The
ENCYCLOPEDIA
of
ELECTROCHEMISTRY

Edited by

CLIFFORD A. HAMPEL

Consulting Chemical Engineer
Skokie, Illinois

REINHOLD PUBLISHING CORPORATION, New York

CHAPMAN & HALL, LTD., LONDON

CONTRIBUTORS

JAMES S. ALLEN, Professor of Physics, University of Illinois, Urbana, Illinois. *Scintillation Counters.*

M. J. ALLEN, Research Scientist, Laboratory of Physical Biology, National Institute of Arthritis and Metabolic Diseases, National Institutes of Health, Bethesda, Maryland. *Bioelectrochemistry.*

RICHARD A. ALLIEGRO, Supervisor, Manufacturing Engineering Department, Refractories Division, Norton Company, Worcester 6, Massachusetts. *Titanium Diboride and Zirconium Diboride Electrodes.*

EDWARD S. AMIS, Professor of Chemistry, University of Arkansas, Fayetteville, Arkansas. *Dissociation.*

ROBERT R. ANNAND, Tracor, Inc., 1701 Guadalupe Street, Austin 1, Texas. *Corrosion Inhibition.*

FRED C. ANSON, Associate Professor of Chemistry, Division of Chemistry and Chemical Engineering, California Institute of Technology, Pasadena, California. *Chronoamperometry; Chronopotentiometry.*

PETER ARNOLD, Sales Manager - Automatic Equipment, The Meaker Company, subsidiary of Sel-Rex Corporation, Nutley, New Jersey. *Electroplating Machines, Automatic.*

F. E. BACON, Metallurgical Engineer, Technology Department, Union Carbide Metals Company, Niagara Falls, New York. *Chromium Electrowinning; Manganese Electrowinning.*

DON H. BAKER, JR., Supervisory Research Metallurgist, Bureau of Mines, U. S. Department of the Interior, Reno, Nevada. *Electrorefining in Molten Salts.*

W. P. BANKS, Senior Research Scientist, Research and Development Department, Continental Oil Company, Ponca City, Oklahoma. *Anodic Protection.*

I. L. BARKER, Resident Metallurgist, Cerro Corporation, 300 Park Avenue, New York 22, New York. *Silver Electrorefining.*

SIDNEY BARNARTT, Manager, Electrochemistry Section, Westinghouse Research Laboratories, Pittsburgh 35, Pennsylvania. *Electrode Potentials, Measurement.*

OTTO BARTH, Professor (Emeritus) of Nonferrous Metallurgy, Royal Institute of Technology, Stockholm, Sweden. *Copper and Nickel Concentrates, Electric Smelting.*

MANUEL BEN, Supervisor, Electrochemistry Department, General Motors Corporation, Research Laboratories, Twelve Mile and Mound Roads, Warren, Michigan; President, American Electroplaters' Society, 1962–1963. *American Electroplaters' Society.*

ELIZABETH S. BENFORD, English Language Institute Librarian, University of Michigan, Ann Arbor, Michigan. *Helmholtz, Hermann L. F.; Héroult, Paul L. T.; Hittorf, Johann W.; Leclanché, Georges; Lewis, Gilbert N.; Sutherland, William; Willson, Thomas L.*

LAWRENCE U. BERMAN, Research Chemist, Organic Chemistry Research, IIT Research Institute, Chicago 16, Illinois. *Electroviscous Effect.*

WALTER J. BERNARD, Technical Assistant to the Director of Engineering, Sprague Electric Company, North Adams, Massachusetts. *Capacitors, Electrolytic—Commercial Types; Capacitors, Electrolytic—Theory of Operation.*

JACOB J. BIKERMAN, Research Associate, Massachusetts Institute of Technology, Cambridge 39, Massachusetts. *Electrokinetic Potentials.*

O. C. BÖCKMAN, Senior Research Engineer, Elektrokemisk A/S, Oslo, Norway. *Electric Smelting Furnaces; Electric Smelting Furnaces—Electrical Circuit; Electric Smelting Furnaces—Metallurgy; Söderberg Anodes in Aluminum Cells; Söderberg Electrodes in Electric Furnaces.*

E. J. BORREBACH, Industrial Systems Engineer, Westinghouse Electric Corporation, Industrial Systems, P. O. Box 10560, Pittsburgh 35, Pennsylvania. *Arc Heating; Dielectric Heating; Induction Heating; Resistance Heating.*

J. I. BREGMAN, Assistant Director of Chemistry Research, IIT Research Institute, 10 West 35th Street, Chicago 16, Illinois. *Corrosion Inhibitors—Commercial.*

ABNER BRENNER, Chief, Electrolysis and Metals Deposition Section, National Bureau of Standards, Washington 25, D.C. *Alloy Electrodeposition.*

iii

CONTRIBUTORS

F. E. BROWN, deceased; formerly, Professor of Chemistry, Iowa State University, Ames, Iowa. *Amalgams.*

HENRY BROWN, Research Director, The Udylite Corp., Warren, Michigan. *Brightening Agents in Electroplating Baths; Cadmium Electroplating.*

JAMES A. BROWN, Technical Service Department, General Chemical Division, Allied Chemical Corporation, Morristown, New Jersey. *Dielectrics—Gaseous; Paschen's Law; Sulfur Hexafluoride.*

T. E. BROWNE, JR., Section Manager, Long Range Major Development, Power Circuit Breaker Division, Westinghouse Electric Corporation, Trafford, Pennsylvania. *Electric Arc Properties.*

JAMES L. BROWNLEE, JR., Assistant Professor, Analytical Chemistry, Department of Chemistry and Chemical Engineering, University of Illinois, Urbana, Illinois. *Acidimetry and Alkalimetry.*

WALTER H. BRUCKNER, Research Professor of Metallurgical Engineering and Technical Director of Cathodic Protection Laboratory, University of Illinois, Urbana, Illinois. *Corrosion Due to Alternating Current.*

WALTER L. BRYTCZUK, Plant Metallurgist, U. S. Metals Refining Co., Division of American Metals Climax, Inc., Carteret, New Jersey. *Copper Electrorefining.*

ROBERT M. BURNS, Senior Scientist, Stanford Research Institute, Menlo Park, California; formerly, Chemical Director, Bell Telephone Laboratories. *Protective Coatings.*

ALLISON BUTTS, Professor of Metallurgy Emeritus, Lehigh University, Bethlehem, Pennsylvania. *Copper Electrowinning.*

JOHN B. CALKIN, deceased; formerly, Consulting Chemical Engineer, 500 Fifth Avenue, New York 36, New York. *Bancroft, Wilder D.*

THOMAS D. CALLINAN, deceased; formerly, Manager of Paper and Ink Research, Thomas J. Watson Research Center, International Business Machines Corp., Yorktown Heights, New York. *Dielectric Chemistry.*

S. R. CAPLAN, Research Associate, Weizmann Institute of Science, Rehovoth, Israel. *Electrochromatography.*

G. H. CARTLEDGE, Consultant, formerly, Group Leader, Chemistry Division, Oak Ridge National Laboratory, * P. O. Box X, Oak Ridge,

* Operated by the Union Carbide Corporation for the U. S. Atomic Energy Commission, Oak Ridge, Tennessee.

Tennessee. *Corrosion Inhibition by Pertechnetate Ion; Flade Potential.*

MYRON CERESA, Engineering Section Manager, Westinghouse Electric Corporation, Electroplating Projects Department, East Pittsburgh, Pennsylvania. *Electrical Currents, Effects on Electrodeposition of Metals; Periodic Reverse Plating.*

MARY L. CHEKEWICZ, International Minerals and Chemical Corporation, Skokie, Illinois. *Kleist, Ewald G. von; Oersted, Hans C.; Tesla, Nikola.*

PAUL CICHY, Senior Engineer, Development Department, The Carborundum Company, Electro Minerals Division, P. O. Box 423, Niagara Falls, New York. *Alumina, Fused.*

THOMAS W. CLAPPER, Technical Director, Research, American Potash & Chemical Corporation, 201 West Washington Blvd., Whittier, California. *Manganese Dioxide, Electrolytic; Perchlorates.*

FRANK M. CLARK, formerly, Consulting Engineer on Dielectrics, General Electric Company, Schenectady, New York. *Askarel; Dielectric Constant; Dielectric Materials.*

GEORGE L. CLARK, Professor of Chemistry Emeritus, University of Illinois, Urbana, Illinois. *Moissan, Henri; Nernst, Walther.*

W. R. CLARK, Assistant to the Vice President of Technical Affairs, Leeds & Northrup Company, Philadelphia 44, Pa. *Galvanometers.*

J. D. COBINE, Physicist, General Electric Research Laboratory, Schenectady, New York. *Dielectric Properties of Vacuum.*

B. E. CONWAY, Professor of Chemistry, University of Ottawa, Ottawa, Canada. *Metal Electrodeposition, Elementary Processes.*

HOWARD F. CONWAY, Research Chemical Engineer, Northern Regional Research Laboratory, Peoria, Illinois, a laboratory of the Northern Utilization Research and Development Division, Agricultural Research Service, U. S. Department of Agriculture. *Dialdehyde Starch Preparation; Periodates, Electrolytic Preparation.*

HUGH S. COOPER, Consulting Chemist and Metallurgist, 16401 South Woodland Road, Shaker Heights, Ohio. *Boron Electrowinning.*

ALBERT J. CORNISH, Senior Research Scientist, United Aircraft Corporation, Research Laboratories, East Hartford, Connecticut. *Joule Effect; Peltier, J. C. A.; Peltier Effect; Seebeck, T. J.; Seebeck Effect; Thermoelectricity; Thomson Effect.*

DANIEL CUBICCIOTTI, Manager, High Temperature Liquids Department, Stanford Research Institute, Menlo Park, California. *Fused Salt Corrosion; Fused Salt Electrochemical Properties.*

L. E. CUPP, Research Superintendent, Nickel Refining Division, The International Nickel Company of Canada, Limited, Port Colborne, Ontario, Canada. *Nickel Electrorefining.*

H. L. DANEMAN, Assistant Sales Manager, Product Sales, Leeds & Northrup Company, Philadelphia 44, Pennsylvania. *Potentiometers.*

ARTHUR W. DAVIDSON, Professor of Chemistry, University of Kansas, Lawrence, Kansas. *Anodic Dissolution, Low Valence States in.*

E. T. DAVIS, Head, Industrial Controls Section, Research & Development Department, Leeds & Northrup Company, Philadelphia 44, Pennsylvania. *Controllers, Automatic.*

ROBERT E. DAVIS, Head, New Products Section, Trona Research Division, American Potash & Chemical Corporation, Trona, California. *Potassium Electrowinning; Rubidium and Cesium Electrowinning.*

ANDRE J. DE BETHUNE, Department of Chemistry, Boston College, Chestnut Hill 67, Massachusetts. *Electrode Potentials (Aqueous); Table of Standard Aqueous Electrode Potentials and Temperature Coefficients at 25°C; Electrode Potentials, Signs of; Electrode Potentials, Temperature Coefficients of; Tension, Cell and Electrode.*

JOSEPH F. DEMENDI, Research Engineer, Pure Carbon Company, Inc., St. Marys, Pennsylvania. *Porous Carbon; Porous Carbon Manufacture.*

RICHARD L. DEMMERLE, Director, Editorial Services, Martin Marietta Corporation, 350 Park Avenue, New York 22, New York; present address: Director of Advertising and Promotion, General Aniline & Film Corp., 435 Hudson Street, New York 14, N.Y. *Castner, Hamilton Y.*

VITTORIO DE NORA, Oronzio de Nora, Impianti Elettrochimici, Via Bistolfi 35, Milan, Italy. *Chlorine Production in Mercury Cells—Electrochemistry; Chlorine Production in Mercury Cells—Industrial Cells.*

ANDREW DRAVNIEKS, Scientific Advisor, Chemistry Research Division, IIT Research Institute, 10 West 35th Street, Chicago 16, Illinois. *Contact Potential.*

GEORGE DUBPERNELL, Technical Advisor, M & T Chemicals, Inc., Detroit 20, Michigan. *Chromium Plating.*

JULES J. DUGA, Senior Research Physicist, Battelle Memorial Institute, Columbus 1, Ohio. *Figure of Merit; Thermoelectric Power.*

ROBERT DUVA, Assistant Technical Director, Sel-Rex Corporation, Nutley 10, New Jersey. *Barrel Plating.*

EDGAR L. ECKFELDT, Staff Scientist, Research & Development Department, Leeds & Northrup Company, North Wales, Pennsylvania. *Conductivity (Electrolytic) Measurement.*

A. P. EDSON, International Nickel Company, Inc., 67 Wall Street, New York 5, New York. *Nickel Electrodes for Fuel Cells and Batteries.*

JUNIUS D. EDWARDS, deceased; formerly, Assistant Director of Research, Aluminum Co. of America, Pittsburgh, Pennsylvania. *Hall, Charles M.*

MORRIS EISENBERG, President and Director of Research, Electrochimica Corporation, Menlo Park, California. *Concentration Polarization.*

RAYMOND T. ELLICKSON, Professor of Physics, University of Oregon, Eugene, Oregon. *Electron.*

PHILIP J. ELVING, Professor of Chemistry, University of Michigan, Ann Arbor, Michigan. *Polarography; Polarography, Organic.*

WILLIAM C. ENGMAN, Dearborn Chemical Company, Chicago 54, Illinois. *Corrosion by Reclaim Waters.*

JAMES U. EYNON, Senior Scientist, Analysis Instrumentation Section, Research & Development Department, Leeds & Northrup Company, North Wales, Pennsylvania. *Conductivity (Electrolytic) Measurement.*

CHARLES L. FAUST, Chief, Electrochemical Engineering Division, Battelle Memorial Institute, Columbus 1, Ohio. *Electromachining; Electropolishing.*

DONALD I. FINCH, Head of the Metallurgical Section, Research & Development Center, Leeds & Northrup Company, North Wales, Pennsylvania. *Thermoelectric Thermometry.*

FREDERICK W. FINK, Chief, Corrosion Research Division, Battelle Memorial Institute, Columbus 1, Ohio. *Corrosion Testing; Fink, Colin G.; Marine Corrosion.*

GORDON R. FINLAY, Assistant Director of Research, Norton Company, Chippawa, Ontario, Canada. *Boron Carbide; Ridgway, Raymond R.*

JOHN M. FINN, Research Chemist, National Carbon Company, Division of Union Carbide

Corporation, Parma 30, Ohio. *Carbon and Graphite Electrolytic Electrodes.*

A. ORMAN FISHER, Corrosion and Metallurgical Laboratories, Monsanto Chemical Company, 800 North Lindbergh Blvd., St. Louis 66, Missouri. *Corrosion Under Heat Transfer Conditions.*

MIKAL FJELLANGER, Chemical Engineer; formerly, Technical Director, Norsk Hydro-Elektrisk Kvaelstofaktieselskab, Oslo, Norway. *Nitrogen Fixation by the Arc Process.*

ARTHUR FLEISCHER, Consulting Chemist, 466 S. Center Street, Orange, New Jersey. *Batteries, Storage; Batteries, Storage—Design and Operation; Planté, Gaston.*

S. N. FLENGAS, Associate Professor, Department of Metallurgical Engineering, University of Toronto, Toronto 5, Ontario, Canada. *Fused Salt Electrode Reactions; Fused Salt Electromotive Series; Fused Salt Overvoltage Measurements.*

G. R. FONDA, 1028 Parkwood Blvd., Schenectady, New York; formerly, General Electric Research Laboratory, Schenectady, New York. *Luminescence.*

HERMAN C. FROELICH, Group Leader, Advanced Development Engineering, General Electric Company, Nela Park, Cleveland 12, Ohio. *Whitney, Willis R.*

RAYMOND M. FUOSS, Sterling Professor of Chemistry, Yale University, New Haven, Connecticut. *Conductance in Nonaqueous Solvents.*

PATRIZIO GALLONE, Research Director, Oronzio de Nora, Impianti Elettrochimici, Via Bistolfi 35, Milan, Italy. *Chlorine Production in Mercury Cells—Electrochemistry; Chlorine Production in Mercury Cells—Industrial Cells; Chlorine Production in Mercury Cells—Overall Process; Heavy Water—Electrolytic Production; Isotopes —Electrochemical Separation; Water Electrolysis.*

REED E. GARVER, Production Superintendent, FMC Corporation, Inorganic Chemicals Division, Buffalo 7, New York. *Hydrogen Peroxide; Peroxygen Chemicals.*

HARRY C. GATOS, Professor, Department of Metallurgy and Department of Electrical Engineering, Massachusetts Institute of Technology, Cambridge 39, Massachusetts. *Semiconductors.*

CHARLES GELMAN, President, Gelman Instrument Company, Ann Arbor, Michigan. *Membranes, Electrolytic.*

ROBERT C. GESTELAND, Research Laboratory of Electronics and Department of Biology, Massachusetts Institute of Technology, Cambridge 39, Massachusetts, and Scientific Engineering Institute, Waltham, Mass. *Microelectrodes.*

GABRIEL M. GIANNINI, President, Giannini Scientific Corporation, 185 Dixon Avenue, Amityville, L.I., New York. *Magnetohydrodynamics; Plasma.*

HUGH P. GODARD, Head of Chemical Division, Aluminium Laboratories Limited, Kingston, Ontario, Canada. *Pitting Corrosion.*

ROBERT BRUCE GOODRICH, Chief, Power Supply Branch, Harry Diamond Laboratories, Washington 25, D. C. *Batteries, Reserve Primary.*

WILLIAM T. GRAY, Research & Development Department, Leeds & Northrup Company, North Wales, Pennsylvania. *Radiation Pyrometry.*

EDWARD C. GRECO, Senior Research Associate, Research Department, United Gas Corporation, Shreveport, Louisiana; President of NACE, 1961–1962. *National Association of Corrosion Engineers.*

C. E. GREEN, Assistant Sales Manager, Analytical Equipment, Marketing Department, Leeds & Northrup Company, Philadelphia 44, Pennsylvania. *Recording Instruments.*

JOHN C. GRIGGER, Senior Research Chemist, Research and Development Department, Pennsalt Chemicals Corporation, Wyndmoor, Pennsylvania. *Lead Dioxide Anode.*

HARRY GRUNDFEST, Professor of Neurology, College of Physicians and Surgeons, Columbia University, New York, New York. *Bioelectrogenesis; Electric Organs.*

CONRADO P. GUTIERREZ, Staff Member, Los Alamos Scientific Laboratory, Los Alamos, New Mexico. *Electrophoretic Deposition.*

NORMAN HACKERMAN, Department of Chemistry, University of Texas, Austin 12, Texas. *Corrosion Inhibition.*

CLIFFORD A. HAMPEL, Consulting Chemical Engineer, 8501 Harding Avenue, Skokie, Illinois. *Adiponitrile Electrosynthesis; Chlorine Industry; Electroplating Terms; Ferroalloys; Galvani, Luigi; Lithium Electrowinning; Northrup, Edwin F.; Tone, Frank J.; Weston, Edward; Zinc and Cadmium Electrowinning.*

ELIZABETH A. HAMPEL, College Department, Rand McNally and Company, Skokie, Illinois. *Franklin, Benjamin.*

J. W. HANLEY, Chief Metallurgical Engineer, Cerro Corporation, 300 Park Avenue, New

York 22, New York. *Lead Electrorefining and Electroplating.*

FOREST K. HARRIS, Chief, Absolute Electrical Measurements Section, National Bureau of Standards, Washington 25, D.C. *Electrical Units and Standards.*

JOHN O. HARRIS, Professor of Bacteriology, Kansas State University, Manhattan, Kansas. *Microbiological Corrosion.*

FRANK HARRISON, Professor of Anatomy, University of Texas, Southwestern Medical School, Dallas, Texas. *Electrophysiology.*

JOSEPH B. HEITMAN, Supervisor, Chemical Engineering Section, Technical Development Department - West, Pennsalt Chemicals Corporation, Tacoma 1, Washington. *Chlorates, Electrolytic Production.*

T. A. HENRIE, Supervisory Research Metallurgist, Bureau of Mines, U. S. Department of the Interior, Reno, Nevada. *Electrorefining in Molten Salts.*

W. STANLEY HERBERT, deceased; formerly, Associate Director of Research, Electric Storage Battery Company, Yardley, Pennsylvania (formerly with Ray-O-Vac Co. Division). *Batteries—Dry Cells; Batteries, Sealed Storage.*

CHARLES K. HERSH, Manager, Propellant Research, IIT Research Institute, Chicago 16, Illinois. *Molecular Sieves; Ozone; Space Power.*

A. HICKLING, Reader in Physical Chemistry, University of Liverpool, Liverpool, England. *Glow-Discharge Electrolysis.*

I. S. HIRSCHHORN, Vice President, Ronson Metals Corporation, Newark 5, New Jersey. *Rare Earth Metals Electrowinning.*

DAVID I. HITCHCOCK, Associate Professor Emeritus of Physiology, Yale University, New Haven, Connecticut. *Buffers; pH; Membrane Equilibrium.*

T. P. HOAR, University of Cambridge, Department of Metallurgy, Cambridge, England. *CITCE; Corrosion—Electrochemical Theory; Electrolytic Polishing Theory; Passivity.*

RAGNAR HOLM, Technical Consultant, Stackpole Carbon Company, St. Marys, Pennsylvania. *Electrical Contacts.*

PAUL L. HOWARD, Vice President, Yardney Electric Corporation, 40–52 Leonard Street, New York 13, New York. *Solar Energy Converters.*

WALTER B. HOWARD, Scientist, Monsanto Chemical Company, Texas City, Texas. *Acetylene by Electric Discharge.*

BRADFORD HOWLAND, Lincoln Laboratory, Massachusetts Institute of Technology, Lexington, Massachusetts. *Microelectrodes.*

H. B. HUNTINGTON, Chairman, Department of Physics, Rensselaer Polytechnic Institute, Troy, New York. *Electromigration in Solid Metals and Alloys.*

RAY M. HURD, Director of Chemical Research, Tracor, Inc., 1701 Guadalupe Street, Austin 1, Texas. *Solion; Streaming Current; Streaming Potential.*

SEIICHI ISHIZAKA, Secretary for General Affairs, Electrochemical Society of Japan, 3. 1-chome, Yarakucho, Chiyoda-ku, Tokyo, Japan. *Electrochemical Society of Japan.*

HENRY F. IVEY, Advisory Scientist, Quantum Electronics Department, Research & Development Center, Westinghouse Electric Corporation, Pittsburgh 35, Pa. *Electroluminescence; Phosphors.*

ALBERT W. JACHE, Associate Research Director, Ozark-Mahoning Co., Tulsa 19, Oklahoma; present address: Olin Mathieson Chemical Corp., New Haven, Conn. *Electron Paramagnetic Resonance in Studies of Electrode Processes; Nitrogen Trifluoride.*

BERNARD JAFFE, James Madison High School, Brooklyn, New York. *Arrhenius, Svante A.; Gibbs, J. Willard; Ostwald, Friedrich W.*

GEORGE J. JANZ, Professor of Chemistry, Department of Chemistry, Rensselaer Polytechnic Institute, Troy, New York. *Reference Electrodes.*

E. W. JOHNSON, Advisory Physical Chemist, Westinghouse Research and Development Center, Pittsburgh 35, Pennsylvania. *Vacuum Arc Properties.*

ROBERT L. KAY, Metcalf Research Laboratory, Brown University, Providence 12, Rhode Island, and Mellon Institute, Pittsburgh 13, Pennsylvania. *Transference Numbers in Solvents; Transference Numbers: Measurement and Data.*

EUGENE J. KELLY, Chemist, Chemistry Division, Oak Ridge National Laboratory,* P. O. Box X, Oak Ridge, Tennessee. *Tafel Lines.*

F. J. KELLY, Research Fellow, Department of Chemistry, Rensselaer Polytechnic Institute, Troy, New York; present address: Mallory Battery Co. of Canada Limited, 2333 North Sheridan Way, Clarkson, Ontario. *Reference Electrodes.*

* Operated by the Union Carbide Corporation for the U. S. Atomic Energy Commission, Oak Ridge, Tennessee.

CECIL V. KING, American Gas & Chemicals, Inc., Box 101, Gracie Station, New York 28, New York; Editor, *Journal of The Electrochemical Society,* and Professor Emeritus, New York University, New York, New York. *Electrochemistry.*

J. D. KINGSLEY, Physicist, General Electric Research Laboratory, Schenectady, New York. *Laser.*

MORTON S. KIRCHER, Hooker Chemical Corporation, Niagara Falls, New York; present address, Dryden Chemicals Limited, Dryden, Ontario, Canada. *Chlorine Production in Diaphragm Cells; Chlorine Production in Diaphragm Cells—Overall Process.*

ERNEST L. KOEHLER, Director, Electrochemical Metallurgy Laboratory, Continental Can Company, Inc., Chicago 20, Illinois. *Cathodic Protection; Sacrificial Protection.*

A. KORBELAK, Vice President, Marketing and New Product Development, Sel-Rex Corporation, Nutley 10, New Jersey. *Precious Metal Electroplating; Silver Plating.*

WALTER G. KRELLNER, Senior Research Engineer, Stackpole Carbon Company, St. Marys, Pennsylvania. *Graphite, Electrothermic Production.*

F. J. KRENZKE, Director, Magnesium Development Department, Dow Chemical Company, Texas Division, Freeport, Texas. *Magnesium Electrowinning.*

JOHN KRONSBEIN, Professor of Mechanical Engineering and Physics, Research Professor of Metallurgy, University of Florida, Gainesville, Florida. *Current Distribution; Current Efficiency; Energy Efficiency.*

WILLIAM E. KUHN, Senior Research Associate, Applied Research Branch, Carborundum Company, Niagara Falls, New York; present address: Senior Scientist, Spindletop Research Center, Lexington, Kentucky. *Furnaces, Inert Atmosphere and Vacuum Arc.*

ROBERT KUNIN, Research Associate, Rohm & Haas Co., 5000 Richmond Street, Philadelphia 37, Pa. *Ion Exchange Membranes; Ion Exchange Resins.*

RICHARD W. LAITY, Frick Chemical Laboratory, Princeton University, Princeton, New Jersey. *Fused Salt Transport Numbers.*

EARL B. LANCASTER, Research Chemical Engineer, Northern Regional Research Laboratory, Peoria, Illinois, a laboratory of the Northern Utilization Research and Development Division, Agricultural Research Service, U. S. Department of Agriculture. *Dialdehyde Starch Preparation; Periodates, Electrolytic Preparation.*

D. T. LAPP, Research Project Engineer, Norton Company, Chippawa, Ontario, Canada. *Furnaces for Hot-Pressing.*

FRANK L. LAQUE, Vice President, International Nickel Company, Inc., 67 Wall Street, New York 5, New York. *Galvanic Corrosion; Galvanic Series.*

FLORENCE H. LARKOWSKI, International Minerals and Chemical Corporation, Skokie, Illinois. *Edison, Thomas A.; Ohm, Georg S.; Watts, Oliver P.*

HENRY LEIDHEISER, JR., Director, Virginia Institute for Scientific Research, 6300 River Road, Richmond 26, Virginia. *Single Crystals of Metals; Single Crystals of Semiconductors.*

JEROME Y. LETTVIN, Research Laboratory of Electronics and Department of Biology, Massachusetts Institute of Technology, Cambridge 39, Massachusetts. *Microelectrodes.*

ROBERT A. LEWIS, Head, Reduction Research Section, Metals Division Research Department, Kaiser Aluminum & Chemical Corporation, Permanente, California. *Aluminum Electrorefining; Aluminum Electrowinning.*

W. E. LEWIS, Manager—Field Sales, Lectromelt Furnace Division, McGraw-Edison Company, Pittsburgh 30, Pennsylvania. *Steel Making in Electric Arc Furnaces.*

W. T. LIBERSON, Chief, Physical Medicine and Rehabilitation Service, Veterans Administration Hospital, Hines, Illinois, and Stritch School of Medicine, Loyola University, Chicago, Illinois. *Electrodiagnosis (Electromyography and Electrostimulation); Electrodiagnosis —Abnormal EMG; Electroencephalography; Electroencephalography—Abnormal.*

JOSEPH Z. LICHTMAN, Materials Engineer, U. S. Naval Applied Science Laboratory, Naval Base, Brooklyn 1, New York. *Cavitation Erosion.*

M. H. LIETZKE, Group Leader, Chemistry Division, Oak Ridge National Laboratory,[*] P. O. Box X, Oak Ridge, Tennessee. *Activity and Activity Coefficient; Electromotive Force and Half-Cell Potentials; EMF Measurements in Aqueous Solutions at High Temperatures;*

[*] Operated by the Union Carbide Corporation for the U. S. Atomic Energy Commission, Oak Ridge, Tennessee.

Enthalpy or Heat Content; Entropy; Free Energy; Heat Capacity; Nernst Equation; Partial Molal Quantities; Soret Potential.

SAMUEL COLVILLE LIND, Consultant in Chemistry at the Oak Ridge National Laboratory* and at the Oak Ridge Gaseous Diffusion Plant, P. O. Box X, Oak Ridge, Tennessee; formerly, Dean of the Institute of Technology, University of Minnesota. *Gases, Electrical Conductance and Ionization.*

ALEXANDER LODDING, Physics Department, Rensselaer Polytechnic Institute, Troy, New York; on leave from Chalmers University of Technology, Gothenburg, Sweden. *Electromigration in Liquid Metals.*

WERNER R. LOEWENSTEIN, Columbia University, College of Physicians and Surgeons, Department of Physiology, New York 32, New York. *Biological Transducers.*

PHILIP B. LORENZ, Physical Chemist, Bartlesville Petroleum Research Center, Bureau of Mines, U. S. Department of the Interior, Bartlesville, Oklahoma. *Electroosmosis.*

NANCY SWENDEMAN LOUD, Newton College of the Sacred Heart, Newton, Massachusetts. *Table of Standard Aqueous Electrode Potentials and Temperature Coefficients at 25°C.*

ARTHUR L. LOWE, JR., Babcock & Wilcox Company, Nuclear Development Center, Lynchburg, Virginia. *Corrosion by Liquid Metals.*

ROBERT E. LUND, Research Superintendent, Zinc Smelting Division, St. Joseph Lead Company, Monaca 7, Pennsylvania. *Zinc, Electrothermic Production.*

WILSON LYNES, Research Department, Revere Copper & Brass, Inc., Rome, New York. *Faraday, Michael.*

ERNEST H. LYONS, JR., Professor of Chemistry, Principia College, Elsah, Illinois. *Complex Ions in Electroplating; Immersion (Displacement) Plating.*

R. M. MACINTOSH, Manager, Tin Research Institute, Inc., 483 West Sixth Avenue, Columbus 1, Ohio. *Tin Electrodeposition.*

MARTIN F. MAHER, Manager, Metal Industries Division, Oakite Products, Inc., 19 Rector Street, New York 6, New York. *Electroplating, Cleaning Before.*

HOWARD V. MALMSTADT, Department of Chem-

* Operated by the Union Carbide Corporation for the U. S. Atomic Energy Commission, Oak Ridge, Tennessee.

istry, University of Illinois, Urbana, Illinois. *Electrometric Titrations.*

R. A. MARCUS, Professor of Physical Chemistry, Polytechnic Institute of Brooklyn, Brooklyn 1, New York. *Electron Transfers at Electrodes.*

R. M. O. MAUNSELL, Technical Department, Albright and Wilson Ltd., 1 Knightsbridge Green, London S.W. 1, England. *Phosphorus, Electrothermal Production.*

WILL MCADAM, Head, Electrical Section, Research & Development Department, Leeds & Northrup Company, Dickerson Road, North Wales, Pennsylvania. *Microvoltmeters and Micro-microammeters.*

W. A. E. MCBRYDE, Chairman, Department of Chemistry; Dean, Faculty of Science, University of Waterloo, Waterloo, Ontario, Canada. *Ionic Equilibria; pH Titration Curves; Stability Constants of Metal Complexes.*

JOHN MCCALLUM, Research Associate, Battelle Memorial Institute, Columbus 1, Ohio. *Fuel Cells; Fuel Cells—Classification.*

HUGH J. MCDONALD, Professor and Chairman, Department of Biochemistry and Biophysics, Stritch School of Medicine, Loyola University, Chicago 12, Illinois. *Electrophoresis.*

J. R. MCDOWELL, Research Engineer, Mechanics Department, Westinghouse Electric Corporation, Research & Development Center, Pittsburgh 35, Pennsylvania. *Fretting Corrosion.*

WILLIAM E. MCEWEN, Department of Chemistry, University of Massachusetts, Amherst, Massachusetts. *Anodic Reductions at Magnesium Electrodes.*

LESLIE D. MCGRAW, Assistant Division Chief, Battelle Memorial Institute, Columbus 1, Ohio; present address: Director of Research, Physical Chemistry, North Star Research and Development Institute, 3100 38th Avenue South, Minneapolis 6, Minnesota. *Fuel Cells; Fuel Cells—Classification.*

JOHN C. MCMULLEN, Research Specialist, Electro Minerals Division, Carborundum Company, Niagara Falls, New York. *Silicon Carbide.*

WAYNE A. MCRAE, Vice President, Research, Ionics, Incorporated, 152 Sixth Street, Cambridge 42, Massachusetts. *Demineralization by Electrodialysis.*

R. B. MEARS, Vice President, New Product Development, United States Steel Corporation, 525 William Penn Place, Pittsburgh 30, Pennsylvania. *Concentration Cells.*

JOHN C. MELCHER, Technical Assistant to Vice President-Marketing, Leeds & Northrup Company, Philadelphia 44, Pennsylvania. *Wheatstone Bridge.*

ROBERT E. MEREDITH, Associate Professor, Department of Chemical Engineering, Oregon State University, Corvallis, Oregon. *Conductivities in Foams and Emulsions; Conductivity, Electrolytic; Kohlrausch, F. W.*

ROBERT E. MEYER, Chemist, Chemistry Division, Oak Ridge National Laboratory,* P. O. Box X, Oak Ridge, Tennessee. *Gibbs-Helmholtz Equation.*

HENRY C. MILLER, Inorganic Research Department, Technical Division, Pennsalt Chemicals Corporation, Box 4388, Philadelphia 18, Pennsylvania. *Fluorine Production.*

HUGH R. MILLER, Principal Chemist, Electrochemical Engineering Division, Battelle Memorial Institute, Columbus 1, Ohio. *Electrographic Printing.*

JACOB M. MILLER, Associate Electrochemist, Metals and Ceramic Research, IIT Research Institute, Chicago 16, Illinois. *Anode; Cathode; Electrode.*

JOHN R. MOSLEY, Staff Member, Los Alamos Scientific Laboratory, Los Alamos, New Mexico. *Electrophoretic Deposition.*

JOHN N. MRGUDICH, Senior Scientist, U. S. Army Electronics Research and Development Laboratories, Fort Monmouth, New Jersey. *Batteries, Solid Electrolyte.*

EDWARD MUELLER, Midwest Research Institute, Kansas City, Missouri, *Bunsen, Robert W.*

GEORGE W. MURPHY, Professor and Chairman, Department of Chemistry, University of Oklahoma, Norman, Oklahoma. *Demineralization of Water by Direct Electrochemical Action.*

JOHN R. MUSGRAVE, Director, Miami Research Laboratory, Chemicals & Metals Division, Eagle-Picher Company, Miami, Oklahoma. *Gallium Electrochemistry.*

RUDOLPH C. NAGY, Administrative Engineer, Research Laboratories, Westinghouse Electric Corporation, Lamp Division, Bloomfield, New Jersey. *Air Ion Generation; Phosphors; Ultraviolet Lamps.*

CLIFFORD V. NELSON, Research Associate, Cardiology Department, Maine Medical Center, 22 Bramhall Street, Portland, Maine. *Electrocardiology.*

JACK H. NICHOLS, Manager, Electrolytic Process Sales, Monsanto Chemical Company, St. Louis 66, Missouri. *Hydrochloric Acid Electrolysis.*

VITO F. NOLE, Corrosion Engineer, Chase Brass & Copper Co., Waterbury 20, Connecticut. *Dezincification.*

SHINZO OKADA, President, Japan Storage Battery Co., Emeritus Professor and former Dean of the Faculty of Engineering, Kyoto University, Kyoto, Japan. *Sodium Sulfate Solution Electrolysis.*

EDGARDO J. PARSI, Assistant Director of Development, Engineering Department, Ionics, Incorporated, 152 Sixth Street, Cambridge 42, Massachusetts. *Electrodialysis; Electrodialysis Applications.*

ROGER PARSONS, Department of Chemistry, University of Bristol, Bristol, England. *Electrode Double Layer; Electrode Reactions, Kinetics.*

ANDREW PATTERSON, JR., Associate Professor of Chemistry, Yale University, New Haven, Connecticut. *Ion Association; Wien Effect.*

R. ROBERT PAXTON, Chief Engineer, Pure Carbon Company, Inc., St. Marys, Pennsylvania. *Porous Carbon; Porous Carbon Manufacture.*

LARRY PENBERTHY, President, Penberthy Electromelt Company, 4301 Sixth Avenue South, Seattle 8, Washington. *Glass, Electric Melting of.*

J. V. PETROCELLI, Applied Science Office, Ford Motor Company, Dearborn, Michigan. *Electromotive Series; Mixed Potential.*

WALTER H. PITTS, Research Laboratory of Electronics and Department of Electrical Engineering, Massachusetts Institute of Technology, Cambridge 39, Massachusetts. *Microelectrodes.*

HERBERT A. POHL, Professor of Materials Science, Department of Chemistry, Polytechnic Institute of Brooklyn, Brooklyn 1, New York. *Dielectrophoresis; Semiconductors, Organic.*

FRANZ A. POSEY, Group Leader, Chemistry Division, Oak Ridge National Laboratory,* P. O. Box X, Oak Ridge, Tennessee. *Billiter Potential; Corrosion, Electrochemical Kinetics; Lippmann Potential.*

MARCEL POURBAIX, Managing Director, Centre

* Operated by the Union Carbide Corporation for the U. S. Atomic Energy Commission, Oak Ridge, Tennessee.

* Operated by the Union Carbide Corporation for the U. S. Atomic Energy Commission, Oak Ridge, Tennessee.

Belge d'Etude de la Corrosion (CEBELCOR), 24 Rue des Chevaliers, Brussels 5, Belgium. *Potential-pH Equilibrium Diagrams.*

R. A. POWERS, Director of Research, Union Carbide Consumer Products Co., 12900 Snow Road, Parma, Ohio. *Crevice Corrosion.*

J. S. PRENER, General Electric Research Laboratory, Schenectady, New York. *Fluorescence; Phosphorescence.*

HAROLD J. READ, Professor of Metallurgy, College of Mineral Industries, Pennsylvania State University, University Park, Pennsylvania. *Addition Agents; Hydrogen Embrittlement; Throwing Power.*

ROBERT B. REIF, Project Leader, Applied Physics Group, Engineering Physics Department, Battelle Memorial Institute, Columbus 1, Ohio. *Electrostatic Coating Processes.*

E. R. RIEGEL, deceased; formerly, Professor of Chemistry, University of Buffalo, Buffalo, New York. *Cottrell, Frederick G.*

D. ROBERTSON, Head of Temperature Measurements Section, Research & Development Department, Leeds & Northrup Company, North Wales, Pennsylvania. *Resistance Thermometers.*

GILSON H. ROHRBACK, Magna Corporation, Anaheim, California. *Biochemical Fuel Cells.*

DAVID ROLLER, Magna Corporation, Research and Development Division, 1001 South East Street, Anaheim, California. *Corrosion Detection Devices.*

BENGT RUDLING, Metallurgist, Technical and Economical Development Department, Bolidens Gruvaktiebolag, Skelleftehamn, Sweden. *Lead, Electrothermic Smelting.*

PAUL RUETSCHI, Manager, Electrochemistry Division, Carl F. Norberg Research Center, Electric Storage Battery Company, Yardley, Pennsylvania. *Exchange Current; Overvoltage, Hydrogen; Overvoltage, Oxygen; Polarization; Transfer Coefficient.*

CHARLES L. RULFS, Professor of Chemistry, University of Michigan, Ann Arbor, Michigan. *Polarography; Polarography, Inorganic.*

W. H. SAFRANEK, Assistant Chief, Electrochemical Engineering, Battelle Memorial Institute, Columbus 1, Ohio. *Copper Electroplating; Electroplating for Decoration and Protection; Nickel Electroplating.*

MARSHALL T. SANDERS, Atlas Chemical Industries, Inc., Wilmington 99, Delaware. *Glucose, Electrochemical Reduction.*

KNUT SANDVOLD, Senior Metallurgical Engineer,

Elektrokemisk A/S, Oslo, Norway. *Electric Smelting Furnaces; Electric Smelting Furnaces— Electrical Circuit; Electric Smelting Furnaces— Metallurgy.*

GEORGE SCATCHARD, Professor of Physical Chemistry, Emeritus, Massachusetts Institute of Technology, Cambridge, Massachusetts. *Ion Transport Across Charged Membranes.*

JAMES C. SCHAEFER, Technical Director-Thin Films, Crystal-Solid State Division, Harshaw Chemical Company, Cleveland, Ohio. *Boron Electrowinning.*

LAWRENCE R. SCHARFSTEIN, Supervisor, Corrosion Research, Carpenter Steel Company, Reading, Pennsylvania. *Corrosion Fatigue; Stress Corrosion.*

LAWRENCE C. SCHOLZ, Research Physicist, IIT Research Institute, 10 West 35th Street, Chicago 16, Illinois. *Work Function.*

WILLIAM J. SCHWERDTFEGER, Electrical Engineer, Corrosion Section, Metallurgy Division, National Bureau of Standards, Washington 25, D.C. *Soil Corrosion.*

JOHN J. SCOTT, Senior Research Engineer, Norton Company, Chippawa, Ontario, Canada. *Magnesia, Fused.*

M. R. SEILER, Solid State Research, Battelle Memorial Institute, Columbus 1, Ohio; present address: North American Aviation, Inc., 4300 East Fifth Avenue, Columbus, Ohio. *Thermoelectric Power Generation.*

M. Ö. SEM, former Technical Director, Elektrokemisk A/S, Oslo, Norway. *Söderberg Anodes in Aluminum Cells; Söderberg Electrodes in Electric Furnaces.*

ROBERT K. SHANNON, deceased; formerly, Executive Secretary, The Electrochemical Society, Inc., 30 East 42nd Street, New York 17, New York. *Electrochemical Society.*

ARTHUR J. SHERBURNE, Consultant, The P. D. George Company, 5200 N. Second Street, St. Louis 7, Missouri; formerly, Manager of Insulation Products Engineering, General Electric Company. *Organic Electrical Insulation.*

JOSEPH M. SHERFEY, Chemist, National Aeronautics & Space Administration, Goddard Space Flight Center, Greenbelt, Maryland. *Electrochemical Calorimetry.*

MERLE E. SIBERT, Staff Scientist, Research Laboratories, Lockheed Missile & Space Company, Palo Alto, California. *Hafnium, Electrolytic Preparation; Titanium, Electrolytic Preparation; Zirconium, Electrolytic Processing.*

CONTRIBUTORS

JOSEPH H. SIMONS, Professor of Chemistry and Chemical Engineering, University of Florida, Gainesville, Florida. *Fluorocarbons, Electrochemical Production.*

M. T. SIMNAD, Visiting Professor, Massachusetts Institute of Technology, Cambridge, Massachusetts, and General Atomic Division, General Dynamics Corp., San Diego, California. *Corrosion, Radiation Effects on.*

C. J. SLUNDER, Senior Metallurgist, Battelle Memorial Institute, Columbus 1, Ohio. *Anodizing.*

PAUL SMISKO, Chief Engineer, Carbon Division, Stackpole Carbon Company, St. Marys, Pennsylvania. *Graphite, Electrothermic Production.*

EDWIN J. SMITH, Director, Research and Development, Research and Development Department, National Steel Corporation, Weirton, West Virginia. *Aluminum Plating; Electrogalvanizing.*

CHARLES P. SMYTH, Professor of Chemistry, Department of Chemistry, Princeton University, Princeton, New Jersey. *Dipole Moment.*

KARL SOLLNER, Chief, Section on Electrochemistry and Colloid Physics, and Professor, Laboratory of Physical Biology, National Institute of Arthritis and Metabolic Diseases, National Institutes of Health, Bethesda 14, Maryland. *Membrane Potentials; Membrane Potentials—Bi-ionic and Polyionic.*

D. N. STAICOPOLUS, Senior Research Physical Chemist, Engineering Materials Laboratory, E. I. duPont de Nemours & Co., Inc., Engineering Station, Wilmington, Delaware. *Electrocapillary Phenomena; Electrostatic Potentials—Effects on Friction and Hardness; Potentiostats—Principles of Design; Potentiostatic Techniques in Corrosion Studies.*

JOHN J. J. STAUNTON, Director Research, Coleman Instruments, Inc., 318 Madison Street, Maywood, Illinois. *Glass Electrode; pH Meter.*

R. STEELE, Manager of Research, J. Bishop & Co. Platinum Works, Malvern, Pennsylvania. *Platinized Electrodes.*

G. D. STENDAHL, Central Research Laboratories, American Smelting & Refining Co., South Plainfield, New Jersey. *Electrorefining; Electrowinning.*

OSCAR A. STOCKER, Sel-Rex Corporation, Nutley 10, New Jersey. *Manual Plating.*

R. W. STOUGHTON, Group Leader, Chemistry

Division, Oak Ridge National Laboratory,* P. O. Box X, Oak Ridge, Tennessee. *Activity and Activity Coefficient; Electromotive Force and Half-Cell Potentials; EMF Measurements in Aqueous Solutions at High Temperatures; Enthalpy or Heat Content; Entropy; Free Energy; Heat Capacity; Nernst Equation; Partial Molal Quantities; Soret Potential.*

M. E. STRAUMANIS, University of Missouri, School of Mines and Metallurgy, Department of Metallurgical Engineering, Rolla, Missouri. *Anodic Disintegration of Metals.*

MICHAEL A. STREICHER, Engineering Materials Laboratory, Engineering Station, E. I. duPont de Nemours & Co., Inc., Wilmington, Delaware. *Difference Effect; Intergranular Corrosion.*

J. D. SUDBURY, Manager, Anotrol Division, Continental Oil Company, Ponca City, Oklahoma. *Anodic Protection.*

KIICHIRO SUGINO, Professor of Applied Electrochemistry, Tokyo Institute of Technology (Tokyo Kogyo Daigaku), Tokyo, Japan. *Bromates, Electrolytic Production.*

DAVID W. SWAN, Materials Laboratory, Queen Mary College, London, E.1, England; present address: Central Research Laboratories, Minnesota Mining and Manufacturing Co., St. Paul 19, Minnesota. *Dielectrics, Liquid.*

SHERLOCK SWANN, JR., Division of Chemical Engineering, University of Illinois, Urbana, Illinois. *Electro-organic Chemistry.*

RAYMOND SZYMANOWITZ, Executive Vice President, Acheson Industries, Inc., Newark, New Jersey. *Acheson, Edward G.*

ICHIJI TASAKI, Laboratory of Neurobiology, National Institute of Mental Health, National Institutes of Health, Bethesda 14, Maryland. *Nerve Impulse Transmission.*

HANS THURNAUER, Head, Ceramic Section, Central Research Department, Minnesota Mining and Manufacturing Co., 2301 Hudson Road, St. Paul 19, Minnesota. *Ceramic Insulation.*

JOHN M. TINNON, Vice President, Engineering, Air Reduction Chemical and Carbide Co., 150 East 42nd Street, New York 17, New York. *Calcium Carbide.*

E. H. TOMPKINS, Senior Chemist, Chemistry Research Division, IIT Research Institute, 10

* Operated by the Union Carbide Corporation for the U. S. Atomic Energy Commission, Oak Ridge, Tennessee.

West 35th Street, Chicago 16, Illinois. *Photoconductivity.*

F. C. TOMPKINS, Secretary and Editor, The Faraday Society, 6 Grays Inn Square, London, W.C. 1; Professor of Chemistry, Imperial College of Science and Technology, London, S.W. 7, England. *Faraday Society.*

A. STUART TULK, Engineering Manager, Solid-State Materials, Chemical & Metallurgical Division, Sylvania Electric Products, Inc., Towanda, Pennsylvania. *Zone Refining.*

MURRAY C. UDY, Vice President, Research and Development, Strategic-Udy Processes, Inc., 3986 Royal Avenue, Niagara Falls, New York. *Udy, Marvin J.*

JOHN D. VAN NORMAN, Assistant Chemist, Brookhaven National Laboratory, Upton, L. I., New York. *Coulometric Techniques in High Temperature Systems; Fused Salt Chronopotentiometry; Fused Salt Polarography.*

PIERRE VAN RYSSELBERGHE, Lecturer in Chemistry and Chemical Engineering, Stanford University, Stanford, California. *Irreversible Electrochemical Processes, Thermodynamics of; Nomenclature, Remarks on.*

GEORGE W. VINAL, 65 Arrowhead Road, Weston 93, Massachusetts; formerly, Chief, Electrochemical Section, National Bureau of Standards. *Volta, Alessandro.*

ROBERT D. WALDRON, Research Scientist, AiResearch Manufacturing Division, The Garrett Corp., Phoenix, Arizona. *Electrostriction; Ferroelectricity; Piezoelectricity.*

J. FREDERICK WALKER, E. I. duPont de Nemours & Co., Inc., Wilmington 98, Delaware. *Davy, Humphry.*

LEWIS E. WALKUP, Group Director, Engineering Physics Department, Battelle Memorial Institute, Columbus 1, Ohio. *Xerography.*

CARMEN W. WALSH, Chief Librarian, International Minerals and Chemical Corporation, Skokie, Illinois. *Ampère, André M.; Becket, Frederick M.; Berzelius, John J.; Burgess, Charles F.; Coulomb, Charles A.; Downs, James C.; Gauss, Karl F.*

PEI WANG, Sylvania Electric Products, Inc., Woburn, Massachusetts. *Electron Beam Melting; Electron Beam Welding.*

RALPH WEHRMANN, Senior Scientist, LTV Research Center, Ling-Temco-Vought, Inc., Dallas 22, Texas. *Tantalum Electrowinning.*

ERWIN K. WEISE, Associate Professor, Department of Mining, Metallurgy, and Petroleum Engineering, University of Illinois, Urbana, Illinois. *Conductivity (Electrical) in Solids; Hall Effect.*

JOSEPH C. WHITE, Head, Electrochemistry Branch, Chemistry Division, U. S. Naval Research Laboratory, Washington 25, D.C. *Batteries.*

WAYNE E. WHITE, Research Director, Ozark-Mahoning Co., Tulsa 19, Oklahoma. *Nitrogen Trifluoride.*

CARL R. WHITTEMORE, Chief Metallurgist, Deloro Stellite Division of Deloro Smelting & Refining Co. Ltd., Belleville, Ontario, Canada. *Cobalt Electroplating; Cobalt Electrowinning and Electrorefining.*

HAROLD J. WIESNER, University of California, Lawrence Radiation Laboratory, Chemistry Division, Livermore, California. *Electroforming.*

LEO D. WILLIAMS, Chemical Engineer, retired; formerly with Electrochemicals Department, E. I. duPont de Nemours & Co., Inc., Niagara Falls, New York. *Sodium, Electrolytic Production.*

FRANK WILLS, Technical Manager, Pyron Division, American Metal Climax, Inc., New York 20, New York. *Electrodeposition of Metal Powders.*

CHRISTOPHER L. WILSON, Head, Departments of Chemistry and Physics, High Point College, High Point, North Carolina. *Kolbe and Related Brown-Walker and Hofer-Moest Reactions; Polymerization (Electrolytic) of Vinyl Monomers.*

N. M. WINSLOW, Consultant, 2115 Riverside Drive, Cleveland 7, Ohio. *Electro-organic Chemistry.*

L. H. WOODMAN, Dow Chemical Company, Midland, Michigan. *Dow, Herbert H.*

JOSEPH J. WYSOCKI, RCA Laboratories, Princeton, New Jersey. *Photovoltaic Effect in Semiconductor Junctions.*

ROBERT P. YECK, Central Research Laboratories, American Smelting & Refining Co., South Plainfield, New Jersey. *Indium Electrorefining.*

SHIRO YOSHIZAWA, Professor of Electrochemistry, Kyoto University, Kyoto, Japan. *Sodium Sulfate Solution Electrolysis.*

WILLIAM J. YOUNG, Head of Research Laboratory, Museum of Fine Arts, Boston 15, Massachusetts. *Electrolytic Restoration of Ancient Metals.*

PREFACE

The "Encyclopedia of Electrochemistry" is an outgrowth of the success of other one-volume ency-clopedias, published by Reinhold, which cover broad fields of science, notably the "Encyclopedia of Chemistry," G. L. Clark and G. G. Hawley, Editors, 1957 (Supplement, 1958), and the "Encyclopedia of the Biological Sciences," Peter Gray, Editor, 1961. After several discussions with G. G. Hawley and Fred P. Peters, Executive Editor and Vice President of the Reinhold Book Division, respectively, about the potential value and scope of an "Encyclopedia of Electrochemistry," I accepted their proposal to undertake the editing of this volume.

At this time, after two and one-half years and the handling of about 4000 letters, the venture seems justified, at least in the minds of the 270 other contributors and the Editor. The support of these contributors has been the major reason for my feeling that the work on this book has been well worth while.

Many people may wonder just what the editor of an encyclopedia does. Stated simply, the editor does everything except write the articles signed by someone else. He selects the contents and the con-tributors, he conducts the voluminous correspondence with the contributors and the publisher, he edits the manuscripts and proofreads the galley proofs and page proofs, and he is ultimately responsible for all the well-known "sins of omission and commission" connected with the final book. Of course, he can also take credit for at least part of whatever success the volume attains. In any event, he initiates and carries on the development of the book through its various phases, as will be described below.

For this book, the scope was first broadly defined as being that of the several divisions of the Electro-chemical Society plus the field of electrochemistry in biology and medicine. Then came the vital job of selecting titles of the specific entries or articles to attain that scope. I first listed everything I could think of and then pestered a variety of friends for their suggestions. After a tentative list of article titles had been compiled, and the approximate length of each article decided, a two-page description of the purpose and details of the book was prepared, and the major task of obtaining the large number of authors for the articles was begun. After preparing my own list of names, I again solicited the aid of friends in determining who might write about what, in addition to perusing the indexes of the *Journal of the Electrochemical Society*, the programs of past meetings of the Society, and other sources to connect names with definite subjects.

The next stage initiated what was to become a flood of correspondence. Letters sent to prospective contributors elicited a host of acceptances, a minor number of declinations for any of a variety of reasons, and suggestions for possible contributors and titles for pertinent subjects for inclusion in the book. Before long, manuscripts began to arrive and another phase of the project was under way: the careful reading of manuscripts, the checking with the author regarding any alterations, additions and deletions which seemed desirable, the marking up of the manuscripts for the printer, and then the submission of batches of them to the publisher.

After a period of time, which was used to find additional contributors and articles, and to jog tardy contributors, galley proofs of each entry were sent out by the publisher—one to the author and one to me. When the author returned his copy to me, I then had to again read each one carefully and in-corporate the corrections for errors found by the author and me on the master set before returning the latter to the publisher. The setting of the type and figures into page forms was then undertaken by the printer, and page proofs were duly forwarded to me. These were checked to be certain that the necessary corrections noted on the galley proofs had been properly made and that tables and figures were correctly located. One set of page proofs was retained by me to use in preparing the index, and another was sent back to the publisher. After the front matter, i.e., the introduction, preface, and the all-important list of contributors had been prepared, the index was compiled.

These several phases of the project were not separated chronologically, and for over a year almost all were going on at one time. Now that the book has been launched, I can more fully appreciate why Peter Gray, who had just recently finished his "Encyclopedia of the Biological Sciences," in reply to my letter asking him for a bit of advice, mentioned: "First let me extend to you my deepest sympathy. I have been through it myself and I fear that you do not yet know exactly what you are in for." Despite this warning, coupled with some qualms about undertaking this major project, I have found it to be most pleasant and rewarding. Not only have I gained a host of new friends, but I have become more impressed than ever by the importance and scope of electrochemistry.

The success of the book has, of course, been vitally dependent on the cheerful cooperation of the contributors, and to each of these busy individuals I again express my sincere appreciation for sharing their knowledge and experience via their contributions.

I wish to acknowledge especially the assistance and advice regarding the contents of and contributors for the book provided by Charles L. Faust and Frederick W. Fink and their associates at Battelle Memorial Institute, by Andrew Dravnieks and Howard T. Francis of IIT Research Institute, by M. H. Lietzke and R. W. Stoughton of Oak Ridge National Laboratory, by Sherlock Swann, Jr. of the University of Illinois, by Albert J. Cornish of Westinghouse Electric Corporation (now of United Aircraft Corporation), by W. R. Clark and Edgar L. Eckfeldt of Leeds & Northrup Company, by T. P. Hoar of Cambridge University, by N. M. Winslow of Cleveland, Ohio, by Paul L. Howard of Yardney Electric Corporation, by M. O. Sem of Elektrokemisk A/S, Oslo, Norway, and by Frank Harrison of the University of Texas, Southwestern Medical School.

With sincere regret I wish to record the deaths of three good friends who contributed to this book. Thomas D. Callinan of International Business Machines Corporation, and author of the entry on "Dielectric Chemistry," died in a plane crash near Rochester, N.Y. on July 2, 1963. W. Stanley Herbert of Electric Storage Battery Company, and author of the articles on "Batteries-Dry Cells" and "Batteries, Sealed Storage," perished with his wife in the crash of an airliner near Elkton, Md. on December 8, 1963. Robert K. Shannon, Executive Secretary of the Electrochemical Society, and author of the article on the "Electrochemical Society," died in New York of a heart attack on January 9, 1964 while attending a meeting of the planning committee for the program of the Spring 1964 meeting of the Society. The positive effect on electrochemistry of each man and the friendly personality of each will long be regarded highly by all those who knew them.

The support and valuable advice of G. G. Hawley, and the all-important processing of the manuscripts and proofs by Alberta Gordon and her associates at Reinhold, have been of great import and are highly appreciated by the Editor.

I also wish to mention the efficient and valuable assistance given me by Carmen W. Walsh, Chief Librarian of the International Minerals & Chemical Corp. library in Skokie, Illinois, in connection with the rather large amount of library work I had to do in the editing of this book.

Finally, I acknowledge with deep appreciation the support and advice of my daughter, Beth, and my wife, Merrylyn. The gracious friendliness of the latter has played a large part in the establishment of the many friendships we have among the electrochemists who have supported this book in one way or another.

CLIFFORD A. HAMPEL

INTRODUCTION

Purpose of this volume. The "Encyclopedia of Electrochemistry" is intended to provide succinct, but authoritative, informative and complete articles on specific subjects related to the various phases of electrochemistry, collected in one volume and presented in encyclopedic fashion. Based on modern concepts and conditions, the articles integrate the myriad aspects of electrochemistry to provide a comprehensive reference source for a variety of readers. The book is designed to be helpful to those seeking an introduction to new areas of science, those looking at some unfamiliar facets of their own general field of physical science, or those wishing to refresh their knowledge of a specific subject. Thus, it is hoped that the book will provide information for teachers and students, as well as for practicing scientists and engineers in universities, research institutes, and industrial organizations.

While the entries contain a host of detailed data, the chief approach has been to present the basic background and phenomena rather than attempt to provide a handbook of data which can be found in specialized books now available. By means of reference lists at the ends of most articles, the reader can seek these and other more detailed works for additional information.

Scope. The "Encyclopedia of Electrochemistry" contains 412 individual articles or entries arranged in alphabetical sequence and especially prepared by 271 contributors. Its subject matter ranges over the whole scope of electrochemistry: Batteries, Corrosion, Electric Insulation, Electrodeposition, Luminescence, Electroorganic, Electrothermics, Industrial Electrolytic Processes, Theoretical Electrochemistry, and Electrochemistry in Biology and Medicine. This scope is described admirably in the article on "ELECTROCHEMISTRY," page 396, by Cecil V. King, Editor of *Journal of the Electrochemical Society.*

As one special feature, the book contains the most complete Table of Electrode Potentials and Temperature Coefficients yet compiled, which includes 467 reactions of 90 elements. It also contains the biographies of 48 scientists whose lives influenced electrochemistry; descriptions of many of the technical societies devoted to electrochemistry; articles dealing with fuel cells, thermoelectricity, semiconductors, and the basic concepts of thermodynamics; and descriptions of the instruments associated with electrochemistry. The coverage of the field of electronics has been minimized because this is handled admirably in Reinhold's companion one-volume "Encyclopedia of Electronics" edited by Charles Susskind.

The content of each individual contribution and the mode of presentation were left entirely to the discretion of the contributor, although the Editor did indicate what was desired and what might be omitted in almost all cases. The length of each entry was also specified to each author, but in several instances the designated length was exceeded. Despite this variation, the average length of the articles is 2.8 book pages or about 2200 words each. The shortest ones are about 500 words and the longest about 4000.

Because so many specific subjects relating to electrochemistry carry titles of more than one word, the locating of entries in alphabetical sequence has not been a simple task. With the thought in mind that the reader will first look for a specific article under the most commonly used title for that subject, most articles have been located so that they will be found under such titles. For instance, **STRESS CORROSION** is found in the "S" section rather than being located as **CORROSION, STRESS** in the "C" section. However, there is a cross-title listing in the "C" section as **"CORROSION, STRESS. See STRESS CORROSION."** This scheme has been followed in all such cases where it was thought helpful to do so for the reader's ease in finding a specific subject. In fact, in this encyclopedia an attempt has been made to include as many cross-titles as possible to assist the reader in finding the subject he is seeking. They and the cross-references listed after most articles also have the purpose of acquainting him with additional material related to specific subjects.

The choice of the titles for the articles has been largely that of the Editor, but it is believed that in no case did the author disagree with the choice of title. This, in turn, means that the groupings of articles on related subjects have been the Editor's choice. Examples are those under **BATTERIES, CORROSION,** and **FUSED SALT.**

No book is ever complete, especially a technical encyclopedia. Even though scores of people assisted in making suggestions for subjects to be included in the book, it is realized that many subjects have been omitted. Many are not present because of the inability to find a contributor who would volunteer to write the article; others are omitted because they were not thought of by the Editor or suggested by someone else; and some are absent because an author did not submit his assigned article for some reason or other and it was too late for the Editor to find another contributor. Fortunately, this last situation rarely occurred.

List of contributors. Because the Editor believes that all too often the List of Contributors for an encyclopedia contains only meager information about each author, he requested each contributor to submit data about his title, affiliation, and address to be listed with his name. The exact titles of each author's articles follow his listing. It is hoped that all this information will be helpful.

References. With few exceptions, at the end of each article there is a reference list requested to be "a judicious selection of a few recent papers or books which will support the author and start the reader on his way to more intensive study." Most of these lists are limited in content, but some are quite extensive. Here it was felt by the Editor that if an author spent several days at a distant library on a special trip to collect references for his article, such a collection deserved to be published in the book. Since such a situation was rare, it is hoped that the inclusion of these few extensive bibliographies will also be condoned by the readers and by the contributors who limited their lists.

Each reference has been presented in a uniform pattern. For books the order is: author's name with initials, book title, place, publisher, and date. For journals the order is: author's name with initials, journal title abbreviated, volume number in bold face type, page number(s), and date. Some contributors also included the title of journal articles and book chapters, while others did not; some gave only the first page of the article, others did not. The Editor left such decisions to the contributors. The references are listed alphabetically by first author's name, and in most cases each reference is numbered. In a very few instances, where the entry text contained no reference numbers, the references were left unnumbered.

Cross-references. Cross-references are indicated in the body of the articles by means of setting the titles of related articles in bold face type, or in some few cases, in italics. They have been inserted by the Editor or by the author in those places where they were considered to be helpful in guiding the reader to additional pertinent information in other articles. In addition, at the end of almost every article a list of the titles of other articles related to the one preceding has been given. While to the expert the titles in these lists may seem redundant or superfluous, they are presented in an effort to be helpful and to indicate that the book contains specific articles on those subjects. In any event, they are not harmful or distractive. It is to be emphasized that the cross-reference lists are not intended to be exhaustive or complete and that the Index should also be consulted for additional sources within the book about any subject.

Index. The preparation of the index to a technical encyclopedia is difficult, and keeping it within bounds presents many problems. The aim of the Editor has been to include in the Index those entries to specific subjects and locations (page numbers) which will be of greatest value to the reader. Patently, it is unwise and unnecessary to list every page where something like "potential" is mentioned. Thus, only those pages where significant information is presented are included in the index. Specific article titles are indicated in the index by means of small capitals, e.g., BATTERIES and BATTERIES—DRY CELLS. While the listing in the index of every article in the book may seem prolix, the Editor feels that a reader looking for something in the index deserves to find it there, rather than to have to leaf through the text pages in addition to the index pages.

Skokie, Illinois
April 28, 1964

CLIFFORD A. HAMPEL

A

ACETYLENE BY ELECTRIC DISCHARGE

Thermodynamic Fundamentals

The formation of acetylene from more saturated hydrocarbons is highly endothermic, i.e., large amounts of energy must be supplied. Furthermore, according to free energy relations high temperatures, of the order of 1000°C or above, are required for the reaction to proceed favorably for acetylene formation. However, the hydrocarbon feed as well as the acetylene product can decompose to carbon and hydrogen at temperatures significantly below that required for acetylene formation. Fortunately, the kinetic relations are such that, at the required acetylene formation temperature, decomposition of feed hydrocarbon and acetylene proceeds relatively slowly compared to the rate of acetylene formation. It is, however, necessary to quench the product gas immediately after the acetylene is formed in order to preserve the product; the total time involved in heating, reacting, and quenching must be of the order of a very few milliseconds.[1, 2] Although many investigators have proposed mechanisms for acetylene formation from hydrocarbons, no mechanism has yet been fully proved.

Electrical Supply of Energy

Electric discharges provide useful means of supplying large amounts of energy at high temperature for manufacturing acetylene from hydrocarbons. Since heat is released directly within the gas in which the electric discharge takes place, the heating can be done very quickly, consistent with the kinetic needs of the system. There remains, of course, the requirement for very quick quenching after acetylene formation. This is usually accomplished by water jets or sprays. Electrical energy requirements per unit weight of acetylene produced by this means are competitive with those of the calcium carbide process. Two electric discharge processes are in commercial operation; several others have been patented. In general all these processes operate at pressures from somewhat below atmospheric to somewhat above.

Gas Phase Processes

Hüls Process. The first electrical synthesis of acetylene was in the 1860's, when Berthelot used an electric discharge between carbon electrodes in a hydrogen atmosphere. Beginning in the late 1920's much interest developed in electrical processes for converting hydrocarbons to acetylene. The most extensive work was done in Germany, and this resulted in development of what is now known as the Hüls arc process. The process has been described in numerous publications, most recently by H. Gladisch.[3] It is the heart of the acetylene plant of Chemische Werke Hüls, A. G., which has a capacity of 200 million pounds of acetylene per year from hydrocarbons. The arc furnace used is shown in Fig. 1.* Hydrocarbon gas to be cracked enters tangentially into a circular chamber at R. This imparts a rapid rotational velocity to the gas which aids stabilization of the d-c arc between the cathode and anode. The power is supplied by specially designed rectifiers which control the current to the negative-characteristic arc, which is about 100 cm long and operates at 7000 volts, 1,150 amperes. Energy requirements are about 5 kwh per pound acetylene produced from methane in the arc, about 4 kwh for acetylene from higher paraffins. A significant development was prevention of deposition of coke on electrode walls by suitable control of process variables. Though electrode wear occurs, construction material is steel and replacement is cheap. It is significant that the gas leaves the arc at about 1750°K and thus has a high heat content

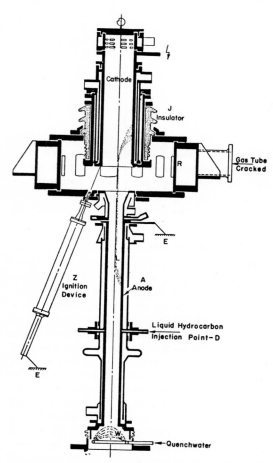

FIG. 1. The latest arc furnace used by Hüls. Note that the arc, L, is about 100 cm long and operates at 7,000 volts and 1,150 amps and draws about 8,200 kw.

which would normally be wasted in quenching the arc gas with water. As shown in Fig. 1, Hüls adds extra, higher, hydrocarbon material below the main area of acetylene formation. The added material is heated and cracked, primarily to ethylene, which is formed at temperatures lower than those required for acetylene formation. Thus, a substantial part of the high energy content of the arc gas is beneficially used instead of wasted. A typical cracked gas from the process contains 15.9 mole per cent acetylene and 7.1 per cent ethylene.

duPont Process. Another commercial plant using an electric arc process to manufacture acetylene is that of duPont at Montague, Michigan. The publicly announced capacity is 50 million pounds of acetylene per year. The details of the process have not been released, nor are energy requirements known with certainty. However, Belgian Patent 604,989,[4] issued to duPont, describes an electric arc reactor which uses a high-speed rotating d-c arc in a metal tube. Rotation is induced by a magnetic field from an externally located electromagnet. Rotational velocities of 7000 revolutions per second are mentioned. The patent also claims injection of higher hydrocarbon material into the arc gas after the arc. The injected material is claimed to be converted primarily to acetylene. The mode of arc current stabilization is not described.

A number of other electric discharge processes for making acetylene have been developed through the pilot plant stage or have been described in patents.

Knapsack and MHD Processes. The newest development in electric discharge acetylene processes is the use of an electric arc to heat a nonreacting gas which, upon its exit from the arc zone, is immediately mixed with a suitable hydrocarbon for cracking to acetylene by utilizing the heat content of the arc gas. For example, it has been known for many years that hydrogen passed through an electric arc can be converted in substantial fraction to atomic hydrogen at temperatures of the order of 3500°C. In this way, the energy content of the gas can be quite high due to the hydrogen dissociation without requiring extreme temperatures. This hydrogen can then be mixed with hydrocarbons to heat them and produce acetylene. Critical factors of such a process include (a) minimization of heat losses from the high temperature arc gas to containing walls before hydrocarbon admixture and (b) extremely fast and thorough mixing of the hydrocarbon cracking stock with the arc gas to avoid overheating of the hydrocarbon and to provide nearly uniform dwell time of the hydrocarbon before quenching. A further important factor is minimization of electrode wear while heating the arc gas to moderately high temperature. Processes of this type are exemplified in patents granted to Knapsack-Greisheim, A. G.[5] and to MHD Research, Inc.[6]

In the Knapsack process the amounts of carbon formed are stated[11] to be an order of magnitude lower than those formed in the more conventional electric arc processes. The effluent gas from the reactor typically has a composition ranging from 12 to 14.2 per cent acetylene and 6.5 to 10.5 per cent ethylene when the cracking feed is a light naphtha ("benzine"). Energy consumption is stated to range from 4.6 to 5.4 kwh per kilogram combined acetylene and ethylene.

Schoch Process. The Schoch acetylene process, developed by E. P. Schoch and associates, progressed through the pilot plant stage.[7] For one of the electrodes the process used a centrifugal blower to blow reactant gas between it and a stationary electrode. The process utilized 60 cycle alternating current and was operated in three phases with three stationary electrodes located 120 degrees apart around the periphery of the blower wheel. Typical energy consumptions and acetylene concentrations when using various feedstocks were as follows:

Feed	Mole % Acetylene	Kwh in electric discharge per lb acetylene
methane	10	4.89
methane	14	5.81
ethane	10	3.63
ethane	14	4.04
propane	12	3.53
propane	16	3.84
naphtha	25*	3.64

* after condensation of unreacted hydrocarbon feed.

The electric current to the negative characteristic electric discharge was controlled by means of an a-c constant current circuit. The T-circuit shown in Fig. 2 was chosen as the most economical control. Such a circuit takes power at constant potential, e.g., from a generator or transformer, and translates it to power at constant current. It also has the advantage of correcting the power factor at the constant potential supply end of the T-circuit. The necessity for having a large X_1 inductance in series with the discharge makes this circuit the cheapest of all possible resonating power supplies for this purpose. The potential of the discharge was controlled by varying the electrode distance.

A recent innovation of electric discharge processes is one which involves a combination of electric discharge and a shock wave.[10] Shock waves are generated by repetitive electric sparks at one end of a shock tube. The shock waves are further intensified by a magnetic field resulting from passage of the lead to one of the electrodes parallel to, and adjacent, the spark gap. Methane in the shock tube is converted in large measure to acetylene.

High Intensity Arc. Baddour (12) has reported on the use of a high intensity (positive characteristic) electric arc between carbon electrodes in hydrogen to produce acetylene. On the basis of thermodynamic calculations of the C-H system he calculated a maximum equilibrium acetylene concentration of 14 per cent at his operating conditions. In contrast he obtained acetylene concentrations as high as 18.6 per cent. The production of the greater-than-equilibrium acetylene concentration was postulated on the basis of quenching not only acetylene existing at the high temperature but also a substantial part of the C_2H, which could join with hydrogen atoms during the quench operation to form acetylene. More recently (13) Baddour has reported further tests feeding methane instead of hydrogen. Acetylene concentrations as high as 52 per cent obtained in contrast to a maximum of 25 per cent theoretically obtainable from methane alone. It was hypothesized that the exothermic reaction of carbon (from electrodes) plus hydrogen to form acetylene could supply energy for the endothermic conversion of methane to acetylene plus hydrogen and thus form additional acetylene. The electrical energy re-

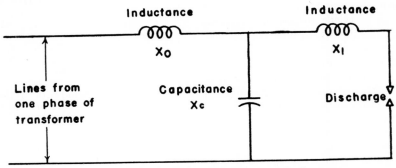

FIG. 2. T-circuit used for power supply for Schoch process.

quirements per unit amount acetylene produced are high for both the arc-in-hydrogen and the arc-in-methane cases.

Liquid Phase Processes

Ediger Process. In contrast to the processes thus far described, in which the electrodes are in the vapor phase, numerous patents have been issued for processes using electrodes immersed in hydrocarbon liquid. One of these is the Ediger process,[8] in which electricity is passed through a multiplicity of granular conductive particles, loosely dispersed as a shallow layer and immersed in a liquid hydrocarbon. Multiple electric discharges take place and as they occur, gas evolution causes movement of the particles and extinction of the arcs, whereupon new arcs are established.

Lonza Process. Another is a process patented by Lonza,[9] in which intermittent electric discharges occur between roller-shaped, rotated electrodes immersed in a liquid hydrocarbon.

By-Products

The story of acetylene from hydrocarbons by electric discharge would not be complete without a discussion of by-products produced along with acetylene. These by-products result from the complex equilibria which exist at the high temperature conditions required for acetylene formation. The amounts of the various by-products formed are functions both of these equilibria and of the relative kinetic rates of equilibrium approach. Mechanisms of formation are not precisely known.

As mentioned earlier, at the temperatures involved all the hydrocarbons present tend to decompose to carbon and hydrogen. As a matter of fact, carbon is commonly a by-product in electric discharge processes. However, on account of the very short times involved and the relatively slow decomposition rates compared to the rate of acetylene formation, comparatively small amounts of carbon are formed. Hydrogen is a major by-product as a result of formation of less saturated hydrocarbons, such as acetylene, from the more saturated hydrocarbon feedstocks; a lesser amount results from the small amount of carbon usually produced.

Hydrocarbon by-products include many types of compounds, all in small amounts. Among these are higher acetylenes, such as methyl acetylene, diacetylene, monovinyl acetylene, dimethyl acetylene, ethyl acetylene, triacetylene,

vinyldiacetylene, and others. Another class is olefins and diolefins, such as ethylene, allene, butadiene, etc. Still another group is aromatics and substituted aromatics, such as benzene, naphthalene, azulene, polynuclear aromatics, phenyl acetylene, styrene, acenaphthene, acenaphthylene, etc. In addition there is usually present some unreacted feedstock; if this be a higher hydrocarbon than methane, small amounts of the lower paraffins will also be formed.

The by-products must be substantially completely removed from the acetylene for the acetylene to be suitable for most utilization processes. Numerous separation systems have been devised.

References

1. KIRK, R. E., AND OTHMER, D. E., Editors, "Encyclopedia of Chemical Technology," Suppl. Vol. II, p. 1, New York, Interscience Publishers, Inc., 1960.
2. McKETTA, JOHN J., JR., Editor, "Advances in Petroleum Chemistry and Refining," Vol. III, p. 379, New York, Interscience Publishers, Inc., 1960.
3. GLADISCH, H., "How Hüls Makes Acetylene by DC Arc." *Hydrocarbon Processing and Petroleum Refiner*, **41**, No. 6, 159 (June, 1962).
4. E. I. duPont de Nemours and Company, Belgian Patent 604,989 (June 14, 1961).
5. SCHALLUS, E., AND GÖTZ, A., (to Knapsack-Griesheim A. G.), U. S. Patent 2,916,534 (Dec. 8, 1959); German Patent 1,012,899 (Aug. 1, 1957); and Belgian Patent 611,880 (Dec. 22, 1961).
6. ORBACH, H. K., (to MHD Research, Inc.), U. S. Patent 3,042,830 (July 3, 1962).
7. "Acetylene from Hydrocarbons by the Schoch Electric Discharge Process," The University of Texas Publication No. 5011, June 1, 1950.
8. Ediger, British Patent 661,105 (Nov. 14, 1951).
9. Lonza Elektrizitätswerke und Chemische Fabriken A. G., Basel, German Patent 1,019,651.
10. LAUER, J. L., AND FRIEL, P. J., (to Sun Oil Co.), U. S. Patent 2,986,505 (May 30, 1961).
11. SENNEWALD, K., SCHALLUS, E., AND POHL, F., *Chemie-Ingenieur-Technik*, **35**, No. 1, 1–6 (January, 1963).
12. BADDOUR, R. F., AND IWASYK, J. M., *Ind. Eng. Chem. Process Design and Development*, **1**, No. 3, 169 (July, 1962).
13. BADDOUR, R. F., "Reactions of Carbon Vapor with Hydrogen and with Methane in a High Intensity Arc," paper presented at 49th National Meeting. AIChE, New Orleans, March 11, 1963.

WALTER B. HOWARD

Cross-references: *Gases, Electrical Conductivity and Ionization.*

ACHESON, EDWARD GOODRICH (1856–1931)

Acheson was born March 9, 1856, at Washington, Pennsylvania, and at an early age took an unusual interest in the operation of the furnace, did a little amateur prospecting in the hills of Armstrong County, and carried on what might be termed extracurricular activities in mathematics, with special emphasis on geometry, trigonometry, and surveying.

In 1872 when the country was on the threshold of a panic, his father had already suffered financial reverses, and Acheson, who had not yet celebrated his seventeenth birthday, was forced to turn his back upon school and seek a job.

Western Pennsylvania was rapidly becoming industrialized, being crossed by railroads and dotted with coal mines, oil wells, blast furnaces, as well as numerous factories and retail establishments of one sort or another. Acheson's employment for the next seven years took him far afield and found him in such varied occupations as timekeeper, salesman, ticket clerk, oil-tank gauger, and surveyor.

This provides the background, minus countless struggles and heartaches, for the young man who was destined to become an important aide to Thomas A. Edison; the inventor of an anti-induction telephone cable which he sold to George Westinghouse; the designer of an electric resistance furnace of great commercial significance; the discoverer of silicon carbide ("Carborundum"), the abrasive so important in mass-production machining operations; the first to establish a practical means for the large-scale conversion of amorphous carbon to the graphite allotrope, which process made possible the manufacture of electrodes so indispensable in electrochemistry and electrometallurgy; and a pioneer in the field of colloid chemistry, developing methods for reducing graphite and other solids to colloidal dimensions and subsequently adapting these colloids to a wide and diversified range of industrial applications.

In addition to the products cited above, Acheson brought into being many other materials and devices for which the United States Government granted him some seventy patents.

Not satisfied simply to create, Acheson, eager to put his creations at the disposal of mankind, founded companies for the manufacture of abrasives, graphite powders, graphite electrodes, inks, and colloidal suspensions of graphite. Numbered among these are The Carborundum Company, Niagara Falls, N. Y.; the Acheson Graphite Company, Niagara Falls (now a part of National Carbon Company, a division of Union Carbide and Carbon Corporation); Acheson Colloids Company, Port Huron, Michigan; and Acheson Colloids Limited, London, England.

During his lifetime, Acheson had numerous honors and awards bestowed upon him. In addition to having received the John Scott Medal on two occasions, he was also awarded the Count Rumford Medal, the Perkin Medal, and his own Acheson Medal. In 1928 he founded the Edward Goodrich Acheson Fund, which under the trusteeship of The Electrochemical Society, provided a cash prize and the Edward Goodrich Acheson Medal "to the person who, in the judgment of the directors of the Society, shall have made such contribution to the advancement of any of the objects, purposes or activities, fostered or promoted by the Society, to merit such an award." The Society unanimously voted him the first recipient of his own medal for his contributions to electrothermics.

The degree of Doctor of Science was conferred upon Acheson by the University of Pittsburgh in 1909, and five years later he was appointed an officer of the Royal Order of the Polar Star by the King of Sweden.

Acheson died in New York City, July 6, 1931.

RAYMOND SZYMANOWITZ

Cross-references: *Graphite, Electrothermal Production; Silicon Carbide.*

ACIDIMETRY AND ALKALIMETRY

The terms "acidimetry" and "alkalimetry" refer to volumetric determinations based upon the titration of a sample with a solution containing an accurately known concentration of acid or base, respectively. In the most elementary terms, the processes involved in acidimetry and alkalimetry include the following: (1) addition of a standardized solution of an acid or base to a solution containing the sample to be determined; (2) the determination by chemical or physicochemical means of that point during the addition of the standardized acid or base wherein the amount of acid or base is chemically equivalent to the reactant in the sample; (3) the calculation of results from values for the concentration of standardized reagent and the volume of this reagent added to reach the equivalence point.

A description of the preparation and standardization of solutions of acids and bases for acidimetry and alkalimetry is beyond the scope of this article. For such information, the reader is referred to one of the standard textbooks on quantitative chemical analysis listed in the bibliography.

In systems susceptible to analysis by the methods of acidimetry and alkalimetry, the samples encountered can usually be classified as being composed of a strong acid or base, a weak acid or base, or the salt of a weak acid or base. The classification of an acid or base as being weak or strong depends upon the extent of its dissociation in solution. In aqueous solution, a strong acid, such as HCl, HNO_3, $HClO_4$, dissociates completely according to the relation:

$$HX + H_2O \rightarrow H_3O^+ + X^-$$

or, more conventionally:

$$HX \rightarrow H^+ + X^-$$

where H^+ is understood to be a hydrated proton. For a strong base, this complete dissociation would be given by:

$$XOH \rightarrow X^+ + OH^-.$$

In both cases, the dissociation is complete in dilute aqueous solution, and no equilibrium exists between the ions and the undissociated molecules. On the other hand, the weak acid HA dissociates according to the expression:

$$HA + H_2O \rightleftharpoons H_3O^+ + A^-$$

where the double arrow indicates an equilibrium exists between the ions, H_3O^+ and A^-, and the undissociated acid, HA. The mathematical relation which expresses the extent to which this dissociation proceeds is:

$$K_{equilibrium} = \frac{[H_3O^+]\,[A^-]}{[HA]\,[H_2O]}.$$

Since the concentration of H_2O is a constant, the two constants can be combined to give:

$$K_a = \frac{[H_3O^+]\,[A]}{[HA]} \quad \text{or} \quad \frac{[H^+]\,[A^-]}{[HA]}.$$

For a weak base, the dissociation is given by:

$$K_b = \frac{[B^+]\,[OH^-]}{[BOH]}.$$

As the dissociation constants for various weak acids and bases decrease, the acids and bases become progressively weaker. Thus, an acid having $K_a = 10^{-9}$ is much weaker than one having $K_a = 10^{-5}$. As a convenience, the dissociation constant of a weak acid or base is often expressed as its negative logarithm, and given the symbol, pK. Thus, for acetic acid, $K_a = 1.75 \times 10^{-5}$,

$$pK_a = -\log_{10} K_a = 4.76$$

Thus, as the pK of a weak acid or base *increases*, the acid or base becomes weaker.

In the acidimetric titration of a strong base with a strong acid, both of which are completely dissociated in dilute solution, the net reaction occurring is:

$$H^+ + OH^- \rightleftharpoons HOH$$

Water, the principal product of such titrations, dissociates slightly according to the equilibrium:

$$H_2O \rightleftharpoons H^+ + OH^-$$

the equilibrium constant for which is given by:

$$K_{eq} = \frac{[H^+]\,[OH^-]}{[H_2O]}$$

Since the concentration of water is essentially a constant in aqueous solutions, the two constants are combined to give:

$$K_w = [H^+]\,[OH^-] = 1.00 \times 10^{-14}$$

at 25°C. In terms of negative logarithms, the above relation becomes:

$$pK_w = -\log K_w = -\log [H^+]_+ - \log [OH^-]$$

$$= pH + pOH = 14.00$$

At the equivalence point in a strong acid-strong base titration, the pH, or negative logarithm of the hydronium ion concentration, is equal to the pOH as indicated by the dissociation of water. Hence, at this point, $pH = \frac{1}{2} \times pK_w$, or pH = 7.00. Thus, in a strong acid-strong base titration, the pH at the equivalence point is 7.00, irrespective of the concentrations of the reactants involved. This is illustrated in Fig. 1, which gives the titration curves of strong acid-strong base systems for various initial concentrations of acid and base.

In the titration of a weak acid or weak base with a strong base or acid (respectively), a situation obtains at the equivalence point which dif-

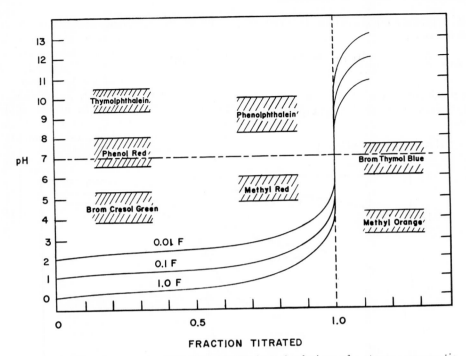

FIG. 1. Titration curves of 1.0, 0.1, and 0.01 formal solutions of a strong monoprotic acid with equal concentrations of a strong base.

fers markedly from that of a strong acid-strong base system. In general, the pH at the equivalence point in a weak acid-strong base, or weak base-strong acid titration differs from 7.00. Using the weak acid acetic acid, HOAc, as an example, the titration reaction can be written:

$$HOAc \rightleftharpoons OAc^- + H^+$$

$$H^+ + OH^- \rightleftharpoons HOH$$

Thus, at the equivalence point of this titration, the solution consists, essentially, of the acetate salt of the strong base titrant. This system can be considered to consist of a Brønsted acid, H_2O, and a Brønsted base, OAc^-, which react to form their conjugate pairs until an equilibrium is established:

$$OAc^- + H_2O \rightleftharpoons HOAc + OH^-$$

The equilibrium expression for this reaction is:

$$K_{eq} = \frac{[HOAc][OH^-]}{[OAc^-][H_2O]}$$

or

$$K_h = \frac{[HOAc][OH^-]}{[OAc]},$$

wherein K_h is composed of $K_{eq} \times [H_2O]$, the product of two constants. If the expression for K_h is multiplied, numerator and denominator, by $[H^+]$, it becomes evident that:

$$K_h = \frac{[HOAc][OH^-]}{[OAc^-]} \times \frac{[H^+]}{[H^+]} = \frac{[HOAc]}{[H^+][OAc^-]}$$

$$\times [H^+][OH^-] = \frac{K_w}{K_a}.$$

Hence, if the dissociation constant, K_a, is known, the hydrolysis constant, K_h, can be determined. The expression from which the pH at the equivalence point in a weak acid-strong base titration can be obtained is:

$$K_a = \frac{[H^+]^3 + [H^+]^2 C_s - K_w[H^+]}{K_w - [H^+]^2}$$

in which C_s is the nominal equivalence-point concentration of the salt of the weak acid and strong base. The only assumption made in deriving the above is the equality of activity and concentration. A useful approximation is given by:

$$pH = \frac{1}{2}(pK_w + pK_a - pC_s)$$

In the titration of a weak base with a strong

acid, the expression equivalent to the exact expression above is:

$$K_b = \frac{K_w{}^2 + K_w C_s\,[H^+] - [H^+]^2\,K_w}{[H^+]^3 - K_w[H^+]}$$

The approximate form of this, in terms of negative logarithms of the various quantities is given by:

$$pH = \tfrac{1}{2}\,(pK_w + pC_s - pK_b)$$

From the foregoing analysis, it is evident that the pH at the equivalence point is dependent upon the concentration of salt formed by the titration, which is dependent upon the initial concentration of the weak acid or base. The equivalence point pH, in addition, is dependent upon the strength of the weak acid or base, as indicated by the value K_a or K_b. This dependence is shown for monobasic weak acids by the curves of Fig. 2.

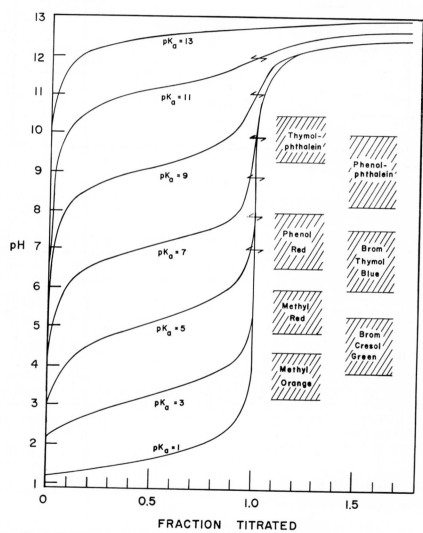

FIG. 2. Titration curves of 0.1 formal solutions of weak acids with 0.1 formal sodium hydroxide, showing equivalence points of acids having successively increasing pK values, and the pH ranges of several indicators. (From Meites and Thomas, "Advanced Analytical Chemistry," New York, McGraw-Hill Book Co. Inc., 1960)

Techniques of Establishing the Equivalence Point

The most simple means for establishing the equivalence point in acidimetric or alkalimetric titrations is through the use of chemical indicators. These indicators are themselves generally weak organic acids and weak organic bases, the undissociated form of which has a color different from the dissociated form. There are a large number of acid-base indicators available; these cover the pH scale from approximately pH = 0 to pH = 13. Each of these indicators undergoes at least one change from an acid color to a basic color over a small range in pH, usually of the order of 1 to 2 pH units. The range of color changes for several of the more analytically useful indicators is indicated by the cross-hatched areas in Figs. 1 and 2.

The use of chemical acid-base indicators poses several problems in certain applications, among which is the fact that the color change is not essentially instantaneous, but occurs over a significant range of pH units. In addition, chemical indicators cannot be used conveniently in colored solutions, nor can they be used to follow the course of acidimetric and alkalimetric titrations, or to monitor continuously industrial process streams. These difficulties can be overcome through the use of potentiometric, and, to a certain extent, conductometric methods.

In the potentiometric determination of pH, measurements are based on differences in potential across a cell consisting of a reference electrode and a hydrogen-sensitive electrode, a portion of which includes the sample solution. In such an arrangement, the potential difference is a function of the pH of the sample solution. Since the pH changes during an acidimetric or alkalimetric titration, the potential difference between the two electrodes also changes, yielding a potentiometric titration curve having the same general shape as the pH *vs* ml of titrant curve.

For the measurement of pH, several electrodes have found widespread use. The most obvious choice, and that which was probably first used for this purpose, is the hydrogen electrode. This electrode responds to the hydrogen ion concentration according to the equilibrium:

$$2H^+ + 2e^- \rightleftharpoons H_2 \text{ (gas, 1 atm)}$$

When this electrode is used, it is often advantageous to use two, one as the indicating electrode, dipping into the sample solution, the second serving as a reference electrode, dipping into a standard solution of known hydrogen ion concentration. In such an arrangement, the potentiometric cell becomes a concentration cell, in which the cell potential difference is given by:

$$E_{cell} = 0.0591 \log \frac{[H^+] \text{ standard}}{[H^+] \text{ sample}} \text{ (at 25°C)}$$

or

$$E_{cell} = 0.0591 (\text{pH}_{sample} - \text{pH}_{standard})$$

Often, the indicator electrode is the saturated calomel electrode, which is assembled more readily than the hydrogen reference electrode. The cell potential difference would then be given by:

$$E_{cell} = 0.246 + 0.0591 \text{ pH}$$

This electrode, the standard to which all pH measurements are referred, suffers from several disadvantages. The most important of these are the sensitivity to oxidizing or reducing agents possibly present in a sample, and the difficulty of assembly and operation. Many of the difficulties found with the hydrogen electrode are overcome by the use of the quinhydrone electrode. This electrode consists of a saturated solution of quinhydrone, an equimolar compound of *p*-benzoquinone (Q) and *p*-benzohydroquinone (H_2Q). In aqueous solution, the following equilibria exist:

$$Q + 2H^+ + 2e^- \rightleftharpoons H_2Q$$

The potential difference of a cell composed of a quinhydrone indicator electrode and a saturated calomel reference electrode is given (theoretically) by:

$$E_{cell} = +0.453 - 0.0591 \text{ pH}$$

in solutions having low ionic strengths. Like the hydrogen electrode and most others in common use, the quinhydrone electrode suffers from several disadvantages. Significant amounts of oxidizing and reducing materials react with the quinhydrone; in solutions having a pH greater than 8, hydroquinone is spontaneously air-oxidized. In addition, hydroquinone is a very weak acid ($K_a \sim 10^{-10}$); hence it will undergo partial neutralization by strong bases in the range pH 8 to 9.

Several indicator electrodes of the type metal-metal oxide have been found to be more or less reversible toward hydrogen ion. Chief among these is the antimony electrode, which consists simply of an electrode of pure antimony metal inserted into the sample solution. In aqueous solution, the surface of the antimony electrode becomes coated with the hydrated antimonous oxide, Sb_2O_3. This electrode then enters into the following equilibrium involving hydrogen ion:

$$Sb_2O_3 + 6H^+ + 6e^- \rightleftharpoons 2Sb + 3H_2O.$$

This electrode has the advantage of being extremely simple and rugged. It is often used in monitoring pH in industrial streams. It suffers from the disadvantage of being sensitive to trace concentrations of citrate, tartrate and other ions forming soluble complexes. In addition, since the oxide is amphoteric, the electrode can be used in neither strongly acid nor strongly alkaline solutions.

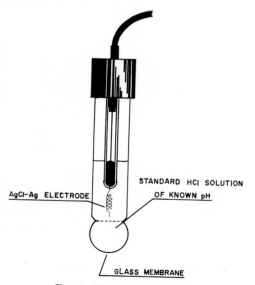

AgCl-Ag ELECTRODE

STANDARD HCl SOLUTION
OF KNOWN pH

GLASS MEMBRANE

FIG. 3. The glass electrode.

By far the most widely used electrode system for pH measurements is the glass electrode, used with a saturated calomel reference electrode. This electrode is possible as a result of the discovery that certain types of glass are permeable to hydrogen ions. Thus, a glass electrode can function as a reversible hydrogen electrode. A typical form of this electrode is shown in Fig. 3. It consists of a glass tube with a very thin bulb of a special type of glass permeable to hydrogen ions. The tube contains a standard solution of standard HCl of known pH, usually at pH 1. Dipping into this solution is a AgCl-Ag° electrode. Contact with external circuitry is often made by means of a drop of mercury. When used with the saturated calomel reference electrode, the following expression relates the overall potential difference with the pH of a sample solution:

$$E_{cell} = 0.094 - 0.0591 \text{ pH}$$

Unlike the other electrodes mentioned above, the glass electrode cannot be used with the ordinary potentiometer-galvanometer arrangement of potentiometry due to its inordinately high resistance of the order of 100 megohms. As a result, the glass electrode is used in conjunction with a stable, high gain d-c amplifier in the form of a "pH meter."

In using the pH meter with a glass electrode-saturated calomel cell system, as in acidimetric and alkalimetric potentiometry with the other electrodes mentioned above, it becomes necessary to standardize the system if accurate measurements of pH are to be obtained. This is made necessary by the existence of liquid junction potentials and asymmetry potentials not included in the various relations mentioned above, and is accomplished by the use of standard buffer solutions such as those developed by R. G. Bates at the National Bureau of Standards. It is also important to adjust the ionic strength of solutions whose pH is to be determined or followed so that they approximate the ionic strengths of the standard buffers used in calibration. By careful calibration, attention to detail, and careful interpretation of data, these various potentiometric systems are capable of very high accuracy and precision in pH measurements. In acidimetric and alkalimetric titrations, in which the electrode-potentiometer system is used only as a means of locating equivalence points, such care is usually unnecessary.

Conductometric measurements deserve brief

mention in that the measurement of conductance of a solution can often be used to locate the position of the equivalence point in acidimetric and alkalimetric titrations. The utilization of this method depends upon the change in conductance of a solution, due to changes in the numbers of ions, during the course of a titration. A pair of platinum or other inert electrodes of fixed area and separation is placed in the sample to be titrated, and the resistance of the solution measured by means of a bridge circuit. The conductance is then obtained by taking the reciprocal of the resistance. When conductance, multiplied by the dilution factor function of milliliters of titrant, curves of the $(V_{sample} + V_{titrant})/V_{sample}$, is plotted as a type shown in Fig. 4 result. The breaks in the curves occur at the equivalence points in the various titrations. Since the breaks are reasonably sharp, fairly accurate location of equivalence points is possible. However, as the total ionic concentration of unreactive species increases, the per cent change in the corrected conductance decreases, so that in solutions of

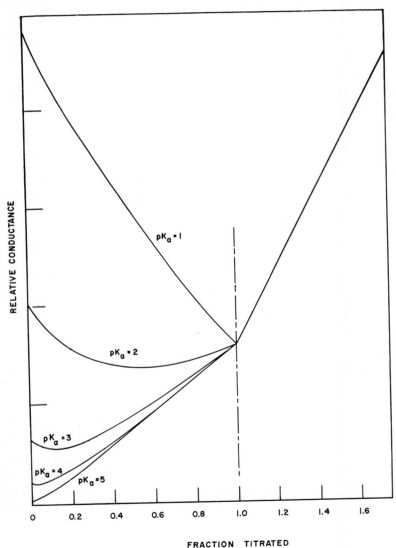

FIG. 4. Conductometric titration curves of successively weaker acids with a strong base. (From Meites and Thomas, "Advanced Analytical Chemistry." New York, McGraw-Hill Book Co., Inc., 1960)

high ionic strength, the accuracy with which the equivalence point can be determined decreases somewhat. This is especially true for weak acids and tends to place a limitation on the usefulness of the method.

Applications of Acidimetry and Alkalimetry

Aside from the acidimetric and alkalimetric determinations of strong and weak acids and bases in aqueous solution for the purpose of obtaining total acidity or basicity of a sample, there are several interesting applications of this technique. A sizeable amount of effort has been directed toward titrations in nonaqueous media, wherein it becomes possible to carry out reactions which are inconvenient or at best, inaccurate in aqueous solution. Proper choice of solvent can greatly enhance the acidic or basic properties of substances that are weak enough to exhibit no break in their aqueous titration curves.

Other applications of acidimetry and alkalimetry include determination of anions of weak acids and cations of weak, including relatively insoluble, bases. In both types of determination, two paths are available: direct titration of the anion or cation, or exchange of the anion or cation for hydroxide or hydrogen ions, respectively, by means of ion-exchange resins. Direct acid-base titrations of metal cations are usually not widely applicable because of the interference of other metals and the inexact composition of the precipitates which often form. As a result, the ion exchange technique has found much wider use. In addition, acidimetric and alkalimetric techniques can be applied to determinations of ionization constants of weak acids and bases, as well as to determinations of equivalent weights. Several examples of the various applications are given in articles listed in the bibliography, along with some general references on the theory behind this technique.

References

1. KOLTHOFF, I. M., AND SANDELL, E. B., "Textbook of Quantitative Inorganic Analysis," *Ch. XXIX, XXXIV*, New York, MacMillan, 1952.
2. LAITINEN, H. A., *Chemical Analysis*, Ch. 3–5, New York, McGraw-Hill, 1960.
3. HILLEBRAND, W. F., LUNDELL, G. E. F., BRIGHT, H. A., AND HOFFMAN, J. I., "Applied Inorganic Analysis," pp. 166ff, New York, John Wiley & Sons, 1953.
4. BATES, R. G., "Electrometric pH Determinations," New York, John Wiley & Sons, 1954.
5. RIDDICK, J. A., "Acid-Base Titrations in Nonaqueous Solvents," (Rev.), *Anal. Chem.*, **32**, 172R (1960).
6. STREULI, C. A., "Titrations in Nonaqueous Solvents," (Rev.), *Anal. Chem.*, **34**, 302R (1962).
7. BATES, R. G., "Electrodes for pH Measurements," (Rev.), *J. Electroanal. Chem.*, **2**, 93 (1961).
8. GASLINI, F., AND NAHUM, L. Z., "Conductometric Titration of Very Weak Acids," *Anal. Chem.*, **31**, 989 (1959).
9. UNDERWOOD, A. L., "Carbonic Anhydrase in the Titration of Carbon Dioxide Solutions," *Anal. Chem.*, **33**, 955 (1961).
10. MATHER, W. B., JR., AND ANSON, F. C., "Coulometric-Acidimetric Titration of Fluoride in Acetic Anhydride," *Anal. Chem.*, **33**, 132 (1961).

JAMES L. BROWNLEE

Cross-references: *Electrometric Titrations; Dissociation; Glass Electrode; pH; pH Meter; Reference Electrodes.*

ACIDS AND BASES. See ACIDIMETRY AND ALKALIMETRY; DISSOCIATION; IONIC EQUILIBRIA; pH; pH METER; pH TITRATION CURVES.

ACTIVITY AND ACTIVITY COEFFICIENT

The Gibbs free energy function F is defined such that at constant temperature and pressure the change in free energy, ΔF, for a system is equal to zero at equilibrium, is negative for a process which would proceed spontaneously as written, and is positive for one which would proceed spontaneously in the reverse direction. The function ΔF also gives a measure of the maximum work which may be obtained from a particular transformation.

In general the absolute value of the free energy is not known. Since the chemist is usually more interested in free energy changes than in absolute values, F for any substance is expressed in terms of $F°$, the (unknown absolute) value in some arbitrary standard state, and a deviation function. The latter provides a definition of the *activity*, a, of the substance with respect to the standard state:

$$F = F° + RT \ln a \tag{1}$$

While the choice of the standard state is completely arbitrary, there are certain conventions which have been found useful. In problems involving pure substances in condensed phases it is usually convenient to choose the pure solid or pure liquid at each temperature (and 1 atm pressure) as the standard state. Accordingly, $F = F°$ and $a = 1$ for the pure solid or pure liquid. For pure gases the standard state at any temperature is usually taken as the gas at unit fugacity. The *fugacity*, f, is defined as numerically equal to the pressure at zero pressure and with a logarithmic relation to the free energy. Thus, the fugacity is always proportional to the activity; indeed, the latter may be defined as equal to the ratio of the *fugacity*, f, to the standard fucagity, $f°$. Then, if the standard state is taken as the gas at unit fugacity,

$$F = F° + RT \ln f = F° + RT \ln a \qquad (2)$$

where the two values of $F°$ are equal, since $f = a$. Since the fugacity is equal numerically to the pressure at zero pressure and approximately equal to it at low pressure, the fugacity may be expressed conveniently as a product of the pressure, p, (or partial pressure in a gaseous mixture) and a *fugacity coefficient*, z

$$f = zp,$$

where z is approximately equal to unity at low pressure.

When treating solutions the important free energy functions are the partial molal free energies, $\bar{F}_i°$, of the components, i.e., the partial derivatives of the total free energy with respect to incremental additions of the various components $(\partial F / \partial n_i)$. These follow the same functional form as the total free energy of a pure substance:

$$\bar{F}_i = \bar{F}_i° + RT \ln a_i$$

In the case of dilute solutions of many nonelectrolytes the activities (or fugacities) of the solute and solvent are nearly proportional to their concentrations. For this reason, as in the case of fugacity vs (partial) pressure of gases, it is convenient to set the activity equal to the concentration times a correction factor or *activity coefficient*, which is equal to unity at infinite dilution of the solute and then deviates from unity as the concentration increases. The standard state of the solvent is usually taken as the pure solvent; that of the solute is taken for convenience as a hypothetical state of unit activity in which the partial molal enthalpy of the solute is equal to the value at infinite dilution.

In the case of solutions of strong electrolytes, complete dissociation into ν_+ positive ions of charge $+z_+$ and ν_- negative ions of charge $-z_-$ per mole is assumed, at least in relatively dilute solutions.

$$A_{\nu_+}B_{\nu_-} = \nu_+ A^{+z-} + \nu_- B^{-z-}$$

and $\nu = \nu_+ + \nu_-$, where $\nu_+ z_+ = \nu_- z_-$. (For a uni-univalent electrolyte $z_+ = z_- = 1$, $\nu_+ = \nu_- = 1$ and $\nu = 2$). It is convenient to express activities of electrolytes in terms of (geometric) mean concentrations and mean activity coefficients, although individual ion activities and activity coefficients have yet to be given an experimental meaning. These may be defined on the mole-fraction N, the molal m or the molar M concentration scales with the respective activity coefficient symbols f, γ and y.

$$\begin{aligned} \bar{F} &= \bar{F}° + RT \ln a \\ &= \bar{F}_N° + \nu RT \ln f_\pm N_\pm \\ &= \bar{F}_m° + \nu RT \ln \gamma_\pm m_\pm \\ &= \bar{F}_M° + \nu RT \ln y_\pm M_\pm \end{aligned} \qquad (3)$$

While the partial molal free energy of the solute, $\bar{F}$, (being on an energy/mole basis) has a unique value, the standard free energy values, $\bar{F}_i°$, are different for the various concentration scales. In each case the activity coefficient, $f_\pm$, $\gamma_\pm$ or $y_\pm$, is defined such that it goes to unity as the concentration, $N_\pm$, $m_\pm$ or $M_\pm$, goes to zero. The mean values of the activity coefficients are usually reported as such and often the $\pm$ symbol is dropped. The mean concentrations are defined as the product $N_\pm{}^\nu = N_+^\nu N_-^\nu$, etc. In the case of mixed electrolytes N_+, m_+ or M_+ is the total concentration of the particular cation in question from all sources, as N_-, m_- or M_- is the total concentration of the particular anion in question, while ν, ν_+ and ν_- depend on the particular electrolyte of interest. Thus, $m_{\pm \text{NaCl}}$ in 1 m NaCl and in a 1 m NaCl − 1 m CaCl$_2$ mixture are 1 m and $\sqrt{1 \times 3}$ m, respectively.

Although all three of the above concentration scales are in common use, the molality scale seems to be the most popular for thermodynamic measurements. Hence the following equations will be expressed in terms of m and $\gamma_\pm$, although they could also be derived in terms of the other scales.

Temperature and Pressure Effects

The variation of the activity coefficient with temperature is given by

$$-\nu RT^2 \left(\frac{\partial \ln \gamma_\pm}{\partial T}\right)_{P,m} = \bar{L} = \bar{H} - \bar{H}^\circ \quad (4)$$

where $\bar{L}$ is the relative partial molal heat content or the difference between the partial molal enthalpy at molality, m, and the value at infinite dilution. The variation of the activity coefficient with pressure may be expressed similarly in terms of the partial molal volume, $\bar{V}$, at molality, m, and the value at infinite dilution, $\bar{V}^\circ$

$$\nu RT \left(\frac{\partial \ln \gamma_\pm}{\partial P}\right)_{T,m} = \bar{V} - \bar{V}^\circ \quad (5)$$

In the integration of these equations account must be taken of the fact that $\bar{L}$ and $(\bar{V} - \bar{V}^\circ)$ are functions of both temperature and pressure.

The Debye-Hückel Equation

The variation of the activity coefficient with concentration involves extra-thermodynamic considerations. One of the most widely used treatments is that of Debye and Hückel, who deduced the expression shown in Eq. (6) for the activity coefficient of an electrolyte.

$$\log \gamma_\pm = -\frac{S\sqrt{I}}{1 + B\mathring{a}\sqrt{I}} \quad (6)$$

In Eq. (6) S is the Debye-Hückel limiting slope, which is a function of temperature, dielectric constant of the solvent and electrolyte valence type; I is the total ionic strength of the solution defined as

$$I = \frac{1}{2}\sum_i m_i z_i^2,$$

where the summation is taken over all the ions of concentration m_i and valence z_i ; B is a constant at any temperature and includes the inverse square root of the product of the dielectric constant of the solvent and the absolute temperature; and $\mathring{a}$ is the "distance of closest approach" parameter. Eq. (6) can be used to represent observed activity coefficients of electrolytes fairly well up to an ionic strength of about 0.1 simply by choosing a value of $\mathring{a}$ characteristic of the electrolytes. For use above this concentration additional terms may be added as needed as shown in Eq. (7):

$$\log \gamma_\pm = -\frac{S\sqrt{I}}{1 + A'\sqrt{I}} + B'I + C'I^2 \quad (7)$$

where the empirical $\mathring{a}$ times the known B is re-placed by the empirical A' and where B' and C' are additional empirical parameters.

Activity coefficients of solutes may be derived from many types of measurements: (1) emf measurements of cells without transference, (2) emf measurements of cells with transference, combined with a knowledge of the transference numbers involved, (3) solubility measurements, (4) measurements of solute vapor pressure, (5) measurements of solvent vapor pressure, (6) measurements of boiling point elevation, (7) measurements of freezing point depression.

The first four of these methods may be considered to be more *direct* than the last three since the former involve a measurement of the free energy (and hence activity) of the solute, while the latter involve a measurement of the free energy or activity of the solvent. Use must then be made of a form of the Gibbs-Duhem equation

$$\sum_i m_i d\bar{F}_i = 0$$

at constant (total) pressure and temperature. Here the sum is taken over all components (2 in the case of a single electrolyte in water). Thus, the activity of the solute at any m is obtained by an integration of the activity of the solvent from $m = 0$ to $m = m$.

References

1. KLOTZ, I. M., "Chemical Thermodynamics," New York, Prentice Hall, Inc., 1950.
2. LEWIS, G. N., AND RANDALL, M., "Thermodynamics," 2nd edition, revised by K. S. Pitzer and Leo Brewer, New York, McGraw-Hill Book, Co., 1961.

M. H. LIETZKE AND
R. W. STOUGHTON

ADDITION AGENTS

In electrodeposition substances that are added to a solution to alter the appearance, properties, or structure of the deposit are known as *addition agents*. Generally their effects seem to be out of proportion to their concentration in the solution. The baths in which they are employed will always yield some kind of deposit without them; it is only the character of the deposit that is altered. The objectives that may be attained by their use are numerous, but they can be classified as (1) compaction or densification, (2) brightness, (3) levelling, (4) alteration of physical properties, (5) alteration of mechanical properties, (6) alteration of structure.

The discussion that follows will be based upon this classification, but it must be emphasized that a given plating solution may contain several addition agents in order to achieve simultaneous control of two or more characteristics of the deposit, e.g., brightness as well as freedom from internal stress in nickel deposits. Because of the great commercial importance of the effects of many addition agents, a great deal of patent activity has taken place in the field, and many proprietary solutions have been developed and promoted. In fact, the use of proprietary solutions in both captive and job shops far outstrips the use of solutions that have never been patented or of those that have come into the public domain.

Compaction

Some metals deposit so readily from certain solutions that only a diffuse moss-like blob of metal is produced. Acid tin solutions are prime examples, but splendid deposits may be obtained by the addition, for example, of small amounts of gelatin or glue to a strongly acidified stannous sulfate solution. In practice, however, several addition agents are often used to attain the best deposits and to assure continuous operation of the solution.

There are at least five general classes of materials that may be used as addition agents for compaction of acid-tin deposits, and it is difficult to find for them any common denominator more specific than the observation that they are all organic compounds.

So far as the mechanism of addition agent action for compaction is concerned, only one basic fact has been well established. Compaction is primarily a matter of preventing the formation of large tree-like crystals in favor of the deposition of small contiguous grains of metal. The details of the mechanisms for bringing about this change in structure are still the subject of inconclusive conjecture.

Brightness

There is probably no more spectacular use of addition agents than for the production of bright deposits, and because of their commercial value there is a bewildering array of patent and journal literature. Contributing in no little measure to the confusion is the fact that there is no useful objective means of measuring brightness. Subjective evaluations involve a host of personal factors, not the least of which is terminology—what may be "full-bright" to an inventor of a process may be a very disappointing and utterly unacceptable "hazy bright" to a waffle-iron manufacturer.

Brighteners have been discovered for almost every plating solution of any consequence, but commercial use is concentrated in baths for nickel, copper, zinc, cadmium, and silver. Of these, nickel baths have received the lion's share of attention owing, probably, to the extensive use of nickel in the automotive and household-appliance industries. Perhaps the omission of chromium will be questioned. The small amount of sulfuric acid or other "catalyst" added to a chromic anhydride solution is not an addition agent. It is needed to make possible the deposition of any metal at all. That a bright deposit is also obtained is only a happy dividend!

It is not surprising that nickel brighteners have received a major share of the work that has gone into the study of the mechanism of addition-agent action. In fact, a great many publications on mechanisms are based *only* on data and phenomena connected with brightness, the authors having forgotten or neglected the many other uses of addition agents. The point here is, of course, that the terms "brighteners" and "addition agents" are too frequently used synonymously.

Very little has been done to organize or systematize the various compounds that can be used as brighteners for most metals. Nickel is an exception and a useful classification has been developed.

The basic division of nickel brighteners, all of which are used in a Watts bath, involves two categories. Brighteners of the first class comprise organic compounds containing the sulfonic-acid group, and they produce bright deposits on buffed surfaces. Brighteners of the second class are not useful alone, but in conjunction with those of the first class they produce brilliant deposits with good auxillary properties over a suitable range of current densities and other operating variables. The auxillary properties include internal stress, ductility, strength, and hardness. Materials falling in the second class comprise both inorganic and organic materials, and in each category there are several subclasses. Although these classifications are of great value in systematizing the compilation of information in this field, they are of no value whatsoever in predicting new *classes* of materials that might be investigated. They provide, of course, a systematic basis on which to assess both the worth and the pertinency of mechanisms of brightening action that have been suggested.

Levelling

See article on **Throwing Power.**

Alteration of Physical Properties

For the most part physical properties of electrodeposits have not been controlled by intent. Although it has long been known that magnetic behavior and electrical resistivity are influenced to a greater or lesser degree by addition agents, these effects have been observed as a by-product of the use of addition agents for other purposes, principally as brighteners. Much attention is now being given to the use of addition agents to control magnetic properties of thin metallic films which are used in computers and other electronic devices. Empirical experimentation is required, for there is no theory that accounts for the alteration of magnetic properties by addition agents. There is some indication that the factors are those that also prevail in internal stress.[1]

Very little is known of the effects of addition agents on electrical resistivity. For nickel brighteners they seem small, but for hardeners used in silver plating solutions the reduction in conductivity may be considerable.

Alteration of Mechanical Properties

Much attention has been given to the measurement of the mechanical properties of tensile strength and ductility of bright deposits, although little has been done on the use of addition agents to achieve specified values of these

TABLE 1. NICKEL HARDNESS FOR A SINGLE ADDITION AGENT

Composition of Bath	Hardness KHN$_{25}$
Watts	320
Watts + 0.2 gpl saccharin	320
Fluoborate	330
Fluoborate + 0.2 gpl saccharin	210
Sulfamate	280
Sulfamate + 0.2 gpl saccharin	460

TABLE 2. MECHANICAL PROPERTIES OF SOME PROPRIETARY NICKEL DEPOSITS

Bath	Tensile Strength, psi	Elongation, %
Watts	46,000	0.47
M	184,000	0.82
N	72,000	0.40
O	198,000	1.23
P	170,000	0.68
Q-1	194,000	0.96

properties. On the other hand, hardness and internal stress have often been controlled by means of addition agents. (Hardness and internal stress are really not properties, but they may be regarded as such.) The effects of addition agents on hardness must be evaluated for each bath and for each set of plating conditions; for, as is shown in Table 1, it is possible to achieve a wide range of hardness with a single addition agent in a variety of plating baths for a given metal.[2]

Not only is it possible to obtain a wide range of strengths and ductility by variation of addition agent, but the strength and ductility do not bear the usual inverse relationship that one expects of them. The data in Table 2 for nickel deposits from a single bath for a variety of addition agents show both the range and the independence of tensile strength and ductility. Unhappily, absolutely nothing is known about the mechanisms by which agents bring about these remarkable changes in mechanical properties.

Both because of the importance of internal stress and the ease with which it can be measured, there is an abundance of data on the effects of specific materials. None of this work makes possible the prediction of the effects of new compounds, for a paper by Newell[3] illustrates the necessity of empirical studies for the selection of an addition agent to do a specific job in a specific environment.

Alteration of Structure

Lattice structure and fibre texture, as well as surface topography, are markedly affected by addition agents. Weil and Read[4] as well as Weil and Paquin[5] have discussed this complex subject and have provided many illustrations with electron micrographs and diffraction patterns. Although some clues are emerging, it is still not possible to predict the effects of untried addition agents.

Attempts have been made to formulate mechanisms to explain the effects of addition agents, but as more and more is learned about the effects that can arise from their use, the less satisfactory are the proposed mechanisms. Hendricks[6] summarized in 1942 the hypotheses that had been suggested at that time. None of them even approach something that is satisfactory today. In fact, there is no current suggestion that is at all acceptable. Recent work in the field of electrode kinetics leads to the hope that considerations of the role of addition agents in the kinetics of deposition may lead to mechanisms of value. So far this has not come to pass, although Vagramyan and Petrova[7] make a brave attempt to do so.

References

1. Wolf, I. W., and McConnell, V. C., *Proc. Am. Electroplaters' Soc.*, **43**, 215 (1956).
2. Read, H. J., *Plating*, **49**, 602 (1962).
3. Newell, I. L., *Proc. Am. Electroplaters' Soc.*, **43**, 101 (1956).
4. Weil, R., and Read, H. J., *Metal Finishing*, **53**, (11), 60 (1959).
5. Weil, R., and Paquin, R., *J. Electrochemical Soc.*, **107**, 88 (1960).
6. Hendricks, J. A., *Trans. Electrochemical Soc.*, **82**, 113 (1942).
7. Vagramgan, A. T., and Petrova, Yu. S., "The Mechanical Properties of Electrolytic Deposits," New York, Consultants Bureau, 1962.

Harold J. Read

Cross-reference: *Brighteners.*

ADIPONITRILE ELECTROSYNTHESIS

An electrochemical process for the tonnage-scale production of adiponitrile, a basic raw material for the synthesis of nylon, by the hydrodimerization of acrylonitrile has recently become an industrial operation. Late in 1963 it was announced by Monsanto Chemical Company that a large plant to make adiponitrile by the process was being erected by Chemstrand Co., a division of Monsanto, at Decatur, Alabama. This represents a major breakthrough in the industrial application of electro-organic chemistry.

The one-step process for the synthesis of adiponitrile consists simply of adding hydrogen to acrylonitrile according to the reaction:

$$2CH_2{:}CHCN + H_2 \rightarrow NCCH_2CH_2CH_2CH_2CN$$

This is called hydrodimerization, the reductive coupling of certain unsaturated or olefinic compounds to give their hydrodimers. Such compounds include alpha, beta-unsaturated acids, such as acrylic acid, and their derivatives, such as acrylonitrile. The electrolytic process accomplishes the above reaction at room temperature at the cathode of a cell with high (90 per cent or more) yields.

While the details of the industrial process have not been disclosed, some essential features have been the subject of recent publications and papers.[1, 2, 3, 4, 5] The aqueous solution fed to the cell contains acrylonitrile and a hydrotropic salt as a supporting electrolyte. The latter, also known as a McKee salt, increases the solubility of the acrylonitrile in water and also ionizes to serve as a conductor of current. Among the suitable salts are those formed by saturated aliphatic or heterocyclic amines or saturated quaternary ammonium compounds with an aryl or aralkyl sulfonic acid with 6–12 carbon atoms.[3] Baizer discusses tetraethylammonium *p*-toluenesulfonate as an example.[1, 2]

The continuous process consists of three essential steps: (1) the mixing of acrylonitrile with the McKee salt to reach a concentration of more than 10 per cent (50 per cent is cited[3]); (2) electrolysis of the acrylonitrile-salt solution in a cell between a platinum anode and a mercury or lead cathode until the acrylonitrile content has been lowered to not less than 10 per cent; and (3) the extraction of adiponitrile from the effluent solution by a suitable solvent, such as methylene chloride, in a liquid-liquid extraction system. The McKee salt is recycled to the cell with fresh acrylonitrile.

The pH of the electrolyte is important and is kept between 7.5 and about 9.5 to prevent side reactions, chiefly the addition of water to the double bond of the acrylonitrile. In a solution of higher alkalinity, bis-(2-cyanoethyl)-ether is formed as an undesirable by-product. If the acrylonitrile concentration in the catholyte falls much below ten per cent, increasing quantities of propionitrile appear as a by-product.

The voltage at which the monomer hydrodimerizes influences the choice of the hydrotropic salt used in the bath. The positively charged cation of the salt must not be discharged at the same voltage at which the hydrodimerization occurs, and the negatively charged anion must not be discharged at the anode. For adiponitrile formation an aqueous solution of at least 30 per cent (on total salt and water content) tetraethylammonium *p*-toluenesulfonate adequately fulfills these requirements.[3]

References

1. BAIZER, M. M., "Electrolytic Reductive Coupling, I. Acrylonitrile," *J. Electrochem. Soc.*, **111**, 215–222 (1964).
2. BAIZER, M. M., AND ANDERSON, J. A., "Electrolytic Reductive Coupling, II. Derivatives of Mono-Olefinic α,β-Unsaturated Acids," *J. Electrochem. Soc.*, **111**, 223–226 (1964); "Electrolytic Reductive Coupling, III. Some Derivatives of 1,3-Butadiene," *Ibid.*, **111**, 226–228 (1964).
3. Belgian Patents 623,657 and 623,691 (to Monsanto Chemical Company), 1963.
4. "Electrochemical Process Yields Organics," *Chem. Eng. News*, **41**, 69 (Oct. 14, 1963).
5. "Blazing New Trail to Nylon," *Chem. Week*, **93**, 85–90 (Oct. 12, 1963).

CLIFFORD A. HAMPEL

Cross-references: *Dialdehyde Starch Preparation; Electro-Organic Chemistry; Glucose Electrochemical Reduction; Kolbe and Related Brown-Walker and Hofer-Moest Reactions; Polymerization (Electrolytic) of Vinyl Monomers.*

AIR ION GENERATION

Air ions are gas molecules, water droplets, or dirt particles with one or more negative or positive charges.* During the past sixty years many investigators have been using air ions in the treatment of respiratory and other types of diseases.[6] Various types of ion generators have been used with apparently appreciable success. Other investigators using the same types of generators have reported little or no effects on the subjects. An analysis of the various methods of ion generation is given to understand better the mechanism of ion formation and to see whether an explanation for the differences in the physiological results can be obtained. The methods used by investigators are: charge separation, thermionic emission, corona discharge, radioactive materials, and ultraviolet radiation.

Separation of Charge

Charge separation occurs when fine dust particles are blown through air ducts. The dust particles momentarily come into contact with the

* One unit charge $= 1.6 \times 10^{-19}$ coulombs.

duct wall, lose an electron, and, thus, become air ions. The separation of the electron from the particle is governed by complex forces similar to the contact potentials of metals (q.v.). The sign of the charge on the particle depends on the type of dust, duct material, and traces of adsorbed gases or impurities on the particles. Many of the common impurities in air form positive ions when blown through iron or aluminum ducts.

Separation of charges and ionization occur rather extensively in nature.[3] As an example, during a rainstorm or snowstorm, a large number of air ions is formed. The breaking of droplets of water on the ocean shore or in a waterfall also results in ionization. Probably the ions reported in the Fohn winds of the Alps and Chinook of North America are also produced by charge separation of the rapidly moving dust.

There have been many reports that these natural air ions are physiologically active. Although no data were found as to the number of electrons attached to each particle, the work of Israel[5] on dust and Lenard[7] on waterfalls shows that each aerosol particle has attached to itself a number of electrons.

In the therapeutic application of hydrosols, Cauer[1] has utilized the method of charge separation in the production of ions. A fine jet of water is sprayed into the air from a nozzle which is at a potential of 40 kv. Wehner[12] has recently summarized most of the work on electroaerosol therapy. He states that each droplet is about 2 microns in diameter and may carry as many as 1600 charges. Electroaerosol therapy is used extensively in Europe in the treatment of bronchial asthma, sinusitis, rhinitis, tuberculosis, silicosis, and many other types of respiratory diseases.

Corona Discharge

Corona discharges have been extensively used in the ionization of dirt in the air. Generally, an electrical potential is applied between two electrodes, one of them being a wire of very small diameter or a needle point. The very high electric field surrounding the small electrode produces large numbers of negative and positive ions. If the wire is the negative electrode, the positive ions are quickly collected and the negative ions repelled to the opposite electrode. The high potential gradient in the space between the electrodes is effective in driving the ions onto the dust particles, resulting in multiple charges on each particle. Penny and Lynch[9] have shown that the number of charges on a particle, as well as the number of charged particles in the moving air, increases as the field strength is increased. Hewitt[4] has shown that particles of 0.1 microns in diameter in a high gradient may hold as many as 25 charges. However, particles in the range of 0.6 microns would hold about 600 charges. Since normal air contains dust particles from less than 0.01 microns in diameter to over 50 microns in diameter, such ionized air would have ions with from one to probably 1000 charges per particle. It has been reported that large ionized particles may not be physiologically active. However, in the measurement of the mobility of ions, these large particles with many charges would be recorded as much smaller ions having higher mobility on most measuring devices because of the multiple charges they have acquired. The mobility of the particles having multiple charges can be calculated by:

$$M = (ne/6\mu a) \cdot C$$

where: M = mobility of ions, cm/sec/v/cm;
e = elementary charge;
μ = viscosity of gas in poises;
a = radius of particle;
C = correction factor for Stokes Law.

Thus, an experimenter working in a dusty atmosphere may believe he has a large number of intermediate or small ions while, in reality, he would have large ions with multiple charges. Contemporary physics divides air-borne ions into three groups according to size. No hard and fast rules exist, but the values in Table 1 are generally accepted. Much of the early work on the physiological effects of air ions was done in rooms with unknown quantities of air-borne dirt which could account for the variation in results sometimes reported by different investigators.

Thermionic Emission of Ions

Metals and other materials emit electrons when heated to high temperatures. The number of electrons emitted is determined by the thermionic emission characteristics and temperature. These electrons will produce ions by attachment to oxygen and small dirt particles. The number of electrons from many heating elements, such as platinum or nichrome, is small. However, if a low thermionic work function material, such as barium oxide, were placed on a hot wire, a large number of ions would be obtained. Martin[8] and Siksna[11] have shown that positive ions are also

TABLE 1. RANGE OF SIZES AND MOBILITIES
OF AIR IONS HAVING ONE CHARGE

	Diameter	Average Range of Mobility in Field of 1 volt per cm
	(Microns)	(cm/sec)
Large or Langevin ions	0.03–0.10	0.0002–0.001
Intermediate ions	0.0003–0.03	0.001–0.12
Small ions	0.001–0.0033	0.12–2.2

generated by hot wires. Martin believes the positive ions are a result of impurities in the air striking the hot filament. This he ably demonstrated by blowing smoke over hot nichrome and platinum wires and measuring the positive ion current under the two conditions.

The pioneer work done by Dessauer[2] and his associate was with a modified thermionic ion generator. Purified magnesium oxide was compressed into a small block and heated to 900 to 1000°C by a platinum wire at 1200°C. Electrons were liberated by both the magnesium oxide and the platinum wire. Air was blown over the hot oxide, dislodging a large number of submicroscopic particles of MgO from the compressed block. Many of these particles were charged negatively because of the excess of thermionically liberated electrons. Those particles that lost electrons became positively charged. Probably a charge separation also occurred due to the rapid movement of the particles in the apparatus. The positive ions were removed by an electrostatic field.

The number of ions measured was of the order of 10 million/cc. However, it should be evident that the size of the particles of MgO would be dependent on the pretreatment of the oxide, the degree of compression, impurities, and rate of movement of the air. Probably many of the ions measured were large charged particles, and a much smaller number of small physiologically active ions were present. Because of the high density of electrons in the vicinity of the generator, it would appear that many of the particles would have a multiple charge.

Radioactive Materials

Various radioactive materials have been suggested and used in the production of air ions. Those materials producing alpha particles are the most efficient ion generators. As an example, a single alpha particle from polonium 210 can produce about 150,000 ion pairs. Electrons are removed from both nitrogen and oxygen molecules. The electron affinity of oxygen molecules is greater than that of nitrogen so that a preponderance of negative oxygen ions is obtained. In the absence of a voltage gradient there is a very rapid recombination of the ions producing neutral atoms. With a proper design for housing the radioactive material, a regulated air flow, and a proper voltage gradient, the positive ions will be removed and mainly negative ions will be emitted. The number of charges on dust particles would be determined by the concentration of the ions and the size of the particle. The process of ion formation by this method is by attachment, and it has been shown by Hewitt[4] that the number of charges on a particle would be less than in a corona discharge where the ions are in a very high field.

Radioactive materials have some disadvantages. Polonium 210 has a half-life of only 138 days and must be specially prepared and covered with thin layers of gold or other foils to prevent the escape of the radioactive material into the air. Radium D has a half-life of 22 years and would be better to use except that this material also emits beta and gamma radiation so that special handling and shielding precautions would be necessary.

Recently tritium dissolved in zirconium has been introduced as an ion generator. Tritium is a beta emitter having a half-life of 12.5 years. The energy of the beta rays is only 0.018 Mev so that most of the ion pair formation takes place within one centimeter from the zirconium surface. The zirconium is at a negative potential to attract the positive ions. The main concentration of ions is in the immediate vicinity of the ion generator. However, if a blower is placed behind the generator, the voltage on the plate must be greatly increased to remove the positive ions.

The mechanism of ion formation with tritium is similar to that for polonium 210. Ion formation is by attachment, and most of the small particles carry only one charge. Of course, the size of the ions would be determined by the amount of dust in the air.

Ultraviolet Radiation

A number of investigators have reported that radiation from quartz ultraviolet lamps will ionize the air. Even the shortest radiation, 1849Å,

from such lamps does not have sufficient energy to ionize oxygen or nitrogen. (See entry on **Ultraviolet Lamps.**) Electrons are produced by the photoelectric effect from nearby metals or dirt particles, and ions are produced by attachment. Ozone is produced by the dissociation of oxygen by radiation below 2000Å. However, if the surrounding metal has a low work function, the short radiation is not necessary for the photoelectric effect. Radiation with a wave length as long as 4000Å can eject electrons from some metals. Picard[10] in 1924 used the photoelectric method in his physiological studies by placing his patients, together with an ultraviolet lamp to generate air ions, in an aluminum sphere.

The number of electrons ejected from the metal is a function of the ultraviolet intensity and the work function of the metal or combination of metals. Since only electrons are ejected from the metal surfaces, only negative ions are produced by ultraviolet radiation. The first step in ion formation is electron attachment to oxygen. The oxygen ions are then attached to dirt particles by polarization in a manner similar to the attachment mechanism occurring when ions are generated by radioactive materials. Again, the number of physiologically active ions would be determined by the amount and type of dust in the air.

Discussion

Under controlled conditions it would appear that all of the different methods for the generation of air ions should produce the same type of physiologically active ions. It is believed that only the intermediate ions of about 0.003 to 0.03 microns having a mobility of 0.001 to 0.12 cm/sec/volt/cm remain in the lungs during respiration. Most of these small particles would hold only one charge with a few of the larger particles having multiple charges. The very large particles (0.3 microns) which may have as many as 100 negative charges would be absorbed in the upper respiratory track.

The number of dust particles in the air is very important in making ion counts or observing physiological effects. Most filters remove particles above 5 microns in size which represent the major weight of the dirt suspended in the air. The electronic precipitators and more modern filters are very effective in removing all of the particles above 0.5 microns. There are about 30,000 to 50,000 particles per cubic foot above

0.5 microns in size in normal air. This number constitutes only one-half of one per cent of the total number of particles in the air. Thus, there may be 5 to 10 million particles per cubic foot below 0.5 microns. About one-half of these would be below 0.03 microns or in the size range of ions considered to be physiologically active.

If all of the dust particles in the air were ionized and had only one charge, it would be a very simple matter to measure only the physiologically active ions in the air. The mobility, M, of any particular size ion could be determined by the formula:

$$M = (d^2v/LV)$$

where: d = distance between plates,
       v = air velocity (cm/sec),
       L = length of plates,
       V = voltage applied to plates.

However, in most ionized air, especially in air ionized by corona discharge, most of the large particles will have multiple charges. The mobility of such large charged particles is proportional to the ratio of the number of charges to their mass. Thus, a highly-charged large particle would be collected, and the number of physiologically active ions would erroneously be assumed to be, as calculated according to the formula:

$$N = (I/qa)$$

where: N = number of ions,
       I = ion current,
       q = 1.6 × 10^{-19} coulombs,
       a = volume of air in cc/sec.

Since there is a very large variability in the number of dust particles in the air, it would seem that most measurements on physiologically active air ions would be in error. This may account for the variable results reported in the literature and for the reluctance of some medical investigators to accept ion therapy. It would appear that basic information on air ions must be obtained in a controlled dust-free atmosphere similar to the so-called "white rooms." In such rooms nearly all particles above 0.2 microns are removed from the air. Most of the remaining particles would accept only one charge regardless of the method of generating the ions.

References

1. CAUER, H., *Z. Aerosol Forschg.*, **3**, 224 (1958).
2. DESSAUER, F., "Zehn Yahre Forschung of dem Physikalisch Medizinischen Grenzgebiet," Leipzig, Georg Thieme, 1931.
3. GUEST, P. G., "Static Electricity in Nature and Industry," Bulletin 368, U.S. Dept. of Commerce, 1938.
4. HEWITT, G. W., *Trans. AIEE*, **76**, Part I, 300 (1957).
5. ISRAEL, H., *Z. Tech. Phys.*, **9**, 289 (1928).
6. KORNBLUEH, I. H., *Archives of Med. Hydrology*, **21**, 1 (1961).
7. LENARD, P., *Ann. Phys.*, **46**, 584 (1892).
8. MARTIN, T. L., *J. Franklin Inst.*, **254**, 267 (1952).
9. PENNY, G. W., AND LYNCH, R. D., *Trans. AIEE*, **76**, Part I, 294 (1957).
10. PICARD, H., *Strahlentherapie*, **16**, 183 (1924).
11. SIKSNA, R., *Arkiv för Fysik*, **5**, 531 (1952).
12. WEHNER, A. P., *J. Physical Med.*, **41**, 24, 68 (1962).

RUDOLPH NAGY

Cross-references: *Gases, Electrical Conductance and Ionization; Ultraviolet Lamps; Work Function.*

ALKALI METALS ELECTROWINNING. See SPECIFIC ELEMENT.

ALKALIMETRY. See ACIDIMETRY AND ALKALIMETRY.

ALKALI PRODUCTION. See CHLORINE INDUSTRY; CHLORINE PRODUCTION IN DIAPHRAGM CELLS; CHLORINE PRODUCTION IN MERCURY CELLS.

ALLOY ELECTRODEPOSITION

A large number of alloys can be electrodeposited from aqueous solutions. These electrodeposits are just as truly alloys as those obtained by melting techniques. Over 100 binary alloys and 15 ternary alloys are shown in Fig. 1. For a metal to be codeposited as an alloy, usually it must be capable of being deposited individually. However, there are a few exceptions, as noted in a later section.

Only a small number of alloys are commercially deposited. Among these are cobalt-nickel, lead-tin, brass, bronze, tin-zinc, nickel-tin, and gold alloys. The processes for depositing a number of other alloys are commercially feasible, but are not utilized. The deposition of most of the alloys, however, has not been developed to the point of being commercially feasible.

Electrodeposited alloys have a variety of uses. The most important are for decorative and pro-

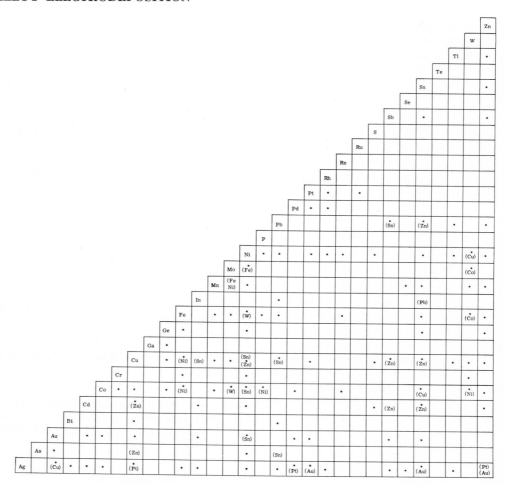

Fig. 1. Alloys which have been electrodeposited from aqueous solution. Binary alloys are indicated by an asterisk at the intersection of a vertical and horizontal column headed by a parent metal. Ternary alloys are indicated by a parenthesis enclosing the symbol of the third element. About 100 binary alloys and 15 ternary alloys are listed. (Reproduced from [3], with permission of the Academic Press, Inc., New York).

tective purposes. For example, gold alloys of various colors are used on jewelry; brass and bronze alloys are used on hardware mainly for their decorative appearance; tin-zinc alloy is used mainly for its protective value but also for its solderability. Electrodeposited alloys also have important engineering applications. For example, lead-tin alloy is used for coating bearings; cobalt-nickel alloy for magnetic tapes; iron-nickel alloy for the memories of computers; and nickel-tin alloy on clock parts because of its hardness and its nontarnishing properties.

The last decade has seen a large increase in the interest in the electrodeposition of alloys. An indication of this is that prior to 1960 there was no monograph on the subject, but in the following three years three books[1, 2, 3] were published.

Conditions for Codeposition of Metals and Nature of Plating Baths

The most important single consideration involved in the codeposition of two metals is their individual equilibrium potentials,* or better still their deposition potentials.* If these are close together, then codeposition usually occurs readily, but if they are far apart, codeposition may

* This refers to the potential of each metal measured separately in a solution similar in composition to the alloy plating bath, except for the absence of the other depositable metal.

not be possible. No definite range of values of the difference in potential can be given for insuring the satisfactory codeposition of two metals, because other considerations enter in. In general, the deposition potentials should be not more than 0.2 volt apart. However, in some instances, codeposition can occur with deposition potentials 0.5 volt apart.

To codeposit metals of which the deposition potentials in simple salt solutions are too far apart, baths containing the metals in the form of complex ions are used. In solutions of complex ions, the deposition potentials of all metals are more negative (less noble*) than in solutions of simple ions. However, the deposition potentials of two metals are often closer together in the solutions of complex ions than in solutions of simple salts. For example, in solutions of their simple salts, the deposition potentials of cadmium and copper are about 0.7 volt apart, with copper as the more noble metal. In a cyanide solution containing some free cyanide, the potential of cadmium is more noble than that of copper. Even in those rare situations in which the potentials of two metals are not brought closer together by formation of complexes, deposition from complex ions seems to facilitate codeposition.

Effect of Variables on the Composition of Electrodeposited Alloys

The composition of an electrodeposited alloy varies considerably with the composition of the bath and with the operating variables: current density, temperature, and agitation. The most important variable is the ratio of the depositable metals in the bath. In a bath containing metals as complex ions, the concentrations of complexing agent (for example, the free cyanide content in a bronze plating bath) and the pH are also important.

One principle of alloy composition, which seems almost self evident, is that an increase in the ratio of the concentration of one metal to the other in the bath causes an increase in the ratio of that metal in the deposit. The ratio in the bath is best expressed as "metal-percentage"

* Deposition potentials are qualitatively compared by referring to them as being more noble or ness noble than one another. Of two potentials, the one that lies closer to the standard potential of gold is called more noble or more positive. The potential that lies closer to the standard potential of sodium is called less noble or more negative.

which is the percentage of a depositable metal based on the total amount of depositable metal in the bath. Fig. 2 shows examples of the increase in the per cent of a metal in an alloy with its metal-percentage in the bath. A few exceptions to this principle have been reported.

There are few other generalizations governing the composition of the alloy. The composition is determined primarily by the relative deposition potentials of the metals, usually the more noble metal depositing preferentially, and secondarily by the variables previously mentioned. The role of the deposition potentials is difficult to evaluate because they are not the same for a metal in codeposition as in individual deposition. More about this is said in a later section. The role of diffusion phenomena is less fundamental, but it is easier to evaluate as the following discussion shows.

In most of the common kinds of alloy plating, the fundamental tendency is for the codeposited metals to approach mutual chemical equilibrium with respect to the solution. This tendency toward equilibrium requires that the concentration of the more noble metal at the cathode-solution interface be considerably reduced relative to that of the less noble metal, and this result is achieved by preferential deposition of the more noble metal. It is a general principle of alloy plating that the ratio of the concentration of the more readily depositable metal to that of the other is smaller at the cathode-solution interface than in the body of the bath:

$$C_m/C_n < C_m{}^\circ/C_n{}^\circ,$$

where C_m and C_n are, respectively, the concentrations of the more readily depositable and less readily depositable metals at the cathode-solution interface, and $C_m{}^\circ$ and $C_n{}^\circ$ are the concentrations in the body of the bath.

Diffusion phenomena play an important role in determining the composition of the alloys, because the unequal reduction of concentrations of metal ions at the cathode-solution interface results in a different concentration gradient in the cathode diffusion layer for each metal. The concentration gradients are approximately

$$\frac{C_m{}^\circ - C_m}{t} \quad \text{and} \quad \frac{C_n{}^\circ - C_n}{t},$$

where t is the thickness of the diffusion layer and in unstirred baths amounts to about ¼ mm. This concentration gradient in many instances

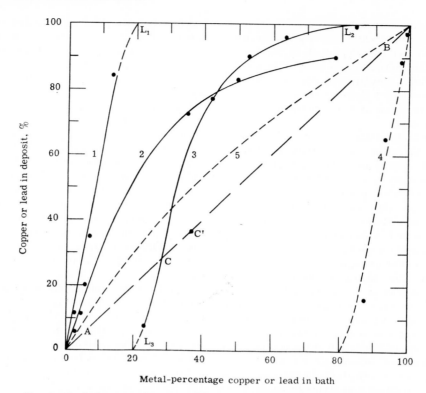

Fɪɢ. 2. Typical curves illustrating the relation between the composition of electrodeposited alloys and the composition of the solution in normal codeposition. The more noble metals are copper and lead.

1. Bismuth-copper alloys deposited from perchlorate bath, 0.35 molar in total depositable metal or about 60–70 gpl total metal. 1 amp/sq dm; rotating cathode; room temperature.

2. Copper-zinc alloys deposited from a cyanide bath. Data are a composite. Total metal content of baths ranged from about 25 to 55 gpl. Current density from 1 to 2 amp/sq dm.

3. Lead-tin alloys deposited from a fluoborate bath, 0.5 M in total metal. Total metal ranged from 65 to 90 gpl. Current density 0.8 amp/sq dm.

4. Dotted Bi-Cu curve represents same data as Curve 1, but plotted against coordinates representing percentage bismuth instead of percentage copper.

5. A hypothetical curve.

AB is the composition-reference line.

(Reproduced from [3], with permission of the Academic Press, Inc., New York)

controls the relative rate of movement of depositable metal ions up to the cathode and hence the composition of the electrodeposited alloy.

To more conveniently discuss the relation of alloy composition to the deposition potentials and plating variables, five categories of deposition characteristics have been set up, which will be referred to as alloy plating systems. These are not characterized by any given type of bath composition.

Regular alloy plating systems (for ex-

ample, deposition of Pb-Sn, Bi-Cu, and Cu-Pb from acid baths).

The baths usually consist of simple salts, but they may also be complex baths. The composition of the alloy is under control of diffusion phenomena and the effects of the plating variables can be predicted. Any factor that tends to increase the metal ion content of the cathode diffusion layer, for example, lowering the current density, or increasing the temperature or agitation of the bath, increases the content of the more noble metal in the deposit, because it increases the ratio, C_m/C_n, at the cathode-solution interface. As the current density increases, the metal ratio of the deposit approaches the metal ratio of the bath.

Irregular alloy plating systems (for example, brass, bronze, and tin-zinc deposited from alkaline baths). These usually consist of baths containing complex ions. The composition of the alloy is determined by the characteristics of the deposition potentials rather than by diffusion phenomena, and the composition of the alloys show no general trends with the plating variables. Some of the trends of a given alloy may be similar to those for the regular system. Usually the deposition potentials of metals are closer together for the irregular system than for the regular system.

Equilibrium Codeposition. In a few of the regular alloy plating systems it is possible to have baths with which the two metals are in mutual chemical equilibrium. Or stated in another way, each metal has the same potential against the solution. Consequently, each has no tendency to displace the other chemically and if the two metals were connected electrically, no current would pass between them. Since each metal has the same tendency to deposit, at a low current density of deposition the ratio of the metals in the deposit is the same as their ratio in the bath. An example is the deposition of lead-tin alloys from a bath containing about 70 metal-per cent of tin (see Fig. 2). This type of codeposition is rare and, hence, not of practicable importance.

Anomalous Codeposition. In the preceeding two types 1 and 2 of codeposition, the more noble metal deposits preferentially. Type 4 is characterized by the anomaly that the less noble metal deposits preferentially. For example, from a solution containing simple salts of both nickel and zinc, the latter deposits preferentially, although the equilibrium potential of zinc in a simple salt solution is more than 0.5 volt more negative than that of nickel. Current density plays an important role because the deposition can make a transition from the normal types 1 or 2 to the anomalous type 4 as the current density is increased. Consequently, the effect of plating variables on the composition of the deposit is not simple and depends on the range of current density used.

Induced Codeposition. Some elements, such as tungsten, molybdenum, germanium, and phosphorus (referred to as *reluctant elements*), have not been deposited individually from aqueous solutions, but they can be readily deposited as alloys with other metals (referred to as *inducing metals*), especially with the iron group metals. This type of alloy plating is called induced codeposition. The phenomenon has not been satisfactorily explained. The content of the reluctant metal in the deposit does not increase continuously as its metal-percentage in the bath is increased but reaches a limit. In this respect induced codeposition differs from the other types.

The effects of the operating variables on the composition of the deposit are not predictable with anomalous and induced codeposition; in general, the effects are much smaller than with regular codeposition.

Relation between Current Density and Cathode Potentials in Alloy Deposition

The relations between the current density and the cathode potentials of the metals deposited individually and of the alloy have been extensively studied, and they are usually depicted as a graph of current density as ordinate plotted against the cathode potential as abscissa. The graph will be referred to as a *cd-ptl* curve. The *cd-ptl* curves qualitatively reflect the changes in alloy composition brought about by variations in the plating variables.

One general qualitative principle is that a variation in a plating condition that brings the *cd-ptl* curves of the metals (individually deposited) closer together increases the percentage of the less noble metal in the electrodeposited alloy and vice-versa. For example, in the deposition of bronze, an increase in the cyanide content of the bath brings the potential of copper (the more noble metal) closer to that of tin, and the content of the latter in the deposit increases. On the other hand, an increase in the caustic content of the bath makes the potential of tin depart further from that of copper, and the content of tin in the deposit decreases.

Electrochemists have attempted to derive more information from *cd-ptl* relations than is warranted, for example, to predict the composition of an alloy from the *cd-ptl* curves of the individual metals. This procedure has no factual basis. The reason that the *cd-ptl* curves cannot be analyzed too closely is that the *cd-ptl* relations of metals individually deposited differ from the *cd-ptl* relations in codeposition. An example

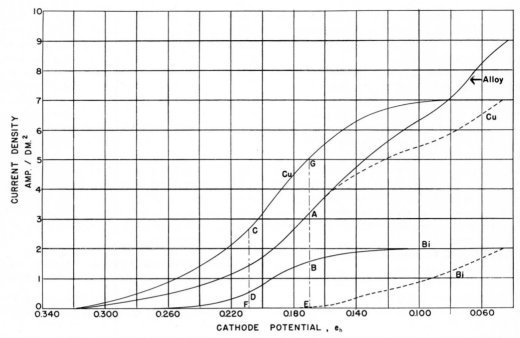

FIG. 3. Comparison of the *cd-ptl* curves for deposition of the individual metals, copper and bismuth, with their corresponding partial *cd-ptl* curves derived from the alloy curve. Composition of bath: Cu, 0.75 *N*; Bi, 0.25 *N*. Metals present as perchlorates. Free perchloric acid, 0.5 *N*. The solid curves for Cu and Bi represent the experimental measurements on the separate deposition of each metal. The dotted lines are the partial *cd-ptl* curves which were computed from the *cd-ptl* curve of alloy deposition and the composition of the deposits. Figure reproduced from [3], with permission of the Academic Press, Inc., New York.

is shown in Fig. 3 for the deposition of copper-bismuth alloy. The actual *cd-ptl* relations of these metals in codeposition was derived from the *cd-ptl* curve for the alloy by using data on the composition of the alloy deposited at each current density.

Replenishment of Alloy Plating Baths

Alloy plating baths can be replenished in the same manner as baths of single metals. For example, in brass or cobalt-nickel plating alloy anodes can be used. In some instances, one metal is supplied by an anode and the other metal by a salt. Individual anodes of the two metals also can be used. This requires that an independent electrical circuit be used for each metal to introduce the metals into the bath in the same ratio that they deposit.

A general principle relating to replenishing the bath is that the metal ratio of the deposit approaches the metal ratio of the anodes (or of the replenishment). Obviously, this relation

does not hold for induced codeposition (see section on Effect of Variables). The metal ratio of the deposit is never the same as that of the bath except for some instances of deposition above the limiting current density or for the rare case of equilibrium codeposition.

Constitution of Electrodeposited Alloys

The constitution (with respect to phases present) of electrodeposited alloys is similar to that of the thermally prepared, annealed alloys. The main difference is that in the electrodeposited alloy a phase may exist over a larger range of alloy composition than in the equilibrium thermal alloy. An extreme example of this is the silver-lead alloy which in the equilibrium condition contains only about 1 per cent of lead in solid solution in silver, but in the electrodeposited state can contain 12 per cent. Such alloys are called supersaturated. The electrodeposited nickel-tin alloy containing about 65 per cent tin is of this type. It consists of an intermetallic compound which is particularly interesting because it cannot be obtained by thermal means with this composition.

Structure and Properties

The microstructure of electrodeposited alloys shows that they are finer grained than cast alloys. Like other electrodeposits the alloys may have a columnar or a laminated structure. The latter occurs more frequently in electrodeposited alloys than in deposits of the individual metals.

Electrodeposited alloys are usually harder and less ductile than the cast metals, otherwise their properties are similar. Some of the electrodeposited alloys have rather unusual properties. For example, the nickel-tin alloy (65 per cent Sn) has much higher corrosion resistance than either of the parent metals; cobalt-tungsten alloys have a high hot-hardness and afford steel unusual protection against rusting in outdoor exposure; the phosphorus alloys of nickel and cobalt are very hard and those containing about 10 per cent of phosphorus are amorphous.

Composition and Operating Conditions of Typical Alloy Plating Baths

In the following list of plating baths the number given after the name or formula of a compound is grams per liter.

Brass (4). Alloy composition: Cu, 80 per cent; Zn, 20 per cent. CuCN, 105 (as Cu, 75); ZnO, 9 (as Zn, 7.2); NaCN, total, 135, (free NaCN, 19); NaOH, 75. Current density, 3 to 16 amp/sq dm. Temp. of bath, 75 to 90°C. Cathode current efficiency, 65 to 100 per cent.

Cobalt-Nickel, Bright (5). Alloy composition: Co, 18 per cent; Ni, 82 per cent. $NiSO_4 \cdot 7H_2O$, 240; $NiCl_2 \cdot 6H_2O$, 30; nickel formate, 45; (total Ni, 76); $CoSO_4 \cdot 6H_2O$, 15 (as Co, 3); boric acid, 30; ammonium sulfate, 0.8; formaldehyde, 2 ml/liter of bath; current density, 5 amp/sq dm. Temperature 65°C. pH, 3.7. Current efficiency, about 90 per cent.

Cobalt-Tungsten (6). Alloy Composition: W, 20 per cent, Co, 80 per cent. $CoSO_4 \cdot 7H_2O$, 120 (as Co, 25); $Na_2WO_4 \cdot 2H_2O$, 45 (as W, 25); Rochelle salt, 400; NH_4Cl, 50; ammonia to a pH of 9. Current density, 2 amp/sq dm. Temperature, 95°C. Current efficiency, 93 per cent.

Lead-Tin (7). Alloy composition: Pb, 50 per cent; Sn, 50 per cent. (The composition may vary somewhat depending on the effectiveness of the glue). Sn, as stannous fluoborate, 45; Pb, as fluoborate, 35; glue 4.0; free acids: fluoboric, 40, and boric acid, 25. Current density, 3 amp/sq dm. Room temperature and mild agitation of bath. Current efficiency, about 100 per cent.

Nickel-Tin (8). Alloy composition: Ni, 35 per cent; Sn, 65 per cent. $NiCl_2 \cdot 6H_2O$, 250 (as Ni, 62); $SnCl_2 \cdot 2H_2O$, 50 (as Sn, 26); $NH_4 \cdot HF_2$, 50; HCl (32 per cent), 8; pH, 2.5. Current density, 2.7 amp/sq dm. Temperature 65°C. Current efficiency, about 100 per cent.

Speculum (9). Alloy composition: Cu, 60 per cent; Sn, 40 per cent. CuCN, 11 (as Cu, 8); $Na_2SnO_3 \cdot 3H_2O$, 90 (as Sn, 40); NaCN, total, 27 (free NaCN, 16); NaOH, free, 16; current density, 3 amp/sq dm. Temperature 65°C. Current efficiency, about 65 per cent.

References

1. ABERKUN, V. A., Editor, "Electrodeposition of Alloys," Moscow, Mashgiz, 1961.
2. FEDOT'EV, N. P., BIBIKOV, N. N., VYACHESLAVOV, P. M., AND GRILIKHES, S. YA., "Electrolytic Alloys," Moscow, Gosudarstvennoe Nauchnotechnichesko Izdatel'stvo Mashinostroitel ' noi Literatur' i, 1962.
3. BRENNER, ABNER, "Electrodeposition of Alloys, Principles and Practice," New York, Academic Press, 1963.
4. ROEHL, E. J., MICHEL, E., AND WESTBROOK, L. R., Plating, 42, 403–405 (1955); U.S. Patent 2,684,937.
5. WEISBERG, L., Trans. Electrochem. Soc., 75, 435–444 (1938); ibid, 77, 223–229 (1940).
6. BRENNER, A., BURKHEAD, P. S., AND SEEGMILLER, E., J. Research Natl Bur. Standards, 39, 351–383 (1947).
7. CARLSON, A. E., AND KANE, J. M., Monthly Rev. Am. Electroplaters' Soc., 33, 255–260 (1946).
8. DAVIES, A. E., Trans. Inst. Metal Finishing, 31, 401–415 (1954).
9. ANGLES, R. M., JONES, F. V., PRICE, J. W., AND CUTHBERTSON, J. W., J. Electrodepositors' Tech. Soc., 21, 19–44 (1946).

ABNER BRENNER

Cross-references: Barrel Plating; Entries with Electroplating titles; specific metals, Electroplating or Plating.

ALTERNATING CURRENT CORROSION. See CORROSION DUE TO ALTERNATING CURRENT.

ALUMINA, FUSED

Fused alumina, together with silicon carbide and boron carbide belongs to the family of artificial abrasives made solely in electric furnaces. It is particularly well-suited for grinding materials of high tensile strength, such as steel. Further, the high melting point (2050°C) and the chemical inertness make it a valuable refractory material.

Fused alumina is also called artificial or electrofused corundum and each company sells it under special trade names such as "Aloxite®," "Alundum," "Exolon," "Borolon," and "Coralox." It has long been known that the abrasive action of naturally-occurring corundum and emery[1] is due to their content of crystalline alumina. Thus, fusing bauxite produces an abrasive superior to naturally-occurring varieties, as proved by Charles B. Jacobs (U.S. Patent 659, 926 (1900).[1]

Different fused alumina abrasives are in use depending on the amount and kind of impurities. *Regular fused alumina* contains 94 to 96 per cent Al_2O_3, 2 to 3.5 per cent TiO_2, 1 to 2 per cent SiO_2 and small amounts of Fe_2O_3, ZrO_2, CaO, and MgO. *Semifriable fused alumina* consists of 96 to 98 per cent Al_2O_3, 1.5 to 2.5 per cent TiO_2 and 0.5 to 1 per cent SiO_2. These two kinds are made from bauxite, the impurities of which are reduced by adding carbonaceous material during melting to form an alloy which is easily separated from the alumina slag. Highly purified calcined alumina, as used in aluminum production, is the starting material for *white fused alumina* whose Al_2O_3 content ranges from 98.5 to 99.5 per cent.

The regular material is the least friable, the white the hardest, and the semifriable of intermediate quality. The friability depends on the TiO_2 content, thermal history, porosity, and microtexture. It should be pointed out that proper chemical composition, if not accompanied by proper microtexture, will not give a material of desired abrasive properties. Calcium oxide ought not to exceed 0.3 per cent and, if uncombined with SiO_2, has an unfavorable effect on the ceramic bond of abrasive wheels.[3]

In addition to the above-mentioned varieties of fused alumina, a pink material is on the market containing above 98.5 per cent Al_2O_3 and 0.05 to 0.2 per cent Cr_2O_3. This abrasive is claimed to be superior to white corundum due to its free cutting action and prolonged resistance to breakdown. Alumina abrasives containing about 10 per cent ZrO_2, 1.0 to 2 per cent SiO_2, and 2.0 to 3 per cent TiO_2 are especially adapted for machining of stainless and high-alloy steels.

Raw Materials

Fused alumina is produced directly or indirectly from bauxite originating from British and Dutch Guiana. The bauxite containing 30 to 40 per cent H_2O as mined is crushed to minus one-half inch and calcined in rotary kilns at a temperature of approximately 1000°C to remove the free and combined water. The chemical analyses of calcined bauxites suitable for abrasive grade alumina are within the following range:[4, 5]

Al_2O_3	Fe_2O_3	SiO_2	TiO_2	Ignition Loss
81–88%	1.2–9.6%	3.0–5.0%	2.8–4.0%	0.1–1.1%

To produce some of the regular and semifriable alumina abrasives, the impurities in the bauxite have to be removed by reduction with carbonaceous matter; e.g., coal, metallurgical coke, petroleum coke, or anthracite. The separation of the impurities like Fe_2O_3, SiO_2, and TiO_2 is based on the selective attack of carbon upon these oxides. First, Fe_2O_3, having the lowest heat of formation per oxygen equivalent, is reduced, then SiO_2 and, finally, TiO_2. To attain the necessary properties in the end product, a part of the TiO_2 has to remain in the oxide state to be recovered in the high-alumina slag. Hence, the carbon to bauxite ratio controls the composition of the final product and a practical example of its calculation is given by Upper.[5] Excesses in carbon have to be avoided by all means as they may lead to the formation of Al_4C_3, which decomposes with moisture from the air, causing the whole pig to degrade into dust and rendering it valueless as an abrasive.

If low-price power is available and the bauxite deposits are near the plant site, uncalcined bauxite can be fed directly into the electric furnace. This practice is used on disapore-type bauxites containing up to 15 per cent bound water. For hydrargillite-type bauxites containing up to 30 per cent bound water, the use of uncalcined bauxite is considered dangerous. The water slowly liberated due to the high temperature of dehydration of bauxite gives rise to gas evolution and to the water-gas reaction with carbon, the latter causing an unbalanced carbon ratio and resulting in unstable furnace operation. In general practice, however, calcined bauxite and dry reducing agents are preferred for the above reasons.

Sintered instead of calcined bauxite is used in sporadic cases,[6] and a 15 per cent higher throughput per unit of time at a 14 per cent lower energy consumption is obtained as compared with the use of raw bauxite containing approximately a total of 25 per cent free and combined water.

The ideal bauxite composition should contain a silicon to iron ratio yielding a ferrosilicon alloy of 11 to 18 per cent Si. Such an alloy is still sufficiently magnetic to permit an easy separation of the metal from the alumina slag. Such bauxites are not widely available, hence, iron oxides, but most frequently, iron borings are added to the furnace charge to bring the Si content within the above-mentioned range. The predominant part of the ferrosilicon falls to the bottom of the bath, provided the alumina remains molten down to the bottom. The rest of the ferrosilicon remains as shot within the alumina. This usually happens in block-type furnaces where the alumina might solidify at the bottom before the pig is completed at the top. The separation of ferrosilicon shot presents no problem as it is easily removed by magnetic separation equipment after the cooled alumina pigs have been crushed.

Production Methods

Production of fused alumina is carried out batchwise in block-type, and continuously in tilt-type or stationary ferroalloy-type electric arc furnaces. The latter two types use three-phase power, the former either single-phase or three-phase.

The block-type furnaces have two or three electrodes and appear in two different modifications. The older type invented by Higgins consists of a truncated conical shell, made out of ¾ to one inch thick steel plate, open at both ends, with the smaller diameter at the top and a bottom lined with graphite or carbon. In the Hutchins-type furnace (U.S. Pat. 1,310,341, (1919)) the shell is also a truncated cone, but closed at the smaller diameter base on which it rests. The shell of both types is cooled by a running film of water. The bottom of the Hutchins pot is lined with carbon for the production of

fused alumina through partial reduction of bauxite. During the production of the latter, ferrosilicon is formed as a by-product.

Direct contact of ferrosilicon with the steel mantle of the pot would be detrimental. Hence, a carbon lining is necessary to avoid the piercing of the mantle. If the Hutchins pot is unlined, it can only be used for making white corundum or pink corundum from Bayer alumina. Where ferrosilicon is formed during melting, the Higgins pot has to have a concave carbon bottom instead of a flat one to avoid the above-mentioned undesirable contact.

The furnace is started up by filling it approximately three feet high with the raw material to be melted, the electrodes are lowered to contact a top layer of coke or graphite, and the power is applied. After the necessary heating time, molten alumina is accumulated under the electrodes to conduct the current and regular operation is commenced. For regular and semifriable fused alumina, the voltage applied is 130 to 140 volts but might vary in special cases from 90 to 150 volts. For white and pink fused alumina, the voltage is higher and the highest voltage quoted is 270 volts.[7]

Block-type furnaces are operated at a power input of 500 to 1500 kw and produce pigs of 4 to 20 tons. The energy consumption for white alumina is in the range of 0.8 to 1.0 kwh per pound. For regular and semifriable types, the energy consumption is higher and ranges from 1.2 to 2.3 kwh per pound of crude fused abrasive. The pigs produced are 4 to 8 feet in diameter and 4 to 6 feet high.

The duration of the operation is 20 to 80 hours, depending on the capacity of the furnace. After the pot is completely filled, the cooling water flow is maintained for 6 to 8 hours. Then, the flow of water is stopped and the pig remains for another 6 to 8 hours in the shell before being dumped and allowed to cool for about a week.

Cooled pigs are crushed by dropping a manganese steel ball of 2,000 to 3,000 pounds from an electromagnet carried by a crane. Several such blows reduce the pig to pieces small enough to be handled by conventional crushers.

The electrodes used are made of carbon or graphite. Also, Söderberg or continuous self-baking electrodes are sometimes used in larger units. The electrode consumption, however, is higher for the self-baking (Söderberg) electrode than for prebaked carbon. The electrode consumption per short ton of fused alumina is approximately 30 to 40 pounds for carbon and 5 to 10 pounds for graphite.

New installations favor the continuously-operating tilt furnace, with power inputs up to 3,500 kw. The furnace is similar to steel melting furnaces except for the absence of a roof. The shell is water-cooled and lined with graphite which, in turn, is protected by a layer of alumina at least twelve inches thick, fused in place, but kept unmolten during regular operation. The furnace shell diameter varies from 10 to 12 feet. Three-phase power at 175 to 200 volts is supplied to three prebaked carbon electrodes which are 14 to 16 inches in diameter. Pours are made every 3 to 4 hours. The energy consumption per pound of 96 per cent fused alumina varies from 0.8 to 1.5 kwh. The amount of ferrosilicon is 12 to 15 per cent of the total amount of materials tapped, depending somewhat on the bauxite analysis. The alumina is tapped into large refractory molds where it cools slowly for 2 to 3 days. The main advantages of these furnaces are their large throughput and lower loss in scrap per unit weight produced in comparison to block-type furnaces.

Fused alumina is also produced in stationary, deep-tap-hole electric arc furnaces like those used in the ferroalloy and calcium carbide industry. The furnace is lined with carbon and has two tap holes, one for fused alumina, the other for ferrosilicon. The furnace described in Ref. (7) operates at 130 volts and at a power input of 2,500 kw. The electrodes are placed in line and their diameter is 100 cm (39.4 in.). Tappings are made regularly at 12-hour intervals. The melt is poured into thick-walled, dish-shaped iron pans which might be water cooled. This method of production, due to the sharp cooling effect, furnishes a rather fine crystalline material. Hence, the product is rarely used for abrasive purposes and is mainly destined for refractory use.

Applications

Fused alumina in combination with 3.0–5.0 per cent Na_2O is further used as a glass tank refractory, in magnesium refining cells, and in Hoopes cells for refining aluminum. These refractories cast in blocks attaining a weight of 2,000 pounds are produced in 2,000 kw tilting-type furnaces similar to the tilting furnace described above.[8]

As an abrasive, fused alumina is used in grit sizes of 4 to 240 and as powder in grit sizes of 280 to 1,000. The finished grain[9] is bonded into wheels, the cutting action of which depends on the kind of abrasive, the grain size, type and amount of bond, and porosity of the wheel. The tougher, high-titania grain is used in snagging wheels for heavy stock removal and in coated products. The finely crystalline type is used in wheels for billet grinding and snagging. The more friable white type is desirable where a freer and cooler cutting action is required, as in grinding hard, heat-sensitive, high-alloy tool steels.

Alumina used in coated abrasives is adapted to application on high-tensile metals, such as alloy and high-carbon steels, on tough bronzes, and on hard woods.

In refractory application, fused alumina finds an outlet in bonded and fused cast refractories. A porous, light-weight alumina brick with high thermal-insulating properties is produced from alumina bubbles. These bubbles form from a molten alumina stream which is dispersed by an air or steam jet.

The abrasion resistance of alumina makes it suitable as a material for linings in ball mills or chutes and for catalyst carriers.[9] The recent annual production of fused alumina in the United States and Canada has been about 200,000 tons, approximately two-thirds of the total production capacity.

References

1. EARDLEY-WILMOT, V. L., "Abrasives, Part IV, Artificial Abrasives and Manufactured Abrasive Products and Their Uses," *Canada Department of Mines, No. 699*, Ottawa, 1930.
2. COLLIE, M. F., "The Saga of the Abrasive Industry" published by the Grinding Wheel Institute and the Abrasive Grain Association, Greendale, Mass., 1951.
3. BURBOT, C., "Electrofused Alumina (Elektrokorund)," from "Ullmann, Enzyklopedie der Technischen Chemie," Third Edition, Vol. 6, pp. 237–242, 1956.
4. BAUMANN, H. N., "Petrology of Fused Alumina Abrasives," *Bull. Amer. Cer. Soc.*, **35**, 387–390 (1956).
5. UPPER, J. A., "The Manufacture of Abrasives," *J. Chem. Educ.*, **26**, 676–680 (1948).
6. VUKOLOV, E. A., NEGOVSKII, A. G., JORDAN, A. E., MALISHEV, V. I., MASHNITSKII, A. A., KLYASHTORNOV, I. A., RAIZ, A. B., AND POLONSKII, S. M., "Fusing Electrocorundum from Bauxite Ag-

glomerates," *Energet.*, **15**, No. 10, 16–18 (1960).

7. WINTER, J. K., COWAN, J. G., AND STRASSER, E. L., "Abrasive Manufacture in Germany," *BIOS Final Report No. 1406*, May, 1946, H. M. Stationery Office, London, England; *PB 80577*, Office of Technical Services, Dept. of Commerce, Washington, D. C.

8. SANDMEYER, K. H., AND MILLER, W. A., "Electric-Arc Fusion-Cast Alumina Refractories," *Trans. Electric Steel Conf.*, AIME, **17**, 257–267, 1959.

9. PARCHÉ, C., "Facts About Fused Alumina," pamphlet of the Carborundum Company, Niagara Falls, New York, 1954.

                                                PAUL CICHY

ALUMINUM ELECTROREFINING

The commercial aluminum electrowinning process produces metal of 99.6 to 99.85 per cent average purity. With selected raw materials and careful cell operation, the maximum purity attainable is about 99.95 per cent. Aluminum of higher purity than this can only be obtained by a refining process. The only commercially successful refining processes utilize molten salt electrolysis and are capable of producing aluminum of purities up to 99.999 per cent.

The principle employed in the aluminum electrorefining processes used today is the electrolytic transfer of aluminum from a molten, anodic aluminum alloy through a fused alkali-alkaline earth chloro-fluoride electrolyte containing aluminum ions, to a high-purity molten aluminum cathode. This is accomplished in a three-layer refining cell of the type schematically shown in Fig. 1. The cell consists of a heavy steel box, open at the top, which contains the thermal insulation, the carbon and refractory lining and the molten anode, cathode and electrolyte. The molten anode, electrolyte, and cathode layers in the cell remain separate by virtue of their density differences.

Current is introduced into the bottom of the refining cell through steel bars which extend into the carbon bottom lining. Current flows from this carbon lining up into the anode alloy layer, through the electrolyte into the molten aluminum cathode, and thence out of the cell via graphite conductors immersed in the top super-purity aluminum layer.

The composition of the anode alloy layer is maintained at approximately 70 per cent aluminum and 30 per cent copper. Commercial grade aluminum is charged into the alloy layer periodically to replace the aluminum removed electrolytically during the cell operation. Minor metallic impurities, primarily iron and silicon, accumulate in the anode layer. The anode layer must be replaced when these impurities begin to crystallize from the anode alloy or deposit electrolytically at the cathode, contaminating the high-purity aluminum.

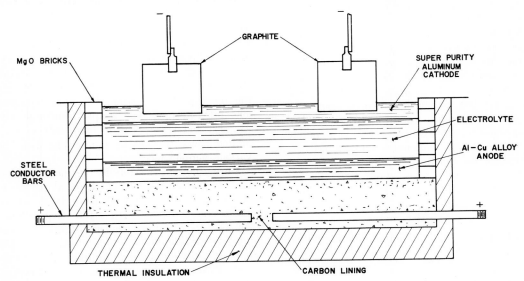

FIG. 1. Three-layer refining cell.

The aluminum to be refined is charged into the anode layer of the larger cells through a forewell, or submerged port, built into the cell for this purpose. In the smaller cells not equipped with such charging wells, molten virgin aluminum is fed into the anode layer through graphite tubes inserted through the cathode and electrolyte layer. Electrolyte additions are usually made via large graphite tubes inserted through the cathode layer. The refined aluminum is removed either by ladling it from the cell with graphite ladles or by siphoning. All of these operations must be carried out carefully to avoid mixing the three layers and upsetting the cell operation.

The anode layer is usually 6 to 8 inches deep, the electrolyte 5 to 7 inches, and the cathode layer 6 to 8 inches deep. A thin protective layer of powdered aluminum flouride, or other electrolyte components, is maintained on top of the super-purity aluminum to minimize oxidation.

Present day aluminum refining cells operate at about 750°C. The electrolyte is composed of cryolite and aluminum fluoride with either barium chloride, or a mixture of calcium and barium fluorides, present in sufficient quantity to maintain the proper density. The structure of the molten electrolyte is complex and incompletely understood. Sodium, chlorine, and fluorine-containing ions are thought to be the main current-carrying ions. Current efficiency is quite good at 98 per cent or higher. The theoretical emf required to transfer aluminum from the anode to the cathode is on the order of only a few millivolts. Polarization at the anode and cathode of the operating cell, however, adds a total overvoltage of 1.0 to 1.2 volts. The electrical conductivity of the electrolyte is poor, and it is necessary to maintain a rather thick layer so that the total cell voltage is about 5 to 7 volts and energy consumption is relatively high at about 8 to 10 kwh per pound of aluminum.

Present day aluminum refining cells range from about 15,000 to 60,000 amperes in capacity. Commercial installations normally consist of a group of about 3 to 20 cells in series.

References

1. PEARSON, T. G., "Chemical Background of the Aluminum Industry," London, Royal Institute of Chemistry, Lectures, Monographs, and Reports, No. 3, 1955.
2. BELYAEV, A. I., "Metallurgie des Aluminiums,"
Band II, pp. 1–69, Berlin, Veb Verlag Technik, 1957.

ROBERT A. LEWIS

ALUMINUM ELECTROWINNING

Practically all of the commercial primary aluminum in the world is produced by electrolysis of aluminum oxide dissolved in molten cryolite electrolyte using carbon anodes and molten aluminum cathode. The present industrial process is essentially the same as that discovered independently by Héroult in France and Hall in America in 1886.

Basic Electrochemistry

In commercial practice, the aluminum cell electrolyte consists of sodium cryolite (Na_3AlF_6) as the major constituent; calcium fluoride, about 4 to 10 weight per cent; aluminum fluoride, about 2 to 5 weight per cent; and alumina, about 2 to 8 weight per cent. The structure of the molten electrolyte is quite complex and is still incompletely understood. The nature and concentration of the various molecular and ionic species present depends upon the composition of the bulk electrolyte and the temperature. The various fluoride salts are partially dissociated and alumina when dissolved in the molten electrolyte also dissociates. Sodium ion (Na^+) appears to be the predominant cation and performs the major role of carrying the current through the electrolyte. Aluminum, oxygen, and fluorine appear to be primarily associated as complex fluoride, oxide, and/or aluminum oxyfluoride ions. Experimental evidence indicates that AlF_4^-, AlF_6^{3-}, AlO^+, Al_2O^{4+}, and $AlOF_2^-$ are the most probable forms that these complex ions may assume. The simple elemental ions Al^{3+}, F^-, and O^{2-} appear to exist only in very limited concentrations in equilibrium with the various complex ions.

During normal electrolysis, the anodic process consists of the deposition of oxygen at the anode at 100 per cent current efficiency from oxygen ion or one of the various possible oxygen donor anions. Overwhelming evidence shows that the primary product of the anodic reaction is 100 per cent carbon dioxide within the range of current densities employed in practice. However, the anode gases evolved from aluminum reduction cells normally contain from 60 to 85 per cent carbon dioxide and 15 to 40 per cent carbon monoxide. It has been shown that the primary carbon dioxide is reduced in secondary reactions by reduced species from the cathode in the electrolyte, such as sodium, finely dispersed aluminum, or monovalent aluminum. The presence of these reduced species in the electrolyte is directly related to the aluminum cathodic current inefficiency. The net effect of the reduction of the primary carbon dioxide as it escapes from the electrolyte is that the oxygen in the carbon dioxide passing from the cell is approximately equivalent to the net aluminum produced at the cathode. The CO_2 content of the anode gases is thus proportional to the cathodic aluminum current efficiency. This relationship is given by the Pearson-Waddington formula:

Aluminum current efficiency, % =
$$\tfrac{1}{2} \ (\% \ CO_2 \text{ in anode gases}) + 50$$

However, depending on the cell geometry and quality of the carbon anodes, the primary carbon dioxide can also be reduced by unpolarized anode carbon to carbon monoxide as it escapes from the cell. Also, losses of cathodic current efficiency can occur without involving reduction of the primary carbon dioxide. The Pearson-Waddington formula, therefore, is an approximation only.

During normal electrolysis in properly adjusted cells, no carbon fluoride gases are present in the anode gases. However, when the alumina concentration in the electrolyte decreases to about 2 weight per cent or slightly less, a critical alumina concentration is reached at which the nature of the anode reaction changes abruptly. The electrolyte ceases to wet the anode, which becomes rapidly covered with a poorly conducting film, probably rich in CF_4, and the condition called "anode effect" ensues. The cell voltage during "anode effect" ranges between about 40 and 90 volts, due to the high resistance at the anode-electrolyte interface. During anode effect, the carbon dioxide content of the anode gases decreases substantially; the carbon monoxide increases, and volatile carbon fluorides (primarily CF_4) are formed at the anode, constituting up to 30 per cent of the total anode gases. The formation of CF_4 appears to result from fluoride ion concentration polarization caused by diminishing oxygen donor ion concentration in the electrolyte. The critical alumina concentration for anode effect is directly proportional to the anode current density.

Unlike the discharge of oxygen at the anode, aluminum is recovered at the cathode at less than 100 per cent current efficiency, the actual current efficiency being between about 84 and 90 per cent in commercial cells. There has been considerbale controversy in the past as to whether sodium or aluminum is the primary deposition product at the cathode. The experimental evidence and modern electrochemical theory now fully supports the view that aluminum is more noble than sodium and is the primary cathodic product under normal operating conditions with a molten aluminum cathode. This consists of the discharge of aluminum from either aluminum ions or one of the possible complex aluminum donor cations. The primary deposition of aluminum does not rule out the possibility of some codeposition of sodium, for the discharge potentials for sodium and aluminum from the aluminum cell electrolyte under normal operating conditions are within a few tenths of a volt of one another. It is quite likely that some sodium codeposition does occur even in normally operating cells, and accounts for a part of the loss of aluminum current efficiency. Factors which promote increased codeposition of sodium are: increasing electrolyte temperature, increasing sodium ion concentration in the electrolyte, and increasing cathodic current density. The deposition potential of sodium is lower on a bare carbon cathode than on aluminum, so that exposure to the molten electrolyte of the cell carbon bottom or side wall lining, which are at cathode potential, also promotes greater deposition of sodium.

For many years the cloudy appearance of the molten electrolyte when in contact with molten aluminum was attributed to a "metal fog" postulated to be either sodium, aluminum, or monovalent aluminum. The "metal fog" was also linked directly to the aluminum cathodic current inefficiency. More recent research shows that the fog can also be attributed to small amounts of hydrogen. It has been shown that aluminum metal is slightly soluble in the aluminum cell electrolyte. The existence of elemental sodium gas bubbles in the electrolyte, on the other hand, is incompatible with experimental facts and electrochemical theory. However, it has been postulated that a monovalent sodium dimer, Na_2^+, can form at the cathode, disperse into the electrolyte, and be reoxidized at the anode. Finally, conditions in the electrolyte-aluminum system are favorable for formation of aluminum monofluoride. Thus at the present time, the exact causes of aluminum cathodic current inefficiency are not completely understood. It appears likely that codeposition of sodium and dispersion of finely divided aluminum (either in elemental or monovalent state) from the cathode into the electrolyte followed by escape of some elemental sodium into the carbon lining, and reoxidation of the aluminum and Na_2^+ at the anode are the major causes of aluminum losses. Minor causes may be: aluminum carbide formation, electrolysis of traces of water, and stray losses of current through frozen bath crust.

The overall aluminum reduction cell reaction may be written as:

$$Al_2O_3 \ (s) + 3/2 \ C \ (s) \rightarrow 2 \ Al \ (l)$$
$$3/2 \ CO_2 \ (g, \ p = 1 \ atm)$$

The reversible decomposition potential for this reaction, calculated from thermodynamic data, is 1.15 volts. In practice the decomposition voltage of aluminum reduction cells is usually about 1.5 to 1.7 volts. The operating cell over-voltage is, therefore, about 0.5 volts. Lack of a suitable reference electrode has prevented accurate measurement of the separate anode and cathode potentials. Indirect measurements by various techniques generally indicate the major portion of the total cell overvoltage is at the anode. The cathodic overvoltage is probably less than 0.2 volt and is thought to be due entirely to concentration polarization. The anodic over-voltage is at least 0.3 volt and appears to be composed of an "activation overvoltage" due to two-step oxidation of the anode carbon to form the primary CO_2 and a concentration polarization inversely proportional to the alumina content of the electrolyte.

Practical Cell Design and Operation

There are two basic types of aluminum reduction cells in commercial operation today which differ only in the type of carbon anode used. These are the multiple prebaked anode cell (Fig. 1) and the continuous self-baking anode, or Söderberg cell (Fig. 2). In both cases, petroleum coke is almost universally used as anode aggregate because of its low cost and high purity. Coal tar pitch is employed as a binder. Theoretical anodic carbon consumption at 100 per cent CO_2 formation and 85 per cent aluminum current efficiency is 0.392 pounds of carbon anode per pound of aluminum produced. In actual practice anode carbon consumption

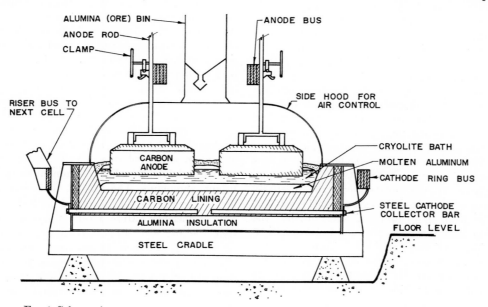

FIG. 1. Schematic cross section of modern prebaked anode cell of 85,000 ampere capacity.

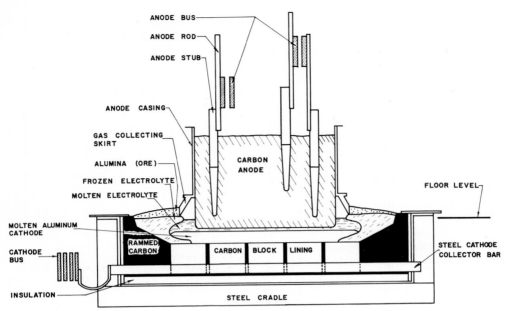

FIG. 2. Schematic cross section of 100,000 ampere vertical stub aluminum reduction cell with Söderberg anode.

ranges from about 0.42 to 0.55. The excess anode consumption above the theoretical is due largely to oxidation of the anodes just above the surface of the molten electrolyte by air and carbon dioxide.

In all aluminum reduction cells, a rugged, heavily reinforced steel shell is used to contain the thermal insulation, the carbon lining, cathode current collector system, and the molten electrolyte. The carbon lining may be installed in the form of prebaked blocks or as a rammed green monolithic lining which is baked in place. In either case, the current collection system to remove cathodic current from the cell consists of steel "collector" bars imbedded in the carbon and extending through the pot shell to connect with the cathode bus system. Anthracite coal is the most commonly used aggregate material for the carbon cell lining, since it is one of the more resistant forms of carbon to the attack and swelling caused by sodium generated at the cathode. The use of silicon carbide-type refractories for side linings in aluminum reduction cells instead of carbon has come into limited use in recent years. Although of greater initial cost, the silicon carbide has the advantages of improving heat dissipation and avoiding sodium deposition, or stray current losses, which can occur with carbon side linings. In opera-

tion, the carbon lining slowly deteriorates from sodium attack, aluminum carbide formation, mechanical disruption by crystal growth of electrolyte components which penetrate into the lining and solidify, and slow oxidation by traces of air diffusing through the insulation. As a result, the lining eventually ruptures, allowing aluminum and/or electrolyte to penetrate to the steel collector bar system, or even completely leak out of the cell. The useful life of aluminum reduction cell linings averages between about 650 and 1100 days.

The normal range of electrolyte compositions used in industrial practice is given above. Alumina is fed intermittently by breaking a portion of the frozen top crust and its preheated alumina down into the molten electrolyte at intervals varying between one and eight hours. The amount of alumina charged per feeding is less than that required to saturate the electrolyte so that excess undissolved alumina will not settle out on the floor of the lining. This would increase the electrical resistance through the lining and alter normal current distribution. The rate of alumina fed is slightly less than the rate of electrolysis so that the cells periodically have an "anode effect" when the alumina concentration is depleted to the critical value. In general, the frequency of anode effects is kept as low as possible, and the duration of anode effect is minimized. Excessively high temperatures are generated in the electrolyte, accompanied by low current efficiency and excessive volatilization of the bath when the anode effect is allowed to continue for more than a minute or two. An anode effect on any given cell also slightly decreases the amperage and voltage of the entire group of cells in series with it, which temporarily decreases their production and efficiency. Thus the anode effect is used primarily as a practical operating guide to prevent overfeeding of alumina to the cells.

In operation, small losses of electrolyte occur due to absorption into the carbon lining, hydrolysis and volatilization. The hydrolysis and volatilization products escape from the cell as traces of gaseous and particulate fluorides in the anode gases. The net result of these processes is a slow increase in the sodium fluoride content of the electrolyte. Sodium fluoride also accumulates in the electrolyte from the traces of sodium compounds in the alumina feed. Therefore, cryolite is added as needed to maintain the operating level of the electrolyte and aluminum fluoride to adjust for the increasing sodium fluoride content.

A continuous pad of molten aluminum is maintained under the electrolyte as the operating cathode. The bottom carbon lining is kept completely covered with this metal pad and the excess aluminum produced is drawn out of the cell through a cast iron "siphon" arrangement at intervals of 24 to 48 hours. The depth of the aluminum metal pad in a cell has an influence on the internal heat balance and the circulation and deformation of the metal pad and electrolyte by electromagnetic forces. In general, deeper

TABLE 1. TYPICAL DISTRIBUTION OF VOLTAGE LOSSES AND ENERGY CONSUMPTION IN AN 85,000 AMPERE COMMERCIAL ALUMINUM REDUCTION CELL

	Volts	Kilowatts
1. Decomposition	1.7	145
2. "Anode effect" polarization	0.1	8.5
3. Normal ohmic resistance		
a. Anode	0.1	8.5
b. Electrolyte	2.0	170
c. Lining	0.5	42.5
d. External conductors, joints, etc.	0.3	25.5
Total	4.7	400.0

TABLE 2. OPERATING PARAMETERS AND PERFORMANCE OF TYPICAL COMMERCIAL ALUMINUM REDUCTION CELLS

	Prebaked	Soderberg
1. *Operating Parameters*		
a. Electrolyte temp., °C.	955–980	945–975
b. Electrolyte depth, in.	6 to 8	5 to 7
c. Al cathode depth, in.	2 to 7	6 to 10
d. Anode current density, amps/sq in.	6 to 9	4 to 7
e. Anode-cathode distance, in.	1.5 to 1.8	1.7 to 2.0
f. Anode effects/cell day	0.8	0.2
2. *Performance*		
a. Current efficiency	86.8	87.0
b. Lb anode C/lb Al	0.486	0.439
c. kwh/lb Al (d-c)	7.31	7.86
d. kwh/lb Al (a-c)	7.70	8.26
e. Lb electrolyte/lb Al	0.04	0.06

metal pads promote better internal heat balance and minimize electromagnetic distortion of the cathode.

Table 1 shows the distribution of voltage losses, and the energy equivalent in kilowatts, in a typical modern aluminum reduction cell. The major ohmic resistance is in the electrolyte. This is where most of the heat is generated in the cell. The next largest ohmic resistance in the cell is between the molten aluminum cathode and the cathode bus system, called the "cathode" or "lining" voltage loss. An average value for the lining voltage loss is given in Table 1. In newly lined cells, this voltage loss is about 0.3 volts, but gradually increases as the cell ages and the carbon lining degenerates. The cathode voltage loss may rise as high as 1.0 volt in cells three or more years old. If the operating decomposition potential of 1.7 volts is regarded as the "useful work" performed by the cell in producing aluminum, then it may be seen that the energy efficiency of the process is about 36 per cent.

Table 2 gives typical cell parameters and operating performance for large, modern aluminum reduction cells. The cell parameters used in practice in any given aluminum plant depend upon the cell design and prevailing economic factors. The aluminum cathode current efficiency, perhaps the most important of all the cell operating characteristics, decreases as the anode-cathode distance decreases, as the electrolyte temperature increases, and as the sodium ion concentration in the electrolyte increases. The best cathodic current efficiency is obtained with the cell carbon side wall covered with frozen electrolyte, and the cell carbon bottom completely covered with the molten aluminum cathode.

The consumption of fluoride electrolyte materials given in Table 2 is the gross consumption. Recovery of electrolyte materials from cell effluent gases and spent linings, which is widely practiced, results in a net consumption of fluoride electrolyte materials much lower than that shown in Table 2.

Commercial aluminum reduction cells range between about 30,000 and 150,000 amperes capacity. Electromagnetic effects present no problems in the operation of cells of less than about 60,000 ampere capacity, unless there is some abnormality in the electrical bus system design. However, in cells larger than about 80,000 ampere capacity, serious attention must be given to the design of the cell and the bus system to minimize possible adverse electromagnetic effects. Electromagnetic forces can result in large static distortions in the surface of the aluminum cathode and/or dynamic agitation of the electrolyte and molten aluminum cathode to such an extent that the efficiency of cell operation is decreased. To a certain extent, however, the electromagnetic stirring of the electrolyte and the metal pad is beneficial in that it promotes more uniform thermal conditions within the cell and minimizes concentration polarization in the electrolyte. The trend in aluminum cell design is toward larger cells and increased automation in the control of cell operating parameters and in materials handling. New materials of construction and modified electrolyte compositions may further improve the efficiency of aluminum reduction cells in the future.

Aluminum Reduction Plants

In practice, aluminum reduction cells are operated in series with from about 100 to 180 cells constituting a "pot line" supplied by a single direct current power source. The cells are usually rectangular in shape and may be placed "side by side" with the long dimensions parallel, or "end to end" with the long dimensions

aligned. The side by side arrangement results in the minimum floor space requirement. The steel "pot shell" of a typical 100,000 ampere Söderberg cell is about 35 feet in length, 16 feet in width and 4 feet in depth. The overall height of such a cell, including the anode and its support, is about 10 feet. Two pot lines consisting of a total of about 300 to 400 cells of 80,000 to 120,000 amperes capacity is about the minimum size plant that can be built economically.

The location of aluminum reduction plants is determined almost solely by the availability of a large, dependable, and relatively low cost electrical power supply. Prior to 1940, power for aluminum reduction plants was derived almost completely from hydroelectric sources. During the 1940's natural gas was used as the energy source for several plants in the United States. In the future, in the United States at least, it appears that any further large expansions in aluminum reduction capacity will have to be based on coal as a source of power.

In the early days of the aluminum industry, motor generator sets and synchronous mechanical converters were used to convert alternating current into direct current for the aluminum pot lines. Beginning about 1930, the mercury arc-type rectifier came into widespread use and is the major type of rectification used by the aluminum industry today. Silicon rectifiers now appear at least competitive with mercury arc rectifiers for new installations and are already in limited use.

References

1. Beck, T. R., *J. Electrochem. Soc.*, **106**, 711 (1959).
2. Grjotheim, K., "Contributions to the Theory of Aluminum Electrolysis," Det KGL Norske Videnskabers Selokabs Skrifter, 1956, NR 5, Trondheim, Norway.
3. Haupin, W. E., *J. Electrochem. Soc.* **107**, 232 (1960).
4. Bockman, O. Chr., and Wlaugel, V., *J. Electrochem. Soc.*, **105**, 417 (1958).
5. Henry, J. L., and Holliday, R. D., *Ind. Eng. Chem.*, **51**, 1289 (1959).
6. Lewis, R. A., *Chem. Eng. Prog.*, **56**, 78 (1960).
7. Pearson, T. G., "Chemical Background of the Aluminum Industry," London, Royal Institute of Chemistry, Lectures, Monographs, and Reports, No. 3, 1955.
8. Piontelli, R., *Metallurgia ital.*, **52**(8), 469 and 478 (1960).
9. Stern, Harry, and Holmes, G. T., *J. Electrochem. Soc.*, **105**, 478 (1958).

10. Vajna, A., *Bull. soc. franç. elec.*, 7th Series, **14**, 85–91 (1952).
11. Rolin, M., and Bernard, M., *Bull. soc. chim. France* **1962**, 939–49.

Robert A. Lewis

Cross-references: *Aluminum Electrorefining; Fused Salt Overvoltage Measurements; Söderberg Anodes in Aluminum Cells.*

ALUMINUM PLATING

There is no convincing evidence that aluminum has ever been deposited from aqueous solutions. The main difficulty is the high negative potential of aluminum. Hydrogen instead of aluminum plates out on the cathode. The absence of overvoltage effects which occur in the electrodeposition of zinc makes it unlikely that aluminum will ever be deposited from an aqueous solution. The electrodeposition of aluminum has, therefore, been accomplished by using nonaqueous solutions. Fused salt baths are one example, while organic electrolytes represent another distinctly different approach. Both types of bath are sensitive to moisture and must be operated under completely anhydrous conditions.

Fused salt baths have been used to coat light-gage steel strips with aluminum in thicknesses ranging from 5 to 100 microinches. Coating adherence is no problem. However, thicknesses in excess of 30 microinches are required to obtain a satisfactory level of porosity. The intended use for this aluminum-coated steel strip has been mainly as a substitute for tin plate in the manufacture of metal containers. For this purpose it has many obvious advantages over solid aluminum.

While organic baths have been investigated for use in the coating of light-gage steel strips, the most extensive use of these baths has been in electroforming. As an example one can cite the electroforming of wave guides where wall thicknesses as heavy as 0.04 inch have been reported. Obviously such baths are well-suited to produce other electroformed goods or for plating small parts.

There are two major points of difference in the operation of the two baths. The fused salt baths operate at temperatures above 300°F. The conductivity of these baths is extremely good. On the other hand, organic baths operate at room temperature, but they are very poor conductors. As a result, organic baths are not suitable for high-current density plating because the voltage requirements would be beyond reasonable operating limits for normal direct current electroplating.

Fused Salt Bath

The first reference to the electrodeposition of aluminum from a fused salt bath dates back to the work of Bunsen and Deville in 1854. Since then many investigators have reported the results of their researches on the use of fused salt baths. Research at National Steel Corporation, Weirton, West Virginia, has shown that an electrolyte containing 80 per cent aluminum chloride, 10 per cent potassium chloride, and 10 per cent sodium chloride will yield excellent deposits of pure aluminum over quite a wide range of operating conditions. For example, the operating temperature may vary from 250°F to as high as 400°F, although the best range extends from 300 to 350°F. Current densities in excess of 200 amp/sq ft have been used with agitation. Without agitation the maximum current density obtained is 100 amp/sq ft. If anode-cathode spacing is less than two inches, the plating voltage required to obtain 50 amp/sq ft will be less than three volts. Current efficiencies exceeding 85 per cent have been recorded below 50 amp/sq ft.

Of considerably more importance than the operating characteristics already mentioned is the maintenance of the purity of the bath. Contamination by small amounts of moisture will seriously affect the operation of the process and the porosity of the deposit. The bath can tolerate up to one per cent water. It is believed that water reacts with the aluminum chloride to form either the mono or dihydroxy chloride of aluminum, both of which are soluble in the bath. This consumes aluminum chloride, and it is important that a minimum level of 75 per cent aluminum chloride be maintained.

Inferior deposits are produced when certain foreign metals contaminate the bath. The worst offenders are iron, nickel and magnesium. Zinc and titanium in low concentrations tend to whiten the deposit. Manganese, surprisingly, brightens the deposit. Concentrations of from 0.4 to 0.5 per cent manganese in the bath cited will yield approximately 16 per cent manganese in the coating. Coatings containing at least 16 per cent manganese are bright and lustrous.

A good grade of aluminum must be used for

the anodes. Satisfactory results have been obtained with 2S (1100). The anodes under normal conditions corrode evenly and without difficulty. There is no evidence of gas forming at the anode surface.

Because of the harmful effect of metallic impurities, the aluminum chloride used must be high purity. Best results have been obtained by using a resublimed grade. The product should be carefully packaged for shipment so that there is a minimum risk of contamination with moisture. Additions to a bath should be made in quantities which correspond to the size of the package in which the material is shipped, otherwise there is again the risk of moisture contamination in the remainder of the package.

Normal cleaning procedures are adequate to prepare the surface for plating. There must be no oils or oxide films on the surface of the strip. If preheating is used to bring the substrate to the temperature of the bath, this should be done in a nonoxidizing or reducing atmosphere. Since it has already been mentioned that iron is harmful if it accumulates in the bath, it is recommended that preheating rather than soaking in the bath be used.

Organic Baths

Several different types of organic baths have been successfully used for electrodepositing aluminum. A bath based on the aluminum chloride-ethyl pyridinium bromide eutectic and its toluene solution is representative of one type.[1, 2] The second type is an ether solution of aluminum chloride to which is added lithium hydride.[3] A description of this bath and its operating characteristics follows.

The constituents of the bath are aluminum chloride, lithium aluminum hydride and ethyl ether. Utmost care must be exercised in handling the chemicals and preparing the bath, and for this procedure the reader is referred to the published work. The plating bath consists of an ethereal solution of three molar aluminum chloride and 0.4 molar lithium aluminum hydride. Stock solutions are prepared from anhydrous materials.

Good deposits have been produced at current densities up to 20 amp/sq ft. Above this current density it is reported that the deposits have a more crystalline appearance. As plated under optimum conditions the deposits are white matte and ductile. The addition agents,

methyl borate and β, β' dichloroethyl ether, promote grain refinement.

The cathode current efficiency is 90 per cent, while the anode current efficiency is close to 100 per cent. At 20 amp/sq ft the plating rate is about one mil per hour.

The hydride bath is operated at room temperature. The life of a given bath or the measure of the amount of good aluminum that can be deposited from a bath varies depending on precautions taken to maintain the concentration of aluminum chloride. Only traces of moisture and carbon dioxide can be tolerated. Periodic additions of lithium aluminum hydride are required. The removal of portions of the bath and replacement with fresh plating solution and the use of paper diaphragms around the anode extends the life of the bath so that as much as 250 gpl of aluminum can be deposited. At this point the bath is spent, and efforts to rejuvenate it have not been successful.

Strips or other articles to be plated must be free of oil films and oxides. They must also be dry. Treatment in certain organic acids as outlined in Ref. (3) already cited will promote adhesion. Good adhesion of aluminum deposits to most of the common metals, except magnesium, has been reported.

References

1. HURLEY, F. H., AND WEIR, T. P., *J. Electrochem. Soc.*, **98**, 203–206 and 207–212 (1951).
2. SAFRANEK, W. H., SCHICKNER, W. C., AND FAUST, C. L., *J. Electrochem. Soc.*, **99**, 53–59 (1952).
3. CONNER, J. H., AND BRENNER, A., *J. Electrochem. Soc.*, **103**, 657–662 (1956).

EDWIN J. SMITH

AMALGAMS

Thomas Aquinas (about 1225–1274) studied solutions of metals in mercury and called them *amalgams*. The naturally occurring amalgams of gold and silver and some artificially prepared amalgams had been known for hundreds of years before his time. An amalgam is commonly defined as "an alloy of mercury with some other metal or metals," or as "an alloy in which mercury is an important component." Mercury forms amalgams not only with metals but also with tellurium, ammonium and other constituents not always considered metals.

Amalgams may be liquid or solid, depending on the temperature, the component or components associated with the mercury, the proportions of the components, and nature of their association. The natures of the associations include: solutions in mercury of individual atoms or associated atoms; suspensions in mercury of particles of colloidal size or larger; compounds in solution in mercury, or in mixtures, or nearly pure; solid solutions; and solid mixtures. Some examples of these states and conditions follow.

A dilute solution of cesium in mercury (m.p., $-38.87°C$) melts at $-46.6°C$. This and many other dilute solutions of metals show a lowering of freezing point corresponding to monatomic particles, and these particles obey the gas laws. Other amalgams have melting points which would indicate diatomic or polyatomic associated-atom solutes. Only one part of iron by weight is soluble in 10^{17} parts of mercury. But an amalgam containing 1% of iron can be made. It has a very large magnetic susceptibility which decreases on standing. When the mercury is evaporated at low temperatures a highly magnetic pyrophoric powder remains. The iron is supposed to form in single magnetic units which combine into much larger particles and partly neutralize each other. Mercury (m.p., $-38.87°C$) mixes with: lithium (m.p., $186°C$); sodium (m.p., $97.5°C$); potassium (m.p., $62.3°C$); and cesium (m.p., $28.5°C$), to form four continuous series of amalgams.

If the percentage of each alkali metal is plotted against the melting point of the alloy it forms, the curve for each metal is a succession of rounded maxima interspersed with sharp minima. The highest melting point on each curve preceded by a formula which represents the composition of that amalgam is respectively: LiHg (m.p., $600.5°C$); $NaHg_2$ (m.p., $360°C$); KHg_2 (m.p., $279°C$); $CsHg_2$ (m.p., $208.2°C$). Such a series of maxima and minima suggest that a rather pure compound is represented by each maximum, and each minimum represents the melting point of a mixture, a eutectic. The maximum melting points, some of them hundreds of degrees higher than the melting point of either component, cannot be explained on any other basis, than formation of compounds.

Amalgams may be prepared as follows: (1) By simple contact between mercury and any of many metals at low temperatures; higher temperatures and/or the presence of a dilute acid either increase the rate of amalgamation or increase the number of metals which can be amalgamated by this method. (2) By contact between mercury and an aqueous solution of a salt of a noble metal. (3) By contact between an aqueous solution of a salt of mercury and an active metal. (4) By contact between an aqueous solution of a salt of the appropriate metal and an amalgam of a more active metal. (5) By electrolysis of an aqueous solution of a salt of the appropriate metal using a mercury cathode. (6) By the electrolysis of an aqueous solution of a mercury salt using the appropriate metal as a cathode.

Amalgams may be used: (1) to deposit metals in thin layers as in silvering mirrors; (2) to plasticize metals or alloys so that irregular cavities may be fitted, as in the use of dental amalgams; (3) to control by dilution the reaction rates of, or facilitate the application of active metals such as sodium, aluminum and zinc when used in the preparation of titanium and other metals, or in the reduction of a great variety of organic compounds; (4) to separate such metals as iron and uranium in analytical chemistry by use of alloys of bismuth and zinc; and (5) as catalysts. In the preparation of pure sodium hydroxide by the electrolysis of brine, the formation of sodium amalgam is a step in one of the processes.

The radical NH_4 has not been prepared in the free state. If it could be prepared it would not be a metal; but when an aqueous solution of ammonia or an ammonium salt is brought into contact with the amalgam of an active metal, or is electrolyzed with a mercury cathode, the mercury becomes one constituent of a spongy mass called ammonium amalgam. If ammonium amalgam is warmed from $-60°C$ to room temperature its volume increases thirty-fold. It displaces such metals as copper, cadmium and zinc from aqueous solutions of their salts. The freezing points of dilute ammonium amalgams are the same as those of amalgams of the alkali metals having equivalent concentrations. Mixed amalgams may be formed by including various metals in ammonium amalgam, but all metals except magnesium decrease the stability. Substituted ammoniums may be deposited in mercury to form amalgams. All ammonium amalgams are unstable even below the melting point of mercury and their stability decreases as the temperature is raised. Their decomposition products are H_2, NH_3 and mercury. The NH_4 is not necessarily a free radical in the amalgam, but could be NH_4Hg_x.

F. E. Brown

Cross-reference: *Chlorine Production in Mercury Cells.*

AMERICAN ELECTROPLATERS' SOCIETY

On March 6, 1909, Charles H. Proctor met with a group of some two-dozen foremen-platers in New York City to create a nonprofit educational organization for the sharing of experiences and information to improve electroplating, metal finishing, and allied arts. As a result of this and subsequent meetings, the National Electro-Platers Association was organized on April 10, 1909, when its Constitution and Bylaws were approved by 60 charter members, and Charles H. Proctor was elected President. The Association was formally incorporated on October 18, 1909, for the principal purposes of: "(1) advancing and disseminating 'knowledge concerning the art of electro-deposition of metals,' (2) maintaining a laboratory equipped for research work, (3) conducting meetings for the purpose of presenting papers upon appropriate technical and scientific subjects, and (4) publishing technical literature." The membership was broadened to include electro-chemists as Active Members, employees of supply houses as Associate Members, and men of "knowledge preeminently valuable to the Association" as Honorary Members. In June, 1910, the first issue of the Association's quarterly magazine, appropriately titled, *Quarterly Review*, was published containing such technical articles as "The Production of Matt Gold Finish" and "The Electrical Side of Electroplating."

In the ensuing years, branches were organized in other eastern cities, the Midwest, and Canada. To meet the challenges of expansion, the Association was reorganized on June 1, 1913, as the American Electroplaters' Society. The new Society held its first annual meeting on that day and elected George B. Hogaboom as its first president. The Constitution reemphasized "the improvement and dissemination of knowledge concerning the art of electrodeposition in all its branches" and stated "all laws and rules must be so formed that the Society will promote no other object than the education of its members in all the principles of electrodeposition and coloring of metals."

The object of the Society was recently (1963) reaffirmed in modern language: "... to improve and disseminate knowledge of the arts and sciences of electroplating and the deposition and finishing of metals and of allied arts. The Society shall be empowered to initiate and sustain research; hold meetings for the presentation and discussion of professional papers; develop, publish, and distribute technical treatises; and pursue other related activities."

Membership in the Society consists of five classes: (1) Active, any person interested in the object of the Society, (2) Student, (3) Member-at-Large, (4) Sustaining Member, any firm or person interested in the object of the Society and in the financial support of the Society research activities, and (5) Honorary. All members are privileged to attend branch, regional, and annual meetings and to receive Society publications. The members differ widely in education and training, from practical experience to doctorate degrees. The common bond uniting this dedicated heterogeneous group is the desire to fulfill the Society objectives. The greatest majority of members are in industry. An increasing number of academic people have affiliated themselves with the Society because of recent scientific interests in metal deposition.

Active and Sustaining Membership dues and income from Society publications support the operation of the Society. There is a degree of uniqueness about the dues. They are proportioned to pay for the subscription to the official journal and contribute to the general fund, Research fund, and branch operation.

The fulfillment of the Society's objective is achieved in many ways. Scientific and technical papers are presented at monthly branch meetings, regional meetings, and annual conventions. The official journal, entitled *Plating*, is published monthly and contains original scientific and technical papers and news of the Society, its members, and the industry in general. The Society publishes one or more times each year a book identified as *Technical Proceedings*. It contains papers presented at the annual convention. The scope was recently broadened to include papers presented at branch or regional meetings, especially if they possess reference value. The Society sponsors publication of symposia papers in book form. *Plating, Technical Proceedings*, and publications of books are supervised by a nine-member technical education board.

A great strength of the Society lies in its 63 branches located in the prime electroplating and metal finishing areas of Australia, Canada, and the United States. The presentation of papers at monthly branch meetings provides personal contact for the members with experts in every phase of electroplating and metal finishing. Educational courses, sponsored by the branches, are presented as a part of adult education in their respective communities.

There are eleven annual technical awards offered. All except the Scientific Achievement Award, recognizing a Society member whose outstanding scientific contributions have advanced the theory and practice of electroplating, are for papers appearing during the year in the Society's publications: Carl E. Heussner Award consisting of the AES Gold Medal Award, best paper; AES Silver Medal Award, second best paper; AES Bronze Award, third best paper; George B. Hogaboom Memorial Award, best paper on nickel plating; Robert S. Leather, best paper on mechanical finishing; Chromium Plating Award, best paper on chromium plating; Precious Metal Plating Award, best paper on plating of gold, rhodium, palladium, and silver; John J. Hanney Memorial Award, best paper on copper plating; Zinc Award, best paper on the plating of zinc die castings; and Organic Finishing Award, best paper on organic finishing.

In addition to the technical awards and Honorary Membership Awards, the Charles A. Proctor Award is presented to a Society member whose leadership has furthered the objectives of the Society.

From its inception, the American Electroplaters' Society has always been considered an "educational society." As such, its members were interested in research and its possible application to industrial practice. The research committee was organized in 1923 to formalize research activities. Its structure was reorganized in 1944 to consist of nine members, three appointed each year for three-year tenures. A research fund was created to insure continuity of fundamental and applied research programs located at well-known Canadian and United States colleges, universities, and re-

search centers by means of prorated Active and Sustaining Membership dues. Since 1944, approximately one-half million dollars have been invested in research. Many doctoral candidates have benefited from this research program.

The duly designated and accredited branch representatives meet annually during the national convention to hear reports; elect Society officers, directors, and a nominating committee; act upon proposed amendments to the Constitution; and counsel the board of directors. The latter group, composed of the Society officers—president, first vice president, second vice president, immediate past president, and treasurer—and 12 directors, is the governing body of the Society. The general manager, an appointive position, is the administrative officer of the board of directors and serves as the secretary of the board of directors. He is responsible for and is in charge of the Society's national headquarters and staff, and the publication of the Society's official journal, *Plating*; annual volume, *Technical Proceedings*; and other special publications. The general manager is assisted in his duties by a staff of workers, including technical editor and editor, at national headquarters office, 443 Broad Street, Newark, New Jersey, 07102.

MANUEL BEN

AMMETERS, MICRO-MICRO. See MICROVOLT-METERS AND MICRO-MICROAMMETERS.

AMMONIUM PEROXYDISULFATE (AMMONIUM PERSULFATE). See HYDROGEN PEROXIDE; PEROXYGEN CHEMICALS.

AMPERE, ABSOLUTE. See ELECTRICAL UNITS AND STANDARDS.

AMPÈRE, ANDRÉ-MARIE (1775–1836)

André-Marie Ampère was born in Lyons January 22, 1775, and brought up nearby in the village of Polémieux. His father, a great admirer of J. J. Rousseau, was almost the boy's only teacher, and his broad molding of his son's mind helped the young man develop a passionate interest in the most diverse sciences of the time. His studies also led him into the fields of literature, philosophy, and poetry. His father perished on the guillotine during the Revolution, and his death profoundly influenced the young man. For almost a year his life seemed entirely planless and only again gained direction with his marriage, at the age of 24, to Julie Carron, who was to be the passion and one affection of his whole life. The young couple settled in Lyons, where he taught mathematics. In 1801 he went to Bourg as professor of physics and chemistry but had to leave his wife behind because of her ill health. She succumbed in 1804 and the second deep blow left a wound which never fully healed.

A mathematical work on problems of probability, in reference to games of chance, drew the attention of the astronomers Lalande and Delambre and led to an appointment at the École Polytechnique in Paris where he continued research and study and was elected to the Académie des Sciences in 1814. His mathematical work alone would have sufficed to put him in the ranks of the great mathematicians of his time, but his widespread scientific research and study were already leading him into the field of chemistry and the molecular theory of gases.

His real claim to glory came as a result of Oersted's great discovery in 1819 that a magnetic needle is acted on by a voltaic current. This led Ampère to feverish activity and in 1820 he identified magnetism and electricity. This science of moving electricity or the creation, in the main, of electrodynamics had been given impetus for development by Galvani and Volta, and the work of Oersted directed its application. It was Ampère, however, who gave this application a form which even today shapes the main part of its content. His mathematical theories explained the already observed electromagnetic phenomena and predicted those to come. Only Faraday was later able to add new and important form and matter.

Ampère's amazing successes depended largely upon his intuition of genius which gave him a clear grasp of the phenomena first pictured by Oersted. This highly complicated discovery was extended through skillful experimentation, with negligible equipment built with his own hands, to a settlement of the idea of electric current. He called the entire process in the discharge wire an electric current with no regard to details. He also made the first sharp distinction between phenomena of electric tension and those of electric current together with the clarification between electrostatics (the science of stationary electricity) and electrodynamics (science of moving electricity) and invented these terms. Further extensive experiments led to the discovery that forces exist between currents in parallel conductors, which in turn led Ampère to a peculiar conception of magnetism.

He died at the age of 61 on June 10, 1836, and apparently remained one of the most attractive and personable of individuals even in his old age. He was often tortured by doubt on both small and large matters, and his letters reveal concern over the dogmas of the Catholic Church. He also suffered some domestic misfortune after his first wife's death. His brilliant achievements prepared for the work of Maxwell which is the basis for the science of physics.

CARMEN W. WALSH

AMPEROMETRIC TITRATION. See ELECTROMETRIC TITRATIONS.

ANCIENT METALS, ELECTROLYTIC RESTORATION. See ELECTROLYTIC RESTORATION OF ANCIENT METALS.

ANODE

In an electrolytic cell, the anode is the electrode at which an oxidation process takes place. Typically, the process may consist of the discharge of negative ions (such as the formation of oxygen in the electrolysis of alkali hydroxides); the oxidation of the electrode (represented by $M \rightarrow M^{+n} + ne$ where M is the oxidizing electrode, M^{+n} the ions formed in the oxidation process, and n the oxidation number of the ions); or the oxidation of other elements.

The anode is the positive terminal in an electrolyte through which current is being forced. Electrons leave (current enters) a cell through the anode. The electrons travel to the cathode through metallic conduction in a circuit external to the electrolyte. Within the electrolyte, anions are attracted to the anode.

In a primary cell, the anode is the negative terminal. In the conventional dry cell, the anode is the zinc container. The anode reaction is $Zn - 2e \rightarrow Zn^{++}$. In the conventional storage battery, the anode consists of finely-divided lead pasted within a lead grid. The anode reaction during discharge is $Pb - 2e \rightarrow Pb^{++}$; during charge it is the reverse.

In electrochemical corrosion the material corroded, attacked, or dissolved is generally the anode in the galvanic circuit.

The number of materials useful as insoluble anodes in electrolytic oxidation processes is rather limited. High-nickel steel, Pt, Ir, Ni, and Pd are employed in alkaline solutions; noble metals and carbon in acid solutions; graphite in chloride solutions. Insoluble lead anodes are useful in the electrodeposition of metals in chloride-free sulfate electrolytes. Lead dioxide anodes are used in bromate and perchlorate cells. When an aluminum electrode is made the anode in sulfuric, chromic, or oxalic acid solutions, an oxide film is formed on the surface of the electrode.

In electroplating, both soluble and insoluble anodes are used. Soluble anodes are used in plating baths where anode dissolution is used to replenish the depleting metal ion content of the bath. Anode composition is usually the same as that of the material being plated on the cathode. Insoluble anodes are used in many cases where, in the absence of an external emf, the bath would chemically attack and dissolve an anode of the same metal as is present in the bath. Platinum is generally used in the laboratory as one of the best examples of insoluble anodes. In many electrolytes, the greater the ease of the oxygen evolution reaction, the greater the likelihood the anode will be insoluble. Carbon and graphite are used as insoluble anodes in solutions which do not evolve much oxygen.

Metallurgical factors, such as previous thermal and mechanical history, often determine behavior of a metal when it is used as an anode.

To produce deburred smooth surface finishes, or in preparation for metallographic examinations, metals are made anodic in electropolishing solutions.

In electrolytic refining, use is made of the fact that different metals oxidize and dissolve from anodes at different voltages, the most active metal dissolving at the lowest voltage.

In an electron tube, the anode is the electrode towards which electrons are attracted. Anodes are also used to focus or accelerate electron streams from cathode to target.

Jacob M. Miller

Cross-references: *Cathode, Electrode.*

ANODIC DISINTEGRATION OF METALS

Some Previous Observations

Gold, if dissolved anodically, produces respectable quantities of gold powder. If the metal is very pure, gold particles trickle down like rain from the anode to the bottom of the vessel through the electrolyte, which is an aqueous solution of $HAuCl_4$. Wohlwill investigated this phenomenon in detail[1] and found that the amount of powder increases with decrease in current density, with increase in purity of the gold, and with the smoothness of the anode. The anodic powder obtained constituted about 10 or more per cent of the weight of the cathodic deposit. The appearance of the gold particles was attributed (a) to partial disintegration of the dissolving anode and (b) to a disproportionation reaction whereby monovalent Au ions are anodically produced in large amounts, especially at low current densities:

$$3Au^+ \rightarrow Au^{3+} + 2Au \qquad (1)$$

This reaction is reasonable in that the presence of Au^+ can be proved and occurs within a solution volume when it is removed from the electrolysis vessel. Furthermore, the Au nuclei formed are stable and dissolve only very slowly in the electrolyte.

The same mechanism can be applied to the anodic dissolution of copper. The copper anode disintegrates partially when the anodic current is flowing and Cu particles are also produced, probably due to the reaction

$$2Cu^+ \rightleftharpoons Cu^{2+} + Cu \qquad (2)$$

The presence of Cu^+ can easily be proved, and the Cu nuclei formed react only slowly with the electrolyte or with air.

However, metallic dust appears also during anodic dissolution of silver in its nitrate solutions. Silver in such solutions is strongly monovalent, as can be followed from the determinations of the Faraday constant from the weight of cathodic deposits. Therefore, reactions simi-

lar to (1) and (2), which would explain the formation of Ag dust at the anode, are excluded. Furthermore, the Faraday constant can be determined with high precision from the weight loss of the anode, but only if the weight of the Ag particles appearing at the anode is taken into the consideration. In this way Craig, Hoffman, Law and Hamer[2] found a value of 96,490.0 ± 2.4 coulombs for the Faraday which is in excellent agreement with the previous best determinations. This result could not have been obtained if Ag dissolved anodically with an uncommon valency,[3, 4] followed by a disproportionation reaction similar to (1) or (2). Therefore, the only reason for the appearance of an Ag sediment during the anodic dissolution of Ag is a partial *disintegration* of the anode into small particles.

Disintegration of other metals occurs also, as reported, e.g., by Hoey and Cohen,[5] Evans,[6] Marsh and Schaschl.[7] If less noble metals are chosen as anodes, their partial disintegration should be more difficult to observe, because of the rapid attack of the dispersed particles by the electrolyte. Nevertheless, Laughlin, Kleinberg, and Davidson[12] observed that beryllium produced a black powder when dissolved anodically in aqueous solutions. X-ray analysis showed the powder to be metallic Be. Hence, the explanation offered for its presence was the reaction

$$2Be^+ \rightarrow Be^{2+} + Be \qquad (3)$$

in analogy with (2). It was assumed that Be went anodically into solution with the uncommon valency of one, and then, upon collision of the monovalent positive ions, disproportionation and formation of comparatively large metallic Be particles occurred in an aqueous solution. Doubts, in contrast to Eq. 2, were cast upon the correctness of (3) because of two reasons: (a) the presence of Be^+ could not be proved, and (b) no one had observed, due to the very active nature of the metal, the growth of Be particles or had obtained Be by cathodic deposition from aqueous solutions. Therefore, it appeared necessary to seek other explanations for the formation of Be particles.

The true nature of the particle formation was revealed by a thorough microscopic study of the size and shape of the particles dispersed in the electrolyte. The author of the present article in collaboration with his associates found[8] that *partial disintegration* of the anode occurred and,

hence, not disproportionation according to (3) during anodic dissolution. This perception removed a series of difficulties in the explanation of various phenomena, as shown in the discussion.

Distintegrating Beryllium

A black deposit was obtained not only during anodic dissolution of Be, but also by simple dissolution of the metal in dilute HCl, HBr, or $HClO_4$.[8] No blackening of the solution occurred when the metal reacted with HF. In HCl, a black deposit of cotton-like appearance (in the dry state) was obtained. The deposit, when examined under a microscope with high magnification, preferably with oil immersion objectives and in reflected light, consisted of innumerable needles, of single but rarely larger chunks, and of parts of deformation twins (Fig. 1).

Disintegration of Be also occurs if the metal is dissolved anodically in neutral aqueous NaCl solutions. Numerous metallic particles, which can be recognized microscopically by their luster, appear throughout the electrolyte, with shapes as shown in Fig. 1, but of smaller size. Separation of the Be fragments from a solid piece could be directly observed and pictures were made. The surface of the dissolving Be casting was covered with deformation twins. The fragments separating from the casting are needle shaped and the needles frequently cross themselves at the twin angle shown in Fig. 2. The separation of a part of a deformation twin from the substrate can also be seen on the same

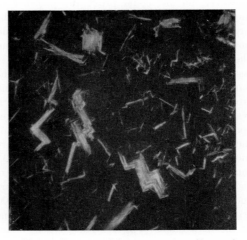

Fig. 1. Be crystal fragments (needles and twins) of the deposit, obtained by dissolving vacuumcast Be in 0.3N HCl. 450X.

FIG. 2. Separation of a twinned particle from the crystalline Be piece (arrow). Etched in about 0.4N HCl. 300X.

picture. This is direct evidence that the Be particles originate from a Be casting or anode by partial disintegration, and not from the secondary reaction (3).

Disintegrating Magnesium

It is well established that the efficiency of sacrificial Mg anodes in cathodic protection is low and may drop sometimes to even below 50 per cent. Thereby the deposit on the surface of the anodes, consisting of MgO or $Mg(OH)_2$, varies in color from white to gray or dark gray. Baborovský (in 1905) assumed that the dark color might be caused by very fine metallic Mg particles dispersed in the oxidation product. However, no one could prove the presence of metallic particles microscopically, except for the presence of some larger chunks,[5] which could not affect the color of the deposits. Bhatia and the author of the present article succeeded in resolving microscopically the structure of the dark, sometimes even black flakes, separating from Mg during anodic dissolution in neutral NaCl solutions.[10] It was found that the flakes consist of an $Mg(OH)_2$ network entangling numerous metallic particles. The particles are much smaller than those of Be, about 6×10^{-5} mm in diameter for the smallest observable particles; they are flat and lie parallel to the corroding Mg surface. There are more than 200,000 particles per sq cm in the denser accumulations of the dark flakes (Fig. 3). The particles react with the electrolyte or with water with evolution of gas (possibly H_2), eventually turning

light gray to white. There is a less dense accumulation of particles in the light gray product (Fig. 4), and no particles in the white flakes.

Dark flakes also separate from Mg anodes when electrolysis is performed in dilute HCl. However, they react so rapidly with the acid that they hardly can be collected for microscopic examination. However, particles can be observed in the dark anodic deposit, if electrolysis is performed in dilute solutions of perchloric acid.

There is little doubt about the metallic na-

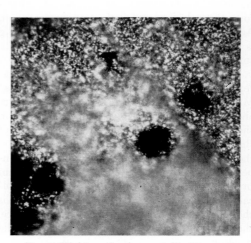

FIG. 3. Highly reflecting metallic Mg particles in the black corrosion product of Mg. 250–300 ma/sq cm; electrolyte — 3% NaCl solution. Holes in the film. 1430X.

FIG. 4. Less dense accumulation of shiny Mg particles in the nearly white flakes. 1430X.

ture of the particles: (a) they have strong metallic luster, reflecting the light of the opaque illuminator of the microscope like tiny mirrors; (b) they appear black in the transmitted light; (c) they produce the x-ray pattern of the metal (Mg or Be); (d) they dissolve in acids and water (Mg) with gas evolution; and (e) the dark anodic product is very stable in dry air as expected from a metallic powder.

Discussion

It has been observed that metals Ag,[2] Be,[8] and Mg[10] partially disintegrate into very fine particles while dissolving anodically. The metals Au and Cu disintegrate also, but the presence of metallic particles in the anodic slime can also be attributed to disproportionation reactions (1) and (2). A more or less coarse disintegration occurs also in case of stainless steel and iron.[6, 7] The same happens with Pb, Sn, and Al.[6] Now, if the weight of the disintegration products dropping out of the anode is not observed, which may occur easily for active metals like Al and Mg, or not considered if differently interpreted (Be),[12] a large deviation from Faraday's law will be found. One explanation of this deviation[12] assumes that the respective metals go anodically into solution as ions of lower valency than normal, and these ions instantly react apart from the anode according to (1), (2), or (3) or with hydrogen ion or *with* H_2O to form ions of normal valency, e.g.:

$$Mg^+ + H^+ \rightarrow Mg^{2+} + 0.5H_2 \qquad (4)$$

As a consequence, a larger amount of metal than calculated from the anodic current using Faraday's law will go into solution. However, the presence of lower valency ions of active metals (e.g., Al^+, Mg^+, Be^+) could not be proved in aqueous solutions.[3, 11, 12]

Alternatively, the *deviation* from Faraday's law can be explained readily *by the breakout* of metallic particles from the working anode, as directly observed with Be (see Fig. 2) and Mg (Figs. 3 and 4). Furthermore, it should be expected that for amalgamated anodes, e.g., of Zn, the metal should not eject particles (how could they penetrate the Hg layer?), but the formation of Zn^+ should not be hampered. It was shown by James and Stoner, using KNO_3 as an electrolyte, that under such conditions neither disintegration nor formation of Zn^+, nor a deviation from Faraday's law occurred.[13] How-

ever, as a deviation was observed with non-amalgamated Zn anodes, it is clear that this is due to partial disintegration of Zn anodes. No lower valency ions are necessary to explain this deviation.

As a possible proof for the formation of lower valency ions, the reducing ability of the anolyte is often mentioned.[12] However, this does not constitute a proof, because the fine particles of the disintegrating anodes of active metals have even a greater reducing ability. Because of their small size they are carried throughout the electrolyte; they may even penetrate membranes and still act as strong reducers.

The anodic disintegration also contributes to the explanation of the negative difference effect:[4] if an electrode consisting, e.g., of Al dissolves at a certain rate, as measured by the rate of hydrogen evolution in HCl, then the rate of hydrogen evolution increases suddenly if the Al is in addition dissolved anodically. The increase in hydrogen evolution rate at a certain current density represents the negative difference effect.[3, 4] The effect is explained by the breakdown of protective layers on Al by the anodic current, and by disintegration of the metal underneath. Both events cause an increase in the rate of hydrogen evolution at the anode while the current is passing the cell. The appearance of the lower valency Al ions is not necessary for the explanation of the effect.

The low efficiency of sacrificial Mg anodes used in cathodic protection is explained similarly: the protective coating breaks down and the metal disintegrates partially while the current is flowing; the particles separated from the bulk metal corrode and do not contribute to the current for cathodic protection.

Finally, if the potential of a corroding active metal becomes more negative (e.g., with increasing concentration of the acid), dissolution of the surface film and disintegration of the metal may well be responsible for that.[14]

Conclusions and Outlook

The reasons for the occurrence of disintegration of dissolving metals are not known. It may be an intrinsic (mosaic) property of the metals themselves. It may also be a consequence of their imperfect structure due to presence of impurities, glide planes, slip lines, vacancies, and dislocations. Hence, the particles will not break out evenly throughout the whole anodic surface but at preferential places, producing beautiful etch patterns, as for Mg.[10] Other sites where the structure of the metal is somehow weakened may also be the starting points of the disintegration process. Studies with single metallic crystals as anodes may contribute to the understanding of the phenomenon and may perhaps reveal the means to prevent disintegration, which may be of benefit in the fields of cathodic protection and batteries.

References

1. WOHLWILL, E., *Z. Elektrochem.*, **4**, 402, 405, 421 (1898).
2. CRAIG, D. N., HOFFMAN, J. I., LAW, C. A., AND HAMER, W. J., *J. Res. of N.B.S.*, **64A**, 381, 392 (1960).
3. STRAUMANIS, M. E., *J. Electrochem. Soc.*, **105**, 284 (1958).
4. STRAUMANIS, M. E., *J. Electrochem. Soc.*, **108**, 1087 (1961).
5. HOEY, G. R., AND COHEN, M., *J. Electrochem. Soc.*, **105**, 245 (1958).
6. EVANS, U. R., "Corrosion and Oxidation of Metals," p. 883, London, Edward Arnold, 1960.
7. MARSH, G. A., AND SCHASCHL, E., *J. Electrochem. Soc.*, **107**, 960 (1960).
8. STRAUMANIS, M. E., AND MATHIS, D. L., *J. Less-Common Met.*, **4**, 213 (1962); *J. Electrochem. Soc.*, **109**, 434 (1962).
9. ROBERTS, C. S., "Magnesium and its Alloys," pp. 199–200, New York, John Wiley & Sons, Inc., 1960.
10. STRAUMANIS, M. E., AND BHATIA, B. K., *J. Electrochem. Soc.*, **110**, 357 (1963).
11. GLICKSMAN, R., *J. Electrochem. Soc.*, **106**, 83 (1959).
12. LAUGHLIN, B. D., KLEINBERG, J., AND DAVIDSON, A. W., *J. Am. Chem. Soc.* **78**, 559 (1960).
13. JAMES, W. J., AND STONER, G. E., *J. Am. Chem. Soc.*, **85**, 1354 (1963).
14. STRAUMANIS, M. E., AND GNANAMUTHU, D. S., Techn. Rep. No. 1 to Office of Naval Research, 1963.

M. E. STRAUMANIS

Cross-references: *Anodic Dissolution, Low Valence States in; Difference Effect.*

ANODIC DISSOLUTION, LOW VALENCE STATES IN

In the whole field of electrochemistry, no law has been more firmly established by generalization from observed data, nor more satisfactorily explained in terms of universally accepted theoretical principles, than Faraday's law of electrolysis: for every 96,487 coulombs (or one faraday) of electricity that passes through an electrolyte, one gram-equivalent of a substance is oxidized at the anode, and one gram-equivalent of the same or another substance is reduced at at the cathode. Specifically, when the anodic reaction consists in the dissolution of a metallic element, a gram-equivalent is defined as a number of grams equal to the atomic weight of the metal divided by the number of units of positive charge on the cation formed from it, or, alternatively expressed, by the number of electrons lost to the anode by each atom of metal entering the solution. Evidently, then, provided that no other anodic reaction occurs simultaneously with such dissolution and that the anode metal is not non-electrolytically acted upon by the solution, the valence or oxidation state of the cation formed must be equal to the number of faradays passed per gram-atomic weight.

As early as 1857, however, it was observed by Wöhler and Buff that the weight of aluminum dissolved from an anode of this metal in the electrolysis of aqueous sodium chloride solution was considerably greater than would correspond, according to Faraday's law, to the quantity of electricity passed through the solution, if the cation formed were assumed to have the charge usually attributed to this cation. A few years later, a similar anomaly was observed by Beetz in the dissolution of a magnesium anode in aqueous magnesium sulfate solution. In both of these instances, in other words, the oxidation state of the cation as calculated from Faraday's law was appreciably lower than that ordinarily associated with the metal in question; thus, a low valence state of the metal had apparently been attained by anodic dissolution.

Although phenomena of this type were reported sporadically during the intervening years, it has been only recently (since 1954), in consequence of more thorough and precise experimental work, that the attainment of low valence states by anodic dissolution has begun to attract wide interest among electrochemists. The method used in these recent studies has been to pass a direct current, in series, through an electrolytic cell (usually divided into anode and cathode compartments by means of a sintered glass barrier) in which a weighed sample of the metal of interest serves as anode, and through a silver coulometer. The results have commonly been expressed in terms of a quantity represented by the symbol, V_i, which is defined by the equation

$$V_i = \frac{\text{number of gram-atomic weights of silver}}{\text{number of gram-atomic weights of metal}}\frac{\text{deposited in coulometer}}{\text{lost from anode}}$$

This quotient, which might alternatively be defined as the ratio of the atomic weight of the metal to its equivalent weight in the anodic process, gives the average number of electrons lost per atom of metal dissolved, and hence has been designated the initial mean valence number of the metal. It is a noteworthy fact that many metals which ordinarily form bipositive or tripositive cations have been observed, under a wide variety of circumstances, to exhibit V_i values markedly smaller than the number which designates the familiar oxidation state of the metal. Furthermore, the low valence numbers so found, although indeed usually nonintegral, are never less than unity.

The anode metals for which lower than "normal" V_i values have been observed on electrolysis of salt solutions in designated solvents include aluminum, gallium, and indium in liquid ammonia and in anhydrous acetic acid; magnesium and aluminum in pyridine; calcium in dimethylformamide; beryllium, zinc, manganese, aluminum, titanium, zirconium, molybdenum, and uranium in concentrated aqueous acetic acid-perchloric acid solutions; and beryllium, magnesium, zinc, cadmium, tin, and aluminum in water. For most of these metals, the minimum V_i value observed was between 1 and 2; in a few instances (calcium in potassium iodide solution in dimethylformamide, beryllium in acetic acid-perchloric acid solution, and tin in aqueous sodium nitrate) the minimum V_i value was unity.

Before a general hypothesis is presented to account for the phenomenon of anomalous anodic dissolution, several significant supplementary facts should be noted. (1) In most of the experiments referred to in the two preceding paragraphs, a control test was provided by suspending in the electrolyte, in close proximity to the anode, a similar rod of the same metal. The fact that this control showed no significant loss in weight during the electrolysis indicated the absence of nonelectrolytic corrosion. (2) In the solutions containing perchloric acid, chloride ion was found to be present in the solution after electrolysis whenever the V_i value was less than the lowest familiar valence number of the anode metal, but never when the V_i value corresponded to a familiar or stable oxidation state. (3) In the

electrolysis of aqueous solutions, evolution of gaseous hydrogen was always observed at an anode of beryllium, magnesium, or aluminum, but never at one of zinc, cadmium, or tin. Furthermore, whereas for the first three metals V_i values lower than 2 were obtained in halide (and in the case of magnesium also in sulfate) solutions, yet for the last three metals the "normal" V_i value of 2 was always exhibited in such solutions. With zinc, cadmium, or tin, the V_i value was lower than 2 only when the electrolyte was a salt with a reducible (or electron-accepting) anion, such as nitrate or chlorate; and in every such instance a product of reduction of the electrolyte could be detected in the anolyte after electrolysis. (4) With a beryllium anode in aqueous sodium chloride solution, and with an aluminum anode in an aqueous sodium chloride-sodium nitrate mixture, after electrolysis had proceeded for a few minutes there appeared throughout the anolyte a finely-divided dark gray to black deposit, which was found to be a mixture of hydrous oxide and free metal.

All of the phenomena thus far described may be satisfactorily explained in terms of a simple hypothesis: namely, that the primary step in the anodic oxidation of any potentially bivalent or polyvalent metal is the loss, by each atom, of a single electron to the anode, with the formation of a unipositive ion. This cation, an active reducing agent, is short-lived, undergoing almost immediate oxidation to the familiar stable polypositive (in the simplest case, bipositive) ion. The second stage of the oxidation, however, may occur in either one of the following two ways. (1) The unipositive ion may, before it leaves the anode, give up its remaining valence electron (or electrons) to this electrode, thus going into solution as a stable cation of familiar oxidation state. When this is the only mode of oxidation, the V_i value, as determined coulometrically, will correspond to the familiar valence number of the metal. (2) In the presence of an oxidizing agent—either the solvent or some other electron acceptor—the unipositive ion may undergo a secondary chemical (nonelectrolytic) reaction in which it is oxidized to a stable cation. If this were the sole mode of oxidation, the V_i value would be unity.

The two oxidation paths described in the preceding paragraph must be supposed to be competitive, so that both reactions may take place simultaneously; when this occurs, the measured V_i value—indicating the *mean* initial oxidation state—will be greater than 1 but smaller than the familiar valence number. Thus, the V_i value may be expected to vary not only from metal to metal, but also for a given metal with any conditions, such as nature of electrolyte, concentration, or temperature, which affect unequally the rates of the two competing types of oxidation.

According to the hypothesis just outlined, it may be supposed that those unipositive ions which are especially readily oxidized—namely, Be^+, Mg^+, and Al^+— undergo in aqueous solution such redox reactions with water as, for example, the following:

$$2Mg^+ \text{ (or } Mg_2^{++}\text{)} + 2H_2O \rightarrow$$
$$2Mg^{++} + H_2 + 2OH^-$$
$$Al^+ + 2H_2O \rightarrow Al^{+++} + H_2 + 2OH^-$$

The stable cation so formed may, of course, be partially or completely precipitated as a basic salt or a hydroxide.

On the other hand, those transitory unipositive ions which are not sufficiently strong reducing agents to be oxidized by water may undergo in aqueous solution secondary reactions with electron-accepting anions, such as the following:

$$6Zn^+ + ClO_3^- + 3H_2O \rightarrow 6Zn^{++} + Cl^- + 6OH^-$$
$$2Cd^+ + NO_3^- + H_2O \rightarrow 2Cd^{++} + NO_2^- + 2OH^-$$
$$8Sn^+ + NO_3^- + 6H_2O \rightarrow 8Sn^{++} + NH_3 + 9OH^-$$

In all three of these cases, the indicated reduction product has been detected in the anolyte after electrolysis, in an amount consistent with the coulometrically determined V_i value.

For the electrolysis of ammonium nitrate with an aluminum anode in liquid ammonia, which is much less readily reduced than water, evidence has been obtained for the secondary reaction

$$5Al^+ + 2NO_3^- + 12NH_4^+ \rightarrow$$
$$5Al^{+++} + N_2 + 6H_2O + 12NH_3$$

and with a beryllium anode in concentrated aqueous acetic acid-perchloric acid solution, for the secondary reaction

$$8Be^+ + ClO_4^- + 8H^+ \rightarrow 8Be^{++} + Cl^- + 4H_2O$$

During electrolysis of an aqueous solution with a beryllium or an aluminum anode, the deposition of black particles of free metal in the anolyte may likewise be readily accounted for in terms of the hypothesis of initial formation of a unipositive ion. There are several well-known instances of disproportionation in aqueous solution of a cation of low positive charge into free metal

and a cation of higher charge. In the cases of beryllium and aluminum, then, it appears highly probable that among the reactions that occur in the anolyte are those represented by the equations

$$2Be^+ \rightarrow Be + Be^{++} \quad \text{and} \quad 3Al^+ \rightarrow 2Al + Al^{+++}$$

Two additional types of evidence that lend support to the hypothesis of one-electron oxidation as the primary step in anodic dissolution of commonly bivalent metals may be briefly cited. First, in the anodic oxidation of magnesium in a pyridine solution of sodium iodide, a V_i value of less than two was observed when, and only when, any one of a number of reducible organic compounds was present in the solution; and in every such case one or more reduction products of the organic additive could be isolated from the anolyte after electrolysis. Second, in the anodic dissolution of beryllium in aqueous potassium chloride solution, an unstable intermediate oxidation product, which could scarcely have been anything but unipositive beryllium ion, was detected polarographically at an auxiliary electrode a few millimeters distant from the anode; the lifetime of this intermediate ion was calculated to be between 10^{-3} and 10^{-1} second.

It would be misleading to leave the reader with the impression that the hypothesis of primary anodic oxidation to unipositive ions, as outlined in this article, has been universally accepted by electrochemists. Two other explanations have been proposed to account for the apparently anomalous valence states indicated by coulometric measurements. The first is that an increase in apparent anodic current efficiency above 100 per cent, or a decrease in V_i value below the usual valence number of the metal, is due to acceleration of nonelectrolytic dissolution of the anode during the passage of the current, resulting from partial breakdown of a protective surface film initially present. Such enhanced corrosion during electrolysis has been designated as a "negative difference effect." The second alternative explanation is that the decrease in weight of the anode metal during electrolysis may be due in part to a splitting off from the anode surface of minute (perhaps microscopic) fragments of metal, which either may later appear as a dark deposit in the anolyte, or because of the extensive surface which they present, may be rapidly dissolved through chemical reaction with the electrolyte. Such nonelectrolytic disintegration of the anode has been

designated as the "chunk effect." It is maintained
by some chemists that both of these effects may
occur simultaneously with anodic oxidation.

References

BENNETT, W. E., DAVIDSON, A. W., AND KLEIN-
  BERG, J., *J. Am. Chem. Soc.*, **74**, 732 (1952).
DAVIDSON, A. W., AND JIRIK, F., *J. Am. Chem.
  Soc.*, **72**, 1700 (1950).
EPELBOIN, I., *Z. Elektrochem.*, **59**, 689 (1955).
HEUSLER, K. E., *Z. Electrochem.*, **65**, 192 (1961).
LAUGHLIN, B. D., KLEINBERG, J., AND DAVIDSON,
  A. W., *J. Am. Chem. Soc.*, **78**, 559 (1956).
MARSH, G. A., AND SCHASCHL, E., *J. Electrochem.
  Soc.*, **107**, 960 (1960).
PETTY, R. L., DAVIDSON, A. W., AND KLEINBERG,
  J., *J. Am. Chem. Soc.*, **76**, 363 (1954).
RAIJOLA, E., AND DAVIDSON, A. W., *J. Am. Chem.
  Soc.*, **78**, 556 (1956).
RAUSCH, M. D., McEWEN, W. E., AND KLEIN-
  BERG, J., *Chem. Reviews*, **57**, 417 (1957).
RUMPEL, M. L., DAVIDSON, A. W., AND KLEINBERG,
  J., *J. Inorg. Chem.*, **2**, 810 (1963).
STRAUMANIS, M. A., *J. Electrochem. Soc.*, **105**, 284
  (1958).

ARTHUR W. DAVIDSON

Cross-references: *Anodic Disintegration of Metals, Anodic Reductions at Magnesium Electrodes,
Difference Effect.*

ANODIC PROTECTION

Anodic protection is now a practical method
for controlling corrosion of storage tanks and
process vessels in the chemical process industry.
Anodic protection may be described briefly as a
method of achieving passivity by flowing anodic
currents at controlled potentials. Passivity results from the formation of a corrosion-resistant
film or layer on the protected metal surface. The
recent development of equipment capable of
precise potential control at high current output
has made anodic protection practical for both
research and field applications.

Apparatus

The apparatus for achieving passivity with
anodic currents is shown in Fig. 1. The vessel or
test specimen is made the anode; an inert metal
is used for the cathode; and an electrochemical
half-cell, such as saturated calomel or silver-
silver chloride, is used as a reference electrode.
The potential controller maintains the potential
of the anode at a predetermined value with respect to the reference electrode by regulating
current flow between the anode and cathode.

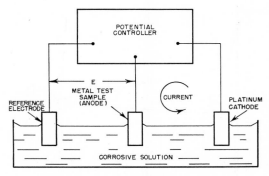

FIG. 1. Anodic protection system.

Theory of Passivity

Fig. 2 shows a typical anodic polarization
curve for stainless steel in sulfuric acid. The
potential, E, of the anode with respect to the
reference electrode is plotted against the current
flowing between anode and cathode. This curve
is defined by shifting the potential in the more
noble direction. The amount of current required
to shift the potential increases until the Flade
arrest is reached. At the Flade arrest, the
amount of current required to shift the potential decreases markedly and remains low until
the transpassive potential region is reached. The
potential region at potentials more active than
the Flade arrest is termed the active region;

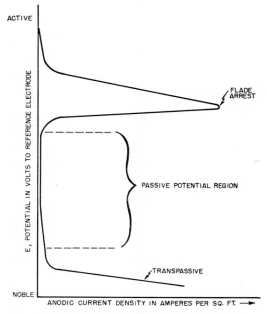

FIG. 2. Typical anodic polarization curve.

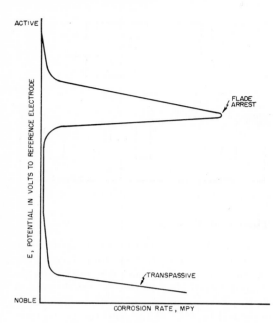

Fɪɢ. 3. Effect of potential on corrosion rate.

corrosion is accelerated in this portion of the curve. Corrosion is halted in the passive region and is accelerated in the transpassive region.

Fig. 3 shows a typical plot of potential, E, against corrosion rate for stainless steel in sulfuric acid. This curve correlates closely with the anodic polarization curve; high current densities correspond to high corrosion rates, and low current densities correspond to low corrosion rates. Corrosion rates thus are very low throughout the passive potential range.

The mechanism of achieving anodic passivity involves the formation of a corrosion-resistant film or layer. The marked decrease in current density at the Flade arrest corresponds to the formation of the passive film. Three principal theories have been presented to explain the formation and structure of the passive film: (1) iron dissolves and reacts with oxygen to form precipitates of iron oxide which protect the metal from corrosion; (2) oxygen adsorbs on the metal to form a protective monolayer; and (3) oxygen is adsorbed initially followed by the formation of an amorphous iron-oxygen structure; iron migrates slowly from the base metal into the adsorbed oxygen film. These theories are the subject of much discussion in the literature.

When anodic protection is applied to large surface areas, the formation of the passive film results in a marked reduction in the current density applied to the passivated surface. Current flow is thus continually diverted from areas initially passivated to areas not yet passive. This promotes the growth of the passive area and accounts for the excellent throwing power of anodic protection in field applications. Because of this, it is possible to passivate large vessels with a minimum number of cathodes.

Applications

Examples of corrosive systems that can be anodically protected are listed in Table 1. Stainless steels are easier to passivate than carbon steel. The current density requirements for establishing passivity decrease with increasing concentration and increase with rise in temperature. The current density, applied voltage, and optimum control potential must be determined for each field application. For example, the current density required for maintaining passivity of carbon steel tanks storing 93 per cent sulfuric acid at 80°F is approximately 0.0015 ampere per square foot at a control potential of +900 mv (noble) to silver-silver chloride. Currents necessary to establish passivity are about fifteen times greater than the current to maintain passivity. Using a typical 12 square inch platinum clad cathode, an applied voltage of 10 volts is sufficient to overcome the electrolyte resistance. For a 30,000-gallon tank with 1,000

TABLE 1. TYPICAL CORROSIVE SYSTEMS WHERE ANODIC PROTECTION IS APPLICABLE

Metal Chemical
Carbon steel
Oleum
Sulfuric acid
Spent (black) sulfuric acids
Super phosphoric acid
Aqueous ammonia
Aqueous ammonium nitrate
Aqueous ammonia—ammonium nitrate mixtures
Aqueous ammonia—ammonium nitrate—urea mixtures
Stainless steel
Sulfuric acid
Sulfuric-nitric mixed acids
Phosphoric acid
Ammonium nitrate solutions
Aluminum sulfate solutions
Sodium hydroxide
Sulfonic acid
Oxalic acid
Sulfamic acid

square feet internal surface area, the power required for anodic protection is less than 1 kilowatt per day. It is not possible to establish passivity in the presence of high concentrations of reducing materials, such as chlorides; however, certain amounts of these additives can be tolerated in oxidizing systems. Anodic protection is not feasible in copper or brass vessels.

A typical field installation is illustrated in Fig. 4. This is identical to the laboratory system in Fig. 1 except that the auxiliary power supply is necessary to provide the larger currents required for establishing and maintaining passivity in large vessels. Such installations have been demonstrated effective in a variety of storage tanks, process vessels, and mobile vessels, such as rail tank cars, trailers, and barges.

The advantages of anodic protection in these installations have included:

(1) *Improvement of product quality due to reduction of iron pickup during storage in carbon steel vessels of H_2SO_4 acids (65–105 per cent)*. For example, the color of a sulfonate detergent was improved by use of low iron content acid in sulfonation.

(2) *Reduction in maintenance and replacement costs*. Corrosion rates in steel and stainless process vessels are reduced by greater than 90 per cent. This is so even in highly agitated vessels. These reduced corrosion rates lead to extended life of vessels with less downtime and costs for repairs.

(3) *Reduction in capital investment*. In many cases it has been possible to replace an expensive alloy with an anodically protected inexpensive vessel. For example, an anodically protected 316 stainless reaction vessel is used to handle 85 per cent H_3PO_4 at 160°C in a system where original design called for Carpenter 20. In other cases, hot sulfuric acid is being handled in carbon steel; whereas, without anodic protection, lead lining or a stainless steel tank would have

been required. Such applications result in considerable savings in initial investment.

References

1. SUDBURY, J. D., RIGGS, O. L., AND SHOCK, D. A., "Anodic Passivation Studies," *Corrosion*, **16**, (2), 47t–54t (February 1960).
2. SHOCK, D. A., RIGGS, O. L., AND SUDBURY, J. D., "Application of Anodic Protection in the Chemical Industry," *Corrosion*, **16**, (2), 55t–58t, (February 1960).
3. RIGGS, O. L., HUTCHISON, M., AND CONGER, N. L., "Anodic Control of Corrosion in a Sulfonation Plant," *Corrosion*, **16**, (2), 58t–62t (February 1960).
4. LOCKE, C. E., HUTCHISON, M., AND CONGER, N. L., "Now: Anodic Corrosion Control," *Chem. Eng. Progress*, **56**, (11), 50–55 (November 1960).
5. DVORACEK, L. M., AND NEFF, L. L., "Use of the Polarization Technique to Study Corrosion in Aqueous Ammonia Systems," *Corrosion*, **18**, (3), 85t–90t (March 1962).
6. GREENE, N. D., "Predicting Behavior of Corrosion Resistant Alloys by Potentiostatic Polarization Methods," *Corrosion*, **18**, (4), 136t–142t (April 1962).
7. EDELEANU, C., "A Potentiostat Technique for Studying the Acid Resistance of Alloy Steels," *J. Iron and Steel Inst.*, **196**, 122–132 (February 1958).
8. MUELLER, W. A., "The Polarization Curve and Anodic Protection," *Corrosion*, **18**, (10), 359t–367t (October 1962).
9. BANKS, W. P., AND SUDBURY, J. D., "Anodic Protection of Carbon Steel in Sulfuric Acid," *Corrosion*, **19**, (9), 300t–307t (September 1963).
10. SUDBURY, J. D., BANKS, W. P., AND LOCKE, C. E., "Anodic Protection of Carbon Steel in Fertilizer Solutions," presented at Second International Congress on Metallic Corrosion, New York, March 11–15, 1963.

J. D. SUDBURY AND W. P. BANKS

Cross-references: *Corrosion; Flade Potential; Passivity; Potentiostat Applications.*

ANODIC REDUCTIONS AT A MAGNESIUM ELECTRODE

In the anodic oxidation of magnesium in aqueous solution[1-4] evidence for the formation of unipositive magnesium is obtained only when the electrolyte contains an oxidizing agent which is reduced by the lower valent species of metal, or when the solvent itself undergoes reduction. In recent years, the anodic behavior of magnesium in pyridine solvent has been investi-

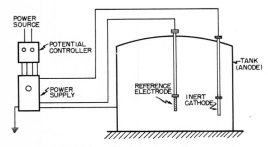

FIG. 4. Field installation of anodic protection.

gated. This solvent has the advantage over an aqueous medium in that it is reduced only with difficulty but is nevertheless a good electrolytic medium. Thus, the behavior of dissolved oxidants can be studied without the interference of complicating solvent effects.

In the anodic oxidation of magnesium in sodium iodide-pyridine medium the metal enters solution with an initial mean valence number of two.[5] However, the presence in solution of any one of a number of potential organic oxidants (benzophenone, 4,4'-dimethylbenzophenone, benzil, nitrobenzene, azoxybenzene, azobenzene, bromobenzene, benzonitrile, benzaldehyde, ethyl benzoate, 1,2-dibenzoylethane, 1,3-dibenzoyl-

magnesium. Since the latter is a one-electron reductant it would appear that the first step in the reduction of any of the additives consists in the transfer of an electron from the +1 magnesium to the organic molecule. Thus, in the specific case of benzophenone, the electron transfer would give the familiar ketyl radical-ion I. Two ketyl radical-ions formed in this manner dimerize to form the pinacolate ion II. The pinacol III is obtained on hydrolysis of the latter. It should not be inferred from the equations shown below that the magnesium ions exist in the simple solvated state. They are probably coordinated with pinacolate ions and help to drive the dimerization essentially to completion.

$$Mg\cdot^+ + C_6H_5-\overset{O}{\overset{\|}{C}}-C_6H_5 \rightarrow C_6H_5-\overset{O^\ominus}{\overset{|}{\underset{\bullet}{C}}}-C_6H_5 + Mg^{++}$$

$$\text{I}$$

$$2C_6H_5-\overset{O^\ominus}{\underset{\bullet}{C}}-C_6H_5 \rightleftharpoons \begin{matrix} C_6H_5-\overset{O^\ominus}{\overset{|}{C}}-C_6H_5 \\ | \\ C_6H_5-\underset{O^\ominus}{\overset{|}{C}}-C_6H_5 \end{matrix} \quad \xrightarrow{H^+} \quad \begin{matrix} C_6H_5-\overset{OH}{\overset{|}{C}}-C_6H_5 \\ | \\ C_6H_5-\underset{OH}{\overset{|}{C}}-C_6H_5 \end{matrix}$$

$$\text{II} \qquad\qquad \text{III}$$

propane, 1,4-dibenzoylbutane) causes the magnesium to dissolve with an initial mean valence number less than two.[5-9] Only with nitrobenzene and azoxybenzene is the magnesium attacked nonelectrolytically by the original solutions employed.

When the initial mean valence number is less than two, a reduction product (or products) may be isolated from the anolyte. Furthermore, in the majority of the cases which have been reported, the quantity of reduction product corresponds quantitatively to that expected from oxidation by the organic additive of the metal from its initial mean valence state to its common +2 state.

In view of the low V_i* values found in the presence of organic additives, and in analogy with the behavior in aqueous solution cited earlier, a strong case can be made that the reducing agent formed electrochemically is unipositive

---

*The initial mean valence number, V_i, for magnesium entering solution is calculated from the loss in weight of the anode and the amount of current passed through the cell, as measured by means of a silver coulometer, by the equation

$$V_i = \frac{\text{wt of Ag deposited in coulometer} \times 24.32}{107.88 \times \text{wt of Mg lost from anode}}$$

Similar mechanisms may be visualized for other "anodic reductions."

Although the data so far accumulated on the anodic oxidation of magnesium can be interpreted in a number of ways, the following hypothesis appears to be particularly attractive, namely, that the magnesium is converted initially solely to the unipositive state. In the absence of an oxidant the +1 magnesium rapidly transfers its remaining valence electron to the anode and goes into solution in the dipositive state. However, if some oxidant is present which reacts with the unipositive magnesium, then the latter is oxidized to the familiar +2 state and "anodic reduction" products are obtained. The observed V_i value is then the result of the relative rates at which the two possible secondary competing reactions occur.[10]

References

1. Beetz, W., *Phil. Mag.*, [4], **32**, 269 (1866).
2. Elsasser, E., *Ber.*, **9**, 1818 (1876); **11**, 587 (1878).
3. Turrentine, J. W., *J. Phys. Chem.*, **12**, 448 (1908).
4. Petty, R. L., Davidson, A. W., and Kleinberg, J., *J. Am. Chem. Soc.*, **76**, 363 (1954).
5. Rausch, M. D., McEwen, W. E., and Kleinberg, J., *J. Am. Chem. Soc.*, **76**, 3622 (1954).

6. RAUSCH, M. D., McEWEN, W. E., AND KLEIN-
   BERG, J., *J. Am. Chem. Soc.*, **77**, 2093 (1955).
7. McEWEN, W. E., KLEINBERG, J., BURDICK, D.
   L., HOFFMAN, W. D., AND YANG, J. Y., *J.
   Am. Chem. Soc.*, **78**, 4587 (1956).
8. HOFFMAN, W. D., McEWEN, W. E., AND KLEIN-
   BERG, J., *Tetrahedron*, **5**, 293 (1959).
9. TSAI, T. T., McEWEN, W. E., AND KLEINBERG,
   J., *J. Org. Chem.*, **26**, 318 (1961).
10. RAUSCH, M. D., McEWEN, W. E., AND KLEIN-
    BERG, J., *Chem. Revs.*, **57**, 417 (1957).

WILLIAM E. McEWEN

Cross-references: *Anodic Disintegration of Metals; Anodic Dissolution, Low Valence States in.*

ANODIZING

Anodizing is the process of forming oxide films or coatings on certain metals and alloys by electrolysis in a suitable solution. Basically, the process is quite simple, consisting merely of applying an electrical potential to a cell in which the metal being treated is made the anode (positive electrode). The passage of current through the cell provides the oxidizing conditions at the anode which convert the surface of the metal to an oxide. A corresponding layer of metal is consumed in the process. This is in contrast to electroplating, where a metal is deposited on the cathode (negative electrode) from a solution by the passage of the electric current. Under proper conditions, the anodic oxide film remains firmly adherent, and is essentially an integral part of the metal. Because the film-forming reaction takes place at the anode, the process is also known as anodic oxidation, and the films are often called anodic oxide coatings.

Metals are usually anodized to improve certain surface properties, or to develop characteristics not present on the original metal surfaces. Among the properties that may be altered by anodizing are corrosion resistance, abrasion resistance, hardness, appearance, dielectric strength, reflection and radiation characteristics, and adsorptive power of the oxide coating. Depending on the metal, and details of the anodizing process, one or more of these properties may be affected.

Although it is possible to anodize a number of metals, commercial application of the process has reached substantial proportions only for aluminum, magnesium, and tantalum. Therefore, much of the information about anodizing

has been developed with special reference to these metals.

Two distinctly different types of anodic oxide films may be produced, depending on the solubility of the oxide in the electrolyte. These may be classified as (1) nonporous films and (2) porous films.

Nonporous Films

If the initially-formed film is relatively insoluble, and has a high electrical resistance, the current flow needed for continued film growth quickly drops to a very low value. The oxide film under these conditions is very thin, dense, and essentially nonporous. The film thickness attained is directly proportional to the applied voltage at constant electrolyte temperature. Unit values of about 13 to 14 Angstroms per volt have been reported, and in practical use the films are usually less than about 1 micron (0.00004 inch) thick.

Procedures to form such films on aluminum and tantalum are used extensively in the production of electrolytic capacitors (q.v.). The extremely thin, compact oxide films have a high dielectric constant and function as the dielectric in the capacitors. Many factors related to the purity of the material and its handling are reported to affect the quality and characteristics of electrolytic condensers. In some cases, the procedures for preparing the components of the capacitors are considered proprietary information and are not available. In general, however, the anodizing step, or forming operation as it is known in the capacitor industry, is merely the means for producing a dielectric film having the thickness and properties to give the desired capacity and performance in the finished capacitor. For aluminum, suitable forming electrolytes are aqueous solutions of the salts of weak acids, such as borates, tartrates, and citrates. A common electrolyte may contain about 10 per cent boric acid and a small amount of borax (generally less than 1 per cent). The borax content is fairly critical. The proportion of borax should be lower when preparing capacitors designed to operate at higher voltages. In the production of capacitor components the aluminum is anodized at an applied potential somewhat higher than the expected working voltage, until the current flow drops to a very low value and does not decrease appreciably on continued anodizing. Temperature of the electrolyte has a marked effect on the thickness of film obtained at any given voltage.

Similarly, anodizing of tantalum in aqueous solutions of acids, alkalis, and salts under proper conditions will form tantalum oxide films suitable for use in electrolytic capacitors. Proprietary processes are said to employ a complicated sequence of operations to produce the desired films. However, formation at constant current in 40 per cent sulfuric or phosphoric acid at 100°C, followed by a period at constant voltage to no more than 110 volts is reported to produce good films on tantalum. Formation by anodizing in a molten salt mixture of sodium nitrate—sodium nitrite at about 250°C is also possible.

The production of these thin nonporous oxide films is a relatively minor application of the anodizing process, and the thicker, porous type anodic oxide coatings have received greater attention and widespread commercial use.

Porous Films

These are formed by anodizing in electrolytes that have some solvent action on the oxide. In this case, the initial nonporous film is partially dissolved and does not stop the flow of current, and the oxide coating can continue to grow. A thin, nonporous barrier layer is constantly maintained at the interface by continued anodizing, but the rest of the film develops a porous structure. Basic studies on aluminum indicate that the pores are initiated at nuclei in the barrier layer. The pores are submicroscopic, varying from about 100 to 300 Angstroms in diameter. Continued growth of the oxide coatings proceeds by conduction of electric current through the electrolyte in the pores. In commercial practice, porous films 0.0001 inch to about 0.003 inch in thickness may be formed. These coatings have many desirable properties that account for the extensive use and development of the anodizing process for aluminum and magnesium. Processing variables and composition of the alloy being anodized have a marked effect on the properties of the finished product.

Anodizing of Aluminum

The relatively thick, porous anodic oxide coatings on aluminum impart certain desirable properties that are adaptable in many commercial applications. Improved resistance to corrosion and abrasion are common objectives of anodizing. Also, the coatings are absorptive and

may be colored by dyes or pigments for decorative applications. These properties may vary widely depending on the alloy being anodized and on the anodizing process variables.

The effect of the alloy composition is related to the behavior of alloying constituents during anodic treatment. Those which are in solid solution in the aluminum generally do not affect the uniformity of the coating. Constituents not in solid solution, but which are not readily dissolved or oxidized, may become trapped in the oxide film in a substantially unchanged condition. Silicon, Al-Mn, and Al-Cr-Fe compounds are in this class. This may have an undesirable effect on the color or clarity of the oxide film. A third possibility arises when the constituent is dissolved preferentially by the anodizing current. In this case, attack of the constituent penetrates into the grain boundaries, and only a relatively small percentage of the current is available to form the aluminum oxide coating. This results in an abnormally thin film. Heavy metal constituents, such as $CuAl_2$, are in this category.

Preparatory treatments also influence the appearance and properties of the coating. Mechanical and chemical cleaning or etching treatments of the surface are, in general, the same as for any other metal finishing process. However, because the aluminum oxide films are translucent or transparent, the original metal surface characteristics may be visible through the coating. Surface pretreatments are available to provide specular, matt, or textured appearance to the anodized aluminum.

Sulfuric, chromic, and oxalic acid solutions, in that order, are the most important anodizing electrolytes. Historically, chromic and oxalic acids were first used commercially, but they have been largely supplanted by sulfuric acid electrolytes because of greater versatility of the latter.

Chromic acid coatings are used mainly to improve resistance to corrosion. The films are quite thin, usually less than 0.0001 inch on most alloys, and, therefore, have little effect on resistance to abrasion. The films tend to be somewhat opaque and are not suitable where a pleasing appearance is needed. However, they provide a good base for paints, enamels, and similar coatings. The current practice is to anodize in an electrolyte containing 100 grams per liter of chromic acid, for a period of 30 to 45 minutes at 95°F with an applied potential of 40 volts.

Anodizing in sulfuric acid is possible over a very broad range of processing conditions. The variables in the process are (1) concentration of the electrolyte, (2) time of treatment, (3) temperature, and (4) current density. The effects of the variables on the thickness and characteristics of the oxide film are interdependent. For example, the growth of the coating is controlled by the current density, which in turn (at a constant applied voltage) is determined by the strength and temperature of the sulfuric acid solution. The latter two variables also affect the rate at which the coating is chemically dissolved. At first, the coating forms faster than it is dissolved, but as the coating becomes thicker, more surface is exposed to the solvent action of the electrolyte. For each set of anodizing conditions, a point will be reached where the coating is being dissolved at the same rate that it is being formed. On continued anodizing, the film thickness remains constant, and the aluminum continues to be consumed at about 100 per cent efficiency. The equilibrium thickness will be lower at the higher acid strengths and temperatures, and vice versa. Considerable heat is generated by the anodizing process. Refrigeration and vigorous agitation of the electrolyte are needed to maintain uniform temperature conditions on the anode surface. The other properties of the oxide, such as hardness, porosity, and protective value, are correspondingly affected by the processing details.

Commercially, the concentration of the sulfuric acid electrolyte may vary from about 7 to 25 per cent by weight. A 15 per cent solution is commonly used. The bath temperature may range from 70 to 80°F. When resistance to abrasion or corrosion is desired, standard coatings up to about 0.001 inch in thickness are produced by anodizing in the more dilute solutions at the lower temperature. For extreme wear resistance and hardness, special techniques have been developed (called hard anodizing), involving low acid strength, low bath temperature (down to 30°F or lower), high current density, and vigorous agitation. Hard coatings are several times thicker and more abrasion resistant than ordinary coatings.

For decorative applications, more adsorptive films are produced by anodizing at higher temperature or in a more concentrated electrolyte.

Such coatings may be dyed by immersing in aqueous solutions of organic dyes, usually at about 150°F. The brilliance of color is affected by the transparency and clarity of the oxide film, and the depth of color may be varied by control of the thickness of the coating.

Where maximum resistance to corrosion is the desired, it is necessary to seal the porous oxide coating. One method of sealing consists of immersion in boiling water for a period approximately equal to the anodizing time. The sealing mechanism, in this case, is said to be due to the increase in volume as Al_2O_3 is converted to $Al_2O_3 \cdot H_2O$ by the boiling water. Additional corrosion resistance may be imparted by sealing in potassium dichromate solutions. The yellow color of the coating after such treatment indicates that a corrosion-inhibiting chromium compound is adsorbed in the coating. Dyed coatings are usually sealed in a hot 0.5 per cent aqueous solution of nickel acetate. Hydrolysis of the acetate to hydroxide within the pores seals the coating and minimizes leaching of the dye.

Anodizing of Magnesium

Several anodizing procedures have been developed for magnesium and its alloys. Two of the newer processes that have achieved success are the HAE process and the Dow-17 process. Anodic coatings on magnesium are not as effective in providing resistance to corrosion and abrasion as those on aluminum. The coatings are often applied to serve as a base for painting.

The Dow-17 process is conducted in an electrolyte composed of ammonium acid fluoride, sodium dichromate, and phosphoric acid. The bath is operated at temperatures ranging from 160 to 180°F. Alternating or direct current may be used, and the thickness and protective value of the film is dependent on the applied voltage. The best properties are obtained by anodizing at 75 to 90 volts, forming a dark green coating about 0.0015 inch in thickness.

The HAE coating is formed in an electrolyte composed of potassium and aluminum hydroxide, potassium fluoride, trisodium phosphate, and potassium manganate. Parts may be anodized at about 15 amperes per square foot using alternating current. The voltage rises from 40 volts at the start to about 100 volts as the coating becomes thicker. A brown coating, having good abrasion resistance is formed in about 60 to 75 minutes. In this process several modifications in the procedure are also available to form thinner and softer coatings. The HAE coatings are alkaline in nature, and this should be taken into account when applying paint coatings over such films.

References

1. "Proceedings of a Conference on Anodising Aluminum," 248 pp., London, The Aluminum Development Association, 1962.
2. WERNICK, S., AND PINNER, R., "Surface Treatment and Finishing of Aluminum and its Alloys," 2nd Edition, 607 pp. Teddington, England, Robert Draper Ltd., 1959.
3. GRAHAM, A. K., Editor, "Electroplating Engineering Handbook," 2nd Edition, New York, Reinhold Publishing Corp., 1962.
4. YOUNG, L., "Anodic Oxide Films," New York, Academic Press, Inc., 1961.
5. MILLER, G. I., "Metallurgy of the Rarer Metals —6, Tantalum and Niobium," pp. 45–59, New York, Academic Press, Inc., 1959.
6. KELLER, F., HUNTER, M. S., AND ROBINSON, D. L., "Structural Features of Oxide Coatings on Aluminum," *J. Electrochem. Soc.*, **100**, No. 9, 411 (September, 1953).
7. MASON, RALPH B., AND FOWLE, PHYLLIS E., "Anodic Behavior of Aluminum and Its Alloys in Sulfuric Acid Electrolytes," *J. Electrochem. Soc.*, **101**, No. 2, 53 (February, 1954).
8. HUNTER, M. S., "The Etching and Forming of Aluminum Electrolytic Capacitor Foil," *Electrochem. Tech.*, **1**, No. 5–6, 151 (May-June, 1963).

C. J. SLUNDER

Cross-reference: *Capacitors, Electrolytic.*

ARC HEATING

Arc heating includes three distinct methods of supplying heat energy. In direct arc heating, the arc spans from the work to an electrode clear of the work. With indirect arc heating, the arc spans between two electrodes, with electrodes and arc all clear of the work. For submerged arc heating, a multitude of arcs form between the work and the electrode which is submerged in the work material. There is a low percentage of resistance heating from the electrode and also from the work material if the current passes through it as in the case of a direct arc or submerged arc operation. However, in all cases, the arc is the main heat source. It dissipates its energy through radiation from the surrounding gases and from the electrode tip, along with some convection and conduction losses. By forcing gaseous flow through the arc area, the amount of convection heat can be increased, and can even become the major heating factor.

The major uses of arc heating are in furnaces for the production of steel, phosphorus, calcium carbide, and various ferroalloys, the smelting of iron and other ores, melting of copper, and refining of zinc. Arc heating is also used in welding and for production of several chemical compounds. It is used for hypersonic wind tunnel operation and in the plasma jet (gas heated and ionized in a constricted arc zone) to provide temperatures up to 50,000°F. It is a most desirable heat source because of its high density of energy emission and its high operating temperature. Other advantages of arc heating are: very little thermal lag time on or off; high intensity of heat input to material that otherwise would be most difficult and expensive to heat; good heat input control for relatively long-time batch processes or continuous processes; no other concentrated electrical heat source is economically operable at the enormous power inputs available through this heating method.

The majority of arc applications are on a-c line frequency, but there are certain cases, such as some arc welding and vacuum arc furnace operations, where d-c power is employed. In either case, an important feature of the arc is its negative coefficient of resistance; that is, the greater the current value of the arc, the less voltage it takes to sustain it. Thus an arc alone in a circuit is unstable, and will degenerate to either a short or open circuit. To obtain a stable circuit, sufficient impedance must be added into the arc circuit to obtain, for the combination circuit, a stable, positive voltage-current characteristic where voltage drop increases as current increases. This stabilizing impedance can be either a resistance or inductive reactance, but for several reasons reactance is employed. First, the use of resistance would increase the losses and make the operation less efficient. Second, reactance limits the short circuit current so that surges in the power company lines are less severe. Third, considering an a-c arc, reactance causes the circuit current to lag the voltage so that at arc current zero, which occurs twice a cycle, there is a voltage across the arc gap tending to cause restrike of the arc. This has a very important stabilizing effect on the continuity of a-c arcs, especially for the direct type arc. While the electrode is often a material that readily emits electrons, the work material is not. This makes arc restrike difficult when the work is the emitter. Deionizing atmospheres also cause problems with restrike. A high voltage across the arc gap increases the likelihood that restrike will occur. This restrike problem is not present with d-c arcs. For the d-c arc obtaining power from rectifiers, reactance is added into the a-c incoming line circuit to the rectifiers to provide the necessary arc stability.

The greatest difficulties of arc operation concern stabilization and control of the direct arc. These problem areas are of far less difficulty in the indirect and submerged arc field. Under differing conditions of material temperature, atmosphere, or electrode and work material composition, the arc stability in a particular circuit may be high or low. The arc voltage gradient (voltage drop per unit length of arc) for a given arc current can vary, depending on conditions, over a 15 or 20 to 1 range. The arc with low voltage gradient will remain in stable operation even though arc length changes appreciably, while the arc with high voltage gradient is difficult to keep in operation as it tends to continually revert to open circuit. The achievement of desired arc stability and control involves the proper selection of circuit impedance, arc current, and arc voltage in accord with the power input and arc voltage gradient requirements.

The electrode is usually made of carbon or graphite. Even though it is consumed at a low rate through oxidation and sublimation due to the high operating temperature of the arc, this type of electrode is considered to be nonconsumable. Certain metal electrodes are meant to be consumed. These are used in welding and also in vacuum arc melting operations where the melted, purified electrode material is the desired product.

Arc voltages may vary from about 20 to 30 volts for welding or vacuum arcs to several hundred volts for the large arc furnaces and to many thousands of volts for production of acetylene or cyanogen. The voltage is varied in each process as necessary to provide the desired power input which may range up to 20 million watts per arc. Unless there is prior operating experience on a particular process, voltage determination for the most part is a cut and dry process on a pilot line basis with figures extrapolated to the production model.

References

PASCHKIS, V., AND PERRSON, J., "Industrial Electric Furnaces and Appliances," New York, Interscience Publishers, 1960.

ROBIETTE, A. G. E. "Electric Melting and Smelting Practice," London, Charles Griffin and Company Limited, 1955.

E. J. BORREBACH

Cross-references: *Calcium Carbide; Copper and Nickel Concentrates, Electric Smelting; Electric Arc Properties; Electric Smelting Furnaces; Furnaces, Inert Atmosphere and Vacuum Arc; Lead, Electrothermic Smelting; Phosphorus, Electrothermal Production; Steel Making in Electric Arc Furnaces; Söderberg Electrode in Electric Furnaces; Vacuum Arc Properties; Zinc, Electrothermal Production.*

ARC PROPERTIES. See ELECTRIC ARC PROPERTIES; VACUUM ARC PROPERTIES.

ARRHENIUS, SVANTE AUGUST (1859–1927)

Arrhenius was born February 19, 1859, at the estate of Wik, near Lake Mäler, Sweden. In 1884, his classic doctoral thesis, "Recherches sur la conductibilité galvanique des électrolytes" was reluctantly accepted by the University of Upsala. This work expounded for the first time the theory of electrolytic dissociation. Arrhenius visited Ostwald in Riga, Kohlrausch in Würzburg, Boltzmann in Graz, and van't Hoff in Amsterdam. In 1887 he published a much matured version of his theory in the *Zeitschrift für Physikalische Chemie.* The essential qualitative idea of his theory, which is now a cornerstone of physical chemistry, is that acids, bases and salts split up spontaneously in water and some other solvents. With this idea, and a quantitative method, since greatly modified, of calculating the degree of electrolytic dissociation, Arrhenius was able to explain an extraordinarily wide number of phenomena, e.g., the constancy of the heat of neutralization, the high osmotic pressure of electrolytes, the increasing molar conductivity, and osmotic pressure of electrolytes with dilution, the equal chemical activity of all strong acids, etc. Another fundamental contribution to chemistry was his suggestion that only "activated" molecules, bearing energies higher than average, can undergo chemical reaction. It remains the basis of our views of the mechanism of chemical reactions. In particular, the Arrhenius equation for the variation of the rate of a chemical reaction with temperature (1889) is very widely applied.

Arrhenius received the Nobel Prize for chemistry (1903), the Davy Medal of the Royal Society, and the Faraday Medal of the Chemical Society, and was the first recipient of the Willard Gibbs Medal of the American Chemical Society (1911). He spent most of his career in Stockholm, becoming professor of chemistry at the University of Stockholm in 1895, and director of the Nobel Institute for Physical Chemistry in 1905. He held the latter post until his death in Stockholm, October 2, 1927.

BERNARD JAFFE

ASKAREL

Askarel is the class name applied to designate a synthetic nonflammable dielectric liquid which when decomposed by heat or the electric arc evolves only nonflammable gaseous mixtures.[1] Commercially available askarels are most commonly chlorinated aromatic hydrocarbon mixtures.[2]

The chemical basis for the nonflammability of the askarels is found in the high reactivity of hydrogen and chlorine.[3] Chlorinated hydrocarbons, when pyrolytically decomposed evolve only carbon and hydrogen chloride if the chlorine is substituted in the parent hydrocarbon in an amount so that the resulting chlorinated product contains a chemical equivalency of hydrogen and chlorine. Because of the engineering requirement for the chemical stability of an insulating liquid over long periods of operation, even at temperatures as high as 100 to 110°C, the askarel liquids in commercial use are chlorinated derivatives of the aromatic hydrocarbons, most commonly of benzene and diphenyl. The chlorinated isomers of these compounds when properly blended are characterized by satisfactorily low temperatures of solidification for engineering use in capacitors and transformers.[4]

From the standpoint of capacitor manufacture and use, the askarel liquids possess the desirable property of high dielectric constant, in addition to their nonflammability. Chlorinated diphenyl compositions which are in wide capacitor use exhibit a dielectric constant as high as 5.5. When such liquid compositions are used in place of

mineral oil for the impregnation of paper insulated capacitors, a reduction in physical bulk as much as 50 per cent may be realized, the actual reduction obtained being dependent to some extent on the type of construction of the capacitor examined.

The askarel liquids are characterized by a high dielectric strength and complete freedom from the susceptability to oxidation and sludge which is exhibited by mineral oil.[2] Because of the high dielectric constant which this type of liquid possesses, electrical stress concentrations in the liquid in series with cellulosic insulation are reduced as compared to mineral oil-treated dielectric systems. This, in association with the characteristically higher dielectric strength of the askarel liquids, permits the application of higher voltages for a given insulating assembly than is possible when mineral oil impregnants are used.

The askarel liquids, being molecularly polar in nature, possess a greater solvent property than do the mineral insulating oils. In order that dielectric losses of the same magnitude as in mineral oil may be obtained, it is necessary, therefor, that such liquids be carefully refined in manufacture and protected from redissolving conducting impurities during their commercial use, if emphasis is placed on the maintenance of low dielectric loss values. Experience in the operation of askarel-filled transformers does not indicate that any practical advantages accrue from the maintenance of the dielectric loss at a low order of magnitude since the dielectric strength itself is unaffected by the presence of the soluble impurity. If such is desired, however, the presence of an absorbent such as dried fuller's earth, or aluminum oxide or hydrate assures its realization.[2, 5, 6]

Because of their marked chemical stability under the usual conditions of their electrical uses, stabilizers, antioxidants and the like are not required in askarel compositions. It has been found desirable, however, when the askarel-treated capacitor is applied on d-c circuits at temperatures higher than about 60°C to incorporate a stabilizer. The material most commonly used for this purpose is anthraquinone or one of its chlorinated derivatives.[7] Because of the formation of hydrogen chloride when the askarel is decomposed by an electric arc, as in the electrical failure of an askarel-filled transformer, a getter is frequently applied to eliminate the corrosive chloride, and to facilitate the repair of the apparatus. Such a getter is tin tetraphenyl or an epoxide type of askarel-soluble material.[2]

References

1. Tentative Method of Testing Askarels, ASTM Designation D901–55T.
2. CLARK, FRANK M., Insulating Materials in Design and Engineering Practice," New York, John Wiley and Sons, Inc., 1963.
3. CLARK, F. M., "The Development and Application of Synthetic Liquid Dielectrics," *Trans. Am. Electrochem. Soc.* **65,** 193–204 (1934).
4. CLARK, F. M., "Dielectric Material for Electric Device," U. S. Patent 1,931,373.
5. CLARK, F. M., "Performance Characteristics of the Askarels," *ASTM Special Tech. Pub.* **95,** 3–20, 1949.
6. CLARK, F. M., "Stabilization of Halogenated Hydrocarbons," U. S. Patents 2,594,872 and 2,594,873 (1952).
7. SAUER, H. A., McLEAN, D. A., AND EGERTON, L., "Stabilization of Dielectrics Operating under DC Potential," *Ind. Eng. Chem.,* **44,** 135 (1959).

FRANK M. CLARK

Cross-references: Entries with *Dielectric* titles.

ASSOCIATION. See DISSOCIATION; ION ASSOCIATION.

AUTOMATIC CONTROLLERS. See CONTROLLERS, AUTOMATIC.

AUTOMATIC ELECTROPLATING MACHINES. See ELECTROPLATING MACHINES, AUTOMATIC.

B

BANCROFT, WILDER D. (1867–1953)

Wilder D. Bancroft was born October 1, 1867, in Middletown, Rhode Island, and graduated from Harvard before obtaining his doctorate degree at the University of Leipzig in 1892. After a few years of teaching at Harvard, he went to Cornell University in 1895 and remained there the rest of his career, becoming full professor of chemistry in 1903 and emeritus professor in 1937. He died February 7, 1953.

Bancroft's contributions to the field of chemistry were manifold and during his lifetime he enjoyed wide recognition for his achievements. Before his thirtieth year, he wrote "The Phase Rule"—the first exposition in English on this subject, based on Bakhuis Roozeboom's work. One of his greatest services was in founding the *Journal of Physical Chemistry* in 1896. He was its editor for over 35 years and financed it from private resources for some time. From 1913 until his death he was associate editor of the *Journal of the Franklin Institute*. His goal was always to further the study of chemistry, encourage pioneer investigations and broaden the applications of scientific knowledge from one branch of study to another. Dr. Bancroft devoted a great deal of time and energy to the education and direction of students. He was always an inspiring teacher.

Bancroft published papers on plasticity of clay, adsorption of gases, chemotherapy, structural colors, qualities of bread-flour, tapping of trees for turpentine and rubber, drug addiction and the chemistry of anesthaesia. But his prime interest was the chemistry of colloids. His book "Applied Colloid Chemistry" appeared in three editions from 1921 to 1932. During those years he lectured on many varied subjects and in 1928 published "The Methods of Research." This book gives three famous lectures delivered at The Rice Institute. Bancroft also served the National Research Council Committee on the Chemistry of Colloids and the Eighteenth An-

nual Colloid Symposium in 1941 at Cornell was called the Wilder D. Bancroft Symposium.

Known for his investigations in electrochemistry, Bancroft in 1902 helped found the American Electrochemical Society and was its President twice—in 1905 and again in 1919. In 1910 he was honored with the Presidency of the American Chemical Society. During World War I, he served his country as Lieutenant-Colonel, Chemical Warfare Service where he made his contribution in the dissemination of data on poison gases. His activities included the Vice-Presidency of the International Union of Chemistry (1922–3); the Board of Visitors of the National Bureau of Standards; the Advisory Board of the Cancer Research Fund; and the National Academy of Sciences.

He was elected Honorary Fellow of The Chemical Society, the Polish Chemical Society and the Societe Chimique de France. Lafayette College and the University of Cambridge awarded him the degree of Honorary Doctor of Science (1919; 1923) and the University of Southern California conferred the Honorary Doctor of Laws degree in 1930.

JOHN B. CALKIN

BARREL PLATING

In barrel plating a multitude of parts to be plated is placed loosely in a nonconductive container (the barrel), which has a cathode to maintain intermittent electrical contact with the parts during plating. The barrel is then submerged and rotated in tanks containing cleaning, pickling, and the plating solutions. The plating tanks contain the anode(s). As the barrel rotates, these parts are tumbled and will gradually receive an electrodeposit as they make electric contact with the cathode. Tumbling is necessary to insure that each part receives the same average current density and is exposed to the same average concentration of plating solution during the plating cycle. The barrel with its load can be advanced through the various steps in the plating cycle in much the same manner as rack or wire plating, and at the end of the process the parts are dumped into suitable containers for final rinsing and drying.

The prime purpose of barrel plating is to improve the economics of electroplating small parts. Many small parts cannot be "still" plated because of the labor costs in the handling of these parts. Also, contact marks and bare spots, which would appear when these small parts are wired or racked, will not show when these same parts are barrel plated. The major advantages of barrel plating are:

(1) The elimination of racking, wiring, and the labor required for such operations.

(2) High productivity because of the large quantities of materials which can be processed in one operation.

(3) Uniformity of metal distribution from part to part, usually more uniform than in the equivalent thickness ranges applied by still plating.

There are two specific disadvantages in barrel plating. First, the possibility of affecting the size and shape of a part by constant tumbling is always a hazard. For example, multipin, hermetically-sealed semiconductor base platforms can readily mangle in a barrel unless proper care is taken to utilize the correct cathode contact design. Second, overall plating efficiency in barrel operations is approximately $\frac{1}{3}$ to $\frac{1}{10}$ of the efficiency of still plating. This involves extended time cycles which tend to slow down production. Although this is apparently contradictory to the second advantage given above, it has been shown that handling time for rack plating far exceeds total time for barrel plating even though "tank time" for barrel operations is from three to ten times longer than for wired or racked work.

In bulk plating there are two basic barrel designs which have been used. The first is an oblique design in which the barrel containing the work load rotates on an axis approximately 45° from the horizontal. Physical limitations precluded by this design include barrel loading, part geometry, and solution level. The second and more common type is the horizontal barrel in which the axis of the rotating cylinder containing the work load is parallel to the plating solution level.

Cathode contact in the oblique barrel is generally made through a supporting yoke or shaft to a disc or studs in the base of the cylinder. In a horizontal barrel, cathode contact can be made in a great variety of ways depending on the geometry of the part to be plated:

(1) Single or double danglers

(2) Axial rod or bar

(3) Axial rod with discs, chain or spokes

(4) Buttons or strips embedded in the cylinder walls

(5) Cylinder end plates, discs, or cones.

Barrel sizes can range from 1 in. diameter by 1 in. high oblique to 3 ft diameter by 5 ft long horizontal units. Barrel size is determined by the size of the part and quantity of the load.

Materials of construction in these barrels will usually be of a nonmetallic composition, such as "Fiberglas," "Lucite," polypropylene, hard rubber, and any other suitable material that will retain its general initial shape after much repeated pounding by the parts being plated. Some heavy construction, such as rubber-coated steel, has been used in the larger-size barrels, so that they physically hold the weight of the parts which they contain.

All barrel plating is empirical with respect to end results. The size, shape and weight of a particular part, the type of barrel, the volume of parts within the barrel, the size and number of perforations in the barrel wall, the barrel load, the anode to cathode ratio in the plating cell, and replenishment of electrolyte within the barrel will all determine the overall barrel efficiency. Each of these variables must be standardized for each part under each of the other conditions, so that a good electrodeposit can be obtained. Parts which tend to nest readily should have incorporated with them during plating a media, either conductive or nonconductive, which will tend to eliminate this nesting characteristic. Parts of varying sizes should not be admixed within the same load, for they will each draw different current densities and subsequently vary appreciably in thickness of electrodeposit. For optimum efficiency a small load is generally handled better than a large load, because the mixing characteristics of the parts to be plated in a small load will allow those parts at the center of the load to become exposed to fresh plating solution more readily.

Generally, all of the necessary pretreatment cycles required for still plating can be applied invariably. The exceptions are few. They include those solutions which will attack the barrel material itself, such as strong acids, bright dips, and hot solvents. Most pretreatment cycles include alkaline cleaners, acid dips, activators, and strikes; and all can be carried out with the parts loaded in the barrel. Sometimes this is impractical because of the physical limitations of the load itself. An example would be the plating of cans for the semiconductor industry where load sizes are of the order of 100,000 units. Here small increments, approximately 25,000 parts at a time, are precleaned and activated prior to being placed in large barrels for plating. A normal processing time would be 15 to 20 minutes in pretreatment, and 4 to 5 hours in actual plating.

Generally, standard plating solutions can be used for the barrel plating of any metal. Handbook formulae are usually satisfactory. More common today are the proprietary plating baths where control is maintained by the simple replenishment by the metals being plated. Additives, such as wetting agents, brighteners, levelers, and stress reducers, can also be added such as they are in still plating. In general, the basis of maintenance additions is an ampere-hour record where Faraday's law applies. A list of the normal plating baths used in barrel plating is given in Table 1.

In all of the above baths, the formulae given are general in nature. Numerous proprietary

TABLE 1. NORMAL PLATING BATHS USED IN BARREL PLATING

(1) *Cadmium*

Cadmium metal	2 oz/gal
Total sodium cyanide	16–18 oz/gal
Sodium hydroxide	2–4 oz/gal
Temperature	Room
Current density	5–10 amp/sq ft
Anodes	Cadmium

(2) *Copper*

Copper metal	4–6 oz/gal
Potassium cyanide	1–2 oz/gal
Rochelle salts	6–10 oz/gal
Potassium hydroxide	2 oz/gal
Temperature	120–140°F
Current density	5–10 amp/sq ft
Anodes	Copper

(3) *Gold*

Gold metal	1 troy oz/gal
Potassium cyanide	4–6 oz/gal
Potassium carbonate	3 oz/gal
Potassium phosphate	3 oz/gal
Temperature	140–160°F
Current density	from ½ to 5 amp/sq ft
Anodes	Stainless steel

(4) *Indium*

Indium metal	2–4 oz/gal
Sodium sulfate	1½ oz/gal
pH	2–2½
Temperature	Room
Current density	up to 5 amp/sq ft
Anodes	Indium and carbon, 1 to 3 ratio

(5) *Iron*

Iron metal	15 oz/gal
Calcium chloride	20–25 oz/gal
pH (with HCl)	1.2–1.8
Current density	up to 20 amp/sq ft
Temperature	190–200°F
Anodes	Iron

(6) *Lead*

Lead metal	25 oz/gal
Fluoboric acid	12 oz/gal
Boric acid	3 oz/gal
pH	1.0–1.5
Temperature	70–80°F
Current density	5–10 amp/sq ft
Anodes	Lead

(7) *Nickel*

Nickel sulfate	20 oz/gal
Nickel chloride	6 oz/gal
Boric acid	4 oz/gal
Temperature	120–140°F
pH	3.0–3.5
Current density	5–10 amp/sq ft
Anodes	Nickel

(8) *Rhodium*

Rhodium metal	5 gpl
Sulfuric acid	20 cc/liter
Temperature	110–120°F
Current density	5 amp/sq ft
Anodes	Platinum

(9) *Silver*

Silver metal	4–10 oz/gal
Potassium cyanide	8–15 oz/gal
Potassium carbonate	3 oz/gal
Temperature	70–80°F
Current density	3–10 amp/sq ft
Anodes	Silver

(10) *Tin*

Tin metal	12 oz/gal
Fluoboric acid	10–15 oz/gal
Boric acid	3 oz/gal
Temperature	70–80°F
Current density	up to 25 amp/sq ft
Anodes	Tin

(11) *Zinc*

Zinc metal	4–6 oz/gal
Total sodium cyanide	12–15 oz/gal
Sodium hydroxide	10–12 oz/gal
Temperature	Room
Current density	2–10 amp/sq ft
Anodes	Zinc and steel 1 to 1 ratio

systems are available which usually give better end results than those obtained from the above formulations. Some of these proprietary systems utilize the above as basic baths and employ additives to improve the plated electrodeposits. Combinations of the above baths can also be used to produce alloyed deposits; most of these baths are also proprietary in nature.

References

GRAHAM, A. K., Editor, "Electroplating Engineering Handbook," New York, Reinhold Publishing Corp., 1955, 1962.

BRENNER, ABNER, "The Electrodeposition of Alloys—Problems and Practices, 2 vols., New York, Academic Press, 1963.

"Metal Finishing Guidebook, (yearly publication), New Jersey, Metals and Plastics Publications, Inc.

ROBERT DUVA

Cross-references: *Addition Agents; Alloy Electrodeposition; Brightening Agents;* entries with *Electroplating* titles; specific metals, *Electroplating* or *Plating; Manual Plating.*

BATTERIES

It could be said that the science of electrochemistry started with the invention of batteries, since electrochemistry, as well as portions of chemistry, physics, and electricity, owe much of their beginning to Alessandro Volta's announcement in 1800 of his voltaic pile and crown of cups. Until that time, electricity was a little understood subject which could be only feebly demonstrated in the laboratory as a static charge. Although Thales, one of the seven wise men of Greece, first observed and reported in 600 B.C. that amber attracted light objects when rubbed, it was not until 1600 A.D. that Gilbert first used the word electricity in describing such a static charge. One hundred and fifty years later, Franklin demonstrated that lightning had some of the same characteristics as the static charge first observed by Thales. It was Galvani's observation in 1790 of the twitching of the muscles of a frog's leg when in contact with metal that stimulated Volta's interest in electricity.

Within a few weeks of the announcement of Volta's discovery, Nicholson and Carlisle used this new source of electrical energy to decompose water into hydrogen and oxygen. By 1807 Davy had used Volta's battery in his celebrated experiment to decompose fixed alkalies. This was soon followed by the classical work of Faraday and Daniell that did so much toward establishing the relationship between electricity and chemistry, or in other words, electrochemistry. During the first half of the 19th Century many other workers attempted to improve on this method of generating power, since it had inspired vast areas of experimental work which had never before been possible. As a result, many of the fundamental laws of electricity, physics, and chemistry were established during this period. It hardly seems necessary to point out the role these early investigations have had in the development of many other scientific areas and related technological accomplishments since that time. Thus, batteries and, therefore, electrochemistry occupy an important place in the history of science.

While many types of primary batteries were developed during this period, they were so low in capacity that their use in experimental work was still quite limited. In 1860 another very important step was made when Planté invented the lead-acid storage battery, which could be recharged and was capable of supplying much higher currents. This new electrochemical source of power made it possible to carry out almost unlimited experimental work and initiated a very definite start in the separation of the physical sciences. Until that time science had been quite general in character, but with Planté's invention it began to subdivide into fields now recognized as electricity, physics, chemistry, and electrochemistry. For several years Planté's batteries could only be charged from primary batteries. However, within fifteen years Planté himself had developed a hand-powered, mechanical generator with which he could charge his storage batteries at a faster rate. Soon after this, direct current generators powered by steam or water were developed, making it possible for light and power to be supplied to many cities. These power systems further increased the demand for lead-acid storage batteries for supplying peak and emergency loads. Thus, during the last half of the 19th Century, secondary or storage batteries came into extensive use. At the end of this period, Edison and Junger both developed various types of alkaline storage batteries which have since been produced in many forms and in large quantities.

At the beginning of the 20th Century, methods were developed for generating and transforming alternating current so that electric power could be transmitted at high voltages from city to city without prohibitive loss. This meant that batteries no longer played such an essential role in everyday life. In the meantime, however, the familiar dry battery was developed from Leclanche's invention into a practical item which has found widespread use in both private and public life. The lead-acid storage battery likewise has received extensive technological development and in addition to its common use in automobiles, it has found considerable application in electric trucks, the telephone service, switch gear control, submarines, and in many emergency standby sources of power.

While batteries are very poor sources of electrical energy for their weight and volume when compared to other sources, there are many important applications where nothing else could possibly be used. For this reason, considerable effort has always been directed toward the improvement and development of increased life and capacity in most types of batteries. This has been particularly true during and since World War II because of the many military applications.

Having seen what an important role batteries have played in the development of science and technology during their first century of existence and particularly, since then, as an essential part of everyday life, the factors involved in producing a battery can be considered.

Batteries make use of spontaneous chemical reactions in which the oxidation and reduction reactions can be arranged to take place at separate electrodes. If these reactions are not readily reversible, the battery is referred to as a primary battery. If they are reversible, the battery is called a secondary or storage battery. If the two reactants are continuously supplied to the electrodes and their products can be simultaneously eliminated, the battery then becomes a continuously acting primary battery or fuel cell. Although a large variety of primary batteries has been developed, only a few are capable of being reversed, thus severely limiting the number of possible storage batteries. Likewise, many combinations of electrochemical reactions are possible in continuously acting primary batteries, but only a few have so far been successful.

Theoretically, almost any of the elements or their compounds should be capable of forming part of a battery when suitably coupled with another in an appropriate electrolyte, provided the anodic reactant has at least one higher state of oxidation and can lose electrons in the reaction, the cathodic reactant has at least one lower state of oxidation and can gain electrons, and the sum of the free energy changes for the two reactions is negative. From the free energy change of the net reaction it is then possible to calculate the open-circuit voltage from the equation

$$-\Delta F = n\mathbf{F}E$$

provided the net reaction is at equilibrium. ΔF is the change in the free energy, n is the number of equivalents involved in the reaction, E, the open circuit voltage and $\mathbf{F}$, the Faraday equivalent in coulombs per gram equivalent. To be useful as a battery, except in very special cases, the potential should be at least one volt and preferably much higher.

A compromise must usually be made between the need to obtain as high a voltage as is possible to get maximum power and at the same time to have a stable system which is compatible with a suitable electrolyte. During the 160 odd years of experience with batteries, only four anodes have so far been commonly employed. These, in the order of their magnitude of use are lead, zinc, iron and cadmium. Recently, some use has been made of magnesium and indium in primary cells, while hydrogen, sodium, and a few hydrocarbons or their partially oxidized products are being used in fuel cells. During this period only a few cathodes have found any appreciable application and they are, listed in an approximate order of their use, the oxides or salts of lead, nickel, manganese, silver, mercury, and copper, and oxygen, itself. More recently, some use has been made of partially oxidized organic compounds. There are a few types of special cells and, of course, fuel cells where oxygen, hydrogen peroxide, the halogens, and SO_3 have been used. It is interesting to note, however, that Grove first demonstrated the operation of the fuel cell with hydrogen and oxygen at platinum electrodes in an acid solution in 1839.

The relationship between the potentials of these few anodes and cathodes presently in use may be best shown by means of a simplified version of the Pourbaix type of diagram, see Fig. 1. While complete diagrams of this kind show the thermodynamic relationship between the reversible potentials, $E°$, of all the various oxidation states of a given element and pH, this simplified version will show only the relationship between the $E°$ of the above electrode re-

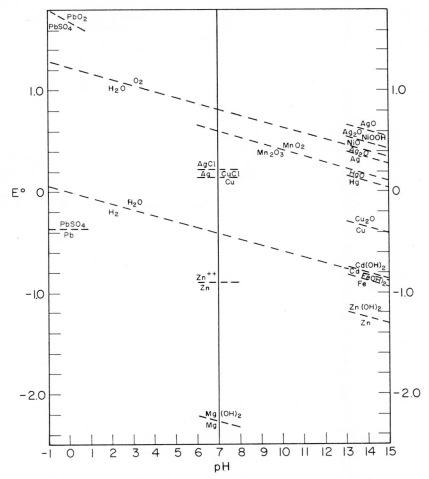

FIG. 1. Potential-pH diagram for the electrode reactions involved in most of the practical batteries.

actions at pH's of 0, 7 and 14, covering the range of most battery electrolytes. The relationship between these and any other electrode reaction may be compared by referring to a table of standard potentials in acidic, basic or neutral solutions.

Other types of batteries use ions in solution which are spontaneously oxidized or reduced at an inert electrode. These batteries have had limited use and are mentioned only because of their historical interest and also to illustrate the manifold ways in which an electrode reaction can be utilized in a battery.

Two other types of batteries have recently been developed which use either a fused salt or a solid membrane as a medium of ion transfer. The former is referred to as a thermal battery and the latter as a solid-state battery. Both

may employ the same couples used in conventional batteries and are different only in the fact that water does not enter into the electrode reactions.

A survey of the published literature and patents in the field of batteries indicates that hundreds of combinations of electrode reactions have been suggested for possible use. There are no doubt many hundreds of others which have been tried, but not reported because of their failure.

Why, then, are there so few successfully developed batteries, in view of the literally thousands of theoretical possibilities and the neverending search for new types? This question can perhaps best be answered by discussing in a general way the role each part of a battery plays in determining its feasibility of manufacture or operational characteristics. The description of specific primary and secondary batteries and fuel cells will be found in subsequent articles.

Electrolyte

The battery electrolyte is an ionic conductor which carries the current by means of ions within the battery. It must not be an electronic conductor or it will act as an internal short between the battery plates. Further, it must be chemically stable in contact with the electrodes. Any medium which meets these requirements may be used as a battery electrolyte. Most commercial cells contain aqueous solutions of strong electrolytes, such as concentrated H_2SO_4 or KOH, to supply heavy currents.

Except for a fortunate quirk of nature, the water in all batteries using an aqueous electrolyte at voltages higher than 1.23 v would theoretically decompose into H_2 and O_2. Thus, electrodes in a successful battery using aqueous electrolyte must have hydrogen and oxygen overvoltages which are high enough to avoid this decomposition of water. This means that many electrode materials with high potentials cannot be directly used. For example, the alkali metals ordinarily cannot be used because their low hydrogen overvoltages result in a spontaneous reaction with water to evolve hydrogen. In some cases, however, it is possible to use amalgamation to raise the hydrogen overvoltage of these anode materials. Overvoltage plays an even more important role in the recharging of storage batteries, since a higher than open-circuit potential must be used which further increases the possibility of producing hydrogen and oxygen at the sacrifice of recharging the electrode material.

The solubility of the reactants and products of both electrodes is a very important factor. They should only be soluble enough to supply sufficient ions to maintain a satisfactory reaction rate. If either the reactants or the products are too soluble, the electrode material may be dissipated in the electrolyte, and in the case of a storage battery, its redistribution during charge may not be uniform over the plates. This factor is not so important in primary batteries, although in some cases an increase in solubility may even enhance the electrode reaction by removing the products from the vicinity of the electrode. In a successful battery, there usually is a relatively narrow range of low solubility which will permit the best utilization of the electrode material.

The electrolyte must be a good conductor to avoid an appreciable loss of power from the voltage drop within the battery during discharge. This means that batteries intended for high rates of discharge must use either a strong acid or a strong base. If high rates are not required, it is sometimes possible to use a salt solution or even an electrolyte which has been immobilized as a gel. A number of batteries have also been developed using sea water as the electrolyte and in other cases the products of the electrode reactions are used to impart conductivity to water.

Controlling Factors in the Electrode Reactions

While many substances are theoretically capable of being utilized as one or the other of the electrodes in a battery, several factors limit their use. The transfer of current from the electrode reaction to the external leads requires that either the electrode material itself must be a good conductor or be made so by the addition of conducting materials, or the electrode material must be physically subdivided in such a way that there are many low-resistance paths to the supporting grid or plate. At the same time this electrode material must have as large a surface area as possible to minimize the current density and yet retain strength sufficient to maintain its shape during manufacture and use. In many cells this material is often referred to as the paste, and its method of preparation in most batteries is an art rather than a science. Thus, most electrodes are fabricated from a very finely-divided material which can be formed into a suitable paste and then applied to a supporting and conducting grid in such a manner that its surface area is high, its resistance low, and the products of its discharge not formed into high-resistance films which would retard further discharge. In a storage battery the discharge products must be retained on the plate without being redistributed. Thus, it can be seen readily that an empirical approach has been necessary in the development of a reasonably satisfactory battery electrode and that the ultimate success of any battery depends primarily on the physical properties of this electrode-active material.

Separation of Battery Plates

Most batteries require some method of physically insulating the two electrodes without appreciably reducing the conductivity of the electrolyte. In some types of nickel oxide-iron and nickel oxide-cadmium storage batteries, due to the rigid construction of the plates, a mere rib or spacer will suffice. Separators, in addition to their simultaneous electron insulating and ionic conducting properties, must be capable of withstanding the high oxidizing potentials, high temperatures, and strong electrolytes which are encountered in many batteries. Materials which have been used include wood, microporous rubber, porous plastic polymers, and very thin ion exchange resin membranes.

Possible Side Reactions

Another important factor which must be considered in producing successful batteries is that all components of construction, as well as any of the accidental or unavoidable impurities, are subject to the reducing potential of the anode and/or the oxidizing potential of the cathode. If either of these electrodes is sufficiently negative or positive to reduce or oxidize these extraneous materials, a side reaction will take place at one or both of the electrodes. This could lead to self-discharge and eventual deterioration of the battery. Battery manufacturers have learned by experience to be careful in the selection of components of construction and in the avoidance of impurities which may be encountered in the manufacture of a given battery.

The high positive plate potential in the lead-acid storage battery is responsible for a difficult corrosion problem associated with the supporting grid for the reactants of this plate. This illustrates another reason why this battery is theoretically impossible because the positive plate itself actually becomes a battery by using a negative active material as a supporting grid for the positive active material. This battery has been in use for a hundred years only because a protective oxide film develops on the grid and yet is conductive enough to allow current to pass. The negative plate of this battery could never be charged except for the unusually high hydrogen overvoltage on lead. Remarkable as Planté's discovery of this battery was, it is doubtful that many years would have passed before someone else would have encountered these remarkable and unusual characteristics of lead. Except for the high density of lead, this battery comes closer to being an ideal battery than any other system.

Polarization

Most of the factors which influence the discharge rates of a battery are usually grouped together under a term commonly referred to as polarization. This inclusive term covers all voltage losses within the battery. It is possible to isolate a number of these factors and thereby gain an insight into those which are important in controlling the overall electrode reaction. These include the resistance of the electrolyte, the active material, and the supporting grid; concentration polarization resulting from the reactants and the products of the electrode reaction; and the rate of the overall electrochemical reaction, which depends on a rather nebulous term known as the activation energy of the reaction. It is often possible to reduce the resistance effects by a physical modification. On the other hand, the activation energy is basic to the initiation of a given reaction and depends on the amount of energy required to transfer an electron through the double layer established between the electrode and its ions in solution. If the activation energy is high, the kinetics of the reaction are quite limited and the reaction is probably not suitable for use in a practical battery.

Except for the special case of the fuel cell, the electrode materials which have been successfully used as anodes are reasonably good conductors which, except in the case of low-rate batteries, must always be used in a finely-divided state having large surface area, so that the current density can be low enough to avoid excessive polarization. Of the metallic oxides which have been successfully used as cathodes, only the higher oxide of lead, PbO_2, has a reasonable conductivity. To utilize nickel oxide and still obtain adequate conductivity, either carbon or nickel flake must be added or else the oxide must be supported on a sintered nickel plaque. While the oxides of silver are poor conductors, metallic silver produced during the discharge reaction reduces electrode resistance.

Curiously enough, the battery with just about the lowest output in watt hours per pound is used to the greatest extent and is the only one that utilizes a single metal and its oxidation products. This is the lead-acid storage battery, in which lead is oxidized to lead sulfate at the anode and lead dioxide is reduced to lead sulfate at the cathode, in a sulfuric-acid electrolyte.

In speaking of batteries, it has become customary to refer to the anodic-active material and its support as the negative plate and the cathodic-active material and its support as the positive plate since, in charging a storage battery, the terminals for these plates are connected respectively to the negative and positive poles of a direct current source.

Cost and Availability

From a practical standpoint, the cost and availability of the necessary materials are of paramount importance, regardless of how well a given type of battery may perform. This automatically eliminates many possible combinations, except where the need is essential or the application unique so that cost is a secondary consideration. This is illustrated by the use of silver in the silver oxide-zinc battery for a number of military and satellite applications. Furthermore, if the world production of a suitable material is limited, then availability may become the controlling factor.

References

1. *J. Electrochem. Soc.*, **99**, No. 8, August, 1952.
2. *J. Electrochem. Soc.*, **99**, No. 9, September, 1952.
3. VINAL, G. W., "Storage Batteries," 3rd ed., New York, John Wiley & Sons, Inc., 1940.
4. VINAL, G. W. "Primary Batteries," 1st ed., New York, John Wiley & Sons, Inc., 1950.
5. LATIMER, W. M., "Oxidation Potentials," 2nd ed., Englewood Cliffs, N. J., Prentice-Hall, 1952.
6. POURBAIX, M. J. N. translated by J. N. Agar, "Thermodynamics of Dilute Aqueous Solutions," London, Arnold Press, 1949.

JOSEPH C. WHITE

Cross-references: subsequent *Batteries* entries; *Anode; Cathode; Conductivity, Electrolytic; Electrode Reactions; Electrode Reactions, Kinetics; Electromotive Force and Half-Cell Potentials; Electromotive Series; Free Energy; Overvoltage; pH; Polarization; Potential-pH Equilibrium Diagrams.*

BATTERIES, DRY CELLS

The term dry cell is a slight misnomer, for it really refers to an "unspillable" cell. The electrolyte is held in a gel or some absorbent material so that the cell can be used in any position. If the cell were truly dry it would not work. The name was adopted about 1890 to distinguish such cells from the wet cells which were previously used. By common usage the term dry cell has become associated with a primary battery and is so used here. The new sealed rechargeable cells are not usually called dry cells, even though they have the same unspillable characteristics. Simi-

larly, reserve batteries which are actually dry until the addition or melting of electrolyte are not classified as dry cells. Some solid-electrolyte cells used for high-voltage piles are really dry. However, they are not included here since they are very specialized and can supply only extremely small currents. The terms *cell* and *battery* are often used interchangably, although a battery is more strictly a group of cells electrically connected together.

Dry cells, like other primary cells, are devices for the conversion of chemical into electrical energy. This is usually accomplished at an efficiency of 85 per cent or better for current drains within the recommended ranges. Dry cells usually consist of a metal anode, an aqueous salt electrolyte, and a readily reducible oxide cathode often mixed with some type of carbon or metal powder for increased conductivity. Separators, such as paper or paste, are used to prevent direct contact between the anode and cathode. The potential of the cell is the sum of the electromotive forces (emf's) of the anode and cathode, as shown below,

$$E \text{ cell} = E \text{ anode} + E \text{ cathode}$$

The emf of each electrode depends on the free energy change as follows:

$$-\Delta F = n\mathbf{F}E_0$$

The free energy change is slightly different from the heat of the reaction according to the entropy factor,

$$\Delta F = \Delta H - T\Delta S$$

Thus, the efficiency of a reversible cell can be expressed as follows:

$$\text{Efficiency (eff.) reversible cell} = \frac{\Delta F}{\Delta H} = \frac{1 - T\Delta S}{T\Delta H}$$

The efficiency of an operating cell is simply E_a/E_0, where E_a is the active cell voltage under load and E_0 is the reversible cell potential.

The performance of the cell under various loads is quite often a very important factor in determining suitable applications for a cell system or battery design. Fig. 1 shows the discharge voltage behavior for the range of current drains usually encountered. Curve A illustrates a heavy discharge rate. Curve B shows the performance at a moderate drain of the type for which the cell is usually designed. At a light drain the operating voltage often has a fairly flat por-

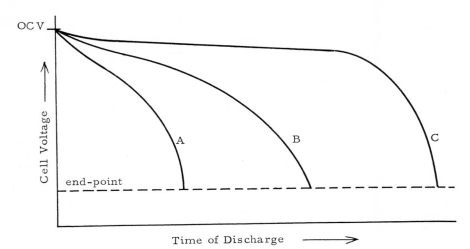

FIG. 1. Dry cell discharge voltage behavior at heavy current drain (A), moderate current drain (B), and light current drain (C).

TABLE 1. COMPARISON OF VARIOUS POSSIBLE ELECTRODE MATERIALS

Metal	Anode Materials				Cathode Materials				
	Emf Sl. acid	Emf Alkaline	Milliamp-hr per g	Amp-hr per cc	Material	Emf Sl. acid	Emf Alkaline	Milliamp-hr per g	Amp-hr per cc
Magnesium	−2.36 v	−2.69 v	2204	3.84	MnO_2	+.80 v	+0.27 v	307	1.54
Aluminum	−1.67	−2.35	2982	8.05	PbO_2	+1.46	+0.25	240	2.26
Zinc	−0.76	−1.25	820	5.65	HgO	+0.85	+0.10	248	2.76
Iron	−0.44	−0.88	960	7.55	CuO	+0.34	−0.36	670	4.32
Cadmium	−0.40	−0.81	477	4.13	Ag_2O	+0.80	+0.35	232	1.67
Tin	−0.14	−0.91	452	3.30	AgO	ca. +1.9	+0.57	432	3.22
Lead	−0.13	−0.54	259	2.94	AgCl	+0.22	+0.22	187	1.04

tion as exhibited in Curve C. The types of curves depend on the inherent characteristics of the cell system and the design employed. In some applications voltage variation is quite critical, so cells giving the type C discharge curve are preferred.

In selecting suitable electrode couples for cells, it is important to use reversible couples for maximum efficiency. The anode and cathode materials for a primary cell must be chosen to give the highest possible potential and capacity per unit weight and volume, but should be sufficiently inactive so that long shelf life can be obtained. The following Table 1 compares some electrode materials which have been studied for use in primary dry cells.

Zinc is the anode material preferred so far because on stand or shelf it reacts only slowly with the electrolyte, due to its high hydrogen overvoltage. Manganese dioxide is the preferred cathode material because of its low cost and

insolubility in electrolyte. There are many factors which must be considered in the choice of suitable electrode materials and electrolytes for dry cells. The importance of dry cells as portable power sources for military applications greatly spurred research and development on new systems, especially during and after World War II and the Korean incident. This has resulted in a much wider variety of dry cells especially suitable for unusual applications. However, the common Leclanché dry cell still enjoys the most widespread usage for noncritical applications because of its low cost and reliable performance.

The standard sizes, electrical tests, and capacity requirements for dry cells are given in Handbook 71 of the National Bureau of Standards. This booklet covers both cylindrical and flat-type Leclanché cells and button and cylindrical mercury cells (see below). The sizes range from the No. 6 or 6 inch telephone cell to the mercury

TABLE 2. SOME CHARACTERISTICS OF COMMERCIAL DRY CELLS*

Cell Name	Chemical System	OCV	Amp-hr	WH/lb	WH/cu in.	Cost†	Cost/WH
Leclanché	Zn/NH_4Cl, $ZnCl_2/$ MnO_2	1.55	4.0	22	1.6	$0.13	3.0¢
Leclanché	Industrial Type	1.65	5.0	26	2.0	0.16	2.8
Mercury	$Zn/KOH/HgO$	1.35	14	46	6	2.25	13.4
Alkaline manganese	$Zn/KOH/MnO_2$	1.50	8	35	3.5	0.50	5.2
Zinc-mercury-carbon	$Zn/ZnSO_4/Hg$ di-oxysulfate	1.36	8	35	3.3 ca	1.00	9.6
Silver-zinc	$Zn/KOH/AgO$	1.86	11	75	6	4.00 est	24
Air cell-alkaline	$Zn/NaOH/O_2$ (air)	1.5	14 est	90	5 est	1.50 est	8
Air cell-neutral	$Zn/NH_4Cl/O_2$ (air)	1.5	14 est	90	5 est	0.25 est	2
Silver chloride	$Zn/ZnCl_2/AgCl$	1.00	2 est	8 est	1 est	—	—

* Based on D flashlight size and for typical light drain or 100 hr rate
† Distributor selling price
OCV = open circuit voltage
WH = watt-hour

button cell of about ½ inch diameter and slightly over ⅛ inch in thickness. The most common dry cells are the standard D-size and baby or C-size flashlight cells and the AA-size penlight cell.

Dry cells are now made in very large quantities and in a wide variety of sizes by high-speed machines. It is estimated that the recent annual production in the U. S. of Leclanché type cells totals about one and one-half billion cells with a value of about $150,000,000. The annual production of mercury cells, which are chiefly used for hearing aids, is estimated to be about 90,000,000 cells with a value of about $20,000,000. The chief commercial uses of dry cells are for flashlights, portable radios, photoflash units, lanterns, motor-operated toys, telephones, and hearing aids. There are many military applications ranging from radio communications to power for firing rockets.

There are several electrochemical systems which have been studied for possible use in primary dry cells. The ones which have attained some amount of commercial success are listed in the adjacent Table 2, which gives their relative performance on both a weight and volume basis. It is notable that dry cells are widely used because of their convenience even though the cost of the electrical energy is very high, i.e., about $30/kwh for ordinary D-size flashlight cells.

The electrochemical system ($Zn/NH_4Cl/MnO_2$) used in the common dry cell was devised by Georges Leclanché (q.v.) and first described by him in 1868. The first *dry* cell of this type was produced by Gassner in about 1888. He also added the innovation of using the zinc anode as the container for a cylindrical shaped cell. The present electrochemical system is Zn/NH_4Cl, $ZnCl_2/MnO_2$, C. The simplified reactions are, at the anode

$$Zn \rightarrow Zn^{++} + 2e \qquad -0.76 \text{ volt}$$

The reactions at the cathode are more complicated depending on the pH and composition of the electrolyte. The most common reaction is thought to be

$$MnO_2 + H^+ + 1e \rightarrow MnO(OH)$$

The overall reaction is often written as

$$Zn + 2MnO_2 \rightarrow ZnO \cdot Mn_2O_3$$
$$\text{(hetaerolite) 1.55 volts}$$

Other reaction products, depending on conditions and the location within the cell, are $Mn_2O_3 \cdot H_2O$, $MnO(OH)$, $ZnCl_2 \cdot 2NH_3$ and various oxychlorides, such as $ZnCl_2 \cdot 4Zn(OH)_2$. During discharge the pH of the electrolyte decreases next to the zinc and, of course, the concentration of $ZnCl_2$ increases here. The pH increases in the porous cathode mix so that various insoluble basic zinc salts are formed. Such precipitation occurs when the original electrolyte pH of about 4.5 goes beyond the precipitation pH for zinc hydroxide which is about 5.2. Diffusion of zinc ions into the depolarizer mix during rest periods results in additional precipitation which may eventually clog up the porous mix. Whatever the exact mechanism, the electrons released at the zinc travel through the external circuit to the carbon positive electrode and are absorbed through reactions in the depolarizing mix.

The construction of a modern flashlight cell

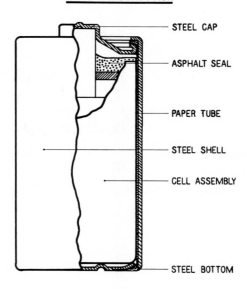

CELL ASSEMBLY

FINAL CONSTRUCTION

- CARBON PENCIL
- SEAL WASHER
- AIR SPACE
- ZINC CAN
- PASTE
- WET MIX
- PAPER SPACER
- BOTTOM DISC

- STEEL CAP
- ASPHALT SEAL
- PAPER TUBE
- STEEL SHELL
- CELL ASSEMBLY
- STEEL BOTTOM

Fig. 2. Cross-section of modern leakproof dry cell. (*Courtesy Ray-O-Vac Co.*)

is shown in Fig. 2. The active materials are held in a zinc can which also functions as the anode. The depolarizing mix, consisting of battery-grade MnO_2, acetylene carbon black, and electrolyte, is pressed around the porous carbon pencil which functions as a gas venting means as well as the positive electrode. The mix and zinc can are separated by an electrolyte paste gelled with corn starch and wheat flour. This inner cell assembly is enclosed as indicated in the final construction to make a modern leakproof cell. Cells of this type were first introduced in 1939 and provided one of the greatest improvements in dry cell performance. Not only was the leakage tendency greatly reduced, but the concurrent improvement in sealing improved the shelf life three or four times. There are now several variations of leakproof cells on the market.

Only certain kinds of MnO_2 are suitable for use in dry cells. The gamma form of natural ore is preferred for general purpose cells. More active forms produced by chemical or electrochemical means are used for cells designed for heavier or more continuous drains. In such industrial type cells, the electrolyte is usually modified so that it has a higher zinc chloride content. In some types of cells the paste layer is replaced by a porous paper having a coating of starch, flour, or methyl cellulose next to the zinc can. The zinc used is usually about 99.9

per cent pure, containing small amounts of lead and cadmium. Copper and other heavy metals are definitely harmful.

When higher voltage batteries are required, the cells are often made in a flat form and stacked in a series in piles to save space. Such flat cells are made in several different designs, but some type of plastic envelope or cup is usually used to contain the cell. The inner cell consists of a zinc disk or plate contacted by a coated paper which separates the zinc from the mix cake. The other side of the zinc is usually coated with a conductive carbon paint, or a conductive carbon plastic layer is used to make contact between the mix and the zinc of adjacent cells. Flat cells are most suitable for low current drains. One of the chief problems has been the drying out of the cells by transmission of water vapor through the plastic envelope. This has now been satisfactorily solved by proper choice of plastics and the addition of wax-type coatings. Flat cells have been made in small button or wafer shapes as small as ½ inch diameter by ⅛ inch height.

Besides the industrial cells mentioned above, there have been many attempts made to modify the Leclanché dry cell to cover a wider range of applications. Since the ordinary cells do not function well below about 0°F, attempts have been made to modify these by the use of special electrolytes and more active forms of the MnO_2

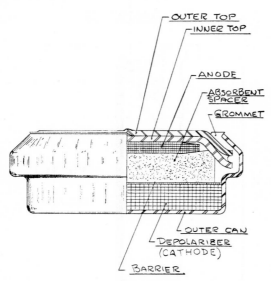

FIG. 3. Button-type mercury cell. (*Courtesy Mallory Battery Co.*)

depolarizer. Electrolytes composed chiefly of LiCl or CaCl₂ have been used since they have freezing points below −30°F. Even with such improvements, the capacity at −30°F is only about 25 per cent of that at room temperature. Attempts have also been made to use aluminum and magnesium as anodes to take advantage of their higher potentials. Different electrolytes are used to control the attack on these more active metals during shelf life. Although practical cells can be made with both aluminum and magnesium, no commercial success has been attained to date. The magnesium cell in particular shows some promise for military applications. There has been a considerable amount of effort recently to utilize organic materials, such as metadinitrobenzene, as depolarizers. Since the electrode potential of such materials is relatively low, they must be coupled with a magnesium anode to produce a cell voltage in the desirable range of 1.0–1.5 volts. Some favorable results have been obtained so far with this system, and development work is in progress to produce a practical cell.

The modern *mercury dry cell* was invented by Samuel Ruben in 1942. The cell system, zinc/KOH/HgO, had been proposed as early as 1884. However, Ruben succeeded in using it in dry cell form by reducing the evolution of gases so that a sealed cell could be produced. Dissolution of the zinc with the consequent evolution of hydrogen gas was prevented by heavy amalgamation

of the zinc and presaturation of the electrolyte with zinc oxide to form a zincate. The cell reaction under these conditions is,

$$Zn + HgO \rightarrow ZnO + Hg \quad 1.345 \text{ volts}$$

The electrolyte is usually about 40 per cent KOH substantially saturated with ZnO. With operation of the cell, the zinc does not dissolve to form zincate but is converted directly to a soft form of ZnO which forms a paste with the electrolyte. It should be noted that in this cell the electrolyte is not changed or used up so that the cell can be operated efficiently with a very small volume of electrolyte. This permits the construction of a cell with a high capacity per unit volume and thus the mercury dry cell finds its chief application where space is limited.

Mercury cells are produced in several sizes of both cylindrical and button types. The construction of a typical button cell is shown in Fig. 3. The cathode consists of a mixture of HgO and finely divided graphite pressed into a pellet and consolidated into the bottom of a nickel-plated steel can. This is covered by a permeable barrier layer of parchment paper or a synthetic microporous plastic. Most of the electrolyte is held in the special absorbent cotton pad located above the barrier layer. The anode is a pressed pellet of amalgamated zinc powder. The negative terminal is composed of tin and nickel-plated caps welded together. The cell is sealed by crimping the outer can over a plastic or rubber grommet. In some cells the zinc pellet is replaced by a corrugated zinc ribbon spirally wound with an absorbent paper. In most cells there is an electrochemical excess of HgO to prevent the formation of gas at the end of discharge.

The mercury cell for a given size can support much larger currents than the Leclanché dry cell. Conversely, a much smaller cell can be used for a given application. A very desirable characteristic of the mercury cell is its relatively flat discharge curve at low and moderate current drains. The capacity of a mercury cell falls off rapidly below about 50°F. Special constructions have been used to overcome this deficiency for military applications. The high cost of mercury has limited the use of the mercury cell chiefly to small sizes where it out-performs the Leclanché cell by a substantial margin. The chief application at present for mercury cells is in hearing aids. Here they have been teamed with transistors to greatly reduce the size and weight of such devices. Recently, rechargeable mercury cells have been marketed as a power source for small flashlights.

The so-called *alkaline manganese dry cells* are a more recent entry into the primary dry cell field. Alkaline electrolytes were first used with manganese dioxide in small "crown" cells on a commercial scale in 1949. These cells were used for portable radio B batteries then and are now being produced in large quantities chiefly for 9 volt transistor radio batteries. In the last few years, cylindrical flashlight cells using the system, zinc/KOH/MnO$_2$, have appeared on the market. The cell discharge reaction is probably

$$Zn + MnO_2 \rightarrow ZnO + Mn_2O_3 \quad 1.52 \text{ volts}$$

The KOH electrolyte is almost saturated with zincate. The reactions of the zinc anode are similar to those for the mercury cell. The reduction of the MnO$_2$ results in a substantial swelling of the cathode. The MnO$_2$ is mixed with graphite to produce cathodes very similar to those used in the mercury cell. In some cylindrical cells the anode is composed of loose zinc powder suspended in a gelled electrolyte, and a thin separator is used between the anode and annular cathode. Crown cells are also made with various blends of HgO and MnO$_2$. In general, alkaline manganese cells utilize the MnO$_2$ more completely than in the Leclanché cell since the electrolyte is not changed during discharge. Thus, for the same size about twice the capacity can be obtained. The alkaline cells are also more suitable for heavy continuous drains, but their advantage is largely lost for intermittent type uses.

The *"zinc mercury-carbon cell"* employing mercuric dioxysulfate as a depolarizer was invented by Samuel Ruben about 1958. The construction used is very similar to that employed in a cylindrical paperlined Leclanché dry cell. A special gel-coated paper separator is used next to the zinc can. The cathode mix contains the depolarizer, HgSO$_4$·2HgO, mixed with acetylene carbon black and wetted with a zinc sulfate electrolyte. The overall reaction on discharge is

$$3Zn + HgSO_4 \cdot 2HgO$$
$$\rightarrow ZnSO_4 + 2ZnO + 3Hg \quad 1.36 \text{ volts}$$

The cells are most suitable for very light drains and on such loads will discharge with a flat curve

at about 1.30 volts. This characteristic is very desirable for electric clocks which have been the chief application so far. Cells for such use have been made in the D, C, and AA sizes.

Alkaline silver-zinc primary dry cells are made very much like the mercury cell, but with the substitution of Ag$_2$O or AgO for the mercuric oxide. The cell potential is about 1.58 for Ag$_2$O and 1.86 for AgO. The larger rectangular cells have been made with both oxides for military applications. Such cells with sponge zinc anodes can sustain very heavy drains so that they can be discharged efficiently at the 1 hour rate and will even give satisfactory performance at the 10 min rate. The relatively flat voltage curve is also a very desirable characteristic. At low drains the AgO cells exhibit a lower voltage plateau due to the Ag$_2$O formed on discharge. Such cells with AgO have the highest performance ratings of any dry cells, namely, about 75 watt-hr per pound and about 6 watt-hr per cu in. Thus, they are especially valuable for missile applications. Very small button cells using Ag$_2$O have been made for use in hearing aids and electric watches. The higher operating voltage gives them a slight advantage over the equivalent mercury cells. The relatively high cost of silver restricts the use of such dry cells to very small sizes or to military applications.

The *alkaline zinc air cell* uses the oxygen from the air as a depolarizer. Thus, it has a very high capacity per unit weight and volume. It has been made as a small cell of thimble size and shape and as a rectangular cell equivalent to two AA penlight cells. Both types of cells were designed for supplying the filament current in the older tube-type hearing aids. The carbon air breathing electrode is covered or enclosed before use. This helps to prevent absorption of CO$_2$ and water vapor from the air. The shelf life in the activated exposed condition is rather limited. These cells perform well for the designed loads, but polarize rapidly at higher drains. On light drains or intermittent drains, the capacity suffers due to improper moisture balance and formation of carbonate from CO$_2$ contained in the air.

The *neutral air cell* is constructed similarly to the pasted Leclanché dry cell, except that the cathode mix contains activated carbon in place of MnO$_2$. Little or no zinc chloride is used in the ammonium chloride electrolyte. Access of the air to the carbon mix is provided either through a hole in the top seal or through a hollow core in the porous carbon pencil. Such cells have about 2 to 3 times the capacity of the Leclanché cell but are suitable for only low drains or slightly heavier drains of an intermittent type. Large rectangular cells of 250 and 500 amp-hrs are made chiefly for railroad signal use in this country. In Europe, #6 size cells, and some larger ones, are made for both railroad and electric fence applications. The shelf life and reliability are considerably inferior to those of the corresponding Leclanché dry cells. Various sizes of air cells were produced in Germany during World War II due to a shortage of battery-grade MnO_2. However, production was converted to the MnO_2 type cell again as soon as suitable grades of MnO_2 became available.

The *silver chloride dry cell* has been made in very small quantities for many years, chiefly for checking the continuity with a galvanometer of electrical blasting circuits. Here its steady voltage and relatively high internal resistance are an advantage. Such cells are only suitable for low current drains.

References

1. VINAL, G. W., "Primary Batteries," New York, John Wiley & Sons, Inc., 1951.
2. Primary Battery Issue, *Journal of Electrochemical Society*, August 1952.
3. GARRETT, A. B., "Batteries of Today," Dayton, Ohio, Research Press, 1957.
4. MOREHOUSE, C. K., GLICKSMAN, R., AND LOZIER, G. S., "Batteries," *Proc. of the I.R.E.*, **46**, 1462–82 (August 1958).
5. "Specifications for Dry Cells and Batteries," *Handbook 71*, National Bureau of Standards, U. S. Dept. of Commerce (December 1959), obtainable from Supt. of Documents, U. S. Government Printing Office, Washington 25, D. C., 25 cents.

W. S. HERBERT

Cross-references: other entries with *Batteries* designation; *Electrode Potentials; Electromotive Series; Leclanché.*

BATTERIES, RESERVE PRIMARY

"Reserve battery" is a term originating from military usage during and following World War II. The U. S. Patent Office classifies the devices under the term *Deferred Action Batteries*. Other terms commonly in use are *one-shot* and *dry-charged* batteries. Patent files first show a significant interest in the subject in the early 1920's

when the shelf storage problems of Leclanché batteries became commercially important.

Simply stated, *reserve batteries* are orthodox, electrochemical power supplies which are designed, manufactured, and stored in a form that insures complete inertness until a specific action is taken by the user or results automatically from the application. The original designs generally involved the separation of the electrolyte from the battery plates until use; later types involve other features. Outstanding benefits are (1) unlimited shelf life when properly packaged, (2) wide freedom in choice of systems to permit the utilization of highly reactive chemistry that offers high rate and/or low temperature performance, and (3) wide freedom in battery design since these devices are normally special purpose and either require or permit unconventional structural design.

Primary has a somewhat broader connotation. The electrochemical systems used run the gamut of all conventional types and include many of an exotic nature. The devices are classified as "primary" only because of the single discharge character of usage. Normally, the term "dry-charged" is applied to any one of the conventional secondary systems in a device form requiring the addition of electrolyte at the time of initial service; service usage is the customary cyclic performance of charge/discharge of the storage battery. A few battery types fall outside these service conditions; included among these might be the Lalande cell and certain of the air depolarized systems, which are hybrid structures.

Classification of Reserve Primary Batteries

There are three basic types of reserve primary batteries. These are systems dependent on the transport and distribution of (1) liquid, (2) gas, or (3) heat. It should be clearly recognized that this broad classification permits the use of many electrochemical systems under each type, for example, the heat-activated systems, i.e., thermal batteries, encompass a range of fused salt chemical systems which are as varied as those available in the aqueous battery field.

A further basis for classification is the method of activation. Activation is the process of energizing the battery system, thereby leading to the term *activation time* which is unique to reserve batteries. The two types are the manually activated structures and the automatically activated types. The former group ranges from simple immersion in electrolyte to hypodermic filling, and for multicell batteries, to relatively complex distribution from a reservoir through a manifolding system. Automatic types are responsive to an externally applied force of either a mechanical or electrical nature. Frequently, the initiating action results from a condition of use, such as the linear acceleration resulting from missile launching or gun firing of a projectile which provides the energy to break an electrolyte ampule. The physical form of initiating systems includes explosive elements, inertia devices, and fluid pumps.

These devices involve the "Special Purpose Battery" concept. Many of the conventional criteria, such as those of energy per unit weight or per unit volume, have only an indirect bearing on the selection and assignment of a device to a using system. Initially, a fully considered target specification covering performance, use environment, storage environment, form factor, acceptable cost, etc. is needed. From these factors decisions can readily be made to narrow the choice of the acceptable battery types and finally the chemical systems within the types. It must be recognized that in the special battery field, the inherent capability to perform a job is paramount. The reserve feature consumes volume which does not produce energy, therefore, the energy densities are lower than normal and are traded off for shelf-life. Other factors often lead in the same direction. These are packaging and a requirement for the relatively inefficient, high-rate performance. In general, the typical (military) reserve design is probably operating at less than 25 per cent of the energy density associated with an advanced technological form of the system as a primary battery.

As typical examples of the art, it is not unusual to assign a silver oxide/zinc battery to an application involving temperatures of −40°C and lower. In some of these cases the noted high-rate performance is required and is obtained by automatic heating features. In other cases, the desired feature is capacity but at a low enough rate to reduce the current density to an acceptable level so that a superficially illogical choice is actually a sound engineering selection. Another example is the lead/fluoboric acid/lead dioxide battery frequently used in artillery rounds. In this case performance at spin rates of several hundred revolutions per second dominates all other requirements. The use of the centrifugal force of the rotating shell to distribute the electrolyte from a centrally located reservoir overcomes and beneficially utilizes a major environmental condition. A third example is in the thermal battery field. Here, molten salt chemistry offers a very wide choice of electrochemical systems with the application controlling the selection. A pulse unit can use chemistry totally unacceptable for an active life requirement of even a minute or two.

Water-Activated Types

Capability. Water-activated batteries satisfy an area of need for radiosondes, particularly meteorological, and for a variety of sea-associated emergency uses including lighting, signal beacons, and markers. Inherently the devices (1) have an active lifetime limited to hours, (2) should be maintained under load when activated, and (3) operate from a few tens of watts, for lighting, to the output level of radio "B" batteries. Electrically, the batteries are noisy due to chemical side reactions but these same reactions provide the heat to make possible low-temperature and, therefore, upper-atmosphere performance. Energy density is relatively high because only active materials in a minimal package (without stored electrolyte) are involved. Values approximate 20 watt-hours per pound and 1.0 watt-hour per cubic inch.

Chemistry. Two chemical systems are used. Each involves a sheet magnesium anode and a water electrolyte with sea or salt water being preferred because of its higher conductivity, which sharply reduces activation time to a few seconds, whereas fresh water may require a few minutes. The key difference is the choice of a silver chloride or cuprous chloride cathode. The same basic capability is provided by both, but one gains many predictable advantages from silver chloride, such as a slightly higher voltage (1.3 vs 1.2 volts per cell), improved high-rate performance, better low-temperature performance, and design and manufacturing advantages due to the working properties and to the inherent electrical conductivity of the material. The only significant basis for the choice of cuprous chloride is economic, and this necessarily reflects a balance of material and manufacturing costs.

Design. Design takes several forms. The simplest is the single-cell, wound structure with a sandwich relationship of cathode/separator/anode, although for certain sea-rescue applications the conventional plate-spacer battery design is incorporated in a buoyant plastic housing, which carries a light bulb already wired to the cell. Series structures normally involve a stack of individually packeted cells to provide electrical isolation. As is evident from the activation by immersion, elimination of intercell leakage requires a self-clearing (or minimizing) of electrolyte bridges, a point uniquely handled for batteries designed to operate when submerged as distinguished from those which operate in air. The chemical side reactions, mentioned above, generate hydrogen, which is captured to displace any standing column of electrolyte from the fill channel and thereby produce the equivalent of in-air operation.

Acid-Activated Types

Capability. Acid-activated types had an early application (1940's) in radiosonde work when multicell structures provided all energy requirements at high rates and over a wide temperature range. These characteristics, coupled with rapid activation of one second or less and an inherent low cost, led to the development of reserve batteries for application in the proximity fuzing of artillery. The system is amenable to miniaturized designs including multicell series structures in a construction capable of withstanding extreme environmental forces with good electrical stability. Operating life of minutes represents a practical limit for the acid-activated primary types. Units capable of even a few hundred watt-minutes are unusual.

Chemistry. Again chemical systems may be varied. Anodes may be electrodeposited zinc, cadmium, or lead with predictable differences in behavior. The electrolytes generally are restricted to those that yield only soluble reaction products during cell discharge. Specifically included are fluosilicic, perchloric, and fluoboric acids. Cathodes normally are lead dioxide in electroplated form. Single-cell voltages range from 1.3 to 1.9 volts at current densities as high as 0.25 ampere per square inch. Nuances in performance requirements present the engineer or user with the question of trade-offs; differences in systems are not profound nor inventive, but reflect the choice of materials to best suit the mechanical, electrical, and cost requirements of the application. Clearly, increasing the reactivity of the materials in composition or form improves the high-rate characteristics, but at the expense of activated life and electrical stability.

The best and most widely used general-purpose system is that consisting of lead/fluoboric acid/lead dioxide.

Design. Many structures and designs have been explored, but only a few have been developed into usable hardware. Representative units are layer built of clad, sheet-metal elements using appropriate spacers. Piece part design and plastic potting produce filling manifolds, or channels, for electrolyte distribution. The electrolyte is retained in a glass ampule in a central cavity until the time of activation when an accelerating force releases and drives the shatterable ampule against a breaker device. Electrolyte distribution may then be by a piston, force-fill mechanism, or in the case of artillery, by the centrifugal forces existent.

Alkali-Activated Types.

Capability. Alkaline primary reserve batteries are dominated by the high-rate, high-energy density silver oxide/potassium hydroxide/zinc system. Again, the dry-charged, commercial item will not be discussed, but attention is directed to the role of the system in the auxiliary (missile) power and weapons' power fields. This system is normally applied in situations requiring more than a few hundred watt-minutes or to situations demanding very high current, i.e., tens or hundreds of amperes. An upper energy limit would be a few tens of kilowatt-minutes. Generally, the devices (1) activate in a fraction to a few seconds, (2) may be made operational over wide temperature ranges by automatic chemical heating, (3) are electrically very stable, and (4) can be built to high levels of reliability. Voltage levels rarely exceed a nominal 28 volts with values of 100 volts and up being virtually nonexistent.

Chemistry. The chemical aspect is again a design variable. There is little basis to select any anodic material but zinc. For other materials, for example, cadmium, not only would costs be higher, but lower rates would be inevitable, and performance would be relatively sluggish and at a somewhat lower voltage per cell. Potassium hydroxide is the universally used electrolyte. The choice of the higher or lower oxide of silver, however, is often the key to a successful unit, for the reserve battery frequently is required to survive high-temperature storage in an evacuated assembly. Degradation of the higher oxide not only affects later capacity and discharge characteristics, but build-up of oxygen pressure may interfere with the filling mechanism. Accordingly, it is not unusual to accept the lower voltage (1.6 rather than 1.8 volts per cell) and a lower capacity to gain reliability and to meet shelf storage requirements. Design current densities range from as low as 0.1 ampere to as high as 5.0 amperes per square inch reflecting use conditions and trade-offs in materials' parameters.

Design. Physical structures have two major distinguishing features. While some units are manually activated, the majority are automatically responsive to an external force, usually electrical. The second feature is the presence or absence of an integral, automatic heat source. Other methods of heating the batteries are used, including built-in resistive heaters or electric blankets, but these techniques are limited in that there must be available stand-by power. The battery pack itself is usually the conventional plate design of a given manufacture with modifications in spacing, separators, etc. to optimize for high-rate, primary application. The electrolyte is retained in a polystyrene, neoprene, silver or stainless steel reservoir and conducted by plumbing to a distribution manifold in the battery pack. A propellant gas generated by an explosive element, or released from a gas bottle, pumps the electrolyte into the battery pack. When heating is required for low-temperature performance, the electrolyte passes through a tubular heat exchanger located between the reservoir and the cell pack. Operation of the exchanger is thermostatically controlled and is dependent on thermite-type materials as chemically stored heat sources. (Fig. 1)

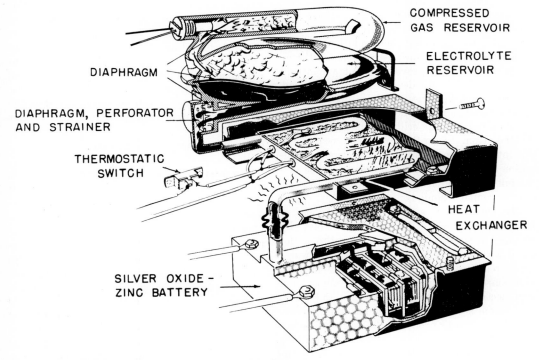

FIG. 1. Exploded view of an automatically activated, temperature-compensated, silver oxide/potassium hydroxide/zinc battery.

It is interesting to note that the adaptation of the reserve concept reached an early inventive peak with the Leclanché dry cell. Despite this fact, there is no known product of this type normally available. It can be expected that with an ever increasing spread of interests to geographical extremes, i.e., arctic and tropic areas, there will be an increasing demand for both better shelf life and performance from this system. Appearance of reserve dry batteries as both military and commercial items can be anticipated.

Gas-Activated Types

Capability. Gas-activated, reserve devices are intriguing but have not yet reached any significant level of development or application. In principle, these systems depend on the interaction between a gas and a salt, or equivalent, to produce an electrolyte. On this basis, interesting high-rate, short-lived batteries of both the multicell and single-cell power types have been demonstrated. The actual capability uniquely provided by these systems is elusive. It would appear to include low-temperature performance in a system capable of miniaturization and of quick activation. (Gas electrode batteries are not considered to be reserve units but storage systems, and as such, a gas electrode then approaches the characteristics of a fuel cell electrode.)

Chemistry. Two basic chemical systems have been explored. The first involves ammonia vapor which diffuses throughout the active structure where it is adsorbed by salts to produce an ammoniacal electrolyte. These solutions contain various thiocyanates, such as potassium, lithium, or ammonium, and provide good low-temperature electrolytes. Anodes of magnesium, lead, and zinc have been used with cathodes of lead dioxide and, to a limited degree, sulfur and heavy metal sulfates. Single-cell combinations produce voltages from 1.5 to 2.5 volts. The system has the interesting possibility of a reversible activation characteristic, if the ammonia can be successfully removed from the electrolyte by vacuum or similar techniques.

The second basic system involves the use of reactive vapors which produce an electrolyte by chemical reaction with a second constituent located within the cell. One combination is water vapor reacting with an acid anhydride, such as phosphorus pentoxide, to yield a phosphoric acid electrolyte. A far more practical and versatile system is boron trifluoride gas which reacts with boric acid to produce a fluoboric acid electrolyte. This electrolyte when coupled with lead anodes and lead dioxide cathodes has performance characteristics generally similar to those for *acid-activated types*.

Design. Design considerations can only be generalized since the field is still one of exploratory development. Layer-built structures of anode, salt-carrying separator, and cathode are normally in a dense pack. Design approaches to gas distribution must consider vapor pressure at low temperatures and provision for adequate access of the gas to the salt to form the electrolyte. Finally, the essential electrical isolation of adjacent cells requires that attention be directed to the prevention of electrolyte bridging which would result in electrical instability. The future for reserve devices based on the gas activation principle is not clear.

Heat-Activated Types

Capability. Thermal batteries are unique in the reserve field because all materials are in place at the time of manufacture; activation is accomplished by the initiation and combustion of an integrally located heat source followed by the transport of heat to the cell elements. No material transport of any kind is required. These features yield devices offering (1) very long shelf life, (2) operation over a wide temperature range (225°F), (3) ruggedness, (4) quick activation, (5) miniaturization, and (6) a wide range of electrical capability. Inherently, the units are short-lived (a few minutes) due to thermal control and they exhibit an upper limit of energy at about 1 to 2 kilowatt-minutes. Conventional series or parallel circuitry may be used to cover a distribution from short-duration pulse batteries through levels of radio requirements to power batteries. Applications are largely military in the area of weaponry and in the emergency, short-duration field of alarms and initiators.

Chemistry. Discussion of chemical systems is difficult. Anodes are invariably magnesium or calcium in sheet or clad form. The significant difference is about 1 volt more per cell with calcium plus improved chemical performance in high-rate systems. Practical electrolytes are nominally eutectic mixtures of lithium and potassium halides with physical properties largely influencing deviations and selection. Depolarizers, or the cathodically reactive chemicals, vary widely with essentially any reducible compound that is thermally stable at operating temperatures of 300 to 600°C being of some value. Voltages and current densities are highly dependent on the choice. They range from less than 1.0 to greater than 3.0 volts per cell and from bias currents to a few amperes per square inch for pulse units. Generally acceptable depolarizers include (1) the soluble types, such as the chromates and heavy metal salts, and (2) the numerous metallic oxides including iron oxide, tungstic oxide, and vanadium pentoxide in the form of a filled inorganic paper.

Design. Several designs of cells have been reduced to practice, but essential features are common. Thin stock (0.010 inch) is normally the structural element with all active materials being blanked and stacked to give layer-built, sandwich units. The electrolyte is made available in the required form by producing an impregnated glass tape as an intermediate. Series or parallel intercell connections are achieved by ingenious materials preparation to permit a maximum use of folding and bridging. Necessary physical connections are made by welding. A common feature of designs is the placement of the pyrotechnic heat source in inorganic paper form against the major surfaces of the individual cells. The heat source is often a blend of zirconium metal fuel and barium chromate oxidizers. The active materials with appropriate thermal and electrical insulation are contained in a hermetically sealed package. Initiation is accomplished with ignition of the heat source by the flame output of a percussion primer, an electric match, or equivalent.

References

1. VINAL, G. W., "Primary Batteries," New York, John Wiley & Sons, Inc., 1950.
2. HAMER, W. J., "Modern Batteries," *IRE Transactions on Component Parts*, Vol. CP-4, pp. 86–96 (September 1957).
3. LINDEN, D., AND DANIEL, A. F., "New Batteries for the Space Age," *Electronics (Engineering Edition)*, **31**, 59–65 (July 18, 1958).
4. MOREHOUSE, C. K., GLICKSMAN, R., AND LOZIER, G. S., "Batteries," *Proc. IRE*, **46**, 1462–1483 (August 1958).
5. HOWARD, P. L., "Wet-Cell Batteries for Power," *Product Engineering*, **31**, 75–82 (February 15, 1960).
6. Proceedings, Sixteenth (1962) Annual Power Sources Conference, and earlier. Sponsored by Power Sources Division, U.S. Army Electronics Research and Development Laboratories, Fort Monmouth, N. J. Available from PSC Publications Committee, P.O. Box 891, Red Bank, N. J.

ROBERT BRUCE GOODRICH

Cross-references: other entries bearing *Batteries* titles.

BATTERIES, SEALED STORAGE

It has been recognized for many years that for some applications it would be desirable to have sealed storage batteries which could be handled in the same manner as dry cells. The possible advantages of such batteries would be their use in any position and absence of leakage or evolution of gases with possible attendant spray. The elimination of maintenance, such as the addition of water and other checking procedures, would also be a decided benefit.

Many attempts have been made to develop sealed batteries with the characteristics as outlined above. Unspillable lead-acid batteries of various types have been on the market for a long time. These batteries are not sealed but have most of the electrolyte retained in absorbent separators and have a special vent trap which prevents leakage of electrolyte even in an inverted position. However, they still must be charged in an upright position and even with the trap there is sometimes the possible danger of some acid spray being evolved with the gases generated on charge.

Probably the first "sealed" storage batteries were small penlight-size nickel-cadmium cells placed on the market about 1951. These cells were sealed in the usual sense of the term. However, a special double-contact terminal was used so that excessive gas pressure within the cell broke contact and thereby disconnected the current and released the excess gas. Further improvements were made in France by Neumann and his associates so that the first real sealed cells were introduced in about 1953. Since that time many millions of small sealed nickel-cadmium cells have been made, and the principles established have led to the introduction of sealed cells with other systems.

The principle employed in most sealed cells is the removal of the gases on one of the cell electrodes, or on a special third electrode which has been introduced. Since most rechargeable cell systems evolve gas on charge and sometimes on stand, this principle is the most widely employed. However, there are other sealed cell systems in which the evolution of gases on charge can be prevented by controlling the rate of charge and the final cell voltage. In this case it is also important that the electrodes do not evolve gases while the cell is standing idle. The development of suitable hermetic long-life insulating seals has resulted in a variety of closures, each with certain advantages and disadvantages. The need for gas recombination has resulted in the use of minimum quantities of absorbed electrolyte and special electrode spacing to permit access of gases to the reacting electrodes. In most cells, the oxygen gas evolved at the positive electrode during charge or over-charge diffuses throughout the cell and combines with the active material of the negative electrode. The relatively small amount of electrolyte actually limits the rates of discharge and charge compared with those of wet or fluid-electrolyte cells. Since the part of the current which sustains gas evolution results in the development of heat from chemical recombination, means must be provided to carry away the heat produced.

Sealed cells, as well as most other storage batteries, are usually given an ampere-hour capacity rating, called C. The charge and discharge rates are expressed as fractions of C, i.e., $C/10$ for a 5 ampere-hour battery, means a discharge or charge at the 0.5 ampere rate. Because of the more critical balance of factors in sealed cells, it is important that the recommended overcharge rates be adhered to quite strictly. For example, constant potential charging at excessive rates can lead to a "thermal runaway" condition in which rupture of the cell may occur. In such cases, the high current used results in a greater rate of evolution of gas which evolves more heat on recombination. The resulting higher temperature in turn decreases the charge acceptance so that still more gas and higher internal pressures are produced. It is also very important that sealed cells connected in series stay "in step" through many cycles. A low cell in series in a battery can actually be reversed on discharge of the battery to low voltages. This cell reversal can result in gas generation with the possible rupture of the cell. Some fairly successful means have been developed to overcome this problem. However, it is usually recommended that no more than about 7 sealed cells be connected in series due to the increased probability of reversal occurring with a larger number of cells.

The following is a brief resumé of the various types of sealed cells which have been developed at the present time.

Nickel-Cadmium System (Alkaline)

Cells of this type are the most highly developed sealed cells and are produced in large numbers and in many sizes and shapes. Flat button cells are available from about 50 ma-hr (⅝ in. dia.) to 450 ma-hr (1¾ in. dia.). Cylindrical cells are produced in sizes ranging from the AA penlight size of 450 ma-hr up to the F-size of about 8 amp-hr. A few special cylindrical

cells have been made up to 50 amp-hr. The prismatic or rectangular cells range in size from about 5 amp-hr up to about 25 amp-hr. Gasket-type seals are used for the button and cylindrical cells. However, ceramic insulating seals have been employed on some of the cylindrical and rectangular types. Some of the latter use safety relief vents for protection against excessive pressures which might develop due to some type of mishandling.

Sealed operation is made possible by using an excess of uncharged negative material (CdO), so that oxygen is evolved on the charged nickel oxide positive. This diffuses, possibly through the separator and through the voids of the cell, to combine with the sponge cadmium metal of the negative. Cadmium is a very desirable material since it does not react with the KOH electrolyte and evolve hydrogen on stand. The active materials are utilized as pressed powders sometimes enclosed in fine screens or are impregnated in sintered nickel plaques. An excellent cycle life of several thousand cycles is obtained at low depths of discharge such as 25 per cent. However, the cycle life falls to a few hundred for deep discharges such as 75 per cent. The cycle life is also adversely affected by extremes of temperature. On constant current charges, such as $C/10$, the voltage levels out at about 1.5 volts. The cell discharges on moderate loads at about 1.2 volts.

The internal pressures on charge range up to about 40 psi. Protection against cell reversal is obtained by incorporating some cadmium oxide as an antipolar mass in the positive nickel electrode. Sometimes, some positive active material is also incorporated in the negative plate. Lately, special high-rate cylindrical cells have been produced by using spiral wound electrodes to obtain large surface areas.

Silver-Zinc System (Alkaline)

Sealed silver-zinc cells were first made available about 1960. They have been used chiefly in missile and space applications, for example, in the successful Mariner space probe of Venus. The cells operate on the controlled charge voltage principle. Charging is terminated at 1.97 volts just before the gassing stage is reached. On moderate drains, the cells discharge at about 1.7 volts at the upper plateau and at about 1.5 volts for the lower plateau. Evolution of hydrogen from the zinc on stand is prevented by relatively heavy amalgamation. Batteries are made in two types which are designated as the flat plate and the pile type. By changes in construction, cells can be made suitable for either light or moderate current drains. Special separators are used to minimize the transfer of soluble and colloidal silver oxide and to reduce the effects of the growth of zinc trees. Because of these conditions, the cycle life is relatively short. However, the high energy density and the high power output make these cells especially valuable for critical applications.

Silver-Cadmium System (Alkaline)

This system has been utilized to incorporate the best and most efficient electrodes of the above two systems. Batteries have been made available on a special pilot plant production basis since about 1961. Cylindrical and button-type cells have been made using both pressed powder and flat electrodes with a conducting matrix. Extremely high discharge currents, i.e., $5C$, can be obtained from cylindrical cells using spiral wound electrodes. The sealed cells operate on the oxygen cycle. The cell has a potential of 1.4 volts and discharges at suitable rates at about 1.0 volt per cell. The cycle life is somewhere between that of silver-zinc and nickel-cadmium cells, depending on conditions.

Lead-Acid System

The development of sealed lead-acid cells was more difficult than for the others, since most of the charging takes place at potentials higher than those required for gas evolution. Some early small sealed cells used plastic cases which bulged due to gas pressure and thereby operated a miniature switch to cut off the current. However, later cells made in Europe operate on the oxygen cycle and are constructed in a semidry condition. In the latter, most of the electrolyte is held in the porous separators or by a gel between the plates. The oxygen evolved from the positive has access to the sponge-lead plates through the peripheral air spaces. The lead alloys and active materials are chosen to give minimum gas evolution on charge and stand. Two new types of maintenance-free sealed batteries were introduced in 1962 in the U.S.A. on a restricted basis. One type is made for deep cycling and can tolerate a moderate overcharge current. It is suitable for at least 300 cycles. The other type of maintenance-free lead acid battery is designed for float-type operation. This cell is used with a special charger which reduces the float current down to a few milliamperes.

Another approach for making sealed lead-acid cells involves the use of a third electrode connected to the negative plate. This is an auxiliary gas electrode which functions similarly to a fuel-cell electrode. In one form it is made of wet-proofed porous carbon catalyzed with silver. The electrode is only partially immersed in the electrolyte. Oxygen gas evolved from the positive plates is consumed at the auxiliary electrode to form water. A similar system may be used for alkaline cells.

In a later version of the above, a hydrogen-consuming fuel-cell type electrode is connected to the positive PbO_2 plates through a diode. The latter regulates the potential of the hydrogen electrode to within the optimum range. This system has important advantages since most negative electrodes evolve hydrogen on stand and this is very difficult to remove when the principle of the oxygen cycle is used. In the hydrogen-cycle system the charge capacity of the plates is regulated so that the negatives are fully charged first and evolve hydrogen. Any oxygen produced on charge or stand is catalytically converted to water on the auxiliary electrodes.

Alkaline Manganese Dioxide System

Rechargeable cells using this system were introduced in about 1959, although it was known before that such primary cells could be recharged to a limited extent. The cells, with a zinc electrode, are made in cylindrical shape in sizes up to the G-size rated at about 4 to 8 ampere-hours depending on the depth of discharge. Since the cell has a potential of 1.5 volts, charging can be carried on up to about 2.1 volts before gassing occurs. Any slight amount of oxygen gas evolved can be absorbed by the finely-divided zinc which is used in the form of an anode electrolyte gel. About 30 to 50 cycles can be obtained at a 25 per cent depth of discharge. Batteries of such cells have been used as power sources for portable TV receivers.

Mercury System (Alkaline)

Sealed rechargeable mercury cells were developed by S. Ruben in about 1951 by making suitable modifications to the structure of the primary dry cell. Silver powder is used in the positive to prevent agglomeration of the mercury in the discharged condition. A helical ribbon of bronze screen coated with zinc is used to facilitate redeposition of zinc on charge. An improved barrier is employed to separate the electrodes and to minimize the effects of zinc treeing and migration of soluble mercury compounds. The cell was introduced commercially in 1962 in rechargeable flashlights. It has a potential of 1.35 volts, and can be satisfactorily recharged up to 1.7 volts without the production of gases. The very slow loss of capacity on stand is a decided advantage.

Lead-Silver Oxide System

This alkaline cell with a lead negative and Ag_2O positive electrode was designed specifically as a low-potential power source for operation of solions. The open-circuit potential is 0.9 volt and on most drains the cell discharges at 0.8 to 0.9 volt. The charging is very critical and must be controlled within the range of 1.09 to 1.15 volts. Lower potentials result in lack of sufficient charge whereas higher potentials cause conversion of the silver electrode to AgO and result in a voltage too high for solion operation. The discharge products are PbO and sponge silver. Cells (with about 1.5 amp-hr capacity) have been made on a limited scale using the mercury button cell construction since about 1957.

References

NEUMANN, G., "Sealed Ni-Cd Cells," U. S. Patents 2,571,927 (Oct. 16, 1951) and 2,636,058 (April 21, 1953).

BARRS, E. G., "Sealed Ni-Cd Cells," Abstracts of Battery Division of Electrochemical Society, Boston Meeting, p. 97, Oct., 1954.

BARRS, E. G., "Working Mechanism of Sealed Ni-Cd Cells," Proc. 12th Annual Battery Research and Development Conf., p. 25, 1958.

SALKIND, A. J., AND DUDDY, J. C., "Thermal Runway Condition in Ni-Cd Cells," *J. Electrochem. Soc.*, **109**, 360 (1962); see also following paper, p. 364, by W. G. Eicke.

DUDDY, J. C., AND ARMS, J. T., "Sealed Ag-Zn Batteries," Proc. 14th Annual Power Sources Conf., p. 84, 1960.

ARMS, J. T., AND DUDDY, J. C., "Sealed Secondary Alkaline Battery Systems," Extended Abstracts, Battery Division of Electrochemical Society, p. 69, Boston Meeting, Sept., 1962.

HOWARD, P. L., AND SOLOMON, FRANK, "Sealed Ag-Cd Batteries," Proc. 14th Annual Power Sources Conf., p. 87, 1960.

SHAIR, R. C., *et al*, "Hermetically Sealed Ni-Cd and Ag-Cd Storage Batteries," *I. R. E. Trans. on Military Electronics*, **MIL-6**, 67, (Jan., 1962).

RUETSCHI, P., "Sealed Lead-Acid and Alkaline Cells with Auxiliary Gas Electrode," U. S. Patent 2,951,106 (Aug. 30, 1960).

RUETSCHI, P., AND CAHAN, B., "Sealed Cells Employing the Hydrogen Cycle," U. S. Patent 3,080,440 (March 5, 1963).

SMYTH, J. R., "Maintenance-free Lead Storage Batteries," paper presented at Lead Industries Association Meeting, St. Louis, May, 1962.

CAMERON, D. B., "Alkaline Manganese Batteries," *Electronics World*, **66**, 33 (Oct., 1961).

RUBEN, S., "Sealed Mercury Cells," U. S. Patent 2,554,504 (May 29, 1951).

GOLDBERG, M. B., AND REED, H. B., JR., (to U. S. Government), U. S. Patent 2,697,736 (Dec. 21, 1954). Extended Abstracts, Battery Division of Electrochemical Society, p. 33, Oct., 1957, "Sealed Silver-Lead Cell."

W. S. HERBERT

Cross-references: other entries with *Batteries* designation.

BATTERIES, SOLAR. See SOLAR ENERGY CONVERTER.

BATTERIES, SOLID ELECTROLYTE

All oxidation-reduction reactions involve a transfer of electrons from the reducing agent to the oxidizing agent. A battery is simply an electrochemical device which forces the electron transfer to take place through an external circuit where it can do work. This is usually accomplished by interposing a layer of an appropriate aqueous acid, base or salt solution between the oxidant and the reductant. Such solutions are insulators to electron flow, while permitting internal ionic charge transport to compensate for external electronic flow.

Thus, in the conventional Leclanché "dry" cell (which is not really dry in a chemical sense), a zinc electrode faces an electrode of manganese dioxide but is separated from it by a starch-immobilized layer of an aqueous solution of zinc and ammonium chlorides. The anode reaction is zinc metal transforming to divalent zinc ions with the release of two electrons. The cathode reaction is tetravalent manganese being reduced to trivalent manganese through the assimilation of one electron. Since the interposed aqueous salt solution is an electronic insulator, neither of these reactions can take place if the required electron transfer is blocked by an open external circuit. When the circuit is closed, however, electrons can flow from the zinc electrode (with simultaneous release of zinc ions to the solution) to the manganese dioxide electrodes where they are assimilated (with simultaneous assimilation of positive ions, ideally zinc ions, from the solution).

Aqueous Solutions as Battery Electrolytes

There are several important advantages favoring the use of aqueous solutions as the electronically-insulative, ionically-conductive electrode separator in batteries: they can be made to exhibit a relatively high ionic conductivity, thus reducing internal IR voltage drop during subsequent battery discharge; their composition can easily be balanced and controlled to yield compatability with a wide variety of anode and cathode materials; they can wet and permeate into powdered or porous anode and cathode materials to facilitate easy ionic migration throughout the entire active mass during discharge; and they have a physical mobility which permits them to compensate for gross-electrode volume changes which may occur as a consequence of discharge (e.g., as the zinc electrode in the Leclanché cell dissolves, the electrolyte slowly flows to maintain contact with the receding zinc surface).

There are also some disadvantages associated with the use of aqueous electrolytes. The first is that such solutions tend to creep and in small batteries, where thin cell components are usually stacked in a repeating sequence to fabricate multicell batteries, the critical creep distance between the electrolytes of adjacent cells can be dangerously small. Even a tiny ionic contact between adjacent cell electrolytes detracts from overall battery shelf-life even if all other adjacent cell electrolytes are perfectly separated.

Another disadvantage is that aqueous electrolytes have appreciable vapor pressure so that cells must be carefully sealed to prevent evaporation losses (or, if the solutions are deliquescent, to prevent moisture absorption). Such sealing can become quite critical if there is a possibility that some unwanted internal side reaction liberates a gas (hydrogen, oxygen or carbon dioxide) which must be vented.

Both of these disadvantages become progressively more pronounced as cell size becomes smaller and smaller. One can synthesize a rather convincing argument that problems of long-time control, confinement, and containment of aqueous electrolytes are the basic factors which determine the miniaturization limit of conventional aqueous electrolyte battery systems. Thus, if the future brings with it a requirement for cells considerably smaller than those now available, the battery industry will probably be forced to search for electrolytes considerably more immobile than those now in use.

A third, and rather obvious, disadvantage of aqueous electrolytes is that they lose practically all of their ionic conductivity when they freeze. In addition, the boiling point of the electrolyte imposes a limit to the maximum temperature at which the battery is operative. Another disadvantage, although perhaps subtle, is that cells using aqueous electrolyte cannot have a really tight and rugged internal structure since high internal packaging pressures would tend to lower the electrolyte's physical ability to separate anode and cathode materials.

It should be emphasized that these disadvantages become of practical significance only when one attempts to make truly miniature batteries without sacrifice of shelf-life.

Solid Ionic Conductors

Background. It has been known for quite some time that certain solid salts exhibit, like aqueous solutions, the property of being ionically conductive and electronically insulative. For example, solid silver iodide between silver electrodes will exhibit an electrical conductivity which Tubandt[1] has shown to be due substantially solely to silver ions moving through a rather open crystalline lattice of iodide ions, and that electronic transport or movement of iodide ions is so small as to be negligible for all practical purposes. Silver chloride and silver bromide behave in a similar manner, although there seems to be some evidence of trace electronic transport at room temperature.[2]

In other cases the conductivity may be completely anionic (e.g., chloride ions moving through $PbCl_2$ or oxide ions through a ZrO_2-CaO ceramic at high temperatures). The conductivity may also be mixed cationic-anionic (e.g., 90 per cent potassium ion and 10 per cent iodide ion through potassium iodide at 610°C). In still other cases (e.g., CuCl) the conductivity can be completely electronic at room temperature, becoming completely cationic as the temperature increases. Friauf[3] has prepared a complete yet remarkably concise tabulation of the conductivity at various temperatures of a large number of solid salts. Lidiard[4] has given a com-

TABLE 1. SOLID ELECTROLYTE BATTERY SYTEMS
UNDER INVESTIGATION IN 1957

System	Cell voltage	Studied by	Refs.
Ag/AgBr/CuBr$_2$	0.74	General Electric Co.	10
Ni-Cr/SnSO$_4$/PbO$_2$	1.2–1.5	P. R. Mallory & Ray-O-Vac	11
Ag/AgI/V$_2$O$_5$	0.46	National Carbon Co.	12
Ag/AgBr-Te/CuBr$_2$	0.80	Patterson-Moos Research	13
Ag/AgCl/KICl$_4$	1.04	Sprague Electric Co.	14

prehensive discussion of the underlying theories emerging from studies of ionic transport through solids, describing the pioneering work of Frenkel, Schottky, Wagner, *et al*, and indicating some interesting avenues that future work may explore in this approach to a better understanding of the solid state.

Solid Ionic Conductors as Battery Electrolytes. Ionically conductive, electronically-insulative solid salts can, of course, be used as the electrolyte of an appropriate solid electrolyte battery. As a matter of fact, primitive cell systems of this type were studied as early as the turn of the century.[5] Interest in such batteries as sources of power, however, did not develop until the early and middle 1950's when Sator,[6] Lehovec and Broder,[7] and van der Grinten,[8] all working independently and with different systems, demonstrated operational feasibility.

These initial efforts implied the basic advantages associated with the use of solid electrolytes; i.e., easy miniaturization through mechanized production, promise of sharply increased shelf-life despite decreased size, improved operational capabilities at higher storage and discharge temperatures, and extremely rugged construction. They also highlighted a major serious disadvantage—a very high internal resistance. This high resistance follows directly from the observed fact that even the most conductive solid salts have specific conductances at room temperature which are from four to seven *orders of magnitude* less than those of most aqueous solutions used as battery electrolytes.

Despite this major shortcoming of high internal resistance, interest in solid electrolyte batteries with their promise of unique advan-

tages was quite high and by 1957, as Shapiro[9] pointed out, five major battery systems began to emerge. These are summarized in Table 1. Development was quite rapid and by 1961 practically all of the concerns involved were in a position to supply solid electrolyte batteries to the market-place or had furnished prototype batteries for test and evaluation by interested potential users.

The development work on these systems did in fact confirm the predicted and unique advantages associated with the use of solid electrolytes. Truly miniature batteries were indeed possible with packaged volumes yielding a voltage "density" as high as about 100 volts per cc. Despite this small cell size shelf-life was quite high at an estimated 10 to 20 years. Manufacture could easily be mechanized (see especially Ref. 12). Finished batteries were operational at and apparently unharmed by temperatures approaching 100°C with some systems. Packaging could be made exceptionally sturdy and rugged.

However, the development work also brought into bold relief the major disadvantage; all battery systems exhibited a very high internal resistance which combined with other polarization losses on discharge to drop specific output to about 0.01 to 0.02 watt-hour per cc at *microampere* drains. This specific output is discouragingly low compared to the better aqueous electrolyte systems with their specific output of 0.25 to 0.35 watt-hours per cc at *milliampere* drains. Thus, at this time (Fall, 1963) only the Sprague system battery is apparently still being produced.

In the Sprague process assembly begins by making a tiny cup (see Fig. 1) out of silver con-

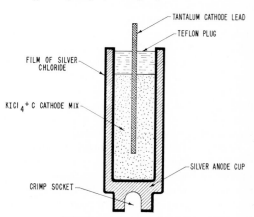

FIG. 1. The Sprague solid electrolyte cell.

taining deliberately added cadmium. This cup is then chlorinated at elevated temperatures to cover the can with a tough, adherent coating of AgCl containing some $CdCl_2$. The presence of divalent cadmium ions in the AgCl crystal lattice creates cation lattice vacancies which serve to increase the ionic conductivity of AgCl. The cup is then filled with an extruded cathodic mix slug consisting of solid $KICl_4$, carbon black and Kel-F ✗90 grease (a product of Minnesota Mining and Manufacturing Company added to protect against trace electronic conductivity in the AgCl). Cell assembly is completed with insertion of a tantalum cathode lead wire and a small Teflon plug. Battery assembly involves mechanical crimping of the tantalum cathode wire of one cell into the crimp socket of another with resultant battery strings, separated by an interleaved Teflon foil, being folded into any desired configuration. The folded strings are then inserted into an appropriate metal container and interstices filled with encapsulating compound.

A commercially available 150 volt Sprague battery has a volume of 16.2 cc, a dead-short flash current of 10 to 20 microamperes, an internal resistance of about 30 megohms, and a total available charge of 10 coulombs. Such a battery can charge a 0.05 microfarad capacitor to 90 per cent charge in 3 seconds, increasing to 15 seconds for a 0.25 microfarad capacitor. Shelf-life is estimated as being in excess of 20 years. Recovery of open circuit voltage after prolonged dead short is essentially instantaneous.

The batteries are particularly well-suited for maintaining a charge on low-leakage capacitors for intermittent discharge through small neon tubes, or to activate a fuse or detonator circuit. They can also be used for direct powering of high-voltage, low-drain devices, such as Geiger counters, scintillation counters or photomultiplier tubes. The batteries can deliver 0.1 microamperes continuously for over 10,000 hours; should be operable at temperatures up to 100°C and at very high pressures; and blasts of nuclear radiation are without noticeable effect.

The low specific output of presently available solid electrolyte batteries, as mentioned above, is their most serious shortcoming. It originates because of low ionic mobilities through the electrolyte and into the cathodic mix. Since the ionic conductivity of all solid ionic conductors increases with temperature, it would be expected that specific output would be improved with higher temperatures and especially so with silver iodide which undergoes a phase transformation at about 145°C into a particularly conductive alpha-phase. Weininger[15] designed and built high-temperature batteries of the type $Ag/AgI/CsI_4$ which showed just this type of improvement when discharged at 300°C.

It is also possible that the room-temperature conductivity of some solid electrolytes can be significantly increased through pretreatment of powdered materials to increase surface conductivity and to lower the resistance across the interface between touching particles in the compressed powder.[16]

Another area which might warrant exploratory effort involves the possibility of rechargeable solid electrolyte batteries along lines suggested by Sator.[6] The technical difficulty here will probably involve prevention of "tree" formation when anode material is plated back on the anode during the charge cycle. It is possible that this prevention can be accomplished through use of amalgamated anodes.[16]

This discussion of solid electrolytes cannot be concluded without reference to their possible use in high temperature fuel cells.[17] One electrolyte now being studied rather intensively is a thin ceramic wafer of 85 per cent ZrO_2 and 15 per cent CaO. Transport through this material is due substantially solely to migration of divalent oxide ions. Although the room temperature conductivity is prohibitively low, it increases rapidly with temperature, being about 10^{-4}ohm^{-1}cm^{-1} at 600°C, 2.5×10^{-3} at 800° and 1.7×10^{-2} at 1000°C. In a cell of the type

$$H_2, \; Pt \mid 0.85ZrO_2 \cdot 0.15CaO \mid Pt, \; O_2$$

(where the Pt serves a dual purpose as catalyst and pick-off electrode), the cathode process is oxygen gas producing oxide ions (with assimilation of electrons from the external circuit). The oxide ions migrate through the ceramic electrolyte to form water with the hydrogen ions generated by the anode process which involves oxidation of hydrogen gas and liberation of electrons, the latter, of course, being supplied to the external circuit for delivery to the cathode process.

A measure of the success of this effort will be the degree to which oxide ion conductivity through the ceramic can be maximized, as well as the chemical and structural stability of the ceramic in service and its impermeability to gases.

References

1. TUBANDT, C., *Z. Elektrochem.*, **26**, 358 (1920); *Z. anorg. allgem. Chem.*, **115**, 105 (1921).
2. LUCKEY, G., AND WEST, E., *J. Chem. Phys.*, **24**, 879 (1956); SHAMOVSKII, L., DUNINA, A., AND GOSTEVA, M., *Soviet Phys., JETP*, **3**, 511 (1956); LUCKEY, G., *Faraday Soc. Discussions*, **28**, 113 (1959).
3. FRIAUF, R. J., "American Institute of Physics Handbook," D. E. Gray, Ed., pgs. 185–197, New York, McGraw-Hill Book Co., 1957.
4. LIDIARD, A. B., "Encyclopedia of Physics," **22**, 246–349, Berlin, Springer, 1957.
5. CZEPINSKI, V., AND WEBER, O. H., *Z. anorg. Chem.*, **19**, 208 (1899); LORENZ, R., *ibid.*, **19**, 283 (1899) and **22**, 241 (1900); SUCHY, R., *ibid.*, **27**, 152 (1901); HABER, F., AND TOLLOCZKO, ST., *ibid.*, **41**, 407 (1904); KATAYAMA, M., *Z. physik. Chem.*, **61**, 566 (1908).
6. SATOR, A., *Comp. rend.*, **234**, 2283 (1952).
7. LEHOVEC, K., AND BRODER, J., *J. Electrochem. Soc.*, **101**, 208 (1954).
8. VAN DER GRINTEN, W. J., *J. Electrochem. Soc.*, **103**, 201C (1956).
9. SHAPIRO, S. J., Proc. Eleventh Annual Battery R & D Conference, Fort Monmouth, New Jersey, p. 3, 1957.
10. WAGNER, B. F., *Electronic Design*, p. 44, Oct. 1, 1957; VAN DER GRINTEN, W. J., U.S. Pat. 2,793,244 (May 21, 1957); VAN DER GRINTEN, W. J. AND MOHLER, D., U.S. Pat. 2,928,890 (March 15, 1960); WEININGER, J. L., AND LEIBHAFSKY, H. A., U.S. Pat. 2,987,568 (June 6, 1961).
11. RUBEN, S., U. S. Patents 2,707,199 (April 26, 1955); 2,816,151 (Dec. 10, 1957); 2,852,591 (Sept. 16, 1958).
12. LOUZOS, D. V., U. S. Pat. 2,894,053 (July 7, 1959); EVANS, G. E., U. S. Pat. 2,894,052 (July 7, 1959); BUCHINSKI, J. J., ET AL., U. S. Pat. 2,932,569 (April 12, 1960); RICHTER, E. W., SHELLEK, D., MCMILLAN, H. E., AND EVANS, G. E., U. S. Pat. 3,004,093 (October 10, 1961).
13. LIEB, H. C., U. S. Pat. 2,930,830 (March 29, 1960).
14. SMYTH, D. M., AND CUTLER, M. E., *J. Am. Chem. Soc.*, **80**, 4462 (1958); SMYTH, D. M., *J. Electrochem. Soc.*, **106**, 635 (1959); anon., *Sprague Engineering Bulletin, No. 11,101* (March, 1962); SMYTH, D. M., AND SHIRN, G. A., U. S. Pat. 2,905,740 (Sept. 22, 1959).
15. WEININGER, J. L., *J. Electrochem. Soc.*, **105**, 439 (1958); *ibid.*, **106**, 475 (1959); U. S. Patents 2,890,259 (June 9, 1959), 2,933,546 (April 19, 1960), and 3,003,017 (Oct. 3, 1961).
16. MRGUDICH, J. N., *J. Electrochem. Soc.*, **107**, 475 (1960).
17. KINGERY, W. D., PAPPIS, J., DOTY, M. E., AND HILL, D. C., *J. Am. Ceram. Soc.*, **42**, 394 (1959); "Fuel Cells," G. J. Young, Ed., contributions by E. B. Shultz, Jr., K. S. Vorres, L. G. Marianowski and H. R. Linden and J. Weissbart and R. Ruka, Vol. 2, New York, Reinhold Publishing Corp., 1963.

JOHN N. MRGUDICH

BATTERIES, STORAGE

The storage battery (secondary battery, accumulator) is a familiar and casually accepted device in this age of the automobile. It is a useful source of instant energy. As such, it has also found an important place in industry and in installations serving the public need. The increasing use of energy as revealed by the developments of the first half of the 20th century and as projected for the future use, leads to the prognostication that the storage battery will continue its role as an auxiliary of power systems. Its role will not be dimmed in a world depending on nuclear and solar power.

The storage battery is an electrochemical device which is capable of storing and yielding energy by the interconversion of chemical energy and electrical energy, the latter in the form of direct current. The fundamental unit of this device, the storage cell or storage battery, is the galvanic cell, an electrolytic cell whose principal parts in its simplest and generalized form so familiar in electrochemistry are positive and negative electrodes placed in juxtaposition and separated by a layer of electrolyte, current leads to the electrodes which are connected through an external circuit, and a container. The cells may be assembled in series or in parallel, most commonly in series, and occasionally wired for combinations for special reasons.

The energy rating of a battery may be expressed in terms of watt-hours and more commonly, in terms of the capacity in ampere-hours and the average voltage, as determined under specified conditions of initial or ambient battery temperature, discharge current, electrolyte composition, and final discharge voltage. The energy relationships are controlled on the theoretical side by the laws of thermodynamics, and in particular by the properties of the Gibbs free energy function. For the practical case, these theoretical and fundamental considerations are supplemented by those phenomena ascribable to electrochemical kinetics, including activation and transfer overvoltages characteristic of the electrode reaction and the nature of the electrode, internal resistance, and mass transfer.

The storage and interconversion of energy in the storage battery is achieved through the agency of a chemical reaction whose direction is determined by that of the current. Such a reaction may be represented by the general equation,

$$A_{(OX)} + B_{(RED)} \underset{r}{\overset{f}{\rightleftharpoons}} A_{(RED)} + B_{(OX)} \qquad (1)$$

where OX and RED represent the oxidized and reduced forms of the species A and B, f corresponds to the discharge reaction, and r to the charge reaction. This general reaction is the sum of two electrode or oxidation-reduction reactions, namely

$$A_{(OX)} + ne^- \underset{r}{\overset{f}{\rightleftharpoons}} A_{(RED)} \qquad (2a)$$

$$B_{(RED)} \underset{r}{\overset{f}{\rightleftharpoons}} B_{(OX)} + ne^- \qquad (2b)$$

The chemical species, A and B, consisting of chemical elements, oxides, hydroxides, and salts, are called the active materials, although this term is commonly also used to designate the materials in the form in which they are incorporated into the electrodes and often to the composite material including addition and modifying agents.

In the f or forward direction of Eq. (1), the cell is under discharge and delivers current and energy to the external circuit. In this state of operation, the positive electrode is the cathode and its reaction is represented by Eq. (2a) proceeding from left to right, as written, while the negative electrode is the anode, with its reaction represented by Eq. (2b). In this state of use, the storage battery operates in the same manner as a primary battery and in principle is indistinguishable in terms of the conversion of chemical energy to electrical energy.

In the r or reverse direction of the reaction according to Eq. (1), the cell is under charge with electrical energy being converted to chemical energy. Any convenient source of direct current may be used for the charging process. This property of accepting a charge, that is, the conversion of electrical energy into chemical energy or the restoration of the active materials to the compositions of matter corresponding to

the ability to function as a primary cell, over many cycles consisting of discharge and charge portions, characterizes the secondary cell. However, the distinction is utilitarian and there have been reports of the conditions under which primary cells may be recharged using due precautions.

The discharge capacity and charge acceptance measured in ampere-hours, coulombs, or faradays are directly related in terms of the electrode construction to the amount of active material incorporated into the electrodes in accordance with the electrochemical equivalents derivable from Eqs. (1) and (2), and the efficiency of their use, often called the coefficient of utilization. The former quantity is fixed theoretically and in this regard the battery technologist and scientist seeks to find practical oxidation-reduction reactions with the highest possible energy-weight or energy-volume ratios. In the matter of the coefficient of utilization, the research is oriented to the highest possible level over a wide range of temperature and current consistent with long life and a minimum of attention.

The theoretical capacities of the positive and negative electrodes and the discharge capacities for a set of conditions need not be the same; the capacity of the positive or negative electrodes may be determined by measuring the voltage curve obtained by using a suitable reference electrode. Under ordinary conditions of use with the storage battery as the source of current for the external use circuit or in parallel with a fixed polarity from a primary source, the capacity on discharge will be controlled by the exhaustion of the electrode with the lower capacity, commonly termed the limiting electrode. On exhaustion, the current in the external circuit will fall to zero. On charge, with current supplied by an external source having ample power, current flow may be continued indefinitely even after the electrodes are fully charged. The completion of electrode reactions (2a) and (2b) and the exhaustion of the uncharged active materials, $A_{(OX)}$ and $B_{(RED)}$, are followed by the electrolysis of the solvent water in the electrolyte solution. This electrolysis produces oxygen gas at the positive electrode and hydrogen gas at the negative electrode. This state is generally referred to as overcharging. It is responsible for the need for watering along with the attendant evaporation and it decreases the efficiency of utilization of the primary power. It is also the reason for providing vented closures, thus avoiding the accumulation of an explosive mixture of hydrogen and oxygen gas under pressure in the container.

Thermodynamically, the electrolysis of water should occur preferentially to the charge reactions for the practical active materials used in storage batteries. The overvoltages for the evolution of hydrogen and oxygen on the active materials and electrodes are such that under battery operating conditions, the charging of the active materials becomes the favored reaction. This is the fortunate circumstance that makes the storage battery a reality. The battery chemist is often plagued with the overlapping of the charge and electrolysis reactions. This is another rich field for research and speculation which may lead to improved batteries.

Electrochemical Reactions

The generalized reaction (1) represents only the apparent overall change of the active materials on charge or discharge. It is a useful means for representing the system, and it is basic in the evolution of the understanding of the principles of operation. The role of the solvent water in the electrolyte insofar as it takes part in the reaction is obscured mainly because information on the changes of hydration of the active materials on reaction is not known with certainty. The exact knowledge is of importance when considering the electrode reaction mechanisms, highly accurate thermodynamic calculations, ageing effects, and phase changes. Similarly, the ions of the electrolyte may and do participate directly in the electrode reactions and are sometimes involved in the phase changes that occur during charge or discharge. The principal function of the electrolyte is to provide ions for the conduction of current by ion migration and thus permit the separation of the overall reaction into component parts.

The reactions in each of the principal storage battery systems will be given in the following, representing the usual overall and electrode reactions by accepted equations. These will then be amplified with statements regarding the implied side effects, often recognized by battery chemists and engineers, but for which there is generally a range of disagreement on the exact representation.

Lead-acid System. The general reaction,

often referred to as the double-sulfate or Gladstone-Tribe reaction, is represented by the following equation:

$$PbO_2 + Pb + 2H_2SO_4 \underset{r}{\overset{f}{\rightleftharpoons}} 2PbSO_4 + 2H_2O \qquad (1a)$$

and the electrode reactions by:

$$PbO_2 + 4H^+ + SO_4^{--} + 2e^- \underset{r}{\overset{f}{\rightleftharpoons}}$$
$$\qquad (2a\text{-}i)$$
$$PbSO_4 + 2H_2O$$

$$Pb + SO_4^{--} \underset{r}{\overset{f}{\rightleftharpoons}} PbSO_4 + 2e^- \qquad (2b\text{-}i)$$

where the reaction in the f direction corresponds to the discharge reaction and in the r direction to the charge reaction.

These reactions show an involvement of the solute ions in the operation of the storage cell with the well-known decrease in sulfuric acid concentration in the electrolyte during discharge. This effect permits the estimation of the state of charge; it also indicates the reason for the limitation in performance at high rates of discharge where sulfate ion migration may be the limiting factor.

Nickel-iron System

Nickel-cadmium System

$$2Ni(OH)_3 + Fe \underset{r}{\overset{f}{\rightleftharpoons}} 2Ni(OH)_2 + Fe(OH)_2 \quad (1b)$$

or

$$2NiOOH + Fe + 2H_2O \underset{r}{\overset{f}{\rightleftharpoons}}$$
$$\qquad (1b')$$
$$2Ni(OH)_2 + Fe(OH)_2$$

$$2NiOOH + 2H_2O + 2e^- \underset{r}{\overset{f}{\rightleftharpoons}}$$
$$\qquad (2a\text{-}ii)$$
$$2Ni(OH)_2 + 2(OH)^-$$

$$Fe + 2(OH)^- \underset{r}{\overset{f}{\rightleftharpoons}} Fe(OH)_2 + 2e^- \quad (2b\text{-}ii)$$

For the corresponding reactions in the nickel-cadmium system, substitute Cd for Fe in Eqs. (1b), (1b'), (2a-ii), and (2b-ii). These equations are idealized versions of the reactions which are suitable as the basis of expressing the system. Studies in recent years have shown that the positive active nickel hydroxides undergo some change in hydration and that the positive ions, K^+ and Li^+, may take part in the electrode reaction at the positive electrode. Also on charge, some of the active material of the nickel electrode is presumably oxidized to tetravalent nickel with additional complications in the phase changes and subsequent behavior on standing in the charged state. There is under question at this time whether the mechanisms of the transformation of the phases occur through a solid state process or through solution process and recrystallization.

Silver-zinc System

$$Ag_2O_2 + 4KOH + 2Zn \xrightleftharpoons[r]{f}$$

$$2Ag + 2K_2ZnO_2 + 2H_2O \qquad (1c)$$

$$Ag_2O_2 + 2Zn \xrightleftharpoons[r]{f} 2Ag + 2ZnO \qquad (1c')$$

$$Ag_2O_2 + H_2O + 2e^- \xrightleftharpoons[r]{f} Ag_2O + 2(OH)^- \qquad (2a\text{-iii})$$

$$Ag_2O + H_2O + 2e^- \xrightleftharpoons[r]{f} 2Ag + 2(OH)^- \qquad (2a\text{-iv})$$

$$Zn + 4(OH)^- \xrightleftharpoons[r]{f} Zn(OH)_4^{--} + 2e^- \qquad (2b\text{-iii})$$

The overall reaction here will depend on the state of the electrolyte; it is probable that both reactions may represent the chemistry depending on the amount of zincate in the electrolyte and the tendency for supersaturation at the operating conditions. The ideal condition is that by which the migration of soluble zinc away from the electrode body is prevented.

In the case of the silver electrode, there are successive reactions, each represented by a voltage plateau. Theoretically, the lengths of the plateaus should be equal; in practice the plateau corresponding to Eq. (2a-iii) is shorter both on charge and discharge, and may disappear completely on discharge at high rates. The electrode reaction at the positive is influenced by the fact that silver (I) oxide, Ag_2O, is a compound having a high electrical resistance and by the thermodynamics permitting the interaction of silver and silver (II) oxide, AgO, to produce silver (I) oxide, according to the reaction,

$$Ag + AgO \rightarrow Ag_2O. \qquad (3)$$

Types and Classifications

Storage batteries are generally classified under two broad headings, namely, by chemical type and by use. Each of these broad types is further classified by a design feature in the first case and by service as stationary or portable in the second case. This dual system of classification has arisen to provide easy reference within frameworks of discussion and to meet the practical need for specifications whose provisions are aimed at minimum requirements to meet the needs in a particular service.

The chemical types that are available from battery manufacturers on a standard procurement basis can be classified by the nature of the electrolyte, namely, acid and alkaline batteries. Except for special uses, the acid batteries use sulfuric acid solutions having specific gravities (60/60°F) of 1.200 to 1.280; generally the lower gravity acid solutions are used in stationary batteries and the higher gravity solutions for portable batteries. Acid batteries generally use lead for the active material and are known as lead or lead-acid batteries. In addition lead batteries may be classified as lead-calcium batteries to indicate that the grid alloy consists of an alloy of lead and calcium, in amounts less than 0.12 per cent, to distinguish from the commonly used lead-antimony alloys.

The alkaline batteries utilize potassium hydroxide solutions varying in concentration from 20 to 45 per cent by weight or 4 to 12 N, usually containing lithium hydroxide for the nickel-iron type, and often added zinc oxide for the silver batteries. It is also customary to classify the alkaline batteries by the principal metallic constituent of the positive and negative active materials, as for example, nickel-iron, nickel-cadmium, silver-zinc, and silver-cadmium, which are the principal types in use. The nickel-zinc alkaline battery has not developed into a commercial type despite extensive studies and tests in the Irish Free State in the thirties.

In addition to the above types of alkaline batteries, developments over the past decade have brought forth a new classification, namely sealed types (q.v.). The previously cited types are referred to as vented types because of the provision of vented openings, often valved, to permit the escape of gas during charge. The sealed cells are permanently sealed, often as nearly hermetically as possible by modern techniques. Sealed nickel-cadmium and silver-cadmium cells and batteries are available commercially, while the sealed silver-zinc batteries are under development and were used successfully in the Mariner II project to study the planet Venus.

Storage batteries when classified by use include the following:

Automobile, often referred to as SLI or Starting, Lighting, and Ignition.
Aircraft
Aerospace or satellite
Emergency lighting
Engine starting
Diesel engine starting
Fire alarm
Marine
Missile
Mine lamp
Railway signalling
Railway car lighting and air conditioning
Radio and radiomarine
Switchgear control
Submarine
Telephone
Truck and tractor motive power
Torpedo

The battery types, sizes, and configurations that are available in these classifications can satisfy most needs except for special and unusual installations. The batteries are available in capacities from fractional ampere-hours to over ten thousand ampere-hours having space requirements from about 0.1 cubic inch (2 cc) to several hundred cubic feet. The battery may consist of a single cell, assemblages of single cells, or convenient packages of multicell trays corresponding to the desired nominal operating voltage of the system. Most applications can be covered by batteries for 6, 12, 24, 32, 64, 120 and 240 volt systems.

Battery Voltage

The theoretical voltage or electromotive force of a cell is an intensive thermodynamic property of the exact cell reaction under equilibrium conditions and differs in this respect from the capacity, which is an extensive property of the system. The electromotive force of a reaction, such as represented by Eq. (1), is determined at a fixed temperature by the thermodynamic relationship expressed by the equation,

$$E = -G/n\mathbf{F} \qquad (4)$$

where E is the electromotive force, G is the Gibbs free energy function for the reaction determined at the equilibrium activities, n is the number of electrons involved in the electrode

reactions, and $\mathbf{F}$ is the Faraday constant equal to 23,062 calories per volt equivalent when G is expressed in calories. For ordinary conditions, the nominal values of the cell voltage for the various types of storage cells are as follows:

Lead-acid	2.0	volts per cell
Nickel-cadmium	1.3	" " "
Nickel-iron	1.35	" " "
Silver-zinc	1.8	" " "
Silver-cadmium	1.4	" " "

The voltage during the discharge of a battery at a given temperature will depend on the discharge rate, which for any battery may be expressed in amperes, amperes per positive plate, time-rate as minutes or hours of discharge, or in fractions or multiples of the nominal or rated capacity, as C_5/t, where C_5 is the nominal capacity at the 5-hour rate of discharge in ampere-hours and t is the time of discharge, in hours. Each rating is ultimately related to an average current density of discharge. Increase in the rate and, correspondingly, in the current density brings about a decrease in average discharge voltage. In many applications, particularly at high rates required in such applications as switch gear control and engine starting, a minimum final discharge voltage is the controlling feature of the specification. The number of cells in a battery is usually selected on the basis of the average voltage on discharge at rates corresponding to the range in the 5-hour to 20-hour rates after ascertaining that the high rate discharge requirements will be met and that the battery charging installation is adequate to achieve recharging in the allowable time.

References

See reference list for subsequent entry: **Batteries, Storage-Design and Operation.**

Arthur Fleischer

Cross-references: Other entries with *Batteries* designation; *Overvoltage*; *Planté*; *Polarization*; *Reference Electrodes.*

BATTERIES, STORAGE—DESIGN AND OPERATION

Battery Design

The practical battery within the broad ranges of capacity and voltage has developed in many forms and structural designs. The most common cell shape is that of a rectangular parallelopiped. The cell container and cover accomodating the cell posts and vent cap must be resistant to corrosion by the electrolyte solution and environment. For lead-acid batteries, the common materials are hard rubber, rubber-base bituminous compositions, and molded synthetic thermoplastics, while for the alkaline batteries, the materials are nickel-clad or nickel-plated steel, occasionally stainless steel, and thermoplastics.

The interior working volume of the cell may be divided into three parts, the bottom space, the element space, and the gas space which is just below the cover of the cell. The element space, usually occupying the bulk of the volume, is occupied by the element, the assembly of electrodes, separators, group straps, and posts, which will be recognized as the very heart of the working battery. The electrodes or plates in the usual industrial connotation are assembled by interleafing the positive and negative plate groups along with insulating separators. The electrolyte occupies the bottom space, all of the unfilled volume of the element space including the pore or void volumes of the plates and separators, and usually some part of the gas space.

The plates, usually rectangular in shape, vary in thickness up to 0.375 inch (9.5 mm). The thickness, area, and number of plates in a storage cell will always be subject to the demands and requirements imposed by economic and manufacturing considerations; on the technical side, the performance of the plates in terms of the current density for the particular active materials will provide the basis of design. Generally speaking, increase in current density will depress the voltage curve and the utilization of the active material on discharge. In design, the decrease of the average current density on a plate is achieved by providing greater area of plate, and since the volume is usually fixed, this means a decrease in the plate thickness. The minimum practical plate thickness will depend to a high degree on the type of construction and the required strength to resist environmental conditions, especially vibration and shock.

The plate must provide for two important operating functions: first, it must be a carrier for the active material which is usually in the form of a finely-divided material having a high surface area, and second, it must have a satisfactorily low electrical resistivity for uniform distribution of the current to all of the active material. These two problems of design are interrelated; plate design has evolved in a number of forms, of which only a few will be described here.

The most widely used type of plate, particularly in the manufacture of lead-acid storage batteries and universally used for automotive batteries, is the Faure or pasted plate. The plate consists of a lattice grid, usually cast of antimonial lead alloy which imparts the desired mechanical properties, into whose open spaces there is applied a paste of active material. The properties of the paste are adjusted to permit a cementing of the mixture to form a coherent porous structure. The art of formulating the paste of active material and its subsequent formation by supplementary processes to produce plates meeting service and life requirements requires an integration of skill, knowledge and experience in blending science, technology and manufacturing.

The pasted plate has to a large extent replaced the original type of lead plate, the Planté type, in which the surface of the lead is formed chemically or electrochemically to produce the desired form of adherent active material. The Planté plate is still in use for stationary applications. Many types of plates incorporating special features have been utilized over the past 100 years of using lead-acid batteries and are in use for special applications. The most prominent of these types is the "Ironclad" whose construction consists of a series of vertical tubes having an outer tube of a porous or slotted nonconductive material, such as woven fabric treated with suitable plastic or plastic tubing, an inner lead spine, and having active material filling the available space. The "Ironclad" type of positive plate is used extensively for batteries in truck and tractor motive power service.

The positive and negative plates of the element are prevented from touching, and thus short-circuiting by providing an electronic flow path, by means of insulating separators. The simplest type is some form of spacer and these in the form of hard-rubber composition or plastic rods are in use in alkaline nickel-iron and nickel-cadmium batteries of the pocket or tubular-plate types, in which the spacing of the plates is adequate. In most secondary batteries, however, the separator is required to serve additional functions. The solubilities of the active materials, such as of lead in sulfuric acid or of silver and zinc in the potassium hydroxide solution, and the tendency for cataphoresis of finely-divided particles of the active materials may be such under certain operating conditions to permit growth and treeing with the result that short circuits are formed between the plates. Because of such effects, it is usual to use sheets of porous, ion-permeable materials between the plates. For many years, specially treated wood was the standard separator in lead-acid batteries. In recent years there have been developed many suitable materials, such as resin-impregnated cellulose, nonwoven synthetic fibers, microporous rubber and plastics, and combinations of woven and nonwoven materials. The search for materials with improved properties continues since the life of batteries in many applications is limited by the changes that occur in a progressive manner as the separator properties change on use and exposure to the electrolyte and the alternating conditions of oxidation and reduction.

For the alkaline nickel batteries, constructions are available in the pocket or tubular types and in the sintered-plate type. In the former, restraining envelopes of tubular shape or flat pocket are made of perforated steel strip, usually nickel plated. These envelopes are filled with the desired active material and then assembled in plate form to the desired size. The flat pockets may be of a definite small size as in the case of the usual iron negative plate or cut from continuous strip to the width of the plate as is the usual case for nickel-cadmium plates. Tubular plates are generally the positive nickel plates, universally used for nickel plates of the nickel-iron batteries.

In the sintered-plate type of construction, carbonyl nickel powder is sintered to a thin metal grid, such as wire mesh cloth, to form a coherent porous matrix having a porosity of about 80 per cent. These plaques are impregnated with nickel or cadmium hydroxides to obtain positive or negative plates, respectively. This type of construction for a battery plate represents an ideal situation in providing a continuous conducting matrix, a high surface area of contact with the active material, a substantial pore system to hold electrolyte, and in the present case a marked resistance of the nickel to corrosion processes.

For the alkaline silver batteries, plates are made by pasting, sintering, and electrolytic deposition procedures, depending on the end-use and type of battery. Silver plates made by sintering silver powder or silver (I) oxide—silver sinters readily at comparatively low temperature in air—are subjected to electrolytic formation to convert the silver to the oxide form, generally to silver (II) oxide. One form of plate uses sintered nickel plaques which are impregnated with silver similarly to the sintered-plate nickel-cadmium type. Zinc plates are generally made by electrolytic deposition of porous dendritic zinc, usually involving compression to the desired thickness. Plates made by pasting zinc oxide or cadmium oxide or by assembly of dry powders with binders are subjected to electrolytic formation and compression. As knowledge and experience accrues in the technology of special types of batteries, there will undoubtedly be a simplification of procedures and a trend to adopt the most economic methods.

Charging of Batteries

The restoration of the battery to the charged (by usual definition meaning the fully charged state) condition is an important part of the operation in service for many reasons besides the obvious requirement to meet the demands for use. The choice of the charging method will depend, among other things, on the type of service. The types of service can be described as cycle service, floating service including trickle charging, and a wide variety of services intermediate in character between the two general types. In cycle service, the battery may be charged during a stated interval, subsequent to which, with or without an idle period or open-circuit stand as it might be called, the battery is discharged. A good example of this type of service is found in motive power batteries as used, for example, in fork lift trucks.

The basic methods of charging batteries for cycle service are the constant-current and constant-potential systems often modified to meet requirements arising from the characteristics of the direct current sources and to achieve efficient charging. In the constant-current method, the battery is charged at a uniform rate for the desired time; it is often modified by using a two-rate regime, the higher initial rate being followed by a lower constant rate. The change is initiated either at a stated ampere-hour input or at the onset of vigorous gassing.

In the constant-potential system of charging,

the upper charging voltage is set at a predetermined value, usually below that for vigorous gassing in the constant-current method. The charge curve with current plotted against time, shows an exponential course starting at high initial values of the current input. It is customary to limit the maximum current and depending on the limitation, the battery may start charging at constant current and pass over to constant-voltage control when the battery voltage reaches the set value of the charge voltage. The modifications often are set by the properties of the electronic control circuits and may cover a wide range of special conditions. In a similar way the constant-current method may be modified with an upper voltage limit to replace the two-rate system, and it might be a matter of quibbling to assign specific titles.

In floating systems, the batteries are continuously connected electrically to the charging source. Under the ordinary conditions of operation, the battery is only discharged for a portion of its capacity. The charging circuit operates at a selected voltage, usually high enough to assure the recharge of the battery in the required time period, but sufficiently below the gassing voltage to assure a minimum electrolysis of water and thus to decrease maintenance. Where the battery capacity is on occasion completely discharged, secondary means of charging are usually provided. Good examples of float type of installations are in switchgear control where batteries may provide a regime of use, and emergency lighting where a battery may be on continuous trickle charge and come into use only on rare occasions. The automotive battery system is a modified float system in that charging is interrupted during periods of nonuse of the vehicle.

Battery Selection

The choice of the optimum battery system for any specific application will be influenced by many properties of the system and the conditions of use. There are to be considered the electrical properties on charge and on discharge over the range of temperature and environment, the life under these operating conditions, and energy-weight and energy-volume properties under the environment, maintenance, and economics. Each type of application is subject to scrutiny and in many cases the deciding factor will be in the net cost; this is especially true where maintenance and life are in proper balance to offset initial investment and interest charges. These situations are usually found where long life, say of the order of ten years or more, is desired. In many cases, as in satellite applications, weight and life may be the deciding factors. For established applications, such as automotive as an example, economy is the principal consideration except for special military applications requiring low-temperature charging. For new uses, such as represented by aerospace applications, all of the conditions should be examined; often the combinations of environment and requirements over a long period represent new regimes of charge-discharge cycling for which only testing can provide a probable optimum selection.

Battery selection is discussed in more detail by Vinal, Hamer, and Morehouse, *et al.*, and weight-energy relationships by Grimes, Howard, and Rappaport in publications cited in "References."

References

American Institute of Electrical Engineers, "Definitions of Electrical Terms. Group 60, Electrochemistry & Electrometallurgy," ASA, C42.60, New York 1957.

Amlie, R. F., and Ruetschi, P., *J. Electrochem. Soc.*, **108**, 813 (1961).

Cahan, B. D., Ockerman, J. B., Amlie, R. F., and Ruetschi, P., *J. Electrochem. Soc.*, **107, 725** (1960).

Dawes, C. L., "A Course in Electrical Engineering. Vol. I. Direct Currents," New York, McGraw-Hill Book Co., Inc., 1937.

Dirkse, T. P., *J. Electrochem. Soc.*, **107, 859** (1960).

Drotschmann, C., "Bleiakkumulatoren," Weinheim/Bergstrasse, Verlag Chemie, GMBH, 1951.

Glasstone, S., "An Introduction to Electrochemistry," New York, D. Van Nostrand Co., Inc., 1942.

Grimes, C. G., and Herbert, W. S., *Soc. Automotive Eng., SAE Reprint* **269D** (1961).

Hamer, W. J., *IRE Transactions on Component Parts*, **CP-4,** 86 (1957).

Hills, S., *J. Electrochem. Soc.*, **108**, 810 (1961).

Howard, P. L., *Product Engineering*, **31**, No. 7, 75–82 (February 15, 1960).

Ives, D. J. G., and Janz, G. J., "Reference Electrodes. Theory and Practice," New York, Academic Press, 1961.

Lewis, G. N., and Randall, M., revised by Pitzer, K. S., and Brewer, L., "Thermodynamics," New York, McGraw-Hill Book Co., 1961.

Morehouse, C. K., Glicksman, R., and Lozier, G. S., *Proc. I.R.E.*, **46**, 1462 (August, 1958).

Potter, E. C., "Electrochemistry, Principles & Applications," New York, The Macmillan Co., 1956.

Power Sources Division, U.S. Army Signal Research & Development Laboratory, "Proceedings of the 16th Annual Power Sources Conference" and earlier volumes, PSC Publications Committee, Red Bank, N.J., 1962.

RAPPAPORT, P. J., *Electronics*, **33**, No. 8, 60 (February 19, 1960).

VINAL, G. W., "Storage Batteries," Fourth Edition, New York, John Wiley & Sons, Inc., 1955.

WHITE, J. C., *et al*, *J. Electrochem. Soc.*, **99**, 233C (1952).

ARTHUR FLEISCHER

Cross-references: Other entries with *Batteries* designation; *Overvoltage; Planté; Polarization; Reference Electrodes.*

BECKET, FREDERICK M. (1875–1942)

Frederick Mark Becket was born on January 11, 1875, in Montreal, Canada. He graduated from McGill University in 1895, taking his work in electrical engineering. His first job was with the Westinghouse Electric and Manufacturing Company, but after a year he joined Charles E. Acker in Jersey City in the development of the Acker fused bath electrolytic process for the production of chlorine and caustic soda. In 1898 he studied in the graduate school at Columbia University and received an A.M. degree in 1899. During the next year he shared in the commercialization of the Acker process at Niagara Falls. The years 1900–02 were spent at Columbia in further electrochemical and metallurgical studies. From 1902–03 he was a member of the Ampere Electrochemical Company engaged in commercial research in the field of metallurgy and steel production direct from iron ores. At this period he began the exacting pioneer research for which he achieved such high distinction.

Becket organized the Niagara Research Laboratories in 1903 and directed their activities until 1906 when they were purchased and absorbed in the Electro Metallurgical Company. He was a pioneer in working with a group of semirare refractory metals, including chromium, tungsten, molybdenum and vanadium, which resulted in the development of several electric furnace processes in the production of low-carbon ferroalloys and metals. He was the first producer of ferrovanadium and low-carbon ferrochrome in America. His work also included a variety of contributions to the metallurgy of steel alloys, among them the use of silicon as a reducing agent and a process to economize the use of silicon by smelting refractory ores with carbon in the presence of enough silica to yield a low-carbon silicide of the metal wanted, which was then resmelted with additional refractory ore, oxidizing out the silicon and further reducing the desired metal. This process became a permanent part of metallurgical practice and was ultimately applied to sulfides as well as oxides.

Becket's improvements in electric furnaces related to electrodes and refractories and the production of alloys for scavenging steel. Other processes which he evolved included the use of a variety of compounds as reducing agents, the production of magnesium and silicon alloys, as well as heat-resistant alloys of chromium and iron. Experiments between 1910 and 1914 dealt with the tungsten alloys and their manufacture, especially in the production of low-phosphorus product from high-phosphorus ores. Such experiments rendered large quantities of phosphorus-tungsten ores available for commercial use and led to a variety of contributions in the area of ore dressing.

In his career with Union Carbide Corp. Becket became president of Union Carbide and Carbon Research Laboratories, Inc., and vice president of Union Carbide Co., Electro Metallurgical Co., and Haynes Stellite Co. A charter member of the Electrochemical Society, he was active in its affairs for many years. He served as president in 1925, was made an honorary member in 1934, and received the Acheson Medal in 1937. The F. M. Becket Memorial Award, a biennial scholarship awarded by the Society, was established in his name in 1956. Becket was also active in the American Institute of Mining and Metallurgical Engineers, of which he was president in 1933 and from which he received the Cresson Medal in 1940. In 1924 he was presented with the Perkin Medal for his work in applied chemistry by the affiliated electrochemical and chemical societies of America.

Becket was awarded about 125 United States patents and received honorary degrees from Columbia (Sc.D.) and McGill (LL.D.) His death on December 1, 1942 ended an outstanding scientific career which was associated with great industrial developments.

CARMEN W. WALSH

BERZELIUS, JONS JACOB (1779–1848)

Jons Jacob Berzelius was born near Linkoping, Sweden, on August 20, 1779. Orphaned early, he worked on his stepfather's farm to obtain a meager living and put himself through high school by doing some private teaching. His strong dislike of authority caused him difficulty in these days, and "doubtful hopes" were predicted for his future. At the university, while studying for his medical degree, he became interested in chemistry, and finally, after discouragements that would have stopped a less strong-minded individual, he received assistance from Professor John Afzelius. A paper on his early experiments in nitrous oxide was rejected by both the College of Medicine and the Academy of Science because he used the new chemical nomenclature of Lavoisier in an effort to clarify chemical writing which, until that time, was a maze of strange pictures and symbols. His early interest in physiological chemistry was greatly enhanced by Alessandro Volta's discovery of the electric cell, and his thesis for his medical degree was on the action of electricity on organic bodies.

Experiments on the electrolysis of salt solutions, ammonia, etc., (made possible through Volta's discovery) led to further experimentation and ultimately to his electrochemical theory. Founded on the supposition that the atoms of the elements are electrically polarized, with either the positive or negative charge predominating, the theory was changed several times by Berzelius and did not long remain in general favor. It did, however, establish him as one of the chief founders of the radical theory. His extension of the efforts of Lavoisier to establish a rational system of chemical shorthand did much to advance the road to chemical learning. Use of the initial letters of the Latin and Greek names of the elements as symbols and small numeral subscripts to indicate the number of each present in a compound gave a clew to the chemical composition of the substance and has not only stood the test of time but formed the basis for naming and symbolizing newly discovered elements and chemical compounds.

Perhaps his greatest task was the investigation of atomic weights. He spent 10 years in the most intensive and skillful manipulation, analyzing about 2,000 simple and compound bodies with the amazing results that he was able to give a set of atomic weights for the 50 different elements known by scientists during that era. Using oxygen as the basis of reference, he evolved the necessary data by relying mainly upon the proportions of oxygen in oxygen compounds. He discovered selenium and thorium, and first exhibited elemental calcium, barium, strontium, tantalum, silicon and zirconium.

Elected to the Stockholm Academy of Sciences in 1807 and made a baron by Charles XIV in 1835, he was recognized as the most eminent chemist in all the world. As permanent secretary of the Academy of Sciences from 1818 on, he published an annual review of the progress of chemistry and mineralogy for the next 27 years. Striken with ill health, he journeyed to France, Austria, and Germany where he met a variety of famous people, including Goethe. Upon his return to Sweden (at age 56) he married the young and attractive daughter of Poppius, the town councillor. The marriage proved to be a happy one and Berzelius continued making important contributions to the scientific world until his death on August 7, 1848.

CARMEN W. WALSH

BILLITER POTENTIAL

The Billiter potential[1] is one of two types of null or zero charge potentials exhibited by metals immersed in electrolytic solutions. The other type of null potential is the Lippmann potential, otherwise known as the potential of the electrocapillary maximum. In the case of liquid metals (Hg, Ga, etc.) which behave as essentially ideally polarizable electrodes in the absence of appreciable faradaic current, electrocapillary curves or plots of surface tension against electrode potential are parabolic in shape. The Lippmann potential is the potential of maximum surface tension, and the thermodynamic theory of capillarity shows that the surface charge density on the metal or solution sides of the interfacial electrical double layer is zero at the potential of the electrocapillary maximum. Both theoretically and experimentally, the interpretation of the Lippmann potential and many other properties of ideally polarizable electrodes is well established, but the Billiter potential has received no comparable quantitative theoretical treatment.

In contrast to measurements of Lippmann potentials, which classically are performed on ideally polarizable electrodes, Billiter potentials are measured with unpolarizable electrodes. In the classical technique for the measurement of the Billiter potential, a small metallic electrode, initially not immersed in solution, is connected through a sensitive galvanometer or other current measuring device to a very much larger electrode of the same metal which is immersed in solution and maintained at a fixed electrode potential by an equilibrium reaction of large exchange current density. The interfacial potential difference of the large electrode is determined by an equilibrium reaction between the metal and its ions in solution or by an oxidation-reduction couple in solution. The exchange current density of the interfacial charge transfer processes is high, and hence the polarization resistance is low so that the potential of the large electrode is essentially unaffected by any current passed through the external circuit on immersion of the small electrode into the solution. The value of the electrode potential may be adjusted by varying the concentration of metal ions or by changing the activity ratio of the oxidation-reduction couple in solution. When the small electrode is placed in contact with the solution, a current is detected on the galvanometer which depends in sign and magnitude on the value of the reversible electrode potential. At a characteristic potential, the Billiter potential (E_B), the sign of the current which passes through the external circuit is reversed. For electrode potentials greater than E_B, positive current flows from the large to the small electrode through the external circuit, while for potentials more negative than E_B, the opposite behavior is observed. At the Billiter potential, no external current is required for the formation of the electrical double layer at the interface of the small electrode upon immersion into the solution.

The value of the Billiter potential is $+0.475$ v vs. the normal hydrogen electrode. It is remarkably independent of the identity of the metal and of the constitution of the solution, provided the electrode potential is poised by an equilibrium reaction of sufficiently large exchange current density. In contrast, Lippmann potentials differ for each metal and vary with solution composition. The addition of capillary-active substances to solution does not change appreciably the value of E_B, although the value of the Lippmann potential is altered significantly. Other types of observations are also pertinent to the problem of the Billiter potential. Experiments on the electrokinetic properties of unpolarizable metals show

that zeta potentials disappear in the vicinity of E_B. In addition, the surface tension of unpolarizable mercury electrodes has a maximum near E_B.

Considerable theoretical interest is attached to the interpretation of the Billiter potential. Historically,[1] attempts were made to interpret the Billiter potential as an absolute potential; that is, the Galvani or inner potential difference ($\Delta\phi$) between metal and solution phases was thought to be zero at the Billiter potential. This view is untenable on the basis of modern electrochemical theory, and the most satisfactory interpretation of the Billiter potential is due to Oel and Strehlow[4] (see, however, the opinion of Frumkin[2]).

The Galvani or inner potential difference ($\Delta\phi = \phi_M - \phi_S$) between metal and solution phases is composed additively of the Volta or outer potential difference ($\Delta\psi = \psi_M - \psi_S$) and the difference between the surface or dipole potentials ($\chi_M - \chi_S$); that is $\Delta\phi = \Delta\psi + \chi_M - \chi_S$.[3] The outer potential difference ($\Delta\psi$) is determined by the excess charge density on metal or solution sides of the electrical double layer, while χ_M and χ_S are potential differences due to the existence of dipolar layers in metal and solution phases, respectively. The surface potential, χ_M, exists even on a metal free of excess charge because the center of electronic charge density does not coincide with the center of charge density of metallic ions constituting the lattice at the surface. The surface potential on the solution side of the double layer, χ_S, is due to the presence of oriented dipoles including solvent molecules, induced dipoles, and specifically adsorbed ionic species at the interface.

In the experimental arrangement for determination of the Billiter potential, Oel and Strehlow suggest that, in the first instant after immersion of the small electrode at the Billiter potential, χ_S is zero because a finite time is necessary for orientation of the dipole layer of solvent (water) molecules at the interface. Since E_B (the measured Billiter potential *vs* a reference electrode) is also a null potential, $\Delta\psi$ is zero because of the absence of excess charge density on either phase and the inner potential difference is given by $\Delta\phi = \Delta\phi_B = \chi_M$ at the moment of immersion. If the electrode were ideally polarizable, subsequent orientation of solvent molecules, producing a surface potential, χ_S, would result in an inner potential difference of $\Delta\phi = \Delta\phi_N = \chi_M - \chi_S$, where $\Delta\phi_N$ is the inner potential difference corresponding to the Lippmann potential. However, the interfacial potential difference is poised at the value of $\Delta\phi_B$ by the reversible interfacial reaction of large exchange current density. In order that overall electroneutrality be preserved during the time of reorientation of solvent molecules, an ionic double layer of potential difference, $\Delta\psi$, is established which is equal and opposite in potential to χ_S at any instant. The current necessary for the establishment of the ionic double layer is derived entirely from the charge transfer processes of the reversible interfacial reaction rather than from the external circuit, so that no current is detectable on the galvanometer. From the definition of the inner potential difference at E_B, $\delta\Delta\phi_B = \delta\Delta\psi + \delta(\chi_M - \chi_S) = 0$, so that $\delta\Delta\psi = \delta\chi_S$ during the formation of the double layer at the Billiter potential. For $E > E_B$ or $E < E_B$, compensation of currents due to changes in $\Delta\psi$ and χ_S with time no longer occurs, and positive or negative currents, respectively, are detected on the galvanometer. In the presence of capillary-active substances, additional dipole layers form on the solution side of the double layer, but again $\Delta\psi$ changes so as to compensate χ_S and no external current is necessary for the formation of the complete double layer at the Billiter potential. The small electrode of the Billiter experiment is a null electrode only at the moment of immersion; in the final state, χ_S has reached its ultimate value and $\Delta\psi \neq 0$, so that excess surface charge density exists on either side of the interface.

Since the Lippmann potential is given by $E_N = \Delta\phi_N + \text{(constant)} = \chi_M - \chi_S + \text{(constant)}$ and the Billiter potential is $E_B = \Delta\phi_B + \text{(constant)} = \chi_M + \text{(constant)}$ at the moment of immersion, the difference $E_B - E_N = \chi_S$ is then the surface or dipole potential of the solution side of the double layer. The value of this difference varies with the identity of the metal because of differences in the interaction strength between various metals and the constituents of the solution. The experimentally established independence of E_B with respect to the nature of the metal requires that the inner potential difference between metal and solution at the Billiter potential vary with the change in the chemical potential of electrons from one metal to another. That is, $\Delta\phi_1 - \Delta\phi_2 = \phi_{M,1} - \phi_{M,2} = (\mu_{e,1} - \mu_{e,2})/\mathbf{F}$, where $\Delta\phi_1$ and $\Delta\phi_2$ are the inner potential differences of two different metals at the Billiter potential, $\mathbf{F}$ is Faraday's constant, and $\mu_{e,1}$ and $\mu_{e,2}$ are the corresponding chemical potentials of the electrons in the metals (the Fermi potentials).

This behavior is analogous to a system of three metals in electronic equilibrium; i.e., the potential difference between the metals Me_1 and Me_3 in the system $Me_1/Me_2/Me_3$ is independent of the identity of the metal Me_2, provided electronic equilibrium is established.

References

1. BILLITER, J., Z. Elektrochem., **8**, 638 (1902); Ann. Physik, **11**, 902,937 (1903); Monatsh. Chem., **53/54**, 813 (1929); Trans. Electrochem. Soc., **57**, 351 (1930).
2. FRUMKIN, A. N., Z. Elektrochem., **59**, 807 (1955).
3. LANGE, E., in WIEN, W., AND HARMS, F., eds., "Handbuch der Experimentalphysik," Vol. 12-2, p. 261, Leipzig, Akademische Verlagsgesellschaft M.B.H., 1933.
4. OEL, H., AND STREHLOW, H., Z. Physik. Chem., N. F., **4**, 89 (1955).
5. VETTER, K. J., "Elektrochemische Kinetik," Berlin, Springer-Verlag, 1961.

FRANZ A. POSEY

Cross-references: *Electrode Double Layer; Lippmann Potential.*

BIOCHEMICAL FUEL CELLS

A biochemical fuel cell is a device for direct conversion of chemical to electrical energy, in which one or both of the electrode processes is promoted or catalyzed by a biochemical agent, rather than by a conventional chemical catalyst. Considerable attention has been given to this new field in the last few years, primarily because of potential usefulness in military and space applications.

In 1912 Potter[1] reported that electrical energy is generated when organic compounds are disintegrated by microorganisms. He constructed biochemical batteries involving yeast plus glucose at one electrode and pure glucose at the other. Cohen[2] did similar work in 1931 and built a biobattery producing 0.07 watts of power for several minutes.

Most of the work on biochemical fuel cells has been done since 1959, however, under research programs supported by the United States Government. These studies are primarily directed toward utilization of human and industrial wastes and of naturally occurring organic matter as fuel sources.

Characterization of Biochemical Fuel Cells. As stated above, electrode reactions in a biochemical fuel cell or battery are promoted or catalyzed by a biochemical agent. The catalysts ultimately responsible for most chemical reactions in living systems are the enzymes, and these are also the active agents in bioelectrode processes.

Enzymes are used in three different forms: living organisms, crude extracts from organisms, and relatively purified enzyme preparations. These represent increasing degrees of isolation of the active ingredient and each has its advantages and disadvantages for specific applications. Thus, living cells can adapt to variations in the environment, but their activity per unit weight is low. Pure enzymes, on the other hand, have a high specific activity, but are subject to deactivation by a foreign environment. Furthermore, the concerted action of a number of different enzymes is usually required to accomplish a given reaction, and the isolation and maintenance of these enzyme complexes in an active state is difficult.

The successful use of these biochemical promotors in electrochemical cells has added greatly to the potential application area of fuel cells. This extension results from several unique characteristics of biochemical fuel cells. One of these is the set of mild conditions under which the reactions occur. The temperature range is that in which most life processes occur in the earth's surface, namely 5 to 40°C. The pH of the solution in which the biochemical reaction takes place is near neutral, and ionic strength must be low relative to that used in conventional cells.

Another unique characteristic supplied by the biochemical catalyst is the ability to utilize a wide range of naturally occurring, relatively inert materials as fuels or oxidants. Thus, for example, any vegetable product or waste therefrom, and many derivatives such as petroleum, are potential fuels, while substances such as sulfate and carbonate may serve as oxidants. Inclusion of photosynthesis in the overall process provides a means of upgrading the available energy from some reactants.

When living organisms are used, catalytic activity is automatically and continuously regenerated by the process of cell division, as long as conditions are favorable to growth. Primarily for this reason, living organisms, in the form of microorganisms, are preferred at the present state of the art. Many microorganisms show considerable resistance to contaminants that would denature their enzyme systems were the latter exposed more directly to the environment. Thus, healthy cells appear to provide the best known vehicle for the required enzymes.

As a result of operating conditions mentioned above, the maximum power density obtainable from biochemical fuel cells is relatively low. The cell voltage is often low because of the low free energy change involved in the overall cell reaction and the low conductivity of the electrolyte that may be used. Current densities are also low because the concentration of biochemical agents that can be maintained in an active state is limited. Despite these limitations, however, power densities of the order of several watts per square foot have been achieved under optimum conditions.

Classification. It is useful to distinguish two different types of biochemical electrode processes relative to the mode of operation. The first type, referred to as "indirect," is one in which the primary reactant is converted to a stable intermediate that is subsequently oxidized or reduced in a conventional electrode reaction. The intermediate is isolated, so that conversion reaction takes place physically remote from the electrochemical reaction.

The other type of process, referred to as "direct," is one in which both biochemical and electrochemical reaction steps occur in contact with the electrode and the rate of the biochemical step is limiting. Such a composite electrode system in which the biologically active substance is in intimate contact with the conductive material supplying or removing electrons, is referred to as a "bioelectrode." Further classification of the composite site of biological and electrochemical reactions is made as either a "bioanode" or "biocathode" to indicate the specific electrode under discussion.

An example of an indirect process is the separate generation of hydrogen by the action of fermentive bacteria on carbohydrates, with the hydrogen then being transported to the anode of a fuel cell where it is electrochemically oxidized. A direct bioelectrode for this same system can be made by placing the bacteria directly on the anode and feeding the carbohydrate into the fuel cell. These two processes are illustrated in Fig. 1.

The characteristics of the indirect process are clearly exactly those of the two separate steps. The principal advantage is that conditions can be optimized independently for both the biochemical and electrochemical processes.

The direct processes are more complex. It is probable that in some systems transient species may be involved in the electrochemical reaction. For example, where hydrogen is produced from an organic fuel, the atomic form may first be produced. Oxidation of this species at the anode would provide a more anodic potential than that of molecular hydrogen.

Whatever the mechanism of the different direct bioelectrode reactions, bioanode processes studied to date operate at potentials somewhat less anodic than the hydrogen anode. Likewise, the biocathode processes, with the exception of the light-activated oxygen electrode, operate at potentials only slightly more cathodic than a hydrogen cathode would under similar conditions. Thus, at the present time, in order to produce a cell voltage of 0.5 volt or more, oxygen is used at the cathode with bioanodes, and active metals are used as anodes with biocathodes. Zinc and magnesium are examples of metals useful for coupling with biocathodes.

Table 1 shows five bioanode systems, three utilizing enzymes and two utilizing living bacteria as the biological promotors. The electroactive species is given as the substance which is known to be a product of the biochemical reaction. As mentioned previously, in the direct process this substance would not necessarily need to be formed as a discreet phase. Transient intermediates, rather, may be involved in the anodic oxidation.

Note that for a given fuel, such as glucose, the specific bioelectrode used greatly influences the energy conversion efficiency. As will be seen below, only two electrons per glucose molecule are obtained by the enzyme-catalyzed reaction; whereas, four electrons are obtained when the reaction is promoted by bacteria. Also, the potential of the reduced form of methylene blue,

TABLE 1. SELECTED BIOANODES

Fuel	Biological Phase	Electro-active species	Estimate of Thermal Efficiency
Glucose	Glucose oxidase	MBH_2	0.1
Glucose	*Clostridium butyricum*	H_2	0.3
Urea	Urease	NH_3	0.5
Lactate	*Desulfovibrio desulfuricans*	H_2S	0.15
Formic acid	Formic hydro-genylase	H_2	0.75

MBH_2, is considerably less anodic than that of hydrogen. Both these factors reduce the conversion efficiency of glucose via the enzyme route.

The biological and electrochemical reactions and the net electrode reaction involved at the glucose-glucose oxidase bioanode are as follows:

Glucose-glucose oxidase:
$$C_6H_{12}O_6 + FAD \rightarrow C_6H_{10}O_6 + FADH_2$$
$$FADH_2 + MB \rightarrow FAD + MBH_2$$
$$MBH_2 \rightarrow MB + 2H^+ + 2e^-$$

$$C_6H_{12}O_6 \rightarrow C_6H_{10}O_6 + 2H^+ + 2e^-$$

FAD is the prosthetic group or coenzyme of glucose oxidase and is an essential part of the total enzyme activity. FAD represents the oxidized form and $FADH_2$ the reduced form. In this system a mediator, methylene blue, MB_1, is required to provide an electrochemically reactive species. Again, MB represents the oxidized form and MBH_2 the reduced form. Note that both the coenzyme and mediator are regenerated and in that sense may be classified as catalysts.

Biocathodes. Three of the most promising oxidants for biochemical cells are sulfate, carbonate, and nitrate. None of these substances can be electrochemically reduced in neutral solutions at ambient temperature except by a biochemical process. The biological and electrochemical reactions as well as the net electrode reaction involved for the sulfate and light-activated carbonate cathodes are as follows:

Sulfate-Desulfovibrio desulfuricans:
$$8H_2O + 8e^- \rightarrow 4H_2 + 8OH^-$$
$$SO_4^{--} + 4H_2 \rightarrow S^{--} + 4H_2O$$

$$4H_2O + SO_4^{--} + 8e^- \rightarrow S^{--} + 8OH^-$$

Carbonate-Algae
$$CO_2 + H_2O \rightarrow (CH_2O)_x + O_2$$
$$O_2 + 2H_2O + 4e^- \rightarrow 4OH^-$$

$$CO_2 + 3H_2O + 4e^- \rightarrow (CH_2O)_x + 4OH^-$$

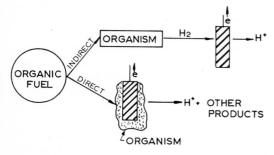

FIG. 1. Direct and indirect processes for biofuel cell.

Potential Application. Biocells are in research and early development stages. Current densities are still low, on the order of a few amperes per square foot. However, interest is high due to long-range possibilities of utilizing sewage, industrial and agricultural wastes. In space vehicles or in air-raid shelters, biocells may offer a sophisticated and efficient way to dispose of human wastes, and yield by-product electricity at the same time. Biocells may find application for generation power in fuel-poor countries, or for remote, unattended or portable power to operate radio receivers for emergency purposes. Obviously, the present potential markets are in military and space, but specialty uses in commercial applications may develop. In general, all fuel cell developments for military and space have numerous foreseeable civilian applications, and it seems likely that this observation will include biocells. The biggest deterrent to application of biocells, at present, seems to be the characteristically low current and power densities, although this does not necessarily mean that energy densities are low.

References

1. POTTER, M. C., "Electrical Effects Accompanying the Decomposition of Organic Compounds," *Proc. Roy Soc. (London),* **B84,** 260–76 (1912).
2. COHEN, BARNETT, "The Bacterial Culture as an Electrical Half-Cell," *J. Bacteriology,* **21,** 18–19 (1931).
3. ROHRBACK, G. H., SCOTT, W. R. (Magna Corp.) AND DEL DUCA, M. G. (Tapco Div. of TRW), "Biochemical Potentialities for Space Flight." Paper presented before the Space Power Systems Conf., American Rocket Society, Santa Monica, Calif., Sept. 27, 1962.
4. WOLFF, MICHAEL F., "Bacteria and Enzymes Product Power in New Biocells," *Electronics,* 30–31 (June 15, 1962).
5. ROSENBLATT, ALFRED, "Bio-Cells—Usable Power from Organic Wastes," *Electronic Design,* **11,** 4–7 (July 5, 1962).
6. SISLER, FREDERICK D., "Electrical Energy from Biochemical Fuel Cells," *New Scientist (Britain),* **12,** 110–11 (Oct. 12, 1961).
7. REYNOLDS, L. W. AND KONIKOFF, J. J., "A Preliminary Report on Two Bioelectrogenic Systems," General Electric, Missile and Space Vehicle Dept., Valley Forge, Penna. Paper presented before the Society for Industrial Microbiology, Corvallis, Ore., August 29, 1962.
8. SISLER, FREDERICK D., "Some Environmental Implications of Natural Biochemical Fuel Cell Systems," General Scientific Corp., Wash. 8, D.C. Paper presented before the Society for Industrial Microbiology, Corvallis, Ore., August 29, 1962.
9. GOLDNER, BERNARD H., OTTO, LUCY ANN, AND CANFIELD, JAMES H., "Application of Bacteriological Processes to the Generation of Electrical Power," Magna Corp., Anaheim, Calif. Paper presented before the Society for Industrial Microbiology, Corvallis, Ore., Aug. 29, 1962.
10. DEL DUCA, M. G., FUSCOE, J. M., AND ZURILLA, R. W., "Direct and Indirect Bioelectrochemical Energy Conversion Systems," Tapco Div. of Thompson Ramo Wooldridge, Cleveland, Ohio. Paper presented before the Society for Industrial Microbiology, Corvallis, Ore., Aug. 29, 1962.
11. COHN, ERNST M., "Perspectives on Biochemical Electricity," NASA, Office of Adv. Res. and Tech., Wash. 25, D.C. Paper presented before the Society for Industrial Microbiology, Corvallis, Ore., Aug. 29, 1962.
12. DAVIS, J. B., AND YARBOUGH, H. F., JR., "Preliminary Experiments on a Microbial Fuel Cell," Socony Mobil Oil Co., Field Res. Lab., Dallas, Tex, *Science,* **137,** 615–16 (Aug. 24, 1962).
13. GILMORE, KEN, "Fuel Cells," *Electronics World,* 84 (September 1962).
14. KALLIO, R. E., MARKOVETZ, A., AND MCKENNA, E. J., paper presented before the Div. of Microbial Chemistry & Technology, Amer. Chem. Soc, 142nd National Meeting, Atlantic City, NJ, Sept. 1962.
15. *Fuel Cell Progress: Survey on Status of Biocells,* St. Louis, Missouri, Fuel Cell Corp, 1962.
16. ROHRBACK, G. H., SCOTT, W. R., AND CANFIELD, J. H., Proceedings 16th Annual Power Sources Conference, Red Bank, N. J., 1962, PSC Publications Committee, 1962.

GILSON H. ROHRBACK

Cross-references: entries bearing *Bio-* titles; *Fuel Cells.*

BIOELECTROCHEMISTRY

The most important requirement of living matter, which must be met if life is to continue, is that it should contain a mechanism by which the free energy from such chemical reactions as the oxidation of ingested food is made available for the performance of energy-requiring reactions and processes instead of being dissipated as heat. Some examples of processes for which energy is required are mechanical work in movement, especially as developed in the higher animals, osmotic work in absorption and secretion, biosynthetic reactions required for the formation of new living matter in growth and reproduction, as well as such special processes as bioluminescence in fireflies or the generation of electricity in the electric eel which is reported to achieve potentials as high as 600 volts.

Until very recently, the electrochemist has devoted very little effort to studies related to life systems. Most of the investigations on these systems were done by biochemists and bacteriologists to whom much credit is due for their realization of the importance of electrochemical phenomena in biological activities.

Although early "physiologists" realized that oxygen-uptake was a very important requirement for animal metabolism and that it was probably involved in all biological processes, it wasn't until Paul Ehrlich's time that the oxidation-reduction phenomena were demonstrated. In 1885 Ehrlich published a monograph describing the different abilities of animal organs to reduce dyes as correlated with the organ's oxygen requirements. These observations were quickly utilized by bacteriologists to develop staining methods for microorganisms.

It is not too difficult to realize the importance of electrochemistry in biologic-metabolism. Oxidative processes, which naturally involve the loss of electrons, are continuously going on in living cells. It is this process that permits the cell to obtain from various foods the necessary energy to perform the required life-functions. This energy is obtained through oxidation-reduction reactions. In many of the cellular redox reactions there is a transfer of hydrogen as well as electrons. As an example we might examine the oxidation of glucose to gluconolactone by the glucose oxidase enzyme.

Glucose

Gluconolactone

The flavin adenine dinucleotide (FAD) moiety accepts the hydrogen and in turn upon reaction with oxygen is regenerated to the oxidized form of the enzyme.

$$EnzFAD-H_2 + O_2 + 2e \rightarrow EnzFAD + H_2O_2$$

Although oxidation-reduction reactions are the predominant source of biological energy there are also hydrolysis reactions which occur with small energy releases amounting to a few hundred calories per mole, whereas the oxidation of glucose liberates approximately 670,000 calories per mole. It is indeed fortunate that the biological system never liberates the energy contained in the nutrient molecule at one time. The results, of course, might be catastrophic; rather it releases the energy in a stepwise manner, a little at a time with each step in the degradation generally being catalyzed by a specific enzyme. There are a number of paths nutrients may take before the final oxidation products, carbon dioxide and water or hydrogen are obtained. An example of one such path is the oxidation of glucose via glucose-6-phosphate to pyruvic acid which can be oxidized further to acetic plus formic acids. This is shown on page 104.

Oxidases and dehydrogenase are the responsible enzymes involved in electron and hydrogen ion transfer. The oxidases require aerobic conditions and the dehydrogenases can function anaerobically. An example of the former would be glucose oxidase and the latter succinic dehydrogenase.

Although there is a considerable amount of data, in the literature, on equilibrium potentials of biological systems, it must be stressed that in these systems a true equilibrium state is rarely if ever reached. Therefore, these potentials can only be considered as apparent E_0 values, determined generally at pH 7.0, and reported vs a normal hydrogen electrode. As a consequence, the symbol, E_0', is used in place of E_0. The following is a list of redox potentials for some of the more important biochemical systems.

Potentials of Biochemical Oxidation-reduction Reactions

Reactants	Products	E_0' (volt)
Acetaldehyde + H_2O	acetate$^-$ + H^+	-0.581
Alanine + H_2O	pyruvate$^-$ + NH_4^+	-0.119
NH_4^+ + H_2O	NH_2OH	$+0.562$
Ascorbate	dehydroascorbic acid	$+0.166$

Reactants	Products	E_0' (volt)
Aspartate	oxoloacetate^{2-} + NH$_4^+$	-0.097
DPNH + H$^+$ (reduced form of diphosphoronucleolide)	DPN	-0.320
Ethanol	acetaldehyde	-0.197
Glucose + H$_2$O	gluconate$^-$ + H$^+$	-0.47
Glucose	gluconolactone	-0.364
Glutamate$^-$ + H$_2$O	a-oxolgutarate^{2-} + NH$_4^+$	-0.121
Glyceraldehyde 3—Phosphate^{2-} + HPO$_4^{2-}$	glyceroylphosphate 3-phosphate^{4-}	-0.286
Glycerate$^-$	hydroxypyruvate$^-$	-0.158
H$_2$O$_2$	O$_2$ (gas)	$+0.295$
Lactate$^-$	pyruvate$^-$	-0.185
Malate^{2-} + H$^+$	pyruvate$^-$ + CO$_2$	-0.330
Pyruvate$^-$ + H$_2$O	acetate$^-$ + CO$_2$	-0.699
Sorbitol	fructose	-0.272

The cytochrome enzymes are of extreme importance too, in biological systems. Their function can best be defined as intracellular ferrous-ferric porphyrin (or related prosthetic group) proteins. It is these substances that are the electron recipients in an oxidation process and which are responsible for electron transfer. From the cytochromes the electrons are passed to the enzyme, cytochrome oxidase, which ultimately discharges the electrons to oxygen. This oxygen then combines with the hydrogen in the substrate to form water. The whole series of reactions can be demonstrated by the following reaction sequence.

Electron Transfer in Cellular Redox Reactions

(1) Substrate·2H·2e + dehydrogenase → substrate + dehydrogenase·2H·2e

(2) Dehydrogenase·2H·2e + flavoprotein → flavoprotein·2H·2e + dehydrogenase

(3) Flavoprotein·2H·2e + 2 cytochrome Fe^{+++} → 2 cytochrome Fe^{++} + flavoprotein + 2H$^+$

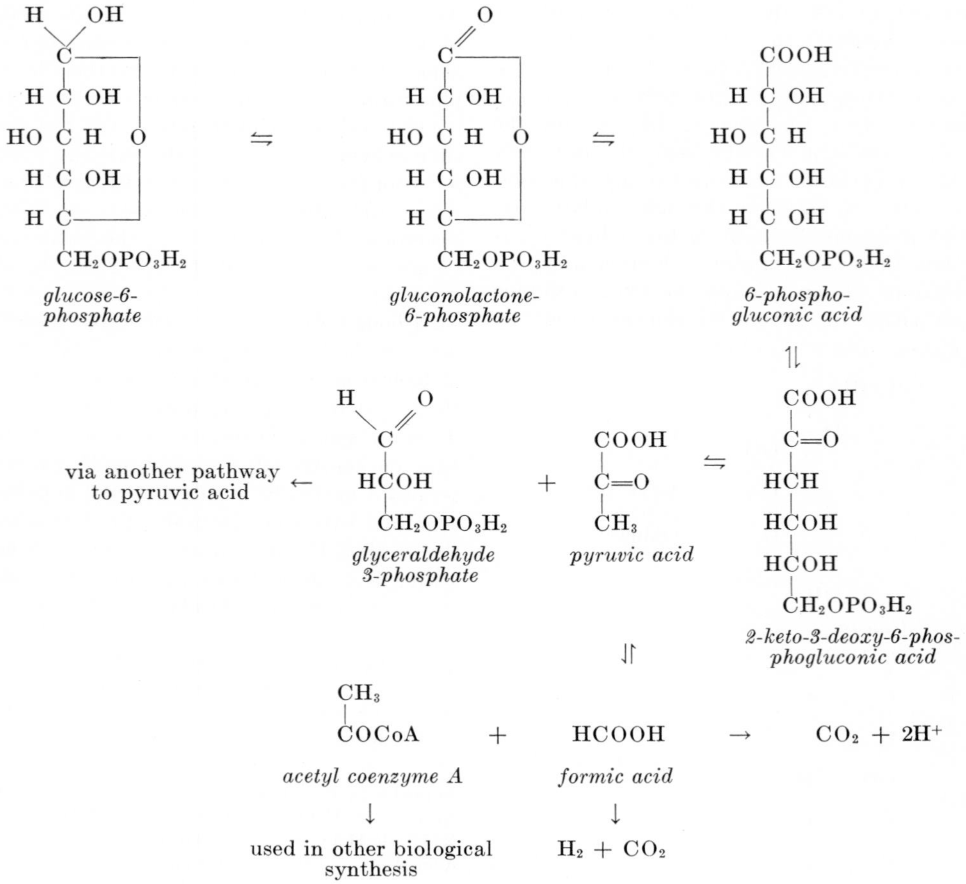

glucose-6-phosphate ⇌ *gluconolactone-6-phosphate* ⇌ *6-phospho-gluconic acid*

via another pathway to pyruvic acid ← *glyceraldehyde 3-phosphate* + *pyruvic acid* ⇌ *2-keto-3-deoxy-6-phosphogluconic acid*

acetyl coenzyme A + *formic acid* → CO$_2$ + 2H$^+$

↓ *used in other biological synthesis*

↓ H$_2$ + CO$_2$

(4) 2 Cytochrome Fe^{++} + 2 cytochrome oxidase Fe^{+++} → 2 cytochrome oxidase Fe^{++} + 2 cytochrome Fe^{+++}

(5) 2 Cytochrome oxidase Fe^{++} + $\frac{1}{2}O_2$ → 2 cytochrome oxidase Fe^{+++} + O^-

(6) $O^- + 2H^+ → H_2O$

It should be noted that there are a number of cytochromes present in nature and that in any one system there are at least three. The electrons are merely passed from one cytochrome to another in the chain according to the following scheme:

Flavoprotein → cytochrome b → c

→ a → a_3 → O_2 .

The E_0' of some of these are shown in the table.

Potentials of Some Cytochrome Systems

Cytochrome	Source	E_0' (volt)
a	Widely distributed	+0.290
c_5	Azotobacter	+0.320
c_4	Azotobacter	+0.300
c_3	Desulfovibrio	−0.205
c_2	Rhodopseudomonas	+0.340
b_7	Arum spadix	−0.030
b_6	Leaves	−0.060
b_1	Bacteria	+0.250
f	Chloroplasts	+0.365

For *in vitro* systems the E_0' data are usually obtained by potentiometric titration at a smooth platinum electrode vs a saturated calomel reference electrode. The values are then corrected by algebraically adding the value obtained to +0.2458 v (SCE vs NHE at pH 7.0 and 20°C). More recently some investigators have used the polarographic method in conjunction with a SCE to obtain E_0'. The half-wave potential ($E_{1/2}$) obtained from the polarographic curve when corrected to the normal hydrogen electrode (NHE) will give the E_0'.

A number of approaches have been used to measure *in vivo* or intracellular redox potentials. Some investigators have inserted platinum microelectrodes into a cell and made their measurements in this manner. Such an approach of course leaves some question as to the validity of the data. The cells are not likely to remain in a healthy condition as a result of such manipulation. Another technique used is to inject into the cell some redox indicator dye. The color change can be used to indicate whether the dye is oxidized or reduced. Using a series of indicators of various E_0' values, the E_0' of the cell may be obtained.

Recently the electrochemical method has been utilized to study the reaction of various oxidizing enzymes with its substrate. The method utilizes a cell containing a smooth platinum electrode and a saturated calomel reference electrode connected to a high impedance recorder. The substrate dissolved in a suitable buffer medium is allowed to react with a particular enzyme or enzyme system. Not only is it possible to obtain kinetic data by this method, but more interestingly it is possible to study the effects of potentiators and poisons on biological redox systems simply and reproducibly.

The method described has been used in studies on the glucose-glucose oxidase and *d*-alanine-*d*-amino oxidase systems. It was of interest to observe in these studies the potentiating effect of metallic iron on the enzymes as indicated by increased open cell potentials (−150 mv vs SCE for glucose-glucose oxidase system as against −590 mv vs SCE for this system with metallic iron). Further electrochemical data indicated that the enzyme itself reacted with the iron prior to its reaction with the substrate.

As mentioned earlier, in relation to the validity of the E_0' values obtained, we are dealing essentially with systems which tend to approach, but never achieve, because of the nature of life itself, an equilibrium state. Therefore, a more dynamic treatment must be given these biologic systems to arrive at a better understanding of their behavior. In other words we must find out to what extent these systems can do work, as indicated by their abilities to produce electrical energy, and for what period of time. A method which produces this data has been developed.

In this procedure an "H-type" cell is used together with two smooth platinum electrodes separated by an ion-exchange membrane. The anode compartment contains the enzyme system or systems in a suitable buffer. A buffered solution of potassium ferricyanide is used in the cathode compartment of such a concentration to prevent the cathode from becoming polarized during the course of the experiment. After addition of the substrate to the anode compartment, the cell is permitted to reach its maximum open cell potential. At this time an appropriate load, e.g., 1000 ohms, is placed across the cell and current vs time recorded until the current drops and plateaus. The curve obtained is very similar to that obtained in a potentiometric titration. The area under the curve to the end-point will give the coulombic value for the system investigated. This approach to the study of life systems has recently been applied to an investigation of the mechanism of the oxidation of glucose by washed *E. coli*. According to the present state of knowledge, the oxidation of glucose by this microorganism can occur via a number of pathways which lead eventually to formic and acetic acids. Two of these paths are illustrated with the following selected intermediates.

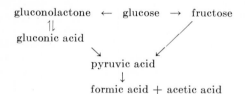

The formic acid is oxidized further to carbon dioxide and hydrogen, and the acetic acid acetylates coenzyme A. If the reaction goes through fructose (or its phosphorlated counterpart), only one equivalent of pyruvic acid will result. However, should the reaction path occur via the gluconolactone-gluconic acid, two equivalents of pyruvic will be produced.

The coulombic values obtained for glucose, fructose, pyruvic, and formic acids are essentially the same. Acetic acid, as anticipated gave a negligible value. Gluconolactone and gluconic acid both give values approximately twice that of formic acid, whereas molecular hydrogen present in a quantity far in excess to the equivalent theoretical amount produced in the oxidation of formic acid gives a considerably lower coulombic value than either glucose, fructose, or pyruvic and formic acids. These results indicate first, the predominant path for the oxidation of glucose by the particular type of *E. coli* used in the experiments appears to be via the fructose; second, as glucose does not give a higher coulombic value than formic acid, the electrical energy producing step in the oxidation of glucose probably is the oxidation of formic acid; and lastly, the energy obtained is not that which could be attributed to a hydrogen-oxygen cell as indicated by the results using molecular hydrogen.

This new approach to the study of redox reaction in life systems may well open the way to investigations, whose results will give a better understanding of biologic phenomena.

It is quite apparent that, although considerable redox potential data have been accumulated over the years, very little other electrochemical information is available on these dynamic biochemical reactions. The difficulty, no doubt, is partly due to the lack of interest and "fear of the unknown" on the part of the electrochemist and, perhaps, lack of communication on the part of the biologist and biochemist. There is no doubt that, with the renewed and increasing interest in biochemical energy conversion phenomena, closer collaboration will take place between the various mentioned disciplines. The organic electrochemist, too, must participate, for *in vivo* and *in vitro* enzyme systems are important tools for electrochemical synthesis. This field of bioelectrochemistry has tremendous scope and is in desperate need of greater scientific interest and effort.

References

1. LONG, C., Ed., "Biochemists Handbook," Princeton, N. J., Van Nostrand, 1961.
2. FRUTON, J. S., AND SIMMONDS, S., "General Biochemistry," New York, John Wiley & Sons, Inc., 1953.
3. DIXON, M., AND WEBB, E. C., "Enzymes," New York, Academic Press, 1958.
4. CLARK, W. M., "Oxidation-Reduction Potentials of Organic Systems," Baltimore, The Williams & Wilkins Co., 1960.
5. CASEY, E. J., New York, "Biophysics," Reinhold Publishing Corp., 1962.
6. BREZINA, M., AND ZUMAN, P., "Polarography in Medicine, Biochemistry and Pharmacy," New York, Interscience Publishers, 1958.
7. BARRON, E. S. G., "The Mechanism of Enzymatic Oxidation-Reductions," "Trends in Physiology and Biochemistry," Barron, Ed., pp. 1–24, New York, Academic Press, 1952.
8. ANFINSEN, C. B., AND KIELLEY, W. W., "Biological Oxidations," *Ann. Rev. Biochem.*, **23**, 17–34, 1954.
9. ALLEN, M. J., AND YAHIRO, A., "The Electrochemical Aspects of Some Biochemical Systems," *Electrochim. Acta*, **8**, 419 (1963).
10. ALLEN, M. J., AND NICHOLSON, M., "Studies on Glucose-Glucose Oxidase Systems," Proc. First Australian Conf. on Electrochem., London, Pergamon Press, (in press) 1964.
11. ALLEN, M. J., BOWEN, R. J., NICHOLSON, M., AND VASTA, B. M., "A New Approach to the Investigation of Electrical Energy Producing Reactions in Biological Systems," *Electrochim. Acta* (in press) 1964.

M. J. ALLEN

Cross-references: entries bearing *Bio-* titles; *Electric Organs*.

BIOELECTROGENESIS

The cell, the working unit of plants and animals, is a complicated electrochemical system. A thin *cell*, or *plasma membrane* separates an aqueous medium which contains a complexly cooperative agglomerate of macromolecules from an aqueous solution predominantly composed of 0.1 to 0.5 M NaCl, but which also contains smaller amounts of KCl, $CaCl_2$, and $MgCl_2$, and other constituents. The nondiffusible macromolecules of the inside are chiefly anions and K is the predominant intracellular cation. The membrane itself is probably a mosaic of anionic and cationic fixed charge sites and behaves as if it were highly permselective for some ions.

Thus, several kinds of electrochemical forces probably operate to establish a potential difference across the membrane. The membrane can change its properties as a response to stimuli in *excitable cells*. If the response involves changes in the membrane permselectivity and conductance for one or several ionic species, the electrochemical conditions of the resting cell are disturbed and a current can flow, inward or outward, depending upon the nature of the change in conductance. These cells therefore are *electrogenic*. The mechanisms by which the cell produces this *bioelectrogenesis* or bioelectric activity are different in nature from those of nonliving electrochemical batteries. There are several varieties of bioelectric activity, some of which are specifically adapted to certain functional requirements, for which the different excitable electrogenic cells are specialized. The cell membrane is itself one of the substructures, or organelles, of the cell substance, and exhibits many functional complexities. In electron micrographs this boundary surface appears as a three-layered "unit membrane," 70–100Å thick. The appearance probably indicates that the membrane is primarily a lamellar organization composed of a bimolecular leaflet. Two sets of hydrophilic polar groups project into the aqueous phases (intracellular for one layer of molecules, extracellular for the other), forming a space between them in which lie the hydrophobic nonpolar groups. The cell membrane is rather poorly permeable to various substances, including ions and water.

The living membrane should not be regarded as a static structure, but rather as a phase boundary of labile composition, with continual interchange going on between the macromolecules which form the framework of the membrane and those in the interior of the cell. Thus, the membrane is likely to be heterogeneous in composition, with nearly every molecular species and functional capacity of the cytoplasm represented in the surface. Local differences probably arise in the membrane due to differences in species and relative concentrations of the various macromolecules. Differences in spatial configurations and charge distributions, in chemical affinities and in the concentration of water would accentuate local heterogeneity of the membrane, not only in its structural aspects but also as to function and chemical reactivity.

Structural heterogeneities are observed in relatively simple lipid or phospholipid films by x-ray analysis, the stable lamellar form of liquid crystal orientation being broken into by regions of hexagonal or other liquid crystal phases. Similar heterogeneities might likewise constitute local structural features of living membranes, to form channels through which various molecular or ionic species could penetrate the cell membrane. However, the number of such channels is probably very small. Only about 10^{-7} of the surface would be available for movement of ions if the membrane were 100Å thick and had a resistance of $10^3 \ \Omega \ cm^2$.

The presence of macromolecules, predominantly as anions, in the intracellular aqueous phase leads to Donnan distribution of the diffusible ions and to an inside-negative potential across the cell membrane. The membrane appears to be differentially permeable to various ions and these permeability characterists are modified by various factors. Some of the factors are clearly physicochemical (e.g., pH); some are less well understood surface actions (e.g., effects of presence or absence of Ca); and others are still more complex biological effects (e.g., changes induced by activity, or which arise with changes in the functional interrelations between cells). There are marked differences between the ionic compositions of the intracellular and extracellular fluids, so that changes in permeability would tend to cause changes in distribution of the ions and a flow of current.

The responses of the membrane of excitable, electrogenic cells may be toward increased or decreased permeability for specific ions. Depending on the ionic species involved and the direction of the changes for each variety, different types and degrees of bioelectrogenesis may be produced.

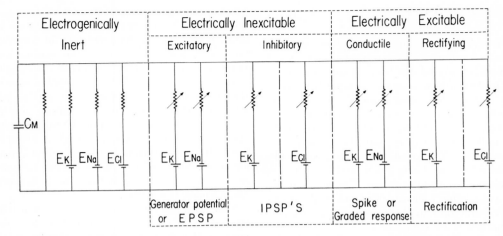

FIG. 1. Generalized electrochemical equivalent circuit of a cell membrane which is capable of electrogenic activity. Lower portion of diagrammatic membrane faces the interior of the cell. The electrogenically inert component of the membrane is probably by far the larger part of its surface. It is represented by channels with invariant permeability characteristics, symbolized by a capacity (Cm) and fixed resistances. Channels or "pores" in the membrane which are not ion specific are indicated as a resistance without a battery in series. Channels specific for the 3 major ions form ionic batteries. Other possible ionic batteries, e.g., for Ca^{++} and/or Mg^{++} are omitted. Two classes of electrogenically reactive membrane are designated by their responsiveness only to specific stimuli (electrically inexcitable components) or to electrical stimuli (electrically excitable components), the reactivity being symbolized by variable resistances of the ion specific channels. The different functional characteristics of the different components are indicated at the top and the types of potentials which develop are listed below. Further description in text.

Since Na, K and Cl are the predominant inorganic ions, bioelectrogenesis probably involves changes in flux for one or several of these species. The change in permeability raises the membrane conductance at the most perhaps 100- to 1000-fold, or decreases it 2- to 10-fold. Thus, the major part of the cell membrane is *electrogenically inert*, and only a small part is *electrogenically* reactive (Fig. 1).

The Resting Potential

While the predominant extracellular cation is Na, the predominant intracellular cation is K. Thus, the cell is not in a Donnan equilibrium, but in a steady state condition of unequal distribution of ions. The preferential concentration of intracellular K is probably achieved by metabolically driven ion exchange mechanisms (or pumps) of unknown nature. These pumps presumably are located in the cell membrane and cause extrusion of Na with intake of K, both against their concentration gradients. However, some investigators dispute this generally accepted view, postulating that the selective accumulation of K is caused by preferential chemical and/or electrostatic binding of K by the cell contents.

The unequal distribution of Na and K should produce emf's of opposite sign according to the Nernst equation:

$$E_{cation} = \frac{RT}{F} \ln \frac{C_0^+}{C_i^+}$$

R is the gas constant; T is the absolute temperature; F is the Faraday; C_0^+, C_i^+ are the external and internal concentrations (or activities) of a particular cationic species; E_K being inside-negative and E_{Na} inside-positive.

In its resting state, however, the cell membrane appears to be relatively impermeable to Na and the resting potential E_M then takes on an inside-negative value, like the Donnan potential, and corresponding approximately to E_K. In other words, the resting cell membrane appears to behave approximately as a K-electrode.

In some cells the intracellular Cl appears to be determined entirely by the Donnan condition, i.e., passively, according to the relation

$$E_{Cl} = E_M = \frac{RT}{F} \ln \frac{Cl_i}{Cl_0}$$

In other cells, however, there appears to be an active or "pump" mechanism setting the level of

Cl_i at some other value. E_{Cl} then may be more or less negative than E_M. Thus, the resting potential depends upon the relative effectiveness of the cell membrane as an electrode at least toward K, Na and Cl, and perhaps toward Ca and/or Mg, as well. This relation is expressed approximately by

$$E_M = \frac{RT}{F} \ln \frac{P_K\, K_0 + P_{Na}\, Na_0 + P_{Cl}\, Cl_i}{P_K\, K_i + P_{Na}\, Na_i + P_{Cl}\, Cl_0}$$

P_K, P_{Na} and P_{Cl} are "permeability" coefficients.

The coefficients P_K, P_{Na} and P_{Cl} can be derived from the Planck flux equations. However, it is doubtful if the latter apply to the non-homogeneous membrane model which is shown in Fig. 1, and which is based on a large body of experimental evidence. Not all the different ion-specific channels which are included in Fig. 1 are necessarily present in every cell membrane. However, if only several varieties of these channels coexist within the very thin membrane, the electrochemical conditions become quite complex. To provide discrimination between cations and anions it is likely that channels exist with either a net negative or a net positive charge. The cell membrane therefore is probably a mosaic of differently charged sites, and some of these are now being characterized specifically. The high degree of specificity of the membrane with respect to K and Na indicates that the negatively charged (cationic) channels are probably distributed as populations of very restricted size-distributions. The different channels behave independently to a considerable degree, indicating that they have different kinds of chemical and physicochemical structures.

These various conditions are in marked contrast with those which obtain in artificial membranes. The cell membrane is also considerably less permeable to water. Furthermore, living cells perform under steady-state rather than under static, equilibrium conditions. The system must be exposed to various phase boundary as well as diffusion potentials and the changes in ionic profile within the membrane occur in extremely confined regions. Thus, rigorous mathematical analysis of bioelectric phenomena has not yet been achieved. However, a qualitative description and, to some extent, a semiquantitative accounting of bioelectrogenesis in terms of ionic permeabilities is now possible.

Bioelectric activity

Living electrogenic membranes possess a transducer action, the capacity to change their permselectivity rapidly, specifically, and reversibly, with a consequent change in their electrode properties (Fig. 2). The latter changes are particularly manifested when the changes in permselectivity lead to a redistribution of ions down their concentration gradients, causing a current flow which changes the charge across the membrane capacity (Fig. 1).

The most commonly studied and best characterized types of electrogenesis are those which are due to Na-activation, increased membrane permeability for Na. The membrane then tends to depolarize, becoming less inside-negative, and may even develop an *overshoot*, becoming inside-positive to a value approaching E_{Na} in the case of spikes. However, there may also be an increased permeability for K (K-activation) or for Cl (Cl-activation). These repolarizing changes may develop in the presence of Na-activation, or without the latter. The different processes may differ in their kinetics and the latter may be modified for one process independently of the others.

All these varieties of change are produced in two apparently fundamentally different types of membrane structures, in which the changes are initiated by different types of stimuli. One of these membrane structures is characteristic of the input surfaces of electrogenic cells. It responds with transducer actions only to specific stimuli; chemical, mechanical, thermal, or photic, but it does not respond to electrical stimuli, except, perhaps, in the case of special electricity receptors of fish.

This *electrically inexcitable* membrane component is specialized for reception of messages, either from sensory stimuli, or messages transmitted across the synaptic junction from the presynaptic neuron to a postsynaptic cell. The latter may be another neuron or an effector cell (muscle fiber, electroplaque, gland or neurosecretory cell). The transducer actions of the second type of membrane are initiated by a change in the membrane potential. These membranes thus are *electrically excitable*. Membranes of cells which are specialized for conductile activity generate spikes (Fig. 3) which propagate along a nerve or muscle fiber without decrement.

In the electrically inexcitable membrane, the process of Na-activation is accompanied by simultaneous or nearly simultaneous K-activation. The membrane potential thus tends to assume a value

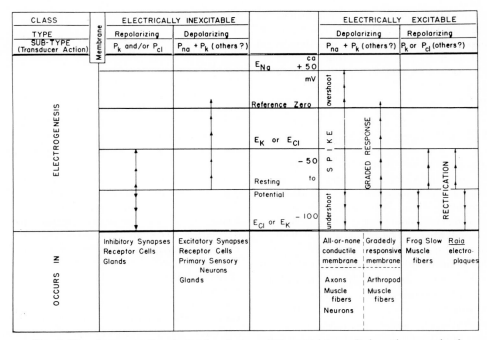

Fig. 2. The changes in the electrochemical conditions which result from increase in the permeability of the different channels. The resting potential (E_M) is indicated (center column) as lying between -50 and -100 mv. E_K and E_{Cl} may be slightly negative or positive to E_M respectively. The changes in permselectivity for different ions are denoted by the coefficients P_k, P_{na}, P_{cl}, respectively. Increase of P_k and/or P_{cl} can cause only small changes in E_M, leading to repolarizing electrogenesis or rectification (two outside columns). The multiple arrow heads indicate that the potentials can assume any intermediate value between E_M and E_K or E_{Cl} (i.e., they are graded responses). The depolarizing electrically inexcitable membrane also generates responses which are graded in amplitude, but which range between E_M and approximately zero potential. Similar changes for P_k and P_{na} which occur in electrically excitable membrane may be regenerative, changing in all-or-none fashion from E_M toward E_{Na}. Some cells exhibit a subsequent hyperpolarization (undershoot) or an after-depolarization. Graded, depolarizing electrically excitable responses are produced by some cells. The cell types in which these various responses occur are shown at the bottom of the diagram.

between E_{Na} and E_K, a depolarization from the resting inside-negativity, approximately to zero membrane potential. This depolarization can act as a stimulus for conductile activity of the electrically excitable component, if the latter is present. The electrically inexcitable electrogenesis accordingly is a functionally specialized activity of receptor neurons, which is termed the *generator potential,* or of the input of postsynaptic cells, where it is the *excitatory postsynaptic potential.*

The two activation processes are somewhat out of phase in electrically excitable, conductile membranes (Fig. 4). The initial process is that of Na-activation, and the membrane potential accordingly tends to change toward E_{Na}. Thus, the spike usually develops an *overshoot* with inside-positivity, before K-activation tends to return the potential toward E_K. The responses of electrically excitable membrane are voltage- and time-dependent, but the kinetics of the activations (and of associated inactivation processes) are remarkably constant in most cells. Their constancy arises largely from the fact that Na-activation, which is initiated by a depolarizing stimulus, itself causes further depolarization, as the membrane capacity is charged toward inside-positivity by the influx of Na. The positive feedback makes the process regenerative and all-or-none. This is an admirable biological adaptation for transmission of a signal in a cable conductor which has very high electrical losses. The same principles, insertion of distributed amplifiers and pulse-shaping or phasing networks, are also utilized in long-lines communication systems. In the nerve

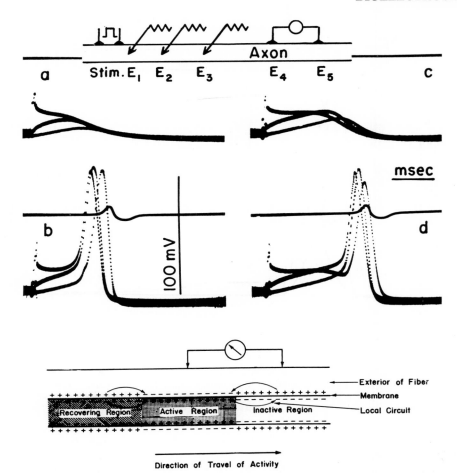

FIG. 3. Initiation and propagation of a spike. *a–d*, recordings from 5 sites of a squid giant axon, three intracellular (E_1–E_3) and two extracellular (E_4, E_5) as shown in the inset diagram. A brief external stimulus was applied to the axon. It was subthreshold in *a* and produced only a local response, which lasted about 1.5 msec. This activity was largest close to the site of stimulation, and probably died out somewhere in the region between E_2 and E_3. The decay of the local response and of its electronic spread to E_3 were passive with the time course of the RC circuit (Fig. 1). *b:* The stimulus was increased slightly and evoked a spike at E_1 which spread progressively to E_2 and E_3 and then to E_4 and E_5, as denoted by the diphasic response on the upper trace, which is also the zero reference line. The excitability in the region of the stimulating electrode was then decreased by microinjection of a chemical agent through E_1 (*c*). The subthreshold stimulus (stronger than in *a*) elicited a large electrotonic potential at E_1, and a local response as well. The latter, however, was now inadequate for evoking a spike. The more excitable regions at E_2 and E_3 each produced local responses which outlasted that at E_1. *d:* A stronger stimulus caused a spike at E_2 which was then followed by a spike at E_3 and a later, smaller response at E_1. Note that the peak of the extracellularly recorded response at E_4 now occurred at about the same time as did that of the spike at E_1. Below: Diagram of the events during propagation of the spike. The spike acts as a local source of current flowing inside the cell toward inactive and recovered regions. The depolarization induced by the local circuit current in the as yet inactive region causes excitation and a spike, with consequent propagation into a more distant, as yet inactive region.

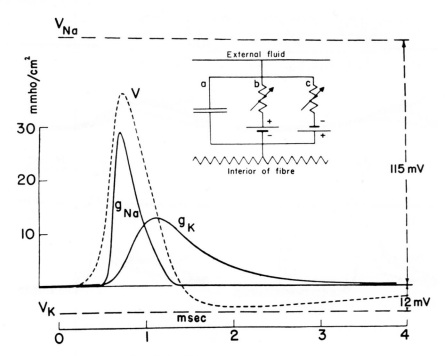

FIG. 4. The time course of changes in ionic conductances (g_{Na} and g_K) which generate a spike (V) of the squid axon, according to the Hodgkin-Huxley theory. The inset diagram shows the inside-positive Na-battery (c), the inside-negative K-battery (b), and the membrane capacity (a). Further description in text.

or muscle fiber locally stored energy is used in the process of spike-production and the system is somewhat analogous to a gunpowder fuse, in which the stimulus (heat) ignites a grain of powder, which produces more heat to ignite adjacent grains, etc.

In both types of membrane, however, there are also varieties which respond only with K- or Cl-activation, Na-activation being absent. The electrogenesis then tends to drive the membrane potential toward E_K or E_{Cl}. If this kind of re-polarizing response occurs in conjunction with the depolarizing type, the latter is diminished. A functionally important combination of the two different types of electrically inexcitable membrane occurs in receptors and at synapses. The depolarizing electrogenesis (generator or excitatory postsynaptic potential) is then diminished or abolished by the simultaneous occurrence of the repolarizing activity of adjacent components of the membrane. The latter are therefore inhibitory to the process of excitation and are termed *inhibitory postsynaptic potentials*. The repolarizing type of electrogenesis does not seem

to play an important independent role in electrically excitable membranes. However, it is known to occur in a few types of cells.

The *I-E* relation is linear (i.e., ohmic) in electrically inexcitable membrane (Fig. 5). There can be no feedback, positive or negative between the electrogenesis and the responsiveness of the membrane. The *I-E* relation remains linear during activity which is induced in the membrane by specific stimuli, but it assumes a different slope depending on the amount of conductance increase during activity. In the presence of applied currents the amplitude of the response is the difference between the two *I-E* lines and above a certain level of the applied current the sign of the potential changes. Thus, the intersections of the resting and active lines represent the *reversal* or *equilibrium potentials* for the electrogenesis of the depolarizing and repolarizing membranes.

The *I-E* relations of electrically excitable membranes reflect the responsiveness of the latter to electrical stimuli and are nonlinear. There are a number of different kinds of behavior, depending on the specific variety of cells and resulting from

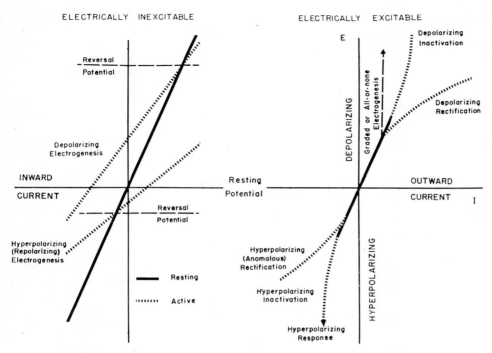

FIG. 5. Characterization of different types of electrogenic activity by their current-voltage (*I-E*) relations. Electrically inexcitable membranes have linear (ohmic) *I-E* relations, but the slope changes during activity, since the membrane conductance increases. The electrically excitable changes in membrane properties cause nonlinearities in the *I-E* relations. A marked change in emf occurs during the membrane changes which lead to graded or all-or-none responses. The rectifying (activating) changes, which indicate increased conductance in one or more ion channels also cause emf changes, but smaller in amplitude (cf. Figs. 1 and 2). The inactivation processes cause increases in membrane resistance which do not usually alter the emf's, but are manifested as large increases in the membrane potential during the flow of the applied current.

different types of activation and inactivation processes. In general they may be reduced to the patterns shown in Fig. 5. The depolarizing activation which changes the membrane conductance for Na also changes the membrane battery (Fig. 4) and results in various types of spikes or depolarizing graded responses. Depolarizing rectification reflects the increased membrane conductance which results from K- or Cl-activation. Similar but less well-understood processes of hyperpolarizing activation are also known. Furthermore, sustained depolarizing or hyperpolarizing currents can produce decreases in membrane conductance or inactivation for specific ions. The different types of membrane responses occur to various degrees and in various combinations in different types of cells. The electrochemical interplays which result from these different electrophysiological phenomena thus give rise to numerous varieties of bioelectrogenic activity.

References

HODGKIN, A. L., The Croonian Lecture, "Ionic movements and electrical activity in giant nerve fibres." *Proc. Roy. Soc. London, Series B*, **148**, 1–37 (1957).

GRUNDFEST, H., "Ionic mechanisms in electrogenesis," *Ann. N. Y. Acad. Sci.*, **94**, 405–457 (1961).

GRUNDFEST, H., "General physiology and pharmacology of junctional transmission." *In* "Biophysics of Physiological and Pharmacological Actions," A. M. SHANES, Editor, Washington, D. C., American Association for the Advancement of Science, Publ. #69, 329–389, 1961.

GRUNDFEST, H., "Impulse conducting properties of cells." *In* "The General Physiology of Cell Specialization," D. MAZIA AND A. TYLER, Editors, New York, McGraw-Hill Book Co., 277–322, 1963.

FINKELSTEIN, A., AND MAURO, A., "Equivalent circuits as related to ionic systems," *Biophys. J.*, **3**, 215–237 (1963).

HARRY GRUNDFEST

Cross-references: *Biological Transducers; Electric Organs; Electrophysiology; Ion Transport Across Charged Membranes; Membrane Equilibrium; Membrane Potentials; Nerve Impulse Transmission.*

BIOLOGICAL TRANSDUCERS

Definition and classification

Living organisms are endowed with a great number of mechanisms of energy conversion which all fall under the heading of biological transducers. Usage, however, restricts this term to the information devices, or sensory receptors, engaged in transforming environmental energy into electrical energy of the nerve impulse. In this restricted sense, biological transducers are the means—in fact, the only means—by which an organism obtains information about its surroundings.

A wide variety of transducer forms have evolved. Among them are simple bare nerve endings, encapsulated nerve structures of the corpuscle type, well-organized epithelial cell-nerve cell associations, and highly differentiated cell systems. (The reader is referred to standard textbooks of neuro-histology for detailed morphological descriptions.) One feature, however,

seems common to all forms: the transducer is an outgrowth of a nerve cell or, at least, in close contact with one. Around the primary nerve element, multiform structures develop, adapting the transducer to a specific function. The scheme of Fig. 1A, which applies to a wide variety of receptors, depicts the case of a transducer of the corpuscle type formed around an outgrowth of a myelinated nerve fiber.

Biological transducers are conveniently classified according to the kind of energy conversion they specialize in: (1) mechanoreceptors, a particularly varied and ubiquitous kind, sensitive to displacements, pressure, stress (this includes also a highly specialized type, sensitive to sound and ultrasound); (2) thermoreceptors, sensitive to temperature changes or gradients; (3) chemoreceptors, excited by certain molecules and often only by a given molecular configuration; (4) photoreceptors, sensitive to the visual band of electromagnetic radiations; (5) infrared-receptors, a relatively rare variety exhibited, for instance, by crotalid snakes; (6) electroreceptors, present in certain species of fish, highly sensitive to electrical fields and/or currents.

Sensitivity

Biological transducers differ greatly in sensitivity. Some are remarkably sensitive and effi-

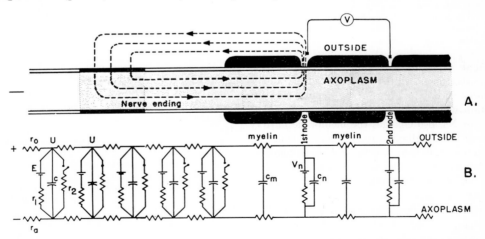

FIG. 1. Biological transducer. Anatomical, A, (upper) and electrical analog, B, (lower) of a transducer of the kind of the Pacinian corpuscle. Transducer membrane is the membrane of the bare (nonmyelinated) nerve ending. Initial portion of the nerve fiber which transmits nerve impulses is shown with its lipid insulator (myelin). Excited transducer membrane area is shown in black; arrows indicate direction of generator current. Transducer potential, V, is led off between two gaps of myelin (nodes). r_o, resistance of fluid around transducer membrane; r_a, resistance of internal media of nerve fiber (axoplasm). Explanation of other symbols in text. From Loewenstein, *Ann. N.Y. Acad. Sci.*, **94**, 510–534 (1961); reprinted by permission N.Y. Acad. Sci.

cient. For example: vertebrate photoreceptor rods detect light energy on the order of 1 quantum. The complex system of the mammalian ear, which transmits mechanical energy from sound waves to the auditory receptors, displays such an extraordinary perfect matching of mechanical impedance, that it can sense external displacements of 10^{-8} cm. Electroreceptors distinguish changes in electrical field of 1 $\mu v/cm$ in the seawater surrounding a fish, and Pacinian corpuscles of mammals are excited by displacements on the order of 10^{-5} cm. The sensitivity of such receptors lies well within the range of random noise, and noise-filtering nerve networks have evolved at various levels in series with the transducers of high sensitivity. The less differentiated receptors have much lower sensitivities. For instance, certain movement receptors in the joints of insects and crustacae have sensitivities on the order of 10^{-3} to 10^{-2} cm displacements, well suited as gating switches.

Transducer structures and mechanisms

The smallness of most biological transducers (most measure on the order of 0.001 mm) places them beyond the reach of the available biochemical and electrochemical techniques. Only a few of them, such as the Pacinian corpuscle of the cat, the stretch receptor nerve cell of the abdominal musculature of crustacae, and the photoreceptors of the horseshoe crab and squid are large enough for analysis. Our present knowledge of biological transducer mechanisms derives almost entirely from these receptors.

In these receptors, application of the appropriate form of energy leads to the following sequence of events:

environmental energy change = stimulus
→ generator current → nerve impulse

The generator current is the earliest detectable sign of excitation. It resembles the transducer current of nonbiological transducers with electrical output: it follows the stimulus at a fixed and short latency, varies continuously over a wide range with the energy content of the stimulus, and saturates at high levels of energy input (Fig. 2B). This current eventually triggers the nerve impulse, the communication signal between the transducer and central nerve system.

All elements of the transducer process seem to be built into the membrane, 75×10^{-7} mm thick, which bounds the nerve element (see **Nerve Im-**

pulse). This is particularly clear in the case of the Pacinian corpuscle in which the entire non-nervous structure has been eliminated experimentaly without impairing the transducer function. In this receptor, energy conversion takes place at the level of the membrane of the non-myelinated nerve ending, which is the transducer proper. There is good indirect evidence that this applies in general to a wide variety of receptors. The following picture of transducer mechanisms has emerged from work of the Columbia group of Loewenstein.

The transducer membrane separates two media of different concentration. On the intracellular side, the medium is notably rich in K ions (and certain large undiffusible organic anions) and poor in Na and Cl ions; while on the extracellular side the situation is reversed. At rest, the membrane offers a high resistance to ion flow. When stimulated, absorption of the appropriate energy form causes the resistance to decrease and ions to flow along their electrochemical gradients. A high energy barrier of about 16,000 cal/mole limits this process. The change in membrane resistance may be directly or indirectly coupled with the stimulus energy. An indirect coupling is present in highly differentiated transducers, such as visual receptors. Here a chemical reaction(s), the rate-limiting step in this case, intervenes in the transducer sequence between the trapping of photons and the production of the generator current. A more direct coupling probably exists in mechanoreceptors. In their simplest form, these appear to operate like certain mechanosensitive monolayers in which diffusion resistance and surface pressure are inversely related. Stretching of the monolayer decreases the molecular packing and the lateral attractive forces between molecules and, thereby, decreases the resistance for diffusion through the monolayer. The corresponding energies of activation are as high as that of mechanoreceptors. Stretching of the transducer membrane may be pictured similarly to lower lateral forces between its constituent molecules, and, thus, to diminish the resistance for ion diffusion; or stated figuratively, to stretch out diffusion channels. Ions, in particular Na^+, K^+, and Cl^-, diffuse through along their gradients; the net transfer of ionic charge constitutes the generator current. It is interesting in connection with this simple model that stretch is known to increase permeability also in other biological membranes, such as those of blood cells, muscle fibers, and nerve fibers,

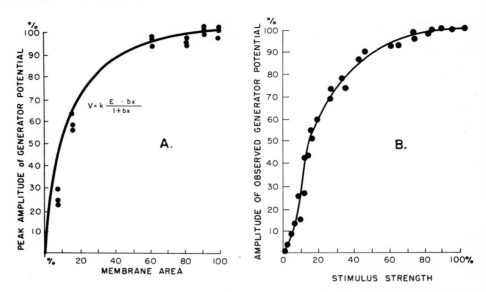

Fig. 2. A, (left). Transducer potential vs excited membrane area. Dots are experimental data from Pacinian corpuscle. The line is the theoretical area-transducer potential relation according to Eq. (1). B, (right). Stimulus energy-transducer potential relation (experimental) in a Pacinian corpuscle. From Loewenstein, *Ann. N.Y. Acad. Sci.*, **81**, 367–387 (1959); reprinted by permission of N.Y. Acad. Sci.

TABLE 1. PROPERTIES OF TRANSDUCER AND CONDUCTILE STRUCTURES

Property	Transducer Membrane Component	Impulse Membrane Component
excitation	highly localized	propagated
charge transfer	continuously variable	all-or-none
transmembrane resistance	approximately constant when probed with inward or outward current	markedly rectifying
membrane current/potential relationship (excited state)	approximately proportional	not proportional
temperature dependence	positive temperature coefficient, $Q_{10} \doteq 2$	$Q_{10} \doteq 1.1$ or negative
energy requirement for excitation	specially low for transducer stimulus	unspecifically low for electrical currents
drug-sensitivity: tetradotoxin	not affected	excitation blocked
: procaine	slightly affected	excitation blocked

which normally are not functioning as mechano-receptors. The sensitivity levels in these cases are, however, several orders of magnitude below those of proper mechanoreceptors.

The membrane portions engaged in the transducer process have a number of distinctive features, as revealed by electrical methods (Table 1). One of the most striking is the local character of excitation. When a small spot within the receptor membrane of a Pacinian corpuscle is stimulated mechanically, this spot alone is excited. The membrane reaction that leads to the conductance change is highly localized. It is localized at and confined to the membrane spot that has been stimulated mechanically. In contrast to a conductile nerve or muscle fiber membrane, excitation in the transducer membrane is not brought about by local circuit excitation (see Nerve Impulse), but only through the external stimulus.

The only coupling agent in the excitation process along the membrane of a biological transducer appears to be the external stimulus. For analytical purposes, the transducer membrane may thus be regarded as composed of functionally independent transducer units, and be represented by a network of the sort shown in Fig. 1 B. Capacitance, C, and transmembrane resistance, r, are considered uniformly distributed over the membrane. Each transducer unit, U, represents thus a fractional value of the total membrane capacitance and resistance. It is thus an analytical unit, and not necessarily a real structural element of membrane. The feature of local excitation is represented by a local drop in transmembrane resistance, r_1. A simple possibility is that this drop is all-or-none with respect to the stimulus energy in each U-unit. Shunt resistor, r_2, performs this so that the local potential, E (resting membrane potential), across a unit drops proportionally to the resistance. The potential, V (rising phase), recorded between two points of the nerve fiber (for instance between two nodes of Ranvier at which the potential is easily recorded) resulting from the flow of generator current between the excited and unexcited region of fiber membrane is thus given approximately by an equation of the form:

$$V = k\,\frac{Ebx}{1+bx}\,(1 - e^{-t/R_1 C}) \qquad (1)$$

where x is the fraction of U-units excited, that is, the ratio of excited transducer membrane area to total excitable transducer membrane area; E, membrane potential at rest; $1 + b$, the ratio between E and the final value to which the membrane potential drops in the excited membrane region due to a stimulus of unlimited energy; R_1, the parallel combination of distributed transmembrane resistance of the entire transducer membrane in parallel with that of the excited membrane; C, the lumped capacitance of the entire membrane; and k, a constant depending on the location of the recording electrodes.

The equation describes the peak value of V ($t \to \infty$), which here will be referred to as the generator potential, increasing at a nonlinear rate with x, the fraction of excited transducer units. To restate this simply: the amount of charge transferred at the transducer membrane, the generator current, increases with excited membrane area.

The biological transducer membrane operates thus essentially like a variable resistance device, attached to a voltage source of low capacity, in which the current depends on the number of in-parrallel shunt resistors. Since the number of shunt resistors, the ion diffusion paths, is very large, the transducer current is continuously variable without visible steps. Under physio-

logical conditions, the determining factor of the current is the stimulus energy. As the stimulus energy increases, the probability for excitation of transducer units (membrane area) increases (see below), and, consequently, the generator current increases (Fig. 2B). At the transducer level, information about environmental energy thus enters the organism in the form of an electrical current the intensity of which is exponentially related with the input energy.

Statistical excitation

The generator current is built up statistically. A number of factors concur to this effect: (1) fluctuation in energy content of the stimulus; (2) quantal absorption of energy by the transducer structure; (3) coarse fluctuation in energy absorption due to unequal accessibility of transducer structure to the stimulus energy; (4) fluctuations in potential gradients and resistance.

Factor *2* is quantitatively important in the case of highly sensitive receptors, such as photoreceptors and probably also in many chemoreceptors. In the majority of receptors, factor *3* is the main fluctuating variable.

In Pacinian corpuscles the mean fluctuation of excited transducer area (mean number of excited transducer units) appears to be proportional to the mean area excited, and the standard deviation of transducer potential, σV, is given by:

$$\sigma_V = \frac{\sigma_x}{x}\,V(1 - V/kE) \qquad (2)$$

where σ_x represents the standard deviation of excited transducer units and the other symbols have the name meaning as in Eq. 1. (σ_x/x is as high as 0.08 in many cases).

The equation predicts that the curve of generator potential fluctuation vs mean generator potential exhibits a peak at $V = kE/2$. Since the mean area excited increases with stimulus energy, it follows that as the latter is progressively increased, fluctuation of generator potential first increases and then declines. The physiological range of stimulus energy falls generally in a region beyond the peak where the fluctuations in generator current are near their lowest.

Aftereffects of transducer excitation

Excitation is followed by a transient inactivation in the transducer membrane. This manifests itself as a marked reduction of generator current in response to a given stimulus. Inactivation, like excitation, is a highly localized process which does not spread beyond the excited membrane area. It has a statistical character and within certain limits increases with stimulus frequency and duration. Inactivation is independent of resting membrane potential and appears to reflect a transient deactivation of the process associated with the conductance change in the transducer membrane.

Nerve impulse initiation

When the generator current reaches a certain critical magnitude, a nerve impulse is produced which travels to the nerve centers. This all-or-none event is the universal communication signal inside organisms wherever information is conveyed over more than a few millimeters. Out of materials, water, a few salts, and organic molecules, which must look rather improbable building blocks to an electrical engineer, nature has made a communication system of nerve cables in which electrical signals are transmitted, in some instances over several meters. As cables, their performance is rather poor. They are so leaky that signals would fade out completely over lengths greater than 1 mm, if they were not continuously reamplified. In vertebrates, crustacae, and insects, the signal is maintained at constant magnitude on its way to the nerve centers along the nerve fiber by booster systems built into the fiber membrane (see **Nerve Impulse**). Only in primitive organisms, where signals traffic over short distances, may the generator current itself serve as communication signal.

Although in many cases, if not in all, both nerve impulse and generator current are produced by a nerve fiber, the membrane components in which they originate are distinctly different. Table 1 summarizes some of the distinguishing qualities. In some cases the two components are coarsely segregated. In Pacinian corpuscles, for instance, the site of impulse initiation appears to be at the first Ranvier node, about 0.2 mm from the transducer membrane of the nonmyelinated nerve ending (Fig. 1A). In other receptors, the two components may be closer, or even intermingled in a mosaic pattern. Their respective electrical outputs are then not directly distinguishable with the available techniques, when simultaneously active. But even then, the two components can be separated by

application of molecules which act selectively on one of the components. The drug tetradotoxin, for example, blocks selectively the impulse component, but leaves the transducer component unaffected.

When an electrical current is passed experimentally through the impulse membrane, outward through the membrane, a nerve impulse is tripped off whenever the current reaches a minimal intensity with a minimal velocity. Within certain limits, the frequency of discharged impulses increases with the intensity of the current. This is the basis of frequency coding of sensory signals. Under physiological conditions, the transducer current has precisely the same direction and effect (Fig. 1). Current, namely the generator current, flows from portions of the transducer membrane excited, i.e., depolarized by action of the external stimulus, to the as yet unexcited, i.e., fully polarized impulse membrane, outward through the latter. The result is the discharge of nerve impulses, the number of which is a function of the intensity and rate of rise of the generator current. This appears to be the way in which information about the outside world is conveyed to the nerve centers. The transducer sequence that started with an intensity code, ends with a code of frequency-modulated signals running to the centers.

Transducer codes

Because nerve fibers conduct only signals of the all-or-none kind over any significant lengths, the only way to convey quantitative information about the transducer energy to the nerve centers is by changing the sequence of the signals. One code that seems to be universally used by biological transducer systems, is a simple frequency code, in which the average frequency of impulses increases as a function of the stimulus energy. The links in the chain leading to this code are the dependences of stimulus energy → excited transducer membrane area → generator current → impulse frequency. The shape of the latter function, within the physiological ranges of stimulus energy, is from linear to exponential in the various types of receptors.

In higher organisms, transducers generally form clusters, all units within the cluster subserving the same function. The density of grouped elements varies greatly in different receptor systems. For example: 2/sq cm for cutaneous Pacinian corpuscles; 1000/sq cm for photoreceptors of a vertebrate retina. Each individual transducer of a cluster, or subgroups of a few, are connected to an independent nerve fiber. Many such fibers, often thousands of them, are packed tightly together in bundles on their way to the nerve centers. Each fiber is well insulated; there is no significant crosstalk of signals between adjacent fibers in a bundle. This permits another way of information coding: receptors of a given cluster have nonuniform thresholds for excitation. Thus, the greater the stimulus energy, the greater the number of excited receptors in the cluster, and hence, the greater the number of parallel nerve fibers engaged in impulse traffic.

There are then at least two ways by which the nerve centers may analyze the content of a transducer message: by counting the number of parallel information channels engaged in signal transmission, and by gauging the frequency and sequence of signals in each information channel. A system in which information is transmitted at the expense of an enormous number of channels must seem, at first glance, a rather wasteful one. But since it is a highly structured system in which transducers and analyzing centers are connected in orderly arrays, it permits transmission of a wealth of information about spatial energy patterns of the environment together with time patterns. Information about distribution of energy in the classical three dimensions appears to be processed through a spatial code built into the fixed transducer-center array, while that about energy distribution in the time dimension, is processed in a separate time-dependent code.

References

ADRIAN, E. D., "The Physical Background of Perception," Oxford, Clarendon Press, 1947.

GRANIT, R., "Receptors and Sensory Perception," New Haven, Yale University Press, 1955.

LOEWENSTEIN, W. R., "The Generation of Electric Activity in a Nerve Ending," *Ann. N. Y. Acad Sci.*, **81**, 367–387 (1959).

LOEWENSTEIN, W. R., "Excitation and Inactivation in a Receptor Membrane," *Ann. N. Y. Acad. Sci.*, **94**, 510–534 (1961).

WERNER R. LOEWENSTEIN

Cross-references: *Electrophysiology; Nerve Impulse Transmission.*

BORON CARBIDE

B_4C—Mol. wt. 55.28; Density 2.50 gm/ml; M. p. 2470°C; Resistivity 0.4 ohm-cm; Knoop Hardness (100 gm load), $K_{100} = 2800$; Crystal structure—Rhombohedral $D_{3d}^5 - R\bar{3}m$, a = 5.19Å, $\alpha = 65.3°$; Thermal expansion, 20–900°C $= 58 \times 10^{-7}/°C$.

Boron carbide is a lustrous black or gray solid of exceptional hardness. It was developed commercially by R. R. Ridgway[1] (q.v.) and the formula of the ideal crystal was established as B_4C. It may be fabricated[2] by hot pressing a finely milled powder into shapes which then have excellent wear-resistant properties. Accordingly, it is used for sand-blast nozzles, mortars for grinding hard materials, bearings for balances, gage blocks and contact points. As a loose powder, it is also used as a lapping agent for polishing sapphire, tungsten carbide die blanks, and other hard materials. To date it has not been successful as a grinding-wheel abrasive.

Boron carbide was first discovered by Moissan in his electric arc furnace (1894). His analysis indicated the composition B_6C. He mentions also another carbide containing less boron, but this was not characterized. Mülhauser, about the same time, prepared a composition which he identified as B_2C_2 which must have contained a large excess of free graphite. In 1906 Tucker and Bliss were unable to reproduce Moissan's results. Their products analyzed from 70–83 per cent B (corresponding to formulas B_3C to B_5C).

Boron carbide is produced in a closed-shell resistance furnace, with a graphite core, from B_2O_3 glass and coke. Alternatively, it may be made in an arc furnace. In some cases, boric acid, H_3BO_3, may be substituted for the anhydrous boric oxide glass. Annual production of crude boron carbide on the North American continent is estimated (1962) as about 40 tons per year, valued at $180,000. The reactions involved in production are as follows:

$$2B_2O_3 + 7C \rightarrow B_4C + 6CO \uparrow$$

or

$$4H_3BO_3 + 7C \rightarrow B_4C + 6CO \uparrow + 6H_2O \uparrow$$

Up to 20 kwh of electrical energy may be required to produce a pound of B_4C, although the theoretical requirement has been calculated as 7.7.

There are two isotopes of boron, B^{10} and B^{11}. The B^{10} isotope (18.8 per cent in natural boron compounds) is an effective absorber for thermal neutrons. Hence, boron carbide finds application in control and shielding of nuclear energy sources.[8] The B^{10} isotope can be concentrated to almost any desired level. $B_4^{10}C$ has been prepared by reacting elemental B^{10} with carbon or graphite for use as a neutron absorber.

Prior to the synthesis of diamond and cubic boron nitride, boron carbide was widely advertised as "the hardest material made by man." Of course, this is no longer the case.

The crystal structure[4, 5] is made up of groups of 12 boron atoms arranged at the vertices of a regular icosahedron which are interspersed in an NaCl type of structure with linear chains of 3 carbon atoms. Thus, the crystal formula might be written $B_{12}C_3$.

The interatomic distances in the structure are as follows:

$$B—B, \ 1.74 \ to \ 1.80\text{Å}$$

$$B—C, \ 1.64\text{Å}$$

$$C—C, \ 1.39\text{Å}$$

Excess boron may be accommodated in the lattice,[3, 6] so that compositions approximating the formula B_6C may be observed before free boron is detected in the system. There is some evidence that one of the three carbon atoms in the chain may be replaced by boron, which would give a structure of the formula $B_{13}C_2$. Alternatively there are available spaces in the $B_{12}C_3$ lattice into which B atoms might fit to produce a similar analysis. Some workers have claimed that excess C atoms can be accommodated in such spaces.[9, 11, 12] However, in annealed specimens, excess carbon is usually present as free graphite.

Normal B_4C analyzes to show 78.3 per cent B and 21.7 per cent C and this composition exhibits the maximum density in the pure boron-graphite system. Technical grades of boron carbide may analyze 65 to 75 per cent boron, the remainder mainly carbon. The boron enriched grades show a slight expansion of the crystal lattice in all directions. They may analyze 80 to 87 per cent B, with the remainder mainly C as before. Enriched materials are readily made by charging a closed-shell resistance furnace with boron carbide and anhydrous B_2O_3 glass.[1]

Boron carbide is a particularly stable material in respect to chemical attack or the effects of heat, abrasion, or radiation. It resists all aqueous acids, salts, and alkalis. It is attacked by fused alkali, by hot nitric acid under pressure, and by electrolytic etching if it is used as the anode in hydrochloric acid or salt solutions. In a nuclear pile there is no great damage to boron carbide at 15 per cent burn-up of the B^{10} atoms. However, granulation of hot-pressed boron carbide does occur at a B^{10} burn-up of 36 per cent.

Analysis of boron carbide is carried out by fusing the powdered sample of boron carbide in sodium carbonate and dissolving the fusion in acid. The neutralized solution, after boiling off carbon dioxide under reduced pressure, is titrated with carbonate-free sodium hydroxide in the presence of mannitol. Carbon is determined by burning the powdered samples in oxygen after mixing with red lead. For details of these and other procedures, see Scott's *Standard Methods of Chemical Analysis*.

Boron carbide is a useful raw material for the manufacture of other boron compounds. It reacts readily with gaseous halogens when heated to redness. Boron trichloride is produced in high purity by the reaction:

$$B_4C + 6Cl_2 \rightarrow 4BCl_3 + C$$

Boron carbide also reacts readily with metal oxides at high temperatures to form metal borides and carbon monoxide. The reaction may be written as, for example:

$$B_4C + 3C + 2TiO_2 \rightarrow 2TiB_2 + 4CO\uparrow$$

Boron carbide may be cemented with metals[7] to give a variety of mixed carbides or borides, some of which have interesting properties as tool bits or wear-resistant parts. Examples are TiB_2/B_4C or SiC/B_4C compacts.

Boron carbide is fabricated to shape by hot pressing a finely milled powder in graphite molds at temperatures approaching 2200°C.[2] Pieces of boron carbide prepared in this way may be cut and ground with diamond wheels and polished with diamond powder. Polished surfaces may be etched electrolytically for metallographic study.

References

1. RIDGWAY, R. R., U. S. Patents 1,897,214 (Feb. 14, 1933); 2,141,617 (Dec. 27, 1938); 2,155,682 (Apr. 25, 1939); *Trans. Electrochem. Soc.*, **66,** 117–33 (1934).
2. RIDGWAY, R. R., AND BAILEY, B. L., U. S. Patents 2,027,786 (Jan. 14, 1936); 2,150,884 (Mar. 14, 1939).
3. ALLEN, R. D., *J. Am. Chem. Soc.*, **75,** 3582–3 (1953).
4. CLARK, H. K., AND HOARD, J. L., *J. Am. Chem. Soc.*, **65,** 2115 (1943).

5. ZHDANOV, G. S., AND SEVAST'YANOV, N. G.,
   Compt. rend. acad. sci. U.R.S.S., **32**, 432–4
   (1941).
6. MEERSON AND SAMSONOV, S.L.A. Translation
   AEC-TR-3317.
7. HAMJIAN, H. J., AND LIDMAN, W. G., *NACA,
   TN 1948*, Sept. 1949; *TN 2050*, Mar. 1950.
8. FINLAY, G. R., *Bull. Am. Ceram. Soc.*, **36**, 109–
   11 (1957).
9. GLASER, F. W., MOSKOWITZ, D., AND POST, B.,
   J. Appl. Phys. **24**, 731–733 (1953).
10. SMITH, D., DWORKIN, A. S., AND VAN ARTSDALEN,
    E. R., *J. Am. Chem. Soc.*, **77**, 2654–6 (1955).
11. National Carbon Co. Research Lab. Progress
    Report No. 3, 1959; *W.A.D.D. Tech. Report
    60-143*, 1959.
12. Armour Research Foundation *ARF-2200-6,
    Quarterly Report #2*, 1960.
13. KING, E. G., *Ind. Eng. Chem.*, **41**, 1298–9
    (1949).
14. ZAGYANSKII, I. L., SAMSONOV, G. V., AND POPOVA,
    N. V., *Doklady Akad. Nauk. S.S.S.R.*, **74**,
    723–4 (1950).
15. GRAY, EDGAR, Thesis #1076, "Recherches sur
    le carbure de bore," Université de Genève,
    1945.

GORDON R. FINLAY

Cross-reference: *Furnaces for Hot-Pressing.*

BORON ELECTROWINNING

Much time and effort has been spent over a long period of years in efforts to make pure boron. One of the earliest workers in this field was Henri Moissan[1] who heated boron oxide with magnesium. This reaction, however, yields only a highly impure product containing about 84 to 92 per cent boron.

Weintraub of the General Electric Company also tried this same process, but concluded that pure boron could not be made in this manner. Later Weintraub[12] attempted to purify this "Moissan Boron" by arc processes, but the pure element was not obtained. In a still later process this same investigator was successful in making small amounts of pure boron by reducing boron trichloride with hydrogen in a high tension arc.

In later work Warth, a fellow worker with Weintraub, modified this process by employing the same reaction but causing the boron to be deposited on a heated tungsten wire or rod. Nchiyama *et al*[6] described a process whereby it is claimed that crude boron can be electrorefined to a purity better than 99 per cent. Boron has also been made by the reduction of boron tri-

chloride with hydrogen using an arc struck between electrodes of tungsten or molybdenum.

Van Arkel prepared boron by dissociation of boron bromide, BBr_3, on a heated tungsten wire. A similar process is described by Laubengayer, Hurd, Newkirk, and Hoard; but in this instance hydrogen was used along with the boron bromide. Kiessling also employed this same method. McCarthy and Carpenter have reported on the synthesis of boron triiodide and its decomposition on tantalum at 800 to 1000°C (1472 to 1832°F) to yield a new crystalline modification of boron. Crystalline boron is also formed when a mixture of hydrogen and BCl_3 is passed over a heated filament of tungsten-tantalum alloy wire or titanium wire. The element can also be deposited from this same mixture on graphite or on individual wires of tungsten, tantalum, or molybdenum.

Further work on the preparation of boron by hot-wire technique is described by Powell, Ish, and Blocher.[8] Here again boron tribromide is reduced with hydrogen on a heated wire (tantalum). A similar method is described by Ellis[5] who notes that the boron diffusion into the wire is serious. Bean and Medcalf[2] describe a process for depositing boron on boron filaments using boron bromide and hydrogen. A new modification of boron prepared by the decomposition of boron bromide on tungsten or rhenium filaments is described by Talley, Post, and La-Placa.[11] Further work on the preparation of boron by reduction of boron bromide with hydrogen on tungsten wire is described by Talley, Line, and Overman.[10] In this investigation the boron is said to be in a massive amorphous form.

Although it is true that boron of high purity can be obtained by thermal decomposition or by hydrogen reduction of boron chloride or bromide or from diborane, in general, the yields are small and the cost is so high as to make such methods useful only in special instances where cost is a negligible factor. There has been a major effort by Fetterley, of the Norton Company, to produce boron on a pilot scale from boron chloride and hydrogen. In this process the boron is deposited on carbon resistor rods heated to about 1400°C (2552°F). Apparently, boron carbide is formed first, adjacent to the graphite, then a layer of boron is deposited which contains, however, about 3 per cent carbon. Production in such a unit proceeds at a rate of about one pound per hour.

Concerning other processes, Andrieux claims

to have made boron of "Moissan purity" by the electrolysis of a molten mixture of boron oxide, magnesium oxide, and magnesium fluoride. Bath temperatures are 1000 to 1100°C (1832 to 2012°F); the anode is carbon; and the cathode is an iron rod. This same investigator and a coworker describe another process in which the electrolysis is performed in baths containing Na_2O and B_2O_3, with and without MgF_2. A British patent and a United States patent disclose a fused salt process in which the initial components of the fused systems are KCl, KF, and B_2O_3. This process was discussed by Nies, McIntyre, and Fajans at a meeting of the Electrochemical Society in 1958. In a later patent[7] Nies described a cell for making boron of about 96 per cent purity. It is claimed by Stern that high purity boron can be obtained from fused salt electrolytes using an anode of boron carbide.[9] Newkirk has reviewed very thoroughly the methods for the preparation of elemental boron.

Cooper has developed two patented processes for making boron, either of which can be used for making industrial quantities of the element. In the first method described by Cooper (U.S. Patent 2,572,248), potassium fluoborate is electrolyzed in a fused bath of potassium chloride. In the second process (U.S. Patent 2,572,249) boron is obtained by electrolysis from a molten mixture of potassium chloride, potassium fluoborate and boron oxide.

In the first process the anode is a graphite-

FIG. 2. Electrolytic boron cell.

lined, heat-resisting alloy pot, and the cathode is preferably a low-carbon iron plate or cylinder. To prevent disintegration of the graphite anode at the top, it is water-cooled. The cathode is bolted to a water-cooled copper terminal which causes some salt to solidify at the surface of the bath, thereby preventing contamination of the boron with copper. A cell of this type operates for extended periods at currents as high as 3,000 amp at voltages of 6 to 12. Current efficiency is about 75 per cent. In this process, chlorine is evolved at the anode, and elemental boron is deposited on the cathode. There is a progressive buildup of potassium fluoride in the bath, coupled with a corresponding rise in voltage. The boron, after removal from the cathode and washing and drying, is predominantly coarsely crystalline, greatly resembling coke. A typical analysis is boron, 99.41 per cent; carbon, 0.29 per cent; and iron, 0.20 per cent.

Details of the operation of the above process in the Atomic Energy Commission plant of Hooker Chemical Corp. are given by Miller.

In the second process the cell construction is quite similar, but in this instance oxygen is liberated at the anode where it combines with the carbon. The boron from this process consists predominantly of fine material which readily passes through a −325 mesh sieve. An electron micrograph of fine boron has shown particle

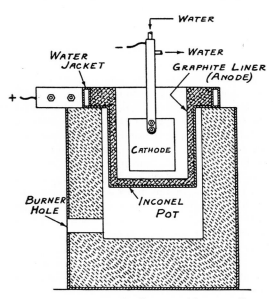

FIG. 1. A schematic diagram of boron cell.

sizes down to less than one-tenth micron and above five micron for the largest particles. Some of the larger particles are believed to be agglomerates of the very small particles. The purity of this metal is quite the same as that made by the other process mentioned. By a special upgrading and purification, boron can be obtained showing a purity of 99.70 per cent, with carbon 0.05 per cent and iron 0.15 per cent. A schematic diagram of a boron cell is shown in Fig. 1 and an actual photograph of a cell is shown in Fig. 2.

A modification of the Cooper cell shown in Fig. 1 has made it possible to reduce the total impurities found in the boron and to extend the graphite liner life, particularly in the process using B_2O_3. The liner is made neutral and graphite anode bars or slabs are suspended one on each side of the flat cathode as shown in Fig. 3. The anodes are cut in width and length such that they cause an equal distribution of current over the entire cathode. Note the smaller width and length with respect to the cathode in Fig. 3. Fig. 2 is a photograph of this arrangement showing the flat cathode in a raised position and the two anodes suspended from bus bars.

Cooper and Schaefer[3] have developed a procedure for essentially continuous operation of the KCl–KBF$_4$ bath previously described. Periodic, or continuous additions of BCl$_3$ to the bath replaces the boron electrodeposited on the cathode and the chlorine liberated at the anode, thereby keeping the bath at a nearly constant composition negating the necessity for frequent bath changes. The same procedure is used for reclaimed bath salts. This procedure is particularly applicable to the electrolysis of expensive isotopic materials on a large scale.

Cooper[4] has also developed a method of forming tenacious coatings of boron up to 0.25 inches

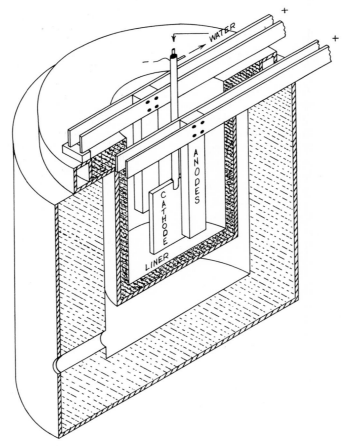

Fig. 3. Boron cell with flat anodes and cathode for improved current distribution.

thick on metallic cathodes from a fused salt bath of B_2O_3-KBF_4. These coatings are especially suited for protection against high neutron radiation. The production procedure is similar to the other Cooper methods but the bath composition is quite different, requiring 15 per cent B_2O_3 in KBF_4.

Nies[7] has developed a cell system suitable for the production of electrolytic boron and borides whereby it is possible to remove the product from the molten bath but without exposing it to the air before it has cooled. Two cells are used with one inverted over the other serving as a cover chamber. After electrolysis the unit is inverted, the cover chamber becomes the cell and the former cell acts as a cooling chamber for the product which is now removed from the bath. When cool the cover cell and its product is removed and another unit is put in its place.

Production of Boron 10

Natural boron is a mixture of the isotopes boron 10 and boron 11 in a 19.57 : 80.43 ratio.

The United States Atomic Energy Commission is interested in producing boron 10 because of its high neutron-capture cross section of 3,850 barns, as compared with 38 barns for boron 11 and 755 barns for natural boron. Boron 10 has become important for control of nuclear reactors, as a shield for nuclear radiation, and for instruments for detecting neutrons. Because of its low neutron-capture properties, boron 11 is of interest in other ways.

In 1953 the United States Atomic Energy Commission authorized the building of a plant for making boron 10. This plant began production in June, 1954, and was operated by Hooker Chemical Corp. for the United States Atomic Energy Commission until about July, 1958, when it was placed on stand-by. The plant has a capacity of 500 kilograms per year of elemental boron enriched to 90 to 95 per cent boron 10 per total boron. To separate the boron 10 from boron 11, a boron fluoride-dimethyl ether complex is employed, the separation being accomplished in large fractionation columns. Following a period of initial operations using the "hot wire" process, the process was altered to substitute fused salt electrolysis for final boron recovery. In the altered process the boron 10 complex from the fractionation columns is reacted with potassium fluoride to produce KBF_4

in which the boron content consists largely of boron 10. Using the Cooper process of U.S. Patent 2,572,248, boron 10 is deposited on a metal cathode from a bath consisting of KCl and the $KB^{10}F_4$ previously described.

Boron 11 has also been produced by means of the Cooper process by substituting $KB^{11}F_4$. This salt was made from the boron 11-rich portion remaining from the isotopic fractionation separation procedure.

References

Note: For brevity, references given in the "Rare Metals Handbook," C. A. Hampel, Editor, chapter on "Boron" by H. S. Cooper, New York, Reinhold Publishing Corp., 1961, covering up to about 1959, have been omitted.

1. MOISSON, H., *Ann. chim. et phys.*, **6**, (7) 296 (1895).
2. BEAN, K. E., AND MEDCALF, W. E., "Utilization of Boron Filaments in Vapor Phase Deposition of Boron," chapter in "Boron," New York, Plenum Press, 1960.
3. COOPER, HUGH S., AND SCHAEFER, JAMES C., "Production of Boron by Fused Salt Bath Electrolysis," U.S. Patent 2,918,417 (Dec. 22, 1959), assigned to Walter M. Weil, Cooper Metallurgical Associates.
4. COOPER, HUGH S., "Deposition of Boron from Fused Salt Baths," U.S. Patent 2,984,605 (May 16, 1961), assigned to Walter M. Weil, Cooper Metallurgical Associates.
5. ELLIS, RAY C., "Various Preparations of Elemental Boron," chapter in "Boron," New York, Plenum Press, 1960.
6. NCHIYAMA, A. A., *et al*, U.S. Patent, 2,940,911 (June 14, 1960).
7. NIES, N. P., "Electrolytic Cell," U.S. Patent 2,909,471 (Oct. 20, 1959).
8. POWELL, C. F., ISH, C. J., AND BLOCHER, J. M., "Preparation of High Purity Boron by Hot Wire Techniques," chapter in "Boron," New York, Plenum Press, 1960.
9. STERN, DAVID R., "Preparation of Boron from Boron Carbide," chapter in "Boron," New York, Plenum Press, 1960.
10. TALLEY, CLAUDE P., LINE, LLOYD E., AND, OVERMAN, QUINTON D., "Preparation and Properties of Massive Amorphous Elemental Boron," chapter in "Boron," New York, Plenum Press, 1960.
11. TALLEY, C. P., POST, B., AND LaPLACA, S., "A New Modification of Elemental Boron," chapter in "Boron," New York, Plenum Press, 1960.
12. WEINTRAUB, E., U.S. Patent 997,879 (July 11, 1911).

HUGH S. COOPER AND
JAMES C. SCHAEFER

BRIGHTENING AGENTS IN ELECTROPLATING BATHS

Most aqueous metal electroplating baths in use today for electrowinning, electrorefining, and for decorative or corrosion protective applications contain, besides the inorganic salt compositions, additives, usually organic compounds, which are employed in small concentrations in the baths to favorably modify, mainly by adsorption processes, the crystalline growth of the metal electrodeposits. Often the improvements obtained are striking.

One or more of the following improvements in electrodeposits can be accomplished with addition agents, usually organic compounds, but sometimes inorganic ions or inorganic compounds: (1) to change coarsely crystalline deposits to microcrystalline deposits, (2) to decrease treeing (dendritic) and nodular growths, (3) to change the structure of a deposit, for example, from columnar to laminar, (4) to increase the limiting cathode current density, (5) to make possible bright deposits, (6) to make possible leveling or smoothening deposits, (7) to modify the tensile or compressive stress of electrodeposits, (8) to make possible both bright and leveled deposits, (9) to change the composition of alloy plates, (10) to decrease or increase the percentage of impurities in the deposit, (11) to increase the hardness of an electrodeposit by the plating out of a uniformly fine dispersion of foreign material in the lattice, thus causing dispersion hardness similar to precipitation hardness, (12) to improve the cathode efficiency of a plating bath, (13) to improve the covering power or throwing power (improved distribution of plate from high current density to low current density areas), (14) to prevent pitting of the deposits caused by adhering hydrogen bubbles, and to minimize spray.

While the exact mode of action of the addition agents is not clearly known, reversible and irreversible adsorption phenomena are involved in the modification of the start and growth of the electrodeposits. In some cases the entire addition agent molecule can be found in the electrodeposit, in other cases, cathodic reduction or degradation products are found in the deposit. It is perhaps not yet proved whether all effective addition agents which clearly modify the deposits always leave some inclusions in the deposit. At least in the cases that have so far received the most study, inclusions from the addition agent have been found in the deposits.

The relationship of the structure of the organic addition agent to its function in a given metal electroplating bath is of fundamental importance not only to the possible understanding of the mechanism of action of the addition agent, but also for the development of improved or more effective addition agents.

One of the oldest and most versatile of addition agents is glue (impure gelatin). It is most often used in the very low concentrations of a few milligrams per liter in the electrowinning of zinc and cadmium from acid baths. It is used to decrease grain size, nodular growth, and treeing of the deposits, that is, to give smoother plate. In the case of zinc, the gelatin also increases the cathode efficiency one or two per cent, which is very important in this very large-scale commercial operation. In lead and copper refining, traces of glue and/or goulac (lignin sulfonates) are used for grain refinement and decreased treeing. Besides these important uses in electrowinning and electrorefining, glue is also used in some acidic tin, lead, and lead-tin alloy plating baths. In alkaline zinc cyanide baths it is used in conjunction with other organic compounds to help obtain bright zinc plate used as a corrosion protection coating on a variety of ferrous articles, such as bolts, nuts, screws, etc. The versatility of this large protein molecule is doubtless due to its proclivity for adsorption on surfaces, and, thus, it affects the growing electrodeposit.

Certain crystal faces may favor adsorption more than others, and thereby not only smaller crystals or grains form, but even the shapes may be altered. It may interfere more with pyramidal growth than cubic growth. In copper deposition from an acid bath, there is evidence that gelatin appears to interfere predominantly with crystal growth on steps growing vertically instead of those growing laterally. If an excess of the addition agent is added, the plate may become hard and very brittle from the excessive filming of the individual crystals, thus decreasing their cohesional as well as their adhesional forces. With the optimum concentration of the addition agent, adsorption takes place on the growing sites, and this will slow down or stop the growth of the crystal. Thus, new ions that are discharged are forced to start new nuclei with the result that finer-grained plate is obtained. The intricate large molecule addition agents like gelatin can also greatly affect the diffusion layer existing at the cathode surface by forming a film of incipient coagulated protein which acts as a membrane of varying permeability to metal ions and hydrogen ions. The coagulation of the gelatin in the cathode film is favored by the decreased hydrogen ion concentration there compared to the body of the solution as the result of hydrogen ion discharge at the cathode. Gelatin is coagulated by neutral salts but solubilized by acid. This membrane can help obtain bright plate as well as greatly improve the throwing power and eliminate treeing if the polarization at the high current points is greatly increased, or if the cathode efficiency is decreased at high current density. In general these dramatic results in quite acidic baths are obtained only with comparatively large concentrations of gelatin in conjunction with another compound, such as phenol or cresol, in, for example, acidic cadmium sulfate and acidic tin (stannous) sulfate baths, which without the addition agents give coarsely crystalline, treed deposits. With these soft metals, the excessive inclusions of the addition agents in the plate do not necessarily cause intolerably brittle plate, as they would with metals like nickel or copper. However, these more dramatic results cannot be used to their fullest extent because gelatin hydrolyzes rather rapidly in these baths, and the baths deteriorate due to the accumulation of an excess of the hydrolytic products (amino acids). Thus, the main use of gelatin in acidic baths is in smaller concentrations.

It is interesting to note that in the case of the acidic stannous sulfate baths, small concentrations of chloride ion tend to nullify the effect of additives, probably due to the preferential adsorption of the chloride ion as part of a coordination complex or basic salt. In alkaline baths, the electric charge on colloidal gelatin particles would be negative due to adsorption of hydroxyl ions or to the ionization of the carboxylate groups, and thus, there is less tendency for excessive adsorption or plating out on the cathode. The presence of glue in a lead-tin acidic fluoborate solution for the deposition of alloy plate not only helps to obtain smooth deposits, but it also tends to increase the tin content of the alloy deposit.

Addition agents are key factors in the electroplating baths used for the deposition of decorative as well as corrosion protective coatings, such as bright nickel plate which confers the brightness and the corrosion protection qualities to the important composite nickel-chromium coatings used on plumbing fixtures, kitchen untensils, automotive hardware, etc. The addition agents which make possible the brilliant leveling nickel plate are more specific, more stable, and more controllable in their effects than the colloidal type of addition agents exemplified by gelatin. The addition agents for producing brightness and/or leveling of the nickel deposits from weakly acidic baths are characterized by the presence of unsaturated bonds. It is believed that adsorption of these addition agents takes place on the freshly depositing nickel through covalency with atomic d-orbitals of the nickel and the π electrons of the unsaturated bond.

The specificity is interesting; for example, dimethyl fumarate is a good leveling agent which produces lustrous semibright plate from the weakly acidic nickel baths, but fumaric acid from which it is derived, does not. The dimethyl fumarate causes no harmful effects to the ductility and the color of the plate, but fumaric acid causes darkish brittle plate. The dimethyl fumarate is hydrogenated at the nickel cathode, though there is also evidence of irreversible adsorption because small percentages of carbonaceous matter are found in the cloudy semibright lustrous nickel plate. The mechanism of leveling in acidic nickel baths by dimethyl fumarate and similarly structured unsaturated compounds involves polarization phenomena caused by the presence of higher concentrations of these unsaturated compounds in the vicinity of edges of microrecesses (polishing scratches) due to the thinner diffusion layer present at these points. Thus, the rate of adsorption at these points is increased, which increases the resistance at these points, diverting the current lines into the microrecesses which produces the leveling effect. Even a slight change in resistance at the edges of the scratches can produce remarkable leveling effects.

To produce brilliant nickel plate instead of cloudy lustrous plate, it is necessary to also have present in the bath an aryl sulfonic acid or sulfonamide. These sulfon-compounds are fissioned by hydrogenolysis at the catalytically active nickel surface, and small concentrations of nickel sulfide are found in the bright nickel plate. Traces of benzene or naphthalene are found in the nickel baths if benzene or naphthalene sulfonic acids were used, respectively, as the brighteners.

To prevent pitting of the deposits caused by

clinging hydrogen bubbles, surface-active agents (wetting agents or detergents) are often used in these plating baths. Not all surface-active agents are compatible with the bath compositions, but the correct ones function to decrease the surface and interfacial tension at the cathode, making possible the easier detachment of the hydrogen bubbles as very small round bubbles with zero contact angle with the cathode, and at the same time to minimize spray from the bath.

For acidic copper sulfate baths, brighteners are available which produce brilliant, high-leveling, ductile copper plate. The importance of chloride ion in small traces of about 10 milligrams/liter in the acid copper sulfate baths to obtain brightness with many of the organic addition agents, such as thioureas, indicates that the cuprous ion is probably of fundamental importance in the mechanism of deposition and brightening action, as are probably coordination complexes involving the thioureas and other negatively valent sulfur compounds with the cuprous ion.

In alkaline copper cyanide baths, traces of lead ions produce brightness, especially if the plating is periodically interrupted for short intervals. The lead plates on copper in alkaline cyanide baths, and banded deposits result. The lead atoms are not compatible in the copper lattice; they are too large, and lead is insoluble in copper. This would also be true of many organic brighteners, and in fact, banded deposits are found in many bright deposits, such as bright nickel and bright copper, obtained with organic addition agents in acidic baths. Another example of a metallic brightener is silver in alkaline high cyanide gold baths where silver is actually more noble than gold.

Studies with radioactive atoms incorporated in organic brighteners, electron microscope work, and theoretical studies of the relationship of the cathodic growth mechanism to the structure of the deposit will help clarify specific adsorption effects of addition agents, synergistic effects, the role of various anions, and the location of included material in the deposits.

References

"Modern Electroplating," special volume of The Electrochemical Society, 1942; and the 1953 edition edited by A. G. Gray, New York, John Wiley & Sons, Inc.; "Extended Abstracts of the Symposium on Addition Agents" of The Electrodeposition Division of The Electrochemical Society (Oct. 1961).

Henry Brown

Cross-references: *Addition Agents;* entries bearing *Electroplating* and *Plating* titles; specific metals; *Throwing Power.*

BROMATES, ELECTROLYTIC PRODUCTION

Bromates are made by electrolysis of bromides in cells designed like those employed for the production of chlorate.

New uses for bromate brought about its commercial production, although in much smaller amounts than chlorate. The biggest consumer of bromates is the beauty shop where they are used exclusively for cold permanent waves. Potassium bromate is used to a smaller extent as an additive for foodstuff (such as improving the quality of flour) as well as for woolen textile finishing, while sodium bromate is effective as an additive for the finishing of metal surfaces by phosphoric acid.

Anodes for Electrolytic Production of Bromate

Electrolytic production of bromate is usually carried out at a graphite anode,[4] the same as in the production of chlorate. The use of graphite, however, has some unfavorable effects. Graphite becomes eroded[2] during electrolysis and forms a mud which makes continuous operation difficult. The final product also turns slightly yellow and can be decolorized only with difficulty. Nevertheless, it seems that graphite is still used commonly as an anode for the production of bromate.

A better anode material for bromate production is a special-type lead dioxide anode[6] manufactured by Sanwa Pure Chemicals, Tokyo, Japan. It consists entirely of lead dioxide and is rectangular in shape. By using this anode, the defects of the graphite anode mentioned above can be eliminated because of its insolubility in electrolyte. Platinized titanium electrodes made by Imperial Chemical Industries Ltd., England, seem to be recognized as an anode material for this object.

Important Factors in Electrochemical Formation of Bromate

Anodic reactions in bromate formation may be represented as follows.

$$6Br^- - 6e \rightarrow 3Br_2 \qquad (1)$$

$$2Br_2 + 2OH^- \rightarrow 2HBrO + 2Br^- \qquad (2)$$

$$Br_2 + 2OH^- \rightarrow BrO^- + Br^- + H_2O \qquad (3)$$

$$2HBrO + BrO^- \rightarrow BrO_3^- + 2HBr \qquad (4)$$

These reactions are similar to those witnessed in chlorate formation except for some small differences. Reaction (4) is about 100 times faster than that in chlorate formation according to Kretzschmar.[3] On the other hand, reactions (2) and (3) seem to occur imperfectly compared with the reactions in chlorate formation by comparing the hydrolysis constant of Br_2 with that of Cl_2.[1] This is confirmed by the fact that bromine separates at the bottom of the cell when the initial pH of the electrolyte is less than 8, and the circulation of the electrolyte is inefficient. Therefore, in the case of bromate, it may be preferable to maintain the pH of the electrolyte slightly alkaline in order to favor these reactions and thus obtain high current efficiency. This condition can be attained easily by using a neutral or slightly alkaline solution of bromide at the start of the electrolysis. Efforts to keep the pH in the desirable range are not necessary except to avoid discharge of hydroxyl ion.

Reactions (2) and (3) may also be accelerated by high temperature, which has a favorable effect on current efficiency. When reactions (2) and (3) are still slow and imperfect compared with reaction (1), the current concentration and current density may have a marked influence on the current efficiency. In practice, however, high current concentration and also high current density [for example, 50 amp/l to 100 amp/l (13 to 28 amp/sq dm)] have no unfavorable effects on the current efficiency. This facilitates design of the cell and also the determination of the operating conditions.

Electrolytic Process for Bromate Using Lead Dioxide Anode[5]

An electrolytic process using special-type lead dioxide anodes is described here. This process was developed by Sanwa Pure Chemicals.

Bromate Cell. A diagram of the bromate cell construction is shown in Fig. 1, which is provided with lead dioxide anodes.

The cell body is constructed of a sheet iron rectangular tank 680 mm long × 520 mm wide × 370 mm high. All inside surfaces of the body are lined with hard vinylchloride polymer. Cell volume is determined so as to keep the cell temperature as constant as possible by balancing the internal heating with natural cooling. Three sheets of hard vinylchloride polymer rest side by side on top of the cell and cover it entirely. The central cover supports 10 anodes and 20 cathodes. These are arranged in 6 rows running the length of the cover. Down the middle are two rows of 5 anodes, and on either side is a row of 5 cathodes. All anodes and cathodes are parallel with each other in each cell.

The lead dioxide anodes (Fig. 2) are 50 mm wide, 7 to 8 mm thick, and 350 mm long, and extend about 55 mm above the cover. The 18-8 stainless steel cathodes are 35 mm wide, 2.5 mm thick, and 400 mm long. The distance from an anode to the nearest cathode is about 13 mm.

Hydrogen discharged at the cathodes causes sufficient circulation of the cell liquor. It is vented through the roof from each cell.

Batch Experiments. Here is an example of batch experiments using the above cell.

The cell was operated batchwise with 90 to 95 l of potassium bromide solution. To decrease anode loss, the temperature was kept at 60

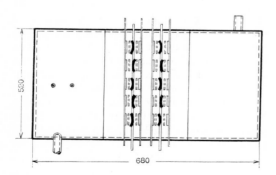

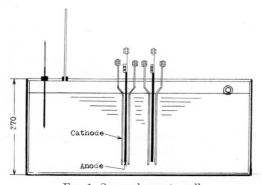

Fig. 1. Sanwa bromate cell.

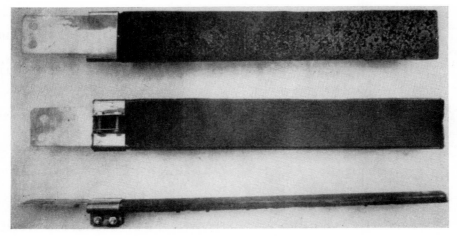

Fig. 2. Special type lead dioxide anode.

to 70°C as constant as possible. The pH was not controlled and reached a maximum of about 10 when a slightly alkaline solution (pH 8.9) of bromide was used at the start of the electrolysis. All electrolyses were conducted at an anodic current density of 20 amp/sq dm. Operating conditions and results are shown in Table 1.

Lead dioxide losses* averaged 53 to 56 mg/ 1000 amp-hr and also 57 to 60 g/ton of product. It indicated that the loss amounted to about 2.2 to 2.6 per cent of the original weight after the anode had been used for one year.

Example of Commercial Production for Potassium Bromate

On a commercial scale, 26 cells are connected in series to make a circuit of 100 v and 510 to 550 amp. The cell system is divided into two solution series of 13 cells each. Electrolyte is introduced into the cell by means of a PVC tube through the cover at one end and is discharged by the same means through the cover at the opposite end. The flow maintains good circulation.

A potassium bromide solution (pH 8 to 9), containing approximately 160 to 170 gpl KBr, 30 to 40 gpl $KBrO_3$, and 2 gpl $K_2Cr_2O_7$, is fed from a constant head tank into the cells. The concentration of bromide is adjusted to prevent crystallization of bromate during electrolysis. In a single pass through the cell, about 110 gpl of bromide is converted to bromate. The

* Lead lost was found in the slight amount of mud on the bottom of the cell.

TABLE 1. PREPARATION OF POTASSIUM BROMATE

Operating conditions

Starting Electrolyte			Current, amp	Cell Voltage, v	Amount of Current, 1000 amp-hr
KBr gpl	$KBrO_3$ gpl	$K_2Cr_2O_7$ gpl			
(1) 173	6	2	506	3.9*	22.2_7
(2) 232	9	2	500	3.7	28.3_2

Results

KBrO₃ produced			KBr Unconverted, kg	Conversion of Bromide to Bromate, %	Current Efficiency, %
Crystal Obtained, kg	In Solution, kg	Total, kg			
(1) 15.7	5.4	21.1	0.4	97.4	91.3
(2) 22.7	4.4	27.1	2.4	88.9	92.2

* Voltage reached about 4.6 v at the end of the electrolysis.

composition of cell effluent* is approximately 230 to 240 gpl $KBrO_3$ and 60 to 70 gpl KBr. Operating data are tabulated in Table 2.

Cell effluent is a very clear solution due to the insolubility of the anode, and filtration is not necessary. After electrolysis, the electrolyte is cooled to 20 to 25°C with circulating water. About 87 per cent potassium bromate crystallizes out. Almost all the remaining potassium bromate in the mother liquor can be crystallized

* The electrolyte is somewhat concentrated by evaporation during the flow. See Table 2, rate of flow.

TABLE 2. CHARACTERISTICS OF POTASSIUM
BROMATE PRODUCTION

Current: 510–550 amp
Anodic current density: 20–22 amp/sq dm
Voltage: 1st cell 4.2 v, 2nd cell 4.0 v, other cells
  3.8 v in 13 cells
Temperature: 65–85°C (1st to 2nd cells, less than
  60°C)
pH: 9.5–10
Rate of flow: cell feed, 42 l/hr; cell effluent, 33 l/hr
Current efficiency: 90–92%
Energy consumption: 3.95 kwh(d-c)/kg $KBrO_3$

TABLE 3. CHARACTERISTICS OF SODIUM
BROMATE PRODUCTION

Current: 490–510 amp
Anodic current density: 20–22 amp/sq dm
Voltage: 3.8–4.3 v
Temperature: 75–85°C (less than 60°C during 5
  hr at the start)
pH: 9.0–9.7
Average operating time: about 100 hrs
Composition of starting electrolyte: 240 gpl NaBr,
  70 gpl $NaBrO_3$
Composition of resulting electrolyte: 418 gpl
  $NaBrO_3$, 2.4 gpl NaBr
Current efficiency: 70–73%
Energy consumption: 6.0 kwh(d-c)/kg $NaBrO_3$

by adding a suitable amount of potassium bromide to return the electrolyte to the original concentration for a new cycle in the bromate cells. By this method, 97 per cent of the bromate produced can be crystallized out without evaporation. Potassium bromate crystals thus produced have excellent purity without recrystallization.

Example of Commercial Production for Sodium Bromate

Sodium bromate can be manufactured by methods similar to those used for the production of potassium bromate. The following is an example of operating data of batchwise productions. Single electrolysis is conducted for about 100 hours in cells containing 100 liters of solution each.

The resulting electrolyte is concentrated to produce crystals of pure sodium bromate. In this case, it is impossible to add $Na_2Cr_2O_7$ in the electrolyte because of a certain reason. This is the reason why the current efficiency is lower than that compared with potassium bromate.

References

1. BRAY, W. C., *J. Am. Chem. Soc.*, **32**, 932 (1910);
  33, 1485 (1911).
2. EWING, D. T., AND SCHMIDT, H. W., *Trans. Am. Electrochem. Soc.*, **47**, 117 (1925).
3. KRETZSCHMAR, H., *Z. Elektrochem.*, **10**, 789 (1904).
4. (For example) MARTIN, C. H., AND HARDY, E. C., (to Morton Salt Co.), U. S. Patent 2,191,574 (1940).
5. OSUGA, T., AND SUGINO, K., *J. Electrochem. Soc.*, **104**, 448 (1957).
6. SUGINO, K., *Bull. Chem. Soc. Japan*, **23**, 115 (1950). (Method (I)).

KIICHIRO SUGINO

Cross-references: *Chlorates, Electrolytic Production; Lead Dioxide Anode.*

BROWN-WALKER REACTION. See KOLBE AND RELATED BROWN-WALKER AND HOFER-MOEST REACTIONS.

BUFFERS

When acid is added to an aqueous solution, the pH falls; when alkali is added, it rises. If the original solution contains only typical salts without acidic or basic properties, this rise or fall may be very great. There are, however, many other solutions which can receive such additions with only a slight change in pH. The solutes responsible for this resistance to change in pH, or the solutions themselves, are known as *buffers*. A weak acid becomes a buffer when alkali is added, and a weak base becomes a buffer on the addition of acid. A simple buffer may be defined, in Brönsted's terminology, as a solution containing both a weak acid and its conjugate weak base. Buffer action is explained by the mobile equilibrium of a reversible reaction:

$$A + H_2O \rightleftharpoons B + H_3O^+$$

in which the base B is formed by the loss of a proton from the corresponding acid A. The acid may be a cation such as NH_4^+, a neutral molecule such as CH_3COOH, or an anion such as $H_2PO_4^-$. When alkali is added, hydrogen ions are removed to form water; but, as long as the added alkali is not in excess of the buffer acid, many of the hydrogen ions are replaced by further ionization of A to maintain the equilibrium. When acid is added, this reaction is reversed as hydrogen ions combine with B to form A.

The pH of a buffer solution may be calculated by the mass law equation

$$pH = pK' + \log \frac{C_B}{C_A}$$

in which pK' is the negative logarithm of the apparent ionization constant of the buffer acid and the concentrations are those of the buffer base and its conjugate acid.

A striking illustration of effective buffer action may be found in a comparison of an unbuffered solution such as 0.1 M NaCl with a neutral phosphate buffer. In the former case, 0.01 mole of HCl will change the pH of 1 liter from 7.0 to 2.0, while 0.01 mole of NaOH will change it from 7.0 to 12.0. In the latter case, if 1 liter contains 0.06 mole of Na_2HPO_4 and 0.04 mole of NaH_2PO_4, the initial pH is given by the equation:

$$pH = 6.80 + \log \frac{0.06}{0.04} = 6.80 + 0.18 = 6.98.$$

After the addition of 0.01 mole of HCl the equation becomes:

$$pH = 6.80 + \log \frac{0.05}{0.05} = 6.80$$

while after the addition of 0.01 mole of NaOH it is

$$pH = 6.80 + \log \frac{0.07}{0.03} = 6.80 + 0.37 = 7.17.$$

The buffer has reduced the change in pH from ±5.0 to less than ±0.2.

Fig. 1 shows how the pH of a buffer varies with the fraction of the buffer in its more basic form. The buffer value is greatest where the slope of the curve is least. This is true at the mid-point, where $C_A = C_B$ and pH = pK'. The slope is practically the same within a range of 0.5 pH unit above and below this point, but the buffer value is slight at pH values more than 1 unit greater or less than pK'. The curve of Fig. 1 has nearly the same shape as the titration curve of a buffer acid with NaOH or the titration curve of a buffer base with HCl. Sometimes buffers are prepared by such partial titrations, instead of by mixing a weak acid or base with one of its salts. Certain "universal" buffers, consisting of mixed acids partly neutralized by NaOH, have titration curves which are straight over a much wider pH interval. This is also true of the titration curves of some polybasic acids, such as citric acid, with several pK' values not more than 1 or 2 units apart. Other poly-

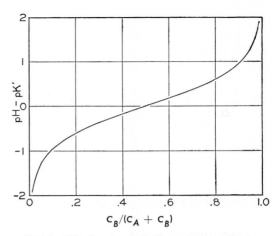

Fig. 1. pH of a simple buffer solution. Abscissas represent the fraction of the buffer in its more basic form. Ordinates are the difference between pH and pK'.

basic acids, such as phosphoric acid, with pK' values farther apart, yield curves having several sections, each somewhat similar to the graph in Fig. 1. At any pH the buffer value is proportional to the concentration of the effective buffer substances or groups.

The following table gives approximate pK' values, obtained from data in the literature, for several buffer systems:

Constituents	pK'
H_3PO_4, KH_2PO_4	2.1
HCOOH, HCOONa	3.6
CH_3COOH, CH_3COONa	4.6
KH_2PO_4, Na_2HPO_4	6.8
HCl, $(CH_2OH)_3CNH_2$	8.1
$Na_2B_4O_7$, HCl or NaOH	9.2
NH_4Cl, NH_3	9.2
$NaHCO_3$, Na_2CO_3	10.0
Na_2HPO_4, NaOH	11.6

Buffer substances which occur in nature include phosphates, carbonates and ammonium salts in the earth, proteins of plant and animal tissues, and the carbonic acid-bicarbonate system in blood.

Buffer action is especially important in biochemistry and analytical chemistry, as well as in many large-scale processes of applied chemistry. Examples of the latter include the manufacture of leather and of photographic materials, electroplating, sewage disposal and scientific agriculture.

References

BATES, R. G., "Determination of pH," Chapter 5, New York, John Wiley & Sons, 1964.

CLARK, W. M., "The Determination of Hydrogen Ions," Chapters I, II, IX, Baltimore, Williams and Wilkins Co., 1928.

KOLTHOFF, I. M., and LAITINEN, H. A., "pH and Electro Titrations," Chapters I, III, New York, John Wiley and Sons, 1941.

MacINNES, D. A., "Principles of Electrochemistry," pp. 275–278, New York, Reinhold Publishing Corp., 1939.

DAVID I. HITCHCOCK

BUNSEN, ROBERT WILHELM (1811–1899)

Robert Wilhelm Bunsen was born March 31, 1811 in Göttingen, Germany. As a boy he showed great interest in geology, but as a student at the University of Göttingen he devoted himself principally to chemistry, physics, mineralogy, and mathematics. In 1831 he obtained his doctorate from the University of Göttingen with a dissertation in the field of physics. The following year he won a travel stipend, of which he made the fullest use.

Back in Göttingen, he became a *Privatdozent* in the field of chemistry; here he discovered an antidote for arsenical poisoning, noteworthy because it represented one of Bunsen's few excursions into organic chemistry. When in 1835 his former teacher, Fredrich Stromeyer, died, he was invited to conduct Stromeyer's lectures on theoretical and practical chemistry. In 1836 he was appointed teacher at the Polytechnic School in Kassel.

From 1837 to 1842 he investigated blast-furnace processes. He found that almost half of the fuel-produced heat was lost, and he demonstrated that this waste could easily be avoided. Upon the invitation of the British Association for the Advancement of Science, he investigated jointly with Lyon Playfair the conditions of British furnaces; he found the waste of heat to be even greater. These investigations resulted in the elaboration of his famous methods of measuring gaseous volumes, published in his book "Gasometrische Methoden" (1857).

Simultaneously he was occupied with practical experiments in producing galvanic current; he succeeded in replacing the expensive platinum of Grove's cells by carbon produced by him artificially. These Bunsen electrolytic cells were used extensively in industry at that time.

After almost 13 years' activity at Marburg, Bunsen accepted the Professorship of Chemistry at the University of Breslau (1851). A year later he went to the University of Heidelberg, succeeding Leopold Gmelin. In 1855 Bunsen moved into the university's new chemical laboratory, then considered the best equipped and largest German university laboratory. Bunsen's laboratory attracted chemists from all over the world, many remaining only a short time to qualify as "students of Bunsen's." Though organic chemistry became increasingly the most popular field of chemistry in the 1860's and 1870's, Bunsen refused to change his allegiance from his chosen area of inorganic chemistry.

Bunsen's achievements in Heidelberg were extensive. Besides devising the famous Bunsen burner, he discovered a method of separating metals by means of electric current. He produced pure chromium and manganese from chloride solutions; light metals in large quantities through electrolysis of their molten chlorides; magnesium, aluminum, sodium, barium, calcium, and lithium. Perhaps it was the dazzling white light generated when magnesium was burned which led Bunsen to a series of photochemical investigations made jointly with Henry E. Roscoe (1855–1862). In this connection he invented the grease-spot photometer. In the years following, Bunsen continued his studies of light. In 1860, in collaboration with Gustav Kirchhoff, he published an epoch-making paper entitled *Chemische Analyse durch Spectralbeobachtungen*. With prophetic insight Bunsen predicted that spectrum analysis was destined to discover new elements. This was borne out in the case of rubidium and cesium, two new elements which he discovered the following year in the Dürkheim saline waters.

In 1853 Bunsen published a general method of volumetric analysis, a method so well known today that few remember its originator, and established standard methods of analysis for silicates, ashes, and nitrogen in organic bodies. His last three investigations (1883–1885) dealt with the condensation of carbon dioxide on smooth glass surfaces and with capillary gas absorption generally. In 1887 Bunsen described a vapor calorimeter with which he determined the specific heat of platinum, glass, and water.

Bunsen died at Göttingen on August 16, 1899.

EUGENE MUELLER

BURGESS, CHARLES F. (1873–1945)

Charles Frederick Burgess was born in Osh-kosh, Wisconsin, January 5, 1873, into a happy wholesome home with thrifty hardworking parents. His father worked as a stonemason, carpenter, and grocery clerk for which he earned enough to keep the family going on a budget of $1.50 a day. His mother was a wonderful homemaker and, although she lacked an education, acted as an inspiration to her budding scientist because of her innate curiosity and mechanical ability. Life was difficult for the family but at the same time satisfying and full of accomplishments. In his boyhood and youth young Burgess sold newspapers, climbed electric poles, tended furnaces, and wound armatures for financial assistance. The family income grew somewhat as the father held various official positions, and it became possible to send Charles and his brother to the University of Wisconsin. Early interest in Edison and the various electrical achievements of the day directed Charles to a career in electrical engineering. His years at the University as a student were busy with plenty of hard work and wonderful associations with students and faculty. Just a month or two after graduation Burgess received a position as assistant in electrical engineering at the munificent salary of $300.00 per year. This was the beginning of an outstanding career as scientist and teacher which led to the organization of the course in applied electrochemistry at the University and a translation of chemical theory into practical application and applied research. Burgess was an inspirational teacher and remained so through his entire life. His interest in technical education never waned.

During his teaching days he had made his small salary serve by supplementing it with research activities for various industrial concerns. In 1910 these activities led to the formation of his Northern Chemical Engineering Laboratories, later the C. F. Burgess Laboratories, Inc., and in 1913 Burgess finally resigned from the university to give the laboratory his undivided attention.

His quest for a better battery began in this era and was carried on with undimmed enthusiasm and led to the establishment of the Burgess Battery Company in 1917. Almost from the beginning, sales of the Battery Company climbed as Burgess produced a better and better product. In 1919 the company became international and only during the depression years in the early thirties did the company experience difficulties which were quickly overcome by strenuous effort on the part of Burgess and his brother George. His interest in the laboratory continued until his death when it dissolved because of the loss of its founder and director.

The records show the great interest Burgess had in both secondary and primary batteries with his main enthusiasm directed to small primary batteries and particularly the dry cell. Battery raw materials, manufacturing processes, and battery accessories were also an endless challenge to him, and his mechanical and chemical mind produced a wide variety of patents applicable to the battery industry. As an electrochemist he was interested in electrodeposition of metals of all sorts, but most particularly in that of iron. In 1904 the Carnegie Institution awarded Burgess a 5-year grant for an "investigation in the properties of electrolytic iron and its alloys". Although the funds ran out, Burgess always maintained his interest in the subject and was planning resumed research on the subject just before his death.

His interest in metal coatings led him to examine electroplating plants, and he made important contributions to the art of preparing metal surfaces for the operation. The specialized problems of corrosion by electrolysis came to his attention early, but he lost much of his interest when he found that scientific ability and technical skill had to be subordinated to political pressures. He published much and studied long on the problem of corrosion of iron and steel and its prevention. Electrochemical processes for the production of chemical compounds, electric furnaces and electrometallurgy, and electrochemical devices came in for their share of attention.

From 1902 one cannot trace the steps of Burgess without noting his connection with the Electrochemical Society. He was a founder and charter member, the fourth president (1907–08), and served independently and on committees for many years. He held many important offices and ultimately received the Acheson Medal (1942) in recognition of his achievements. The literature is full of a long stream of outstanding papers presented by him over the years. His death on Feb. 13, 1945 ended a long rich life heaped with honor and success and a long line of scientific contributions to the good of mankind. Honors came his way, including a Doctor of Science degree from the University of Wisconsin in June 1926 and a Doctor of Engineering from Illinois Institute of Technology in 1944. He was elected to the Royal Institution of Great Britain in 1929 and received the Perkin Medal from the American Section of the Society of Chemical Industry in 1932. Burgess' influence will be felt by many generations to come in science, technology, labor, and business.

CARMEN W. WALSH

C

CADMIUM ELECTROPLATING

Cadmium is a beautiful, silvery-white, ductile metal with a faint bluish tinge. Electroplated coatings of cadmium constitute by far its largest use. It has been an important electrodeposited coating for the corrosion protection of iron and steel, and to a much less extent, of copper, brass, and other alloys since Udy in 1919 introduced the first commercially practical alkaline cyanide cadmium plating process.

Cadmium, like zinc, is anodic to steel, copper, and brass and, therefore, protects these metals electrochemically even when the coating is scratched through. In its effectiveness in the protection it provides steel, it is even superior to zinc in a marine atmosphere but inferior in an industrial atmosphere. Unlike zinc, it does not form voluminous or encrusted corrosion products and is, therefore, often preferred for plating bolts, nuts, and fasteners. It plates much more readily than zinc on malleable iron and cast iron. Other important advantages are its low electrical contact resistance, ease of soldering, resistance to attack by alkali, self-lubricating qualities, low electrical current requirements, and high resistance to salt corrosion. For all these reasons it is used extensively.

Physical and Chemical Properties

Cadmium (Cd), atomic weight 112.4, sp. gr. 8.64, is whiter than zinc. Its melting point, 321°C, and boiling point, 767°C, are lower than those of zinc, and it is also softer and much more malleable than zinc, but slightly harder than tin. Cadmium, like zinc, loses its luster in moist air and, therefore, its use for atmospheric corrosion protection is far more important than its use for decorative appearance. Cadmium is rapidly corroded by moist ammonia fumes and by moist sulfur dioxide, and is readily attacked by most acids, although more slowly than zinc. Cadmium, unlike zinc, is not readily attacked by caustic; it is, however, very rapidly dissolved by concentrated ammonium nitrate solutions, and this is often used in stripping cadmium coatings.

Toxicity

Cadmium coated articles should not come into contact with food or drinks, nor should cadmium plated articles be welded or heated in ovens, because while cadmium metal as such is not poisonous, the fumes of heated cadmium are toxic, as are its compounds and solutions of its compounds.

Acid Plating Baths

The acid cadmium sulfate and fluoborate baths are far less important in the plating industry than the alkaline cyanide bath. The acid cadmium sulfate bath is used in certain analytical procedures involving separations from other metals. Its main industrial use is in electrowinning. (See **Zinc and Cadmium Electrowinning.**) Acidic cadmium fluoborate solutions are employed in a few special cases where good throwing power is not required, but where high rate of deposition and thick coatings are needed. The acidic baths are also valuable where as close to 100 per cent efficiency as possible is desired to minimize hydrogen embrittlement of a susceptible metal, for example, the cadmium plating of hardened steel. There is definitely less hydrogen embrittlement, and the hydrogen relief baking treatment can either be eliminated or reduced. In general the acidic cadmium fluoborate solution is used in these applications instead of the cadmium sulfate bath because it gives fewer treeing problems. The disadvantage of these acidic baths is their poor throwing power (distribution of plate thickness over a complex contour) compared to the alkaline cyanide baths and the matte appearance of the deposits. The highest adhesion of cadmium to steel can, however, be obtained from the acid baths, though this is important only in rare instances for special applications with thick plate. The adhesion obtained with cyanide cadmium baths is completely satisfactory for all usual applications.

Since the plain acidic cadmium sulfate baths have poor throwing power and give coarse-grained plate with remarkably extensive treeing, the baths are practically useless without an addition agent. (See **Addition Agents** and **Brightening Agents**.) The usual inorganic composition of the bath is about 100 to 250 gpl cadmium sulfate and 3 to 75 gpl of sulfuric acid with about 2 to 4 gpl of 2-naphthol-6-sulfonic acid as one of the best and most stable addition agents to use. The bath is operated at room temperature at current densities of about 1 to 5 amps/sq dm (approx. 10 to 50 amps/sq ft).

The usual composition of the cadmium fluoborate bath is about 240 gpl (32 oz/gal) cadmium fluoborate, $Cd(BF_4)_2$, and about 60 gpl of ammonium fluoborate, with the pH maintained between 4 and 5. The optimum temperature of operation of the bath is 20 to 27°C (70 to 80°F). The usual cathode current densities employed are 2 to 6 amps/sq dm (about 20 to 60 amps/sq ft). With strong agitation of the solution or the cathodes, higher current densities can be employed. The anode area used is usually about twice the cathode area. The most common addition agent for this bath is licorice, (0.3 to 1 gpl). Sometimes about 0.3 to 0.4 gpl aloin is used instead. The addition agent control is best done by a small scale beaker plating test, or the Hull Cell plating test.

Cyanide Plating Baths

In the plating industry the cyanide bath is used almost exclusively because of its very good throwing power and ease of operation, and because it gives deposits of pleasing brightness. Stable noncritical addition agents consisting of organic compounds, such as dextrins, cellulosic derivatives, caramelized sugars and cereals, etc., used together with traces of dissolved nickel in these baths make possible highly lustrous cadmium plate of excellent covering power. Various proprietary baths are on the market, and the differences among them lie mainly in the different types of organic addition agents which are used.

The articles to be plated and the method (see **Barrel Plating; Electroplating Machines, Automatic;** etc.) to be used govern the optimum solution composition for best results.

For work to be plated on racks, the solution composition differs slightly from that used in barrel plating (bulk plating of small parts, such as bolts, nuts, screws, fasteners, etc.). The baths are made up from sodium cyanide which is dissolved in water and to which wetted cadmium oxide is slowly added and dissolved with the formation of the complex sodium cadmium cyanide and sodium hydroxide. The exact composition of the cyanide complex is not known, though it is usually considered to be $Na_2Cd(CN)_4$. The extra sodium cyanide that is present in the baths to help in the electrolytic corrosion of the anodes and to help throwing and covering power is called the "free cyanide." The baths are usually operated on the basis of cadmium metal content, total cyanide, and caustic as determined by analysis.

Typical bath compositions are given below:

	Still (Rack) Plating	Barrel Plating
Cadmium	3 oz/gal (22.5 gpl)	2.4 oz/gal (18 gpl)
Total sodium cyanide	16.5 oz/gal (124 gpl)	16.2 oz/gal (121 gpl)
Total caustic soda	2.6 oz/gal (19.5 gpl)	2.0 oz/gal (15 gpl)
Brightener	As required	As required

Occasionally with articles that have very deep recesses which must be covered, the following composition with low metal content and high cyanide and caustic soda is necessary: cadmium 1.8 oz/gal, total sodium cyanide 17 to 18 oz/gal, total caustic soda 4 oz/gal. Such baths have lower cathode efficiency.

The operating bath temperature is usually 70 to 100°F with cathode current densities of 10 to 50 amps/sq ft used in the still tanks and 5 to 25 amps/sq ft used in barrel plating. Approximately 2 to 5 volts at the tank are needed in still plating and 8 to 14 volts in barrel plating. At 20 amps/sq ft and with about 90 to 95 per cent cathode efficiency it takes only 7 to 8 minutes to plate 0.0002 in. thickness of plate. Because of the variation of plate thickness over a complex shape, usually a longer plating time is necessary than those given by thickness charts to meet minimum thickness specifications at any one point which must be checked by thickness measurements. Also, barrel plating takes about double the time used in still plating.

Pure cadmium anodes must be used; the purity usually averages 99.98 per cent. The price of cadmium in 1964 was about $3.00/lb.

Adequate anode area must be maintained and the current density on the anode should be about 20 to 25 amps/sq ft under most conditions. It is very important to regularly analyze and maintain the sodium cyanide content to provide good anode corrosion and good solution conductivity. Neglect of the cyanide maintenance is one of the chief causes of serious imbalance of the bath. The amount of caustic soda formed from the cadmium oxide is the satisfactory concentration. The pH of the bath should be approximately 13. Plain steel tanks are most commonly used to contain the baths, though vinyl or hard-rubber linings are sometimes used where stray current losses may be serious. Proper cleaning, pickling and rinsing facilities are required for best plating operation.

Surface Treatments

Bright dipping in a properly adjusted chromic acid-sulfuric acid dip, which may also contain nitrates, is frequently used to equalize the luster and passivate the cadmium surface after plating and rinsing. This passivation treatment also minimizes staining and tarnishing. Thicker iridescent chromate films are also easily applied to the cadmium surface from differently adjusted solutions of chromic acid with sulfates and nitrates than those used for the bright dip, and these visible films give added corrosion protection against salt-spray and humidity. It is important not to allow the chromic acid solutions to contaminate the cadmium bath or the rinses preceding the cadmium plating operation because blistering of the plate will result due to passivation effects of the chromic acid.

For high-speed plating from alkaline cyanide cadmium baths for engineering uses, more concentrated baths are used and greater agitation. In these baths, triethanolamine at 10 to 30 ml/liter and traces of dissolved nickel are the best addition agents to use to obtain ductile, thick, fine-grained plate.

References

"Modern Electroplating," special volume of The Electrochemical Society, 1942; and the 1953 edition edited by A. G. Gray, New York, John Wiley and Sons, Inc.; "Metal Finishing Guide Book," 1957–1962; Hampel, C. A., Ed., "Rare Metals Handbook," New York, Reinhold Publishing Corp., 1961.

HENRY BROWN

Cross-references: *Addition Agents; Brightening Agents;* entries bearing *Electroplating* and *Plating* titles; *Zinc and Cadmium Electrowinning.*

CADMIUM ELECTROWINNING. See ZINC AND CADMIUM ELECTROWINNING.

CALCIUM CARBIDE

Calcium carbide is formed by the reduction of calcium oxide by carbon at elevated temperatures in accord with the following equation:

$$CaO + 3C \rightarrow CaC_2 + CO - 111 \text{ kcal}$$

A temperature of 1800 to 2100°C is required for a reasonable reaction rate and to obtain a liquid product. Electric furnaces have so far proved the only practical way to provide this temperature. Willson (q.v.) first produced calcium carbide in this country in the 1890's.

Commercially, lime and coke are used as the raw materials. An excess of lime is used to give a product in the range of 70 to 85 per cent calcium carbide. This is done to give a lower melting product more readily removed from the furnace and to limit dissociation of the product carbide which mounts rapidly as temperature is increased. Fig. 1 shows the liquidus of the calcium carbide-calcium oxide system based on data reported by Aall.[1]

The requirement, then, in manufacturing calcium carbide is to introduce a lime-coke mixture to temperatures approaching that of the electric arc, to allow evolution of the carbon monoxide by-product, and to provide a means of removing molten calcium carbide from the reaction area. This is universally done today in a three-phase furnace consisting of three vertical carbon electrodes about which the mixed charge is introduced. This is sketched in Fig. 2. The charge reacts beneath the electrodes to form molten calcium carbide. As the molten carbide is removed from the furnace, the charge works downward. The depth of penetration of the electrode in the charge is controlled to give constant power consumption.

Furnaces in use today range in size up to 50,000 kw and the major share of calcium carbide produced today is in furnaces rated 25,000 kw or over. The operating voltage on these large furnaces runs from 150 to 300 volts between phases. Although frequently called an

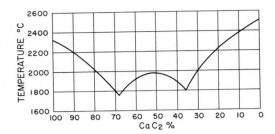

FIG. 1. Liquidus of the calcium carbide-calcium oxide system, based on data by Aall.[1]

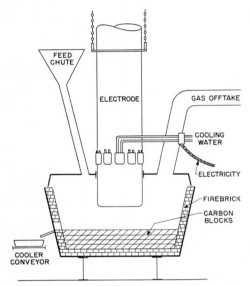

FIG. 2. Schematic diagram of typical calcium carbide furnace.

"arc" furnace, it is fairly well accepted that the major portion of the power input is absorbed by the resistance of the charge between the electrode and the bottom of the furnace. The normal penetration of the electrode into the furnace charge is 3 to 6 feet.

A 30,000 kw furnace typically has a diameter of about 30 feet and a height to the furnace cover of 15 feet. Such a furnace produces about 250 tons per day of calcium carbide.

A major problem in furnace design is providing a path for power from the transformers to the electrodes with minimum resistance and reactance. Transformers are located as close to the furnace as practicable with heavy copper bus bars to the furnace. Since the electrodes ride up and down in the furnace, flexible copper cable is provided from the bus bars to the electrode holder.

The sensible heat of carbon monoxide from the reaction is only partially recovered as it passes through the charge and thus temperatures are high above the furnace. On open furnaces, this is aggravated by combusion of the carbon monoxide at the surface. Heat is also conducted upward through the carbon electrodes. Thus, the electrode holders and other structures immediately above the furnace must be water-cooled.

Although an in-line arrangement was once used in many furnaces for convenience in the electrical connections to the electrodes, large furnaces today almost entirely have a delta arrangement of electrodes. These electrodes range from 50 to 60 inches in diameter on the large furnaces and carry currents up to 125,000 amps. The reaction area in which carbide is formed is primarily directly under the electrodes, extending a foot or so beyond the periphery of the electrodes. The electrodes must be spaced close together to achieve interconnection between the molten carbide pools under the various electrodes.

So-called Söderberg electrodes (q.v.) are used on most large furnaces. The Söderberg electrode consists of a steel casing into which a thoroughly mixed composition of petroleum coke, anthracite coal, and pitch is charged at a level well above the furnace top. This composition is baked by the furnace heat as the electrode is consumed and new sections moved down into the furnace. Originally, prebaked amorphous carbon electrodes were used for carbide furnaces, and these are still used on many of the smaller open-top furnaces.

Originally, the lime-coke mixture to be charged to the furnace was shoveled manually into the area around the electrodes. Today, a number of charge chutes are provided to feed the charge to the area around the electrodes. It is desirable to obtain a reasonably level charge bed, and, thus, a multiplicity of chutes has to be used. Slow oscillation or rotation of the entire furnace body is considered helpful by some in keeping the charge porous to the flow of carbon monoxide.

Most furnaces today are covered, with a slight positive pressure maintained over the furnace. Thus, there is some leakage of the gas evolved from the furnace at openings in the shell such as are required for the electrodes. The furnace gas is piped from the furnace and burned, preferably usefully, or the dust removed to provide carbon monoxide for chemical synthesis.

The choice of raw materials is quite critical to the success of a carbide operation. Typical of the quality of lime used is the following analysis:

Lime	
Calcium oxide	97.0%
Calcium carbonate	1.0
Magnesia	0.6
Silica	0.6
Iron oxide and alumina	0.6
Sulfur trioxide	0.2
Phosphorus	0.02

Silica and alumina, present in both coke and limestone, increase power requirements as they must be heated to molten carbide temperatures and to some extent undergo side reactions. Magnesia is reduced and volatilized before reaching the reaction zone of the furnace, and, if the lime contains more than several per cent, it will tend to build up in the charge section of the furnace, interfering with the free passage of carbon monoxide and greatly increasing power consumption.

Ferrosilicon, formed in the reaction zone from lime and coke impurities, tends to settle out in the bottom of the furnace. Some furnaces are tapped deliberately to remove accumulated ferrosilicon. Otherwise, it is tapped with the calcium carbide from which it can be separated magnetically.

All basic types of coke as well as some European anthracite coals are usable for carbide production. It is, of course, desirable to minimize ash. Also, if a coke contains more than several per cent moisture, it is desirable to predry it before mixing with lime to avoid slaking of the lime. Product specifications on carbide sold for the generation of acetylene for welding and cutting use also require a limitation on the sulfur and phosphorus level in the carbide raw material.

An important criterion in the choice of cokes is the electrical resistivity of the coke. Petroleum coke is particularly favored because of high resistivity and low ash.

Although early small furnaces were generally able to take an unsized raw material, larger size modern furnaces with greater electrode penetration require careful attention to the proportion of fines introduced into the furnace. It is generally necessary to screen out the fines

to allow adequate passage of the carbon monoxide by-product through the charge. Failure to do this can result in "blows" in which gas and hot materials are expelled explosively from the furnace to the hazard of personnel and equipment.

Furnaces may be tapped intermittently or a continuous flow maintained to remove the molten calcium carbide. Another point of variation between various furnace designs is that a single tapping point may be used, or, alternately, three points located where the three electrodes are closest to the furnace shell. Tapping is initiated, and maintained in continuous tapping, by an electric arc from a graphite tapping electrode of perhaps four inches in diameter to the adjacent furnace electrode.

The molten carbide may be tapped either into cast-iron chill cars or into some sort of continuous wheel or conveyor made up of numerous cast-iron pans. If the cars are used, the chills are lifted from the cars by a crane and stored on pads to give more rapid cooling. The cooled chills, or the material from the continuous conveyor, are then crushed and, if to be shipped in commercial channels, sized.

Gas yield specifications for calcium carbide moving in commercial channels require the production of about 80 per cent calcium carbide. This is normally also a good operating point for power and raw material efficiency. When calcium carbide is used as an acetylene source within a company, it may be found desirable to operate closer to the eutectic point (see Fig. 1) to facilitate tapping from the furnace.

The furnace bottom and shell are less significant factors in furnace design. A bottom of carbon or coke is provided, backed by several layers of firebrick. On the sides, inactive charge serves as the main refractory except perhaps around the taphole. Several layers of a low-grade firebrick are used to line the steel shell.

Power consumption in producing calcium carbide in modern equipment is in the range of 2700 to 3000 kwh per ton of 80 per cent carbide. Corresponding raw material requirements are: lime, 0.9T; coke, 0.6T; electrode paste, 20 to 25 pounds.

The major share of acetylene for chemical use is generated at the carbide plant or from carbide shipped in bulk or in 5-ton containers that are used directly as the hopper on the acetylene generator. The standard container for carbide shipped to the compressed gas industry and consumers for welding and cutting is a 100-pound, nonreturnable drum. However, many special size returnable containers are in service. Commercial carbide in the larger particle size ranges must have a gas yield of 4.50 cu ft of acetylene per pound of calcium carbide, and the acetylene must not contain more phosphine than 0.05 per cent by volume.

In the United States, more than 99 per cent of the carbide produced is used for the generation of acetylene. The reaction is:

$$CaC_2 + 2H_2O \rightarrow C_2H_2 + Ca(OH)_2 + 31 \text{ kcal}$$

Traditionally, in most acetylene generators calcium carbide has been added to excess water with the evolution of acetylene and the co-production of a 10 to 15 per cent lime hydrate slurry. An alternate procedure now used is to add the stoichiometric amount of water to the carbide, plus an additional amount to be vaporized and so remove the heat of reaction. The co-product is a dry lime hydrate. Although once discarded in ponds as a waste material, the by-product hydrate is now generally utilized as a chemical raw material and in acid neutralization, or it is reburned to lime for recycling to the carbide furnaces.

United States production of calcium carbide was 1,042, 088 tons in 1961, the volume remaining essentially the same as over the pervious five years. The traditional market in welding and cutting processes for the generated acetylene now consumes only about 20 per cent of this production. The remaining 80 per cent of acetylene is used almost entirely as a chemical raw material.

Major chemicals derived from acetylene and therefore calcium carbide are: neoprene, produced by the dimerization of acetylene with subsequent reaction with hydrogen chloride; vinyl chloride, the reaction product of acetylene and hydrogen chloride; trichlorethylene, from acetylene and chlorine; vinyl acetate, from acetylene and acetic acid; and acrylonitrile, from acetylene and hydrogen cyanide.

Because petroleum sources have been less available, the chemical industry in other countries has placed greater reliance on calcium carbide and acetylene as raw materials. Worldwide carbide capacity is approximately 10,000,-000 tons per year of which only 1,400,000 tons per year is in the United States. Cyanamide, melamine, and hydrogen cyanide, the latter both cyanamide derivatives, require large quantities of calcium carbide in many countries. United States requirements of cyanamide and melamine are supplied primarily from Canadian carbide production. Acetaldehyde, acetic acid, and acetic anhydride are important calcium carbide derivatives in many countries.

References

1. AALL, C. H., *Chemical Products*, **8**, 14 (1945).
2. KASTENS, M. L., AND MCBURNEY, W. G., *Ind. Eng. Chem.*, **43**, 1020 (1951).
3. ANON., *The Industrial Chemist*, **36**, 320 (1960).
4. ABBOTT, A. J., "Encyclopedia of Chemical Technology," R. E. Kirk and D. F. Othmer, Eds., Vol. 2, p. 834, New York, Interscience Publishers, 1948.

JOHN M. TINNON

Cross-references: *Söderberg Electrodes in Electric Furnaces; Willson, Thomas L.*

CALOMEL ELECTRODE. See REFERENCE ELECTRODES.

CALORIMETRY, ELECTROCHEMICAL. See ELECTROCHEMICAL CALORIMETRY.

CAPACITORS, ELECTROLYTIC—COMMERCIAL TYPES.

Since all electrolytic capacitors are characterized by a high capacity/volume ratio, the choice of one type over another is dictated by the requirements of size, cost, weight, reliability, voltage rating, temperature and frequency dependence, dissipation factor, and leakage current. Since no single type will optimize all these factors, it is evident that a compromise must be made in the selection of a capacitor for a given application. There are capacitors available today in literally hundreds of different voltage and capacity ratings, sizes, and designs; even within a single major class, as with aluminum foil capacitors, there is a great diversity in materials of construction, types of seals and enclosures, geometry of terminals, and provisions for mounting in circuits. A discussion of these complexities is best reserved for manufacturers' bulletins and will not be attempted here. Rather, a brief treatment is given of the major classes of electrolytic capacitors to point out their particular advantages and limitations.

Figs. 1 to 4 give a comparison of the frequency

and temperature dependence of capacitance and dissipation factor for the four types of capacitors described here. It should be emphasized that these curves merely demonstrate a general relationship between these types and are not intended to be universally applicable. Depending on the voltage and capacitance rating and the particular design, quite large variations in these properties may be obtained within a single class of capacitor.

Aluminum Foil Capacitors

This type of electrolytic capacitor is the most widely used and will probably retain its pre-eminent position for some time. It has several distinct advantages over all other types, the most prominent being its low cost. High-purity aluminum in thin foil form is many times less expensive than either tantalum foil or powder (the cost per pound differs by about a factor of 40

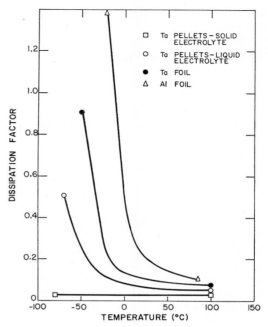

Fig. 3. Dissipation factor at 1000 cps as a function of temperature.

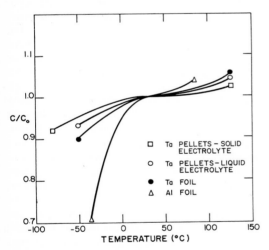

Fig. 1. Capacitance change at 1000 cps as a function of temperature. C_0 represents the value at 25°C.

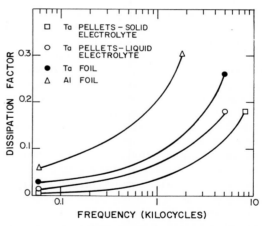

Fig. 4. Dissipation factor at 25°C as a function of frequency.

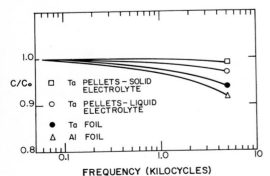

Fig. 2. Capacitance change at 25°C as a function of frequency. C_0 represents the value at 60 cps.

at current market prices), and this is naturally reflected in the final price of the capacitor. In addition, aluminum has a density of 2.7 g/cc as compared to 16.0 for tantalum, and this results in a further economy as well as a lower weight, which may be important for some applications. Because of this combination of low cost and weight, aluminum is the only practical material to use for very large devices as, for example, a capacitor in a 5⅝ in. x 3 in. diameter container and with a capacitance of 1000 μF rated at 425 volts.

Most electrolytic capacitors are polar and must be operated with the oxidized anode as the positive electrode. However, by using two anodized foils for the electrodes a nonpolar device may be obtained. This construction finds employment for some applications but, of course, suffers, a large decrease in capacitance over the comparable polar type.

Aluminum electrolytic capacitors usually employ etched foil for both anode and cathode to obtain maximum capacitance. Physical separation of the electrodes to prevent short circuiting is accomplished by interleaving porous paper separators between the layers of metal. The paper, which is absorbent, serves an additional function by retaining the electrolyte with which the capacitor is subsequently impregnated. The number of layers of paper and the choice of properties, such as porosity and thickness, are determined by the voltage at which the capacitor will be operated, and also by the conductivity and composition of the electrolyte.

The electrolytes which find the widest application are based on the glycol-borate system. These solutions have properties which are well suited to the maintenance of the aluminum oxide film, but they create temperature limitations for the capacitors: (1) the resistivity of these solutions rises rapidly at low temperatures and at about $-25°C$ the resistance causes the dissipation factor to become undesirably large and a serious reduction in capacitance is suffered; (2) the upper temperature limit is usually $85°C$ because of the presence of volatile compounds in the electrolyte. The dissolution of boric acid or borates in ethylene glycol results in the production of water through esterification and, depending on the method of preparation, part or all of this water may be retained in the electrolyte. These so-called "dry" electrolytes may contain several per cent by weight of water which results in a high vapor pressure within the capacitor at elevated temperatures. Since these capacitors are in general not hermetically sealed, water vapor may be lost, bringing about a change in electrolyte composition and subsequent degradation of electrical properties. For high-temperature applications present technology is directed toward the development of electrolytes containing higher boiling solvents and the design of hermetically sealed enclosures.

The sensitivity of anodic aluminum oxide to water as well as to other reactants creates what can be an inherently unstable condition while the capacitor is not on voltage. The shelf life of a capacitor is determined by the extent of this degradation of the oxide and is an important property of a capacitor. A large range in quality of commercial aluminum capacitors is found today due to the differences in manufacturers' processes and techniques in oxide film stabilization.

Aluminum electrolytic capacitors have the advantage of being operable at higher voltages than other types. They can be obtained in ratings as high as 500 volts and are the only choice for most applications in excess of 250 volts. The exceptions are some tantalum foil capacitors which may be obtained in voltage ratings of 400 volts.

Tantalum Foil Capacitors

The principal advantages enjoyed by foil-type tantalum electrolytic capacitors are wider useful temperature range, generally lower dissipation factors, and longer life. In addition, tantalum and its oxide exhibit high chemical stability and, under some conditions, capacitors of this metal have a much greater reliability than aluminum foil capacitors. Solutions with higher conductivities than the glycol-borate electrolytes may be used, and it is feasible to employ materials of construction that for various reasons are unsuitable for aluminum capacitors. Tantalum oxide has a relatively high dielectric constant (27, as compared to 8.5 for anodic aluminum oxide), and the mechanical strength of the metal permits the application of very thin foil, 0.5 mil material being in common use, whereas aluminum capacitors use foil varying in thickness from 1.5 to 4.0 mils. Because of these two factors the volume efficiency of capacitance of tantalum is enhanced and a size advantage is obtained from certain voltage ranges. A comparison for all types is shown in Fig. 5. As with aluminum, it is possible to etch tantalum foil to increase its surface area, but not to the same extent.

Opposed to these advantages are the limitations of greater weight and the much greater cost of tantalum foil. It is likely that with the improvements being made in aluminum capacitor technology, many of the present applications of tantalum capacitors will be supplanted by aluminum types.

Next to aluminum capacitors, tantalum foil units have the highest operating voltages. Most ratings are available up to 250 volts, and some may be obtained as high as 400 volts. Operating temperatures of 125°C are possible with these capacitors because of the excellent seals which have been developed for this type of device. For special applications requiring high reliability and long operating life, true hermetically-sealed containers have been produced. The success of this device is dependent on a glass-to-metal seal involving the tantalum lead wire. During the life of the capacitor, hydrogen is evolved within the unit in proportion to the charge passed, but with high-quality capacitors the leakage current is too small to generate a critical volume of gas.

Porous Pellet Capacitors

The capacitors with the highest volume efficiency of capacitance are constructed of porous pellets. The pellets are made of high-purity tantalum powder with a particle size in the range of a few microns. The metal powder, along with an organic material to act as a binder, is compacted in a die and the resulting pellet is sintered into a mechanically stable, porous mass by heating in the region of 2000°C in a high vacuum. The binder is completely volatilized during this process along with some of the impurities introduced into the tantalum in the course of manufacture. As a result the sintered pellets may be of higher purity than foil material. By varying the temperature and sintering time, the density of the pellet is controlled. Devices of extremely high surface area prepared this way may be anodized in the same manner as foil and then impregnated with a suitable electrolyte.

Liquid Electrolyte Capacitors. Because of the long path length to the interior of the pellet, the use of one of the usual electrolytes for tantalum capacitors would result in an impractically high dissipation factor. Therefore, solutions of high conductivity (e.g., aqueous sulfuric acid) are used for the electrolyte. These serve very well in controlling the dissipation factor but at the same time the maximum operating voltage of the capacitor is limited to about 150 volts. The use of aqueous electrolytes does not impose a serious temperature limitation because of well-sealed, sturdy construction. Some liquid pellet capacitors may even be operated at 200°C, but the very costly construction places such devices out of consideration for most commericial applications.

This type of capacitor employs a heavy silver can for the container, the interior wall of which

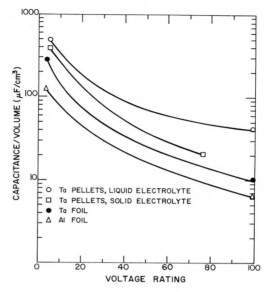

Fig. 5. Volume efficiency of capacitance vs the operating voltage.

serves as the cathode. The problem of hydrogen evolution within the capacitor is often reduced by incorporating a substance, such as a copper or silver salt, in the electrolyte which will deposit on the cathode in preference to hydrogen.

Solid Electrolyte Capacitors. The appearance within recent years of this modification of the pellet capacitor has resulted in the further extension of applications of electrolytically-formed devices. Some of the limitations of liquid systems are overcome: for example, the poor characteristics at low temperature and high frequency. The use of manganese dioxide, an electronically conducting solid, as the cathodic contact to the oxide film results in a capacitor whose properties approach those of an electrostatic capacitor.

The process of manufacture, except for the anodization step, is unlike that used for other types of capacitors. After oxidizing to the desired voltage the pellet is impregnated with an aqueous solution of a manganous salt and then heated to bring about thermal conversion of the salt to manganese dioxide. This process may be repeated several times to build up a cathode layer of sufficient thickness. The cylindrical surface of the pellet is next coated with graphite and a metallic conductor, such as silver paint, to which a suitable metallic lead may be affixed.

In capacitors with liquid electrolytes the anode lead and terminal within the container must be of the same metal as the anode itself because of the mobility of the electrolyte, but this is not demanded of the solid electrolyte capacitor, and a solderable lead may be attached to the tantalum lead wire within the container. This simplifies the design of a true hermetic seal for this structure, and the resulting capacitor has an extremely long and reliable life with stable electrical parameters. Furthermore, there are virtually no problems concerning shelf life.

The volume efficiency of capacitance for solid electrolyte pellet capacitors is somewhat less than the corresponding wet pellet types. This is a consequence of a large derating for this device, that is, the operating voltage is a smaller fraction of the formation voltage than is used with liquid systems. The reason for this is to be found in the nature of dielectric breakdown and repair in the oxide-solid electrolyte system. One of the consequences of breakdown appears to be the conversion of the manganese dioxide to a compound of lower conductivity at the point of breakdown, but the dielectric strength of this substance is not great enough to support electric fields of the intensity normally applied to capacitors using liquid electrolytes, in which electrochemical healing is more effective. Therefore, solid electrolyte capacitors are operated at a lower electrical stress than comparable liquid-containing capacitors.

All types of liquid electrolyte capacitors show a very low resistance when cathodically-biased and, therefore, unless the cathode has been previously anodized to some protective level, the permissible reverse voltage is very low. The presence of a solid electrolyte, however, results in more symmetrical conducting properties and an appreciably larger negative voltage may be impressed on these devices. This is a distinct advantage for some applications.

The use of a solid electrolyte is not limited to the pellet structure. It has been applied to foil devices, although without great commercial success, and to small wire anodes where it has been extremely successful in low capacitance applications.

Other Types

Electrolytic capacitors using niobium as the anode material are available in low-voltage ratings both as solid electrolyte pellets and as conventional foil units; their electrical characteristics are at present inferior to the corresponding

tantalum devices and they are not yet a commercially important product. The interest in developing niobium to replace tantalum is due to its lower density (8.0 vs 16.0 for tantalum) and to the belief that the comparative cost of niobium will eventually be much lower.

Aluminum as an anode for solid electrolyte capacitors is an even more attractive material than niobium. There are serious problems in the fabrication of useful porous structures, however, and the high reactivity of aluminum presents obstacles to the successful deposition of a solid electrolyte in intimate contact with the oxide surface. This latter difficulty appears to have been largely overcome recently, and to a limited extent solid electrolyte foil aluminum capacitors have been commercially produced. These devices have capacitance and dissipation factor characteristics at low temperatures and high frequency which are superior to those of aluminum foil capacitors and which approach those of solid tantalum capacitors, but leakage currents are poor and the volume efficiency of capacitance shows only a slight advantage over aluminum liquid electrolytic capacitors. As improvements develop, however, these may become important devices.

One of the most promising types of capacitors is one which uses no electrolyte. This is the metallized tantalum capacitor whose properties are close to those of a true electrostatic capacitor. The cathode is applied directly on the surface of the oxide by an electroless process in which nickel appears to be the most useful metal. The success of the method is dependent on having an oxide film free of any serious flaws or defects and on the control of the cathode thickness to only a few thousand angstroms. If these conditions prevail, serious short-circuiting is avoided and the capacitor then has the ability to heal itself during localized dielectric breakdown by a clearing process similar to that which occurs with conventional metallized dielectric types. This capacitor at present is limited to a very low capacitance range.

References

1. BOONE, S., VOETEN, H., AND HENDRICKS, H., *IEEE Trans. Component Pts.*, **CP-10**, 3 (1963).
2. FRANKLIN, R. W., *Proc. Inst. Elec. Engrs.* (*London*), *Pt. B, Suppl.*, **109**, 525 (1962).
3. GÜNTHERSCHULZE, A., AND BETZ, H., "Elektrolyt-Kondensatoren," 2d ed., Berlin, Technischer Verlag Herbert Cram, 1952.

4. Georgiev, A. M., "The Electrolytic Capacitor," New York, Murray Hill Books, 1945.

Walter J. Bernard

Cross-references: *Aluminum; Anodizing; Capacitors, Electrolytic-Theory of Operation;* entries with *Dielectric* headings; *Tantalum.*

CAPACITORS, ELECTROLYTIC—THEORY OF OPERATION

Electrolytic capacitors are characterized both by a dielectric which has been formed by electrochemical oxidation and by the presence of an electrolyte within the final capacitor structure. However, since the essential feature of the electrolytic capacitor is the extremely thin dielectric film which can only be obtained through anodic oxidation and which is responsible for the characteristically high capacitance of the device, the designation is frequently extended to other capacitors employing this type of dielectric—for example, the so-called solid electrolyte tantalum capacitor and the metallized tantalum oxide capacitor. The conventional capacitor, containing a liquid or paste electrolyte, represents the type which was the first to be manufactured and which today is still the most important commercial form.

Dielectric Formation

The dielectric of an electrolytic capacitor is a thin film of oxide, formed on the surface of a certain class of metals by electrolytic oxidation in a suitable electrolyte. The only metals which demonstrate this and which are commercially important are aluminum, tantalum and—to a slight extent at present—niobium, but this property is also exhibited by zirconium, titanium, bismuth, and silicon, among others. Of these, titanium offers some promise as a capacitor material. When one of these metals is made the anode in the proper electrolyte and a constant current is applied to the electrochemical cell, an insulating layer of oxide forms on the surface, and the applied potential must therefore be increased to keep the current constant. If the entire charge passed is used in forming oxide, the rise in voltage is linear. With reasonably close electrode spacing and moderately high electro-

lyte conductivity there is only a small, usually negligible, voltage drop in the cell, and the measured cell voltage may be considered to be entirely across the anodic film. The voltage at which oxidation is terminated is the so-called formation voltage (V_F in Fig. 1). Application of a constant voltage beyond the time required to attain V_F causes the current flowing through the cell to decay, and it is usually allowed to reach a value which is low compared to the initial anodizing current before removal of voltage. A typical current-time plot is shown in Fig. 2. The particular value observed under a given set of conditions is called the leakage current; it may

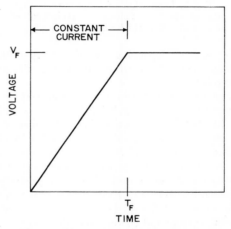

Fig. 1. Voltage-time relationship during formation of an anodic oxide film.

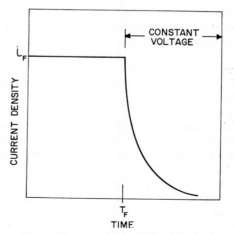

Fig. 2. Current-time relationship during formation of an anodic oxide film.

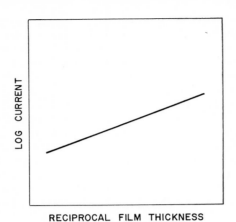

FIG. 3. Logarithm of ionic current density at constant voltage vs reciprocal of the anodic film thickness.

vary widely depending on the temperature, voltage, time of formation, anode material and electrolyte.

The relation between current and voltage is generally recognized as being best expressed by the Mott-Cabrera equation, $i = \alpha e^{\beta F}$, where F is the electric field (applied voltage divided by film thickness), and α and β at a given temperature are constants which are characteristic of a particular metal, and quite probably the electrolyte in which it is anodized. Examination of the equation shows that the thickness of a film is related to both current and voltage, and, thus, both must be defined to define the thickness. A somewhat loose practice has evolved in which it has become customary to refer to an anodic film as having a certain thickness per volt. This is approximately correct when the formation current has reached such a low value that the rate of oxide formation has become negligible. A plot of the logarithmic form of the Mott-Cabrera equation at constant voltage, $\log i = \log \alpha + \beta v/d$, where d is the film thickness, demonstrates this relationship (see Fig. 3).

The values of d considered here are very small. For aluminum, at current densities between 10^{-3} and 10^{-7} amp/sq cm, the thickness of the oxide is 11 to 15 angstroms/volt, and for tantalum the thickness of the oxide at low current densities approaches 20 angstroms/volt. This corresponds to only a few thousand angstroms for films formed to the order of hundreds of volts and demonstrates the intense electric fields which may be withstood by these anodic films; at a current density of 10^{-3} amp/sq cm, the field

is about 10^7 volts/cm. In practice the fields are somewhat less than this since capacitors are operated at voltages well below the formation voltage. It is because of the high dielectric strength and the ease with which the dielectric thickness may be controlled that capacitors of high capacitance may be made. It is apparent that for low-voltage applications where, under some circumstances, a dielectric film of only a few hundred angstroms thickness may be necessary, the volume efficiency of electrolytic capacitors is extremely large and unapproached by any other type of capacitor.

The electrolytes used for the anodic oxidation of aluminum and tantalum have been determined more or less empirically, but their selection is dictated to some degree by the chemical behavior of the metals and their oxides. The most common electrolytes for the oxidation of aluminum are those consisting of aqueous solutions of boric acid and its salts, particularly sodium or ammonium borate. Aqueous solutions of the salts of some organic acids—among which are citric acid and tartaric acid—are also frequently used, but borate solutions have a broader applicability. The concentrations of the solutes are controlled to give the pH and conductivity that experience has shown result in the optimum oxide formation for the particular voltage range of interest. Although the concentration may vary widely, the pH is controlled to keep the solution only slightly acidic. This is a consequence of the behavior of anodic aluminum oxide which tends to be soluble in both acidic and basic solutions. Tantalum, on the other hand, may be anodized in nearly any solution with a pH less than 7, since tantalum oxide is completely unaffected by common acids. Alkaline solutions are prohibited, however, because of the solubility of the oxide.

The maximum voltage which may be applied to an oxidized electrode is determined principally by the composition and concentration of the electrolyte. In general, the maximum voltage is inversely proportional to the conductance of the solution. The highest voltages may be attained with dilute solutions of boric acid. Voltages in excess of 700 volts are commonly achieved on aluminum, and about 600 volts on tantalum is possible. At the maximum formation voltage, film breakdown occurs and sparking (often described as scintillation) at the electrode surface may be observed.

Film formations are strongly affected by the presence of impurities in the metal and in the anodizing solution. The metallic impurities may become occluded during anodization as conducting oxides within the dielectric film, reducing the maximum voltage and causing higher leakage currents. Metallic impurities in tantalum and niobium are also believed to be the source of a phenomenon peculiar to these metals, that of field-induced crystalline oxide growth (observed as gray areas) in which the original anodic oxide is replaced by a thicker dielectric of poorer quality. Once initiated, this new growth may spread over the entire metal surface. This effect is largely suppressed by using the highest purity tantalum available. Aluminum is not subject to this form of dielectric perturbation, but, like tantalum, the leakage current of its oxide is affected by extremely low concentrations of contaminants. Iron, for example, in an amount greater than its solid solubility (< 0.01 per cent), can give rise to abnormally high leakage currents. As a result of such experiences, aluminum foil for capacitors is fabricated from metal of high purity (99.97 per cent or higher).

Contaminants in the oxide-forming electrolyte may be equally obnoxious, but their effect is manifested in a different manner. Aluminum undergoes severe electrochemical attack by chlorides, bromides, nitrates, sulfates, and many other common substances. A concentration of only a few parts per million of halide ions in aqueous solution may result in a serious reduction in the current efficiency of oxide formation, pitting of the electrode, and, in some cases, complete suppression of the formation of a dielectric film. The presence of such contaminants within the final capacitor structure results in increased leakage current and reduced capacitor life. Tantalum, which is much more stable electrochemically than aluminum, does not demonstrate this effect and, in fact, may be successfully anodized in halide solutions.

Leakage Currents

The leakage current consists of two components, their relative importance being determined principally by the applied voltage. Part of the current is ionic, so designated because ions in the film conduct current between electrode and solution; the remainder of the current is electronic. Ionic current results in film growth and is the major component during formation. At high total current the ionic component usually predominates to such an extent that the electronic current is obscured, and the process appears to be 100 per cent efficient in regard to oxide formation.

The passage of electronic current results in an electrochemical process at the anode other than oxide formation; in aqueous solution it is usually the evolution of oxygen. The magnitude of electronic current depends upon the purity and surface condition of the metal, the composition of the electrolyte, the applied field, and the temperature. After an oxide film has been on voltage for several hours and the current shows no further tendency to decrease, it is assumed that the residual current is electronic. This is usually the correct interpretation, but in the analysis of leakage currents the possibility must also be considered that the final leakage current contains a constant ionic component persisting because of a slow and minute chemical attack on the oxide film by the anodizing solution. It is clear that if a film of constant and uniform thickness is to be maintained, a compensating ionic current must flow.

Surface Area Increase

A further capacitance advantage over other types of capacitors is achieved by the electrochemical etching of foil anodes, whereby a severalfold increase in surface area of the electrode may be realized. Aluminum may be etched more effectively than tantalum for this purpose. The etch ratio — determined by comparing the capacitance of etched foil to that of smooth foil, after anodization to a given formation voltage — is controlled by the thickness of the metal as well as by the parameters of the etching solution. Because of its thinness, the oxide follows the contours of the etched foil and thus utilizes the increased surface area. However, as the film grows in thickness, the consumption of metal has a smoothing effect on the original etch structure and the etch ratio at the higher formation voltages is reduced.

Another high-capacitance device is obtained through the manufacture of sintered porous compacts of tantalum powder. These compacts are generally prepared as cylindrical pellets and in this form they are widely used for solid electrolyte capacitors, as well as for the more conventional liquid types. In making such compacts, the high surface area of the original tantalum powder is largely retained and the available capacitance of the final device reflects this property.

Oxide Composition and Structure

The formed dielectric is usually referred to as an oxide film, the tacit assumption being made that the anodic product consists only of stoichiometric aluminum oxide, tantalum oxide, etc. In general, this appears to be essentially correct, but there are instances in which the dielectric shows an important deviation from oxide stoichiometry. This is demonstrated by the films formed on aluminum in dilute solutions of phosphates; these films contain several per cent of what may be described for convenience as aluminum phosphate. Probably all electrolytes influence the oxide film to varying degrees, although chemical evidence of slight changes in film composition may be difficult to obtain. The oxide films formed at low voltages are amorphous, or so nearly so that no crystalline form can be observed by the usual x-ray and electron diffraction techniques. On aluminum at higher voltages—usually above 100 volts—the formation of the crystalline $\gamma'-Al_2O_3$ is observed; the amount of crystalline oxide increases with increasing voltage, but it is apparently never formed to the complete exclusion of the amorphous oxide.

Operating Electrolytes

An electrolyte is introduced within the final capacitor structure to establish electrical contact between the oxide film and the counter-electrode (cathode). When the electrolyte is a liquid it serves an additional function by maintaining electrochemical repair of the oxide during the life of the capacitor. Thus, the selection of the electrolyte is governed by several considerations: ability to act as an efficient oxide-forming electrolyte, chemical compatibility with the metal-metal oxide system, conductivity, vapor pressure over the temperature range of interest, freezing point and viscosity. The aluminum electrolytic capacitor commonly employs an electrolyte prepared by the reactive dissolution of boric acid and its salts in a polyhydric alcohol, usually ethylene glycol. Such solutions are preferred over aqueous electrolytes because of the more favorable physical properties of ethylene glycol and because of the chemical instability of anodic aluminum oxide in most aqueous solutions. This instability is manifested by a slow reaction with water in which the oxide is converted to a noninsulating hydrated oxide, and through electrochemical attack by low concentrations of contaminants (chlorides, etc.) which is enhanced in an aqueous environment.

The chemical stability of tantalum and its oxide permits a broader choice of electrolytes for capacitors using this metal. Although glycolborate solutions are sometimes employed, other more highly conducting electrolytes are common. Organic solvents and concentrated aqueous solutions find application here, and in special cases, such as the porous pellet type, solutions of sulfuric acid may be used. The limitations on electrolytes for tantalum capacitors are usually dictated by the chemical reactivity of the other materials of construction and the mechanical problem of seals and enclosures.

The conducting medium in the solid electrolyte tantalum capacitor is manganese dioxide, introduced to the pellet structure by the *in situ* thermal decomposition of manganous nitrate or other manganous salt. It is not clear whether this "electrolyte" functions as an electrochemical oxide-former, even though some of its electrical characteristics appear similar to those of liquid electrolytes.

Cathodes

To utilize the high capacitance available from anodic films, the cathode, whose double layer capacitance is effectively in series with the anode capacitance, must be designed to give as high a value as possible. In foil capacitors the cathode is of the same material as the anode and is etched to present a large surface area to the electrolyte. Except for very low-voltage capacitors, this procedure is sufficient to prevent any important loss in available anode capacitance. Liquid-impregnated pellet capacitors use the interior wall of the container as the cathode. This surface may be etched and platinized to maximize its capacitance. The oxide in solid electrolyte capacitors is in contact with an electronic conductor and, therefore, the problems imposed by liquid systems are not present in this case.

Rectifying Properties

Dielectric films on aluminum and tantalum, and on other film-forming metals as well, exhibit noninsulating properties when the base metal is made cathodic in the presence of an electrolyte. Even when the metal has been anodically oxidized to several hundred volts, the application of only a volt or two of opposite polarity is sufficient to cause a high current flow. Various theories have been proposed to ac-

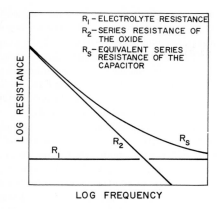

References

1. BURNHAM, J., *IRE Trans. Component Pts.*, **CP-4**, 73 (1957).
2. FRANKLIN, R. W., *Proc. Inst. Elec. Engrs. (London)*, *Pt. B, Suppl.*, **109**, 525 (1962).
3. GÜNTHERSCHULZE, A., AND BETZ, H., "Elektrolyt-Kondensatoren," 2d ed., Berlin, Technischer Verlag Herbert Cram, 1952.
4. MCLEAN, D. A., AND POWER, F. S., *Proc. IRE*, **44**, 872 (1956).
5. YOUNG, L., "Anodic Oxide Films," New York, Academic Press, 1961.

WALTER J. BERNARD

Cross-references: *Aluminum; Anodizing; Capacitors, Electrolytic-Commercial Types;* entries with *Dielectric* headings; *Tantalum.*

FIG. 4. Frequency dependence of the principal resistive components and the total equivalent series resistance of an oxide-electrolyte system.

count for this property, but it is likely that the effect is due to the presence of small-scale physical flaws in the film which permit the electrolyte to make contact with the base metal and to evolve hydrogen upon cathodic bias.

Dissipation Factor

A higher dissipation factor is observed with electrolytic capacitors than with most other types and is especially noticeable at high frequencies and low temperatures. This is mainly due to the series resistance of the electrolyte, whose relative contribution to tan δ ($= \omega RC$) becomes larger under these conditions, since the equivalent series resistance of the capacitor is (principally) the sum of the electrolyte resistance and the series resistance of the oxide. With increasing frequency the oxide resistance decreases, and since the electrolyte resistance is frequency-independent, the dissipation factor increase is due to the electrolyte. These relationships are demonstrated graphically in Fig. 4. At lower temperatures the oxide resistance is nearly constant, but the electrolyte resistance increases rapidly, creating an effect comparable to the high-frequency case.

The electrolyte is also largely responsible for the high dissipation factor in low-voltage capacitors. In this case the oxide resistance is small and the capacitance is large; these conditions tend to enlarge the role of the electrolyte and to make it the controlling factor in determining the dissipation factor.

CARBON ELECTRODES, ANION- AND CATION-RESPONSIVE. See DEMINERALIZATION OF WATER, DIRECT ELECTROCHEMICAL.

CARBON ELECTRODES, SÖDERBERG. See SÖDERBERG ANODES IN ALUMINUM CELLS; SÖDERBERG ELECTRODES IN ELECTRIC FURNACES.

CARBON AND GRAPHITE ELECTROLYTIC ELECTRODES

This article will be devoted to the reactivity in protonic electrolytes of carbon and graphite electrodes.

The ability of carbon to form a multitude of compounds is widely appreciated. Less known is the fact that carbon, as the element, exists in many forms with widely differing properties of great technical and scientific interest. Certain bulk, artificial carbons have found wide use as electrodes in chlorine and fluorine technology. There is a wealth of engineering knowledge in regard to the selection and use of such electrodes; however, this article will emphasize the principles upon which utility rests.

In the manufacture of graphite anodes for the chlor-alkali industry the common starting materials are calcined petroleum coke and coal tar pitch. The two materials, as a plastic mix, are formed in suitable "green" plates or rods. The green shapes are heated in a baking furnace for six to nine weeks to temperatures of 750 to 1000°C. The "carbon" bars or rods are then subjected to temperatures of up to 2600 to

3000°C in electric "graphitizing" furnaces. This last heat treatment requires from three to five weeks, counting the programmed heating and cooling stages. Finally the "graphite" pieces are normally machined and impregnated with a drying oil.

The utility of carbon and graphite electrolytic electrodes depends on their excellent chemical stability when polarized in contact with the particular electrolyte. Of course, laboratory interest in the inertness of carbon and graphite electrodes in electrochemical systems preceded the large-scale industrial acceptance. The industrial interest in turn stimulated more detailed laboratory studies such as the extensive, classical work of Foerster (1923).

Most of the fundamental studies of carbon and graphite electrodes reported in the literature preceded the development of the modern physics of solids. It is now recognized that the nature of defects in the crystal lattice and the effects of foreign atoms in the carbon network may be of crucial importance even in near-ideal graphites. In carbons with structures remote from the ideal graphite lattice the structural peculiarities are even more important in determining the properties. Knowledge of carbon electrode reactivity is subject to much further expansion as it becomes possible to characterize the defect state more completely and trace its consequences.

In passing it may be noted that carbons and graphites are of great importance in the high-temperature electrolysis of fused salts, especially in the aluminum and magnesium industries; however, the discussion here is limited to "protonic electrolyte" systems such as water and anhydrous HF.

Brine Electrolysis

Graphite anodes are universally used in the chlorine cells of the chlor-alkali industry (Hardie, 1959; Mantell, 1960). The major, and the desired, reaction at these anodes is conversion of chloride ion to chlorine. This process is accompanied by the production of some oxygen, carbon dioxide, and smaller amounts of other substances. The occurrence of the carbonaceous by-products is symptomatic of the gradual corrosion of the graphite anode. Anodes retain utility for at least a year or two before replacement is necessary. In long-term average, a ton of chlorine is produced for every four to eight pounds of graphite.

Graphite anodes are used in brine electrolysis in preference to carbon or coke anodes because of the superior corrosion resistance of the graphite. The greater durability of graphite is related to the lower concentration of sites for edge-atom attack therein. Furthermore, graphite exhibits greater mechanical strength and lower electrical resistance than hard carbons or gas coke.

A fully corrosionproof graphite for the chlorine cell is greatly to be desired, as also is attainment of power economy by the use of anode graphites of the lowest possible overvoltage. In fact, the concept of overvoltage is basic to any understanding of the process at the working chlorine anode, for, if thermodynamic voltages governed the process, then carbon dioxide and oxygen would occur as the major anode products and little chlorine would be obtained. In actual experience, chlorine evolves in high purities (97+ per cent), indicating that overvoltage for carbon dioxide and oxygen is high enough compared to chlorine to more than compensate for their lower theoretical equilibrium voltages.

TABLE 1. CALCULATED STANDARD VOLTAGES

$C + H_2O \rightarrow CO + 2H^+ + 2e^-$	+0.52 v
$C + 2H_2O \rightarrow CO_2 + 4H^+ + 4e^-$	+0.21 v
$C + 4Cl^- \rightarrow CCl_4 + 4e^-$	+1.19 v
Oxygen electrode	+1.23 v
Chlorine electrode	+1.36 v

An understanding of the overvoltage and corrosion behavior of a graphite anode is complicated by the presence of 25 to 30 per cent by volume of pores in its structure as a result of which the area available for electrolysis is considerably larger than the exterior dimensions of the anode would imply. The current density calculated from the projected area is an upper limit under which the average real current density lies. The distribution of real current densities is nonuniform and current diminishes to a negligible value on the pore walls in the interior of the anode.

The theory of the operation of the porous electrode had early importance in its application to the Leclanché dry cell and has attracted recent interest in connection with the fuel cell. Porous electrode theory is also pertinent to the graphite chlorine anode and has been developed for this area, i.e., by Stender and Ksenzhek. The parameters "specific surface" and "resistivity of electrolyte in pores" (a function of pore structure) appear in the Stender-Ksenzhek equations; the authors used surface and pore resistivity values of uncorroded graphite. However, constants for unused graphite are not significant for the working graphite chlorine anode because the surface thereon has been altered by corrosion.

Graphite porosity is a highly favorable attribute since it reduces both the polarization and the electrochemical corrosion by reducing local current density, thereby achieving both power and material economies.

Internal corrosion of anodes, a condition obtained by percolation of the chlorine-sodium chloride solution to the anode interior, is combated by impregnation with a catalyst-bearing drying oil, a procedure practiced for diaphragm cell anode graphite but not for mercury cell graphite. A properly cured oil film protects the interior pore walls from corrosion. It is an equally essential property of such a film that it removes itself from the working surface of the anode, otherwise the insulating properties of the film would impede electrolysis.

Brine electrolysis with graphite anodes is also carried out for the purpose of chlorate manufacture. Here the anode chlorine and the cathode sodium hydroxide are allowed to react with each other. The reactivity of the anode graphite is greater under such conditions of higher pH but is not considered different in kind from behavior in the chlorine cell. In fact, chlorate cell conditions have been proposed as an expedient for rapid testing of chlorine cell graphites (Wranglen, et al., 1962).

The Structural Basis of Anode Reactivity

To understand the importance of graphite structure as it relates to its use in electrochemical systems, a more detailed consideration of crystal lattice development is necessary. X-ray study shows that even amorphous carbon blacks are somewhat crystalline, their structures having something in common with that of the ideal graphite crystal lattice. This lattice is a useful basis for discussion even though many important carbons are structurally remote from ideal graphite. Beginning with the amorphous carbon blacks, there is a series of carbon forms increasing in crystal perfection up to the polycrystalline graphite used in electrodes. The latter has been termed "near ideal" because in it the graphite lattice is comparatively well-defined.

Interaction between layers in ideal graphite is small in comparison with nearest-neighbor bonding in the carbon atom planes. Thus, layer-stacking and carbon-network bond defects may be distinguished (Ubbelohde and Lewis). Under "network bond" are included edge, bond isomerism, foreign atom incorporation, and gross defects of partly graphitized carbons. In the latter carbons there exist graphite particles joined together by regions of "amorphous" carbon. The physico-chemical properties of such carbons are dependent on the arrangement of atoms at the internal surfaces of the pores. Hence, it is here that the concepts of "pore," internal surface, and grain size of graphite electrolytic anodes are important.

A detailed understanding of carbon electrode reactivity in terms of the modern physics of solids lies in the future. Present knowledge is in terms of classical chemical concepts and, to some extent, other structural features such as porosity. Chemical reaction may be regarded as occurring at edge atoms (at plane boundaries or defects), at exterior intraplanar atoms or by intrusion between the planes. Limiting conditions occur under which these types of process occur separately. In general two or all three of the modes of reaction may occur at the same time.

As a general rule environments which are anodically reactive with the edge atoms affect the more amorphous carbons most. On the other hand, attack by interplanar intrusion is more pronounced with highly graphitized carbon. Amorphous carbons are protected from such attack by their defects, some of which are analogous to the cross-links in high polymers.

Carbon Electrode Reactions

Reaction of the carbon electrode is determined not only by the nature of the carbon but also by the acidity, dilution, and specific nature of the electrolyte (Thiele). The electrolysis of an alkaline solution occurs at about 0.8 volts at a graphite anode and yields oxygen. To a small extent oxidative destruction of the graphite occurs with the formation of carbon dioxide and humic acids, recognized by the brown coloration which passes from the anode into the solution. Attack is primarily at edge atoms; therefore, amorphous carbons are more vigorously attacked in alkali than is graphite, carbon dioxide and humic acid formation being intensive.

Attack mainly at edge atoms occurs also in

acids and salts in the "phosphoric acid group": phosphoric, acetic, chloracetic, chromic, hydrochloric, hydrobromic, and hydroiodic acids. In the acid media, electrolysis occurs at higher polarizations, about 1.7 volts. No evolution of oxygen occurs at graphite in these media, at least initially. Rather, the graphite is brought to a state so oxidized that it will set free bromine from bromides and chlorine from chlorides. Consistent with the edge-atom attack mechanism, amorphous carbon anodes are attacked more severely than graphites by electrolysis in phosphoric acid group electrolytes.

Interplanar intrusion occurs at graphite anodes in solutions of the "sulfuric acid group": sulfuric, nitric, chloric, perchloric, and hydrofluoric acids and salts. Relatively little oxygen is evolved and polarization is of the order of 1.8 volts in the acid systems. Swelling is induced in the graphite causing it to exfoliate. The behavior of the two groups of electrolytes may be contrasted in terms of typical members, as follows: in $2N$ sulfuric acid graphite takes up far more oxygen, capable of subsequent liberation, than is taken up in quite concentrated phosphoric acid. Another characteristic of the sulfuric acid group electrolytes is that anodic treatment of graphite therein leads to the formation of graphite oxide, the highest oxidation product of graphite still retaining extensive network structure.

Finally, concentrated acids of the sulfuric acid group produce anode swelling and a lustrous deep-blue graphite oxide at graphite anodes. When water is added to this product graphite and oxygen result. However, the graphite does not recover its original volume nor can it be made to do so in any direct manner.

Explanation of the detailed mechanism of reaction with carbons in terms of organic functional groups was pushed to an advanced stage by Sihvonen (1938), and what immediately follows is derived from that source. In general, oxidative reactions have attracted most interest. The reaction of carbons with oxygen, carbon dioxide, and water vapor involve intermediate functional groups which have also been used to explain reactions of carbon electrolytic electrodes.

Edge reaction unaccompanied by any appreciable intraplanar or interplanar reactions occurs at a very porous, pure graphite anode at low current density in sulfuric acid. The 1,2-diketo groups on the edges of the graphite planes are first converted to α-keto acid groups. This reaction may be symbolized as follows:

$$(C_xO)_2 + H_2O \rightarrow C_{2x-2} \, COCO_2H + H^+ + e,$$

where x denotes lattice carbons. The broken carbon-carbon bond implied by the equation is repaired on its other side by the formation of a new keto group by subsidiary oxidation. In a second step the α-keto acid group is converted into carbon monoxide and carbon dioxide:

$$C_{2x-2} \, COCO_2H \rightarrow C_{2x-2} + CO + CO_2 + H^+ + e.$$

Again the other side of the broken C—C bond is oxidized with the formation of a fresh keto group. It is noted that the equation implies equal volumes of CO and CO_2. Such is actually found in the system under conditions of maximum CO formation.

In alkaline electrolysis one of the processes is the discharge of hydroxyl ions on the crystal planes of graphite followed by dehydration to oxygen atoms bonded to two carbons:

$$2C_xOH \rightarrow C_{2x}O + 2H_2O.$$

Molecular oxygen then forms in additional steps. At edge positions hydroxyl discharge leads to the molecular adsorption product of oxygen with subsequent desorption. In addition some hydroxyl ions discharge at edge positions with the formation of keto groups.

Fluorine Technology

The versatility of carbon as an electrode material is further illustrated by the important part played by ungraphitized carbon anodes in fluorine technology. In this service, resistance to attack by the highly reactive elemental fluorine is necessary and also inertness in the presence of the $KF \cdot 2HF$ electrolyte. Carbon electrodes provide the desired properties while the more crystalline graphite disintegrates under bath conditions.

Disintegration of graphite in the fluorine electrolyte is a consequence of interplanar reactions with the formation of intercalation compounds. $(CF)_x$ is known to be formed by the treatment of graphite with gaseous fluorine at 400°C. The anodic electric field may encourage $(CF)_x$ formation at 80 to 110°C, the fluorine cell range. However, room-temperature formation of the other intercalation fluoride, $(C_4F)_x$, is known to occur when a gaseous mixture of HF and F_2

is passed over graphite. $(C_4F)_x$ is to be expected under cell conditions.

In contrast to other halogen intercalation compounds of graphite, $(CF)_x$ is practically an electrical insulator whereas $(C_4F)_x$ conducts at only 1 per cent of the efficiency of graphite itself. Both fluorides decompose explosively on heating to give mixtures of volatile carbon fluorides and solid products. These properties lead to and explain the uselessness of graphite in the fluorine application. On the other hand, the same intercalation compounds are invoked to account for the utility of ungraphitized carbon which is actually used.

Because of its grossly defective structure, ungraphitized carbon resists formation of intercalated fluorides beyond an exceedingly thin surface layer. However, the surface layer is very important. It is wetted neither by water nor $KF \cdot 2HF$; hence, penetration of the electrolyte into the pores is prevented. The unflooded pore structure provides a means of escape for the fluorine. Such an escape route is necessary because electrolyte nonwetting implies wetting by the fluorine gas. This occurs with the formation of very adherent lenticular bubbles which, under unfavorable circumstances, can mask the working surface of the anode and lead to an appreciable decrease in the electrolysis current.

Graphite Crystal Compounds

The graphite intercalation compounds need not be regarded solely from the point of view of their function in limiting or permitting the use of carbon electrodes. These compounds are of considerable scientific interest and may have some practical utility (Ubbelohde and Lewis).

One of the modes of formation of intercalation crystal compounds of graphite is electrochemical, and the compounds have been classified on this basis (Ubbelohde and Lewis). In this mode of formation the carbon network appears to function as a macrocation. One of the longest-known intercalation compounds is graphite bisulfate of approximate composition $C_{24}{}^+(HSO_4)^-2H_2SO_4$. This was first prepared chemically in anhydrous acid oxidizing media but also is formed by electrode reactions in which well-ordered graphitic carbon is made anodic in strong sulfuric acid. Better control of the amount of material intercalated with the possibility of simultaneous measurement of

physical properties make anodic oxidation preferable to chemical methods of preparation.

Nitrate, perchlorate, biselenate, pyrophosphate, phosphate, and arsenate have been prepared by methods similar to those for the acid bisulfates. In addition, anodic treatment can be used to prepare acid salts from organic acids which are sufficiently strong. Finally, $C_{24}{}^+HF_2 \cdot 2H_2F_2$ and compounds of lower fluorine content result on anodic oxidation of graphite in anhydrous HF.

The chemical properties of crystal compounds of graphite are not fully established. In regard to the electrochemical compounds, it is known that these may be reduced by cathodic polarization or by chemical means. However, stripping of the intercalate from the graphite is incomplete, the resulting graphite with tightly-held adduct being known as a "residue compound."

As already mentioned, graphite oxide, $C_x{}^+(OH)_y{}^-(H_2O)_2$, may be formed by electrolytic means, a particularly suitable medium being dilute nitric acid containing an oxidizing agent. Caution is required because graphite oxide formation may lead to an explosion of the carbon electrode under certain circumstances. In chemical methods of preparation the acid salts, such as the bisulfate, are intermediates, and an electrically conducting colloidal dispersion is the final product. It is interesting to note that mirrors of graphite have been formed by the electrolysis of such colloidal systems. Electrolysis of the graphite oxide gels has also resulted in the formation of long dendritic crystals which are reported to give the x-ray pattern of natural graphite.

References

1. FOERSTER, F., "Electrochemie Wässeriger Lösungen," Leipzig, J. A. Barth, 1923.
2. HARDIE, D. W. F., "Electrolytic Manufacture of Chemicals from Salt," London, New York, Toronto, Oxford University Press, 1959.
3. MANTELL, C. L., "Electrochemical Engineering," 4th Ed., New York, Toronto, London, McGraw-Hill Book Co., 1960.
4. RUDGE, A. J., "The Manufacture and Use of Fluorine and Its Compounds," London, New York, Toronto, Oxford University Press, 1962.
5. SIHVONEN, V., Trans. Faraday Soc., 34, 1062 (1938).
6. STENDER, V. V., AND KSENZHEK, O. S., Zhur. Priklad. Khim., 32, 110 (1959). (Consultant's Bureau Translation available.)
7. THIELE, H., Trans. Faraday Soc., 34, 1033 (1938).

8. UBBELOHDE, A. R., AND LEWIS, F. A., "Graphite and Its Crystal Compounds," London, Oxford University Press, 1960.
9. WRANGLEN, G., SJÖDIN, B., AND WALLEN, B., *Electrochimica Acta*, **7**, 577 (1962).

JOHN M. FINN

Cross-references: *Carbon, Porous; Chlorine Production in Diaphragm Cells; Chlorine Production in Mercury Cells; Chlorates, Electrolytic Production; Fluorine Production; Graphite, Electrothermal Production.*

CARBON, POROUS. See POROUS CARBON.

CARBORUNDUM. See SILICON CARBIDE.

CASTNER, HAMILTON YOUNG (1858–1899)

A modest bronze placque on a wall in Columbia University's main chemistry building, Havemeyer Hall, commemorates the technical accomplishments of one of her most distinguished alumni, Hamilton Young Castner, class of 1879. Generations of students have read the inscribed list of his impressive contributions to chemical technology made during the last thirteen years of his relatively short life (1858–1899).

At the top of the list is Castner's chemical process for the production of sodium, a development that made possible the world's first truly commercial process for making aluminum. Yet Castner is rarely thought of as a pioneer in the aluminum industry because his contribution was, within a few years of its inception, completely eclipsed by the Hall process for the manufacture of aluminum by electrolysis.

Whether or not this turn of fate worked to deny Castner the broad recognition to which he is entitled will never be determined. The fact remains that little is known about this genius of American industrial chemistry.

Castner was born on September 11, 1858, in Brooklyn, New York. He enrolled in Columbia's School of Mines in September, 1875, as a student in analytical and applied chemistry. Highly inventive and independent in thought, he soon became impatient with the nonscientific courses required for a baccalaureate degree and chose to concentrate all his efforts in the field of chemistry, a decision that denied him his degree. In spite of his devotion to scientific pursuits,

Castner did find time for extracurricular activities, notably crew. He rowed the bow position on the first freshman crew Columbia ever sent to an intercollegiate regatta.

His creative mind and scientific curiosity soon caught the attention of Dean Charles F. Chandler, one of Columbia's greatest chemists and teachers. Chandler's deep respect and affection for his student were evidenced by the several addresses he gave in Castner's honor after the latter's death.

At the end of his third year at Columbia, Castner left to begin work as an analytical and consulting chemist in a small laboratory on Pine Street in lower Manhattan. His business grew and prospered, and he moved his laboratory to larger quarters on West 20th Street where he was able to devote his free time to the investigation of processes to produce the alkali metals and their compounds.

In early 1886 he was granted a patent for his process to manufacture metallic sodium by the reduction of caustic soda by means of iron carbide or an eqiuivalent. His process was considerably more efficient than previous processes and reduced the price of sodium to 25 cents a pound. On October 12, 1886, Castner delivered a lecture on his process at the Franklin Institute that attracted world-wide attention. He later won the Institute's coveted gold medal for his work.

At this point in time a series of events which had been put in motion four years before Castner was born, and three thousand miles from his birthplace, began to exert a strong influence on his career. In 1854, the French chemist, Henri Sainte-Claire Deville, announced a process for the production of aluminum by the reduction of aluminum sodium chloride with metallic sodium. The announcement caught the attention of Emperor Napoleon III of France, a patron of the arts and sciences who also possessed the military ambitions of his famous uncle. The emperor thought aluminum would be an ideal metal from which to fabricate light, strong items of field equipment for his army and offered to subsidize Deville in the improvement of his process.

At the Paris Exposition of 1855, at which Napoleon III entertained many of the crowned heads of Europe, Deville was able to exhibit some bars of aluminum made by his process. The cost of the aluminum was prohibitively high because three pounds of the then costly sodium were required to make one pound of aluminum by the Deville process. Deville was never able to reduce the cost of sodium below a dollar a pound. During the next thirty years many investigators worked to lower the cost of sodium still further. None was successful until Castner did it thirteen years after the death of Napoleon III.

Unable to obtain capital to finance his process in the United States, Castner went to England during the winter of 1886–87 where he became managing director of the newly formed Aluminum Co. Ltd. His company captured the world market for aluminum and for about two years enjoyed a virtual monopoly of the metal. By that time the impact of the much less costly Hall process, which did not require sodium, was felt in world markets in spite of the later (1891) development by Castner of an electrolytic process to make sodium still more cheaply. The Deville-Castner process was doomed and Castner's role as a pioneer in aluminum was expunged from the pages of history.

Castner turned his attention to finding other uses for sodium in organic syntheses, the preparation of sodium peroxide bleaching agents, and in the manufacture of pure commercial cyanides for gilding, electroplating and the extraction of low-grade ores. In these attempts he was very successful.

In 1891 he developed a process for the production of sodium and potassium by the electrolysis of fused caustic soda and caustic potash, respectively, and in 1894 he was granted a patent for a process to manufacture caustic soda and chlorine by the electrolysis of salt. His ingenius use of a rocking electrolytic cell and a mercury cathode in this process solved a problem that had stumped chemists for years. In this development he ultimately joined forces with an Austrian chemist, Karl Kellner, who independently and almost simultaneously had developed a similar process. The two men sold their patent rights to Solvay et Cie.

American rights to the mercury cathode caustic-chlorine cell process were acquired by Mathieson Alkali Works which installed the process in 1897 at its Niagara Falls plant. There the Castner rocking cells were operated continuously until 1960. The Castner fused-caustic sodium cell also had a remarkably long industrial life. First used in 1891, the last major operation of it ceased in England in 1952. Both are tributes to the value and soundness of Castner's inventions.

Castner's final contribution to electrochemistry was his development of graphite anodes which were more durable than ordinary carbon anodes in electrolytic processes.

In 1898, Castner's health began to fail. He spent a winter in Florida in an attempt to regain it and then went to Saranac, New York, where he died on October 11, 1899, a month after his forty-first birthday, of tuberculosis, the disease that had previously brought death to his father and two brothers. Castner had no children, but was survived by his wife, the admiration of his associates, and a rich legacy to industrial chemistry.

References

1. EDWARDS, J., FRARY, F. C., AND JEFFRIES, Z., "The Aluminum Industry," First Ed. pp. 4–12, New York, McGraw-Hill Book Co., 1930.
2. GEER, WALTER, "Napoleon the Third," pp. 171–73, New York, Brentano's, 1920.
3. HALTON, V. L., "Hamilton Young Castner, 1858–99," *Journ. Chem. Ed.*, **19**, 353–56 (1942).

RICHARD L. DEMMERLE

Cross-References: *Chlorine Production in Mercury Cells—Electrochemistry; Hall, Charles M.; Sodium, Electrolytic Production.*

CATAPHORESIS. See ELECTROPHORESIS.

CATHODE

The negative electrode of an electrolytic cell through which current is being forced is called a cathode. It is the electrode at which reduction reactions take place. Representative cathodic reactions are:

1. Hydrogen ions + electrons → hydrogen atoms
2. Oxygen + water + electrons → hydroxyl ions
3. Metal ions + electrons → metal atoms

The cathode is the electrode at which electrons enter (current leaves) an electrolyte. The electrons combine with cations which migrate to the cathode under the influence of an emf. Among the reducing reactions which take place at the cathode are the discharge of positive ions, the formation of negative ions, and the reduction of elements from higher to lower valence states.

In a battery, the cathode is the positive terminal. In the conventional primary dry cell it is a carbon rod embedded in a mixture of manganese dioxide and carbon black or graphite. In the conventional storage battery the cathode consists of lead peroxide pasted within a lead grid. The cathode reaction during discharge is $Pb^{++++} + 2e \rightarrow Pb^{++}$; during charge it is the reverse.

In the electrorefining of metals, the cathode (as sheet or rod) is usually made of the metal being deposited. Iron or steel is commonly used as the cathode material in the production of caustic and chlorine in electrolytic cells, although mercury is the cathode in the mercury cathode chlor-alkali cells.

The cathode does not generally participate chemically in the cathodic reactions of corrosion processes; hence it is not attacked. In cathodic protection a current from an external d-c source is applied between an auxiliary anode and the material being protected (the cathode) or the material is coupled to a sacrificial anode and thereby protected by the direction of the galvanic current. An example of cathodic protection is the attachment of zinc blocks to the hull of a steel ship.

In electroplating, the cathode is the electrode which receives the deposit. The condition and composition of the cathode will, in general, affect the electrodeposit to the extent of chemical and mechanical bonding.

In electrolytic reduction (other than metal deposition), the nature and physical condition of the cathode can markedly influence the type of reaction products obtained. Among the factors affecting the type of product obtained are minor impurities on the cathode surface (which can lower the hydrogen overvoltage) and grain size (which can affect yields).

In electrolytic refining use is made of the fact that different metals plate out on the cathode at different voltages, the least active plating at the lowest voltage.

In an electron tube, the negative electrode is the cathode. It is the electrode from which electrons are emitted. It is heated by the tube filament and chemically coated in order to increase emittance.

JACOB M. MILLER

Cross-references: *Anode, Electrode.*

CATHODIC PROTECTION

Cathodic protection is a means of preventing or deterring the corrosion of metallic structures by liquid media. It was one of the first practical applications of electrochemistry. Sir Humphrey Davy in 1824 described his experiments for protecting the copper sheathing on the hulls of naval vessels. He considered tin, zinc, and iron as possible sacrificial materials and determined the ratio of sacrificial metal to copper for obtaining the optimum result with respect to cost and the retardation of corrosion and fouling.

Principle of Application

Application of cathodic protection is simply illustrated in Fig. 1. Four things are required: 1. the metallic structure to be protected (cathode); 2. an auxiliary electrode or anode; 3. a continuous electrolytic path between the two electrodes; and 4. a source of direct current. Note that there must be a continuous electrical circuit, with the current being carried by ions through the electrolyte and by electrons through the external circuit. The method is not applicable for metallic areas in the atmosphere or in nonconducting liquids. The current causes the corroding element to be a cathode to the exclusion of anodic or oxidation processes which are in effect transferred to the auxiliary anode. The source of electrical current may be external, as shown, or it may be galvanic. If a metal electrochemically more active (anodic) in the corroding medium than the protected metal is used as the auxiliary anode, the system becomes a galvanic cell in which the protected electrode is the cathode. In this case, the external current source is eliminated, and a direct electrical connection is made between the two electrodes. Magnesium and zinc are metals frequently used for this purpose. (See **Sacrificial Protection.**)

Electrochemical Theory

Since making an area anodic causes metallic destruction to occur, it would appear logically to follow that making it cathodic would retard such destruction. A useful visualization of the mechanism of cathodic protection has been advanced by T. P. Hoar and by R. H. Brown and R. B. Mears. According to the local-cell theory, corrosion is the result of galvanic action between anodes and cathodes on the metal surface. At the anodes a metal-consuming oxidation process, such as

$$Fe \rightarrow Fe^{++} + 2e$$

takes place. In the presence of anions such as chloride or sulfate, an acid salt solution is formed at the anodes. The most common reduction reactions at the local cathodes are

$$1/2\ O_2 + H_2O + 2e \rightarrow 2OH^-$$

and

$$2H_2O + 2e \rightarrow H_2 + 2OH^-$$

Note that each of these reactions produces hydroxyl ions at the cathodes, making the electrolyte basic near the cathodes. If the anodes and cathodes could be physically separated, the anodes would exhibit a potential against a reference electrode which is negative (more active) to that of the cathodes. On passage of a current to the anodes or cathodes, the above reactions would proceed at a rate equivalent to the current. Electrode areas polarize as a function of current, resulting in a potential shift in the negative direction for cathodes and a potential shift in the positive direction for anodes (see Fig. 2). For a corroding system, the corrosion current (i_{corr}) and the corrosion potential (e_{corr}) are determined by the intersection of the anodic and cathodic polarization curves.

If the corroding system is now polarized as a cathode to some more negative (active) potential, e_1, the polarization curves indicate that the current on the local cathodes is i_{c_1} and the current on the local anodes (equivalent to corrosion rate) is i_{a_1}. The protective current provided by the auxiliary anode is $(i_{c_1} - i_{a_1})$. This amounts to partial protection, with the corrosion rate (current) being reduced from i_{corr} to i_{a_1}. It is seen from the figure that, to obtain complete protection, the structure must be polarized to the open circuit potential of the anodes, e_2. At complete protection, the current on the local anodes is zero. The protective current from the auxiliary anode needed to do this is i_{c_2}.

Further Considerations

Helpful though the above visualization may be, it leaves many unanswered questions of both a fundamental and a practical nature.

It is not always possible to consider a metallic structure in terms of definite anodes where all of the oxidation takes place and definite cathodes where all of the reduction takes place. More generally, the corrosion potential is to be

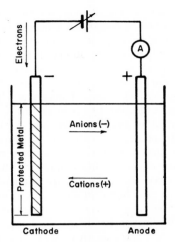

FIG. 1. Method of applying cathodic protection.

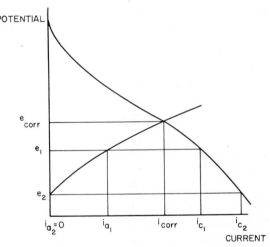

FIG. 2. Representation of electrochemical principle in cathodic protection.

considered as a mixed potential for all possible reactions on the metallic surface. The polarization curves, as in Fig. 2, are then partial reaction curves for the anodic processes and the cathodic processes, respectively, upon the entire metallic surface. For iron, complete protection is related to the reversible Fe/Fe^{++} potential and occurs at that potential above which iron passes into solution and below which iron plates out of solution at the ferrous ion concentration prevailing. It is, however, less than satisfying to explain the cathodic protection of aluminum in such terms. There are still some gaps in our understanding.

Inspection of Fig. 2 indicates that the protective current necessary to achieve full protection must be equal to or greater than the corrosion current. It is often observed, however, that the protective current is less than the corrosion current. For rapid corrosion in acid solution this has been ascribed to the "chunk effect," in which corrosion proceeds by removal of "chunks" of metal rather than by oxidation of individual atoms. In other cases, however, it appears related to mixed potential interactions, resulting from cases where the anodic and cathodic polarization curves, as in Fig. 2, are not truly independent of each other. Making an area cathodic, for example, may affect its anodic properties. One such effect is the result of changes in pH at anodic and cathodic areas. When aluminum is made a cathode, hydroxyl ion produced by an excessively high protective current destroys the oxide film and causes accelerated corrosion. For this reason, care must be exercised in not overprotecting amphoteric metals, such as aluminum and lead. Zinc may be used to sacrificially protect aluminum, but magnesium is too strongly anodic and may stimulate "cathodic" corrosion on aluminum. With iron, on the other hand, an increase of pH at the cathode causes passivation which assists protection. Of great importance is the fact that natural waters generally contain calcium and magnesium salts, bicarbonates, and carbon dioxide in solution. Under such conditions the increase in pH at the protected structure causes precipitation of a tightly adhering, high-resistance coating of insoluble carbonates. This coating diminishes the current required for full protection; redistributes the impressed current, causing it to protect the more inaccessible areas of the structure; and continues to protect the structure in the event of a temporary interruption of the protective current.

Cathodic protection is used most frequently in conjunction with some type of protective coating so that the cathodic protection is needed only at gaps in the protective coating system. Alkali produced at the cathode may destroy the bond between the metal and the coating. In some cases the coating also may be damaged by electroosmotic transport of water through the coating.

Applications

Cathodic protection is widely used for the protection of underground structures, such as pipelines and cables, for marine structures, such as inactive ships, for tanks of various types and,

in one way or another, for many other applications. Although the principles involved in cathodic protection may be simple, many complications are encountered in practice which require the guidance of an expert. As the size of the system increases, resistance effects become more important. There may be uncertainties as to the resistance of soils. Changes which might occur in service, shielding effects of other underground structures, and possible effects of the protective current on other underground structures must be considered.

A minimum potential of -0.85 volt with respect to a copper/copper sulfate reference electrode has been generally accepted as the criterion of protection for steel structures which are underground or beneath water. This potential corresponds quite well with what might be expected from the theoretical considerations outlined above. Where there is reason to believe that the potential may be in error because of the IR drop between the reference electrode and the area to be protected, an appropriate allowance must be made. To cope with varying requirements which may occur, it may be desirable to employ an automatic system to maintain the structure at constant potential. This has the advantages of maintaining full protection most economically at all times and preventing breakdown of coatings by excessive currents.

It is necessary that the current be carried across the junction of the auxiliary electrode and the electrolyte which serves as the corroding medium by some oxidation process. This means that on the anodes either oxygen must be evolved or metal must be destroyed. A metal which responds to the impressed current by thickening of a protective film cannot be used, since it would require an ever increasing potential to maintain a current. Galvanic anodes are necessarily consumed in operation. Scrap-steel or iron anodes are consumed in use and require replacement. It might be thought that graphite anodes would last indefinitely, but this is not necessarily the case. For underground use the anodes are generally surrounded by coke. Lead-alloy anodes are relatively inexpensive and suitable for marine applications. Platinum has the advantage that in almost all environments it evolves oxygen without being consumed. In spite of its high cost, it is occasionally used—sometimes coated on titanium to reduce cost.

Dependent on conditions, underground anodes may be point anodes, distributed anodes, or con-

159

CAVITATION EROSION

tinuous anodes. Deep underground anodes have advantages in minimizing surface interference difficulties and providing more uniform current distribution. It may be necessary to provide for irrigation and venting of underground anodes to keep them operative.

References

DAVY, HUMPHREY, *Phil. Trans. Roy. Soc.* (London), **114**, 151 (1824); **114**, 242 (1824); **115**, 328 (1825).

UHLIG, H. H. (Editor), "Corrosion Handbook," pp. 923–934 by John M. Pearson and pp. 935–950 by Robert Pope, New York, John Wiley & Sons, Inc., 1948.

EVANS, U. R., "The Corrosion and Oxidation of Metals," p. 283 and p. 890, New York, St. Martin's Press, 1960.

WAGNER, C. J., *J. Electrochem. Soc.*, **99**, 1 (1952); **104**, 631 (1957).

SUDRABIN, L. P., *Materials Protection*, **2**, 8 (1963).

HOAR, T. P., *J. Electrodep. Tech. Soc.*, **14**, 33 (1938).

ERNEST L. KOEHLER

Cross-references: *Corrosion-Electrochemical Theory; Galvanic Corrosion; Polarization; Sacrificial Protection.*

CAVITATION EROSION

Cavitation erosion is the localized damage and removal of a solid boundary material resulting from exposure to a cavitating liquid environment. It is usually associated with high-velocity liquid flow systems, including marine propellers, hydraulic turbines, valves, nozzles, Venturi tubes, and centrifugal pumps. Cavitation erosion may also occur in quasi-static liquid systems, such as ultrasonic cleaning and magnetostriction machines, and cylinder liners of diesel engines, in which high-frequency pressure fluctuations are produced in the liquid. Cavitation, which is the conversion of liquid to vapor in the form of vapor bubbles, will tend to occur in these systems when the pressure in the liquid drops below its vapor pressure. The degree of cavitation of a liquid or its tendency to cavitate is related to the magnitude of the cavitation number, σ. This dimensionless number is defined by the equation:

$$\sigma = \frac{P - p_V}{\frac{1}{2}\rho V^2}$$

where:

P = absolute field static pressure of the liquid, lb/sq ft

p_V = liquid vapor pressure, lb/sq ft

ρ = mass density of the liquid, d/g, (lb/cu ft)/(ft/sec²)

V = liquid reference velocity, ft/sec

The degree of cavitation increases with decrease in σ and vice versa.

Cavitation Erosion Mechanisms

The vapor bubbles formed by cavitation collapse on reaching regions of higher pressure. When this occurs at or near a solid boundary, the energy of collapse may be sufficiently high to cause damage to the boundary material. Theoretical calculations of the pressures resulting from collapse of a vapor bubble were made by Rayleigh.[1] He showed these pressures to approach infinity at final collapse, assuming an incomprehensible liquid and absence of any gas content. Modifications to Rayleigh's theory have been made on the basis of physical properties of real liquids, including temperature, vapor pressure, density, surface tension, viscosity, compressibility, and gas content, as well as thermodynamic properties of the liquid and vapor. Investigations to determine experimentally the collapse pressure have been largely inconclusive because of the high rate of pressure changes (in the order of 1 to 10 microseconds) and the small area of pressure impingement (0.005 to 0.010 inches in diameter). Recent experimental measurements[2, 3] of pressure intensities have shown them to be in the order of 6000 to 200,000 psi. Naudé and Ellis[3] have also observed that bubbles in contact with a boundary collapse nonuniformly, and that a liquid jet forms during this asymmetrical collapse, impinging on the boundary. This jet impingement produces a higher stress on the boundary than collapse of a bubble away from the boundary.

The mechanisms of cavitation erosion have been a source of controversy among investigators of this phenomenon for many years. The association of cavitation erosion with mechanical effects of stress impingement has been based largely on the stress intensities predicted and observed as described above, and the deformation and erosion of low yield metals, Fig. 1, and the damage to nonmetallic materials. The erosion resistance of alloys is related to mechanical and metallurgical properties, including strain energy,[4, 5] hardness, tensile strength, fatigue strength, grain size, and cold working properties. In general erosion resistance increases with increase in strain energy, hardness, tensile

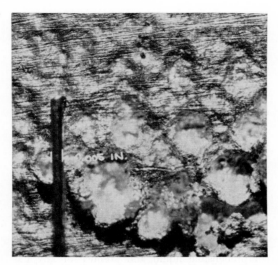

FIG. 1. Cavitation impingement damage of aluminum 1100-0 (10 seconds exposure in rotating disk apparatus at 150 ft/sec and 15 psig).[6]

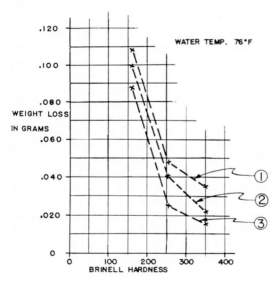

FIG. 2. Effect of liquid corrosivity and hardness on cavitation erosion of ductile iron, Leith.[7] (1) Halifax sea water; (2) Montreal tap water; (3) distilled water.

strength, and fatigue strength, and with decrease in grain size. Cold working resulting in increase in hardness (strain hardening) also tends to increase erosion resistance. The erosion resistance of polymeric materials has been shown[6]

to be related to the elasticity (related to the hysteresis or relaxation time), tensile strength, tear strength, and extensibility, the cavitation erosion resistance increasing with increase in these properties. High strength elastomeric materials are observed to be more erosion-resistant than metallic and plastic materials, and serve effectively as erosion-resistant coatings when adequate adhesive strength is provided.

Contributions of Corrosion

The importance of corrosion in contributing to cavitation erosion has been demonstrated by Leith,[7] Plesset,[8] and others. They observed relationships between erosion rates and corrosivity of the liquid, as shown in Fig. 2. Investigations[7, 8] of the application of cathodic protection to suppress cavitation erosion in corrosive liquids have shown a decrease in erosion rate with increase in current density, Fig. 3. However, it was observed in these investigations that hydrogen bubble generation accompanied such cathodic protection. As aeration of water also has been found to be effective in decreasing cavitation erosion,[9] it is believed that decrease of erosion by application of cathodic protection is associated with the formation of hydrogen bubbles. These bubbles increase the compressibility of the liquid and tend to cushion the cavitation bubble collapse. Plesset[10] has confirmed this hypothesis by using anodic currents sufficiently high to generate oxygen on the specimen surface. He then observed a similar decrease in erosion rate with increasing anodic current density and increasing oxygen evolution. Preiser and Tytell[11] also have shown that relatively low-level cathodic protection current can reduce cavitation damage in corrosive environments.

It has also been suggested that corrosion contributes to metallic damage in areas exposed to cavitation bubble collapse because of galvanic potentials resulting from velocity and stress gradients. Galvanic potentials may result from continual removal of corrosion product films in regions of cavitation. These bared surfaces are anodic to the adjacent filmed surfaces which will exhibit a more noble (cathodic) potential. Galvanic effects may also result from an increase in anodic potential caused by impingement stresses. Adjacent unstressed areas will be cathodic to the stressed area. The continual removal of corrosion products also permits corro-

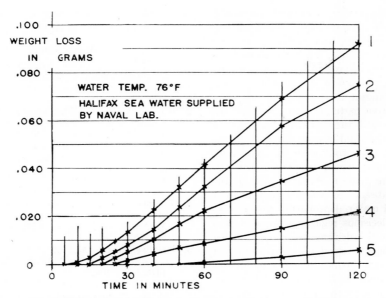

FIG. 3. Effect of cathodic protection on cavitation erosion of cast steel in sea water, Leith.[7] (1) No current; (2) 0.032 amps cathodic protection; (3) 0.190 amps cathodic protection; (4) 0.360 amps cathodic protection; (5) 0.500 amps cathodic protection.

sion to proceed at higher rates of attack on the bared surfaces. The increased rate of deterioration and weakening of metal by corrosion increases the rate of mechanical erosion due to cavity bubble collapse.

The feasibility of diminishing the contribution of corrosion to cavitation erosion by the use of corrosion inhibitors has been investigated.[12] Generally, however, this has not been found to be as effective in the laboratory as in service systems. The laboratory studies have shown that with the exception of a heat-treated low-alloy cast iron, none of the alloys used showed a significant increase in resistance to erosion with increase in sodium chromate concentration in fresh water. The discrepancy between conclusions shown by service and laboratory tests may be due to changes in significance of the chemical and mechanical factors in the two exposures.

Other means of suppressing erosion, in addition to the use of corrosion- and erosion-resistant structural alloys and weld overlays, elastomeric coatings and aeration, include pressurization to prevent the liquid pressure from dropping below its vapor pressure and design of the flow system to prevent severe pressure drops.

Laboratory Methods and Correlations with Service Erosion

Laboratory devices used to determine the relative cavitation erosion resistance of boundary materials and the effectiveness of control systems have included: (1) high-velocity flow systems, such as Venturi tubes, rotating disks, and ducts containing specimens in throat sections, (2) vibratory devices in which the liquid is essentially still, such as magnetostriction and ceramic transducers, and (3) impinging jet devices in which a cyclic jet impingement simulates the cyclic cavitation bubble collapse and jet (or energy) impingement on the boundary material without an actual occurrence of cavitation.

Differences in magnitude of parameters of different laboratory devices (e.g., different frequencies, amplitudes, and specimen shapes) give different erosion rates for the same test material. Orders of merit of different materials may be similar, depending on the relationships between the material properties and test parameters. Plesset,[8] thus, found that the effects of vibration pulsing on erosion rates were dependent on the specimen alloy and liquid medium in which the specimen was exposed. Erosion rates obtained under laboratory conditions and under actual service conditions (in which parameters, such as cavitation shedding frequency, liquid velocity, and pressure, may be difficult to define) also may differ considerably.

The mechanisms of erosion damage in a particular exposure are seen to be dependent on the conditions of exposure. In the exposure of a chemically reactive material in a corrosive environment, chemical processes may contribute significantly to the total erosion damage; in the absence of such chemically reactive conditions, the erosion damage would be determined primarily by the mechanical characteristics of the system. In the absence of detailed knowledge of flow, liquid, and material properties under service conditions, decisions regarding imposed protection in the initial designs are subject to error; also, sufficient correlations are not yet available to indicate the most effective manner of protection in service on the basis of laboratory investigations of different protection systems. Methods of protection if required may be specified on inspection of the machine after it has been operating under cavitating conditions, and the effectiveness of these methods determined by subsequent observation. Progress is being made[4, 5] in developing relationships between liquid, flow, and boundary material characteristics, and laboratory cavitation erosion measurements to permit accurate predictions of erosion control requirements. Further progress will depend on a greater understanding of the hydrodynamics of cavitating flow and resistance of materials to erosion and corrosion.

The cavitation erosion of materials appears to be related to other erosion processes, including abrasion, impingement erosion, and rain erosion. All show a major dependence on mechanical properties. Relationships between material hardness, elasticity, and extensibility properties and the resistance to these erosion processes are similar, highest resistance being shown by alloys of high hardness, strain energy, corrosion fatigue, and ductility, and by elastomeric materials of high tensile strength, tear strength, and extensibility.

For further study on the subject of cavitation erosion the reader is referred to the extensive reviews and bibliographies of Godfrey[13] and Eisenberg.[14]

(Note: The opinions or assertations contained in this paper are the private ones of the author and are not to be construed as official or reflecting the views of the Naval Service at large.)

References

1. LORD RAYLEIGH, "On the Pressure Developed in a Liquid During the Collapse of a Spherical Cavity," *Phil. Mag. (London)*, **34**, 94–98 (1917).
2. SUTTON, G. W., "A Photoelastic Study of the Strain Waves Caused by Cavitation," *J. Appl. Mech.*, **24**, No. 3, 340–348 (Sept., 1957).
3. NAUDÉ, C. F., AND ELLIS, A. T., "On the Mechanism of Cavitation Damage by Nonhemispherical Cavities Collapsing in Contact with a Solid Boundary," *Trans ASME*, **83**, Ser D, No. 4, 648–656 (Dec., 1961).
4. GOVINDA RAO, N. S., AND THIRUVENGADAM, A., "Prediction of Cavitation Damage," Trans. Am. Soc. Civil Engrs., **127**, 309–334, Paper No. 3308 (1962).
5. THIRUVENGADAM, A., "A Unified Theory of Cavitation Damage," *ASME Paper* **62-WA-118,** Nov., 1962.
6. KALLAS, D. H., LICHTMAN, J. Z., and CHATTEN, C. K., "Cavitation Erosion Resistant Coatings," **ONR-13,** Vol 2, pp 422–442, Washington, Office of Naval Research, 1962. Proceedings Seventh JANAF Conference on Elastomer Research and Development.
7. LEITH, W. C., AND THOMPSON, A. LLOYD, "Some Corrosion Effects in Accelerated Cavitation Damage," *Trans ASME, Basic Engineering,* **82,** Ser D, No. 4, 795–807 (Dec., 1960).
8. PLESSET, M. S., "The Pulsation Method for Generating Cavitation Damage," *ASME Paper* **62-WA-315,** presented at ASME Annual Meeting, Nov., 1962.
9. RASMUSSEN, R. E. H., Paper 20, "Some Experiments on Cavitation Erosion in Water Mixed With Air," National Physical Laboratory Symposium, "Cavitation in Hydrodynamics," London, Her Majesty's Stationery Office, 1956.
10. PLESSET, M. S., "On Cathodic Protection in Cavitation Damage," *Trans ASME, J. Basic Engineering,* **82,** Ser D. No. 4, 808–820 (Dec., 1960).
11. PREISER, H. S., AND TYTELL, B. H., "The Electrochemical Approach to Cavitation Damage," *Corrosion,* **17,** 11, 535t–549t (Nov., 1961).
12. RHEINGANS, W. J., "Accelerated Cavitation Research," *Trans ASME,* **72,** 705–724 (July, 1950).
13. GODFREY, D. J., "Cavitation Damage—A Review of Present Knowledge," *Chemistry and Industry (London),* **23,** 686–691 (June, 1959).
14. EISENBERG, P., "Cavitation," Section 12, V. L. Streeter, Ed., "Handbook of Fluid Dynamics," New York, McGraw-Hill Book Co., 1961.

JOSEPH Z. LICHTMAN

Cross-references: *Cathodic Protection;* entries bearing *Corrosion* headings.

CERAMIC INSULATION

The successful performance of electrical equipment depends upon the correct choice of the electrical insulating material. Frequently selection according to dielectric properties is of secondary importance; more often limiting factors for a specific insulating material are mechanical, chemical, or thermal characteristics. They are of particular significance for electrochemical processes which are carried out under corrosive and high-temperature conditions. For example, the process of fused salt electrolysis can be cited where the insulator may come in contact with molten salts or corrosive fumes emanating from the bath. In this case, special attention must be given to the corrosion resistance and to the high-temperature performance of the insulating material.

Heat affects insulation more than any other single environmental factor. The limiting temperature of usefulness for plastics is 300°C; above this temperature only ceramics can be considered.

What are Ceramics?

Ceramics, derived from the Greek word "keramos," meaning "burnt stuff," originally referred to pottery or earthenware. In its modern meaning, ceramics comprise products made from inorganic, nonmetallic materials undergoing a fusion or sintering process through the application of heat. A very large variety of materials falls under this definition. From an electrical point of view, ceramic materials may vary from electrical conductors to semiconductors, and finally to insulators. They may exhibit ferromagnetic properties (ferrites), or ferroelectric properties (titanates, niobates). From a chemical point of view, they may be compounded of oxides, single or mixed, and also of carbides, silicides, nitrides, selenides, or sulfides. While many of these materials and their properties are of interest to the electrochemist, the discussion will be confined to those which are electrical insulators.

Ceramics as Electrical Insulators

Ceramics which are electrical insulators are mainly oxide types and are either in the glassy or polycrystalline state. Consider briefly the facts which make these materials good electrical insulators. If a material is placed in an elec-

trical field, its interaction with the field is governed by electronic and ionic movements through the material. In case of metals, the bonding electron energy bands contain a high concentration of mobile electrons which account for electrical conductivity. In ceramic insulators, the band gap is sufficiently large that electrons are unable to move through the material. The minute electrical conductivity which is observable at room temperature (volume conductivity) is due to the movement of charged ions rather than electrons. Ionic conductance is temperature-dependent. It is extremely low for ceramic dielectrics at room temperature, but noticeable at elevated temperatures, especially if small cations of high mobility, such as charged alkali ions, are present.

Another contributing factor to electrical conductance is the surface condition of a material. Accumulated moisture from the air or contamination of the surface by salts, soot, etc., have a profound effect on surface conductance. Glazed surfaces are therefore preferred in all cases of adverse atmospheric conditions. Extending the surface area of an insulator by corrugating is another way of combating surface conductivity; the well-known "skirts" of high-voltage outdoor insulators are good examples of this design practice.

Dielectric strength of ceramic insulation is influenced by many factors, such as composition, form, thickness, and temperature. Dielectric breakdown is initiated by cumulative effects of dielectric losses and electrical conductance, which cause heating and further instability until final breakdown occurs.

Dielectric constant and dissipation factor are important considerations for the choice of insulating materials used for high-frequency applications. The dielectric constant of ceramic materials can be varied over a wide range, depending on composition and crystal structure. It may range from as low as 4 for special glasses to 10,000 for titanate ceramics. Dissipation factor, a measure of the loss of energy in an alternating field, can also be controlled by composition and crystal structure.

Mechanical Properties

Mechanical properties of ceramics vary considerably for different types of compositions and are dependent on structure, density, and manufacturing methods. Composition and manufacturing processes affect not only density, but also the types and size of crystallites, and the ratio of glassy to crystalline phases.

One property is common to all ceramic materials: brittleness. If metals are compared with ceramics, it is found that rupture of metals under load is preceded by intergranular slip. Ceramics break more suddenly and the total workload necessary to break them is considerably lower than for metals. Therefore, metals may be considered as tough and ductile, ceramics as brittle. Attempts to obtain a certain amount of ductility in ceramics have not been successful; on the other hand, their strength has been improved in recent years, so that by proper choice of material and design, brittleness of ceramic insulators is no longer a serious problem.

An advantage of lack of deformation before rupture is the high degree of rigidity of ceramic materials. They are almost ideal elastic bodies which do not cold-flow and do not change shape under load. Ceramics are therefore preferred insulators in electronic equipment where alignment and spacing of metallic conductors is an important consideration. High-strength ceramics, such as sintered alumina, have modulus of elasticity and compressive strength values of the same order of magnitude as steel. Tensile and flexural strengths, however, are considerably lower.

Chemical Resistance, Corrosion Resistance

Generally speaking, chemical and corrosion resistance of ceramics is excellent. Most ceramics withstand attack by acids with the exception of hydrofluoric acid; exposure to strong alkalies and superheated steam, however, requires careful selection of suitable materials. There are ceramic formulations which give excellent service under these conditions.

Types of Ceramic Insulation

One of the oldest types of ceramic insulation and the most desirable from a cost point of view is *porcelain*. Raw materials for its manufacture: clay, $Al_2O_3 \cdot SiO_2 \cdot 2H_2O$; flint, SiO_2 ; and feldspar, $(KNa)_2O \cdot Al_2O_3 \cdot 6SiO_2$, are readily available, and the formability of the ceramic before firing is such that economical production in a variety of shapes is possible. Glazed porcelain is the most widely used ceramic for all-purpose insulation, both outdoors and under corrosive conditions.

The search for improved specific properties, such as lower dielectric losses, higher dielectric constant, higher mechanical strength, thermal shock resistance, and others, led to the development of special types of ceramics, which merit a brief description. Only the more prominent ones which are commercially available will be mentioned. They are generally named after the main crystalline phase present in the fired ceramic body. *Mullite porcelain, $3Al_2O_3 \cdot 2SiO_2$* , is an improvement of high-tension feldspatic porcelain. It has higher mechanical strength over a wider temperature range, also good thermal shock and corrosion resistance. Its main application of interest to the electrochemist is for thermocouple protection tubes which may be immersed in gases or liquids up to 3000°F.

Sintered alumina, Al_2O_3, ceramics offer the best all-round properties of any ceramic insulating material. Only the relatively high cost of manufacture restricts wider applications, especially for large-size insulators. Sintered alumina products, ranging from 75 to 99 per cent alumina content, are available on the market; the higher alumina content offers better temperature resistance, lower dielectric loss properties, and higher mechanical strength. Originally designed for spark plug insulation, this group of materials is also used extensively in electronic devices. Vacuum- and pressure-tight insulators are used for metal-ceramic seals and in all cases where highest mechanical strength is important. Because of their extreme hardness, they find use in applications where wear resistance is an important factor. Fig. 1 illustrates the great variety of alumina ceramics available.

Steatite, $MgO \cdot SiO_2$, is an excellent ceramic insulating material for high-frequency applications. It combines low loss characteristics with good mechanical strength and low cost. It is made from the basic raw material, talc, a hydrous magnesium silicate. Talc is one of the softest, naturally-occurring minerals which can be formed into intricate shapes by automatic high-speed dry pressing and extrusion methods. (See Fig. 2.) Very little die wear is experienced during pressing and extrusion, a fact which contributes to the ability to maintain close dimensional tolerances at economical prices.

Forsterite, $2MgO \cdot SiO_2$, ceramics have still lower dielectric losses than steatite and find applications as UHF insulation.

Cordierite, $2MgO \cdot 2Al_2O_3 \cdot 5SiO_2$ ceramics are distinguished by very low coefficient of thermal

Fig. 1. Intricate shapes of alumina ceramics. (American Lava Corp.)

expansion. They have excellent heat-shock resistance and can be used for arc chambers where the insulator comes into direct contact with an electric arc.

Machinable Ceramics. Because of hardness and brittleness, most ceramics cannot be machined with ordinary machine tools. They must be formed and shaped before firing, while they are still in the soft or "green" state. If precision shaping after firing is required, it must be done by grinding or lapping with abrasive grains, either of silicon carbide or diamond. There are, however, certain ceramic materials which can be machined in the finished state. *Boron nitride, BN,* in the hexagonal crystalline form has lubricating properties similar to graphite, but in contrast to graphite is a good electrical insulator. It can be hot-pressed and thereafter machined with ordinary tools.

Glass-bonded mica, consisting of either natural or synthetic mica flakes, bonded with glass, has limited machinability. Also, it can be formed into intricate shapes by hot compression, transfer, or injection molding. Metal inserts can be molded into the material because molding temperatures are relatively low.

Certain dense types of *block talc, 3MgO·4SiO₂·H₂O,* or *pyrophillite, Al₂O₃·SiO₂·H₂O,* are used for model work or small production runs. These materials are soft and can be cut and machined to desirable and accurate dimensions and hardened by a firing process.

Ceramics with High Dielectric Constant. A special class of ceramic materials is comprised of those with high dielectric constants, ranging from 12 to 10,000. These materials are based on *titanium dioxide* and combinations of *titanium dioxide with alkaline earth oxides.* Within this class also fall some of the *niobates and tantalates.* These ceramics are not used as insulators, but rather as dielectric media in capacitors, dielectric amplifiers and energy-conversion devices, such as piezoelectric transducers.

Glasses. Glass as an electrical insulator is as old as porcelain. The demand to provide insulation for the whole frequency spectrum of electromagnetic waves resulted in the development of a variety of special electrical glasses with

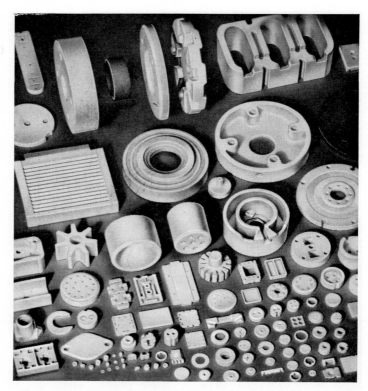

Fig. 2. These ceramics are principally steatites produced by dry pressing. (American Lava Corp.)

specific properties. The problem of reducing electrical conductivity through glass was solved by developing glasses with low alkali content. Fused silica glass, SiO_2, is one of the best electrical insulators.

The choice of glass as an insulator in preference to polycrystalline ceramics is due less to its dielectric properties than to its formability. The fact that glass is formed from the molten state makes it a versatile material from the designer's point of view. Glass is the only ceramic which can be drawn into continuous fibers. Fibrous glass as cloth, tape, or sleeving provides excellent flexible temperature-resistant insulation.

A major advancement among ceramic insulating materials has been the development of *Glass Ceramics*. These combine the advantage of polycrystalline ceramics, high-temperature resistance, and strength, with the versatility of forming glass by conventional glass-forming techniques. Glass ceramics are produced from standard glass ingredients, but in addition contain certain constituents as crystal nucleating agents. By special heat treatment, the glass is converted into a polycrystalline body. Glass ceramics have extremely small crystals and are practically free of voids. They resist deformation up to higher temperatures than the original glass and have higher thermal conductivity, hardness, and strength.

Fabrication Methods

To become useful products, ceramics must be formed to specific shapes with controlled dimensional tolerances. Great strides have been made in recent years in ceramic processing methods and have advanced the fabrication of ceramics from an art to an engineering science. *Raw materials* used for ceramic manufacture have been improved. These run from natural minerals, clays, talc, feldspar, etc., beneficiated by purification processes, to synthetic compounds formed by solid state reaction or fusion of refractory oxides. The raw materials are comminuted into powders of controlled particle size and carefully blended into a formable mass or "body." Depending on size, shape, tolerances, and similar

TABLE 1. COMPARATIVE VALUES OF PHYSICAL PROPERTIES

		Porcelain, high-voltage	Mullite porcelain	Alumina 95%+	Steatite	Forsterite	Cordierite	Boron nitride, hot-pressed	Glass-bonded synthetic mica	Titanium dioxide	Barium titanate	Glass, boro-silicate, low expansion	Glass ceramics
Density	g/cc	2.4	3.2	3.7	2.6	2.8	2.1	2.1	3.2	4.0	5.6	2.2	2.6
Safe Operating Temperature	°C	900	1400	1600	1000	1000	1200	800	800	1000	1000	400	1000
Thermal Expansion, Linear Coefficient	10^{-6}/°C	6	6	8	8	10	2	2	12	8	10	3	5
Flexural Strength	10^3 psi	11	18	50	20	20	16	10	10	20	15	8	20
Thermal Shock Resistance	—	Fair	Good	Good	Fair	Poor	Excellent	Excellent	Fair	Fair	Poor	Good	Excellent
Te Value (1×10^6 Ω at °C)	°C	350	600	850	800	1050	500	1000	550	500	—	450	450
Dielectric Strength	volt/mil	250	250	250	240	240	220	100	250	100	80	250	300
Dielectric Constant, at 1 MC	—	5.5	6.5	9	6	6.2	5.3	4	7	85	up to 10,000	4.6	5.6
Dissipation Factor at 1 MC	—	.01	.004	.0003	.002	.0004	.005	.0002	.002	.0005	.01	.005	.002
Loss Factor at 1 MC	—	.05	.026	.003	.012	.002	.026	.001	.014	.043	—	.023	.011

factors, a variety of forming methods can be selected.

Plastic forming, one of the earliest processes, takes advantage of the unique property of clay: plasticity. It is used extensively for forming high-voltage porcelain insulators. The so-called "jiggering process" has been highly mechanized. In this process, a lump of plastic body is placed on the surface of a plaster of Paris mold which has the contour shape of the lower surface of the article. The mold is rotated and a profile tool forms the upper surface. There are numerous variations of this method.

Slipcasting is a process whereby a ceramic "slip," a deflocculated water suspension of solid particles, is poured into a plaster of Paris mold. The mold absorbs part of the water and a coating of solids forms against the surface of the mold. The method lends itself to the production of hollow ware or complicated shapes.

Dry powder pressing is a process of compacting dry granules in metal dies under high pressures. It is an excellent method for the production of precision items in large quantities, because it can be carried out on high-speed mechanical presses either of the rotary or single-stroke type. Skill and experience are required in designing dies to obtain uniform compacting and efficient operation.

Extrusion is the accepted method of forming articles in rod or tubular form. A powder-water mix of stiff mud consistency is forced through a steel orifice under high pressure, and after ex-

trusion cut to appropriate length. Extruded shapes can be machined on automatic lathes before firing.

Injection molding of ceramics can be done by adding a thermoplastic binder to the ceramic powder and molding according to standard organic plastic injection molding procedures. The organic binder is burned out during the firing process and the final product is sintered to high density.

Isostatic pressing is a forming method which produces articles of very uniform density. The powder is compressed in a rubber mold to which fluid pressure is applied externally.

Table of Properties

The accompanying Table 1 is an attempt to give a survey of some of the more important physical properties of ceramic insulators. It should be emphasized that the quoted figures are by no means absolute, but relative values, given only for the purpose of a general comparison between the types of materials cited in the table. Manufacturers' property figures should be consulted where actual applications are considered.

References

1. BIRKS, J. B., "Modern Dielectric Materials," New York, Academic Press, Inc., 1960.
2. VON HIPPEL, A. R., "Dielectric Materials and Applications," New York, John Wiley & Sons, Inc., 1954.
3. "Insulation, Directory/Encyclopedia Issue,"

Libertyville, Ill., Lake Publishing Corp., **8**, No. 6 (1962).

4. KINGERY, W. D., "Ceramic Fabrication Processes," New York, Technology Press and John Wiley & Sons, Inc., 1958.

5. KINGERY, W. D., "Introduction to Ceramics," New York, John Wiley & Sons, Inc., 1960.

6. KOHL, W. H., "Materials and Techniques for Electron Tubes," New York, Reinhold Publishing Corp., 1960.

7. PHILLIPS, C. J., "Glass, Its Industrial Applications," New York, Reinhold Publishing Corp., 1960.

8. SHAND, E. B., "Glass Engineering Handbook," New York, McGraw-Hill Book Co., 1958.

9. SALMANG, H., "Ceramics, Physical and Chemical Fundamentals," London, Butterworths, 1961.

10. ZWIKKER, C., "Physical Properties of Solid Materials," New York, Interscience Publishers, 1954.

HANS THURNAUER

CERIUM ELECTROWINNING. See RARE EARTH METALS ELECTROWINNING.

CESIUM ELECTROWINNING. See RUBIDIUM AND CESIUM ELECTROWINNING.

CHLORATES, ELECTROLYTIC PRODUCTION

Sodium and potassium chlorate are produced commercially by electrolysis of aqueous solutions of the corresponding chlorides. Other chlorates, which have only limited commercial use, are made from sodium chlorate by metathesis.

The sodium salt, $NaClO_3$, is made in an electrolytic cell having no diaphragm and usually having anodes made from impregnated graphite. A few cells in this country now use lead dioxide anodes, while magnetite is also employed to some extent in European cells. Anodes may also be made of platinum or platinum-clad titanium. Mild steel is widely used for cathodes, although stainless steel and graphite are also employed. Steel, plastic, or concrete are used for cell bodies. Cell covers are plastic, asbestos-cement, or some other inert, nonconductive material.

The overall cell reaction for the electrolysis of a salt solution to form sodium chlorate can be expressed by the following equation:

$$NaCl + 3H_2O + 6 \text{ Faradays} \rightarrow NaClO_3 + 3H_2$$

However, in the cell a number of simultaneous reactions take place. Chloride ion is discharged at the anode:

$$2Cl^- \rightarrow Cl_2 + 2e^-$$

At the cathode, hydroxide ions are formed and hydrogen is liberated:

$$2HOH + 2e^- \rightarrow H_2 + 2OH^-$$

The chlorine can react in two ways: (a) with water to form hypochlorous and hydrochloric acid, and (b) with hydroxide ion to form hypochlorite and chloride ions:

$$(a) \quad Cl_2 + H_2O \rightarrow HClO + H^+ + Cl^-$$

$$(b) \quad Cl_2 + 2OH^- \rightarrow ClO^- + Cl^- + H_2O$$

The chlorate is then formed by a relatively slow reaction between hypochlorous acid and hypochlorite ions:

$$2HClO + ClO^- \rightarrow ClO_3^- + 2H^+ + 2Cl^-$$

This reaction is favored at temperatures above 30°C and at a pH below 7. Under alkaline conditions and temperatures below 30°C the hypochlorite will remain unreacted. A typical chlorate cell is shown in Fig. 1.

Chlorate cells are operated at such a low temperature that not all of the heat produced can be carried off by evaporation of water from the electrolyte. Therefore, cooling coils are customarily employed. These coils are usually of steel, located within the cell, and are bonded to the cathode to provide protection against corrosion. External cooling of circulated electrolyte may also be used. Owing to the decrease of overvoltage at higher temperatures, and its effect on heat generation, the thermal conditions are inherently stable and cooling water may be controlled by a setting on a hand operated valve. The difference between the cell voltage and the theoretical decomposition voltage (2.3 volts) represents the heat which must be removed from the cell by cooling methods.

Electrical supply and arrangement of chlorate cell systems are similar to those used in chlorine plants. Cells are usually connected in one or more electrical series operating at up to 600 volts, but the electrolyte and cooling water flows are in parallel.

The cell covers are provided with a gas duct system to vent the byproduct gas. Cell gas, principally hydrogen contaminated with oxygen and chlorine to the degree that it is usually not

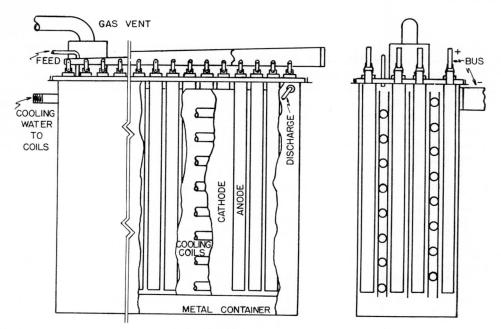

Fɪɢ. 1. Typical chlorate cell.

recovered, is vented to the atmosphere. In some systems air is drawn in over the vapor space and mixed with the hydrogen to drop its concentration below the explosive limit. Cells may also be sealed and operated with a high hydrogen content in the vent gas.

Some facilities employ cells having bipolar electrodes which are arranged to divide a long narrow cell container into a large number of parallel chambers, each being an individual cell. One side of each electrode is anodic with the opposite side being the cathode in the next chamber. Current is introduced into the first electrode of the battery and leaves from the last. This arrangement allows a very simple electrical bus system and a compact arrangement of the cells.

No outstanding advantages can be attributed to any particular cell design. The operating success of a plant is usually a function of the chlorate plant in its entirety. Whereas past practices have involved cells containing a large volume of dead space to allow retention time for the conversion of hypochlorite to chlorate and various cascade systems to allow for liquor flow through groups of cells in series, present practice tends toward large cells having no dead space and simple parallel liquor flow through individual cells. Advantages of this trend arise

from the greater electrolyzing capacity per unit area of floor space and from simplified operation of the cells. These changes in design have not resulted in any apparent loss in current efficiency.

Chlorate cells are not particularly sensitive to variations in operating conditions and will produce satisfactorily within a wide range for each variable. Thus, it is customary for each facility to operate its cells in such a manner as to obtain maximum fiscal economy, taking all plant expenses into consideration. Therefore, it is not possible to set forth exact operating data for chlorate cells and the following table merely contains a representative range of characteristics based on the use of graphite anodes.

As in the case of chlorine cells, chlorate cells must be dismantled at the end of the useful life of the anodes for cleaning and anode replacement. The absence of a diaphragm in the chlorate cell makes this repair relatively simple.

It is customary to add several grams per liter of sodium chromate to the electrolyte to assist in maintaining pH on the acid side and to reduce corrosion effects on the metallic portions of the cell (not useable with lead dioxide anodes). In the event that either the cell container or the cooling coils are of metal, they are bonded to the cathode to provide cathodic protection against corrosion. Fig. 2 is a basic flowsheet for sodium chlorate production.

Chlorate cell systems are generally provided with a so-called rundown tank which provides cell feed, process feed, loss collection, and makeup for the entire system. Intermediate storage tanks may also be provided. The rundown tank is located in or near the cell room and receives the electrolyte discharge from the cells. It also furnishes the feed to the cells, which is at approximately the same concentration as

TABLE 1. CHLORATE CELL CHARACTERISTICS

Cell potential, volts	3.0–4.0
Cell current, amperes	1,000–30,000
Current density, amps/ft²	30–80
Current efficiency, %	70–85
Electrolysis power (a-c basis), kwh/ton NaClO₃	6,000–7,000
Sodium chlorate in electrolyte, gpl	150–600
Sodium chloride in electrolyte, gpl	50–200
Sodium chromate in electrolyte, gpl	1–7
Temperature, °C	30–50
pH	6.0–7.0
Anode height, inches	30–40
Anode thickness, inches	1–2.5
Anode width, inches	2–10
Graphite consumption, lb/ton NaClO₃	15–25
Life of anodes, years	1–3
Anode-cathode spacing, inches	0.3–0.5

the discharge, i.e., there is very little increase in the chlorate concentration of the electrolyte per pass through the cells. The rundown tank also is fed with strong brine from the sodium chloride make-up system and, in addition, provides feed liquor to the crystallization process. The size of the rundown tank is such that it permits satisfactory operation of the cell system for many hours in case the brine feed and/or crystallization systems are not functioning. The concentration of sodium chloride and chlorate in the rundown tank may, as a result, vary through rather wide limits on occasion and, therefore, the subsequent crystallization system is designed to function within these variances.

Both sodium chloride and sodium chlorate are present in the rundown tank, cell feed, and cell discharge to an appreciable extent as shown in the preceding table (cf. concentrations in electrolyte). A side stream is continually transferred from the rundown tank for crystallizer feed which, after the removal of a portion of its chlorate, is returned to the rundown tank with depleted chlorate content and with an unreduced amount of chloride. The removed chlorate is replaced with an equivalent amount of chloride which is added to the rundown tank as saturated brine. The function of the electrolytic cells as a part of this system is to continually

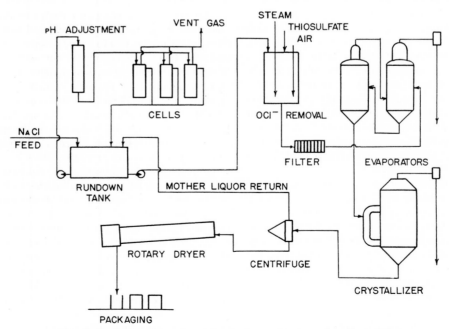

FIG. 2. Basic flowsheet for electrolytic production of sodium chlorate.

convert a portion of the chloride to chlorate to an extent sufficient to offset chlorate removal.

The sodium chloride feed to the rundown system consists of a saturated solution of sodium chloride either in water or in spent mother liquor from the crystallizer system. It is customary to remove calcium and magnesium salts and sulfates from feed brine prior to delivery to the rundown tank. Chemical precipitation, using the appropriate reagents, is employed.

The liquor in the cells has a tendency to become alkaline owing to the loss of chlorine from the electrolyte. Therefore, the stream being returned to the cells from the rundown tank is acidified with chlorine or hydrochloric acid using automatic control based on pH.

The feed to the crystallization system contains hypochlorite ion which must be removed by heating, air blowing, and/or acid or thiosulfate treatment. The feed is also made slightly alkaline with caustic soda following hypochlorite removal. Failure to remove hypochlorite and acid will cause serious corrosion problems in the evaporator. The liquor is subsequently filtered to remove anode mud and other solids. If required by the concentration of chlorate, the purified liquor may then be evaporated in continuous, multi-effect evaporators until chlorate just starts to precipitate. The liquor is then transferred to either an evaporative or a surface cooled crystallizer where crystallization takes place. In some systems "salting out" of chlorate with sodium chloride is employed.

Crystallizers may operate at temperatures as low as −10°C. The slurry from the crystallizer is continuously centrifuged to remove chlorate crystals, with the mother liquor being returned to the rundown tank. The wet crystals are dried in a steam-tube or hot-air, rotary dryer and are then ready for packaging. An inorganic conditioning agent may be added to prevent caking. The product is packaged in drums, hopper cars, or, in the case of some large users, is shipped as a 50 per cent solution.

The appearance of sodium chlorate varies to some extent with the conditions extant in the crystallizer. The usual crystal form consists of small regular tetrahedrons which may be considerably rounded. Pure sodium chlorate is white but the commercial form may have various graduations of yellow color. The color is caused by a very small amount of chromate introduced from the cell liquor. The depth of yellow color depends on the amount of chromate used and the temperature of the crystallizer.

The manufacture of potassium chlorate is similar to that of sodium chlorate except that, owing to its solubility characteristics, the necessity for water evaporation is eliminated. Potassium chlorate systems involve the addition of potassium chloride to hot, purified sodium chlorate cell liquor. Upon cooling in the crystallizer, potassium chlorate crystallizes out. The mother liquor from the crystallizer contains appreciable quantities of potassium ion and this material is recirculated to the cells. No difficulty is encountered from the presence of both sodium and potassium ions in the electrolyte, provided the cells are used entirely in conjunction with a potassium chlorate system. In the event that potassium salts alone are electrolyzed, the current efficiency is reduced because of the lower solubility of potassium salts. Care is taken that the crystallization of potassium chlorate is relatively sharp with little sodium ion present in the product. Sodium chlorate, being slightly hygroscopic, interferes with the use of potassium chlorate in matches and pyrotechnic devices which comprise the principal market for the product.

Pure sodium chlorate is not strongly corrosive inasmuch as the chlorate molecule is large and does not tend to react readily with metals. However, the solutions used in the plant may be somewhat acidic and contain hypochlorite. At all points chloride ion is present. Accordingly, corrosion can easily occur. The portion of the facility handling acid- or hypochlorite-containing liquor must employ halogenated plastics such as polyvinylchloride, cement-asbestos, glass, ceramics, rubber, etc. Metal cell cans and cooling coils, which are cathodically protected, are an exception to this. Tanks are generally tile or plastic lined. Following treatment to remove hypochlorite and neutralize the acid, the liquor may be handled in copper, bronze, cast iron, stainless steel, or other metals which are somewhat inert to chloride corrosion. Titanium is probably suitable at most points in the system.

Chlorates are reasonably stable but, since they are very powerful oxidizing agents, have a tendency to react strongly with reducing agents. Accordingly, great care must be taken that all equipment and plant facilities are kept clear of wood, oil, combustible organic materials, sulfur, ammonium salts, dust, and easily oxidizable metals such as aluminum and magnesium. Moving equipment must either be run dry or lubricated with water or fluorinated lubricants. Pump packings must be of the noncombustible type. Chlorate solutions are especially dangerous with respect to materials that are both absorbent and oxidizable. Rubber and plastics, although organic in nature, may be relatively safe for certain applications provided that they do not become impregnated with solution, that they do not exude organic materials such as oils and plasticizers, and that their temperature is kept well below the ignition point. Good safety practice requires that employees in chlorate facilities wear a complete change of clean clothing every day and that it be washed after each shift. Clothing should also be changed immediately in the event that it is splashed with chlorate solution since, when dry, chlorate-saturated fabric becomes violently combustible. Rubber shoes should also be worn since leather easily impregnates with chlorate solutions and becomes hazardous. Chlorate solution will easily creep into small cracks and other interstices in equipment and then form crystals. Upon crystallization, expansion occurs which may cause serious leaks. Chlorate solutions will also creep and deposit crystals in cell vents. Therefore, daily washdowns of plant facilities are advisable.

Sodium chlorate is employed principally for pulp bleaching (reactant for chlorine dioxide generation), as a herbicide, and as an intermediate for the production of ammonium perchlorate, the oxidizer for most solid rocket propellants. Potassium chlorate is used in matches, flares, and pyrotechnic devices.

The commercial production of sodium chlorate in the United States had increased from 33,000 tons in 1951 to about 117,000 tons in 1963. Producers are: American Potash & Chemical Corporation with plants at Henderson, Nevada, and Aberdeen, Mississippi; Hooker Chemical Corporation with plants at Niagara Falls, New York, and Columbus, Mississippi; Pennsalt Chemical Corporation with a plant at Portland, Oregon; Penn-Olin Chemical Company with a plant at Calvert City, Kentucky; and Pittsburg Plate Glass with a plant at Lake Charles, Louisiana.

References

1. WHITE, N. C., *Trans Electrochem Soc.*, **92**, 15–21 (1947).
2. JANES, MILTON, *ibid.*, 23–44.
3. HAMPEL, CLIFFORD A., AND LEPPLA, P. W., *ibid.*, 55–65.
4. MANTELL, C. L., "Industrial Electrochemistry," 4th Ed., 342–347, New York, McGraw-Hill Book Company, Inc., 1960.
5. KIRK, R. E., AND OTHMER, D. F., Ed., "Encyclopedia of Chemical Technology," Vol. 3, 707–715, New York, The Interscience Encyclopedia, Inc., 1949.

JOSEPH B. HEITMAN

CHLORINE INDUSTRY

The chlorine industry, also called the chloralkali or chlorine-caustic industry, produces the two greatest tonnage products of the electrochemical industry: *chlorine* and *caustic soda* (sodium hydroxide or NaOH). This statement neglects the production of steel made in electrical furnaces. As chemical raw materials, chlorine and caustic soda individually are exceeded only by salt, lime, sulfuric acid and soda ash, Na_2CO_3, in the quantities consumed.

The chlorine industry uses over 2 per cent of all the electrical energy consumed in the United States.

Well over 90 per cent of the chlorine made in this country is produced by the electrolysis of sodium chloride solution which yields caustic soda as a co-product. The availability of caustic soda from this source has reduced to a minor amount the quantity of it made by other processes, chiefly the lime-soda process, which formerly was a major source of caustic soda. The demands for chlorine, which have more than doubled since 1950, from 2,150,000 tons to about 5,400,000 tons in 1963, account for the growing production of caustic soda by electrolysis of salt. In fact, so much caustic soda is available that it has displaced soda ash in many of the uses where the latter has been predominant for many years.

Over the past several years the installation of additional chlorine capacity has been influenced by the problem of finding outlets for the accompanying caustic soda. This matter of the unbalance of markets for chlorine and caustic soda is expected to become an even greater factor in the industry in the future.

Production Data

The annual United States production data for the past several years, as well as for 1954 for

TABLE 1. CHLORINE-CAUSTIC SODA PRODUCTION
ANNUAL TONS

	Chlorine	Caustic Soda	
		Electrolytic	Lime-Soda
1954	2,895,100	2,770,000	468,000
1958	3,600,000	3,620,000	435,000
1959	4,285,000	4,375,000	300,000 est.
1960	4,840,000	4,596,000	300,000 est.
1961	4,603,193	4,697,000	200,000 est.
1962	5,142,876	5,262,500	200,000 est.
1963*	5,400,000	5,450,000	200,000 est.

* Preliminary.

comparison, are given in Table 1 for both chlorine and caustic soda.

The production of soda ash, in contrast, has remained relatively constant over the past few years: 5,611,600 tons in 1958; 5,387,751 tons in 1960; and 5,639,000 tons in 1962.

Sources of Chlorine

Approximately 74 per cent of the 1963 chlorine capacity installed in the United States is in diaphragm cells, 20 per cent in mercury cells, 5 per cent in sodium cells, and less than 1 per cent in nonelectrolytic processes. The major trend in recent years has been the increased capacity in mercury cells, which in 1945 accounted for only 4 per cent of the total production facilities. In other parts of the world the mercury cell is dominant. The various cells are discussed in other articles on **Chlorine Production** and on **Sodium, Electrolytic Production.**

Currently (1963) some 91 per cent of the chlorine produced is equivalent to electrolytic caustic soda production, 1.5 per cent to potassium hydroxide production, about 4 per cent to sodium production, and the remainder to other products. The same proportions have existed for several years, and no major change is apparent in the immediate future.

The chlorine industry is currently operating at an everage of 93 per cent of capacity, with some plants operating at 97 to 98 per cent. At the end of 1963 the installed United States capacity was about 5,860,000 annual tons of chlorine.

End-Use Pattern

Estimates vary on the markets and uses for both chlorine and caustic soda, but the major use

by far for chlorine is in the manufacture of other chemicals whose number runs into the hundreds. Among the more prominent are chlorinated solvents, plastics and resins, automotive fluids, insecticides and herbicides, and refrigerants. The most vital single use for chlorine is in sanitation, where chlorine has been responsible for the purification of potable water supplies which has reduced to almost zero the incidence of water-borne diseases, such as typhoid.

Caustic soda's chief use is also in chemical manufacture, but the proportion so used is much smaller than it is for chlorine.

A breakdown of estimated end-uses for both chlorine and caustic soda is given in Table 2.

Plant Location

For the first 30 or so years the chlorine industry in the United States was centered in Niagara Falls where large amounts of cheap power and a source of salt some 90 miles east in New York state provided the two main production requirements. Other states, such as West Virginia, Ohio, and Michigan, soon became chlorine producers, mainly because of on-site salt deposits. Today, the picture is quite different.

In installed capacity, Texas leads with some 28 per cent of the total, followed by Louisiana with some 13 per cent. Michigan and West Virginia account for about 11 and 10 per cent, respectively, while New York has about 8 per cent, Alabama and Ohio about 5 per cent each, and Washington somewhat more than 4 per cent. The remaining capacity is widely distributed in New England, New Jersey, Maryland, Virginia, North Carolina, Georgia, Kentucky, Ten-

TABLE 2. U.S. CHLORINE-CAUSTIC SODA
END-USE PATTERN[5]

Chlorine		Caustic Soda	
Organic chemicals	59%	Chemicals	43%
Inorganic chemicals	10	Rayon and film	12
		Pulp and paper	10
Pulp and paper	15	Aluminum	7
Water treatment	4	Petroleum	5
Others	12	Textile	5
		Soap and detergents	4
		Other	14
	100%		100%

(Source: The Dow Chemical Co.)

nessee, Illinois, Wisconsin, Kansas, Arkansas, Colorado, Oregon, California, and Nevada.

Between 70 and 75 per cent of the chlorine production is captive, a fact that accounts to a degree for the widespread distribution of the chlorine plants, even though cheap power and cheap salt may not both be available at a given site. Close proximity of a consuming process for either or both chlorine or caustic soda, as in a captive plant operation, often overcomes the economic advantages of other sites where either or both cheap power and salt is available. For example, chlorine must be liquefied to be shipped any distance, so use of it near the cell plant saves both liquefaction and freight costs.

Future Trends

A few factors about the chlorine industry in the future might be mentioned. The growth of the industry is healthy. While the annual growth rate during the 1940–1950 decade was 12.5 per cent, for the next decade, 1950–1960, it dropped to 8 per cent, and for the more recent years it has levelled off to about 6 per cent annual growth rate. This rate is expected to continue for some time.

There is a continuing need for more caustic soda markets and for methods of producing chlorine without alkalis as co-products. Even through processes are available to electrolyze hydrochloric acid, a by-product of many organic chlorination processes, no major installation of them has been made. This situation may change in the near future because the two problems of disposal of by-product HCl and of producing chlorine without alkali would then be solved.

References

1. HAMPEL, C. A., AND EHLERS, N. J., *J. Electrochem. Soc.*, **106**, 906 (1959).
2. EHLERS, N. J., AND HAMPEL, C. A., *ibid.*, **107**, 791 (1960).
3. CURREY, J. E., AND HAMPEL, C. A., *ibid.*, **108**, 1001 (1961).
4. CURREY, J. E., AND HAMPEL, C. A., *Electrochem. Tech.*, **1**, 56 (1963).
5. CURREY, J. E., AND SWANBERG, D. E., *ibid.*, **1**, 191 (1963).
   Note: The above five articles are the annual reports of the Chlor-Alkali Committee of the Industrial Electrochemistry Division of the Electrochemical Society. These reports will continue to be published in *Electrochem. Tech.* each year.
6. SCONCE, J. S., Editor, "Chlorine, Its Manufac-

ture, Properties and Uses," New York, Reinhold Publishing Corp., 1962.

CLIFFORD A. HAMPEL

Cross-references: entries bearing *Chlorine Production* headings; *Hydrochloric Acid Electrolysis; Sodium, Electrolytic Production.*

CHLORINE PRODUCTION IN DIAPHRAGM CELLS

The diaphragm chlor-alkali cell is important as the principal twentieth century method of chlorine production. Approximately 75 per cent of United States chlorine is produced in diaphragm cells as of 1962. For additional information on chlorine production see entry on **Chlorine Industry.** The diaphragm cell is exceptionally simple in principal and in operation; yet, the processes involved in the diaphragm remain a challenge to the electrochemist.

The great growth in chlorine demand and the availability of new materials of construction have opened up opportunities for development so that during recent years more effort has been directed toward diaphragm cell development than at any previous time.

Chemistry

In the operation of a typical diaphragm cell (see Fig. 1) sodium or potassium chloride brine, nearly saturated and at a temperature approximately 60 to 70°C, is fed into the anolyte compartment, from which it flows through the diaphragm into the catholyte compartment where alkali is formed. Flow is continuous, with a differential head maintaining flow through the diaphragm. Chlorine gas is formed at the anode and hydrogen and alkali are formed at the cathode. Only a portion of the alkali metal chloride entering the cell is electrolyzed, and the unreacted portion leaves with the hydroxide solution from the catholyte compartment.

Modern cells operate with a cathode efficiency (hydrogen) very close to 100 per cent and an

---

Editor's note: This article and the following one are adapted from Chapter 5 by the author in "Chlorine, Its Manufacture, Properties and Uses," J. S. Sconce, Editor, New York, Reinhold Publishing Corp., 1962.

anode efficiency (chlorine) of approximately 97 per cent.

Anode Reactions. The principal anode reaction is

$$2Cl^- \rightarrow Cl_2 + 2e \qquad (1)$$

This simple reaction represents approximately 97 per cent of the anode discharge under good operating conditions; however, the following reactions representing minor losses are of particular significance since they have a considerable effect on anode life, diaphragm life, and purity of the products.

Chlorine formed at the anode saturates the anolyte and an equilibrium is established as follows:

$$Cl_2 + OH^- \rightleftharpoons Cl^- + HOCl \qquad (2)$$

$$HOCl \rightleftharpoons H^+ + OCl^- \qquad (3)$$

Reactions (2) and (3) indicate the importance of hydrogen ion concentration on the solubility of chlorine in the anolyte. Normally the pH of the anolyte is in the range of 3.0 to 4.0.

Hypochlorous acid and hypochlorite tend to react to produce chlorate according to the reaction used in electrolytic chlorate cells as shown:

$$2HOCl + OCl^- \rightarrow ClO_3^- + 2Cl^- + 2H^+ \qquad (4)$$

In addition to chloride ion, other anions may discharge at the anode. Under usual operating conditions, OH^- discharge is the most important reaction competitive with chloride discharge

$$4OH^- \rightarrow O_2 + 2H_2O + 4e \qquad (5)$$

With graphite electrodes, which are the only type presently used in commercial production, Reaction (6) also occurs as shown:

$$4OH^- + C \rightarrow CO_2 + 2H_2O + 4e \qquad (6)$$

The source of OH^- ions discharged at the anode is the cathode liquor, from which the OH^- ions migrate under the influence of the electrical potential across the diaphragm. Under steady state conditions the amount of OH^- ion entering the anolyte must equal the amount used in other reactions, e.g., chlorate formation plus the amount discharged at the anode. Hence, a certain pH is established in the anolyte which is sufficiently high to cause the required rate of discharge at the anode.[23] The pH established depends not only on the rate of migration of OH^- through the diaphragm but also on the characteristics of the anode material (the relative oxygen and chlorine discharge potentials).

For a given rate of oxygen discharge, the anolyte pH with different anode materials would tend to be in the following order:

Carbon anodes $<$ untreated graphite $<$ treated

graphite $<$ platinum

The reactions undoubtedly are much more complicated than represented. Peroxygen compounds, organic hydroxides, organic acids, and carbon monoxide probably are formed as intermediates. Traces of organic compounds resulting from anodic oxidation are always present to some extent in the caustic liquor from graphite anode cells; also small quantities of carbon monoxide, carbon tetrachloride, chloroform, and hexachloroethane are always present in the chlorine. Vaaler[26] has studied the mechanism of oxygen and carbon dioxide discharge at chlorine cell anodes.

Presence of anions other than OH^-, e.g., HSO_4^-, ClO_3^-, OCl^-, is also a factor in the anodic formation of oxygen and carbon dioxide. In small quantities such anions do not affect the total amount of oxygen formation because oxygen (or CO_2) discharge according to any mechanism also involves the formation of an equivalent quantity of H^+ ion. Hydrogen ion formed by such processes tends to neutralize an equivalent of hydroxyl ion and hence to reduce the extent of Reactions (5) and (6) correspondingly.

Cathode Reactions. At the cathode, the primary reaction is discharge of hydrogen ion

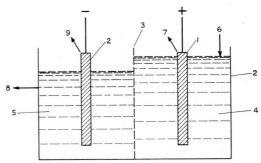

FIG. 1. Diagram of percolating diaphragm chloralkali cell. 1. anode; 2. cathode; 3. diaphragm; 4. anolyte-chlorine container for anolyte and chlorine; 5. catholyte hydrogen container for catholyte and hydrogen; 6. brine inlet; 7. chlorine outlet; 8. caustic outlet; 9. hydrogen outlet.

from the alkaline solution as shown:

$$2H^+ + 2OH^- \rightarrow H_2 + 2OH^- - 2e \qquad (7)$$

Discharge of hydrogen from the aqueous solution leaves an equivalent OH^- ion derived from water.

Reduction of HOCl to Cl^- also takes place at the cathode. However, for all practical purposes, the current efficiency of hydrogen discharge is 100 per cent.

History

The first formation of chlorine by electrolysis is attributed to Cruickshank in 1800.[27] Commercial production of chlorine by oxidation of hydrogen chloride by manganese dioxide (Weldon process) and air (Deacon process) became important during the last half of the nineteenth century. Hydrogen chloride was derived from the Le Blanc soda ash process and the chlorine was converted to bleaching powder. By 1900, 150,000 tons per year of bleaching powder were being produced in England.[12]

British patents on chlorine-alkali cells to Cook in 1851, Watt in 1851, and Stanley in 1853 indicated an awareness of the possibilities of commercial electrochemical chlorine. The development of the dynamo about 1865 gave impetus to research on electrochemical processes which, until this time, had been quite academic. The observations of Watt indicate a remarkable insight into the problem which was not appreciated until nearly fifty years later. The theoretical work on electrolysis of brine by Fritz Foerster[8] and his students in Germany was outstanding and remains important today.

The first commercial electrochemical production of chlorine was by the Griesheim Company in Germany, in 1888. Actually the chlorine was a by-product of KOH manufacture. The first commercial electrochemical production of chlorine in the United States and of caustic soda in the world was started by the Electrochemical Company of Rumford Falls, Maine, in 1892. Because there was no U.S. production of bleaching powder and cheap hydroelectric power was available, the infant U.S. electrochemical chlor-alkali industry was given a chance to survive competition with bleaching powder imported from England and Germany.[4, 17, 27]

The first cells operated as a batch process with no electrolyte flow through the diaphragm. Anode materials used were platinum, amorphous carbon, and magnetite.

Discovery of the principle of allowing the anolyte solution to flow into the catholyte to minimize migration of OH^- ions toward the anode and the discovery of a process for manufacture of graphite for use as anodes provided the technical basis for development of diaphragm cells from approximately 1900. From 1900 to 1928 nearly all commercial cells employed one or two sheets of asbestos paper as a diaphragm material. The asbestos paper was placed over a perforated steel plate or steel screen cathode and fastened in place opposite the anodes. The hydrostatic head of brine held the diaphragm in place against the screen or perforated plate. Cells were classified as (1) vertical (a) rectangular, (b) circular, (c) filter press, or (2) horizontal.

In 1913 Marsh introduced a multifinger shaped cathode over which asbestos paper was wrapped. This cell was used in two installations for a period of fifteen years but the problem of sealing the edges of the diaphragm prevented any major expansion.

Stuart in 1928 developed a deposited asbestos diaphragm for the Marsh-type cell which overcame the difficulty of sealing the edges. The deposited diaphragm is made by applying a layer of asbestos to a cathode screen by immersion of the screen in an asbestos slurry and applying a suction to the screen.

The deposited diaphragm made possible the design of cells with a relatively intricate cathode and, hence, relatively large cathode areas per cell. Furthermore, the deposited diaphragm provided a more rugged and more uniform diaphragm. The deposited diaphragm is the basis for all the major diaphragm cells in use at the present time.

Present Diaphragm Cells

During the past 12 years all new diaphragm cells have been of two basic types: the Stuart (Hooker) type and the Dow type. These types are similar, the only difference being that the Dow cell incorporates a multiplicity of unit cells into a filter press or box structure. Both types have (1) vertical graphite anodes, (2) steel screen cathodes and (3) deposited asbestos diaphragms. The Stuart type cell includes the Hooker Type S, S-3, S-3A, S-3B, S-3C and S-3M, Columbia-Hooker cells and Diamond cells. The Dow cell includes the Hunter-Otis-Blue cell design,[15] and the Lucas-Armstrong design.[18]

Hooker Type Cell. The Hooker Type S cell

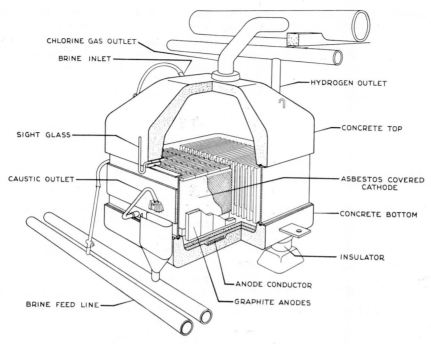

CHLORINE GAS OUTLET

BRINE INLET

HYDROGEN OUTLET

CONCRETE TOP

SIGHT GLASS

CAUSTIC OUTLET

ASBESTOS COVERED CATHODE

CONCRETE BOTTOM

INSULATOR

ANODE CONDUCTOR

GRAPHITE ANODES

BRINE FEED LINE

Fig. 2. Sectional diagram of Hooker Type S-3C cell.

has evolved in various models known as the S-1 (the original Type S cell) S-3, S-3A, S-3B, S-3M and S-3C cells. This description is based on the Type S-3C cell which is currently recommended[2] by Hooker for most installations. The cells are nearly cubical in shape and consist of three sections, bottom, middle, and top, placed one upon the other (Fig. 2). The anode assembly includes a concrete bottom in which is placed a casting of lead which contains the two flat copper anode connector bars and 128 vertically projecting graphite anode blades. The copper bars are 12 in. wide and ¾ in. thick at the ends and are tapered in the direction of diminishing current. The anode blades are 1¼ x 6¼ x 25 in. long. The lead casting is sealed into the concrete bottom by a mastic system of asphaltic material. It is a feature of the cell that the anode section, which requires renewal least frequently, is at the bottom and does not need to be disturbed when the diaphragm is renewed.

The cathode section consists of a steel frame with flanged top and bottom and with a copper conductor bar welded to the frame. A steel screen structure including 30 fingers is welded to the inside of the steel frame forming an integral cathode unit. The diaphragm is applied to this unit by immersing the cathode into a bath of asbestos slurried in cell liquor (the caustic liquor containing approximately 11.5 per cent NaOH, 15 per cent NaCl) and applying a vacuum according to a time schedule. The cathode with deposited diaphragm is placed over the graphite anodes, using a rubber cord gasket and putty for seal. Since the top of the cell is completely open, spacing between anode and cathode may be carefully adjusted. The concrete cell top is placed directly on the cathode with a seal of putty. The weight of the cell parts is sufficient to seal the cell so that no fasteners are required to make the cell liquid-tight. Electrical connections from one cell to the next are made with L-shaped copper connector bars slotted to provide for flexibility of assembly. Cells are removed for renewal from the circuit individually, using the portable jumper switch which operates on a monorail in back of the cells and which may service cells on either side of a double row. The jumper is applied without any interruptions of current to the circuit.

The cell is rated for operation at 30,000 amperes but may be operated within the range of 20,000 to 32,000 amperes. A sectional view of the cell is shown in Fig. 2. The cell bottom contains graphite anodes projecting upward from their anchorage in cast lead. The cathode section, with deposited asbestos fibre diaphragms, is placed on the bottom, fingers of the cathode alternating with the anode blades.

Brine is introduced into the cell through a

TABLE 1. PERFORMANCE DATA FOR DIAPHRAGM CELLS

	Hooker S-3B or S-3C	Diamond D-3
Electrical data		
Current, amperes	30,000	30,000
Current efficiency, per cent	96.0	96.5
Voltage/cell, circuit average	3.95	3.82
Power, d-c kwh/short ton Cl₂	2820	2720
Chlorine production, lb/day/cell	2016	2020
Caustic soda		
NaOH production, lb/day/cell	2274	2280
NaOH in cell liquor, per cent	11.6	10.5*
Temperature of catholyte, °F	211	196
Hydrogen production, lb/day/cell	59.1	59.2
Graphite		
Consumption, lb/short ton Cl₂	5.3	7.5
Anode life, days	280	230
Diaphragm life	2 or 3 during life of anode	115 days

* Can be operated to produce 11.2 per cent NaOH with cell voltage increase of 0.02 volts.

tantalum orifice placed in a glass tube set into a rubber stopper in the cell top. The head of brine on the orifices is controlled for the entire circuit and may be varied according to the current load and the strength of caustic which is desired.

This arrangement provides for a uniform feed of brine to each cell and a uniform rate throughout the life of the cell. The level of anolyte automatically adjusts itself in accordance with the porosity of the diaphragm. A cell with a new diaphragm will have a level approximately 5 in. above the top of the cathode. As the diaphragm becomes old and plugged with impurities, the level will rise to approximately 17 in. at which time the cell is shorted out for diaphragm replacement. The caustic liquor flows from the percolation pipe out of the cell whereas the hydrogen collected within the cathode is removed from the back of the cell through an insulator to the hydrogen header. Chlorine formed on the anodes bubbles up through the brine, accumulates at the top of the cell, and is withdrawn through a pipe to the chlorine header. The piping for brine, hydrogen, and caustic liquor is generally constructed of steel, whereas the chlorine line is usually constructed of ceramic, "Haveg" or "Hetron" polyester pipe. A typical cell room of Type S cells is shown in Fig. 4 of the article following this one. Performance data are shown in Table 1.

Diamond Alkali D-3 Chlorine Cell. The Diamond Alkali D-3 chlorine cell is rated at

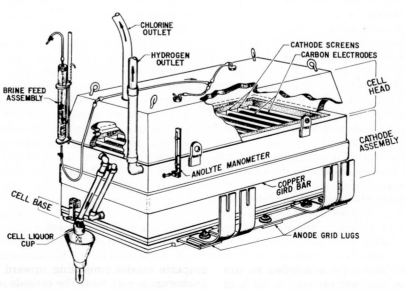

FIG. 3. Diagram of Diamond D-3 cell. (*Courtesy, Diamond Alkali Company.*)

30,000 amperes and can be operated at 33,000 amperes for extended periods. A diagram of the cell is shown in Fig. 3. The cell is rectangular in shape and is 7 ft long, 3 ft 7 in. wide, and 4 ft 9 in. high. The base of the cell consists of a shallow cast iron pan, housing flat copper grids. The copper grids and graphite anodes are imbedded in lead and the lead is sealed with protective coatings.

The cathode assembly is a rectangular steel can. The inner section of this assembly consists of lateral rows of double metal screens, upon which a diaphragm of asbestos fiber has been deposited. These rows of screens fit between the anodes when the cathode is lowered into the base, thus forming the anolyte and catholyte sections of the cell. The cell is completed by placing a concrete head on top of the cathode assembly. This head contains the chlorine outlet and the salt brine feed hoses. Electrical connections are made to a copper bar around the outside of the cathode and to lugs which extend from the anode grids. Performance data are shown in Table 1.

Dow Bipolar Cells. Dow has developed the bipolar filter-press type of cell through many modifications. The filter-press cell provides a very compact unit with large productive capacity for unit floor area. In addition, the investment cost is relatively low because the metal conductors between the anodes of one cell and cathode of the next cell are reduced to the minimum as is the container for electrolyte.

References

1. ALLMAND, A. J., AND ELLINGHAM, H. J. T., *"The Principles of Applied Electrochemistry,"* London, Arnold Co., 1931.
2. Anon., Hooker Chemical Corporation, Bulletin 20-A (1959).
3. Anon., *Chem. Eng.*, **64**, (6), 154 (1957).
4. BARTON, C. R., *Trans. Am. Inst. Chem. Engrs.*, **13**, 1 (1920).
5. CARRIER, C. F., JR., *Trans. Electrochem. Soc.*, **35**, 239 (1919).
6. DE NORA, V., *Trans. Electrochem. Soc.*, **97**, 347 (1950).
7. ENGLEHARDT, V., *"Handbuch der Technischen Elektrochemie."* Vol 2 (1), Leipsig, Akademische Verlagsgesellschaft, 1933.
8. FOERSTER, FRITZ, "Electrochemie, Wasseriger Losungen," 4th ed., Barth, 1923.
9. GARDINER, W. C., *Chem. Eng.*, **52**, (7), 110 (1945).
10. GRISWOLD, T. JR., U. S. Patent 987,717 (1911).
11. GRISWOLD, T. JR., U. S. Patent 1,070,454 (1913).
12. HARDIE, D. W. F., *"Electrolytic Manufacture of Chemicals from Salt,"* Oxford University Press, 1959.
13. HASS, K., *"Ullmanns Encyklopadie der Technischen Chemie,"* Vol. 5, pp. 324–376, Munich, 1954.
14. HOOKER, A. H., *Trans. Am. Inst. Chem. Engrs.*, **13**, 61, (1920).
15. HUNTER, R. M., OTIS, L. B., AND BLUE, R. D., U. S. Patent 2,282,058 (May 5, 1942).
16. KIRCHER, M. S., ENGLE, H. R., RITTER, B. H., AND BARTLETT, *Trans. Electrochem. Soc.*, **100**, 448 (1953).
17. LE SUEUR, E. A., *Trans. Electrochem. Soc.*, **63**, 187 (1933).
18. LUCAS, J. L., AND ARMSTRONG B. J., U. S. Patent 2,858,263 (Oct. 28, 1958).
19. MARSH, C. W., U. S. Patent 1,075,362 (1913).
20. MANTELL, *"Industrial Electrochemistry,"* 3rd Ed., p. 421, New York, McGraw-Hill, 1950.
21. MOORE, *Chem. Met. Eng.*, **23**, 1011, 1072, 1125 (1920).
22. MURRAY, R. L., *Ind. Eng. Chem.*, **41**, 2155 (1949).
23. MURRAY, R. L., AND KIRCHER, M. S., *Trans. Electrochem. Soc.*, **86**, 83 (1944).
24. STENDER, W. W., ZIVOTINSKY, P. B., AND STROGANOFF, M. M., *Trans. Electrochem. Soc.*, **65**, 189 (1934).
25. STUART, K. E., LYSTER, T. L. B., AND MURRAY, R. L., *Chem. Met. Eng.*, **45**, 354 (1938).
26. VAALER, L. E., *Trans. Electrochem. Soc.*, **107**, 691 (1960).
27. VORCE, L. D., *Trans. Electrochem. Soc.*, **86**, 69 (1944).
28. WARD, L. E., U. S. Patent 1,365,875 (1921).

MORTON S. KIRCHER

CHLORINE PRODUCTION IN DIAPHRAGM CELLS—OVERALL PROCESS

The production of chlorine and caustic soda involves many more factors than the operation of the electrolytic cells. Salt brine of proper purity and direct courrent at requisite voltage and amperage must be provided. The chlorine and hydrogen gases must be collected, cooled, and treated for subsequent use. The cell liquor must be evaporated to separate most of its salt content and to concentrate the caustic soda. These and other operations are handled in the various departments of a chlor-alkali plant.

A typical modern caustic-chlorine plant using diaphragm cells is shown in the schematic flow sheet of Fig. 1 and also in photographs of various sections of the plant (Figs. 2 to 5). Rock salt is dissolved in water (or brine is produced from underground salt deposits by water injection in a well), and the usual impurities, calcium and magnesium sulfates and chlorides, are precipitated from the brine by addition of soda ash and caustic soda. Brine is clarified by settling

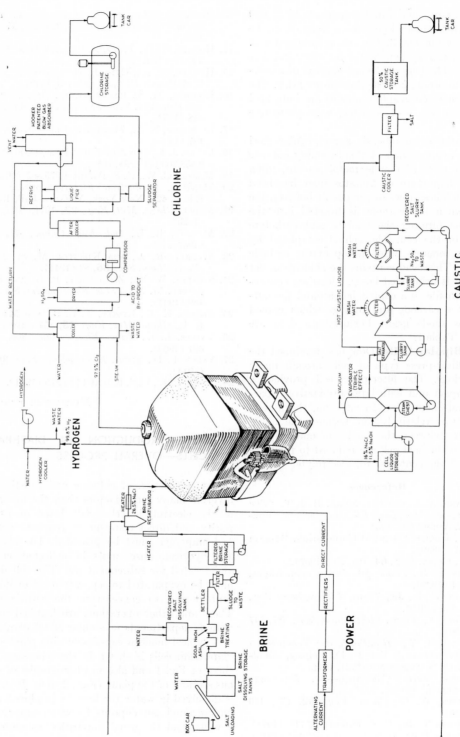

Fig. 1. Schematic flowsheet of typical caustic-chlorine plant using diaphragm cells.

FIG. 2. Brine treating plant.

and filtration (Fig. 2). To increase the salt content to a practical maximum, brine is heated and saturated with purified salt, obtained from the evaporation of cell liquor, before going to the cells. The brine is fed in parallel to the cells from a brine header for each bank of cells.

Direct current is supplied to the cells from an alternating current source by mercury arc, silicon, or other types of rectification equipment (Fig. 3). The cells are arranged in banks connected electrically in series, the number per bank dictated by the voltage of the supply and the voltage drop per cell, e.g. about 25 cells on a 100 volt line.

Electrolysis of the brine in the cell results in the formation of chlorine gas, hydrogen gas, and caustic. The gases leave the cells saturated with water vapor. Caustic leaves the cell as cell liquor which contains about 11.5 per cent NaOH by weight and about 16 per cent NaCl by weight. The three products are withdrawn separately and processed in different departments. A typical cell room, containing Hooker type S-3A cells, is shown in Fig. 4.

Hydrogen gas is scrubbed with water sprays to cool and remove any traces of salt or caustic. It is then compressed for supplying various processes or for use as a fuel.

Chlorine cell gas is cooled by direct contact with water in a packed tower and then dried with sulfuric acid. The dried gas is compressed to 25 to 60 psi and then liquefied by refrigeration (Fig. 5). The liquid chlorine is then transferred to tank cars, to process or to storage. Some processes can use the wet cell gases, other processes require dry cell gas and some need liquid chlorine. The "blow gas" from the chlorine liquefier contains noncondensable gases and some chlorine. The chlorine in the blow gas may be recovered by patented processes, such as absorption in carbon tetrachloride (Diamond[3]), and absorption in water (Hooker[3]), or it may be absorbed in alkali for the production of hypochlorite or for disposal. In the Diamond process,

FIG. 3. Silicon rectifiers.

FIG. 4. Typical cell room, Hooker Type S-3A cells.

chlorine is recovered from carbon tetrachloride solution by heating and stripping. In the Hooker process, chlorine is removed from the blow gas by absorption in water and recovered by using the chlorine-containing water for cooling the direct contact cell gas cooler. Before leaving the cooler, the water is acidified and heated with steam to strip it of chlorine.

FIG. 5. Chlorine compressors.

Evaporation of the cell liquor until the NaOH content is 50 per cent by weight is carried out in double- or triple-effect evaporators. Modern evaporators circulate the liquor rapidly in each effect through an external shell-and-tube heat exchanger. As the NaOH content increases, salt crystallizes and is separated from the caustic liquor by decantation and filtration. Salt is then washed free of caustic, dissolved, and recycled to the brine system. Additional salt is removed from 50 per cent caustic by cooling and settling. Standard 50 per cent caustic containing only 1 per cent salt is shipped as such in tank cars or it may be evaporated in single-effect evaporators to 73 per cent caustic. Several processes can be used for further reducing the salt content of the standard liquor to convert it to rayon grade. The most widely used process for desalting is the so-called "DH process" of Columbia-Southern which employs liquid ammonia extraction of the impurities from the caustic.

Fused caustic, either solid or flake, is produced by evaporation and fusion of either 50 per cent or 73 per cent caustic. Fused caustic is usually shipped in metal drums.

References

See reference list for preceding article.

MORTON S. KIRCHER

CHLORINE PRODUCTION IN MERCURY CELLS— ELECTROCHEMISTRY

The mercury cathode cell process for the production of chlorine, an alkali metal hydroxide, and hydrogen involves a two-stage electrochemical operation. In the first stage an alkali metal chloride solution is electrolyzed in a cell between a graphite anode and a flowing mercury cathode. Chlorine is liberated at the anode, and the alkali metal is deposited into the mercury to form an alkali metal amalgam. The latter is transferred into a decomposer vessel where the alkali metal of the amalgam reacts with water to form the hydroxide and hydrogen. This is a galvanic reaction occurring in the presence of a shortcircuiting conductor like graphite. The denuded mercury is returned to the electrolysis cell and the hydroxide is withdrawn as a concentrated solution of high purity. The brine entering the electrolysis cell is only partially depleted and is recycled through a brine purification and concentration operation before being returned to the cell.

This entry discusses the electrochemistry of the process, and in subsequent entries the industrial cells and overall process are described.

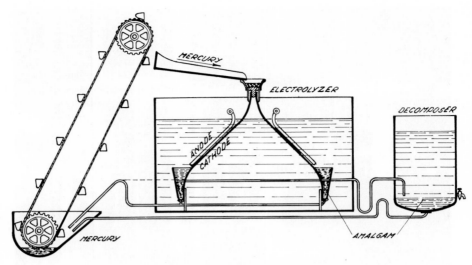

Fig. 1. Hermite-Dubosc mercury cathode cell.

Historical and General Outlines

Like most inventions, the idea of taking advantage of the properties of a liquid cathode, for a more efficient separation of a metallic product obtained by electrolysis, was not the outcome of one single flash of genius. The first efforts in this direction must be credited to technologists conversant with treatment of gold and silver ores by amalgamation.[22]

The inventors to which is rightly attributed the merit of having, first and independently, succeeded in developing a continuous mercury cathode process for application to chlor-alkali industry are H. Y. Castner[9] and C. Kellner.[18] However, also in this particular field there were forerunners like E. Hermite and A. Dubosc,[16] whose setup (Fig. 1) clearly anticipates some modern attempts to use vertical or nearly vertical cathode arrangements.

The original setup of Castner's *rocking cell*, as disclosed in the relevant patent, is shown in Fig. 2. The sodium chloride solution was electrolyzed in the two side-compartments of the vat, between carbon anodes and a mercury layer acting as a cathode; the alkali metal amalgam thus formed was periodically transported into the central compartment by the rocking motion imparted to the vat, where sodium plated out and reacted with the water of an overlying caustic solution, thus producing sodium hydroxide and hydrogen. That early cell type had a rated capacity of 550 amperes. With some modifications, this model was operated in one major

American plant until 1960, when it was replaced with mercury cells of modern design, rated at 100,000 amperes.

In spite of the ingenuity of those successful pioneers, and strange as it may look to our hindsight, they seem to have nourished for quite a long time the illusion that by electrically connecting the decomposing section in series with the electrolysis cell to the outer source of direct current, as shown in Fig. 2, not only would there be a possiblity of recovering the chemical energy of amalgam decomposition in the form of useful electric energy, but that such an electrical hookup was an indispensable *must* to carry out the deamalgamation process at all.[18] Actually, this forcible electric interdependence of the two processes resulted, instead, in a twofold nuisance. One nuisance, indeed, was associated with the inevitably lower current efficiency of the cathodic process in comparison with anodic decomposition. In fact, the quantity of electricity that has to be passed through the mercury cathode, in order to discharge a certain amount of sodium, must also take into account a current loss due to some hydrogen evolution and other side reactions, whereas no such loss occurs in the anodic process, by which the same amount of sodium is plated out again. It ensues that the excess current leaving the anodic side of the amalgam layer will oxidize an equivalent amount of mercury in the decomposing compartment.

The second nuisance of said electrical interdependence resided in that the overall resistance opposed to the passage of current by the galvanic

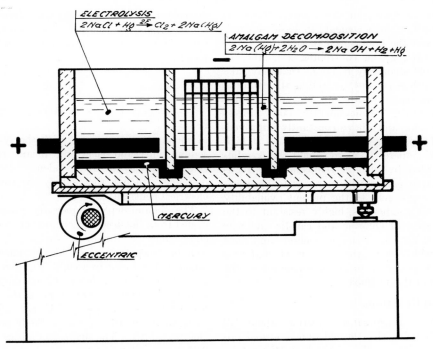

FIG. 2. Castner mercury cathode cell.

cell in series to the electrolysis cell was greater than its electromotive force; consequently, energy was thereby dissipated instead of being recovered.

The first of said troubles was soon realized and was counteracted by inserting a resistive shunt across the denuding stage, so as to bypass a controlled amount of current, equal to the excess required by the electrolysis stage.[19] However, it took about seven years more to realize that "all these manipulations had proved inappropriate for this purpose," as stated by Kellner in his patent application concerning the now obvious simplification of providing a short-circuiting conductor between the cathode in the decomposing cell and the amalgam.[20]

Nonetheless, another important step still remained to be accomplished to further enhance the decomposition rate and thus reduce the size of the equipment and the holdup of expensive mercury in the denuding stage. This was achieved when it was realized that, by putting a mass of nonreactive, conductive, and nonamalgamable material in direct and simultaneous contact with the caustic solution and the body of amalgam as well, it was not only possible to obtain a further simplification, but also to provide shorter and wider paths for the galvanic

current performing the decomposition.[6] For this purpose, grids of carbon or of cast iron were used at first and eventually replaced with graphite, when the method of graphitizing carbon, formerly discovered by Castner, was industrialized by E. G. Acheson about 1899. Moreover, since artificial graphite makes a superior chlorine anode, it also succeeded in gradually replacing carbon as well as platinum wire in this application.

With the last mentioned improvement in the decomposition stage, the status of the technique had acquired maturity for the development of cell design into the horizontal elongated shape, with sloping bottom for mercury flow, that is still now almost universally adopted. Its prototype was the Solvay cell developed by A. Brichaux and H. Wilsing about 1900. As in many models still in use, the decomposer also consisted of a long and narrow trough, lying parallel to the electrolyzer with a countersloping bottom, while a device for lifting the mercury from the lower end of the decomposer to the upper end of the electrolyzer provided a closed mercury circulation.

Since its inception, the history of this process has mainly been a history of patents. In seventy years, more than 250 patents have been issued in the United States on this subject. However, some important achievements in basic research have backed the operating experience in properly interpreting and controlling a number of primary and secondary reactions that may take place at both electrodes,[7] as well as the catalytic phenomena that can promote dangerous hydrogen evolution.[1-5, 15] Consequently, both process efficiency and safety have constantly improved, while cell capacities have reached values as high as 200,000 amperes, so as to exploit the possibilities afforded by modern semiconductor rectifiers. A large part of the merit as to improvement in design goes to the present availability of synthetic compounds, highly resistant to the aggressiveness of chlorine and caustic and now being used instead of simple concrete and hard rubber, which were the only inert materials practically available for cell construction at the beginning of this technology.

Main Cell Reactions

Consider a nearly saturated brine (about 310 gpl NaCl) being electrolyzed under normal operating conditions. The desired reactions take place in the following way:

mercury cathode is supplied with electrons from the external circuit. Such a mechanism for the cathodic process would be represented as follows:

$$
\begin{array}{ll}
Na^+(aq) & \rightarrow Na^+(Hg) \\
e^- & \rightarrow e^-(Hg) \\
\hline
Na^+(aq) + e^- & \rightarrow Na^+(Hg) + e^-(Hg)
\end{array}
$$

in which (Hg), associated with the symbols for sodium ions and electrons, means that both charged species are independently dissolved in mercury, although they satisfy the condition of electrical neutrality.

The sodium-depleted mercury stream is recycled from the decomposer into the electrolyzer, equicurrent to the brine stream; its residual sodium concentration at the cell inlet may be about 0.01 per cent by weight. The mercury flow rate is so adjusted, depending on ampere load, that the sodium concentration in the amalgam leaving the cell is close to 0.15 per cent. Under such conditions the average cathode potential is close to -1.8 v.[11] The slight overvoltage of about 0.05 v is mostly due to concentration polarization at the phase boundary.

Anodic half-reaction:	$2Cl^-(aq)$	$\rightarrow Cl_2(aq) + 2e^-$
	$Cl_2(aq)$	$\rightarrow Cl_2(g)$
Cathodic half-reaction:	$2Na^+(aq) + Hg + 2e^-$	$\rightarrow 2Na(Hg)$
Overall cell reaction:	$2NaCl(aq) + Hg$	$\xrightarrow{2F} Cl_2(g) + 2Na(Hg)$

The average electrolysis temperature is about 65°C (corresponding to 55°C at the cell inlet and 75°C at the outlet) and the average brine concentration is 290 gpl NaCl (i.e., 310 and 270 gpl at inlet and outlet, respectively). Under these conditions, the equilibrium potential of the anodic half-reaction would be $+1.32$ v.[21] However, the actual potential is considerably higher, on account of irreversible phenomena giving rise to an overvoltage, which, at said average temperature and for a current density of 0.5 amp/sq cm, is about 0.3 v.

The cathodic half-reaction, in contrast, is one of the few examples in industrial electrolysis in which the electrode process develops very nearly the state of thermodynamic reversibility, also at high current densities. This may be explained with the assumption that, in dilute amalgams, sodium is mostly dissociated into sodium ions and free electrons;[7] accordingly, the sodium discharge process would merely imply a phase boundary passage by sodium ions, while the

Cell Voltage Balance

At an average temperature of 65°C, a cathodic current density of 0.5 amp/sq cm, and an anode-to-cathode distance of 5 mm, other operating conditions being as already assumed, a typical overall voltage balance in a modern cell is made up as follows:

Reversible cell voltage	3.07
Overvoltage	0.35
Ohmic drops	
through electrolyte	0.60
through electrode contacts with	
outer connections	0.10
through outer connections	0.23
	———
	4.35 volt

Accurate voltage balances have been worked out by several authors, for current density conditions prevailing in the past[11] as well as for the present trends in mercury cell design and operation.[21, 24]

Amalgam Decomposition Reaction

In the decomposer the reaction takes place between the concentrated amalgam leaving the electrolyzer and a countercurrent stream of water. The sodium content in the amalgam stream thus gradually decreases from the inlet to the outlet, while the sodium hydroxide concentration constantly increases in the aqueous solution.

When dealing with a strongly alkaline electrolyte, such as in the decomposer, the affinity of the overall decomposition reaction is about 18,000 cal per mole of NaOH produced, corresponding to an emf of 0.78 v.[17, 21] This driving force is too weak, if compared with the exceedingly large magnitude of hydrogen overvoltage on mercury; this is indeed one of the most outstanding characteristics of polarographic analysis, which mainly on this account acquires its wide field of application. Consequently, if hydrogen had only the possibility to discharge on mercury itself, when displaced by sodium from the water molecule, hydrogen could not plate out, and the reaction would not proceed at any appreciable rate.

This shortcoming can be turned around by providing a conductive, nonamalgamable material, such as graphite, in contact with the amalgam as well as with the electrolyte, on the surface of which hydrogen is allowed to discharge at a relatively low overvoltage. The contact with the amalgam establishes a short circuit for the galvanic reaction, in which the graphite mass will perform as a cathode, while the amalgam body behaves as a soluble anode, according to the following processes:

temperature is kept above 100°C, so as to prevent the caustic product from freezing and to maintain at the same time the reaction at a sufficiently high rate to achieve amalgam decomposition. When the effluent does not exceed 50 per cent NaOH, the normal operating temperature is about 80°C. In such case, the heat of reaction is sufficient to maintain the temperature.

Competing Reactions

As already indicated, the reversible voltage of the electrolytic reaction that brings about chlorine discharge at the anode, together with sodium amalgam buildup at the mercury cathode, is higher than 3 v. On the other hand, for *water electrolysis* (q.v.) under the same conditions it is close to 1.25 v. Therefore, on a pure thermodynamic basis, sodium chloride electrolysis taking place instead of hydrogen and oxygen discharge would be inconceivable, all the more so as the anode usually consists of graphite; in such case, indeed, the combination reaction of nascent oxygen with carbon

$$2O^0 + C \rightarrow CO_2$$

is characterized by a positive affinity, so that it further facilitates oxygen discharge, even though in the form of carbon dioxide.

The reason of such a wide discrepancy between the ideal realm of thermodynamics and the real state of affairs resides, as always, on kinetic grounds.

As soon as the brine becomes saturated with dissolved chlorine, its pH value approaches 2.5,

Anodic half-reaction: $2Na(Hg)$ $\rightarrow 2Na^+ + Hg + 2e^-$
Cathodic half-reaction: $2H_2O + 2e^-$ $\rightarrow 2OH^- + H_2(g)$
Overall decomposition reaction: $2Na(Hg) + 2H_2O \rightarrow 2NaOH(aq) + H_2(g) + Hg$

The decomposition reaction is of the first order;[13] indeed, sodium concentration, c, in the amalgam decreases as a function of time, t, at a rate obeying the following relationship:

$$-dc/dt = kc$$

where k is a constant.

The control of water feed rate is usually effected in such a way that the caustic strength at the decomposer outlet is between 40 and 50 per cent NaOH; however, a substantially higher concentration can be obtained (up to the eutectic point of 73 per cent NaOH) if the reaction

on account of the hydrolysis reaction

$$Cl_2 (aq) + H_2O \rightarrow H^+ + Cl^- + HOCl$$

As already mentioned, when graphite anodes are used, oxygen in cell gas is mostly present as CO_2. Accordingly, the relevant anodic reaction to be considered is the following:

$$C + 2H_2O \rightarrow CO_2 (g) + 4H^+ + 4e^-$$

The equilibrium potential of this reaction against the standard hydrogen electrode, at the operating temperature of 65°C, can be formulated as follows:

$$E = 0.201 - 0.067 \, pH + 0.0168 \, \log \frac{(CO_2)}{(H_2O)^2}$$

The partial pressure of carbon dioxide in the cell gas is usually in the order of 0.5 per cent. If this value is considered, together with pH 2.5, the equilibrium potential calculated from the above equation is approximately zero volt.

On the other hand, the actual electrode potential, as measurable under chlorine discharge at the current density of 0.5 amp/sq cm, is about +1.6 v. Accordingly, the overvoltage for the above reaction leading to carbon dioxide formation is found, by difference between the actual and the equilibrium potential, to be close to 1.6 v, for an oxygen discharge current density of only 5 ma/sq cm, as can be calculated from the product of the relative concentration of CO_2 in cell gas (0.5 per cent), times the overall current density (0.5 amp/sq cm), times the value of 2, which equals the ratio of the electron numbers involved in the anodic formation of one molecule of CO_2 and one molecule of Cl_2, respectively.

As to cathodic hydrogen discharge, its overvoltage can be calculated from the parameters of the Tafel line for mercury[23] and from the knowledge of the relevant current density. If other side reactions which tend further to decrease the cathodic current efficiency with respect to sodium discharge are neglected, the fraction of electricity involved in hydrogen evolution is proportional to the hydrogen fraction in the cell gas. At the cathodic current density of 0.5 amp/sq cm and for a normal hydrogen concentration of 0.5 per cent in the cell gas, the partial current density equivalent to such evolution is 2.5 mamp/sq cm; the corresponding hydrogen overvoltage at 65°C found by calculation is about −1 v.

By difference between this value and the actual electrode potential of −1.8 v, the hydrogen equilibrium potential is about −0.8 v, under the average conditions that normally prevail at the sodium amalgam cathode. On the other hand, since hydrogen evolution takes place at nearly atmospheric pressure, its equilibrium potential must be very close to a value obeying the equation

$$E = -2.303 \, \frac{RT}{F} \, pH$$

From this and from the E value of −0.8 v as previously calculated, it can be deduced that the pH at the cathodic boundary layer must be definitely higher than 10, in spite of the acidic conditions of the chlorine-saturated solution. This circumstance could have been realized also *a priori*, since sodium amalgam, when contacted with any solution at any acidic pH, can be shown to decompose at a much faster rate than that corresponding to normal hydrogen content in the chlorine gas from the mercury process.

The important conclusion to be drawn from the preceding discussion is that cell construction, operation, and maintenance must be such that the streaming state of the mercury layer should be as laminar as possible; indeed, any turbulence giving rise to ripples or eddies would upset the alkalinity of the boundary layer, by superimposing a convective motion to the regular diffusion of hydrogen ions toward the cathode and hydroxyl ions away from it.

Other Loss Reactions

Anodic side reactions involve not only hydrolysis of chlorine, with a consequent buildup of hypochlorite, but also chlorate formation,[7] according to the same processes that are enhanced in chlorate cells.

Beside being unfavorable to some of the chemical purification steps that the depleted brine stream must undergo after being resaturated with raw salt, these side products have a tendency to decrease the anodic as well as the cathodic current efficiency.

The hypochlorite ion tends indeed to compete with chlorine in the anodic discharge, giving rise to evolution of oxygen, which reacts with the graphite anodes and thus accelerates their consumption, while decreasing the gas purity.

As to the influence of such anodic side reaction products on the cathodic current efficiency, it can be recognized in the following set of equations, which summarize the main reactions that are responsible for current losses at the cathode:

$$2e^- \, (Hg) + 2H_2O \rightarrow 2OH^- + H_2 \, (g)$$

$$2e^- \, (Hg) + Cl_2 \, (aq) \rightarrow 2Cl^-$$

$$2e^- \, (Hg) + OCl^- + H_2O \rightarrow Cl^- + 2OH^-$$

$$6e^- \, (Hg) + ClO_3^- + 3H_2O \rightarrow Cl^- + 6OH^-$$

The first reaction, giving rise to hydrogen evolution, has already been discussed. The second represents a reversal of the anodic process, since it involves a regression of chlorine from molecular to ionic state. Such regressive tendency can be counteracted by keeping the anode not exceedingly close to the cathode, so as to prevent as far as possible chlorine gas bubbles from upsetting the cathodic boundary layer and making the mercury cathode accessible to dissolved chlorine.

As to the cathodic reduction of hypochlorite and chlorate ions, indicated by the third and the fourth equations, it can be prevented by feeding the cell with acidic brine (pH 3 or 4) so as to displace the equilibrium of the formation reactions toward smaller concentrations of said ions.[7] By feeding the cell with an acidic brine, the further advantage is obtained that calcium, normally present as an impurity, will thus diminish its tendency to precipitate on the mercury, and build up a sluggish "mercury butter" hindering the laminar flow.

Despite the accuracy with which the mercury process may be carried out, it is not possible to avoid such loss reactions completely. Therefore, the current efficiency is usually not higher than 95 per cent.

References

1. ANGEL, G., AND LUNDÉN, T., *J. Electrochem. Soc.*, **99,** 435 (1952).
2. ANGEL, G., AND BRÄNNLAND, R., *ibid.*, **99,** 442 (1952).
3. ANGEL, G., LUNDÉN, T., AND BRÄNNLAND, R., *ibid.*, **100,** 39 (1953).
4. ANGEL, G., LUNDÉN, T., BRÄNNLAND, R., AND DAHLERUS, S., *ibid.*, **102,** 124 and 246 (1955).
5. ANGEL, G., BRÄNNLAND, R., AND DAHLERUS, S., *ibid,.* **104,** 167 (1957).
6. BAKER, E. C., AND BURWELL, A. W., U. S. Patent 739,140 (Sept. 15, 1903).
7. BARR, L., *J. Electrochem. Soc.*, **101,** 497 (1954).
8. BILLITER, J., British Patent 832,196 (April 6, 1960).
9. CASTNER, H. Y., U. S. Patent 518,135 (April 10, 1894).
10. CURREY, J. E., AND HAMPEL, C. A., *Electrochem. Technology*, **1,** 56 (1963); Currey, J. E., and Swanberg, D. E., *ibid*, **1,** 191 (1963).
11. DE NORA, V., *J. Electrochem. Soc.*, **97,** 346 (1950).
12. GALLONE, P., *Chimica (Milan)*, **6,** 78 (1951).
13. GALLONE, P., *Chimica (Milan)*, **5,** 132, 201 (1950).
14. GARDINER, W. C., *et al*, U. S. Patent 2,872,393 (Feb. 3, 1959).
15. HAUCK, G., *Chem.-Ing.-Tech.*, **34,** 369 (1962).
16. HERMITE, E., AND DUBOSC, A., U. S. Patent 501,783 (July 18, 1893); French Patent 217,887 (Dec. 7, 1891).
17. HINE, F., OKADA, M., YOSHIZAWA, S., AND OKADA, S., *J. Electrochem. Soc. Japan*, **27,** 134 (1959).
18. KELLNER, C., U. S. Patent 578,457 (March 9, 1897).
19. KELLNER, C., U. S. Patent 586,729 (July 20, 1897).
20. KELLNER, C., U. S. Patent 631,468 (Aug. 22, 1899).
21. MACMULLIN, R. B., "Chlorine," Sconce, J. S., Ed., pp. 127–199, New York, Reinhold Publishing Corp., 1962.
22. NOLF, A. L., U. S. Patent 271,906 (Feb. 6, 1883).
23. PARSONS, R., "Handbook of Electrochemical Constants," p. 95, London, Butterworths Scientific Pub., 1959.
24. SCHMIDT, H., AND HOLZINGER, F., *Chem.-Ing.-Tech.*, **35,** 37 (1963).

VITTORIO DE NORA AND
PATRIZIO GALLONE

CHLORINE PRODUCTION IN MERCURY CELLS—INDUSTRIAL CELLS

In a previous entry, "Chlorine Production in Mercury Cells-Electrochemistry," the fundamental aspects of the electrolytic process are discussed. This entry will describe the cells used industrially in the process and the operating factors involved.

Cell Types and Operating Characteristics

The two stages forming the mercury cathode process, namely, the alkali metal chloride electrolysis and the alkali metal amalgam decomposition (see previous article), are performed in two distinct parts of equipment, interconnected by the mercury circuit: they are the *electrolysis cell* proper and the *amalgam decomposer*, or *denuder*.

The simplest arrangement is exemplified by the original setup of the Solvay cell (Fig. 1). This sort of arrangement is known under the denomination of *horizontal construction*, because of the relatively large floor space it occupies, if compared with the shallow depth of the trough-shaped cell and decomposer. However, these are not perfectly horizontal, but slightly inclined with opposite slopes of about 0.5 to 1 per cent, so that mercury is allowed to flow by gravity.

The horizontal cell design is still the most widely used. Although remaining basically similar to the prototype, developed at the beginning of the century, it has undergone substantial refinements, especially with the purpose of raising the unit cell capacity, so as to obtain a better

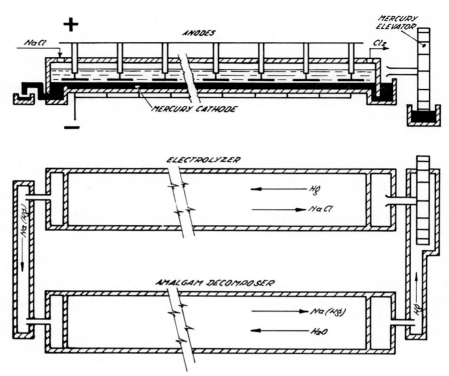

FIG. 1. Solvay prototype cell.

balance between capital, operation and energy costs.

Cell capacity has been increased by steadily enlarging the cell size and by raising the current density; nonetheless, it has been possible to maintain the cell voltage at a nearly unaltered value by continuously improving some constructional details, such as electrical connections and anode design,[13, 16, 19] and by introducing anode adjustment devices, whose function is to keep under constant control the spacing between the mercury cathode and the graphite anodes, notwithstanding the gradual consumption undergone by the latter.

The amalgam decomposer, or denuder, can be of horizontal or of vertical type.

In the former case it has the shape of an elongated steel trough running at the electrolyzer side or, as more generally practiced in modern design, underneath the cell. The cathodic mass in the trough consists of slotted graphite grids. Typical examples of such design are the Krebs B.A.S.F. cell and the models offered by Solvay and by Uhde.

The vertical decomposer is one of the characteristics of the de Nora cell and of the Olin-Mathieson cell. It is a vertical tower packed with lumps of broken graphite. Fig. 2 illustrates it in conjunction with one of the cells offered by de Nora, rated at 200 kiloampere. Fig. 3 shows a cell room containing similar cells rated at 150,000 amperes at a large chlorine plant in Texas.

A good review of the best-known mercury cell types has been made by MacMullin.[19] The most widely used lining material for the electrolysis cell sides and covers is hard rubber. However, special techniques have been developed by de Nora for the application of a lining made of natural stone or synthetic materials. The cell bottom consists in most cases of a bare steel surface, accurately machined to obtain perfect evenness and consequently a regular flow of mercury. In some few cases the bottom is lined with an insulating material, so as to allow only a part of the steel surface to establish an electrical continuity between the mercury and the cathodic connection with the outer circuit.

Several sorts of vertical anode and cathode assemblies have been devised, too, with the main object of saving floor space. However, as regards their operating characteristics, particu-

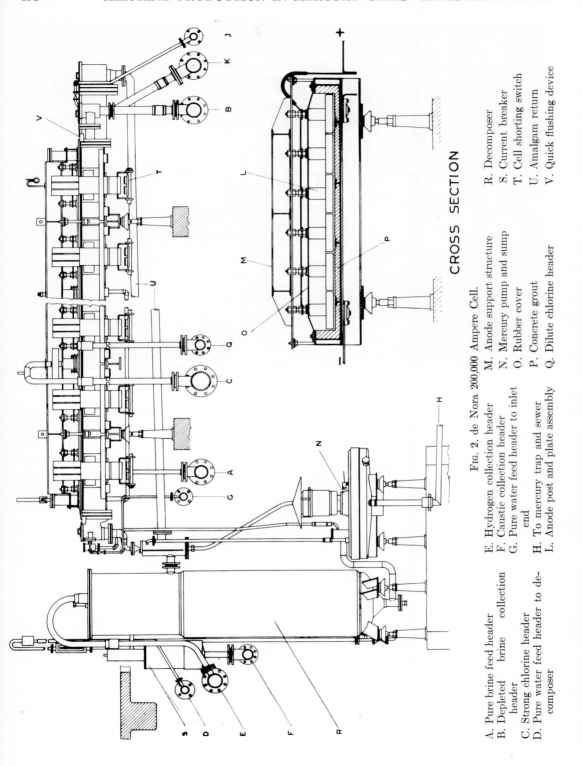

CROSS SECTION

FIG. 2. de Nora 200,000 Ampere Cell.

A. Pure brine feed header
B. Depleted brine collection header
C. Strong chlorine header
D. Pure water feed header to de-composer
E. Hydrogen collection header
F. Caustic collection header
G. Pure water feed header to inlet end
H. To mercury trap and sewer
L. Anode post and plate assembly
M. Anode support structure
N. Mercury pump and sump
O. Rubber cover
P. Concrete grout
Q. Dilute chlorine header
R. Decomposer
S. Current breaker
T. Cell shorting switch
U. Amalgam return
V. Quick flushing device

Fig. 3. Cell room containing de Nora mercury cathode cells rated at 150,000 amperes at a large chlorine plant in Texas.

larly in connection with current efficiency and voltage, the results obtained so far are not so satisfactory as with the horizontal construction. Indeed, their main and common drawback resides in the mechanical difficulty of providing a convenient anode adjustment so as to compensate for gradual graphite wear. The interest in the vertical construction could be revived by the advent of metallic anodes, such as platinized titanium, provided their operating life is sufficiently long to give economic advantages.

Hereunder are listed some typical values relating to the operating characteristics of the mercury cell process.

Rated cell capacity	40 to 200 ka
Cathode current density	0.5 amp/sq cm
Average cell voltage	4.35 v
Current efficiency	95%
D-C energy	3100 kwh/ton Cl_2 (1 ton = 2000 lb)
Anode life	10 months
Graphite consumption	5 lb/ton Cl_2
Mercury loss	0.2 lb/ton Cl_2
Cell gas analysis	
Cl_2	99%
H_2	0.5%
CO_2	0.5%
Caustic strength	50% NaOH

More detailed operating data for several of the cells used industrially can be found in Ref. 19, pp. 182–185.

Comparison between the Mercury Cathode and the Diaphragm Process

The outstanding characteristic of the mercury cathode cell is that the caustic solution leaving the process is already pure and concentrated, whereas the corresponding product of a diaphragm cell is a dilute mixture of alkali hydroxide and salt. Consequently, the finishing cost, involving cell liquor evaporation and purification, is substantially higher in the latter case.

On the other hand, the mercury cathode process requires about 15 per cent more energy per ton of product than the diaphragm process; indeed, the average cell voltage is about 0.5 v higher in the former case. However, for smaller plant capacities the greater cost for electricity is more than offset by the saving in investment and operation as regards the caustic finishing equipment. For major plants many other factors come into consideration in the choice of the best suited method.

In the mercury process the depleted brine is recirculated after resaturation with solid salt;

consequently, where the chlor-alkali industry is to exploit local resources of natural well brine, a particularly elegant and convenient arrangement consists of combining the mercury and the diaphragm process together. By such combination, the diaphragm cell circuit is fed with natural brine and the pure salt obtained by cell liquor evaporation is used as such to resaturate the brine to be recycled in the mercury cell circuit.

The technological advances of the latest decades have contributed considerably to the safe operation of the mercury process, in particular because of the better knowledge that has been acquired on the influence of certain impurities, such as vanadium, chromium, and molybdenum, in catalyzing the hydrogen evolution on the mercury cathode.[1-5, 15]

A breakdown of the processes used by the chlor-alkali industry in the United States in recent years[9] shows that diaphragm cells account for 74 per cent and mercury cells for 20 per cent of the production (the residual 6 per cent being obtained with sodium cells and nonelectrolytic processes). The predominance of the diaphragm cell in this country is largely ascribed to the great availability of natural brine resources. However, in other countries, like Germany and Italy, the mercury process is responsible for more than 95 per cent of the total chlorine production.[14]

Other Products Associated with the Mercury Cathode Process

Caustic Potash. Electrolysis of potassium chloride by the mercury cathode process does not present any particular difficulty, although the cathodic potential at which potassium discharge takes place is by a few hundredths of a volt more negative than for sodium. The only consequence of this is that the process is slightly more sensitive to impurities in brine, as regards a possible tendency to hydrogen evolution. Energy consumption per ton of chlorine is about the same as with sodium chloride.

As a rule, caustic potash production by the mercury process is cheaper than by the diaphragm process; indeed, the evaporation plants required by the latter are considerably larger and more expensive when handling caustic potash instead of caustic soda.

Lithium Hydroxide. Electrolysis of lithium chloride can also be successfully carried out by the mercury cathode process.[12] In particular,

this is one of the processes used for the electrolytic separation of lithium *isotopes* (q.v.).

Amalgam By-products. Because of the outstanding reducing properties of alkali metal amalgams, they can be used to obtain a number of interesting byproducts. An extensive review of the several possibilities was published by MacMullin.[18] The following examples are limited to some of the processes that have found industrial application.

Sodium sulfide can be made, in strengths up to about 58 per cent Na_2S, by reacting sodium amalgam with a sodium polysulfide solution.

Benzidine is manufactured on a commercial scale by reduction of nitrobenzene to hydrazobenzene with sodium amalgam. Hydrazobenzene is then converted to the final product, benzidine, by the usual methods.[10]

Sodium methylate is obtained as a byproduct of chlorine and caustic by reacting the sodium amalgam with anhydrous methyl alcohol, followed by final amalgam depletion in a conventional decomposer for caustic production.

Sodium hydrosulfite can be produced by reacting sodium amalgam with a bisulfite solution.

Recovery of the Amalgam Decomposition Free Energy

The former attempts by Castner and Kellner to recover the free energy of the galvanic reaction taking place in the decomposer were unsuccessful, mainly because of the high polarization opposed by the hydrogen discharge on usual cathodic materials, such as graphite or iron. Indeed, the only practical method to recover such energy would be to insert the denuding cell in series to the electrolysis cell and the current rectifier; however, because of the exceedingly high cathodic overvoltage, the galvanic cell would actually oppose a counterelectromotive force to the flow of the electrolytic current.

Nonetheless, a new interest has been aroused by the possibility of using for the cathode the special materials, such as sintered nickel, that have been developed for the hydrogen-oxygen fuel cells. Mainly by virtue of their porous structure and of the consequently large area on which the electrode reaction can develop, the real current density is much smaller than the apparent value calculated from the geometrical area. Accordingly, overvoltage is much reduced, so that, for an apparent current density of 0.1 amp/sq cm at its cathode, the galvanic cell operating at 70°C can deliver a useful voltage of about 0.7 v.[20, 21]

Others[8] have also proposed to depolarize the hydrogen discharge by activating the porous electrode with oxygen, either pure or atmospheric. In such case, no hydrogen would be produced and the electrochemical reactions in the denuding cell would be the following:

Anode: $2Na(Hg)$
$$\rightarrow 2Na^+ + Hg + 2e^-$$
Cathode: $H_2O + \frac{1}{2}O_2 + 2e^-$
$$\rightarrow 2OH^-$$

Overall reaction: $2Na(Hg) + H_2O + \frac{1}{2}O_2$
$$\rightarrow 2NaOH(aq) + Hg$$

By thus sacrificing the hydrogen, otherwise obtainable as a by-product, the voltage output of the denuding cell could be theoretically increased by an amount corresponding to the free energy of water formation, or 1.25 v (see *Water Electrolysis*). Actually, the practical voltage gain is limited to about 0.8 v, so that the total voltage output could be raised to 1.3 to 1.6 v.[21]

It seems, however, that considerable difficulties are still to be solved, in order to render any such possibility practical and economical, in view of the further complications involved in the equipment and in the circuit. It is therefore likely that, in case the hydrogen by-product does not find any captive purpose, the first sort of electrochemical energy to be industrially recovered in chlorine-alkali electrolysis plants (either with mercury cathode or with diaphragm cells) will be obtained by utilizing the hydrogen in an independent system of fuel cells, hooked into the rectifying circuit so as to return to the electrolysis process a part of the electric energy formerly used.

As to the other problem arising from amalgam energy recovery, on account of the unbalance in current efficiency between the process of cathodic sodium discharge on the mercury and of anodic sodium redissolution from the amalgam, theoretically correct solutions have been proposed by several authors.[17, 20] The all too simple arrangements as described in Castner's and Kellner's patents, and basically consisting of a resistive shunt across the denuding cell, would indeed serve an opposite purpose to that which is wanted, that is, bypassing a part of the electrolytic current around the denuding cell. In fact, any shunt across the latter would establish a partial shortcircuit between its terminals

and thus increase the galvanic current output over the electrolytic current, instead of reducing it.

References

1. ANGEL, G., AND LUNDÉN, T., *J. Electrochem. Soc.*, **99**, 435 (1952).
2. ANGEL, G., AND BRÄNNLAND, R., *ibid.*, **99**, 442 (1952).
3. ANGEL, G., LUNDÉN, T., AND BRÄNNLAND, R., *ibid.*, **100**, 39 (1953).
4. ANGEL, G., LUNDÉN, T., BRÄNNLAND, R., AND DAHLERUS, S., *ibid.*, **102**, 124 and 246 (1955).
5. ANGEL, G., BRÄNNLAND, R., and DAHLERUS, S., *ibid.*, **104**, 167 (1957).
6. BAKER, E. C., AND BURWELL, A. W., U. S. Patent 739,140 (Sept. 15, 1903).
7. BARR, L., *J. Electrochem. Soc.*, **101**, 497 (1954).
8. BILLITER, J., British Patent 832,196 (April 6, 1960).
9. CURREY, J. E., AND HAMPEL, C. A., *Electrochem. Technology*, **1**, 56 (1963); CURREY, J. E., AND SWANBERG, D. E., *ibid.*, **1**, 191 (1963).
10. GALLONE, P., *Chimica (Milan)*, **5**, 132, 201 (1950).
11. GALLONE, P., *Chimica (Milan)*, **6**, 78 (1951).
12. GARDINER, W. C., *et al*, U. S. Patent 2,872,393 (Feb. 3, 1959).
13. GARDINER, W. C., AND SAKOWSKI, W. J., *Electrochem. Technology*, **1**, 53 (1963).
14. HASS, K., *Chem.-Ing.-Tech.*, **34**, 337 (1962).
15. HAUCK, G., *Chem.-Ing.-Tech.*, **34**, 369 (1962).
16. JEITNER, F., *Chem.-Ing.-Tech.*, **34**, 353 (1962).
17. KANDLER, L., *Chem.-Ing.-Tech.*, **34**, 349 (1962).
18. MacMULLIN, R. B., *Chem. Eng. Progress*, **46**, 440 (1950).
19. MacMULLIN, R. B., "Chlorine," Sconce, J. S., Ed., pp. 127–199, New York, Reinhold Publishing Corp., 1962.
20. VIELSTICH, A., JUSTI, E., AND WINSEL, A., U. S. Patent 3,068,157 (Dec. 11, 1962).
21. VIELSTICH, A., *Chem.-Ing.-Tech.*, **34**, 346 (1962).

VITTORIO DE NORA AND
PATRIZIO GALLONE

CHLORINE PRODUCTION IN MERCURY CELLS— OVERALL PROCESS

Although the cells are the heart of the chlor-alkali plant, many other steps are requisite for the production of chlorine and alkali and the operation of the cells. Indeed, the investment in the equipment for the nonelectrolytic operations in the plant is much larger than that for the cells themselves. This entry describes the overall process for the production of chlorine and alkali in mercury cathode cells.

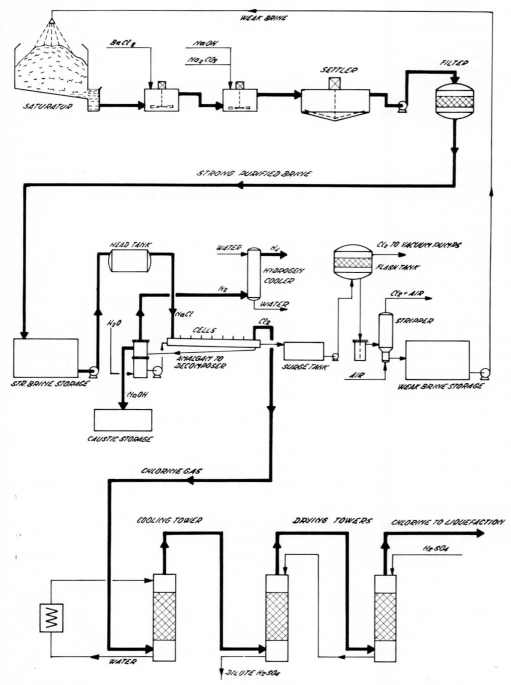

FIG. 1. Flowsheet for chlor-alkali plant using mercury cathode cells, showing brine treatment and chlorine cell gas handling.

A schematic flowsheet for the overall process is shown in Fig. 1.

Hereunder are listed the main steps into which the overall process is subdivided from the starting material (solid salt or well brine) to the electrolytic products (chlorine, caustic soda or caustic potash, and hydrogen) ready for further processing.

Electrolysis

Conversion of electric power from alternating to direct (rectified) current

Brine preparation and purification

Chlorine gas cooling, washing, drying, and liquefaction

Caustic concentration

Hydrogen gas cooling, washing and storage

A brief description of each operation will be given.

Electrolysis

The electrolysis circuit is always sheltered in a well-ventilated *cell house,* equipped with fans providing 8 to 10 air changes per hour. The cells, which are connected in series, lie side by side and are usually arranged in two parallel cell banks; the circuit will thus form a loop to reduce as far as possible the extension of copper bus bars and the ensuing ohmic losses.

All the cells in each bank are interconnected by two pipe headers, for the supply of the nearly saturated and purified brine and for the discharge of the weak brine. The stray currents that are thus allowed to circulate between the cells through these headers are kept down to a negligible value by providing the pipe headers with a chemically inert and electrically insulating lining, as well as with insulating flanges and current-break connections between the manifolds and the cells.

A countercurrent flow of brine with respect to mercury would in principle be more convenient as regards temperature and voltage uniformity throughout the cell length, which would imply a better current distribution. Despite this, the two streams are always kept equicurrent, since the buildup of solid deposits upsetting the even flow of mercury on the cell bottom is thus rendered more difficult, while it becomes easier to remove any such deposits by *flushing* the cell from time to time. This is accomplished by breaking the mercury seal at the outlet end and thus allowing the outrushing brine to drive out the solid matter deposited in the electrolysis compartment.

The gas line through which chlorine is withdrawn is kept under a slight suction of a few mm water column, so as to prevent chlorine and mercury vapors from leaking into the atmosphere.

The caustic solution leaving the decomposers is collected by a common manifold, with the interposition of appropriate devices to break the stray current that would otherwise circulate in the caustic line, due to the relatively high conductivity of the concentrated alkaline solution.

The hydrogen pressure inside the decomposer is kept slightly positive to prevent air from entering the system and building up an explosive mixture; the back pressure at the gas holder and the pressure drop along the line are usually sufficient to keep safety conditions during operation.

Electric Power Conversion

The motor-generator sets, which were the only equipment available for production of d-c power at the outset of the electrochemical industry, have been supplanted by mercury arc rectifiers and, more recently, by contact converters (currently called mechanical rectifiers) and semiconductor rectifiers, mostly of germanium or silicon. The latter have rapidly been taken advantage of because of their high conversion efficiency even at low voltage. This has encouraged cell design toward ever larger current ratings, which decrease the cell number for a given plant capacity, with a corresponding saving in capital, operation, and maintenance costs.

Brine Treatment

The simplified flow diagram of Fig. 1 illustrates a typical brine circuit system.

The acidic weak brine is recycled from the electrolysis cells to the brine treatment plant, where it is first stripped of most of the active chlorine saturating it in the amount of about 0.7 gpl in the form of dissolved gas, as well as of hypochlorous acid and hypochlorite ion, which are in mutual equilibrium according to the reaction:

$$Cl_2(aq) + H_2O \rightleftharpoons HOCl + HCl$$

The hypochlorous acid is partially dissociated ($HOCl \rightleftharpoons H^+ + OCl^-$) and tends to react with the OCl^- ion, with the production of ClO_3^-. Now, a considerable buildup of OCl^- and ClO_3^- ions decreases the current efficiency of the electrolytic process, as discussed in the article "Chlorine Production in Mercury Cells-Electrochemistry." Another obnoxious effect of any active chlorine content in brine is its tendency to form undissociated compounds with iron and heavy metals, so that it becomes more difficult to precipitate them efficiently by chemical treatment, which is necessary to remove such promoters of hydrogen evolution on the mercury cathode.

Brine dechlorination is usually achieved first by acidifying the cell effluent with HCl down to about pH 2, so as to shift the above written reaction toward the left. The gaseous chlorine thus set free is then flashed off under a vacuum of about 400 mm mercury, produced by a water-ring seal pump or by an ejector. Another fraction of the residual chlorine is finally removed by blowing air through the brine stream in a system of stripping towers.

The highly concentrated chlorine gas that is sucked off from the flash tank joins the cell gas to drying and liquefaction, while the mixture of air and chlorine leaving the stripping towers is sent to the hypochlorite plant. The residual free chlorine in the dechlorinated brine stream is thus brought down to about 20 mg/l.

The dechlorinated brine is refortified with solid salt, either by dumping sodium chloride into the brine stream or by letting the latter flow through a salt pile contained in a dissolving vessel, or saturator. The NaCl content is thus brought up from about 270 gpl to about 310 gpl.

Calcium, magnesium, iron, and the sulfate ion are the most common impurities in solid salt and the most easily dissolved in the acidic brine. Of these, magnesium and iron are the most harmful, owing to their synergetic action in promoting hydrogen evolution on the mercury cathode when they are present together even in small concentrations.[1, 7]

Calcium, similarly to magnesium, tends to precipitate as a hydroxide when reaching the alkaline boundary layer of the mercury cathode, thus making the amalgam more sluggish and favoring hydrogen discharge. However, this impurity can be tolerated in much higher concentrations than magnesium and iron. These two metals can both be easily precipitated and filtered out by raising the brine pH to the value of 10. On the other hand, calcium can be precipitated by the addition of sodium carbonate and also by allowing the sulfate content to reach the limit of the solubility product for calcium sulfate.[5]

The sulfate ion, however, promotes oxygen discharge and consequently a faster consumption rate of the graphite anodes; therefore, its concentration is usually prevented from exceeding a certain limit by the addition of barium carbonate or barium chloride, so as to obtain the precipitation of the $SO_4^=$ ion as insoluble barium sulfate.

To satisfy the requirements as set forth in the foregoing considerations, the brine is passed through a system of reactors in which it undergoes a chemical treatment that can be exemplified as follows (see Fig. 1).

First reactor: addition of barium chloride to precipitate the sulfate ion.

$$BaCl_2 + SO_4^= \rightarrow BaSO_4 \downarrow + 2Cl^-$$

Second reactor: addition of sodium carbonate and caustic soda to precipitate calcium, as well as iron and magnesium, by raising brine alkalinity to pH 10.

$$Ca^{++} + Na_2CO_3 \rightarrow CaCO_3 \downarrow + 2Na^+$$

$$Mg^{++} + 2NaOH \rightarrow Mg(OH)_2 \downarrow + 2Na^+$$

$$Fe^{+++} + 3NaOH \rightarrow Fe(OH)_3 \downarrow + 3Na^+$$

The insoluble products thus formed are settled in a Dorr-type clarifier, and removed by a battery of sand or pressure leaf filters.

The brine is now saturated and purified and ready to be recycled to the mercury process, after a pH readjustment to a suitable value. For many years after the inception of the mercury process it was thought that at least the feed solution should be definitely alkaline, on the argument that, from a strictly thermodynamic standpoint, the hydrogen discharge potential can be shifted toward more negative values by raising the alkalinity of the medium. In the past decade, however, it has become a standard practice to preacidify the feed brine so as to obtain a pH value between 2.5 and 5. In fact, by acquiring a deeper insight of the kinetic conditions prevailing at the cathode boundary layer,[2] it is possible to realize that, by keeping acidic conditions throughout the bulk of the solution, not only is the overall current efficiency improved because of reduced buildup of hypochlorite and chlorate ions, as well as because of lesser consumption rate of graphite,[6] but also hydrogen evolution is better checked. Indeed, the tendency for metals in general, and for calcium and magnesium in particular, to precipitate as insoluble or sparingly soluble hydroxides over the mercury cathode is hindered at the very beginning of the brine inflow by the acidity of its bulk, so that calcium can be tolerated in amounts as high as 1 gpl or even more.[3, 4]

A typical feed brine analysis is the following:

NaCl	310 gpl	Ca	100 mg/l
SO_4^-	3 gpl	Mg	1 mg/l
ClO_3^-	2 gpl	Al	0.1 mg/l
		Fe	0.1 mg/l
		V + Cr + Mo less than	0.01 mg/l
pH	4	other heavy metals less than	0.01 mg/l

Chlorine Gas Treatment

The cell gas leaves the mercury process with a water vapor content corresponding to saturation over brine at about 70°C, plus some salt carryover. Most of the water vapor is removed together with the salt mist by means of a countercurrent stream of water through a packed tower. Final gas drying is carried out in a series of towers, where chlorine is passed countercurrent to a stream of sulfuric acid.

Dried chlorine is sent to liquefaction, which in modern plants is usually achieved by deep cooling (−30 to −50°C) so as to obtain liquefaction at a relatively low gage pressure (about 2 atm).

Caustic Concentration

By virtue of the fact that the caustic-producing reaction is completely separated from the electrolytic reaction, the alkaline solution can be produced at such a high degree of purity and concentration that in many cases it does not require any further processing.

An example of this is given by a captive chlor-alkali production associated with the manufacturing of rayon. Otherwise, caustic finishing merely consists of submitting the solution to evaporation under reduced pressure, so that the final concentration can be raised up to the solid product known as *fused caustic* (98–99 per cent NaOH).

Hydrogen Gas Treatment

The hydrogen gas leaving the amalgam decomposers, beside containing caustic mist and water vapor, is saturated with mercury vapor, which at the temperature of 70°C corresponds to about 80 mg mercury per cu m of hydrogen. The gas is first passed through a water-cooled vapor condenser, from which a large part of the mercury is recovered. Beside submitting the gas to further drying procedures, such as described for chlorine, the residual mercury may be removed by some chemical agent, such as chlorinated water and sulfur dioxide, if hydrogen is to be used for foodstuff hydrogenation.

References

1. ANGEL, G., AND LUNDÉN, T., *J. Electrochem. Soc.*, **99**, 435 (1952); for other references to G. Angel and coworkers see under the article "Chlorine Production in Mercury Cells—Industrial Cells."
2. BARR, L., *J. Electrochem. Soc.*, **101**, 497 (1954).
3. GALLONE, P., *J. Electrochem. Soc.*, **102**, 358 (1955).
4. GARDINER, W. C., AND WOOD, J. L., U. S. Patent 2,787,591 (Apr. 2, 1957).
5. TAYLOR, M. C., AND GARDINER, W. C., U. S. Patent 2,248,137 (July 8, 1941).
6. VAALER, L. E., *J. Electrochem. Soc.*, **107**, 691 (1960).
7. WALKER, J. W., AND PATTERSON, C. S., *J. Electrochem. Soc.*, **3**, 185 (1903).

PATRIZIO GALLONE

CHLORINE PRODUCTION IN SODIUM CELLS. *See* SODIUM, ELECTROLYTIC PRODUCTION.

CHROMIUM ELECTROWINNING

Most electrolytic chromium is produced from a solution of trivalent chromium alum. This process has advantages over plating from the hexavalent chromic acid bath in that at 100 per cent current efficiency, theoretically, 701 ampere-hours are required to deposit one pound of chromium from a trivalent solution, while double that amount is needed for deposition from the hexavalent solution. Actually, five times as much metal per kilowatt hour of energy is deposited from a trivalent bath, due chiefly to higher current efficiency and lower voltage, as well as only half the valence charge to overcome. Other advantages are lower cost of chromium in the form of chrome alum and fewer toxicity problems. The disadvantages of the process are the requirement of a diaphragm cell and close cell control.

While chrome alum can be prepared from leached chromite ore, the large number of steps necessary to produce a sufficiently pure electrolyte renders this process so costly from both operating and construction viewpoints that it is not used. Instead, a commercially available intermediate product, high-carbon ferrochrome, has been found to be the cheapest source of chromium, so this discussion will be limited to a process using it as a source of chromium.

Four to six per cent carbon ferrochrome is used as the starting material. A typical flowsheet for the process is given in Fig. 1.

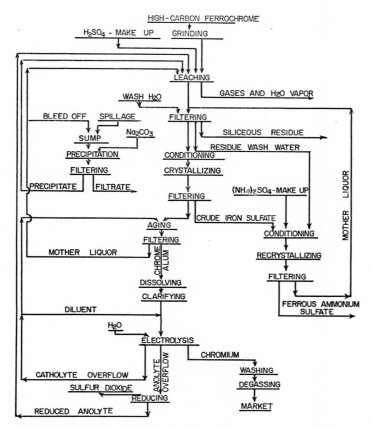

HIGH-CARBON FERROCHROME

FIG. 1. Flow sheet of Marietta Plant for electrolytic chromium.

High-carbon ferrochrome crushed and sized to 20 mesh is slowly fed to a brick-lined, lead-protected steel tank in which it is leached in a mixture of reduced anolyte, chrome alum mother liquor, and make-up sulfuric acid. The tank is equipped with a coil to keep the temperature near the boiling point and with a condenser to control the spray. Leaching plus digestion time is 48 hours. Since a large volume of hydrogen is evolved during the reaction, a ventilating system capable of maintaining the hydrogen concentration below explosive limits is required to exhaust the gases to a scrubber.

After leaching, the slurry is transferred to a holding tank where cold mother liquor from the ferrous ammonium sulfate crystallization is introduced to lower the temperature to 80°C. Silica and the undissolved solids are filtered from the solution in a rubber-covered filter. The filtrate is transferred to a brick-lined, lead-protected steel conditioning tank in which the chromium is transformed to the non-alum forming

condition by holding for several hours at elevated temperatures. The temperature of the liquid is then reduced to about 5°C, and the crude iron sulfate crystals that form are separated from the mother liquor on an acid-proof drum vacuum filter. For the best iron separation, the liquor must be well conditioned and rapidly cooled to prevent resolution.

The by-product resulting from washing the leach residue is used to dissolve the crude iron sulfate. Ammonium sulfate is added to the solution which is conditioned at elevated temperatures for several hours. The ferrous ammonium sulfate is recovered and sold as fertilizer and for other uses.

Getting back to the main circuit, the mother liquor freed from the crude iron sulfate is clarified in an acid-proof filter press, and sent to the aging circuit where it is aged in Koroseal-lined steel thickeners holding about 10 days' production. Aging and crystallization take place at about 30°C, and about 80 per cent of the

TABLE 1. TYPICAL ANALYSES IN GPL OF SOLUTIONS
IN ELECTROLYTIC CIRCUIT

| | Chromium | | | | Fe | NH₃ | H₂SO₄ |
	Total	+6	+3	+2			
Cell feed	130	0	130	0	0.2	43	3
Circulating mixture	65	0	63	2	0.1	68	1
Catholyte	23	0	11.5	12.5	0.035	84	—
Anolyte	15	13	2	0	0.023	24	280

TABLE 2. CELL OPERATING DATA

Cathode current density	70 amp/ft²
Cell potential	4.2 volts
Current efficiency	45%
Electrical consumption	8.4 kwh/lb
pH	2.1 to 2.4
Catholyte temperature	53 ± 1°C
Time of deposition	72 hours
Cathode material	Type 316 stainless steel
Anode material	1 to 99 Ag-Pb

TABLE 3. ANALYSIS OF COMMERCIAL CHROMIUM

| Element | Process | | |
	Electrolytic	Silicon Red.	Aluminum Red.
Cr	99.80%	98.00%	97.80%
Fe	0.14	0.75	0.85
C	0.01	0.18	0.15
Si	Nil	0.60	0.50
P	Nil	0.03	0.02
S	0.25	0.008	0.018
Al	Nil	0.02	0.04
Mn	Nil	0.07	0.40
Cu	0.001	0.01	0.01
Pb	0.002	0.001	0.001

chromium is stripped as ammonium chromium alum in this circuit. The crystal slurry is filtered and washed, and the filtrate is pumped to the leach circuit. The washed chromium alum crystals are dissolved in hot water and filtered to produce cell feed.

Successful operation of the cells depends on close pH control of the catholyte and the preservation of divalent chromium formed at the cathode. The sulfuric and chromic acids that form at the anode must be prevented from mixing with the catholyte to prevent oxidation of the divalent chromium and to maintain the pH. To accomplish this, the cells are fitted with diaphragms of limited porosity. A description of the cells is given by Bacon in another encyclopedia (see Bibliography).

In one commercial installation the cells are set up in two banks of 44 each, and direct current is supplied to each bank by a 10,000-ampere generator. Cell feed is continuously supplied to the operating cells. The feed is mixed with circulating catholyte to lower the chromium content since it is quite viscous even when hot. Due to oxidation of divalent chromium, which lowers the current efficiency, the amount of circulating catholyte must be held to a minimum. The amount of feed to the circulating system and to each cell is controlled by periodic chemical analysis.

The flow of catholyte through the diaphragm into the anolyte compartments controls the pH within narrow limits. The sulfuric acid content of the anolyte is held at 250 to 300 gpl by the addition of water.

Excess catholyte, which is withdrawn from the circulating stream, is returned to the aging circuit. Anolyte is treated in packed towers with sulfur dioxide to reduce hexavalent chromium, and then returned to the ferrochrome leaching circuit. Complete reduction of the chromic acid is necessary because high-carbon ferrochrome will not dissolve in the presence of oxidizing agents.

The cathodes are removed from the cells on a 72-hour cycle; they are placed in racks and taken to the plate-handling area. Here, they are treated with hot water to remove adhering salts, and the brittle chromium deposit (⅛ to ¼ inch thick) is stripped by hand.

The metal thus obtained is crushed by rolls to 2-inch size and washed with hot water to remove any soluble salts. It is then placed in stainless steel cans and heated in an electric furnace to dry and dehydrogenate.

The stripped cathodes are shot blasted, straightened, degreased with a detergent, treated with dilute sulfuric acid, rinsed with water, and returned to the cells.

Typical solution analysis and cell operating data are given in Tables 1 and 2.

Comparative analyses of electrolytic chromium and electrothermic chromium produced by reduction with silicon and aluminum are given in Table 3.

Electrolytic chromium is used in preparing alloys, especially those based on cobalt-chromium and nickel-chromium. It is also used for the production of chromium carbide and cermets, and as fine powder for powder metallurgy.

The price of electrolytic chromium as of late

1963 was $1.15 per pound. A low-oxygen grade of metal produced by heating in hydrogen sells for a considerably higher price ($28/lb).

References

1. American Society for Metals, "Ductile Chromium," American Society for Metals, Cleveland, Ohio, 1957.
2. ROSENBAUM, J. B., *et al., Bureau of Mines R.I. 5322* (1957).
3. BACON, F. E., "Encyclopedia of Chemical Process Equipment," W. J. Mead, Ed., New York, Reinhold Publishing Corp., (in production, 1964).
4. FOUNTAIN, R. W., "Chromium," in "Rare Metals Handbook," C. A. Hampel, Ed., 93–113, New York, Reinhold Publishing Corp., 1961.

F. E. BACON

CHROMIUM PLATING

The electrodeposition of chromium on a noteworthy scale commenced in 1925, after the discovery of the controlling factors of deposition from chromic acid solutions by Fink and Eldridge in 1924.[1] The major attention had been focused on the electrolysis of trivalent and bivalent solutions since the work of Bunsen in 1854, and electrochemists were slow to discover that chromic acid solutions are in many ways more easily reduced to the metal than trivalent salts and provide a simple plating process when used with insoluble lead anodes and solution replenishment with chromic acid itself, instead of with soluble chromium anodes.

Chromium anodes dissolve well enough, in fact too well, and in the form of chromic acid, but since the efficiency of chromium deposition at the cathode is always low, generally 10 to 25 per cent, the high anode efficiency can only result in unbalancing the solution. Lead anodes on the other hand evolve oxygen freely, and serve to reoxidize any chromic acid reduced at the cathode during chromium deposition, and thus stabilize the bath.

Actually, pure chromic acid, while rich in metal, is not reduced by the current, and the reduction to metallic chromium requires the presence of a small amount of some other anion, generally sulfate, which acts as a catalyst and permits the reduction without being reduced or oxidized itself. On the other hand, the presence of too much sulfate or sulfuric acid is injurious, and favors the reduction of chromic acid too much, and the only reaction which occurs is the formation of trivalent chromium at a low cathode potential, and the solution is said to be "over-sulfated."

At intermediate concentrations of sulfate ion, around 1 per cent by weight of the amount of chromic acid present, chromium metal plates out readily, although not at the very lowest current densities; and, simultaneously, there is a brisk evolution of hydrogen at the cathode and also the formation of some trivalent chromium. Thus, early formulas of chromium plating solutions contained 400 gpl (53 oz/gal) of chromic acid and 4 gpl (0.53 oz/gal) of sulfate ion, or 250 gpl (33 oz/gal) of chromic acid and 2.5 gpl (0.33 oz/gal) of sulfate ion.

The more concentrated solution has a higher conductivity and may plate at a lower voltage, but the efficiency is low. The lower concentration has a higher efficiency but somewhat lower conductivity. Still lower concentrations may be used, as long as the ratio of chromic acid to sulfate ion is about 100 to 1, and have still better efficiencies, but a higher voltage is required and the concentrations become more critical.

Cold chromium plating baths give relatively smooth, dull deposits, with poor adhesion. The current efficiency is high, 35 to 40 per cent, and the deposits are relatively soft, about 600 kg/sq mm Knoop, Brinell, or Vickers diamond pyramid hardness number. There is evidence that they consist primarily of a hexagonal hydride, which slowly decomposes to the more stable body-centered cubic metal at room temperature over a period of several weeks.[2]

When the solutions are heated above room temperature, hard (1000 to 1100 kg/sq mm hardness number) bright deposits of the body-centered cubic structure are obtained, but the efficiency is somewhat lower, and higher current densities are required. The current densities used in chromium plating are commonly in the range of 5 to 100 amps/sq dm (50 to 1000 amps/sq ft), according to the bath temperature and composition; and tank voltages will run about 5 to 10 volts and higher according to the conditions.

An improvement in the current efficiency, hardness, brightness, and other characteristics of chromium plating was made by Stareck and collaborators in 1948 and 1949 by the use of the proper proportions of both sulfate and fluosilicate catalysts added to the chromic acid bath simultaneously.[3] Fluosilicate is difficult to control by chemical analysis, but this difficulty is

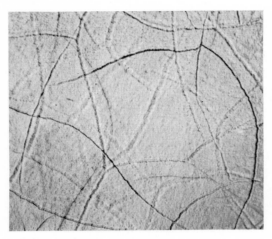

FIG. 1. Bright chromium plate 0.001 in. thick from 250 gpl chromic acid—2.5 gpl sulfate ion bath at 45°C and 72 amps/sq ft. Magnification 1000×.

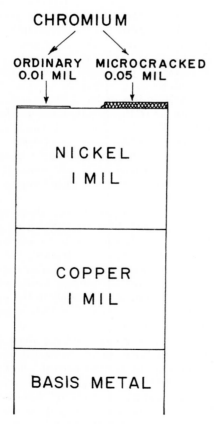

FIG. 2. Typical thicknesses of decorative copper, nickel and chromium deposits drawn to scale.

surmounted by the use of a salt having just the right limited solubility, thus achieving "self-regulation." A further control is achieved by means of the common ion effect, so that the concentrations of both sulfate and fluosilicate ions can be suppressed to whatever proportions are desired for more dilute baths. A substantial and increasing proportion of all chromium plating is now done in self-regulating baths.

Chromium plating has found widespread use in two different fields of application, as a decorative final finish over nickel or copper and nickel plate, and for wear resistance or other "industrial" applications, commonly called hard chromium plating.[4]

In the decorative field, thin bright coatings 0.00001 to 0.00002 in. thick have been used over nickel undercoats for more than thirty years to give a bright finish of substantial durability. It was not found possible to replace nickel with chromium plate, but rather the two finishes supplement each other, and the chromium plate improves the tarnish resistance and durability of nickel coatings.

Thicker chromium coatings which have only a few cracks per inch, actually decrease the corrosion resistance of the combined nickel-chromium deposits when the chromium is more than 0.00002 in. thick. Fig. 1 shows a typical thicker chromium deposit, with cracks in various stages of formation and plating over or "healing shut." It is also possible to produce both bright and dull crack-free chromium plates by special adjustments of the conditions and solution composition.[2]

Seyb and Rowan[5] found that thicker decorative chromium coatings which were quite finely cracked could be used to advantage, and resulted in substantially increased corrosion resistance over heavy, bright nickel undercoats. Such microcracked chromium deposits are now coming into widespread use. Fig. 2 shows the relative thickness of copper and nickel plate which might be used on an automobile bumper, for example, and also the typical thicknesses of both thinner and thicker decorative chromium plates.[6] While the chromium deposits are still relatively thin, they exert a powerful effect on the overall corrosion resistance, which is dramatically increased by the thicker chromium.

Due to the hardness, heat resistance, and special surface qualities, chromium plate has received extremely wide application in industrial or engineering applications of the most varied nature.[4] The normally passive surface has a very low coefficient of friction and substantial resistance to galling or wetting by other materials, and yet can be dissolved, plated with adherent layers of other metals, coated with printing ink, etc., as desired. This great adaptability is hardly matched by any other metal.

The field of hard chromium plating ranges very widely from small tools to large hydraulic rams, from power mower motors to railroad and marine diesel engine cylinders, from 30 calibre rifle bores to the bores of 16 inch guns, from printing plates to large rolls for printing cloth or linoleum, for forming photographic film, or drums for drying chemicals, etc.

The thickness of chromium plate used varies widely from decorative thicknesses (0.00001 in.) up, without any particular limit. The thickness of the chromium plate tends to vary inversely with the hardness and load-bearing capacity of the basis metal. Thus, cutting tools and files which are fully hardened are only lightly flashed with chromium similar to decorative plating, for improved performance, while engine cylinders and large rolls may be plated with 0.005 to 0.010 in. and more of chromium. Frequently, worn surfaces are built up with heavy deposits of chromium, and the salvaged part may give better service than a new one.

Due to unusual "microthrowing power," the effect of hard chromium plating is to heal metal surfaces which have been torn open or microcracked by being machined or ground or otherwise cold-worked, and this healing action is partly responsible for decreasing the friction on the surface and making it more durable. It is also the great merit of hard chromium plating in warm or hot solutions that a very firmly-bonded plate is obtained under almost all conditions, so that the process is not a critical one and is relatively foolproof.

Many new processes for chromium coating have been and are being investigated, but electrodeposition from chromic acid solutions has basic merits which will make it difficult to displace if new processes are introduced.

References

1. DUBPERNELL, G., "The Development of Chromium Plating," *Plating*, **47**, 35–53 (1960).
2. DUBPERNELL, G., chapter on "Chromium Plating" in "Modern Electroplating," Ed., F. A. Lowenheim, pp. 80–140, New York, John Wiley & Sons, Inc., 1963.
3. STARECK, J. E., PASSAL, F., AND MAHLSTEDT, H., "Self-Regulating High-Speed Chromium Plating," *Proc. American Electroplaters' Soc.*, **37**, 31–49 (1950).
4. MORISSET, P., OSWALD, J. W., DRAPER, C. R., AND PINNER, R., "Chromium Plating," 586 pages, Teddington, Middlesex, England, Robert Draper Ltd., 1954. Also MORISSET, P., "Chromage dur et decoratif" (Hard and Decorative Chromium Plating), 895 pages, Paris VIII, Centre D'Information Du Chrome Dur., 1961.
5. SEYB, E. J., AND ROWAN, W. H., "Thicker Decorative Chromium For Better Corrosion Resistance," *Plating*, **46**, 144–149 (1959).
6. SEYB, E. J., "Duplex Chromium—Thicker, More Corrosion-Resistant Chromium Plate," *Products Finishing*, **23**, 64–78 (July, 1959).

GEORGE DUBPERNELL

CHRONOAMPEROMETRY

Chronoamperometry consists of electrolysis experiments in which the potential of an electrode of interest is instantaneously adjusted from its equilibrium value (where no net current passes) to a new value where a net current flows. The electrode potential is held constant at the selected value, and the resulting current is observed as a function of time. The electrolysis cell typically contains the same three electrodes (working, reference, auxiliary) employed in chronopotentiometry and the two techniques have a great deal in common. The solution is maintained quiescent and an excess of supporting electrolyte is used so that the reactant moves toward the working electrode solely by diffusion (linear, spherical, or cylindrical depending on the shape of the electrode).

In a typical chronoamperometric experiment in which conditions of semi-infinite linear diffusion are provided and the electrode potential is held at a value sufficiently removed from the equilibrium potential so that the concentration of reactant at the electrode surface is essentially zero, the current obtained decays with time according to the following formula due originally to Cottrell and sometimes called the Cottrell equation:

$$i = \frac{nFACD^{1/2}}{\pi^{1/2}t^{1/2}}$$

where i is the current (amperes), n is the number of faradays per molar unit of reaction, $\mathbf{F}$ is the Faraday (96, 493 coulombs), A is the electrode area (sq cm), C is the initial concentration (moles/cc) of reactant in the body of the solution, D is the diffusion coefficient of the reactant (sq cm/sec), and t is time (sec). This equation is not valid as t approaches zero because diffusion of the reactant to the electrode is no longer the current-limiting process at very short times. However, the equation has been shown to give the correct description of the current-time behavior for times sufficiently greater than zero to ensure that diffusion of the reactant is the current-controlling process.

The magnitude of the current decays continuously with time, but at any time it is directly proportional to the concentration of reactant in solution. In principle this proportionality could be taken advantage of for analytical purposes but relatively little effort has been expended in this direction. The magnitude of the current at any time is independent of the potential at which the electrode is held during the experiment so long as it is in the range corresponding to a negligible concentration of reactant at the electrode surface and no secondary reactions (e.g., decomposition of the solvent) are occurring. If the electrode potential is not as far removed from the equilibrium value and a finite concentration of reactant persists at the electrode surface at equilibrium, the equation giving the current-time behavior must be modified. In the case of a redox couple that obeys the Nernst equation the modified equation is:

$$ i = i_d \left[1 + \left(\frac{D_1}{D_2} \right)^{1/2} \exp \pm \frac{n\mathbf{F}}{RT} (E - E^\circ) \right]^{-1} $$

where i_d is the current given by the unmodified equation above, D_1 and D_2 are the diffusion coefficients of the reactant and product, respectively, R is the gas constant, T is the absolute temperature, E is the potential of the electrode measured with respect to some suitable reference electrode, E° is the standard potential for the redox couple measured with respect to the same reference electrode, and the solution initially contains only one-half of the redox couple. The plus and minus signs are to be taken for reduction (E becomes more negative) and oxidation (E becomes more positive) reactions, respectively.

The uses to which the chronoamperometric technique has been put are not as many or as varied as those for chronopotentiometry or polarography. Adherence to the Cottrell equation has been used as a means of demonstrating that conditions of semi-infinite linear diffusion have been achieved. It is possible to obtain excellent experimental agreement with this equation, and advantage has been taken of this fact to measure relative diffusion coefficients.

It is interesting to note that chronoamperometry and chronopotentiometry with a current that decreases with the inverse square root of time are in fact identical techniques. In the former cases the electrode potential is maintained constant by the experimenter, and the current is observed to decay with the square root of time. In the latter case the current is made to decrease with the square root of time by the experimenter, and the electrode potential is observed to remain constant. A detailed discussion of this topic is given in Ref. 3.

References

1. DELAHAY, P., "New Instrumental Methods in Electrochemistry," Chapt. 3, New York Interscience Pub., Inc., 1954.
2. VETTER, K. J. "Electrochemische Kinetik," Berlin, Springer-Verlag, 1961.
3. MURRAY, R. W., AND REILLEY, C. N., *J. Electroanalyt. Chem.*, **3**, 64 (1962); **3**, 182 (1962).

FRED C. ANSON

CHRONOPOTENTIOMETRY

Chronopotentiometry is the name given to electrolysis experiments in which the time-dependent variations of the potential of an electrode caused by the passage of current through it are measured. Most often the current passed through the electrode is maintained constant, but chronopotentiometric experiments may also be carried out in which the current is some selected function of time. The electrolysis cell usually contains three electrodes: a working electrode at which the reaction of interest proceeds; a reference electrode (e.g., saturated calomel electrode) against which the potential of the working electrode is measured; and an auxiliary electrode that completes the electrolysis circuit.

The solution and electrodes are maintained quiescent, and a large concentration of inert supporting electrolyte is present so that the reactant moves to and from the electrode surface entirely by diffusion.

Under these conditions as the electrolysis current flows, the reactant is consumed, and its concentration in the solution at the surface of the working electrode decreases. The resulting concentration gradient causes reactant from the body of the solution to diffuse toward the electrode, but before long the diffusive supply of reactant to the electrode surface is insufficient to maintain the constant current which is flowing. At this point a second electrode reaction must commence in order to keep the current constant. For solutions containing only one component of interest this second reaction is most often the decomposition of the solvent (hydrogen gas evolution in the case of reductions and oxygen gas evolution in the case of oxidations in aqueous media). Since the secondary reactions ordinarily occur at electrode potentials quite different from those at which the primary reactant was consumed, a sharp change in the measured electrode potential results. The time that passes between the initiation of the current through the cell and the sharp potential inflection corresponding to consumption of essentially all of the reactant at the electrode surface is called the transition time, τ.

A typical potential-time plot as obtained in a chronopotentiometric experiment with a solution of ferric iron is shown in Fig. 1.

The relationship between the transition time, the current, the concentration and diffusion coefficient of the reactant, and the electrode area depends on the geometry of the electrode and cell. In the usual case in which conditions of semi-infinite linear diffusion of the reactant to the electrode are provided, the transition time, τ (sec), is given by the Sand equation:

$$\tau^{1/2} = \frac{\pi^{1/2} n \mathbf{F} A D^{1/2} C}{2i}$$

where C is the initial concentration (moles/cc.), of reactant in the body of the solution, i is the constant electrolysis current (amperes), D is the diffusion coefficient of the reactant (sq cm/sec), $\mathbf{F}$ is the Faraday (96, 493 coulombs), A is the electrode area (sq cm), and n is the number of faradays per molar unit of reaction.

This equation is to chronopotentiometry as the Ilkovic equation is to polarography, and it forms the basis of chronopotentiometric analysis. A measurement of τ with a known current, i, allows C to be calculated if the electrode area and diffusion coefficient are known or have been measured (e.g., by performing a calibration experiment with a known concentration of the reactant). The accuracy and precision obtain-

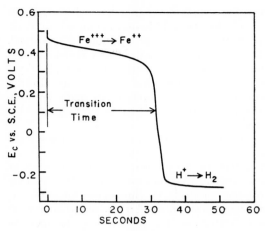

Fig. 1. Typical potential-time plot obtained in a chronopotentiometric experiment with a solution of ferric iron.

able in chronopotentiometric analysis are comparable to those achievable with polarographic analysis, although the fact that an electrode of constant area is used in chronopotentiometry can be an advantage because of the smaller contributions that result from the charging of the electrical double layer at the electrode surface.

The equation for the potential-time plots obtained in chronopotentiometric experiments (these plots are called chronopotentiograms) with redox couples that obey the Nernst equation at 25° C is the following:

$$E = E_{1/4} \pm \frac{0.059}{n} \log \frac{\tau^{1/2} - t^{1/2}}{t^{1/2}}$$

where $E_{1/4}$ is the potential when $t = \tau/4$ and is equal to the standard potential for the couple to a good approximation, τ is the transition time, t is the time since the current was turned on, and the plus and minus signs correspond, respectively, to reductions and oxidations in solutions initially containing only one-half of the redox couple.

The analytical usefulness of chronopotentiometry has been well established, but the technique has found an equal if not greater acceptance as a method for the study of electrode reaction mechanisms and kinetics. This is because of the significant advantages chronopotentiometry offers in mechanistic studies compared with the more classical techniques (e.g., polarography, potentiometry). One major advantage is the flexibility of the time scale that is available in chronopotentiometric experiments. Transition times can range from approximately 60 seconds to less than 20 milliseconds before serious deviations from the Sand equation are observed. This variable time scale allows chronopotentiometry to be used to study, for example, rapid chemical reactions that precede the electron transfer reaction as well as the more leisurely reactions that are amenable to polarographic study.

Another major advantage of the chronopotentiometric technique is the possibilities it offers for studying the products of electrode reactions immediately after they are formed. The electrode reaction products in chronopotentiometric experiments are contained in the diffusion layer at the electrode surface. By reversing the direction of the current that formed the products, they may be caused to react at the electrode and a transition time obtained that corresponds to the consumption of all of the product at the electrode surface. In cases where the reactant and product are stable species that simply diffuse to and from the electrode (e.g., Fe^{+++} and Fe^{++}), the transition time following current reversal turns out always to be one-third as long as the time between the start of the experiment and the point of current reversal. However, if the initial products of the electrode reaction are unstable and undergo chemical conversions to further stable products, the transition time following current reversal may be less than one-third of the generation time and more than one chronopotentiometric wave may be observed. Chronopotentiometry with current reversal can expose the existence of such chemical reactions following the electrode reaction and can frequently be used to measure the rates of the reactions. In a number of instances the presence of suspected but unproven transitory intermediates has been established for the first time by means of chronopotentiometry with current reversal.

Chronopotentiometry has also been used to study the adsorption of reactants on electrode surfaces, the nature of electrode reactions in fused salts, the behavior of oxide films on metallic electrodes, the diffusion of reactants through membranes covering electrode surfaces, and the electrode reactions of substances confined in thin films of solution next to an electrode. The theory of various modified chronopotentiometric techniques has been worked out so that, for example, if a current that varies with time in some prescribed way is substituted for the usual con-

stant current, the effect on the transition time can be computed.

The electrochemical behavior of solid electrodes has, in general, been studied much less systematically than that of the dropping mercury electrode. This has been due in part to the lack of a simple and reproducible experimental technique for use with solid electrodes. Chronopotentiometry has done much to fulfill this need.

References

1. DELAHAY, P., "New Instrumental Methods in Electrochemistry," Ch. 8, New York, Interscience Publishers, Inc., 1954.
2. LINGANE, J. J., "Electroanalytical Chemistry," New York, Interscience Publishers, Inc., 1957.
3. VETTER, K. J., "Electrochemische Kinetik," Berlin, Springer-Verlag, 1961.
4. MURRAY, R. W., AND REILLEY, C. N., *J. Electroanalytical Chem.,* **3,** 64 (1962); **3,** 182 (1962).
5. REINMUTH, W. H., *Anal. Chem.,* **32,** 1514 (1960); *ibid.,* **33,** 322 (1961).
6. REINMUTH, W. H., AND TESTA, A. C., *ibid.,* **32,** 1512, 1518 (1960); **33,** 1320, 1324 (1961).

FRED C. ANSON

Cross-references: *Fused Salt Chronopotentiometry; Polarography.*

CHRONOPOTENTIOMETRY IN FUSED SALTS See FUSED SALT CHRONOPOTENTIOMETRY.

CITCE

The *Comité Internationale de Thermodynamique et Cinétique Electrochimiques* (CITCE) (International Committee for Electrochemical Thermodynamics and Kinetics) held its foundation meeting in Brussels in 1949. Some thirteen electrochemists from four or five countries assembled to discuss such matters as electrochemical nomenclature, potential/pH diagrams, and polarization curves, and to lay plans for future more extensive meetings. Annual meetings have since been held in Milan, Berne, London and Cambridge, Stockholm, Poitiers, Lindau, Madrid, Paris, Vienna, Brussels, Montreal, Rome, and Moscow. In 1963, the membership comprised nearly 400 persons from 34 countries. The Committee has maintained low membership dues for all active academic workers in electrochemistry, who are in a position to share and discuss their results with complete freedom. Workers in industrial organizations are also welcomed, provided that the organization becomes a sustaining member with considerably higher dues, on the grounds that, since industrial work cannot always be communicated completely freely, the financial contribution on behalf of such industrial workers should be appropriately greater.

The founder President of CITCE was P. Van Rysselberghe (U.S.A.). He was followed by T. P. Hoar (U.K.), and M. Pourbaix (Belgium), who each held the office for 3 years. The President for 1961–64 is H. Fischer (W. Germany). M. Pourbaix acted as Secretary-General for the first 8 years of the Committee; he was followed by N. Ibl (Switzerland) 1958–63, and M. Fleischmann (University of Newcastle, England) 1963–.

Eight subcommittees or Commissions are active, dealing with nomenclature and definitions, electrochemical equibrium diagrams, electrochemical kinetics, experimental techniques, corrosion, batteries, high-temperature electrochemistry, and semiconductor electrochemistry. Members of CITCE may join any Commission, if they are active in the field covered by it, and may attend any meetings.

At the annual meetings, which last for 5 to 6 days, papers are presented either to plenary sessions or to Commission sessions. There are usually 50 to 70 papers at a meeting. In addition, several Commissions, notably that on Nomenclature, hold roundtable discussions to provide and to improve internationally standardized terminology, standards, and the like in electrochemistry.

The proceedings of the Milan (1950) meetings are published by Tamburini (Milan); those of the Berne (1951) meeting by Manfredi (Milan), and those of the Poitiers (1954), Lindau (1955), Madrid (1956), and Paris (1957) meetings by Butterworth, London. Since 1959, papers given at CITCE meetings (after suitable refereeing) have appeared in *Electrochimica Acta*, the international journal of pure and applied electrochemistry published by Pergamon Press (Oxford, London, New York, and Paris), under the auspices of CITCE, which provides the advisory and executive editorial boards, the Editor-in-Chief being T. P. Hoar.

Apart from the publication of several hundred original papers on very various aspects of electrochemistry, and the encouragement of the subject on a world-wide basis by its meetings and the contacts that they produce, CITCE has played a large part in two major projects in academic electrochemistry. First, through its Nomenclature Commission, which is closely associated with the Electrochemistry Committee of the International Union of Pure and Applied Electrochemistry (IUPAC), it has produced a detailed set of standard definitions in the subject. Although there is still some argument on semantics in a few matters, there is now (1963) general agreement over a very broad field. Not least in importance was the agreement, in association with the IUPAC (Stockholm 1953), to make sodium negative and silver positive in the electrochemical series. Secondly, the publication of a long series of papers on potential/pH diagrams by the Pourbaix school, culminating in the "Atlas d'Equilibres Electrochimiques" (Gauthier-Villars, Paris, 1963), while not originating in CITCE nor sponsored by it, owes a great deal to the long collaboration of the CITCE Commission on such diagrams, and its members.

T. P. HOAR

CLEANING FOR ELECTROPLATING. See ELECTROPLATING, CLEANING BEFORE.

COATINGS, PROTECTIVE. See PROTECTIVE COATINGS.

COBALT ELECTROPLATING

Cobalt plating has not to date attained commercial importance due in part to cost and the more important use of cobalt in alloys and chemical compounds. Cobalt also oxidizes more readily than nickel or chromium, and improvements in nickel and chromium plating have deterred research in cobalt plating.

Industrial applications require a bright and nonbrittle cobalt electroplate. Brightness is based on the size of crystals, their preferential orientation, and the lamellar structure of the deposit.

Cobalt plate has a pleasing appearance, somewhat like that of nickel, with a slightly bluish cast. Brinell hardness of cobalt deposits vary between 270 and 311 compared with 180 to 420 for nickel.

In the electrochemical series, cobalt lies between thallium and nickel, the standard electrode potential for Co → Co^{++} at 25°C being

+0.278 volt. The deposition potential of cobalt from solutions of sulfate and chloride in different acidities, temperatures, and current densities has been noted by Mellor.[3]

The early work of Watts,[4] and the extensive investigations of Kalmus and coworkers[2] form the basis of the most promising cobalt plating baths.

The Centre d'Information du Cobalt (Bruxelles) has investigated over one thousand variables. Notable cobalt plating baths are the double salt of Co-NH₄, Co-fluoborate, Co-sulfamate and the Co-sulphate-chloride bath which has proved the most efficient. Conditions have been studied at different pH values, temperatures, and current densities in conjunction with various brighteners and mineral additives, with the objective of obtaining a bright and crack-free deposit at a current density competitive with conventional nickel plating baths.

The composition of the sulfate-chloride 10:1 bath is as follows:

Composition		Brighteners	
$CoSO_4 \cdot 7H_2O$	300 gpl	Co salt of p-toluolsulfonic	6 gpl
$CoCl_2 \cdot 6H_2O$	30 gpl	glyoxal (30% soln)	1 cc/l
H_3BO_3	40 gpl	SN-1*	2 gpl
Na laurylsulfate (10% sol)	1 cc/l	$FeSO_4$	12 gpl
		$ZnSO_4$	1 gpl

* SN-1 = Naphthalenetrisulfonic acid salt.

Working Conditions. At a temperature of 25°C, a current density of 2 amp/sq dm, and a pH of 3.3, a semibright, crack-free, and ductile deposit is obtained. With a current density of 1.3 amp/sq dm and a pH of 1.5 the deposit is bright and free of cracks.

Cobalt-Nickel

Electrodeposited cobalt-nickel having the same or superior qualities to nickel deposits and with baths capable of tolerating a higher current density permit commercial production in a highly competitive field.

The cobalt-nickel electroplating baths are based on the Watts type $NiSO_4$ bath and the cobalt content can be adjusted to give whatever per cent of cobalt is desired in the deposit.

A basic chemical composition for bright cobalt-nickel plating solutions is as follows:

Composition	
$NiSO_4 \cdot 7H_2O$	270 gpl
$NiCl_2 \cdot 6H_2O$	27 gpl
$CoSO_4 \cdot 7H_2O$	30 gpl
$CoCl_2 \cdot 6H_2O$	3 gpl
H_3BO_3	40 gpl
$CdSO_4 \cdot 7H_2O$	0.30 gpl
Brightner—Cobalt salt of difulsonic acid coumarin	6 gpl

Working Conditions. Working at pH 4.0, temperature 50°C, and with 6 amp/sq dm, the deposit is bright, adherent, and ductile.

Cast cobalt-nickel alloyed anodes contribute to the bath uniformity and permit any desirable cobalt content. It is preferable to encase the anodes in suitable bags and continuously purify the solution at a low current density (2 to 5 amp/sq dm) to remove Fe, Zn, Cu, etc. Organic impurities are removed by filtering through activated charcoal.

Bright deposits of cobalt-nickel alloys are produced by additions of sodium formate, formaldehyde and the cobalt salt of disulfonic acid coumarin.

The continuous removal of impurities is necessary to give smooth, bright, hard but relatively ductile deposits with low porosity.

Cobalt-nickel baths operate over a pH range of 3.5 to 3.7 for maximum throwing power and brightest deposit and a pH of 2.0 to 2.7 for ductile and easily buffed deposits. Current density varies from 4.3 to 6.5 amp/sq dm and 4 to 5 volts. Bath temperature ranges from 50 to 70°C.

Use of the periodic reverse current decreases nodule formation when using a cathodic period of 2 seconds or less and an anodic period of ½ to ¹⁄₂₅ of a second.

Cobalt-Tungsten

The commercial interest in the cobalt-tungsten alloys[6] relates to their hot-hardness which approaches that of Stellite.

A satisfactory plating solution for the electrodeposition of cobalt-tungsten alloys has the following composition:

Cobalt (as chloride or sulfate)	25 gpl
Tungsten (as sodium tungstate)	25 gpl
Rochelle salt	400 gpl
Ammonium chloride or sulfate	50 gpl
Ammonium hydroxide to a pH of 8.5	

Working Conditions. The operating conditions are, 90 to 100°C; pH 8.5; a current density of 2 to 5 amp/sq dm. The concentration of the tungsten may be varied to the point of saturation, depending on the composition of the deposit desired. As tungsten is added the deposits become brighter.

References

1. DELMONTE, J., AND SPRETER, V., "Bright Cobalt Electroplating," First Report April 4, 1957, Second Report July 8, 1957, Centre d'Information du Cobalt, Bruxelles.
2. KALMUS, H. T., HARPER, C. H., AND SAVELL, W. L., "Cobalt Electroplating," Canada Dept. of Mines, Rept. No. 334 (1915); and *Trans. Am. Electrochem. Soc.,* **27,** 75 (1915).
3. MELLOR, J. W., "A Comprehensive Treatise on Inorganic and Theoretical Chemistry," Vol. XIV, London, Longmans, Green and Co., 1935.
4. WATTS, O. P., "The Electrodeposition of Cobalt and Nickel," *Trans. Electrochem. Soc.,* **25,** 99–152 (1913).
5. YOUNG, R. S., "Cobalt, Chemistry, Metallurgy and Uses," ACS Monograph 149, New York, Reinhold Publishing Corp., 1960.
6. BRENNER, A., BURKHEAD, P., AND SEEGMILLER, EMMA, "Electrodeposition of Tungsten Alloys Containing Iron, Nickel and Cobalt," J. Research National Bur. Standards, **39** (Oct. 1947).
7. Centre D'Information du Cobalt, "Cobalt Monograph"–35, Rue Des Colonies, Brussels, Belgium, 1960.
8. SHELTON, F. K., CHURCHWARD, RUTH E., STAHL, J. C., AND DAVIS, C. W., "Electrolytic Cobalt —A Commercially Feasible Process," Trans. Electrochem. Soc. **91,** 115 (1947).
9. BROWN, H., U.S. Pat. 2,654,703, "Electrodeposition of Bright Nickel, Cobalt and Alloys," (Oct. 6, 1953).
10. RENZONI, L. S., "Electro-Refining of Nickel & Cobalt," U.S. Pat. 2,394,874 (Feb. 12, 1946).
11. DE MERRE, M., "Separation of Nickel Contained in Nickeliferous Cobalt Alloys," U.S. Pat. 2,651,562 (Sept. 8, 1953).

CARL R. WHITTEMORE

COBALT ELECTROWINNING AND ELECTROREFINING

The electrolytic recovery of a metal from solution derived by leaching an ore or intermediate product is designated electrowinning.

The electrowinning of cobalt metal[5, 7, 8] forms an intricate part of processing copper ores at Union Minière du Haut Katanga in the Congo and Rhokana Corporation Limited, Northern Rhodesia.

At Union Minière cobalt is not deposited with the copper in the copper electrolysis circuit, and the spent solution is returned to the leaching circuit to become enriched in cobalt.

To recover the cobalt and to maintain the proper equilibrium, measured volumes of solution are bled from the copper circuit.

The bleed solution, removed both at the exit of the copper electrolytic cells and at the overflow of the copper washing thickeners, contains 20 to 25 gpl copper and 15 to 25 gpl cobalt. This solution passes through a two-stage electrolytic decopperizing step and is subsequently neutralized with lime to precipitate iron and alumina hydrates. The clarified solution is further decopperized in a two-stage operation with lime. The copper hydrates from the first stage are used for the purification of iron in the main copper circuit. After the second purification the pulp is thickened; the precipitate is returned to the cobalt circuit's neutralization and iron-precipitation section, and the solution is passed over beds of annealed metallic cobalt granules to remove traces of copper by cementation. A further treatment of the solution with milk of lime yields a precipitate containing cobalt, the magnesia being left in solution. The filtered cobalt hydrate is repulped in an acid solution, and the mixture is fed to the cobalt electrolytic cells.

Electrolytic deposition of cobalt is conducted in a neutral solution obtained by electrolyzing a pulp containing an excess of cobalt hydrate (up to 70 gpl) in suspension. The cobalt hydrate acts as a neutralizing agent for the acid generated at the anode. Air is blown through specially designed anodes to avoid the harmful effect of the cobalt hydrate. Power consumption during electrolysis is 3.3 kwh per pound of cobalt at a current density of 5 amp/sq dm. Before recycling, part of the electrolyte is treated for the elimination of its nickel content by the De Merré selective cementation—sulfidization process.

The cobalt cathodes contain in per cent, Co 92 to 94, Ni 0.25 to 0.30, Fe 0.05 to 0.08, Cu 0.01 to 0.03, Mn 0.1 to 0.9, Zn 1.0 to 2.5, and S 0.1 to 0.3.

Refining of the cobalt cathodes is accomplished in an electric arc furnace under slightly oxidizing conditions for manganese removal, desulfurizing by a high-lime reducing slag and zinc removal by volatilization and poling. The molten cobalt is then granulated in water and polished for market. The average composition in per cent is Co 99.15, Ni 0.45, Fe 0.15, Si 0.07, S 0.01, C 0.05, Cu 0.02, Mn 0.01, and Zn 0.01.

Cobalt metal at Rhokana Corporation Limited is a by-product of copper. Concentration of the sulfide ore which yields a primary copper concentrate and a cobalt concentrate assaying 3 to 4 per cent cobalt, 25 per cent copper, and 17 per cent iron.

The cobalt concentrate is roasted to sulfate to yield the maximum proportion of cobalt sulfate with minimum sulfates of copper and iron.

The sulfated concentrate is leached with water at 80°C to yield a primary filtrate containing Co 10 gpl, Cu 8 gpl, and Fe 0.2 gpl and a copper bearing residue which is smelted.

Copper is partially removed from the cobalt solution by cementation on annealed cobalt. The remaining copper and iron are precipitated with lime at pH 5.8. The cobalt bearing solution and precipitate are separated by thickening, the precipitate being returned to the initial leach pulp.

The purified cobalt solution is treated with milk of lime at pH 8.3 to form cobalt hydrate which is filtered off and added to the spent electrolyte to which sulfuric acid is added to give a final pH 5.9. The cobalt-enriched electrolyte is clarified and contains 20 to 30 gpl cobalt.

Electrolysis is carried out at 60°C in lead-lined cells with hard lead anodes and mild steel cathodes. The cathodic current density is 1.6 amp/sq dm and a 5-day cathode cycle yields about 50 pounds of cobalt metal per cathode. The cathode cobalt is stripped by hand and broken up in a roller crusher.

The electrolytic cobalt metal may be marketed as "broken cathode metal" or in shot form by melting in an arc furnace and shotting in water. Purity is in excess of 99 per cent cobalt.

Electrorefining

Cobalt is present in small quantities in the copper-nickel ores at Sudbury, Canada, and accompanies the nickel throughout processing. Recovery of cobalt commences at the nickel refinery.

High-purity cobalt metal is recovered during the course of purifying the impure nickel anolyte, containing about 50 gpl Ni and 0.1 gpl Co, by the selective oxidation and hydrolysis of the iron, cobalt, arsenic, and lead and the comentation of copper. Iron is precipitated by aeration and hydrolysis and removed by filtration. Cobalt is precipitated from the resulting solution, together with remaining iron and some copper by selective oxidation with chloride followed by hydrolysis to cobaltic hydroxide. Basic nickel carbonate from the cobalt purification circuit is used to maintain a pH of 4.0.

The impure cobaltic-nickelic slime is slurried with water, selectively reduced with sulfur dioxide, and dissolved with sulfuric acid at pH 4.5. The nickel and cobalt are in the reduced state whereas the other elements are only partly reduced. A further amount of primary cobaltic hydroxide is added to raise the pH to 4.3 and to reoxidize and reprecipitate the iron, lead, and arsenic. Filtration yields a solution essentially free from iron, arsenic, and lead, and containing about 25 gpl cobalt and 50 gpl nickel plus copper. Copper is removed by cementation with nickel powder and the resulting solution is treated with sodium hypochlorite, sodium carbonate and sulfuric acid at pH 2.3 and 100°F for the cobalt-nickel separation.

The cobaltic hydroxide is calcined to oxide and leached with water to remove soluble sulfur salts. The oxide contains in per cent Co 70, Ni 0.8, Fe 0.15, Cu 0.01, S 0.15, and Pb 0.01, and is mixed with 17 per cent petroleum coke, reduced, melted, and cast into anodes. The anodes contain in per cent about 95 Co, 1.5 Ni, 0.8 Fe, 0.4 Cu, and 0.6 S.

Cobalt anodes are refined in divided cells, analogous to electronickel refining.

The electrolyte contains 60 gpl cobalt, 40 gpl sodium, 170 gpl sulfate, 10 gpl chloride, and 10 gpl boric acid. Nickel is held below 2.0 gpl. Electrolyte purification involves precipitation of copper and nickel with sodium sulfide. Iron is removed by oxidation with chlorine at 500 mv redox potential on the platinum-saturated calomel cell. Cobalt carbonate additions maintain pH 4. Purified cobalt electrolyte flows to the cathode compartments at pH 3.3 and 140°F. Cobalt deposition proceeds at 1.6 amp/sq dm.

The cobalt deposits on stainless steel plates to a thickness of about 0.10 inch in 7 days. It is stripped off, acid and water washed, dried, and sheared to 2-inch squares for market.

A typical analysis in per cent is cobalt 99.5, nickel 0.40, copper 0.005, iron 0.005, sulfur 0.001, carbon 0.02, and lead 0.0001.

References

1. DELMONTE, J., AND SPRETER, V., "Bright Cobalt Electroplating," First Report April 4, 1957, Second Report July 8, 1957, Centre d'Information du Cobalt, Bruxelles.
2. KALMUS, H. T., HARPER, C. H., AND SAVELL, W. L., "Cobalt Electroplating," Canada Dept. of Mines, Rept. No. 334 (1915); and *Trans. Am. Electrochem. Soc.*, **27**, 75 (1915).
3. MELLOR, J. W., "A Comprehensive Treatise on Inorganic and Theoretical Chemistry," Vol. XIV, London, Longmans, Green and Co., 1935.
4. WATTS, O. P., "The Electrodeposition of Cobalt and Nickel," *Trans. Am. Electrochem. Soc.*, **25**, 99–152 (1913).
5. YOUNG, R. S., "Cobalt, Chemistry, Metallurgy and Uses," ACS Monograph 149, New York, Reinhold Publishing Corp., 1960.
6. BRENNER, A., BURKHEAD, P., AND SEEGMILLER, EMMA, "Electrodeposition of Tungsten Alloys Containing Iron, Nickel and Cobalt," J. Research National Bur. Standards, **39** (Oct. 1947).
7. Centre D'Information du Cobalt, "Cobalt Monograph"–35, Rue Des Colonies, Brussels, Belgium, 1960.
8. SHELTON, F. K., CHURCHWARD, RUTH E., STAHL, J. C., AND DAVIS, C. W., "Electrolytic Cobalt —A Commercially Feasible Process," *Trans. Electrochem. Soc.*, **91**, 115 (1947).
9. BROWN, H., U.S. Pat. 2,654,703, "Electrodeposition of Bright Nickel, Cobalt and Alloys," (Oct. 6, 1953).
10. RENZONI, L. S., "Electro-Refining of Nickel & Cobalt," U.S. Pat. 2,394,874 (Feb. 12, 1946).
11. DE MERRE, M., "Separation of Nickel contained in Nickeliferous Cobalt Alloys," U.S. Pat. 2,651,562 (Sept. 8, 1953).

CARL R. WHITTEMORE

COMPLEXES (METAL) STABILITY CONSTANTS. See STABILITY CONSTANTS OF METAL COMPLEXES.

COMPLEX IONS IN ELECTROPLATING

Metal ions to be electroplated are often attached to anions or to neutral molecules added to the bath, rather than to water molecules, as is the case with the so-called simple ions. Such aggregates are called *complex ions*. Thus, silver, copper, zinc, cadmium, gold, and some other metals are plated from baths containing cyanide ions, with which the metal ions form complexes; $[Ag(CN)_2]^-$, $[Cu(CN)_3]^{--}$, $[Zn(CN)_4]^{--}$, $[Cd(CN)_4]^{--}$, $[Au(CN)_2]^-$ are the predominant species, and substantially none of the simple metal ions re-

main. Likewise, in stannate baths, tin is associated with hydroxide ions: $[Sn(OH)_6]^{--}$; in chromium baths, the metal is linked with oxide ions: $[Cr_2O_7]^{--}$. Pyrophosphate complexes are also used, and baths containing amines, such as $[Zn(NH_3)_4]^{++}$ and $[Cu(NH_2 \cdot CH_2 \cdot CH_2 \cdot NH_2)_2]^{++}$, have been employed.

Deposition from such complex ions, compared to that from simple salt baths, differs in that: (1) the equilibrium electrode potential is more negative; (2) polarization is generally greater; (3) throwing power is frequently very much improved; (4) the appearance and physical form of the deposit is altered, often quite profoundly; (5) current efficiencies and limiting current densities are usually lowered; and (6) anodic dissolution may be affected. For technical purposes, specific complexes are selected which exert beneficial influences, but complexes do not necessarily give superior results, as was once supposed.

Alteration of electrode potential is helpful where immersion deposits, with faulty adhesion, would otherwise be formed. For example, zinc surfaces can be plated satisfactorily in cyanide copper baths, but not in copper sulfate. The potential of zinc in the cyanide bath is not sufficiently more negative than that of copper to cause the latter metal to plate without external current, as it does in the sulfate bath. When copper is plated on steel, the advantage of cyanide baths is probably kinetic; potentials calculated from thermodynamic data indicate that copper should be deposited by immersion, but these potentials are not actually observed, presumably because the deposition reaction is too slow (exchange current infinitesimal). Alloy plating baths employ complexing to bring the potentials of two or more metals to approximately the same value so that simultaneous deposition becomes possible; brass is the most prominent example.

The factors determining throwing power (q.v.) are only now becoming understood, but in part the effect of complexing is exercised through its influence on current efficiency. Thus, with cyanide zinc or copper baths containing a high ratio of cyanide to metal, efficiency falls off sharply as current density is increased; accordingly, a portion of the cathode surface at which heavier than average current is flowing does not receive a proportionately heavier deposit. However, kinetic factors are often important, for throwing power may be quite high in baths which operate at current efficiencies approximating 100 per cent, such as zinc baths with high alkalinity and low cyanide-to-metal ratio, high-efficiency copper cyanide baths, and gold and silver baths. Microthrowing power is often adversely affected by complexing, but macrothrowing power is usually improved; the chromium bath is an exception.

Deposits from cyanide baths are generally smoother, finer grained, and somewhat more lustrous than those from simple baths (in the absence of brightening agents); this is especially notable with silver, where deposits from the simple ion are so crystalline and loose as to be useless. The reasons for this are not clear, but apparently cyanide or the complex ions themselves are adsorbed on the cathode surface and interfere with the ready growth of undesirable large crystal grains of the depositing metal; that is, the complex functions as its own addition agent. Nevertheless, further improvements may be obtained by adding other agents. Many complex ions give very poor deposits; as already mentioned, technical baths employ specifically selected complexes.

Complexing agents do not always promote dissolution of the anode. For example, copper anodes form an insoluble coating of copper cyanide, $CuCN$, which blocks the flow of current unless considerable excess cyanide is present to convert the insoluble salt to a soluble complex. However, this excess cyanide lowers cathode current efficiencies so sharply that it is preferred to add tartrates instead; apparently the anode dissolves as a tartrate complex without filming, and this complex is subsequently converted to the cyanide complex.

In the technical practice of plating, the complexing agent is lost along with the metal by dragout (carry out of solution on wet work surfaces). Furthermore, cyanide is also lost by hydrolysis and possibly by electrolytic oxidation. Consequently, replenishment of the complexing agent may become a significant cost; in cyanide zinc baths it may be several times that of the metal deposited.

It was formerly assumed that the complex ion dissociates to form the "simple" ion from which deposition actually takes place. It was apparently not recognized that the simple ions, on account of their hydration (amounting to a "water complex," e.g., $[Cu(H_2O)_4]^{++}$, $[Ni(H_2O)_4]^{++}$, $[Zn(H_2O)_6]^{++}$) are not necessarily more accessible for deposition processes than are the complex ions. Recently it has become possible to identify the species from which deposition actually occurs at very low current densities. In most complex baths, metal is deposited directly from a complex ion, although not always from the predominating complex. Thus, silver is deposited from the $[Ag(CN)_2]^-$ ion, as might be expected, but copper is produced from the $[Cu(CN)_2]^-$ ion, although most of the metal is found as $[Cu(CN)_3]^{--}$. In cyanide zinc baths deposition proceeds from the complex $[Zn(OH)_2]$, at least at low current densities, even though the zinc is almost entirely in the form of $[Zn(CN)_4]^{--}$. Evidently transformation between the complexes is very rapid. The old explanation that the complexing agent improves the deposit by diminishing the concentration of simple ions in the bath is plainly inadequate.

As a rule, several species of complex ions coexist in the bath. In cyanide copper baths, $[Cu(CN)_2]^-$, $[Cu(CN)_3]^{--}$, $[Cu(CN)_4]^{---}$, and possibly $[Cu(CN)_5]^{----}$, are present; and in cyanide zinc baths, to which sodium hydroxide is usually added, $[Zn(CN)_3]^-$, $[Zn(CN)_4]^{--}$, $[Zn(CN)_5]^{---}$, $[Zn(OH)_3]^-$, and $[Zn(OH)_4]^{--}$ are found. It is seldom known how much of the complexing agent remains "free," that is, not coordinated with metal ions. The addition of more complexing agent converts some of the lower to higher complexes and is associated with diminished current efficiencies at the cathode, presumably because deposition occurs most readily from the lowest complex. For these reasons, the cyanide-to-metal ratio is a more significant parameter for control purposes than a hypothetical "free" cyanide.

The strength of the bonding (coordination) of the complexing species (ligand) to the metal ion varies greatly from metal to metal and from ligand to ligand. If the bond is exceptionally strong, as in $[Ni(CN)_4]^{--}$, $[Fe(CN)_6]^{----}$, $[Ti(OH)_6]^{----}$, etc., the potential required for deposition may be greater than that required for hydrogen production, or the rate of dissociation is so low that metal polarization exceeds that of hydrogen, and hydrogen is produced rather than metal. It has been shown that complexes with "inner orbital" or "spin-paired" electronic structures tend to be too stable for deposition, although there are exceptions. Some fairly strong complexes yield spongy, impure deposits, apparently because dissociation of the complex is too slow to be complete.

Most complex ions used in electroplating are anionic and, therefore, are repelled by the negative charge at the cathode. In spite of this repulsion, they probably become attached to the cathode as a first step in the deposition process either by specific adsorption or after conversion to neutral or cationic forms in the double layer. Depletion of the complex anions near the cathode surface during deposition is partially compensated by diffusion of more ions from the unaltered bulk of the bath, which is very much more rapid than migration away from the cathode in response to the electric charge.

References

1. LOWENHEIM, F. A., "Modern Electroplating," 3rd Ed., Chap. I, New York, John Wiley & Sons, Inc., 1963.
2. LYONS, E. H., JR., in "The Chemistry of Coordination Compounds," J. C. BAILAR, JR., Ed., Chapt. 19, New York, Reinhold Publishing Corp., 1956.
3. LYONS, E. H., JR., J. Electrochem. Soc., 101, 363 (1954).

ERNEST H. LYONS, JR.

CONCENTRATION CELLS

If the electrode potential of a metal specimen immersed in an aqueous solution containing one concentration of ions of that metal is compared to that of a similar metal specimen immersed in an aqueous solution containing an appreciably different concentration of ions of that metal, the two potentials will be different. The potential of the specimen immersed in the more dilute solution will be negative to that of the specimen in the more concentrated solution. If the vessels containing these two different solutions are connected by a salt bridge and if the two specimens are connected together by a metallic conductor, current will flow between them. The specimen in the more dilute solution will be the anode and will suffer corrosive attack, while the specimen in the more concentrated solution will be the cathode, and will either remain uncorroded or at least will be less corroded. Electrochemical cells of this type are termed "concentration cells."

For thermodynamically reversible cells of this type, the potential generated can be calculated using the Nernst Equation.[1] This can be expressed as

$$E = \frac{RT}{n\mathbf{F}} \log \frac{a_1}{a_2} + E_L$$

where

E = cell potential, in volts

R = gas constant, in joules per degree per mole

T = absolute temperature

n = number of electrons transferred in the potential determining reaction

$\mathbf{F}$ = Faraday's constant, in coulombs per equivalent

a_1 and a_2 = activities of the metal ions in the two solutions

E_L = liquid junction potential, in volts

However, under less well-controlled or service conditions, the reactions are generally neither simple nor thermodynamically reversible, and this prevents rigorous adherence to the Nernst Equation. One of the main reasons for this lack of agreement is that frequently the solutions differ in the concentration of ions other than those of the metal that composes the electrodes. In particular, if the two solutions are exposed to air, the concentration of oxygen dissolved in the two solutions is likely to differ. Oxygen is more soluble in dilute solutions of metal salts than in more concentrated solutions of such salts. The pH, which is a measure of the hydrogen ion concentration, is also likely to be different in the two solutions. There may be other compositional differences also that may affect the electrode reactions. Thus, under service conditions, it can only be predicted that the solution potentials of similar specimens exposed to solutions containing different concentrations of their ions will differ without being able to predict in advance either the magnitude or even the direction of this difference.

The same is true when two specimens of the same metal are immersed in solutions that differ in concentration of the ions of some different substance. For example, if one specimen of copper is immersed in a 1 N solution of sodium chloride and another specimen of copper is immersed in a 0.1 N solution of sodium chloride, it will be found that a difference in potential exists between the two specimens. Under stagnant conditions and with both solutions exposed to air, the copper specimen exposed to the more concentrated solution is anodic to the specimen exposed to the more dilute solution. Specimens of other metals give qualitatively similar results.[2,3] Here again, the concentration of oxygen in the more concentrated salt solution is probably lower than that in the more dilute solution

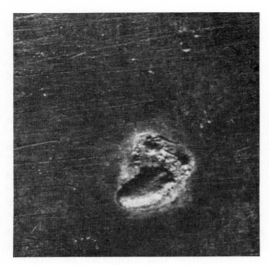

FIG. 1. Pitting of lead under glass bead in 0.2N ammonium chloride solution.

localized corrosion that occurs under service conditions.

Differential aeration cells can be caused by crevices, lap joints, or settled debris, since the stagnant solution within the crevice or joint becomes depleted of oxygen, whereas the liquid at freely-exposed areas is maintained continuously saturated with air. Under such conditions, the metal surfaces within the crevice or joint or under the particle or settled debris become anodic to adjacent, freely-exposed metal areas and suffer local corrosion.

Local corrosion resulting from such differential aeration cells can be easily demonstrated in the laboratory by completely immersing a sheet lead specimen in a beaker that is maintained partly full of a dilute ammonium chloride solution. If a glass bead is placed on the surface of the lead, severe corrosion pits will develop on the lead surface under the glass bead. (See Fig. 1.)

Another method of demonstrating the effect of differential aeration is to place a rubber band around a stainless steel specimen and then immerse the specimen in a ferric chloride solution. Severe local attack will develop under the rubber band. (See Fig. 2.)

As was mentioned above, under service conditions the concentrations of more than one type of ion may differ at various locations in the solution contacting the metal surface. Some metals are more sensitive to differential aeration cells than others. In many solutions metals, such as aluminum, iron, lead, zinc (and their alloys), are sensitive to differential aeration cells whereas copper, silver, and their alloys are more sensitive to metal ion concentration cells. With the former group of metals, surfaces that contact

and this may be an important factor in determining the direction of the potential difference.

Under laboratory conditions, it is possible to study the specific effect of differences in oxygen concentration.[4] Here two similar steel specimens are partially immersed in a beaker containing a dilute salt solution. The specimens are separated from each other by a semipermeable membrane. If air or oxygen is now bubbled into the compartment containing one specimen, it will become cathodic to the other specimen. The potentials of the specimens reverse if the air or oxygen is bubbled into the other compartment. Oxygen concentration cells of this type are frequently termed "differential aeration cells."[5] They are responsible for much of the severe

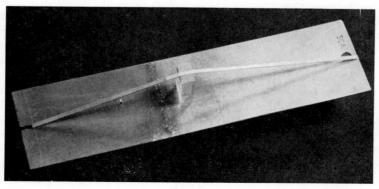

FIG. 2. Severe crevice attack of AISI type 304 stainless steel by contact with rubber band in 2 per cent ferric chloride solution. Only left portion of specimen was immersed. Approximately ¾ actual size.

moving streams of air-saturated liquid will be cathodic to those contacting stagnant liquid (because of differential aeration cells) whereas, with the second group of metals, surfaces that contact moving streams of air-saturated liquid will be anodic to those contacting stagnant liquid (because concentration cells resulting from differences in metal ion concentration are more important than are differential aeration cells). The pH and composition of the solution can affect the relative importance of these two types of cells. Lynes concludes that in the pH range of 5 to 9, the potential of oxygen concentration cells is greatest.

The activity of oxygen concentration cells is affected by other factors. For example, if a deposit is formed on the surface of the cathode, either as a result of electrolysis of the solution or as a result of corrosion of the cathode in cases where it does not receive a sufficiently high current density to completely suppress corrosion, this deposit can gradually reduce contact of the cathodic areas with the oxygen-containing solution. Thus, the potential of the oxygen concentration cell will gradually decrease.[6]

There is another complicating factor which interferes with the activity of oxygen concentration cells. If the conditions are such that rapid corrosion occurs on the metal surface exposed to solution of higher oxygen content, corrosion of the metal surface adjacent to it, but exposed to solution of lower oxygen content, may be suppressed. This effect can be illustrated by experiments in which one steel rod is laid across a second steel rod so that they are in contact. If these contacting rods are immersed an an air-saturated 0.05 N sodium carbonate solution, corrosion of the rods will occur at small areas surrounding the point of contact.[7] This corrosion is the result of an oxygen concentration cell. However, if deep saw cuts are made in the rods on each side of their point of contact, but 0.6 cm distant, corrosion always occurs at the saw cuts, and this reduces the probability of corrosion occurring at the contact area. The highly anodic areas at the saw cuts give partial cathodic protection to the contact area.

Similarly, if the contacting steel rods are exposed to air-saturated sodium chloride solution, the rods corrode all over, and attack adjacent to the contact area is actually less than elsewhere. Oxygen concentration cells cause the greatest intensity of local corrosion in cases where the metal surface adjacent to the air-saturated solution suffers little or no attack. In such cases, there is a large cathode area and a small anode area where the corrosion current densities are high. It is for this reason that local corrosion in crevices or under scattered particles of foreign debris is much more severe on alu-

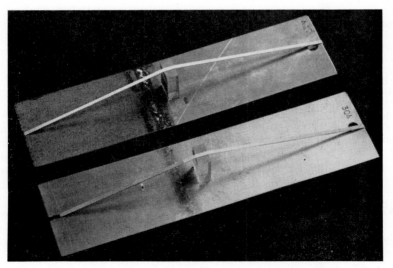

Fig. 3. Severe general corrosion in Type 410 stainless steel (top specimen) prevented localized attack in crevice formed by rubber band. Type 304 stainless exhibited severe crevice attack with little or no general corrosion on exposed surfaces. Left portions of specimens were exposed in 2 per cent ferric chloride solution. Approximately ¾ actual size.

minum or stainless steel than on carbon steel when these metals are exposed to nearly neutral, chloride solutions containing dissolved oxygen.

This effect is illustrated in Fig. 3. Notice that fairly general attack occurred on Type 410 stainless steel exposed to a 2 per cent ferric chloride solution but that attack at the crevice under the rubber band was not much more severe that on adjacent edge areas that were freely exposed. In the case of the Type 304 stainless steel specimen, little attack occurred at freely exposed areas, but very severe localized attack developed at the crevice adjacent to the rubber band.

Bacterial activity can cause concentration cells by altering the oxygen ion, hydrogen ion, or metal ion concentration adjacent to local areas of a metal surface exposed to solutions, natural waters, or soil.[8] Localized corrosion can result from such cells.

References

1. GLASSTONE, S., "An Introduction to Electrochemistry," p. 195, New York, D. Van Nostrand Co., Inc., 1942.
   IVES, D. J. G., AND JANZ, G. J., "Reference Electrodes," p. 48, New York, Academic Press, 1961.
2. MEARS, R. B., AND BROWN, R. H., *Ind. Eng. Chem.*, **33**, 1007 (1941).
3. BECK, W., KEIHN, F. G., AND GOLD, R. G., *J. Electrochem. Soc.*, **101**, 396 (1954).
4. EVANS, U. R., "Metallic Corrosion Passivity and Protection," p. 168, London, Edward Arnold & Company, 1937.
5. A technical review by Wilson Lynes in the *J. Electrochem. Soc.*, **103**, 467 (1956), summarizes information on oxygen concentration cells.
6. SCHASCHL, E., AND MARSH, G. A., *Corrosion*, **16**, 461t (1960).
7. MEARS, R. B., AND EVANS, U. R., *Trans. Faraday Society*, **30**, 421 (1934).
8. HARRIS, J. O., Symposium on Microbiology of Petroleum, American Petroleum Institute, December 4, 1962.

R. B. MEARS

CONCENTRATION POLARIZATION

Electrode reactions, being heterogeneous in nature, are associated with the formation of concentration gradients resulting from mass transfer phenomena which are part of the overall electrode process. Broadly speaking, the ionic mass transport to and from an electrode may occur by one or more of the following three mechanisms: diffusion, migration, and convection. The total rate of mass transfer, N_t, can therefore be expressed as

$$N_t = -D_i \frac{\delta C}{\delta x} - C u_i \frac{\delta \phi}{\delta x} - UC \qquad (1)$$

where D_i is the diffusion coefficient, u_i is the ionic mobility, ϕ is the potential, U is the velocity of bulk fluid movement in the direction of transfer, x is the distance orthogonal to the surface of the electrode, and C is the concentration of reacting species, i.

In cells employing solid and semisolid electrolytes, convection is absent and the rate due to diffusional transport can be calculated from an appropraite solution of the diffusion equation for a suitable set of boundary conditions. In liquid electrolytes some form of convection is usually present (even if only free convection in the gravitational field of the earth), and a hydrodynamic analysis is then required.

In recent years, mass-momentum analogy methods and similar analytical techniques have been successfully employed for the calculation of the interfacial concentration of a reacting species at an electrode surface.[1, 2, 3]

Once the interfacial concentration has been calculated (or estimated from some experimental techniques), one can calculate the additional loss of potential which results from the existence of such a concentration gradient. This loss of potential is equal to the electromotive force (emf) of a concentration cell without transference. Thus, the concentration polarization can be simply defined as

$$\Delta E_{conc} = \frac{RT}{nF} \ln \frac{C_i}{C_0} \qquad (2)$$

where C_i and C_0 represent the interfacial and bulk concentrations of the reacting species. If more than one species is potential-determining, for instance, as is the case with a redox reaction, two gradients will usually form (a buildup of the concentration of one species and a decrease of the other) so that ratios of concentrations of both species must be considered in the calculation of concentration polarization (see, e.g., Ref. 4).

Thus, concentration polarization represents a *shift in the potential of a single electrode* as a consequence of concentration changes in the electrolyte in the immediate vicinity of its surface resulting from a net passage of current. It is important to recognize that concentration polarization must be separately considered for *each* electrode in a cell since it can only be discussed in relation to each half-cell reaction.

The so-called mass transfer coefficient, k_L, is defined by the equation

$$N_t = k_L \cdot \Delta C \tag{3}$$

where N_t is the total rate, and ΔC is the concentration difference. These can be related to the electrochemical rate and to the so-called diffusion boundary layer thickness, δ, as follows:

$$N_t = \frac{I(1 - t_i)}{n\mathbf{F}} = k_L \Delta C = \frac{D}{\delta} \Delta C \tag{4}$$

Thus, from mass transfer coefficient data, the boundary layer thickness for the electrochemical mass transfer, δ, can be simply obtained. t_i is the transport number of the potential determing ion. As shown in Eq. (4), mass transfer rates should be equated only to the nonmigrational part of the total current. The mass transfer boundary layer thickness, δ, is generally different from the hydrodynamic boundary layer thickness.

The boundary layer thickness, δ, is commonly identified with the Nernst diffusion layer thickness indicated in Fig. 1. This thickness is smaller than the true thickness of the boundary layer, δ_E, which reaches to the point where the concentration is actually equal to the bulk concentration, C_0.

The hydrodynamic boundary layer represented by the gradient of the velocity, U, has a so-called Prandtl boundary layer thickness, δ_{PR}, which is obtained by an analogous asymptotic extrapolation. The Prandtl layer thickness, δ_{PR}, (which is again smaller than the true thickness, δ_0), is generally larger than the Nernst diffusion layer thickness, δ, and, under conditions of a turbulent flow, related to it as follows:

$$\delta_{PR}/\delta = (PR)_m^{1/3} \tag{5}$$

where $(PR)_m$, the Prandtl Number for mass transfer (often referred to as the Schmidt Number), represents the dimensionless ratio of the kinematic viscosity and the diffusion coefficient for the reacting species.

It is convenient to relate the concentration polarization to the applied current density, I, and the limiting current density, I_L. The latter is the value obtained when the concentration difference is the maximum, i.e., when $\Delta C = C_0$, the bulk concentration. It can be shown from Eqs. (2) and (4) that concentration polarization (for a consumptive electrode process) is:

$$\Delta E_{conc} = \frac{RT}{n\mathbf{F}} \ln \left(\frac{I_L - I}{I_L} \right) \tag{6a}$$

where I_L is the limiting current density for the consumptive process, and I, the applied current density. Concentration polarization, of course, also occurs at the opposite electrode at which a species is generated and the concentration builds up. For this case, its value is:

$$\Delta E_{conc} = \frac{RT}{n\mathbf{F}} \ln \left(\frac{I_L' + I}{I_L'} \right) \tag{6b}$$

The derivation of the above equations is based on a linear relationship between the concentration difference, ΔC, and the current density, I. This may not always be the case. For instance, in one important mode of convection, namely, free convection at vertical electrodes (resulting naturally from the buoyancy force due to a density gradient in the presence of the gravitational field), the current density is proportional to $(\Delta C)^{5/4}$ (see Ref. 5). On the basis of such a relationship, it can be readily shown that the expression for concentration polarization for a consumptive process, equivalent to Eq. (6a), is:

$$\Delta E_{conc} = \frac{RT}{n\mathbf{F}} \ln \left[1 - \left(\frac{I}{I_L} \right)^{4/5} \right] \tag{7}$$

Concentration polarization within the electrolyte of a cell can be very significant when either low bulk concentrations are employed or when large concentration gradients result from poor mass transfer within the cell. Good mass transfer in electrochemical cells is essential for high rate processes.

The above discussion concerns the traditional concept of concentration polarization at working electrodes as related to concentration gradients of reactants and products within the liquid elec-

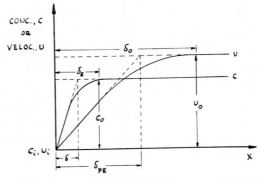

FIG. 1. Hydrodynamic and concentration boundary layers at the electrode interface.

trolyte. With the recent rise of interest in gas electrodes employed in fuel cells, it became important to define another form of concentration polarization and develop appropriate analytical methods.[6] This mode of polarization, termed "Gas-side Concentration Polarization," is related to the mass transport of gaseous reactants and products through the pores of a porous electrode to the triphase equilibrium sites of the working electrode.

The gas-side concentration polarization becomes of particular significance when the reactant gas must diffuse through an inert, stagnant gas layer, as would be typical in the operation of an air electrode, in which, roughly, 21 mole per cent is the reactant gas, oxygen. Within the pores of the electrode, oxygen must diffuse through the stagnant nitrogen. Thus, the gas-side concentration polarization can be related to the ratio of the partial pressure of the oxygen in the bulk of the gas phase, $(p_0)_1$, to that at the reaction zone within the pores, $(p_0)_2$. Hence, for this gas, the gas-side concentration polarization can be expressed as

$$(\Delta E_{conc})_g = \frac{RT}{n\mathbf{F}} \ln \left[\frac{(p_0)_1}{(p_0)_2} \right] \qquad (8)$$

The partial pressure of the reactant gas at the reaction zone (e.g., the value of $(p_0)_2$), required for the calculation of this form of concentration polarization, can be obtained through considerations of gas diffusion theory in porous media (see, e.g., Ref. 6). This calculation generally requires knowledge of the volume fraction porosity, the effective diffusional pore length, the binary or effective diffusion coefficient for the reacting species, and finally, of course, the current density for which the calculation of this partial pressure is made.

For an analysis of a more complex case of the simultaneous counterdiffusion of a gaseous reaction product, the reader is referred to Ref. 7.

The relative significance of gas-side concentration polarization on the kinetics of a gas diffusion electrode depends, of course, on the structure of the electrode (size, length, and tortuosity of the pores) in addition to the usual effects of reactant concentration, temperature and true current density. Regardless of its relative significance, the operation of porous gas-diffusion electrodes is accompanied by both the gas-side concentration polarization and the usual concentration polarization on the electrolyte side.

The relative significance of concentration polarization of one form or another, as part of the total polarization of an electrode, represents an area requiring mass transfer analysis for each individual case. This necessity, often overlooked in early treatment of electrode kinetics, has sometimes led to improper interpretation of experimental data.

The direct measurement of concentration polarization by static techniques is not possible, since what one measures is a sum total of all modes of polarization (for instance, the sum of concentration polarization and activation polarization). Only interrupter techniques and certain pulse techniques lend themselves (through the interpretation of the electrode potential decay curve) to a separation of activation polarization, a rapidly decaying component, from concentration polarization, which decays much slower as it is associated with mass transport phenomena.

References

1. TOBIAS, C. W., EISENBERG, M., AND WILKE, C. R., *J. Electrochem. Soc.*, **99**, 359c (1952).
2. EISENBERG, M., TOBIAS, C. W., AND WILKE, C. R., *J. Electrochem. Soc.*, **101**, 306 (1954).
3. IBL, N., BUOB, K., AND TRUMPLER, G., *Helv. Chim. Acta*, **37**, 2251 (1954).
4. PETROCELLI, J. V., *J. Electrochem. Soc.*, **98**, 187 (1951).
5. WILKE, C. R., EISENBERG, M., AND TOBIAS, C. W., *J. Electrochem. Soc.*, **100**, 513 (1953).
6. EISENBERG, M., *Electrochemica Acta*, **6**, 93 (1962).
7. EISENBERG, M., "Design and Scale-Up of Fuel Cells," in "Advances in Electrochemistry and Electrical Engineering," Vol. II, p. 235, New York, Interscience Publishers, 1962.

MORRIS EISENBERG

Cross-references: *Electrode Reactions, Kinetics; Overvoltage; Polarization.*

CONDUCTANCE. *See* CONDUCTIVITY HEADINGS.

CONDUCTANCE IN FUSED SALTS. *See* FUSED SALT ELECTROCHEMICAL PROPERTIES.

CONDUCTANCE IN GASES. *See* GASES, ELECTRICAL CONDUCTANCE AND IONIZATION.

CONDUCTANCE IN NONAQUEOUS SOLVENTS

Most nonaqueous solvents differ from water in two fundamental properties which markedly influence the conductance of dissolved electrolytes: they have *in general* no hydrogen-bonded structure and their dielectric constants are *usually* lower than that of water. Alcohols, amines, carboxylic acids, and other compounds with active hydrogen do form hydrogen bonds, of course. Furthermore, formamide has a dielectric constant of 109, which is considerably higher than 78.5, that of water; liquid hydrogen cyanide has a constant equal to 158 at 0°. Limitations of space will necessarily prevent detailed discussion of exceptions such as these to the general statements which will be made here.

The first consequence of no active hydrogens is to limit solute-solvent interaction primarily to electrostatic effects (charge-dipole); a corollary is that very few inorganic salts are soluble in nonaqueous solvents (with the special exceptions of liquid sulfur dioxide and ammonia, hydrogen fluoride, amides, and some others) and these are 1-1 salts. (It will be recalled that the energy of hydration of electrolytes is so high that a net decrease in free energy occurs when a solid salt dissolves in water, despite the high lattice energy. But if insufficient energy of solvation is available as driving force, no dissolution can occur.) Only when the ionic charges are shielded or distributed in at least one of the ions (e.g., quaternary ammonium cations, picrates, tetraphenylborides) are electrolytes appreciably soluble in organic solvents. Finally, as will be explained shortly, the analog of the "weak" electrolyte of classical (i.e., aqueous) physical chemistry does not exist in nonaqueous solutions. The consequence of the lower dielectric constant follows directly from Coulomb's law (q.v.), which states that the potential energy, u, between two charged spheres in contact is inversely proportional to the dielectric constant, D, of the medium in which they are immersed:

$$u = -\epsilon_1\epsilon_2/aD \qquad (1)$$

where ϵ_1 and ϵ_2 are the charges and a is their center-to-center distance. In water, u/kT is about unity, and therefore the tendency of pairs of ions of opposite charge to stick together is overcome by the kinetic energy, kT, of collisions with solvent molecules. Hence, in dilute aqueous solution (or in other solvents of high dielectric constant), we see only the effects of long range interionic forces. But in nonaqueous systems, where the dielectric constant can drop as low as 2 (and recall that the ratio u/kT appears as an *exponent* in the Boltzmann factor which describes local

ionic concentrations), we expect and find increasing stability of contact pairs, accompanied by a corresponding decrease in conductance, because a $(+)(-)$ pair will act as a dipole in an external field, and hence cannot contribute to charge transport. At sufficiently low dielectric constants (less than about 8-10), it is necessary to include not only pairwise short-range electrostatic interaction of ions, but configurations of three, four, and even more ions then begin to acquire potential energies larger than kT. Finally, since the conductance process necessarily involves friction as the ions move through the solvent, the conductance is higher for a given electrolyte at a given concentration in the solvent of lower viscosity (at the same dielectric constant, of course). Thus the two controlling variables which describe conductance in a given solvent (at a given temperature) are viscosity, η, and dielectric constant, D; the conductance is naturally much more sensitive to D than to η, because the former dependence is exponential through the Boltzmann factor while the latter is merely one of (approximate) inverse proportionality.

The directly observed quantity in conductimetric studies is the specific conductance, κ, which is defined as the ratio of current density, i, to field strength, X. The current density depends on the product of charge, ϵ_i, velocity, v_i and concentration, n_i, of each species of ion in solution:

$$i = \sum_i n_i \, \epsilon_i \, v_i \qquad (2)$$

The mobility, u_i, of a given ion is v_i/X, its velocity in unit field (usually one volt per cm; if charge in (2) is in electrostatic units, $u_i = v_i/300 \, X$, for field strength also in esu). The quantity of theoretical interest is Λ, the equivalent conductance, defined by

$$\Lambda = 1000\kappa/c \qquad (3)$$

where c is stoichiometric concentration in equivalents per liter. Combining (2) and (3)

$$\Lambda = A \sum_i \gamma_i \, u_i \qquad (4)$$

where γ_i is the fraction $n_i/10^{-3} \, Nc$ of ions of species i which are free to transport charge (N is Avogadro's number). From (4), it is clear that Λ will in general depend on concentration through γ_i and u_i. For 1-1 salts, (4) becomes,

$$\Lambda = A\gamma(u_1 + u_2) \qquad (5)$$

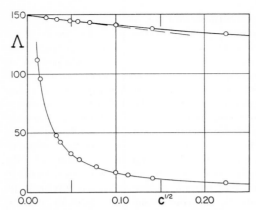

FIG. 1. Top curve: potassium chloride in water at 25°, Shedlovsky, T., *J. Am. Chem. Soc.*, **59** 1411 (1932); bottom curve: acetic acid in water at 25°, Mac Innes, D. A., and Shedlovsky, T., *ibid.*, **54**, 1429 (1932).

The subsequent discussion will be limited to 1-1 salts; this restriction represents no real loss of generality, because practically no electrolytes of higher valence type are soluble in nonaqueous solvents.

Arrhenius assumed that $\gamma = \Lambda/\Lambda_0$ where Λ_0 is the conductance of infinite dilution, the limit of $(1000 \ \kappa/c)$ as c approaches zero, and assumed mobilities independent of concentration. Using the law of mass action to describe the postulated equilibrium

$$AB \rightleftharpoons A^+ + B^- \qquad (6)$$

between neutral molecules and free ions, the Ostwald dilution law

$$c\Lambda^2/(1 - \Lambda/\Lambda_0) = K\Lambda_0^2 \qquad (7)$$

results. In classical times, this equation was found to reproduce conductance data for aqueous solutions of carboxylic acids and of amines in water (the "weak" acids and bases), but it failed completely for substances like hydrochloric acid, sodium hydroxide, and sodium chloride. Debye (1923), on the other hand, postulated that $\gamma = 1$ at all concentrations (i.e., complete dissociation), and ascribed the change of conductance with concentration to a change of mobility with concentration, produced by the electrostatic forces which the ions exert on one another. This hypothesis led to the limiting relationship

$$\Lambda = \Lambda_0 - Sc^{1/2} \qquad (8)$$

where S is a constant for a given system, the value of which was predicted by Onsager (1927) in terms of D, η, absolute temperature, T, valence

type, and single ion mobilities. It was found that the conductance curves for strong electrolytes in water and in other solvents of high dielectric constant approached a limiting tangent whose slope was given by (8). In general, on a Kohlrausch $\Lambda - c^{1/2}$ plot (phoreogram), the conductance curves for strong acids, bases and salts approach the Onsager tangent from above. The upper curve of Fig. 1 for potassium chloride in water is typical. On the same scale, the phoreograms for the organic acids and bases are sharply concave-upwards at low concentrations, and are located far below the limiting tangent. The lower curve of Fig. 1 for acetic acid in water illustrates this type of phoreogram. Stated as inequalities, for strong electrolytes, Λ (obs.) $\geq (\Lambda_0 - Sc^{1/2})$ while for weak electrolytes in the same range of concentration, Λ (obs.) $\ll (\Lambda_0 - Sc^{1/2})$. It thus became clear that weak and strong electrolytes in water were both qualitatively and quantitatively different.

When experimental results for nonaqueous systems were examined from the theoretical point of view, a real problem immediately appeared; the conductance curve for sodium bromide in liquid ammonia ($D = 22$), for example, resembles the curve for acetic acid in water rather than that for sodium chloride in water, while the curve for acetic acid (actually ammonium acetate, of course) in ammonia does not differ much from that for sodium chloride in the same solvent. Furthermore, as Kraus and Bray (1913) showed, the conductance of sodium bromide and similar salts in ammonia conformed within a fair approximation to the Ostwald dilution law; i.e., to use classical language, the alkali halides are strong electrolytes in water but weak ones in ammonia. In fact, for a long time no "strong" electrolytes were known in nonaqueous solvents of dielectric constant less than about 40, if a strong electrolyte is defined as one whose conductance curve approaches the Onsager tangent from above. The upper curve of Fig. 2 is for sodium bromide in ammonia; note that the abscissa scale is one tenth that of Fi.g 1, i.e., the curve would be ten times as steep if drawn on the scale of Fig. 1. The lower curve of Fig. 2 is for o-dinitrophenol, which is practically a nonconductor in water but is a fair electrolyte in ammonia because relative to the phenol, ammonia acts as a strong base.

Bjerrum (1926), who had been one of the first to argue complete dissociation for strong electrolytes in water, made the suggestions that pairs of unlike ions of higher valence type (e.g., Mg^{++} ·

SO_4^{--}) would be stable aggregates in water, and that ions in pairs should not be counted as members of the atmospheres of the other ions. Fuoss and Kraus (1933) applied the concept of ion pairs to the problem of conductance of nonaqueous solutions of electrolytes, arguing that a Bjerrum pair could be stabilized by lowering the dielectric constant of the solvent of medium. Using this hypothesis, a wide body of data for nonaqueous systems was rationalized in terms of several simple theoretical assumptions. While Arrhenius and Ostwald assume the γ of (5) variable with mobility fixed, and Debye and Hückel, and Onsager assumed $\gamma = 1$ and mobility variable, Fuoss and Kraus postulated that both quantities were in general functions of concentration. They thereby arrived at the conductance equation

$$\Lambda = \gamma(\Lambda_0 - Sc^{1/2}) \qquad (9)$$

where the fraction, γ, of unpaired ions was related to the stiochiometric concentration, c, by the algebraic analog of the mass action equation

$$(1 - \gamma)/c\gamma^2 f^2 = K_A \qquad (10)$$

In (10) f, the activity coefficient, is assumed to be given by the Debye-Hückel equation

$$-\ln f = \beta c^{1/2}/(1 + \kappa a) \qquad (11)$$

where β is a theoretically predictable coefficient. The association constant, K_A, implies that the primary process is association of free ions to nonconducting pairs

$$A^+ + B^- \rightleftharpoons A^+ \cdot B^- \qquad (12)$$

rather than a dissociation of neutral molecules into free ions as implied by the Arrhenius postulate (6). (It had long been known from x-ray work that the crystal of sodium chloride contains only ions; there are no "neutral molecules" to dissociate.)

The semantic anomaly of sodium chloride being "strong" in water and "weak" in ammonia was resolved by the introduction of a new nomenclature. Sodium chloride is an ionophore, a compound whose crystal lattice is ionic. Whether the conductance curve lies above or below the Onsager tangent is determined by the dielectric constant of the solvent medium. If the dielectric constant is high, few pairs will be present, and practically all the ions contribute to the current; if it is low, many ions will be in pairs, and the conductance will be low. For a given dielectric constant, pairs will dissociate into free ions as

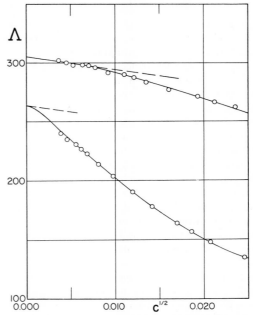

FIG. 2. Top curve: sodium bromide in ammonia at $-33°$; bottom curve, o-dinitrophenol in ammonia at $-33°$; Franklin, E. C., and Kraus, C. A., *Am. Chem. J.*, **23**, 277 (1900).

the concentration is decreased; simultaneously, the mobility will increase, because the retarding effects on mobility will be decreased, due to the greater mutual distances between ions on dilution. The ions in ion pairs (and higher clusters) do not lose their identity as ions. Acetic acid, on the other hand, is an ionogen, a substance whose crystal lattice is made up of neutral molecules, which, on reaction with suitable solvents, can generate ions. Depending on the magnitude of the molecular dissociation constant for the reaction with solvent, the conductance will be higher or lower. Water is practically the only solvent whose self-ionization must be considered. Here we have the equilibria, for the case of acetic acid,

$$HAc + H_2O \rightleftharpoons H_2O \cdot HAc \rightleftharpoons H_3O^+ \cdot Ac^- \qquad (13)$$

$$H_3O^+ \cdot Ac^- \rightleftharpoons H_3O^+ + Ac^- \qquad (14)$$

and as is well known, equilibrium (13) lies far to the left at ordinary concentrations. In ammonia, on the other hand, the reaction

$$HAc + NH_3 \rightleftharpoons NH_4^+ + Ac^- \qquad (15)$$

is essentially complete, because ammonia is a much stronger base than water and the self-ionization

$$2NH_3 \rightleftharpoons NH_4^+ + NH_2^- \qquad (16)$$

is negligible; hence, electrolytically sodium chloride and ammonium acetate in ammonia are qualitatively and quantitatively alike.

For solvents with dielectric constant down to about ten, the $\Lambda - c^{1/2}$ plot is a convenient and informative means of presenting experimental results. But for lower dielectric constants, the free ion population becomes so low at ordinary concentrations that the observed equivalent conductance looks like zero over much of the concentration range on a scale which shows Λ_0; the phoreogram would on such a scale be practically indistinguishable from the axes. In benzene, for example, equivalent conductances are below 10^{-2} at concentrations below several hundredths normal, compared to $\Lambda_0 \approx 30$. In order to show structure, it is therefore conventional to present conductance data in solvents of low dielectric constant on $\log \Lambda - \log c$ plots, as shown in Fig. 3. The upper curve is for tetramethylammonium picrate in ethylene dichloride ($D = 10.23$) and is given to effect the transition from $\Lambda - c^{1/}$

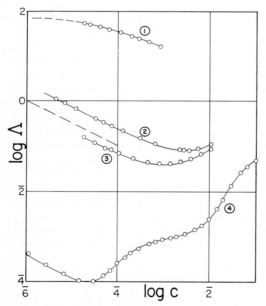

FIG. 3. Curve 1, tetramethylammonium picrate in ethylene dichloride at 25°, Mead, D. J., Fuoss, R. M., and Kraus, C. A., *Trans. Faraday Soc.*, **32**, 594 (1936). Curves 2 and 3, tetrabutylammonium nitrate in ethylene dibromide (2) and in anisole (3) at 25°; Cox, N. L., Kraus, C. A., and Fuoss, R. M., *ibid.*, **31**, 749 (1935). Curve 4, tetra-*i*-amylammonium thiocyanate in benzene at 25°, Fuoss, R. M., and Kraus, C. A., *J. Am. Chem. Soc.*, **55**, 21, 3614 (1933).

curves to $\log \Lambda - \log c$ curves. On the former, the curve approaches the Onsager tangent from below in this range of dielectric constant. Going the other direction (i.e., toward higher concentrations), the curve passes through an inflexion region (where it simulates linearity, with a slope considerably greater than the Onsager value), and then becomes concave-up. Sometimes, depending on the dielectric constant, the curve actually goes through a minimum towards higher concentrations. On the logarithmic plot, the curve has an S-shape for $D \approx 10$ and approaches a horizontal asymptote ($\log \Lambda_0$) as concentration goes to zero ($\log c \rightarrow \infty$).

In solvents of dielectric constant below ten, a minimum in conductance usually appears; the middle two curves (tetrabutylammonium nitrate in ethylene dibromide, $D = 4.76$, and in anisole, $D = 4.29$) illustrate this behavior. The minimum has been accounted for in terms of association between ion pairs and free ions to give clusters of three ions, either $(-+-)$ or $(+-+)$, whose presence increases conductance. The minimum shifts to lower concentrations with decreasing dielectric constant (approximately as D^{-3}) and the conductance becomes simultaneously lower. The conductance curve from one decade above the minimum to several decades below is given by the simple equation

$$\Lambda = A c^{-1/2} + B c^{1/2} \qquad (17)$$

where the constants have physical significance in terms of association constants and limiting conductances. We note in passing that despite the complete chemical dissimilarity of ethylene bromide and anisole, the conductance curves are quite similar, differing only quantitatively, with the curve for anisole below that for ethylene dichloride, as expected from the lower dielectric constant. This pattern is general, and serves to emphasize the introductory statement that the dielectric constant is the primary controlling parameter in determining the conductance pattern of a given electrolyte in a nonaqueous solvent. It will be noted that the curves simplify to linearity on the low concentration side of the minimum. (For these examples, the eventual downward concavity and approach to the horizontal asymptote would not appear until the experimentally inaccessible concentration range of 10^{-9} to 10^{-10} stoichiometric moles per liter.) This linearity, with slope of -0.5 on a $\log \Lambda - \log c$ scale, confirms the hypothesis that the ion-ion pair equilibrium controls at low concentrations in nonaqueous solvents of low dielectric constant. The long range mobility terms of (9) become negligible, reducing (9) to (7) and Λ/Λ_0 becomes negligible compared to unity; hence

$$\Lambda \approx \Lambda_0 \sqrt{K/c} \qquad (18)$$

becomes a usable approximation.

For solvents of dielectric constant less than about four, the conductance curve in the range $c > 10^{-4}$ or 10^{-3} begins to show a wide pattern of complicated behavior which at best is only qualitatively understood. The lower curve of Fig. 3 for tetra-i-amylammonium thiocyanate in benzene is typical. The minimum has moved down to the order of 10^{-5} normal, where equivalent conductance is about 10^{-4}, corresponding to only about 0.0003 per cent of the solute in the form of free ions. On the low concentration side of the minimum, we would expect linearity with slope -0.5 if data could be obtained. Going to higher concentrations, the following pattern is observed for quaternary salts with small anions (e.g., thiocyanate, nitrate, halides). First, a rise in Λ, corresponding to 3-ion clusters appears; then comes a range of decelerating increase in Λ or even a plateau where the curve is nearly horizontal. This behavior is compatible with the association of ion pairs to quadrupoles. The conductance increase then accelerates for a while; for some salts, such as the picrates of tertiary amines, the rate of increase can become as rapid as proportional to the cube of concentration. But eventually, assuming that the solubility limit does not terminate the curve, the conductance goes through a maximum and finally, assuming complete miscibility of solute and solvent, it approaches the conductance of the fused salt. The appearance of the maximum is evidently a hydrodynamic effect because the product of equivalent conductance and viscosity ($\Lambda\eta$) is a monotone increasing function of concentration as it approaches the value of the product for the molten salt. It should be mentioned that some salts (e.g., quaternary picrates, silver perchlorate in benzene) show no structure between the 3-ion minimum and the viscosity maximum except the expected single inflection point.

To summarize, the conductance of dilute solutions of electrolytes in nonaqueous solvents is primarily controlled by the ion-ion pair equilibrium, which is in turn controlled by the dielectric constant. The lower the dielectric constant, the lower the conductance, and at an exponential rate; to a good approximation

$$\log \Lambda = A - B/DT - (\tfrac{1}{2}) \log c \qquad (19)$$

at concentrations below the minimum in conductance in solvents of low dielectric constant. Up to and through the minimum, observed conductances can be described in terms of equilibria between free ions and 2- and 3-ion clusters, with appropriate corrections for long range effects of electrophoresis and relaxation field in solvents of intermediate dielectric constant. In solvents of high dielectric constant, ion association becomes negligible, and the long range effects alone determine the rate of decrease of conductance with increasing concentration. At higher concentrations in all solvents, what scanty information is available is empirical and descriptive. Much remains to be done here by both theoretician and experimenter.

References

1. KRAUS, C. A. "The Properties of Electrically Conducting Systems," New York, Chemical Catalog Company, 1922.
2. WALDEN, P., "Electrochemie nicht-wässriger Lösungen," Leipzig, Akademische Verlagsgesellschaft, 1924.
3. DAVIES, C. W., "The Conductivity of Solutions," London, Chapman and Hall, 1933.
4. FUOSS, R. M., AND ACCASCINA, F., "Electrolytic Conductance," New York, Interscience, 1959.
5. DAVIES, C. W., "Ion Association," Washington, Butterworths, 1962.
6. KRAUS, C. A., *J. Phys. Chem.*, **58,** 673 (1954); *ibid.,* **60,** 129 (1956).

RAYMOND M. FUOSS

CONDUCTIVITIES IN FOAMS AND EMULSIONS

Unlike many physical properties of mixtures, one may not obtain the effective electrical conductivity of heterogeneous mixtures by volume averaging the conductivities of the individual phases in the mixture. Indeed, the general case is extremely difficult to treat in a rigorous or theoretical manner, especially when the system contains several discrete phases with particles of arbitrary shape and size.

The rigorous approach is implicit in the theory of potential which requires that the propagation of electrical energy in the steady state must be such as to satisfy the Laplace equation

$$\nabla^2 \phi = 0 \qquad (1)$$

everywhere, i.e., including the boundaries of the

system under consideration. The physical consequence of this restriction implies that the lines of flow describing the path of electric charge show no discontinuities. The lines of flow are thus "smooth" and orthogonal to equipotential surfaces. Such streamlines converge in regions of high conductivity and diverge where the conductivity is low. Qualitatively, then, it is to be expected that a volumetric averaging of the conductivities of individual phases leads to unacceptable values of the effective conductances of multiphase mixtures. Indeed, such simple averages give effective conductance figures which easily may be in error by 100 per cent.

Fortunately, most multiphase mixtures of interest to electrochemists fall within the easily defined subdivisions of the general case. These, for instance, include foams which are dilute with respect to the gaseous phase and which may then be characterized as dilute dispersions of nonconducting spheres in an otherwise continuous medium. Also included are either oil in water (O/W) or water in oil (W/O) emulsions where one phase consists of spherical particles which are dispersed in the second phase. In the case of emulsions it is possible for both phases to be electrically conducting.

The simple system that consists of a dilute dispersion of spherical particles of conductance, κ_d, imbedded in a medium of conductance κ_c has been treated by Maxwell (1881). If we denote the effective conductance of the mixture by κ_m and the volume fraction of the dispersed phase as f, Maxwell's relation becomes

$$K_m = \frac{K_d + 2 - 2f(1 - K_d)}{K_d + 2 + f(1 - K_d)} \qquad (2)$$

where $K_m = \kappa_m/\kappa_c$, and $K_d = \kappa_d/\kappa_c$.

Eq. (2) was derived by considering a single sphere in a continuum when the electrical field was unidirectional and linear at great distances from the sphere. By solving the Laplace equation (Eq. 1) in spherical coordinates for the potential both inside and around the sphere, and using the principle of continuity, Maxwell obtained an expression describing the variation of potential in the continuous phase due to the presence of this single sphere. Following this, the effective conductance of dilute dispersions was obtained by regarding the dispersion itself as a sphere. This was done by setting the effect of the dispersion on the potential in the continuous phase outside of the spherical boundary equal to that

obtained for the case in which the sphere consisted of a single phase only.

Because of the assumptions employed in the derivation of Eq. (2), this relation is rigorously valid only for very dilute dispersions of spherical particles. In practice it has been found, however, that conductance data may be accurately represented by the Maxwell relation up to a dispersed phase volume fraction of about 0.2.

Another expression which is well-obeyed by dilute dispersions is

$$(1 - f) = \frac{K_m - K_d}{K_m^{1/3}(1 - K_d)} . \qquad (3)$$

This equation was derived by Bruggeman (1935) by expanding the Maxwell equation in a Taylor's series and treating the first two terms by a special integral technique. A subsequent interpretation of the mathematical steps used by Bruggeman indicates that the model employed was such that each dispersed spherical particle was considered as being very different in size from its nearest neighbor. This size difference is such that the distortion of the field due to a particle's smaller neighbors is negligible. Under these conditions, Maxwell's equation is valid in the neighborhood of each particle, and thus this latter relation may be applied to calculate the change in conductivity that arises after the addition of each particle. In the limit, one obtains Eq. (3).

This relation has received wide acceptance for a number of reasons. First, it makes an attempt at pointing out the correction necessary for concentration effects, although in reality a practical mixture never meets the conditions on which the theory is based. Second, it shows that for two cases of equal volume fraction a difference in conductivity would be obtained depending upon the size distribution of the particles in the two dispersions. Third, this equation and the Maxwell equation appear to form boundaries on most of the data that have been obtained on dispersions of spherical particles. Finally, the Bruggeman equation reduces to a very simple form for two of the common cases, i.e., for $K_d \rightarrow 0$,

$$K_m = (1 - f)^{3/2}$$

and, for $K_d \rightarrow \infty$,

$$K_m = (1 - f)^{-3}$$

As mentioned above, most of the effective conductivity values obtained on dispersions of uniform size spherical particles appear to lie between the values predicted by Eqs. (2) and (3). This is true, for example, with the data of Clark (1948) for studies of foams containing high volume fractions of the dispersed phase; with the data of De La Rue (1959) for studies on dispersions of nonconducting spherical particles; with the data of Pierce (1955) on dispersions of spheres in a cubical array; and with the data of Fradkina (1950) for emulsions where $K_d > 1$.

The nature of the data mentioned above and the "correction" to Maxwell's equation by Bruggeman has been analyzed by Meredith and Tobias (1960). These latter investigators in turn derived

$$K_m = \left[\frac{2(K_d + 2) + 2(K_d - 1)f}{2(K_d + 2) - (K_d - 1)f} \right] \left[\frac{(2 - f)(K_d + 2) + 2(K_d - 1)f}{(2 - f)(K_d + 2) - (K_d - 1)f} \right] \quad (4)$$

by considering that most dispersions of spherical particles, whether the particles were of uniform size or not, behave as if they contained two equal volume fractions of spheres which differ in size from each other by an order of magnitude.

Eqs. (2) (3) and (4) are compared with some experimental data in Figs. 1 and 2.

When properly interpreted, the expressions given above may also be employed to evaluate the effective thermal conductivity, dielectric constants, magnetic permeability, diffusion coefficients, refractive indexes, etc. of mixtures. These phenomena are related inasmuch as the potentials involved in each case obey Eq. (1) and the concepts differ only in the name given to the constant of proportionality that applies at the boundary conditions.

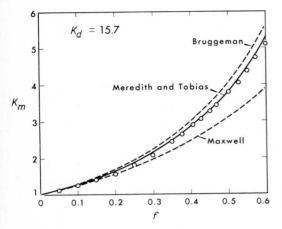

FIG. 1. Conductivity data by Meredith and Tobias on an emulsion with $k_d = 15.7$. Comparing Maxwell (Eq. 2), Bruggeman (Eq. 3) and Meredith and Tobias (Eq. 4). Reproduced with permission from Vol. II "Advances in Electrochemistry and Electrochemical Engineering," P. Delahay and C. W. Tobias, Interscience, 1962.

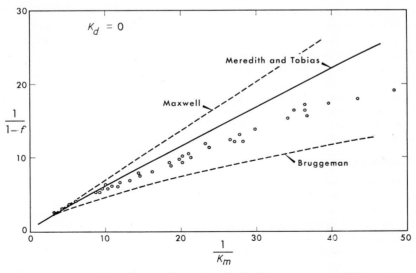

FIG. 2. Conductivity data on foams by Clark. Plot accentuates high volume fraction effects. Comparing Maxwell (Eq. 2), Bruggeman (Eq. 3) and Meredith and Tobias (Eq. 4).

Reproduced with permission from Vol. II "Advances in Electrochemistry and Electrochemical Engineering," P. Delahay and C. W. Tobias, Interscience, 1962.

References

1. BRUGGEMAN, D. A. G., *Ann. Physik*, **24**, 636 (1935).
2. CLARK, N. O., *Trans. Faraday Soc.*, **44**, 13 (1948).
3. DE LA RUE, R. M., Univ. of Calif., M.S. Thesis (1955).
4. MAXWELL, J. C., "A Treatise on Electricity and Magnetism," 2nd Ed., Vol. 1. p. 435, Oxford, Clarendon Press, 1881.
5. MEREDITH, R. E., "Studies on the Conductivities of Dispersions," *Univ. of Calif. Lawrence Radiation Lab. Report* **UCRL-8667**, 133 (1959).
6. MEREDITH, R. E., AND TOBIAS, C. W., "Advances in Electrochemistry and Electrochemical Engineering," edited by P. Delahay and C. W. Tobias, Vol. II, 15, New York, Interscience Publishers, 1962.
7. MEREDITH, R. E., AND TOBIAS, C. W., *J. Electrochem. Soc.*, **108**, 286 (1961).

ROBERT E. MEREDITH

CONDUCTIVITY (ELECTRICAL) IN SOLIDS

Electric charges in a solid body can move in an electric field either with or without simultaneous motion of matter. In the latter case—pure electronic conductivity—the whole current is carried either by negative electrons or positive holes. On the other hand, decomposition and irreversible changes of the electrical characteristics of the conductor usually occur in the case of pure or partial electrolytic or ionic conductivity.

Electrolytic conductivity (q.v.) is often indicated by the appearance of a decomposition voltage as a kink in the voltage-current characteristic. Experimentally this kink is sometimes disguised by diffusion of the deposits from one or both of the electrodes back into the bulk material, or by filamentary deposits shorting the conductor, or by electrostatic space charges building up near one or both of the electrodes. Special techniques, suitable for the individual materials, have been developed for practical applications.

Pure Ionic Conductivity

Faraday's Law (q.v.) is found valid and transfer numbers for the cations, n_c, and the anions, n_a, can be determined. It is $n_c = 1$ in unipolar cation conductors, $n_a = 1$ in unipolar anion conductors, and $n_a \neq 1$, $n_c \neq 1$, $n_a + n_c = 1$ in bipolar conductors. Examples are given in Table 1.

Mixed Conductivity

The ionic contribution to the total conductivity can be determined by weighing the deposits on the electrodes and applying Faraday's Law. The ratio of electronic and ionic conductivity in mixed conductors changes both with temperature and with current. Examples are given in Table 2a, b.

In some materials mixed conductivity occurs only in a limited temperature range. At lower temperature the ionic conductivity can disappear and at higher temperatures the electronic con-

TABLE 1. TRANSFER NUMBERS OF PURE IONIC CONDUCTORS

Material	T, °C	n_c	n_a
Unipolar Cationic Conductors			
AgCl	20–350	1.00	0
α-CuI	440–535	1.00	0
β-CuI	400–440	1.00	0
Unipolar Anionic Conductors			
PbF_2	200	0	1.00
$PbBr_2$	250–365	0	1.00
Bipolar Conductors			
PbI_2*	155	0.004	0.996
	194	0.03	0.97
	228	0.12	0.88
	255	0.3–0.35	0.7–0.65
	270	0.4–0.5	0.6–0.5
	290	0.55–0.65	0.45–0.35
	338	0.79–0.85	0.21–0.15
	376	0.92–1.00	0.08–0

* PbI_2 is a unipolar anionc conductor at lower temperatures. With increasing temperatures it gradually changes into a bipolar conductor and, finally, into a unipolar cationic conductor.

TABLE 2. PARTIAL ELECTRONIC CONDUCTIVITY IN β-Ag_2S

a. Depending on Temperature; Current Constant

T, °C	Electronic Conduct. (%)
170	18.8
150	16.0
100	10.1
60	7.0
20	1.5

b. Depending on Current; Temperature Constant (150°C)

Current (ma)	Electronic Conduct. (%)
1.8	16.8
5	17.1
7	17.8
40	18.8
75	20.6

ductivity, respectively. Examples are given in Table 3.

It is noteworthy that these materials in the range of pure ionic conductivity can be turned into mixed conductors upon addition of a small anion excess; this brings about an additional electronic conductivity which increases with anion concentration.

The range of the conductivity of solid ionic conductors is given by the extremes of 500 Ω^{-1} cm^{-1} for Ag_2S at 20°C and of about 10^{-20} Ω^{-1} cm^{-1} for NaCl at 20°C.

Impurities have a large influence on conductivity. The direction of the change depends on the nature of the particular impurities.

Grain size has an influence on the conductivity of polycrystalline bodies. Usually single crystals (q.v.) have the highest conductivity at higher temperatures.

The conductivity of ionic conductors is time-dependent for most materials. Generally, conductivity slowly decreases with time down to a constant value. This value is dependent on temperature and current.

In materials with high resistivity, a logarithmic dependence of conductivity on field strength sometimes occurs.

The change of conductivity with temperature

TABLE 3. TRANSITION FROM ELECTRONIC TO IONIC CONDUCTION WITH TEMPERATURE

Ionic Conduct. (%)	Temperature (°C)		
	CuCl	γ-CuBr	γ-CuI
0	0°	40°	180°
50	297°	280°	328°
100	370°	390°	440°

TABLE 4. VALUES OF A AND B CONSTANTS

Material	A	B
$PbCl_2$	6.55	5535
TlI	5×10^2	8100
TlBr	5.1×10^3	9900
TlCl	1.6×10^4	10300

TABLE 5. VALUES OF A_1 ; A_2 ; B_1 ; B_2 CONSTANTS

Material	A_1	B_1	A_2	B_2
NaCl	0.8	10300	3.5×10^6	2.4×10^4
NaBr	0.5	9430	1.1×10^6	2.1×10^4
NaI	2.3×10^{-2}	6440	1.3×10^5	1.7×10^4
PbI_2	3×10^{-4}	4140	8.0×10^4	1.5×10^4

for many unipolar ionic conductors is given by

$$K = A \cdot e^{-B/T} = A \cdot e^{-E/RT}$$

where A, B, E, R are constants. E is interpreted as the ionization energy of the respective mobile ions. Examples for values of A and B are given in Table 4.

For some materials formulas with more than one term have been found, e.g., a two-term formula for alkali halides. See Table 5. Remarkably, a two-term formula has also been used for AgCl and AgBr, known as unipolar cation conductors.

Pure Electronic Conductivity

Pure electronic conductivity occurs in two groups of electrical conductors which can be distinguished by the values of conductivity, K, and its temperature coefficient, α:

a. Metallic conductors
    $K > 0.1$ Ω^{-1} cm^{-1};

$$\alpha = \frac{1}{K} - \frac{dK}{dT} < 0$$

b. Semiconductors
    $K < 10$ Ω^{-1} cm^{-1};

$$\alpha = \frac{1}{K} - \frac{dK}{dT} > 0$$

Between $K = 0.1$ Ω^{-1} cm^{-1} and 10 Ω^{-1} cm^{-1}, α changes its sign in going through zero. Exceptions to these rules are, for example, materials with a positive temperature coefficient and a small conductivity, as in some "diluted" metallic conductors.

Both elements and compounds can be found in the group of metallic conductors as well as in the group of semiconductors.

A rule has been established which allows a prediction about the character of electrical conductivity of most compound materials. The elements with positions in the periodic table of one to four places ahead of a noble gas usually form negative anions in nonmetallic compounds with other metals. These compounds are usually semiconductors.

The elements in positions of five to seven places ahead of a noble gas cannot form negative anions. Their compounds usually have metallic character. For some magnesium compounds this is shown in Table 6. This general rule has exceptions, especially at the boundary between the two groups.

The conductivity of metallic conductors decreases almost linearly with temperature above

TABLE 6. COMPOUNDS OF Mg WITH ELEMENTS 1 TO 7 PLACES AHEAD OF A NOBLE GAS

Metallic			Nonmetallic			
I	II	III	IV	V	VI	VII
Mg_3Ag	Mg_3Cd	Mg_4Al_3	Mg_2Si	Mg_3P_2	MgS	$MgCl_2$
$MgAg$	$MgCd$	$MgAl$	Mg_2Ge	Mg_3As_2	$MgSe$	$MgBr_2$
$MgAu$	$MgCd_3$	Mg_3Al_4	Mg_2Sn	Mg_3Sb_2	$MgTe$	MgI_2
		$MgAl_3$	Mg_2Pb	Mg_3Bi_2		

Debye's characteristic temperature.* At lower temperatures the conductivity changes with a higher power of the temperature and can be split into two parts, one of which expresses the temperature dependence, whereas the other is temperature-independent. The latter increases with increasing impurity contents. This behavior is understood by assuming scattering of the electrons by lattice imperfections leading to reduction of the mean free path of the charge carriers. The concentration of the electrons is assumed to be practically constant with changing temperature. At still lower temperatures, near the absolute zero point, superconductivity can be found in many metallic conductors; the resistance drops abruptly to immeasureably small values.

The conductivity of semiconductors changes with temperature in obeying a logarithmic law; it is assumed that this temperature dependence is brought about essentially by increase of the concentration of the charge carriers with increasing temperature. (See **Semiconductors.**)

There are two kinds of charge carriers in semiconductors—negative electrons and positive holes which contribute to the total conductivity to a larger or lesser extent. This variance leads to three different types of semiconductors: (1) n-type semiconductors with prevailing conductivity by negative electrons; (2) p-type semiconductors with prevailing conductivity by positive holes; and (3) intrinsic semiconductors with both negative and positive charge carriers.

A decision about which type a particular material belongs to can, for example, be made from the results of Hall-effect measurements.

If pure materials are semiconductors, they usually belong to the third type. On addition of small

* In the quantum theory of the specific heat it is shown that it can be expressed in a wide temperature range as a function of T/θ where T is the usual absolute temperature and θ is the so-called characteristic, or Debye temperature. θ is an individual constant for every material. This constant can be found from thermal, optical, or elastic measurements.

amounts of special other substances, generally called "impurities," the materials turn into either n or p-type semiconductors. In the following, examples are given both for elements and for compounds.

Elements which are intrinsic semiconductors in the pure state are found in the fourth group of the periodic table, as Ge, Si, gray tin. The first two can be converted into n-type conductors by addition of small amounts of elements of the third group, as B, Al, Ga, In. Addition of elements of the fifth group, as P, As, Sb, leads to p-type conductivity.

The behavior of compounds is analogous. The concentration of electrons (holes) is increased (decreased) if small amounts of another compound with cations of a higher valency are added, as for example $CuO + Cr_2O_3$. The concentration of electrons (holes) is decreased (increased) if cations of a lower valency are added, as for example $CuO + Li_2O$. In both cases the total conductivity is increased.

In n-type compounds, the concentration of negative electrons is increased (decreased) if cations of a higher (lower) valency are added which leads to an increase (decrease) of the conductivity. Examples are $ZnO + Al_2O_3$ and $ZnO + Li_2O$, respectively.

In p-type compounds, the concentration of positive holes is decreased (increased) if cations of a higher (lower) valency are added. Examples are $NiO + Cr_2O_3$ and $NiO + Li_2O$, respectively.

Modification of the type of conductivity by this principle of "controlled valency," as described, is not restricted to cation interchange. The substitution of a small amount of anions of the host lattice by suitable anions of a differing valency is doubtless possible with analogous effects of changing conductivity.

The fact that certain compounds of transition elements can be converted into semiconductors by reduction or removal of anions can be understood as the result of a substitution of cations of a higher valency by the same kind of cations of a lower valency. An example is given by the reduced titanates in which a part of Ti^{4+} ions are changed into Ti^{3+} ions; a similar case is magnetite, Fe_3O_4.

Organic materials can also be semiconductors as has been found for some polycyclic aromatic substances which exhibit intrinsic conductivity by electrons and holes. (See **Organic Semiconductors.**)

Semiconductors have a great importance as electrical circuit elements in the form of transistors, thermistors, and rectifiers. High thermoelectric power (q.v.) as exhibited by some intermetallic compounds is promising for applications in refrigerators and power generators.

For a complete understanding of all phenomena of electrical conductivity in solids, going beyond a mere description of the behavior of individual solid materials, intensive studies of pertinent factors are now in progress. Such factors are crystallographic structure, structure of the systems of electronic energy bands, type of bonding, etc. Results are lacking especially for the heavier elements with mixed ionic-covalent bonds. Most advanced seems to be the understanding of materials with diamond structure and prevailing covalent bond.

E. K. WEISE

Cross-references: *Conductivity, Electrolytic; Hall Effect; Semiconductors; Single Crystals.*

CONDUCTIVITY, ELECTROLYTIC

The electrical conductivity exhibited by metals or metal-like substances is attributed to the presence of "free electrons" within the body of the specimen. For certain nonmetallic substances one also observes the phenomenon of electrical conductivity; however, in this case, the charge is carried by "free ions." Materials in the first class are said to exhibit metallic or electronic conductivity while the remainder (i.e., solutions of salts, etc.) are said to be electrolytes and exhibit electrolytic conductivity.

Although one commonly thinks of an electrolyte as being typified by an aqueous solution of an inorganic salt, it is important to note that organic compounds (e.g., acetic acid), pure liquids (e.g., water), and chemicals in the solid state (e.g., ion exchange resins) can also exhibit electrolytic conductivity in various degrees.

Specific Conductance

The conductivity exhibited by a body of electrolyte depends upon the nature of the material, the temperature, and the geometry of the system with respect to the electrodes used in the measurement. However, its value may be calculated in a manner in which the conductivity is no longer a function of this latter variable. This calculation is performed by referring the measurement to a particular type of cell geometry which contains a cube of solution having edges one centimeter long and which employs square electrodes that are one centimeter on a side mounted on opposite sides of the solution. The value of the conductivity obtained in this particular type of cell is termed the specific conductance (or specific conductivity).

For cells of arbitrary design, the specific conductance, κ, is related to the measured resistance, R, and the cell constant, C, through

$$\kappa = C/R.$$

The cell constant (which is normally obtained by measuring the resistance of the cell while it contains a solution of known specific conductance) has the units of reciprocal centimeters (i.e., cm^{-1}). Since the resistance is normally measured in ohms, the specific conductance has the units of reciprocal ohm-centimeters or $ohm^{-1}\ cm^{-1}$. To avoid the printing difficulties associated with units which contain only reciprocal variables, values of specific conductance are often quoted in units of mho/cm where mho $= 1/ohm$.

The specific conductance for most electrolytes is quite sensitive to variations in temperature. The conductance of many inorganic compounds in water varies about 2 per cent per °C. For a plus or minus ten degree variation around 25°C one may make a temperature correction for electrolytes with an expression of the following form:

$$\kappa_t = \kappa_{25°C}\,[1 + \alpha(t - 25)],$$

where α has a value of about 0.02 in aqueous solutions. This expression, however, does not correctly follow the behavior of electrolytes which contain active hydrogen and hydroxyl ions since these ions exhibit abnormal conductance behavior as noted below.

A knowledge of the specific conductance is useful inasmuch as it is directly related to the electrolytic resistance of a body or solution. This in turn indicates the voltage drop or power loss due to the electrolyte in various electrochemical processes. On the other hand, the specific conductance, because of its sensitivity to the concentration of the conducting species, is a poor parameter by which to judge or compare the intrinsic conducting abilities of various electrolytes.

Molar Conductance

For solutions the difference in electrical conductivities among electrolytes is more appreciated when the specific conductance is converted to a common molecular concentration basis. When so compared, one can notice that some compounds yield higher conductance values with the same number of molecules than other chemicals which apparently lack the ability to dissociate into ionic form. Such a parameter is characterized by the molar conductance which is defined as:

molar conductance

$$= \frac{\text{specific conductance of electrolyte}}{\text{conc. of electrolyte in g-moles per cc}}$$

or if c denotes the concentration in g-moles per liter of solution, we have

$$\text{molar conductance} = 1000(\kappa/c)$$

Equivalent Conductance

The ability of an electrolyte to carry current depends not only on the ionic concentration but on the electrochemical valency, or the g-equivalence (n_e), of the electrolyte. The equivalent conductance (Λ), defined by

$$\Lambda = \frac{\text{molar conductance}}{n_e}$$

or

$$\Lambda = \frac{1000\,\kappa}{c n_e}$$

takes the valency or ionic charge into consideration and is thus the more informative of the conductance parameters. The commonly employed units of Λ are ohm^{-1} cm^2 or mho cm^2.

The g-equivalence, as used above, is obtained by considering the ionic dissociation of the molecule. For example, let us examine the hypothetical molecule, $A_x B_y$, which yields xA^{z+} cations and yB^{z-} anions. There are xz^+ or yz^- equivalents of charge for each molecule of $A_x B_y$ which dissociates. Because of electrical neutrality, xz^+ has

the same numerical value as yz^-, and either of these products is designated as n_e (examples: KCl, $n_e = 1$; Al$_2$(SO$_4$)$_3$, $n_e = 6$). The effective equivalence number of chemicals, such as H$_3$PO$_4$ or H$_2$CO$_3$, can only be obtained by considering equilibrium constants since these compounds dissociate in degrees and yield several ionic species at any one time.

Because a molecule may dissolve into a solvent without dissociating into ionic species, the conductance is not always a linear function of the total concentration. Chemicals which apparently dissolve only through ionic dissociation are called "strong" electrolytes, whereas compounds such as ammonium hydroxide or acetic acid, which dissolve in most solvents partially in ionic but mostly in molecular form, are termed "weak" electrolytes.

Equivalent Conductance at Infinite Dilution

For many electrolytes as the solution becomes dilute the equivalent conductance varies linearly with the square root of the concentration. It also increases to a limiting value as the concentration gets very low. This latter value has been appropriately called the equivalent conductance at infinite dilution and is denoted by the symbol Λ_0.

For strong electrolytes with common anions, it is possible to assign any difference in Λ_0 which may exist among the systems to the cations. This is shown in the table below for the cations of sodium and potassium in aqueous solutions. Similar behavior, of course, is also observed for anions.

TABLE 1. COMPARING VALUES OF Λ_0 AT 24°C IN mho-cm^2

Electrolyte	Λ_0	Electrolyte	Λ_0	Difference
KCl	149.9	NaCl	126.5	23.4
KNO$_3$	145.0	NaNO$_3$	121.6	23.4
K$_2$SO$_4$	153.3	Na$_2$SO$_4$	129.9	23.4

Observations of this nature led Kohlrausch, in 1879, to the formulation of his theory of the independent migration of ions in dilute solutions. From this one can conceive that:

$$\Lambda_0 = (\lambda+)_0 + (\lambda-)_0$$

where $(\lambda-)_0$ and $(\lambda+)_0$ are the individual equivalent conductances of the anion and cation respectively. For example, at 25°C in water

$$\Lambda_0(\text{HCl}) = (\lambda_{\text{H}^+})_0 + (\lambda_{\text{Cl}^-})_0$$

$$= 349.8 + 76.3 = 426.1 \text{ mho-cm}^2$$

From this it also follows that:

$$\Lambda_0(\text{HCl}) = \Lambda_0(\text{HNO}_3) + \Lambda_0(\text{NaCl}) - \Lambda_0(\text{NaNO}_3)$$

$$= 421.2 + 126.4 - 121.5$$

$$= 426.1 \text{ mho-cm}^2$$

A number of relations have been proposed for the purpose of allowing one to obtain Λ_0 from a knowledge of Λ.

Arrhenius proposed that

$$\Lambda/\Lambda_0 = a,$$

where a was designated as the "degree of dissociation." For a completely dissociated salt a would have the value of unity, and for this case one would expect no difference between Λ and Λ_0. The Arrhenius model, however, is not fulfilled in practice by compounds, such as NaCl or KCl in water, which are known to be completely dissociated at most concentrations.

More in conformance with the true nature or behavior of electrolytes is the model inherrent in the Debye-Huckel-Onsager Theory which yields

$$\Lambda = \Lambda_0 - \left[\frac{29.15(z^+ + z^-)}{\eta\sqrt{(DT)}} + \frac{9.90 \times 10^5 \Lambda_0\, w}{\sqrt{(DT)^3}} \right] \sqrt{c(z^+ + z^-)}$$

where D is the dielectric constant of the medium of viscosity, η (c.g.s. units), T is the temperature in °K and c, z^+, and z^- have meanings previously defined above. The value of w for *uni-uni*valent electrolytes is 0.586; for other valence states, a knowledge of ionic transference numbers and mobilities is required in order to evaluate this parameter.

The Influence of Solvents on Ionic Conductance (Walden's Rule)

Although there are always exceptions, Walden in 1923 found that when the conducting properties of any one compound are studied in a variety of solvents that the product of the solvent viscosity, η_0, and the equivalent conductance at infinite dilution, Λ_0, is approximately a constant, i.e.,

$$\Lambda_0\eta_0 = \text{constant}$$

Of course the same type of relation would also hold for $(\lambda +)_0$ and $(\lambda -)_0$. The value of the constant, for example, for tetraethylammonium iodide in organic solvents is approximately 0.64 mho-gram-cm/sec. This conductance-viscosity relation is known as "Walden's Rule."

The Abnormal Conductance of Hydrogen and Hydroxyl Ions

Hydrogen and hydroxyl ions appear to have abnormally high conductance values in solvents which exhibit hydrogen bonding. In the case of the hydrogen ion, one cannot attribute this increased conductance to the small size of the proton since unquestionably the proton is solvated and exists in water, for example, as H_3O^+. The diffusing specie in water is thus approximately the size of a sodium ion; yet, the limiting conductance obtained is approximately eight times as large as that obtained with sodium.

Some authors have attributed the increased conductance of the hydrogen ion to the apparent large mobility that the ion would have in a mechanism of the following type:

Here the H_3O^+ specie is visualized as transfering a proton to an adjacent water molecule, which in turn passes it on to its neighbor, etc., with the result that the net diffusing specie is the H^+ entity rather than the H_3O^+ ion. A similar mechanism may be postulated for the hydroxyl ion, and both of these ions in turn may exhibit analogous behavior in nonaqueous solvents which permit the hydrogen bonding required in the above model.

References

1. DAVIES, C. W., "The Conductivity of Solutions," New York, John Wiley and Sons, Inc., 1930.
2. GURNEY, R. W., "Ionic Processes in Solution," New York, McGraw-Hill Book Co., Inc., 1953.
3. ROBINSON, R. A., AND STOKES, R. H., "Electrolyte Solutions," London, Butterworth's Scientific Publ., 1955.
4. FUOSS, R. M., AND ACCASCINA, F., "Electrolytic Conductance," New York, Interscience Pub., Inc., 1959.
5. HARNED, H. S., AND OWEN, B. B., "The Physical Chemistry of Electrolytic Solutions," 3rd Ed., New York, Reinhold Publishing Corp., 1958.

ROBERT E. MEREDITH

CONDUCTIVITY (ELECTROLYTIC) MEASUREMENT

The measurement of electrolytic conductivity reveals important fundamental information on the structure of matter and is often used in practical applications to indicate solution composition. The measurement when used for analytical purposes, though nonspecific, gives high speed of response with good reproducibility and can be accomplished ordinarily with low maintenance requirements using inexpensive equipment.

Electrolytic conductivity is measured by measuring the effect of current flow in a solution when a d-c or a-c voltage field is applied. D-c is not commonly used because of complicating polarization effects. An a-c field can be applied with or without immersing electrodes in the solution. In the latter case, the technique is termed oscillometry if a high-frequency field is used and "electrodeless" measurement if a low frequency is used. By and large the measurement is most precisely and satisfactorily carried out with electrodes immersed, and this technique will be briefly discussed.

Cells

The sample solution is brought into a measurement region (a cell) having a definite solution space and fixed electrodes. Circuit means are provided for making an a-c resistance measurement across the electrodes. Precision cells of the Jones type are shown in Fig. 1. It is not necessary to use a rectangular shaped cell of known dimensions.

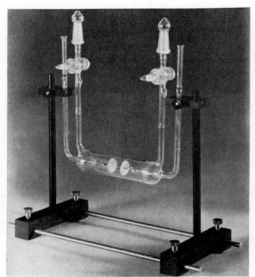
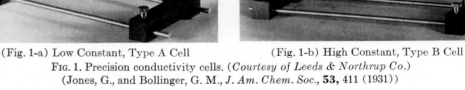

(Fig. 1-a) Low Constant, Type A Cell   (Fig. 1-b) High Constant, Type B Cell

Fɪɢ. 1. Precision conductivity cells. (*Courtesy of Leeds & Northrup Co.*)

(Jones, G., and Bollinger, G. M., *J. Am. Chem. Soc.*, **53**, 411 (1931))

Type	Available Cell Constant cm^{-1}	Approximate Volume (incl. filling tubes) ml
A	0.05	65
A	0.25	65
A	1.0	65
B	5.0	30
B	25.0	30
B	150.0	30

Because the cell establishes reproducible conditions, measurements with the same cell but on different solutions will give resistance values that are proportional to the specific resistances of those solutions. The proportionality factor is termed the cell constant. The cell constant, K, in reciprocal centimeters is evaluated by applying Eq. 1, using the measured cell resistance, R, in ohms obtained on a solution of known specific conductance, G, in mhos per centimeter.

$$K = RG \qquad (1)$$

Potassium chloride solutions of specified concentration and known conductivity (Table 1) are commonly used to establish cell-constant values. Once the constant has been established for a cell, the cell can be used to measure unknown solutions to obtain their conductivities by applying the relationship of Eq. 1.

For precise work, cells are designed to reduce measurement errors. A representative sample is insured by a cell arrangement which permits thorough rinsing with solution. Contamination is avoided by the use of inert materials of construction. Because temperature has a large effect on electrolytic conductivity (about 2 per cent per degree C), the solution temperature during measurement is commonly controlled by operating the cell immersed in a constant-temperature bath, or the effect of varying temperature is compensated by circuit means. A-c interferences in the operation of the cell and circuit become significant at high cell impedances, unless the equipment is very carefully designed. A-c coupling effects are minimized or eliminated by employing favorable cell geometry and by the use of guarding arrangements in cells employing two or three electrodes. The cells of Fig. 1 to avoid a-c interference (Parker effect) have their leadwires remote from conducting portions of solution.

The electrodes behave imperfectly when a-c passes, giving rise to a phase shift and an in-phase resistance at the surface of the electrodes (polarization resistance) which adds to the cell resistance and constitutes an error in the measurement.[6,8] The polarization resistance error decreases with increase in a-c frequency and can be estimated from measurements made at several frequencies (usually in the range of several hundred to several thousand cycles per second).

The line obtained by plotting the measured resistance against the square root of the reciprocal of the frequency is extrapolated to zero value

TABLE 1. POTASSIUM CHLORIDE REFERENCE
SOLUTIONS FOR STANDARDIZING
CONDUCTIVITY CELLS

Approximate Normality	Precise Composition Vacuum Weight Grams of KCl in 1000 Vacuum Weight Grams of H_2O	Temp., C	Conductivity, mhos per cm ($\times 10^6$)
1.0	71.1352	0	65176
		18	97838
		25	111342
0.1	7.41913	0	7137.9
		18	11166.7
		25	12856.0
0.01	0.745263	0	773.64
		18	1220.52
		25	1408.77

Jones, G., and Bradshaw, B. C., *J. Am. Chem. Soc.*, **55**, 1780 (1933).

of the frequency function (infinite frequency) at which point polarization resistance is assumed zero. Polarization resistance and phase shift can be greatly reduced by using electrodes of good design. Electrodes should have sufficient area, should be mounted normal to the solution conductance path, and especially, should be of platinum metal, covered with an electrolytically deposited coating of platinum black.[6] Even with a well-designed cell it is not advisable to let the measured cell resistance become less than about 100 ohms, for reason of polarization resistance, nor greater than about 50,000 ohms for reason of a-c interferences. These conditions can be met by proper choice of cell constant value. As evident from Eq. 1, a high-constant cell is suitable for making measurements on solutions of high conductivity. Such a cell in effect has a long, narrow column of solution between the electrodes. Conversely, a low-constant cell is suitable for measurements on poorly conducting solutions and in effect has a short, large-area column of solution between electrodes.

Additional requirements are imposed on cells for practical measurements in industry. The electrode problems are accentuated, because much instrumentation for these purposes operates at 60 cycles and without adjustment of phase angle. Furthermore, cells for these applications must be compact and adaptable to permit introduction into available spaces in tanks, pipelines, and reaction vessels for making measurements on either batch or flowing samples. Such cells must also be able to make measurements under unfavorable conditions of tempera-

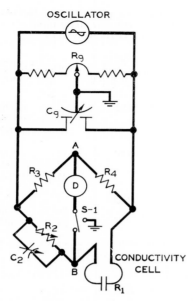

Fig. 2. High-accuracy bridge circuit.

ture, pressure, corrosion, rough handling, and minimal maintenance, without fouling of electrodes or solution stoppage taking place.

Circuits

The most generally used circuit is the null-balance a-c bridge, because it is capable of the greatest sensitivity, stability, and accuracy. Using complex bridge apparatus and refined techniques, it is possible to achieve measurement accuracy within 0.01 per cent. Conditions for attaining high accuracy have been discussed in detail.[2, 3, 5, 7, 9, 10] The basic principles for minimizing errors in bridge measurements were established by Jones[5, 7] and Shedlovsky,[9] and most modern bridges for precise measurement of conductance utilize refinements of these principles. For bridge balance, the potentials at points A and B (Fig. 2) must be the same in magnitude and phase, and this is achieved by adjusting R_2 and C_2. Measurements are frequency-dependent because cells exhibit capacitance effects.[8] A close approximation to the true cell resistance can be obtained, when black-platinized electrodes are used, by extrapolating measurements to infinite frequency as has been described. When gray-platinized or bright electrodes are used, significant errors arise in this approximation, and other techniques, such as the double-cell method of Feates,[3] may be required.

The ratio resistors, R_3 and R_4, of the bridge of Fig. 2 are equal in resistance (usually 1000 ohms) and exhibit negligible phase angle, i.e., their impedances at frequencies up to several kilocycles are essentially the same as their d-c resistances. The variable standard resistance, R_2, uses similarly constructed resistive elements, arranged to minimize inter-element capacitance. The adjustable air capacitor, C_2, provides for phase-angle balance. A Wagner-type grounding system consisting of adjustable resistance, R_g, and capacitance, C_g, in conjunction with switch, S_1, permits elimination of undesirable hum and noise in the detector caused by stray capacitance. Although not shown in Fig. 2, shielding of the bridge elements is required.

Important auxiliaries to the bridge are the oscillator and detector which either should be of such design that they do not introduce into the bridge circuit additional capacitances to ground, or should be connected to the bridge by means of shielded transformers. The oscillator should provide an output of adjustable and calibrated frequency and should produce a good sine waveform at output voltages ranging from a fraction of a volt up to about 10 volts. The classic detector for a-c bridges, a telephone headset and tuned amplifier, has been supplanted by the cathode-ray oscilloscope and other electronic devices which are more versatile and less fatiguing to the operator. Applying the bridge unbalance signal and the oscillator output signal, respectively, to the vertical and horizontal

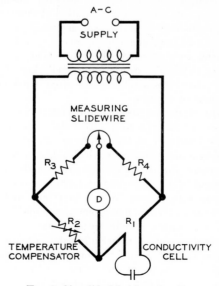

Fig. 3. Simplified bridge circuit.

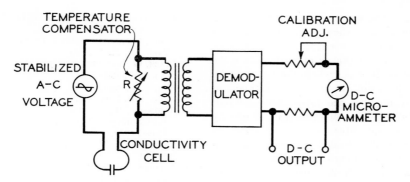

FIG. 4. Ohmmeter-type circuit.

FIG. 5. Conductivity instrument employing ohm-meter-type circuit. (*Courtesy of Leeds & Northrup Co.*)

amplifiers of the oscilloscope produces an elliptical trace which becomes a straight, horizontal line at balance.

Some bridges of modern design use transformer ratio arms instead of ratio resistors. One such bridge[4] features simplicity of construction by the use of unitized commercial components and can be used not only for conventional two-terminal measurements but also for three-terminal measurements to eliminate effects of the cell leadwires. Another bridge design[1] is adaptable to conductance measurements with either electrodeless cells or conventional cells.

A simplified bridge circuit as indicated in Fig. 3 can be used where only moderate accuracy is needed (0.1 to 1.0 per cent). The Wagner ground system and the provisions for phase-angle balancing are eliminated. The bridge is energized from the 60 cycle power line or a fixed frequency oscillator (usually 1000 cps). The detector may be an a-c galvanometer or a cathode-ray "magic eye" tube. The resistance, R_2, is often made adjustable in steps to provide

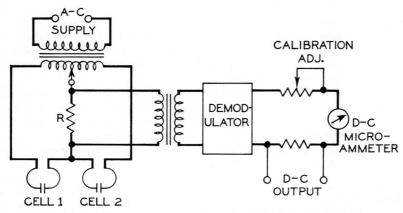

FIG. 6. Ohmmeter-type conductance-difference circuit.

decade range selection, or it may function as a temperature-sensitive element to compensate for electrolytic conductance changes with temperature. The latter function is of particular value in industrial applications where the temperature of the sample is not controlled. Adjustment of the slidewire modifies the ratio arms and balances the bridge. The slidewire scale is usually calibrated to read directly in conductance or resistance. Simplified bridge circuits in addition to being used in a variety of portable, manually-balanced indicators are also used in servo-balancing recording instruments, some of which employ quadrature-rejecting amplifiers.[11]

A nonbridge-type circuit similar to that used in the ohmmeter is sometimes preferred, because at low cost it provides direct, continuous indication of 1 to 3 per cent accuracy with no balancing operation required. As shown in Fig. 4, a stabilized a-c voltage is applied to the cell and a resistor, R, connected in series. Because the resistance of R is kept small in value compared with the cell resistance, the current flowing in the circuit, and therefore the a-c signal appearing across resistor R, will be approximately proportional to the cell conductance. This signal is transformer-coupled to a demodulator, and the rectified output is measured by a d-c meter calibrated directly in micromhos. The rectified output flowing through a precision resistor will develop a voltage suitable for driving other d-c readout devices, such as a recorder or data-logger. Temperature compensation is obtained by making resistor R a temperature-variable element, the coefficient of which matches the temperature-resistance change of the measured electrolyte. A typical instrument of this type is shown in Fig. 5.

Conductance difference measurements can be made by using the circuit modification shown in Fig. 6. Equal, stabilized voltages applied to the two cells cause opposing (subtracting) currents to flow through resistor R in the common branch. The voltage developed across resistor R by the net current will be proportional to the conductance difference.

References

1. CALVERT, R., CORNELIUS, J. A., GRIFFITHS, V. S., AND STOCK, D. I., *J. Phys. Chem.*, **62**, 47 (1958).
2. EISENBERG, H., AND FUOSS, R. M., *J. Am. Chem. Soc.*, **75**, 2914 (1953).
3. FEATES, F. S., IVES, D. J. G., AND PRYOR, J. H., *J. Electrochem. Soc.*, **103**, 580 (1956).
4. JANZ, G. J., AND McINTYRE, J. D. E., *J. Electrochem. Soc.*, **108**, 272 (1961).
5. JONES, G., AND BOLLINGER, D. M., *J. Am. Chem. Soc.*, **51**, 2407 (1929).
6. JONES, G., AND BOLLINGER, D. M., *J. Am. Chem. Soc.*, **57**, 280 (1935).
7. JONES, G., AND JOSEPHS, R. C., *J. Am. Chem. Soc.*, **50**, 1049 (1928).
8. ROBINSON, R. A., AND STOKES, R. H., "Electrolyte Solutions," p. 93, New York, Academic Press, 1959.
9. SHEDLOVSKY, T., *J. Am. Chem. Soc.*, **52**, 1793 (1930).
10. SHEDLOVSKY, T., "Technique of Organic Chemistry," Vol. I., p. 1651, "Physical Methods," (Editor: Weissberger), New York, Interscience Publishers, 1949.
11. WILLIAMS, A. J., AND PAYNE, J. F., *Trans. AIEE*, **72**, 611 (1953).

EDGAR L. ECKFELDT AND
JAMES U. EYNON

Cross-reference: *Controllers, Automatic.*

CONDUCTOMETRIC TITRATION. See ELECTROMETRIC TITRATION.

CONTACT POTENTIAL

Contact potential, or Volta potential, is a historic term describing the potential difference that is established between two phases when they are electrically connected. The work required to bring a small amount of charged species, i, from infinity into some point deep within the phase consists of several parts, as shown in the diagram on p. 237.

Here z_i is the electrical valence of i, $\mathbf{F}$, the Faraday (96,494 coulombs), and χ and ψ are potentials in volts. The real potential of electrons (α_e) is numerically equivalent to the work needed to extract electrons from the phase and is called the electronic work function (q.v.). Frequently it is expressed in electron-volts. The contact potential between two phases is numerically equivalent to the difference between their work functions.

Sometimes the term "contact potential" is used to describe the potential drop across a junction of two conductors subjected to a flow of current. This drop relates to contact resistance and should not be referred to as a contact potential.

The μ_e component of the electron work function originates from interaction of electrons with the intermolecular and intramolecular forces in the particular phase, which is usually a solid or

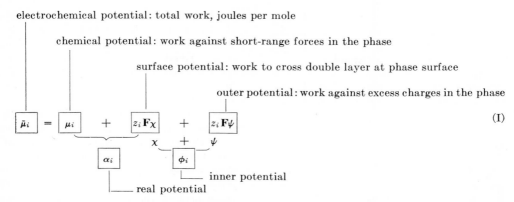

$$\bar{\mu}_i \;=\; \mu_i \;+\; z_i \mathbf{F} \chi \;+\; z_i \mathbf{F} \psi \tag{I}$$

where, above the terms:

electrochemical potential: total work, joules per mole

chemical potential: work against short-range forces in the phase

surface potential: work to cross double layer at phase surface

outer potential: work against excess charges in the phase

and below: $\chi + \psi$, α_i, ϕ_i, inner potential, real potential

liquid. The typical magnitude of μ_e is several electron-volts. The surface potential, χ, results from the electrostatic effect of the dipole sheath (double layers) existing at phase boundary:

$$\chi_e = (-)4\pi n\sigma = (-)3.77 \times 10^{-15} n\sigma \text{ volt} \tag{2}$$

where n is the number of dipoles per sq cm aligned normal to the boundary and σ is the strength of each dipole in Debye units (1 Debye $= 10^{-18}$esu). On clean metals, the image dipole reduces the contribution of the absorbed dipole by a factor of 2. The dipole is positive when its positive end points away from the surface. The magnitude of χ can be up to 1.5 volts.

Several contact-potential sign usages are encountered in the literature. The contact potential of phase 2 with respect to phase 1 sometimes is defined as:

$$\Delta(\alpha_e) = (\alpha_e)_2 - (\alpha_e)_1 \tag{3}$$

Since the electron work functions (α_e) are positive numbers, the sign of $\Delta(\alpha_e)$ depends on the choice of reference $(\alpha_e)_1$. No universal reference has been accepted, and hence this convention is not strictly followed. When a phase 2 with a surface dipole film is compared with the same phase 2 without the film, the relation holds $\Delta(\alpha_e) = \Delta(\chi_e^1)$ where χ_e^1 indicates that part of the surface potential which originates from the film. "Positive" film usually means one with positive dipole ends pointing outwards, away from the underlying phase.

Positive film contributes (Eq. 2) negative surface potential increment and decreases the electronic work function of the underlying phase. The direction of resulting change in the contact potential, however, will depend entirely on the relative magnitudes of the electronic work functions, $(\alpha_e)_1$ and $(\alpha_e)_2$, in Eq. 3. This point must be carefully checked when comparing data of various authors. Arbitrary conventions can also be encountered in selecting the sign for $\Delta(\chi^1)$. Sometimes the material or film with the higher electronic work function (e.g., Pt) is called "noble" while the one with lower function "active."

Measurement of $\Delta(\alpha_e)$ is based on Eq. 1. When two phases with unequal α_e are electrically connected, their electrochemical potential difference, $\Delta(\bar{\mu}_e)$, becomes nil by exchange of electrons. This exchange generates a Volta potential difference, $\Delta(\psi)$, which is measurable and at $\Delta(\bar{\mu}_e) = 0$ is equal to $\Delta(\alpha)_e$. Contact potential refers to one mode of connecting the phases.

In the experimental devices for measurement of the contact potentials, the existence of $\Delta\psi$ is indicated by an electric effect. A potential difference, ΔE, is introduced into the circuit connecting the phases and is varied until the effect disappears. Then numerically

$$|\Delta E| = |\Delta\psi| = |\Delta\alpha_e|$$

Four typical arrangements for measuring the contact-potential differences are shown in Fig. 1. In A, the plates of the specimens are put in contact and presence of potential difference is indicated by deviation of a quadrant-electrometer when the plates are parted. Frictional electrical charging upsets such measurements.

In B, gas space formed by two phases with surfaces facing each other is ionized with a weak radioactive source, e.g., polonium 210, or with x-rays, ultraviolet radiation, etc. As long as there is a Volta potential difference between phases, a field exists between the surfaces and an ionic current flows through the space, causing current detectable by the microammeter (m). The setting on P is varied until the current disappears.

In C, the so-called Kelvin method, one surface is moved with respect to the other, vibrating it

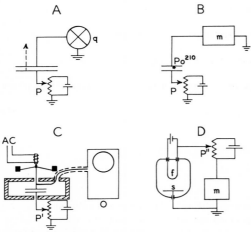

FIG. 1. Methods for measurement of contact potentials.

electromechanically, pneumatically, or even by tapping. Rotation of a segmented surface above another segmented one is also employed. Detector o, usually an oscilloscope, indicates an a-c current when the field between the surfaces is not compensated by P^1. The a-c signal disappears when P^1 compensates $\Delta(\alpha_e)$.

In D, the diode method, thermal electron current flows between a hot filament, f, and the experimental surface, s. From the shape of the curve representing the current versus applied voltage, P'', it is possible to establish the point of equivalence, $\Delta(\alpha_e) = P''$. The curve frequently deviates from the ideal shape, complicating the interpretation. In studies of surface-potential change, such a curve merely shifts over by $\Delta\chi$ and the measurement is simpler.

On a smooth surface consisting of areas with different work functions, the capacitor method measures an area-weighed average while the diode method produces complex curves since the current varies exponentially with the work functions.

The diode method needs reasonable vacuum and is best suited for measurements on clean surfaces or on strongly adsorbed films. The other methods adapt easily to use with any solid or liquid that is in a gas. With the capacitor method, resolutions within ± 0.002 millivolt have been reported. Resolution within ± 2 millivolt is possible with simple devices. However, the contact-potential differences themselves are much less reproducible.

For comparisons of contact potentials, an invariable reference surface with constant α_e is de-

sired. Such ideal surfaces are not available since the electronic work functions are very sensitive to surface preparation. In vacuum, gold ($\alpha_e = 4.54$ ev) and tungsten ($\alpha_e = 4.51$ ev) are frequently employed because they are easily cleaned. In air, among surfaces used are aged gold, freshly wire-brushed copper or silver, or else gold or other metal coated with a low-energy film of paraffin wax, certain fluorocarbons, or stearic acid. Preparations of tellurium-dusted gold surfaces have been reported to reproduce within less than 0.0002 volt, but their work function is sensitive to adsorption of polar vapors. The χ component of the electronic work function on clean metals in vacuum results from asymmetry of electron distribution around the outer layer of metal ions. For sodium, $\chi = -0.4$ volt has been estimated. Surface potentials of different crystallographic planes can vary by as much as one volt. In ionic salts, unequal sizes and polarizabilities of ions lead to existence of surface dipole sheaths, usually with the larger negative ions protruding beyond the last plane of positive ions. In semiconductors, space charges can create double layers. In solids and liquids, surface force fields generate polarization and orientation effects in the outer layer. Water surface in air has $\chi = -0.45$ volt. Adsorbed species can form dipole sheaths by orientation and polarization. In chemisorption, dipole layers are formed by electron shifts. Since adsorption equilibria and orientations of adsorbed molecules are temperature-sensitive, the values of the surface potential term can change by several tenths of a volt in the range of 20 to 50°C. The μ_e term, on the other hand, is temperature-insensitive, changing for metals by a fraction of millivolt per °C. In semiconductors, the work function decreases with increase in temperature for the hole-type conductivity.

Metals in air acquire thin films of oxides, and the contact-potential measurements apply then to these films. Polar vapors (H_2O and CO_2) from air adsorb on films and modify the surface potential. The contact-potential shift on adsorption is not a reliable criterion for distinguishing between physical adsorption and chemisorption. In adsorption of organic molecules at the water surface, polar groups point toward water.

All these surface effects cause continuous drifts of contact potentials at newly prepared surfaces. Drifts may easily be at 0.005 volt per minute, and hours may be needed to arrive at steady poten-

TABLE 1. SOME MEASUREMENTS OF CONTACT POTENTIALS BETWEEN METALS

In Vacuum vs Au*	In Air vs Au†	In Air vs Pt‡	
		Abraded Dry, stored 1 hr in desiccator	Abraded Wet, stored 1 hr above water
Pt +0.71	—	0	+0.16
Ag −0.30	−0.25	−0.08	−0.02
Au 0	0	−0.16	−0.13
Cu −0.11	−0.28	−0.27	−0.12
Fe −0.22	−0.25	−0.44	−0.16
Cr −0.07	—	−0.58	−0.59
Ni +0.26	−0.03 to −0.25	−0.61	−0.39
Sn −0.47	−0.50	−0.69	−0.66
Pb −0.56	−0.60	−0.79	−0.69
Zn −0.84	−0.90	−1.08	−0.92
Al −0.84	−0.90	−1.16	−1.08
Mg −1.12	—	−1.51	−1.67

* Michaelson, H. B., *J. Appl. Phys.*, **21**, 536 (1950).
† Schaafs, W., *Z. angew. Phys.*, **10**, 424 (1958).
‡ Uhlig, H. H., *J. Appl. Phys.*, **22**, 1309 (1951).

tials. Reproducibility, even with the same method of surface preparation, is rarely better than within 0.02 volt. Data from different authors may spread over several tenths of volt. A recent compilation of the electronic work functions can be found in "Landolt-Börnstein Zahlenwerte u. Funktionen," Band II, Teil 6, p. 913, Berlin, Springer-Verlag, 1959.

In Table 1, representative contact-potential data are shown with the sign convention of Eq. 3. The reference was gold in Michaelson's and Schaaf's data and platinum in Uhlig's work.

Contact-potential measurements are used to study adsorption phenomena, solid and liquid surface structure, catalytic processes, surface states in semiconductors, etc. Because of the sensitivity to adsorbable contaminants, one of the applications may be in detection of odors and other vapors in air. Several attempts to develop contact-potential olfactometry have been reported, and others are known to be in progress.

References

1. LANGE, E., "Wien-Harms Handbuch d. Experimental Physik," *XII*, Teil II, p. 265, Leipzig, Akad. Verlaggesellschaft, 1933.
2. PARSONS, R., in J. O'M. Bockris, "Modern Aspects of Electrochemistry," p. 103, London, Butterworths Sci. Publ., 1954.
3. PRITSCHARD, J., AND TOMPKINS, E. C., *Trans. Faraday Soc.*, **56**, 540 (1960).
4. GOTTLIEB, M. H., *J. Phys. Chem.*, **64**, 427 (1960).
5. CHAPMAN, C. R., Ph.D. Thesis, Purdue University, 1955: available as Doct. Dissert. Series Publ., *14,384*, University Microfilms, Ann Arbor, Michigan.

ANDREW DRAVNIEKS

Cross-references: *Dipole Moment; Electrode Double Layer; Work Function.*

CONTROLLERS, AUTOMATIC

Control systems providing precise control of industrial processes were unknown fifty years ago. The urgent requirements for improved metallurgical and chemical products during World War I created a need for more accurate measurement and control devices. One result of this need was the development of the self-balancing potentiometer recorder and its early adaptation for control of industrial processes. Since that time, the development of industrial process measurement and control systems has proceeded at an ever-increasing rate. The emphasis on more advanced control systems during the 20's, 30's, and 40's was directed largely toward pneumatic controls, particularly for the petroleum industry and for certain chemical applications where the presence of explosion hazards encouraged their use. Advanced types of electric control systems became available in the late 30's and were used in large quantities, along with pneumatic controllers to meet the needs of industry during World War II. Since the early 50's, strong emphasis has been placed on the development of electronic control systems and these are now widely accepted, even in the petroleum and chemical industries. While hydraulic systems have had less extensive industrial use in recent years, they are sometimes used for applications where extremely high speed of response is required.

The controllers of today range from very simple ones to those of great complexity. They utilize electric, pneumatic, or hydraulic elements and sometimes a combination of such elements.

For the control of chemical processes it is often necessary or desirable to control such process conditions as temperature, pressure, rate of flow, liquid level, electrolytic conductivity, hydrogen ion concentration, gas analysis, etc.

It is axiomatic that a measurement of the process condition must be made as a prerequisite to controlling that condition. It is not within the scope of this article to discuss in detail the various primary elements available for measuring the various process conditions enumerated above. However, a large variety of devices for such measurements is available, some producing a pneumatic output signal and others producing an electrical output signal related to the process condition. Another entry deals with *recording instruments* (q.v.) to provide a continuous or periodic curve of the measured variable on a recorder chart in response to electrical input signals. This entry will discuss control systems which use such recording instruments as a basis of measurement, as well as other control systems which operate without use of a recorder.

Some controllers provide a very simple on-off type of control action, as obtained, for example, by the opening and closing of electrical contacts which operate in response to changes in the process variable. Others provide more refined and complex control actions, the more common of which are listed and very briefly described as follows:

Proportional control action provides a continuous linear relation between input and output.

Proportional plus rate control action provides an output proportional to a linear combination of the input and rate-of-change of input.

Proportional plus reset control action provides an output proportional to a linear combination of the input and the time integral of the input.

Proportional plus reset plus rate control action provides an output proportional to a linear combination of the input, the time integral of the input, and the rate-of-change of input.

The selection of an instrument embodying any of the above or other control actions will depend on a number of factors, including the response characteristics of the process to be controlled, the degree to which close control is required, cost considerations, etc.

Two common applications will be briefly considered together with typical control instrumentation for each.

Conductivity Control—All-Electronic Type

Maintaining the conductivity of chemical solutions is often important to industrial process operation. It may, in some instances, be desired to regulate the conductivity at a particular value by the addition of a suitable reagent. In other instances, for example, boiler water, it may be necessary only to monitor the conductivity of the solution and take action only under certain off-limit conditions by sounding an alarm and/or diverting the out-of-tolerance solution to waste.

A typical electronic-type on-off conductivity controller or alarm device is shown in Fig. 1.

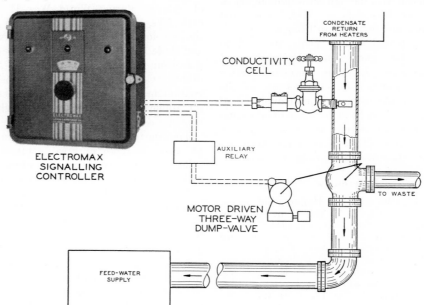

FIG. 1. Conductivity control system.

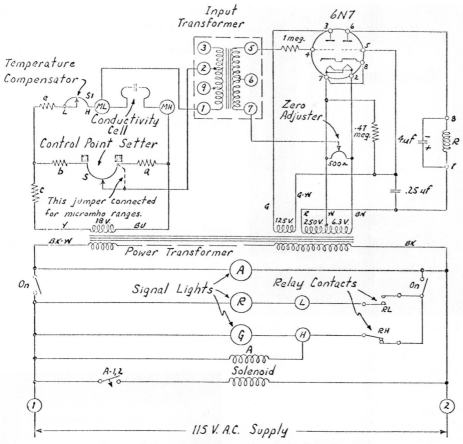

FIG. 2. Schematic drawing of conductivity controller.

A conductivity cell forms one arm of an a-c Wheatstone bridge circuit (a-c is typically used on the conductivity bridge to avoid errors due to d-c polarization). An electronic detector and amplifier operates an output relay, when the conductivity exceeds a predetermined balance point of the Wheatstone bridge, to energize suitable regulating or alarm devices. The balance point of the bridge is set by a variable resistor, which is calibrated in terms of ohms or mhos as sensed by the conductivity cell. A second dial, calibrated in degrees, is used to adjust a bridge resistor that compensates for variations in solution resistance due to temperature changes.

Indicating lights are included in the controller and serve to show whether the conductivity of the solution is above or below the bridge balance point as set on the control or alarm point adjusting dial.

The circuit for this device, including the bridge circuit, amplifier, and output relay circuits, is shown in Fig. 2.

Hydrogen Ion (pH) Control (Using Recorder for Measurement)

It is often desired to maintain the pH of a solution at a given value by controlling the flow of an acid or alkaline reagent being fed into the process stream. A common type of control equipment used to regulate pH embodies a recorder-controller system, where the recorder serves to measure the controlled quantity as sensed by a pH electrode assembly and at the same time provides an error input signal to the control system.

In such a system the control action will typically include a combination of proportional, reset, and rate action to provide the precise control action usually required to produce satisfactory control of pH where process disturbances

FIG. 3. Recorder with pneumatic control system.

may be frequent and process transportation and measuring lags unfavorable.

The control system may be of the pneumatic type as shown in Fig. 3. The servomechanism of this recorder operates a pneumatic nozzle and baffle assembly which converts recorder movement into air output changes. This air signal generally actuates a pneumatically operated control valve to suitably regulate the process input. Air supply and output air gages and means for transferring the controller output from automatic to manual regulation and vice versa may be seen mounted on the front of the instrument.

Another typical recorder-controller system may be of the electric type as shown in Fig. 4. Automatic to manual transfer provisions, a meter for monitoring the controller output, and means for manually adjusting the output signal are again located on the front of the control unit where they are accessible to the operator. Such electronic controllers are available with up to three-function control action (proportional, reset, and rate) and may deliver a modulated current output suitable for operating an electropneumatic transducer as shown in Fig. 5 to provide a modulated pneumatic signal for the operation of pneumatically operated valves or cylinders.

Where operation of electrically operated valves is preferred, electronic-type controllers are also available with relay output circuits for modulating the position of motor-operated drive units, which consist of a reversing motor, a suitable gear train, output shaft, and built-in position feedback device.

Other All-Electronic Control Systems

Where a record of the process condition is not needed, a wide variety of controllers is available which operate directly from the measurement signal without benefit of a recorder in the measuring system. In such instances, a suitable transducer or analyzer is used to generate an electrical signal responsive to the process condition being measured. This signal is then compared to an electrical signal derived from a set point device, and the difference between these two signals serves as the "error" signal to the controlling system.

In such all-electronic systems, the recorder, if used, is generally of the "miniature" size. The associated control components are also typically

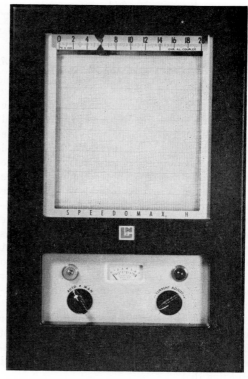

FIG. 4. Recorder with electric control system.

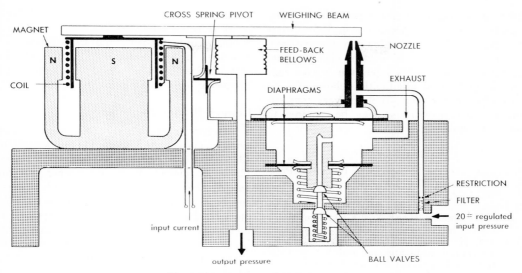

FIG. 5. Electropneumatic converter.

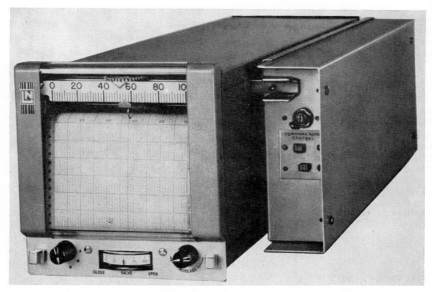

FIG. 6. Miniature recorder and controller.

of small size to conserve panelboard area. Fig. 6 shows such a typical control system, including the set point unit, manual station, controller, and monitoring recorder. This particular control and recording station is approximately 6 in. high x 8 in. wide, including the side-mounted controller.

In addition to conventional control loops, a wide variety of other arrangements is available for producing control action related to two or more input signals. Typical of each system is "ratio control," where one quantity is regulated as a function of another quantity, for example, where one flow is controlled so as to be maintained in a predetermined ratio to another flow which may vary in a random manner. Another typical system involving more than one measured quantity is "cascade control," where the output from one controller is used to adjust the set point of another controller, for example, where a temperature controller may be used to adjust the control point of a flow controller.

Such an arrangement has merit in controlling upsets in a fast responsive loop before they become disturbances in a slower responsive loop.

The wide variety of control elements and systems available today offers the process control designer an almost limitless choice of tools to provide either very simple or very sophisticated control systems as may be required to meet his needs.

References

1. ECKMAN, D. P., "Principles of Industrial Process Control," New York, John Wiley & Sons, Inc., 1945.
2. BROWN, G. S., AND CAMPBELL, D. P., "Principles of Servomechanisms," New York, John Wiley & Sons, Inc., 1948.
3. LAUER, H., LESNICK, R., AND MATSON, L. E., "Servomechanism Fundamentals," New York, McGraw-Hill Book Company, Inc., 1947.
4. NIXON, F. P., "Principles of Automatic Controls," New York, Prentice-Hall, Inc., 1953.
5. Report of ASME, "Automatic Control Terminology," American Society of Mechanical Engineers, 1952.
6. CHESTNUT, H., AND MAYER, R. W., "Servomechanisms and Regulating System Design," New York, John Wiley & Sons, Inc., 1951.
7. FARRINGTON, G. H., "Fundamentals of Automatic Control," London, Chapman & Hall, Ltd., 1951.
8. AHRENDT, W. R., AND TAPLIN, J. F., "Automatic Feedback Control," New York, McGraw-Hill Book Company, Inc., 1951.
9. CONSIDINE, D. M., "Process Instruments and Controls Handbook," New York, McGraw-Hill Book Company, Inc., 1957.

E. T. DAVIS

Cross-references: *Conductivity (Electrolytic) Measurement; pH Meters; Recording Instruments.*

COPPER ELECTROPLATING

Copper is electroplated on many parts as an undercoat for nickel and chromium, for color effects, as a stop-off against carburizing, and for other special purposes. Nearly all zinc alloy die castings are electroplated first with copper to protect them from dissolution in the acid, nickel sulfate solutions commonly employed for electroplating bright nickel. Some steel parts are copper plated and subsequently buffed for smoothing purposes, prior to being plated with nickel and chromium. For preserving nonmetallic mementos, such as baby shoes, they are plated with thick copper deposits (up to 0.03 inch). Electroformed objects, such as electrotypes, record stampers, and wave guides, are produced in large numbers by copper electroplating. Steel wire is plated with copper for producing high-strength, electrical cable.

Copper Plating Solutions

Commercial copper plating solutions are classified as (1) copper cyanide, (2) copper sulfate, (3) copper fluoborate, or (4) copper pyrophosphate. In type (1) baths, the copper is monovalent. The others are prepared with divalent copper salts. The cyanide solution is used for most of the articles plated with copper as an undercoat for nickel and chromium plate, partly because it has good throwing power and deposits copper more uniformly than the other solutions which are employed mostly for other purposes.

The chief constituents of the copper cyanide plating baths are copper cyanide, sodium or potassium cyanide, sodium or potassium carbonate, and sodium or potassium hydroxide. Copper cyanide, insoluble in water, is dissolved in solutions containing sodium or potassium cyanide, to form a soluble complex compound, as follows:

$$CuCN + 2NaCN \rightleftarrows Na_2Cu(CN)_3$$

Sodium cyanide in excess of $Na_2Cu(CN)_3$ is termed "free cyanide," which controls the ionization of the complex compound, as follows:

$$Na_2Cu(CN)_3 \rightleftarrows 2Na^+ + Cu(CN)_3^{--}$$

$$Cu(CN)_3^{--} \rightleftarrows Cu^+ + 3CN^-$$

The "free cyanide" must be carefully controlled within relatively narrow limits to control the anode and cathode efficiencies and the smoothness of the copper electroplates. A high "free cyanide" favors electrolytic dissolution of the copper anodes, but tends to reduce the cathode efficiency. Optimum concentration levels depend on the temperature, current density, copper concentration, and other factors. Regular additions of sodium or potassium cyanide are required to compensate for consumption by dragout, oxidation, and hydrolysis.

Potassium salts are more soluble than the sodium salts and more tolerant to organic impurities. Hence, they are favored in cases where relatively high cathode current densities are desired for fast plating. Many commercial solutions are prepared and maintained with a mixture of sodium and potassium salts.

About 2 oz/gal of sodium or potassium carbonate is added to each new copper cyanide plating bath, to improve the conductivity of the solution. Carbonates build up in the electrolyte, because of oxidation and hydrolysis of the cyanide radical. A concentration above about 9 oz/gal should be avoided, or the copper deposits will tend to become rough or "pebbly." Carbonate control below this level is especially important for the high-efficiency baths containing brighteners that preclude buffing. Carbonates are precipitated by adding calcium hydroxide, which restores the hydroxyl ion concentration desired for maximum solution conductivity and maximum copper plate smoothness. Treatment with calcium hydroxide at regular intervals to control both the carbonate and the hydroxyl ion concentrations is important for reproducing smooth, porefree copper plates.

The "strike" solution in Table 1 containing only 15 gpl of copper cyanide customarily precedes the high-efficiency bath, to prevent displacement deposits of copper on zinc or steel. The "strike" bath is relatively inefficient and usually is employed for only 2 to 4 minutes. The Rochelle bath can be used as a "strike" solution or directly for depositing up to about 0.0001 inch of copper (which requires 3 to 5 minutes, depending on the cathode current density).

In the high-efficiency bath containing 75 to 100 gpl of copper cyanide, copper is deposited at the rate of about 0.003 inch/hour when the cathode current density is adjusted to the customary level of about 30 amp/sq ft. Proprietary brighteners consisting of mixtures of selenium or thallium salts with other metal compounds or with organic compounds frequently are added to the high-efficiency solutions. Surface active organic compounds sometimes are added to prevent pitting.

Divalent Copper Solutions

Among the divalent copper solutions, the copper sulfate is the best known. A copper strike in a cyanide solution must precede any of the divalent solutions, however, in the case of steel and zinc articles to prevent displacement coatings of copper that do not adhere well to the substrate.

Copper sulfate pentahydrate and sulfuric acid are the chief constituents of the copper sulfate bath, but grain refining agents, such as molasses and gelatin, or proprietary brightening agents, such as derivatives of thiourea and certain amines, are frequently added. Typical concentrations are given in Table 2. Cathode current densities normally range from about 20 to 40 amp/sq ft except for solutions operated with vigorous air agitation when current densities up to about 200 amp/sq ft may be employed without burning. In general, copper sulfate solutions are more tolerant of ionic impurities than many other plating solutions.

The fluoborate bath is suited for operation with higher current densities than are practical for any other copper plating solution. Satisfactory deposits are obtained without agitation at a current density of 350 amp/sq ft. Copper fluoborate, fluoboric acid, and boric acid are the primary constituents. Table 3 shows representative "high" and "low" concentration baths. To prevent uneven plating at edges, addition agents usually are incorporated, especially for thick deposits.

TABLE 1. COMPOSITION OF COPPER CYANIDE PLATING SOLUTIONS

Constituent or condition	Copper Cyanide Strike	Rochelle Copper Bath	High-Efficiency Copper Cyanide Bath[a]	Barrel Plating Bath
Sodium cyanide, gpl	25	35	90 to 120	50
Copper cyanide, gpl	15	25	75 to 100	20
Sodium carbonate, gpl	15 to 30	15 to 30	15 to 30	15 to 30
Rochelle salts, gpl	None	30 to 60	None	None
Free sodium cyanide	6 to 10	6 to 10	40 to 20	20 to 25
pH (electrometric)	About 10.5	12.6	12.6[b]	About 10.5
Temperature, °F	100 to 120	120 to 140	150 to 170	100 to 110
Cathode current density, amp/sq ft	10 to 20	20 to 50	20 to 40	5 to 15
Cathode efficiency, per cent	30 to 40	40 to 60	95 to 99	30 to 40
Anode current density, amp/sq ft	15 to 30	20 to 30	20 to 30	15 to 15

[a] Equivalent weights of potassium salts often are substituted for the sodium salts. Proprietary addition agents usually are added for brightening.
[b] About 40 gpl of sodium hydroxide or 56 gpl of potassium hydroxide is needed to adjust the pH of a new bath to 12.6.

TABLE 2. COMPOSITION OF COPPER SULFATE
PLATING BATHS

Constituent or Condition	Customary Range
Copper sulfate, CuSO$_4$·5H$_2$O, gpl	150 to 250
Sulfuric acid, gpl	45 to 110
Specific gravity at 75°F	1.115 to 1.21
Resistivity, ohm-cm	4.0 to 4.5
Cathode current density, amp/ sq ft	20 to 40[a]
Temperature, °F	70 to 100
Anode current density, amp/sq ft	20 to 40[a]

[a] Higher current densities up to 200 amp/sq ft are practical with considerable agitation. Copper is deposited at the rate of 0.011 inch/hr at this current density.

TABLE 3. COMPOSITION OF COPPER
FLUOBORATE PLATING BATHS

Constituent or Condition	Low Concentration	High Concentration
Copper fluoborate, Cu(BF$_4$)$_2$, gpl	224	448
Fluoboric acid, gpl	15	30
Boric acid, gpl	15	30
pH (electrometric)	1.2 to 1.7	0.3 to 0.6
Specific gravity at 80°F	1.17–1.18	1.35–1.36
Cathode current density, amp/sq ft	20 to 50	40 to 60[a]
Temperature, °F	70 to 95	75 to 100
Anode current density, amp/sq ft	20 to 100	40 to 150[a]

[a] Higher current densities up to 350 amp/sq ft are practical with considerable agitation. Copper is deposited at the rate of 0.02 inch/hr at this current density.

TABLE 4. CONDITIONS FOR ELECTROPLATING
IN THE COPPER PYROPHSOPHATE BATH

Constituent or Condition	Customary Range
Copper ions, gpl	22 to 38
Pyrophosphate ions, gpl	150 to 250
Oxalate ions, gpl	15 to 30
Nitrate ions, gpl	5 to 10
Ammonia, gpl	1 to 3
pH (electrometric)	8.2 to 8.8
Temperature, °F	122 to 140
Cathode current density, amp/sq ft	10 to 75
Air agitation, cu ft/min/sq ft of surface area	1 to 1.5

The pyrophosphate bath (Table 4) is prepared with sodium or potassium pyrophosphate which forms a highly soluble complex compound with copper pyrophosphate and with ammonium or potassium oxalate to stabilize the pH of the solution and assist anode dissolution. Nitrate ions may be added to inhibit the reduction of hydrogen ions at high current density areas of the cathode. The pH of the solution must be maintained in the range of 8.2 to 8.8. The copper complex compound is unstable at a lower pH. If the pH is too high, the anode efficiency is reduced. During operation, the pH may be raised by adding ammonia. Like the copper sulfate and copper fluoborate baths, the copper pyrophosphate solution normally dissolves copper anodes with an efficiency of 100 per cent. The cathode efficiency for these divalent solutions also is about 100 per cent. There is less tendency for nonuniformity in thickness and for rough, uneven deposits with the pyrophosphate bath, by comparison with the other divalent solutions.

Anodes

High-purity, oxygen-free copper is recommended for the anodes in cyanide, sulfate, fluoborate, and pyrophosphate baths. Silver as an impurity in very small amounts causes rough copper deposits in cyanide solutions. Lead in small amounts is a harmful impurity in the sulfate and fluoborate baths.

Copper anodes containing phosphorus have been introduced for operation in sulfate solutions. Gelatinous films containing phosphides tend to hold small particles of undissolved copper or impurities and prevent them from entering the plating solution.

In cyanide solutions, films of cuprous oxide tend to form on anode surfaces, if the temperature is too low or the current density is too high. Particles of the oxide that fall off the anode and reach the cathode surfaces before they are dissolved by the cyanide ions will cause rough deposits. In the sulfate and fluoborate baths, the anodes generally become coated with finely-divided particles of copper or copper oxide. If agitation removes the particles and if they are not dissolved by the free acid, they will cause roughness in the copper plate. To prevent such particles from reaching the cathode surfaces, the anodes are customarily bagged, at least when more than 0.0001 or 0.0002 inch of copper is being plated. Nylon is a widely-used material for the anode bags.

Properties of Copper Electroplate

The properties and characteristics of copper plate depend on the conditions for plating the copper. The dependency of the properties on the bath composition and operating conditions is well established. Very small concentrations

TABLE 5. HARNDESS, TENSILE STRENGTH, AND DUCTILITY OF ELECTRODEPOSITED COPPER

Type of Bath	Hardness (Vickers or Vickers Equivalent)		Tensile Strength, psi		Elongation in 2 in., per cent	
	Min.	Max.	Min.	Max.	Min.	Max.
Copper cyanide[a]	100	220	—	43,000	6	50
Copper sulfate[b]	51	170	17,100	90,000	3.0	39
Copper fluoborate[c]	41	77	17,100	37,600	6.0	14.5
Copper pyrophosphate	160	190	—	—		~10

[a] The hardness of copper electroformed in cyanide solutions is given as 100 to 160 VPN without periodically reversed current, and from 150 to 220 VPN with PR. With no PR, elongation is 30 to 50 per cent. With PR, elongation is only 6 to 9 per cent.

[b] With no addition agents, the hardness of copper deposited in copper sulfate baths is about 85 Vickers or Knoop; tensile strength ranges from 20,000 to 40,000 psi, depending on the bath temperature and cathode current density. Elongation values range from 16 to 39 per cent. Higher values for hardness and tensile strength and lower values for the elongation are reported for solutions containing addition agents.

[c] The lower values for hardness and tensile strength are obtained for the low-concentration bath described in Table 3. Higher values for hadrness and tensile strength result from copper deposited in the high-concentration solution.

of addition agents cause profound changes in brightness, smoothness, hardness, and strength. Variations in temperature and current density have equally important effects for some solutions. Data for the hardness, tensile strength, and ductility of electrodeposited copper are given in Table 5. The footnotes describe the influence of some of the most important variables.

Soft copper deposits usually are associated with a coarse, columnar microstructure, similar to the structure of cast copper. A fibrous structure in copper electroplate exhibits slightly higher hardness and tensile strength values. The fine-grained structure such as that produced by adding β-naphthoquinoline to the copper sulfate bath is about twice as hard and strong as the copper with a columnar structure and is similar to the fine-grained rolled sheet used for deep drawing.

To avoid cracking in electrodeposits, stress must be kept at a low value. Unless unusual addition agents are added to copper electroplating baths, stress values are generally lower than the stress in nickel, chromium, and other electrodeposited metals. Representative stress data for copper are as follows:

Copper cyanide solutions, 6,000 to 10,000 psi
Copper sulfate solutions, 0 to 3,000 psi.

Lead as an impurity in the copper cyanide solution can increase the stress to as much as 15,000 psi. Gelatin additions to the copper sulfate bath causes a stress as high as 21,000 psi.

References

1. LOWENHEIM, F. A., Editor, chapters on "Rochelle Copper," "High Efficiency Copper," "Pyrophosphate Copper," and "Acid Copper Electroplating" in "Modern Electroplating," Third Edition, sponsored by The Electrochemical Society, New York, John Wiley & Sons, Inc., 1963.
2. "Physical and Mechanical Properties of Electroformed Copper," American Society for Testing Materials, Special Publication No. 318, 1962.

W. R. SAFRANEK

Cross-references: *Addition Agents; Brightening Agents;* entries bearing *Electroplating* and *Plating* titles.

COPPER ELECTROREFINING

The behavior of metals in an electrolytic refining process is determined by their relative position in the electromotive series of chemical elements.[1] The electromotive series is a list of the metals arranged in the decreasing order of their tendencies to pass into ionic form by losing electrons. In electrorefining a metal, a solution or electrolyte is selected that will, upon passage of an electric current, ionize the metal to be refined and all those above it in the electromotive series but will deposit or deionize only the most noble one of those dissolved.

In copper electrorefining, a solution of copper sulfate in sulfuric acid will dissolve copper and all metals above it, such as Zn, Fe, Ni, Sb, and Pb when such metals are present in the anode or positive electrode in an electrolytic cell. The elements below copper in the electromotive series will remain un-ionized and, therefore, undissolved at the anode, leaving a residue or slime. By proper balance of ionizing current with decomposition potential it should be possible to deposit the copper alone. In actual practice the definition is not as clear cut due to complex ion formation and controls have to be used to minimize codeposition of impurities.

TABLE 1. SMELTING AND REFINING PRODUCTS

Element	Anode	Cathode	Slime
Au oz/ton	1.0	0.001	100
Ag "	40	0.20	4,000
Cu %	99.3	99.99	20.0
Fe %	0.002	0.0015	
S %	0.005	0.0015	
As %	0.05	0.0002	1.5[a]
Pb %	0.10	0.0015	10.0
Sb %	0.08	0.0001	5.2[b]
Bi %	0.005	0.0005	0.3[c]
Se %	0.07	0.0004	7.0
Te %	0.02	0.0001	2.0
Sn %	0.002	0.00002	0.2
Ni %	0.12	0.0007	0.8[d]

[a] About 30 per cent of arsenic goes into slime and 70 per cent into electrolyte.
[b] About 65 per cent of antimony goes into slime and 35 per cent into electrolyte.
[c] About 60 per cent of bismuth goes into slime and 40 per cent into electrolyte.
[d] About 5 per cent of nickel goes into slime and 95 per cent nto electrolyte.

Electrolytic copper has a specification (ASTM B-5-43) of a minimum purity of 99.900 per cent, with silver being counted as copper and a maximum resistivity of 0.15328 ohm/meter-gram at 20°C. The purity of commercial copper exceeds these specifications and assays over 99.95 per cent copper are not uncommon. Resistivity is usually reported in its reciprocal or conductivity standard with 100 per cent being equivalent of 0.15328 ohm resistivity. Most of the copper now available has conductivity of 101 per cent or better by this criterion. Electrolytic refining is the only method developed to date that will consistently produce copper of this quality.

In addition to the removal of deleterious impurities, the electrolytic method often pays for itself in the recovery of precious metals, such as gold, silver, and platinum group elements. It has been estimated that as high as 80 per cent of the world silver and 15 per cent of the world gold production are recovered as by-products from copper, lead, nickel, and cobalt refining.

Thus, electrorefining produces copper of the highest degree of purity required for electrical conductor use and also makes possible the recovery of precious metals which are present in the ores in such small amounts that recovery is not practical by any other method. Other metals and salts are also recovered as by-products of electrorefining, among them nickel, selenium, and tellurium.

Listed below is a typical upgrading of copper

in electrorefining showing the anode and cathode analysis and anticipated slime assay with a slime fall of 20 pounds per ton refined.

Systems

With a single exception[2] all electrorefining of copper is by the multiple system wherein a number of electrode pairs (usually 22 to 48) are placed in a single cell. The alternate electrodes are connected to common busses; thus, the current flow is split up in parallel circuits or in "multiple" arrangement.

Electrodes connected to the positive bus are called anodes and dissolve supplying the metal ions to the electrolyte. The alternate electrodes are connected to the negative bus (cathodes) and take copper out of the electrolyte, pure copper depositing on a thin sheet and building it up to about a ½ in. thickness.

The decomposition voltage for copper sulfate at the cathode face is counterbalanced by the energy of formation at the anode face, therefore, only sufficient voltage has to be provided to overcome electrolyte resistance plus a small overvoltage at each electrode. This results in the relatively low power consumption for electrorefining of copper of 150 to 250 kwh per ton. Cell voltages are in the order of ¼ volt with amperage flow of 10,000 amperes (at current density of 15 to 20 amps per sq ft).

Fig. 1 shows the cell room of an electrolytic copper refinery.

Tanks

Since the electrolyte is a corrosive acid and the tanks are electrically connected, two major items have to be kept in mind when constructing a refinery: (1) tanks must be made of an acid-resistant material, and (2) tanks must be electrically insulated from ground and from other tanks (only the electrode should make contact with the bus or power system).

For uniform operation, several hundred or more tanks are connected to a common circulating system and electrolyte is flowed gently through each cell. This permits heating and conditioning of the electrolyte at one common point. The gentle flow is required to keep electrolyte stirred without agitating the slime.

Tanks are electrically connected in series with other tanks to give sufficient voltage for a circuit, since each tank in the multiple system will

FIG. 1. Electrolytic copper refinery; general view of the deposition tanks and crane lifting out a load of cathodes. (*Courtesy U. S. Metals Refining Co.;* photograph by Max Heberlein)

have a voltage drop only slightly higher than the individual cells in that tank of 0.2 to 0.4 volts. Normal refining practice uses 15 to 20 amperes per sq ft active surface, but the multiple arrangement permits current flows of 5,000 to 20,000 amps per cell. Thus, placing say 500 cells in series will give a circuit loading of 100 to 200 volts at 5,000 to 20,000 amperes (d-c).

Tanks have been made of wood but the tendency now is toward concrete.[3] In the multiple system, tanks are usually lead-lined using antimonial sheet lead about ⅛ in. thick. In the series system, due to the higher voltage drop in each tank, the lining must be nonconducting, otherwise a portion of the current will flow through the tank lining from one end of the cell to the other in preference to going through the electrodes. Series tanks are therefore lined with an asphaltic mastic or other insulating materials.

Tanks for either system have to be sturdily constructed, for the walls of the tanks support the weight of the electrodes which is about 10 tons for an average size tank. In addition each tank will contain more than 3 tons of electrolyte.

Tanks generally vary from 8 ft to 14 ft in length and 2.75 to 3.5 ft in width with a depth of 3½ to 4 ft. Increasing depth creates difficulties in maintaining spacing between electrodes and in keeping cathodes free of settleable impurities.

Operating Conditions

Anodes for the multiple system are cast slabs of fire-refined copper weighing from 400 to 700 lb each, 35 to 40 in. long, 28 to 36 in. wide and 1¼ to 2 in. thick. There are 22 to 48 anodes used per tank and usually one cathode more than anodes.

Anodes remain in tanks from 20 to 30 days and will produce two or more sets of cathodes. At the end of the anode period there will still be 6 to 20 per cent of the anode left undissolved, and this is returned to anode furnaces for remelting and recasting. At the time of replacing anodes, usual practice calls for cleaning out any mud or slime accumulated on the anode and in the bottom of the tanks. This slime is processed primarily for precious metal recovery, but other less precious metals, such as Se, Te, Pb, and Sn, are recovered in the process.

Cathodes for copper refining are made by electrodeposition of a thin film on an oiled or treated blank ³⁄₁₆ to ¼ in. thick in a portion of the electrorefinery. This deposit is removed daily producing a "starting sheet" 0.02 to 0.03 in. thick that is used as an expendable cathode in the remainder of the refining tanks.

Cathode quality is controlled by adjusting

operating conditions so as to give a fine, dense, crystalline deposit with a minimum of irregular growths (needles, trees, or nodules). This is usually accomplished by adding some form of colloid which helps control crystal size plus other modifiers or buffers, such as lignones,* thiourea and "Avitone."

Electrolyte

For electrorefining a solution of an ionizable metal salt is required. In refining of copper an aqueous solution of copper sulfate is used with added sulfuric acid to improve its electrical conductivity.

Factors affecting conductivity of electrolyte and power consumption with usual operating range are as follows:

Acid content	180 to 210 gpl free H_2SO_4
Copper content	35 to 45 gpl Cu as $CuSO_4$
Impurity content	25 gpl Ni and 15 gpl As (max)
Temperature	140 to 150°F
Circulation	2 to 4 gal/min
Spacing of electrodes	1 to 2 in. face to face
Conditioning reagents	Usually glue with other modifiers
Current density	15 to 20 amp per sq ft

The electrolyte gradually becomes fouled from other impurities in the anode in addition to the Ni and As so that the composition is not as simple as given above. After a certain amount of impurities has accumulated, part of the electrolyte must be removed for purification.

The first step in purification entails the removal of copper ions by either electrodeposition using insoluble anodes or by partial evaporation and crystallization as copper sulfate or by a combination of the two. The copper-free electrolyte is then treated for removal of other compounds. Frequently, concentration by evaporation is sufficient to crystalize out an impure nickel sulfate which will keep other impurities also in control. The remaining acid after crystallization of nickel sulfate is reused in the copper refinery.

Slimes Treatment

The slime collecting in the bottom of the electrolytic cells will contain the undissolved metals

* Lignones are materials such as "Bindarene," "Goulac," "Glutrin," "Encore," "Orzan A," "Lignin-sulfite," "Sulfite-lignose," "Lig-inhibitor," "Lignone," and other similar sulfite waste residues from paper mills.

and intermetallic compounds as well as salts and complexes precipitated from the electrolyte. For example, lead dissolves from the anode in preference to copper, but is precipitated as $PbSO_4$.

The slimes are processed for recovery of the various metals contained.[4] Briefly, the processes used for slime treatment involve removal of copper by oxidation and leaching, and extraction of selenium and tellurium by fuming or fusion with fluxes. The treated slime is smelted and refined in small furnaces where base metals are slagged or fumed off and impure silver is cast in anode form for electrolytic refining of the silver and recovery of more precious metals, such as gold and the platinum group of metals.

References

1. Tables on "Electromotive Series of Elements" or "Oxidation Potentials of Elements," "Handbook of Chemistry and Physics," Cleveland, Chemical Rubber Publishing Co., latest edition, 1962–63.
2. HARLOFF, C. S., AND JOHNSON, H. F., "The Nichols Series System of Electrolytic Copper Refining," *Trans. AIME*, **106**, 398 (1933).
3. SCHLOEN, J. H., AND FORBES, S. S., "Industry Report on Modern Tank House Practice," 401–431, "Extractive Metallurgy of Copper, Nickel and Cobalt," New York, Interscience Publishers, 1961.
4. SCHLOEN, J. H., AND ELKIN, E. M., "Treatment of Electrolytic Copper Refinery Slimes," p. 265, "Copper, The Metal, Its Alloys, and Compounds," New York, Reinhold Publishing Corp., 1954.

WALTER L. BRYTCZUK

COPPER ELECTROWINNING

Production of copper from ore is accomplished by one of two main types of processing. The principal one employs electrolytic refining as the last of several steps. The other, accounting for perhaps 10 per cent of the total production of copper, has only two main steps: (1) leaching the ore (usually without prior concentration) with a suitable aqueous solvent to dissolve the copper minerals, and (2) recovery of the copper from the leaching solution.

Treatment of the solution for recovery of copper is usually by electrolysis. Chemical precipitation is employed in some cases, but the precipitated copper then is impure, so that the additional steps of melting and refining the precipitate must follow.

Electrowinning is the term given to the electrochemical method of extracting the copper from the leaching solution. A more definitive phrase would be "electrodeposition from leaching solutions" or "electrolytic precipitation from leaching solutions," but the simpler "electrowinning" is usually preferred.

The product of copper electrowinning is of the same quality as electrolytically refined copper. The nature of the impurity contained in the cathodes may differ slightly, such as being lower in silver, but with a total impurity content as low as 0.1 per cent or less, the difference in composition between electrorefined copper and copper obtained by electrowinning is of little or no practical importance. In both cases the exact composition will vary slightly from one plant to another.

Of greater importance is the fact that similarity of the product has sometimes led to disregard of the fundamental differences between electrorefining and electrowinning.

In brief, electrowinning consists of using the leaching solution as electrolyte, electrolyzing it with an insoluble anode, and depositing its copper content as pure copper on the cathode. When electrowinning is employed, the leaching solvent is sulfuric acid, so that the electrolyte, as also in electrorefining, is an aqueous solution of copper sulfate containing free sulfuric acid. In decomposing the copper sulfate, sulfuric acid is regenerated, and the resulting solution is again used for leaching. Thus, the hydro-electrometallurgical process is cyclic, a feature which is essential to its economy. Because of the necessity of obtaining a chemically pure and physically dense, adherent cathode deposit, the composition of the electrolyte must be kept within limits; hence only a portion of its copper content, ranging from 15 to 60 per cent, is deposited in each cycle, the remainder being carried as a circulating load.

Perhaps the best approach to consideration of the theory and practice of electrowinning will be by discussing the essential differences between electrorefining and electrowinning.

Chemical Reaction

The reaction in electrorefining is reversible, except for the small amount of impurities dissolved at the anode. The reaction in electrowinning is irreversible:

$$CuSO_4 + H_2O \rightarrow Cu + H_2SO_4 + \tfrac{1}{2}O_2 .$$

$$\Delta H = +56,620 \text{ cal}$$

Thus, an equivalent of sulfuric acid is formed for every equivalent of copper deposited at the cathode, and 11.2 liters of oxygen gas are liberated at the anode for every 63.6 g of copper deposited. The acid becomes available for dissolving more copper in the leaching cycle, and the amount of acid that must be purchased for leaching is essentially only that required to account for losses, such as in solution entrained in the ore after leaching and washing and acid used in dissolving iron and other impurities.

Source of the Copper

In electrorefining the copper is dissolved from the anode, which has been obtained by smelting and furnace refining operations. In electrowinning, the copper comes from the solution (electrolyte), which had been obtained by leaching.

Nature of the Anode

In electrorefining, the anode is impure copper, soluble in the electrolyte except for a small content of insoluble impurities, which enter the "anode slimes." In electrowinning, the anode is wholly insoluble; there are no slimes.

A suitable material for the anode has been a source of difficulty. The requirements are insolubility, resistance to the mechanical and chemical effects of oxygen liberated on its surface, low oxygen overvoltage, and resistance to breakage in handling. Lead anodes containing 6 to 15 per cent antimony have been used in most plants. Such anodes are attacked by chloride if present in the electrolyte. This is the case at the huge plant at Chuquicamata, Chile, where it is necessary to remove cupric chloride dissolved from the ore by passing the solution over cement copper, reducing the cupric to insoluble cuprous chloride. At this plant there was also developed an anode of a copper-silicon alloy, called the Chilex anode, used in a portion of the tankroom. It has a longer life but raises the power consumption because of greater resistance and greater oxygen overvoltage.

Nature of the Cathode

This is the same in both processes. In both a "starting sheet" of pure copper is used to receive the deposit initially. The starting sheets are made in a special section of the tankroom.

Nature of the Electrolyte

In electrorefining, the electrolyte usually contains 34 to 52 g of Cu per liter with 125 to 225 g of free H_2SO_4 per liter. Its composition changes between rather narrow limits during operation, although there is a slow accumulation of impurities dissolved from the anode, which makes purification necessary. In electrowinning, the composition of the electrolyte is more variable, dependent on the composition of the ore being leached. When it flows from the leaching tanks to become the "feed" to the electrolytic cells, its copper content averages somewhat lower than that of the electrorefining electrolyte, and as it flows through the series of tanks its content of copper is further reduced. The free acid content is much lower in electrowinning, being adjusted for maximum dissolving ability and minimum cost for leaching. It is lowest in the "feed" to the electrolytic cells and builds up during electrolysis as the copper content is reduced. Impurities enter during the leaching cycle, none during electrolysis. Purity is controlled by treatment and by drawing off part of the flow and discarding it after removal of its copper content.

The temperature of the electrolyte is commonly 30 to 50°C, compared with 50 to 65°C in electrorefining.

Current

With a more dilute solution, a lower current density must be used. It ranges between 5 and 13 amp per sq ft, as against 15 to 30 amp per sq ft in electrorefining.

One of the impurities dissolved from the ore in leaching is iron. This will exist in the electrolyte as both ferric and ferrous sulfate. A loss in current efficiency results, largely because ferric sulfate will redissolve some of the deposited copper:

$$Fe_2(SO_4)_3 + Cu \rightarrow 2FeSO_4 + CuSO_4$$

Some of the current may also be expended in reducing ferric to ferrous sulfate; this reaction consumes only the equivalent of 1624 cal per gram of iron, whereas reduction of $CuSO_4$ to Cu consumes 3156 cal per gram of copper. Ferrous sulfate transported to the anode may be oxidized to ferric sulfate, thus setting up the so-called ferro-ferric cycle. However, with a total iron content below 4 per cent, as is usually the case, this action is slight, and the presence of ferrous iron is not considered harmful. In some plants ferric iron is reduced to ferrous by passing SO_2 through the solution prior to electrolysis:

$$Fe_2(SO_4)_3 + SO_2 + 2H_2O \rightarrow 2FeSO_4 + 2H_2SO_4$$

At the plant of the Inspiration Consolidated Copper Company in Arizona, the ferric iron content of the solution leaving the tankhouse is about 11 gpl, falling below 4 gpl during treatment. This high content is purposely carried to leach sulfide copper from the ore, but there results a current efficiency as low as 75 per cent. At other plants this runs from 81 to 92 per cent, compared with an average of about 93 per cent in electrorefining.

Voltage

In electrorefining, the energy absorbed in liberating copper at the cathode is counterbalanced by energy generated in dissolving copper at the anode. Hence, the reaction potential is negligible. In electrowinning, the reaction potential is that equivalent to the energy absorption of 56,620 cal, as shown above. Calculation by Thompson's rule gives the reaction potential as 1.2 volts. In electrorefining, the only voltage requirement is that for overcoming the ohmic resistance of the electrolyte and resistances of electrodes, slimes clinging to the anode, and contact resistances. These same resistances, except for slimes, occur in electrowinning, the resistance of the electrolyte being somewhat greater because of its lower content of acid and copper. In addition, the oxygen gas voltage in electrowinning is a relatively large factor. It can be minimized, but not avoided. It varies at different plants.

For the sake of comparison, the following analysis of cell voltages in copper electrorefining, copper electrowinning, and zinc electrowinning is given, with the understanding that the actual voltages may depart somewhat from those stated.

TABLE 1. ANALYSIS OF CELL VOLTAGES

Source	Copper Electro-refining	Copper Electro-winning	Zinc Electro-winning
Reaction potential	0.0	1.2	2.25
Electrolyte IR drop	0.15	0.25	0.75
Resistance of contacts, etc.	0.10	0.10	0.15
Oxygen gas voltage	—	0.35	0.45
Hydrogen gas voltage	—	—	0.10
Total	0.25	1.90	3.70

It will be seen that the tank voltage required in copper electrowinning is about 8 times that in electrorefining, and about one-half that in zinc electrowinning.

Power Consumption

The power requirement in electrowinning is 8 to 10 times that in electrorefining, the voltage ratio being augmented by the difference in current efficiency. In electrowinning, it is about 0.9 to 1.1 kwh per pound of copper produced, except at Inspiration, where the low current efficiency raises it to about 1.3 kwh per pound of copper.

Chemical Precipitation

An alternative method to electrowinning for recovering copper from leaching solutions is chemical precipitation. Although a number of precipitating agents are possible, only iron in the form of scrap iron or sponge iron has been used with commercial success. The chemical action is a simple replacement of copper by iron due to the higher position of iron in the electromotive series of metals:

$$CuSO_4 aq + Fe \rightarrow FeSO_4 aq + Cu.$$

$$\Delta H = -35,360 \text{ cal}$$

Precipitation of copper in this manner is called *cementation* and the product is *cement copper*. A major disadvantage of the process is the impurity of the cement copper, which cannot be cleanly separated from the remaining iron on which it precipitates. It is commonly as low as 90 per cent Cu, and must be melted and refined to produce pure copper for the market. Also, the process is not applicable to a closed circuit; the acid is not regenerated.

The process may be carried out in tanks, towers, or launders, depending on the form of iron used. Scrap iron, such as detinned cans, for example, is cheap but more impure. Sponge iron gives more rapid and efficient operation, but is more expensive. The consumption of iron is always considerably greater than the chemical reaction requires, because of attack on iron by sulfuric acid or ferric sulfate as well as mechanical losses. It averages 1 to 2 lb of iron per pound of copper. Other important applications of the process are in recovering copper from wash solu-

tions in leaching operations or from solutions discarded to control accumulation of impurities; also it is used to recover copper from mine waters or copper-bearing water in small streams and from solutions obtained in heap leaching. It has also been used in connection with leaching in place.

Another advantage of cementation in addition to its simplicity and adaptability to discontinuous operation is its effectiveness with very dilute solutions, far too dilute for use in electrowinning. Impurities in the solution are of little consequence.

For continuous and large-scale operation, electrowinning is preferred.

The leaching process which precedes electrowinning, yielding the solution which serves as electrolyte, will not be described here; it is discussed in some of the references given below.

The hydro-electrometallurgical process of producing copper from ore has certain advantages in comparison with the flotation-smelting-converting-refining type of process. Briefly these are:

(1) It is suitable for low-grade ores (sometimes under 1 per cent Cu) without concentration to a higher percentage of copper.

(2) It requires neither fuel nor flux.

(3) The equipment needed, primarily leaching tanks and their accessories, is lower in cost than the furnaces needed in the other types of process.

On the other hand, there are large limitations, as follows:

(1) It is largely limited to oxidized ores, since copper sulfide minerals are not soluble in sulfuric acid. This objection may sometimes be counteracted by incorporating ferric sulfate as a solvent, or by a combination process in which the sulfides are removed by flotation and smelted, while the oxides are leached.

(2) It is not suitable for the many ores containing important amounts of gold and silver, since these metals are not dissolved in acid leaching.

(3) Consumption of sulfuric acid may be prohibitive if the gangue of the ore contains large amounts of carbonates or other minerals attacked by the acid.

Flowsheets and most operating details vary widely at different plants, depending on the nature of the ore and other circumstances. Accordingly, none can be cited as standard or even typical. In general, tankhouse layouts and cell design follow closely those used in electrorefining of copper. The multiple system is employed. There may be several hundred tanks, each containing many anodes and cathodes. Tanks are rectangular in section and may be from 20 to 60 ft in length, 3 or 4 ft wide, and 4 or 5 ft deep. They are usually built of reinforced concrete, lined with antimonial lead sheet. In some instances the lining has been asphalt mastic, in others this has proved unsatisfactory. In one recent installation polyester resin reinforced with fiber glass is used for launders and other parts, taking the place of lead. Small tanks and pump boxes are lined with this material. Polythene piping has there replaced lead for pipelines up to 4 in. in diameter.

Anodes are spaced 3 to 4 in. center to center, with cathodes between. Direct current is obtained by use of motor-generator sets or mercury arc rectifiers. Details of operation and construction at a number of individual plants may be found in the references cited below.

The principal plants at which electrowinning is practiced are those of the Chile Exploration Company, Chuquicamata, Chile; Inspiration Consolidated Copper Company, Inspiration, Ariz.; Andes Copper Mining Company, Potrerillos, Chile; Union Minière du Haut Katanga, Katanga, Africa; and Nchanga Consolidated Copper Mines Ltd., Chingola, Africa. The new plant of the Bagdad Copper Corp., Bagdad, Ariz., uses the cementation process, producing about 20 tons of cement copper per day.

References

1. CHAPMAN, F. H., AND PAGE, E. W., "Leaching and Electrowinning of Copper from Nchanga Oxide Concentrate," in "Extractive Metallurgy of Copper, Nickel, and Cobalt," Queneau, P., Ed., pp. 317–45, New York, Interscience Publishers, 1961.
2. McARTHUR, J. A., AND LEAPHART, C., "Leaching of Chuquicamata Oxide Copper Ores," *idem*, pp. 347–61.
3. GRUNENFELDER, J. G., "The Hydrometallurgy of Copper," in "Copper, the Metal, Its Alloys and Compounds," Butts, A., Ed., pp. 300–36, New York, Reinhold Publishing Corp., 1954.
4. MANTELL, C. L., "Electrochemical Engineering," 4th ed., pp. 198–210, New York, McGraw-Hill Book Co., Inc., 1960.
5. NEWTON, J. AND WILSON, C. L., "Metallurgy of Copper," pp. 318–78, New York, John Wiley & Sons, Inc., 1942.
6. VAN ARSDALE, G. D., "Hydrometallurgy of Base Metals," pp. 103–205, New York, McGraw-Hill Book Company, Inc., 1953.

ALLISON BUTTS

Cross-references: *Cadmium Electrowinning, Copper Electrorefining, Electrorefining, Electrowinning, Zinc and Cadmium Electrowinning.*

COPPER AND NICKEL CONCENTRATES, ELECTRIC SMELTING

Metallurgical Considerations

The electric furnace can be used as a replacement of the fuel-heated reverberatory furnace for the smelting of sulfur-bearing copper, or copper-nickel, or nickel concentrates and ores.

As shown in Fig. 1, the furnace charge may be roasted (hot charge smelting) or unroasted (wet charge smelting). The main product is a matte containing iron sulfide and the copper, or copper-nickel, or nickel in the form of sulfides. This is separated from the waste slag which contains chiefly the iron from the concentrates in the form of fayalite. Oxide nickel ores give a ferronickel alloy instead of a matte.

If the matte contains only copper, it is blown in the converter in two steps, first to white metal, Cu_2S, and then to blister copper. The iron sulfide in the matte forms a fayalite (iron silicate) slag with the siliceous flux added to the converter. If the matte contains copper and nickel, it is blown in the converter to a "Bessemer matte," a mixture of Cu_2S and Ni_3S_2. The blister copper is treated in the electrorefining process to produce pure copper, and the Bessemer matte is separated into copper and nickel in special processes. The converter slag is returned to the electric or reverberatory furnace where its 2 or more per cent copper and nickel is largely recovered. Details of these operations can be found in books dealing with copper or nickel metallurgy.

Thermal Considerations

Large quantities of slag are formed from the concentrates and converter slag; therefore, the electric furnace cannot be heated by the electric arc in the same manner as are electric steel furnaces or furnaces for the smelting of copper cathodes. In copper and nickel matte furnaces the liquid slag floating on the matte is resistance-heated according to the I^2R relationship, where I is the current in amperes, and R is the resistance of the slag in ohms. The controlling factor is R, whose value depends on the composition and temperature of the slag.

At any given installation the composition of the copper and nickel concentrates is quite constant; therefore, the composition of the slag shows little variation. In the ternary system diagram: SiO_2-FeO-CaO, all these slags are located on or near the quasi-binary section: $2FeO \cdot SiO_2$-$CaO \cdot SiO_2$, ranging from the monosilicate, acidity 1.0, to the bisilicate, acidity 2.0, with rising CaO content. Generally the acidity of these slags is from about 1.2 to 1.4, and increasing content of CaO, MgO, Al_2O_3 and other basic oxides lowers the conductivity. The liquid slag is dissociated. The anion, SiO_4^{4-}, has a large ionic radius and has the tendency to build up two- and three-dimensional chains which render difficult the movement of energy. On the other hand, the cations, especially Fe^{2+}, have a much smaller ionic radius, and they can move more easily as carriers of energy. The larger the ionic radius, e.g., Ca^{2+}, the lower the mobility and the lower the conductivity of the slag. The slags always contain magnetite, Fe_3O_4, but its influence on the conductivity is not yet clear. A certain resistance in the slag is absolutely necessary, so that the current is not too high. On the other hand, if the resistance is too high, the voltage must be increased.

The electrical energy is transmitted by electrodes dipping to varying depths in the slag. The electrode material is carbon or graphite, materials not attacked by the liquid slag. How deep the electrodes must dip into the slag depends on the slag resistance (or conductivity) and the furnace voltage. There are two paths for the flow of current, the first through the slag between the electrodes, and the second from the tip of one electrode to the matte and from the matte to the tip of the other electrode. The matte has a much higher conductivity than the slag and, therefore, there is little heating of the matte during the passage of current.

However, there is an exception. If the quantity of matte in the furnace is low, the cross-section is small and the current density is high. In that case, there is not only a considerable heating of the matte, but also an electrodynamic movement and circulation which may damage severely the furnace bottom. In the same way, if the voltage is too low and the electrodes too deep in the slag, the slag directly under the

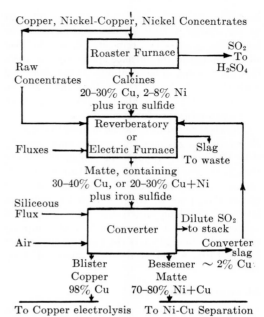

FIG. 1. Flowsheet for the pyrometallurgical refining of copper and copper-nickel concentrates.

electrodes is heated too much and damage to the furnace bottom occurs.

In contrast to reverberatory furnace practice, there must be sufficient matte, at least 30 to 50 cm thick, and sufficient slag depth so that with high voltage the distance between the tip of the electrode and the surface of the matte is great and the heating of the slag is chiefly at the surface where the charge floats. The first electric furnaces at Sulitjelma, Norway and Imatra, Finland operated at 80 to 100 v and a slag layer of 30 to 50 cm. Today the electric furnaces operate at 200 to 300 v and a slag layer of 80 to 100 cm. The Russian furnaces are said to operate at up to 400 v and slag layers up to 150 cm.

The smelting heat is produced by the passage of current in the slag and is transferred from the slag to the charge. Thus, there is a principal difference between the fuel-heated reverberatory furnace and the electric furnace. In the former the heat of the combustion gases in the combustion space is transferred to the charge in part directly by convection and in part indirectly by radiation from the heated furnace roof. The heat passage is from the combustion space to the charge to the slag to the matte, that is from top to bottom. In the electric furnace the slag is heated and transfers its heat to the charge floating on the slag surface. The heat flow is thus the opposite: from the slag to the charge to the furnace space, that is, from bottom to top. The contact of the hot slag with the matte is the reason that the matte in the electric furnace is about 100°C hotter than in the reverberatory furnace.

The electric furnace has no combustion gases; therefore, the gas quantity is very small, chiefly SO_2, CO_2, water vapor, and leakage air. Since the gas temperature is not more than 600°C, the furnace roof of the electric furnace may be made of fire clay, possibly covered with an insulating layer of kieselgur, while the roof of the reverberatory furnace, exposed to high-temperature combustion gases, is the most sensitive part of the furnace and is generally made of magnesite.

Electrical Connections

The electric energy is generally three-phase a-c, usually separated into three single-phase currents by three single-phase transformers. In this way only a third of the transformer capacity is necessary as reserve. The transformers are partly water-cooled (where the transformer oil is cooled by water) and partly air-cooled. All modern transformers have the provision for changing the voltage under load in steps of 5 to 10 v. Moreover, the transformer may be switched from Y to delta connection and the different steps changed from v to $v\sqrt{3}$. The current is carried to the electrodes by copper bus bars. Their current density is about 1 amp/sq mm. The connections from the bus bars to the electrodes are copper cables whose current density is also 1 amp/sq mm, and then water-cooled pipes, whose current density is about 2 amp/sq mm. The electrode contact plates are also water-cooled.

Electrodes

The electrodes are chiefly Söderberg electrodes. To replace the electrode consumption, about 2 to 5 kg/metric ton of solid charge, the electrodes must be lowered, either by a Wisdom ribbon or by a pneumatic or hydraulic device. The latter permits both lowering and raising of the electrode; the Wisdom ribbon permits only lowering, but has a higher safety factor. If one of the two ribbons breaks, the remaining one can hold the electrode. With the employment of Wisdom ribbons the wall thickness of the interior cylinder can be about 1.0 to 1.2 mm thick, while the pneumatic device requires a cylinder wall thickness of 2.0 to 2.2 mm with electrodes of 800 mm or more diameter.

The green material for the Söderberg electrodes can be preheated and softened before filling the forming cylinder or cold solid material can be used. In the first case the electrode will be denser, the consumption of the electrode per ton of solid charge will be lower, and an eventual breakdown of the electrode can be avoided. The interior cylinder should be filled with green electrode material to a point one meter above the contact plates. The cooling water for the contact plates should not be more than 60°C. The electrodes can be fed by hand or automatically, and the regulation can be adjusted for constant current or constant kw per phase.

For electrodes of large diameter the current density for carbon and Söderberg electrodes is 2 to 3 amp/sq cm, and for graphite electrodes is 8 amp/sq cm.

Furnace Design

The furnaces can be oval-shaped, round, or rectangular. The first type has three electrodes in Y connection, the round ones three electrodes in delta connection, and the rectangular ones six electrodes or three single-phase connections in one large smelting hearth. This last form with six electrodes is preferred for all modern furnaces larger than 10,000 kva. The center to center spacing of the electrodes is from 2.5 to 3.6 meters in the large furnaces, such as at Thompson, Canada and Petsamo, Finland (now Russia), 12,000 kva; Boliden in Sweden, 12,000 kva; and Thompson, International Nickel Company, Canada, 18,000 kva. This spacing gives good current efficiency and a power factor of 0.95 to 0.98.

In contrast to the reverberatory furnace with a compact foundation and a furnace bottom of slag, the electric furnace is built on concrete pillars. See Fig. 2. On the pillars are pig iron plates with ribbons to cool the bottom, because the matte is hotter than in a reverberatory furnace. The bottom itself is composed of several layers of fire clay and then two layers of magnesite bricks, about 70 to 80 cm thick. The form of the furnace bottom is that of a reverse arch. The joints are arranged in a zigzag, instead of going straight through. The side walls

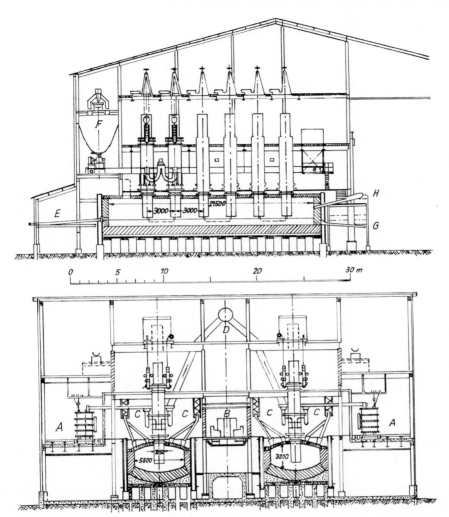

FIG. 2. Electric furnaces, 12,000 kva, at Petsamo, Finland (now Russia) for the smelting of nickel concentrates. A, transformers; B, control room; C, Redler conveyer; D, waste gas discharge; E, slag launder; F, ore bin; G, nickel matte launder; and H, return converter slag launder.

up to the slag level are built of magnesite bricks, 60 to 70 cm thick. The upper part of the side walls can be fire clay, just as the furnace roof. The lower part of the side walls, as well as the two front walls, are protected by pig iron plates with ribbons up to the upper slag level. The furnace is tied with strong I-beams. The draw rods on the roof must have a center piece of nonmagnetic steel. The expansion of magnesite at about 1000°C is nearly one per cent. Therefore, the joints are designed so that half of the expansion comes at the joints, the other half at the springs at both ends of the ties.

The interior smelting area is 1 sq m/100 kva transformer capacity. With long furnaces, e.g., 21.5 m at Petsamo, 23.5 at Boliden, and 27.5 at Thompson, there should be two gas outlets at the two ends of the furnace in addition to two more in the middle to avoid the escape of waste gas around the electrodes. At one front wall there are two or three tap holes for the matte and at the opposite front wall two or more tap holes on different levels for the slag. The matte tap holes, 1 to 2 in. diameter, are lined with an especially hard magnesite and stand about 100 to 200 taps before being replaced. Sometimes the tapping blocks are surrounded by a water-cooled copper block.

Furnace Operation

The furnaces are charged through tubes at the side walls. In contrast to the reverberatory furnace, where the charge is smelted only in the first half of its length and area while the other half toward the slag end acts as kind of a settler, the electric furnace heated by current over the entire smelting surface is able to smelt materials in the back end to lower the copper or nickel content of the slag. The concentrate, cold or hot, is transported to the furnace from the roasters by cars, by steel containers, or by Redler conveyors. The converter slag is fed to the furnace in a liquid state.

The furnace slag runs toward the slag tap holes with an interior laminar movement, but in the electric furnace there is an additional turbulent movement vertical to the first. Near the electrodes the slag is overheated and saturated with CO from a partial reduction of Fe_3O_4 and FeO in the slag by the carbon of the electrodes, and there is an ascending flow in the slag near the electrodes. From there the slag flows along the surface to the side walls, giving a circulation and turbulent movement. In this way the slag transfers its heat by convection to the charge floating on the surface. However, this double movement is a hindrance for the settling of small matte drops, and the slags in an electric furnace are higher in copper or nickel than in a reverberatory furnace. They are also higher in Fe_3O_4 and the settling of the Fe_3O_4 on the furnace bottom is less than in a reverberatory furnace, although a certain layer of magnetite on the furnace bottom is desired for protection. This layer of magnetite can be controlled with the aid of thermocouples in the furnace bottom and side walls. By lowering the voltage and lowering the electrodes it is possible to dissolve part of this magnetite, and the thermocouples give a good means for the control of the magnetite segregations. In contrast to the reverberatory furnace it is not necessary to shut down the electric furnace because of difficulties caused by too much magnetite.

The electric furnaces smelt converter slag, partly wet concentrate (Sulitjelma) and wet ore (Petsamo), mixtures of cold, wet concentrate and cold calcines (Imatra), or hot, 500 to 600°C, calcines (Boliden and Thompson). The charge is fed continuously at the side walls, the converter slag is poured in as a liquid, and the furnace slag is tapped continuously or at intervals. Usually the slag is granulated. The matte is tapped according to the operations of the converters. The tap hole is closed manually by a clay cone or with a clay gun, similar to practice in iron blast furnaces.

The electric furnace must be started up carefully by preheating with fuel oil over a period of several weeks, followed by the melting of slag until all temperature conditions are satisfied.

The smelting capacity of an electric furnace varies from 3 to 6 metric tons/24 hr day/sq m of smelting area. The power consumption with wet concentrate and wet ore is about 700 to 800 kwh/metric ton of solid charge (without liquid converter slag), about 500 to 600 with mixed charge, and 350 to 400 with hot calcines. The power factor is 0.85 to 0.90 in furnaces with three electrodes and low voltage, and 0.95 to 0.98 in furnaces with six electrodes and high voltage. The heat loss of the furnaces, depending on the slag temperature, is 3 to 5 kw/sq m furnace surface. The temperature of the matte is 1050 to 1100°C and of the slag is 1200 to 1250°C, with the exception of Petsamo where it is up to 1360°C.

Installations

There are six electric furnaces smelting copper concentrate in Europe (Scandanavia) and Africa with a transformer capacity of 3,000 to 12,000 kva each. One other furnace, 3,000 kva, produces black copper by the reduction of calcines at Brixlegg, Austria, and another of 6,000 kva melts copper sulfide from the flotation of nickel-copper Bessemer matte at Inco, Copper Cliff, Canada. The slags contain up to 50 per cent FeO and 38 per cent SiO_2, with varying amounts of CaO, MgO, Al_2O_3 and ZnO. The matte contains 30 to 40 per cent Cu. It is blown to blister copper in the converter. There are eight furnaces smelting nickel material, three in Canada (Inco, Thompson) smelting concentrate and five in Russia smelting nickel ore (two in Petsamo and three in Montjegorsk). The nickel furnaces have a transformer capacity of 12,000 to 15,000 kva, but the transformers of the Petsamo furnaces have been increased to 22,000 kva. The nickel-copper matte contains about 20 to 30 per cent Ni + Cu. The slag at Thompson contains, by per cent, 35 SiO_2, 47 to 50 FeO, 6 Al_2O_3,

4 CaO, 5 MgO, and 0.2 Ni. At Petsamo it contains 35 SiO_2, 37 to 40 FeO, 6 Al_2O_3, 1 CaO, 15 MgO, and 0.2 Ni.

Production of Ferronickel

There are two other plants smelting nickel oxide ore, garnierite, in electric furnaces to produce ferronickel. The ore at Riddle, Oregon has 17 to 25 per cent moisture and in the dry state, by per cent, 45 to 55 SiO_2, 25 to 28 MgO, 8 to 15 Fe, and 1.5 Ni. This ore is first calcined in rotary kilns after being dried, crushed and screened. The calcine at 700°C goes into four electric furnaces, 14,000 kva each. In these furnaces the ore is not reduced but only melted. In addition to the four smelting furnaces, there is one 13,500 kva ferrosilicon furnace. The Perrin process of the Société d'Électro-Chimie, d'Électro-Métallurgie et des Aciéries Électriques d'Ugine is used for the reduction of NiO in the molten ore by ferrosilicon containing 45 per cent Si. The melting furnaces are about 8 m diameter and about 3 m high with no roof. The molten ore is tapped at about 1650°C into a ladle together with solid pieces of ferrosilicon and so-called "seed metal." Then the molten ore and solid ferrosilicon are mixed by pouring back and forth into a second ladle. The nickel settles in the form of ferronickel, and the remaining slag is granulated and goes to the waste dump containing only 0.15 per cent Ni. The ferronickel contains 45 per cent Ni and is refined in an electric steel furnace. The nickel recovery from the ore with 1.5 per cent Ni is 91 to 92 per cent. Power consumption is 58 kwh/kg Ni in the ferronickel, and about 10 kwh are used in the production of ferrosilicon and the refining. This process has a certain disadvantage: when mixing the molten ore in the ladles it is impossible to prevent the cooling of large amounts of the slag which forms skulls at the ladle walls. These skulls must be crushed and the nickel recovered by magnetic separation for return to the process. The 1959 production in this plant was about 20,000 metric tons of ferronickel containing 46 per cent Ni.

The other nickel ore smelting plant is that of S. A. Le Nickel at Doniambo, New Caledonia. The garnierite, contains about 20 to 30 per cent moisture, and in the dry state, by per cent, about 37 SiO_2, 23 MgO, 14 Fe, and 3 Ni. These ores are calcined too in rotary furnaces and fed hot into four electric furnaces of 12,500 kva each. Reduction coal is added and the nickel reduced to ferronickel containing about 22 to 23 per cent Ni. This material is first desulfurized in a Kalling furnace and then blown in converters to eliminate carbon and silicon. The power consumption is about 600 kwh/metric ton of dried ore. About 94 per cent of the 3 per cent Ni in the ore is recovered. The slag contains 52 per cent SiO_2, 7 FeO, 38 MgO, and 0.2 Ni. The production is about 50,000 metric tons per year of ferronickel containing about 12,000 metric tons of nickel.

Altogether there are eight electric furnaces for the treatment of garnierite.

References

1. EGER, G., "Handbuch der Technischen Elektrochemie," Vol. 4, Part 3, by Barth, O., "Kupfer, Nickel, Kobalt und Blei," Leipzig, Akademische Verlagsgesellschaft, Geest und Portig K. G., 1956.
2. QUENEAU, P. "Extractive Metallurgy of Copper, Nickel and Cobalt," "Electric Furnace Smelting," p. 241, 263 and 287, New York, Interscience Publishers, 1961.
3. BARTH, O. Z. Erzbergbau u. Metallhüttenwesen, 1, 244 (1948); ibid., 15, 1 (1962).
4. HERNERYD, O., SUNDSTRÖM, O., AND NORRÖ, A., J. Metals, 7, 330 (1954).
5. BUTTS, A., "Copper-The Science and Technology of the Metal, Its Alloys and Compounds," New York, Reinhold Publishing Corp., 1954.

OTTO BARTH

CORROSION, CREVICE-TYPE. See CREVICE CORROSION.

CORROSION DETECTION DEVICES

Devices for detecting corrosion can be divided into two main categories: those which assess corrosion occurring on materials, and those which assess the corrosivity of either the natural or induced environments surrounding the material. Those devices in the former category are more direct, but usually involve disturbing either the corroding material or the surrounding environment. Devices in the latter category are more indirect because they involve detecting changes in either the composition or physical properties of the environment, but they need not involve disturbing either the corroding material or the environment.

Devices for detecting corrosion can also be

divided into one of the following classes based upon their mode of operation: visual, mechanical, electrical, sound (ultrasonics), radiography, chemical, and magnetic. While many devices have been conceived and used, few have been found to be widely adaptable because they are inherently difficult to operate outside a laboratory due to their complexity, fragility, cost, and operational requirements. This has limited their utility in many laboratory and field applications.

Visual devices, either for microscopic or macroscopic examination, have found considerable application due to ease of operation and interpretation of data. Various types of microscopes can provide an indication of the type and degree of corrosion, including structural effects, which the material is undergoing. Visual devices have also been used to determine gas evolution or absorption resulting from the corrosion process. Another widely-used device for detecting corrosion is the analytical balance used to measure gravimetrically the gain or loss of weight of the corroding material. For many types of corrosive attack, particularly highly-localized or pitting corrosion, gravimetric analyses are of little use and may be misleading. Problems associated with retention of corrosion products, inadvertent contamination of the material by extraneous matter, and nonuniform attack can introduce considerable errors. Various scoring systems and standardized methods of observation have been developed for use with visual devices to record more precisely the observer's data.

Devices which measure changes in optical properties of metal surfaces or thin metal films have been used to detect corrosion and to determine corrosion-time curves. Changes in spectral and diffuse reflectivity due to corrosion or tarnishing have been used where metals are used as reflectors. Devices based on this principle of operation, such as a photometer or an optical smoothness-meter, have been used in both field and laboratory applications to evaluate the surface finish of metals and coated metals since their use rarely affects the metal or the corrosion process.

The transmission of light through very thin films of metals has been used to detect tarnishing and oxidation of metals, since the film of corrosion products is more transparent than the parent metal. The maximum thickness of metal which will transmit light to a measurable degree is about 1000 Angstroms. Much thinner films introduce complications due to varying reflections of light which complicate data interpretation. Nonuniform corrosion or oxidation and changes due to stress relievement of the film also complicate corrosion detection by these optical methods.

Electron diffraction studies of metal films by either transmission or reflection techniques have been used to detect corrosion and, particularly the effect of periodic exposure to various gases and oxidation. Since a high vacuum is needed to make measurements, both the metal film and any corrosion products must withstand this environment. Electron diffraction, electron probe, and similar techniques are principally used in the laboratory for special examinations such as the identification of corrosion products, phrase transformations, and size and orientation of constituent crystals.

Several devices have been used to detect corrosion by measuring the change in *mechanical properties* of a specimen located in the environment. In general, these devices require placing a tensile or fatigue specimen in a corrosive environment and determining the change in properties of corroded and uncorroded specimens. More sophisticated devices of this type can apply a continuous or variable tensile stress to the specimen during exposure to the corrosive media. Measurements assess the susceptibility of the material to stress or fatigue corrosion by determining residual mechanical properties after specified exposure periods, or by determining the exposure period required to reduce the mechanical properties to an arbitrary level by continuing the test to failure.

Devices which depend on the change in *electrical properties* of corroding material and/or the surrounding environment have often been used to detect corrosion because the general method has certain inherent advantages. These include detecting corrosive activity *in situ* without affecting either the material or the environment, making accurate and repetitive measurements at a relatively remote location removed from the test site, and reducing errors due to corrosion products, extraneous materials, and certain environmental factors such as temperature.

Measurements of the change in electrical resistance of either the material itself or a specially designed probe made of the material have been used extensively in the laboratory and field for detecting corrosion. Since the electrical resistance of a metal depends on its cross-sectional area, a decrease in thickness due to corrosion may be evaluated quantitatively from the increase in resistance. Since the resistance of nonmetals is very high in comparison with metals, corrosion products and other extraneous materials do not affect the measurements. The use of specially designed metal probes has found many applications where *in situ* corrosion measurements are desired, including monitoring the effect of applied mechanical stresses, determining the protectiveness afforded by protective coatings, monitoring the deterioration of metal inside concrete and other nonmetallics, and evaluating biologically induced attack. A variety of probes are available to fit almost any combination of environmental conditions using most commercially available metals and alloys. With suitable instrumentation and probes, resolution of the order of 0.5 microinches penetration is obtained using a metal specimen 4 mils thick. Effects of temperature changes are compensated for in the probe design and by using a modified Kelvin bridge.

Thin metal films of about 1000 Angstroms thickness are also being used to detect the cumulative history of corrosive conditions of the surrounding environment. The films corrode irreversibly and can furnish quantitative information regarding environmental corrosivity either visually or electrically. By sensitizing the metal film with suitable chemical salts comparable with inadvertent contamination of metal parts, the metal films can be designed to corrode faster than actual hardware, thus furnishing a warning that the environment is potentially corrosive. By using different metals and sensitizing salts, indicators can be made which are particularly sensitive to a limited corrosive environment. For example, a silver film contaminated with a metal oxide salt will react in the phase only with such strong oxidizers as fluorine and ozone. Using suitable instrumentation with these metal films, very high sensitivities to a corrodent are possible.

Detection of corrosion by either measuring changes in the electrical properties of the corrodent, such as conductivity, or, by measuring changes in capacitance or conductance between the specimen and the corrodent have also been used extensively. The former method generally employs electrodes of a particular design connected to a Wheatstone bridge to monitor the progressive change in conductivity as corrosion progresses. The latter method usually employs the specimen as one electrode and either a dupli-

cate specimen or another metal as the other electrode. The change in capacitance or conductance of painted metals immersed in sea water has been used as a measure of failure of the coating and subsequent metal corrosion.

Another electrical method used to detect corrosion is based on measuring the change in impedance of a probe of the desired metal when it is placed in close proximity to the coil of an oscillator circuit. The generation of eddy currents in the metal produces an opposing magnetic field in the probe which can be continuously monitored with reasonable accuracy and with simple, light-weight equipment. A modification of this method involves moving the eddy current probe over the corroding structure and modulating the beam intensity of a cathode ray tube with the electrical signal from the eddy current probe. Devices based upon eddy current measurements show significant promise but field applications appear relatively limited and interpretation of test results must be done carefully.

The use of *ultrasonics* to detect corrosion nondestructively has found considerable application because continuous measurements can be made without disturbing either the environment or the material. In general, a transducer is placed against the material to introduce the ultrasonic sound waves or pulses and receive the attenuated signal. This signal must be monitored by suitable instrumentation and a trained observer. Under most conditions material thickness can be measured with accuracies from $\frac{1}{2}$ to 4 per cent from one side of the material without excessive interference from corrosion products, coatings or environmental factors.

Though many modifications have been developed, two general techniques are used: resonance and pulse ultrasonics. Resonance techniques depend on sonically inducing vibration of the material at a given frequency. A limitation of using resonance methods is that the material being tested must have parallel sides within 10 per cent slope. Pulse ultrasonics involves vibration of the transducer, the sending of sound pulses into the material, and the generation of multiple back-reflection patterns. The distance between each back reflection is proportional to the thickness of the material since the instrumentation basically is a time-measuring device.

Radiography has been used more frequently in recent years for both laboratory and field detection of corrosion and metal flaws. Penetrating radiation, such as x-rays or gamma-rays, are passed into the metal, and measurements are made of those passing through or, alternatively, those which are back-scattered, to determine metal thickness and density. A Geiger tube measuring head is held against the metal to count the number of radiation pulses transmitted, generally with a reproducibility of about 1 per cent. Advantages include instrumentation compactness, portability and small operating expense, while disadvantages are a high initial cost, possible hazards to operating personnel, relatively long exposure periods, interference from scale or other materials, and, often, the need for calibration curves.

A number of *chemical methods* have been used to detect corrosion, especially chemical indicators to sense the presence of particular corrosion products, anions and cations in solution, and corrosive environmental conditions. Identification of anodic points on a metal surface which may undergo corrosion has been accomplished by spreading gelatin or other materials containing an appropriate colorimetric indicator on the metal's surface. Chemical spot tests, involving observations of precipitates or color changes, and crystal tests, involving formation of characteristic crystals, have been used to detect metal ions in the corrosive medium or excessive humidity and other deleterious contaminants in the environment. The use of cobaltic chloride to detect high humidities which may cause corrosion of metallic materials is widely used because of the simple color change and low chemical cost associated with the detection system.

Chemical penetrants have been used to detect intergranular corrosion by applying the penetrant, removing it with a chemical cleaner, applying a developer chemical, and finally, viewing the part for color contrast between the penetrant drawn out and the background surface. A dual penetrant technique has also been used to detect surface corrosion between two close-fitting flat surfaces. The second penetrant forces the first penetrant out of any uncorroded areas without removing it from the corroded pockets. Subsequent application of the developer brings both penetrants to the surface, but corrosion is indicated only by the presence of the first one.

Indicator chemicals are relatively easy to apply and, in many cases, give quick, qualitative assessment of metal deterioration or corrosive environments. However, many chemical methods are not widely used due to high costs, difficulty in chemical application and removal, and other problem areas.

Various *electromagnetic methods* for measuring metal thickness and, thereby, detecting corrosion have been devised. The force required to pull a magnet of known strength from the surface of a metal plate can be used to determine the average amount of metal lost. Another method is based on the amount of steel that must be inserted into an electromagnetic coil to balance exactly the magnetic flux from a similar electromagnetic coil which is held in contact with the specimen.

An electromagnetic device has been used to detect localized corrosion of tubes from the inside based on drawing the device through the tubing. When the electromagnetic coils are disturbed to an extent depending on the mass of the metal, the out-of-balance current is observed on an appropriate meter. Meter readings are affected by both the diameter and the depth of the pit, so this method can only be used to give a rough indication of the depth of pitting.

Corrosion detecting devices which depend on changes in electromagnetic properties must be used with magnetic material rather than nonmagnetic metals to provide sufficient sensitivity. These methods also are subject to errors from various sources, such as variations in the air gap between the pole pieces and the specimen, mechanical stresses in the metal, and the effects of the shape of the sample.

Magnetic particle inspection to detect corrosion and determine structural flaws has been used extensively to determine corrosion-fatigue cracks. The method utilizes equipment that magnetizes the part, fluorescent powder particles that line up along any surface discontinuity or corrosion pit which produces a flux-leakage field, and an ultraviolet light for observing the powder particle build-up. While this test is extremely sensitive and can detect minute flaws, it is rather slow, tedious, and requires that the material be capable of being magnetized.

References

1. HINSLEY, J. F., "Non-destructive Testing," London, MacDonald & Evans, Ltd., 1959.
2. McMASTER, R. C., "Nondestructive Testing Handbook," Vols. I and II, New York, The Ronald Press, 1959.
3. EWING, S., "Soil Corrosion & Pipe Line Protection," Chapters V, VIII, and X., New York, American Gas Association, 1938.

4. ROLLER, D., AND SCOTT, W. R., *Corrosion Technology*, **8**, No. 3, 71, (1961).
5. CHAPMAN, F. A., "Corrosion Testing Procedures," Chapters VIII and IX, London, Chapman and Hall, 1952.
6. "Corrosion Problems of the Petroleum Industry," SCI Monograph No. 10, p. 157, New York, The Macmillan Company, 1960.

DAVID ROLLER

Cross-reference: *Corrosion Testing.*

CORROSION DUE TO ALTERNATING CURRENT

Corrosion of metals receiving alternating current can occur under various circumstances. The conditions which are effective in causing a-c corrosion may be a function of one or more of the following factors: (1) types of similar or dissimilar metals in the circuit, (2) pH of the electrolyte, (3) types of cations and anions in electrolyte, (4) current density of a-c, (5) frequency of a-c, (6) presence or absence of d-c component and current density of d-c, and (7) rectification potentiality of corrosion films formed. The a-c may have an indirect effect in accelerating natural corrosion due to changes in anode or cathode polarization or due to thermal activation from a-c heating at or near the electrodes.

The most serious corrosion loss due to a-c can occur when the following set of conditions exists: (a) the metal is dependent upon a uniform oxide film for its corrosion resistance, (b) the oxide has good rectifying characteristics and permits mainly cathode behavior, and (c) the oxide is soluble with increased pH at the electrode resulting from cathode behavior.

The metals Mg and Al and to a lesser extent Zn and Pb behave as cited above and, thus, may suffer serious a-c corrosion loss. An additional factor in a-c corrosion of these metals may be the existence of a barrier to diffusion at the electrodes provided by imbedding the metals in soil or by a perforated dielectric coating which will permit the pH to increase rapidly.

The use of the metals Mg, Al and Zn as sacrificial anodes for cathodic protection of steel is well-known in practice. It has been demonstrated in the writer's laboratory that with sufficient a-c in a system of steel cathodically protected with Mg the potential of Mg to steel may reverse thus making steel the anode. The maximum d-c may reach a value of 10 per cent of the a-c as indicated on a d-c ammeter provided with paralleled capacitance to by-pass a-c out of the d-c meter circuit. When the Mg-Fe potential has been reversed by a-c, rapid corrosion of both metals occurs due to the effects of the periodic d-c provided by rectification.

For electrodes of Fe (steel buried underground as an example) the effects of the a-c in causing corrosion are decreased as the pH is raised from 5 to 9. High a-c corrosion rates have been found by some investigators for Fe in aqueous solution (neutral) when current density is above 70 ma/sq in and the frequency is 50 cps. For frequencies below 50 cps a-c corrosion loss occurs at lower current density than 70. For other metals (Pb as a specific example) a-c corrosion is experienced below and above 60 cps. Some investigators have found the a-c to cause the d-c component to increase or decrease, depending upon the type of anion in the electrolyte or depending upon the initial value of the d-c density at Fe electrodes.

References

1. KULMAN, F. E., "Effects of Alternating Currents in Causing Corrosion," *Proc. Amer. Gas Assn.,* **42**, (1960); *Corrosion,* **17**, 34 (1961).
2. BRUCKNER, WALTER H., "Progress Report on AC Corrosion Research," *Proc. Amer. Gas Assn.,* **44**, (1962).
3. WALTERS, F. O., "A-C Corrosion," *Materials Protection,* **1**, 3, 26–32 (Mar. 1962).
4. FUCHS, W., STEINRATH, H., AND TERNES, H., "Investigations Concerning A-C Corrosion of Iron as a Function of Current Density and Frequency," *Das Gas und Wasserfach,* **99**, (1958) (in German).
5. FUJITAKA, S., SAKAJUDIO, Y., AND KIKUCHI, S., "The Influence of Form Factor and Direct Current on the Corrosion of Fe Electrodes by Alternating Current," *J. Chem. Soc. (Japan),* **51** (1958) (in Japanese).
6. TORIGOE, Y., "Action of Alternating Current on Corrosion Process of Iron," *J. Electrochem Soc. (Japan),* **5**, No. 1–2 (1958) (in Japanese).
7. AMY, L., AND MOUNIES, C., "Investigations of A-C Corrosion," *Rev. Gen. Elec.,* **66** (1957) (in French).

WALTER H. BRUCKNER

CORROSION, ELECTROCHEMICAL KINETICS

The destruction of the crystalline lattice of a metal by corrosion in a liquid environment is governed by the kinetics of electrochemical reactions occurring at the metal-solution interface. These electrochemical reactions involve the transfer of ions or electrons across the interface under the influence of an electrical potential difference which exists between the phases. According to Faraday's law of electrochemical equivalence, a current (or current density) corresponds to each reaction flux, and the total current crossing an interface is equivalent to the algebraic sum of the rates of all the electrochemical reactions. Rates of electrochemical reactions, including corrosion reactions, depend on the value of the interfacial potential difference, as well as on the composition and structure of the metallic phase, the constitution of the solution, the temperature and pressure, and, in some cases, the time. The concepts and methods of electrochemical kinetics may be used to analyze the relations among these variables, and provide important insights into the mechanisms of corrosion reactions which are difficult to obtain by any other method of corrosion research.

In the absence of electrical current supplied from an external source, an electrode immersed in solution exhibits the reversible or equilibrium potential of the reaction which occurs on its surface, provided no interfering reactions are present. This equilibrium potential, measured with respect to a reversible reference electrode, receives thermodynamic explanation on the basis of the Nernst and Gibbs-Helmholtz equations (q.v.). However, in the case of corroding electrodes, several different interfacial reactions occur simultaneously on the surface, and the electrode exhibits a mixed potential (q.v.) in the steady state. The concept of the mixed potential, together with the principle of superposition of partial current-potential curves, forms the basis of the electrochemical kinetic theory of corrosion.

The formation of the mixed potential of a corroding metal electrode is illustrated in the polarization diagram of Fig. 1, where the current density (i) is plotted against electrode potential (E) (European sign convention). Here, $i_1(E)$ is the (steady state) polarization curve corresponding to the dissolution of the metal (Me) to form metal ions in solution (Me^{z+}) (reaction 1). This overall process is composed additively of $i_{a,1}(E)$, the anodic partial reaction ($Me \rightarrow Me^{z+} + ze^-$), and of $i_{c,1}(E)$, the cathodic partial reaction ($Me^{z+} + ze^- \rightarrow Me$). That is, $i_1(E) = i_{a,1}(E) - i_{c,1}(E)$ by the principle of superposition and the $i_1(E)$ vs. E line would be the measurable polarization curve provided no other reaction occurred at the electrode surface. If the rates of both partial reactions are determined by the charge transfer

steps of each process, the reactions are said to be under activation control. In this case, electrochemical kinetic theory shows that

$$i_{a,1}(E) = i_{o,1} \cdot \exp\left(+ \frac{\alpha_{a,1} z_1 \mathbf{F}}{RT} \eta_1\right)$$

and

$$i_{c,1}(E) = i_{o,1} \cdot \exp\left(- \frac{\alpha_{c,1} z_1 \mathbf{F}}{RT} \eta_1\right),$$

so that $i_1(E)$ is given as a function of electrode potential by Eq. 1.

$$i_1(E) = i_{o,1}\left[\exp\left(+ \frac{\alpha_{a,1} z_1 \mathbf{F}}{RT} \eta_1\right) - \exp\left(- \frac{\alpha_{c,1} z \mathbf{F}}{RT} \eta_1\right)\right] \tag{1}$$

Here, $\eta_1 = E - E_{0,1}$ is the overvoltage of reaction 1, where $E_{0,1}$ is the reversible potential of the reaction. The exchange current density of the reaction is denoted by $i_{0,1}$, $\alpha_{a,1}$ and $\alpha_{c,1}$ are the transfer coefficients of the anodic and cathodic partial reactions ($\alpha_{a,1} + \alpha_{c,1} = 1$), z_1 is the number of charges transferred in the electrochemical step, and $RT/\mathbf{F}$ is the thermal volt equivalent. The exchange current density, $i_{0,1}$, denotes the rate at which the partial reactions proceed in either direction at the reversible potential, $E_{0,1}$.

In the presence of a second electrochemical process (reaction 2) which has a reversible potential ($E_{0,2}$) more noble than $E_{0,1}$, reaction 1 is polarized anodically, a net corrosion process occurs ($i_1(E) > 0$), and a mixed potential (E_{corr}) is established such that $E_{0,1} < E_{corr} < E_{0,2}$. This situation is also shown in Fig. 1, where the hydrogen evolution reaction ($2H^+ + 2e^- \rightarrow H_2$) has been selected as a typical cathodic process. The net rate ($i_2(E)$) of reaction 2 is given by Eq. 2, where all quantities have

$$i_2(E) = i_{0,2}\left[\exp\left(+ \frac{\alpha_{a,2} z_2 \mathbf{F}}{RT} \eta_2\right) - \exp\left(- \frac{\alpha_{c,2} z_2 \mathbf{F}}{RT} \eta_2\right)\right] \tag{2}$$

the same meaning as the corresponding quantities of Eq. 1. The $i_2(E)$ vs. E line would be the polarization curve observable for reaction 2 if no other process occurred on the surface.

When $E_{0,2} \gg E_{0,1}$ and $i_{0,1}$ is comparable in magnitude to $i_{0,2}$, the resulting mixed electrode potential (E_{corr}) is neither very near to $E_{0,1}$ nor

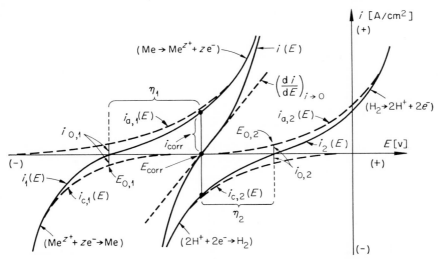

FIG. 1. Formation of the steady state mixed potential of a corroding electrode
by superposition of partial current-potential curves.

to $E_{0,2}$. In this case, the rate of the cathodic partial reaction, $Me^{z+} + ze^- \rightarrow Me$, is negligible compared to the rate of the anodic partial reaction (the corrosion reaction), $Me \rightarrow Me^{z+} + ze^-$; hence $i_1(E) = i_{a,1}(E) - i_{c,1}(E) \cong i_{a,1}(E)$. Similarly, the rate of the anodic partial reaction, $H_2 \rightarrow 2H^+ + 2e^-$, is small compared to the rate of the cathodic hydrogen evolution reaction, $2H^+ + 2e^- \rightarrow H_2$, so that $i_2(E) = i_{a,2}(E) - i_{c,2}(E) \cong - i_{c,2}(E)$. Since $i(E) \cong i_{a,1}(E) - i_{c,2}(E)$ is the total current density of the mixed electrode system, Eqs. 1 and 2 may be combined to yield Eq. 3, which expresses $i(E)$ as a function of the exchange current densities

$$i(E) = i_{0,1} \cdot \exp\left(+\frac{\alpha_{a,1} z_1 \mathbf{F}}{RT} \eta_1 \right)$$
$$- i_{0,2} \cdot \exp\left(-\frac{\alpha_{c,2} z_2 \mathbf{F}}{RT} \eta_2 \right) \tag{3}$$

and overvoltages of the two different reactions occurring at the electrode surface.

A more convenient form of Eq. 3 is obtained by use of the substitutions, $\eta_1 = E_{corr} - E_{0,1}$ and $\eta_2 = E_{corr} - E_{0,2}$. At $E = E_{corr}$, $i(E) = 0$ and the corrosion rate in the absence of externally applied current (see Fig. 1) is given by

$$i_{corr} = i_{0,1} \cdot \exp\left[+\frac{\alpha_{a,1} z_1 \mathbf{F}}{RT} (E_{corr} - E_{0,1}) \right]$$
$$= i_{0,2} \cdot \exp\left[-\frac{\alpha_{c,2} z_2 \mathbf{F}}{RT} (E_{corr} - E_{0,2}) \right]$$

Substitution for $E_{0,1}$ and $E_{0,2}$ then leads to Eq. 4

for the relation between $i(E)$ and E as a function of i_{corr}. Eq. 4 is identical in form to Eqs. 1

$$i(E) = i_{corr} \left\{ \exp\left[+\frac{\alpha_{a,1} z_1 \mathbf{F}}{RT} (E - E_{corr}) \right] \right.$$
$$\left. - \exp\left[-\frac{\alpha_{c,2} z_2 \mathbf{F}}{RT} (E - E_{corr}) \right] \right\} \tag{4}$$

and 2; the corrosion rate in the absence of applied current, i_{corr}, is analogous to the exchange current density of a reversible electrode (i_0), and the polarization, $(E - E_{corr})$, is analogous to the overvoltage (η).

For small polarization, $(E - E_{corr}) \ll RT/\mathbf{F}$, the exponential factors in Eq. 4 may be expanded to first-order terms and the resulting equation differentiated to give Eq. 5. This expression relates the slope

$$\left[\frac{di(E)}{dE} \right]_{i \to 0} = \frac{i_{corr}(\alpha_{a,1} z_1 + \alpha_{c,2} z_2) \mathbf{F}}{RT} \tag{5}$$

of the polarization curve of a corroding electrode at the open circuit potential (see tangent in Fig. 1) to the corrosion rate at that potential. The importance of Eq. 5 arises from the fact that corrosion rates may be estimated accurately by use of electrochemical measurements alone. The major uncertainty in the use of Eq. 5 for electrode systems under activation control involves the value of the charge transfer parameter, $(\alpha_{a,1} z_1 + \alpha_{c,2} z_2)$; however, values of α generally lie near $\frac{1}{2}$ and values of z may sometimes be in-

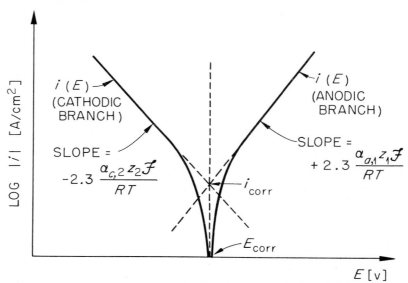

FIG. 2. Semilogarithmic plot of polarization curve of a corroding electrode showing Tafel lines of partial reactions under activation control.

ferred from the stoichiometry of the appropriate partial reactions.

Polarization curves are frequently presented graphically in semilogarithmic form, as shown in Fig. 2 where the $i(E)$ curve of Fig. 1 is plotted schematically. In potential regions where the rate of a single partial reaction predominates, this type of plot yields straight lines [known as *Tafel lines* (q.v.)] for reactions under pure activation control. Thus, when $E \gg E_{\text{corr}}$, $i_{a,1} \gg |i_{c,2}|$ and the slope of the line may be obtained from Eq. 4 as

$$\left[\frac{d \ln i(E)}{dE}\right]_{E \gg E_{\text{corr}}} = +\frac{\alpha_{a,1} z_1 \mathbf{F}}{RT}.$$

Alternatively, when $E \ll E_{\text{corr}}$ and $|i_{c,2}| \gg i_{a,1}$, the slope is given by

$$\left[\frac{d \ln i(E)}{dE}\right]_{E \ll E_{\text{corr}}} = -\frac{\alpha_{c,2} z_2 \mathbf{F}}{RT}$$

Both Tafel lines extrapolate to i_{corr} at E_{corr}; this procedure provides another method for estimating corrosion rates from electrochemical measurements. In addition, the slopes of the Tafel lines are of mechanistic interest and may be used to compute the value of the charge transfer parameter, $(\alpha_{a,1} z_1 + \alpha_{c,2} z_2)$, of Eq. 5. Complications to the simple picture presented above arise when the velocity of mass transfer processes to or from the interface affect the overall rate of one or more of the electrochemical reactions occurring at the corroding surface. Concentration polarization (q.v.) occurs when the rate of the charge transfer step of a partial reaction becomes comparable to the rate of diffusion of reactants or products from (or into) the bulk of the solution. In this case, concentrations at the electrode surface differ from bulk concentrations, and Eq. 4 must be corrected for this effect. Tafel lines (see Fig. 2) are not found in the presence of concentration polarization, and steady state measurements are no longer useful for the calculation of kinetic parameters of the charge transfer steps of partial reactions. Instead, limiting currents are observed which correspond to the finite flux of reactants or products to (or from) the surface as a consequence of the finite rate of molecular or ionic diffusion in solution. Limiting currents are most frequently encountered during the application of high current densities or in the presence of low concentrations of reactive species. Concentration changes due to natural and forced convection are often superimposed on changes due to diffusion alone. Changes in solution density occur during the passage of polarizing current which lead to natural convection and hence to convective diffusion. Solution flow in forced convection may be either laminar or turbulent and limiting currents obtainable in stirred solutions depend on the mode and velocity of stirring. Experimental methods for circumventing concentration polarization effects and theoretical treatments of pertinent mass transfer problems in natural and forced convection are described in specialized monographs.[3, 5, 8]

Further refinements to the simple electrochemical kinetic picture of corrosion may be needed in some cases to account for the effect of the structure of the electrical double layer at the metal-solution interface on the rates of partial reactions.[4, 8] Ions are distributed according to the Boltzmann distribution law in the diffuse region of the double layer, so that differences exist between concentrations of ions near the electrode surface and concentrations outside the double layer. The equations of electrochemical kinetics may be corrected for the distribution of ions in the diffuse double layer and the correction is particularly important for dilute electrolytic solutions. In addition, specific adsorption of ionic or molecular species on the corroding surface may affect reaction rates or may be an important step in reaction mechanisms, as in the case of organic and inorganic corrosion inhibitors.[2]

Chemically and physically inhomogeneous surfaces frequently exist on corroding metals because of the presence of discrete phases of alloying elements or impurities and because polycrystalline surfaces present areas of differing crystallographic orientation to the solution. In general, reaction rates vary according to the type of surface and the unequal distribution of reaction rates over the surface is the origin of so-called local currents. The mixed potential concept and the principle of superposition provide a basis for the interpretation of local currents on corroding surfaces and of the polarization characteristics of galvanic couples.[7, 8]

Films of corrosion products or insoluble salts form at the metal-solution interface under certain conditions and considerably complicate the interpretation of electrochemical measurements. A number of metals possess the ability to form compact oxide lattices on their surfaces in certain regions of potential; the presence of the oxide phase drastically alters the kinetics of corrosion reactions and the metal is said to be passive. Research on the kinetics of the passive state on metals is an important part of present studies on the electrochemical kinetics of corrosion.[9]

Techniques for the measurement of polarization curves and other properties of corroding metals include nearly all the standard methods of electrochemical kinetics.[6] In the galvanostatic or constant current method, the variation of electrode potential is observed as a function of the value of a constant current applied to the electrode from an external current source with the aid of an auxiliary polarizing electrode. In the potentiostatic or constant potential method, an electronic potentiostat maintains the electrode at a fixed potential relative to a reference electrode by supplying the necessary current through a polarizing electrode. In addition to the potentiostatic and galvanostatic methods, other techniques are sometimes useful in corrosion studies. Measurements of the impedance of the metal-solution interface by use of alternating currents (or potentials) are capable of yielding information on the rates of partial reactions, the magnitude of the double layer capacity, and the contribution of mass transfer processes to the overall kinetics. Current interrupter methods and single or double pulse techniques provide similar information. The kinetics of formation and decomposition of surface compounds may be studied by chronopotentiometry. Details of experimental cells and techniques are available in standard works on electrochemistry and electrochemical kinetics.[1, 8]

References

1. BOCKRIS, J. O'M., in Bockris, J. O'M., Ed., "Modern Aspects of Electrochemistry," Vol. 1, p. 180, London, Butterworths, 1954.
2. CARTLEDGE, G. H., *Corrosion*, **18**, 316t (1962); Fischer, H., *Werkstoffe u. Korr.*, **6**, 26 (1955).
3. DELAHAY, P., in Delahay, P., Ed., "Advances in Electrochemistry and Electrochemical Engineering," Vol. 1, p. 233, New York, Interscience, 1961.
4. GRAHAME, D. C., *Chem. Revs.*, **41**, 441 (1947); Parsons, R., in Delahay, P., Ed., "Advances in Electrochemistry and Electrochemical Engineering," Vol. 1, p. 1, New York, Interscience, 1961.
5. LEVICH, V. G., "Physicochemical Hydrodynamics," Englewood Cliffs, N. J., Prentice-Hall, 1962.
6. MAKRIDES, A. C., *Corrosion*, **18**, 338t (1962).
7. POSEY, F. A., *J. Electrochem. Soc.*, **106**, 571 (1959).
8. VETTER, K. J., "Elektrochemische Kinetik," Berlin, Springer-Verlag, 1961.
9. YOUNG, L., "Anodic Oxide Films," New York, Academic Press, 1961.

FRANZ A. POSEY

CORROSION, ELECTROCHEMICAL PRINCIPLES

Corrosion is the interaction of a metal or alloy with its nonmetallic environment. Since metals and alloys are electronic conductors and are built up of cations and electrons that are more or less easily dissociable, and since many environments contain, or produce in contact with the metal lattice, ionically conducting species, most corrosion reactions are electrochemical.

"Dry" Corrosion

When a metal surface is exposed to dry air, electrons from the metal reduce adsorbed O_2 molecules to O^{2-} ions (except in the case of gold). Cations from the metal lattice, freed from electrons, associate with the O^{2-} anions to form either a monolayer of oxide or a number of oxide nuclei. Growth of the monolayer or nuclei outwards from the metal surface continues by the passage of metal cations or oxygen anions, or both, through the solid oxide electrolyte; the nuclei, if formed, also grow sideways to form a complete film that proceeds to grow in thickness. In this film growth, the metal/film interface is the anode, the film/atmosphere surface the cathode, and the film itself both electron-conductor and electrolyte in a short-circuited cell (Fig. 1). If the emf of this cell is E; the overall specific conductivity (by a-c measurement) of the film substance, κ; the transport numbers of anions, cations, and electrons, respectively, n_a, n_c, and n_e; the density and the gram-equivalent weight of the film substance, respectively, ρ and J, then by Ohm's and Faraday's laws the rate of film growth is

$$dy/dt = \frac{E\kappa(n_a + n_c)n_e J}{\rho \mathbf{F}} \cdot 1/y, \qquad (1)$$

where y is the film thickness at time, t. This leads by integration to

$$y^2 = \frac{2E\kappa(n_a + n_c)n_e J}{\rho \mathbf{F}} \cdot t \qquad (2)$$

(for $y = 0$, $t = 0$), the familiar "parabolic law" of film thickening. The "parabolic law" is, of course, an "ideal" law, but it is nonetheless approximately obeyed for the oxidation of copper at 600°C or so, with E taken as equivalent to the free energy of formation of cuprous oxide, and for several other oxidations and sulfidations.

Deviations from the parabolic equation occur from many causes. Thus, E is usually not constant owing to varying polarization at anode and cathode, and κ often varies throughout the film thickness because it is strongly dependent on the nonstoichiometry of the film substance. For thin films, the field is sometimes too high for Ohm's Law to hold for ion conduction, and for very thin films electron conduction may be by tunnel effect. Many films break down through the mechanical stresses set up during their growth, either by cracking or flaking, which increases the growth rate; alternatively, the production of cavity "barriers" within the film or at the metal/film interface, often by vacancy condensation, may reduce the growth rate. These and other effects frequently lead to one or other "logarithmic" laws of film growth; these are best interpreted as deviations from the ideal "parabolic" behavior caused by one or several of the causes mentioned. Generally, fairly thick films growing at fairly high temperatures correspond most nearly to the "parabolic" ideal.

Duplex films, either of two oxides of the same metal or of two or more different metals in the case of alloys, grow according to the same principles. The relative conductivities and ion mobilities in the several oxides are here the decisive factors in the overall film morphology and composition.

Generally, metals and alloys showing low rates of "dry" corrosion are those forming oxides with very low specific conductivity, or those in which either ion or electron mobility is particularly low (see Eq. 1). Aluminum is a common example of a metal that is very slow to oxidize or tarnish in dry air, even at moderately enhanced temperatures, through the very small conductivity of

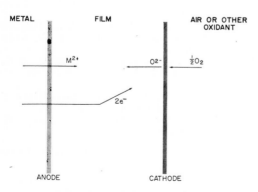

Fig. 1. Simplified model for film growth, for bivalent metal.

Al_2O_3; as an alloying addition it can confer similar properties on silver and copper, through its selective oxidation. On the other hand, metals and alloys, such as unalloyed silver and copper, that tarnish readily in polluted atmospheres do so because of the relatively high conductivity of the sulfide films that form on them preferentially by reaction with polluting sulfur compounds.

"Wet" Corrosion

The oxide films that form on metals at ordinary temperatures in the atmosphere by the mechanism just described soon cease to thicken appreciably because the current in the film-cell falls to extremely minute values and $dy/dt \rightarrow 0$. When such metal is exposed to an aerated electrolyte solution, the initial invisible (50 to 150 Å) oxide film may grow further to "visible" thickness, as shown by its exhibiting interference colors (e.g., tin in dilute carbonate solution). Probably anion exchange of OH^- for O^{2-} in the film increases its conductivity. However, solutions containing "corrosive" anions, of which Cl^- is the prime example, lead to the onset of corrosion in all but noble metals and metals that form insoluble compounds with these anions (silver with Cl^-, lead with SO_4^{2-}). Usually, film breakdown occurs at singularities on the metal surface (grain-boundaries, inclusions, locally worked areas) where the film may be expected to be least impervious. The mode of action of corrosive anions in promoting film breakdown is still not fully understood. Anion exchange (Cl^- for O^{2-}) certainly occurs, and although the increased flow of cations outwards at such weakened points is partly checked by the immediate formation of further oxide or hydroxide, an equivalent of hydrogen ion forms also; this soon gives the lowered pH necessary for continued anodic dissolution to *soluble* products, which in turn leads to undermining of the film and the extension of the anode to large areas. In an unbuffered nearly neutral saline solution, the first anodic reaction is thus

$$M + zH_2O \rightarrow M(OH)_z + zH^+ + ze, \quad (3)$$

where z is often 2. This is followed by

$$M + xH_2O \rightarrow M \cdot xH_2O^{z+} + ze \quad (4)$$

when the anolyte pH has fallen sufficiently, depending on the particular hydrolytic equilibrium

$$M \cdot xH_2O^{z+} \rightleftarrows M(OH)_z + zH^+ + (x-z)H_2O. \quad (5)$$

Most "corrosive" anions, like Cl^-, form strong acids and do not sequester H^+; anions, such as PO_4^{3-}, CO_3^{2-}, etc., form weak acids and sequester H^+, thus tending to favor the formation of *solid* hydroxide or oxide at anodes instead of *soluble* $M \cdot xH_2O^{z+}$, and they are in many cases inhibitory of corrosion.

The corresponding cathodic reaction in aerated nearly neutral saline solutions is

$$\frac{1}{2}O_2 + H_2O + 2e \rightarrow 2OH^-,$$

taking place on the surface of the oxide film (Fig. 2). The specific sluggishness of the cathodic reduction of oxygen is a major reason for the relatively slow corrosion of reactive metals such as iron. In acid solutions, hydrogen evolution can occur,

$$2H^+ + 2e \rightarrow 2H_{ads} \rightarrow H_{2\,gas}$$

with reduction of any initial oxide film often occurring also. Hydrogen-ion reduction is much less sluggish than oxygen reduction, so that corrosion by acids is commonly much more rapid than that by aerated neutral solutions. It also occurs in neutral and even in alkaline solutions with the reactive metals, such as zinc and aluminium, because the operating cathode potential is sufficiently low.

The state of affairs at the electrodes of a piece of corroding metal is conveniently illustrated by polarization curves such as those of Fig. 3. These can often be determined experimentally, and the rate of metal weight loss can be correlated with the corrosion current. This current can be determined in several ways: (a) by dividing (in suitable special cases) the metal anode and cathode mechanically and using direct external measurement (Fig. 4); (b) by measurement of the current/potential relationships (usually logarithmic) at high anode and high cathode polarizations, and backward extrapolation to the potential obtaining during natural corrosion (Fig. 5); (c) by suitable potential or current measurements in the surrounding electrolyte solution (Fig. 6).

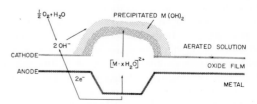

FIG. 2. Simplified model for wet corrosion in aerated, nearly neutral saline solutions, for bivalent metal.

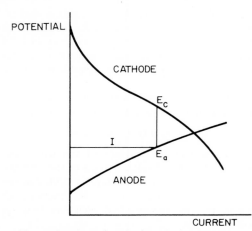

FIG. 3. Anode and cathode polarization curves for corroding metal (schematic).

The anode and cathode polarize one another until the difference of their working potentials, $E_c - E_a$, divided by the corrosion current, I, equals the overall resistance of the circuit.

When anodes and cathodes are very close together, $E_c - E_a \to 0$, and the corrosion current and overall corrosion potential are given by the intersection of the curves.

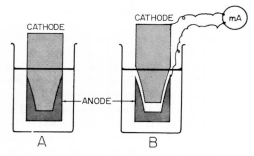

FIG. 4. Direct measurement of corrosion current by divided specimen.

(a) Undivided specimen to determine location of anode and cathode.

(b) Divided specimen for subsequent current measurement.

The anodes and cathodes on a piece of corroding metal may be yards or miles apart, as on pipe lines running through deaerated soil and then through a highly aerated stream; they may be a centimeter or so apart, as in a "beaker" experiment; or they may be at adjacent atoms, as in metal dissolution—general attack—in acids with hydrogen evolution. In the first two cases they can be readily investigated separately; in the third, their conjoint presence on the same visible area of metal must always be presumed. At any instant, a metal atom about to undergo an anodic act of dissolution is normally sited at

an edge, or especially a kink in an edge, of atoms on the lattice; the metal atoms still in close-packed surface array require a higher free energy of activation to react. Cathodic reduction of H^+ or indeed of O_2 may be also easier at similar singularities—in fact, a particular surface site may consecutively be cathode and anode. It is simplest to regard the whole surface of a generally dissolving metal as both the total poten-

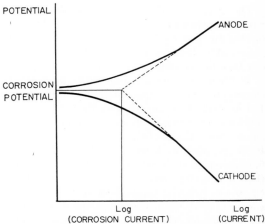

FIG. 5. Determination of corrosion current by extrapolation.

——, Experimental polarization curves.

- - -, Extrapolation of "Tafel" portion to corrosion current and potential.

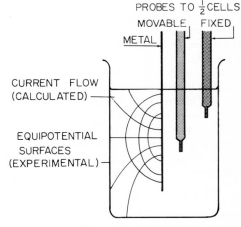

FIG. 6. Determination of corrosion current by p.d. measurement in solution.

Right-hand side of beaker: Arrangement of probes.

Left-hand side of beaker: Experimental plot of equipotentials, from which current can be calculated, since potential and current surfaces form an orthogonal system.

tial anode area *and* the total potential cathode area: at any atomic site, the time taken for an individual anodic or cathodic act is so small ($ca\ 10^{-12}$ sec) compared with the average interval between them ($ca\ 10^{-3}$ sec for a dissolution rate of 1 mm/h) that there is virtually no interference between such individual acts.

Corrosion rates are reduced by *inhibitors* (q.v.). These act either by adsorption at the metal surface (amphipathic organic molecules) or by producing solid precipitates at the anodes or cathodes by reaction with the primary anodic or cathodic products. Some anodic inhibitors can increase the rate of corrosion penetration because they reduce the anode area without a concomitant reduction in anode current, thus increasing the anode current density. However, if present in *sufficient* amount, such anodic inhibitors can either block the anodes entirely with a solid precipitate, or lead to such a high anode current-density that anodic passivity (see **Passivity**) is produced.

Corrosion rates are also reduced by *cathodic protection* (q.v.). If the potential of a dissolving anode is moved in the negative direction by an outside agency, such as a more negative "galvanic" anode or an unattackable or expendable anode with an external emf, its current density diminishes (Fig. 7). If the potential is made sufficiently negative, all corrosion ceases. The current at the cathode zones of such protected metal of course increases, and the anode zones may indeed be made cathodic by the application of sufficient polarization. The increased pH of the solution surrounding such cathodic metal, and especially any precipitate that it may lay down on the surface (e.g., $CaCO_3$ from a "hard" water or sea water), are important additional effects in cathodic protection. *Anodic protection* is considered elsewhere (see **Anodic Protection** and **Passivity**).

Corrosion rates are increased, often by many orders of magnitude, by cathodic or anodic stimulators. Thus, nitric acid is a powerful cathodic stimulator, because it is reduced at high rates with very little activation polarization below its high positive potential, and because its high solubility allows very rapid supply to cathode surfaces by convection-diffusion. Complexing agents such as cyanide act as anodic stimulators by making the anode potential more negative rather than by reducing anode activation polarization, although they may provide means of preventing concentration polarization (q.v.). Gen-

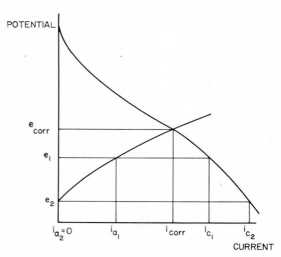

FIG. 7. Principle of cathodic protection.

$\left.\begin{array}{l} i_{corr} \\ e_{corr} \end{array}\right\}$, natural corrosion $\left\{\begin{array}{l} \text{current} \\ \text{potential} \end{array}\right.$

$\left.\begin{array}{l} i_{a_1}\text{, anode current} \\ i_{c_1}\text{, cathode current} \\ e_1 \quad\text{, potential} \end{array}\right\}$ for partial

cathodic protection; external current is $i_{c_1} - i_{a_1}$

$\left.\begin{array}{l} i_{a_2} = 0\text{, anode current} \\ i_{c_2}\text{, cathode current} \\ e_2\text{, potential} \end{array}\right\}$ for complete cathodic protection.

erally, increased access of either cathodic or anodic reactants to the appropriate reaction zone, as achieved by stirring and agitation, leads to reduced concentration polarization and much increased corrosion rate.

Corrosion may also be much stimulated by very stagnant conditions, such as those obtaining in crevices or pits or under porous deposits. The considerable acidity that may be produced by anodic reactions such as (3) is there neither swept away by convection, nor neutralized by the alkali concomitantly formed at the cathode outside the crevice or deposit; further, access of dissolved oxygen, which might tend to turn the zone into a cathode, is greatly hindered. Crevice, pit, and subdeposit anodes, therefore, tend to be self-perpetuating, and in some cases (notably zinc and aluminium) develop so much acidity that local cathodic hydrogen evolution can begin, with a considerable increase in corrosion. Resistant metals such as titanium are almost immune to this kind of attack, because even at quite low pH they tend to form adherent solid oxide, rather than soluble aquocations, as the initial anodic product.

Stress corrosion cracking and *corrosion fatigue* (q.v.) are examples of conjoint action of a corrosive environment and mechanical stress—the former occurring under static tensile stress and the latter under alternating stress well below the yield-point. There is much evidence that cold-worked metal is more specifically anodically active than annealed metal, probably because its surface contains a greater density of active anode sites. Further, *rapidly yielding* metal (as at the advancing edge of a stress-corrosion crack), may give 10^4 to 10^5 times as great an anodic current density for the same polarization as static metal (as on the sides of the crack)—the probable explanation of at least some types of stress corrosion cracking. The detailed dislocation structure formed on deformation is probably linked with the anodic "mechanochemical" effect just described, and may also be important in the less well-understood phenomenon of corrosion fatigue.

References

1. EVANS, U. R., "The Corrosion and Oxidation of Metals," London, Edward Arnold, 1961.
2. EVANS, U. R., "An Introduction to Metallic Corrosion," 2nd Edition, London, Edward Arnold, 1963.
3. UHLIG, H. H., "Corrosion and Corrosion Control," New York, John Wiley and Sons, Inc., 1963.

T. P. HOAR

Cross-references: See entries bearing *Corrosion* titles; *Anodic Protection; Cathodic Protection; Passivity; Polarization; Potential-pH Diagrams; Tafel Lines.*

CORROSION FATIGUE

A metal is said "to fail from fatigue" when repeated (not continuous) stressing causes the development of surface cracks, eventually resulting in complete fracture. This property of metals has probably been known for centuries. However, it has been only 45 years since the first written record was made of the observation that the environment surrounding the metal was capable of drastically altering the nature of the fatigue process. The phenomenon whereby the environment alters the fatigue process from that found in air or vacuum is now referred to as "corrosion fatigue."

The reverse stressing of a metal below a defi-

nite limit of stress does not seriously affect the metal. It is true that some gliding may occur initially but if the stress is sufficiently low there is no further damage and the deformation process behaves elastically. The stress limit below which the structural changes in the metal are slight is called the "fatigue limit." It is presumed that the life of a specimen undergoing reversed stresses, in air or vacuum, at stress levels below the fatigue limit is very, very long.

At stresses higher than the fatigue limit, slip occurs along certain crystallographic planes; slip lines appear on the grains, and as time proceeds the lines appear to thicken. Sooner or later the gliding planes gradually join up to produce a crack in the region where considerable slip has already occurred. Once a crack is formed it is easily propagated by further stress cycles due to a stress intensification factor at the root of the crack. The metal will then fail. The upper curve in Fig. 1 represents a relationship between the logarithm of the number of cycles completed before fracture occurred in a metal undergoing fatigue at different stresses without corrosion.

When the environment is capable of substantially altering the surface of metal, fatigue behavior usually follows the lower curve of Fig. 1. There will be no fatigue limit. Whereas the ordinary fatigue limit may be approximately one-half of the ultimate tensile strength, failure by corrosion fatigue can occur at low stresses and in relatively short times. In recent years it has become apparent that accelerated failure by environmental conditions may even have occurred

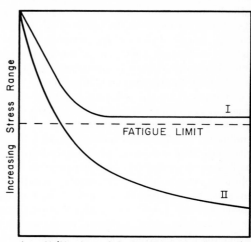

Log N (Number of Cycles Needed for Fracture)

FIGURE I

FIG. 1. (I) Fatigue without corrosion
(II) Fatigue with corrosion

in tests on specimens of certain metals tested in air. The peculiarities of environment were never more clearly evident than when data were reported by the National Bureau of Standards that transparent pressure-sensitive tape applied to the surfaces of aluminum alloy fatigue specimens tested in air disclosed the presence of gas bubbles issuing from fatigue cracks. The presence of the tape both increased the fatigue life of one alloy and retarded crack development in others.

For simplification it is easiest to consider corrosion fatigue as a two-stage process. The first stage is corrosion. It is doubtful if slow uniform corrosion would have more than a slight effect on the fatigue process. The corrosion processes most harmful to the fatigue behavior of the metal will be those which interfere with elastic deformation and lead to plastic deformation. These would be various forms of localized attack, such as pitting and grooving. They not only interfere with gliding but by virtue of the groove or notch produced, intensify the stress. The second stage is therefore a pure fatigue failure.

There are three related modes of metal failure under stress. Besides ordinary fatigue and corrosion fatigue, one must consider stress corrosion cracking. The tendency to ascribe the mode of failure through analysis of the cracking pattern is commendable but often leads to incorrect conclusions since there are really no "hard and fast" rules about the cracking patterns in each of these categories. In fact, if hydrogen embrittlement is considered as a special case of stress corrosion cracking, rules concerning the path of the crack and number of cracks are impossible. The textbook advice on cracking patterns is most reliable for ordinary fatigue. Here one looks for lone cracks, usually transgranular. Of course, the history of the metal should be known as well, since the environment must be inocuous for a pure fatigue failure. An example of how misleading the actual crack may be, is a hypothetical failure in some steel where the crack path is transgranular and the cracks are few in number. If this metal was also susceptible to hydrogen embrittlement, it is conceivable that failure in the air after a period of time (and cyclic stressing) could occur either through ordinary fatigue or embrittlement from retained hydrogen absorbed during its pickling. A choice between corrosion fatigue and stress corrosion cracking purely on the basis of crack patterns is even more dubious. In both cases the cracks

are either few or many, branching or straight, intergranular or transgranular. It requires much experience, knowledge of the materials and their history, and "a little bit of luck" to be 100 per cent certain of cause.

In the brief period of the last 45 years, interest in studying corrosion fatigue has been declining. The greatest number of papers were published immediately after the discovery of the phenomenon. The number has declined with a few brief flurries of productivity. It is not likely that the interest *per se* in the phenomenon has declined, since a continuing increase in the related subject of stress corrosion cracking is evident by an upsurge of papers on that subject. It is more likely that the difficulties in experimentation in studying corrosion fatigue have made experimenters choose the easier (experimentally) study of stress corrosion cracking. When studying corrosion fatigue the following variables must be considered:

1. Magnitude and type of applied stress. The stresses generated during testing will, of course, depend on the fatigue-testing device. There are two main types; in one, a rod is alternately in tension and compression due to a push-pull action; in the other, a wire or rod is made to rotate into a slight bow so that the surface will be both in tension and compression simultaneously. Work performed on the electrochemistry of the corrosion processes occurring during corrosion-fatigue testing has shown that current will flow from a cell generated by the surface in tension and compression simultaneously. Undoubtedly the currents are different in the push-pull machine.

2. Nature of the stress cycle. This includes not only the way the stress varies with time or the frequency of the cycle, but could include excursions into periods of dry fatigue.

3. Environment
4. Temperature
5. Surface
6. Metallurgical structure.

Since corrosion fatigue can be divided into corrosion and fatigue, most of the methods for lengthening the life of materials depend on preventing or retarding corrosion. The devices used to accomplish this result are: coatings, shot-peening (to place the surface in compression), cathodic polarization, and inhibitors.

In summary, corrosion fatigue is a fairly recently observed phenomenon. Its effects are exceedingly dangerous, since the normal fatigue behavior of a specific alloy gives no clue to the expected life of a part undergoing cyclic stresses in a slightly corrosive environment. In this age when new alloys appear on the market at the rate of hundreds each year, and alloys are being exposed to progressively more severe environments, it seems that a rash of increasing corrosion fatigue failures will result. Against this there is a decline in corrosion-fatigue testing. Perhaps the increased interest in metal physics will result in a better understanding of the mechanism and permit more confidence in the application of new alloys. But at the present time, it does appear that a vital subject is overlooked by ignoring the study of corrosion fatigue.

References

1. Gough, H. J., *J. Inst. Metals*, **49,** 17 (1932).
2. Gilbert, P. T., *Metallurgical Reviews*, **1,** Part 3, (1956).
3. Evans, U. R., "The Corrosion and Oxidation of Metals," pp. 701–730, New York, St. Martin's Press, 1960.
4. Wood, W. A. and Davies, R. B., *Proc. Royal Soc.* (A), **220,** 255 (1953).
5. Holshouser, W. L., and Bennett, J. A., "Gas Evolution from Metal Surfaces During Fatigue Stressing," *ASTM 1962 Preprint* **62.**

Lawrence R. Scharfstein

Cross-references: *Hydrogen Embrittlement; Pitting Corrosion; Stress Corrosion.*

CORROSION, FRETTING. See FRETTING CORROSION.

CORROSION BY FUSED SALTS. See FUSED SALT CORROSION.

CORROSION, GALVANIC. See GALVANIC CORROSION.

CORROSION INHIBITION

Corrosion inhibition is the *in situ* treatment of a metal to reduce its corrosion rate. Corrosion processes always involve mass transfer of atoms, ions, or molecules to and from the metal/corrodant interface. With the possible exception of the action of liquid metals, these processes also involve charge transfer from metal atoms to some reactive species. In the vast majority of systems and certainly in all of the well-studied systems, the corrosion reactions are electrochemical, i.e., some localized areas in the metal surface serve as anodes; others serve as sites for the cathodic reac-

tion. The two electrochemical half-reactions are spatially separated but electrically connected by the metal and by the solution.

Corrosion inhibitors function by one or more of the following mechanisms: (1) By forming or causing to form a material barrier to the transport up to the metal surface of the reactive species or to the transport of the products away from this interface; (2) by forming a film which has an electrical resistance high enough to restrict the flow of electrons between anodic and cathodic reaction sites; and (3) by causing the metal to become less subject to reaction, i.e., by ennobling the surface. The most effective inhibitors probably utilize more than one means.

Because the corrosion process in aqueous solutions of electrolytes is electrochemical, an understanding of the interrelationships of the three inhibition processes can be accomplished by reference to the mixed potential theories which have evolved from studies of the electrochemical kinetics of corrosion reactions.

Mixed Potential Corrosion Theory

When a metallic electrode is in equilibrium with a solution of its ions, it adopts a reversible potential, E_M, which depends on the temperature of the solution and activity of the ions in accordance with the Nernst equation. The magnitude and sign of this potential are functions of the position of the metal in the electrochemical series, of the activity of the ions, and of the temperature. Under equilibrium conditions, the rate of the deposition half-reaction,

$$M^{n+} + ne \rightarrow M^\circ,$$

equals that of the dissolution half-reaction,

$$M^\circ \rightarrow M^{n+} + ne.$$

If this half-cell is connected to another suitable half-cell, but isolated from it by means of an electrolyte bridge, and if a current is impressed between the two so that the deposition reaction is made to predominate by the magnitude and direction of current flow, then the current density, i_c, and the overvoltage, $\eta = E_{rev} - E$, are related by Tafel's empirical equation

$$\eta_c = a + b \log i_c.$$

This relation is equally applicable to the dissolution reaction.

It is known that when an impure metal corrodes in aqueous electrolyte solutions, the impurity sites may function as cathodes for the electrochemical half-reaction,

$$2H^+ + 2e \rightarrow H_2 \;.$$

Other sites are dissolution (anodic) sites. Thus, a current passes through the bulk metal between these cathodic sites and the anodic sites, and the solution completes the circuit by electrolytic conductance, i.e., the system is a short-circuited voltaic cell. The phenomenon is most pronounced when dissimilar metals exist in a segregated matrix. In this case, the metal which stands lowest (most noble) in the electrochemical series becomes the cathode and the base metal dissolves. A dissimilar metal is not *necessary*, however, because sulfides, phosphides, etc. can also serve as the sites for cathodic reaction.

Using the Tafel relation, the polarization curves of Fig. 1 may be used to explain corrosion mechanisms. In the idealized case of an *active* metal electrode initially in equilibrium with a very dilute solution of its ions at E_M , line A expresses the $E - \log I$ relationship when this electrode is polarized anodically by means of an impressed current. Curve C arises in the idealized case of cathodic polarization of an *inert* electrode in a deaerated solution with both hydrogen gas and hydrogen ions initially in equilibrium at the electrode surface. A similar curve is observed for aerated solutions in which the dissolved oxygen reacts preferentially to the hydrogen ions. Curves

A', C', and B arise under various conditions of inhibition which are discussed below.

If the cathodic and anodic reactions are occurring on the same piece of metal as in corrosion, only one potential of this electrode is possible because the surface anodic and cathodic sites are short circuited through the bulk metal. This potential is E_{corr} (Fig. 1). The corresponding i_{corr} can be determined from Faraday's law by measuring the rate of dissolution of the metal by determining either the weight loss of the electrode or the concentration increase of the M^{n+} ions. In deaerated acidic solutions, an identical value is obtained from the rate of evolution of hydrogen. Thus,

$$i_H = i_M = i_{corr} \;,$$

where the i's represent current density.

Mechanisms of Inhibition

The above concepts are summarized by polarization diagrams such as Figs. 1 and 2. Using Fig. 1, it is possible to determine a number of possible effects which can be used to inhibit corrosion. It should be noted that evolution of hydrogen is not the only possible cathodic reaction. Under proper conditions a number of materials may be reduced at the cathodic sites either preferentially or along with the hydrogen ions.

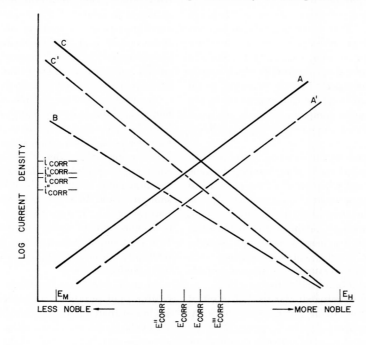

POTENTIAL

FIG. 1. Polarization diagram.

When this occurs, the cathode reaction is said to be depolarized. Dissolved oxygen is the most common depolarizer although heavy metal ions (e.g., Fe(III)) and organic molecules (e.g., nitrobenzene) can serve this purpose also. These circumstances are more complicated, but the principles of inhibition are the same.

The development so far predicts five effects which can result in a decrease in i_{corr}.

(1) Compounds which cause a parallel shift of the cathodic curve, C, toward less noble potentials (e.g., C') also produce a new corrosion potential, E'_{corr}, which is *less* noble than before and a new corrosion current, i'_{corr}, which is lower than before. Organic compounds which are selectively adsorbed on the cathodic sites and thereby reduce the cathodic surface area produce this effect. The types of organic compounds which function at least partly in this manner cover the whole range of functional groups which contain the elements, O, S, N, and P. Probably compounds containing other members of periodic groups V and VI are equally effective. The masking process is effective when the rate of supply of the reactive solute (e.g., rate of diffusion) limits the uninhibited corrosion rate.

(2) Compounds which cause a decrease in the slope of the cathodic curve, C, (e.g., corresponding to B) will produce inhibition ($i''_{corr} < i_{corr}$) accompanied by a potential shift in the *less* noble direction (E''_{corr}). This effect is produced by ions of metals which are reduced to the metallic state by the corroding system, e.g., As(III), Sb(III), Sn(II), Hg(I), added to solutions in which steel is corroding. It is necessary that the deposited metal have a very high overpotential compared to the base metal. Organic compounds which are good catalyst poisons, e.g., amines and sulfides, behave similarly.

(3) Compounds which cause a shift of both E_H and E_M toward each other leaving the new Tafel lines (A' and C') parallel to the old lead to decreased corrosion current (i'''_{corr}). This effect is produced by inhibitors which are generally physically adsorbed at both anodic and cathodic sites. These inhibitors are usually sparingly soluble, high molecular weight, colloidal organic substances. They are frequently of natural origin, e.g., gelatin, egg albumin, dextrin, or agar.

(4) and (5) Reasoning similar to that of effect (2) applied to the anodic polarization curve, A, predicts that compounds which can cause a decrease in slope of this curve will also decrease the corrosion current. This effect produces a *more*

noble E_{corr}. It is often observed but usually occurs in conjunction with the other anodic effect which is analogous to (1). Compounds which produce a shift in the anodic polarization curve toward *more* noble potentials will produce a *more* noble E_{corr} and will decrease i_{corr}. This effect, which is illustrated by A' in Fig. 1, is distinctly different from passivation. It has only recently been recognized as an effect resulting from the adsorption of nitrogen-containing molecules as well as other nonoxidizing inhibitors. Formerly it was supposed that amine molecules in acid solutions were inhibitors because they exist in the protonated, cationic form which would be electrically attracted to cathodic sites.

This electrical attraction mechanism does not explain the observed noble shift of the corrosion potential. Furthermore, it is now known that the adsorption behavior of any species, cationic, anionic, or neutral, is governed by the difference between the electrode potential and the null potential of the adsorbate surface and not necessarily by its cathodic-anodic function. In addition, the mixed potential diagram (Fig. 1) clearly shows that the potential of cathodic and anodic sites need not be different and therefore general, rather than selective adsorption, is the expected rule. It is observed that steel which contains on its surface irreversibly adsorbed unprotonated amines (from benzene) is inhibited when transferred (without exposure to air) to aqueous sulfuric acid. All of these factors lead to the conclusion that *general chemi*sorption is one of the major functions of soluble, adsorption inhibitors and that this is often accompanied by an ennobling effect.

In order to account for all the observed phenomena exhibited by the many compounds which have been studied, it is necessary to recognize that few compounds produce only a single effect. Furthermore, it is evident that the best inhibitors, compounds or mixtures, are those which produce a complement of effects which best fit the corrosion situation. In this connection, two other important effects should be discussed. The most often encountered is the question, "Why should two compounds which differ only slightly in molecular structure exhibit greatly different inhibitor effectiveness?"

In acid solutions, piperidine is a better inhibitor than pyridine; ortho-substituted anilines are better than meta- or para-substituted anilines; the cyclic saturated imines, deca- and octamethyleneimine are better than their secondary alkyl analogs, di-*n*-amylamine and di-*n*-butylamine.

It is known that the *chemical* reactions of polarizable atoms, such as N, S, and O, may be influenced by structural changes at remote positions even in saturated molecules. The changes are wrought by structurally induced changes in the orbital geometry of the unshared electrons of the polarizable atom. It is reasonable then to assume that these changes will have a distinct effect on the chemisorption bond between an inhibitor and a metal surface. Work is in progress in several laboratories to clarify this point.

The second effect concerns the influence of the metal-solution interface. Even in the absence of any specifically adsorbed substances, a metal-solution interface exhibits a double-layered charge structure, i.e., there is an accumulation of charge next to the metal which is balanced by an equal accumulation of the opposite sign on the solution side of the double layer. The structure of this double layer, i.e., which charges are next to the metal, depends on the potential of the metal. In fact, the phenomenon is used to define a scale of potentials as plus or minus with respect to the zero point of charge (zpc) or null potential, i.e., that potential at which the charges (+ and −) are randomly distributed in both layers. Inhibitor adsorption is influenced by the displacement of the potential from the zpc, not necessarily by whether an anodic or cathodic reaction is taking place. The further the potential is removed from the zpc, the more difficult it is for a neutral mole-

cule to adsorb; the more negative with respect to the zpc, the more likely for a positively charged molecule to adsorb; and, the more positive with respect to the zpc, the more likely for a negative ion to adsorb. Furthermore, the kinetics of electrochemical reactions are known to be strongly influenced by the nature of the double layer; hence, corrosion rates are also sensitive to such changes in double layer structure. The difficulty lies in the fact that the zpc is well-known only for mercury, and in addition, is not easily defined for impure polycrystalline metals.

Inorganic and Passivating Inhibitors

The inhibitors discussed so far for the most part have been organic. Most of the inorganic inhibitors are passivating inhibitors and as such, require an extension of the polarization diagram. In order to lay the foundation for an understanding of their mode of action, consider an experiment in which an iron (steel, Co, Si, or Ni) electrode is made the anode of an electrochemical cell in sulfuric acid media. If the potential is stabilized at any desired value by use of a potentiostat, and if the current passing through the cell is measured at increasing anodic (more noble) potentials over a range which is extended from that of Fig. 1, the nonlinear curve illustrated in Fig. 2 will be observed. At first, increased dissolution of the iron is observed; however, at more noble potentials, the current falls to a very low value in a more or

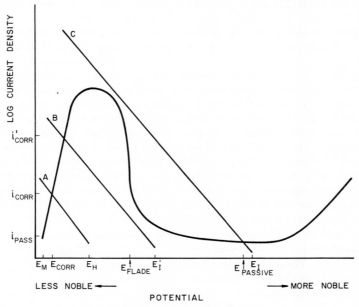

FIG. 2. Anodic polarization diagram.

less broad, passive region. The transition point between active and passive states is known as the Flade potential (q.v.). It has a unique pH dependence in any given system. A thin, pore-free, electronically conducting film formed by the products of an electrochemical reaction constitutes the passive surface.

Using similar "mixed-potential" reasoning to that applied to the mechanism of adsorption inhibitors the mode of action of inhibitors, such as OsO_4^{--}, CrO_4^{--}, TcO_4^-, MoO_4^{--}, NO_2^-, and $C_6H_5COO^-$, can be described using the curves in Fig. 2. The cathodic polarization curve of hydrogen is represented by curve A. It intersects the anodic curve at E_{corr} and i_{corr} which are the uninhibited values. Cathodic polarization curves for reduction of an inhibitor, e.g., OsO_4^{--}, are represented by curves C and B. The curves are displaced along the potential axis depending on inhibitor concentration. At the higher concentration, the reversible potential is E_I. If OsO_4^{--} is added at this concentration to an acid solution in which an iron electrode is corroding at a rate represented by i_{corr} and potential, E_{corr}, reduction of the inhibitor will polarize the iron so that it follows the heavy curve to its intersection with C at $E_{passive}$. Note that $E_{passive}$ is much more noble than E_{corr} and that the corrosion current (rate) is stabilized at a low value over quite a potential range *after* going through a maximum. If the inhibitor is added in such a low concentration that its reversible potential is E_I', it acts as a depolarizer and serves to *increase* the corrosion rate to i_{corr}'. This phenomenon has led to the application of the term, "dangerous," to this type inhibitor.

In point of fact OsO_4^{--} is the only inhibitor of this type which will passivate an iron surface in the absence of oxygen. All the rest require dissolved oxygen before passivation occurs. In addition, some of the very weak oxidizers (benzoate, phthalate) require high pH. Oxygen dependence is not explained by the mixed potential approach. Neither the specific properties of the inhibitor, nor the composition or properties of the film, nor the specific interaction between the inhibitor and the solid surface by adsorption or otherwise, nor the effect of the inhibitor on the kinetics of the reaction are considered by the electrochemical theory discussed above. These phenomena have given rise to two other theories and a hypothesis, each emphasizing a different aspect.

A purely chemical theory has been developed principally on the basis of film stripping experiments using PO_4^{---} and CrO_4^{--}. Analyses of the stripped films show them to contain chiefly Fe(III). From this point, logic indicates that inhibition occurs because of the barrier formed by the films. Further, film growth and repair require both an oxidative and a buffering action so that pores are plugged by oxidation of the Fe(II) which diffuses through them followed by precipitation of hydrous oxides. By extension of the concepts to include precipitation of iron phosphates and oxidation by dissolved oxygen, inhibition by ions such as PO_4^{---} and CrO_4^{--} is explained. The picture is not complete, however, because TcO_4^- does not convert Fe(II) to Fe(III) under conditions where it inhibits. It is also a very weak base and so far as is known does not form insoluble salts with iron. It must be concluded, therefore, that the chemical theory does not embody a complete picture either.

Adsorption at the metal-corrodant or film-corrodant interface is well established in a few cases and inferred in others. The process is reversible and follows well-known isotherms in some cases. In general, it may be assumed that the adsorbed species blocks sites which are active in one of the corrosion processes. It may also be assumed that the adsorbed inhibitor interferes with anodic catalytic processes, such as those postulated for adsorbed FeOH, by decreasing the surface available for catalytic action or by substituting a slow alternative process for a fast catalytic one. The marked lack of inhibitor action by ReO_4^-, in contrast to TcO_4^- which is almost an identical twin in size, charge, and geometrical configuration, is not explained by this reasoning, however.

Electrostatic polarization has been considered as a working hypothesis whereby the above $TcO_4^- - ReO_4^-$ contrast (as well as others) has been considered to be due to varying degrees of polarity in the metal-oxygen bonds of the inhibitor ion. Simple coulomb law calculations have shown that ions of polar type should induce a space charge at a semiconducting surface which is opposite in sign to that from covalent bonds. Such effects may cause the same kind of double layer effect on the kinetics which are observed in other electrochemical reactions.

Nonaqueous Systems

Corrosion inhibitors for nonaqueous or even partially aqueous systems usually cause precipitation of some metallic compound. However, in the case of liquid sodium, the best inhibitors primarily decrease the oxygen content and secondarily form a protective film. The more usual case is similar in principle to the use of HF to passivate aluminum and iron alloys for use with fuming nitric acid. The HF forms a tenacious surface film of insoluble metal fluoride. Similarly, zirconium and titanium inhibit mass transfer of steels by liquid bismuth, mercury and probably lead by reacting with the surface of these steels to form adherent deposits of nitrides or nitride plus carbide.

In some cases the inhibitor must catalyze the formation of a film of corrosion product which is both dense and adherent enough to prevent further corrosion. Thus, in the corrosion of iron in 60 per cent LiBr, in the absence of inhibition a magnetite film grows on the iron surface as large, loosely adherent pyramidal crystals. These crystals clearly show that they have been nucleated by screw dislocations in the surface of the metal. On the other hand, in the presence of $LiMoO_4$ as an inhibitor, the film is dense and adherent and thereby effectively decreases the corrosion rate after its formation. These films are very fine-grained and contain small amounts of molybdenum. In this case, the molybdate is nucleating film crystal formation in many more places than the surface defects, and thereby is promoting a film which is resistant to scaling and other ruptures which allow corrosion to continue through the film in the uninhibited case.

Vapor Phase Systems

Two corrosion circumstances which are often encountered and which require vapor phase inhibitors are situations where a solvent is alternately evaporated and condensed or where a tightly closed system may be obtained so that the atmosphere may be controlled and proper concentration of inhibitor maintained. In the first case, corrosion is usually caused by a dissolved gas, e.g., CO_2 in boiler water, which is carried along by the solvent so that the condensates are quite corrosive. This circumstance is combated by using ammonia or a volatile amine, such as dicyclohexylamine, cyclohexylamine, or morpholine. These compounds accomplish inhibition by two mechanisms. The free amine will combine with the dissolved CO_2, thus rendering the atmosphere less corrosive, and it will adsorb to form a protective layer. In addition to forming a barrier to the approach of the reactant, this adsorbed layer may cause an ennobling of the surface in the same manner as that which occurs on addition of these compounds to aqueous acid solutions.

With the advent of new packaging techniques using plastic films, it is possible to protect equipment from such corrosive environments as marine atmospheres by placing the article to be protected in a sealed, plastic cocoon containing a small amount of a salt of a volatile amine as an inhibitor, e.g., dicyclohexylammonium nitrite. Frequently, a desiccant is also included in these packages. Generally, the same compounds which are useful in steam boilers, etc., are also useful for this purpose.

Miscellaneous Systems

Many useful inhibitors do not fit any of the schemes discussed so far. The most important of these are soluble compounds which cause precipitation at the metal surface. On iron, for example, the most effective precipitated coatings are predominantly cubic iron oxide, e.g., γ-Fe_2O_3, containing inclusions derived from the precipitant. These films are built up in oxygenated neutral or alkaline solutions starting from the air-formed oxide coat present on the metal surface at the time of immersion into the corrodant. By reaction with the products of the corrosion reaction, compounds such as $Zn(OH)_2$, $Ca(OH)_2$, $FePO_4$, or $FeCO_3$ can be precipitated at a corroding metal surface by use of the appropriate soluble inhibitor. Those weak spots in the inhibitive coating, which allow corrosion to continue and thus allow an accumulation of corrosion products, are plugged by the precipitating action of the inhibitor, and the film is thereby maintained in repair. The fact that the films continue the cubic crystalline structure probably accounts for their ready growth and relative tenacity. Those compounds which decrease the aggressiveness of the corrodant, such as hydrazine and sodium sulfite used for oxygen reduction or ethanolamines used for scrubbing hydrogen sulfide, are not inhibitors within the meaning of the previously stated definition, but they are often used in corrosion control and therefore are mentioned.

Conclusion

In summary, corrosion inhibitor molecules generally become deeply involved at the interfaces between corrodant and metal or corrodant and oxide film (or other corrosion product film). They either displace the reactive species to form a protective film of inhibitor molecules or else they participate in the formation of a dense protective film of corrosion product. The thickness of very protective films is often only one or a few molecular layers at most, so that it is clear that they are not always purely physical barriers; the ennobling of the metal surface caused by adsorption of the inhibitor is also important. Thus, the keys to further practical knowledge of corrosion inhibition lie in the application to corrosion studies of such diverse disciplines as electrochemistry, surface chemistry, physical organic chemistry, and solid-state chemistry.

References

1. ANTROPOV, L. I., "*Kinetics of Electrode Processes and Null Points of Metals*," Ranchi, India, Catholic Press, 1960.
2. EVANS, U. R., "*The Corrosion and Oxidation of Metals: Scientific Principles and Practical Applications*," London, Edward Arnold, Ltd., 1960.
3. First International Congress on Metallic Corrosion, especially see N. Hackerman and R. M. Hurd, "Corrosion Inhibition and Molecular Structure," and L. I. Antropov, "Inhibitors of Metallic Corrosion and the *phi*-scale of Potentials."
4. FISCHER, H., *Korrosion*, **12**, 1369 (1960).
5. HOAR, T. P., "Mechanism of Anodic Inhibitors of Corrosion," *J. Appl. Chem.*, **5**, 381, (1955).
6. PUTILOVA, I. N., BALEZIN, S. A., AND BARANNIK, V. U. P., "Metallic Corrosion Inhibitors," New York, Pergamon Press, 1960.
7. STERN, M., "The Mechanism of Passivating-Type Inhibitors," *J. Electrochem. Soc.*, **105**, 638 (1958).
8. SYMPOSIUM Européen sur Les Inhibiteurs De Corrosion, Xème Manifestation de la Fédération Européeme de la Corrosion, Ferrara (Italie) 1960, (Universita Degli) Studi Di Ferrara, 1961.
9. Symposium on Corrosion Theory, published in *Corrosion*, **18**, No. 9 (1962). Especially see G. H. Cartledge, "Recent Studies in the Action of Inorganic Inhibitors," 316t and N. Hackerman, "Recent Advances in Understanding of Organic Inhibitors," 332t.
10. UHLIG, H. H., *Z. Electrochem.*, **62**, 626–31 (1956).

ROBERT R. ANNAND AND
NORMAN HACKERMAN

Cross references: *Corrosion Inhibition by Pertechnetate Ion; Corrosion Inhibitors; Flade Potential; Mixed Potential; Passivity; Tafel Lines.*

CORROSION INHIBITION BY PERTECHNETATE ION

Most of the inorganic inhibitors of corrosion other than nitrite have the formula $XO_4{}^{n-}$, in which n lies between zero and 3. Included in the group are OsO_4, $TcO_4{}^-$, $CrO_4{}^{2-}$, $MoO_4{}^{2-}$, $WO_4{}^{2-}$, and $PO_4{}^{3-}$. With the exception of the various phosphatic inhibitors, all these substances are potential oxidizing agents, though their oxidizing properties differ considerably. Since oxidation is required in the passivation of iron, the phosphates are effective inhibitors only in well-aerated systems. At the other extreme is osmium (VIII) oxide, which has so noble an electrode potential and so high an exchange current density that it passivates iron very rapidly in the absence of oxygen, provided the pH value is sufficiently high and activating electrolytes are at a sufficiently low concentration.[1] The presence of the pertechnetate ion, $TcO_4{}^-$, in this group of inhibitors is of interest because of its extreme effectiveness, its uniqueness in being derived from a man-made element, and, finally, because it differs in so many respects from other similarly constituted inhibitors that it provides a new and useful material for the study of inhibition. The theories of the mechanism of inhibition by these substances have been reviewed recently.[2]

The discovery of the inhibitory action of the pertechnetate ion came from attempts to find a reason why the sulfate ion, for instance, does not inhibit in the presence of oxygen, whereas certain other $XO_4{}^{n-}$ ions of similar charge, size and geometrical configuration are very effective inhibitors. It appeared difficult to account for all the facts by assumption of oxidation, buffering, or precipitation of a protective film as the general explanation of the phenomena. A hypothesis was developed from the assumption of a short-range electric field derived from the internal polarity of the $XO_4{}^{n-}$ particles. It was calculated that the externally similar sulfate and chromate ions would generate oppositely directed fields when adsorbed on the substrate if, as is likely, the S-O bonds were essentially covalent and the Cr-O bonds largely ionic. This consideration suggested that if inhibition is somehow related to the resultant surface fields, technetium, in Group VII of the periodic system, should form a good inhibitor in its highest state of oxidation; its moderate oxidation potential, compared to that of permanganate ion, should be favorable in permitting the ion to remain unreduced on the surface. The prediction from this hypothesis was confirmed experimentally in 1952, when it was demonstrated that the pertechnetate ion surpasses even the much-used chromate ion in effectiveness in certain respects.[3]

Technetium does not occur naturally on the

earth, but is produced in nuclear reactors with a fission yield of about 6 per cent. It is recovered and is available from the Oak Ridge National Laboratory. The principal isotope is Tc^{99} with a half-life of 2.15×10^5 years. Its beta radiation of 0.29 Mev maximum energy is useful for determination of the amount of technetium on a corrosion specimen. It is also suitable for studying the distribution of the element by autoradiographic techniques. The compounds of technetium provide a combination of properties that differentiate the pertechnetate ion sharply from all the other inhibiting substances. These differences are helpful in the examination of the various explanations of inhibitor action that have been advanced. Thus, the $Tc(VII–IV)$ couple has a less noble potential but higher exchange current density on passive iron than the $Cr(VI–III)$ couple. The pertechnetate ion is the anion of a very strong acid and consequently has no buffering action, whereas all the other inhibiting anions in the group derive from weak acids. The pertechnetate ion also contrasts with the other anions in its univalence and the considerable solubility of its salts with heavy metals.

Investigation of the inhibiting action of the pertechnetate ion has been limited to iron and steel up to the present. With these materials, inhibition depends upon the maintenance of a certain minimum concentration of inhibitor in the aqueous environment. This minimum concentration depends somewhat upon the composition and surface state of the metal. With abraded electrolytic iron or low-carbon steel, inhibition is effected equally at either 25 or 250°C by $5–10 \times 10^{-5}$ f pertechnetate (5–10 ppm Tc). (f denotes formality, the number of formula weights of the compound in question in a liter of solution.) These tests were made in contact with air, a platinum-lined bomb being used at the elevated temperature (116-hr test). Cast iron or steels with higher carbon content require higher concentrations of the inhibitor. Inhibition persists apparently indefinitely, since two specimens of low-carbon steel (0.1 per cent C) have been under observation for 10 years, part of the time at 85°C. The specimens are unchanged in weight and brightness, and their beta activity has remained constant, showing that there has been no continuing consumption of inhibitor. The observed beta activity comes from a very small amount of $Tc(OH)_4$ deposited on the metal during the initial passivation reaction.

Inhibition seems unrelated to the deposited $Tc(OH)_4$ in the film, however, since addition of rather low concentrations of foreign ions (10^{-2}–10^{-3} f SO_4^{2-}, for example) destroys the effect of the inhibitor when its concentration is also low (10^{-3} f, for example). It appears that a competing adsorption is involved in some way in the mechanism, since the same activating effect of foreign ions has been observed with all the XO_4^{n-} inhibitors.

The radioactivity of technetium and the radiolytic products arising therefrom do not appear to be important factors in the inhibition. This was demonstrated by use of the perrhenate ion, ReO_4^-, in tests for inhibition. It was found that potassium perrhenate has no inhibitory action at any concentration up to saturation, or at temperatures from 5 to 100°C in the presence of air. When a radioactive isotope Re^{186} was used at such a specific activity as to match the radiation in the inhibiting pertechnetate solutions, there was still no inhibition.

A thoroughly deaerated pertechnetate solution does not oxidize aqueous iron(II) ions to iron(III) in weakly acidic solution under conditions which nonetheless permit inhibition to occur. In alkaline solutions this is no longer the case. Polarization measurements with a passive-iron electrode in oxygenated or thoroughly deoxygenated pertechnetate solutions at pH ca. 6 showed that reduction of oxygen is several times faster than reduction of pertechnetate ions at potentials in the neighborhood of the Flade (passivation) potential. Any film of $Tc(OH)_4$ deposited on the electrode accelerates cathodic processes. A similar acceleration results from deposition of $Os(OH)_4$ on the electrode; with the reduction product from chromate ions, no similar catalytic effect is observed. With both pertechnetate and chromate solutions, reduction of oxygen is the faster process under the conditions stated; with osmium(VIII) oxide, reduction of oxygen is greatly subordinate to reduction of the inhibitor.[4] These observations of relative reduction rates are consistent with the fact that the long-term experiments previously mentioned disclose no continuing consumption of pertechnetate by reduction.

Inhibitor ions are known to interact with metallic or oxidic surfaces by either simple adsorption or a true ion-exchange mechanism. The surface state of the substrate is therefore a function of the composition of the environment, the competing actions of which determine the ionic population of the surface. This, in turn, modifies the electric field gradient across the total interface, and the adsorption hypothesis is an attempt to correlate such effects with the inhibiting or noninhibiting action of the different ionic species.[5] The electrostatic polarization hypothesis assumes that the induced space charge changes the energetics of all charge-transfer processes occurring at the corrosion interface in such a way that the overall rate of corrosion is diminished. Similar effects of surface constituents are well-recognized in certain properties of semiconductors.

The radioactivity and relatively high cost of technetium ($90 a gram currently) render its general use as an inhibitor improbable, though its unique properties may make it applicable in special circumstances. As a tool for research, however, it is in a class by itself because of the important respects in which it differs from all other available inorganic inhibitors.

References

1. CARTLEDGE, G. H., *J. Phys. Chem.*, **60**, 1571 (1956).
2. CARTLEDGE, G. H., *Corrosion*, **18**, 361t (1962).
3. CARTLEDGE, G. H., *J. Am. Chem. Soc.*, **77**, 2658 (1955).
4. CARTLEDGE, G. H., *J. Phys. Chem.*, **65**, 1361 (1961).
5. CARTLEDGE, G. H., *Z. Elektrochem.*, **62**, 684 (1958).

G. H. CARTLEDGE

Cross-references: *Flade Potential; Passivity; Polarization.*

CORROSION INHIBITORS—COMMERCIAL

Plant operations of vast magnitudes are dependent upon successful application of commercial corrosion inhibitors. It has been estimated that as much as $50,000,000 annually is spent in the United States alone for this purpose. An understanding of the nature of these commercial corrosion inhibitors, therefore, is of considerable importance to the industrial electrochemist.

While a large number of different types of inhibitors are available, the bulk of commercial materials sold for this purpose consists of surprisingly few different chemicals and combina-

tions of them. This is due to many factors involving the inhibitor properties and the requirements of the system to which it is added, but the main reason is an economic one. The price of the inhibitor times the amount used must come to a figure which represents a substantial savings over the cost of the corrosion that is being prevented. When subjected to this stringent criterion, the list of commercially satisfactory inhibitors is drastically reduced.

It should be stressed that proper selection of inhibitors for specific systems is critical. An inhibitor that is effective for one system may be valueless, and perhaps even dangerous for another one. Even within one type of system, a change in the operational characteristics may dictate the choice of a different inhibitor. Considerable economic damage has resulted from careless extrapolation of inhibitor types and dosages from one system to another.

Another factor influencing the selection of inhibitors is the need for chemical additives to prevent other problems in the system, such as scale deposition, bacterial growth, or foaming. Specific corrosion inhibitors may be helpful or harmful as far as these other problems are concerned, and this must be given due consideration, since a "package" treatment for all the system difficulties is the most frequently used approach.

The use of proper application techniques can be as important to good protection as the selection of the correct corrosion inhibitor. The principles involved in inhibitor application are straightforward and amount to laying down a protective film at the proper location as rapidly as possible. When possible, the metal surface should first be cleaned so as to help film adherence and prevent local cells from developing under the inhibitor. The inhibitor is preferably applied at a high dosage level to cover the surface as rapidly as possible. The treatment is then cut back to that necessary to maintain the film. Use of this technique will not only minimize corrosion, but it will cut down treatment costs, since the dosage required for film repair will be substantially less than the normal use level, and the initial high inhibitor cost will rapidly be recovered in savings.

For the purpose of this discussion, inhibitors will be broken down into two major categories—inorganic and organic. Chemicals of major commercial use in each category will be discussed individually, as well as in combinations. This latter point is very important, since most corrosion inhibitors used industrially today represent blends of inhibitors designed to achieve specific objectives.

Inorganic Corrosion Inhibitors

The use of pH control as an effective inhibition measure is widely practiced. It is not only valuable *per se*, but also as an auxiliary treatment to make the primary corrosion inhibitor most effective at its minimum dosage. A wide variety of inorganic chemicals is used for this purpose.

Boiler water treatment represents one area where alkaline pH control is practiced widely. *Sodium hydroxide*, recirculation of *alkaline boiler water* to the make-up, the *"coordinated pH"* approach involving a high ratio of *trisodium phosphate* to sodium hydroxide, and maintenance of the *ratio of sodium sulfate to alkalinity* above a certain value all are utilized for corrosion inhibition in the feedwater and boiler systems. *Ammonia* is used to volatilize with the steam, and produce a noncorrosive condensate having a neutral or alkaline pH. *Lime* and alkali are used in municipal treating plants or distribution systems to adjust the pH value and form a protective eggshell-thin layer of calcium carbonate. A key factor in good corrosion inhibition in boiler systems is the application of the inhibitor at the proper location. This may be in the feedwater, at various locations in the boiler itself, or in the return condensate system. The inhibitor selected and the amount used depend on the local corrosive conditions. Sodium hydroxide, *sodium carbonate*, calcium oxide, and an *ammoniacal copper carbonate* are used for alkaline pH adjustment in refinery operations. The latter reagents react with the corrosive agents in crude oil to form alkali metal salts that are stable and are removed in the distillation residues. Ammonia is used in overhead systems, together with film-forming amines. The ammonia raises the pH to a specific point, e.g., 7.0, and the other inhibitor then provides protection on an efficient cost-dosage basis.

A surprising corrosion inhibitor is *sulfuric acid*. Cooling tower system waters must be kept above 6.0 to 6.5 to prevent corrosion, but below 7.5 to 8.0 to prevent scaling. Since almost all of the concentrated cooling waters are naturally alkaline, sulfuric acid is used for cheap and effective pH adjustment downwards.

Borax is used as the major portion of certain treatments for diesel and automobile radiators. It is frequently the major antifreeze corrosion inhibitor in formulations because of its low cost. The main purpose of the borax is to maintain the pH of the treated water above 8, although there is some feeling that it is also an effective corrosion inhibitor itself.

Another category of inorganic inhibitors functions by removal of oxygen from the system. Typical inhibitors are *sodium sulfite* and *hydrazine* used in boiler water treatment. Sodium sulfite may be used together with a catalyst such as copper, cobalt, or even activated carbon. The hydrazine is much more effective at lower dosages and is more frequently used.

Molecularly dehydrated phosphates are among the most widely-used inhibitors. They are effective for both corrosion inhibition and scale prevention. A variety of these materials is in use today. The more common ones include pyrophosphate, triphosphate, and a number of different glassy polyphosphates. Commercial glasses are generally characterized in terms of the molecular ratio of their Na_2O and P_2O_5 contents. Probably the most common commercial glass, Calgon, has a Na_2O/P_2O_5 mole ratio of about 1.1 and is also called "hexametaphosphate." Other glasses in common commercial usage are called tetrapoly- and septapolyphosphate. The use of the calcium and magnesium salts of glassy polyphosphates has become fairly prevelant, and offers a controlled slow solubility.

The use of extremely low dosages of glassy polyphosphates (1 or 2 ppm) in boiling water or municipal and home systems is known as "threshold treatment," and is based on the fact that low polyphosphate concentrations will prevent the deposition of calcium carbonate. Higher levels are necessary only when the water is held at high temperatures for a long period of time so that reversion to orthophosphate becomes appreciable, or else when foreign solids are present that will adsorb considerable amounts of the polyphosphate. A recent innovation is the use of polyphosphates containing divalent metals, with the one having zinc being especially effective. Less dosage is required, the film forms faster, and reversion is less.

The largest use of polyphosphates is in cooling tower systems. The inhibitor dosage is generally from 10 to 25 ppm as PO_4 with a higher initial dosage used to lay down a film rapidly. Thus, for example, an initial dosage of 100 ppm as PO_4 for one week on a clean system will allow subsequent film maintenance with good inhibition at the 10 ppm level, whereas lack of pretreatment may require the 25 ppm level. The addition of certain metallic cations, such as zinc, in dosage levels of one or two ppm will improve the inhibiting properties of phosphate combinations. Ferrocyanide is also added for improved corrosion inhibition by a "synergistic" mechanism, while fluoride ions may be used to complex cations, such as aluminum or iron, which might interfere with inhibitor action.

The *chromate ion* is the most effective and widely-used inorganic inhibitor. It can be used in many applications either alone or else as the key ingredient in a formulation of a number of inhibitors. Advantages of straight chromate treatment are its effectiveness, low cost, and applicability to a number of metals. Disadvantages include a pitting tendency at weak points or discontinuities in the film, and toxicity to fish and plant life. Probably the best known and most effective cooling tower formulation is the polyphosphate-chromate combination. The term "dianodic treatment" is usually applied to this mixture which gives very effective corrosion inhibition and prevents pitting. The chromate-phosphate ratio may be varied over a wide range depending on the requirements of the system. Zinc, trivalent chromium, or molybdate anion may be added for additional effectiveness.

The most widely-used treatment for diesel cooling systems consists of formulations based on chromates or dichromates. Typical formulations include sodium or potassium chromates and dichromates, sodium nitrate (primarily for solder protection), borax and sodium carbonate for pH adjustment, and sodium silicate for aluminum inhibition. These chromate inhibitors have the advantage of being very effective for all of the various metals found in a diesel system and have been successfully used in large quantities for many years.

Sodium silicate is used as an inhibitor in cooling systems to a lesser extent than chromates or polyphosphates. The protective film can form over a corroded surface, which is a definite advantage. The presence of calcium is beneficial, while chlorides are harmful, and insufficient quantities of silicate can lead to localized pit-

ting. Sodium silicate is also commonly used in once-through systems. It will prevent corrosion of domestic water piping and will protect iron, steel, galvanized steel, brass, copper, or lead. Household hot water can be treated by bypassing a small part of it through a tank containing a highly insoluble glass of the composition $Na_2O:3SiO_2$. For waters below pH 6.0 a glass containing a higher ratio of sodium to silica is used.

"Boron-nitrite" formulations consisting of a blend of several inhibitors, with borax and nitrite being especially prominent, have been "tailor-made" for diesel and automotive cooling systems. The borax accounts for about half of the inhibitor composition and serves to maintain the pH in the required range. The *sodium nitrite* is an excellent inhibitor for iron and will protect aluminum, but is aggressive to solder. *2-Mercaptobenzothiazole* (MBT) or its sodium salt is frequently present for the protection of copper and brass. Sodium silicate is commonly added for the protection of aluminum, and *sodium nitrate* is added as an inhibitor for solder and aluminum.

The last major class of inorganic inhibitors that will be considered here consists of *arsenic* compounds and formulations. Their use as corrosion inhibitors for "sweet" oil wells is second in volume today only to the long chain organic nitrogeneous inhibitors. Commonly used formulations include mixtures of arsenous oxide, sodium hydroxide and water, and occasionally boric acid in varying proportions, depending upon the desired physical properties. The protection attained against corrosion is excellent.

In the use of inorganic inhibitors it is especially desirable to guard against the deleterious effects of "underdosing." Some inhibitors are considered "dangerous" in that if too low a dosage is used, intense pitting attack will occur at locations that are not covered by a protective film. On the other hand, too high an inhibitor concentration in the material being fed to the system may cause severe attack at the point of entry.

Organic Corrosion Inhibitors

Organic corrosion inhibitors are in use today for a wide variety of applications, with the majority having to do with corrosion in oil-water systems. There are a number of factors common to most of these inhibitors. Invariably, there will be a "long-chain," usually $C_{18}H_{37}$, for solubility in the oil layer and a polar end to form a bond with the metal surface. The polar groups usually are nitrogenous or sulfonic. These two types of inhibitors constitute the overwhelming majority of organic inhibitors in industrial use today, and this brief discussion will be limited to them.

The more common long-chain nitrogenous corrosion inhibitors can be broken down into the following categories: *aliphatic fatty acid derivatives, imidazolines* and their derivatives, *quaternaries*, and *rosin derivatives*. Examples of the first category are as follows:

a) Monoamines: RNH_2

b) Diamines: $RNHCH_2CH_2CH_2NH_2$

c) Amides: $RCONH_2$

d) Polyethoxylated materials: as in a), b), and c) above with $(CH_2CH_2O)_xH$ groups attached to the nitrogen atoms.

e) Amphoteric compounds:

$$CH_3CHCH_2COOH$$
$$|$$
$$RNH$$

The commercial inhibitors are generally derived from tallow, soya, or coco fats, and these terms are used in their commercial names. Thus, the term "R" is replaced by tallow-, soya-, or coco-, leading to names such as *n*-tallow propylene diamine, rather than using the correct designation for the mixture of long chains in tallow.

The straight chain monoamines are inferior to the diamines in oil-water systems. They find considerable application as inhibitors for steam condensate corrosion in boilers. Formulations are commonly based upon octadecylamine or its salts. Blending with a suitable wetting agent will improve the wetting characteristics and also eliminate the corrosion problems that may arise at the point where the acetate salt is fed.

Diamines are very effective inhibitors. The *n*-tallow propylene diamine in the form of the oleic or naphthenic acid salts is one of the most frequently-used inhibitors for primary production of oil. The distilled coco aliphatic diamine is among the best waterflooding inhibitors, and its adipic acid salt has the unusual property (for this general class of inhibitors) of inhibiting corrosion even in the presence of appreciable oxygen concentrations.

Amides of fatty acids and imidazolines find occasional use. Polyethoxylated materials are especially worthwhile in that by varying the amount of ethylene oxide on the molecule, the solubility of the inhibitors can be adjusted to any desired value. The proper degree of water or oil solubility or dispersibility is important in allowing the inhibitor to reach and adhere to the surface that it is supposed to protect. The ethoxylated diamines are especially good inhibitors for a number of applications, since they combine the effectiveness of the diamines with the ability to "tailor-make" their solubility properties as a result of the presence of the ethoxy groups.

Amphoteric materials are beginning to receive considerable attention and have been quite successful in field applications. Amidic acid salts are now being evaluated, and a new type of inhibitor, a diamine salt of an acylsarcosine, has shown very good effectiveness in laboratory testing. The acylsarcosine has the structure $RCON(CH_3)CH_2COOH$.

The second category of nitrogenous inhibitors, the imidazolines, are usually used as such, as salts, or as derivatives. A wide variety of glyoxalidine derivatives for this purpose can be prepared by the reaction of acids, such as oleic or stearic, with aliphatic polyamines, such as aminoethylethanolamine or diethylenetriamine. Salts are then made with acids, such as sebacic, salicylic, oleic, dimeric, and alkaryl sulfonic. The acid serves to impart desirable dispersing and solubility characteristics. Derivatives of imidazolines that have been used include imidazolidinones, imidazolidinethiones, dimidazolines, and various sulfur derivatives. The latter group has been explored quite thoroughly and has generated a number of excellent inhibitors.

The organic inhibitors described in this section are of especial value for oil production and refinery applications. The older technique of applying a constant dosage of corrosion inhibitor to a producing well has been replaced to a great extent by the "Inhibitor Squeeze Technique." A drum or more of an inhibitor formulation is squeezed into the formation in the expectation that the inhibitor will adsorb on the formation and gradually desorb. By this technique, the inhibitor can desorb into the system at a fixed rate for anywhere from 3 months to 1 year each time a well is squeezed. An "overflush" of oil of a few to more than 50 barrels is used to insure that the inhibitor is moved back into the formation. This method treats wells that are packed off or have high fluid levels and are difficult to treat by other methods. Frequency of treatment is reduced drastically, and a steady supply of inhibitor is insured over a long period of time. Less manpower is required, errors are fewer, the entire length of tubing is treated, shut-in times are reduced, and wear and tear on equipment is minimized. Disadvantages include a considerable economic loss in case of an error in treatment, and the possibility of developing emulsion-blocks or reverse wetting in the formation.

Quaternaries may be based on either the long-chain amines or imidazolines. Examples of the former include soya or tallow trimethyl ammonium chloride or dicoco dimethyl ammonium chloride, while especially effective imidazoline quaternaries are based on 1-hydroxyethyl-2-heptadecenyl glyoxalidine. They are useful in in waterflooding applications because they function as bactericides and dispersing agents as well as corrosion inhibitors. Rosin amines, and especially their ethylene oxide derivatives, are used in substantial quantities in producing wells and refineries and are among the earliest and least expensive inhibitors for those purposes.

In waterflooding, the inhibitor application technique is critical. The inhibitor may be applied by batch techniques, continuously, or some combination of both. The batch treatment is used in most supply wells where submerged pumps are installed. The inhibitor is injected, flushed, and recirculated to insure proper distribution. At least three complete cycles are made, with slug treatments of 10 to 15 gallons of inhibitor per 100 to 200 gallons of water applied weekly. Injection points are chosen as far back in the system as possible to insure protection for the entire system, with appropriate care being taken to insure that the inhibitor is not removed by the filter.

A somewhat different type of organic amine is the volatile neutralizing amine used in the prevention of steam condensate corrosion. The most common amines of this type are *morpholine* and *cyclohexylamine*. The vapor pressure characteristics of these amines are quite superior to that of ammonia for this purpose.

The most commonly used *organic sulfur compounds* are the high molecular weight petroleum *sulfonates*. The most valuable sulfonates as corrosion inhibitors are those that have a molecular weight of over 400. These sulfonates are termed oleophillic and have structures like $(C_nH_{(2n-10)}-SO_3)_xA$, where A can be a metal of valence x or else it may be an amine.

One of the most commonly-used sulfonates is a neutralized mahogany petroleum sulfonic acid. It has been reported that a high molecular weight fraction of this material (MW-548 as Na salt) is about three times as effective as the original unfractionated material. Other sulfonates in use include barium salts of dinonylnaphthalene sulfonate, ammonia-neutralized sulfonated didodecylbenzene, and sodium diisopropylnaphthalene sulfonate. Sulfonates are also the key ingredient in a class of inhibitors known as the *soluble oils*. These inhibitors are widely used in automobile radiators, antifreeze, and to some extent in diesel systems. They consist of a combination of an oil and an emulsifying agent. The latter is usually polar in nature with long-chain high molecular sulfonates being frequently used.

Other organic sulfur compounds that are being used commercially are primarily derivatives of thiourea. These are especially favored as corrosion inhibitors for acids, and have the general formula $(RNH)_2CS$.

References

Most corrosion inhibitors are sold under commercial trade names, and information concerning their chemical identities is kept secret. For this reason, the literature concerning corrosion inhibitors has been involved primarily with their application rather than with information concerning their compositions. A truly meaningful bibliography, therefore, must be limited to a small number of references, and the reader is referred to the following articles:

1. BREGMAN, J. I., "Corrosion Inhibitors," New York, Macmillan Company, 1963.
2. "Comptes Rendus Du Symposium European Sur Les Inhibiteurs De Corrosion," Annali Dell' Universita Di Ferrara, N. S., Sez. V., (1961). (Individual papers published in language of author.)
3. PUTILOVA, I. N., BALEZIN, S. A., AND BARANNIK, V. P., "Metallic Corrosion Inhibitors," New York Pergamon Press, 1960.
4. EVANS, U. R., "The Corrosion and Oxidation of Metals," New York, St. Martin's Press, 1960.
5. "Corrosion of Oil and Gas Well Equipment," American Petroleum Institute, 1958.

J. I. BREGMAN

CORROSION, INTERGRANULAR. *See* INTER-
GRANULAR CORROSION.

CORROSION BY LIQUID METALS

Liquid metal corrosion is a phenomena normally associated with high-temperature heat
transfer systems which utilize low melting metals or alloys for the coolant. The development
of the mercury boiler which used mercury vapor
instead of steam for the generation of electricity
is a prime example and among the first commercial applications of a liquid metal as a heat
transfer medium. Others include the use of mercury, and either sodium or sodium alloys in
chemical processes and, more recently, such metals as bismuth, lead, sodium, and lithium for
coolants in nuclear systems. Liquid metal coolants offer several advantages over conventional
systems such as stability at high temperature,
high specific heats, and low operating pressures.
However, with these advantages there are problems, one of which is the corrosive effect of the
liquid on the container material. For most liquid
metals this may be overcome by the proper
selection of materials or by the use of corrosion
inhibitors for certain of the metals.

Theory

Two principal modes whereby liquid metals
attack solids have been defined. One is the process of solution. The other is the process of
chemical reaction.

In the process of solution, the alloy may be
attacked by any one of three processes: (1)
either of the major constituents of the alloy may
be dissolved; (2) a minor alloy element may be
leached out; or (3) grain boundary constituent
may be dissolved. In a chemical reaction, either
the liquid metal or some impurity may react
with the solid.

In solution attack, there are two possible
mechanisms. In one, the boundary film which
is in contact with the solid is saturated with
the solute and the corrosion rate is fixed by the
rate of diffusion of the dissolved material into
the liquid metal. In the second, the boundary
film is never saturated with the solute and the
corrosion rate is controlled by the solution of
the material and not by the rate of diffusion into
the liquid metal. These two mechanisms are illustrated in Fig. 1.

Liquid metal systems wherein solution attack
occurs and a temperature differential exists may
be subject to a phenomena known as mass transfer. The material dissolved in the hot zone of
the system reaches saturation in the cold zone
and is precipitated because of supersaturation.
The resulting transfer of material from the hot
zone of the system to the cold zone is known as
mass transfer. The process is described in Fig. 2.

Corrosion resulting from chemical reactions
can normally be described in terms of ordinary
chemical kinetics relationships which take into
account the specific reaction under consideration
and should properly define the rate at which the
process proceeds. This type of reaction appears
to give satisfactory agreement with experimental results in certain systems, such as sodium
in stainless steel.

In general, there is no evidence that electrical
phenomena are of importance in the corrosion
of liquid metal systems although some electrical
phenomena have been associated with liquid
metals. Sodium-potassium alloy, for example,
separates into its constituents under the influence of a strong electrostatic field. This has not
been construed to indicate that electromotive
forces may be a factor. However, more recent
work on the bismuth system indicates that electromotive forces may be influential in the corrosion phenomena of that particular system.

Test Methods

The method of evaluating corrosion by liquid
metal is of prime importance to the interpretation and application of data. In general, a test
system which simulates the actual application is
the most reliable. Since this is elaborate and expensive, it is essential that more economical
methods be used to screen the variables which
can influence liquid metal systems. There are
four methods of testing which produce results
of varying degrees of reliability.

Static Test. These tests are used primarily
for screening of alloys and/or liquid metals.
They are normally conducted in a metal container which has a high degree of resistance to
the liquid metal being evaluated. Specimens of
various shapes or sizes are suspended within the
liquid metal a predetermined length of time at a
prescribed temperature. The liquid metal may
or may not be agitated. The specimens are removed after testing and evaluated for corrosion,
usually as a function of weight change. The re-

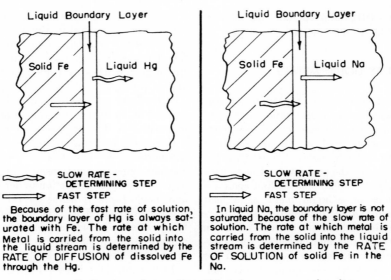

Mechanism of corrosion of iron by mercury and sodium.

FIG. 1. Mechanisms of corrosion by solution attack. (Ref. 3)

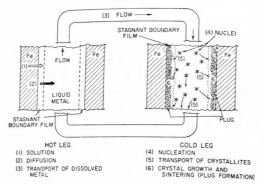

FIG. 2. Process of mass transfer in liquid metal systems. (Ref. 3)

sulting data give a relative indication of the resistance of the materials tested.

Tilting Capsule Test. This type of test is of value in the evaluation of materials which are subject to mass transfer in liquid metals. It, like the static test, is designed primarily for screening applications. The test apparatus is constructed on a piece of pipe of the material being evaluated. The liquid metal is placed inside the pipe and both ends sealed. One end of the capsule is heated to the maximum temperature expected in the system and the other end of the capsule is heated to the lower temperature expected in the system. The capsule is then rocked, allowing the liquid metal to flow alternately from the hot end to the cold end of the capsule and vice versa. The results obtained from testing by this method are qualitative and give a relative indication of the corrosion resistance of the system.

Thermal Convection Loops. Convection loops are closed systems wherein the liquid metal is circulated as a result of thermal convection, as in Fig. 3. The liquid metal moves upward in the heated section and downward in the cold section, thereby producing flow in the system. Specimens are placed in the hot and cold sections of the loop and exposed for various periods of time, after which they are removed and evaluated. This method of evaluation is more reliable than either of the described static tests; however, it is usually more expensive to conduct.

Pumped Loops. Fig. 4 shows schematically the ultimate in liquid metal testing: the pumped loop which is a mock-up of the actual system in which the liquid metal will be used. The loop contains a hot section and a cold section at temperatures simulating those of the actual application. The liquid metal is pumped through the system by either an electromagnetic or a mechanical pump. The data obtained from the loop are more reliable than those from any of the other tests described. However, the pumped loop is the most expensive method of testing and should only be conducted after extensive screening tests. As a result, it is used primarily as a type of final proof test.

Evaluation of Corrosion Data

Corrosion by liquid metals can be affected by any factor in the system from operating conditions to the types of materials within which the metals are contained. For this reason, the evaluation of corrosion data and the extrapolation of existing data to new applications must be done with caution. This is particularly true if the test conditions are not identical with those of the application. However, one may make a reasonable extrapolation of the general corrosion if the relative effects of the primary variables are considered. Variables which must be considered are:

Maximum Temperature. This is important where the container material is soluble in the liquid metal. If the temperature is kept below a certain temperature for the particular liquid metal, the solution rate is slow enough not to be a problem. Normally, increasing temperature accelerates the corrosion rate.

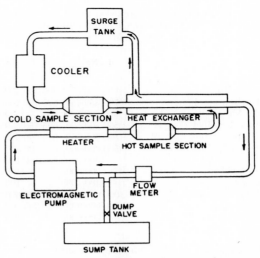

Electromagnetic-pump loop used for corrosion tests.

FIG. 4. Schematic of pumped test loop. (Ref. 3)

Temperature Gradients. The smallest of temperature gradients can contribute significantly to mass transfer and the larger the gradient the greater will be the rate of mass transfer. This factor is particularly important in liquid metal systems with which mass transfer is associated because the cold section of the system can be completely blocked in a matter of hours.

Purity. The purity of the liquid metal is important in systems where chemical reactions are a controlling factor. The smallest variation in impurity level can produce a large effect on the corrosion behavior. The inclusion of corrosion inhibitors should be noted along with their concentration and relative effects.

Velocity. Systems which may be affected by corrosion may also be affected by the velocity of the fluid. This may be a contributing factor to cavitation or erosion.

Pressure. Normally the liquid metal systems operate at atmospheric pressure, but an overpressure may be placed on the system to prevent cavitation where this is shown to be a problem.

Corrosion Data

It is impossible to tabulate all the liquid metal corrosion data within the scope of this section. As a guide to the relative corrosiveness of the more useful metals the following tabulation, Table 1, is presented. For more detailed infor-

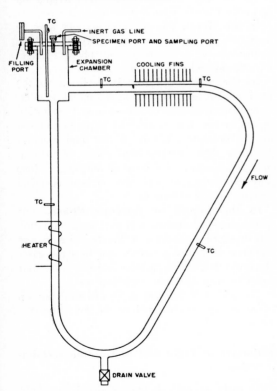

FIG. 3. Thermal convection loop. (Ref. 3)

TABLE 1. MAXIMUM TEMPERATURE, °C, AT WHICH
SELECTED MATERIALS RESIST CORROSION
BY LIQUID METALS

	Bi	Na	Na-K	Pb	Li	Hg
Cast iron	800	250	250	500	600	400
Carbon steel	700	450	450	625	400	400
Cr-Mo steel	600	500	500	625	—	500
Low-Cr steel	500	500	500	625	450	500
High-Cr steel	500	900	900	625	800	550
18-8 stainless steel	500	900	900	550	500	500
Nickel	—	900	900	—	400	100
Inconel	—	900	900	—	—	100
Copper	—	400	400	—	—	100
Molybdenum	1000	900	900	900	900	600
Tantalum	700	900	900	1000	900	200
Zirconium	—	600	600	600	—	100

mation, one of the references should be consulted.

References

1. LYON, B. N., Ed., "Liquid-Metals Handbook," 2nd Edition, Report **NAVEXOS-P-733** (Rev), U. S. Atomic Energy Commission, U. S. Navy, Washington, D. C., U. S. Government Printing Office, June, 1952 (Revised 1954).
2. LIPTON, C. R., JR., Ed., "Reactor Handbook," Volume 1, "Materials," 2nd Edition, pp. 994–1020, New York, Intersciences Publishers, Inc., 1960.
3. VAN ANTWERPEN, F. J., Ed., "Liquid Metals Technology," Part 1, Chemical Engineering Progress Symposium Series, Vol 53, No. 20, American Institute of Chemical Engineers, 25 W. 45th St., New York 36, New York, 1957.
4. JACKSON, C. B., Ed., "Liquid Metals Handbook, Sodium NaK Supplement," 3rd Edition, U. S. Atomic Energy Commission, U. S. Navy, Washington, D. C., U. S. Government Printing Office, July, 1955.
5. "Liquid Metals and Solidification," Cleveland, American Society for Metals, 1958.
6. "Proceedings of the International Conference on the Peaceful Uses of Atomic Energy," Vol 9, "Reactor Technology and Chemical Processing," New York, United Nations, 1956.

ARTHUR L. LOWE, JR.

CORROSION BY MICROORGANISMS. See MICROBIOLOGICAL CORROSION.

CORROSION, PITTING. See PITTING CORROSION.

CORROSION POTENTIAL. See MIXED POTENTIAL.

CORROSION, RADIATION EFFECTS ON

Radiation may influence the corrosion and surface reactions of metals by altering the properties of (1) the metal, (2) the solid reaction products, and (3) the corrodant. These effects have been reviewed in two papers[1, 2] to which reference may be made for more detailed information. Radiation can give rise to effects which may either increase or decrease the rates of corrosion, depending on the particular mechanisms and combination of factors that govern the corrosion reaction. The extent of damage depends not only on the energy, the flux, and the type of the radiation, but also on the nature, the composition, and temperature of the material and of the corrodant. The most severe damage is caused by neutrons and charged heavy particles, which may displace atoms from their lattice sites, produce ionization or dissociation, give rise to thermal pulses in small regions in the solid, or create impurity effects as a result of nuclear transmutations.

The changes that can result from irradiation and influence corrosion include the following:

In the Metal. The chemical activity may be increased, dimensional changes may take place, embrittlement may occur and phase changes may be induced.

In the Surface Film. In addition to the kinds of damage produced in the metal, irradiation may cause severe ionization and excitation in the surface film capable of producing effects on the protective nature of the solid reaction products. The electronic conductivity of the film may be increased, the rates of diffusion of ions may be increased, and the surface chemical activity may be enhanced.

In the Liquid or Gaseous Phase. The mechanisms of energy transfer from radiation flux or charged particles in liquids and gases are complex. In liquid solutions and in some gases the formation of free radicals and new molecular products may alter the corrosion rates.

The effects of different types of irradiation on corrosion are summarized in the following sections.

Influence of Light and of Gamma Irradiation

As early as 1818, it was reported that light could influence the electrochemical behavior of metals in aqueous solutions. A review of work in this field[3] cites many observations of enhanced corrosion of metals exposed to light. For example, copper in distilled water tarnishes more rapidly when exposed to light. The effect of light on lead, zinc, aluminum, and iron in aerated salt solutions is to make the illuminated electrode markedly cathodic, the maximum effect being obtained with light in the violet and near ultraviolet. With other metals, the direction of change in potential is governed by the nature of the electrode reactions. The oxidation rate of aluminum shows a marked increase under ultraviolet radiation.

The results of experiments on the effects of high-level gamma radiation on the corrosion of aluminum, copper, and iron in aqueous solutions show significant changes.[4] Aluminum tubes were exposed to the gamma radiation in both tap water and distilled water. The irradiated samples gained less weight than the nonirradiated ones, and metallographic examination showed that the surface pits on the irradiated specimens were shallower than those on the control samples. On the other hand, experiments with copper and iron in $2N$ hydrochloric acid showed an opposite effect, namely, that radiation increased the rate of corrosion. Other studies have shown that the rate of solution of nickel in N sulfuric acid increased by exposure to gamma radiation, whereas the solution of 18-8 stainless decreased.[5]

Influence of Charged Particles

Electron irradiations (0.8 mev) of Al/Zr couples in a 3 per cent sodium chloride solution have been reported to result in a sharp increase in the current flowing between the couples, which is ascribed to the increase in electronic conductivity of the semiconductor film of ZrO_2.[6]

An extensive series of experiments with 260-mev proton irradiated metals and oxides have shown changes in surface properties.[1] The electrode potentials in salt solution of irradiated tungsten are anodic (less noble) to the annealed specimens by as much as 80 millivolts. The rate of solution of ferric oxide in hydrochloric acid is increased. In the hydrogen reduction of nickel oxide, proton irradiation shortens the induction period and also increases the rate of reduction. The catalytic effect of copper in the decomposition of formic acid is enhanced by proton irradiation.[7] Thorium foils irradiated with 9 mev protons at about $-140°C$ corrode more actively than unirradiated foils in water.[2]

Deuteron bombardment of zirconium in water at 315°C increases the corrosion rate ten-fold.[8] It also accelerates the corrosion of mild steel in hot water.

Alpha-particle bombardment of silicon renders the surface soluble in aqueous HF.[2]

Influence of Nuclear Reactor Irradiation

Aqueous Solutions. In water the action of nuclear irradiation is to produce molecular or ionic species, (such as hydrogen, hydrogen peroxide, and the free radicals H and OH) capable of either oxidation or reduction of certain solutes. Several chemical reactions, not normally expected in hot water, may take place in a reactor system.[9] For example, the presence of nitrogen dissolved in the water results in the formation of ammonia or nitric acid depending on whether oxygen or hydrogen is present in excess.

In studies of the corrosion of Zircalloy-2 fuel cladding it has been noted that these are covered with more than twice the expected amount of oxide in hot water at 280°C.[10] In experiments on the corrosion of Zircalloy-2 in steam at 340°C a 30–40 per cent increase in corrosion rate is observed in the presence of a neutron flux level of 3×10^{13} nv (fast). Also, the time to transition (break-away) is decreased and the post-transition corrosion rate is increased by a factor of 8. In the cases where radiation increases the corrosion rate, there is a proportional increase in hydrogen pickup. The corrosion behavior of zirconium and its alloys, titanium, platinum, and stainless steels in uranyl sulfate solutions at high temperatures and pressures has been studied extensively in connection with the aqueous homogeneous reactor.[11] In general, the corrosion rates of the zirconium specimens are governed by the fission power density. The results are correlated by a relationship between the corrosion rate, R, (mils per year), the fission power density, P (watts/ml), and the uranium sorption factor, α, by

$$\frac{1}{R} = \frac{2.23}{P\alpha} + \frac{1}{40}$$

The role of the oxide film has been confirmed by heating zirconium in oxygen at 250°C in the presence of mixed neutron and fission fragment flux. The weight gains were greater and the structure of the oxide was affected.

The results of titanium specimens indicate that in-pile titanium corrosion is affected by

TABLE 1. EFFECT OF IRRADIATION ON THE
CORROSION RESISTANCE OF URANIUM
ALLOYS IN WATER

Alloy	% Atom Burnup	Corrosion Resistance
U-3% Nb	none	No failure after 2000 hours at 260°C
	0.1	Disintegrated after 1 hour at 260°C
U-5% Zr-1.5% Nb	none	No failure after 365 days at 265°C
	0.04	Cracking after 63 days at 260°C

some uniform change in the solution under radiation to a greater extent than by fission recoil irradiation of the specimen surfaces. The corrosion of platinum is negligible. The stainless steel specimens have an average corrosion rate of attack which increases with increasing fission power density, above 2 watts/ml.

The effect of nuclear irradiation on the corrosion of uranium and of a number of uranium alloys is quite catastrophic. Table 1 includes examples of pre- and post-irradiation corrosion resistance of uranium alloys.[12]

In some cases irradiation actually improves the corrosion resistance, such as in uranium molybdenum alloys, by stabilizing the gamma phase. If these alloys are tested in high temperature water after irradiation they can fail rapidly, since they revert to the less corrosion-resistant two-phase condition.

Irradiation appears to decompose or to make radioactive most corrosion inhibitors for stainless, low alloy, and carbon steels. The pH of the solutions is maintained at about 9.5 to 11.5 by means of lithium hydroxide additions, since it has sufficient solubility and stability and little radioactivity. Hydrogen is also a suitable additive for reducing corrosion by suppressing the dissociation of water and for removing oxygen by gamma flux combination. Experiments have shown also that radiation tends to accelerate the deposition of corrosion products. The corrosion of aluminum in water does not appear to be much affected by irradiation.

The semiconductor materials germanium and silicon show a change in etching behavior after neutron irradiation.[13] The irradiated crystals show a finer surface granulation when etched with CP-4 solution. This is ascribed to the presence in irradiated samples of localized re-

gions or centers of lattice disorder produced by "thermal spikes."

Organic Systems. Radiation produces free radicals in organic liquids and it might be expected that some metals might react with free radicals to form organo-metallic compounds. However, the recombination time of the free radicals with each other is so short that they do not have time to reach a surface and react with it. No evidence of free radical attack has been observed in the presence of polyphenyl mixtures used for reactor cooling at 300 to 350°C at a total flux of 10^{20} nvt (thermal). The production of hydrogen from the radiation decomposition of organic materials will cause hydriding attack on metals, such as zirconium or uranium, and precludes the use of these metals in organic coolants. Trouble has also been noted with halogen-containing organic protective coatings and paints, gaskets and lubricants, since the effect of irradiation is to liberate the halogen atoms or acids and this leads to enhanced corrosion of metals.[2]

Gases. The existence of nitrogen fixation in air within a reactor and its effect in accelerating the corrosion of metals has been observed in several reactors.[14] Exposure of metals, such as aluminum, copper, lead, nickel, and Inconel, which are subject to nitric acid attack, to humid air in a reactor results in the formation of nitrates on the surface of the specimen. Oxides form in copious amounts when lead is exposed to radiation in humid oxygen. No reactions are observed when the oxygen, nitrogen, or air is dry. The corrosion products may be hygroscopic, spreading by wiping or capillarity, or they may be nonadherent and transported mechanically or by gas convection currents.

The oxidation rate of niobium at 400°C is not changed by reactor irradiation.[15] However, the oxidation rate of copper does increase in the presence of reactor irradiation at temperatures below about 200°C.[16] There is also an increase in the rate of formation of the thin films (below about 400 Angstoms) on irradiated copper at 150°C.[17]

References

1. SIMNAD, M. T., "The Effects of Radiation on Materials," (edited by J. J. Harwood, *et al*), p. 126, New York, Reinhold Publishing Corp., 1958.
2. STOBBS, J. J., AND SWALLOW, A. J., *Metallurgical Reviews*, **7**, (25), 95 (1962).

3. Young, L., *Atomic Energy Research Estab. Rept.*, **M/TN-2** (1950).
4. Hittman, F., and Kuhl, O. A., **BNL-2257** (1955).
5. Proskurnin, M. A., and Kolotyrkin, Ya. M., Vol. 29, p. 52, Geneva Conf., 1958.
6. Rozenfeld, I. L., and Oshe, E. K., *Doklady Akad. Nauk. S.S.S.R.*, **114**, 143 (1957).
7. Roberts, R., Spilners, A., and Smoluchowski, R., *Bull. Amer. Phys. Soc.*, **3**, 116 (1958).
8. Rockwell, T., and Cohen, P., Vol. 9, p. 423, Geneva Conf., 1955.
9. Wroughton, D. M., and Cohen, P., Vol. 7, p. 427, Geneva Conf, 1958.
10. Krenz, F. H., "Proc. 1st Intern. Congress on Metallic Corrosion," p. 496, London, Butterworths, 1961.
11. Jenks, G. H., and Baker, J. E., **ORNL-2962** (1962).
12. Kittel, J. H., Greenberg, S. Paine, S. H., and Draley, J., *Nucl. Sci. and Eng.*, **2**, 431 (1957).
13. Chang, R., *J. Applied Physics*, **28**, 385 (1957).
14. Primak, W., and Fuchs, L. H., *Nucleonics*, **13**, (3), 38 (1955).
15. Cathcart, J. V., and Young, F. W., *Corrosion*, **17**, (2), 55t (1961).
16. Tobin, M. J., **GA-3349** (1963).
17. Carpenter, F., Simnad, M. T., and White, J. L., **TID-7597** (1960).

M. T. Simnad

CORROSION BY RECLAIM WATERS

Industrial cooling water frequently is circulated through open systems, such as spray ponds, evaporative condensers, cooling towers, and similar devices, to reduce their temperature before they are reintroduced into heat-transfer units. The use of such reclaim waters is dictated by economic reasons as well as by the availability of raw water of satisfactory temperature and composition. Raw water is used only for make-up purposes to replace that quantity of water lost by evaporation, windage and blow-down.

However, the use of reclaim waters or concentrated raw waters creates a variety of problems, among them corrosion, the main topic of this article. In addition to corrosion, the scale-forming tendencies of reclaim waters must be considered. Scaling is of initial concern inasmuch as the function of the cooling water systems is to dissipate heat and any build-up of scale deposits interferes with this aim. It is for this reason that scale formation and its prevention will be covered briefly.

Scale

Formation of scale is primarily due to dissolved solids reaching their solubility limits as the reclaim water becomes more and more concentrated during recycling. The prime offender is calcium bicarbonate which enters the system with the raw water make-up. Calcium carbonate is formed as carbon dioxide is driven off at elevated temperatures, and this deposits in the form of a hard scale on heat-transfer surfaces. Other deposits, such as calcium silicate, magnesium silicate, calcium sulfate, etc., may also be formed. Control over the concentration of solids in the water in the system (cycles of concentration) is practiced by controlled blow-down where windage is not sufficient to limit the build-up to an acceptable level.

Organic and inorganic surface-active agents are also in use and can be effective in certain areas. These agents build up electrical charges, causing precipitates or colloidal particles to repel each other, resulting in a reduction or elimination of deposits.

In most cases, however, blow-down control by itself or in conjunction with surface-active agents is not sufficient and cannot cope with the scale-forming tendency of a reclaim water. It becomes necessary to substitute cations of hardness salts or aid the process by changing the raw water salts.

External water treatment for the removal of calcium and magnesium has been utilized. However, initial investment in the equipment necessary usually eliminates it from consideration.

Sulfuric acid is generally used to convert $Ca(HCO_3)_2$ to the more stable and rather more soluble $CaSO_4 \cdot 2H_2O$ (gypsum).

$$Ca(HCO_3)_2 + H_2SO_4 \rightarrow CaSO_4 + 2CO_2 + H_2O$$

Consequently, a previously unacceptable water supply may be used and concentrated, or a higher number of cycles may be tolerated in the system, resulting in reduced blow-down and raw water savings. The criterion as far as the number of cycles to be carried now becomes the solubility of gypsum, together with other ions affecting solubility, at the temperatures encountered.

Corrosion

The major cause of corrosion in cooling water systems is electrochemical action. It depends on the transfer rate of metal ions into water. Electricity flows between metal areas through water, the electrolyte. At the point where the current leaves the metal (anode) corrosion occurs and it is here that the following type of reaction takes place:

$$Fe \rightarrow Fe^{++} + 2e$$

As can be seen from the above reaction, two electrons are released by the metal atom at the anode, and the atom becomes a positively charged ion. These ions are attracted by negatively charged hydroxyl ions gravitating freely in the electrolyte and pass into solution as follows:

$$Fe^{++} + 2OH^- \rightarrow Fe(OH)_2$$

The final oxidation reaction takes place as the ferrous hydroxide formed above combines with oxygen, which is present in adequate quantities in reclaim waters, to form ferric hydroxide or common rust:

$$4Fe(OH)_2 + O_2 + 2H_2O \rightarrow 4Fe(OH)_3$$

At the same time reduction reactions take place at the cathode. Electrons arriving at the cathode neutralize hydrogen ions from the electrolyte, forming hydrogen gas:

$$2H^+ + 2e \rightarrow H_2$$

This hydrogen gas, if permitted to remain at the cathodic area, would reduce the corrosion rate and eventually, as the entire area is covered, would stop corrosion at the anode. This is called polarization. However, hydrogen is removed by combining with oxygen from the electrolyte to form water:

$$4H^+ + 4e + O_2 \rightarrow 2H_2O$$

As the reaction continues, hydroxyl ions are formed:

$$2H_2O + 4e + O_2 \rightarrow 4OH^-$$

These hydroxyl ions attract more ions from the anodic area and the corrosion process continues.

Other anodic-cathodic areas develop because of a variety of conditions, such as foreign metallic inclusions in the metal, presence of dissimilar metals used in fabrication or erection of system components, stresses in metal or grain boundaries themselves, and dissimilar oxygen concentration cells on metal surfaces where an oxygen cell having the lowest oxygen content becomes the anodic area and an oxygen cell having a higher oxygen content becomes the cathodic area. These cells may form under crevices, porous scale, or organic growths. Other corrosion is found to be directly attributable to acidic conditions at biological growth points.

Protection against corrosion

Optimum corrosion control may be achieved by a single approach or a combination of corrosion-control methods. Selection of any one approach depends on the most economical means to attain minimum amounts of corrosion.

Design considerations should be stressed prior to installation of a cooling system. Corrosion can be held to a minimum by selecting proper materials of construction and by selecting the least corrosive water supply (if more than one source is available). All too often, however, corrosion-protection measures are not considered until real problems arise, leaving a fixed set of conditions around which a control program has to be built.

The major cause of corrosion in an active system is due to galvanic cells created between the base metal and its corrosion products. Other foreign matter, such as scale, entrained silt and algae, contributes much to the corrosion potential by creating an undesirable environment. It is therefore almost always necessary to clean the system prior to instituting a corrosion-prevention program. This may be accomplished mechanically or by acid cleaning or a combination of both. Good engineering practices will do much to reduce corrosion.

Of major concern are gases which are entrained in reclaim waters in cooling towers. It can be assumed that the predominant gas is oxygen. However, other gases may also play a decisive role depending on the location of the tower within an industrial complex. The solubility of these gases at varying pressures and temperatures is of concern. As reclaim water temperatures increase at heat transfer surfaces these gases are liberated unless sufficient pressure is available. Backpressure on exchangers or other equipment will reduce or eliminate liberation of these gases. Creating the proper backpressure for any given set of conditions is not easy and cannot always be considered. Reclaim water flow rates are controlled at the outlet of a given exchanger, thus creating desirable backpressure. However, surveys have shown that many operators will control flow rates at the inlet side. Therefore, it is well to make certain that this practice be discontinued if it exists.

Some large vessels in reclaim water systems have been protected successfully against corrosion through cathodic protection (q.v.). However, the maze of piping and intricate equipment found in such a system limits the use of cathodic protection.

Metal surfaces in reclaim water systems are best protected by preventing the electrolyte from getting to the metal surfaces. Formation of scale or application of protective coatings will achieve this goal. It is theoretically possible to control deposition of calcium carbonate scale by adjusting pH, alkalinity and calcium content of a water to give satisfactory results at a given temperature level, but temperatures encountered in cooling systems vary widely and although some areas will be protected properly, heavy scale will deposit on others and limit heat transfer, while still other areas will not be protected at all. Controlled formation of scale can therefore be discarded.

Protective coatings (q.v.) are applicable to certain types of equipment and prevent or reduce corrosion. Physical characteristics of components within the system limit their use. Together with corrosion inhibitors, which will be discussed next, they aid in the prevention of corrosion and perform a definite function.

Effective, economic control over corrosion is carried out through the use of anodic- or cathodic-type corrosion inhibitors (q.v.). Chromates and phosphates, generally considered the most effective inhibitors, belong to the anodic type. Zinc, nickel, arsenate, and cyanide belong to the cathodic type. Depending on the compound used, certain conditions, such as pH limitations, of reclaim waters have to be met. Inasmuch as anodic areas are usually considerably smaller than cathodic areas, it is desirable to stifle corrosion at the anode by using anodic-type inhibitors. Cathodic inhibitors are sometimes used in conjunction with the former to give added protection. Certain proprietary complex organic compounds are also blended with the above inhibitors to increase their affinity to the base metal, to lay down a more uniform film, and to increase their effectiveness under adverse pH conditions.

Selection of a specific inhibitor should be based on control requirements, i.e., necessary monitoring and chemical testing as well as the ease of feeding the chemical to the system. Obviously, the better a system is controlled, the better the results will be. However, a less sophisticated approach may have to be used because of limitations as to quality or quantity of operating personnel.

References

1. Langelier, W. F., *J. Am. Water Works Assoc.*, **28**, 1500–1521 (1936).
2. Denman, W. L., *Ind. Eng. Chem.*, **53**, 817–822 (1961).
3. Brooke, J. M., and Witt, B. G., *Corrosion*, **17**, No. 8, 22–25 (1961).
4. Kerst, Herman, *Corrosion*, **16**, No. 10, 523t–529t (1960).
5. Hess, William A., *Corrosion*, **16**, No. 7, 18–21 (1960).
6. "Report on Study of Wood Maintenance for Water-Cooling Towers," June, 1959, available from the Cooling Tower Institute, 1120 West 43rd St., Houston, Tex.
7. Fisher, A. Orman, *Materials Protection*, **1**, No 10, 54–68 (1962).

William C. Engman

CORROSION-RESISTANT COATINGS. See PROTECTIVE COATINGS.

CORROSION IN SEA WATER. See MARINE CORROSION.

CORROSION IN SOIL. See SOIL CORROSION.

CORROSION, STRESS. See STRESS CORROSION.

CORROSION TESTING

The first step in the selection or planning of a corrosion test is to define clearly the objective of the investigation.[1-5] One may wish to establish the mechanism of the attack on a container material in a chemical plant, or other corrosive situation, and establish the cause of a failure. It may be desirable to establish the quality of a new design in a corrosive environment. A new process may be available, and corrosion experiments may be needed to establish the limits of the factors that affect corrosion behavior.

Corrosion tests are used to establish specific information, such as whether the quality (e.g., of a protective coating) is similar to previous experience. A suitable environmental test may establish whether a normally corrosion-resistant alloy is off composition or is improperly heat treated. Corrosion tests are conducted on finished parts, subassemblies, or coupons.

If the objective of a program is to develop alloy compositions or surface treatments that are resistant to the external atmosphere, it usually is necessary to resort to outdoor-exposure tests. Since the corrosiveness of the atmosphere varies from one location to another, from day to day, and from year to year, it is essential (1) to initiate the exposure of all samples in a given comparison on the same day, and (2) to run replicate samples at several different sites. Much more useful data are obtained if repeat tests are started at periodic intervals during the year. Furthermore, to enable rough cross-comparisons to be made with older data, it is necessary to include several previously calibrated materials in the new experiments.

Simulated, accelerated environmental tests conducted in the laboratory, in a few cases, have been able to predict service life. However, long years of experimentation were necessary to develop them. Usually they apply to a narrow range of materials. For example, in recent years the CASS test[6] and the Corrodkote test[7] have found favor for the laboratory evaluation of the quality of electroplated coatings. After screening out metal-coating systems of poor quality, the more promising ones can be exposed to actual environments. Accelerated tests also are used to evaluate rust preventives.[8]

Lacking a well-established corrosion test, one must resort to ingenuity and draw on past experiences. To simulate service in the tropics, for example, one will want to consider the many environmental variables present. In most areas there is a daily hot-and-cool temperature cycle. A drenching rain may be followed by intense sunlight. An environmental cabinet can be set to simulate the daily temperature and humidity cycles. Simulated radiation also can be provided for. In addition, one should consider whether corrosive dust, fungi, or other contaminants on the metal surface may be a factor in the problem.

In conducting laboratory studies, one suggestion is to employ three or four simple designed tests, each providing information on the problem but varying in themselves. A broader picture usually is developed than when one relies on the results of a single test. Another point is to avoid over-accelerating the environmental factors in the design of the corrosion test. A laboratory-developed corrosion test can be judged potentially useful if it gives the same order of merit for a group of materials whose service behavior is well known. A preliminary estimate, then, can be obtained for unknown materials.

Perhaps one of the best developed is the 65 per cent boiling nitric acid test for evaluating the quality of stainless steels. Truman[9] demonstrates the need for rather precise control of the vapor phase. Much useful information on the effects of heat treatment, composition, and quality of a heat is given by this test.

Good design of specific corrosion tests involves an intimate knowledge of the factors in the problem.[10] A checklist of some factors to consider is given below:

Environmental Factors	Metal and Design Factors
Temperature	Heat treatment
Heat transfer	Composition
Oxygen or oxidizing agent	Cold work
	Grain orientation
Depth	Surface condition
Pressure	Crevices
Volume per exposed area	Galvanic couples
Velocity	Joints
Concentration	Welds
Purity	Stress
Deposits	Fatigue
Hydrogen evolution	Precipitates
Time	Inclusions
Cycle of exposure	Metallography
Humidity	

In some corrosion problems electrolysis may be involved. Stray alternating currents affect corrosion behavior in some cases. Hydrogen in the metal may affect the corrosion behavior or lead to deterioration, e.g., hydride formation.

For many situations, years of laboratory studies have shown that actual-service experience is essential for a complete evaluation of a material of construction.

References

1. HUGHSON, Roy V., "Ideas and Techniques for Corrosion Testing," *Chem. Eng.*, **69**, 9, 132–136 (April 30, 1962).
2. GORDON, S. A., "The Philosophy of Simulated Service Testing," *ASTM Bulletin No.* **193**, 27–31 (October 1953).
3. LaQUE, F. L., "Theoretical Studies and Laboratory Techniques in Sea Water Corrosion Testing Evaluation," *Corrosion*, **13**, No. 5, 303t–314t (May 1957), 28 ref.

4. LaQue, F. L., "Corrosion Testing," ASTM Edgar Marburg Lecture (June 29, 1951).
5. Fontana, M. G., "Corrosion Testing in Pilot Plants," *Ind. Eng. Chem.* **41**, 101A, 103A, and 95A (March, April, and May 1949).
6. Nixon, C. F., Thomas, J. D., and Hardesty, D. W., *Proc. Am. Electroplaters' Soc.*, **46**, 159–163 (1959).
7. Bigge, D. M., *Proc. Am. Electroplaters' Soc.*, **46**, 149–153 (1959).
8. Preston, R. St. J., and Stroud, E. G., "Application of an Accelerated Atmospheric Corrosion Test," *J. Inst. Petroleum*, **36**, No. 319 (July 1950).
9. Truman, J. E., "Factors Affecting the Testing of Stainless Steels in Boiling Concentrated Nitric Acid," *J. Applied Chem.*, **4**, 273–283 (May 1954).
10. Champion, F. A., "Corrosion Testing Procedures," New York, John Wiley & Sons Inc., 1952.

Frederick W. Fink

CORROSION UNDER HEAT TRANSFER CONDITIONS

Despite countless corrosion failures under heat transfer conditions in the chemical processing industry, only a few efforts have been made to obtain corrosion data where both corrosion and heat transfer are involved. The lack of knowledge concerning the role of heat transfer and temperature upon corrosion has persisted for a number of reasons. First, the method of testing surfaces under heat transfer conditions is more complicated than that used in the more conventional immersion tests. Second, it is almost impossible to duplicate field conditions in the laboratory. Third, and perhaps most important, plant operating personnel and management are generally more interested in production than in equipment life.

Several attempts have been made to study the effect of heat transfer upon corrosion in the laboratory. Typical apparatus for this purpose is shown in Fig. 1. This is an adaptation of equipment originally developed by Norman D. Groves, now of Carpenter Steel Company, while with the Atomic Energy Commission at Hanford, Washington. Heat from a 550 watt soldering iron is transmitted through a flat, ground aluminum heating head to a ¼ inch thick metal test specimen which in turn transfers the heat to a solution contained in a one-liter glass flask. The flask is fitted with a 2 inch diameter glass pipe bottom outlet to which the metal test specimen is fastened with a standard cast iron flange. The flask also contains condenser, agitator, and thermometer well from which a non-heat transferring metal control specimen is suspended in the test solution. With this apparatus the metal heat transfer surface is maintained at a higher temperature than the solution, a condition not possible in the conventional immersion test.

Thermocouple temperatures are taken in the aluminum head for the purposes of heat transfer calculations, and in the center of the flat heat transferring specimen. The heat transfer specimen can be heated to 210°C and the heat transfer can be adjusted from 5,000 to 30,000 Btu/hr/sq ft.

Additional modification of the equipment, Fig. 2, permits testing of heated and cooled vapor-liquid interface surfaces under pressures to 30 psig. Glass-lined steel pipe fittings have been adapted to this technique and permit testing under pressures of 30 to 150 psig.

Fig. 3 shows schematically the relationship between the flow of heat through a metal wall and the drop in temperature from the hot to the cold fluid. Temperature T_1 represents the temperature of the specimen taken in the specimen thermocouple hole, while T_2 represents the skin temperature calculated from the Fourier equation. The magnitude of T_3 and T_4 depends upon the type of fluid, velocity conditions, and the solubility of any corrosion products. The temperature of the test environment is represented by T_5 which is taken as the metal temperature of the control specimen in the apparatus described.

Corrosion rate data obtained using this test method are plotted against metal temperature, T_1, for heat transferring specimens and T_5 for control specimens on semilog paper. In most systems a sharp break in the corrosion rate is observed at a "critical" temperature. For example, for 316 stainless steel in 75 per cent H_3PO_4, the critical temperature occurs at 105 to 120°C depending upon the impurity in the acid; and for 304 stainless steel in 93 per cent H_3PO_4, the critical temperature is in the range of 70 to 90°C.

In most commercial studies data of this nature are quite satisfactory as they define the corrosion-temperature parameter of a system under heat transfer conditions. By utilizing this information, it is then possible to design and

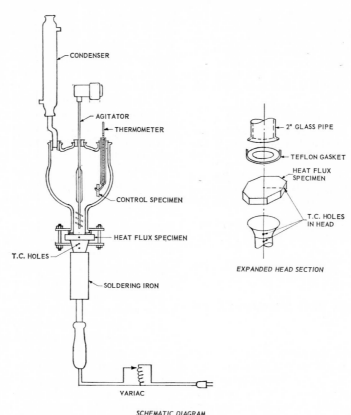

SCHEMATIC DIAGRAM

Fɪɢ. 1. Modified disc heat flux apparatus, 2 in. unit.

operate within the limitations of the system or to select a more resistant alloy which does not undergo "break away" corrosion in the environment.

For academic reasons it may be desirous to go one step further with the data obtained in the apparatus described. This involves the plotting of corrosion rates versus the skin temperature, T_2, of the heat transferring specimens. This plot is then compared with data obtained from the non-heat transferring immersion specimens T_5. If both sets of data fall on the same curve, as is the case with 316 stainless steel in 77 per cent H_3PO_4 in the range of 38 to 182°C at atmospheric pressure, one concludes that temperature and not heat transfer rates or film formation is the controlling variable in the corrosion reaction. Similar treatment of data on 304 stainless steel in 65 per cent nitric acid between 60 and 120°C at atmospheric pressure, however, has shown differences in corrosion rates between heat-transferring surfaces and immersion surfaces at the same temperature. Further

investigation of this system has revealed that the variation in mechanical agitation across the specimen surface does not fully account for the differences in corrosion of the two 304 stainless steel surfaces. Differences in film formation and corrosion product character and solubility are suspected.

From these and other limited studies, it has been postulated that the corrosion of a metal surface is not necessarily affected by the transfer of heat other than the influence caused by the increased temperature of the metal surface. In some systems, however, it appears that the presence and magnitude of heat flow might influence corrosion because of film effects and possible localized thermal galvanic cells. These effects are extremely difficult to measure experimentally, and, although perhaps important from an academic standpoint, they do not appear to be significant in most applications in the process industries where heat flux rates are usually kept below 10,000 to 20,000 Btu/hr/sq ft.

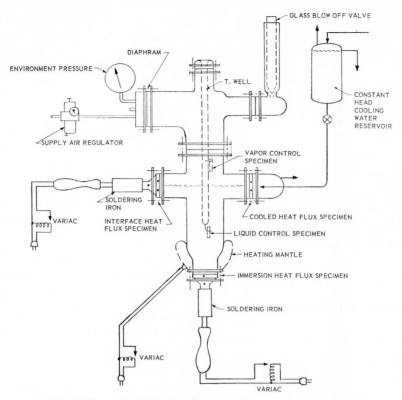

FIG. 2. Pressurized-interface heat transfer corrosion apparatus.

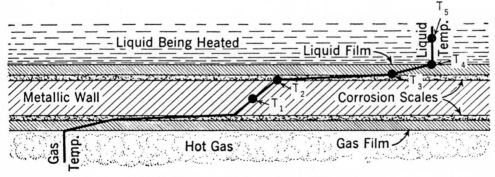

FIG. 3. Heat transfer through a metallic wall.

In conclusion, each system requires careful study before the true relationship between temperature and heat transfer upon corrosion can be ascertained. However, it is believed that below the boiling point, heat transfer has little influence and that skin temperature is controlling. Under normal boiling conditions it seems likely that changes in the magnitude of heat flux may exert some influence upon corrosion over and above that caused by the change in temperature. This would be explained as follows: an increase in heat transfer rate at the boiling point creates more nucleation sites and turbulence at the surface. This causes increased corrosion and liquid film breakdown due to the higher local velocities resulting from the increase in rate of vapor formation. When the heat-transferring surface reaches a point where it is entirely covered by a vapor film, "blanketing" results; then further increases in heat transfer cause a sharp increase in wall temperature. What effect this has upon corrosion is not predictable, since the environment is now a vapor rather than a liquid. In fact, the mechanism involved in heat transfer alone, under boiling or turbulent conditions, is itself so nebulous at present that attempts to fully explain the effect of heat flux upon corrosion at boiling conditions seem futile at this writing.

References

1. FISHER, A. O., AND WHITNEY, F. L., JR., "Laboratory Methods for Determining Corrosion Rates Under Heat Flux Conditions," *Corrosion*, **15**, 257t-261t (1959).
2. FISHER, A. O., "New Methods of Simulating Corrosive Plant Conditions in the Laboratory," *Corrosion*, **17**, 215t-221t (1961).

A. ORMAN FISHER

COTTRELL, FREDERICK GARDNER (1877-1948)

Frederick Gardner Cottrell was the first to apply the principle of electrical precipitation of suspended dust and droplets from chimney or other gases. The device became the electrical precipitator, which now bears his name.

The simplest construction of a Cottrell precipitator would include a vertical pipe, in the central axis of which hangs an insulated metal wire. The pipe is grounded. A unidirectional high voltage current, varying from 15,000 to 100,000 volts in the different installations, is fed to the wire, so that a powerful electric field is created. Dusty air or fumes travel up the pipe; the electric field ionizes the air or gas; the ions in turn charge the suspended particles by contact. The charged particles travel to the relatively uncharged wall, there depositing the negatively charged particles. Periodically the pipe is rapped so that the deposit drops down into a container box. Suspended droplets are similarly deposited on the pipe wall, where they coalesce and travel downward as a liquid to a suitable outlet. The cleaned air or gas leaves at the top of the pipe.

The unipolar corona discharge is secured by impressing the negative polarity on the wire, which is the discharge electrode. The only exception to this rule are the installations for air-cleaning operations, where the positive polarity is impressed on the wire, because of the lower ozone generation. The Cottrell for full scale smelter or factory installation is more often de-signed to provide narrow rectangular passages between flat plates, which are then the collecting electrodes, with a series of spaced wires suspended in the center plane of the space. The distance the charged particle travels is a few inches, perhaps 3 or 4, before it strikes the collecting electrode.

Dr. Cottrell began his work on the electrostatic precipitation of dust and droplets in 1910, when he was 33 years old. He was born in Oakland, California, January 10, 1877, graduated from the University of California, taught high school for a while, then went to Leipzig for graduate studies, coming home in 1902 with the degree of Ph.D. He was instructor and assistant professor at his Alma Mater until 1911. His field of study and research was physical chemistry, and his experimental work in that period was in phase relations, electrochemistry and the liquefaction of gases. From 1911-1921, Dr. Cottrell was successively chief chemist, chief metallurgist and Director of the U. S. Bureau of Mines. From 1922-1927 he was Director of the Fixed Nitrogen Research Laboratory, and after that, he remained as Division chief in the Department of Agriculture.

Tall and thin, always bubbling over with ideas, Dr. Cottrell was a rapid talker, yet at the same time, always modest, unselfish, and little concerned with the acquirement of money or with personal gain. In 1912, he founded the Research Corporation, now of 405 Lexington Avenue, New York 17, to develop electrical precipitation on a large scale for industries, and distribute the profits to researchers for the development of fundamental research—a lasting and continuing legacy. He advised several other university foundations on patent administration. In 1948, over $750,000 were donated to young research workers in the smaller colleges.

Among his other chemical engineering interests were the production of helium from natural gas with a helium content, and the pebble-heat-exchanger as a means of attaining high heat, a project now in process of realization.

Death came to Dr. Cottrell on November 16, 1948, while he was attending a meeting on the National Academy of Sciences at the University of California in Berkeley. Knowing that he would have wished the meeting to continue, his friends went on with it despite this shock. Thus ended the life of a scientist appropriately called by his biographer a "Samaritan of Science."

References

CAMERON, FRANK, "Cottrell, Samaritan of Science," Garden City, New York, Doubleday & Company, Inc., 1952.

E. R. RIEGEL

COTTRELL PRECIPITATOR. See COTTRELL, FREDERICK G.

COULOMB, CHARLES AUGUSTIN (1736–1806)

Charles A. Coulomb, born June 14, 1736, came from an excellent family in the south of France. He studied mathematics and science in Paris, then entered the army and became an officer in the engineers. During nine years in Martinique he supervised the building of fortifications, and it was not until his return in 1776 that he found time for purely scientific work. During the years before the outbreak of the Revolution, he carried out his fundamental electric and magnetic investigations. It was with Coulomb that the electrical and magnetic phenomena began to develop into a science, and he made the first quantitative determinations of the laws of the two phenomena which bear his name. The first law of electricity states the forces with which electric charges attract and repel one another and that these forces are always proportional to the quantities acting upon one another and inversely proportional to the square of their distance apart. The law for magnetism is exactly similar. The recognition and proof of these laws was another masterpiece of experimental skill in view of the smallness of the forces to be examined. By measuring the torsion of a wire from which hung the electrified body being observed, he was able to measure the forces in action. He had previously applied this method in studying compasses and magnetism and created the torsion balance. The mathematical theory of these phenomena was developed by Laplace and completed by Poisson.

Coulomb's army career led to various questions of mechanics which brought about research of a practical nature, and resulted in his works on friction and the laws applied thereto, as well as research on hydraulics which promoted studies on the viscosity of fluids. In 1784 he was made intendent-general of the waters and fountains of France. His work brought recognition in the academic world and membership in the Academy, although his outspoken technical reports frequently made him disliked in governmental high places. During the Revolution he retired to his small estate near Blois and devoted himself entirely to science. Not until Napoleon's time did he get back his former posts which he occupied until death at the age of 70 on August 23, 1806.

When consideration is given to how much detailed knowledge had been gathered together upon the subject of electricity without any real comprehensive idea of it, we can best appreciate the fundamental achievement of Coulomb. The ancients knew of the lodestone or magnetic iron ore, but no further progress in electrical and magnetic observation was evidenced before the year 1600 when Gilbert, Queen Elizabeth's doctor, made somewhat elaborate scientific experiments with artificial magnets. His contribution, however, was limited to the fact that other substances besides amber could be electrified by electric and magnetic forces. Seventy years later Guericke made the first step toward the construction of an electrical machine and Leibnitz observed the electric sparks produced thereby. Another 60 years passed before Stephen Gray in London found that electricity can be conducted and shortly thereafter Dufay discovered the two kinds of electricity (positive and negative). Kleist, Franklin, and Wilke all added to the imposing number of observations, but the idea of two electricities and their actions upon one another and upon like charges was still very indefinite. It was Coulomb who brought this state of uncertainty to an end with the announcement of his laws. Even the work of Faraday 50 years later on the influence exerted by the insulators surrounding the conductors left the law intact and only necessitated the addition of the dielectric constant.

The name of coulomb has been given to the unit of quantity of electrical current.

CARMEN W. WALSH

COULOMB'S LAW

Early research in electrostatics had determined that electrically charged bodies repelled each other if they were charged with the same type of electricity and attracted each other if they were charged oppositely. The first quantitative investigation of this law of force was published in 1788 by Charles-Augustin Coulomb (1736–1806). Coulomb had earlier investigated the torsional forces associated with the twisting of wires, and, with these investigations as a guide, he had constructed an ingenious torsion balance with which he could determine the magnitude of small forces with considerable precision. Using this balance, he was able to determine within the limits of accuracy of his instrument that the forces of repulsion and attraction between two charged bodies are inversely proportional to the square of the distance between them. At that time, the concept of quantity of charge was not precise enough for quantitative investigation, but other investigators later determined that the force between charged bodies was proportional to the product of the magnitudes of the charges contained by the two bodies. The law describing the forces between charged bodies, therefore, now states that the force between two point charges varies directly as the product of the magnitude of their charges and varies inversely as the square of distance between them, and this law is called *Coulomb's Law.*

Strictly speaking, Coulomb's Law holds only for point charges, although it is observed to be approximately valid if the dimensions of the charged bodies are small compared to their separation. This law received remarkable verification for extremely small charged bodies from Sir Ernest Rutherford's famous experiments in 1910–11 on the scattering of alpha particles as they passed through metal foils.[2] Rutherford found that when alpha particles were passed through metal foils many more particles were scattered at large angles, i.e., bounced back, than could be explained on the basis of existing theories of the atom, which assumed that the positive charge of an atom was contained in a large sphere about 2×10^{-8} cm in diameter. If he assumed that the positive charge of an atom was concentrated in a very small nucleus of dimension on the order of 10^{-12} cm, he found that the application of Coulomb's Law to the repulsion of the positively charged alpha particles and the atomic nucleus explained his results quantitatively. Thus, at the same time he verified Coulomb's Law for extremely small charged bodies and proposed an essentially correct theory of the atom.

Mathematically, Coulomb's Law may be expressed by Eq. (1),

$$F = \frac{kq_1q_2}{r^2} \qquad (1)$$

where q_1 and q_2 are the magnitudes of the charges and r is their separation. The value of the constant, k, is determined by the particular system of units in use. In the electrostatic system of units, forces are expressed in dynes, distances in centimeters, and the constant, k, is taken to be unity. The unit of charge is therefore defined to be of such magnitude that Coulomb's Law will be satisfied, and this unit of charge is called the *statcoulomb*. It has a charge about equal to that of 2×10^9 electrons.

More commonly used today is the rationalized mks system. In this system, Coulomb's Law is written as follows:

$$F = \frac{1}{4\pi\epsilon_0} \frac{q_1q_2}{r^2} \qquad (2)$$

The constant, k, is written as $1/4\pi\epsilon_0$ so that certain equations in electrostatics derived from Coulomb's Law and more commonly used may have a simple form. The unit of charge is the *coulomb*, which is defined as that charge passed in one second through a cross section of a conductor by a current of one ampere. The ampere is the common practical unit of current. The coulomb is almost 3×10^9 times as large as the statcoulomb and has, therefore, a charge about equal to that of 6×10^{18} electrons. In the rationalized mks system, the unit of length and the unit of force are the meter and the newton, respectively. The constant, ϵ_0, in Eq. (2) has the value 8.85×10^{-12} coulomb^2 newton^{-1} meter^{-2}.

Unfortunately, there are other systems of units also, and there is no common usage of any one system. In any given text or article, one must be careful to determine exactly which system of units is in use.

Coulomb's Law will give the correct measured force between two charged bodies only if there is no intervening matter between the point charges. If matter is present, the two charges will induce charges on the intervening matter, and the forces will therefore be altered due to the presence of these induced charges. Coulomb's Law is still valid, of course, because the force between the two charged bodies, due only to the charges on the bodies, will not be changed. An accurate calculation of the measured force would have to apply Coulomb's Law also to all of the induced charges, a task that would be very difficult. For many cases it can be shown, however, that a satisfactory approximation may be obtained by using the concept of the dielectric constant (q.v.). If the charges are immersed in a homogeneous isotropic fluid of dimensions large compared to the separation of the charges, then the measured force will be given by Eq. (3)

$$F = \frac{1}{4\pi\epsilon_0 K}\frac{q_1 q_2}{r^2} \qquad (3)$$

where K is the dielectric constant. It will be noted that the force is the same as that force calculated if the charges were in a vacuum but multiplied by a factor, $1/K$. The dielectric constant has the value unity for vacuum, very close to unity for gases at normal pressures, 81 for water, and values ranging from 1 to 100 for other substances. Some of the titanates have dielectric constants of several thousand.

Coulomb's Law is basic to all of electrostatics, for from it are derived the concepts of the electric field and the potential, and the potentials of cell electrodes are surely among the most important variables of electrochemistry.

References

1. Magie, W. F., "A Source Book in Physics," p. 408, New York, McGraw-Hill Book Co., 1935.
2. Rutherford, E., *Philosophical Magazine*, **21**, 669 (1911).

Robert E. Meyer

COULOMETER. See FARADAY'S LAWS.

COULOMETRIC TECHNIQUES IN HIGH-TEMPERATURE SYSTEMS

Coulometric techniques have been developed for the study of fused salt and other high temperature systems. Various coulometric titrations have been developed to determine analytically components of fused salt systems, and coulometric generation has been used for preparative purposes. Coulometric techniques are also very valuable for the study of electrode processes in high-temperature systems. The simplicity of these techniques is one of their main advantages; current measurement is simple and when used as an analytical method coulometry does not require ideal diffusion conditions as does the case for chronopotentiometry or polarography. The measurement of the number of coulombs is done either by the passage of a constant current for a known period of time or by using a coulometer, chemical or electronic.

One of the first applications of a coulometric technique to a high-temperature system was performed by Wagner[10] in his investigations on silver sulfide. By passing a known amount of current through the solid-state galvanic cell

$$Ag \mid AgI \mid Ag_2S \mid Pt$$

he was able to vary the silver to sulfur ratio in the Ag_2S phase. If a positive current is passed through the cell from left to right, Ag^+ ions enter the Ag_2S phase from the AgI, and the electrons are furnished at the platinum electrode; if the current is reversed, Ag^+ and electrons are removed from the Ag_2S phase. Since both Ag^+ ions and electrons are mobile in Ag_2S, a uniform Ag/S ratio is obtained in the Ag_2S. In this manner Wagner was able to measure the potential of this galvanic cell from an Ag/S ratio of greater than two, i.e., silver in the Ag_2S, to a critical lower ratio corresponding to the formation of liquid sulfur as a new phase, and thus evaluate the variability of the Ag/S ratio in αAg_2S from 200 to 300°C and in βAg_2S below 176°C. He termed this technique "a solid state coulometric titration" and later used it for the study of similar high-temperature solid state systems.

Egan[1] adapted this technique to a study of the thermodynamics of liquid Mg-Bi alloys. By coulometrically depositing magnesium into the bismuth alloy, he varied the mole fraction of magnesium from 0.55 to 0.60 in the galvanic cell

$$Mg(l) \mid NaCl\text{-}KCl\text{-}MgCl_2(l \text{ eutectic}) \mid Mg\text{-}Bi(l)$$

in the temperature range 720 to 830°C. He was able to evaluate the activity of magnesium in bismuth in this critical region, from emf measurements.

Laitinen and Liu[5] utilized a coulometric technique for the preparation of their $Pt(II) \mid Pt$ reference electrode in fused LiCl-KCl eutectic. A platinum foil was anodized at a constant current for a known period of time, the anodization proceeding with a current efficiency of 100 per cent. This reference electrode was shown to be suitable and was stable over long periods of time. Preparation of reference electrodes by coulometric generation has been used in many other fused salt systems and has become a standard procedure in fused salt technology. Reference electrodes of the metal-metal ion type are contained in isolated compartments with frits, asbestos wicks, or thin glass membranes to furnish contact with the fused salt system.

The first coulometric titrations in fused salts were accomplished by Laitinen and Bhatia[4] who titrated chromium (II) to chromium (III) and vanadium (II) to vanadium (III) in the LiCl-KCl eutectic with iron (III) as the oxidant. The iron (III) was coulometrically generated *in situ* by anodizing, at a constant current, a carbon rod in contact with a solution of iron (II) and chromium (II) or vanadium (II) in the LiCl-KCl eutectic at 450°C. They determined the end point potentiometrically or amperometrically with one or two indicator electrodes. Analyses were performed with accuracies better than ±2 per cent.

Hill, Perano, and Osteryoung[3] coulometrically titrated uranium (III) to uranium (IV) in the LiCl-KCl eutectic at 450°C with platinum (II). The platinum (II) was directly generated by anodizing a platinum foil in the melt at a constant current with the end point of the titration being determined potentiometrically. Again, accuracies of ±2 per cent were achieved for these analyses.

These coulometric titrations were based on the fact that anodic processes in fused salts generally proceed with 100 per cent current efficiency. Liu[7] showed that this was also the case in the LiSO₄-K₂SO₄ eutectic at 625°C. He coulometrically titrated copper (I) to copper (II) using a palladium electrode as the anode. He found that copper (I) in the sulfate melt was at first directly oxidized to copper (II); when the copper (I) concentration became too low to sustain the constant current, palladium (II) was generated which then oxidized the remaining copper (I). The end point was determined potentiometrically with an accuracy of ±2 per cent.

Coulometric titrations of the type described have proved to be quite accurate for analytical purposes. Their value, however, is limited since it is difficult to obtain selectivity and a foreign ion or metal is always introduced into the system. The technique of controlled potential coulometry eliminates these objections. There are now many commercially available automatic instruments capable of electrolyzing at a controlled potential with simultaneous electronic integration of current. Van Norman[9] used controlled potential coulometry for analyses in the LiCl-KCl eutectic. He was able to determine both zinc (II) and cadmium (II) in the chloride eutectic with an accuracy of ± 1 per cent, by the

controlled potential coulometric stripping of the predeposited metal from a liquid bismuth electrode. Mixtures of cadmium (II) and zinc (II) were also analyzed by selective stripping of zinc and cadmium from a bismuth pool, following a predeposition step. The advantage of the anodic process over the cathodic process for analyses was the elimination of background due to the irreversible reduction of hydroxide impurity which interfered with accurate determinations. The hydroxide impurity was probably reduced as follows:

$$2OH^- + 2e^- \rightarrow 2O^= + H_2 \uparrow$$

Van Norman also showed that ions of metals too noble to be stripped from bismuth, e.g., nickel, could be determined by predeposition on a platinum gauze electrode followed by controlled potential coulometric stripping. Again, the anodic process was used since impurities interfered with the cathodic process. It is apparent that pure fused salt solvents must be meticulously purified for electrochemical investigations.

Coulometric techniques in fused salts are not limited to analyses but can also be used for preparative purposes. Gruen and MacBeth[2] used a coulometric technique to prepare samples of vanadium (II) in the LiCl-KCl eutectic for subsequent spectrophotometric studies. Laitinen and Rhodes[6] coulometrically reduced vanadium (V) in a solution of V₂O₅ in the LiCl-KCl eutectic to form the insoluble reduction product for x-ray analysis.

One extremely interesting adaptation of a coulometric technique in a high-temperature system was devised by Ratchford and Rickert.[8] They combined a "Knudsen"-cell with the solid-state galvanic cell

$$Pt,Ag \mid AgI \mid Ag_2Se,Pt,$$

in which the silver iodide is practically a pure ionic conductor. The constant current passed through the cell, with the Ag₂Se as the positive pole, is a measure of the rate of outflow of selenium vapor from the "Knudsen"-cell while the potential of the galvanic cell is a direct measure of the chemical potential of selenium. From the rate of outflow of selenium vapor and the corresponding chemical potential, thermodynamic properties of selenium molecules were calculated.

References

1. EGAN, J. J., *Acta Metall.*, **7**, 560 (1959).
2. GRUEN, D. M., AND MACBETH, R. L., *J. Phys. Chem.*, **66**, 57 (1962).

3. HILL, D. L., PERANO, J., AND OSTERYOUNG, R. A.,
       J. Electrochem. Soc., **107**, 698 (1960).
4. LAITINEN, H. A., AND BHATIA, B. B., *Anal.
       Chem.*, **30**, 1995 (1958).
5. LAITINEN, H. A., AND LIU, C. H., *J. Am. Chem.
       Soc.*, **80**, 1015 (1958).
6. LAITINEN, H. A., AND RHODES, D. R., *J. Electro-
       chem. Soc.*, **109**, 413 (1962).
7. LIU, C. H., *Anal. Chem.*, **33**, 1477 (1961).
8. RATCHFORD, R. J., AND RICKERT, H., *Z. Electro-
       chemie*, **66**, 497 (1962).
9. VAN NORMAN, J. D., *Anal. Chem.*, **34**, 594
       (1962).
10. WAGNER, C., *J. Chem. Phys.*, **21**, 1819 (1953).

JOHN D. VAN NORMAN

Cross-references: *Electrometric Titrations;* entries bearing *Fused Salt* titles.

COULOMETRIC TITRATION. See ELECTRO-
METRIC TITRATIONS.

CREVICE CORROSION

Crevice corrosion (sometimes known as contact corrosion) is observed as localized and usually accelerated corrosion within a crevice occurring between two metal surfaces or between a
metal and a nonmetal.

In terms of elementary corrosion theory,
crevice corrosion may be regarded as a special
type of galvanic cell arising from a difference in
composition between the environment within the
crevice and that in contact with the main body
of the metal part or parts. As an example,
imagine that air is bubbled into a steel tank of
water which previously had been maintained
in an oxygen-free condition. As air is introduced
into the tank the water in contact with the walls
becomes saturated with oxygen, but in the
crevices where two steel plates are joined together the stagnant water remains essentially
oxygen free. Thus, a galvanic cell develops in
which the walls of the tank in contact with oxy-
gen-saturated solution become the cathode and
the metal within the crevice becomes the anode,
resulting in accelerated corrosion within and
adjacent to the crevice. It is important to note
that for crevice corrosion to occur the differences
in environment must be such that the bulk of
the metal becomes cathodic to that within the
crevice.

The conditions which lead to crevice corrosion
in practice can arise in many ways. First of all,
the crevice does not have to be a structural item,
such as a seam or a rivet, but can result from
any object resting on the metal surface. The
object can be a marine organism, a grain of sand,
loose corrosion products, or an imperfect protective coating. Factors which can lead to a difference in environment between the crevice and
the rest of the system are:

1) Normal corrosion processes, such as consumption of oxygen from the solution within the
crevice, the depletion of inhibitors, or the presence of dissimilar metals in the crevice area.

2) Deliberate or accidental changes in the
bulk solution, such as addition of oxidizing
agents or corrosion inhibitors, change of pH or
composition due to chemical reactions, or replacement of one solution by another.

3) Mechanical, biological, or chemical destruction of surface films or protective coatings in the
crevice area under conditions where they cannot
be reformed or replaced.

Materials, such as stainless steel and aluminum, which depend on protective films or oxidizing environments for their corrosion resistance are particularly subject to crevice corrosion
as are metals protected from corrosion by special
coatings or treatments. Once the protective barrier within the crevice has been lost for any
reason, it is almost impossible to replace. This
together with the large difference in potential
which can exist between the protected and unprotected metal often leads to very rapid localized corrosion in the crevice area.

Laboratory studies of crevice corrosion may
be carried out in a number of ways and are useful in demonstrating its occurrence with a particular combination of materials and environments. The most simple method is to overlap
and clamp together two pieces of the metal concerned to form a crevice adjacent to a larger
area of exposed material. The sample is then
immersed in the desired solution and the incidence and extent of corrosion in the crevice
observed. A useful variation of this technique
consists of machining one of the surfaces so that
a wedge-shaped opening is formed, giving a
measure of what constitutes a dangerous crevice
in a given situation. In some instances the use
of a ball or a cylinder with a flat surface is used
to simulate a crevice. Where the environment
that might exist within a crevice is known,
measurements of potential and current flow between the same metal in different environments
are quite useful in predicting a tendency toward
crevice corrosion or in suggesting possible means

of prevention. Unwitting crevice corrosion often complicates and confuses laboratory studies of other corrosion phenomena and the laboratory worker as well as the equipment designer should be aware of its implications. The use of hooks and spacer rods to support and separate corrosion coupons introduces unknown crevice effects into many weight loss tests as does the use of bundles of coupons bolted together with insulating or conducting spacers. It may not be possible or practical to eliminate all sources of potential crevice corrosion in many tests, but their existence should at least be recognized in the recording of data and interpretation of results.

The prevention of crevice corrosion is best accomplished by careful design, fabrication, and use of metal equipment and structures. The only sure measure is to avoid or eliminate crevices or potential trouble spots before corrosion starts. The same factors responsible for crevice corrosion make its treatment or prevention by chemical inhibitors or electrochemical means very difficult or impossible.

References

1. DePaul, D. J., "Corrosion Engineering Problems in High Purity Water," *Corrosion*, **13**, 75t (1957).
2. Ellis, O. B., and LaQue, F. L., "Area Effects in Crevice Corrosion," *Corrosion*, **7**, 362 (1951).
3. Evans, U. R., "The Corrosion and Oxidation of Metals," pp. 207–212, New York, St. Martins Press Inc., 1960.
4. Freedman, A. J., and Dravnieks, A., "Evaluation of Refinery Corrosion Inhibitors," *Corrosion*, **14**, 567t (1958).
5. Lymes, W., "The Oxygen Concentration Cell as a Factor in the Localized Corrosion of Metals," *J. Electrochem. Soc.*, **103**, 467 (1956).
6. Wyche, E. H., Voigt, L. R., and LaQue, F. L., "Corrosion in Crevices," *Trans. Electrochem. Soc.*, **89**, 149 (1946).

R. A. Powers

Cross-references: *Concentration Cells;* entries bearing *Corrosion* titles.

CRYSTAL GROWTH. See ZONE REFINING.

CURRENT DISTRIBUTION

Current distribution is the local density of current on an electrode in an electrolytic cell expressed as a function of position on the electrode. The electrode may also be inserted in the main body of electrolyte for exploring purposes, in which case it serves to ascertain the distribution of current within the body and boundaries of the cell.

Anode, cathode, and bipolar electrode current distributions are easily distinguished, but "primary" and "polarization" current distributions are more basic but also more difficult to separate. There is also an "effective" current distribution which is of practical importance.

The measurement is in terms of current passing through a small area of electrode divided by that area and, hence, may be expressed by the derivative, dI/da, where I is the current in amperes and a the area in suitable units, so that da is the arbitrarily small area of electrode through which the current, dI, passes. In general this quantity varies from point to point over the surface of the electrode under consideration. All positive values up to a theoretically infinite limit, and including also zero, may occur. Only a small number of known electrode configurations and cell geometries yield uniform current distribution (and therefore constant current density) over the entire cathode and anode area. Examples are: 1) a rectangular tank whose sides and bottoms are insulators (also the surface immediately above the electrolyte) and whose ends are anode and cathode, respectively; 2) an infinite (i.e., very large) tank with a single circular electrode at an arbitrary point, the electrode of opposite polarity being infinitely (extremely) far removed; 3) a spherical electrode surrounded by a concentric spherical electrode of opposite polarity, the entire space between being filled with electrolyte; 4) a cylindrical anode surrounded by a concentric cylindrical cathode, the space between (say, up to unit height) being filled with electrolyte, and the bottom of the cylindrical space a perfect insulator.

The more basic concept of "primary" current distribution is found in an idealized cell in which the electrodes are assumed to be perfect conductors. This entails a constant potential difference (voltage) between them at every point and requires that the electrolyte does not polarize the electrodes. The current distribution is then easily formulated mathematically in terms of the "first boundary value problem": To find the potential function (a function of position generally varying from point to point within the electrolyte) which assumes an arbitrary positive constant value over the entire surface of the anode, and another arbitrary constant negative value with respect to that of the anode over the entire surface of the cathode; this last constant may be chosen to be zero without restriction of generality. The potential function, V, so defined is uniquely determined throughout the electrolytic cell. It has the fundamental property that the current is so distributed under its control that a minimum of heating of the electrolyte occurs.

The current distribution may also be described by the potential drop per unit distance from a point of either electrode into the electrolyte, or, as it is more conveniently expressed: the "normal" derivative of the potential function, dV/dn, where dV is the small potential (voltage) drop measured from a point on the electrode to a point within the electrolyte situated a small distance, dn, from that point, in a direction at right angles to the surface of the electrode. The two definitions given must obviously be identical. Consequently, the current distribution function and the potential function are related to one another in pairs so that a potential function in one cell arrangement may also serve as a current distribution function in another, and conversely.

The problem here stated for primary distribution of current always has a (mathematical) solution so that in principle prediction of the distribution on anode and cathode is possible. This is nowadays within reach of the electrochemist by programming for modern fast digital computers. Conformal mapping is also a useful mathematical tool for a number of configurations.

Some general statements can be made which are of practical use. 1) Sharp edges and external corners(whatever be the angle) always exhibit infinite (in practice, very large) current density, causing excessive deposition of metal or "burning," or operation of cells at densities where unwanted products occur locally, or excessive consumption of electrodes at corners and edges until change of shape to a more rounded configuration occurs (as in electric furnaces or, e.g., aluminum depositing cells). For right angles rounding off of corners causes adjustment of current to a value of approximately the inverse of the cube root of the radius: $i = A/\sqrt[3]{R}$ (A is a constant). 2) Internal angles always exhibit zero current density (regardless of angle); rounding of such an internal corner redistributes the local current density so that it is in direct proportion to the radius, at least for right angle corners.

The somewhat abstract formulation given can be illustrated by the practical example of an electrolytic cell consisting of an insulated (e.g., rubber-lined) tank with liberally dimensioned copper electrodes (i.e., so that their ohmic resistance can be neglected) and carefully adjusted conventional copper sulfate electrolyte operated at fairly low average current density so as to avoid the onset of polarization of the electrodes. Sharp external corners of the anodes are quickly eaten away to rounded corners due to the excessive current density there.

It is a proper question to inquire whether shaping of anode or cathode might always make uniform current distribution possible over the entire electrode. This can be answered affirmatively for primary distribution provided that the electrode on which uniform current distribution is desired has no true internal or external corners or sharp edges, i.e., has a smooth contour in every direction. It is then possible either by suitable arrangement or providing additional electrodes of the opposite polarity to achieve uniform current distribution. This statement loses its validity if the electrode consists of multiple pieces, e.g., if more than one cathode is present, or if the cathodes are at varying potentials with respect to the anodes, in which case they will act as bipolar electrodes.

The problem can be generalized still further be asking for a *given* current distribution over an electrode. In electrodeposition this would permit imparting an arbitrary shape to that electrode either by building up by cathodic deposition, or by dissolution at a given rate by making the electrode an anode (so-called "electrolytic machining"). This problem can be stated mathematically as the "second boundary value problem," as follows: given a cathode to determine a potential function, V, so that at every point of the cathode a prescribed current density is obtained, $dV/dn = f$, where f is a function describing the current distribution over the cathode. This is a mathematically solvable problem but, a necessary condition is again the smooth contour of the electrode to be shaped. In practice this problem is unsolved, even with solutions producing considerable electrode polarization, or the insertion of insulating or conducting shields to lower local current density.

Uniformity of current distribution on one electrode, the cathode, say, does not imply uniformity on the other electrode (the anode), and geometrical similarity of anodes and cathodes is no assurance of similarity of current densities on the electrodes.

When bipolar electrodes occur in a cell, a portion of the surface is positive (anodic) and the remainder is negative (cathodic). The dividing line or surface represents a configuration of zero current density. The division is not in general a simple fraction of the surface area.

When the walls of the electrolytic cell are conducting, they form an additional electrode of potential intermediate to that of the cathode and anode (provided these are distinct from the walls, and primary distribution—no polarization —is assumed).

When polarization of the electrodes occurs, the exact nature of the polarizing film must be known before the resulting modified current distribution is ascertainable. The polarizing film effectively modifies the shape of the electrode and precludes the establishment of exactly uniform potential difference between anode and cathode. The effective electrode surface may be visualized as moved to somewhere within the electrolyte, where the potential is once more constant. Once this is known, the previous discussions on primary current distribution apply.

The simplest polarization is "linear." The primary current distribution is then modified so that the current density over the electrode is proportional to the potential itself: $dV/dn = AV$, where A is some constant. This modification can again be formulated as a "boundary value problem," but considerable complications are introduced which make the explicit mathematical calculation impossible in most cases. Only one special case has been explicitly solved by C. Kasper of the U. S. Bureau of Standards. The existence of a solution under fairly general conditions has been proved by mathematicians and the availability of modern high-speed computers should make practical calculations of more difficult cases possible.

More general and usually more complicated types of polarization also occur, but are beyond the scope of the present article. Generally speaking, polarization tends to make current distribution more uniform over the electrodes and thereby helps to avoid the extremes described in the foregoing.

Current distribution in a cell is considerably modified from that described due to changing ohmic resistance of, or voltage drop within, the electrodes themselves. These are not now assumed to have only negligible ohmic resistance, so that the potential difference varies from point to point. Appreciable voltage drop occurs between the point at which the current enters (or leaves) the electrode and any given other point of the same electrode. This is referred to as "electrode current distribution." The previous theory can nevertheless be applied by searching for the potential distribution function over the electrodes first, and then applying this over limited sections of the electrode-electrolyte interface where the potential may be assumed approximately constant. The phenomenon is neglected in most practical cases. If it does occur, however, nonuniformity of current distribution will be increased and produce an effect prior even to the primary distribution. It is noticeable in cells where extremely high current densities are employed as in certain types of commercial chromium plating from chromic acid solutions.

"Effective" current distribution must also be mentioned. It arises when the current efficiency of a process at an electrode is less than 100 per cent, the unwanted product escaping, e.g., in the form of gas. The current efficiency is generally least at places of highest current density, and, thus, the largest amount of unwanted product appears at locations of high current density. The consequence is that at these places less wanted product appears and thus the impression of more uniform current distribution is created. An example is presented by commercial chromium depositing electrolytes of the aqueous chromic oxide type which have average cathode current efficiencies of 5 to 8 per cent, the unwanted product, hydrogen, escaping at the cathode in the form of gas. The current density over a cathode even of simple shape may vary between 50 amp/sq ft and 500 amp/sq ft; in locations of the first the current efficiency may be as high as 15 to 20 per cent, while at 500 amp/sq. ft. it may be as low as 1 per cent or even less. Thus, when the customary decorative layers of ten to fifty millionths of an inch thickness are deposited over nickel, say, the thickness is found to be almost entirely uniform, giving the impression of uniform current distribution. If the aim is uniform thickness of deposit in cases of this kind, an effectively uniform current distribution apparently occurs.

Recent investigations show that still more complicated arrangements involving porous electrodes are amenable to theoretical analysis of current distribution.

References

1. KRONSBEIN, J., *et al*, "Current and Metal Distribution in Electrodeposition," American Electroplaters' Society Research Report No. 24, 1953.
2. NEWMAN, JOHN S., AND TOBIAS, CHARLES W., "Theoretical Analysis of Current Distribution in Porous Electrodes," *J. Electrochem. Soc.*, **109**, 1183–1191 (1962).

JOHN KRONSBEIN

Cross-references: *Current Efficiency; Energy Efficiency; Electroplating; Electrorefining; Polarization; Throwing Power.*

CURRENT EFFICIENCY

Current efficiency is the fraction, expressed as a percentage, of current passing through a cell which accomplishes the intended effect based on Faraday's third law of electrolysis, according to which 96,500 coulombs or 26.8 ampere-hours produce or convert a gram-equivalent of substance. If this is achieved, the current efficiency is said to be 100 per cent. It is related to energy efficiency which is measured by total I^2R losses in the cell compared with the minimum possible: the decomposition voltage plus the intrinsic ohmic resistance of the cell times the current. In the expression, $E = I^2R$, where E is the energy, the factor I must contain the current efficiency.

At least two essentially different current efficiencies are distinguished: anode and cathode efficiencies, respectively. The former is the fraction of current multiplied by 100 giving the ratio of actual desired anode product or conversion to that theoretically possible by Faraday's law mentioned above; cathode efficiency is defined similarly with reference to cathode product or conversion. Anode and cathode efficiency need not be the same, nor less than 100 per cent, but they are never less than zero. The two electrodes may be enclosed in separate compartments; if the anode efficiency exceeds that of the cathode, anode products accumulate in its compartment unless removed at a rate suitable to maintain the balance, and correspondingly for the cathode compartment. If the compartments do not exist, i.e., if the electrodes are not kept in separate spaces, it is still possible for one or the other

electrode to have greater current efficiency, in which case the excess electrode products accumulate in the cell as a whole either by concentrating the electrolyte or remaining suspended, or precipitating to the bottom of the cell by gravitational action. Such effects may or may not be desirable. If undesirable, corrective controls must be exercised, the choice of which will depend on the desired ultimate effects or the ingenuity of the controller. Anode and cathode efficiencies are not constant throughout the cell nor over the entire electrode area; they may change with electrolyte composition caused by the current efficiency or from point to point of electrode with changes in current density. If electrolyte composition has been made constant by external intervention or due to equality of anode and cathode efficiencies, the latter still may be changed by current density control and electrode shape. Generally speaking, uniform current distribution over the electrode area improves current efficiency, and, equally generally, an increase in overall average current density decreases current efficiency. Whether or not this is true will, of course, depend upon the desired electrode product; if the cell is used for production of substance previously considered unwanted, the efficiencies reverse, the previous electrode inefficiency becoming its efficiency.

These generalities must not be taken to represent immutable laws, since polarization of the electrodes also changes current efficiencies. In many cases polarization increases with overall average current density, and this in turn may improve the current efficiency by increasing the particular electrode product desired. On the other hand, polarization also generally causes an increase in ohmic resistance of the cell and thereby decreases its energy efficiency. Hence, a proper balance between electrode current efficiency, polarization, energy efficiency, controllability of electrolyte, etc., must be kept in mind. Current efficiency is therefore a function of local as well as average current densities, concentration of electrolyte, polarization, temperature, electrode composition, or surface condition, addition agents or impurities, shape and nature of container and state of electrolyte.

This last item implies the introduction of still another type of current efficiency not included in the previous discussion. It is possible for the electrolyte to be present in two or more phases or compositions; it may then happen that pure electronic conduction current without electrolysis occurs in the cell. Current consumed due to such causes obviously contributes to inefficiency. This phenomenon is generally confined to cells with fused electrolytes, since it rarely occurs that, e.g., solid and liquid phases are present simultaneously in aqueous electrolytes. Another source of current inefficiency, also usually found in fused electrolyte cells with separated anode and cathode spaces, is caused by diffusion of electrode products into the electrolyte, recombination, secondary undesirable reaction with electrolyte, volatilization (generally due to excessive temperatures), seepage or diffusion through porous barriers or diaphragms, and reactions with the atmosphere (gaseous or vapor) above the electrolyte.

There is also a current inefficiency in cells not used for production of chemicals or metals or for deposition or dissolution, but ostensibly for heating the electrolyte, as exemplified by the Hultgren salt bath furnace or a fused cyanide hardening furnace in which potassium and sodium cyanides and other salts are fused for the purpose of heat treating metals. Such cells are generally operated by alternating current to prevent chemical dissociation, but in many cases unequal electrode polarization sets in, causing electrolytic decomposition of the fused salt, e.g., by the rapid and excessive formation of sodium carbonate in sodium cyanide hardening crucibles. The percentage of current consumed for this unwanted effect in many cases reduces the ohmic resistance of the cell, and causes formation of products with higher melting points, making temperature control difficult or impossible, and numerous other minor effects. Such cells will not be considered further.

Examples of the above general statements will illustrate typical occurrences in industrial installations. First of all, it should be mentioned that a current efficiency in excess of 100 per cent does not imply a failure of Faraday's third law but the occurrence of secondary electrode reactions which maintain themselves as long as current passes through the cell. An example of 100 per cent anode efficiency is found in the electrolytic oxidation of anthracene to anthraquinone; another is found very closely approximated in silver cyanide plating solutions operated at fairly low average current densities. In fact, the latter furnishes an example of practically 100 per cent anode and cathode efficiency at all reasonable commercially customary average electrode current densities which may range from 2 to 10 amperes per square foot.

This contrasts with copper cyanide electroplating solutions which have cathode current efficiencies from 40 to 60 per cent depending on an average cathode current density which may vary from 10 to 60 or more amperes per square foot, and anode efficiencies from 30 to 50 per cent under similar conditions. It follows that in this case the electrolyte is depleted in copper in time, and correction becomes necessary either by addition of suitable copper salts or by dummy electrolysis with porous pot-encased cathodes to inhibit current deposition at the cathode while causing electrolytic dissolution of copper from the anodes. At times, due to the addition of excessive free alkali cyanides or other addition agents, the anode efficiency may rise to an extent where undesirable accumulation of copper occurs in the cell. Such a condition may be corrected by use of inert (nickel or iron) anodes, either permanently or temporarily, with or without soluble anodes mixed with insoluble ones.

Copper plated from an acid sulfate solution, on the other hand, exhibits cathode efficiencies of 92 to 98 per cent in commercial practice, even in copper refining where bipolar electrodes are used. Thus, even though the metal is divalent in this cell, the high current efficiency as compared to that of the cyanide electrolyte offsets the valency disadvantage with its theoretical output cut in half.

An example of fused salt electrolysis is that of aluminum from (purified)Al_2O_3 dissolved in sodium aluminum fluoride plus calcium fluoride, where 70 to 90 per cent current efficiency is common for the cathode product, aluminum. In brine electrolysis, diaphragm separation of anode and cathode is customary, and the primary cathode product is sodium metal, but this is immediately converted to sodium hydroxide which is the cathode compartment product. Thus, the sodium cathode efficiency is zero, but the secondary product (NaOH) efficiency is practically 100 per cent, aberrations being found due to diffusion and other causes. In addition hydrogen is obtained from the cathode, thus illustrating in effect 200 per cent cathode efficiency as far as cathode product is concerned. This apparent discrepancy is of course due to the nonelectrolytic reaction of sodium with water at the cathode.

Another example, but of zero current efficiency, this time at the anode, is found in commercial electrodeposition of chromium from aqueous chromic acid solutions. Lead anodes are used which are practically insoluble, lead peroxide forming only as a surface layer. The anode efficiency with chromium anodes is greater than 100 per cent, dissolution of chromium being accelerated near the anode at a rate greater than that accounted for by the current passed through the cell. The cathode efficiency on the other hand is 5 to 8 per cent, copious hydrogen evolution taking place as unwanted product at the cathode. In the Castner cell for brine electrolysis the current efficiency is about 93 to 96 per cent at the mercury cathode, but here the energy efficiency is only about 50 per cent. In electroplating practice the energy efficiency is rarely considered, current efficiency, and especially cathode efficiency, being a main consideration.

JOHN KRONSBEIN

Cross-references: *Current Distribution; Electroplating; Electrorefining; Energy Efficiency;* and *Polarization.*

D

DAVY, SIR HUMPHRY (1778–1829)

Humphry Davy was the first to isolate the alkali metals and recognize the fundamental identity of chemical and electrical energy. He was born in Penzance, Cornwall, on December 17, 1778, of humble parents. Following apprenticeship to a local physician, he turned to chemistry and was eventually put in charge of the laboratory of Dr. Beddoes' Medical Pneumatic Institute at Bristol in 1798. Here, his experiments on the preparation and physiological action of gases resulted in the discovery of the unusual effects of nitrous oxide ("laughing gas") on the human body. As a result of this discovery and a naturally attractive personality he received an appointment as lecturer at the Royal Institution by Count Rumford in 1801 and was promoted to a professorship in 1802. His success led to knighthood in 1812 and he became a baronet in 1818. He died on May 29, 1829 at the age of 50.

His interest in electricity led him to study the electrolysis of salts and water. His application of electricity to the decomposition of molten caustic potash resulted in the isolation of metallic potassium in 1807. The same technique also resulted in the discovery of sodium in the same year. This was followed by the electrolytic preparation of amalgams of the alkaline earths from which he isolated the elements magnesium, calcium, strontium and barium. These discoveries supported his hypothesis concerning the electrical nature of chemical combination. Experiments with chlorine, which was believed to be the oxide of the muriatic radical, convinced him that this gas was an element and contained no oxygen. He gave it its present name.

In the field of applied science, Davy is best known for his development of the miner's safety lamp or Davy lamp which he did not patent but donated for free use by the mining industry. In this invention, the flame from the wick of an oil lamp was surrounded by a cylinder of wire gauze and could be used safely in an explosive atmosphere. Davy also found that the copper sheathing employed on ship bottoms at that time could be protected from corrosion by the use of small pieces of zinc. However, the invention was not successful, since the electrolytically protected metal was soon covered with seaweed and barnacles.

Davy's recognition of Michael Faraday, whom he hired as an assistant, also represents one of his valuable contributions to the advancement of science.

A silver dinner service donated to Davy by the Newcastle mining industry was used in accordance with his will to found a medal after his death. This Davy medal was awarded annually for the outstanding discovery in chemistry.

In addition to his chemical accomplishments Davy was recognized by his contemporaries as an amateur poet. Both Coleridge and Southey testify to his ability in this avocation.

J. Frederic Walker

DEBYE EQUATION. See DIPOLE MOMENT.

DEBYE-HÜCKEL EQUATION. See ACTIVITY AND ACTIVITY COEFFICIENT.

DEMINERALIZATION BY ELECTRODIALYSIS

Demineralization by electrodialysis is a process for removing dissolved low molecular weight electrolytes from aqueous or nonaqueous solutions in which they occur. The process has been chiefly applied to the production of potable water from brackish or other mineralized waters, although the literature contains descriptions of successful application to the removal of electrolytes from solutions containing nonelectrolytes and/or colloids. The process is one application of electrodialysis with ion selective membranes which is discussed elsewhere in the encyclopedia. (See, for example, **Electrodialysis, Ion Exchange Membranes,** and **Ion Transport Across Charged Membranes.**)

Although the concept of electrodialysis in multicompartment apparatus using ion selective membranes was first described by Meyer and Strauss in 1940,[1] commercial applications awaited the development of mechanically-robust, low-resistance ion selective membranes. The latter were announced in 1950 by Juda and McRae[2] and by Kressman.[3] Since that time several hundred publications have appeared relating to demineralization by electrodialysis and to the preparation of ion selective membranes therefor. A recent monograph edited by Wilson[4] is devoted entirely to demineralization by electrodialysis and is recommended to those who wish both a broader and deeper understanding of this field than it is possible to present here. The reader is cautioned that important advances will undoubtedly appear in the next few years in this rapidly expanding field. The rapidity of this expansion may be illustrated by noting that since 1952 when demineralization by electrodialysis with ion selective membranes was announced,[5] over 150 plants have been installed using this process. The locations and characteristics of some of these plants are listed in Table 1.

The milestones in the field are:

(a) In 1959[6] the installation and start-up at Coalinga, California, of the first municipal demineralization plant in the United States;

(b) In 1959[4] the installation and start-up of the 125,000 gallon per hour Free State Geduld demonstration plant by the Council for Scientific and Industrial Research and associated mining companies of the Union of South Africa. This was the first electrodialysis plant having a capacity in excess of 1 million gallons per day;

(c) In 1962[7] the installation and start-up of the 650,000 gallons per day Buckeye, Arizona, plant by the City of Buckeye, Arizona. This plant is the first to demineralize the entire water supply of any municipality in the world by any process and the first demineralization plant in the United States to be financed by a long-term municipal bond issue approved in an election by qualified voters. The plans and specifications were prepared by John A. Carollo, Consulting Engineers. The design and engineering were performed by Ionics, Incorporated. The plant was constructed by N. P. Van Valkenburgh Construction Company; and

(d) In 1962[8] the installation and start-up of full scale plants for the demineralization of whey by electrodialysis with ion selective membranes. The plants were a joint project of Wyeth Laboratories, Incorporated; Foremost Dairies, Incorporated; and Ionics, Incorporated. These plants are believed to be the forerunners of many future plants demineralizing solutions other than saline water.

Ion selective membranes are thin plastic sheets of either cation or anion exchange resins and respectively selective to the migration of cations and anions. Transport numbers for cations in a cation selective membrane and anions in an anion selective membrane approach unity; in addition, each type of membrane can exhibit some selectivity for different ions of like charge. Other important properties of such synthetic membranes are their high electrical conductivity and low permeability to the passage of water.

Fig. 1 is a schematic diagram of the configuration of a multiple-compartment membrane cell stack of the type used in demineralization by electrodialysis. For illustration purposes, the demineralization of an aqueous solution of sodium chloride is presented. Electrodialysis stacks for this type of application generally consist of a large number of alternating anion and cation selective membranes separated from each other by electrically resistive gaskets, or spacers. These spacers have a central area cut out to permit solution and current to flow between the membranes. At each end of the stack are located electrodes connected to a source of direct current. Two inlet streams and two outlet streams are manifolded to the alternate compartments, or cells, formed by each pair of membranes and the separating gaskets.

When the flows are started and the current is applied to the stack, the cations (represented in Fig. 1 by Na^+) in all cells migrate toward the cathode, and the anions (represented by Cl^-) migrate toward the anode. In a diluting cell, the cations move out of the process stream through the cation membrane into the adjacent concentrating cell, and the anions migrate in the opposite direction through the anion selective membrane into the other adjacent concentrating cell. Because of the high ion selectivity of the membranes, ions are restrained from migrating from concentrating cells; in a concentrating cell

TABLE 1. LOCATION AND CHARACTERISTICS OF SOME SALINE WATER ELECTRODIALYSIS PLANTS.

	Date of Start Up	Feedwater parts per million	Product Capacity Gal/Day
Municipal			
Coalinga, California, U.S.A.	2/59	2,400	28,000
Zarzis, Tunisia	3/61	6,300	6,600
Buckeye, Arizona, U.S.A.	9/62	2,200	650,000
State of Kuwait, Arabian Gulf	4/63	4,000	240,000
Oil Drilling and Exploration			
Libya Shell, N.V., Libya	8/59	4,000	5,000
Cam Drill International, Inc., Libya[1]	11/59	17,100	1,600
Santa Fe Drilling Co., Libya[2]	6/60	1,700	6,000
AGIP Mineraria, Libya[3]	10/61	5,300	10,000
Sonpetrol, Spanish Sahara	1/62	varies[5]	varies[5]
C. Deilmann Bergbau G.m.b.H., Spanish Sahara	1/62	5,000	6,000
Petroleum Services Libya, Inc.[3]	5/63	varies[5]	varies[5]
Oil Production and Refining			
Bahrain Petroleum Co., Ltd., Bahrain, Arabian Gulf	6/55	3,150	86,400
Oasis Oil Company, Libya[4]	8/59	varies[5]	varies[5]
Getty Oil Company, Kuwait	12/59	3,000	15,000
Arabian American Oil Co., Dhahran, Saudi Arabia	8/61	2,700	115,000
Esso Libya, Libya[3]	10/61	3,780	4,000
National Iranian Oil Company, Iran	5/62	2,900	12,000
Sinclair Oil Company, Algeria	2/64	2,200	5,000
Trapsa, Tunisia	2/64	3,000	20,000
Military			
Government of U.A.R. (Egypt)[6]	6/56	varies[5]	varies[5]
U.S. Air Force, Havre, Montana, U.S.A.[7]	7/56	1,800	14,000
French Army, Southern Algeria	11/58	2,300	15,000
U.S. Air Force, Gettysburg, South Dakota, U.S.A.	4/59	2,300	40,000
U.S. Air Force, Hanna City, Illinois, U.S.A.	3/60	1,700	70,000
Royal Air Force, El Adem, Libya[8]	6/60	3,980	10,000
U.S. Air Force, Ellsworth, South Dakota, U.S.A.[9]	7/61	2,100	86,000
U.S. Air Force, Roswell, New Mexico, U.S.A.[10]	7/61	5,010	65,000
U.S. Air Force, Fortuna, North Dakota, U.S.A.	7/61	2,088	44,500
U.S. Navy Bureau of Yards and Docks, Subic Bay, Philippines	2/62	2,200	6,000

[1] Two additional plants in use in Libya and one in the Spanish Sahara.
[2] Three additional plants in use in Libya.
[3] Second identical plant in Libya.
[4] Six additional plants in use in Libya.
[5] Indicates portable unit where water data vary considerably.
[6] Additional portable unit delivered in 1958.
[7] Second unit with four times the capacity of the first installed in 1960.
[8] Royal Air Force is operating two additional units in Libya and four in Bahrain.
[9] Two additional plants in operation.
[10] Five additional plants installed in July of 1961.

cations are restricted from migration toward the cathode by an anion selective membrane, and anions are restricted by a cation selective membrane. In effect, the current passing through the cation selective membrane is carried principally by cations and through an anion selective membrane, principally by anions. The "membrane" current efficiency for a given ion can be considered as that fraction of the total current flowing through a membrane which is carried by the named ion. The composite result of these ion transfers is that the process stream in the diluting cells is demineralized and the transfer stream in the concentrating cells becomes enriched in electrolyte.

In the electrode compartments, electrode reactions take place
at the anode:

$$\tfrac{1}{2}H_2O \rightarrow H^+ + \tfrac{1}{4}O_2(g) + e^-$$

and/or

$$Cl^- \rightarrow \tfrac{1}{2}Cl_2(g) + e^-$$

at the cathode:

$$H_2O + e^- \rightarrow OH^- + \tfrac{1}{2}H_2(g)$$

In addition to the migration of the ions, some water or other electrolytic solvent is transferred from the diluting cells into the concentrating cells. The ratio of the chemical equivalents of

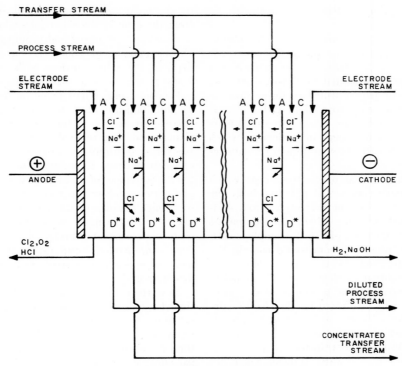

FIG. 1. Demineralization by electrodialysis.

A = anion selective membrane
C = cation selective membrane
Cl⁻ = anion
Na⁺ = cation
D* = diluting cell
C* = concentrating cell

electrolyte transferred to the volume of solution transferred expressed as equivalents per liter is generally greater than the concentration, in the same units, of the solution from which transfer is taking place. Published data on various ion selective membranes indicate that the transfer of some common uni-, di-, and trivalent ions is accompanied by 0.1 to 0.3 liter of water per equivalent of salt transferred varying slightly with the ion, the concentration, and the nature of the membrane studied.

Depending on the solutions being considered for processing, either or both of the diluting and concentrating features of the membrane configuration of Fig. 1 may be desired. The system may be employed to (a) remove an undesirable electrolyte from a solution, so that the liquid remaining in the process stream may be utilized, (b) remove valuable constituents from a solution to facilitate recovery from the transfer stream, and (c) effect the concentration of an electrolyte or nonelectrolyte.

Whereas many chemical solutions are valued in terms of units of cents per gallon, potable water is valued in terms of units of cents per thousand gallons. To operate at low electrical energy costs, membranes of high electrical conductivity must be employed; the current efficiency over the range of concentrations to be encountered must be high; and water transfer should be low to avoid loss of feed and partially demineralized water. The membranes must be either very inexpensive or else chemically and physically rugged so that replacement costs will be low. Initial investment per unit of demineralizing capacity must also be low.

Other potential uses of the dilution function of electrodialysis include the treatment of waste streams for the removal of valuable or polluting constituents prior to disposal or reuse of the waste streams.

The ability of membrane systems to concentrate electrolytes depends on the high normality of the electrolyte transfer; for example, sea water can be concentrated to 20 to 25 per cent by weight to prepare a brine feed for electrolytic caustic-chlorine cells provided that the brine is treated to remove those sea water constituents (for example, magnesium and calcium) which would interfere with the operation of the caustic-chlorine cells.

Another application of electrodialysis which has considerable commercial potential is in the separation or removal of electrolytes from solutions of nonelectrolytes. Membrane equipment using the configuration of Fig. 1 is employed. In this case the process stream would contain the nonelectrolyte, such as glycerine, sucrose, or gelatin, in addition to electrolyte. The nonelectrolyte material in the process stream passes through the cells unaffected by the electric current, and the salts go, as indicated in Fig. 1, into a transfer stream for recovery or disposal. The usual feed to the transfer stream is mill water. Because of the water transfer which accompanies electrolyte transfer, the concentration of nonelectrolyte is usually greater in the product stream than in the feed stream. In all applications of this type investigated to date, this concentration effect has been of some economic benefit by decreasing subsequent demand for evaporation. Indeed, commercial applications are known in which the electrodialysis is carried out for the sole purpose of concentrating a heat-sensitive nonelectrolyte or colloid. In this case it may even be desirable to add substantial amounts of salt to the feed stream to increase the concentration effect. Some loss of low molecular weight nonelectrolyte may also occur with the water being transferred, but in general this can be reduced to practical levels by utilizing special membranes.

A pilot plant program investigating the application of demineralization by electrodialysis to the treatment of sugar-mill and refinery liquors is now underway in Maui, Hawaii.[9] The pilot plant has a demineralization capacity for approximately 450 gallons per hour of evaporator syrup. Dissolved salts, principally potassium chloride, are removed from the evaporator syrup prior to crystallization, permitting a greater recovery of raw sugar and decreased production of molasses. The salts picked up from the soil

by the sugar cane during growth are extracted from the cane in the sugar juice along with the sucrose in the crushing and grinding operations. During subsequent concentration and crystallization, the salts interfere with the complete recovery of sucrose as acceptable raw sugar.

Economic projections based on data obtained to date indicate that costs for the membrane process are less than for conventional ion exchange and that the value of the extra sugar recovered substantially exceeds the total cost of electrodialysis. Evaluations have been made for the treatment of mill juice, evaporator syrup, and various molasses; syrup is generally favored over juice because of the higher electrical conductivity of the more concentrated syrup. For economic reasons it is preferable to remove salts from concentrated syrup rather than from the molasses which results from syrup which is not demineralized.

As in the case of ion exchange, long-term continued exposure to raw cane sugar juice or syrup or to molasses may result in decreased effectiveness of the anion selective membranes through absorption of color bodies. The principal effect is an increase in electrical resistance and, hence, in power consumption. Such decrements in performance have been found to be reversible and may be avoided by the proper choice of membranes and operating conditions.

Other applications for the ion selective membranes in the separation of electrolytes from nonelectrolytes include as examples: (a) the removal of sulfuric or hydrochloric acids or their salts from the solutions encountered in the production of dextrose by hydrolysis of starch, (b) demineralization of gelatins produced in the hydrolysis of animal substances by acids and bases, (c) removal of salts from glycerin waters. Laboratory and field data on all of these processes have shown favorable economics compared to alternative processes.

Since electrodialysis depends on the current-carrying ability of the electrolytes in solution, strong and weak electrolytes can also be separated. By proper selection of operating conditions, such as pH, separations approaching those between electrolytes and nonelectrolytes are possible. Electrodialysis has been employed for the separation of acetic acid from sulfuric and hydrochloric acids and for the separation of organic acids from each other.[10] Similarly, aconitic acid has been recovered from blackstrap molasses.

Mixtures of amphoteric materials, such as amino acids resulting from protein hydrolysis, can be fractionated by use of ion selective membranes and adjustment of pH. As the pH is lowered, various amino acids successively become cationic and transfer through cation permeable membranes. Stage-by-stage modification of pH and passage through a membrane electrodialysis unit have been used to separate desired amino acids from a crude mixture.

A thorough discussion of the economics, design, and operation of electrodialysis equipment is beyond the scope of this article. The interested reader should refer to the publication by Mason and Kirkham[11] and the monograph by Wilson.[4] Approximate methods for estimating the membrane area required and the energy consumption involved are discussed under **Electrodialysis.**

Other factors which must also be considered in a complete evaluation are: (a) the extent and the effect of water transfer; (b) the quantity of water (or solution) required for the concentrating stream; (c) the life of the membranes and electrodes; (d) the consumption of any chemicals used to maintain operation—for example, acid is frequently added to the electrode stream to prevent precipitation of basic salts in the cathode compartments; (e) operating and maintenance labor; (f) energy requirements for pumping; and (g) flow sheets from which piping, instrumentation, and space requirements may be determined. Generalized relationships have been developed by electrodialysis equipment manufacturers who have been cooperative in preparing detailed estimates. Reliable estimation of some factors, such as membrane life, must be based on experience obtained under at least approximately equivalent operating conditions and is best performed by the manufacturers.

References

1. MEYER, K. H., AND STRAUSS, W., *Helv. chim. acta,* **23,** 795 (1940).
2. JUDA, W., AND MCRAE, W. A., *J. Am. Chem. Soc.,* **72,** 1044 (1950).
3. KRESSMAN, T. R. E., *Nature, London,* **165,** 568 (1950).
4. WILSON, J. R., "Demineralization by Electrodialysis," London, Butterworths Publications, Limited, 1960.
5. (a) *Chem. Eng. News,* **30,** 898, 900 (1952).
   (b) *Chem. Eng.,* **59,** No. 3, 102, 106 (1952).
   (c) HOWE, E. D., *J. Am. Water Works Assoc.,* **44,** 690 (1952).
   (d) LANGELIER, W. F., *J. Am. Water Works Assoc.,* **44,** 845 (1952).
6. CARY, E. S., ONGERTH, H. J., AND PHELPS, R. O., *J. Am. Water Works Assoc.,* **52,** 585 (1960).
7. KIRKHAM, T. A., paper presented before the Division of Water and Waste Chemistry, American Chemical Society, Los Angeles, California, April 4, 1963.
8. *Chem. Eng. News,* **40,** No. 41, 44 (1962).
9. PAYNE, J. H., SLOANE, G. E., HAINES, W. S., AND OGASAWARA, E., paper presented to the Division of Carbohydrate Chemistry, American Chemical Society Meeting, April 7–12, 1957.
10. LIGHTFOOT, E. N., and FRIEDMAN, I. J., *Ind. Eng. Chem.,* **46,** 1579 (1954).
11. MASON, E. A., AND KIRKHAM, T. A., *Chemical Engineering Progress Symposium Series,* **55,** No. 24, 173 (1959).

WAYNE A. McRAE

Cross-references: *Electrodialysis; Electrodialysis Applications; Ion Exchange Membranes; Membranes, Electrolytic.*

DEMINERALIZATION OF WATER, DIRECT ELECTROCHEMICAL

The approach to water demineralization with pairs of cation- and anion-responsive electrodes has been under laboratory development since 1957. Calculations indicate that it will be economically competitive with the best methods now available for desalting brackish water.

Cation-responsive electrodes are defined as those which as cathodes take up cations, while anion-responsive electrodes are those which as anodes take up anions. The pair of electrodes, therefore, constitutes a demineralization apparatus. Systems in which such electrodes are employed are reversible, so that in a second phase of a demineralization-regeneration cycle cations and anions are given to a reject solution from the respective electrodes upon reversal of polarity. Electrode pair voltages in this process are typically 0.5 volt, well below the decomposition voltage of water.

Carbon in the form of finely-divided graphite, charcoal, or carbon black, is cation-responsive. The electrochemical capacity of some of these materials is about the same as that of a good synthetic ion-exchange resin. The mechanism of ion-responsive behavior is complex, involving both physical and chemical factors, but interpretations thus far have been in terms of electrochemical half-cell reactions. The surface of the carbon is acidic due to the partially-oxidized surface. Among others, hydroquinone-quinone groups are known to be present in considerable abundance on the surface. Based on these groups alone, a satisfactory explanation of cation-responsive behavior can be represented by the following half-cell reaction:

$$\diagdown C=O + Na^+ + e \rightarrow \diagdown C-O^- Na^+.$$

The structure represented is that at the edge of a graphite lattice. In this and the following discussion the salinity is presumed to be entirely sodium chloride.

In the reduced state, the surface of the carbon thus carries a negative charge and is a cation exchanger. The carbon can therefore be regarded as a cation exchanger whose capacity depends on the state of oxidation. Demineralization systems based on such electrode pairs are equivalent in function to electrically-regenerable ion exchange bed systems.

In the preparation of an electrode, the treated finely-divided carbon is dispersed as a thick colloidal mud. Tannic acid has been used for cation-responsive electrodes, and quaternary nitrogen polyelectrolytes, such as quaternized polyvinylimidazole, for anion-responsive electrodes. The dispersion is then impregnated onto a fibrous backing material, commonly polyester felt or paper. Drying of the electrode, followed by oven heating at 110°C, coagulates the colloid, thus producing a coherent electrode.

The use of quaternary nitrogen polyelectrolytes as dispersants almost invariably converts a cation-responsive electrode material into an anion-responsive material, a fact that suggests a model of anion-responsive behavior. The polyelectrolyte could form a closely-fitting film around the normally cation-responsive particle, with positive nitrogens tending to neutralize negative sites, thus displacing the mobile cations that would normally be present. If the hydroquinone-quinone model of cation-responsive behavior is correct, then upon oxidation the transition from hydroquinone to quinone would have to be balanced electrically by the uptake of anions.

Another model of anion-responsive behavior has been proposed for carbons containing nitrogen in the surface structure. Many samples of such carbons have been prepared by chemical treatment of normally cation-responsive carbons. A prototype half-cell reaction for such a carbon is

$$\diagdown C-NR_2 + Cl^- \rightarrow \diagdown C=\overset{+}{N}R_2Cl^- + e.$$

Since such carbons have to be dispersed with quaternary nitrogen polyelectrolytes, which by themselves impart the anion-responsive function, it has not been possible to verify the above model independently.

The electrode arrangement of a demineralization cell can be designed in two ways, parallel or series. In any case, insulating porous spacers lie between individual electrodes, and solution flows parallel to them. Maximum electrical efficiency results from the closest possible electrode spacing consistent with mechanical and hydrodynamic requirements. Typically the spacing is 0.020 inch. In the parallel arrangement, there are many alternating pairs of cation- and anion-responsive electrodes connected in electrical parallel. Such an arrangement requires a large amount of current at very low voltage. The series principle can be adopted if a cation- and anion-responsive pair is laminated together with a conductive, but water-impervious, film. Such a film can be made by loading large amounts of conductive carbon into polymers like polyethylene or rubber. The resulting electrode can be referred to as a bipolar electrode or CA laminate. Stacking of many such bipolar electrodes in a cell permits operation at relatively low current (the same current goes through each laminate), and at a cell voltage determined by multiplying the individual pair voltage by the number of pairs.

Basic factors that determine the economic promise of the process are the low cost of materials—carbon at a few cents per pound—and the simplicity of construction and maintenance of demineralization units.

References

1. USDI Office of Saline Water Research and Development Progress Reports No. 45 PB 171129 (Sept. 1960); and No. 58, PB 181142 (March 1962). For sale by the U.S. Department of Commerce, Office of Technical Services, Washington 25, D.C.

2. Blair, J. W., and Murphy, G. W., "American Chemical Society Advances in Chemistry Series," No. 27, p. 206, 1960.
3. Arnold, B. B., and Murphy, G. W., *J. Phys. Chem.*, **65**, 135 (1961).
4. Murphy, G. W., Smith, F. W., Blair, J. W., and Satler, A., Dechema Monographien, Band 47, pp. 639–672, Verlag Chemie, G.M.B.H., Weinheim/Bergstrasse, W. Germany, 1962.
Cross-references: *Carbon and Graphite Electrolytic Electrodes; Ion Exchange Resins.*

GEORGE W. MURPHY

DEUTERIUM, DEUTERIUM OXIDE. See HEAVY WATER-ELECTROLYTIC PRODUCTION.

DEZINCIFICATION

Dezincification is the selective solution of zinc from copper-zinc alloys (brasses) and is readily recognizable by the copper-colored appearance of the corroded metal. This is well-known in yellow brasses and modifications thereof which contain less than about 80 per cent copper. Those containing more copper are relatively immune to this type of attack. There is considerable evidence indicating that the copper may be residual or redeposited. In the former process, the zinc atoms are leached directly from the crystal lattice leaving the copper atoms essentially in their original position while in the latter process, the copper and zinc go into solution together in the presence of an electrolyte and the copper is immediately redeposited in the form of a porous mass or layer having poor mechanical strength. The most usual form involves re-

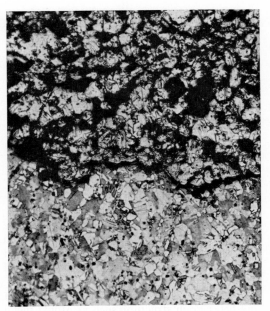

Fig. 2. Microstructure of dezincified leaded yellow brass of Fig. 1. Uncorroded brass is at bottom while the dezincified area is at the top. 50×.

deposition of the copper. The zinc constituent may be carried away as a soluble salt or deposited in place as an insoluble compound.

The attack may occur in highly localized areas in the form of a plug or local type of dezincification (Figs. 1 and 2). The plugs of dezincified material are generally held in place and permit only slight seepage. If the section of brass is bent, the porous plugs of copper will pop out leaving hemispherical pits. Frequently, the site of plugs is readily located through the brownish-white zinc-rich salts which form directly over the areas where dezincification has occurred. When dezincification proceeds by formation of a more or less uniform layer of copper, it is known as uniform or layer type of dezincification. (Fig. 3). On occasion, layer type dezincification may result from a merging together of a large number of small plugs.

Plug type dezincification generally occurs in neutral, alkaline, or slightly acidic environments and seems to be prevalent in alloys of low zinc content, such as cartridge brass, 70 per cent (70 per cent copper, 30 per cent zinc). Uniform or layer type dezincification is more apt to take place in strongly acidic media and favors the higher zinc brasses, such as Muntz metal (60 per cent copper, 40 per cent zinc).

In addition to local or uniform dezincification,

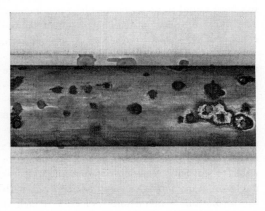

Fig. 1. Section of a leaded yellow brass water pipe showing plug type dezincification on inner wall. 0.7×.

FIG. 3. Section of a Muntz metal plumbing pipe which has suffered uniform dezincification on inside surface. 0.7×.

FIG. 4. Microstructure of dezincified Muntz metal of Fig. 3. Uncorroded brass, alpha and beta phases, at bottom. Dezincified area is dark. Light alpha grains in dezincified area show how the beta grains are dezincified before the alpha grains. 50×.

the attack may occur preferentially along the grain boundaries. This may weaken the metal because of brittleness of the copper deposit and poor adhesion to the surface of the grains of brass.

Copper-zinc alloys having a two phase (alpha and beta) grain structure, such as Muntz metal or Naval brasses which contain about 60 per cent copper and between 39 and 40 per cent zinc often dezincify in two stages. Since the beta phase may contain as much as 40 per cent zinc and 60 per cent copper while the alpha phase may contain as little as 35 per cent zinc and 65 per cent copper, the zinc-rich (beta) areas are attacked first. (Fig. 4). As the corrosion proceeds, the alpha grains are attacked. If under severe conditions the attack spreads to both the alpha and beta phases, complete dezincification may result with the formation of a layer of porous copper which sometimes can be peeled or pulled from the surface of brass, leaving an irregular surface.

Dezincification is ordinarily encountered in stagnant aqueous solutions or slowly moving solutions because the chances are better for the formation of scale or settling out of foreign matter from the solution. The rate of corrosion underneath such deposits is usually accelerated from concentration cell attack or from the increase in temperature caused by the insulating effect of the deposit or both. It occurs frequently in non-scale forming fresh or salt waters with the pH ranging from 5.0 to 8.0 or higher. The rate of attack is generally increased with increasing temperature, and there is a tendency for plug-type dezincification rather than uniform dezincification.

Dezincification may be retarded by mechanical cleaning, chemical cleaning, keeping the tem-

perature relatively low, and by increasing the water velocity. The latter prevents deposits from attaching themselves to the metal surface and setting up concentration cells.

Copper-zinc alloys containing more than about 80 per cent copper are highly resistant to selective solution. The addition of tin to brasses effects a slight improvement in resistance to dezincification while the addition of very small amounts (0.02–0.05 per cent) of antimony, arsenic, or phosphorus greatly reduces the tendency of alpha brasses to dezincification. The latter elements are not particularly effective in inhibiting dezincification of the beta constituent in alpha-beta brasses.

The mechanism of the protective action imparted by antimony, arsenic, or phosphorus has been found to be a surface film phenomenon. The inhibitors have no significant effect on the resistance of brasses to other types of corrosion.

Selective solution is not confined to copper-zinc alloys. It has been found on occasion to take place in other copper-base alloys, such as de-aluminumization in copper-aluminum alloys, de-cuprification in copper-silver alloys and in copper-gold alloys, demanganization in copper-manganese alloys, denickelification in copper-nickel alloys, etc. In each instance, the more noble or cathodic element remains and the less noble or more active element is dissolved with the formation of metal ions. Selective attack is also encountered in alloys other than copper-base alloys, for example, graphitization of cast iron, selective solution of silver in gold-silver alloys and of tin in lead-tin solders.

References

1. BENGOUGH, G. D., AND MAY, R., *J. Inst. Metals,* **32,** 181 (1924).
2. MITCHELL, N. W., *Oil Gas J.,* p. 43 (Oct. 29, 1936).
3. ROATH, E. W., U.S. Patent 2,061,921 (Nov. 24, 1936).
4. FINK, F. W., *Trans. Electrochem. Soc.,* **75,** 441 (1939).
5. HOLLOMON, J. H., AND WULFF, J., *Trans., Am. Inst. Mining Met. Eng.,* **143,** 93 (1941); **147,** 183 (1942).
6. POLUSHKIN, E. P., AND SCHULDENER, H. L., *Metal Tech.,* AIME Tech. Publ. No. 1742, Oct. 1944; *Corrosion,* **2,** 1 (1946).
7. BURGHOFF, H. L., "Corrosion of Metals," Cleveland, American Society for Metals, 1946.
8. COLEGATE, G. T., *Metal Ind.,* Dec. 17, 24 and 31, 1948.
9. KENWORTHY, L., AND O'DRISCOLL, W. G., *Corrosion Tech.,* p. 241 (Aug., 1955).

VITO F. NOLE

Cross-references: *Concentration Cells;* entries bearing *Corrosion* titles.

DIALDEHYDE STARCH PREPARATION

For a number of years, the structure of starch has been investigated by reacting it with the very specific oxidant periodic acid. The reaction is quantitative at 32°F. Analytical methods are available for following the reaction closely. Jackson and Hudson[5] established that the oxidation of starch by periodate results in cleavage of the anhydroglucose units between carbon atoms 3 and 4 and in the production of a mole of iodic acid per mole of periodic acid consumed. The change in structure is shown in Fig. 1. The polymeric aldehydes thus produced are known as dialdehyde starches.

Because of its unique functional structure, dialdehyde starch was first evaluated as a tanning agent; subsequently it was employed to impart high wet strength to paper, as an adhesive for plywood, and as a hardener for gelatin. These industrial applications made it apparent that a process for its production and recovery was needed that would be more economical than the existing laboratory methods employed only to elucidate the structure of the starch molecule. For an industrial process to be economical, the dialdehyde starch product should be in a dry form, and the expensive oxidant should be recoverable.

Starch exists in nature in the form of small granules packed within the original kernel or berry, and most processes for separating and purifying it do not disturb this granular integrity. Jackson and Hudson[5] found that when granular starch was mixed with a solution of periodic acid, the starch within the granule could be oxidized with no apparent change in the granule. The granular oxidized starch could be separated easily from the oxidant liquors by filtration and purified by subsequent washing.

Mehltretter *et al*[10] combined the oxidation of granular starch with an electrolytic method for converting the iodate produced to the periodate, both processes occurring in the same container. They thus achieved a pseudo-electrochemical oxidation of granular starch with iodic acid in a catalytic role. Conway and Sohns,[3] working with an extension of the basic Mehltretter cell in the in-cell process, successfully produced several thousand pounds of dialdehyde starch for product evaluation purposes.

The principal difficulty in the original in-cell process was in providing sufficient agitation to prevent the starch granules from either coming in contact with a zone of high alkalinity surrounding the diaphragms or being damaged otherwise by high temperatures and long exposure times without oxidation. To overcome the difficulties and to simplify the process, Pfeifer *et al*[12] developed an alternative two-stage process in which only the periodate was produced in the electrolytic cell, by a modification of the method of Mehltretter.[9, 11]

In the original in-cell process the oxygen was made available at a linear rate in time, and high starch concentrations were employed relative to the amount of oxidant that could be made available. Reducing the starch concentration in the cell improved the agitation and reduced the time, so that the probability of contact with alkali decreased. Even when a hydrodynamically unsound cell was used, successful oxidations were accomplished. Increasing the iodate content of the anolyte shortened the reaction time by providing more oxidant during the diffusional reaction.

To shorten the time of reaction without decreasing the starch concentration and reducing efficiency meant that the free volume of the cell had to be small relative to the anode area. To accomplish this a cell was constructed with

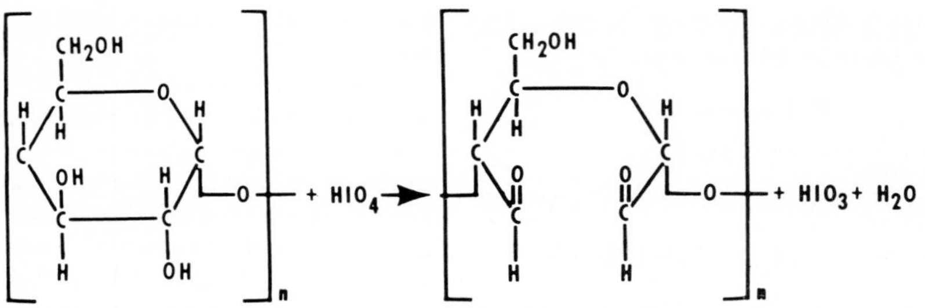

Fig. 1. Preparation of dialdehyde starch by reacting starch and periodic acid.

TABLE 1. COMPARISON OF METHODS FOR OXIDIZING STARCH

Method	Reaction Mixture Composition, lb/gal electrolyte		Current, amp/mole starch	Anode Area, sq dm/mole starch	Reaction Time, hr
	Starch	Iodate as HIO_3			
In-cell, original pilot-plant cell design[3]	3.15	0.33	2.0	0.83	48
In-cell, highly baffled pilot-plant cell, low starch conc.[2]	1.27	0.33	3.7	1.53	23
In-cell, pilot-plant annular cell[2]	2.14	0.54	11.7	7.10	6
Two-stage process[12]	0.50	0.59	25.6*	10.7*	3

* The anode area and current are adjusted to estimate re-oxidation of iodate at the starch oxidation rate.

a small distance between the anode and diaphragm, and the cell contents were agitated in this space. With a cell employing ceramic thimbles, a convenient method is to make the anode cylindrical and concentric with the diaphragm and to agitate by circulating the contents through a low-volume pump. Dialdehyde starch was produced in a small cell of this type in 6 hr at an unusually high overall current efficiency. An unexpected result was that the close spacing in this cell promoted much better efficiencies in converting iodate to periodate.[2, 6, 7]

In the in-cell process, starch is mixed with iodic acid (approximately 25 per cent suspension in a solution containing 7 to 8 g/100 ml iodic acid, equal to 0.1 mole equivalent HIO_3/mole of starch). This suspension is then placed in the cell and the electrolysis started. During electrolysis some of the iodate is converted to periodate which in turn oxidizes some of the starch and is reduced to iodate. After the starch

is 25 to 50 per cent oxidized, periodate gradually accumulates since it is being generated at a rate greater than it is being consumed. The rate of starch oxidation is diffusion controlled after the initial stage. Electrolysis is continued for approximately 48 hr to achieve 90 per cent conversion to dialdehyde starch.

In the two-stage process the oxidant is prepared by electrolytic oxidation of a solution containing 7 to 8 g/100 ml iodic acid. This oxidation is continued until the iodic acid is 80 to 95 per cent converted to periodic acid. After the periodic acid is prepared, it is withdrawn from the cell system to a mixing tank where the starch is added; the amount depends on the concentration and conversion of the oxidant solution equal to 1.2 mole HIO_4/mole starch. The starch concentration is approximately 4.5 per cent. The time required to reach 90 per cent conversion to dialdehyde starch is about 2 hr at a reaction temperature of 105°F.

Recovery of dialdehyde starch is the same for either the in-cell or two-stage method of oxidation. The starch and spent oxidant solution are separated by filtration. The spent oxidant is recycled either for reuse in the cell or for reoxidation to periodic acid. Most of the oxidant can be recovered easily by filtration* and almost all by concentrating the first 4 lb of wash water used for purification of the product. A total

* In the case of waxy starches, such as waxy corn and milo, and of potato starch, the granules swell excessively at the temperatures and acidities ordinarily employed. Although dialdehyde starch is formed efficiently from these starches, swelling prohibits use of high starch concentrations as in the in-cell process, and recovery is made almost impossible by conventional methods. Alcohol washing and filtration at low pressures and rates can be used to prepare experimental lots. Partially crosslinked potato starch behaves well. Wheat and high-amylose corn starch filter more slowly than ordinary corn starch because of their smaller granule size, but they do not swell.[1]

of 15 lb of wash water is required per pound of product. There is an economic balance between the cost of evaporation and the value of the iodate, however, so that the loss of iodate amounts to about 1 lb per 100 lb of product. More efficient recovery methods could reduce this loss. Because starch is a good adsorbent and releases the last traces of iodate reluctantly, probably no method would give perfect recovery.

In the following table, typical results of four methods of preparing dialydehyde starch are compared. The choice between oxidation methods depends on an assessment of convenience; control of the important variables; and relative costs of space, inventory, and fabrication. With starches, the difficulties to be overcome from using the in-cell production method are formidable, but the apparent cost of both processes is about the same. With a material like cellulose, which responds differently to the oxidation environment, both methods should be seriously considered.

References

1. CONWAY, H. F., AND LANCASTER, E. B., *Cereal Chem.* (1963) submitted.
2. CONWAY, H. F., AND LANCASTER, E. B., *Electrochem. Technol.* (1963) submitted.
3. CONWAY, H. F., AND SOHNS, V. E., *Ind. Eng. Chem.*, **51**, 637 (1959).
4. DVONCH, W., AND MEHLTRETTER, C. L., *J. Am. Chem. Soc.*, **74**, 5522 (1952).
5. JACKSON, E. L., AND HUDSON, C. S., *J. Am. Chem. Soc.*, **59**, 2049 (1937).
6. LANCASTER, E. B., AND CONWAY, H. F., *Electrochem. Technol.*, **1**, 253 (1963).
7. LANCASTER, E. B., CONWAY, H. F., AND WOHLRABE, F. C., to U. S. Secretary of Agriculture, U. S. Patent pending.
8. MEHLTRETTER, C. L., to U. S. Secretary of Agriculture, U. S. Patent 2,713,553 (July 19, 1955).
9. MEHLTRETTER, C. L. to U. S. Secretary of Agriculture, U. S. Patent 2,830,941 (April 15, 1958).
10. MEHLTRETTER, C. L., RANKIN, J. C., AND WATSON, P. R., *Ind. Eng. Chem.*, **49**, 350, (1957).
11. MEHLTRETTER, C. L., AND WISE, C. S., *Ind. Eng. Chem.*, **51**, 511 (1959).
12. PFEIFER, V. F., SOHNS, V. E., CONWAY, H. F., LANCASTER, E. B., DABIC, S., AND GRIFFIN, E. L., JR., *Ind. Eng. Chem.*, **52**, 637 (1960).
13. SLAGER, JAMES E., to Miles Laboratories, Inc., Elkhart, Ind., U. S. Patent 3,086,969 (April 23, 1963).

HOWARD F. CONWAY AND
EARL B. LANCASTER

Cross-reference: *Periodates, Electrolytic Preparation.*

DIAPHRAGM MEMBRANES. See ION EXCHANGE MEMBRANES; MEMBRANES, ELECTROLYTIC.

DIELECTRIC CHEMISTRY

The chemistry of dielectrics is concerned with the transformations which insulating materials undergo due to chemical, thermal, and electrical ambients. Insulating materials are substances which possess volume resistivities greater than 10,000 megohm-cm. The application of this science to the solution of practical problems in electrical engineering is called the science of electrical insulation; the employment of the principles for analytical purposes is called the science of dielectric spectroscopy.

Early studies on the chemistry of dielectrics were concerned with the development of high-voltage cables, capacitors, generators, motors, reactors, transformers, and other transmission equipment. For this reason, emphasis was placed on the effect of severe voltages on materials and on the relationships of conductivity, dielectric constant, and dielectric loss factor to chemical composition. This was followed by intensive studies of long-term aging of dielectrics under moderate temperature and electric field conditions because of the enormous growth of the telecommunications industry. Recently the increased interest in outer space exploration and the development of thermoplastic and cryogenic memory devices for computers have encouraged studies on the effect of severe thermal and chemical ambients on insulating materials.

The insulating materials used extensively in these applications have dielectric constants in the range 1–10, dielectric loss factors 0.0005–0.01, volume resistivities 10^{12}–10^{21} ohm-cm, surface resistivities 10^{10}–10^{19} ohm, electric strengths 100–8,000 volts per mil and arc resistances of 3–>280 seconds. Such characteristics are dependent upon the state and temperature of the substance and the frequency and intensity of the applied electric field.

The chemical properties of dielectrics may be discussed in terms of the changes which the materials undergo (1) because of their inherent composition, (2) because of the interaction with the electrodes with which they are in contact, and (3) because of the nature of the atmospheres in which they reside.

Of the hundreds of thousands of materials synthesized by chemists, only a small fraction fulfill the requirements of a dielectric and a still smaller fraction are capable of being insulants. This is because most materials are chemically unstable and deteriorate rapidly due to either internal changes or interaction with the atmosphere. Thus, organic materials oxidize readily, inorganics ionize easily, metals conduct electricity, and metal-organics undergo internal fragmentation. The exceptions constitute the dielectrics used in practice.

Among the organic compounds, therefore, the saturated rather than the unsaturated, the fluorinated rather than the iodinated, the high molecular weight rather than the low, the ester rather than the alcohol, in short, the items which have already become inert through a multitude of previous reactions are used extensively as insulants. Thus, mineral oil, "Teflon," polystyrene, and polyethylene terephthalate find extensive use, but not their monomers. In the field of the inorganics, the calcium and aluminum silicates as well as the Group II, III, and IV oxides rather than the phosphates, borates, or oxides of Group I serve as practical insulants. While many metals are not considered suitable as conductors, even the worst according to such a scale cannot be considered a dielectric. This is true of most of the metal-organics except for the widely used polymeric siloxanes.

Since the fundamental law of dielectrics for a chemist may be stated as: "a chemically reactive substance is electrically unstable under similar conditions," enormous effort has been expended by dedicated scientists in synthesizing compounds free of deleterious contaminants, developing stabilizers for other materials, and elucidating the exact conditions of transformation. This has led to the establishment of a vast literature on procedures for analyzing materials for such contaminants as chloride and sulfate ions, dissolved water and oxygen, and colloidal aggregates, and for identifying their concentrations in parts per million (0.001 per cent). It has also resulted in the development of a large number of additives, e.g., anthraquinone, which have extended the life of insulants in actual service by three to one hundredfold. Efforts to synthesize new and improved organic insulants have been successful and such complex materials as partially fluorinated diesters of 3-methyl glutaric acid have been developed possessing high dielectric constants, low dielectric loss factors, high electrical strengths, and long life even under extreme conditions.

Similar exertions on the part of scientists in the field of inorganic materials have resulted in the development of the barium titanates, glass-, quartz-, and ceramic-fiber papers, nonwoven fabrics and textiles, and pyroceram. The doping of metals with minute quantities of electron donors and acceptors, followed by the creation of junctions is a present concern of specialists, especially since the junction properties are affected importantly by the surface and its ambient. Finally, much work is in progress on the development of new metal-organic polymers and complexes; unfortunately, most of those reported at this time are seriously deteriorated by moisture.

Since the electrode and insulant in a practical system form an interface, the chemistry of each affects appreciably the stability of the other. Thus, the most minute change in the composition of the copper conductors in an oil-cooled transformer can change the life of the oil by fivefold. Similar effects have been observed on the embrittlement rate of phenolic varnishes, the development of chlorides in aluminum-pentachlorodiphenyl capacitors and the deterioration of electrolytic condensers. The failure mechanism involves the catalytic transformation of the material similar to classical Friedel-Crafts reactions. Obviously, the presence of traces of such contaminants as silicon and silver can reduce the rate of transformation (thereby increasing the life of the insulant) while others like phosphorus can increase the deterioration.

The atmosphere in which the dielectric resides plays a significant role in the stability and usefulness of an insulant. While sodium chloride single crystals maintained in moisture-free chambers have good dielectric properties, a trace of water converts the surface of such a crystal into a conductor. Since most materials are affected by water (160 ppm dissolve in mineral oil; esters hydrolyze and salts ionize in its presence) the chemistry of practical dielectrics involves the development of substances which resist moisture. Three solutions are used extensively and successfully: the generation of atomic linkages which are stable to aqueous attack, the synthesis of high molecular weight aggregates which are inherently inert because of their mass, and the generation of molecules having protective atomic configurations. Needless to say, similar approaches have been employed against atmospheres such as trichlorobenzene and freon.

Besides chemical atmospheres, the temperature plays an important part in both the functioning and life of an insulant. Obviously, the electrical properties as well as the mechanical and physical characteristics depend significantly on it. Because most materials become more reactive at elevated temperatures and because this enhanced reactivity usually results in an increase in the rate at which deleterious products form, the life of insulation is markedly dependent on temperature. Since many organic materials have been found to react twice as fast when the temperature is raised by only 10 degrees, much research has been concerned with developing substances with very low rates of reaction or ones which change into nonconductive and even more stable items. In general, the aromatic hydrocarbons, the fluorinated straight chains, and the polymeric amides and esters have proved satisfactory.

Thus far the chemistry of dielectrics presented here does not differ significantly from the chemistry of materials which are stable to different chemical and thermal ambients. Insulants, however, must also be stable to the passage of electrons; they must retain their dielectric properties even when subjected to the ionizing radiation which arises in intense electrical fields.

The electrical properties of dielectrics are distinguished as those exhibited by the chemicals at low fields, intense fields, and at rupture or breakdown. At low fields orientation and polarization of the molecule occurs and some deposition of ion masses occurs which results in a cleansing of the dielectric. At intense fields, electrons passing through the dielectric collide with others or at least perturb them; this results in the creation of more excited molecules than are usually present due to thermal agitation. As a consequence the life of a dielectric is reduced appreciably. It has been found empirically, that the life of many dielectrics is inversely proportional to the 5th power of the voltage. Slight overvoltages or surges can, therefore, reduce appreciably the life of an insulant. Much research has gone into this problem and additives, e.g., tin tetraphenyl are now employed to increase the life of highly stressed dielectrics.

The chemistry of dielectric failure, like the chemistry of most of the ultimate or rupture characteristics of matter is not known at this time, although much effort has been expended on the subject. Two approaches to the problem have been tried with limited success: in one case highly refined, select organic liquids have been subjected to rupture fields and the circuit response and product composition examined; in the other, single crystals have been subjected to post-rupture evaluation. The problem will probably not be solved until a deeper understanding of radiation chemistry is evolved.

Besides interest in the effect of electrons which pass through a dielectric, practical problems in printed circuits, panel boards and bus bar insulants have posed questions on the effect of electrons on the chemistry of insulating surfaces. This is referred to in electrical standards as the arc-resistance of a material. In general, aromatic materials have low arc-resistance, as do halogenated compounds, while oxygen constituted materials like cellulose and nitrogenous polymers like melamine-formaldehyde have high arc-resistance values. The inorganic oxides usually have arc-resistance values many times higher than those found for the organic dielectrics.

From this it can be seen that the chemistry of dielectrics is concerned with reactivities of materials of low conductivity under various conditions of chemical, thermal, and electrical ambients. As such it utilizes the subdisciplines of chemical kinetics, radiation chemistry and electrolytic chemistry as well as the more classical sections of organic and inorganic synthesis. Dielectric chemistry is therefore a "systems chemistry."

References

1. SMYTH, C. P., "Dielectric Behavior and Structure," New York, McGraw-Hill Book Co., Inc., 1955.
2. VON HIPPEL, A. R., "Dielectric Materials and Applications," New York, John Wiley & Sons, 1954.

THOMAS D. CALLINAN

DIELECTRIC CONSTANT

The force exerted by one unit of electric charge on another in any fixed medium varies inversely as the square of the distance between them. (See *Coulomb's Law*). However, if the medium itself is changed at a fixed distance of separation of the charges, the force involved is also altered by a factor which is a characteristic of each medium tested. The effect of substituting a liquid or solid medium in place of a gas or vacuum is to reduce the force existing between two unit electrical charges by a factor of $1/k$ of its previous value. This factor, $1/k$, enters into all considerations of electric charge transfer from one level of potential to another. The quantity, k, is known as the *dielectric constant*. It is usually expressed as the ratio of the capacitances of a given material and air or vacuum, each measured with a fixed electrode configuration and gap distance. The ratio value obtained is frequently affected by changes in the temperature of the measurement and the frequency of the voltage applied.

The dielectric constant of a material is a basic property reflecting its molecular configuration and composition. The various gases exhibit values only slightly higher than 1 (air = 1.000590 at 0°C) as compared to a vacuum. Nonpolar liquid and solid dielectric materials are characterized by values in the range below 2.5 (mineral oil = 2.0 to 2.2; polyethylene resin = 2.2). The dielectric constants of polar organic dielectric materials in common engineering use are most generally found in the range of values less than about 7 (pentachlorodiphenyl 5; phenolformaldehyde resin 6 to 6.5). Polar organic materials, such as nitrobenzene and glycerol, however, are characterized by substantially higher values. Inorganic bodies, such as those generally used in electrical power equipment, exhibit dielectric constant values in the range less than 10 (ceramics = 5 to 8; mica = 6 to 7; glass = 3 to 5) although much higher values characterize certain metal oxides (titanium oxide = 100) and their more complex salts (the titanates = 1200 and higher).

The high-dielectric constant materials, because of their polarity, are characterized by a greater solvency for the polar materials commonly encountered in industrial practice than are the nonpolar materials. Because of this, they present a greater problem in their engineering applications in electrical equipment. Impurities in polar products invariably result in higher electrical losses than when present in nonpolar media. The effects of changes in the conditions of equipment operation in service are also more severe when polar materials are used.

In electrical machine design, the dielectric constant plays an important role in determining the distribution of electric stress across composite dielectric assemblies. The electric stress absorbed by equal thicknesses of series-arranged insulations is inversely related to the dielectric constant of each material. When, as is common in electrical power equipment, the insulations in series consist of mineral oil and cellulose sheets or tapes, the mineral oil with its lower dielectric constant (2.2) absorbs more than twice as much stress than does the cellulose material (dielectric constant 5). When air (dielectric constant 1) is substituted for the mineral oil, as in air-operating devices, the concentration of the electric stress in the air layer is even greater than in the oil dielectric. Since the dielectric strength of the lower dielectric constant material in the cases cited (oil and air) is lower than that of the cellulosic solid, the hazard to the successful operation of such insulating assemblies is correspondingly increased. Because of the varying response of the dielectric constant of different materials to the effects of changes in temperature and voltage frequency, the distribution of the electric stress between dielectric materials arranged in series will vary depending on the exact conditions under which the composite assembly is operated in electrical equipment.

The ferroelectric materials are outstanding in their response to the effects of temperature and pressure. Such materials may exhibit dielectric constant values of several thousand. Barium metatitanate, for example, possesses a dielectric constant of approximately 9000 when tested at 40°C under normal pressure. Materials of this type show the saturation effects of dielectric flux density and are characterized by a critical temperature (Curie temperature) above which the nonlinearity of the dielectric constant-voltage relation disappears. The more important ferroelectric materials include the titanates of barium, lead and strontium, together with combinations of these.

The effect of temperature on the dielectric constant of a ferroelectric material varies with its composition. Thus, in barium titanate, when the ratio of the barium oxide to the titanium oxide is less than 1:5, the dielectric constant falls with an increase in the testing temperature; when the ratio is greater than 1:5, the dielectric constant increases with the testing temperature. The effect is most pronounced in the case of barium metatitanate ($2BaO:3TiO_2$).

The dielectric constant of the ferroelectric materials increases in a substantially linear relation to the hydrostatic pressure applied. In the case of barium titanate crystal, the electrical capacitance is increased equivalent to a 1.2×10^{-5} sq cm/kg increase in pressure over the range from 300–2000 atmospheres. The effect is reduced when calcium or lead atoms are introduced into the molecule.

FRANK M. CLARK

Cross-references: *Askarel; Ceramic Insulation;* entries with *Dielectric* titles; *Ferroelectricity; Organic Electrical Insulation.*

DIELECTRIC HEATING

Dielectric heating is the frictional heating of a nonconducting material through the use of a varying electrical field for inducing molecular motion in the material. It is applicable in several industries for such processes as cooking and sterilizing food, vulcanizing rubber, laminating wood, preheating thermosetting plastics, and for drying various materials. It is in general applicable only to materials that have a high dielectric constant.

Dielectric heating takes place when the material to be heated is placed between two conducting plates or electrodes to which an alternating voltage of high amplitude and high frequency is applied. The work and the electrodes act as a capacitor, and an alternating field is set up between the two electrodes. This alternating field passes uniformly through the work and displaces or stresses the molecules of the work first in one direction and then the other as the field alternates. The molecular motion in the work causes the generation of heat uniformly throughout the material.

There are several advantages to this type of heating. It permits the heating of nonconductive materials which are otherwise difficult to heat. Heating is faster since it is unnecessary to wait for the heat to penetrate from the outside surface to the core. It provides high accuracy of control with a resultant uniformity of process. It provides an improved product due to the uniform heating made possible.

There are certain features of this heating method that must be taken into consideration. First, because of heat radiation from the surface, the center of the work may be hotter than the outer layers. Corrective procedures can be taken for this condition when it becomes an im-

portant factor. Second, heating will not be uniform if the work material varies in density, composition, moisture content, or shape. In certain cases the nonuniformity of heating may be minor, or it may even be beneficial in certain drying cycles. In other cases, however, it can make dielectric heating unusable for a task where otherwise it appears attractive.

The power transmitted to the work can be expressed as a function of five factors of the work material or power source: voltage gradient, or volts per unit thickness of work between electrodes; frequency; dielectric constant; power factor; and volume.

It is desirable to use the highest voltage gradient that can be applied safely based on the dielectric strength of the work material. This is because power input varies as the square of the voltage applied. However, there are definite limits to the voltage level that can be applied, and often a much lower voltage level than the maximum safe value is used as a precautionary measure against voltage breakdown. This safety measure must be tempered by the need for sufficient power input. The use of a high-frequency source is required to obtain the necessary power input with a reasonable level of voltage gradient. The dielectric constant is a measure of the capacitive capability or, it may be called, the electrical storage capability of a material. The power factor is an indication of leakage current through the material that produces heat loss. For the imperfect capacitor represented by the electrodes and work, there is a component of current in-phase with the applied voltage. The power factor of the work material is a function of this current component. The product of the dielectric constant and power factor is called the loss factor. This single value is often used for simplifying computations.

Water has a dielectric constant of about 80 compared to other materials with values ranging from 1 to 12. Since power input is proportional to the dielectric constant of the material to be heated, dielectric heating provides an excellent means to drive water from various materials, or to heat materials that have a moisture content sufficient to assure rapid, efficient heating. Moisture content is the foundation for many uses of this heating method.

The high-frequency generator or oscillator must be properly matched to the load in order to obtain a reasonable and efficient transfer of power from the oscillator to the load. In one method of circuit design, the load becomes part of the oscillator circuit and makes up the greatest portion of the oscillator tuned-circuit capacitance. This permits the maintenance of a reasonably uniform power input level to the work, and load changes with temperature result mainly in frequency changes rather than in circuit detuning. A second method it to match the impedance of the load and leads to the impedance of the oscillator circuit, with the load tuned to resonance by means of an adjustable inductance. As the capacitance of the load varies during the heating cycle the total circuit will become detuned and the oscillator load changes. The circuit is carefully designed so that this variation remains within acceptable bounds.

To obtain uniform heating along the length of the electrode, it is absolutely necessary to prevent standing waves from arising. Otherwise, the potential along the electrode will vary over a wide range, approaching zero at the wave nodes. Uneven heating would result. For this reason, the electrode length should be limited to $\frac{1}{8}$ wave length if possible, or should be physically divided into two or more electrodes, with each electrode so limited in length. It is also possible to make the heating along the electrode more uniform by adding inductances (tuning stubs) to the electrodes to tune the minimum potential points to resonance.

Dielectric heating frequencies range from 1 to 500 megacycles, but the majority of applications lie below 50 megacycles. The theoretically minimum frequency at which a heating requirement can be carried out is:

$$F = \frac{12.4 \, MCT}{D^2 \, tL} \text{ megacycles}$$

where

M = density, lb/cu inch
C = specific heat, Btu/lb°F
T = desired temperature rise, °F
D = maximum safe voltage gradient, kilovolts/inch
L = loss factor
t = desired heating time, minutes

M, C, D, and L all pertain to the work material.

This equation disregards losses, etc., and merely provides a lower frequency boundary to which the design is limited. The chosen frequency will normally be much greater than this minimum value. Obviously, a great deal of information on the properties of the work material is required to make even this basic calculation. These values are normally not precisely known, and actual tests are often used as a simple method of determining satisfactory power levels and supply requirements, heating rates, and circuit layout.

References

1. BROWN, G. H., HOYLER, C. N., AND BIERWIRTH, R. A., "Theory and Application of Radio Frequency Heating," New York, D. Van Nostrand Company, 1947.
2. "Bibliography on High-Frequency Dielectric Heating," New York, American Institute of Electrical Engineers, 1947.
3. CABLE, J. W., "Induction and Dielectric Heating," New York, Reinhold Publishing Corp., 1954.

E. J. BORREBACH

DIELECTRIC MATERIALS

Materials which are capable of sustaining a difference of electric potential without the passage of an electric arc are said to possess insulating properties, and are designated as dielectric materials. As such, however, they exhibit a wide range of electrical properties.[1] Pure air approaches the characteristics of a perfect dielectric in that when submitted to a difference of potential the resulting flow of current is small. Its ability to sustain the potential difference, however, is limited to relatively low values. On the other hand, certain solids, the phenol-formaldehyde resins for example, are capable of sustaining substantially larger potential differences, but, even at low values, permit the passage of a significant amount of current.

The most fundamental property of a dielectric material is its *dielectric constant*. Other characteristics which play an important role in the engineering application of these materials are the dielectric strength (the minimum voltage which causes their electric breakdown) and the dielectric loss (frequently expressed as the dissipation factor or the power factor on a-c voltage circuits).

Among the gaseous dielectric materials, air has been most widely used. Its relatively low dielectric strength under normal atmospheric conditions, however, has been a severe handicap in many of its applications because of the accompanying increase in the physical bulk of the equipment. Recourse has been made to the application of higher than atmospheric pressures. The dielectric strength of air increases with the increase in the applied pressure up to a value of about 200 atmospheres. More recently, the electronegative gases of the fluoride type (sulfur hexafluoride, the Freon gases,[2] etc.) have been demonstrated to possess a substantially higher dielectric strength than air or similar gases, even under normal room temperature conditions. Properly selected and applied, pressurized gases of this type approach the dielectric strength of mineral insulating oil.

Mineral oil has been the most widely used type of dielectric liquid. Despite the development of the askarel liquids and other synthetic compositions, it is still the most generally applied liquid in power equipment, such as transformers, circuit breakers, and electric cables. In electric capacitors, however, its low dielectric constant (approximately 2.2) has been the basis of its replacement by the chlorinated diphenyl compositions (dielectric constant as high as 5.5).

Cellulose is the solid insulating material which has been used traditionally throughout the whole field of electrical equipment. Properly dried and impregnated, it is characterized by a satisfactorily low loss and high dielectric strength. The basic problems in its use have been concerned with its drying and impregnation and with its mechanical and electrical stability in the higher temperature ranges of its normal commercial operation in electrical equipment. The presence of residual moisture leads to high dielectric loss and low dielectric strength. The presence of unimpregnated areas (gas pockets and voids) leads to destructive ionization at relatively low voltages. Chemical instability of the cellulose leads to the ultimate destruction of the apparatus of which it may be a part because of mechanical and electrical degradation. Most commonly the drying and impregnation of the cellulose dielectric is performed under the lowest possible pressure (generally in the range from 50 to 100 microns for cables and capacitors and frequently higher for transformers) and at a temperature in the range from 100 to 120°C.

With the engineering demand for the operation of electric equipment at higher and higher temperatures and voltages, the continued engineering reliance on cellulose dielectrics is being questioned. It degrades sufficiently at temperatures above 115°C to prevent its use at higher values. Its high dielectric constant (about 5) leads to a destructive charging current when used in electric cables at high temperatures and voltages. Its dielectric loss, even under the best drying and impregnating conditions, is too high for its successful application in many of the highly stressed, high-temperature equipments of present engineering demand. For such applications, the synthetic resin dielectric materials offer a greater promise for successful use.

The phenol-formaldehyde resins have been used as varnish impregnants and binders in laminated cylinders, plates, and similar insulating structures. Since World War II other synthetic resins have found engineering applications in specialized uses dependent on their particular property advantages. Polytetrafluoroethylene, (Teflon (2)), resin is characterized by a low dielectric constant, a low dielectric loss, and a thermal stability which permits its use at temperatures at least as high as 200°C. Silicone resin exhibits a similar usability. Polyethylene, polypropylene, and polystyrene are characterized by a very low dielectric loss, even at high frequency, which permits their use in electronic apparatus, high-frequency cables and the like. Their use, however, is limited to operating temperatures not greater than from 60 to 110°C, depending on the composition applied. The easy molding and casting applications of the polyester and the epoxy resins offer distinct manufacturing advantages in many types of electrical equipments. Polyvinyl chloride resin is applied as a wire insulation in low-voltage circuits.

The use of oleoresin varnishes and enamels is being replaced by synthetic resins. In the construction of enameled wire, polyvinyl formal (Formvar) has been widely used as the insulating film. The development of the polyurethane enamel compositions, however, has produced an enameled wire which is more easily solderable, eliminating the necessity of physically removing the enamel before the soldering operation, as is necessary with the Formvar compositions. The polyamide resin (Nylon) enamels have a similar utility. Polyester terephthalate resin enamels (Alkanex[3] and the like) possess a thermal stability suitable for use at temperatures as high as 130°C.

Among the industrial resin fibrous materials which have been applied in electrical equipment are Dacron (polyethylene terephthalate), Delrin (polyoxymethylene), and Orlon (acrylonitrile-methylacrylate copolymer) of the DuPont Company, and the various vinyl polymers and copolymers including Acrilan[4] and Creslan[5] (vinyl acetate-methyl vinylpyridine copolymer), Zefran[7] (vinyl pyrrolidone), Verel[7] and Dynel[8] (vinyl chloride compositions), and other similar polymers and copolymers.

Natural rubber has been almost entirely displaced as the insulation for electric wires and cables by the development of synthetic substitutes. Among these is butyl rubber (polyisobutylene-isoprene copolymer) which exhibits a greater heat stability than natural rubber, a greater oxidation and ozone resistance, increased tear and flexural strength, improved elongation characteristics and a greater resistance to gas penetration. The use of butyl rubber, however, does not eliminate the problem of solvent resistance and offers no improvement over natural rubber in abrasion resistance. Other synthetic elastomers which have been applied in electrical equipment include the polyacrylate rubbers, chloroprene rubbers (Neoprenes[2]), polysulfide polymer compositions (Thiokol[9]), chlorosulfonated polyethylene (Hypalon[2]), the polyurethane rubbers and silicone elastomers, together with their variously fluorinated derivatives.

Ceramic bodies are widely applied as electrical insulators because of their remarkable chemical and mechanical stabilities under severely adverse conditions of use. Their ability to resist degradation over wide ranges of temperature and humidity, even in the presence of an electrical discharge, has been the engineering basis of their applications in the construction of power bushings, transmission line insulators, and the like. Porcelain and alumina ceramics are most widely applied in power equipment. Insulator-type porcelain commonly consists of mullite-quartz. In alumina ceramics the major crystalline phase is alpha alumina (corundum).

The high dielectric constants exhibited by selected titanate ceramics have promoted their application in capacitors designed for electronic use. A composition comprising $2BaO:3TiO_2$ (barium metatitanate) possesses a dielectric constant as high as 9000 at 40°C. Materials of this type are commonly designated as ferroelectrics in order to indicate the analogy which correlates their dielectric behavior with the magnetic behavior of the ferromagnetic materials.

For extremely high-temperature use and under conditions where the dielectric material is subjected to recurring corona discharge during its normal commercial operation, mica insulation is most widely applied in the form of pasted tapes or sheets, or in molded form in which a resin or glass binding material is used. Glass-bonded mica, frequently referred to as Mycalex,[10] consists of ground mica flakes and a suitably selected glass composition. It is characterized by high dielectric strength, low dielectric loss, and marked chemical stability, and is impervious to water. It is generally applicable when high temperature or highly humid atmospheres are to be encountered. It is machineable, moldable to close tolerances, and possesses excellent dimensional stability.

Mica tapes and sheets are built up from mica splittings, bonded together by an organic or inorganic adhesive. Mica paper, which is applied in place of the usual mica tape or sheet in some types of rotating equipment and in certain gas cooled transformers, is made from reconstituted mica. The natural mica is broken into small particles in an aqueous suspension, and mica paper is formed from the slurry in a manner similar to that by which cellulose paper is formed. Mica paper is available in thicknesses of less than 0.002 inch. For engineering use, the paper is dried and impregnated with resin to obtain suitable electrical and mechanical properties.

For improved stability at high temperature, especially in laminated structures in which thermally stable, high-temperature resins are used, glass cloth or glass roving are preferably substituted for the cellulosic paper or board normally applied. Glass insulated wires, impregnated with a properly selected resin binder suitable for high-temperature use are of similar utility. Glass "ribbon" films have been applied in the manufacture of small, dry-type capacitors for electronic devices.

References

1. CLARK, FRANK M., "Insulating Materials for Design and Engineering Practice," New York, John Wiley & Sons, Inc., 1963.
2. E. I. DuPont de Nemours & Company, Inc., Wilmington, Delaware.
3. General Electric Company, Schenectady, New York.
4. Chemstrand Company, New York, N.Y.
5. American Cyanamid Company, New York, N.Y.
6. Dow Chemical Company, Midland, Michigan.
7. Eastman Chemical Products Company, Kingsport, Tenn.
8. Carbon and Carbide Chemical Company, New York, N.Y.

9. Thiokol Chemical Corp., Trenton, N.J.
10. Mycalex Corporation of America, Clifton, N.J.

FRANK M. CLARK

Cross-references: *Askarels; Ceramic Insulation; Ferroelectricity; Organic Electrical Insulation;* entries with *Dielectric* titles.

DIELECTRIC PROPERTIES OF VACUUM

High vacuum, in theory, represents a perfect loss-free dielectric of very high electric strength. There are many factors, largely involving surface phenomena, that can cause departures from the ideal properties. Electric breakdown in vacuum can be schematically distinguished from that at low pressures by means of Fig. 1. In this figure the gas portion (right-hand side) is represented by the familiar Paschen law curve, wherein the breakdown voltage for a uniform electric field is shown as a function of the product of gas pressure and gap length (pd). Actually the Paschen curve should be shown with gas *density* rather than *pressure* in the abscissa, otherwise a standard temperature must be assumed. It will be noted that for small values of pd the breakdown voltage of a gas increases very rapidly as pd decreases. This low pressure portion of the Paschen curve is sometimes carelessly, and incorrectly, referred to as a vacuum breakdown. When the gap is kept constant and low pd is obtained by decreasing the gas pressure, the transition zone between gas and vacuum characteristics occurs at pressures such that the gap is of the order of a mean-free-path. Below this somewhat arbitrary pressure the vacuum-type breakdown occurs and the principal variable is gap length. The vacuum breakdown curve is thus shown schematically in the left-hand portion of Fig. 1, with only gap length as the independent variable. The exact nature of this curve depends on many factors, a few of the most important of which will be discussed in the following sections.

Vacuum Breakdown from Points

The most clearly understood type of vacuum breakdown is that between a point and a plane. Current that is drawn in vacuum from a point, when the electric field is very high, is called "cold" or "field" emission. Field emitted current is determined by the Fowler-Nordheim relation.[1]

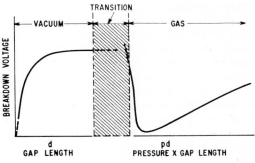

FIG. 1. Vacuum and gas breakdown characteristics.

$$J = \left(1.54 \times 10^{-6}\,\frac{F^2}{\phi}\right) \exp\,[-6.83$$

$$\times 10^{-7}\,\phi^{3/2}\,f(y)/F] \quad (1)$$

where $f(y)$ is the Nordheim elliptic function

$$y = 3.79 \times 10^{-4}\,\frac{F^{1/2}}{\phi}. \quad (2)$$

In these equations J is the current density in amp/sq cm, F is the electric field at the surface in volts/cm, and ϕ is the work function of the surface in electron-volts. It is usually simpler to use tables or curves in determining J than to solve the equation. Very clean surfaces will yield measurable field currents at 10^6 to 10^7 volts/cm, whereas surfaces contaminated by low work-function impurities may exhibit considerable field emission for $F = 10^5$ or even less. It is clear that current from a point in vacuum does not spontaneously appear at some clearly defined electric field. The pre-breakdown field currents often produce x-rays and fluorescence of the glass container long before a true breakdown occurs. It is thus necessary to define what is meant by vacuum breakdown. Breakdown occurs when sufficient metal is vaporized from the electrodes to establish an arc discharge. The arc in vacuum is not usually as stable as it is in gases, and often snaps out due to a deficiency of metal vapor. However, this high current discharge usually lasts long enough so that breakdown is clearly indicated, both visually and by a large decrease in voltage.

It has been established by Dyke and his associates[2] that point breakdown occurs in vacuum when the current density *in* the point due to field emitted electrons *from* the point is of the order of 10^8 amps/sq cm. The I^2R energy dissipated in the point at this current density is sufficient to vaporize the point. This results in a vapor arc with a current at least 100 times the value of the field emitted current and a consequent destruction of the point. Thus, breakdown of a point is established at the value of voltage necessary to produce an electric field so that the field current essentially "explodes" the point. This can occur in times as short as 5 × 10⁻⁸ sec. The corresponding field strength, of course depends on the size and sharpness of the point.

Large-Surface Vacuum Breakdown

The electrical breakdown of a gap between large flat or blunt surfaces in vacuum[3] is by no means as clearly explained as for the sharp, clean points discussed above. Pre-breakdown currents are quite sensitive to the surface conditions. These currents are by no means clearly identified as governed by the field emission equation (Eq. 1). Usually the breakdown voltage increases with the number of measurements, and often the ultimate value is more than double the value of the first breakdown. This "conditioning," as it is called, can be due to the effects of changing the gas layer on the surfaces, loosely attached insulating particles, oxide layers, surface irregularities, points, etc. In ordinary high vacua, i.e., pressures of the order of 10⁻⁶ Torr, a monolayer of gas is always present because it is formed in about one second at this pressure (if the residual gas can stick to the surface). However, after ultrahigh vacua processing at a pressure of the order of 10⁻¹⁰ Torr or lower, a freshly cleaned surface may remain free of gas for hours. In this case the effects of changing gas coverage may be detected. Conditioning breakdowns undoubtedly

are effective in smoothing the sharper irregularities of the surface as well as dispersing oxide layers and insulating particles. Thus, after a sufficiently large number of breakdowns, a fairly uniform surface may result with corresponding high and relatively regular breakdown voltage.

The curve of Fig. 2 is representative of experimental data taken of breakdown voltage as a function of the gap length in vacuum for plain parallel electrodes. It is clear that the breakdown voltage increases as some fractional power of the gap length. Actual data may vary considerably from this curve because of differences in surface roughness, material, contaminants, as well as whether the measuring voltage is direct current, high- or low-frequency alternating current, or an impulse. There is a similar difference in the pre-breakdown current of a plain gap, i.e., the current that may flow by field induced emission at voltages less than the breakdown value.[4]

It is generally believed that vacuum breakdown results from the cumulative effects of charged particles drawn from one electrode (usually the anode) gaining energy from the electric field and giving this energy up at the other electrode. At a critical value of voltage, a copious amount of metal vapor develops so that a vapor *arc* is formed in the gap. The particles are variously conceived of as being loose clumps, atoms vaporized at the anode by electron beams from locally sensitive sites on the cathode, or gas atoms on the surface of the anode detached and ionized by electrons from the cathode. There also exists the possibility that the necessary initiating particles are torn from the metal surface by the electric field. This might tend to explain the fact that it has been found that the breakdown voltage increases with the mechanical strength of the metal; however, this could also be associated with the lower vapor pressures exhibited by those same materials. The various assumptions usually demonstrate that the breakdown voltage should vary as some power, usually between 0.5 and 1, of the gap length.[5, 6] It has also been shown that *impulse* voltages can cause the exponent of the gap length[7] to vary between 5/6 and 5/2. Not to be ignored are the effects of the photoelectric electron emission produced by the x-rays which are generated by electrons striking the anode. These x-rays can produce showers of electrons from both metal and insulating surfaces that can accelerate breakdown.

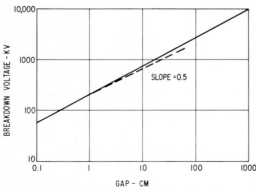

FIG. 2. Approximate breakdown strength of vacuum gaps. Dotted line has slope of 0.5 for comparison.

References

1. "Handbuch der Physik," XXI, p. 188, Berlin, Springer-Verlag, 1956; DOLAN, W. W., *Phys. Rev.*, **91**, 510 (1953).
2. DYKE, W. P., AND TROLAN, J. K., *Phys. Rev.*, **89**, 799 (1953) (and subsequent articles.)
3. HAWLEY, R., *Vacuum*, **10**, 310 (1960).
4. Little, R. P., and Whitny, W. T., *J. Appl. Phys.*, **34**, 2430 (1963).
5. CRANBERG, L., *J. Appl. Phys.*, **23**, 518 (1952).
6. MAITLAND, A., *J. Appl. Phys.*, **33**, 2628 (1962).
7. FARRALL, G. A., *J. Appl. Phys.*, **33**, 96 (1962).

J. D. COBINE

Cross-references: *Electric Arc Properties; Paschen's Law.*

DIELECTRICS, CERAMICS. See CERAMIC INSULATION.

DIELECTRICS, GASEOUS

Electrical insulation may be solid, liquid, or gas. Although solid insulation must have adequate electrical properties, it is primarily used as structural support for the electrical components of the system. In many areas of an electrical system, electrical insulation is needed but structural support is not necessary. In areas such as these a gas or a liquid may be used. Liquids are quite heavy, however, and certain gases can provide adequate electrical insulation with great savings in weight and increased ease of maintenance.

Gases are used as insulation and heat transfer media in many types of electrical equipment. Electronegative gases, such as sulfur hexafluoride, SF_6, and the fluorocarbons, have shown increased use in transformers. For years hydrogen has been used in large rotating units, such as generators, and air is widely used as an interrupting medium in large power circuit breakers. Sulfur hexafluoride in recent years has held considerable interest as an interrupting medium. Gases are also used in x-ray equipment, coaxial cables, pressurized transmission cables, and microwave equipment.

The oldest dielectric gas known and the one still used the most is air. It was not until late in the 1800's that work was done to find other gases for use as dielectrics. In 1887 Thompson reported the dissociation of various halogens by spark discharge. In 1889 Natterer studied the effect of electrical discharge on a large number of gases, including CO_2, HCN, and CCl_4. Berthelot in 1900 made the first report on the unique stability of SF_6 to spark breakdown, working with a sample prepared by Moissan. Very little study of breakdown of gases except air was done from this time until 1937. Then Charlton and Cooper reported the dielectric strength of some 80 gases and indicated the exceptional strength of compounds containing fluorine or sulfur.

All gases have some dielectric properties, but beside high dielectric strength, a commercially useful dielectric gas must have other good qualities. It must be thermally and chemically stable so that it will not react with or corrode materials of construction. It must also be nonflammable, nontoxic, and nonexplosive. It must remain a gas at all operating temperatures and, therefore, have a low condensation temperature. And it must have the ability to transfer heat to insure that all parts of the system are operating within their temperature limitations. Availability and cost of the gas are also an obvious concern.

The electrical breakdown of a gas involves its transition from an insulating to a conducting state. This transition takes place by ionization. Air, for example, filling the gap between two electrodes at a potential difference is subject to bombardment by electrons which have gained sufficient energy to escape from the cathode surface. These electrons are accelerated toward the anode by the electric field. Some travel far enough, and thereby gain enough energy, to ionize gas molecules and create additional electrons. These additional electrons can ionize still other gas molecules and release still more electrons. Thus, an electron avalanche moves toward the anode. Photons emanating from electron-ion recombination or positive-ion bombardment of the cathode create more electrons by photoemission at the cathode. This sustains the discharge and the conductive state between the electrodes.

The electrical stress in volts needed to initiate sparkover in a gas is called the "dielectric strength" or breakdown strength. Dielectric strength depends on many factors, including gas pressure, gap spacing, uniformity of the electric field, and type of voltage application. Generally the dielectric strength of any gas increases as its pressure increases. It also increases as the gap increases. In recent years the term "relative dielectric strength" has been used. This is the

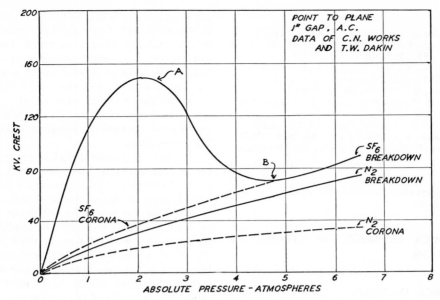

FIG. 1. Sparkover and corona onset voltages for SF₆ and N₂.

ratio of the dielectric strength of the gas to the dielectric strength of some reference gas, usually nitrogen. The dielectric strength of both gases expressed in volts is determined under similar conditions of pressure, spacing, etc. As this is a ratio, the "relative dielectric strength" has no units.

In a uniform electric field, such as that formed by two parallel plates or two spheres in which the area of the plates or the diameter of the spheres is large as compared to the gap, most gases obey Paschen's law. This law states that the breakdown strength is proportional to the product of the gap distance and gas pressure. At high pressures, deviations from this law occur. The dielectric strength of a gas in a uniform field is about the same for all types of voltage applications, i.e., power frequency (60 cycles), direct current, and impulse voltages.

In a nonuniform electric field, such as that formed in a point-to-plane electrode system, gases such as nitrogen, hydrogen, argon, and helium obey Paschen's law. Gases containing an electronegative atom, such as oxygen or fluorine, show deviations, however. These are noted in compounds, such as SF_6, CCl_2F_2, CO_2, and also in air due to the presence of O_2. In plotting the breakdown voltage in kilovolts versus the gas pressure for gases such as these, a maximum is observed in the breakdown curve as indicated by point A of Fig. 1. The pressure at which this maximum occurs depends on the distance between electrodes. As the distance increases, the pressure at which the sparkover maximum occurs is lower.

The breakdown voltage then decreases with increasing pressure until a second inflection point is reached at some higher pressure, point B in Fig. 1, after which the normal direct variance of breakdown strength with pressure is again observed. This second inflection point is called the "critical pressure" (not to be confused with the similar term used to denote the pressure of a gas at its critical temperature). At pressures below the critical pressure, breakdown is preceded by corona. Above the critical pressure, breakdown and corona occur almost simultaneously.

The latter phenomenon is called corona stabilized breakdown and has been attributed to a space charge formed around the sharp electrode. The charge "rounds off" the sharp electrode, reduces the field divergency, and increases the breakdown voltage. Polarity of the electrode contributing to the field divergency is also a factor in corona stabilization. If the point electrode is negative, breakdown voltage is higher than when the point is positive or subject to alternating current.

The breakdown voltage of a gap subjected to a power frequency of 60 cycles/sec is about equal to the d-c breakdown voltage. At higher frequencies, though, the breakdown voltage is slightly lower. If the frequency is raised, a point is reached at which positive ions have too little time to cross the gap in one-half cycle. When this occurs, a positive space charge builds up in the gap, distorts the field, and lowers the breakdown voltage below that of the d-c value. At still higher frequencies, electrons will oscillate in the gap causing cumulative ionization. This increased ion density further lowers the voltage necessary for breakdown.

Further information on the subject of gaseous insulation can be found in the following sources.

References

1. MEEK, J. M., AND CRAGGS, J. D., "Electrical Breakdown of Gases," London, Oxford University Press, 1953.
2. LOEB, L. B., "Basic Processes of Gaseous Electronics," Los Angeles, University of California Press, 1955.
3. CHARLTON, E. E., AND COOPER, F. S., "Dielectric Strength of Insulation Fluids," *General Electric Review*, pp. 438–442 (Sept. 1937).
4. NARBUT, P., AND BERG, D., "Factors Controlling Electric Strength of Gaseous Insulation," *A.I.E.E. Trans.*, III, **78**, 545–50 (1959).

JAMES A. BROWN

Cross-references: *Paschen's Law; Sulfur Hexafluoride.*

DIELECTRICS, LIQUID

The term liquid dielectrics is usually taken in its broadest sense to mean liquids having high resistivity (as high as 10^{20} ohm-cm), and having the ability to withstand very high electrical stress before breakdown takes place. These liquids may be conveniently divided into two groups: first, the industrial oils of complex molecular structure which are used extensively for electrical insulation where relatively high electrical stress occurs, for example, in transformers and in certain types of cables and capacitors; and second, both organic and inorganic liquids of more simple structure which can be prepared with a high degree of purity. Liquids in this latter category, while frequently not having any direct practical application have been used to examine the fundamental processes involved in the phenomena of electrical conduction and breakdown of the liquid phase. Full reviews of the recent and more reliable experimental data concerning the behaviour of liquids

subject to electric stress have appeared,[5, 8, 9] and it is evident that, despite the skill and ingenuity which have been applied, there is still no completely satisfactory explanation of the breakdown mechanism. Solid and gaseous dielectric breakdown is comparatively well understood and the theoretical explanations of the processes involved have reached an advanced stage, but the liquid state remains in many ways an enigma, being is some ways analogous to a solid and in others to a gas.

The electrical behavior of dielectric liquids has been examined in two ways; either by direct measurement of the electric field necessary to cause breakdown or by a more fundamental, and in many ways more difficult, technique whereby the prebreakdown phenomena are investigated.

Simple measurements of the breakdown strength of a range of liquids have shown that an "intrinsic" strength does not appear to exist for the liquid phase, this being defined as the magnitude of the homogenous electric field existing in a region of the dielectric necessary to disrupt this region or establish a conducting path across it, initiating processes from outside this region being excluded. All liquids which can be classified as dielectrics appear to have strengths of about 10^6 volts per centimeter, but the actual measured value depends on a variety of parameters. Of particular importance is the influence of the electrode material, but electrode configuration, electrode spacing, equilibrium gas content, hydrostatic pressure above the liquid, and impurity concentration all affect the measured breakdown strength. The technique of testing is also important as very different results are obtained with short impulse voltages of a few microseconds duration and with direct voltage.

The interpretation of direct stress breakdown measurements is simplified to some extent by the absence of any time variations in the individual processes which lead to the initiation of the discharge, but may be complicated by the formation of space charges and by the influence of solid impurities. With microsecond and submicrosecond impulse voltages, however, the movement of ions and impurities is largely curtailed, but the temporal variations of the breakdown processes become significant. Since each of these processes, whatever they may be, is associated with a certain probability, a statistical interpretation of impulse measurements is required, and serious errors may be made unless the correct statistical theory for a given set of conditions is used. This has not been generally realized in the past, and it has recently been shown that previous interpretations are in many cases erroneous.[6]

The fundamental processes which lead to breakdown are generally considered to be the production of free electrons in the gap by electron emission from the cathode, the acceleration of these electrons by the field and the loss of energy through collisions with the liquid or impurity molecules, and ionization leading to an instability.

Prebreakdown conductivity studies have shown conclusively that cathode emission occurs at stresses well below breakdown, and the importance of electron emission as a necessary condition for breakdown is clearly demonstrated by the dependence of electric strength on cathode material and surface condition in certain circumstances. The insulating deposits formed on the electrodes by each discharge with organic liquids have probably masked electrode effects in many instances, but recent work with liquefied gases in which solid deposits do not occur has demonstrated that very strong electrode effects are present.

While the dependence upon cathode material is to be expected if the breakdown mechanism is intimately connected with electron emission, perhaps the most surprising fact which has been demonstrated during studies with liquefied argon is that the anode can also control the actual measured strength, and can even mask changes in cathode conditions. The anode effect is only observed when the electrons are attached to neutral molecules to form low mobility ions, this effect being absent in pure argon liquid, in which the electrons remain free.[9] It is believed that the anode surface, which would normally have a thin insulating or semiconducting oxide layer on it, can only neutralize negative ions at a certain rate without forming a space charge extending back into the liquid. If the rate of arrival of ions at the anode is sufficient to set up such a space charge, then field distortion will occur and the breakdown strength may be changed from the value to be expected if space charge were absent.

One possible mechanism whereby such a change in strength may be brought about is that in the region of enhanced field near the anode surface additional positive ions may be produced by collision ionization. These positive charges will then move to the cathode and cause enhanced electron emission, which can lower the electric strength. If only a few positive ions are necessary to cause a breakdown in the case where the anode is not important,[10] than a slight increase in ionization due to an anode space charge would be very effective in lowering the breakdown strength. It is likely than an anode effect also occurs in other liquids where the negative ion is a massive structure, and neutralization at the electrode surface is not immediate.

Collosion ionization is perhaps the most controversial of all aspects of the breakdown mechanism, and evidence both for and against the occurrence of such a process has been recently obtained.[7, 8] Those investigators who favor ionization in the liquid believe that the breakdown is essentially a Townsend discharge in which electrons from the cathode ionize the liquid, the resulting positive ions returning to the cathode where emission is enhanced. At a certain critical stress, a current instability occurs and breakdown follows. Other investigators who do not believe that ionization of the liquid occurs have suggested that the actual discharge takes place in a gas or vapor bubble which is produced by cavitation in the liquid or as a result of thermal heating at the cathode due to a large emission current density.[8] An appreciable dependence of electric strength on hydrostatic pressure lends support to the "bubble" theory, but against this the recent discovery of a strong anode influence can best be explained by ionic space charge influencing ionization of the liquid.

It is quite possible that both mechanisms occur in practice, one or other being predominant. For example, the cathode current density could be enhanced because of space charge formation due to ionization in the liquid, until at a certain stress level vaporization of the liquid would occur and a discharge develop in the gaseous phase. More detailed investigations are necessary to resolve these difficulties.

The possibility of using dielectric liquids for radiation detectors and counters has also been examined with some success. The naturally occurring residual current in the absence of any radiation constitutes the noise level of the detector, and by careful shielding from stray radiation this undesirable current may be reduced to a very low level. With purified n-hexane as the dielectric the current has been found to be proportional to the intensity of radiation, and ion pulses resulting from individual α-particles are observed with fields in excess of 2×10^4 volts per centimeter with a resolution of about 10 per cent.[1] Prior to this work the pulses of single α-particles had not been observed in liquids other than argon and helium, in which recombination within the ionized column occurs to a much smaller extent as a result, presumably, of the very large negative ion mobility.

In this connection it is interesting to note that α-particle induced currents in argon and helium liquids are much greater than in liquid oxygen or liquid nitrogen, and this has been attributed to the large differences between the mobilities of positive and negative ions in the liquefied rare gases.[3] In liquid argon the negative ion mobility corresponds to that of a free electron, being particularly sensitive to small concentrations of molecular impurity, and is about 10^4 times greater than the positive ion mobility. In liquid helium, however, the situation is very different. The negative ion mobility is found to be slightly less than that of the positive ion[7] and it would be expected that the α-particle induced current in this liquid would be of similar magnitude to that in oxygen or nitrogen, where strong electron trapping is known to occur and where columnar recombination drastically reduces the current. One possible explanation for this apparent anomalous behavior is that initially the negative ion in helium is also a free electron of high mobility as in argon, but that trapping by either the helium itself or by impurities subsequently reduces the mobility to that of a massive ion.

Measurements of naturally-occurring currents in liquid normal paraffins have shown that with direct stress close to breakdown the influence of moisture is particularly strong, giving rise to a stable emission, but that if care is taken to remove traces of water, small particles of solid impurities moving between the electrodes cause the current to oscillate erratically. Elimination of these particles is very difficult, if not impossible. Using microsecond duration pulse voltages the current is found to be several orders of magnitude greater than with direct-stress, and liquid purity is not important. It is believed that polarizing space charges near the electrodes are responsible for the fall in current with extended stress application. Observation of the field distribution between two electrodes using the Kerr optical technique has shown that space charges at the electrodes are formed, but that considerable time is necessary in order to establish these.[2]

A theory of dielectric breakdown based entirely on the interaction of the applied field with solid impurities has been developed by Kok.[4] He supposes that the particles are polarizable spheres with dielectric constant greater than that of the liquid. Because of surface irregularities on the electrodes local field gradients exist which cause the particles to move into the high field region and ultimately to form a bridge between the electrodes. The magnitude and variation of breakdown strength with such parameters as temperature and particle size predicted by theory do not appear to be in accord with experiment and it is difficult to see how the many factors which influence the electric strength in practice can be introduced into the theory.

References

1. BLANC, D., MATHIEU, J., AND BOYER, J., "Nuclear Electronics I," p. 285, Vienna, International Atomic Energy Agency, 1962.
2. CROITORU, Z., *Bull. Soc. Franç. Elect.*, Ser. 8, **1**, 362 (1960).
3. GERRITSEN, A. N., *Physica*, **14**, 381 (1948).
4. KOK, J. A., "Electrical breakdown of insulating liquids," London, Cleaver-Hume Press Ltd., 1961.
5. LEWIS, T. J., "Progress in Dielectrics," Vol. 1, p. 97, London, Heywood and Co. Ltd., 1959.
6. LEWIS, T. J., AND WARD, B. W., *Proc. Roy. Soc. (London)*, **A269**, 233 (1962).
7. REIF, F., AND MEYER, L., *Phys. Rev.*, **119**, 1164 (1960).
8. SHARBAUGH, A. H., AND WATSON, P. K., "Progress in Dielectrics," Vol. 4, p. 201, London, Heywood and Co. Ltd., 1962.
9. SWAN, D. W., *Brit. J. Applied Physics*, **13**, 208 (1962).
10. SWAN, D. W., *Proc. Phys. Soc. (London)*, **78**, 423 (1961).

DAVID W. SWAN

DIELECTRICS, ORGANIC. See ORGANIC ELECTRICAL INSULATION.

DIELECTROPHORESIS

Dielectrophoresis is defined as the motion of matter induced by electrical polarization in nonuniform fields. It is analogous to the moving of a piece of soft iron toward a magnet. In both cases, matter moves to where the field is stronger.

Consider first the behavior of matter in a "uniform" field, such as that in the central region of a charged parallel plate condensor. A charged body freely suspended between the plates will move

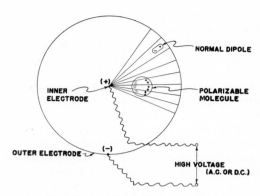

Fɪɢ. 1. Diagram of forces acting on dipoles and polarizable molecules suspended in an inhomogeneous electric field. The radial lines of electric force converge toward the central electrode, and the field grows stronger toward the center.

(From Ref. 1 by permission.)

parallel to the field toward the plate bearing the opposite charge. On the other hand, a neutral body will be polarized, perhaps rotated, but will stay put. It is not impelled by a uniform field. In the external electric field the electrons and nuclei are pulled in opposite directions so that the center of negative electricity no longer coincides with that of the positive. The amount of net separation produced by a given electric field is called the polarizability and varies widely for different substances.

If, however, the field is made nonuniform and is stronger on one side of the particle than on the other, there will be a net pull on the particle towards the stronger field. This is shown in Fig. 1 for an inner electrode concentric with a cylinder. In this case the polarizable molecule moves toward the center.

This arises because the electrical force, $\mathbf{F}$, on a charge, Q, in a field, $\mathbf{E}$, is:

$$\mathbf{F} = Q\mathbf{E}$$

The net force, F_e, can be pictured as arising on an induced dipole having charges Q_+ and Q_-, separated by a distance, d, in the particle. Then, for example,

$$F_e = F_{strong} \cdot q_+ - F_{weak} \cdot q_-$$

Note that the net force on the uncharged body is in the same direction no matter which electrode is positive and which is negative. The

polarity of the field does not matter, only the field strength and rate of change of field strength matters. As a consequence, an alternating voltage applied to the electrodes can produce the same dielectrophoretic action as a static field. The motion of the particle due to the nonuniform field effects is called dielectrophoresis.

Compared to the movement of charged particles in an electric field, (i.e., to electrophoresis), dielectrophoresis is a relatively mild effect, and historically speaking has been relatively neglected. Fields of from 100 to 10,000 volts/cm are usually required to produce appreciable forces. The effects, however, have many uses.

It can be shown that the effective translational force, $\mathbf{F}_e$, on a spherical particle suspended in a fluid medium is:

$$\mathbf{F}_e = \mu_e \cdot \boldsymbol{\nabla} \, | \, \mathbf{E} \, |$$

$$= 4\pi a^3 K_1{}' \epsilon_0 \left(\frac{K_2{}' - K_1{}'}{K_2{}' + 2K_1{}'} \right) | \, \mathbf{E} \, | \cdot \boldsymbol{\nabla} \, | \, \mathbf{E} \, |$$

$$= 2\pi a^3 K_1{}' \epsilon_0 \left(\frac{K_2{}' - K_1{}'}{K_2{}' + 2K_1{}'} \right) \boldsymbol{\nabla} \, | \, \mathbf{E} \, |^2$$

The force is seen to be proportional to the cube of the particle radius, a, to the difference of its dielectric constant, $K_2{}'$, from that of the medium, $K_1{}'$; and proportional to the gradient of the square of the electric field strength, $\mathbf{E}$. The latter statement contains the implication that the direction of the force is the same whether alternating or static voltage is applied.

As examples, the values of $\boldsymbol{\nabla} \, | \, \mathbf{E} \, |^2$ are given below for electrodes with cylindrical and spherical symmetry:

Cylindrical:

$$\boldsymbol{\nabla} \, | \, \mathbf{E} \, |^2 = \frac{-2\mathbf{r}_0 V_1{}^2}{r^3 [\ln \, (r_1/r_2)]^2}$$

Spherical:

$$\boldsymbol{\nabla} \, | \, \mathbf{E} \, |^2 = \frac{-\mathbf{r}_0 4 V_1{}^2 r_1{}^2 r_2{}^2}{r^5 (r_1 - r_2)^2}$$

where

V_1 = applied voltage on inner electrode
r_1, r_2 = radii of inner and outer electrodes, respectively
$\mathbf{r}_0$ = unit radius vector

r = radius of cylinder or sphere
ϵ_0 = permittivity of free space,

$$= \frac{1}{36\pi \times 10^9} \; ; \text{[coulombs/volt-meter]}$$

A careful comparison of the two distinct phenomena, dielectrophoresis and electrophoresis, shows these contrasts:

DIELECTROPHORESIS	*ELECTROPHORESIS*
1. Arises from ability of matter to become polarized in an electric field and move into regions of stronger field.	1. Arises from the electrostatic attraction of charged electrodes for charged particles.
e.g., Image forces on a charged particle near a polarizable surface.	e.g., Motion of ions between charged electrodes.
2. Produces motion of the particles, the direction of which is toward higher field strength, but is *independent* of field direction.	2. Produces motion of the particles, the direction of which is dependent on the field direction.
3. Is best observable in relatively coarse particles. (e.g., particle diameter $\geq 0.4 \ \mu$)	3. Is observable with particles of any molecular size or larger.
4. Requires both high field strength and highly divergent fields simultaneously.	4. Operates in either uniform or divergent fields.
5. Requires relatively high field strengths for easily observable results, (e.g., about 100 volts/cm or more.)	5. Operates even in relatively low voltage gradients.
6. Is most readily observable where the dielectric constants, K_2' and K_1', of particle and medium differ by over 5 per cent.	6. Is readily observable with relatively few free charges per unit volume.

Having clearly differentiated between the phenomena of dielectrophoresis and electrophoresis, some of the more interesting experimental results of applying nonuniform electric fields can be presented.

Using them, one can efficiently pump liquids without the use of moving parts; can cause continuous separations of suspensions; can cause selective precipitation; can cause separations of mixed powdered substances, often where it had been impractical hitherto; and can even cause mixing. One of the more spectacular uses contemplated is to create modest sized regions of "artificial gravity" for use in outer space.

By way of illustration consider the following experiments.

Precipitation and Mixing

In Fig. 2 is shown a fine wire serving as one electrode surrounded by a suspension in a grounded container.

A suspended powder having a dielectric constant higher than that of the poorly-conducting fluid (e.g., carbon black in kerosene) is drawn rapidly to the central electrode after a moderate field is applied. If, instead of a moderate field, the field is made quite intense, there results a partial breakdown of the molecules nearest the inner electrode, and this causes charge release. Particles entering the region of this "incipient corona" become charged themselves and are then pushed away from the electrode by electrophoresis. The result is an active stirring and mixing as shown in the lower sketch. A properly designed dielectrophoretic cell has commercial application in the purification of certain high polymers. Here the material coming from the reaction vessel is freed of contaminating catalyst particles by dielectro-

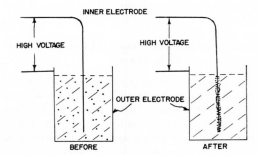

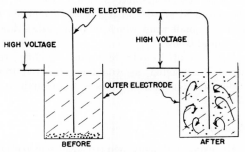

Fig. 2. Dielectrophoretic precipitation and mixing; (upper) suspended powder attracted to central electrode under moderate field; (lower) mixing of suspended particles under intense field.

(From Ref. 1 by permission.)

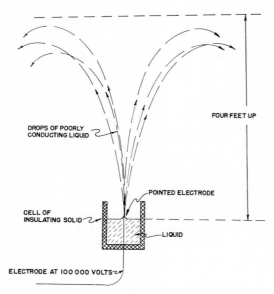

FIG. 3. Pumping action of strong divergent electric field.

(From Ref. 1 by permission.)

phoresis. The process can be made continuous by using arrangements similar to that shown in Ref. 3.

Repulsion and Attraction of Liquids by Non-uniform Field Forces

When a high voltage is applied between a metal dish holding a liquid and a center electrode pointed at the surface of the liquid, the field apparently repels the liquid below. In reality this is but a secondary manifestation of the divergent field effects upon the air in the neighborhood of the pointed electrode. Air is pulled to the electrode by dielectrophoretic action, charged by the extreme field at the tip region, then repelled to create a small wind which in turn pushes down the liquid below.

If the pointed electrode is raised slightly, the liquid is attracted, as would be expected from earlier discussion, and forms a hump under the electrode.[1]

Pumping

By using a sharply pointed electrode passing up almost through or just through the liquid, the liquid (or even dry powders!!) can be pumped. This action is sketched in Fig. 3.

Pumping efficiencies of up to 50 per cent are achievable. Here care must be taken to distinguish how the work is done. Dielectrophoresis acts to pull matter toward a stronger field. Unless some transformation of its dielectric constant occurs asymmetrically at the field (as by heating which then supplies the energy for the work of pumping), dielectrophoresis can only supply the limited amount of work occasioned by "filling" the field with the most polarizable substance present. In the pump of the type shown in Fig. 3 above, electrophoresis and, hence, actual work input by charge transfer is active so that continuous power input and continuous pumping is possible.

Separations: The Isomotive Cell

Mention was made earlier of the cylindrical cell which causes particles of high dielectric constant to collect at the small electrode. The cylindrical arrangement, however, has a serious drawback. The force it exerts on a particle drops off sharply (as $1/r^3$) with increasing distance from the axis. The effect is particularly bothersome when one tries to separate a suspension of two solid powders rather than merely to pull out one solid from a suspension.

A solution to this problem is found in a device called the *isomotive cell* (because it exerts an equal force on identical particles regardless of their position).[3] Here a flat-bottomed trough made of an insulator is sandwiched between a pair of charged plates. The lower electrode is flat, the upper one curved. With proper plate curvature the field across the width of the trough varies in such a way as to make the dielectrophoretic forces the same at all points. When the trough is tilted down at about 60° and a powder mixture is shaken onto the top end, the particles are subjected to a sideways dielectrophoretic force as they slide down. If the particles of the mixture have different dielectric constants, as is very often the case, one set of particles is pulled more strongly than the other. Separation may then be achieved by giving the trough a slight twist angle so that gravity can begin to counteract the dielectrophoretic force on the more weakly polar particles. At the bottom of the trough the separated powders emerge through separate chutes. Sparks, corona, and other discharge effects are avoided by immersing the isomotive cell in a nonconducting liquid, such as kerosene or a Freon. The isomotive cell beautifully separates minerals, diamond dust, phosphors, etc. from other powders often when other methods fail or are undesirable.

In conclusion, it should be noted that the effects of nonuniform electric fields are many and varied, often surprisingly spectacular (as in the pump), and can be quite useful. This is a long neglected area of a rather exciting branch of science, one which is seeing an awakening.

References

1. POHL, H. A., *J. Applied Phys.*, **29**, 1182 (1962).
2. POHL, H. A., *Scientific American*, **203**, No. 6, 107 (1960).
3. POHL, H. A., AND PLYMALE, C. E., *J. Electrochem. Soc.*, **107**, 390 (1960).

HERBERT A. POHL

DIFFERENCE EFFECT

Dissolution of metals immersed in aqueous solutions is a result of local-cell action. This action is a combination of oxidation and reduction processes which, in the absence of external currents, proceed at the same rate. For example, aluminum dissolves in alkaline solutions at anodic sites and hydrogen gas is evolved at ca-

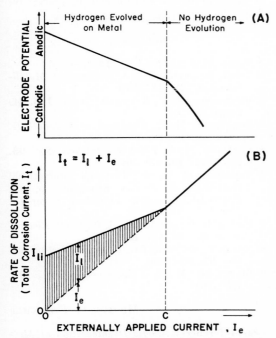

FIG. 1. The positive difference effect: schematic curves based on data obtained on aluminum dissolving in sodium hydroxide solutions.

thodic sites of numerous, continually shifting local cells. The weight of aluminum dissolved during a given exposure period is electrochemically equivalent to the volume of hydrogen gas evolved and may be converted by Faraday's law into a "corrosion current." By means of an auxiliary electrode (cathode) and a source of emf, an external *anodic* current may be superimposed on the local-cell current. When applied to aluminum dissolving in sodium hydroxide, the anodic external current decreases the rate of evolution of hydrogen on the aluminum. This shows that the local-cell corrosion current has been decreased. The change produced in local-cell action of a corroding metal by the application of an external anodic current is known as the "Difference Effect." If local-cell action (hydrogen evolution) is decreased, as above, it is a "positive" difference effect. In some cases the applied anodic current results in an apparent increase in local-cell action. This phenomenon is known as the "negative" difference effect for reasons which are apparent from the following mathematical definition.

I_{ii} = local-cell corrosion current observed initially before application of external current. This is calculated from the rate of hydrogen evolved, (V_{ii}).

I_i = local-cell corrosion current during application of external current. This may be derived from the rate of evolution of hydrogen or from $I_i = I_t - I_e$, where I_t is the current derived from the total weight loss per unit of time (corrosion rate) and I_e is the external anodic current to the metal.

Δ = difference effect.

$I_{ii} - I_i = \Delta$.

The difference effect is positive when $I_{ii} > I_i$, and negative when $I_i > I_{ii}$.

Thiel and Eckell[1, 2] first described the difference effect and also observed that Δ is directly proportional to the external anodic current.

The most extensively investigated system[3-6] is aluminum dissolving in sodium hydroxide solutions. Data obtained[5] on this system are typical for the positive difference effect and are shown schematically in Fig. 1-B. Without external current the local-cell current is I_{ii}. When the external anodic current is applied via an auxiliary cathode, the total rate of dissolution (I_t) increases. It is the sum of local-cell dissolution (hydrogen evolution) (I_i) and dissolution by external current (I_e). As the external current is increased there is a linear decrease of the local-cell current (cross-hatched area) until a current density, C, is reached at which there is no more evolution of hydrogen on the anodic specimen. From this point on, the weight of aluminum dissolved is equivalent to the external current and, as expected, increases along a line which extrapolates to the origin.

Electrode-potential measurements show that the positive-difference effect is associated with anodic polarization which decreases the potential difference in local cells (Fig. 1-A). When all hydrogen evolution is suppressed by the external current at C, local anodes have been polarized to the open-circuit potential of local cathodes, and there is a break in the straight-line polarization curve.[5, 6]

Suppression of local-cell action by anodic polarization is analogous to suppression of local-cell action (corrosion) in cathodic protection. In this latter case, cathodic polarization is used to polarize local cathodes to the open-circuit potential of local anodes for complete protection.[7] This does not imply that local-cell action may be suppressed by application of an external anodic or cathodic current on any corroding metal. Whether or not a surface can be polarized to the open-circuit potentials of local-cell anodes or cathodes depends on the nature of the metal and the solution, its concentration and temperature. However, the appearance of the positive difference effect and/or of cathodic protection provides proof of an electrochemical mechanism of metal dissolution.

In hydrochloric acid solutions, anodic polarization of aluminum appears to increase local-cell action, i.e., the rate of hydrogen evolution or the calculated value of I_l is greater than $I_{l\iota}$ (negative difference effect). This apparent increase is not the result of a higher rate of dissolution per unit area of actively corroding surface, but of an enlargement of the total surface area which is corroding. Application of an anodic, external current breaks down or strips protective films. Another factor which may contribute to apparent increases in local-cell action is dropping of metal particles in the form of grains produced by intergranular attack or in the form of tiny blocks. For example, on aluminum containing from 0.01 to 0.1 per cent iron and copper impurities, attack by hydrochloric acid proceeds along cubic planes of particles about 5×10^{-4} cm in size.[8] As a result, such blocks are dislodged, drop from the surface, and

may markedly increase weight losses observed on anodically polarized metals. Dissolution in the form of blocks has also been observed on magnesium, beryllium, and silver.

The difference effect has been studied on magnesium, zinc, cadmium, copper, steel, titanium, and some alloys in solutions of acids, bases, and salts.

Real and apparent variations in local-cell action produced by external currents, when not recognized, can lead to erroneous calculations of the valences of ions formed in the dissolution of metals. Thus, if a certain self-dissolution rate (local-cell action) is observed before anodic polarization, and it is assumed mistakenly that this rate remains constant when current is applied, the valence calculated from the weight loss and the external current will be incorrect. Similarly, dropping of grains or blocks, if unobserved, will lead to calculated valences which are lower than the correct values. These factors are of importance in investigations of unusual valence states.[9] In practical applications of electrochemistry the nature of the difference effect determines the efficiency of sacrificial anodes used for cathodic protection, affects the dissolution of anodes used in electroplating, and controls the phenomenon of anodic protection and the leveling process required for electrolytic polishing of metals.

References

1. THIEL, A., *Z. Elektrochem.*, **33**, 370 (1927).
2. THIEL, A., AND ECKELL, J., *Korrosion u. Metallschutz*, **4**, 121, 145 (1928).
3. STRAUMANIS, M. E., *Z. physik. Chem.*, **148**, 349 (1930).
4. STRAUMANIS, M. E., *Korrosion u. Metallschutz*, **14**, 67, 81 (1938).
5. STREICHER, M. A., *Trans. Electrochem. Soc.*, **93**, 285 (1948); **96**, 170 (1949).
6. STREICHER, M. A., in "Pittsburgh International Conference on Surface Reactions," p. 105, Pittsburgh, Corrosion Publishing Company, 1948.
7. BROWN, R. H., AND MEARS, R. B., *Trans. Electrochem. Soc.*, **81**, 455 (1942).
8. ROALD, B., AND STREICHER, M. A., *J. Electrochem. Soc.*, **97**, 283 (1950).
9. STRAUMANIS, M. E., *J. Electrochem. Soc.*, **108**, 1087 (1961).

MICHAEL A. STREICHER

Cross-references: *Anodic Disintegration of Metals; Anodic Protection; Cathodic Protection; Mixed Potential; Polarization.*

DIFFERENTIAL AERATION CELLS. See CONCEN-TRATION CELLS.

DIPOLE MOMENT

A dipole moment is a vector quantity measuring the size of a dipole. An electric dipole consists of a pair of electric charges, equal in size but opposite in sign and very close together. The dipole moment, sometimes called the "electric moment," is the product of one of the two charges by the distance between them. A polarized dielectric material has an electric moment, a slab of the material behaving like an assembly of electric dipoles parallel to one another.

The electric dipole moment is normally a molecular property arising from asymmetry in the arrangement of the positive nuclear charges and the negative electronic charges in the molecule. A moment may be induced in a molecule by an electric field, which displaces the positive and negative charges relative to one another. A permanent moment arising from electrical asymmetry is usually much larger than the induced moment. Its order of magnitude is that of the product of an electronic charge, 4.80×10^{-10} electrostatic units, times an atomic radius, 10^{-8} cm, that is, 4.80×10^{-18}. The moment values are, therefore, expressed in 10^{-18} esu cm, which is commonly called a "debye."

The dielectric constant of a molecular material is roughly proportional to the number of molecules per cc, the polarizability of the molecule, and the square of the permanent molecular dipole moment. The relationship is more exactly expressed by the Debye equation

$$\frac{\epsilon - 1}{\epsilon + 2} = \frac{4\pi N_1}{3}\left(\alpha_0 + \frac{\mu^2}{3kT}\right)$$

in which ϵ is the dielectric constant; N_1 is the number of molecules per cubic centimeter; α_0 is the molecular polarizability, that is, the dipole moment induced per molecule by unit electric field (1 esu = 300 volts/cm); μ is the permanent dipole moment possessed by the molecule; k is the molecular gas constant 1.38×10^{-16}, and T is the absolute temperature. The order of magnitude of α_0 is 10^{-23} for molecules of ordinary size. The actual moment per molecule induced by any electric field of intensity F is $F\alpha_0$, but a dielectric material normally breaks down before the field can become large enough to induce a moment of magnitude comparable to that of the permanent molecular moment. Although the induced moment per molecule is much smaller than the permanent moment, the induced moments all act in the direction of an externally applied field, while the permanent moments give only a mean moment per molecule, $F\mu^2/3kT$, in the direction of the field, F. For dipolar molecules, this mean moment is usually larger than the induced moment, but of the same general order of magnitude, 10^{-23}. The amount of molecular orientation produced in the material by an externally applied field of 300 volts/cm (1 esu) is so small that the complete orientation of only one molecular dipole in every hundred thousand would produce a dielectric constant of the magnitude observed.

Since the Debye equation for the relation between dielectric constant and dipole moment is based on the assumption that the molecules can orient freely in the applied alternating field used in measuring the dielectric constant, hindrance or prevention of orientation by molecular association or by freezing the molecules into a crystal lattice changes the dielectric constant, which can, therefore, be measured as a means of investigating molecular freedom. Molecular rotational freedom has thus been observed in many solid phases.

In polyatomic molecules, the molecular dipole moment is the vector sum of the moments of dipoles associated with bonds or groups of atoms in the molecule. Dipole moments are widely used to determine the geometric structures of molecules and also to investigate the distribution of electronic charge.

Dipole moments are usually calculated by means of the Debye equation from the results of dielectric constant measurements on gases, dilute solutions, or pure liquids. Some very exact values have been obtained for simple molecules from microwave spectroscopic measurements. A few, usually approximate, values have been obtained for molecular moments by means of molecular beam measurements and for bond moments by means of infrared intensity measurements.

In a molecular dielectric material, the permanent dipole moment is responsible for the dielectric loss and for any part of the dielectric constant in excess of the small contribution from the induced charge shift. It is, therefore, a quantity of theoretical importance in determining electrical forces in matter and of practical importance in determining the properties of insulating materials.

The induction of small dipole moments by the electric field of a light wave depends on the polarizability α_0, which is related to the optical refractive index, n, by the Lorentz-Lorenz expression

$$\frac{n^2 - 1}{n^2 + 2} = \frac{4\pi N_1}{3} \alpha_0$$

The induction of small dipoles in molecules by the electric fields of neighboring molecules gives rise to intermolecular attraction.

References

1. SMITH, J. W., "Electric Dipole Moments," London, Butterworths Scientific Publications, 1955.
2. SMYTH, C. P., "Dielectric Behavior and Structure," New York, McGraw-Hill Book Co., 1955.

CHARLES P. SMYTH

Cross-reference: *Dielectric Constant.*

DISSOCIATION

Dissociation can be broadly defined as the separation from union or as the process of disuniting. In chemistry, dissociation is the process by which a chemical combination breaks up into simpler constituents due, for example, to added energy as in the case of the dissociation of gaseous molecules by heat, or to the effect of a solvent upon a dissolved substance, as in the action of water upon dissolved hydrogen chloride. Dissociation may occur in the gaseous, liquid, or solid state or in solution.

Elementary substances, if polyatomic in the molecule, will dissociate under conditions of sufficient energy. Chlorine and iodine, which are diatomic, are half dissociated at 1700 and 1200°C, respectively. Just above the boiling point the molecule of sulfur is S_8. Its molecular weight decreases from 250 at 450°C to 50 at 2070°C. Thus there are some monatomic sulfur molecules at 2070°C. The dissociation probably takes place in reversible steps and can be represented by the equation:

$$S_8 \rightleftharpoons 4S_2 \rightleftharpoons 8S. \tag{1}$$

Many chemical compounds dissociate readily upon heating or otherwise supplying them with energy. Acetic acid vapor consists of double molecules just above the normal boiling point, but dissociates completely into single molecules at 250°C. Nitrogen tetroxide (N_2O_4) is a pale reddish brown gas at temperatures near its normal boiling point of 21.3°C. On heating the density of the gas becomes less and the color becomes darker until it is almost black. At 140°C the molecular weight is 46 which is that of NO_2 molecules. The dissociation can be written:

$$N_2O_4 \rightleftharpoons 2NO_2 . \tag{2}$$

If one mole of gas yields ν moles of gaseous products, and α is the fraction of the one mole which dissociates, then the total number of moles present is:

$$1 - \alpha + \nu\alpha = 1 + \alpha(\nu - 1). \tag{3}$$

Now the density of a given weight of gas at constant pressure is inversely proportional to the number of moles, and if d_1 is taken as the density of the undissociated gas and d_2 that of the partially dissociated gas, then:

$$\frac{d_1}{d_2} = \frac{1 + \alpha(\nu - 1)}{1} \tag{3a}$$

or

$$\alpha = \frac{d_1 - d_2}{d_2(\nu - 1)} \tag{4}$$

Therefore, the *degree of dissociation* of a substance can be found by measuring the densities of the undissociated and partially (or completely) dissociated substance in the gaseous state. Molecular weights may be substituted for densities giving

$$\alpha = \frac{M_1 - M_2}{M_2(\nu - 1)} \tag{5}$$

The degree of dissociation can be used to calculate the *equilibrium constant* for dissociation. The equilibrium constant may be expressed in terms of concentrations, for example, moles per liter (K_c), or in terms of partial pressures (K_p). The degree of dissociation and equilibrium constants are important theoretically and practically, e.g., the latter can be used to ascertain the extent of a chemical process.

The temperature dependence of dissociation is expressed in terms of the equilibrium constant and is

$$\frac{d \ln K_p}{dT} = \frac{\Delta H}{RT^2} \text{ or } \frac{d \ln K_c}{dT} = \frac{\Delta H}{RT^2} \tag{6}$$

where ΔH is the heat of dissociation. Integrating between the limits T_1 and T_2 one obtains

$$\ln \frac{K_{p_2}}{K_{p_1}} = \frac{\Delta H}{R}\left(\frac{T_2 - T_1}{T_1 T_2}\right)$$

$$\ln \frac{K_{c_2}}{K_{c_1}} = \frac{\Delta H}{R}\left(\frac{T_2 - T_1}{T_1 T_2}\right) \tag{7}$$

Electrolytes, depending upon their strength, dissociate to a greater or less extent in polar solvents. The extent to which a weak electrolyte dissociates may be determined by electrical conductance, electromotive force, and freezing point depression methods. The electrical conductance method is the most used because of its accuracy and simplicity. Arrhenius proposed that the degree of dissociation, α, of a weak electrolyte at any concentration in solution could be found from the ratio of the equivalent conductance, Λ, of the electrolyte at the concentration in question to the equivalent conductance at infinite dilution, Λ_0, of the electrolyte. Thus

$$\alpha = \frac{\Lambda}{\Lambda_0} \tag{8}$$

This equation involves the assumption that mobilities of the ions coming from the electrolyte are constant from infinite dilution to the concentration in question. From the degree of dissociation and the concentration, the ionization constant or protolysis constant of a weak electrolyte can be obtained.

Water is a weak electrolyte, ionizing according to the equation:

$$H_2O + H_2O \rightleftharpoons H_3O^+ + OH^- \tag{9}$$

The specific conductance, L, of water at 25° is 5.5×10^{-8} mho cm^{-1}, and the equivalent conductance of water at infinite dilution is found from the equivalent conductance of its constituent ions (H_3O^+ and OH^-) to be 547.8 mhos. The equivalent conductance, Λ, of water at 25°C is LV, where V is the volume of water (18 ml) containing 1 gram equivalent of water. Hence, $\Lambda = LV = 5.5 \times 10^{-8} \times 18 = 9.9 \times 10^{-7}$. Therefore, $\alpha = \Lambda/\Lambda_0 = 9.9 \times 10^{-7}/547.8 = 1.81 \times 10^{-9}$. Now $C_{H_3O^+} = C_{OH^-} = 5.55 \times 1.81 \times 10^{-9} = 1.00 \times 10^{-7}$ and

$$K = \frac{C_{H_3O^+} X C_{OH^-}}{C_{H_2O}^2} \tag{10}$$

but C_{H_2O} is a constant, namely 55.5 moles/l and therefore

$$K_w = (55.5)^2 K = C_{H_3O^+} X C_{OH^-} = 1.00$$
$$\times 10^{-7} \times 1.00 \times 10^{-7} = 1 \times 10^{-14} \tag{11}$$

The ionization constant of pure water varies as shown below

Temperature, °C	0	10	25	40	50
$K_w \times 10^{14}$	0.113	0.292	1.008	2.917	5.474

Inserting corresponding values of K_w and absolute temperature into Eq. (7) and solving for ΔH, one finds the heat of ionization per mole of water to be 13.8 kilocalories.

Ionization or dissociation in general can be repressed by adding an excess of a product of the dissociation process.

The acid formed when a base accepts a proton is called the conjugate acid of the base and the base formed when an acid donates a proton is the conjugate base of the acid. Thus, in the reaction

$$HA + H_2O \rightleftharpoons H_3O^+ + A^- \tag{12}$$

HA and A$^-$ are conjugate acid and base and H_2O and H_3O^+ are conjugate base and acid, respectively.

The common ion effect can be found as the following example shows when using acetic acid to which the common acetate ion in the form of sodium acetate has been added, the ionization can be represented by the equation

$$HC_2H_3O_2 + HOH \rightleftharpoons H_3O^+ + C_2H_3O_2^- \tag{13}$$

The acetate ion $C_2H_3O_2^-$ is the conjugate base of acetic acid $HC_2H_3O_2$. The ionization constant can be written

$$K = \frac{C_{H_3O^+} X C_{C_2H_3O_2^-}}{C_{HC_2H_3O_2}} \tag{14}$$

and

$$C_{H_3O^+} = K \frac{C_{HC_2H_3O_2}}{C_{C_2H_3O_2^-}} \tag{15}$$

or

$$pH = pK + \log \frac{C_{salt}}{C_{acid}} \tag{16}$$

Thus, $C_{H_3O^+}$ and hence the degree of ionization of the acid $HC_2H_3O_2$, is decreased with increasing concentration of salt. The salt effect of adding electrolytes with no common ion to a solution of a partially ionizable substance can be seen from the following considerations and using the equilibrium represented by Eq. (14), which in terms of activities becomes:

$$K = \frac{a_{H_3O^+} X a_{C_2H_3O_2^-}}{a_{HC_2H_3O_2}}$$
$$= \frac{C_{H_3O^+} X C_{C_2H_3O_2^-}}{C_{HC_2H_3O_2}} \cdot \frac{f_{H_3O^+} X f_{C_2H_3O_2^-}}{f_{HC_2H_3O_2}} \qquad (17)$$

This ionization constant in terms of activities is called the true or thermodynamic ionization constant. It does not differ too much from the K in Eq. (14) for sufficiently low ionic strengths. The two differ more markedly for appreciable ionic strengths. Now suppose a salt with no common ion is added to the solution. The ionic strength of the solution will be increased. The increase in ionic strength causes a decrease in the activity coefficients of the ions except in very concentrated solutions. Thus, for K of Eq. (17) to remain constant the concentrations of the ions must increase to offset the decrease in their activity coefficients. The acetic acid must therefore increase in ionization and K as defined by Eq. (14) must increase. This is known as the salt effect.

Ampholytes in solution give equal concentrations of a weak acid and a nonconjugate weak base. The amino acids are ampholytes which contain within their molecules equal amounts of a weak acid, the COOH group and a weak nonconjugate base, the NH_2 group.

According to Arrhenius those substances which yield the hydrogen ion in solution are acids, whereas bases produce the hydroxyl ion. As long as water was considered the only "ionizing" solvent these definitions were relatively simple. In the case of nonaqueous solvent chemistry at least three other concepts have been advanced. These are: (1) Franklin's *solvent system concept*, first limited to water and ammonia but since extended to nonprotonic media and defining an acid as a substance yielding a positive ion identical with that coming from autoionization of the solvent and a base as a substance yielding a negative ion identical with that coming from autoionization of the solvent; (2) the *protonic concept* of acids as proton donors and bases as proton acceptors advanced by Bronsted and by Lowry; and (3) Lewis' electronic theory according to which an acid is a molecule, radical, or ion which can accept a pair of electrons from some other atom or group to complete its stable quota of electrons, usually an octet, and forming a covalent bond, and a base is a substance which donates a pair of electrons for the formation of such a bond.

In liquid ammonia as in water autoionization takes place. Ammonium and amide ions are formed by the dissociation or protolysis according to the following equation

$$2NH_3 \rightleftharpoons NH_4^+ + NH_2^- \qquad (18)$$

The acid and base analogs of ammonia as a solvent is specified by this equilibrium as NH_4^+ and NH_2^- ions. All substances which undergo ammonolysis and hence bring about an increase in the ammonium ion concentration yield acid solutions. Thus, P_2S_5 dissolves a liquid ammonia to give an acid solution as follows:

$$P_2S_5 + 12\,NH_3 \rightarrow 2PS(NH_2)_3 + 3(NH_4)_2S. \qquad (19)$$

The solution is acid since an ammonium salt is formed and also because a solvo acid is obtained.

Many substances dissolve in liquid sulfur dioxide to yield ionic, conducting solutions. It has been found that such conductance data extrapolated to very high dilution yield the limiting conductance of sulfur dioxide. Both the Ostwald dilution law and the law of independent mobility of ions hold for "strong" electrolytes in highly dilute solutions.

The order of increasing dissociation and conductivity of salts in liquid sulfur dioxide apparently parallel the order of increasing cationic size. Probably because of solvation effects a similar relationship does not hold with respect to anion size. The mobilities of various ions in liquid sulfur dioxide have been studied. The van't Hoff i factors or mole numbers have been obtained by the ebullioscopic method for a wide variety of solutes in liquid sulfur dioxide. For nonelectrolytes the mole number is one within experimental error. In liquid sulfur dioxide, univalent electrolytes give mole numbers which indicate large effects of ion-association of some kind. As would be expected the mole numbers of these electrolytes approach two in very dilute solutions. See Jander and Mesech, *Z. physik. Chem.*, **A183**, 277 (1939). The mole number in general can be found from the ratio of the value of a colligative property of the solute in solution to the value of the same colligative property for a normal solute, such as sugar, both solutes being at the same molal concentration.

The protonic concept of acid and bases is applicable to many of these high-temperature solvent systems such as the fused ammonium salts which possess the "onium" ion or solvated proton, and the fused anionic acids which are salts possessing a metallic ion and a hydrogen containing anion. One of the most useful of the anionic acids is KHF_2 which is used to dissolve ore minerals containing silica, titania and other refractory oxides.

In many high temperature reactions there is an absence of hydrogen containing ions. The Lewis electron pair concept of acids and bases can be used to advantage in such systems. In such systems strong anion bases such as the O^{--} ion coming from basic compounds such as metallic oxides, hydroxides, carbonates, or sulfates react with acidic oxides such as silica through the intermediate formation of polyanionic silicate complexes. The average ionic size of these complexes depends no doubt on the temperature and the amount of added base.

Anion bases include the sulfide and fluoride ions coming from the corresponding alkali metal compounds. Likewise, metaphosphate and metaborate melts are acid in nature. Also proton-like character can be ascribed to any positive ion. The smaller the positive particle and the higher its charge, the greater is its polarizing tendency in bringing about deformation of negative ions, and the more reasonably can such an ion be looked upon as an acid analog.

Association is the opposite of dissociation. In chemistry, association is the process by which a chemical combination is formed from simpler constituents, due, for example, to van der Waals or Coulombic forces, and to hydrogen bonding or other bonding phenomena. In some cases association constants are determined. Thus, association constants for the formation of ion pairs and ion triplets in molten salts are often determined using conductivity, electromotive force or other measurements.

For example, the association constants, K_1, K_2, and K_{12}, for the formation of the ion pair AgBr and of the ion triplets $AgBr_2^-$ and Ag_2Br^+, respectively, have been evaluated from electromotive force measurements in silver nitrate-sodium bromide-sodium nitrate ($AgNO_3$-NaBr-$NaNO_3$) mixtures at 402, 438, 460 and 500°C. (See Manning, Bansal, Braunstein and Blander, *J. Am. Chem. Soc.*, **84**, 2028 (1962).) Thus, the value of K_1 at 402°C was found to be 633 in mole fraction units. We can write the expression for the reaction involved as

$$Ag^+ + Br^- \rightleftharpoons AgBr \qquad (20)$$

and K_1 becomes

$$K_1 = \frac{N_{AgBr}}{N_{Ag^+} \cdot N_{Br^-}} = 633 \text{ at } 402 \text{ °C} \qquad (21)$$

where N_{AgBr}, N_{Ag^+} and N_{Br^-} are the mole fractions of silver bromide (AgBr), silver ion (Ag^+) and bromide ion (Br^-), respectively, in the molten salt mixture. The large value of K_1 indicates that the mole fraction of silver bromide is large compared to the product of the mole fractions of the silver and bromide ions.

The values of K_2 and K_{12} were likewise large at 402°C. K_1 was 246 and K_{12} was 280. Thus, the processes for the formation of ion triplets, namely,

$$AgBr + Br^- \rightleftharpoons AgBr_2^-$$

and

$$AgBr + Ag^+ \rightleftharpoons Ag_2Br^+$$

proceed to the extent that the concentrations of the ion triplets are large relative to the products of the concentrations of the ion pairs and simple ions. Since the bromide ion was produced from the addition of sodium bromide (NaBr) to one electrode compartment of the cell used in the electromotive force measurements at concentrations of Ag^+ and Br^- ions too low to precipitate silver bromide, and since the association constants were so large, it is evident that practically all of the Br^- ions were tied up in the ion pairs and the ion triplets.

The values of K_1, K_2 and K_{12} were used to calculate different properties of the molten system; for example, the "specific bond free energies" for the ion pair AgBr and the ion triplets $AgBr_2^-$ and Ag_2Br^+ were calculated.

The dissociation constants are the reciprocals of the association constants.

An extensive discussion of the structures and properties of ionic melts using various approaches is given in *Discussions of the Faraday Society*, **32**, 5–267 (1961).

References

DANIELS, FARRINGTON, AND ALBERTY, ROBERT A., "Physical Chemistry," 2nd Edition, New York, John Wiley and Sons, Inc., 1961.

IVES, DAVID J. G., AND JANZ, GEORGE J., "Reference Electrodes," New York, Academic Press, 1961.

KORTUM, G., AND BOCKRIS, J. O'M., "Textbook of Electrochemistry," Vol. I and II, New York, Elsevier Publishing Company, 1951.

MACINNES, D. A., "The Principles of Electrochemistry," New York, Reinhold Publishing Corp., 1939.

MANNING, D. L., BANSAL, R. C., BRAUNSTEIN, J., AND BLANDER, M., *J. Am. Chem. Soc.*, **84**, 2028 (1962).

MOELWYN-HUGHES, E. A., "Physical Chemistry," New York, Pergamon Press, 1957.

YATSIMIRSKII, H. B., AND VASIL'EV, V. P., "Instability Constants of Complex Compounds," New York, Pergamon Press, 1960.

EDWARD S. AMIS

Cross-references: *Acidimetry and Akalimetry; Conductivity, Electrolytic; Conductivity in Nonaqueous Solvents; Fused Salt Electrochemical Properties; Ion Association; Ionic Equilibria.*

DONNAN EFFECT. See MEMBRANE EQUILIBRIUM.

DOUBLE LAYER. See ELECTRODE DOUBLE LAYER.

DOW, HERBERT HENRY (1866–1930)

Although born in Belleville, Ontario (1866), Herbert Henry Dow, founder of The Dow Chemical Company, was of New England parentage, and in Birmingham, Conn., (now Derby), spent most of his early boyhood. When he was 12, Dow's family moved to Cleveland where he later received his college education at Case School of Applied Science. His father, Joseph Dow, was a master mechanic and something of an inventor, with a consuming interest in turbines. From him the younger Dow acquired a similar interest in the mechanics of power which he retained throughout his life. As a result, in later years he was inclined to badger supplies to design larger and more efficient equipment than was in current use, and, for a time, served as a consultant to Westinghouse.

As a chemistry student at Case he became interested in the chemical content of brines and discovered that both chlorine and bromine could be released from them by appropriate voltages of electric current. After graduation he briefly took a teaching position in order to carry on his experiments, and in 1890, with the backing of a family friend, set up shop in a shed in Midland, Mich., with the intention of producing bromine compounds from the brines underlying that area. The early years were in the best Horatio Alger tradition, with financial problems frequently more potent than technical ones. The company

which today bears his name was organized in 1897 to extract chlorine from the same brines, and subsequently took over the earlier bromine operation.

With a restless and inventive mind, Herbert Dow sought constantly to broaden the exploitation of his raw materials and set a pattern of aggressive diversification which characterizes the company to this day. Under his guidance was accomplished the first synthesis in this country of indigo and phenol as well as production of magnesium and the extraction of bromine from sea water.

Before his death in 1930 Dow's company was manufacturing scores of products, in both the organic and inorganic categories, and enjoying sales of nearly $20,000,000 a year. He had personally been honored for his accomplishments with the award of the Perkin Medal in January of that year, and had earlier received honorary doctorates from Case and from the University of Michigan. He had contributed some 100 patents to the chemical industry and several other fields.

Among the many characteristics for which he is remembered are: preoccupation with cheap starting materials—brine, salt, sulfur, etc.; insistence on the most efficient power facilities obtainable; early adherence to large-scale equipment, continuous process and automatic control; a doctrine of origination rather than mimicry.

L. H. WOODMAN

DOWNS, JAMES C. (1885–1957)

James Cloyd Downs, inventor of the Downs sodium cell, was born November 6, 1885, in Newark, N. J. He died at the age of 72 in Saranac Lake, N. Y., after an illustrious career in the chemical industry.

Downs attended public schools in Newark and Cooper Union School in New York and after completing electrical engineering studies in 1904, his first job involved testing meters in New York City. He began his career in the chemical industry two years later by joining the Acker Process Company of Niagara Falls, N. Y. When the plant burned down in 1907, Downs moved to the Niagara Electro Chemical Company in electrical construction and experimental work. The

Niagara Company was managed and partially owned by the Roessler & Hasslacher Chemical Company and was finally absorbed by R&H in 1925.

In 1911 Downs transferred to the new Perth Amboy Plant of R&H which had been erected two years previously for the manufacture of a new bleaching compound. At Perth Amboy he worked with R. J. McNitt in developing a new type of sodium cell. In 1914 he returned to Niagara Falls to work on the design and construction of nine McNitt sodium cells at Niagara. Two years later, he became engineer and assistant manager of a new plant in St. Albans, W. Va., for the installation of the new cell. In 1920 Downs returned to Niagara Falls to begin work on an improved cell which would overcome some of the difficulties of the McNitt cell. As a result of this work, the Downs cell for production of metallic sodium and chlorine from fused salt was developed and adopted by Roessler and Hasslacher. Downs received the Schoellkopf Award in 1934 from the Western New York Section of the American Chemical Society for his contributions to sodium technology.

In 1926 Downs developed tuberculosis and retired to Saranac Lake, N. Y. However, he served as consultant from his home in Saranac Lake for the R&H Company. After R&H was purchased by Du Pont in 1930, Downs continued as a consultant for Du Pont.

He was married and had four sons and a daughter. He died December 18, 1957.

CARMEN W. WALSH

DRY CELLS. See BATTERIES—DRY CELLS.

E

EDISON, THOMAS ALVA (1847–1931)

This American inventor and scientist developed over a thousand patented practical applications of electricity, an overwhelming sum considering that Edison, born February 11, 1847 in Milan, Ohio, attended school for only three months. His mother, a schoolmistress, dissatisfied with his progress, tutored him at home in Port Huron, Michigan, where his family had moved in 1854.

Edison's interest in science was due largely to his mother. She introduced him to several scientific textbooks, including Parker's *Natural and Experimental Philosophy*, which he consulted throughout his life.

Throughout childhood, Edison experimented with chemicals. At 12, while employed as a railroad newsboy, he began concentrating on electricity, using the train cars as a laboratory. During this period he studied telegraphy and became an operator at 15. He spent the next few years vagabonding about the country, working, studying, and experimenting, his inventive nature overpowering his need for steady employment.

Realizing his limited background in science, Edison studied Faraday's work, appreciating the simple, nonmathematical explanations. Edison's retentive brain and indefatigable nature enabled him to solve complex problems with facility. These solutions were from a practical standpoint as is evident from his accomplishments.

His first patented invention, at 21, an electrical vote recorder, was not well received. Thus, Edison resolved to patent only inventions having commercial value. Later, conscious of the economic and social impact of his work, he pursued only research that benefited the public.

By 1877, he had patented over two hundred inventions including stock tickers, duplex, quadruplex, sextuplex, automatic and printing telegraphs, and an electric pen (developed into the mimeograph). He also had persuaded financiers and industrialists to establish a laboratory for his work at Menlo Park, New Jersey. Edison became known as the "Wizard of Menlo Park." The public began sending letters of appreciation for his inventions.

All of these inventions were not original ideas, for he capitalized on the work of others. Reviewing their experiments gave him insight as to the purpose and problems involved. Working quickly and logically, day and night, he would bring their conceptions into practical being. An example of this method is his invention of the incandescent lamp (1878–1879).

J. W. Swan and a few others invented carbon incandescent electric lamps. However, these lamps worked only for short periods and were expensive. Edison devised a lamp using less costly materials. He investigated relationships between electrical resistance, shape, and heat-radiation of filaments; he studied the specific heat of materials, realizing that low-volume current with high voltage and low amperage was cheaper and safer. More than 1600 kinds of materials from tar to cheese plus a variety of vegetable fibers were tried before he obtained success with a carbonized thread loop. It remained incandescent for forty hours in a vacuum bulb. The cost of this research was $40,000. Through Edison's compromise with Swan, who held the English patent, the lamp was known as the "Ediswan" in England.

"The Edison Effect" (1883) is considered his major scientific contribution. Carbon filaments of the bulbs deposited a nonuniform blackening on the glass, being lighter in the plane of the carbon loop. Thus, carbon atoms shot off from some parts of the filament were being obstructed by those from other parts and did not reach the glass surface. By setting a small metal plate on a wire sealed through the bulb between the legs of the carbon filament, Edison noted that if the positive leg was connected through a galvanometer to the plate, a low current was registered when the filament was made incandescent. No current registered if the negative leg was connected. He concluded that the incandescent lamp permitted only negative electricity to pass. This experiment gave impetus to the development of the radio tube.

One of his first inventions at Menlo Park was the carbon transmitter (1877–1878). It brought Bell's telephone into practical use. Placing compressed lamp-black buttons in the primary circuit of an induction coil connected with a voltaic battery and a Bell-type distant receiver in a secondary coil's circuit enabled the transmission of voices by high voltage currents, which would overcome the resistance of long wires.

His phonograph, deemed an original invention by the U.S. Patent Office in 1877, was not popularly received. It consisted of a cylinder, covered with tin-foil, turned by a hand crank, and costing $18. Therefore, ten years later he developed a motor-powered machine with cylindrical wax records. A disk form which reproduced sound with a diamond point and the "Ediphone" used for office dictation evolved later.

Following the death of his first wife, Mary Stillwell, in 1884, Edison moved to Orange, New Jersey. He married Mina Miller in 1886 and profoundly altered his life. The untidy, rough, pioneering nature changed to a more orthodox conception of a well-to-do American. Although he never used the desire for money as a spur to invention, large amounts began to come in. Deafness, which began in childhood, continued yet never interfered with his work.

Other inventions of note were the details of central electric power systems (1879–1889); transmission of telegraphic signals by induction from moving trains or between ships (1885); kinetoscopic camera (1891); concentration of iron ore by a magnetic field (1891–1900); a storage battery using an alkaline solution, the negative material being iron oxide and the positive, nickel hydrate (1900–1910); and the manufacture of Portland cement (1900–1910).

Due to his varied interests, Edison worked on as many as fifty inventions simultaneously. Failure in any experiment was, to him, a method of learning. He instilled this fact in his assistants, highly qualified specialists, who explored the possibilities of his ideas.

Edison also worked on naval problems for the government and on chemical production, such as phenol, during World War I. At 81, he was admitted to the National Academy of Science. He was working on the problems of synthetic rubber production when he died on October 18, 1931.

Congress estimated that Edison contributed fifty billion dollars a year, for fifty years, to the national economy. His brain was assayed as being worth fifteen billion dollars by "The New York Times." Edison, the shrewd but modest man, called his genius "2 per cent inspiration and 98 per cent perspiration."

FLORENCE H. LARKOWSKI

ELECTRICAL CONDUCTIVITY IN SOLIDS. See CONDUCTIVITY (ELECTRICAL) IN SOLIDS.

ELECTRICAL CONTACTS

The term electrical contact means a releasable junction between two conductors which is apt to carry electric current. One distinguishes stationary, sliding, and switching contacts. The general requirement is that the contact consumes relatively little energy. The stationary contact should not change with time. Switching contacts should endure opening and closing operations without "too much wear." In order to explain how contacts can respond to these and other requirements a short survey of the theory is presented.

The mks-unit system is applied. Notice that the equations require all variables expressed in the same unit system; for example, in Eq. (2), P is in Newtons (1 Nw = 0.102 kg force), and H is in Newtons/sq meter.

Contact resistance is a misnomer but is a commonly used term. There is no perceivable transition resistance in the contacts, and what appears are volume effects, certainly a "constriction resistance," and often in addition the resistance in an alien film in the interspace of the contact. The *constriction resistance* arises from the fact that the conducting area is very small, often consisting of small contact spots at elevations of the contact surfaces. Thus, the current flow is constricted to paths narrowing into the small spots and, therefore, exerting high resistance which, of course, is located within the conductors on both sides of the contact area.

Perfectly clean contacts have only constriction

resistance, R_c. They appear in vacuum or where plastic deformation at contact make has moved away disturbant films. In air first thin, invisible so-called adhesion films of oxygen, etc., are deposited on free surfaces; later visible tarnish films (oxides, sulfides, etc.) may develop. With R_f being the film resistance the total "contact resistance" in ohms is

$$R = R_c + R_f \tag{1}$$

One distinguishes load bearing area, A_b, and conducting area, A_c, within A_b. Usually only parts of A_b are conducting, i.e., A_c is a fraction of A_b. The initial load bearing area, A_b, is more or less generated by plastic deformation, and its size, therefore, depends on the mechanical load, P, and the hardness, H, according to Eq. (2), where H is force per unit of the indentation area in the ball indentation test (Vickers or Meyers method).

$$P = \xi H A_b \tag{2}$$

ξ is a factor ≤ 1, often as small as 0.3. It corrects for the fact that complete plastic deformation seldom is reached. Repeated contact make at the same place may lead to solely elastic reaction in the then increased A_b.

For a single circular contact spot with the radius, a, between equal members with dimensions much greater than a, the constriction resistance is

$$R_c = \frac{\rho}{2a} \tag{3}$$

where ρ is the resistivity of the material of the members in ohm-meters. Eq. (4) is a rule of thumb for the resistance of a contact under practical circumstances when the members have the resistivities, ρ_1 and ρ_2, the mechanical load is P and the hardness of the softer member is H.

$$R = \frac{\rho_1 + \rho_2}{2} \sqrt{\frac{H}{P}} \tag{4}$$

Eqs. (3) and (4) are valid in case the current does not heat the contact considerably, which is indicated by a low contact voltage, say below 0.05 volt. The effect of higher voltages on metallic clean contacts is illustrated by Table 1, giving supertemperature in the contact area above the temperature of the bulk of the members as a function of the voltage.

This relation is true for contacts with metallic conducting spots, even for members initially film-covered if metallic conducting spots have been generated by plastic yielding at contact make. The relationship is the consequence of a physical law that is valid when heat generated by electric current flows in the same paths as the current, which is the case with electric contacts. Of course, if the spots are small and consequently the constriction resistance is great, even a small current can produce a considerable voltage.

In order to avoid promotion of oxidation by high temperature, contact voltage should be kept below 0.07 volt, i.e. $IR < 0.07$. The load, P, which secures the right resistance is dependent on the cleanness of the contact. To take an example: for installation of bus bar contacts under common circumstances it is advisable to choose P about 30 times higher than required by Eq. (4) and the rule $IR < 0.07$.

P will often be produced by means of a screw, and it is valuable to have the following rule of thumb for the pressure force, P, in Newtons produced by a screw with the diameter, D, in meters on which the torque, M, in Newton-meters is applied:

$$P = 3 \frac{M}{D} \tag{5}$$

Melting in the contact is indicated by the "melting voltage" which is

for Ni	Cu and Au	Mo	Ag	W	Pt	
0.65	0.43	0.75	0.37	1.1	0.65	volts

This, of course, is the upper limit for any contact voltage. For carbon a similar limiting voltage of 5 volts is observed.

The region of high supertemperatures is so thin that it cannot be scanned with thermoelements. Neither can the concentrated equipotential surfaces near the contact surface be tested by means of probes.

The distance from contact spots to probes measuring the contact resistance should be at least $20a$, where a is the spot radius. This is usually an easily satisfied requirement.

The reason why high contact temperature, even far below melting, must be avoided is that high temperature accelerates oxidation. However, in cases when available voltage suffices to break through films or the contact force is able to partly wipe them away, a certain oxidation may be tolerated.

Classification of contacts

Table 2 gives physical data about properties of a few important contact materials.

Stationary or permanent contacts. Examples of this type include plug and socket, clamped, and wrapped contacts. For obtaining lasting good conductance, it is necessary that metallic spots be generated by plastic deformation at contact make. Even a short opening of such spots gives the air opportunity to contaminate their clean metallic character. Therefore, the pressure producing means should be able to maintain the pressure in spite of possible vibrations and in spite of the tendency of the material to creep away from the pressure. This means that the system should be elastic, for example, act with "washers." Permanent contacts between different metals should be avoided because of their tendency toward electrolytic corrosion.

Sliding contacts. With respect to the wear it is recommended that metal members of considerably different hardness be chosen. The harder member provides a smooth sliding surface. With equal hardness both surfaces become uneven, and wear is accelerated because of interlocking. Of course, one must consider whether tarnish films on the harder metal can produce insulation.

Carbon is a contact material with exceptional properties. It does not weld and is self lubricating in sliding contacts, because it deposits a thin (sometimes invisible) lubricating film of graphite flakes on the sliding surfaces. Only under high-altitude conditions (dryness), the film does not always adhere where it is needed, and severe wear appears. Other valuable properties are exploited in brushes on commutators. The constriction resistances in the brushes are favorable for so-called resistance commutation, and brushes preferably should have a small Young's modulus that enables them to adapt their faces to the curvature of the commutator. The adaption is necessary to prevent loss of contact with commutator segments in phases where contact opening would lead to detrimental arcing.

TABLE 1

Contact voltage	0.1	0.2	0.3
Supertemperature in the contact surface, °C	130	400	700

TABLE 2. PROPERTIES OF COMMONLY USED CONTACT MATERIALS

Metals	Electrical Resistivity, 10^{-8} ohm — m	Thermal Conductivity, (watt/ m-deg)	Hardness, H, 10^8 (Nw/ m²)
Material			
Ag	1.65	418	4
Au	2.3	310	3
Cu	1.8	380	6
Mo	5.8	140	18
Ni	8	70	16
Pd	10.8	70	7
Pt	11	70	5
W	5.5	190	25
electrographite	3000	30	2
Alloys			
Ag, 40Pd	21	30	9.5
Cu, 10Sn	18	50	7
Cu, 40Zn	8.5	100	10
Pt, 10Ir	25	40	10
Compounds			
W, 35Cu, 0.5 Ni	5.3	150	15
WC, 13 Co	20	70	20

Switching Contacts

Light duty and high-repetitive-operation contacts. An example of the type is found in automotive regulators. The troubles are high resistance contamination, material transfer, and adherence. Because of their inertness (except against sulfur) silver and silver alloys (particularly Ag + Pd) are preferred as contact materials. Arc "quenching" is used to diminish material transfer at arcing. An effective quenching consists of shunting the arc by a circuit containing a capacitor and a rectifier, that leads current from the opening contact into the capacitor, thus weakening or killing the arc, and prevents high discharge current from the capacitor at closure.

In the cases when the load is strong enough or the voltage high enough to puncture highly resistive films, hard materials as W or WC can be used to prevent cold weld, i.e., disturbing adherence.

Medium and heavy-duty circuit breakers and contactors. Strong arcs are inevitable. The problem is to limit their life. The requirements are different for d-c and a-c.

In *a-c breakers* the arc is weakened every time the current passes through zero. Its cathode- and anode-drop regions become ineffective at once, but the plasma (also called column) of the arc remains hot and highly ionized for some time and has the tendency to take over current and recover as soon as high voltage reappears. Fortunately the circuit usually is not able to produce reigniting voltage before about 10^{-4} second. Meanwhile the plasma can be killed by cooling in arc chutes, in case of moderate current (<3000 amp) or by being blown to pieces and cooled in an air blast or oil vapor that is generated in the oil of the switch by the arc itself.

In *d-c switches* the arc has no natural weak phase, and the switch has to kill the arc at full current. The active phenomena are the cooling and the lengthening of the arc plasma until it requires a greater voltage than is available in the circuit. Lengthening is produced by magnetic blowing whereby the arc may be driven between walls which in addition cool it.

So-called low-voltage breakers often have a main contact and an arcing contact that, operating after the main one, produces final breaking with arcing. The main contact is responsible for the conduction through the closed switch.

Of course, it is required that the contact members do not oxidize when heated by the arc to such an extent that conducting contact can not be regained at closure. Neither should the members be deformed beyond certain limits.

Silver satisfies the requirements with respect to good conduction and no oxidation in air, but its mechanical properties and low melting temperature do not guarantee conservation of shape. Copper does not oxidize in oil breakers, but it deforms as silver does under the influence of the arc heat. In compound materials, such as silver-tungsten, the silver provides the good conduction, whereas the tungsten framework not only strengthens the material against deformation but also prevents much melting of the compound material and welding. The reason for this is that the refractory metal, without melting, endures heating to a sufficiently high temperature for emission of the electrons needed by the arc. Thereby, the current density in the cathode spot becomes relatively low, and the silver or copper of the compound material is, so to say, dispensed from participating in the delivery of electrons, because Ag and Cu could contribute to the arc current only in case of a very high current density accompanied by an extremely high field at the cathode. The wear on these sintered electrodes is up to 10 times less than electrodes of copper or silver would

suffer. It is an advantage that the components do not alloy, because in an alloy the silver or copper could not provide the good conduction. With the good conductors Ag and Cu one combines refractory materials as W, Mo, and WC. Nickel is admixed as a binder which, during the sintering, produces a favorable liquid phase. These compound materials are very hard and are difficult to machine. Compositions of silver and nickel are readily machined and formed, but they are suitable only for medium duty service.

In *mercury switches* one or both contact members are liquid mercury in a sealed container. Oxygen must be excluded. The operation involves making one electrode flow until it contacts the other, either by inclining the container or using a plunger that displaces mercury, or by heating the gas filling so as to alter the pressure on the mercury. The solid connectors are of platinum or molybdenum. Advantages are: 1) the electrodes have no wear, since the mercury evaporated by the arc redeposits and returns to its contact member; 2) the conductance of the switch remains good; and 3) the switch can be operated by small forces. A drawback is that the current is limited to moderate values.

In a *"vacuum switch"* the arc, of course, does not burn in vacuum but in the vapor of the electrodes which is produced initially by boiling metal in the decreasing contact spot, then by heat from the arc. This vapor condenses in a couple of microseconds at the zero phase of a-c, so that full dielectric strength is rapidly obtained. This is the reason why vacuum switches can be made with relatively small dimensions. A disadvantage is that the arc is so unstable that it may extinguish at such a high current as 50 amp (chopping), thereby inducing detrimental voltages in the circuit. Advantages are that the switch is nonexplosive and nontoxic. The contact material is preferably tungsten. The upper current limit seems presently to be about 4000 amp (much higher for capacitor discharge) and this holds at about any practical circuit voltage.

References

1. HOLM, R., "Electric Contacts Handbook," Berlin, Springer-Verlag, 1958.
2. KEIL, A., "Werkstoffe für elektrische Kontakte," Berlin, Springer-Verlag, 1960.

R. HOLM

Cross-references: *Dielectric Properties of Vacuum; Electric Arc Properties.*

ELECTRICAL CURRENTS, EFFECTS ON ELECTRODEPOSITION OF METALS

Metals are usually electrodeposited with low voltage d-c supplied by a rectifier or a motor generator. The wave form of the current of a rectifier or a motor generator has some ripple when compared to the current wave form of a pure d-c source such as the storage battery. The manipulation or alteration of this normally used d-c as supplied by rectifiers, motor generators, and storage batteries to form a modulated current usable for electrodeposition of metals has been a field for research and investigation starting about the time of Coehn's work in 1893.[8] Shortly thereafter in 1896, Roesing published a paper on the use of fast-cycle PR (periodic reverse) current for the deposition of zinc and copper.[3] Since these initial studies, much research has been done, but very few production installations used modulated current for electrodeposition before the 1940's.

In the United States during the early 1940's, a form of current modulation which is the superimposition of a-c on d-c was promoted for production plating by Chester.[10] In the late 1940's and early 1950's, further research work on modulated currents resulted in production installations using interrupted d-c (IDC) and periodic reverse (PR). (See **Periodic Reverse Plating**.) Outside of some possible isolated instances, the commercial use of modulated current for the electrodeposition of metals can be limited to slow-cycle interrupted d-c, superimposed a-c on d-c, and slow-cycle PR current. The current modulations which seem to attract the most commercial use are slow-cycle interrupted d-c and slow-cycle PR, with slow-cycle PR current being by far the most widely used at the present time in all parts of the world. Baeyens published a thorough review of the literature on electroplating with modulated current in 1954.[5]

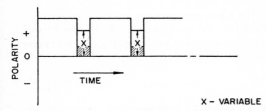

Fig. 1. Polarity classification of fundamental types of modulated current cycles; Type 1—current wave form cycles that do not change polarity.

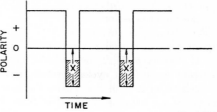

Fig. 2. Polarity classification of fundamental types of modulated current cycles; Type 2—current wave form cycles that change polarity.

When the frequency, intensity, wave shape, and other variables are taken into consideration, there is no limit to the variety of current wave-form cycles that can be generated for the deposition of metals. With these variables and the numerous possible combinations from the two polarity wave-form classifications, the number of wave-form cycles that can be conceived is only limited by the imagination.

Since Baeyens' review, most of the references in the literature to the use of various types of modulated currents for the electrodeposition of metals have been of Russian origin. As an example, of the more than 30 references on modulated current from 1958 through 1960 in the *Chemical Abstracts*, 23 are of Russian publication. Russian studies report on the superimposition of a-c on d-c, pulsed d-c, PR, and interrupted d-c.[2]

Types of Current for the Electrodeposition of Metal

Polarity Wave Form Classification. There are two fundamental types of modulated current wave-form cycles. Type I, (Fig. 1), would include all the current wave form cycles where the current does not change polarity. Type II, (Fig. 2), would include all the current wave-form cycles that have positive and negative current values.

Examples of a Type I current wave-form (Fig. 1) are:

Type I—Polarity does not reverse
1. Rippled d-c (current supplied by a rectifier or generator).
2. Interrupted d-c.
3. Pulsed d-c.
4. Superimposed a-c on d-c.

Examples of a Type II current wave form (Fig. 2) are:

Type II—Polarity Reverses

1. Superimposed a-c on d-c.
2. Periodic reverse current (PR).

A superimposed a-c on d-c could fit in Type I or Type II. For example, Type I would include those current wave-form cycles formed by the superimposition of a-c on d-c where the maximum negative a-c value is never more than the d-c value at the same instantaneous time. The superimposition of a-c on d-c would come under Type II when the maximum negative a-c value is greater than d-c value at the same instantaneous time. To obtain actual deposition of metal with Type II would require that the plating coulombs times the cathode efficiency would have to exceed the deplating coulombs times the anode efficiency.

Frequency Classification. Types I and II modulated current wave forms classified according to polarity reversal or nonreversal for the electrodeposition of metals can be further divided into two time or frequency classes. Frequency ranges studied have been from millions of cycles per second to several cycles per day. This subdivision of Type I and II is based on the present availability of the equipment or the practicality of obtaining equipment to pro-

duce the required current modulated for production plating. These two time or frequency types of modulated current under Types I and II will be designated as fast cycle and slow cycle (Fig. 3). A fast cycle will be those modulated current cycles that have a frequency of more than one cycle per second, while a slow cycle will be the modulated current cycles that have a frequency of less than one cycle per second. To obtain slow-cycle current, it is only necessary to use presently available rectifiers or motor generators with the proper contactors or timing equipment. To produce fast-cycle current in the amperage ratings required for production plating would require specialized power generating equipment not ordinarily used for the electrodeposition of metals. Much of this specialized equipment has many drawbacks and limitations. Due to these shortcomings, modulated currents of more than one cycle per second have not been used more extensively in production plating.

Rippled D-C (Current Supplied by Generators and Rectifiers)

Currents supplied by generators and rectifiers are pulsating unidirectional currents usually referred to as a rippled d-c when compared to a steady d-c from a storage battery.

Rectifiers can be designed so that the output current has a d-c wave form or ripple comparable to the d-c wave form or ripple supplied by a d-c generator. In such cases, the deposition of metal with the rectifier would be comparable to that obtained with the d-c generator. It has been established from production experience that the d-c output of a three-phase, full-wave rectifier would be as satisfactory as current supplied by a d-c generator for the deposition of any metal. However, the current outputs of single-phase, half-wave and full-wave rectifiers have limitation in the deposition of certain metals, especially if specific physical properties or bright deposits are required.

Rectifiers can be designed, depending on the circuitry, to produce currents of the following wave forms which have a ripple that is expressed in a percentage (Fig. 4).

Type of Rectifier	Per cent Ripple Range
1. Single-phase, half-wave	123–125
2. Single-phase, full-wave	46–52
3. Three-phase, half-wave (no load)	18–20
4. Three-phase, full-wave (no load)	Under 5

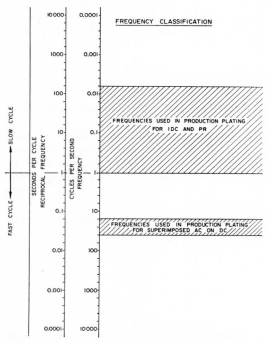

FIG. 3. Frequency classification of modulated current cycles.

The ripple or wave shape can be observed by connecting an oscilloscope across the output terminals of a rectifier.

The single-phase, half-wave circuit is never used in commercial rectifier units for electroplating. The single-phase, full-wave circuit is often used in small bench rectifiers. The three-phase, half-wave and three-phase, full-wave are used in all large rectifiers. It might be suspected that such large variation in ripple from a single-phase, full-wave rectifier would affect the deposition of metal. Many plating processes, for example, the electroplating of copper, silver, and gold, seem to be unaffected. This view is supported by the successful use of many small single-phase, full-wave rectifier units used in the plating of jewelry. However, with the development of new organic and inorganic brightener systems that can be used with the deposition of these metals, consideration should be given to the percentage of ripple in the rectifier output.

The deposition of other metals appears to be more critical, especially the bright plating of chromium, nickel, cadmium, and zinc. Since there is considerable difference in the initial cost and subsequent maintenance between a three-phase, full-wave rectifier and a three-phase, half-wave rectifier, their application for the deposition of various metals must be evaluated.

It is the general opinion of many authorities in the plating field that rectifiers of low ripple, less than 5 per cent, should be used for decorative chromium plating, bright cadmium plating, and bright nickel plating.[1, 6, 7] This suggestion is made even in view of the fact that the three-phase, half-wave rectifier with 18 per cent ripple has been recommended and used successfully in all commercial electroplating processes.[1]

Interrupted Direct Current

Interrupted direct current is formed by periodically interrupting the normally-used direct current so that the current value is zero for a specified time. Interrupted direct current, in the slow-cycle time range, is the easiest type of modulated current to produce with rectifiers or d-c generators. Timing mechanisms are required to permit variation in the plate and off times. The plate and off times can be varied independently while the plating current is readily varied in the normal manner as in d-c plating. Interrupted d-c can also be produced by a half-

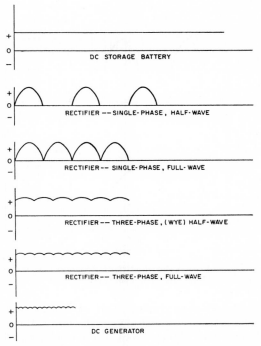

FIG. 4. Direct current wave forms (storage battery, rectifier, and d-c generator).

wave rectifier, and the frequency is dependent on the a-c supplied to the rectifier. The fast-cycle interrupted d-c produced in this manner has been primarily of academic or research interest. Fast-cycle interrupted d-c has been found to be detrimental for the bright plating of nickel, chromium, zinc, and cadmium. Coehn, Madsen, and others studied the use of interrupted d-c for the deposition of metal, but very little if any interrupted d-c was used in production plating before 1950.[5, 8]

Pulsed Direct Current

A pulsed direct current is a modulated current wave form which is generally produced by periodically imposing peaks of current of equal or varying magnitude and frequency upon the d-c. Pulsed d-c was first used for alloy plating in 1931 by Winkler.[9] Winkler claimed that with pulsed d-c he was able to plate compositions of alloys that could not be deposited by d-c. Grimm also used pulsed d-c for alloy plating by switching the pulses to inert anodes.[5] Fig. 5 shows fast-cycle pulsed d-c wave forms obtained by the imposition of 1800 and 3600 cycles per second on d-c. The apparatus required to produce a fast-cycle pulsed d-c shown in Fig. 5 is very

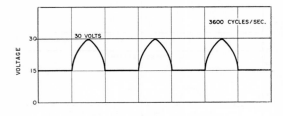

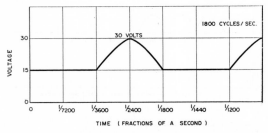

FIG. 5. Pulsed direct current wave forms; comparison of 1800 and 3600 cycles per second.

expensive and complex. The equipment consists of a high-frequency oscillator, a transformer, and rectifier tubes. The oscillator is fed by a 60-cycle transformer with a rating higher than necessary in order to maintain the consistent voltage. After entering the oscillator, the 60-cycle a-c is rectified to d-c and then converted to a high-frequency a-c which can be varied from 300 to 3600 cycles per second. Upon leaving the oscillator, the high-frequency a-c enters a rectifier tube and the lower half of the sine wave is blocked off. In this case, the magnitude of the pulse is independent of the frequency. In this particular installation for pulsed d-c, the time of duration of each pulse is equal to the time between pulses and cannot be varied. To generate slow-cycle pulsed d-c the equipment would be simple and would be practical to use in production plating. However, little if any value has been noted from the use of slow-cycle pulsed d-c.

Superimposed Alternating Current on Direct Current

The superimposition of a-c on d-c usually referred to in the literature would be the superimposition of a-c faster than 25 cycles per second. The commercially available 25 to 60 cycles per second was used for most research investigations and production plating by Chester and others.[10]

Superimposed a-c on d-c was used initially by Wohlwill for the refining of gold from a gold chloride-hydrochloric acid solution.[5] Chester in the 1940's was granted numerous United States patents for the deposition of copper, zinc, cadmium, arsenic, and antimony using superimposed a-c on d-c and had limited production success with the deposition of copper, cadmium, and zinc with this form of current modulation.[4] Primarily due to equipment problems, the use of superimposed a-c on d-c has had only limited production application to the electrodeposition of metals.

Chester maintained that just enough a-c voltage should be applied so that the effective plating current is reversed for a small fraction of every cycle. Fig. 6 shows a typical set of curves and voltage values for such work. In Fig. 6C, an a-c of 6 volts peak value is superimposed on a steady d-c of 4 volts. The resulting voltage applied to the electrodes shown by the current in shaded areas varies from approximately 10 volts in the positive direction (plate) to approximately 2 volts in the opposite direction (deplate). For proper operation, the exact amount of reverse current and time that is applied must be controlled accurately.

The importance of reversing the plating current for a small portion of each cycle lies in the

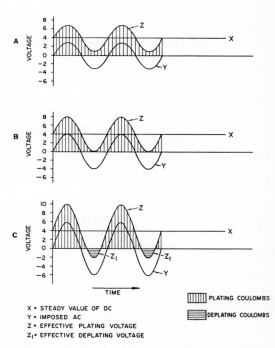

X = STEADY VALUE OF DC
Y = IMPOSED AC
Z = EFFECTIVE PLATING VOLTAGE
Z_1 = EFFECTIVE DEPLATING VOLTAGE

FIG. 6. Superimposed a-c on d-c wave forms.

fact that this breaks up the anode passivity, which is the tendency for the electrochemical process to approach a saturated or inactive condition. This anode passivity is one of the limiting factors in conventional d-c plating. By reducing or eliminating it, the rate of metal deposition is increased, and the entire plating operation is made more efficient.

Superimposition of a-c on d-c also affects the hydrogen over-voltage. This in turn reduces the starting voltage normally required for the deposition of metal in the plating bath.

Definitions

1. *Ripple*—The ratio of the alternating current component in the output of a rectifier to the average direct current component.

$$\text{Per cent ripple} = \frac{\text{RMS a-c Voltage}}{\text{Average d-c Voltage}} \times 100$$

2. *Modulated Current*—A modulated current is any current usable for electroplating that changes in value, either absolute or in sign. The change in current value is cyclic and repetitive during the plating operation.
3. *Superimposed A-C on D-C*—A modulated current which is formed by superimposing alternating current on direct current. The resultant current can change in sign as well as in absolute value (Fig. 6).
4. *Interrupted D-C (IDC)*—A modulated current which is formed by interrupting the d-c periodically, that is, the current value is zero for a specified time. Usually slow cycle.
5. *Periodic Reverse Current Plating Process (PR)*—A process involving the periodic reversal of the plating current for appreciable time intervals so that the reverse current will remove a substantial amount of the previously plated metal.
6. *Slow Cycle*—A modulated current which has a frequency of less than one cycle per second.
7. *Fast Cycle*—A modulated current which has a frequency of more than one cycle per second.
8. *Pulsed D-C*—A modulated current which is formed by periodically imposing on the d-c peaks of current of equal or varying magnitude and frequency.
9. *Covering Power*—The ability of a plating solution under a specified set of plating conditions to deposit metal on the surface of a recess or deep hole.
10. *Leveling Action*—The ability of a plating solution or the type of wave form of the current applied to a plating solution to produce a surface smoother than that of the basis metal.
(Also see **Electroplating Terms.**)

References

1. GRAHAM, A. K., "Electroplating Engineering Handbook," 1st Edition, Chapter 30, p. 551-583, New York, Reinhold Publishing Corp., 1955.
2. VAGRAMYAN, A. T., AND SOLOV'EVA, Z. A., "Technology of Electrodeposition," Chapter 3, p. 95–117, Teddington, England, Robert Draper, Ltd., 1961.
3. ROESING, B., "Metal Deposition by Means of Alternating Current," *Z. Elektrochem.*, **2**, 550–552 (1896).
4. BIRDSALL, G. W., "Superimposed AC on DC," *Steel*, (March 12, 1945).
5. BAEYENS, P., "Electroplating and Modulated Current," 4th International Conference on Electrodeposition and Metal Finishing, London, (April 23, 1954)—[*Transaction Metal Finishing*, **31**, 429–452 (1954)].
6. DARRAH, ROBERT J., "Is Your Plating Rectifier Defective," *Product Finishing*, **24**, 44–51 (October, 1960).
7. SCHNEIDERS, F. A., "AC Ripple in Rectifier Output," *Plating*, **46**, No. 11, 1279–1281 (November, 1959).
8. COEHN, A., German Patent 75,482 (1893).
9. (a) Winkler, J., German Patent 576,585 (1931). (b) Winkler, J., British Patent 396,191 (March 15, 1933).
10. (a) Chester, A. E., (Assignor to Poor & Co.), U.S. Patent 2,443,599 (June 22, 1948). (b) Chester, A. E., (Assignor to Poor & Co.), U.S. Patent 2,515,192 (July 18, 1950). (c) Chester, A. E., (Assignor to Poor & Co.), U.S. Patent 2,548,867 (April 17, 1951). (d) Chester, A. E., (Assignor to Poor & Co.), U.S. Patent 2,606,147 (August 5, 1952). (e) Chester, A. E., (Assignor to Poor & Co.), U.S. Patent 2,651,609 (September 8, 1953). (f) Chester, A. E., (Assignor to Poor & Co.), U.S. Patent 2,651,610 (September 8, 1953).

MYRON CERESA

Cross-references: entries with *Electroplating* or *Electrodeposition* titles; *Periodic Reverse Plating; see specific metals.*

ELECTRICAL UNITS AND STANDARDS

Basic Considerations

The physical standards in terms of which electrical quantities are evaluated are the embodiment of the defined electrical units, or of fractions or multiples of these units. Such standards form the basis for the calibration of measuring devices and systems. The defined electrical units, uniform throughout the world by international agreement, are related to the mechanical units of length, mass, and time—the meter, the kilogram, and the second—in such a way that the electrical and mechanical units of energy—the watt-second and the joule

—are identical. These *absolute* electrical units were defined for the United States by a Congressional Act (Public Law 617 of the 81st Congress); and Section 12 of this law contains the following statement—"It shall be the duty of the National Bureau of Standards to establish the values of the primary electric units in absolute measure, and the legal values for these units shall be those represented by, or derived from, national reference standards maintained by the National Bureau of Standards." These "legal" units will be described in later paragraphs. Their establishment is based on "absolute" measurements, so called because the values of the "absolute" electrical units are experimentally realized in terms of appropriate mechanical units.

Two types of *absolute* measurements have been used in assigning numerical values to the basic electrical standards in terms of mechanical units. The *ohm* is evaluated in terms of the mechanical units of length and time; the *ampere* in units of mass, length, and time. The *absolute-ohm* determinations on which the *legal* ohm is based have involved an inductor so constructed that its value can be computed from its measured dimensions together with the conventionally assigned permeability of the space around it. This inductance is supplied with a periodically varying current, and its reactance at the known frequency is, in effect, compared with the resistance of a standard resistor.[1] This experiment could equally well involve the comparison of a capacitive reactance and resistance. Indeed, such a determination offers decided advantages in that the electric field of a capacitor can be completely confined by shields so that the value of capacitance is independent of neighboring objects outside the shield, whereas the magnetic field of an inductor cannot be limited to be free from proximity effects. Absolute ohm determinations have been made recently in terms of computable capacitors,[2] although their results have not yet (1964) been incorporated into the "legal" ohm. In an *absolute-ampere* determination, a pair of coils is arranged so that the force (or torque) between them when they carry current can be measured in terms of the force of gravity acting on a known mass. Such an arrangement is called a *current balance*. The current, measured in *absolute* amperes, is passed through a resistor whose value is known in *absolute* ohms. The resulting voltage drop is com-

pared to the emf of a standard cell, whose value is thus assigned in *absolute* volts.[3]

Values having been assigned to physical standards of resistance and of voltage on the basis of absolute measurements, the values of the other electrical quantities can be derived from them. Alternatively, values of inductance (or of capacitance) could be assigned directly in terms of the calculable inductor (or capacitor) constructed for the absolute-ohm experiment. However, the *ohm* and *volt* are considered to be the basic units of electrical measurement, and their physical embodiments in resistance coils and standard cells become the fundamental electrical standards and the basis of the "legal" units.

"International" and Absolute Units

The assignment of values to electrical standards based on a system of absolute units, has been recognized as desirable ever since it was first proposed by the British Association for the Advancement of Science. But difficulties encountered in absolute measurements led to rather large uncertainties in the values of the units. This resulted in the adoption (1894) of an auxiliary set of "international" units, which were intended to be a "reasonable approximation" of the absolute units and which, it was hoped, could be reproduced with sufficient accuracy for measurement purposes. These units were specified in terms of the resistance of a uniform mercury column of a certain length and mass, and by the current that would deposit silver at a certain rate from a silver nitrate solution. These units—the "mercury" ohm and "silver" ampere—could be reproduced within a few hundredths per cent; but better accuracy was eventually required. With the general improvement in measurements, the techniques of absolute measurements also improved, and it became possible to assign values of the units within about 10 ppm by absolute methods. Accordingly, on January 1, 1948, the "international" system of units was abandoned and the "absolute" system universally adopted. This required small adjustments in the values assigned to the various units, because of differences between the magnitudes of the "international" units (last assigned in 1910) and the newly determined "absolute" units. The table below may be used to convert the United States version of the "international" units to "absolute" units.

United States Values

1 international ohm = 1.000495 absolute ohms
1 international volt = 1.000330 absolute volts
1 international ampere
  = 0.999835 absolute ampere
1 international coulomb
  = 0.999835 absolute coulomb
1 international henry = 1.000495 absolute henrys
1 international farad = 0.999505 absolute farad
1 international watt = 1.000165 absolute watts

Maintenance of the Electrical Units

The National Bureau of Standards has the duty to maintain the electrical units defined by Public Law 617 of the 81st Congress. It also makes these units available by measuring the basic standards of other laboratories.*

The absolute measurements on which the assignment of the National reference standards is based, are time-consuming and require great care and skill. Their occasional repetition, to maintain a surveillance on the constancy of the National units, is desirable. But for the purpose of providing a continuing measurement capability, groups of wire-wound resistors and of standard cells constitute the National standards and form the basis for the "legal" system of units.

Resistance Standards

The National reference standard of resistance is a group of 10 one-ohm resistors of special construction. Their values were initially assigned from the various *absolute-ohm* determinations; and the *legal* unit of resistance is preserved in terms of the average of the group. These resistors are intercompared regularly, and also are compared at regular intervals (through measurements made at the International Bureau at Sevres, France) with the standards maintained by the national laboratories of other countries. It is believed very unlikely that the *legal* unit—the Washington Ohm—which is preserved in terms of the group average, differs from the defined *absolute* ohm by as much as 4 ppm. The group comprising the National standard are of the Thomas type,[5] wound of No. 12 AWG manganin wire, vacuum annealed at

* This service is performed on request of the laboratory desiring the measurement. With some exceptions, the National Bureau of Standards is required to recover the cost of these tests, and a "Fee Schedule" detailing the conditions and cost of tests is available from the Bureau.

550°C, and sealed in double-walled containers. The maximum net change in any member of the group with respect to the group average has been a little over 2 ppm during the 30 years that have elapsed (1964) since the group was set up. These resistors can be intercompared, or compared with other similar standards, to about 1 part in 10^7. By suitable series and parallel combinations, ratios of resistance can be established to a few parts in 10^7; and the National standard can be used to extend the range of measurement to higher and lower resistance values. Other standards can be assigned values stepwise from the National reference group to a maximum of 10^8 ohms and a minimum of 10^{-5} ohm. Wire-wound construction is not feasible for resistors of 10^9 ohms or more, and a film of resistive material on an insulating base is regularly used. Such resistors are generally less stable than wire-wound units, and their values may depend on humidity, voltage, and other factors. Accurately known stable standards are not available in the very high resistance region. The usual techniques of measurement can be applied, but with increasing difficulty, up to about 10^{12} ohms, but higher resistances cannot be determined stepwise from the basic standard. A group of selected hermetically sealed resistors, in the range 10^9 to 10^{14} ohms, has been watched over a period of years by a loss-of-charge method.[6] Under specified measurement conditions, the best of this group appears to be drifting at rates that range from 0.1 per cent per year for 10^9-ohm units to 0.5 per cent per year for 10^{14}-ohm units.

Voltage Standards

The National reference standard of emf is a group of 44 saturated cadmium cells, maintained at a temperature of 28°C within 0.01°C at all times and held at a constant temperature within 0.001°C during intercomparison. Eleven of the cells have been in the reference group since 1906; seven made in 1932 and 26 made in 1949 were added to the group in 1955. New cells made periodically of carefully purified materials, are kept under the same conditions as the reference group and compared with it regularly. Thus, a cell having a known history of constancy is always available for replacement, if one of the cells in the National reference group should fail. The cells of the National reference group are intercompared regularly, and their average value is assumed to be constant. It is in terms of this group average and its assignment from absolute measurements, that the "legal" volt is maintained. This unit is compared on a regular basis with those of other countries through the International Bureau in Sevres.

The cell universally used as a reference standard of emf has a positive electrode of mercury and a negative electrode of cadmium-mercury amalgam (about 10 per cent Cd), with cadmium sulfate as electrolyte and mercurous sulfate as a depolarizer. In the usual H form of the saturated cell, a paste of mercurous sulfate and cadmium sulfate crystals covers the mercury electrode in the positive limb, and the solution of cadmium sulfate is saturated in the presence of $CdSO_4 \cdot 8/3H_2O$ crystals in each limb to maintain saturation for all temperatures within its working range.

Laboratory reference standards of emf are usually cadmium cells of the saturated type, although unsaturated cells (generally used with potentiometers as working standards) sometimes serve also as the basic reference standard of a laboratory. The temperature coefficient of emf of a saturated cadmium cell is much larger than that of an unsaturated cell, and its temperature must be held constant within 0.01°C if its emf is to be constant to $1\mu v$. The international formula (adopted in 1908) relating the emf of a saturated cadmium cell to its temperature is

$$E_t = E_{20} - 40 \times 10^{-6} (t - 20) - 0.95$$
$$\times 10^{-6} (t - 20)^2 + 0.01 \times 10^{-6} (t - 20)^3,$$

where E_t is the emf at temperature, t. This formula is stated to apply to either neutral or acid cells and to hold within about a microvolt* for temperatures between 0 and 40°C.

Capacitance Standards

Capacitors whose values can be computed accurately from their measured dimensions are necessarily small (100 pf or less), and are of 3-terminal construction with gas (or vacuum) dielectric. A 3-terminal construction is required in order that the geometry of the active electrode system may be completely defined, and that the solid insulating supports for the electrodes be so located that they do not influence either the computed capacitance or the quadra-

* For further discussion of temperature coefficients see Vigoreux, P., and Watts, S., *Proc. Phys. Soc. (London)*, **45**, 172, (1933).

ture relation between voltage and current. Until recently such capacitors were usually built as a parallel-plate guard-ring configuration, or as a system of coaxial guarded cylinders, and the accuracy of the assigned value was at best around 0.01 per cent. The situation as regards computable capacitors has changed completely since 1956, thanks to a new theorem in electrostatics announced by D. G. Lampard of the Australian National Standards Laboratory.[7] This theorem may be stated in the following general terms—"If four infinite cylindrical conductors of arbitrary section are assembled with their generators parallel, to form a completely enclosed hollow cylinder, in such a way that the internal cross-capacitances are equal, then in vacuum each of these cross-capacitances is $\ln2/4\pi^2$ stat-farads per cm length." A practical realization of such a capacitor consists of four equal closely spaced cylindrical rods with their axes parallel and at the corners of a square.[8] The internal cross-capacitance amounts to about 2 pf per meter length and, if end effects are eliminated, this capacitance can be computed as accurately as 1) the length can be measured, and 2) the permittivity of vacuum can be calculated from its assigned permeability and the speed of light. Transformer ratio-arm bridges[9] are available in which 1 pf capacitors can be intercompared to a precision better than 1 ppm, and 10 to 10^3 pf capacitors can be assigned values with about this same precision. Thus, in the range 1 to 10^3 pf, 3-terminal reference standards of capacitance are possible with an initial assignment good to 1 to 2 ppm, and sealed units are available at the 10^2 and 10^3 pf level that are stable within 20 ppm per year.

Solid-dielectric capacitors, in which thin sheets of clear mica are interleaved with metal foil, are used as working standards from 10^{-3} to $1\mu f$. The phase-defect angle of the best mica capacitors may amount to 1 to 2 minutes in the audio frequency range, and the capacitance may be expected to remain constant within 0.01–0.02 per cent over many years.

Inductance Standards

Self inductors and mutual inductors whose values can be computed from their measured dimensions, have been constructed at various national laboratories for use in absolute measurements. Computable self inductors are single-layer solenoids wound on marble, porcelain, low-expansion glass, or fused silica cylinders; in some instances a screw thread has been cut into the face of the cylinder to control the spacing of the winding.[10] Computable mutual inductors generally follow a design by Campbell, or Wenner's modifications of it.[11] The primary consists of single-layer windings on a cylindrical form, the winding sections being spaced so that there is a relatively large annular space around the central portion of the cylinder in which the field is very small. A multi-layer secondary winding is located in this low-field belt, so that its dimensions and location are relatively less critical. Such mutual inductors can be computed as accurately as can self inductors. However, such self or mutual inductors are not generally useful outside their special field of application—absolute measurements.

Self inductance standards for laboratory use may be multilayer coils of cylindrical shape designed to have maximum inductance for a given size and length of wire, or may be a multilayer coil on a toroidal form, lap wound to reduce self capacitance. Accurate computation of inductance is not possible in either instance, and the value of such an inductor is usually established in terms of other inductors or a combination of capacitance and resistance. Inductors wound as multilayer cylindrical coils designed to achieve maximum time constant are subject to "pickup" from stray fields. This effect is reduced by dividing the coil into two equal sections wound in opposite directions so that the emfs induced in them by an alternating external field tend to cancel. (Such an arrangement is called astatic). A much greater degree of astaticism is achieved by a toroidal coil whose winding is uniformly distributed around the torus.

All inductors are frequency sensitive to some extent because of distributed self-capacitance, eddy currents, and imperfect insulation between turns and layers of the winding. The effect of distributed capacitance is to increase the effective inductance. At frequencies well below resonance, this amounts to $L_{eff} = L_0 (1 + \omega^2 L_0 C)$, where L_0 is the inductance at zero frequency. The effect of eddy currents is to decrease the effective inductance, and the effect of imperfect insulation (equivalent to shunt resistance) is also to decrease the effective inductance.

Frequency Standards

Standards of frequency are derived from the standard of time, the second, which is defined in terms of the motion of the earth. The United States Naval Observatory regulates the standard of time from observations of the passage of stars through the vertical meridian. The basic standard of frequency is a 100 kilocycle quartz-crystal oscillator maintained by the National Bureau of Standards, and checked for constancy by using it to operate a clock that is compared with Naval Observatory time. Standard frequencies, obtained from the crystal through multiplier and divider circuits, are continuously broadcast by WWV, the National Bureau of Standards transmitter near Washington, D. C.

Quartz crystals are used in great numbers to control oscillator frequencies in measurement and communication applications. Their constancy depends on the close control of temperature and pressure. Tuning forks can be used as laboratory standards at audio frequencies. A precision fork, operating at constant temperature, may be stable to 10 ppm or better.

References

1. Thomas, J. L., Peterson, C., Cooter, I. G., and Kotter, F. R., *NBS J. Res.*, **43**, 291 (1949).
2. Cutkosky, R. D., *NBS J. Res.*, **65A**, 147 (1961).
3. Driscoll, R. L., *NBS J. Res.*, **60**, 287 (1958); Driscoll, R. L., and Cutkosky, R. D., *NBS J. Res.*, **60**, 297 (1958).
4. Brooks, H. B., *Trans. AIEE*, **50**, 1318 (1931).
5. Thomas, J. L., *NBS J. Res.*, **5**, 295 (1930); **36**, 107 (1946).
6. Scott, A. H., *NBS J. Res.*, **50**, 1947 (1953).
7. Lampard, D. G., *Nature*, **177**, 888 (1956); and *Proc. IEE*, **104C**, 271 (1957).
8. McGregor, M. C., *et al*, *Trans. IRE*, **7-I**, 253 (1958).
9. Thompson, M. F., *Trans. IRE*, **7-I**, 245 (1958).
10. Curtis, H. L., Moon, C., and Sparks, C. M., *NBS J. Res.*, **21**, 371 (1938).
11. Campbell, A., *Proc. Roy. Soc. (London)*, Ser. A, **79**, 428 (1907); Thomas, J. L., Peterson, C., Cooter, I. G., and Kotter, F. R., *NBS J. Res.*, **43**, 325 (1949).

General Bibliography

Campbell, A., and Childs, E. C., "Measurement of Inductance, Capacitance and Frequency," Princeton, Van Nostrand, Co., Inc., 1935.
Curtis, H. L., "Electrical Measurements," New York, McGraw-Hill Book Co., 1937.
Drysdale, C. V., and Jolley, A. C., "Electrical Measuring Instruments," 2nd Edition, New York, John Wiley & Sons, Inc., 1952.
Golding, E. W., "Electrical Measurements," New York, Pitman, 1946.
Handbook 77 (Volume 1), "Precision Measurement and Calibration," Electricity and Electronics, Washington, National Bureau of Standards, 1961.

HARRIS, F. K., "Electrical Measurements," New York, John Wiley & Sons, Inc., 1952.

Historical Reports of the Committee on Electrical Standards Appointed by the British Association for the Advancement of Science, Cambridge, Cambridge University Press, 1913.

Keinath, "Die Technik elektrischer Messgerate," Munich, Oldenbourg-Verlag, 1928.

Palm, "Elektrische Messgerate," Hamburg, Springer-Verlag, 1948.

VINAL, G. W., "Primary Batteries," New York, John Wiley & Sons, Inc., 1950.

FOREST K. HARRIS

ELECTRIC ARC PROCESS FOR ACETYLENE. *See* **ACETYLENE BY ELECTRIC DISCHARGE.**

ELECTRIC ARC PROCESS FOR NITROGEN FIXATION. *See* **NITROGEN FIXATION BY THE ARC PROCESS.**

ELECTRIC ARC PROPERTIES

The electric arc has been known as a spectacular mystery from prehistoric times onward: first as lightning—the thunderbolts of the ancients; later as a laboratory curiosity; and thence to the present day either as a useful tool for lighting, welding, smelting, chemical synthesis and the like, or as a terrifying and destructive aspect of electrical power line accidents. Under the control of engineers and scientists it can accomplish many things which would be practically impossible without it. Its uses and ranges of application are so varied that one should perhaps speak of *arcs* rather than *the arc*.

Physical Aspects

First of all, an arc is an electrically conducting channel in a normally insulating medium, generally a gas. It has a characteristic anatomy, consisting of anode and cathode regions or "spots" joined by a more or less uniform column. Its conductivity is the result of ionization of the gas, generally maintained thermally, that is, by very high temperature. Fig. 1 is a photograph of a high-current arc in the open air.[1] This arc was carrying a 60-cycle alternating current of 15,000 amperes RMS value between electrodes 12 inches apart. The lead arrangement caused a magnetic force tending to blow the arc to the right. The apparently dark plumes extending from the electrodes were actually so bright that photographic reversal due to extreme overexposure occurred. These brilliant flames reveal the paths of intense vapor jets produced by a combination of rapid boiling of the metal electrode surfaces and a magnetic "pinch" effect. They are surrounded by a less brilliant but still very bright discrete core which is several inches in diameter in this case. Surrounding the core is a large diffuse halo of glowing but still less luminous gas. Although there is little difference in appearance between the anode and cathode spots in the high-current arc, each has an essentially different electrical function. Electrons, which carry most of the arc current, are released at the cathode and collected at the anode. By the usual definition, an essential feature of the arc is the production of electrons at the cathode with a voltage drop of the order of only ten volts. This may be by thermionic emission, high electric field emission, or some process or combination of processes not yet fully understood. Both electrodes absorb heat from the arc and by this cooling action tend to concentrate the discharge at the terminals.

The arc column, the major component of a long arc, is a source of heat and so may be compared with an electrical heating element.[2] As such it can be an extremely powerful heat source, dissipating sometimes millions of watts per cubic centimeter. The flow of this heat and the temperature profile associated with it are the most important physical features of the arc column. Although much energy may be radiated from an arc in a wide spectrum, the principal mechanisms of heat loss are thermal conduction and convection. This is ilustrated by Fig. 2, taken from a study by Hagenah[3] of a 10-ampere carbon arc in air. The axial temperatures of such arcs have been found by King[4] to vary with the rate of heat dissipation according to an empirical relation,

$$T_0 = 1500 \ (W)^{2/7} \text{ degrees Kelvin} \qquad (1)$$

where W is watts per centimeter length. This shows the somewhat surprising fact that cooling influences, such as adjacent cold surfaces or gas blasts, actually cause an arc to heat up since they increase the power dissipation. The cored structure of the arc column, observable as radial nonuniformities in both Figs. 1 and 2, results from wide and somewhat complex fluctuations in both the thermal and electrical properties of the gas as it goes through the extreme range of temperatures from normal ambient to the level of many thousands of degrees Kelvin observed in the arc core. This high temperature in the arc leads to molecular dissociation and atomic excitation and to resultant chemical reactions in mixed gases.

The very high rates of energy production and loss in the arc coupled with its limited thermal storage capacity—relatively small volume and low gas density—lead to the possibility of high-speed response. Thus, the dynamic properties of arcs are very important in applications and lead to many useful results as well as to some difficulties.

Electrical Properties

To the electrical engineer the arc most often appears as a circuit element which is nonlinear in its static behavior and exhibits short time constants in responding to electrical changes.

Static Characteristic. Perhaps the most familiar electrical property of the normal arc under steady conditions is its falling volt-ampere characteristic, illustrated by the curve in Fig. 3. More properly, this is the characteristic of a *low-current* arc at the level of 10 amperes or so. At hundreds or thousands of amperes the characteristic always flattens out so that the arc voltage is almost independent of current and at very high currents the voltage tends to rise slightly with current increase. Study of the electrical properties of arcs has led to a number of suggested empirical equations associated with the names of such experimenters as Ayrton, Steinmetz, and Nottingham. Since actual arc characteristics show so much individual variation,

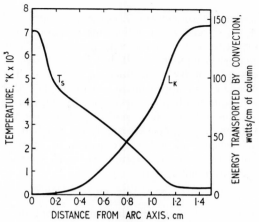

FIG. 2. Distribution of temperature, T_S, and convection loss, L_K, in a vertical 10-ampere carbon arc (*courtesy of British Welding Journal and Springer-Verlag*).

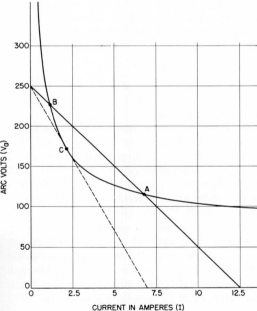

FIG. 3. Static characteristic of a 1.5 inch copper electrode arc in air according to the Nottingham equation.

depending especially on the current range, arc length, electrode composition, and composition, density, and state of motion of the ambient gas medium, any such equation for general use can be only approximate. The following form for the voltage of unconfined arcs seems to the writer to be most useful in general, at least as a basis for discussion:

$$V_a = A + (B + CI^{-n})\, L \qquad (2)$$

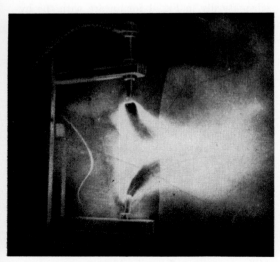

FIG. 1. 15,000 ampere arc in air.

where I is arc current, L is the arc length, and A, B, C, and n are adjustable constants. The exponent, n, is found to vary from about 0.3 to somewhat more than 1.0, but it may often be taken as unity with sufficient accuracy. The meaning and approximate values of the other constants can best be ascertained by considering extreme cases. In the case of very short arcs, the voltage drop approaches simply the constant, A, independent of either arc length or current. For large enough currents the term containing I drops out so that

$$V_a = A + BL \qquad (3)$$

independent of current, and for very long high-current arcs the constant, A, may be omitted, yielding only

$$V_a = BL \qquad (4)$$

As another extreme, long arcs carrying only small currents, such as line charging or magnetizing current arcs at the contacts of high-voltage air-break switches, may be approximated by

$$V_a = C\,L/I^n \qquad (5)$$

with n near unity. This shows that such an arc requires an approximately constant power input, C, per unit length.

No exact numerical values can be given, but a few general magnitudes may be useful. The almost constant total drop at the electrodes, A in the equations, generally is of the order of 20 to 40 volts. The voltage gradient, B, for arcs in the open air at currents above 50 amperes or so is about 12 volts per centimeter. At low currents, of the order of one ampere, laboratory studies of long open air arcs have shown the value C to be near 100 watts per centimeter and n to be nearly one. Thus, an order of magnitude numerical approximation for the static characteristic of an *open air* arc might be

$$V_a = 30 + (12 + 100/I)\,L \text{ volts} \qquad (6)$$

where L is arc length in centimeters and I is arc current in amperes. As already indicated, open arcs carrying tens of thousands of amperes or smaller current arcs in confined spaces require at least one additional term containing the current with a positive fractional exponent.

Stability Requirement. An immediate consequence of the falling volt-ampere characteristic is that a steady arc cannot be maintained in a constant emf circuit without a stabilizing series resistance. The curve through BCA in Fig. 3 has been drawn for a 1.5-inch-long copper-electrode arc in air according to Eq. (2), using constants given by Nottingham. The solid straight line in the figure gives the available voltage at the terminals of an arc in a 250 volt d-c circuit including a series resistance of 20 ohms. Steady arc conditions can exist in this circuit only at the intersection points A or B where the available circuit voltage is just equal to the arc voltage. The arc can operate *stably*, however, only at point A where the slope of the circuit characteristic is steeper than that of the arc characteristic. The dotted line tangent to the arc characteristic at C corresponds to the maximum circuit resistance, about 36 ohms, at which this arc can be maintained with a source emf of 250 volts. If conditions for stability are lost, either by circuit resistance increase or by arc lengthening, the arc will suddenly "go out." That is, the current will drop to zero, and the terminal voltage will jump to the open-circuit voltage. Any inductance in the circuit will cause a momentary overvoltage to appear at the arc terminals. In extreme cases the overvoltage may reach dangerous values, even in low-voltage circuits.

Dynamic Arc Characteristics. With currents changing slowly enough the voltage drop in an arc will follow the static characteristic but, as the current is changed more and more rapidly, hysteresis effects become evident so that the arc voltage departs from the static characteristic by an amount depending on the rate of current change and the nature and condition of the arc. This behavior is illustrated schematically in Fig. 4 for an arc with the hyperbolic static characteristic AB. Superimposed on a steady current component, i_o, for which the steady arc voltage is v_o, is a sinusoidal current oscillation between the limits i_a and i_b. At a low enough frequency, f_1, the voltage will retrace the single curve AB along the static characteristic. At a somewhat higher frequency, f_2, current oscillation between the same limits will cause the arc voltage to follow the near-elliptical loop about the single curve AB. With rising current some additional power is required to expand the arc column and so the loop lies above AB; with falling current the reverse situation causes the loop to return below AB, as indicated by the arrow points. At a still higher frequency f_3, the oscillation curve will follow the ellipse shown and approach the straight line A'B' at some sufficiently high frequency, f_4, above 100,000 cycles per second for an arc in air. The arc may be said to have an inherent natural frequency of response, f_0, lying between the values f_2 and f_3, at which the elliptical locus approaches a circle.

The falling *static* characteristic for the arc column clearly results because the column resistance adjusts itself to the current when the current changes slowly enough. The factors determining the steady burning voltage of the arc column at any given current are complex, but depend mainly on conductive and convective cooling processes in and around the column. The *dynamic hysteresis* is caused by storage in and near the arc column of energy in the form of heat, molecular dissociation, and ionization associated with the column conductance.

Alternating Current Arcs. The dynamic volt-ampere characteristics of a-c arcs somewhat resemble those for the superimposed oscillation in Fig. 4, but are symmetrical about the zero current axis. At relatively low frequencies, say 60 cps for an arc in hydrogen or 5 to 10 cps for an arc in the open air, the dynamic characteristic may follow the static characteristic closely except in the immediate vicinity of current zero where both current and voltage reverse.

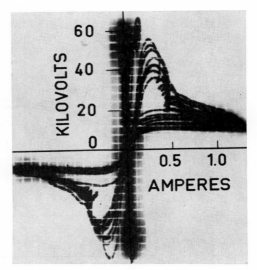

Fig. 5. Cathode-ray volt-ampere cyclogram of a vertical 60-cycle arc drawn to a length of 48 inches in a 40-kv circuit in air.

Fig. 5 shows a time exposure of a repetitive cathode-ray volt-ampere trace for a 60-cycle magnetizing current (1.5 amperes rms) arc drawn vertically in the air to 48 inches length in a 40 kv circuit. The arc lasted for about one second and then spontaneously "went out." At this low current amplitude the actual rate of current change is so low that there is evident a strong tendency to follow a constant-power-loss static characteristic, but a large loop is still present in the dynamic characteristic. The rising (outer) portions of these traces tends to approach rectangular hyperbolas given by $D = 300$ watts per inch [120 watts per cm, near the value in Eq. (6)] but the falling portions drop rather far below this. The *maintenance* requirement for these arcs could be expressed in terms of rms open-circuit voltage gradient times short-circuit current as 240 volt-amperes per cm, just twice the per cm wattage value approached by the upper loops.

The natural or response frequency of an arc is affected very considerably by the current magnitude and the nature and density of the ambient gas, depending particularly on the thermal properties of the medium. Arc natural frequencies are especially high in hydrogen and in some more complex denser gases, such as sulfur hexafluoride. They may be greatly increased by gas blasts or other cooling effects.

Figure 6 is another example of a 60-cycle a-c arc characteristic plotted from an oscillogram of

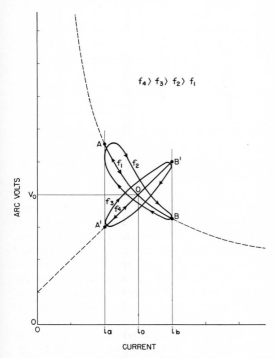

Fig. 4. Dynamic characteristics of d-c arc with superimposed current oscillation.

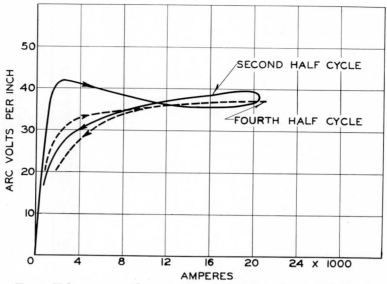

FIG. 6. Volt-ampere cyclograms of a vertical 60-cycle arc 12 inches long in air, 15,000 amperes RMS.

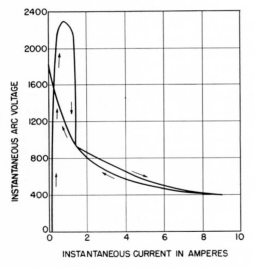

FIG. 7. Volt-ampere cyclogram of a 60-cycle arc in hydrogen between copper electrodes 1.5 inches apart. Atmospheric pressure.

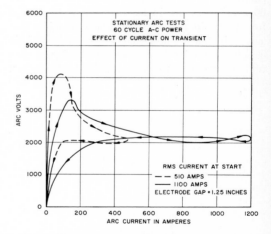

FIG. 8. Hydrogen arc volt-ampere traces at 69 atmospheres pressure.

a 15,000 ampere open air arc like that of Fig. 1. This shows the typical flatness of the volt-ampere trace for higher current arcs, including also the slight tendency for the arc voltage to rise with current at large current values. Fig. 7 shows the tendency of a lower current a-c arc in hydrogen to follow its static characteristic quite closely except very near current zero. Also illustrated is the tendency, especially noticeable in hydrogen, for the arc column to

exist in two distinct forms, with a sudden transition between the two. In addition to the normal concentrated and high-natural-frequency form, there exists right after current reversal a visually diffuse "glow-like" form with a lower natural frequency and higher arc voltage than for the normal form. Fig. 8 shows the characteristics of much higher current arcs in high-pressure (69 atm) hydrogen.[5] This illustrates the flatness of the high-current characteristic, the relatively lower reignition voltage for high current amplitudes, and the increase in arc voltage gradient with gas pressure. Arc column gradients generally increase as the absolute gas pressure raised to some power between 0.5 and 1.0.

Mathematical Models of Arc Column

So important are the transient or dynamic properties of arcs in electric circuits that it is often worthwhile to express these properties mathematically so that arcs may be treated as circuit elements in circuit transient calculations. The mathematical models devised so far represent the behavior of arc columns only and so are limited to relatively long arcs.

These models are all based on the assumption that the arc column conductance can be expressed as a prescribed function of the added stored energy (often called heat content), Q, associated with the conducting state of the column, or

$$1/R_a = F(Q) = F[\int (W - N) \, dt] \text{ mho}, \quad (7)$$

where R_a = column resistance, ohms; W = electrical power input, watts; N = rate of energy loss, watts; and t = time, seconds.

Particular arc model equations depend on the forms assumed for $F(Q)$ and N. Relatively simple and, therefore, useful models have been proposed and studied by Cassie,[6] Mayr,[7] and others.[8, 9, 10] All of these models are characterized dynamically by a time constant, θ, where

$$\theta = Q/N \quad (8)$$

or an equivalent ratio of some specifically defined energy storage quantity, Q_0, to a power loss quantity, N_0. Possibly most useful is Mayr's nonlinear differential equation for the arc conductance,

$$R_a \frac{d}{dt}\left(\frac{1}{R_a}\right) = \frac{1}{\theta}\left(\frac{V_a I - N_0}{N_0}\right) \quad (9)$$

This and other similar equations can be linearized by special assumptions and can be combined in various ways with associated circuit equations to obtain useful results in the theory of circuit breakers[6, 7, 10] and other arc-employing devices.

Electrode Regions. Conditions at the arc electrodes are more variable and less well understood than those in the arc column.[11] Complications arise from multiple possible mechanisms of electron emission from the cathode, associated with different current densities, cathode materials, and surface temperatures. High-velocity vapor blasts from one or both electrode "spots" may markedly affect conditions at the

spots and in adjacent portions of the arc column. Thus, definition of the electrical behavior of short arcs by means of mathematical equations is not so well established as for long arcs. One possible application which may have enough validity to be useful is the use of dynamic arc equations to predict overvoltages[9] due to current chopping by vacuum arcs. Such arcs, whose properties are mainly those of their cathode spots, frequently have values of the apparent time constant, θ, two or three orders of magnitude smaller than those of normal gaseous arc columns.

Concluding Remarks

The electrical rather than the physical properties of arcs have been emphasized in this article partly because of the impossibility, with our present state of knowledge, of calculating all observable arc properties from basic principles. The electrical properties, however, may be determined experimentally. Approximate equations can be devised for both static and dynamic arc characteristics, and these can provide useful starting points for analysis of circuits and devices involving arcs.

References

1. STROM, A. P., "Long 60-Cycle Arcs in Air," *Trans. AIEE*, **65**, 113–117 (March, 1946).
2. MILNER, D. R., SALTER, G. R., AND WILKINSON, J. B., "Arc Characteristics and their Significance in Welding," *Brit. Welding J.*, 73–88 (February 1960).
3. HAGENAH, W., "Das Stromungsfeld im Freien Kohlebogen," *Z. Physik*, **128**, 279–288 (1950).
4. KING, L. A., private communication to the author, July 1960.
5. Unpublished results of arc studies by Westinghouse Electric Corporation Astronuclear Laboratory, 1962.
6. CASSIE, A. M., "Arc Rupture and Circuit Severity: A New Theory," *CIGRÉ* Report No. 102, 1939.
7. MAYR, O., "Beiträge zur Theorie des statischen und des dynamischen Lichtbogens," *Archiv für Elektrotechnik*, 37, 588–608 (1943).
8. BROWNE, T. E., JR., "A Study of A-C Arc Behavior Near Current Zero by Means of Mathematical Models," *Trans. AIEE*, **67**, 141–153 (1948).
9. BROWNE, T. E., JR., "The Electric Arc as a Circuit Element," *J. Electrochem. Soc.*, **102**, 27–37 (1955).
10. BROWNE, T. E., JR., "An Approach to Mathematical Analysis of A-C Arc Extinction in Circuit Breakers," *Trans. AIEE*, **78**, Part III, 1508–1517 (1959).
11. ECKER, G., "Electrode Components of the Arc

Discharge," *Ergebnisse der Exakten Natur-wissenschaft*, **33**, 1–104 (1961).

T. E. BROWNE, JR.

Cross-references: *Electric Smelting Furnaces-Electrical Circuit; Furnaces, Inert Atmosphere and Vacuum Arc; Vacuum Arc Properties.*

ELECTRIC ARC PROPERTIES IN VACUUM. See VACUUM ARC PROPERTIES.

ELECTRIC FISH. See ELECTRIC ORGANS.

ELECTRIC HEATING. See ARC HEATING; DIELECTRIC HEATING; INDUCTION HEATING; RESISTANCE HEATING.

ELECTRIC MELTING OF GLASS. See GLASS, ELECTRIC MELTING.

ELECTRIC ORGANS

In almost all animals millions of nerve and muscle fibers, receptor and gland cells, and in the human brain billions of neurons become generators of electric currents during activity. However, little of their electrical output circulates in the fluids of the body or on its surface. Prime factors are the low voltage of the output, which in different cells ranges from a few to about 150 mv, high internal resistance of the generators, and considerable shunting in the external circuits.

Specialized *electric organs*, structured so that they can deliver appreciable currents to the external medium occur in 7 families of *electric fishes*. The strongly electric fish can give painful and even dangerous shocks to an observer. Thus, their effects on humans or animals were a source of wonder before the nature of electricity was recognized. These strongly electric fishes are the marine cartilagenous family of Torpedinidae (electric rays), and two fresh water teleosts, the electric eel of tropical America (*Electrophorus*) and the electric catfish of tropical Africa (*Malapterurus*). The maximum observed external electrical outputs in air are about 60 v in Torpedinidae, and 500 v or more in *Malapterurus* and *Electrophorus*. The giant *T. nobiliana* can deliver about 50 amp on short circuit during the brief single discharge of about 5 msec duration, and *Electrophorus* about 0.5 amp dur-

ing the pulse which lasts about 2 msec. The discharges of *Astroscopus* (*stargazer*), the only marine teleost electric fish, are up to about 15 v in amplitude and are barely felt. Fresh water weakly electric fishes are the close relatives of the electric eel, the electric knifefishes (Gymnotidae), the African elephant noses (Mormyridae) and their relative *Gymnarchus*. The electric skates (Rajidae) are weakly electric marine cartilagenous fishes. The outputs of these forms range between about 0.5 v and 10 v. While small in comparison with the discharges of the strongly electric fishes, they nevertheless are much larger than the electric activity of the brain recorded from the scalp (up to about 100 μv) or of the heart, as obtained from chest leads (several mv).

The individual cells (*electroplaques*) of the electric organs are modified muscle fibers. The organs owe their specialized capacity for high electrical output to the polarization of the electroplaques in both anatomical and physiological respects, and the orderly array of the polarized cells in series-parallel combinations (Fig. 1). Electroplaques generate pulses lasting 0.5 to 20 msec in different forms. Each pulse is only about 150 mv at its peak, and in certain cases does not exceed 50–70 mv. However, the series arrays may number several thousand cells in the strongly electric fishes, with equally large numbers of parallel arrays.

The electroplaques of weakly electric fish have basically the same properties as do those in organs of the strongly electric fish. The low outputs are due entirely to the smaller number of cells in both the series and the parallel arrays. Indeed, in some respects the electric organs and cells of the weakly electric fishes are more highly specialized than are those of strongly electric fishes. The knifefishes emit pulses continuously at frequencies which range between about 5 per second and 1500 per second, depending upon the species. *Gymnarchus* also emits continuously at frequencies between about 200 and 400 per second. This repetitive activity during the entire life of the fish depends upon highly organized central nervous pathways and makes severe demands upon metabolic requirements of nerve cells and electroplaques. The Mormyridae are also capable of high frequency activity, but the discharges usually come as brief trains of impulses. In all these weakly electric fishes the electrical output is apparently used to power sense organs which are highly sensitive current detectors. Obstacles in the water, or even

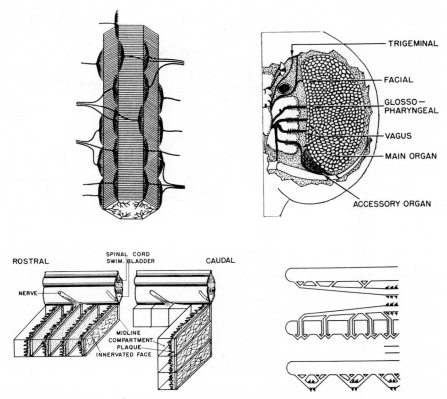

FIG. 1. Shows samples of electric organ and electroplaque structures. (Upper left) Column of torpedine electroplaques in series array: the thin cells are all innervated on their ventral surface. Four bundles of nerve fibers are shown. (Upper right) A dorsal view, showing the parallel array of the columns of the main organ of a small Torpedine, *Narcine brasiliensis*: in this form there is also an accessory organ, in which the electroplaques are innervated on their dorsal surface, as are all the electroplaques of *Astroscopus* which are also arranged in the same dorso-ventral orientation. (Lower left) The series-parallel longitudinal arrays in the electric eel: somewhat similar arrays occur in other electric fishes, but in the Rajidae the electroplaques are innervated on their rostral faces. (Lower right) Mormyrid electroplaques are innervated on one or several stalk processes which arise from the caudal surface. In some, the stalk then penetrates through the cell and the innervated sites (heavy dots) lie ahead of the electroplaque. In *Malapterurus* there is a single stalk which arises from the center of the caudal face.

changes in salinity which produce small changes in the field that is generated by the electric organs, are detected by the fish. Thus, the organs may form a component of an electrical guidance system.

With a few exceptions, the electroplaques are waferlike cells, only 10 to 100μ thick, but presenting two major surfaces of considerable area, up to about 20 sq mm in the electric eel and 75 sq mm in the giant North Atlantic *Torpedo*. They exhibit the same electrochemical properties as do the muscle fibers from which they have descended. However, their special adaptation for electrical output frees them from the requirement to activate contractile machinery. Therefore, evolutionary variants of electrogenic ac-

tivity could persist more readily and the occurrence of such variants has made electroplaques particularly suitable material for study of the general aspects and properties of bioelectrogenesis. The large size of most electroplaques and other anatomical features are also helpful for experimental analysis of the bioelectric activity.

Gymnarchus has not yet been studied with microelectrode recordings from single electroplaques. In one group of Gymnotidae, the Sternarchid ghost fishes, the anatomical relations of the electroplaques present some difficulties and the data are as yet unclear. However, the responses of most of the other forms have been well characterized. While there are as yet no

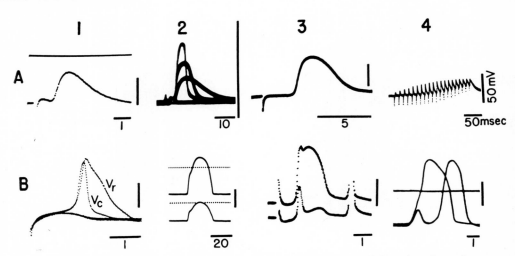

FIG. 2. Responses of single electroplaques recorded with intracellular microelectrodes. The recording traces are initially between 50 and 90 mv inside-negative. Responses of the electrogenically reactive membrane to appropriate stimuli are excursions toward inside-positivity (depolarizations). All calibrations in msec and in 50 mv.

A. Marine electric fishes: (1) *Astroscopus*, (2) *Raja erinacea*, (3) *Torpedo nobiliana*, (4) *Narcine brasiliensis* accessory electric organ. All the responses are *postsynaptic potentials*, depolarizations of electrically inexcitable membrane and are all evoked by stimulating the nerve supply of the cell. They arise only after a synaptic latency of 1 to 5 msec in different forms. The peak of the maximum depolarization (ca. 60 mv) does not cause an overshoot into inside-positivity (A_1, A_3). The amplitude of the potential may be graded by stimulating more nerve fibers (A_2) or by repetitive stimulation (A_4).

B. Some fresh water forms: (1) *Hypopomus*, (2) *Sternopygus*, (3) *Malapterurus*, (4) *Electrophorus*. In all these forms the cell can produce one or several varieties of spikes as well as a depolarizing (excitatory) postsynaptic potential. In a response to a nerve impulse the latter occurs first and evokes the spike or spikes of the electrically excitable membrane components. (1): *Hypopomus* is a weakly electric gymnotid relative of the electric eel, but the rostral as well as the caudal surfaces of the electroplaques generate spikes. Both spikes occurred as all-or-none responses, that of the rostral surface (V_r) being longer lasting. The record shows simultaneous registrations of the potentials across the two surfaces, evoked by a direct stimulus to the cell. A second sweep during which the stimulus was slightly subthreshold is also superimposed. (2): *Sternopygus* is another gymnotid but only the caudal surfaces of the electroplaques are electrogenically reactive. Exceptionally among electric fishes the cells are elongated and the record shows simultaneous registration with two intracellular electrodes, *upper* near the caudal surface, *lower*, 0.8 mm rostral. The response is during a normally occurring repetitive discharge of the whole organ. The spike was markedly attenuated in the short distance of propagation. Also exceptionally among excitable cells, the electroplaques of this and a few other gymnotids show an intracellular difference of potential (broken line is the zero reference). (3): *Malapterurus* is the strongly electric African catfish. The contribution of each electroplaque to the organ discharge is the difference of potential between the large spike of the rostral surface and the smaller, briefer response of the caudal surface. The cell was stimulated by an externally applied current. The start and finish of the 5 msec pulse appear as deflections in the records. The two traces were separated for easier display. (4): The electric eel is also a strongly electric fish, but only the innervated caudal surface of the cell is electrogenically reactive. The record shows responses to stimulation of the nerve recorded at two sites of this membrane 0.8 mm apart. The nerve impulses, which are distributed all over the innervated surface, evoked simultaneous excitatory postsynaptic potentials at both sites. However, the e.p.s.p. was larger at one site and evoked a spike in this region. The latter, being generated in electrically excitable membrane, then propagated to the other site at a velocity of about 0.5 meter per sec.

quantitative data on the kinetics of the ionic movements during activity, comparable to those of some axons, neurons, and muscle fibers, a number of features of interest to the theory of bioelectrogenesis are nevertheless clear cut.

Electrophysiological Differences in Cell Membranes

Electrogenically Reactive and Inert Components. In certain fish only one of the two major surfaces of the electroplaques, that which is innervated, is electrogenically reactive. The opposite, uninnervated face is electrogenically inert. Nevertheless, both surfaces have permselective membrane and the same inside-negative resting potential appears across both major faces. The permselectivity of the inert face is particularly noteworthy because the resistance of the membrane is very low. The current which flows through the inert face during activity of the cell causes very little IR drop so that nearly the full output of the generator of the active surface is delivered to the external circuit.

Electrically Inexcitable Electrogenic Membrane. The membranes in the innervated faces of the electroplaques of Torpedinidae and *Astroscopus* respond with activity to stimulation of their nerve supply, but not to electrical stimuli, i.e., they are *electrically inexcitable*. The depolarizing electrogenesis which results from applying neural or chemical stimuli therefore is a *postsynaptic potential* (p.s.p.) (Fig. 2A). Since these cells produce p.s.p.'s which are uncomplicated by other electrically excitable responses, the pulses exhibit in "pure" form the properties which are characteristic of electrically inexcitable electrogenesis. The pulses are graded in amplitude, rather than all-or-none, as are spikes. At their peaks they show little or no overshoot and there is no refractory period, so that a sustained depolarization results when sustained stimulation is applied. This type of activity also occurs in the input membranes of neurons, receptors, and effector cells, but may be obscured by the electrically excitable electrogenesis.

Innervated Membrane with An Intermingled Electrically Excitable Component. In some Gymnotidae, including the strongly electric eel and the weakly electric *Eigenmannia* and *Sternopygus*, the innervated membrane also has an electrically excitable spike-generating component intermingled with the electrically in-

excitable synaptically activated component (Fig. 2B). The electrogenic surface of these electroplaques thus resembles in its properties the cell membrane in neurons of the vertebrate central nervous system. However, in the much larger electroplaques the existence and the nature of the interactions of two components with distinctive properties are more readily demonstrated. As in Torpedinidae and *Astroscopus*, the electroplaques of these Gymnotids develop unidirectional pulses. The current is inward in the active membrane, and it flows out of the opposite, unreactive, low resistance face.

Second Surface Also Electrically Excitable. Both major surfaces are electrogenic and the uninnervated face is electrically excitable in the electroplaques of *Malapterurus*, the Mormyridae and certain Gymnotidae (*G. carapo*; *Hypopomus*; *Steatogenys*) (Fig. 2 B_1 and B_3). The direction and amount of external current depends upon the temporal relations and relative amplitudes of the potentials generated by the two active faces. In *Malapterurus* and in some Mormyrids and Gymnotids, the spike of one face is larger and longer lasting than that of the other face, so that the net current is unidirectional, but in other Mormyrids and Gymnotids it is bidirectional. Bidirectional (diphasic) discharges are found only in weakly electric fish and the steeply changing current may possibly aid in sharpening the sensitivity of the electrical guidance system. However, as already noted, other Mormyrids and Gymnotids and *Gymnarchus* emit monophasic pulses which are adequate for their guidance systems.

Morphological and Functional Correlations

The fact that the membranes on the two major surfaces may differ profoundly in their properties is of considerable theoretical importance. These differences are not revealed by morphological studies, even with the highest resolutions currently available in electron microscopy. The inadequacy of these methods indicates that the functional differences reside in heterogeneities of the macromolecular structure of the membrane and emphasizes the need for developing new methods to resolve these structural differences.

References

1. BENNETT, M. V. L., AND GRUNDFEST, H., "Studies on Morphology and Electrophysiology of Electric Organs. III. Electrophysiology of

Electric Organs in Mormyrids." *In* "Bioelectrogenesis," C. Chagas and A. Paes de Carvalho, Editors, p. 102–112, Amsterdam, Elsevier, 1961.
2. BENNETT, M. V. L., "Modes of Operation of Electric Organs," *Ann. N. Y. Acad. Sci.*, **94,** 458–509 (1961).
3. GRUNDFEST, H., "The Mechanisms of Discharge of the Electric Organ in Relation to General and Comparative Electrophysiology," *Prog. Biophys.*, **7,** 1–85 (1957).
4. GRUNDFEST, H., "Electric Fishes," *Scientific American*, 150–157 (October, 1960).
5. GRUNDFEST, H., AND BENNETT, M. V. L., "Studies on Morphology and Electrophysiology of Electric Organs. I. Electrophysiology of Marine Electric Fishes," *In* "Bioelectrogenesis," C. Chagas and A. Paes de Carvalho, Editors, p. 57–101, Amsterdam, Elsevier, 1961.
6. KEYNES, R. D., BENNETT, M. V. L., AND GRUNDFEST, H., "Studies on Morphology and Electrophysiology of Electric Organs. II. Electrophysiology of Electric Organ of *Malapterurus electricus*." *In* "Bioelectrogenesis," C. Chagas and A. Paes de Carvalho, Editors, p. 102–112, Amsterdam, Elsevier, 1961.

HARRY GRUNDFEST

Cross-references: *Bioelectrogenesis; Electrophysiology; Ion Transport Across Charged Membranes; Membrane Equilibrium; Membrane Potentials; Nerve Impulse Transmission.*

ELECTRIC SMELTING FURNACES

The work of Moissan,[12] beginning in 1890, on the reduction of metallic oxides in the electric furnace is considered the scientific basis for the early development of the electric furnace in metallurgy. The first commercially applied electric smelting process, however, was the production of calcium carbide, invented by Willson (q.v.) in 1892. In Fig. 1 is shown the furnace developed by Willson. The furnace crucible rests on rails in a furnace brick construction that is used for raw materials preheating. The process was discontinuous, because the crucible was removed and allowed to cool after the smelting period. Fulton[8] has reviewed the early history of calcium carbide manufacture in the United States and Canada. Keller[9] and Lyon *et al*[11] have reported on the early application of the electric furnace in metallurgy.

The calcium carbide industry grew rapidly before 1900, resulting in overproduction. During a commercial crisis in the carbide industry attempts were made about 1900 in using the carbide furnaces for production of ferroalloys, pig iron, and steel. Experiments with the production of some ferroalloys, e.g., ferrochrome and ferrosilicon, were successful, and the processes soon were applied commercially. The production of pig iron in electric furnaces failed or was only partially successful until the low shaft furnace was developed in the late twenties.[6] For production of quality steels by melting steel scrap the electric furnace was successful and soon replaced the old crucible process. However, electric steel melting will not be considered here. (See **Steel Making in Electric Arc Furnaces.**) In this entry only electric smelting furnaces will be dealt with, i.e., electric furnaces used for extracting the metals from their ores, and for the production of calcium carbide and phosphorus (q.v.).

Fig. 2 illustrates the phases in the development of the modern smelting furnace.

Fig. 2a is the old built-up ingot furnace. The electric current passes between one top electrode and the furnace bottom. The furnace operates discontinuously, starting with the electrode in low position and raising it as the smelting proceeds. After completion of the smelting period the furnace is allowed to cool, the side walls usually removed, and the product taken out in lumps. This process is still used for the production of metals, alloys, and minerals with extremely high melting points, such as ferrotungsten.

Shortly after 1900 the process was made continuous by tapping the molten product through a tap hole, see Fig. 2b. When a sufficient quantity of product has accumulated in the furnace hearth, the tap hole is opened by mechanical working, by melting with a pivot electrode, or by using oxygen. After tapping, the hole is closed with a plug of clay. As the smelting proceeds, more raw materials are added from the top of the furnace. The power on the furnace is controlled by raising or lowering the electrode.

The current supply to the furnace bottom made it necessary to use an electrically-conductive bottom lining, usually carbon. This limited the furnace to produce carbon-saturated products. In addition, the large current loop produced a high inductance of the furnace circuit. By using only top electrodes these limitations were overcome. Fig. 2c illustrates a single-phase furnace with two top electrodes. The advantage of three-phase power systems soon led to the use of three top electrodes. The first three-phase furnaces were made rectangular or oval with the three electrodes on a line, as shown in Fig. 2d.

Because of different inductive conditions of the two end electrodes, at equal voltage the one developed more and the other less power than the middle electrode (the "wild" and "dead" electrodes). This effect is especially pronounced when using high electrode currents at low voltage, i.e., when smelting a low-resistance charge.

Some big calcium carbide producers still adhere to this furnace design. The electrode cross section then usually is rectangular or oblong, as shown by the dotted line in Fig. 2d. The arrangement of three or even six electrodes in line is also maintained for smelting of copper and nickel ores[3] (q.v.) and a few other processes. In several of these cases a thin layer of solid charge is floating on the slag bath, with the electrodes more or less submerged into the liquid slag.

The latest step in the development of furnace shape was taken by making the hearth circular with the electrodes at the corners of an equilateral triangle, as shown in Fig. 2e. Most modern furnaces follow this design pattern. By the symmetry of this design the inductive conditions of the three electrodes are equal.

The development of furnace design and size may be comprehended by comparing the early furnace of Willson, Fig. 1, with Fig. 3, which is a cross section of a modern calcium carbide furnace. Electrodes 60 inches, or even more, in diameter are used, the furnace shell may be 40 ft or more in diameter, and furnace load as high as 50 mw. Such large furnaces may produce

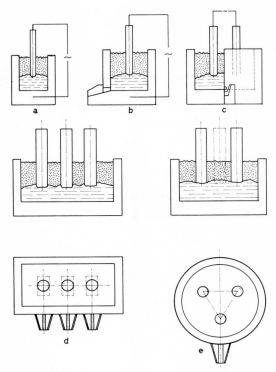

Fig. 2. Stages in the development of electric smelting furnaces. (a) An early furnace for batch operation wherein the furnace was partly torn down for removal of cooled product and rebuilt for the next run; (b) an early furnace equipped with a tap hole for continuous operation; (c) single-phase furnace with two top electrodes; (d) three-phase furnace with three electrodes on a line in a rectangular or oval furnace; (e) three-phase furnace with three electrodes positioned in a triangle in a circular furnace.

calcium carbide at a rate of 15 to 18 short tons per hour. (See **Calcium carbide**.)

The approximate world production capacity, given as mva installed, of different smelting processes is shown in Table 1 (eastern block excluded).

In Table 2 typical operating conditions for various smelting processes and furnace sizes for recent installations are given. Operating data naturally vary with local conditions, such as richness and type of raw materials, preparation and pretreatment of the same, quality of the product, etc. New procedures under development, as for instance preheating and prereduction of the materials, may influence furnace capacity and operating data considerably. The

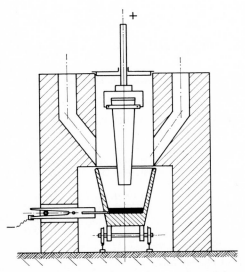

Fig. 1. Willson's pioneer furnace for calcium carbide production.

TABLE 1. APPROXIMATE WORLD PRODCTUION CAPACITY (EASTERN BLOCK EXCLUDED), MVA INSTALLED

	MVA
Calcium carbide, ferroalloys and silicon metal	2700
Pig iron	1260
Phosphorus	1200
Copper and nickel matte	96

values given in Table 2 represent the range of present practice.

Furnace Design and General Arrangement

The Furnace Hearth. The furnace hearth consists of a steel shell with a refractory lining. For carbon-saturated products the bottom lining usually is made of carbon. The hearth may be stationary, or rotating as shown in Fig. 3.[7] The rotating hearth may be supported by wheels resting on a circular rail or by a large ball bearing. The electrodes remain stationary, and for closed furnaces a stationary cover is used with a gas seal to the rotating hearth. The rotation is very slow, one revolution taking one to three days.

Electrodes. Söderberg electrodes are now commonly used in carbide and ferroalloy furnaces all over the world. (See **Söderberg Electrode in Electric Furnaces.**) In furnaces for the production of elementary phosphorus, as well as for certain other purposes, prebaked carbon or graphite electrodes still cover most of the market in the United States.

The electrodes extend above the furnace, and floors are provided for electrode work. The electrodes are suspended by hoists for raising or lowering the electrodes, by which the furnace load and operating conditions are controlled. In the current supply flexible cables are used near the electrodes to allow the vertical movement of the electrodes.

Furnace Transformers. The transformers supplying the low-tension power to the furnace are set up close to the furnace to make the high-current busses as short as possible.

Open Furnaces. Some processes have to be carried out in open furnaces. This may be required because of the exessive heat developed

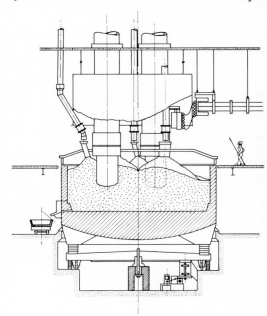

FIG. 3. Large, modern calcium carbide furnace.

TABLE 2. MAXIMUM FURNACE SIZE AND OPERATING CONDITIONS FOR DIFFERENT SMELTING PROCESSES

Product	Max. furnace size, mw	Unit energy consumption, mwh per short ton	Crater voltage, volts	Kelley's K, ohm-inch	Approx. vol. of gas, cu ft NTP per short ton of product
Calcium carbide	40–50	2.7–3.0	150–170	0.19–0.22	14,000
Ferrosilicon 75%	20	7.5–9	80–110	0.16–0.20	55,000
Ferrosilicon 90%	20	10–12	80–110	—	—
Ferromanganese	12	2.5–2.8	80–90	0.08–0.13	28,000
Ferrochrome	7–10	4.5–5.5	85–100	0.35–0.65	32,000
Pig iron	25–40	1.6–1.9	110–155	0.40	20,000
Phosphorus	50	12[a]	200–300	0.75–1.00	65,000[a]
Cu-Ni matte	6–9	0.5[b]	60–75	—	—

[a] Per short ton of elemental phosphorus.
[b] Per short ton of charge.

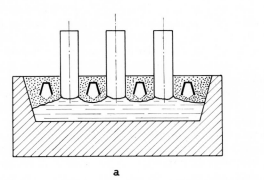 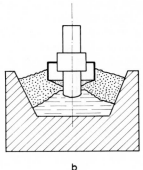

a   b

FIG. 4. Types of partly-closed furnaces showing gas collection devices.

on top of the charge, which makes it difficult to apply a cover, or because of the need for easy poking into the charge. The furnace gases then are burned on top of the charge, and a hood and chimney are provided to carry away the hot gases. Normally the gases are mixed up with large quantities of excess air.

Closed Furnaces. In most smelting processes large quantities of gas rich in CO are evolved. Table 2 gives the approximate value of gas evolved per short ton of product for different processes. The general trend is to close the furnace when possible to collect the gas, which may be used for heating or synthesis purposes. Integrated works may use the gas profitably, for instance in steel shops or rolling mills. The gas also may be used in drying and sintering raw materials or for the burning of limestone and less frequently for chemical syntheses. Recently, great interest has been paid to the use of the gas for preheating and prereduction of the ore fed to the furnace.[5] Phosphorus furnaces naturally have to be closed, as the phosphorus vapors are carried away with the gas. The hot gases are cleaned in electrostatic filters and elemental phosphorus recovered by condensation.

Partly closed furnaces. In rectangular furnaces with three electrodes on a line, a simple and efficient method has been developed for partial collection of the gas. As shown in Fig. 4a, water-cooled inverted U-channels are buried in the charge between the electrodes of oblong cross section, and the gas sucked off from the space formed below the channels.

For partial closing of furnaces with circular electrodes the gas collecting sleeve of Fig. 4b recently has been developed.[1] For simplicity only one electrode is shown on the figure, but the

system is suited as well for three-phase furnaces. The lower edge of the water-cooled sleeve may be submerged into the charge, or may be positioned slightly above the charge. Most of the gas escapes near the electrode, and more than 90 per cent of the gas may be collected by the sleeve.

In the semiclosed furnaces a good possibility of poking the charge still exists.

Fully enclosed furnaces. For fully enclosing the furnace a cover is used extending over the complete top surface of the furnace. The cover may be made of water-cooled steel channels and refractory brick, or may be a water-cooled all-steel cover. Openings are provided for the electrodes, for feeding the raw materials, and for poking and inspection doors, through which correction materials also may be added. Efficient gas seals for all openings are essential.[1]

A slight positive pressure is maintained within the furnace by automatic controllers to prevent the undesirable entrance of air. Extremely rapid and sensitive controllers are required, which also must withstand substantial pressure shocks. In a well-designed gas collecting system a gas containing more than 90 per cent CO in some cases may be obtained.

Preventing Air Pollution. In most smelting processes part of the charge is vaporized in the hot zone of the furnace and carried by the furnace gas as metallurgical fume. In large smelting works the fumes may constitute a serious air pollution problem. For cleaning the gas from open furnaces, bag filters or electrostatic precipitators are used. Because of the large gas volumes such installations usually are expensive.

In closed furnaces the gas is sucked off without burning, and the volume thus kept low.

Cleaning the gas then is more easily done and at a lower cost. The dust content of the unburned gas usually in in the range 15 to 65 grains per cu ft NTP. The particle size of the dust in the gas from closed furnaces usually is in the range 0.1–1 microns. For cleaning the gas from closed furnaces, wet scrubbers of the rotating or venturi type most commonly are used.

Feeding the Charge. From the storage bins the ore, coke, and fluxing materials are proportioned in a weighing system and transported to smaller feeding bins above the furnace. For this transport a telpher, skip hoist, conveyor, or other arrangement may be used. From the feeding bins the materials flow by gravity into the furnace through chutes.

For open furnaces the lower ends of the chutes often are made moveable. By means of a gate system the materials are fed from time to time into the furnace in different directions according to the requirements of furnace operation. A charging machine moving freely on the furnace platform also may be used. The raw materials then are weighed up in steel boxes which are emptied into the furnace by the machine. By exchanging the steel box with a stoking rod, these machines also may be used for stoking in the furnace charge.

For closed furnaces the chutes may be directly connected to the roof. In most cases, however, the chutes deliver the raw materials into shafts arranged in the roof around the electrodes. This arrangement is seen in Fig. 3. The columns of raw materials in the shafts then act as a gas seal for the furnace. The descending raw materials can be easily observed in the gaps between the chutes and the shafts, thus making possible a visual control of furnace operation. The shafts also serve as a safety valve in case of gas eruptions.

Tapping Equipment. For furnaces with a stationary hearth the tapping arrangement also is stationary. If the hearth is rotating, the receivers are movable on circular rails on the tapping floor. Tapping is usually performed at intervals, more seldom continuously. The furnace may be equipped with one or more tap holes. For slag forming processes (pig iron, ferromanganese, etc.) metal and slag are tapped more or less simultaneously. Through a runner arrangement the metal is conducted into a ladle or into pans. The slag usually is separated by a skimmer arrangement in the runner and may be collected in ladles or slag pans, or it may be granulated directly with water. In some cases metal and slag go to the same ladle from which the slag overflows.

Main Dimensions *vs*. Furnace Load. Selection of the main dimensions for a furnace of prescribed production capacity still is a matter of accumulated experience, and generally valid rules do not exist. The most important points of view

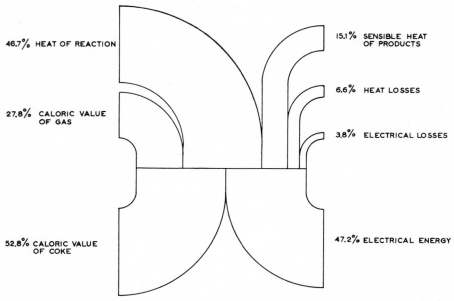

FIG. 5. Energy balance in an electric pig iron furnace.

in selecting dimensions may be summarized as follows:[13]

The charge to be smelted determines the resistivity of the smelting crater and provides the basis for calculating the electric circuit of the furnace (see below).

For large electrodes the current density normally does not exceed 50 amps per square inch. For some products, for instance ferromanganese, a smaller current density has proved to be favorable.

The ratio of furnace power load to hearth area must be adjusted to the process. Morkramer[13] has given values of this ratio for different smelting processes.

Correct electrode spacing is essential to obtain proper smelting zones with easy tappings and long life of the furnace lining.

Energy Balance. Specific energy consumptions for different electrothermal processes cover a range of about 1 to 15 mwh per short ton of product. Energy balances differ accordingly. However, as an example, the energy balance of a large pig iron furnace is shown diagramatically in Fig. 5.

References

1. ANDERSEN, H. C., paper presented at Symposium on Electric Arc Furnaces, Montreal, 1963.
2. ANDREA, F. V., *Trans. Electrochem. Soc.*, **63**, 345 (1933).
3. BARTH, O., *Z. f. Erzbergbau u. Metallhüttenwesen*, **1**, 244 (1948).
4. BÖCKMAN, O. C., *J. Electrochem. Soc.*, **107**, 688 (1960).
5. COLLIN, F. C., AND GRYTTING, O. A., *J. Metals, AIME*, **8**, 1464 (1956).
6. COWES, H., *Iron Age*, **150**, No. 23, 41 (1942); **150**, No. 24, 50 (1942).
7. ELLEFSEN, T., *Trans. Electrochem. Soc.*, **89**, 307 (1946).
8. FULTON, W. J., *Elec. Furnace Conf., Proceedings*, **16**, 196 (1958).
9. KELLER, A., *J. Iron Steel Inst.*, **63**, 161 (1903).
10. KELLY, W. M., *Carbon and Graphite News*, **5**, No. 1 (1958).
11. LYON, D. A., KEENEY, R. M., AND CULLEN, J. F., "The Electric Furnance in Metallurgical Work," *Bulletin* **77**, Department of the Interior, Bureau of Mines, Washington, Government Printing Office, 1914.
12. MOISSAN, H., "The Electric Furnace," translated by V. Lenher, 1904.
13. MORKRAMER, M., *J. du Four Elec.*, **65**, 61 (1960); *ibid.*, **65**, 113 (1960).

OLUF C. BÖCKMAN AND
KNUT SANDVOLD

Cross-references: *Calcium Carbide; Copper and Nickel Concentrates, Electric Smelting; Ferroalloys; Lead, Electrothermic Smelting; Phosphorus, Electrothermal Production; Söderberg Electrodes in Electric Furances; Steel Making in Electric Arc Furnaces; Zinc, Electrothermic Production.*

ELECTRIC SMELTING FURNACES—ELECTRICAL CIRCUIT

Operating Characteristics

Most modern three-phase furnaces are equipped with three single-phase transformers arranged as shown in Fig. 1. In a symmetrically loaded system, let E_T and I_T be the low-tension voltage and current of the transformers. The power on the furnace then is

$$P = 3\,E_T I_T \cos \phi$$

where $\cos \phi$ is the power factor.

The electrode current, I, is equal to $\sqrt{3}\,I_T$, and the electrode-to-hearth voltage, E, is $E_T/\sqrt{3}$. The power, therefore, also may be expressed as

$$P = 3\,EI \cos \phi$$

The power factor may be expressed as

$$\cos \phi = \frac{R}{Z} = \frac{R}{\sqrt{R^2 + X^2}}$$

where Z, R, and X are impedance, resistance, and inductance of the electrode circuit, respectively.

Resistance of the busses normally is a small fraction of total resistance. For this purpose, therefore, let R be the crater resistance of one electrode. As the electrodes are lowered, R will decrease and at constant voltage the current, I, will increase. When short circuiting the furnace, R is zero, and the current will obtain its largest value.

$$I_{max.} = \frac{E}{X} \qquad (1)$$

When at constant voltage R decreases from large values, the power, P, will increase until a maximum value is obtained when $R = X$ and $\cos \phi = 1/\sqrt{2} = 0.707$. This maximum power is

$$P_{max} = 3EI \cos \phi = \frac{3EI}{\sqrt{2}}$$

Noting that $I = E/Z$ and that for $X = R$,

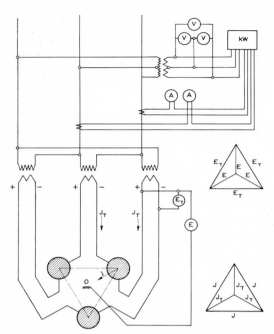

FIG. 1. Electrical layout for a modern three-phase furnace. (J = electrode current.)

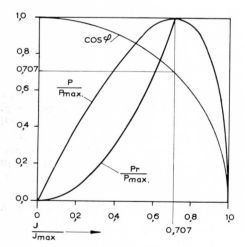

FIG. 2. Electrical operating characteristics of smelting furnaces. (J = electrode current.)

$Z = \sqrt{2}\, X$, the maximum power will be

$$P_{max} = \frac{3}{2} \frac{E^2}{X} \qquad (2)$$

By further reduction in R, the power factor will decrease rapidly and the load on the furnace will decrease.

It may be shown that for any operating condition of the furnace, the electrode current and furnace power are related to their largest values by

$$I/I_{max} = \sin \phi$$

$$P/P_{max} = \sin 2\phi$$

Similarly, it may be shown that the reactive power, P_r, is given by

$$P_r/P_{max} = 2 \sin^2 \phi$$

These relationships are used for constructing the graph of Fig. 2 demonstrating the characteristic behavior of the electric circuit of a smelting furnace. When taking into account the resistance of the current supply to the furance, the maximum of useful heat will be shifted to a slightly lower electrode current and a correspondingly slightly higher power factor.

The Furnace Inductance

The importance of the inductance, X, of the electrode circuit is seen from Eqs. 1 and 2. For a given voltage the inductance, X, sets the limit of maximum current and power.

To keep the inductance at a low level the busses are interlaced from the transformers and to a point as near as possible to the electrodes. The contribution of this part of the circuit to the total inductance usually is small. The part of the circuit made up by the flexible cables, the water-cooled copper tube conductors to the electrode holders, and the electrodes themselves, as well as the current path in the charge, form large current loops with appreciable inductance. With increasing size of the furance the size of these loops will increase and, hence, the inductance of the circuit. The inductance of well-designed, large, modern furnaces seldom exceeds 0.9×10^{-3} ohm at a frequency of 50 cycles per second.

Crater Resistance

The crater resistance depends on the raw materials, and covers a range of approximately 10^{-3} to 10^{-2} ohm. With a high crater resistance, the furnace will operate on a high voltage and power factor, and electrode current will be low. Furnace operators, therefore, seek to prepare the charge to this end. However, except for phosphorus furnaces, most large furnaces operate near the power maximum of Fig. 2.

The ohm-inch Rule

Andrea[1] has pointed out that the product of crater resistance and electrode diameter, D, is fairly constant for differently sized furnaces operating on the same raw materials. He multiplied by π to obtain the peripheral ohm-inch factor

$$K = \pi DR$$

Kelly[3] has reported values for K for different smelting processes. He also reports that K will vary to some extent with the power density of the furnace. The ranges of his values for K are included in Table 2 of **Electric Smelting Furnaces.** These K-values reflect the range of charge resistivity.

The ohm-inch rule of Andrea is valuable for scaling up data from existing to larger furnaces or from small scale tests to industrial size furnaces. It may be shown[2] that this rule implies that for differently sized furnaces operating on the same raw materials the electrode current and ohmic crater voltage are related to furnace power by

$$I = \text{const.} \ (PD)^{1/2}$$
$$E_R = \text{const.} \ (P/D)^{1/2}$$

As P increases with furnace size approximately proportional to the square of electrode diameter, the ohmic voltage increases slightly with furnace size. The inductive voltage increases more rapidly with furnace size, and power factor decreases.

Electrode current

For large smelting furnaces the electrode current may be well above 100 ka.

Power supply

Transformers for smelting furnaces usually are supplied with a series of voltage taps to meet the voltage requirements of changing smelting conditions. By connecting the high-tension side of the transformers in delta or star, the number of voltage taps may be doubled. Change of voltage usually is made under full power load on the furnace.

The high-tension voltage of the furnace transformers usually is kept moderate, about 5 to 30 kv, because of the danger of current leakage in the dust-laden atmosphere. If the power line operates at higher voltage, step-down transformers are interconnected. In recent times, however, higher primary tensions, up to about 100 kv, have been applied on furnace transformers.

Large smelting furnaces may draw large reactive power from the power line. To improve the power transmission, capacitors often are installed to take up a part of the inductive current of the furnace. The capacitors are installed at the high-tension side of the transformer, and may be in parallel or in series with the load.

Instrumentation

Fig. 1 indicates the main instrumentation. All current measurements usually are made on the high-tension side of the transformer. Measurement of electrode current and electrode-to-hearth voltage is most important to furnace operators, but a number of other instruments commonly are installed for control and account purpose.

Electrode regulators are used for automatic control of electrode position. The input to the regulators is taken from the power supply to the furnace, the output operates on the electrode hoists. Usually the regulators are designed to keep constant the impedance of each crater, but constant current regulation also is used.

References

1. ANDREA, F. V., *Trans. Electrochem. Soc.,* **63,** 345 (1933).
2. BÖCKMAN, O. C., *J. Electrochem. Soc.,* **107,** 688 (1960).
3. KELLY, W. M., *Carbon and Graphite News,* **5,** No. 1 (1958).

OLUF C. BÖCKMAN AND
KNUT SANDVOLD

Cross-references: *Electric Arc Properties;* see list for *Electric Smelting Furnaces.*

ELECTRIC SMELTING FURNACES—METALLURGY

Main Types of Processes

Depending on the nature of the materials to be smelted, electric smelting is carried out in different ways. The main points of difference are the presence or absence of a slag bath, and the position of the electrodes relative to the liquid bath at the furnace bottom.

The majority of smelting processes work with the tips of the electrodes at a clear and often considerable distance (mostly 2 to 6 feet) from the liquid bath. The electrodes are submerged to a considerable extent (2 to 4 feet) in the solid charge which is filled up to a high level in the furnace pot.

Some of these processes work without slag formation, e.g., ferrosilicon and calcium carbide (q.v.). Impurities in the raw materials are partly vaporized and partly introduced into the product. Purity of the product is obtained by selecting pure raw materials.

If the ore contains substantial amounts of rocky minerals, a slag is formed. Fluxes are added to produce a slag of proper fluidity and to impart to the slag proper affinity to impurities, especially to sulfur.

Temperature level of the smelting zone is partly determined by the melting point of the ore and the resulting slag. At sufficiently high temperatures, chemical reactions are rapid and the ore on melting is transformed rapidly into metal and slag which accumulate at the furnace bottom. The metallurgical reactions are mainly completed while the charge is moving downwards to the bath through the smelting zone. In the bath changes may occur only to a limited extent and then mostly as a refining or equalization action. Smelting processes belonging to this category are pig iron, ferromanganese and many other ferroalloys.

If the melting point of the ore is low, a phenomenon called "melting before smelting" occurs. At the melting point of the ore, the temperature is insufficient for rapid chemical reactions and poorly reacted slag will accumulate. To avoid excessive amounts of molten ore, the feed of raw materials must be limited to give a thin layer of unreacted materials above the smelting zone. Smelting of ilmenite is a moderate example of this tendency.

In extreme cases the tips of the electrodes have to dip more or less in the molten slag or to be positioned slightly above the slag bath. The slag is then heated by the passage of current to temperatures sufficient to allow chemical reactions to proceed rapidly. The main reactions then occur within the molten slag, and in the thin layer of solid charge resting on the slag bath. Smelting of copper and nickel ores (q.v.) offers typical examples of this smelting technique.[1]

Smelting Zones

With the electrodes at a clear distance from the liquid bath, the electric current passes mainly from the tips of the electrodes through the charge to the metal pad at the furnace bottom, which acts as a common ground connection

for the three electrode currents. Depending on the electrode position and temperature distribution, part of the current may pass from one electrode through the solid charge to the two other electrodes.

Power density is high near the electrodes, and normally a definite smelting zone is established around each electrode. The three smelting zones may overlap to some extent. The charge is partly preheated by the ascending reaction gases, but prereduction normally occurs only on a limited scale. The metallurgical reactions occur mainly in the smelting zones. More distant from the electrodes the downward movement of the charge is slower. Near the furnace wall the charge is more or less stationary, and this protects the furnace lining.

In some processes, e.g., pig iron and ferromanganese, a coke bed is established below each electrode. This helps to complete the metallurgical reactions and stabilizes the electric current.

For smooth and efficient furnace operation it is essential to establish proper conditions for the smelting zones. The reacted products of metal and slag should move downwards to the bottom in a regular way, the gas escaping upwards spreading over a larger section of the furnace. Narrow smelting zones may cause violent reactions, with the furnace gas escaping near the electrodes at high velocity. In other irregular cases of improper energy distribution conditions for rapid reactions will not be obtained.

The Furnace Charge

The character and preparation of the raw materials have a great influence on the smelting conditions. The present trend is to put more effort into the selection and treatment of the raw materials.

A porous and well-sized charge will descend smoothly in the furnace and allow an even escape of the gas. A dense charge will force the gas to escape at high velocity near the electrodes, sometimes with crust formations and eruptions. The porosity of the charge is mainly determined by the content of fine particles, which should be kept as low as possible.

Special attention should be paid to the reducing agent. This is the main conductor for the electric current in the charge, the charge conductivity varying considerably with type and particle size of the reducing agent. Generally, small particle size gives a high charge resistivity.

The charge components should be properly weighed and blended. If necessary, correction materials may be added directly to the furnace. Because of the limited height of the charge such corrections are quickly effective.

Furnace Operation

The furnace must be operated to give a power and temperature distribution that will provide proper reaction zones and that will meet the heat requirements of the reactions. Proper temperature of the molten metal is essential for easy tapping, and excessive temperatures that will damage the furnace lining must be avoided.

To this end the furnace operator must select the proper operating voltage and properly compose and prepare the furnace charge.

A high operating voltage will force the electrodes to a high position to establish sufficient resistance in the charge. Much heat will be developed high up in the furnace with consequent high smelting zones. The furnace bottom may be insufficiently heated and tappings become difficult. The preheating effect of the escaping furnace gas will be reduced.

When a low operating voltage is used, the electrodes will be in a low position. The smelting zones will be narrow and the furnace bottom may become overheated.

Improper position of the electrodes may also be corrected by changing over to other coke or coke size, as this will influence charge conductivity. The temperature level may partly be controlled by adjusting the melting point of the slag.

Visual observation of charge descent, electrode movements and, in open furnaces, gas distribution helps the operator to judge the operating situation.

Rotating Hearth

Some processes, especially ferrosilicon and calcium carbide, tend to form crusts of partly reacted charge, resulting in narrow smelting zones. Rotating the furnace hearth then will help in keeping the furnace volume open. The crusts are melted away as they move relative to the stationary electrodes. It has been proved that production in this way is improved and wear on the furnace lining is more even.

Dependability and Flexibility

The modern electric furnace is a reliable production unit if a well-organized maintenance system is provided. The average annual operating time factor normally is above 95 per cent, and frequently 98 per cent or even more is obtained.

The lifetime of the furnace lining naturally varies with conditions. For pig iron furnaces the lifetime usually is more than ten years, for ferromanganese furnaces a lining lasts about four to five years.

The electric load curve is in most cases even and regular with small fluctuations.

Normally the electric furnace may be operated at reduced load without significant influence on specific consumption figures and a reduction to half the maximum load in most cases is possible.

Electric smelting furnaces normally operate continuously. Accidental break off of power supply for several hours, however, does not harm the furnace or furnace operation.

References

1. Barth, O., Z. f. Erzbergbau u. Metallhütten-wesen, 1, 244 (1948).
2. See Reference list for **Electric Smelting Furnaces.**

Oluf C. Böckman and
Knut Sandvold

Cross-references: see list for *Electric Smelting Furnaces.*

ELECTRICAL SMELTING OF COPPER AND NICKEL CONCENTRATES. See COPPER AND NICKEL CONCENTRATES, ELECTRIC SMELTING.

ELECTRIC STEEL MAKING. See STEEL MAKING IN ELECTRIC ARC FURNACES.

ELECTROALUMINIZING. See ALUMINUM PLATING.

ELECTROANALYSIS. See ELECTROMETRIC TITRATIONS.

ELECTROCAPILLARY PHENOMENA

Electrocapillary phenomena are "electrokinetic" or "quasi-electrostatic" in nature. The two major types of electrokinetic phenomena are electroosmosis, the movement of liquid with respect to a stationary solid (q.v.); and electrophoresis or cataphoresis,[1] the movement of dispersed particles through a fluid (q.v.). These phenomena result from changes in interfacial tension brought about by electric fields externally imposed or spontaneously developed at interfaces. For example, if an electrical potential is applied between the ends of a capillary tube (or a system of capillaries such as a porous-cup diaphragm) filled with a liquid, the liquid is displaced along the capillary. If, on the other hand, a solid phase is finely dispersed in the fluid matrix, the solid particles move with respect to the liquid when the electrical potential is applied. When at least one of the phases is a fluid, the existence of such phenomena can be detected by measuring changes in surface tension.

Electroosmosis and electrophoresis are reversible phenomena in that a charge separation and, therefore, a potential difference is developed when the fluid is forced through the capillary or when a finely divided suspensoid is moved relative to the surrounding fluid. This potential is known as the streaming potential (q.v.) From direct measurement of the streaming potential, E, it is possible to derive a characteristic potential difference, ζ, the zeta potential, which corresponds to the charge transfer between the streaming fluid and the stationary capillary.

Thus,

$$\zeta = \frac{4\pi\eta\kappa E}{PD}$$

where η is the viscosity of the fluid, κ is its electrical conductivity, D is the dielectric constant, and P is the pressure under which the liquid is forced through the capillary.

In electroosmosis the volume of liquid, V, transported per unit time through a capillary of cross section, q, under the action of a potential gradient, $\mathbf{E}$, is proportional to the zeta potential and inversely proportional to the viscosity of the fluid:

$$V = \frac{q\zeta\mathbf{E}D}{4\pi\eta}$$

The charge transfer, and thus the zeta potential, is the result of preferential adsorption or aggregation of ions at the interface. Thus, the addition of electrolytes can bring about a change in the magnitude as well as in the sign of the zeta potential. The effect is illustrated in Fig. 1, which shows experimental values for the zeta potential at a glass-water interface, determined from measurements of the streaming potential with a capillary tube.[2]

This figure shows specific effects due to the nature and the valence of the cation and of the anion on the zeta potential. The initial increase in the negative zeta potential on addition of KCl and BaCl2 suggests that the chloride ions are preferentially adsorbed on the already negatively charged capillary wall. This adsorption, however, reaches a limiting value and further additions of electrolyte diminish the zeta potential, an effect brought about by the increased adsorption of the positive ions. On the other hand, the presence of high-valence ions, such as La^{3+} and Th^{4+}, reduces the negative zeta potential, and a reversal in sign may result. When, however, a sufficiently large positive potential is attained, selective adsorption of the anions begins, and another reversal in sign may result, as in the case of $Th(NO_3)_4$ additions.

Quasi-electrostatic electrocapillary phenomena of considerable importance involve a liquid electrical conductor, e.g., molten metals and alloys or amalgams, and a liquid electrolyte. The changes in the surface tension of, for example, mercury produced by electrolytic polarization have been ascribed to two main effects: (1) a purely electrostatic one, due to the tendency of

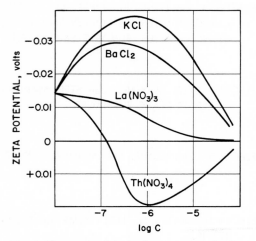

Fig. 1. Zeta potentials in the presence of salts.

an electric charge at a surface (i.e., the mercury side of the interface) to expand and so to reduce the surface tension; and (2) changes in concentration of ions near the surface (i.e., the solution side of the interface), brought about by the polarization.

Original observations were made by Lippmann[3] with the capillary electrometer, which measures the interfacial tension between mercury and an electrolytic solution by a modified capillary-height method. For example, it is possible to support a column of mercury about 50 cm high in a glass tube, whose lower end is an open-end capillary about 10^{-3} cm diam., immersed in an electrolytic solution. Polarization of the mercury-solution interface by an external source of current results in a change in the interfacial tension and, thus, a change in the height of the mercury column supported. Extended studies of electrocapillary phenomena on liquid metals have been made,[4-13] and theories reviewed.[6, 14] The effect on the capillary curve (i.e., the curve representing surface tension as a function of metal-solution interface potential) of various substances has been exhaustively studied by Gouy. Capillary-active substances may be divided roughly into three classes: (1) Those that depress the curve on the positive branch (i.e., at potentials less negative than the "electrocapillary maximum" (E_{ecm})), the depression disappearing in the negative branch (i.e., active anions, e.g., I$^-$); (2) Substances that depress the negative branch (active cations, e.g., tetraalkyl ammonium ions); (3) Substances that depress the curve about the maximum, the depression disappearing at a distance from the maximum on each side (active neutral molecules, e.g., amyl alcohol). Their behavior is diagramatically shown in Fig. 2, in which the electrocapillary curve of a typically inactive electrolyte (Na_2SO_4) is also shown.

"Electrocapillary" phenomena on solid metals cannot be readily observed by the measurement of the changes in surface tension of the solid metal. However, other surface properties of the metal-solution interface (e.g., frictional properties[15, 16] or hardness[17] have been used for their detection. (See entry on **Electrostatic Potentials: Effect on Friction and Hardness.**)

References

1. PRAUSNITZ, P. H., AND REITSTÖTTER, J., "Elektrophorese, Elektroosmose, Electrodialyse," Dresden, 1931.
2. FREUNDLICH, H., AND ETTISCH, G., *Z. physik. Chem.*, **116**, 401–19 (1925).
3. LIPPMANN, G., *Pogg. Ann.*, **149**, 547 (1873); *Ann. chim. phys.*, (5) **5**, 494 (1875).
4. PALMAER, W., *Z. physik. Chem.*, **59**, 187 (1907).
5. GOUY, G., *Ann. phys.*, (Paris), (9) **6**, 5 (1916).
6. BUTLER, J. A. V., *Proc. Roy. Soc. (London)*, **A 113**, 549–605 (1927).
7. FRUMKIN, A., *Ergeb. exakt. Naturw.*, **7**, 258 (1928).
8. BUTLER, J. A. V., *Proc. Roy. Soc. (London)*, **A 122**, 399–416 (1929).
9. KOENIG, F. O., *Z. physik. Chem.*, **A 154, 454** (1931).
10. HANSEN, L. A., AND WILLIAMS, J. W., *J. Phys. Chem.*, **39**, 439 (1935).
11. PARSONS, R., AND DEVANATHAN, M. A., *Trans. Faraday Soc.*, **49**, 673 (1953).
12. GRAHAME, D. C., AND SODERBERG, B. A., *J. Chem. Phys.*, **22**, 449 (1954).
13. BLOMGREN, E., AND BOCKRIS, J. O'M., *ibid.*, **27**, 1475 (1959).
14. BOCKRIS, J. O'M., "Modern Aspects of Electrochemistry," Vol. I, p. 127 ff, London, Academic Press Inc., 1954.
15. BOCKRIS, J. O'M., AND PARRY-JONES, R., *Nature*, **171**, 930 (1953).
16. STAICOPOLUS, D. N., *J. Electrochem. Soc.*, **168**, 900–904 (1961).
17. REHBINDER, P., AND WENSTRÖM, E., *Acta Physicochim.*, **19**, 36 (1944).

D. N. STAICOPOLUS

Cross-references: *Electrokinetic Potential; Electroosmosis; Electrophoresis; Lippmann Potential; Streaming Potential.*

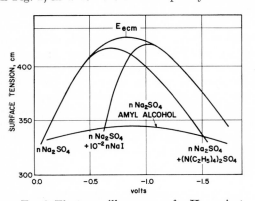

FIG. 2. Electrocapillary curves for Hg against various electrolytic solutions.

ELECTROCARDIOLOGY

Genesis of Cardiac Potentials

Heart muscle, like nerve and skeletal muscle, has the property of excitability, i.e., when part of the muscle is stimulated, the impulse spreads through the entire muscle. The electrical activity of the entire heart depends upon the electrical action of the individual cardiac cells.

The unstimulated mammalian cardiac fiber has a transmembrane potential difference, or resting potential, of about 90 mv, with the interior of the cell negative with respect to the external fluid. The magnitude of the resting potential varies for different tissues within the same heart and for hearts of different species. The resting potential is due chiefly to the difference in concentration of ions inside and outside the cell. A concentration ratio of $(K_i^+/K_o^+) = 31$ when substituted in the Nernst equation gives very nearly the correct potential. The discrepancy is due to a small permeability of the resting membrane to Na^+ and other ions. This theory is supported by the fact that increasing the external K^+ concentration lowers the resting potential.

Upon stimulation, the transmembrane polarity is reversed, with the cell interior becoming 20 to 30 mv positive to the oustide, corresponding to an action potential of 110 to 120 mv. This depolarization is caused by an increase in permeability of the membrane to the Na^+ ion, which is normally about 24 times as concentrated outside the cell as inside. The theory developed by Hodgkin and Huxley for depolarization of nerve fibers has been applied to cardiac muscle, although not with uniform success. Both types of tissue respond to a decrease in external sodium by a diminished action potential magnitude and slower change of voltage. Due to the decreased impedance of the membrane to Na^+, this ion flows into the cell until a new equilibrium is reached, with the inside positive to the outside.

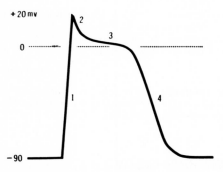

Fig. 1. Transmembrane potential of single cardiac muscle fiber. At rest the interior of the fiber is 90 millivolts negative with respect to the external medium. Depolarization is represented by phase 1 and repolarization at varying rates by phases 2, 3 and 4.

Ions other than Na^+ may also contribute to the process.

A typical cardiac fiber transmembrane potential as recorded by a microelectrode is shown in Fig. 1.

The potential values are those of the cell interior relative to the external fluid. The action potential has four phases. Phase 1 corresponds to depolarization and includes the "overshoot." Phases 2, 3 and 4 are different stages of repolarization, or the gradual restoration of the resting potential of about -90 mv. The repolarization time of cardiac muscle is much greater than that of nerve or skeletal muscle. Repolarization time ranges from 100 to 500 msec or more depending on type of cardiac tissue and animal species. The ionic mechanisms responsible for repolarization are not completely known. Possible causes are a decrease in membrane permeability to Na^+, flow of K^+, and active transport, i.e., flow of ions against the electrochemical gradient, by metabolic processes involving coupling with organic molecules.

Dipole Concept of Electrical Action of the Heart

When a cardiac fiber is stimulated, the impulse is propagated along this fiber. The excited portion develops a transmembrane potential difference with the outside negative, whereas the outside of the resting portion remains positive. There is thus a potential-difference vector directed along the fiber, with the positive pole in the direction of excitation. The moment of this vector is given by

$$M = I\,d$$

where $I =$ current between excited and unexcited regions, and $d =$ effective distance between positive and negative regions. The current from each fiber dipole spreads throughout the surrounding volume. Since the heart is made up of very many such fibers, the currents summate to produce a net current field throughout the body. This current field produces potential differences at the surface, which may be measured by means of electrodes on the body connected to an amplifier and recording device. Since the fibers are oriented in different directions, vector summation must be used.

Anatomy of the Heart (Fig. 2)

The heart consists of 4 chambers, the right and left auricles, or atria, and right and left

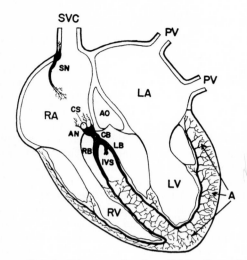

FIG. 2. Diagram showing distribution of specialized heart muscle. RA and LA are right and left auricles, RV and LV are right and left ventricles, and IVS is the interventricular septum. AO is the ascending aorta and CS the mouth of the coronary sinus. SVC is the superior vena cava and PV are the pulmonary veins. SN is the sinus node, AN is the A-V node, CB is the common bundle, RB and LB are the right and left bundle branches. A is the peripheral Purkinje net. (Adapted from Fig. 8 of "Clinical Electrocardiography. The Arrythmias," by Louis N. Katz and A. Pick, published in 1956 by Lea & Febiger, Philadelphia.)

ventricles. Blood which has circulated through the body enters the right auricle (RA) through the great veins—the superior vena cava (SVC) and the inferior vena cava (not shown), and passes through the right ventricle (RV) to the lungs. Oxygenated blood returning from the lungs enters the left auricle (LA) through the pulmonary veins (PV), and passes to the left ventricle (LV) which pumps it to the body tissues through the aorta and other arteries. Blood supply to the heart muscle flows through the coronary arteries and returns to the right auricle via the coronary veins and coronary sinus.

Impulse Conduction

The impulse which starts the heart beat arises at the sino-auricular node (SN). The SA node is a small piece of specialized tissue which has the property of automaticity, i.e., the impulse occurs spontaneously without external stimulation. The rate of impulse formation may be altered by nerves from the autonomic nervous sys-

tem, such as the vagus nerve, but the SA node will continue to fire even if these nerve connections are severed. The mechanism of impulse generation is not known, but because of this property the heart has been compared with a relaxation oscillator.

From the SA node, the impulse spreads over the walls of the auricles in a wave-like fashion at a rate of about 80 cm/sec. The resulting auricular depolarization produces the P wave of the typical electrocardiogram (ecg) (Fig. 3). After crossing the auricles, the impulse reaches the auriculoventricular node (AN), located at the top of the interventricular septum (IVS). The A-V node connects to a tract of rapidly conducting fibers (CB), which divide into a right bundle (RB) and left bundle (LB). Although conduction through the A-V node is very slow, conduction in the bundle fibers is rapid, of the order of 2 to 4 m/sec. The left and right branches run down the IVS, and branch further into a network of fibers, called Purkinje fibers, which pervade the ventricular wall muscle, or myocardium. The Purkinje fibers in the septum itself cause an activation of the septum from left to right. As the excitation spreads down the bundles and through the Purkinje network, depolarization of the ventricular walls starts from within outwards. Excitation of the septum and ventricular myocardium gives rise to the QRS complex of the ecg. Repolarization of the ventricles is indicated by the T wave. The letters P-T were assigned arbitrarily by Einthoven to indicate successive deflections in the electrical record.

Vector Field Theory of the Electrocardiogram

The deflections at different points on the body surface can be interpreted qualitatively by the

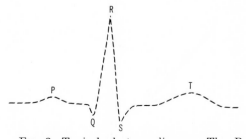

FIG. 3. Typical electrocardiogram. The P wave represents depolarization of the auricles and the Q, R, S waves the depolarization of the ventricles. The T wave occurs during the gradual repolarization of the heart fibers.

equation for the potential due to a dipole in an infinite fluid medium.

$$V = \frac{M \cos \Theta}{4 \pi k r^2}$$

As shown in Fig. 4, M is the dipole moment of the vector, r is the distance of the measured point from the dipole center, and θ is the angle between M and r; k is the fluid conductivity. The potential is maximum in the direction of the vector and zero perpendicular to it. M can be chosen to represent a given region of the heart, or even the resultant electrical force of the entire heart. During the cardiac cycle, for a given body point, M, r and θ may all vary. The ecg is thus a function of both space and time, and the records obtained at different sites may be quite different.

The value of M depends on the number of fibers or the heart volume excited at a given instant of time. In cases of hypertrophy, or thickening of the muscle wall, M is abnormally high. The mean direction of M varies among different individuals and in certain disease conditions. Potentials registered by electrodes on the chest wall are generally higher than those obtained by limb electrodes, because r is smaller (chest electrode closer to dipole center). The successive loci of M during the cycle may be altered by disturbances in impulse conduction, such as left or right bundle branch block. Areas of injury to the myocardium result in partial depolarization, producing alterations in the d-c level of the patterns. The equation is not adequate for quantitative studies, since it neglects important factors, such as the effect of the finite boundary on the current field, and the effect of differences in resistivity of tissues, such as the intracardiac blood.

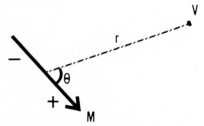

FIG. 4. The potential due to a dipole in free space. The potential, V, depends on the magnitude of M, the distance, r, from the dipole center and upon the angle, θ, between the direction of the dipole, M, and r.

Recording Methods

In 1856, Kölliker and Müller found that an electric current was produced at every beat of the frog heart without external stimulus. The electrocardiogram was first recorded by Sanderson and Page in 1878, by photographing the shadow of a capillary electrometer on a moving sensitive plate, using leads on the surface of the heart. Waller recorded the human ecg in 1889 using the same instrument. Clinical electrocardiography became a practical possibility with Einthoven's development of the string galvanometer. Although good records were obtained with this instrument, the response depended on string tension and it had a relatively low input impedance. The string galvanometer was followed by the vacuum tube amplifier. Modern electrocardiographs consist of multistage balanced amplifiers, using either tubes or transistors. Another method of recording is to apply two voltages, proportional to two orthogonal components of the heart-vector, to the X and Y plates of an oscilloscope. The resulting Lissajous pattern is called the vectorcardiogram.

Leads

Bipolar limb leads measure the potential difference between two limbs: lead I = left arm-right arm, II = left leg-right arm, III = left leg-left arm; the right leg is connected to ground. Einthoven represented the body as an equilateral triangle with the heart at the center, and deduced the direction of the vector in the frontal plane from these leads.

Unipolar leads are measured relative to a reference electrode which is as constant and as close to the mean heart potential as possible. The most widely used system was devised by Wilson, and consists of three leads from the left arm, right arm, and left leg, connected together via resistors to form a central terminal or reference electrode. In clinical practice, 3 bipolar limb leads, 3 unipolar limb leads, and 6 or more unipolar chest leads are usually taken.

Recent Advances

During the last decade, much work has been done on fundamental aspects of electrocardiology, due partly to the increased participation of engineers, mathematicians, and physicists. In 1954, it was shown that the resultant dipole moment of any system of charges in a volume conductor can be determined by a surface integration involving potential, surface contour, and conductivity. Thus,

$$M = k \iint VndS$$

where k = conductivity, V = potential, and n = unit normal vector. Using this theorem, it has been found that the magnitude of the peak vector in the human is of the order of 3 ma-cm. By means of electrolytic tank experiments in models with the shape of the human thorax, more accurate vector lead systems have been developed. Multipole representations of the heart have been derived, and advanced mathematical techniques, such as correlation studies, factor analysis and tensor analysis have been applied. Analog and digital computers are being used for diagnostic purposes as well as for theoretical studies.

References

1. BAYLEY, R. H., "Biophysical Principles of Electrocardiography," New York, Hoeber-Harper, 1958.
2. BRODY, D. A., BRADSHAW, J. C., AND EVANS, J. W., "The elements of an electrocardiographic lead tensor theory," *Bull. Math. Biophys.*, **23**, 31–42 (1961).
3. GABOR, D., AND NELSON, C. V., "Determination of the resultant dipole of the heart from measurements on the body surface," *J. Appl. Physics*, **25**, 413–416 (1954).
4. GESELOWITZ, D. B., "Multipole representation for an equivalent cardiac generator," *Proc. I.R.E.*, **48**, 75–79 (1960).
5. HAMILTON, W. F., AND DOW, P. (Eds.), "Handbook of Physiology," Section 2, "Circulation," Vol. 1, Baltimore, Williams & Wilkins, 1962.
6. HECHT, HANS H. (Ed.), "The Electrophysiology of the Heart," *Ann. N.Y. Acad. Sci.*, **65**, Art. 6 (1957).
7. HODGKIN, A. L., AND HUXLEY, A. F., "A quantitative description of membrane current and its application to conduction and excitation in nerve," *J. Physiol.*, **117**, 500–544 (1952).
8. HOFFMAN, B. F., AND CRANEFIELD, P. F., "Electrophysiology of the Heart," New York, Blakiston, 1960.
9. JOHNSTON, F. D., AND LEPESCHKIN, E., "Selected Papers of Dr. Frank N. Wilson," Ann Arbor, Edwards Bros., 1954.
10. PIPBERGER, H. V., "Use of computers in interpretation of electrocardiograms," *Circ. Research*, **11**, 555–562 (1962).
11. SCHER, A. M., YOUNG, A. C., AND MEREDITH, W. M., Factor analysis of the electrocardiogram," *Circ. Research*, **8**, 519–526 (1960).
12. WILLIUS, F. A., AND DRY, T. J., "A History of the Heart and Circulation," Philadelphia, Saunders, 1948.
13. WOLFF, L., "Electrocardiography, Fundamentals and Clinical Applications," Third Ed., Philadelphia, Saunders, 1962.

CLIFFORD V. NELSON

Cross-references: *Electrophysiology; Membrane Equilibrium; Membrane Potentials; Nerve Impulse Transmission.*

ELECTROCHEMICAL CALORIMETRY

Electrochemical processes almost invariably involve the evolution or absorption of heat. The measurement of this heat—"electrochemical calorimetry"—is a much-neglected and potentially fruitful area of research. This paper outlines the significance of the measured heat in terms of other familiar thermodynamic quantities. It also describes the work that has been done in this field and outlines briefly the apparatus and methods that have been used. Mention is made of several areas where electrochemical calorimetry might prove to be a useful research tool.

Energy Relations

The relations between the heat effect of an electrochemical process and the other energy changes involved can be illustrated by considering the discharge of an electrochemical cell or battery.

The electrical energy expended by the cell under reversible, isothermal conditions would be measured as the product of voltage, current, and time (E, I, t). Under these reversible conditions this work output is the maximum obtainable and equals free energy change (ΔF) of the cell reaction. The heat which must be evolved or absorbed by the cell to maintain temperature constancy is given by the product of the absolute temperature (T) and the entropy change (ΔS). The enthalpy change (ΔH) is to be identified with the change in the energy content of the system due to its changed chemical composition. This is externally undetectable. The above quantities are related by the familiar relation $\Delta F = \Delta H - T\Delta S$.

It is important to note that for a reversible process it is the entropy term ($T\Delta S$) that is solely responsible for the heat effect. Failure to recognize this fact is a common source of confusion.

In practice complete reversibility is never attained and, as a consequence, the electrical work obtained from the cell is less than maximum and, therefore, does not equal the theoretical ΔF of the cell reaction. All of the "lost work" appears as heat in the cell. Under these partially reversible conditions there are two heat effects in the cell, that caused by the entropy effect $(T\Delta S)$, which can be either exothermic or endothermic, and that caused by the "lost work", which is always exothermic. The latter is a consequence of irreversible effects, such as electrode polarization and the resistance of the electrolyte.

The completely irreversible process can be exemplified by short-circuiting the cell internally. From a thermodynamic standpoint this is the same as reversible discharge through a resistor which is considered as a part of the system. Even though the latter process is impossible, the heat effect can be divided conceptually into two parts, that dissipated by the resistor (ΔF) and that due to the entropy effect $(T\Delta S)$. Since the sum of these equals the enthalpy change (ΔH), it follows that for a completely irreversible process, and only for such a process, the heat effect equals the enthalpy change (ΔH).

In summation, the operation of a cell always involves a fixed heat effect $(T\Delta S)$ which is independent of reversibility. The only other heat effect is that caused by irreversibility. This can vary from zero for the completely reversible process to ΔF for the completely irreversible process.

The above discussion is based on molar quantities and assumes either pressure constancy or that gases are not involved. If gases are evolved or absorbed at constant volume, ΔH must be replaced by ΔE, the change in internal energy. The above discussion also assumes that heat is either evolved or absorbed at constant temperature. It is usually more convenient experimentally to isolate the system and relate the heat effect to the heat capacity of the system and its temperature change. Provided the latter is not greater than a few degrees Centigrade, the error thus introduced is rarely significant.

Two important conclusions can be drawn from the above treatment: first, the difference between the electrical energy done by (or on) an electrochemical cell and the heat evolved (or absorbed) by the cell equals the enthalpy change (ΔH) of the cell, this statement being independent of the reversibility of the process; second,

the heat effect of an electrochemical cell equals $T\Delta S$ plus the sum of the heat effects due to irreversible phenomena, the latter primarily a result of electrode polarization and the resistance of the electrolyte. Lead and electrode resistance can also play a significant role.

Measurement of ΔH

The most common application of conventional calorimetry is the measurement of ΔH. It is this application of electrochemical calorimetry that will be considered first.

In drawing a comparison between conventional and electrochemical calorimetry it must be borne in mind that the techniques and apparatus of the former have been thoroughly studied and highly refined. Work with the latter, on the other hand, has been very limited and has only served to indicate its feasibility and utility. In spite of this lack of experience with the electrochemical technique, certain conclusions regarding its potential usefulness can be drawn.

Certainly, it is severely limited in its applicability because it is restricted to reactions which can be carried out electrochemically. Also, the apparatus required is somewhat more complicated. The principal advantage of the electrochemical method lies in the fact that it often affords a direct, one-step measurement and thus avoids the devious, multistep determination which would be required by conventional calorimetry.

For example, the heats of formation of metal salts in solution can often be obtained directly by dissolving the metal anodically or depositing it cathodically. In particular the heat for formation of sodium tungstate has been obtained[1] by measuring the ΔH of the reaction: $W + 2NaOH$ (aq) $+ 2H_2O \rightarrow Na_2WO_4$ (aq) $+ 3H_2$.

Another advantage of the electrochemical approach lies in the fact that the rate of the reaction and, hence the rate of heat evolution is essentially uniform and under the operator's control. Such processes are ideally suited to adiabatic calorimetry. The adiabatic technique eliminates the heat leak correction and simplifies the problem of calorimeter design.[2]

Apparatus and Procedure

The essential features of both procedure and apparatus follow. A more detailed treatment can be obtained from the literature.[1,2]

Before attempting to measure the ΔH of the reaction, its current efficiency must be measured, and the nature and extent of any secondary reactions must be ascertained. In general only one electrode process will be of interest, e.g., the anodic dissolution of tungsten in the reaction above. The judicious choice of a counter electrode process will simplify the calorimetry and increase accuracy.

Gas evolution should be avoided if possible and every effort should be made to minimize irreversible effects. The latter can be accomplished by (a) the choice of a suitable reaction, (b) the use of large, rough, closely spaced electrodes, and (c) by minimizing electrolyte resistance. If irreversible effects are large, the enthalpy change (ΔH) will be obtained as a small difference between two large measured quantities, the electrical energy supplied, and the heat energy developed. This inevitably decreases the accuracy of the measurement.

The apparatus can be divided into two parts, the electrical circuit and the calorimeter. The former consists of a source of direct current with suitable controls and various instruments which afford a measure of both current and voltage as a function of time. Recent developments in electronics have made available constant current sources with regulation better than 0.01 per cent. These could supplant the lead cells used heretofore as a d-c source and, thus, simplify both apparatus and procedure.

A calorimeter made from a glass Dewar flask is well suited to electrochemical calorimetry. The glass is generally immune to chemical and electrochemical attack, and the rate of heat leak is much less than that through an all-metal calorimeter. The glass Dewar is not easily adapted to accurate work if isothermal calorimetry is used because of its unpredictable heat-leak. However, this objection is invalid if applied to adiabatic calorimetry.

In use the calorimeter is immersed in a light hydrocarbon or silicone oil which serves as an adiabatic environment. A sensitive thermopile with one set of junctions in the calorimeter and the other in the oil bath serves to detect temperature differences between the two and makes it possible to minimize these differences by means of a heater in the oil bath. A method of making a satisfactory thermopile is given in Ref. 2.

The various calorimeter components pass through the oil bath and then through seals in the calorimeter lid before entering the calorimeter. With the exception of the stirrer the commonly-used compression-type seal is satisfactory. The stirrer shaft can enter the calorimeter through a seal based on the "mercury seal stirrer," the oil acting as a sealant in place of mercury.

The calorimeter is essentially filled with the electrolyte which also acts as a calorimeter fluid. It must also contain the two electrodes, a platinum resistance thermometer, one end of the thermopile, a heater, and a stirrer. The latter should be driven by a synchronous motor and should operate in a tube to obtain maximum stirring effectiveness with minimum stirring heat. The position and size of the various components are important and should be considered carefully. For example, it is probably best to place the heater inside the stirrer tube. Also, the arrangement should insure effective stirring of the solution between the electrodes.

The procedure to be followed in making a ΔH determination consists of three experiments: a stirrer experiment, a heater experiment, and an electrolysis experiment. All measurements during these experiments are made under steady state, adiabatic conditions.

During the stirrer experiment only the stirrer is operated. The heater experiment entails the use of both heater and stirrer. For both of these experiments the temperature rise during a known time interval (e.g., $\frac{1}{2}$ hour) is noted. With these data and the energy dissipated by the heater it is then possible to compute the heat capacity of the calorimeter and the rate at which heat is generated by the stirrer.

The electrolysis experiment involves operation of the stirrer and the electrolytic cell. It is again necessary to measure the temperature rise corresponding to a known time interval. The number of faradays passed through the cell and the total electrical energy supplied to the cell must also be obtained. With these data and those from the stirrer and heater experiments it is then possible to compute the desired ΔH. A detailed description of the procedure and the method of calculation is given in Ref. 2.

Measurement of ΔS

The second application of electrochemical calorimetry to be considered is the measurement of the entropy change of half-cell processes. The first investigator in this field was Carhart[8, 9] who compared the entropy changes in the two halves of the Daniell cell. Carhart was followed by Lange[3] whose basic approach can be described as follows.

A calorimeter is divided into two symmetrical halves by means of a vertical partition. Both compartments are filled with the same electrolyte and each has one of two identical electrodes. A hole in the partition permits the passage of the electrolytic current. When current is passed between the electrodes the heat developed in either compartment is characteristic of the half-cell process taking place in that compartment. Since these half reactions are identical except for direction, one compartment will be heated and the other cooled by an equal amount. Because the currents used are very small, the process is essentially reversible, and the heat effect in either compartment can, therefore, be related to the $T\Delta S$ of the half-reaction taking place there.

Division of this measured $T\Delta S$ by the absolute temperature gives the entropy change of the half-reaction. Having this value, the entropy of the ion involved is easily computed provided only that the entropies of the other (nonionic) reactants and products are available in the literature. This is most commonly the case.

Literature values for ionic entropies are based on a scale which arbitrarily assigns a value of zero to the hydrogen ion at all temperatures. Values obtained by Lange's method, on the other hand, are independent of this convention and are based on the same absolute scale as are the literature values for the entropies of elements and compounds. It would seem that Lange's measurements would make it possible to measure "absolute" ionic entropies and, thus, fix the additive constant which relates one scale to the other.

Lange demonstrated that this is not the case, however. This finding grew out of his measurements on the half-cells: Ag, AgCl, HCl and Ag, AgCl, LiCl. He found that the entropy changes of these two half-cells differ by about 8 cal mole^{-1} deg^{-1}. According to the teachings of classical chemical thermodynamics, this difference could only be caused by a one hundred-fold difference between the activities of the chloride ion in these two half-cells. However, Lange found the 8 E.U. difference when comparing the two half-cells above with both of them dilute and at the same concentration.

Even though single ion activities are not thermodynamically defined, it is not reasonable to assume that any such one hundred-fold difference exists. One must, therefore, conclude that there is a heat producing phenomenon in half-cells other than that attributable to the chemical process indicated by the half-cell equation. Lange ascribed this anomalous effect to "transport entropies" as defined by Eastman.[4]

The quantitative treatment of such transport processes requires the methods of "steady state" or "irreversible" thermodynamics (q.v.). This subject, as it applies to electrochemistry has been reviewed by de Bethune.[5, 6] Qualitatively, the Eastman theory predicts that the ordered movement of ions must be accompanied by a simultaneous movement of heat. It is important to note in this connection that the quantity of heat thus transported depends only on the initial and final states of the system and is independent of the reversibility of the process. It is, therefore, not an irreversible phenomena in the usual sense.

Thus, according to the Eastman theory, the "reversible" half-cell heat effect measured by Lange is the sum of two effects. The first is predicted by classical chemical thermodynamics and is caused by the half-cell chemical change. The second is due to the movement of heat from one compartment of the calorimeter to the other, and must find its explanation in the thermodynamics of the steady state. Since there is no known method for measuring these separately, the elusive "absolute" ionic entropies—if indeed this phrase has any meaning—remain unknown.

Lange's work with half-cell heat effects has been refined and extended by the author.[2] In this study it was shown that it is possible in one calorimetric experiment to determine the cell ΔF, ΔH, each of the two half-cell ΔS values, and from the sum of these, the cell $T\Delta S$. Also included was a study of the relation between half-cell heat effects and the corresponding thermocell potentials. This relationship is in need of a simple theoretical interpretation that is consistent with the observed facts.

Other Applications

There are other applications of electrochemical calorimetry, both proved and potential, which have not been mentioned. It has been used, for example, to determine the rate of heat evolution of the sealed nickel-cadmium cells used in space applications.[7] This information is needed by the design engineer responsible for the thermal balance of the spacecraft.

These same cells can be used to exemplify another potential application of electrochemical calorimetry, the study of side reactions. During overcharge, oxygen is evolved at the nickel electrode and is subsequently absorbed by the cadmium electrode. These phenomena are only poorly understood in spite of the importance of this type of cell to the space program.

Electrochemical calorimetry should prove a most useful tool in the study of membrane phenomena and the processes which take place at liquid junctions.

In short, electrochemical calorimetry is a technique which can make contributions to both the theory and practice of chemistry. Its usefulness is limited primarily by the resourcefulness and imagination of the experimenter.

References

1. SHERFEY, J. M., AND BRENNER, ABNER, J. Electrochem Soc., **105**, 665 (1958).
2. SHERFEY, J. M., J. Electrochem Soc., **110**, 213 (1963).
3. LANGE, E., AND HESSE, TH., Z. Electrochem., **29**, 374 (1933).
4. EASTMAN, E. D., J. Am. Chem. Soc., **50**, 283, 929 (1928).
5. DE BETHUNE, ANDRE J., LICHT, T. S., AND SWENDEMAN, N., J. Electrochem Soc., **106**, 616 (1959).
6. DE BETHUNE, ANDRE J., J. Electrochem Soc., **107**, 829 (1960).
7. METZGER, WM. H., JR., WEINREB, M., AND SHERFEY, J. M., Goddard Space Flight Center internal document number 1-650-62-15 (to be published as a Goddard Technical Note).
8. CARHART, H. S., Phys. Rev., **11**, 1–13 (1900).
9. CARHART, H. S., "Thermoelectric Force in Electric Cells," pp. 52–66, New York, D. Van Nostrand Co., 1920.

JOSEPH M. SHERFEY

Cross-references: Enthalpy; Entropy; Irreversible Electrochemical Processes, Thermodynamics of.

ELECTROCHEMICAL NOMENCLATURE AND DEFINITIONS. See NOMENCLATURE, REMARKS ON; TENSION, CELL AND ELECTRODE.

ELECTROCHEMICAL SEPARATION OF ISOTOPES. See ISOTOPES, ELECTROCHEMICAL SEPARATION.

ELECTROCHEMICAL SOCIETY

The Society was founded April 3, 1902 by a group of 52 members who met in Philadelphia, Pennsylvania, to organize the American Electrochemical Society. There were 357 charter members. Joseph W. Richards of Lehigh University served as the first president. The name of the Society was changed to its present title, The Electrochemical Society, Inc., and its membership made international in scope in 1930.

Objectives

Its objectives are the advancement of the science and technology of electrochemistry; the encouragement and reporting of research for the dissemination of knowledge in its related fields; and insuring of adequate training for chemists, engineers and metallurgists.

Membership

There are three classes of individual membership: Active, Associate, and Student. Corporations affiliate with the Society by becoming Patron or Sustaining Members.

The current membership is about 3800.

Divisional Scope and Areas of Interest

The technical scope and areas of interest embraced in the Society are defined and represented by its several Divisions as follows:

Battery includes primary and secondary cells for the chemical production of electrical energy.

Corrosion covers behavior of materials in such environments that cause corrosion, oxidation, and related surface reactions; to study the special technical terms in its own and related fields and to make recommendations to simplify, standardize, and increase the comprehension of its oral and written presentations.

Electric Insulation includes the physics, chemistry and application of dielectrics.

Electrodeposition includes fields of electroplating, electroforming, electrorefining, electrowinning, electropowders, anodic processes, such as electropolishing and anodizing, and allied processes.

Electronics covers the chemical and physical properties of electronically active systems emphasizing chiefly semiconducting and luminescent materials.

Electro-Organic includes all fields of electro-organic chemistry.

Electrothermics and Metallurgy covers reactions taking place at high temperature, said temperature resulting from the utilization of electrical energy, the study and teaching of various metallurgical processes or properties, said metals being of unusual or special scientific note.

Industrial Electrolytic includes improvement in existing industrial electrolytic processes and provides a sound basis for the establishment of new processes covering applied research, engineering and industrial practices. The term electrolytic processes includes the electrolysis of aqueous, nonaqueous, and fused salt electrolytes, electrowinning, electrodialysis, etc. Associated processes, such as cell feed preparation, product handling, electrode manufacture, power sources, etc., are also included.

Theoretical includes the general field of theoretical electrochemistry.

Local Sections

Local sections are organized in 18 areas and members affiliate with the local section, if one exists, in their area. Local meetings are held periodically throughout the year.

National Meetings

National meetings of the Society are held in the spring and fall of each year, when its divisions arrange for its technical sessions. Prior to each meeting the program, with a 75-word abstract of each paper to be presented, is published in the *Journal*. Enlarged abstracts of 500–1,000 words are also available.

Publications

The Journal of The Electrochemical Society is a monthly publication and contains technical papers covering fundamental research. It also has a current affairs section which keeps members informed of Society activities and news items of general interest.

Electrochemical Technology is a new bimonthly publication and is devoted to practical aspects of electrochemistry, including engineering, technology, design, devices, economics and appropriate reviews.

Review of Papers. Papers submitted for publication in the *Journal* and in *Electrochemical Technology* are reviewed by authorities in the field and must be approved before publication. This procedure establishes high standards of scientific evaluation.

Monographs and Special Publications containing papers presented at symposia which are organized to provide a comprehensive treatment of special subjects, are published from time to time.

Extended Abstracts containing 500 to 1,000 words of papers presented by divisions at its national meetings are published each year. Separate books are printed for each divisional program.

Honors and Awards

Edward Goodrich Acheson Gold Medal and $1,000 Prize, established in 1928, is awarded biennially to a person who shall have made a distinguished contribution to the advancement of any of the objectives, purposes, or activities of the Society.

Palladium Medal, founded in 1950, is awarded biennially to a scientist in recognition of original contributions to fundamental knowledge of corrosion processes or theoretical electrochemistry.

F. M. Becket Memorial Award, a biennial award amounting to approximately $1,500, was established by the Union Carbide Corporation. Its purpose is to commemorate the memory of F. M. Becket by providing a grant-in-aid to an outstanding student of science or engineering specializing in electrothermics or high-temperature technology.

Summer Fellowship Awards, three in number, of $800 each are made annually to students who wish to continue their studies during the summer months in pursuance of work between the degree of B.S. and Ph.D., who have received a nine months' grant preceeding the summer period, and who will continue their studies after the summer period for at least one more quarter or semester. These awards are named the Edward Weston Summer Fellowship, Colin Garfield Fink Summer Fellowship, and the Electrochemical Society Summer Fellowship.

Joseph W. Richards Memorial Lecture, founded in 1929, is provided for from income from a special fund used at periodical intervals to defray the expenses incurred by a distinguished scientist invited to lecture at a meeting of the Society.

Young Author Prizes, one consisting of a cash award of $100 by the Society, and the other of $100 worth of scientific and technical books contributed by the Reinhold Publishing Corporation in memory of Francis Mills Turner, are awarded each year to young authors under 31 years of age who have published the best papers in the *Journal*.

Perkin Medal. The Society, among others, is represented on a Committee for Awarding the Perkin Medal of the Society of Chemical Industry.

ROBERT K. SHANNON

ELECTROCHEMICAL SOCIETY OF JAPAN

This Society was established in 1933 to promote the science and technology of electrochemistry and also to promote the electrochemical industry of Japan. Since then the activities of the Society have developed to include such functions as publication of technical journals and monographs, sponsorship of symposia and other meetings, arrangement of industrial plant tours for members, and drafting recommendations to other organizations. The Society, being responsible for prosperity in the electrochemical industry, has often submitted recommendations to the Japanese Government regarding the problems of electricity which is the basis of the electrochemical industry. In April, 1963, the Society celebrated its 30th anniversary.

Two journals are published by the Society. *Denki-Kagaku [Journal of the Electrochemical Society of Japan,* (Japanese Edition)] appears monthly mainly for domestic members. The *Journal* has included applied physical chemistry since 1961. The specific fields covered are: 1) Theoretical Electrochemistry and Applied Physical Chemistry, 2) Electroorganic, 3) Electroanalysis, 4) Electrodeposition and Surface Treatment, 5) Industrial Electrolytic, 6) Batteries, 7) Corrosion and Prevention, 8) Electronics and Materials for Electrical Industry, 9) Extractive Metallurgy, 10) High Temperature Chemistry and Fused Salts, 11) Electricdischarge Chemistry and Radiation Chemistry, and 12) Instrumentation and Quality Control. The Journal consists of an Essay, Reviews, Technical Reports, Lectures, and News. *Journal of the Electrochemical Society of Japan* (English Edition) appears quarterly mainly for overseas members and contains original papers and abstracts from the Japanese Edition. The journals are operated for the Society by an editorial staff composed of a

chief editor and five technical editors, based upon approval of and consultation with the publication committee. The chief editor concurrently holds the post of chairman of the committee. In addition to these *Journals*, the Society sponsors various monographs such as "Denkikagakubenran" (Electrochemistry Handbook), "Denkikagaku-no-Shimpo" ("Progress of Electrochemistry") and "Japan's Electrochemical Industry" (English). Since its first publishing in 1942, 23,000 copies of the Handbook have been distributed in Japan. It was revised in 1952 and is scheduled to be revised again at the end of 1963 as an activity of the 30th anniversary. "Japan's Electrochemical Industry" was published in 1958 for foreign persons interested in obtaining information on Japanese industries.

Six standing committees on the science and technology of a specific area are organized under the Society: Primary Batteries, Prevention of Corrosion, High Purity Metals, Fused Salt Chemistry, Materials for Electronics, and Electrothermal Chemistry. These committees are playing important roles in each field in Japan by holding conferences and sponsoring technical meetings.

There are six local sections, organized by regional members of the Society, which sponsor the general meetings, technical meetings, and educational functions of the respective local section.

Three awards are offered by the Society: The Tanahashi Prize to Predominant Author, The Tanahashi Prize for "contribution to the advancement of the electrochemical industry," and The Sano Prize to Young Authors.

In the membership, six types of members are recognized: 2291 regular members, 208 student affiliates, 1 honorary member, 128 overseas members, 50 patron (special sustaining) members (firms), and 154 sustaining members (firms). Each numerical figure shows the number of members as of 1962.

A general meeting is held every April when the annual program and budget are planned, the balance of income and expenditure is approved, and the members of the Board of Directors are appointed. The annual meeting for presentation of papers, symposia, and plant tours are also arranged. The Society cosponsors symposia and technical meetings with The Chemical Society of Japan, The Polarographic Society of Japan, and The Japan Society for Analytical Chemistry.

Funds for operation of the Society are derived from individual and corporate dues, income from publications, and benefits from various grants.

Business matters of the Society are conducted by a manager under the supervision of a Board of Directors. The latter is composed of a president, four vice-presidents, a chief editor, five technical editors, four auditors, two secretaries for general affairs, two treasurers, and several of the other members. The board members are selected at the regular general meeting of the Society, and the president and the vice-presidents are elected by the members themselves. The length of their terms is two years. The manager is appointed by the Board of Directors, and the length of his term is indefinite. The manager is assisted in his duties by a staff of workers at the Society office: 3, 1-chome, Yurakucho, Chiyoda-ku, Tokyo, Japan.

Seiichi Ishizaka

ELECTROCHEMICAL THERMODYNAMICS. See **IRREVERSIBLE ELECTROCHEMICAL PROCESS, THERMODYNAMICS OF;** also see **SPECIFIC TERMS, SUCH AS FREE ENERGY; ENTROPY; ETC.**

ELECTROCHEMISTRY

Electrochemistry has been defined in "Webster's New Unabridged International Dictionary" as "a science that deals with the relation of electricity to chemical changes and with the interconversion of chemical and electrical energy (as in electric cells or in electrolysis) and has many applications in industry (as in the production of aluminum, alkalies, and chlorine, or in electroplating)." While this statement is excellent as a brief definition, obviously more space is needed to survey the scope of electrochemistry both as an empirical art and as a theoretical science.

Broadly interpreted, electrochemistry deals with all systems which involve chemical preparation and electrical charge or potential. This includes electrical production of high temperatures for chemical purposes (electrothermics, electrometallurgy); electric insulation and dielectric materials; electrolysis of either organic or inorganic substances; plating in any form; all electric cells whether rechargeable or not; and many electronic devices, such as semiconductor and phosphor products. In addition to

industrial processes and research on industrial materials, the science includes laboratory studies of great importance in the theories of chemical structure, reactivity, energy relations, and kinetics, of electrolytes and ionization in solutions and melts, of electric cells, of oxidation-reduction systems, and of most types of metallic corrosion. Various types of electroanalysis are included (polarography, amperometric, and coulometric methods, as well as classical constant current and constant potential electrodeposition). Electrobiology is essentially electrochemistry applied to biological systems.

Modern electrochemistry may be said to have begun with the assembly of electric cells (galvanic cells) which could produce appreciable current in an outside circuit, due to chemical reaction within the cell. A modern example is the zinc "dry cell," a refined version of the original Leclanché cell. It consists essentially of a zinc or zinc-lined can containing ammonium chloride paste and a central "spool" having a carbon rod conductor surrounded by a paste of manganese dioxide, MnO_2, and graphite. There is little or no chemical reaction until the zinc and carbon electrodes are connected (for example, through copper wires and a flashlight bulb); then the following reactions take place:

$$Zn \rightarrow Zn^{+2} + 2\epsilon \text{ (anode, oxidation)}$$

$$2MnO_2 + 2H^+ + 2\epsilon \rightarrow Mn_2O_3 + H_2O$$

(cathode, reduction)

The symbol, ϵ, stands for the electron, and it is the fact that electrons can move away from the zinc through the circuit to the carbon, where they are used in reducing the MnO_2, which makes the chemical process possible. In the early days of the study of such cells the electron was not known and it was postulated that a current of positive charge flowed from carbon to zinc.

While there is some evidence that electrochemical cells with copper and iron electrodes were known and used at least 2000 years ago, the art was forgotten and Alessandro Volta is generally credited with the discovery of such cells, about 1790. While sometimes called voltaic cells, they are more often called galvanic cells, after Luigi Galvani, whose experiments with metallic couples were initiated a few years earlier.

Current from such cells was used for many years to study electrolysis and other phenomena. In the early 1800's Sir Humphry Davy was able to produce sodium and other active metals by electrolysis of their molten salts or hydroxides. In modern terminology we write the equations:

$$Na^+ + \epsilon \rightarrow Na \text{ (cathode, reduction)}$$

$$2Cl^- - 2\epsilon \rightarrow Cl_2 \text{ (anode, oxidation)}$$

Michael Faraday formulated his laws relating electrical and chemical quantities from experiments on electrolysis of aqueous solutions of acids, bases and salts, using chemical cells to provide current. Our modern equations show these laws by the number of electrons indicated: if the symbol Na in the above equation stands for a gram-atomic weight of sodium (23 grams), the symbol ϵ stands for Avogadro's number of electrons, carrying 96,490 coulombs of charge.

Galvanic cells provide only low-voltage current, usually less than 2 volts per cell; this is inherent in the nature of the chemical oxidation-reduction reactions which produce current. To study electrolysis it was necessary to connect 2 or more cells in series (a battery), and to study some phenomena, as electric discharge in gases, many cells had to be connected. Today high-voltage "B" batteries are used for portable radios, radiation survey meters, etc.; a 45-volt battery may consist of 30 zinc cells, a 300-volt battery of 200 cells in series.

In the early days of galvanic cells it was hoped that large electric currents could be produced, using inexpensive materials, e.g., carbon for the anode (to be oxidized) and atmospheric oxygen for the cathode. Research has been revived in this direction in recent years (*fuel cells*), and while the low voltage of single cells is a great disadvantage, there is reason to believe that economically useful batteries will be developed. In the fuel cell, as with most dry cells or primary cells, there is ordinarily no attempt to regenerate the fuel or the oxidant, while in the storage battery or accumulator the anode and cathode materials are regenerated by current from an outside source. Some thought has been given to the possibility of decomposing the oxidized product of a fuel cell with the high temperatures attainable in a nuclear reactor. The fuel would then be used over and over, and the whole process would serve to obtain electrical energy from nuclear energy.

Electrothermics

Since the first days of large-scale production of electricity, electric furnaces have been used for chemical reactions which require high temperatures. While not strictly electrochemistry, electrothermics has come to be known as a branch of the subject. Both *resistance* and *arc* furnaces are used. Carborundum (silicon carbide, SiC) and other abrasives; calcium carbide, CaC_2; calcium cyanamide, $CaCN_2$; and elementary phosphorus are electric furnace products. Some metallurgical processes employ electric furnaces because of the excellent temperature control, and electric blast furnaces for the reduction of iron ore are not unknown.

Dielectric Materials

Electrical insulating materials are important in many industrial applications, from the coating on a wire to the fluids used in electrical voltage transformers. The study of such materials may again not be electrochemistry in a strict sense, but much chemical research is involved in developing substances to meet strict electrical requirements. Silicones, fluorinated hydrocarbons, and certain plastics are examples. In electrical condensers or *capacitors* the properties of the liquid or solid medium between metallic plates is important; in *electrolytic capacitors* true electrochemical processes are involved at the electrodes.

Industrial Electrolysis

Many of the active metals and nonmetals, and compounds of an unusual nature, are made by electrolysis of melts or of aqueous solutions. All the alkali and alkaline earth metals are included as well as beryllium, indium, magnesium, aluminum, and even some zinc, copper and lead. Many of the "exotic" metals, such as titanium, tantalum, zirconium, hafnium, and boron, are obtained by electrolysis in fused salt systems.

Chlorine is obtained at the anode from molten or aqueous chlorides. Fluorine is made in special electrolysis cells using HF and KF as the source. Sodium and other hydroxides are obtained from aqueous solution with hydrogen as a by-product. Chlorine bleaches (containing hypochlorites, as NaClO), chlorates, perchlorates, persulfates, perborates, and other oxidizing agents are anodic products; lead dioxide and manganese dioxide are among these. Hydrogen peroxide, H_2O_2, is the indirect product from an electrolytic procedure. Many other compounds made by oxidation or reduction can be obtained by electrolysis, but often direct chemical methods or even bacterial action are more economical.

Electrodeposition and Electrorefining

Electroplating is well-known as a means of depositing a thin layer of a corrosion-resistant metal on a more susceptible one. Impure copper, nickel, tin, and other metals can be refined by anodic dissolution and simultaneous cathodic deposition in suitable solutions of their salts; more noble metals do not dissolve as easily at the anode while baser metals do not deposit as readily at the cathode. Some ores can be leached with acids or other reagents, the metals recovered by electrolysis of the resulting solution (*electrowinning*). Certain *colloids* whose particles are electrically charged can be deposited electrolytically; in this way thin layers of rubber can be formed on molds which serve as electrodes.

Semiconductors

Substances which normally do not conduct electricity well, as germanium and silicon, whose atoms each have *four* valence electrons to share in covalent bonds with neighboring atoms are called semiconductors. The crystals of these elements are never quite pure or perfect, and a few electrons are free to conduct. More are freed at higher temperature (the resistance decreases, in contrast to the resistance of metals, which increases with rising temperature). By refining these elements to unusual purity and then adding small amounts of elements whose atoms have either *three* or *five* valence electrons, the useful p- and n-semiconductors result and serve as the basis for transistors and other electronic devices. The study of semiconductors is considered at least partly a branch of electrochemistry since a combination of chemical and electrical properties is involved.

Phosphors

Phosphors emit light when bombarded with electrons (as on a television screen) and may be considered electrochemical products; the same is true of materials used in scintillation counters for the study of radioactivity, the phosphors which emit light on electric stimulation (*electroluminescence*), and even the *lasers* which transform heterogeneous white light into intense beams of "coherent" monochromatic light.

Electrochemical Theory in the Laboratory

Electrical studies of chemical materials have provided a powerful tool for the theoretical explanation of the properties of matter, and have led to many practical applications.

Determination of *dielectric constants* of gases and liquids has enabled calculation of the *dipole moment* of molecules, a measure of their electrical symmetry or dissymmetry, and, consequently, an indication of their structure. For example, the water molecule, H_2O, is shown to have a triangular configuration with the valence electrons drawn toward the O-atom, while carbon dioxide CO_2 is linear with the O-atoms equally spaced on either side of the C-atom as a time average. The dielectric constant of a liquid is important in ionization theory; the attractive force between ions of opposite charge is proportional to the product of the charges and inversely proportional to the dielectric constant of the medium and the square of the distance between them: force $= q_+q_-/Dr^2$.

Electrolysis with *direct current* has led to the measurement of relative and actual speeds of ions, and the fraction of the current carried by individual ions. In dilute solutions the ions travel rather slowly, a few centimeters per hour at room temperature with voltages which do not heat the solution. In dilute hydrochloric acid the H^+ ion travels four times as fast as the Cl^- ion and so carries four-fifths of the current; on electrolysis this leads to unequal concentration changes at anode and cathode unless the solution is well stirred.

In *electrophoresis*, chemical compounds of very high molecular weight are separated by electrolysis, since their ions move at different speeds. The proteins of blood plasma have been separated and identified in this way, and the electrophoretic method was used as a guide in the larger-scale separation of blood proteins.

In *polarography*, electrolysis is carried out with the "falling mercury drop" as one electrode. A new mercury drop becomes the cathode (or anode) every few seconds, presenting an uncontaminated surface for metal deposition or other processes. Each reaction takes place at a characteristic potential, and the components of a solution, for example a dilute mixture of metal salts, can be identified and their concentrations determined.

Direct current is used in studies of *electrode kinetics* and the molecular mechanism of electrode processes. If current is forced between two electrodes in a solution, the voltage required is greater than the "reversible potential," i.e., the electrodes become "polarized" because some step in formation of a product requires more energy than the calculated minimum. It is of great theoretical importance to understand why this is true and what the slow steps are.

Quantitative study of the *conductance* of ionic solutions is made with alternating current of low amplitude and fairly high frequency (as 1000 cycles per second), using platinum electrodes with specially prepared surfaces. This avoids the electrode polarization mentioned above and insures that only the resistance of the solution is measured, not a special resistance at the electrode-solution interface. Comparison of electrical conductance with other physical properties of solutions, such as freezing point depression and boiling point elevation, led Arrhenius in the 1880's to his ionization theory and to the distinction between strong, weak, and nonelectrolytes. Quantitative measurements have enabled calculation of ionization constants ("strength constants") of weak acids and bases, and of water and other solvents. Conductance is used to measure the rates of some chemical reactions, in analysis by titration, to follow the purity of boiler feed-water and the contamination of industrial effluents, and for many other purposes.

Study of the *electromotive force* (emf) of *reversible cells* is of major importance in accurate determination of the energy produced or consumed in chemical reactions. Provided the emf can be measured with an instrument which requires very little current (potentiometer), and if small currents can be drawn from or pushed through the cell without electrode polarization, the "free energy" of the cell reaction is obtained from the equation, $\Delta G = -n\mathbf{F}E$. Here E is the emf in volts, $\mathbf{F}$ is the Faraday constant (96,490 coulombs per chemical equivalent), and n is the number of electrons appearing in the partial equations. If the free energy corresponding to standard conditions (unit activity of each reactant and product) can be obtained, the equilibrium constant of the cell reaction can be deduced, and from this the possible yield of products. Once extensive tables of emf's or free energies have been built up, the values can be combined in such a way that even the extent of reactions which have not been studied can be predicted.

Corrosion of Metals

Corrosion is in most cases an electrochemical reaction in that the metal is oxidized, losing electrons to something in the surrounding medium. For example, if a drop of water is allowed to evaporate on a clean steel surface, a rust stain results. The initial anodic reaction is:

$$Fe - 2\epsilon \rightarrow Fe^{+2}$$

The corresponding cathodic reaction is reduction of dissolved oxygen:

$$O_2 + 2H_2O + 4\epsilon \rightarrow 4OH^-$$

These reactions are followed by precipitation of solid ferrous hydroxide and its further oxidation to hydrated ferric oxide (rust).

Such corrosion mechanisms suggest ways to prevent or delay corrosion: keep oxygen out, add an inhibitor which is adsorbed on the metal and prevents oxygen from touching it, make the metal cathodic in an electric circuit so that outside electrons reduce the oxygen, instead of electrons from the iron. Such *cathodic protection* is widely used to mitigate corrosion of pipe lines, water mains, and other underground equipment, as well as ships' hulls (where the paint coating is never perfect) and many metal structures immersed in sea water. Current is supplied by generators or rectified a-c, or by attaching more active metals as Mg and Zn to steel (sacrificial anodes); when such a metallic *couple* is immersed in a conducting medium the more active one becomes anodic and is oxidized, as in any galvanic cell.

Sometimes a metal may be protected by making it the anode in a circuit, thus forming an impervious *passivating* film of oxide; or by addition to the medium of a strong oxidizing agent (as chromate) to form the film.

Electrochemistry in Life Processes

Ever since Galvani found that frog muscle twitched on application of a small electric potential, it has been apparent that electricity and current flow are intimately involved in life processes. Differential diffusion of ions through individual cell membranes results in electrical potential differences, and due to the orderly array of cells appreciable potentials are found between different parts of the living body. In the extreme case of the "electric eel" the voltage and current available are sufficient to stun or kill the fish's prey.

Nerve impulses, while not due to electronic conduction as in a wire, are certainly carried along the nerve fibers by a series of chemical processes which transmit an electric potential difference. Storage of information in the brain (memory) and its retrieval are almost certainly electrochemical in nature. Experiments have shown that electrical stimulation at certain points in the brain can make the subject recall "forgotten" events; stimulation at other points can result in pleasant, or unpleasant, feelings. The heart beats as the result of periodic stimuli, apparently electrochemical in nature; heartbeat has been revived by slight electric shock, and irregular beat or flutter can be brought under control by periodic electric impulses supplied by a battery-operated electronic device.

The study of electrochemical processes in living biological systems is evidently of utmost importance and holds great promise for the future.

References

1. HUTCHINSON, E., "Physical Chemistry," Philadelphia, W. B. Saunders Co., 1962.
2. MACINNES, D. A., "The Principles of Electrochemistry," New York, Reinhold Publishing Corp., 1939; reprinted by Dover Publications, New York, 1961.
3. SHEDLOVSKY, T., (Editor), "Electrochemistry in Biology and Medicine," New York, John Wiley and Sons, 1955.
4. UHLIG, H. H., "Corrosion and Corrosion Control," New York, John Wiley and Sons, 1963.

CECIL V. KING

ELECTROCHROMATOGRAPHY

As the name implies, electrochromatography is a method of carrying out an essentially chromatographic separation in an electric field. Chromatographic separations are based on repeated transfer of substances between two phases, one stationary and the other moving. For example, a moving liquid phase may be used to wash a small quantity of a mixture of substances through a cylindrical column packed with a porous material. The stationary phase may be the surface of the packing itself (adsorption chromatography), or a second liquid supported in the packing (partition chromatography). A particularly versatile supporting medium is filter paper, which can be used in the form of strips or sheets directly. Under favorable conditions the mixture separates into its components, which migrate as a series of discrete bands or zones at different rates down the col-

umn or filter paper strip. The resolving power of chromatography is extraordinarily great. It depends on slight differences in the distribution of similar substances between the two phases, the effects of which are multiplied enormously as the zones migrate. The ratio of the rate of movement of a given substance to the rate of movement of the flowing solvent is defined as the R_F value.[1] In an ideal situation, where there is instantaneous equilibrium between phases and no diffusion, it is equivalent to the proportion of the substance in the mobile phase.

In electrochromatography, an electric gradient may be either substituted for the hydraulic gradient responsible for the flow of mobile phase, or superimposed upon it. The method is, of course, only applicable to charged colloidal particles and substances which ionize in solution. In the first case the electrophoretic mobilities of the substances in the "mobile" phase are wholly responsible for the migration of the zones. An additional factor, therefore, comes into play in the separation: if the mobilities of the components of a mixture bear an inverse relation to their sorbabilities on the stationary phase, the chromatographic resolution will be enhanced. In the second case, the electrical gradient is most profitably superimposed transversely on the hydraulic gradient. This procedure, generally known as "two-dimensional electrochromatography," is carried out on rectangular sheets or beds of supporting material. It leads to migration along a path which is the resultant of the electrophoretic movement of a zone and its movement in the direction of the flowing solvent. In certain circumstances *continuous* electrochromatographic separations can be carried out in this way, as will be shown below.

Closely related to the above two types of electrochromatography are the procedures used for carrying out purely electrophoretic separations in a stabilizing ("anticonvection") medium. Generally known as *zone electrophoresis*, such separations depend essentially or entirely on mobility differences between the components of a mixture, which may be maximized by suitable choice of buffer or complexing agent. Unfortunately, the terms zone electrophoresis and electrochromatography have frequently been used synonymously. To emphasize the distinction other terms have been introduced, such as "ionography" for the former and "electrochromatophoresis" for the latter. However, the words electrophoresis (q.v.) and chromatography have well-defined meanings, and it is a pity to blur the implication of electrochromatography by using it in an all-embracing operational sense.

One-dimensional electrochromatography

If u_r represents the electrophoretic mobility of substance r, and x_r the distance travelled by a zone of r in a given time, then the degree of separation of a binary mixture is determined by

$$\frac{x_1}{x_2} = \frac{u_1 R_{F_1}}{u_2 R_{F_2}}$$

where the ratio of R_F values is obtained from a simple chromatographic separation using the same supporting material and electrolyte. Clearly, the latter separation cannot be improved on by electrochromatography if the mobilities of the two components are identical. On the other hand, separations by electrochromatography are readily carried out in media of very low porosity, in which chromatography as such is not feasible owing to high mechanical resistance to flow. In cases of this kind, the evaluation of the relative contributions of electrophoresis and chromatography may not always be straightforward.

Numerous methods of utilizing packed media for electrochromatographic and zone electrophoretic separations have been described. The media used include glass beads, starch granules, cellulose powder, polyvinyl chloride resins, foam rubber, starch and agar gels, ion-exchange resins, and the ubiquitous filter paper. Whatever the medium, certain problems always arise in regard to experimental design and theoretical interpretation of the results. To obtain the greatest possible resolution, the mixture must be applied to the medium as an extremely narrow zone—preferably a fine line—normal to the direction of the field. During the experiment it is necessary to control the effects of electroosmosis (q.v.), heating and consequent evaporation and diffusion of electrode products into the region in which the separation takes place, and to regulate automatically voltage or current. Since an increase in temperature is accompanied by a decrease in the electrical resistance, constant current regulation is generally preferred. Considerations relating to zone mobilities must take into account the porosity and tortuosity of the medium, its electrokinetic potential (q.v.), and its affinity for the substances undergoing separation, as well as the composition of the supporting electrolyte.[2-7]

Most commonly the experimental arrangement comprises a sheet or strip of filter paper or a thin, flat layer of one of the other media, supported horizontally on a plastic rack. At opposite ends of the rack are electrode vessels in the form of troughs containing the electrolyte solution. When paper is used it is moistened with electrolyte first, and then placed in position in such a way that the ends overhang and dip into the troughs; with other media paper or cloth wicks are used to make the contact. The electrodes are usually of platinum. To restrict diffusion of the products of electrolysis, isolating systems of baffles and porous plugs have been devised. The water content of the medium is often critical, and it may be necessary to separate it from the wicks by means of cellophane membranes. The whole system is covered during an experiment, so as to form a moist chamber in which evaporation can be controlled. Below field strengths of about 20 volts per centimeter no additional cooling is necessary beyond that brought about by evaporation. However, high-voltage separations at field strengths ranging up to 100 volts per centimeter are frequently more efficient for low-molecular weight materials, since sharper zones are produced. Furthermore, for preparative work high voltages are generally more economical.[8] In this case special measures are necessary to insure adequate cooling.[4, 6]

Examples of one-dimensional electrochromatographic separations include the fractionation of haemoglobins in agar by Zuelzer *et al*[3] and the resolution of higher monoalkylammonium ions on filter paper by Edward and Crawford.[5] Filter paper is an excellent medium for the separation of many basic organic substances, such as alkaloids, dyes, and amino acids. Spiegler has described the use of columns of granular ion-exchange resin and strips of ion-exchange membrane for the separation of metal ions.[9] In all such work the methods of detection and quantitative estimation are by and large those which are universally used in paper chromatographic studies.[1, 4]

Two-dimensional electrochromatography

Virtually all the procedures published make use of a vertical sheet (or "curtain") of filter paper, generally freely suspended in a moist chamber.[10] The upper edge of the curtain dips into a trough containing the supporting electrolyte, which serves also as an eluant. The lower edge is serrated, and arranged so that the teeth are inserted individually into a row of small funnels which either lead the eluant to waste or to a rack of collecting tubes. Down the side edges of the curtain are attached the electrodes, preferably within dialysis tubing through which buffer can be circulated. The mixture to be separated is applied to the curtain as a small spot, near the upper edge and on the side farthest from the electrode towards which the predominant migration is expected to take place.

As before, the degree of separation of two components in the horizontal or electrochromatographic direction is determined by the expression above, while their degree of separation in the vertical or chromatographic direction depends on the ratio R_{F_1}/R_{F_2}. Thus. a mixture will be resolved into a pattern of zones scattered over the curtain, the distribution of which can be predicted from paper-strip chromatography and one-dimensional electrochromatography carried out alone under identical conditions. Pučar has given a beautiful example of the complete resolution of a mixture of seven dyes by this procedure using a borate buffer electrolyte: chrysoidine Y, nitraniline, rosolic acid (two components), tropeolin O, fluorescein, and chlorophenol red. By one-dimensional electrochromatography the first two travel in one zone, the last three in another, and the others are separated. By paper chromatography the first and the last are separated, the remainder travelling practically as a single zone in between. Strain and Sullivan have separated by this means complex mixtures of metal ions, for example, Ni-Co-Fe-Ag-Cd-Cu in an electrolyte containing 0.01 M ammonium tartrate, 0.005 M dimethylglyoxime, and 4 M ammonia.[10]

Continuous electrochromatography

The arrangement described above for two-dimensional electrochromatography has been used with great success for continuous separations.[10] The mixture is fed continuously to the point of application through a fine capillary or auxiliary wick. Once steady-state conditions are set up, the components stream downwards across the curtain along a series of stable paths, which terminate at different points on the serrated lower edge. In this way, for example, continuous fractionation of mixtures of amino acids and peptides can be performed. Instead of filter-paper curtains, narrow rectangular troughs packed with glass powder have also been employed.

It has been pointed out by Pučar[10] and Caplan[11] that the separations obtained in these systems are not influenced by adsorption, and depend only on the ratio u_1/u_2. They are thus electrophoretic, not electrochromatographic. The adsorbed substances are immobilized with respect to both gradients, consequently the *direction* of the resultant of the horizontal and vertical zone velocities must be independent of adsorptive retardation. On the other hand, continuous electrochromatographic separations can be achieved by using ion-exchange resin media rather than surface adsorbants. These may be troughs of resin granules, or even ion-exchange membrane curtains.[11] In this way a stationary phase capable of highly selective sorption is provided, within which charged particles are immobilized with respect to eluant flow but not with respect to current flow. The direction of the resultant is then no longer independent of sorption. If a "separation coefficient," D_2^1, is defined as the ratio $\tan \theta_1/\tan \theta_2$, where θ_r is the angle through which the path of a substance, r, is swept from the vertical under the influence of an applied potential, then

$$D_2^1 \approx \frac{\bar{u}_1 R_{F_2}}{\bar{u}_2 R_{F_1}}$$

where $\bar{u}$ represents electrophoretic mobility measured within the resin. As an example of this process, Caplan has obtained sharp continuous electrochromatographic separations of the alkali metals, Li-Na-K, in a pack of cation-exchange membrane "curtains" interleaved with thin filter paper.

References

1. CONSDEN, R., GORDON, A. H., AND MARTIN, A. J. P., "Qualitative Analysis of Proteins: a Partition Chromatographic Method Using Paper," *Biochem. J.*, **38**, 224 (1944).
2. WUNDERLY, CH., "Paper Electrophoresis," in Bier, M., Ed., "Electrophoresis," New York, Academic Press Inc., 1959.
3. KUNKEL, H. G., AND TRAUTMAN, R., "Zone Electrophoresis in Various Types of Supporting Media," in Bier, M., loc. cit.
4. WIELAND, T., "Applications of Zone Electrophoresis," in Bier, M., loc. cit.

5. McDonald, H. J., "Theoretical Basis of Electrophoresis and Electrochromatography," in Heftmann, E., Ed., "Chromatography," New York, Reinhold Publishing Corp., 1961.

6. Michl, H., "Techniques of Electrochromatography," in Heftmann, E., loc. cit.

7. Strain, H. H., "The Basis of Selectivity in Chromatography, Electrochromatography, and Continuous Electrochromatography," *Anal. Chem.*, **33**, 1733 (1961).

8. Caplan, S. R., "Optimum Voltage for Preparative Electrophoresis," *Chem. and Ind.*, 226 (1960).

9. Spiegler, K. S., "On the Electrochemistry of Ion-Exchange Resins," *J. Electrochem. Soc.*, **100**, 303C (1953).

10. Pučar, Z., "Continuous Electrophoresis and Two-Dimensional Electrochromatography," in Lederer, M., Ed., "Chromatographic Reviews," Vol. 3, Amsterdam, Elsevier, 1961.

11. Caplan, S. R., "Continuous Electrochromatography on Ion-Exchange Membranes," *J. Electrochem. Soc.*, **108**, 577 (1961).

S. R. Caplan

Cross-references: *Electrokinetic Potentials; Electroosmosis; Electrophoresis.*

ELECTROCLEANING. See ELECTROPLATING, CLEANING BEFORE.

ELECTRODE

The electrodes of an electrolytic cell are the terminals or poles by which current enters and leaves the cell and at which electrochemical reactions may occur. There is a change at each electrode from conduction by electrons to conduction by charged particles of matter or ions. The basic electrolytic cell consists of an electrolyte and two electrodes (anode and cathode). During the passage of current through an electrolytic conductor, the constituents of the electrolyte move to the electrodes and take part in oxidizing or reducing reactions at the electrodes. Substances set free at the electrodes sometimes react with the solvent and can be observed at the electrodes. For example, in the electrolysis of water and solutions of the alkali hydroxides, the products are hydrogen at the cathode and oxygen at the anode. In general, electrode reactions produce phase changes at the electrode surfaces.

The measurement of the emf of an electrode requires the use of a reference electrode. The requirements of a reference electrode are that its potential be independent of the experimental operation and show reproducible behavior throughout the course of the measurement. Among the most commonly used reference electrodes (q.v.) are the calomel, silver-silver chloride, and the normal hydrogen (Nernst) electrodes. The calomel electrode is essentially a mercury-mercurous ion electrode. The hydrogen (gas) electrode consists of a piece of platinized platinum exposed to a stream of hydrogen and partly immersed in a normal acid solution.

The quinhydrone electrode is an organic reference electrode used for the measurement of pH in neutral or acid solutions. Another convenient means of measuring pH is with the glass electrode (q.v.). This electrode consists of a glass membrane separating solutions of different pH with a resultant potential difference across the membrane.

The dropping mercury electrode can, under favorable conditions, provide for a qualitative and quantitative analysis of several substances in a solution. This electrode is extensively used in the field of polarography (q.v.).

The anode in a polarograph usually consists of a large mercury pool at the bottom of a solution. The cathode consists of mercury drops falling through the solution to the anode from the cathode mercury reservoir. Rotating mercury electrodes can be used at concentrations for which the polarographic method cannot be applied.

Dilute amalgam electrodes can be used in some cases where the pure metal would react with the solution (i.e., the sodium amalgam half-cell).

An "electrode of the first kind" is an electrode which is reversible with respect to ions of the electrode material. An "electrode of the second kind" consists of a metal, a sparingly soluble salt of the metal, and a solution of a soluble salt of the same anion. This electrode is reversible with respect to the anion.

A null electrode is an electrode which has a potential difference of zero between metal and solution.

Electrochemical corrosion involves electrodes of dissimilar materials in a circuit, or spatially separated electrode areas on the same piece of material in contact with a conducting medium.

Graphite and carbon electrodes are extensively used in the steel-making and welding industries, among others. These materials make excellent electrodes because of their chemical inertness, electrical conductivity and thermal shock resistance. In reduction furnaces, the Söderberg continuous, self-baking carbon electrode is widely used.

Choice of electrode material for use in electrolytic oxidation or reduction processes is very important. The overpotential of the electrode as well as its catalytic properties help determine its effectiveness when used as an anode or cathode.

JACOB M. MILLER

Cross-references: *Anode, Cathode.*

ELECTRODE DOUBLE LAYER

At any phase boundary there is always some redistribution of electrical charge because of the inhomogeneous field. This may be represented as two parallel sheets of charge of opposite sign, known as a double layer. This name is retained even if the structure is more complex. The double layer at a metal-electrolyte interface is of particular interest because it occurs between two conductors and of particular importance because its structure has a considerable influence on the rates of electrode reactions.

Two ideal types of electrode may be considered: the perfectly polarizable electrode in which no transfer of electric charge across the interface can occur, and the perfectly nonpolarizable electrode in which unhindered exchange of charge is possible. Real electrodes may approach these idealizations or may have intermediate properties. Most information on the structure of the electrode double layer has been obtained from studies of electrodes which may be considered as perfectly polarizable. It seems reasonable to assume that the structure of the double layer at a nonpolarizable electrode is similar in most respects.

Most of the precise information about the structure of the electrode double layer has come from measurements of electrode capacity and electrocapillary curves of mercury electrodes. This is because with a liquid metal it is easy to form a clean surface which is smooth and also to measure its interfacial tension in a electrolyte. It can be shown from Gibbs' adsorption isotherm that the interfacial tension (γ) of a pure metal electrode in contact with a solution containing, say NaCl in water is given by

$$-d\gamma = q \cdot dE_- + \Gamma_{Na^+} \cdot d\mu_{NaCl} \qquad (1)$$

at constant temperature and pressure. Here q is the charge per unit area on the metal side of the interface (the charge on the solution must be equal and opposite so that the interface as a whole is electrically neutral), E_- is the potential of the electrode with respect to a reference electrode reversible to the anion (e.g., a silver-silver chloride electrode), Γ_{Na^+} is the Gibbs surface excess (per unit area) of the sodium ions and μ_{NaCl} is the chemical potential of NaCl in the solution. In a system of more components Eq. (1) will have more $\Gamma \cdot d\mu$ terms, but the principle remains the same. Eq. (1) shows that the interfacial tension of a perfectly polarizable electrode depends on the concentration of the salt in the solution and also on the potential difference applied between the electrodes. The curve of γ against E_- at constant composition is called an electrocapillary curve. It is roughly parabolic in shape (Fig. 1) and it follows from Eq. (1) that the slope is directly related to the charge per unit area on the metal:

$$-(\partial\gamma/\partial E_-)_{\mu_{NaCl}} = q \qquad (2)$$

This equation is often called the Lippmann equation (q.v.). It is clear from Eq. (2) that the charge will be zero at the maximum of the electrocapillary curve. This point is called the electrocapillary maximum or, preferably, the point of zero charge. The charge, q, arises from an excess or deficiency of electrons on the metal surface and the corresponding charge in the solution from an excess of cations over anions (or vice versa) on the solution surface. At the point of zero charge it may not be concluded that there is no potential drop across the interface because even in the absence of a double layer of free charges oriented dipoles of water, etc. will produce a potential difference.

Measurements of the interfacial tension as a function of the solution composition lead to values of the ionic surface excesses:

$$-(\partial\gamma/\partial\mu_{NaCl})_{E_-} = \Gamma_{Na^+} \qquad (3)$$

Since the charge on the solution is equal and opposite to that on the metal

$$q = e(\Gamma_{Cl^-} - \Gamma_{Na^+}) \qquad (4)$$

where e is the charge carried by a sodium ion. Clearly from Eqs. (2), (3) and (4) the values of Γ_{Cl^-} may be obtained.

The existence of the parallel sheets of charge,

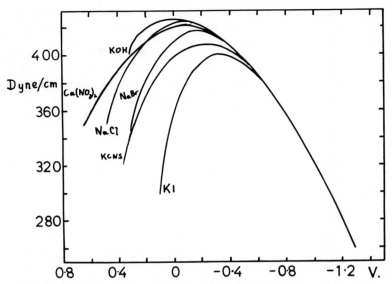

FIG. 1. Interfacial tension of mercury in contact with 1 N aqueous solutions of the salts named at 18°C as a function of applied potential difference. (From D. C. Grahame, *Chem. Rev.*, **41**, 441 (1947), with permission.)

one on either side of the interface, suggests that the electrode may have the properties of a parallel plate condenser. This is found experimentally to be the case. If the test electrode is combined with another electrode of much larger area (lower impedance) and the system is put into one arm of an a-c bridge network, the measured impedance may be analyzed into the capacity of the test electrode in series with the solution resistance (if the test electrode is not perfectly polarizable, the electrode impedance will also have a resistance in parallel with the capacity). The electrode capacity is found to be high (20–40 microfarads/ sq cm) and strongly dependent on the d-c potential applied across the electrode (Fig. 2). For this reason meaningful results for the capacity are obtained only by using a very small alternating potential across the electrode (~5 mv peak to peak). The capacity then measured is the differential capacity which is usually expressed per unit area of the interface:

$$C = (\partial q / \partial E)_\mu \qquad (5)$$

From a comparison of Eqs. (2) and (5) it is clear that the capacity of the interface is simply equal to the curvature of the electrocapillary curve:

$$-(\partial^2 \gamma / \partial E^2)_\mu = C \qquad (6)$$

consequently, measurement of the capacity provides a second route for the study of the charge

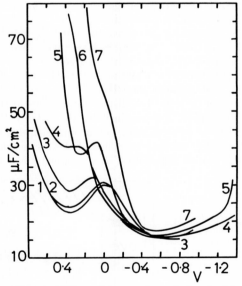

FIG. 2. Differential capacity of the double layer between mercury and the following solutions: (1) N NaNO$_3$; (2) N KNO$_3$; (3) N H$_2$SO$_4$; (4) N Na$_2$SO$_4$; (5) N NaCl; (6) N Na$_2$CO$_3$; and (7) N NaI. (From D. C. Grahame, *J. Am. Chem. Soc.*, **63**, 1207 (1941), with permission.)

and surface excesses. The capacity is more sensitive to the detailed structure of the double layer but is less easy to interpret than electrocapillary measurements. The capacity is also a property which can be measured on solid as well as on liquid metals. However, misleading results may be obtained unless the solid surface is very smooth.

Other methods of studying the structure of the double layer include the direct determination of adsorption by either measuring the change of the bulk concentration of a constituent using a variety of analytical methods or the amount adsorbed using a radioactive method. The electrode capacity may also be found by passing a constant direct current through the electrode and observing the potential as a function of time or by observing the decay of potential on open circuit after polarizing the electrode. Measurement of contact angles, hardness, and frictional properties provide some information about the point of zero charge.

The simplest model of the electrode double layer treats the metal as a perfectly plane sheet of infinite polarizability. The solution consists of ions moving in a dielectric continuum. Under the influence of a charge on the metal, ions of the opposite sign are attracted towards the metal up to a distance, x_2, determined by the ionic radius. The plane at x_2 is called the outer Helmholtz plane (OHP). The double layer may then be considered in two parts: a charge-free or *inner layer* between the metal and the OHP and a *diffuse layer* between the OHP and the bulk of the solution (Fig. 3). The distribution of ions in the diffuse layer is determined by the balance between the force of attraction or repulsion due to the charge on the electrode and the thermal kinetic motion. The diffuse layer is in fact precisely

analogous to the charge cloud around an ion in the Debye-Hückel theory of electrolytes and the distribution of ions is governed by the same equations. The potential drop between the metal and the solution (ϕ^{M-S}) may be divided into two parts, ϕ^{M-2} across the inner layer and ϕ^2 across the diffuse layer

$$\phi^{M-S} = \phi^{M-2} + \phi^2 \qquad (7)$$

Therefore

$$\frac{d\phi^{M-S}}{dq} = \frac{d\phi^{M-2}}{dq} + \frac{d\phi^2}{dq}$$

or

$$1/C = 1/C^i + 1/C^d \qquad (8)$$

This means that the total electrode capacity, C, may be considered as a series combination of the inner layer capacitance, C^i, and the diffuse layer capacitance, C^d. The latter may be found from the Debye-Hückel equations as:

$$C^d = -dq^d/d\phi^2 = (\epsilon\kappa/4\pi)\cdot\cosh(z\phi^2\mathbf{F}/2RT) \qquad (9)$$

where q^d is the charge on the diffuse layer, ϵ is the dielectric constant in the diffuse layer, κ is the Debye-Hückel characteristic reciprocal length and it is assumed that a single z-z-valent salt is present in the solution. Since κ is proportional to the square root of the concentration, so is C^d. It has a minimum value at $\phi^2 = 0$ ($q^d = 0$) which for a 1-1-electrolyte is $7.22 \mu F$ cm^{-2} (microfarads/sq cm) at $10^{-3} M$; $22.8 \mu F$ cm^{-2} at $10^{-2} M$; $72.2 \mu F$ cm^{-2} at $0.1 M$ and $228 \mu F$ cm^{-2} at $1M$. At the higher concentrations these values are so much higher than the experimental capacity that

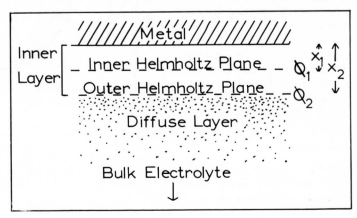

FIG. 3. Schematic diagram of the double layer between a metal and an electrolyte. (From R. Parsons in "Advances in Electrochemistry and Electrochemical Engineering," P. Delahay, Ed., Interscience Publishers, Inc., 1961, by permission.)

it is evident that the latter is virtually equal to the inner layer capacity at all values of q. At lower concentrations experiments show (Fig. 4) a sharp minimum in the capacity at the point of zero charge which is in agreement with the expected contribution of C^d at such concentrations. In the case of a mercury electrode in aqueous NaF, it is found that C^i is practically independent of the NaF concentration (though strongly dependent on q) and the concentration effect on the capacity is attributable entirely to C^d. Thus, the simple model is in good agreement with these experiments. A further consequence of the model is that there can be no adsorption of ions when $q = 0$ because the adsorption is due to the attraction of the charge. Then, from Eq. (3) the interfacial tension at the maximum of the electrocapillary curve is independent of the salt concentration. This is also confirmed experimentally for aqueous NaF.

The vast majority of salts do not give results which fit the above simple model. The maximum of the electrocapillary curve is lowered with increase of concentration and the simple equivalent circuit implied by Eq. (8) is invalid. It is therefore concluded that ions are subject to a specific adsorption force as well as the general electrostatic force. This may be a chemical bond with the electrode or the fact that the ion does not fit readily into the structure of the solvent in the bulk but is more stable at the surface. It is generally assumed that this force acts over only a short range and that only ions or molecules in the first layer next to the electrode are affected. Their centers then lie in a plane, the inner Helmholtz plane (IHP), at a distance, x_1 from the electrode, where $x_1 < x_2$ (Fig. 3). It is now convenient to consider the charge on the solution in two parts: the specifically adsorbed charge (q_1) on the IHP and the diffuse layer charge (q_d), the sum of which is equal and opposite to the charge on the metal:

$$q = -(q_1 + q_d) \qquad (10)$$

Although the potential drop across the double layer may still be divided according to Eq. (7), ϕ^{M-2} is no longer a function of q only but also of q_1, so that the first term of Eq. (8) becomes

$$\frac{1}{C^i} = \frac{d\phi^{M-2}}{dq} = \left(\frac{\partial \phi^{M-2}}{\partial q}\right)_{q_1} + \left(\frac{\partial \phi^{M-2}}{\partial q_1}\right)_{q} \frac{dq_1}{dq} \qquad (11)$$

The second term of Eq. (8) is also more complex:

$$\frac{d\phi^2}{dq} = \left(\frac{\partial \phi^2}{\partial q_d}\right)\left(\frac{\partial q_d}{\partial q}\right) = \frac{1}{C^d}\left\{1 + \frac{\partial q_1}{\partial d}\right\} \qquad (12)$$

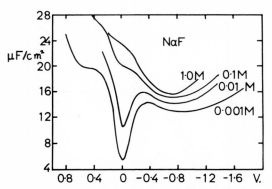

FIG. 4. Differential capacity of the double layer between mercury and aqueous sodium fluoride solutions at 25°C. Concentrations are marked by the curves. (From D. C. Grahame, ONR Report No. 6, May 25, 1951, by permission.)

When ions are specifically adsorbed, the second term in Eq. (11) is often negative so that the inner layer capacity may rise to very high values; this is in agreement with experimental observations.

Specific ionic adsorption is also clearly revealed by measurement of the surface excesses of the ions. In Fig. 5 it is clear that at negative charges on the metal the cation is attracted to the metal while the anion is repelled. In contrast, at positive charges both ions are positively adsorbed. This is accounted for by assuming that the anion is so strongly specifically adsorbed that $|q_1| > |q|$ and the diffuse layer charge must become positive. With inorganic salts the anion is usually more strongly adsorbed than the cation. In fact, the negative branches of capacity and electrocapillary curves are very insensitive to the nature of the cation (Figs. 1 and 2), which is positively adsorbed, unless it is a very large cation, such as an organic cation. This suggests that the specific adsorption of simple cations is weak or nonexistent. The variety of behavior on the positive branches of these curves illustrates the specific adsorption of anions which seems to be the rule; fluoride is apparently the only anion which is not specifically adsorbed on mercury from aqueous solution.

The adsorption of nonionic substances from aqueous solution most often occurs over a limited potential range where the charge on the metal is small. This is because of the unusually high polarizability per unit volume of water which therefore tends to displace other molecules from regions of high field strength. Thus, the interfacial tension is lowered over a limited potential

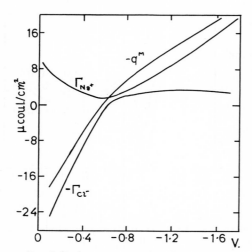

Fig. 5. Surface excesses of sodium and chloride ions at a mercury electrode in a 0.3 N NaCl solution at 25°C. Surface excesses are expressed in terms of their contribution to the charge on the solution side of the double layer. (From D. C. Grahame, *Chem. Rev.*, **41**, 441 (1947) with permission.)

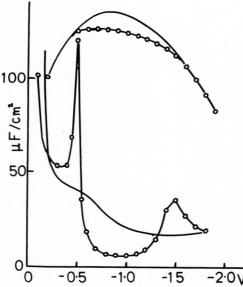

Fig. 6. Electrocapillary curves (above) and capacity curves (below) for mercury electrodes in aqueous N Na₂SO₄ (curves without points) and in the same with addition of 0.1 M butyl alcohol (curves with points).

range (Fig. 6) and because of the relation given in Eq. (6) the capacity curve has the characteristic double peaked form shown in Fig. 6. The lowering of the capacity in the middle region

arises from the increase of the first term in Eq. (11) as a result of a lower dielectric constant and/or an increased thickness of the inner layer. The peaks in the capacity curve are related to a term analogous to the second term in Eq. (11) and arise because the amount of substance adsorbed changes rapidly with potential.

Although most of the detailed knowledge of the structure of the electrode double layer has been obtained using mercury electrodes, there is evidence that other metals will behave in a very similar way. It is important in comparing the double layer properties of different metals that the potentials should be referred to the point of zero charge in a solution of an electrolyte which is not specifically adsorbed. This type of potential scale is called the "rational" potential. The potential of the zero point is a characteristic constant for each metal and is not directly related to other electrochemical properties of the metal. Some values are given in Table 1. As a first approximation it is reasonable to expect capacity and electrocapillary curves for different metals and the same solution plotted on the rational scale to coincide. This is most likely to be correct for electrolytes which are not specifically adsorbed because the strength of specific adsorption of a given ion is likely to be dependent on the nature of the metal. The potential of the point of zero charge is dependent on the chemical state of

TABLE 1. POTENTIAL OF THE POINT OF ZERO CHARGE WITH RESPECT TO THE NORMAL HYDROGEN ELECTRODE IN AQUEOUS SOLUTION AT ROOM TEMPERATURE

Metal	E^z(v)	Solution
Ag	-0.70	$0.01\ N\ Na_2SO_4$
Cd	-0.90	$0.001\ N\ KCl$
Cu	-0.02	$0.02\ N\ Na_2SO_4$
Co	-0.33	$0.02\ N\ Na_2SO_4 + 0.1\ N\ H_2SO_4$
Cr	-0.45	$0.1\ N\ NaOH$
Fe	-0.29	$0.02\ N\ Na_2SO_4 + 0.1\ N\ H_2SO_4$
Ga	-0.60	$1\ N\ KCl\ 0.1\ N\ HCl$
Hg	-0.192	$0.001–1\ N\ NaF$
Ni	-0.06	$0.001\ N\ HCl$
Pb	-0.69	$0.001\ N\ KCl$
PbO₂	1.80	$0.01\ N\ HClO_4$
Pt(smooth)	0.27	$1\ N\ Na_2SO_4 + 0.1\ N\ H_2SO_4$
Pt(oxidized)	$0.4–1.0$	$1\ N\ Na_2SO_4 + 0.01\ N\ H_2SO_4$
Te	0.61	$1\ N\ Na_2SO_4$
Tl	-0.80	$0.001\ N\ KCl$
Zn	-0.63	$1\ N\ Na_2SO_4$

the surface. It may be displaced considerably if, for example, the surface is oxidized. Thus, the double layer structure may differ very much at the same potential (with respect to a reference electrode) for the same metal in a clean and oxidized state.

References

1. DAMASKIN, B. B., *Russian Chemical Reviews* (translation of *Uspekhi Khimii*), **30**, 78 (1961).
2. FRUMKIN, A. N., *J. Electrochemical Soc.*, **107**, 461 (1960); *Z. Elektrochem.*, **59**, 807 (1955).
3. FRUMKIN, A. N., AND DAMASKIN, B. B., "Modern Aspects of Electrochemistry," Vol. 3, (Ed. J. O'M. Bockris) London, Butterworths, 1963.
4. GRAHAME, D. C., *Chem. Rev.*, **41**, 441 (1947).
5. PARSONS, R., "Modern Aspects of Electrochemistry," Vol. 1, Chap. 3, (Ed. J. O'M. Bockris) London, Butterworths, 1954.
6. PARSONS, R. "Advances in Electrochemistry," (Ed. P. Delahay), Chap. 1, New York, Interscience, 1961.

ROGER PARSONS

Cross-references: *Corrosion, Electrochemical Principles; Electrocapillary Phenomena; Electron Transfers at Electrodes; Lippmann Potential; Polarization.*

ELECTRODEPOSITION. See SPECIFIC METAL; ALSO ELECTROPLATING ENTRIES. ELECTRODEPOSITION OF ALLOYS FROM AQUEOUS SOLUTIONS. See ALLOY ELECTRODEPOSITION.

ELECTRODEPOSITION CURRENTS. See ELECTRICAL CURRENTS, EFFECTS ON ELECTRODEPOSITION OF METALS; PERIODIC REVERSE PLATING.

ELECTRODEPOSITION OF METAL POWDERS

Electrodeposition of metal powders involves the use of electrochemical methods to produce fine, discreet metal particles. The particle shapes and sizes which can be obtained by this method can be varied widely and depend primarily on the metal being deposited, the type of electrolyte, and the deposition conditions. The operations and equipment used in the electrodeposition of metal powders are similar to conventional electroplating and electrowinning, with the basic difference that operating conditions are so adjusted that a nonadherent or brittle deposit is obtained. Metal powders are generally classified as discreet particles within a size range of 1 to 1000 microns and include the full range of particle shapes from needle-like structures to irregularly-shaped and flat platelet-type particles. Metal powders find their major application in the field of powder metallurgy and in the production of metallic pigments.

Most metals have been electrodeposited as powders or other finely-divided forms on an experimental or pilot plant operation. To be of commercial interest, however, powders produced by electrolysis must either be economically competitive with other production methods or offer unique properties not obtainable by other processes. Electrodeposition may also be used to yield a finely-divided metal merely as an intermediate product in the recovery of the metal by electrolytic methods.

Electrolytic powders are generally characterized by their high purity, unique particle shape and uniformity of product. Due to these properties, electrolytic iron powder when processed by powder metallurgy techniques results in structural parts having higher strength than parts produced by any other type of iron powder. Similarly, electrolytic copper powder when processed into parts results in easier machining and gives improved wear properties. These two metals represent the major commercial application of the electrodeposition of metal powders.

Two instances of the electrodeposition of powders as an intermediate step are the production of silver and, at one time, uranium.

All electrolytic refining of silver (q.v.) results in a silver crystal deposit for which there is only a small demand. These crystals are either used as produced or ground and classified to the desired size range. The predominant quantity of crystals, however, is melted and cast into ingots which are the commercial form in which silver is used.

The first tons of uranium produced during the start of the Manhattan project were produced as electrolytic powder and subsequently melted. A later direct reduction process, however, yielded an improved metal and eliminated the electrolytic process.

Theory

The basic electrochemical theory of deposition of metal powders is identical to that of electrorefining and electroplating. The electrochemical conditions affecting the type of deposit, however, are controlled in powder production so as to yield either a brittle or a nonadherent deposit. Three general factors will produce such operating conditions:

1) Low metal overvoltage.
2) Conditions which will cause depletion of the metal content of the cathode film.
3) Formation of basic compounds in the cathode film.

The last condition will generally be present only in electrolytes with a neutral or slightly acid pH.

There are many changes that can be made in the operating variables of an electrodeposition system to affect the above conditions of powder deposition.

The following changes of these variables generally produce the deposition of coarser and denser particles:

1) Increasing the metal ion concentration in the solution.
2) Raising the solution temperature.
3) Increasing the interval of deposit removal from the cathode.
4) Increasing the acid concentration.
5) Addition of complexing agents to the solution.
6) Lowering the circulation rate.
7) Lowering the current density per electrode area.

The more these conditions approach conventional plating practice for the metal in question, the more adherent, smooth, and continuous the deposit will become. Reversing these conditions within practical limits will generally produce a finer deposit.

Detailed discussions of the underlying factors causing powder electrodeposition are given by G. Wranglen,[1] E. Mehl,[2] with a good overall summary by C. L. Mantell.[3]

General Considerations

The electrolytes used in the deposition of metal powders are generally the same as in electrorefining or electrowinning operations. Aqueous solutions of the metal to be deposited predominate, although fused salt and liquid metal systems are also employed. Since one major advantage of the electrochemical deposition of metal powders is a product of high purity, the choice of electrolyte and the ease of its removal from the high-surface-area metal powder becomes a matter of first importance. Fused salt systems present serious problems in this respect. Since generally a pure metal powder is desired, the starting material (either anode or electrolyte if electrowinning is used) must also be of high purity. Many attempts have been made to use low-grade starting materials. It has so far been found commercially impractical, however, to separate the deposited powder from the included and codeposited impurities contained in the slimes.

Corrosion and general material handling problems of powder deposition are similar to electrorefining operations. The high surface area and consequently high chemical reactivity of the metal powder will generally complicate operations. Re-solution in the electrolyte of deposited powders occurs readily in acid electrolytes, whereas oxidation and entrainment become problems with the high-temperature fused salt systems which are generally used for refractory metals. The two commercially most important metals produced as powders will be reviewed in more detail.

Copper

The major commercial electrolytic copper powder operations are based on an acid copper sulfate electrolyte. Deposition tanks are very similar to those used in conventional copper electrorefining. Operating conditions for powder production and electrorefining are summarized below.

Anode starting material is electrolytic copper, generally cathodes produced in the electrorefining operation. Sheets, rods, and even wires have been used as cathodes, with antimonial lead giving best service in the form of sheets.

TABLE 1. COPPER ELECTRODEPOSITION

	Copper Powder Deposition	Copper Electrorefining
Electrolyte	Cu sulfate	Cu sulfate
Cu content, gpl	5–8	35–45
H_2SO_4, gpl	130–150	180–210
Temperature, °F	100–140	140–150
Circulate rate (gal/min)	5–6	2–4
Electrical conditions:		
Tank voltage (volts)	1	0.2–0.3
Anode current density (amps/sq ft)	55–60	15–20

Stainless steel, graphite, aluminum, and copper have also been used.

During electrolysis some of the powder falls to the bottom of the tank and the remainder adheres to the cathode and must be brushed off at definite intervals. The longer the interval, the coarser and denser the resultant powder. Other major process variables which affect powder characteristics are copper content, acid content, and current density. Effective control of copper content of the electrolyte, which increases during electrolysis due to less than 100 per cent cathode efficiency, is made in a series of electrowinning tanks using insoluble anodes.

When the copper anode is depleted, electrolysis is halted. The powder is removed from the tanks and washed free of electrolyte. This step must be carefully controlled since any remaining acid or copper sulfate will render the powder unstable. The wet powder is subsequently dried and processed through a classifying and blending system. Since the predominant use of electrolytic copper powder is in the production of parts by powder metallurgy techniques, certain properties are required which cannot be fully controlled by the deposition conditions. A furnace treatment under reducing conditions is consequently used as a means of obtaining the desired characteristics. A detailed description of the major U.S. producer is given by Wills and Clugsten.[4]

Iron

Electrolytic iron powder is the other major commercial application of electrolysis to obtain a powder with specific properties. Unlike copper powder production, the electrolysis results in a hard, brittle cathode which after extensive grinding yields a fine iron powder. To be of value in the powder metallurgy field, however, the powder must be annealed to remove the hardening introduced both during the grinding and by hydrogen embrittlement during deposition. Solid cathodes are produced rather than powder because the excessive power requirements for direct powder production do not render this method economically competitive.

The process is based on the use of a mixed ferrous and ammonium sulfate solution at a pH of 5 to 6. Anodes are of Armco iron and cathodes are Type 430 stainless steel. Current density is 25 amp/sq ft and operating temperature 120 to 140°F. Since plating efficiency is less than 100 per cent, a sludge buildup occurs which settles to the cell bottom. This material is periodically removed. At the end of the plating cycle, the cathodes are removed, thoroughly washed and the 3/32 to 1/4 in. thick iron deposit removed by flexing of the sheet. The iron sheet is broken into about 1 in. chips which are ground to powder for powder metallurgy application. The only plant operating at the present time in the U.S. has been described by Shafer and Harr.[5]

Other Metals

Electrodeposition of tantalum powder (q.v.) in a fused salt system,[7, 8] is the predominant of three commercially used methods for producing tantalum powder. Other methods involve reduction of oxides.

Manganese is generally produced by electrowinning the metal from solution (q.v.). The cathode produced is generally broken into small chips and the major share used in that form as melting stock. Some powder is produced, however, by grinding of these chips and in this regard the operation is similar to electrolytic iron powder production except that the reactivity of the powder can present processing problems.

Several processes based on fused salt mixtures of beryllium and alkali chlorides have been proposed for the production of beryllium powder.

Considerable work has been reported on fused salt processes for production of titanium and zirconium[9] powder or metal particles (q.v.).

References

1. WRANGLEN, G., *J. Electrochem. Soc.,* **97,** 353 (1950).
2. MEHL, E., *Powder Metallurgy,* **1/2,** 33 (1958). (Inst. Metals, London, Powder Metallurgy Joint Group, 17 Belgrade Sq., London, 5W1.)
3. MANTELL, C. L., *J. Electrochem. Soc.,* **106,** 70 (1959).
4. WILLS, F., AND CLUGSTEN, E. J., *J. Electrochem. Soc.,* **106,** 362 (1959).
5. SHAFER, W. M., AND HARR, C. R., *J. Electrochem. Soc.,* **105,** 413 (1958).
6. JONES, W. D., "Fundamental Principles of Powder Metallurgy," pp. 142–176, London, Edward Arnold Publishers, Ltd., 1960.
7. MILLER, G. L., "Tantalum & Niobium," "Metallurgy of the Rarer Metals," Vol. 6, pp. 211–239, New York, Academic Press, 1959.
8. HAMPEL, C. A., Ed., "Rare Metals Handbook," 2nd Ed., pp. 474+, New York, Reinhold Publishing Corp., 1961.
9. STEINBERG, M. A., SIBERT, M. E., AND WAINER, E., *J. Electrochem. Soc.,* **101,** 63 (1954).

FRANK WILLS

**ELECTRODEPOSITION OF METALS, ELEMEN-
TARY PROCESSES. See METAL ELECTRO-
DEPOSITION, ELEMENTARY PROCESSES.**

ELECTRODE POTENTIALS (AQUEOUS)

The electrode potential of a metal in contact with an aqueous electrolyte has often been understood to mean the electrical potential of the metal minus the electrical potential of the electrolyte, i.e., ϕ(metal)—ϕ(electrolyte) (or the negative of the above quantity to those who prefer the Latimer "oxidation potential" convention, see **Electrode Potentials, Signs of**). In the above, ϕ denotes the "inner" electrostatic potential of each phase, the potential that would be measured by means of a "purely electrical" test charge, i.e., a test charge devoid of any "chemical" interactions with the phase. Given the generalized cell

$$(V) \ 1/2/3/4/5/1' \ (V') \tag{1}$$

where 2 and 5 are metals, 3 and 4 aqueous electrolytes, and 1 and 1′ the two pole pieces (of the same kind of metal), the measurable cell emf, E, (on open circuit) can be expressed as

$$E = V' - V = (\phi_{1'} - \phi_5) + (\phi_5 - \phi_4)$$
$$+ (\phi_4 - \phi_3) + (\phi_3 - \phi_2) + (\phi_2 - \phi_1) \tag{2}$$

where the V's denote the measured electrical potentials of the two pole pieces, but the several interfacial potential differences, $\Delta\phi$, and, in particular, the two "electrode potentials," $\phi_5 - \phi_4$ and $\phi_2 - \phi_3$, are not measurable, since a "purely electrical" test charge does not exist as such in nature. The liquid junction potential, $\phi_4 - \phi_3$, is calculable, in principle, from the known composition of the electrolytes and can usually be minimized to a millivolt or less by a properly selected salt bridge (KCl, NH_4NO_3, etc. . . .). $\Delta\phi$ can be calculated if the net electrical dipole moment, p, per unit area of the interface is known and is then

$$\Delta\phi = p/\epsilon_0 \tag{3}$$

where $\epsilon_0 = 8.854 \times 10^{-12}$ amp-sec volt^{-1} m^{-1}.

The outer electrostatic potential, ψ, of a phase is measured by means of a test charge in free space brought to within 10^{-4} cm (i.e., to a distance at which the image attraction does not exceed 1.44 millivolts) of the surface of the phase,

and is measurable. The cell emf can then be expressed as

$$E = V' - V = (\psi_{1'} - \psi_5) + (\psi_5 - \psi_4)$$
$$+ (\psi_4 - \psi_3) + (\psi_3 - \psi_2) + (\psi_2 - \psi_1) \tag{4}$$

provided the surface properties, as well as the bulk properties, of the two pole pieces, 1 and 1′, are identical. The several contact potential differences, $\Delta\psi$, are measurable. For two metals, 1 and 2,

$$\psi_2 - \psi_1 = w_1 - w_2 \tag{5}$$

where w is electronic work function (q.v.), a property of a metal that can be strongly affected by its surface condition. For the standard calomel electrode, the contact p.d. (potential difference) was measured under argon by Klein and Lange and found to be

$$\psi°(\text{Hg}) - \psi°(\text{Hg}_2\text{Cl}_2 , \text{Cl}^- \text{ aqueous},$$
$$\text{at unit activity}) = +0.16 \text{ volt} \tag{6}$$

The $\Delta\psi$ of the calomel electrode has been found to follow the Nernst equation (see below Eq. 13) in the normal way.

Since the interfacial potential difference, $\Delta\phi$, is not measurable, and since the contact potential difference, $\Delta\psi$, while measurable, is sensitive to variations in surface properties, it has become customary to designate the *electrode potential as the potential of an electrode as measured by reference to a reference electrode*, such as the standard hydrogen electrode (SHE) or the saturated-KCl calomel electrode (SCE). In cell (1), let the electrode/electrolyte system, 2/3, be a reference SHE: Pt/H_2(1 atm), H^+ aq(unit activity). Let V and V' denote the measurable electrical potentials in the two pole pieces (of the same kind of metal) when the cell is on open circuit, then the *measured emf of the cell, $E = V' - V$, defines the electrode potential (referred to SHE) of the 4/5 electrolyte/electrode system (or the 5/4 electrode/electrolyte system*, since the value of $V' - V$ is not affected by a reversal of the cell diagram to 1′/5/4/3/2/1). Let this *electrode potential (referred to SHE)* be denoted by $V(5/4)$ or $V(4/5)$, i.e.,

$$V(5/4) = V(4/5) = V' - V$$

in cell (1), when 2/3 (or 3/2) is a reference SHE. The electrode potential defined here follows the Gibbs-Stockholm sign convention, i.e., $V(5/4)$ is positive if the pole piece, 1′, is the (+) terminal of cell (1).

The decomposition of the electrode potential, $V(5/4)$, into its component $\Delta\phi$'s according to Eq. 2 is at present not possible. The decomposition into $\Delta\psi$'s according to Eq. 4 is possible, provided the liquid junction potential is negligible, by means of Eqs. 5 and 6, together with Eq. 7.

$$V°(\text{Hg/Hg}_2\text{Cl}_2, \text{Cl}^- \text{ aqueous at unit activity}) \tag{7}$$
$$= +0.2676 \text{ volt at } 25°\text{C},$$

referred to SHE.

For a reversible electrode, the electrode potential is thermodynamically related to the free enthalpy (Gibbs free energy) of the half-cell reactions, viz.:

$$\Delta G \text{ (anodic oxidation)} = +n\mathbf{F}V \tag{8}$$

$$\Delta G \text{ (cathodic reduction)} = -n\mathbf{F}V \tag{9}$$

Take, for example, the standard zinc electrode Zn/Zn^{++}

$$V°(\text{Zn/Zn}^{++}) = -0.76 \text{ volt} \tag{10}$$

$\text{Zn} = \text{Zn}^{++} + 2e^-$

$$\Delta G° = +n\mathbf{F}V° = +2\mathbf{F}(-0.76 \text{ volt}) \tag{11}$$
$$= -1.52 \text{ vF} = -35.0 \text{ kcal}$$

$\text{Zn}^{++} + 2e^- = \text{Zn}$

$$\Delta G° = -n\mathbf{F}V° = -2\mathbf{F}(-0.76 \text{ volt}) \tag{12}$$
$$= +1.52 \text{ vF} = +35.0 \text{ kcal}$$

These free enthalpy values are to be combined, in all cases, with

$$\Delta G° = 0 \text{ for } \text{H}_2 = 2\text{H}^+ + 2e^-.$$

For a reversible nonstandard electrode, the electrode potential is governed by the Nernst equation, which takes the general form

$$V = V° + (RT/n\mathbf{F}) \ln (Ox)/(Red) \tag{13}$$

where (Ox) and (Red) denote the activities, or activity products, of the electromotively active materials on the oxidized and reduced sides, respectively, of the generalized half-cell reaction

$$Red = Ox + ne^- \tag{14}$$

The Nernst coefficient $RT/\mathbf{F} = 25.69$ millivolts, and $2.30259\, RT/\mathbf{F} = 59.16$ millivolts, at 25°C.

Potentials of some of the more common reference electrodes (q.v.) are listed as follows, referred in all cases to the SHE at the same temperature, $t°\text{C}$:

Decinormal Calomel Electrode

$V(\text{Hg/Hg}_2\text{Cl}_2, 0.1N \text{ KCl})$ mv
$$= +333 - 0.07(t - 25)$$

Normal Calomel Electrode

$V(\text{Hg/Hg}_2\text{Cl}_2, 1N \text{ KCl})$ mv
$$= +280 - 0.24(t - 25)$$

Saturated Calomel Electrode (SCE)

$V(\text{Hg/Hg}_2\text{Cl}_2, \text{ saturated KCl})$ mv
$$= +241 - 0.66(t - 25)$$

(the above constant, including the salt bridge potential, is changed from $+241$ to $+245$).

Standard Calomel Electrode

$V°(\text{Hg/Hg}_2\text{Cl}_2, \text{ Cl}^- \text{ at unit activity})$ mv
$$= +267.6 - 0.32(t - 25)$$

Standard Silver Chloride Electrode

$V°(\text{Ag/AgCl}, \text{Cl}^- \text{ at unit activity})$ mv
$$= +222.2 - 0.65(t - 25)$$

Saturated Copper Sulfate Electrode

$V(\text{Cu/CuSO}_4 \text{ saturated})$ mv
$$= +300 + 0.02(t - 25)$$

Standard Copper Electrode

$V°(\text{Cu/Cu}^{++} \text{ at unit activity})$ mv
$$= +342 + 0.008(t - 25)$$

The temperature coefficients listed above are the *isothermal temperature coefficients* of the electrode potentials in mv/°C (see **Electrode Potentials, Temperature Coefficients of**).

The potential of an electrode which is passing an anodic (or cathodic) current may be shifted in the positive (or negative) direction by the appearance of a polarization potential (overpotential) analogous to the ohmic-IR drop potential required for current flow through a resistance. Resistances of a chemical and/or mechanical (mass transfer) nature localized at or near the electrode surface give rise to this polarization. Polarization resistances, expressible in ohmssquare centimeters (ohm-sq cm) can be either 1) constant (film resistances, resistances due to poorly conducting layers of electrolyte), or 2) functions of current and/or potential. For activation (chemical) polarization, the resistance has its maximum value at zero current where it is

$b/2(2.3i_0)$ where b is the "Tafel constant" in volts and i_0 the reversible exchange current density in the Tafel equation. The resistance decreases with increasing current density, i, according to the relation

$$r_{act} = (b/i) \log (i/i_0) \qquad (15)$$

and the overpotential is ir_{act}. For concentration (mass-transfer) polarization (q.v.), the resistance has its minimum value at zero current where it is $RT/n\mathbf{F}i_d$ where n is the valence of the particle carrying current to the electrode and i_d, the so-called "limiting diffusion current," is the maximum current density that the given rate of mass-transfer can sustain. The resistance increases with increasing current density, i, according to the relation

$$r_{conc} = (RT/n\mathbf{F}i)[-\ln(1 - i/i_d)] \qquad (16)$$

and becomes infinite as i approaches i_d. The concentration polarization is ir_{conc}. Since activation and concentration polarizations act like resistances in series, the effective polarization resistance of an electrode can often be approximated by a constant up to the limiting current where the resistance becomes very large until another electrode reaction takes over (e.g., H_2 or O_2 evolution).

An ideal polarized electrode is an electrode at which charge transfer through the interface is forbidden. The potentials of such electrodes vary, from a certain characteristic point known as the zero point of charge (z.p.c.) or electrocapillary maximum (e.c.m.) or isoelectric point (iso), according to the laws of electrical condensers. For mercury in the presence of K or Na salts of capillary inactive anions (F, CO_3, OH, SO_4)

$$V_{iso} = -0.20 \text{ volts} \qquad (17)$$

referred to SHE. The capacitance, C, of the mercury/electrolyte interface has been measured and found to lie in the range 10–100 microfarads per square centimeter. On the negative side of the isoelectric point, the capacitances are 16–20 microfarads per square centimeter. The charge density of the electrical double layer can then be computed from the integral

$$q = \int C \, dV$$

between the limits V_{iso} and V.

The subsequent "Table of Electrode Potentials" lists the values of the Gibbs-Stockholm poten-

tials, $V°$, of the standard aqueous electrodes at 25°C and, where known, their thermal and isothermal first temperature coefficients, and their isothermal second temperature coefficients.

References

KLEIN, O., AND LANGE, E., Z. Elektrochem., **43,** 570 (1937).

LEWIS G. N., RANDALL, M., PITZER, K. S., AND BREWER, L., "Thermodynamics," Chapter 24, New York, McGraw-Hill Book Co., 1961.

VETTER, K. J., "Elektrochemische Kinetik," Berlin, Springer, 1961.

TAFEL, J., Z. physik. Chem., **50,** 641 (1905).

GRAHAME, D. C., Chem. Reviews, **41,** 441 (1947).

LATIMER, W. M., "Oxidation Potentials," New York, Prentice Hall, 1952.

DEBETHUNE, A. J., Corrosion, **9,** 336 (1953).

DEBETHUNE, A. J., J. Chem. Physics, **29,** 616 (1958); **31,** 847 (1959).

DEBETHUNE, A. J., LICHT, T. S., AND SWENDEMAN, N., J. Electrochem. Soc., **106,** 616 (1959).

SALVI, G. R., AND DEBETHUNE, A. J., ibid, **108,** 672 (1961).

VAN RYSSELBERGHE, P., Z. Elektrochem., **58,** 530 (1954).

ANDRE J. DEBETHUNE

Cross-references: *Electrode Potentials* entries; *Electromotive Force and Half-Cell Potentials; EMF Measurements in Aqueous Solutions at High Temperature; Electromotive Series; Nomenclature, Remarks on; Reference Electrodes.*

TABLE OF STANDARD AQUEOUS ELECTRODE POTENTIALS AND TEMPERATURE COEFFICIENTS AT 25°C

Introduction

The standard electrode potential, $V°$, is given a positive value if the electrode is the (+) terminal of a cell whose second electrode is the standard hydrogen electrode, SHE (Gibbs-Stockholm electrode potential). The Latimer "oxidation potentials" have the opposite sign. The thermal temperature coefficient, $(dV°/dT)_{th}$, is given a positive value if the hot electrode is the (+) terminal in a thermal cell of two such electrodes at two different temperatures, the thermal liquid junction potential being taken as zero in KCl solutions. The first and second isothermal temperature coefficients are given positive values if $d(V' - V)/dT$ and $d^2(V' - V)/dT^2$ are positive, respectively, in the isothermal cell: (V)Cu/SHE// Electrolyte/Electrode/Cu$'(V')$. Values given are calculated from thermodynamic data, except where marked x which denotes a direct experimental value. The thermodynamic relations are

$$V° = \Delta G°(\text{oxidation})/n\mathbf{F}$$

where $\Delta G°$ is that for the oxidation reaction

$$\text{Red} \rightarrow \text{Ox} + ne^-$$

and

$$(dV°/dT)_{isoth} = \Delta S°(\text{reduction})/n\mathbf{F}$$

$$(dV°/dT)_{th} = (dV°/dT)_{isoth} + 0.871 \text{ mv/°C}$$

$$(d^2V°/dT^2)_{isoth} = \Delta C_p°(\text{reduction})/n\mathbf{F}T$$

where $\Delta S°$ and $\Delta C_p°$ are those for the reduction reaction

$$\text{Ox} + (n/2)\text{H}_2 \rightarrow \text{Red} + n\text{H}^+.$$

Note that 1 volt-faraday = 23060 calories and that 1 mv$\mathbf{F}$/deg = 23.06 cal/deg.

Nonstandard potentials, V, are related to standard potentials, $V°$ by the Nernst equation

$$V = V° + (RT/n\mathbf{F}) \ln (Ox)/(Red)$$

$$= V° + (0.05916 \text{ v}/n) \log (Ox)/(Red)$$

$$\text{at } 298.15°\text{K.}$$

The standard potential, $V°(t)$, at temperature, t°C, referred to SHE at the same temperature, can be calculated from

$$V°(t) = V°(25) + (dV°/dT)_{isoth}(t - 25)$$

$$+ (1/2)(d^2V°/dT^2)_{isoth}(t - 25)^2.$$

References

LATIMER, W. M., "Oxidation Potentials," New York, Prentice Hall, 1952.

ROSSINI, F. D., WAGMAN, D. D., EVANS, W. H., LEVINE, S., AND JAFFE, I., "Chemical Thermodynamic Properties," National Bureau of Standards, Circular 500, 1952.

deBETHUNE, A. J., LICHT, T. S., AND SWENDEMAN, N., "Temperature Coefficients of Electrode Potentials," J. Electrochem. Soc., 106, 616 (1959).

SALVI, G. R., AND deBETHUNE, A. J., "Temperature Coefficients of Electrode Potentials, II," J. Electrochem. Soc., 108, 672 (1961).

CLARK, W. M., "Oxidation-Reduction Potentials of Organic Systems," Baltimore, Williams and Wilkins, 1960.

POURBAIX, M., "Atlas d'Equilibres Electrochimiques," Paris, Gauthier-Villars, 1963.

ANDRE J. de BETHUNE AND
NANCY SWENDEMAN LOUD

Electrode	$V°$, v	$(dV°/dT)_{th}$ mv/deg	$(dV°/dT)_{isoth}$, mv/deg	$(d^2V°/dT^2)_{isoth}$, μv/deg^2
Acid Solutions				
$HN_3(g) = (3/2)N_2 + H^+ + e^-$	−3.40	−0.322	−1.193	−0.562
$HN_3(aq) = (3/2)N_2 + H^+ + e^-$	−3.09	−0.70	−1.57	—
$Li = Li^+ + e^-$	−3.045	+0.337	−0.534	—
$K = K^+ + e^-$	−2.925	−0.209	−1.080	—
$Rb = Rb^+ + e^-$	−2.925	−0.374	−1.245	—
$Cs = Cs^+ + e^-$	−2.923	−0.326	−1.197	—
$Ra = Ra^{++} + 2e^-$	−2.916	+0.28	−0.59	—
$Ba = Ba^{++} + 2e^-$	−2.906	+0.48	−0.395	—
$Sr = Sr^{++} + 2e^-$	−2.888	+0.680	−0.191	—
$Ca = Ca^{++} + 2e^-$	−2.866	+0.696	−0.175	—
$Na = Na^+ + e^-$	−2.714	+0.099	−0.772	—
$Ac = Ac^{+++} + 3e^-$	−2.6	—	—	—
$La = La^{+++} + 3e^-$	−2.522	+0.956	+0.085	—
$Ce = Ce^{+++} + 3e^-$	−2.483	+0.972	+0.101	—
$Pr = Pr^{+++} + 3e^-$	−2.462	+0.986	+0.115	—
$Nd = Nd^{+++} + 3e^-$	−2.431	+0.995	+0.124	—
$Pm = Pm^{+++} + 3e^-$	−2.423	+0.991	+0.120	—
$Sm = Sm^{+++} + 3e^-$	−2.414	+1.007	+0.136	—
$Eu = Eu^{+++} + 3e^-$	−2.407	+1.008	+0.137	—
$Gd = Gd^{+++} + 3e^-$	−2.397	+1.018	+0.147	—
$Tb = Tb^{+++} + 3e^-$	−2.391	+1.017	+0.146	—
$Y = Y^{+++} + 3e^-$	−2.372	+1.05	+0.18	—
$Mg = Mg^{++} + 2e^-$	−2.363	+0.974	+0.103	—
$Dy = Dy^{+++} + 3e^-$	−2.353	+1.025	+0.154	—
$Am = Am^{+++} + 3e^-$	−2.320	+0.960	+0.089	—

Electrode	$V°$, v	$(dV°/dT)_{th}$ mv/deg	$(dV°/dT)_{isoth}$, mv/deg	$(d^2V°/dT^2)_{isoth}$, μv/deg²
Acid Solutions—*Continued*				
Ho = Ho^{+++} + 3e$^-$	−2.319	+1.032	+0.161	—
Er = Er^{+++} + 3e$^-$	−2.296	+1.037	+0.166	—
Tm = Tm^{+++} + 3e$^-$	−2.278	+1.050	+0.179	—
Yb = Yb^{+++} + 3e$^-$	−2.267	+1.059	+0.188	—
Lu = Lu^{+++} + 3e$^-$	−2.255	+1.064	+0.193	—
H$^-$ = (1/2)H$_2$ + e$^-$	−2.25	−0.70	−1.57	—
H(g) = H$^+$ + e$^-$	−2.1065	+1.382	+0.511	+0.221
Sc = Sc^{+++} + 3e$^-$	−2.077	+1.12	+0.25	—
Al + 6F$^-$ = AlF$_6$$^{---}$ + 3e$^-$	−2.069	+0.67	−0.20	—
Pu = Pu^{+++} + 3e$^-$	−2.031	+0.93	+0.06	—
Th = Th^{+4} + 4e$^-$	−1.899	+1.15	+0.28	—
Np = Np^{+++} + 3e$^-$	−1.856	+0.817	−0.054	—
Be = Be^{++} + 2e$^-$	−1.847	+1.44	+0.565	—
U = U^{+++} + 3e$^-$	−1.789	+0.80	−0.07	—
Hf = Hf^{+4} + 4e$^-$	−1.70	—	—	—
Al = Al^{+++} + 3e$^-$	−1.662	+1.375	+0.504	—
Ti = Ti^{++} + 2e$^-$	−1.628	—	—	—
Zr = Zr^{+4} + 4e$^-$	−1.529	—	—	—
Si + 6F$^-$ = SiF$_6$$^{--}$ + 4e$^-$	−1.24	+0.22	−0.65	—
Yb^{++} = Yb^{+++} + e$^-$	−1.21 (−0.58^x?)	—	—	—
Ti + 6F$^-$ = TiF$_6$$^{--}$ + 4e$^-$	−1.191	−0.09	−0.965	—
V = V^{++} + 2e$^-$	−1.186	—	—	—
Mn = Mn^{++} + 2e$^-$	−1.180	+0.79	−0.08	—
Sm^{++} = Sm^{+++} + e$^-$	−1.15	—	—	—
Nb = Nb^{+++} + 3e$^-$	−1.099	—	—	—
Pa + 2H$_2$O = PaO$_2$$^+$ + 4H$^+$ + 5e$^-$	−1.0	—	—	—
H$_2$Po = Po + 2H$^+$ + 2e$^-$	<−1.00	—	—	—
Ti + H$_2$O = TiO^{++} + 2H$^+$ + 4e$^-$	−0.882	—	—	—
B + 3H$_2$O = H$_3$BO$_3$(aq) + 3H$^+$ + 3e$^-$	−0.8698	+0.390	−0.481	—
B + 3H$_2$O = H$_3$BO$_3$(c) + 3H$^+$ + 3e$^-$	−0.869	+0.632	−0.239	—
Si + 2H$_2$O = SiO$_2$ (quartz) + 4H$^+$ + 4e$^-$	−0.857	+0.497	−0.374	+0.594
2Ta + 5H$_2$O = Ta$_2$O$_5$ + 10H$^+$ + 10e$^-$	−0.812	+0.494	−0.377	+0.514
Zn = Zn^{++} + 2e$^-$	−0.7628	+0.962 (+1.^{x})	+0.091 (+0.166^x)	— (+3.84^x)
Zn(Hg) = Zn^{++} + Hg + 2e$^-$	−0.7627^x −0.7625^x	— —	(+0.100^x) (+0.103^x)	(+0.62^x) (+1.6^x)
Tl + I$^-$ = TlI + e$^-$	−0.752	+0.721	−0.150	—
Cr = Cr^{+++} + 3e$^-$	−0.744	+1.339	+0.468	—
H$_2$Te(aq) = Te + 2H$^+$ + 2e$^-$	−0.739	—	—	—
H$_2$Te(g) = Te + 2H$^+$ + 2e$^-$	−0.718	+1.151	+0.280	—
Tl + Br$^-$ = TlBr + e$^-$	−0.658	+0.458	−0.413	—
2Nb + 5H$_2$O = Nb$_2$O$_5$ + 10H$^+$ + 10e$^-$	−0.644	+0.48	−0.39	—
U^{+++} = U^{+4} + e$^-$	−0.607	+2.27	+1.40	—
AsH$_3$(g) = As + 3H$^+$ + 3e$^-$	−0.607	+0.82	−0.05	—
Tl + Cl$^-$ = TlCl + e$^-$	−0.5568	+0.311	−0.560 (−0.579^x amalgam, −0.611 crystal^x)	—
Ga = Ga^{+++} + 3e$^-$	−0.529	+1.54	+0.67	—
SbH$_3$(g) = Sb + 3H$^+$ + 3e$^-$	−0.510	+0.81	−0.06	—
P(white) + 2H$_2$O = H$_3$PO$_2$ + H$^+$ + e$^-$	−0.508	+0.45	−0.42	—
H$_3$PO$_2$(aq) + H$_2$O = H$_3$PO$_3$(aq) + 2H$^+$ + 2e$^-$	−0.499	+0.51	−0.36	—
Fe = Fe^{++} + 2e$^-$	−0.4402	+0.923	+0.052	—
Eu^{++} = Eu^{+++} + e$^-$	−0.429	—	—	—

x = direct experimental values.

Electrode	$V°$, v	$(dV°/dT)_{th}$ mv/deg	$(dV°/dT)_{isoth}$, mv/deg	$(d^2V°/dT^2)_{isoth}$, μv/deg^2

Acid Solutions—*Continued*

Electrode	$V°$, v	$(dV°/dT)_{th}$ mv/deg	$(dV°/dT)_{isoth}$, mv/deg	$(d^2V°/dT^2)_{isoth}$, μv/deg^2
$Cr^{++} = Cr^{+++} + e^-$	-0.408	—	—	—
$Cd = Cd^{++} + 2e^-$	-0.4029	$+0.778$ ($+0.788^x$)	-0.093 (-0.053^x)	— ($+2.2^x$)
$H_2Se(aq) = Se + 2H^+ + 2e^-$	-0.399	$+0.843$	-0.028	—
$Ti^{++} = Ti^{+++} + e^-$	-0.369	—	—	—
$Pb + 2I^- = PbI_2 + 2e^-$	-0.365	$+0.747$	-0.124 (-0.095 amalgam, -0.111 solid^x)	—
$Pb + SO_4^{--} = PbSO_4 + 2e^-$	-0.3588	-0.144	-1.015	-1.555
$Cd(Hg) = Cd^{++} + Hg + 2e^-$	-0.3516	$+0.62$	(-0.250^x)	($+1.6^x$)
	-0.3515		(-0.252^x)	(-0.56^x)
	-0.3514		(-0.292^x)	($+0.20^x$)
$Pb(Hg) + SO_4^{--} = PbSO_4 + Hg + 2e^-$	-0.3505	-0.043	(-0.914^x)	(-1.71^x)
$In = In^{+++} + 3e^-$	-0.343	$+1.27$	$+0.40$	—
$Tl = Tl^+ + e^-$	-0.3363	-0.456 (-0.525^x)	-1.327 (-1.314^x)	— (-0.85^x)
$(1/2)C_2N_2 + H_2O = HCNO + H^+ + e^-$	-0.330	$+0.283$	-0.588	—
$Pt + H_2S(aq) = PtS + 2H^+ + 2e^-$	-0.327	$+0.606$	-0.265	—
$Pt + H_2S(g) = PtS + 2H^+ + 2e^-$	-0.297	$+1.039$	$+0.168$	—
$Pb + 2Br^- = PbBr_2 + 2e^-$	-0.284	$+0.530$	-0.341	—
$Co = Co^{++} + 2e^-$	-0.277	$+0.93$	$+0.06$	—
$H_3PO_3(aq) + H_2O = H_3PO_4(aq) + 2H^+ + 2e^-$	-0.276	$+0.51$	-0.36	—
$Pb + 2Cl^- = PbCl_2 + 2e^-$	-0.268	$+0.396$	-0.475 (-0.45 amalgam, -0.47 solid^x)	—
$V^{++} = V^{+++} + e^-$	-0.256	—	—	—
$V + 4H_2O = V(OH)_4^+ + 4H^+ + 5e^-$	-0.254	—	—	—
$Sn + 6F^- = SnF_6^{--} + 4e^-$	-0.25	$+0.178$	-0.693	—
$Ni = Ni^{++} + 2e^-$	-0.250	$+0.93$	$+0.06$	—
$N_2H_5^+ = N_2 + 5H^+ + 4e^-$	-0.23	$+0.03$	-0.84	—
$S_2O_6^{--} + 2H_2O = 2SO_4^{--} + 4H^+ + 2e^-$	-0.22	$+1.39$	$+0.52$	—
$Mo = Mo^{+++} + 3e^-$	-0.20	—	—	—
$HCOOH(aq) = CO_2(g) + 2H^+ + 2e^-$	-0.199	-0.065	-0.936	—
$Cu + I^- = CuI + e^-$	-0.1852	$+0.671$	-0.200	-6.028
$Ag + I^- = AgI + e^-$	-0.1518	$+0.587$ ($+0.414^x$)	-0.284 (-0.328^x)	-6.016 (-7.2^x)
$Ge + 2H_2O = GeO_2 + 4H^+ + 4e^-$	-0.15	$+0.54$	-0.335	—
$Sn(white) = Sn^{++} + 2e^-$	-0.136	$+0.589$	-0.282	—
$HO_2 = O_2 + H^+ + e^-$	-0.13	—	—	—
$Pb = Pb^{++} + 2e^-$	-0.126	$+0.420$ ($+0.45^x$)	-0.451	—
$W + 3H_2O = WO_3(c) + 6H^+ + 6e^-$	-0.090	$+0.471$	-0.400	$+0.480$
$HS_2O_4^- + 2H_2O = 2H_2SO_3 + H^+ + 2e^-$	-0.082	—	—	—
$PH_3(g) = P(white) + 3H^+ + 3e^-$	-0.063	$+0.767$	-0.104	—
$2Hg + 2I^- = Hg_2I_2 + 2e^-$	-0.0405	$+0.890$	$+0.019$	-5.883
$Hg + 4I^- = HgI_4^{--} + 2e^-$	-0.038	$+0.91$	$+0.04$	—
$D_2 = 2D^+ + 2e^-$	-0.0034	—	—	—
$H_2 = 2H^+ + 2e^-$ (SHE)	±0.0000	($+0.871^x$)	±0.000	±0.000
H_2(sat'd, t.p. 1 atm) $= 2H^+ + 2e^-$	$+0.0004$	($+0.904^x$)	$+0.033$	—
$Ag + 2S_2O_3^{--} = Ag(S_2O_3)_2^{-3} + e^-$	$+0.017$	—	—	—
$Cu + Br^- = CuBr + e^-$	$+0.033$	$+0.426$	-0.445	—
$UO_2^+ = UO_2^{++} + e^-$	$+0.05$	$+1.45$	$+0.58$	—
$HCHO(aq) + H_2O = HCOOH(aq) + 2H^+ + 2e^-$	$+0.056$	—	—	—

x = direct experimental values.

Electrode	$V°$, v	$(dV°/dT)_{th}$ mv/deg	$(dV°/dK)_{isoth}$, mv/deg	$(d_2V°/dT_2)_{isoth}$, μv/deg^2
Acid Solutions—*Continued*				
$Ag + Br^- = AgBr + e^-$	$+0.0713$	$+0.363$	-0.508	-5.901
	$(+0.0711^x)$	$(+0.320^x)$	(-0.488^x)	(-5.97^x)
	$(+0.0713^x)$	$(+0.327^x)$	(-0.499^x)	(-6.90^x)
	$(+0.0712^x)$	$(+0.38^x)$	(-0.526^x)	(-4.80^x)
$Ti^{+++} + H_2O = TiO^{++} + 2H^+ + e^-$	$+0.099$	—	—	—
$SiH_4(g) = Si + 4H^+ + 4e^-$	$+0.102$	$+0.674$	-0.197	-0.302
$CH_4(g) = C(graphite) + 4H^+ + 4e^-$	$+0.1316$	$+0.662$	-0.209	-0.266
$Cu + Cl^- = CuCl + e^-$	$+0.137$	$+0.236$	-0.635	—
$2Hg + 2Br^- = Hg_2Br_2 + 2e^-$	$+0.1397$	$+0.729$	-0.142	—
$H_2S(aq) = S(rhombic) + 2H^+ + 2e^-$	$+0.142$	$+0.662$	-0.209	—
$Np^{+++} = Np^{+4} + e^-$	$+0.147$	$+2.23$	$+1.36$	—
$Sn^{++} = Sn^{+4} + 2e^-$	$+0.15$	—	—	—
$2Sb + 3H_2O = Sb_2O_3 + 6H^+ + 6e^-$	$+0.152$	$+0.496$	-0.375	—
$Cu^+ = Cu^{++} + e^-$	$+0.153$	$+0.944$	$+0.073$	—
$Bi + H_2O + Cl^- = BiOCl + 2H^+ + 3e^-$	$+0.160$	$+0.526$	-0.345	—
$H_2SO_3 + H_2O = SO_4^{--} + 4H^+ + 2e^-$	$+0.172$	$+1.68$	$+0.81$	—
$2At^- = At_2 + 2e^-$	$+0.2$	—	—	—
$Ag + Cl^- = AgCl + e^-$	$+0.2222$	$+0.213$	-0.658	-5.744
	$(+0.2225^x)$	$(+0.210^x)$	(-0.638^x)	(-6.61^x)
	$(+0.2224^x)$		(-0.646^x)	(-5.961^x)
	$(+0.2224^x)$		(-0.656^x)	(-4.746^x)
	$(+0.2225^x)$		(-0.645^x)	(-6.554^x)
			(-0.65^x)	
$Hg + 4Br^- = HgBr_4^{--} + 2e^-$	$+0.223$	$+0.45$	-0.42	—
$(CH_3)_2SO + H_2O = (CH_3)_2SO_2 + 2H^+ + 2e^-$	$+0.23$	—	—	—
$As + 2H_2O = HAsO_2(aq) + 3H^+ + 3e^-$	$+0.2476$	$+0.361$	-0.510	—
$Re + 2H_2O = ReO_2 + 4H^+ + 4e^-$	$+0.2513$	—	—	—
$2Hg + 2Cl^- = Hg_2Cl_2 + 2e^-$	$+0.2676$	$+0.554$	-0.317	-5.664
	$(+0.2681^x)$	$(+0.55$ to	(-0.317^x)	(-5.986^x)
	$(+0.2679^x)$	$+0.59^x)$	(-0.312^x)	(-6.74^x)
	$(+0.26790^x)$		(-0.320^x)	(-5.961^x)
$Bi + H_2O = BiO^+ + 2H^+ + 3e^-$	$+0.320$	—	—	—
$U^{+4} + 2H_2O = UO_2^{++} + 4H^+ + 2e^-$	$+0.330$	-0.40	-1.27	—
$Cu = Cu^{++} + 2e^-$	$+0.337$	$+0.879$	$+0.008$	—
	$(+0.3419^x)$	$(+0.83$ to	(-0.016^x)	
		$+0.93^x)$		
$Ag + IO_3^- = AgIO_3 + e^-$	$+0.354$	$+0.303$	-0.568	-5.956
$S + 4H_2O = SO_4^{--} + 8H^+ + 6e^-$	$+0.3572$	$+0.703$	-0.168	$+1.278$
$V^{+++} + H_2O = VO^{++} + 2H^+ + e^-$	$+0.359$	—	—	—
$Fe(CN)_6^{-4} = Fe(CN)_6^{-3} + e^-$	$+0.36$	—	—	—
$Re + 4H_2O = ReO_4^- + 8H^+ + 7e^-$	$+0.362$	$+0.36$	-0.51	—
$HCN(aq) = 1/2C_2N_2(g) + H^+ + e^-$	$+0.373$	$+0.275$	-0.596	—
$2NH_3OH^+ = H_2N_2O_2 + 6H^+ + 4e^-$	$+0.387$	$+0.43$	-0.44	—
$Tc = Tc^{++} + 2e^-$	$+0.4$	—	—	—
$S_2O_3^{--} + 3H_2O = 2H_2SO_3 + 2H^+ + 4e^-$	$+0.400$	-0.39	-1.26	—
$Rh + 6Cl^- = RhCl_6^{---} + 3e^-$	$+0.431$	$+0.73$	-0.145	—
$S + 3H_2O = H_2SO_3 + 4H^+ + 4e^-$	$+0.450$	$+0.21$	-0.66	—
$2Ag + CrO_4^{--} = Ag_2CrO_4 + 2e^-$	$+0.464$	-0.287	-1.158	—
$Sb_2O_4(c) + H_2O = Sb_2O_5(c) + 2H^+ + 2e^-$	$+0.479$	—	—	—
$2Ag + MoO_4^{--} = Ag_2MoO_4 + 2e^-$	$+0.486$	—	—	—
$ReO_2 + 2H_2O = ReO_4^- + 4H^+ + 3e^-$	$+0.510$	—	—	—
$S_4O_6^{--} + 6H_2O = 4H_2SO_3 + 4H^+ + 6e^-$	$+0.51$	-0.44	-1.31	—
$C_2H_6(g) = C_2H_4(g) + 2H^+ + 2e^-$	$+0.52$	$+0.246$	-0.625	-0.343
$Cu = Cu^+ + e^-$	$+0.521$	$+0.813$	-0.058	—
$Te + 2H_2O = TeO_2(c) + 4H^+ + 4e^-$	$+0.529$	$+0.501$	-0.370	—
$2I^- = I_2(c) + 2e^-$	$+0.5355$	$+0.723$	-0.148	-5.965
$3I^- = I_3^- + 2e^-$	$+0.536$	$+0.657$	-0.214	—
$CuCl = Cu^{++} + Cl^- + e^-$	$+0.538$	$+1.521$	$+0.650$	—

x = direct experimental values.

Electrode	$V°$, v	$(dV°/dT)_{th}$ mv/deg	$(dV°/dT)_{isoth}$, mv/deg	$(d^2V°/dT^2)/_{isoth}$ μv/deg²
Acid Solutions—*Continued*				
$Ag + BrO_3^- = AgBrO_3 + e^-$	+0.546	—	—	—
$Te + 2H_2O = TeOOH^+ + 3H^+ + 4e^-$	+0.559	—	—	—
$HAsO_2 + 2H_2O = H_3AsO_4(aq) + 2H^+ + 2e^-$	+0.560	+0.507	−0.364	—
$Ag + NO_2^- = AgNO_2 + e^-$	+0.564	+0.606	−0.265	—
$MnO_4^{--} = MnO_4^- + e^-$	+0.564	—	—	—
$2H_2SO_3 = S_2O_6^{--} + 4H^+ + 2e^-$	+0.57	+1.97	+1.10	—
$Pt + 4Br^- = PtBr_4^{--} + 2e^-$	+0.581	+1.02	+0.15	—
$2SbO^+ + 3H_2O = Sb_2O_5(c) + 6H^+ + 4e^-$	+0.581	—	—	—
$CH_4(g) + H_2O = CH_3OH(aq) + 2H^+ + 2e^-$	+0.588	+0.836	−0.035	—
$Tc^{++} + 2H_2O = TcO_2 + 4H^+ + 2e^-$	+0.6	—	—	—
$Pd + 4Br^- = PdBr_4^{--} + 2e^-$	+0.60	+1.11	+0.235	—
$Ru + 5Cl^- = RuCl_5^{--} + 3e^-$	+0.601	—	—	—
$2Hg + SO_4^{--} = Hg_2SO_4 + 2e^-$	+0.6151	+0.045	−0.826	−1.537
	(+0.6151^x)		(−0.803^x)	(−0.854^x)
	(+0.6119^x)			(−1.685^x)
$U^{+4} + 2H_2O = UO_2^+ + 4H^+ + e^-$	+0.62	−2.26	−3.13	—
$Pd + 4Cl^- = PdCl_4^{--} + 2e^-$	+0.62	+0.75	−0.12	—
$CuBr = Cu^{++} + Br^- + e^-$	+0.640	+1.331	+0.460	—
$Ag + C_2H_3O_2^- = AgC_2H_3O_2 + e^-$	+0.642	+0.074	−0.797	—
$Po = Po^{++} + 2e^-$	+0.65	+0.44	−0.43	—
$2Ag + SO_4^{--} = Ag_2SO_4 + 2e^-$	+0.654	−0.311	−1.182	−1.608
$Au + 4CNS^- = Au(CNS)_4^- + 3e^-$	+0.655	—	—	—
$PtCl_4^{--} + 2Cl^- = PtCl_6^{--} + 2e^-$	+0.68	+0.54	−0.33	—
$H_2O_2(aq) = O_2(g) + 2H^+ + 2e^-$	+0.6824	−0.162	−1.033	—
$3NH_4^+ = HN_3(aq) + 11H^+ + 8e^-$	+0.695	+0.373	−0.498	—
$C_6H_4(OH)_2 = C_6H_4O_2 + 2H^+ + 2e^-$	+0.6994	(+0.140^x)	(−0.731^x)	—
	+0.6998	(+0.135^x)	(−0.736^x)	(−0.629^x)
$At_2 + 2H_2O = 2HAtO + 2H^+ + 2e^-$	+0.7	—	—	—
$TeO_2 + 2H_2O = TeO_4^- + 4H^+ + 3e^-$	+0.7	—	—	—
$OH(g) + H_2O = H_2O_2(aq) + H^+ + e^-$	+0.71	+1.411	+0.540	—
$H_2N_2O_2 = 2NO + 2H^+ + 2e^-$	+0.712	−0.861	−1.732	—
$Pt + 4Cl^- = PtCl_4^{--} + 2e^-$	+0.73	+0.64	−0.23	—
$C_2H_4(g) = C_2H_2(g) + 2H^+ + 2e^-$	+0.731	+0.291	−0.580	−0.508
$Se(gray) + 3H_2O = H_2SeO_3(aq) + 4H^+ + 4e^-$	+0.740	+0.351	−0.520	—
$Np^{+4} + 2H_2O = NpO_2^+ + 4H^+ + e^-$	+0.75	−2.26	−3.13	—
$2CNS^- = (CNS)_2 + 2e^-$	+0.77	—	—	—
$Ir + 6Cl^- = IrCl_6^{---} + 3e^-$	+0.77	+0.84	−0.03	—
$Fe^{++} = Fe^{+++} + e^-$	+0.771	+2.059	+1.188	—
$2Hg = Hg_2^{++} + 2e^-$	+0.788	—	—	—
$Ag = Ag^+ + e^-$	+0.7991	−0.129	−1.000	−0.924
		(−0.22, −0.170^x)		
$Po^{++} + H_2O = PoO_2 + 4H^+ + 2e^-$	+0.80	+0.61	−0.26	—
$Rh = Rh^{+++} + 3e^-$	+0.80	—	—	—
$N_2O_4(g) + 2H_2O = 2NO_3^- + 4H^+ + 2e^-$	+0.803	+0.978	+0.107	—
$Os + 4H_2O = OsO_4(c, yellow) + 8H^+ + 8e^-$	+0.85	+0.438	−0.433	—
$H_2N_2O_2 + 2H_2O = 2HNO_2 + 4H^+ + 4e^-$	+0.86	+0.36	−0.51	—
$CuI = Cu^{++} + I^- + e^-$	+0.86	+1.086	+0.215	—
$2Rh + 3H_2O = Rh_2O_3 + 6H^+ + 6e^-$	+0.87	+0.47	−0.40	+0.50
$Au + 4Br^- = AuBr_4^- + 3e^-$	+0.87 (60°C)	+0.39	−0.48	—
$Hg_2^{++} = 2Hg^+ + 2e^-$	+0.920	—	—	—
$PuO_2^+ = PuO_2^{++} + e^-$	+0.93	+1.58	+0.71	—
$HNO_2 + H_2O = NO_3^- + 3H^+ + 2e^-$	+0.94	+0.07	−0.80	—
$Au + 2Br^- = AuBr_2^- + e^-$	+0.956	—	—	—
$NO + 2H_2O = NO_3^- + 4H^+ + 3e^-$	+0.96	+0.899	+0.028	—
$Pu^{+++} = Pu^{+4} + e^-$	+0.97	+2.27	+1.40	—
$Pt + 2H_2O = Pt(OH)_2 + 2H^+ + 2e^-$	+0.98	+0.561	−0.310	—

x = direct experimental values

Electrode	$V°$, v	$(dV°/dT)_{th}$ mv/deg	$(dV°/dT)_{isoth}$, mv/deg	$(d^2V°/dT^2)_{isoth}$, μv/deg^2
Acid Solutions—*Continued*				
$Pd = Pd^{++} + 2e^-$	+0.987	—	—	—
$IrBr_6^{-4} = IrBr_6^{-3} + e^-$	+0.99	—	—	—
$NO + H_2O = HNO_2 + H^+ + e^-$	+1.00	+1.574	+0.703	—
$Au + 4Cl^- = AuCl_4^- + 3e^-$	+1.00	+0.24	−0.63	—
$VO^{++} + 3H_2O = V(OH)_4^+ + 2H^+ + e^-$	+1.00	—	—	—
$IrCl_6^{---} = IrCl_6^{--} + e^-$	+1.017	−0.24	−1.11	—
$TeO_2 + 4H_2O = H_6TeO_6(c) + 2H^+ + 2e^-$	+1.02	+1.00	+0.13	—
$2NO + 2H_2O = N_2O_4 + 4H^+ + 4e^-$	+1.03	+0.860	−0.011	—
$Pu^{+4} + 2H_2O = PuO_2^{++} + 4H^+ + 2e^-$	+1.04	−0.69	−1.56	—
$2Cl^- + ½I_2 = ICl_2^- + e^-$	+1.056	—	—	—
$2Br^- = Br_2(l) + 2e^-$	+1.0652	+0.242	−0.629	−6.210
$2HNO_2 = N_2O_4 + 2H^+ + 2e^-$	+1.07	+0.145	−0.726	—
$2Br^- = Br_2(aq) + 2e^-$	+1.087	+0.393	−0.478	—
$Pt(OH)_2 = PtO_2 + 2H^+ + 2e^-$	ca + 1.1	—	—	—
$Pu^{+4} + 2H_2O = PuO_2^+ + 4H^+ + e^-$	+1.15	−2.95	−3.82	—
$H_2SeO_3 + H_2O = SeO_4^- + 4H^+ + 2e^-$	+1.15	+1.424	+0.553	—
$NpO_2^+ = NpO_2^{++} + e^-$	+1.15	+1.45	+0.58	—
$4Cl^- + C + 4H^+ = CCl_4 + 4H^+ + 4e^-$	+1.18	+0.226	−0.645	−5.934
$2H_2O(g) = O_2 + 4H^+ + 4e^-$	+1.185	+0.641	−0.230	−0.173
$ClO_3^- + H_2O = ClO_4^- + 2H^+ + 2e^-$	+1.19	+0.46	−0.41	—
$½I_2 + 3H_2O = IO_3^- + 6H^+ + 5e^-$	+1.195	+0.507	−0.364	+1.813
$Pt = Pt^{++} + 2e^-$	ca + 1.2	—	—	—
$HClO_2 + H_2O = ClO_3^- + 3H^+ + 2e^-$	+1.21	+0.62	−0.25	—
$2H_2O(l) = O_2 + 4H^+ + 4e^-$	+1.229	+0.025	−0.846	+0.552
$2S + 2Cl^- = S_2Cl_2 + 2e^-$	+1.23	+0.23	−0.64	−6.261
$Mn^{++} + 2H_2O = MnO_2 + 4H^+ + 2e^-$	+1.23	+0.210	−0.661	—
$Tl^+ = Tl^{+++} + 2e^-$	+1.25	+1.76	+0.89	—
$Am^{+4} + 2H_2O = AmO_2^+ + 4H^+ + e^-$	+1.261	—	—	—
$2NH_4^+ = N_2H_5^+ + 3H^+ + 2e^-$	+1.275	+0.69	−0.18	—
$HClO_2 = ClO_2 + H^+ + e^-$	+1.275	−0.57	−1.44	—
$PdCl_4^{--} + 2Cl^- = PdCl_6^{--} + 2e^-$	+1.288	+0.42	−0.45	—
$N_2O(g) + 3H_2O = 2HNO_2(aq) + 4H^+ + 4e^-$	+1.29	+0.544	−0.327	—
$2Cr^{+++} + 7H_2O = Cr_2O_7^{--} + 14H^+ + 6e^-$	+1.33	−0.392	−1.263	—
$NH_4^+ + H_2O = NH_3OH^+ + 2H^+ + 2e^-$	+1.35	+0.34	−0.53	—
$2Cl^- = Cl_2 + 2e^-$	+1.3595	−0.389	−1.260 (−1.26^x)	−5.454
$HAtO + 2H_2O = HAtO_3 + 4H^+ + 4e^-$	+1.4	—	—	—
$N_2H_5^+ + 2H_2O = 2NH_3OH^+ + H^+ + 2e^-$	+1.42	−0.01	−0.88	—
$Au + 3H_2O = Au(OH)_3(c) + 3H^+ + 3e^-$	+1.45	+0.665	−0.206	—
$(1/2)I_2 + H_2O = HIO + H^+ + e^-$	+1.45	+1.29	+0.42	—
$Pb^{++} + 2H_2O = PbO_2 + 4H^+ + 2e^-$	+1.455	+0.633	−0.238	—
$H_2O_2(aq) = HO_2(aq) + H^+ + e^-$	+1.495	—	—	—
$Au = Au^{+++} + 3e^-$	+1.498	—	—	—
$Mn^{++} = Mn^{+++} + e^-$	+1.51	+2.10	+1.23	—
$Mn^{++} + 4H_2O = MnO_4^- + 8H^+ + 5e^-$	+1.51	+0.21	−0.66	—
$½Br_2(l) + 3H_2O = BrO_3^- + 6H^+ + 5e^-$	+1.52	+0.453	−0.418	+1.871
$PoO_2 + H_2O = PoO_3 + 2H^+ + 2e^-$	+1.52?	—	—	—
$2BiO^+ + 2H_2O = Bi_2O_4 + 4H^+ + 2e^-$	+1.593	—	—	—
$½Br_2(l) + H_2O = HBrO + H^+ + e^-$	+1.595	—	—	—
$Bk^{+++} = Bk^{+4} + e^-$	ca + 1.6	—	—	—
$IO_3^- + 3H_2O = H_5IO_6 + H^+ + 2e^-$	+1.601	—	—	—
$Ce^{+++} = Ce^{+4} + e^-$	+1.61	—	—	—
$(½)Cl_2 + H_2O = HClO + H^+ + e^-$	+1.63	+0.73	−0.14	—
$AmO_2^+ = AmO_2^{++} + e^-$	+1.639	—	—	—
$HClO + H_2O = HClO_2 + 2H^+ + 2e^-$	+1.645	+0.32	−0.55	—

x = direct experimental values.

Electrode	$V°$, v	$(dV°/dT)_{th}$ mv/deg	$(dV°/dT)_{isoth}$, mv/deg	$(d^2V°/dT^2)_{isoth}$, μv/deg^2
Acid Solutions				
$Ni + 2H_2O = NiO_2 + 4H^+ + 2e^-$	+1.678	—	—	—
$PbSO_4 + 2H_2O = PbO_2 + SO_4^{--} + 4H^+ + 2e^-$	+1.682	+1.197	+0.326 ($+0.347^x$)	+2.516 ($+2.493^x$)
$Au = Au^+ + e^-$	+1.691	—	—	—
$Am^{+++} + 2H_2O = AmO_2^{++} + 4H^+ + 3e^-$	+1.694	—	—	—
$MnO_2 + 2H_2O = MnO_4^- + 4H^+ + 3e^-$	+1.695	+0.205	−0.666	—
$Am^{+++} + 2H_2O = AmO_2^+ + 4H^+ + 2e^-$	+1.721	—	—	—
$2H_2O = H_2O_2 + 2H^+ + 2e^-$	+1.776	+0.213	−0.658	—
$Xe + 3H_2O = XeO_3 + 6H^+ + 6e^-$	+1.8	—	—	—
$Co^{+2} = Co^{+3} + e^-$	+1.808	—	—	—
$NH_4^+ + N_2 = HN_3 + 3H^+ + 2e^-$	+1.96	+0.73	−0.14	—
$Ag^+ = Ag^{++} + e^-$	+1.980	—	—	—
$2SO_4^{--} = S_2O_8^{--} + 2e^-$	+2.01	−0.39	−1.26	—
$O_2 + H_2O = O_3 + 2H^+ + 2e^-$	+2.07	+0.388	−0.483	+0.655
$2F^- + H_2O = F_2O + 2H^+ + 4e^-$	+2.15	−0.313	−1.184	—
$Am^{+++} = Am^{+4} + e^-$	+2.18	−2.40	+1.53	—
$Fe^{+++} + 4H_2O = FeO_4^{--} + 8H^+ + 3e^-$	+2.20	$+0.02^x$	−0.85	—
$H_2O = O(g) + 2H^+ + 2e^-$	+2.422	−0.277	−1.148	+0.427
$N_2 + 2H_2O = H_2N_2O_2 + 2H^+ + 2e^-$	+2.65	+0.78	−0.09	—
$H_2O = OH + H^+ + e^-$	+2.85	−0.984	−1.855	+1.078
$Pr^{+++} = Pr^{+4} + e^-$	+2.86	—	—	—
$2F^- = F_2(g) + 2e^-$	+2.87	−0.959	−1.830	−5.339
$XeO_3 + 3H_2O = H_4XeO_6 + 2H^+ + 2e^-$	+3.0	—	—	—
$2HF(aq) = F_2(g) + 2H^+ + 2e^-$	+3.06	+0.27	−0.60	—
Basic Solutions				
$Ca + 2OH^- = Ca(OH)_2 + 2e^-$	−3.02	−0.094	−0.965	—
$Ba + 2OH^- + 8H_2O = Ba(OH)_2·8H_2O + 2e^-$	−2.99	+1.25	+0.38	—
$H(g) + OH^- = H_2O + e^-$	−2.9345	+0.548	−0.323	−7.050
$La + 3OH^- = La(OH)_3 + 3e^-$	−2.90	−0.08	−0.95	—
$Sr + 2OH^- = Sr(OH)_2 + 2e^-$	−2.88	−0.09	−0.96	—
$Ce + 3OH^- = Ce(OH)_3 + 3e^-$	−2.87	—	—	—
$Pr + 3OH^- = Pr(OH)_3 + 3e^-$	−2.85	−0.05	−0.92	—
$Nd + 3OH^- = Nd(OH)_3 + 3e^-$	−2.84	—	—	—
$Pm + 3OH^- = Pm(OH)_3 + 3e^-$	−2.84	—	—	—
$Sm + 3OH^- = Sm(OH)_3 + 3e^-$	−2.83	—	—	—
$Eu + 3OH^- = Eu(OH)_3 + 3e^-$	−2.83	—	—	—
$Gd + 3OH^- = Gd(OH)_3 + 3e^-$	−2.82	—	—	—
$Ba + 2OH^- = Ba(OH)_2 + 2e^-$	−2.81	−0.06	−0.93	—
$Y + 3OH^- = Y(OH)_3 + 3e^-$	−2.81	−0.08	−0.95	—
$Tb + 3OH^- = Tb(OH)_3 + 3e^-$	−2.79	—	—	—
$Dy + 3OH^- = Dy(OH)_3 + 3e^-$	−2.78	—	—	—
$Ho + 3OH^- = Ho(OH)_3 + 3e^-$	−2.77	—	—	—
$Er + 3OH^- = Er(OH)_3 + 3e^-$	−2.75	—	—	—
$Tm + 3OH^- = Tm(OH)_3 + 3e^-$	−2.74	—	—	—
$Yb + 3OH^- = Yb(OH)_3 + 3e^-$	−2.73	—	—	—
$Lu + 3OH^- = Lu(OH)_3 + 3e^-$	−2.72	—	—	—
$Mg + 2OH^- = Mg(OH)_2 + 2e^-$	−2.690	−0.074	−0.945	−6.079
$2Be + 6OH^- = Be_2O_3^{--} + 3H_2O + 4e^-$	−2.63	—	—	—
$Be + 2OH^- = BeO + H_2O + 2e^-$	−2.613	−0.301	−1.172	−6.596
$Sc + 3OH^- = Sc(OH)_3 + 3e^-$	−2.61	—	—	—
$Hf + 4OH^- = HfO(OH)_2 + H_2O + 4e^-$	−2.50	—	—	—
$Th + 4OH^- = Th(OH)_4 + 4e^-$	−2.48	−0.12	−0.99	—
$Pu + 3OH^- = Pu(OH)_3 + 3e^-$	−2.42	—	—	—
$U + 4OH^- = UO_2 + 2H_2O + 4e^-$	−2.39	−0.349	−1.220	—
$Zr + 4OH^- = H_2ZrO_3 + H_2O + 4e^-$	−2.36	−0.24	−1.11	—

x = direct experimental values.

Electrode	$V°$, v	$(dV°/dT)_{th}$ mv/deg	$(dV°/dT)_{isoth}$, mv/deg	$(d^2V°/dT^2)_{isoth}$, μv/deg²
Basic Solutions—*Continued*				
$Al + 4OH^- = H_2AlO_3^- + H_2O + 3e^-$	−2.33	—	—	—
$Al + 3OH^- = Al(OH)_3 + 3e^-$	−2.30	−0.06	−0.93	—
$U(OH)_3 + OH^- = U(OH)_4 + e^-$	−2.20	—	—	—
$U + 3OH^- = U(OH)_3 + 3e^-$	−2.17	—	—	—
$P + 2OH^- = H_2PO_2^- + e^-$	−2.05	—	—	—
$B + 4OH^- = H_2BO_3^- + H_2O + 3e^-$	−1.79	−0.276	−1.147	—
$Si + 6OH^- = SiO_3^{--} + 3H_2O + 4e^-$	−1.697	—	—	—
$U(OH)_4 + 2Na^+ + 4OH^- = Na_2UO_4 + 4H_2O + 2e^-$	−1.618	—	—	—
$H_2PO_2^- + 3OH^- = HPO_3^{--} + 2H_2O + 2e^-$	−1.565	—	—	—
$Mn + 2OH^- = Mn(OH)_2 + 2e^-$	−1.55	−0.208	−1.079	—
$Mn + CO_3^{--} = MnCO_3(c) + 2e^-$	−1.50	−0.361	−1.232	—
$Mn + CO_3^{--} = MnCO_3(ppt) + 2e^-$	−1.48	−0.433	−1.304	—
$Cr + 3OH^- = Cr(OH)_3(c) + 3e^-$	−1.48	−0.11	−0.98	—
$Zn + S^{--} = ZnS(wurtzite) + 2e^-$	−1.405	+0.02	−0.85	—
$Cr + 3OH^- = Cr(OH)_3(hydrous) + 3e^-$	−1.34	−0.12	−0.99	—
$Cr + 4OH^- = CrO_2 + 2H_2O + 3e^-$	−1.27	—	—	—
$Zn + 4CN^- = Zn(CN)_4^{--} + 2e^-$	−1.26	+1.19	+0.32	—
$Zn + 2OH^- = Zn(OH)_2 + 2e^-$	−1.245	−0.131	−1.002	−5.978
$Ga + 4OH^- = H_2GaO_3^- + H_2O + 3e^-$	−1.219	—	—	—
$Zn + 4OH^- = ZnO_2^{--} + 2H_2O + 2e^-$	−1.215	—	—	—
$Cd + S^{--} = CdS + 2e^-$	−1.175	0.00	−0.87	—
$6V + 33OH^- = HV_6O_{17}^{-3} + 16H_2O + 30e^-$	−1.154	—	—	—
$Te^{--} = Te + 2e^-$	−1.143	—	—	—
$HPO_3^{--} + 3OH^- = PO_4^{---} + 2H_2O + 2e^-$	−1.12	+0.38	−0.49	—
$S_2O_4^{--} + 4OH^- = 2SO_3^{--} + 2H_2O + 2e^-$	−1.12	+0.16	−0.71	—
$Zn + CO_3^{--} = ZnCO_3 + 2e^-$	−1.06	−0.293	−1.164	—
$W + 8OH^- = WO_4^{--} + 4H_2O + 6e^-$	−1.05	−0.49	−1.36	—
$Mo + 8OH^- = MoO_4^{--} + 4H_2O + 6e^-$	−1.05	−0.49	−1.36	—
$Zn + 4NH_3(aq) = Zn(NH_3)_4^{++} + 2e^-$	−1.04	—	—	—
$Ni + S^{--} = NiS(\gamma) + 2e^-$	−1.04	—	—	—
$Ge + 5OH^- = HGeO_3^- + 2H_2O + 4e^-$	−1.03	−0.42	−1.29	—
$Cd + 4CN^- = Cd(CN)_4^{--} + 2e^-$	−1.028	—	—	—
$In + 3OH^- = In(OH)_3 + 3e^-$	−1.00	−0.10	−0.97	—
$CN^- + 2OH^- = CNO^- + H_2O + 2e^-$	−0.970	−0.340	−1.211	—
$Pu(OH)_3 + OH^- = Pu(OH)_4 + e^-$	−0.963	—	—	—
$Fe + S^{--} = FeS(\alpha) + 2e^-$	−0.95	−0.10	−0.97	—
$Pb + S^{--} = PbS + 2e^-$	−0.93	−0.03	−0.90	—
$HSnO_2^- + H_2O + 3OH^- = Sn(OH)_6^- + 2e^-$	−0.93	—	—	—
$SO_3^{--} + 2OH^- = SO_4^{--} + H_2O + 2e^-$	−0.93	−0.518	−1.389	—
$Se^{--} = Se + 2e^-$	−0.92	−0.02	−0.89	—
$Sn + 3OH^- = HSnO_2^- + H_2O + 2e^-$	−0.909	—	—	—
$2Tl + S^{--} = Tl_2S + 2e^-$	−0.90	−0.07	−0.94	—
$2Cu + S^{--} = Cu_2S + 2e^-$	−0.89	−0.17	−1.04	—
$PH_3 + 3OH^- = P(white) + 3H_2O + 3e^-$	−0.89	−0.067	−0.938	—
$Fe + 2OH^- = Fe(OH)_2 + 2e^-$	−0.877	−0.19	−1.06	—
$Sn + S^{--} = SnS + 2e^-$	−0.87	−0.14	−1.01	—
$Ni + S^{--} = NiS(\alpha) + 2e^-$	−0.830	—	—	—
$H_2 + 2OH^- = 2H_2O + 2e^-$	−0.82806	+0.037	−0.8342	−7.272
$Cd + 2OH^- = Cd(OH)_2 + 2e^-$	−0.809	−0.143	−1.014	—
$Fe + CO_3^{--} = FeCO_3 + 2e^-$	−0.756	−0.422	−1.293	—
$Cd + CO_2^{--} = CdCO_3 + 2e^-$	−0.74	−0.361	−1.232	—
$Co + 2OH^- = Co(OH)_2 + 2e^-$	−0.73	−0.193	−1.064	—
$Ni + 2OH^- = Ni(OH)_2 + 2e^-$	−0.72	−0.17	−1.04	—
$2FeS(\alpha) + S^{--} = Fe_2S_3 + 2e^-$	−0.715	—	—	—
$Hg + S^{--} = HgS (black) + 2e^-$	−0.69	+0.08	−0.79	—

x = direct experimental values.

Electrode	$V°$, v	$(dV°/dT)_{th}$ mv/deg	$(dV°/dT)_{isoth}$ mv/deg	$(d^2V°/dT^2)_{isoth}$, μv/deg²
Basic Solutions—*Continued*				
$AsO_2^- + 4OH^- = AsO_4^{-3} + 2H_2O + 2e^-$	-0.68	—	—	—
$As + 4OH^- = AsO_2^- + 2H_2O + 3e^-$	-0.675	—	—	—
$2Ag + S^{--} = Ag_2S(\alpha) + 2e^-$	-0.66	-0.21	-1.08	—
$Sb + 4OH^- = SbO_2^- + 2H_2O + 3e^-$	-0.66	—	—	—
$Co + CO_3^{--} = CoCO_3 + 2e^-$	-0.64	—	—	—
$Cd + 4NH_3(aq) = Cd(NH_3)_4^{++} + 2e^-$	-0.613	—	—	—
$ReO_2 + 4OH^- = ReO_4^- + 2H_2O + 3e^-$	-0.594	—	—	—
$Re + 8OH^- = ReO_4^- + 4H_2O + 7e^-$	-0.584	-0.59	-1.46	—
$Pb + 2OH^- = PbO(r) + H_2O + 2e^-$	-0.580 (-0.577^x)	-0.292	-1.163 (-1.188^x)	-6.841^x ($\simeq -6.7^x$)
$Re + 4OH^- = ReO_2 + 2H_2O + 4e^-$	-0.577	—	—	—
$S_2O_3^{--} + 6OH^- = 2SO_3^{--} + 3H_2O + 4e^-$	-0.571	-0.275	-1.146	—
$Te + 6OH^- = TeO_3^{--} + 3H_2O + 4e^-$	-0.57	-0.36	-1.23	—
$Fe(OH)_2 + OH^- = Fe(OH)_3 + e^-$	-0.56	-0.09	-0.96	—
$O_2^- = O_2 + e^-$	-0.563	—	—	—
$Pb + 3OH^- = HPbO_2^- + H_2O + 2e^-$	-0.540	—	—	—
$Pb + CO_3^{--} = PbCO_3 + 2e^-$	-0.509	-0.423	-1.294	—
$Po + 6OH^- = PoO_3^{--} + 3H_2O + 4e^-$	-0.49	—	—	—
$Ni + 6NH_3(aq) = Ni(NH_3)_6^{++} + 2e^-$	-0.476	—	—	—
$2Bi + 6OH^- = Bi_2O_3 + 3H_2O + 6e^-$	-0.46	-0.343	-1.214	-6.828
$Ni + CO_3^{--} = NiCO_3 + 2e^-$	-0.45	-0.400	-1.271	—
$S^{--} = S + 2e^-$	-0.447	-0.06	-0.93	—
$Cu + 2CN^- = Cu(CN)_2^- + e^-$	-0.429	—	—	—
$Hg + 4CN^- = Hg(CN)_4^{--} + 2e^-$	-0.37	$+1.65$	$+0.78$	—
$Se + 6OH^- = SeO_3^{--} + 3H_2O + 4e^-$	-0.366	-0.447	-1.318	—
$2Cu + 2OH^- = Cu_2O + H_2O + 2e^-$	-0.358	-0.455	-1.326	-6.828
$Tl + OH^- = Tl(OH)(c) + e^-$	-0.343	$+0.003$	-0.868	—
$Ag + 2CN^- = Ag(CN)_2^- + e^-$	-0.31	$+0.958$	$+0.087$	—
$Cu + CNS^- = Cu(CNS) + e^-$	-0.27	—	—	—
$OH(g) + 2OH^- = HO_2^- + H_2O + e^-$	-0.262	—	—	—
$OH(aq) + 2OH^- = HO_2^- + H_2O + e^-$	-0.245	—	—	—
$Cr(OH)_3(hydr) + 5OH^- = CrO_4^{--} + 4H_2O + 3e^-$	-0.13	-0.804	-1.675	—
$Cu + 2NH_3 = Cu(NH_3)_2^+ + e^-$	-0.12	$+0.09$	-0.78	—
$Cu_2O + 2OH^- + H_2O = 2Cu(OH)_2 + 2e^-$	-0.080	$+0.15$	-0.725	—
$HO_2^- + OH^- = O_2 + H_2O + 2e^-$	-0.076	—	—	—
$TlOH + 2OH^- = Tl(OH)_3 + 2e^-$	-0.05	-0.069	-0.940	—
$Mn(OH)_2 + 2OH^- = MnO_2 + 2H_2O + 2e^-$	-0.05	-0.458	-1.329	—
$Ag + CN^- = AgCN + e^-$	-0.017	$+0.992$	$+0.121$	—
$At_2 + 4OH^- = 2AtO^- + 2H_2O + 2e^-$	0.0	—	—	—
$NO_2^- + 2OH^- = NO_3^- + H_2O + 2e^-$	$+0.01$	-0.388	-1.259	—
$Os + 9OH^- = HOsO_5 + 4H_2O + 8e^-$	$+0.015$	—	—	—
$2Rh + 6OH^- = Rh_2O_3 + 3H_2O + 6e^-$	$+0.04$	-0.36	-1.23	-6.772
$SeO_3^{--} + 2OH^- = SeO_4^{--} + H_2O + 2e^-$	$+0.05$	-0.316	-1.187	—
$Pd + 2OH^- = Pd(OH)_2 + 2e^-$	$+0.07$	-0.193	-1.064	—
$2S_2O_3^{--} = S_4O_6^{--} + 2e^-$	$+0.08$	-0.24	-1.11	—
$Hg + 2OH^- = HgO(r) + H_2O + 2e^-$	$+0.098$	-0.249	-1.120 (1.127^x)	-6.775 (-6.749^x)
$2Ir + 6OH^- = Ir_2O_3 + 3H_2O + 6e^-$	$+0.098$	—	—	—
$Co(NH_3)_6^{++} = Co(NH_3)_6^{+3} + e^-$	$+0.108$	—	—	—
$Pt(OH)_2 + 4OH^- = Pt(OH)_6^{--} + 2e^-$	$+0.1$ to $+0.4$	—	—	—
$2NH_4OH + 2OH^- = N_2H_4 + 4H_2O + 2e^-$	$+0.11$	-0.22	-1.09	—
$Mn(OH)_2 + OH^- = Mn(OH)_3 + e^-$	$+0.15$	-0.032	-0.903	—
$Pt + 2OH^- = Pt(OH)_2 + 2e^-$	$+0.15$	-0.273	-1.144	—
$Co(OH)_2 + OH^- = Co(OH)_3 + e^-$	$+0.17$	$+0.07$	-0.80	—

x = direct experimental values.

Electrode	$V°$, v	$(dV°/dT)_{th}$ mv/deg	$(dV°/dT)_{isoth}$, mv/deg	$(d^2V°/dT^2)_{isoth}$, μv/deg²
Basic Solutions—*Continued*				
$PuO_2OH + OH^- = PuO_2(OH)_2 + e^-$	+0.234	—	—	—
$PbO(r) + 2OH^- = PbO_2 + H_2O + 2e^-$	+0.247	−0.323	−1.194	—
$I^- + 6OH^- = IO_3^- + 3H_2O + 6e^-$	+0.26	−0.291	−1.162	−6.755
$Ag + 2SO_3^{--} = Ag(SO_3)_2^{-3} + e^-$	+0.295	—	—	—
$ClO_2^- + 2OH^- = ClO_3^- + H_2O + 2e^-$	+0.33	−0.60	−1.47	—
$2Ag + 2OH^- = Ag_2O + H_2O + 2e^-$	+0.345 (+0.342^x)	−0.466	−1.337 (−1.325^x)	−6.718 (≃6.7^x)
$ClO_3^- + 2OH^- = ClO_4^- + H_2O + 2e^-$	+0.36	−0.37	−1.24	—
$Ag + 2NH_3 = Ag(NH_3)_2^+ + e^-$	+0.373	+0.411	−0.460	—
$TeO_3^{--} + 2OH^- = TeO_4^{--} + H_2O + 2e^-$	ca. +0.4	—	—	—
$4OH^- = O_2 + 2H_2O + 4e^-$	+0.401	−0.809	−1.680	−6.719
$OH^- + HO_2^- = O_2^- + H_2O + e^-$	+0.413	—	—	—
$2Ag + CO_3^{--} = Ag_2CO_3 + 2e^-$	+0.47	−0.506	−1.377	—
$I^- + 2OH^- = IO^- + H_2O + 2e^-$	+0.485	—	—	—
$Ni(OH)_2 + 2OH^- = NiO_2 + 2H_2O + 2e^-$	+0.490	—	—	—
$AtO^- + 4OH^- = AtO_3^- + 2H_2O + 4e^-$	+0.5	—	—	—
$MnO_2(pyrolusite) + 4OH^- = MnO_4^- + 2H_2O + 3e^-$	+0.588	−0.907	−1.778	—
$MnO_2 + 4OH^- = MnO_4^{--} + 2H_2O + 2e^-$	+0.60	—	—	—
$RuO_4^{--} = RuO_4^- + e^-$	+0.6	—	—	—
$Ag_2O + 2OH^- = 2AgO + H_2O + 2e^-$	+0.607	−0.246	−1.117	—
$Br^- + 6OH^- = BrO_3^- + 3H_2O + 6e^-$	+0.61	−0.416	−1.287	−6.748
$ClO^- + 2OH^- = ClO_2^- + H_2O + 2e^-$	+0.66	−0.583	−1.454	—
$IO_3^- + 3OH^- = H_3IO_6^{--} + 2e^-$	+0.7	—	—	—
$Fe(OH)_3 + 5OH^- = FeO_4^{--} + 4H_2O + 3e^-$	+0.72	−0.75	−1.62	—
$N_2H_4 + 2OH^- = 2NH_2OH + 2e^-$	+0.73	−0.94	−1.81	—
$2AgO + 2OH^- = Ag_2O_3 + H_2O + 2e^-$	+0.739	—	—	—
$Br^- + 2OH^- = BrO^- + H_2O + 2e^-$	+0.761	—	—	—
$3OH^- = HO_2^- + H_2O + 2e^-$	+0.878	—	—	—
$Cl^- + 2OH^- = ClO^- + H_2O + 2e^-$	+0.89	−0.208	−1.079	—
$Xe + 7OH^- = HXeO_4^- + 3H_2O + 6e^-$	+0.9	—	—	—
$HXeO_4^- + 4OH^- = HXeO_6^{-3} + 2H_2O + 2e^-$	+0.9	—	—	—
$Cu(CN)_2^- = Cu^{++} + 2CN^- + e^-$	+1.103	—	—	—
$ClO_2^- = ClO_2(g) + e^-$	+1.16	−1.35	−2.22	—
$O_2 + 2OH^- = O_3(g) + H_2 + 2e^-$	+1.24	−0.447	−1.318	−6.617
$OH^- = OH(g) + e^-$	+2.02	−1.818	−2.689	−6.194

x = direct experimental values.

Alphabetical Index for
Table of Standard Aqueous Electrode Potentials, by Elements

Under each element are listed, in order of increasing Gibbs-Stockholm electrode potential (i.e., from the most active to the most noble), the potentials associated with the oxidation-reduction reactions of each element. Potentials marked B will be found in the basic solutions section of the Table.

Alphabetical Index—*Continued*

Cadmium—*cont.*	+0.033	+1.195	+0.1397
−0.613B	+0.137	+1.45	+0.223
−0.4029	+0.153	+1.601	+0.2676
−0.3516	+0.337	Iridium	+0.6151
Calcium	+0.521	+0.098B	+0.788
−3.02B	+0.538	+0.77	+0.920
−2.866	+0.640	+0.99	Molybdenum
Carbon	+0.86	+1.017	−1.05B
−0.970B	+1.103B	Iron	−0.20
−0.330	Dysprosium	−0.95B	Neodymium
−0.199	−2.78B	−0.877B	−2.84B
+0.056	−2.353	−0.756B	−2.431
+0.1316	Erbium	−0.715B	Neptunium
+0.23	−2.75B	−0.56B	−1.856
+0.373	−2.296	−0.4402	+0.147
+0.52	Europium	+0.36	+0.75
+0.588	−2.83B	+0.72B	+1.15
+0.6994	−2.407	+0.771	Nickel
+0.731	−0.429	+2.20	−1.04B
+0.77	Fluorine	Lanthanum	−0.830B
+1.18	+2.15	−2.90B	−0.72B
Cerium	+2.87	−2.522	−0.476B
−2.87B	+3.06	Lead	−0.45B
−2.483	Gadolinium	−0.93B	−0.250
+1.61	−2.82B	−0.580B	+0.490B
Cesium	−2.397	−0.540B	+1.678
−2.923	Gallium	−0.509B	Niobium (Columbium)
Chlorine	−1.219B	−0.365	−1.099
+0.33B	−0.529	−0.3588	−0.644
+0.36B	Germanium	−0.3505	Nitrogen
+0.66B	−1.03B	−0.284	−3.40
+0.89B	−0.15	−0.268	−3.09
+1.16B	Gold	−0.126	−0.970B
+1.19	+0.655	+0.247B	−0.330
+1.21	+0.87	+1.455	−0.23
+1.275	+0.956	+1.682	+0.01B
+1.3595	+1.00	Lithium	+0.11B
+1.63	+1.45	−3.045	+0.373
+1.645	+1.498	Lutetium	+0.387
Chromium	+1.691	−2.72B	+0.695
−1.48B	Hafnium	−2.255	+0.712
−1.34B	−2.50B	Magnesium	+0.73B
−1.27B	−1.70	−2.690B	+0.77
−0.744	Holmium	−2.363	+0.803
−0.408	−2.77B	Manganese	+0.86
−0.13B	−2.319	−1.55B	+0.94
+1.33	Hydrogen	−1.50B	+0.96
Cobalt	−2.9345B	−1.48B	+1.00
−0.73B	−2.25	−1.180	+1.03
−0.64B	−2.1065	−0.05B	+1.07
−0.277	−0.82806B	+0.15B	+1.275
+0.108B	−0.0034	+0.564	+1.29
+0.17B	0.0000	+0.588B	+1.35
+1.808	+0.0004	+0.60B	+1.42
Columbium, see Nio-	Indium	+1.23	+1.96
bium	−1.00B	+1.51	+2.65
Copper	−0.343	+1.51	Osmium
−0.89B	Iodine	+1.695	+0.015B
−0.429B	+0.26B	Mercury	+0.85
−0.358B	+0.485B	−0.69B	Oxygen
−0.27B	+0.5355	−0.37B	−0.563B
−0.1852	+0.536	−0.0405	−0.262B
−0.12B	+0.7B	−0.038	−0.245B
−0.080B	+1.056	+0.098B	−0.13

Alphabetical Index—*Continued*

Oxygen—*cont.*
-0.076B
+0.401B
+0.413B
+0.6824
+0.71
+0.878B
+1.185
+1.229
+1.24B
+1.495
+1.776
+2.02B
+2.07
+2.422
+2.85

Palladium
+0.07B
+0.60
+0.62
+0.987
+1.288

Phosphorus
-2.05B
-1.565B
-1.12B
-0.89B
-0.508
-0.499
-0.276
-0.063

Platinum
-0.327
-0.297
+0.1B
+0.15B
+0.581
+0.68
+0.73
+0.98
+1.1
+1.2

Plutonium
-2.42B
-2.031
-0.963B
+0.234B
+0.93
+0.97
+1.04
+1.15

Polonium
-1.00
-0.49B
+0.65
+0.80
+1.52

Potassium
-2.925

Praseodymium
-2.85B

-2.462
+2.86

Promethium
-2.84B
-2.423

Protactinium
-1.0

Radium
-2.916

Rhenium
-0.594B
-0.584B
-0.577B
+0.2513
+0.362
+0.510

Rhodium
+0.04B
+0.431
+0.80
+0.87

Rubidium
-2.925

Ruthenium
+0.6B
+0.601

Samarium
-2.83B
-2.414
-1.15

Scandium
-2.61B
-2.077

Selenium
-0.92B
-0.399
-0.366B
+0.05B
+0.740
+1.15

Silicon
-1.697B
-1.24
-0.857
+0.102

Silver
-0.66B
-0.31B
-0.1518
-0.017B
+0.017
+0.0713
+0.2222
+0.295B
+0.345B
+0.354
+0.373B
+0.464
+0.47B
+0.486
+0.546

+0.564
+0.607B
+0.643
+0.654
+0.739B
+0.7991
+1.980

Sodium
-2.714

Strontium
-2.888
-2.88B

Sulfur
-1.12B
-0.93B
-0.571B
-0.447B
-0.22
-0.082
+0.08B
+0.142
+0.172
+0.23
+0.3572
+0.400
+0.450
+0.51
+0.57
+0.77
+1.23
+2.01

Tantalum
-0.812

Technetium
+0.4
+0.6
+0.7

Tellurium
-1.143B
-0.739
-0.718
-0.57B
+0.4B
+0.529
+0.559
+1.02

Terbium
-2.79B
-2.391

Thallium
-0.90B
-0.752
-0.658
-0.5568
-0.343B
-0.3363
-0.05B
+1.25

Thorium
-2.48B

-1.899

Thulium
-2.74B
-2.278

Tin
-0.93B
-0.909B
-0.87B
-0.25
-0.136
+0.15

Titanium
-1.628
-1.191
-0.882
-0.369
+0.099

Tungsten
-1.05B
-0.090

Uranium
-2.39B
-2.20B
-2.17B
-1.789
-1.618B
-0.607
+0.05
+0.330
+0.62

Vanadium
-1.186
-1.154B
-0.256
-0.254
+0.359
+1.00

Xenon
+0.9B
+0.9B
+1.8
+3.0

Ytterbium
-2.73B
-2.267
-1.21

Yttrium
-2.81B
-2.372

Zinc
-1.405B
-1.26B
-1.245B
-1.215B
-1.06B
-1.04B
-0.7628

Zirconium
-2.36B
-1.529

ELECTRODE POTENTIALS IN FUSED SALTS. See **FUSED SALT ELECTRODE REACTIONS; FUSED SALT ELECTROMOTIVE FORCE SERIES.**

ELECTRODE POTENTIALS, MEASUREMENT

The absolute potential of a single electrode is the potential difference between a point within the solid (or liquid) conductor and a point in the electrolyte adjacent to the surface of the conductor. Unfortunately, there is no known method of determining the absolute single electrode potential,[1] but the difference in potential between two electrodes is readily measured. There is a defined zero-potential electrode, and all other electrode potentials are given relative to this.

The defined zero is the potential of the standard hydrogen electrode. This consists of a metal conductor, usually platinized platinum, in contact with hydrogen gas at 1 atm and with an electrolyte containing hydrogen ion at unit activity. The sign convention for single electrode potentials is such that active metals (e.g., magnesium and zinc) have negative potentials in aqueous solutions while noble metals (e.g., silver and gold) have positive potentials.

Any electrode whose potential is reproducible and time-invariant may be calibrated against the hydrogen electrode and is then useful as a *reference electrode* (q.v.).[2] To determine the unknown potential of an electrode under study, the latter is electrolytically connected to a reference electrode of predetermined potential. The emf of this cell is a measure of the unknown potential. Since the measured voltage, V, of any electrolytic cell is given as a positive number, its relation to the pair of single electrode potentials is:

$$V = E_+ - E_-$$

Here E_+ refers to the more positive or less negative electrode of the pair, whether it be the reference electrode or the unknown.

General cell arrangement and potentiometric measurement

A typical cell for potential measurements is shown schematically in Fig. 1. In this example the solution (S_r) surrounding the reference electrode (e_r) is not the same as the solution (S_u) around the unknown (e_u). The junction (j) between the two solutions is usually made within a porous separator, through which the reference solution flows at a finite but very small rate. Of the many reference electrodes available, one is selected such that the voltage drop across the junction of the two solutions (the "liquid junction potential") is either negligible* or calculable.[2]

The emf of the cell is most accurately measured by the "Poggendorff compensation" method.[3] The cell is connected to a potentiometer, P, through a sensitive galvanometer, G, as shown in Fig. 1. Here the reference electrode has the more positive potential of the pair and hence must be attached to the positive side of the potentiometer, so that the cell voltage opposes the potentiometer voltage. The latter is adjusted to balance the cell emf, i.e., no galvanometer deflection on momentarily closing the push-button switch, B. At balance no current passes through the cell, so that the emf is being measured at "open circuit."

While the balance point is being sought, the resistance, R, limits the current in the cell to minute values. Passage of any appreciable quantity of electricity during the measurement will disturb the voltage being measured. After initial balance is obtained, the resistance, R, is lowered for greater sensitivity and a new balance established, then this procedure is repeated until the desired precision of measurement is obtained. The potentiometer is calibrated just before each measurement by replacing the test cell with a Weston cell (1.019 volt):

$$(+) \ Hg/Hg_2SO_4 \ (satd), \ CdSO_4/Cd(Hg) \ (-)$$

The emf of a commercial Weston cell is generally standardized to within ±0.01 mv.

There are two important modifications of the cell arrangement depicted in Fig. 1. The first concerns the situation where the two solutions (S_r and S_u) are the same. The electrodes (e_r and e_u) are then placed in a single vessel filled with S_u and no liquid junction is present.

The second case concerns a test electrode to which current is passed from a third electrode. The third electrode may be located within the same vessel as the test electrode (e_u), but often is in a separate vessel and is electrolytically connected by means of a siphon tube. When current is passed, the test electrode is in an electric field, and IR drops exist in the electrolyte around it. To minimize the IR drop included in the potential measurement, the siphon tube from

* See **Electrode Potentials.**

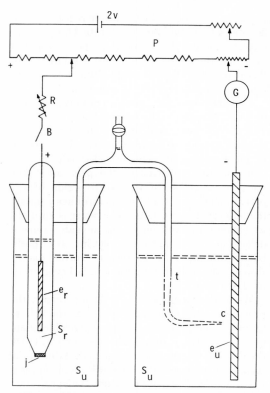

FIG. 1. Apparatus for potential measurements.

the reference may be brought close to the electrode (to point c in Fig. 1). In the absence of current flow, IR drops are absent and the siphon tube may be terminated anywhere in the test solution (e.g., position t, Fig. 1).

IR Drop Corrections

For test electrodes under current flow ("polarized" electrodes), tip, c, is drawn to a fine capillary of diameter, d, and is placed no closer than a distance $2d$ from the electrode surface to prevent "shielding" errors (due to distortion of the field at the electrode surface).[4] As illustrated by Fig. 2, potential mapping studies have shown that the potential inside a capillary at a distance $2d$ from a planar electrode is the same as that at a distance $(2d - d/3)$ in the undistorted field away from the capillary.[5] Thus, the IR voltage in the electrolyte between capillary and electrode, V_{IR}, may be evaluated from

$$V_{IR} = (2d - d/3)i/\kappa \qquad (1)$$

where i is the current density and κ the conductivity of the electrolyte.

The measured cell voltage must be corrected by this amount. The following table gives V_{IR} corrections calculated from Eq. 1, for a fine capillary of diameter 0.02 cm situated 0.04 cm from a planar electrode.

i (amp cm^{-2})	V_{IR} (mv)	
	$\kappa = 0.1$ (ohm cm)$^{-1}$	$\kappa = 0.001$ (ohm cm)$^{-1}$
3×10^{-1}	100	10,000
3×10^{-2}	10	1,000
3×10^{-3}	1	100
3×10^{-4}	0.1	10

Larger capillaries yield proportionately larger IR drops (Eq. 1). It is evident that accurate potential measurements on polarized electrodes can be made by the method of Fig. 1 only if the IR correction is evaluated with precision.

The sign of the IR drop depends only on whether the current to the test electrode is anodic (I_a) or cathodic (I_c). If the polarized electrode is anode:

$$V = E_+ - E_- - |I_a R| \qquad (2)$$

and if it is cathode:

$$V = E_+ - E_- + |I_c R| \qquad (3)$$

Eq. 2 and 3 are independent of whether the

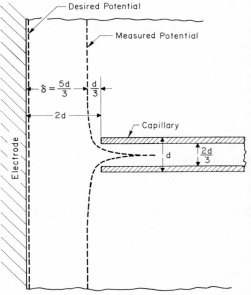

FIG. 2. Potential drop in electrolyte between capillary tip and electrode surface.

polarized electrode has the more positive potential (E_+) or the more negative one of the pair.

Electronic meters for potential measurements

While the Poggendorff compensation method described above yields the most accurate potentials, it is not usable with electrodes of high impedance, such as the glass electrode employed for pH measurements (q.v.). The current passing through high-impedance electrodes must be extremely low (10^{-10} amp or less) to avoid measurable IR drops in the cell. Such low currents cannot be detected by galvanometers of the usual deflection type, even those of high sensitivity.

Vacuum-tube voltmeters (VTVM) can be used for these high-impedance cells, although they lack the precision of the Poggendorff method. Since the VTVM is also useful for low-impedance cells where highest accuracy is not required, and since it provides simpler and more rapid measurements, it has become the most commonly used instrument for potential determinations.

Modern commercial VTVM circuits have been described by Bates.[6] The emf to be measured is connected to the grid of a vacuum tube, and a current of 10^{-10} to 10^{-12} amperes is drawn continuously from the cell. For most measurements such currents do not disturb the emf being measured. Where lower cell currents are required, however, electronic voltmeters utilizing an electrometer vacuum tube, a vibrating reed electrometer, or a vibrating condenser can be used.[6] Electrometer voltmeters drawing roughly 10^{-14} amperes from the test cell are available.

An electronic instrument of the type just described functions simply as a d-c voltmeter. When used for a potential measurement with polarized electrodes, the reading will include the IR drop between the polarized electrode and the capillary tip. More complex instrumentation has been described,[7, 8] called an "electronic commutator," which yields potential measurements that exclude the IR drop. The functioning of this device is based on periodic interruption of the polarizing current. The decay of the emf being measured is followed as a function of time during the current-off interval, when no IR drops are present in the test cell. It is necessary to extrapolate the decay curve back to the instant of current interruption, because the emf decay is initially rapid. Usually the extrapolated emf will have an uncertainty of 10 mv or more unless switching is sufficiently rapid to permit emf measurements within about 5 μsec.[8]

References

1. GUGGENHEIM, E. A., "Thermodynamics," p. 332, New York, Interscience Publishers, Inc., 1949.
2. IVES, D. J. G. AND JANZ, G. J., "Reference Electrodes," New York, Academic Press, 1961.
3. GLASSTONE, S., "An Introduction to Electrochemistry," Princeton, N. J., D. van Nostrand Co., Inc., 1942.
4. BARNARTT, S., *J. Electrochem. Soc.*, **99**, 549 (1952).
5. BARNARTT, S., *J. Electrochem. Soc.*, **108**, 102 (1961).
6. BATES, R. G., "Electrometric pH Determinations," New York, John Wiley and Sons, 1954.
7. HICKLING, A., *Trans. Faraday Soc.*, **33**, 1540 (1937).
8. STAICOPOULOUS, D., YEAGER, E., AND HOVORKA, F., *J. Electrochem. Soc.*, **98**, 68 (1951).

SIDNEY BARNARTT

ELECTRODE POTENTIALS, REFERENCE. *See* REFERENCE ELECTRODES

ELECTRODE POTENTIALS, SIGNS OF

Two conventions have arisen governing the algebraic signs of electrode (half-cell) electromotive force (emf) data: 1) the Nernst-Lewis-Latimer "American" half-cell emf, sign bivariant, E convention; 2) the Gibbs-Ostwald-Stockholm "European" electrode potential, sign invariant, V convention. In 1953, the International Union of Pure and Applied Chemistry (IUPAC) at Stockholm unanimously recommended that, while either convention is permissible, only convention 2) may be designated the *electrode potential*, V. Since the E convention was formerly, and is still sometimes erroneously, referred to as the "electrode potential," the V convention may be conveniently and unambiguously designated the *Gibbs-Stockholm electrode potential*.

In convention 1), *the sign of the emf, E, assigned to a single electrode or half-cell (referred to the standard hydrogen electrode, SHE, as the zero-point) is determined by the sign of the free enthalpy change* (Gibbs free energy change), ΔG, of the half-cell reaction *which transfers n faradays, $\mathbf{F}$,*

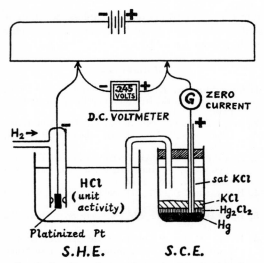

FIG. 1. A cell made up of standard hydrogen electrode (SHE) and a saturated calomel electrode (SCE). "Open circuit" electromotive force measured with a potentiometer by the Poggendorf compensation method.

of positive electricity through the electrode interface *from left to right* (as written in a half-cell diagram), by means of the relation

$$\Delta G = -n\mathbf{F}E \qquad (1)$$

The half-cell emf, E, is sign bivariant, i.e., a reversal of the half-cell reaction (and diagram) reverses the sign of ΔG and also the sign of E, notwithstanding the fact that the observed d-c polarity of the electrode remains unchanged. E values may be designated as *oxidation emf's* (*oxidation potentials*) or *reduction emf's* (*reduction potentials*) according as the half-cell reactions are written in the *anodic oxidation* or *cathodic reduction* directions. Oxidation potentials have been extensively used in the tabulations of W. M. Latimer. Reduction potentials coincide in sign with the electrode potential, V.

In convention 2), the sign of the (*Gibbs-Stock-*

holm) *electrode potential*, V, *is determined by the observed polarity of the terminal* of the d-c potential-measuring instrument *connected with the electrode* in question, when the second terminal (of the same kind of metal) is connected with a standard hydrogen electrode, SHE, and the circuit is closed and balanced. Fig. 1 illustrates the measurement of the potential of the saturated calomel electrode, SCE: Hg, Hg_2Cl_2, KCl sat. aq., by reference to the SHE. As seen in Fig. 1, the electrode potential of the saturated calomel electrode, V(SCE) = +0.245 volt at 25°C, and is sign invariant, i.e., a reversal of an infinitesimal current flowing through the galvanometer G does not change the observed polarities in the (−)SHE/SCE(+) cell.

Since the *electrode potential*, V, is sign invariant, while the *free enthalpy change*, ΔG, is necessarily sign bivariant, two separate relations must be written between these two quantities, *viz.*,

$$\Delta G = +n\mathbf{F}V \quad \text{(for anodic oxidations)} \qquad (2)$$

$$\Delta F = -n\mathbf{F}V \quad \text{(for cathodic reductions)} \qquad (3)$$

while relation (1) is retained for electromotive forces (whole cell and half cell emf's).

Consider the two cells

$$(+) \text{ SHE } // \text{ Zn}^{++}/\text{Zn } (-) \quad E° = -0.76 \text{ volt} \qquad (4)$$

$$(-) \text{ SHE } // \text{ Cl}^-, \text{ Cl}_2/\text{Pt } (+) \quad E° = +1.36 \text{ volt} \qquad (5)$$

with the given standard $E°$ cell emf values and the indicated d-c polarities. The double bar // denotes that the liquid junction potential has been eliminated or minimized, e.g., by a salt bridge. The whole cell emf, E, is conventionally related to the electrode potentials by

$$E\text{(cell)} = V\text{(right)} - V\text{(left)}. \qquad (6)$$

The E and V half-cell sign conventions and their free enthalpy relationships can be illustrated by the examples

Half-Cell	Half-Cell Reaction	Electrode Potential, V	Half-Cell Emf, E	Free Enthalpy, ΔG	
	Anodic	(v)	(v)	(vF)	(kcal)
Zn/Zn^{++}	$Zn = Zn^{++} + 2e^-$	−0.76	+0.76*	−1.52	−35.05
Pt/Cl_2, Cl^-	$2Cl^- = Cl_2 + 2e^-$	+1.36	−1.36*	+2.72	+62.72
	Cathodic				
Zn^{++}/Zn	$Zn^{++} + 2e^- = Zn$	−0.76	−0.76†	+1.52	+35.05
Cl^-, Cl_2/Pt	$Cl_2 + 2e^- = 2Cl^-$	+1.36	+1.36†	−2.72	−62.72

* Oxidation emf's (oxidation potentials)
+ Reduction emf's (reduction potentials)

TABLE 1. SIGNS AND DESIGNATIONS OF ELECTRODE POTENTIALS

Observed d-c Polarity of Electrode with respect to SHE	(+)	(−)
Potential Designation on *noble—active* scale	noble more noble less active	active less noble more active
The Electrode Potential, V (Gibbs-Stockholm electrode potential)	+	−
The Half-Cell Emf, E Oxidation Emf (oxidation potential) Reduction Emf (reduction potential)	− +	+ −
Direction of Current Flow galvanic electrolytic	cathodic anodic	anodic cathodic
Potential Designation in battery and corrosion work in polarization and polarographic work	cathodic anodic	anodic cathodic

The signs of the electrode potentials, V, of zinc (negative) and of chlorine (positive) correspond to the polarities observed in cells (4) and (5) and remain invariant upon a reversal of the half cell reaction, while the E values change their signs so as to have always the opposite sign to the ΔG values. For the latter, the conversion factor, 1 volt-faraday = 23.06 kcal, is convenient. *The electrode potential, V, always has the same algebraic sign as the oxidation free enthalpy change, and as the reduction emf (reduction potential) while the oxidation emf (oxidation potential) has the opposite sign.* Note that, while the half-cell reactions are properly labelled anodic or cathodic depending on their direction, the electrodes themselves are here considered to be reversible and on open circuit, i.e., they are not to be thought of as anodes or cathodes passing anything more than the infinitesimal current needed to activate the potential-measuring device.

Other designations for electrode potentials are: *cathodic* and *anodic*, or *noble* and *active*. In battery and corrosion work, a *positive electrode potential* (Gibbs-Stockholm) is *cathodic*, while in polarization work (e.g., in polarography) a *positive potential* is *anodic*. By reference to the emf series of the metals, it is seen that a *positive electrode potential* is characteristic of a metal *more noble* than hydrogen; a *negative electrode potential*, of a metal *more active* than hydrogen.

The various designations and their relations to the electrode sign conventions are summarized in Table 1 above.

References

1. CHRISTIANSEN, J. A., AND POURBAIX, M., *Compt. rend. 17th Conf. I.U.P.A.C., Stockholm*, 1953, pp. 82–84; Christiansen, J. A., *J. Am. Chem. Soc.*, **82**, 5517 (1960).
2. NERNST, W., *Z. physik. Chem.*, **4**, 129 (1889); *Ber.*, **30**, 1547 (1897).
3. LEWIS, G. N., AND RANDALL, M., "Thermodynamics," Ch. XXIX and XXX, New York, McGraw-Hill Book Co., 1923.
4. PITZER, K. S., AND BREWER, L., "Lewis and Randall's Thermodynamics," 2nd Edition, Ch. 24, New York, McGraw-Hill Book Co., 1961.
5. LATIMER, W. M., "Oxidation Potentials," 2nd Edition, New York, Prentice Hall, 1952.
6. GIBBS, J. WILLARD, "The Equilibrium of Heterogeneous Substances," *Trans. Conn. Acad.*, **3**, 108, 343 (1875–8); reprinted in "Collected Works, Vol. I, Thermodynamics," pp. 55–349, notably pp. 332–333 and 349, New Haven, Yale University Press, 1949.
7. GIBBS, J. WILLARD, Letter to Wilder D. Rancroft, May 1899, reprinted in "Collected Works," Vol. I, "Thermodynamics," p. 429, New Haven, Yale University Press, 1949.
8. OSTWALD, W., *Z. physik. Chem.*, **1**, 583 (1887).
9. DEBETHUNE, ANDRE J., *Corrosion*, **9**, 336 (1953); *J. Electrochem. Soc.*, **101**, 252C (1954); **102**, 288C (1955).
10. LICHT, T. S., AND DEBETHUNE, ANDRE J., *J. Chem. Educ.*, **34**, 433 (1957).
11. Van Rysselberghe, P., *Z. Elektrochem.*, **58**, 530 (1954).

ANDRE J. DE BETHUNE

Cross-references: *Nomenclature, Remarks on.*

ELECTRODE POTENTIALS, TEMPERATURE COEFFICIENTS

The temperature coefficient of the potential, V, of an electrode can be defined experimentally by reference to (a) the potential of the standard hydrogen electrode, SHE, at the same temperature, (b) the potential of the same electrode at a fixed temperature. These two definitions give rise to the *isothermal* and *thermal temperature coefficients* of electrode potentials, respectively.

Consider the isothermal cell

$$\text{SHE//Electrolyte/Electrode} \qquad (1)$$

at uniform temperature, T, where the double bar means that the liquid junction potential has been eliminated, or minimized, e.g., by the use of salt bridges. The cell emf, E(cell), equal to V(right) − V(left) on open circuit, where the V's are the electrical potentials of two pieces of the same kind of metal connected with the two electrodes, defines the sign-invariant Gibbs-Stockholm potential, V, of the right-hand electrode. The *isothermal temperature coefficient*, $(dV/dT)_{iso}$, is dE(cell 1)$/dT$, and is given thermodynamically for reversible electrodes by

$$(dV/dT)_{iso} = \Delta S/n\mathbf{F} = (\Delta H - \Delta G)/n\mathbf{F}T \quad (2)$$

where ΔS, ΔH and ΔG are the entropy, enthalpy, and free enthalpy (Gibbs free energy) changes of the reaction which reversibly transfers n faradays of positive electricity through cell (1) from left to right, i.e., the reaction

$$\text{Ox} + (n/2)\text{H}_2(a = 1) = \text{Red} + n\text{H}^+(a = 1) \quad (3a)$$

if the right-hand electrode reaction can be written

$$\text{Ox} + ne^- = \text{Red.} \qquad (3b)$$

The entropy change used in Eq. 2 is then

$$\Delta S = S(\text{Red}) - S(\text{Ox}) + nS°(\text{H}^+) \\ - (n/2)S°(\text{H}_2). \qquad (4)$$

The *second isothermal temperature coefficient* is

$$(d^2V/dT^2)_{iso} = \Delta C_p/n\mathbf{F}T \qquad (5a)$$

where

$$\Delta C_p = C_p(\text{Red}) - C_p(\text{Ox}) \\ + nC_p°(\text{H}^+) - (n/2)C_p°(\text{H}_2). \qquad (5b)$$

Conventional ionic entropies and heat capacities, based on $S°(\text{H}^+) = 0$ and $C_p°(\text{H}^+) = 0$ may be used in Eqs. 2–5. The conversion factor is 23.06 calories/degree = 1 millivolt-faraday/degree.

Consider next the thermal cell

$$\text{Cu}(T_1, V)/\text{Electrode } (T_1)/\text{Electrolyte } (T_1)/$$

$$\text{Electrolyte } (T_2)/\text{Electrode } (T_2)/ \qquad (6)$$

$$\text{Cu}(T_2)/\text{Cu}(T_1, V + dV)$$

where $T_2 = T_1 + dT$ and the cell emf, dE(cell 6), is given by the potential difference, dV, on open circuit. The *thermal temperature coefficient of the electrode potential*, $(dV/dT)_{th}$, is dE(cell 6)$/dT_2$. From Carnot's theorem, the electrical work output $n\mathbf{F}dE$(cell 6) $= Q^*dT_2/T_2 = S^*dT_2$ where Q^* is the Peltier heat of the thermal cell (for n faradays) and S^* is the entropy of transport of the cell, i.e., the entropy transported reversibly from the hot to the cold heat reservoir by the passage of n faradays of positive electricity through the cell from the cold to the hot electrode (before the onset of thermal diffusion, *v.i.*), so that

$$(dV/dT)_{th} = S^*(\text{cell})/n\mathbf{F} \qquad (7)$$

and is of the order of tenths of millivolts per degree. The entropy of transport, S^*, is made up of three contributions: an entropy, S_E^*, of electrochemical transport which arises from the two electrode reactions, an entropy, S_M^*, of migration transport which determines the thermal liquid junction potential (tljp), and the entropy of transfer, $-nS_M^*(e^-$ in Cu$)$, of the electrons in the external copper leads. The total entropy of transport is given by

$$S^*(\text{cell 6}) = S_E^*(\text{cell}) \\ + S_M^*(\text{cell}) - nS_M^*(e^- \text{ in Cu}) \qquad (8a)$$

$$= S_E^*(\text{Red}) - S_E^*(\text{Ox}) - nS_E^*(e^- \text{ in Cu}) \\ - \Sigma(t_i n/z_i)S_{Mi}^* - nS_M^*(e^- \text{ in Cu}). \qquad (8b)$$

The term S_E^*(cell) in (8a) determines the electrode temperature effect, while, in (8b), S_E^* (Red or Ox) denotes the entropy of electrochemical transport of the chemical species indicated; for neutral substances this coincides with the partial molal third-law entropy; for aqueous ions of valence, z_i,

$$S_{Ei}^* = \bar{S}_i + z_i(-4.48 \text{ cal/deg})(\text{at } 25°\text{C}) \quad (9)$$

where $\bar{S}_i$ is the (conventional) partial molal entropy of the ith ionic species. The constant, -4.48 cal/deg mole, is the standard entropy of electrochemical transport of aqueous hydrogen ion at 25°C, and is based on the experimentally observed thermal temperature coefficient of the standard hydrogen electrode with a saturated KCl bridge

$$(dV°/dT)_{th}(H_2/H^+aq/sat\ KCl) \tag{10}$$
$$= +0.871\ mv/°C$$

(the hot electrode is the (+) terminal) under the assumption that the tljp of the KCl bridge and the electronic terms can be neglected. The electronic terms coalesce to give $\bar{S}(e^-) = S_E{}^*(e^-) + S_M{}^*(e^-)$, the *entropy of the moving electrons* in the copper leads, which can be estimated from a third-law integral of the thermoelectric Thomson coefficient of copper to be -0.045 cal/deg equiv, a negligible value in most thermal cell studies. The summation in Eq. 8b represents the entropy of migration transport, $S_M{}^*$, of the cell, which determines the tljp, and involves the transport numbers, t_i, and the ionic contributions, $S_{Mi}{}^*$. These can be estimated from data on the Soret effect of aqueous electrolytes, and represent the entropy absorbed from the surrounding heat reservoir by the solution that the ion leaves. Referred to $S_M{}^*(Cl^-) = 0$, $S_{Mi}{}^*$ values for most simple inorganic ions range between -2 and $+3$ cal/deg equiv, except that $S_M{}^*(H^+) = +10$ and $S_M{}^*(OH^-) = +13.5$ cal/deg mole. The ionic migration transport entropy, $S_{Mi}{}^*$, is approximately concentration-independent, while the ionic electrochemical transport entropy, $S_{Ei}{}^*$, has a mass-action dependence which parallels that of the conventional partial molal entropy, i.e.,

$$S_{Ei}{}^* = S_{Ei}{}^{*°} - R\ln a_i - RT(d\ln a_i/dT) \tag{11}$$

Thermal cells are subject to thermal (Soret) diffusion, unless prevented by convection. This normally tends to concentrate electrolytes in the cold region and superimposes a concentration emf (usually of a few hundredths of a millivolt per degree) on the thermal emf of Eq. 7. If the cell reaches Soret equilibrium, the final emf is given by

$$(dV/dT)_{th,\ fin} = \bar{S}(cell)/n\mathbf{F}, \tag{12}$$

TABLE 1. POTENTIALS AND THERMAL TEMPERATURE COEFFICIENTS OF REFERENCE
ELECTRODES IN WATER AT 25°C

A positive V value means that the electrode is the (+) terminal of a cell whose other electrode is the SHE. A positive thermal temperature coefficient means that the hot electrode is the (+) terminal in a thermal cell. Isothermal coefficients can be computed from the thermal coefficients by subtracting 0.871 mv/deg C.

Electrode	V(v)	$(dV/dT)_{th}$(mv/deg C)	
		calc.	obs.
{SHE/sat KCl			
H$_2$ (a = 1)/H$^+$ (a = 1)/sat KCl	0.000	(+0.871)	+0.871
H$_2$ (a = 1)/H$^+$ 0.1M/sat KCl	−0.065	(+0.640)	+0.640
Hg/Hg$_2$Cl$_2$/0.01M KCl	+0.388	+0.961	+0.94
Hg/Hg$_2$Cl$_2$/0.1M KCl	+0.333	+0.774	+0.79
Hg/Hg$_2$Cl$_2$/1.0M KCl	+0.280	+0.573	+0.61, .59, .57
Hg/Hg$_2$Cl$_2$/3.5M KCl	+0.247	+0.48	+0.47
Hg/Hg$_2$Cl$_2$/3.8M KCl	+0.244	+0.475	+0.475
Hg/Hg$_2$Cl$_2$/sat. KCl (SCE)	+0.241	+0.165	+0.22
Hg/Hg$_2$Cl$_2$/(a = 1) KCl	+0.2676	+0.554	—
Ag/AgCl/0.001M KCl	+0.401	+0.81	+0.77
Ag/AgCl/0.01M KCl	+0.343	+0.621	+0.617
Ag/AgCl/0.1M KCl	+0.288	+0.434	+0.431
Ag/AgCl/1.0M KCl	+0.235	+0.235	+0.250
Ag/AgCl/(a = 1) KCl	+0.2222	+0.213	—
Cu/CuSO$_4$ 0.08M	+0.287	+0.694	+0.64
Cu/CuSO$_4$ 0.1M	+0.289	+0.700	+0.72
Cu/CuSO$_4$ 0.5M	+0.298	+0.733	+0.75
Cu/CuSO$_4$ 1.0M	+0.303	+0.747	+0.69, .79
Cu/CuSO$_4$ 1.4M	+0.305	+0.755	+0.75
Cu/CuSO$_4$ sat	+0.30	+0.782	+0.90
Cu/CuSO$_4$ (a = 1)	+0.342	+0.879	—

where

$$\bar{\bar{S}}(\text{cell}) = \bar{\bar{S}}(\text{Red}) - \bar{\bar{S}}(\text{Ox}) - nS(e^- \text{ in Cu}), \quad (13)$$

and the entropy, $\bar{\bar{S}}$, for a neutral species coincides with its (partial molal) third-law entropy; for an ion, $\bar{S}_i = S_{Ei}^* + S_{Mi}^*$ is called the *entropy of the moving ion* or *transported entropy of the ion*, and is directly measurable from final thermal emf's.

Mass action effects on reversible electrode potentials are given by the Nernst equation

$$V = V^\circ + (RT/n\mathbf{F}) \ln (\text{Ox})/(\text{Red}). \quad (14)$$

The temperature derivatives of this equation can be applied equally well to *isothermal* and *thermal temperature coefficients*, provided liquid junction effects can be neglected. Let $(\text{Ox}) = \Pi m(\text{Ox})\gamma(\text{Ox})$, with a similar expression for (Red), then the first coefficient is

$$dV/dT = dV^\circ/dT + (R/n\mathbf{F}) \ln (\text{Ox})/(\text{Red})$$
$$+ (RT/n\mathbf{F})d \ln [\Pi_\gamma(\text{Ox})/\Pi_\gamma(\text{Red})]/dT \quad (15)$$

and the second coefficient is

$$d^2V/dT^2 = d^2V^\circ/dT^2$$
$$+ (2R/n\mathbf{F})d \ln [\Pi_\gamma(\text{Ox})/\Pi_\gamma(\text{Red})]/dT$$
$$+ (RT/n\mathbf{F})d^2 \ln [\cdots]/dT^2. \quad (16)$$

for both isothermal and thermal coefficients. Molalities do not appear in Eq. 16, and there is no mass-action dependence of the second coefficient if all γ's are temperature invariant, e.g., in ideal solutions.

The application of Eq. 15 to the thermal temperature coefficients of reference electrodes is illustrated in Table 1.

In the Table of Electrode Potentials (q.v.), the V values are accompanied, wherever possible, by values of the thermal and isothermal temperature coefficients and second isothermal temperature coefficients. The values are computed from thermodynamic data, except where noted as direct experimental. Isothermal coefficients can be computed from thermal coefficients by subtracting 0.871 mv/°C.

References

1. deBethune, A. J., Licht, T. S., and Swendeman, N., *J. Electrochem. Soc.*, **106**, 616 (1959).
2. deBethune, A. J., *ibid.*, **107**, 829, 937 (1960)
3. Salvi, G. R., and deBethune, A. J., *ibid.*, **108**, 672 (1961).
4. Agar, J. N., *Rev. Pure Applied Chem.* (*Roy. Aust. Chem. Inst.*), **8**, 1 (1958).
5. Richards, T. W., *Z. physik. Chem.*, **24**, 39 (1897).

Andre J. de Bethune

Cross-references: *Electrode Potentials entries; EMF Measurements in Aqueous Solutions at High Temperature; Nomenclature, Remarks on; Soret Potential.*

ELECTRODE REACTIONS IN FUSED SALTS. See FUSED SALT ELECTRODE REACTIONS.

ELECTRODE REACTIONS, KINETICS

Reactions which occur at electrodes include: the deposition of metals, e.g.,

$$Ag^+ + e \rightarrow Ag \quad (1)$$

the evolution of gases,

$$2H^+ + 2e \rightarrow H_2 \quad (2)$$

the deposition of solid salts,

$$Pb + SO_4^{2-} \rightarrow PbSO_4 + 2e \quad (3)$$

simple electron transfer reactions,

$$Fe^{3+} + e \rightarrow Fe^{2+} \quad (4)$$

and more complex oxidation-reduction reactions,

$$(COOH)_2 + 2H^+ + 2e \rightarrow CHOCOOH + H_2O \quad (5)$$

Such reactions are similar to heterogeneous catalytic reactions in that they occur only at the interface, in this case between a metal (or other electronic conductor) and an electrolyte. The important distinction from the usual type of heterogeneous catalytic reaction is that electrode reactions always involve a net transfer of electric charge between the two phases. Hence, the continuous occurrence of an electrode reaction is associated with the flow of an electric current across the metal-electrolyte interface. As Faraday showed, there is a quantitative relation between the amount of reaction occurring and the quantity of electricity passed through the electrode. Consequently the current flowing is a measure of the rate of the electrode reaction and provides the most usual way in which the kinetics of electrode reactions are studied.

Electrode reactions may take place in a number of steps which include:

1. Transport of reactants to and from the interface.

2. Reactions in which charge is transferred

across the interface (these may be considered to be the essential electrode reactions).

3. Chemical reactions preceding or following the charge transfer reaction. They may occur in the bulk of the electrolyte or at the interface only.

4. Phase forming reactions, i.e., nucleation and crystal growth, or formation of gas bubbles.

For example, the deposition of silver from a concentrated cyanide bath involves processes of all these types: the $Ag(CN)_3^{2-}$ complexes diffuse towards the electrode, near which they dissociate to $Ag(CN)_2^-$ complexes which actually take part in the charge transfer reaction. The deposited silver ions then migrate to growing points on the crystal surface where they are incorporated into the metal lattice.

Steps of type 3 can be treated by the usual methods of chemical kinetics, but those of type 2 require some modification of these methods. Owing to the transfer of electricity between phases, the free energy change associated with charge transfer reactions depends on the potential difference between the two phases. A change in electrode potential, ΔE, results in a change in the free energy of reaction by $z\mathbf{F}\Delta E$ per mole of reaction, where $\mathbf{F}$ is the Faraday and z the number of electrons transferred in a unit reaction. Like any chemical reaction, this type of reaction system passes through an intermediate state of high energy known as the activated complex before reaching its final state. It may be assumed that the free energy of formation of the activated complex (the free energy of activation, $\Delta G^{\ddagger}$) is also dependent on the electrode potential, but to a smaller extent than the free energy of the whole reaction. Thus the free energy of activation for the cathodic reaction is changed by $\alpha z\mathbf{F}\Delta E$, while that for the anodic reaction is changed by $(1 - \alpha)z\mathbf{F}\Delta E$, where α is a proper fraction and is called the *transfer coefficient*. The rate constant of a reaction is proportional to $\exp(-\Delta G^{\ddagger}/RT)$ so that the rate constant of the cathodic reaction may be written as $k_c \cdot \exp(-\alpha z\mathbf{F}\Delta E/RT)$, where k_c is the rate constant at the potential from which ΔE is measured and ΔE is taken as positive if the electrode is made more anodic. Similarly, the rate constant of the reverse reaction is $k_a \cdot \exp[(1 - \alpha)z\mathbf{F}\Delta E/RT]$. The net rate of a reaction like (4) may thus be expressed as:

$$v = i/z\mathbf{F} = k_a \cdot \exp[(1 - \alpha)z\mathbf{F}\Delta E/RT]c_{Fe^{2+}}$$
$$- k_c \cdot \exp(-\alpha z\mathbf{F}\Delta E/RT) \cdot c_{Fe^{3+}} \quad (6)$$

where i, the current per unit area of the electrode (*current density*), is taken as positive for an anodic reaction and $c_{Fe^{2+}}$, $c_{Fe^{3+}}$ are the concentrations of the reactants at the electrode surface.

Clearly the rate constants, k_a, k_c, depend on some arbitrary potential from which ΔE is measured and it would be advantageous to avoid this arbitrariness. The most useful way of doing this is to use the value of the equilibrium potential of the system being studied. At equilibrium there is no net reaction ($i = 0$); $\Delta E = \Delta E_r$, the reversible potential, and the reactant concentrations are equal to those in the bulk of the solution, $c_{Fe^{2+}}{}^b$ and $c_{Fe^{3+}}{}^b$. Although there is no net reaction, the equilibrium is of course dynamic, the rates of the cathodic and anodic reactions being equal. These equal rates are expressed by the exchange current:

$$i_0/z\mathbf{F} = k_c \cdot \exp(-\alpha z\mathbf{F}\Delta E_r/RT) \cdot c_{Fe^{3+}}{}^b$$
$$- k_a \cdot \exp[(1 - \alpha)z\mathbf{F}\Delta E_r/RT] \cdot c_{Fe^{2+}}{}^b \quad (7)$$

Therefore

$$\exp(z\mathbf{F}\Delta E_r/RT) = k_c \cdot_{Fe^{3+}}{}^b/k_a \cdot c_{Fe^{2+}}{}^b \quad (8)$$

and the exchange current may be expressed as

$$i_0/z\mathbf{F} = k_c^{1-\alpha} k_a^{\alpha} (c_{Fe^{3+}}{}^b)^{1-\alpha} (c_{Fe^{2+}}{}^b)^{\alpha}$$
$$= k_s (c_{Fe^{3+}}{}^b)^{1-\alpha} (c_{Fe^{2+}}{}^b)^{\alpha} \quad (9)$$

The *standard rate constant*, k_s, is characteristic of the rate of the electrode reaction without any arbitrariness and is therefore the most satisfactory measure of the intrinsic rate of an electrode reaction. The exchange current is also useful as a measure of the rate of the reaction in a particular solution. The standard rate constant and its temperature variation may be interpreted in terms of a pre-exponential factor (related to the entropy of activation) and an exponential factor involving the energy of activation, in a way somewhat similar to that used for ordinary chemical reactions.

The equation for the net rate (Eq. 6) takes its simplest form when the potential is expressed as the deviation from the reversible value, i.e., the overpotential

$$\eta = \Delta E - \Delta E_r, \quad (10)$$

also with the aid of Eq. (7) the exchange current is introduced to obtain

$$i = i_0\{\exp[(1 - \alpha)z\mathbf{F}\eta/RT]$$
$$- \exp(-\alpha z\mathbf{F}\eta/RT)\} \quad (11)$$

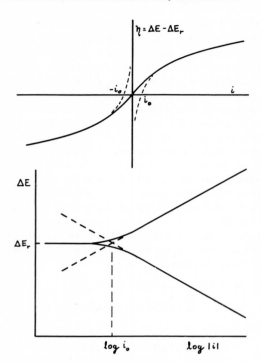

FIG. 1. Current-voltage curves according to Eq. (11) (above), also expressed in terms of log (current) (below)

This double exponential form of the current-voltage relation (Fig. 1) is characteristic of simple electrochemical reactions. It has two useful limiting forms:

a) When $|i| \gg i_0$, one of the exponentials may be neglected and the overpotential is proportional to $\log |i|$. This was observed experimentally by Tafel in 1905 and the plot of η against $\log |i|$ is called a *Tafel line* (q.v.).

b) When $|i| \leq i_0$ the exponentials may be expanded and terms higher than the second neglected to obtain

$$i = i_0 z \mathbf{F} \eta / RT. \qquad (12)$$

Since the current is now a linear function of the overpotential, the electrode behaves as a simple or "ohmic" resistance.

More Complex Reactions

When the overall electrode reaction is the same as the charge transfer reaction and the latter is much slower than the rate of transport of reactants to and from the electrode, the experimental current-voltage curves agree well with Eq. (11). Most electrode reactions are more complex. If

the reaction involves a sequence of chemical and/or electrochemical steps, these may be treated by the usual methods of chemical kinetics, e.g., use of the steady state condition if the reaction is studied under such conditions, or if one reaction is very much slower than the remainder, the overall rate may be put equal to the rate of this reaction and the other reactions may be assumed to depart negligibly from equilibrium conditions. When rate-determining chemical steps precede the charge transfer steps, the rate of the overall reaction will tend to be independent of the electrode potential, i.e., a *limiting current* is observed. On the other hand, if a chemical step follows the charge transfer step the overall reaction rate may be potential dependent because the concentration of the products of the charge transfer step is potential dependent.

Steps of types 1 and 4 require a treatment which differs from that of ordinary chemical kinetics. Transport to and from the electrode occurs by diffusion (supplemented by migration if the transport number of the relevant species is appreciable) which occurs as a result of the concentration gradients set up near the electrode when a reactant is consumed or produced in the electrode reaction. In general these concentration gradients are time dependent, and the rate of diffusion depends very much on the experimental conditions used. Under steady state conditions the rate of diffusion to an electrode per unit area is given by

$$i/z\mathbf{F} = D(c^b - c^e)/\delta, \qquad (13)$$

where D is the diffusion coefficient, c^b is the bulk concentration and c^e that at the electrode surface. δ is a characteristic length known as the diffusion layer thickness. In the simplest case of an electrode in the form of a disk rotating about an axis perpendicular to the plane of the disk, it is given by

$$\delta = 1.62 \, D^{1/3} \nu^{1/6} \omega^{-1/2} \qquad (14)$$

where ν is the kinematic viscosity and ω the angular velocity of rotation. Exact expressions for other types of convective electrodes are not known. In the absence of convection, δ is given for a large flat electrode by $\sqrt{\pi D t}$ where t is the time after beginning electrolysis. For a dropping mercury electrode this becomes approximately $\sqrt{(3/7)\pi D t}$. Clearly, there is no stationary state for such electrodes, although with the dropping electrode a limit is put on δ by the termination of the process when the drop falls, i.e., when $t = \tau$ the drop period.

One important characteristic of transport processes is that they can lead to the occurrence of a limiting current, since it follows that i in Eq. (13) has a maximum value when $c^e = 0$. This limiting current may usually be distinguished from that due to a chemical reaction by changing the diffusion conditions, e.g., the rate of electrode rotation or rate of mercury flow.

A crystallization step may involve the transport of adsorbed particles across the electrode surface, but it also involves nucleation and crystal growth. These may be potential-dependent processes because they depend on the interfacial free energy of the crystal against the electrolyte, which like the interfacial tension of a liquid metal-electrolyte boundary is dependent on the potential difference across the interface. Apart from this the process is treated in the same way as the growth of crystals of neutral molecules from gas or liquid phases.

Methods for studying electrode reactions

The rates of electrode reactions vary over a wide range. It is estimated that the maximum rate constant for a simple oxidation-reduction reaction is between 10^3 and 10^5 cm sec^{-1}. Most of the reactions which have been studied have rate constants greater than 10^{-15} cm sec^{-1}. The technique by which the reaction is studied depends very much on the speed of the reaction under the conditions used. When the exchange current is less than about 10^{-5} amp/sq cm, the steady state method is adequate and transport processes are rapid compared with the electrode reaction itself. A three-electrode type of cell is used (Fig. 2). Current is passed through the working electrode (W) and the auxiliary electrode (A), while the change in the potential of the working electrode is measured with respect to an unpolarized reference electrode (R). Besides the change in the electrode potential, the observed potential change may have a contribution from the potential drop occurring in the solution which carries the current to the working electrode. This contribution (the ohmic pseudo-overpotential) is minimized by using a "Luggin capillary" (L) which runs from the reference electrode compartment to a point close to the electrode surface. Thus, only a small element of solution carrying the current is included in the potential measuring circuit.

If there are no complications, the current-potential curve measured in this way is time independent and it may be analyzed according to Eq. (11) to obtain α and i_0. The simplest way of doing this is to plot the Tafel line; α is obtained from the slope and i_0 from the intercept. Variation of reactant concentration permits the orders of reaction to be determined and also the standard rate constant, k_s (cf. Eq. 9), although in some reactions results are not immediately interpretable because of the adsorption of reactants on the electrode surface. From the temperature coefficient of the standard rate constant the heat of activation of the reaction may be found in the usual way.

Reactions which are faster by about two powers of ten may be studied by the stationary current-potential curve method if the electrode is rotated, or if a dropping mercury electrode can be used. The effect of the rate of transport (step 1) can be eliminated either by theoretical calculation or by extrapolation; the resulting curve may then be analyzed as before.

Reactions which are even faster require more elaborate techniques which may be classified as *relaxation methods*. The simplest in principle are those in which either the current or the potential is changed abruptly to a new value and the other variable is studied as a function of time. The potential step or potentiostatic method provides results which are more readily interpreted because the rate constants are functions of potential. However, the apparatus required is fairly elabo-

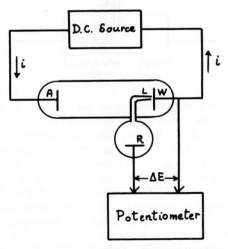

Fig. 2. Schematic diagram of the circuit for measuring steady state current-voltage curves.

rate. The current step or galvanostatic method is simpler in practice but more difficult to interpret. Both depend on the fact that when such a step function is applied to an electrode, the electrode reaction is able to occur almost at once with a speed unhindered by the transport processes. As time elapses the reactants near the electrode become depleted, and the rate is retarded. The elimination of transport control is often obtained best by an extrapolation. An important factor in the interpretation of the transients is that some of the current passed through the electrode must be used to charge the double layer at the electrode surface when the potential is changed. This current must be subtracted from the total current to obtain the current due to the electrode reaction (the faradaic current). An improved galvanostatic method uses a short, high-current pulse to charge the double layer, followed by the normal pulse.

Fast reactions may also be studied by alternating current methods. In the faradaic impedance method the working and auxiliary electrodes are inserted into an impedance bridge powered by an alternating voltage of a few mv. If the auxiliary electrode has a sufficiently large area, its impedance is negligible compared with that of the rest of the cell. The measured impedance is thus the resistance of the solution in series with the impedance of the working electrode. In the simplest case of a reaction like (4) the latter may be analyzed in the form:

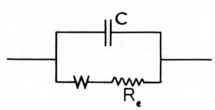

where C is the capacity of the double layer and R_e is the resistance due to the electrode reaction. The symbol —W— represents the part of the impedance due to the transport of the reactants; it is known as the Warburg impedance. It is a frequency dependent impedance with a phase angle constant at 45°. R_e may be found by first subtracting (vectorially) the double layer capacity and then extrapolating the remaining impedance to high frequency where the Warburg impedance vanishes. From Eq. (12) R_e is found to be RT/zFi_0 and hence the exchange current

may be calculated. A second, a-c method known as faradaic rectification depends on the fact that the current-voltage characteristic of an electrode is nonlinear. If no direct current is allowed to pass through the electrode, then passage of an alternating current will cause the potential of the electrode to shift from its equilibrium value and the exchange current can be found from the measurement of this shift.

In the study of fast reactions it is rarely possible to pass currents much larger than i_0. Hence, most of the methods described for fast reactions yield i_0 only. The value of α must be obtained from the concentration dependence of i_0 according to Eq. (9). This involves some difficulties if the reaction is complex, since the exponents to which the concentrations are raised in Eq. (9) in this case contain reaction orders as well as the transfer coefficient. However, fast reactions rarely go through many steps so that this does not often cause much trouble. In the case of faradaic rectification, α is obtained directly because the nonlinearity of the current-voltage characteristic is expressed by higher terms in the series expansion of Eq. (11).

Some Results

Simple reactions of type 1 tend to be fast, for example, the discharge of mercurous ion onto liquid mercury from 1 mM solution in 1 M $HClO_4$ occurs with an exchange current of about 0.25 amp/sq cm and $\alpha = 0.24$. The deposition of silver from 0.2 M $AgClO_4$ is slower ($i_0 \simeq 0.1$ amp/sq cm and $\alpha = 0.5$), and there is evidence that both the charge transfer step and the crystal formation step contribute to the control of the total rate. The slower deposition of copper ($i_0 \simeq 5 \times 10^{-3}$ amp/sq cm from 1 M $CuSO_4$ + 1 M H_2SO_4) is attributable to the effect of the rate-determining $Cu^{2+} + e \rightarrow Cu^+$ reaction, which also accounts for the low value of α (0.29). The deposition of transition metals is considerably slower and for iron ($i_0 \simeq 10^{-6}$ amp/sq cm in 0.5 M $FeSO_4$) this appears to result from the greater complexity of the reaction which involves intermediate species FeOH and $FeOH^+$.

Reactions of type 2 exhibit a very wide range in rate. Hydrogen evolution from a normal aqueous acid solution occurs with an exchange current of about 10^{-3} amp/sq cm on Pt and about 10^{-13} amp/sq cm on Pb. This variation is due primarily to the variation in the stability of the essential intermediate, atomic hydrogen, which is adsorbed to a greater or less extent on the electrode surface. When about half the surface is covered with adsorbed hydrogen at equilibrium, the highest exchange currents are found. The mechanism of the reaction may be deduced from the transfer coefficient and other kinetic parameters though the interpretation has many difficulties. It seems likely that, except for the metals at which hydrogen is evolved fastest, the reaction $H^+(aq) + e \rightarrow H(ads.)$ is rate-determining. Oxygen evolution occurs by a more complex sequence of reactions and can be studied only using the small number of unattackable metals. On platinum ($i_0 \simeq 10^{-10}$ amp/sq cm) it seems probable that the initial discharge step, $H_2O \rightarrow H^+(aq) + OH(ads.) + e$, determines the rate. The slowest known electrode reaction, the evolution of nitrogen from azide ions, has an exchange current of about 10^{-76} amp/sq cm on Pt. This is, of course, an extrapolated value using the plot of an experimental Tafel line and a calculated equilibrium potential.

The deposition of $PbSO_4$ according to Eq. (3) occurs by the initial dissolution of lead and the precipitation of $PbSO_4$ in the solution immediately adjacent to the electrode. If a constant current is used, the electrode becomes "passive," i.e., the current can no longer be carried by this reaction, and the potential rises until another reaction can occur. At this electrode the second reaction is the oxidation of $PbSO_4$ to PbO_2. Oxide films may be formed directly, for example, by the anodization of Ta in aqueous solution. The growth of such films is a relatively slow process and probably is determined by the rate of migration of the metal ions through the oxide lattice, although the oxygen ions may also migrate.

Simple electron exchange reactions of type 4 occur rapidly unless a major reorganization of the co-ordination shell about the ion is required. The Fe^{3+}/Fe^{2+} reaction has an exchange current of 5×10^{-3} amp/sq cm at a Pt electrode when both reactants are 0.015 M. The effect of the co-ordination shell is illustrated by the Cr^{3+}/Cr^{2+} reaction. In 1 mM solution the exchange current is 10^{-6} amp/sq cm when the aquo-ions are used, but 3×10^{-3} amp/sq cm when the hexacyano ions are used. The α values for this type of reaction are usually close to 0.5 and the electrode material has little effect on the rate.

Organic electrode reactions frequently occur by alternating proton and electron transfers, the former usually being the more rapid. Intermediate free radicals are formed and may be adsorbed at the electrode surface. In reaction (5) at a mercury electrode the first step is an electron transfer to the neutral oxalic acid molecule and this is the step which is rate-determining.

References

1. DELAHAY, P., "New Instrumental Methods in Electrochemistry," New York, Interscience, 1954.
2. VETTER, K. J., "Elektrochemische Kinetik," Berlin, Springer, 1961.
3. YOUNG, L., "Anodic Oxide Films," New York, Academic Press, 1961.
4. BOCKRIS, J. O'M., Ed., "Modern Aspects of Electrochemistry," London, Butterworths, Vol. 1, 1954, Chap. 4, "Electrode Kinetics," Bockris, J. O'M., Vol. 2, 1959, Chap. 4, "The Anodic Behaviour of Metals," Hoar, T. P.
5. DELAHAY, P., AND TOBIAS, C. W., (Eds.) "Advances in Electrochemistry and Electrochemical Engineering," New York, Interscience, Vol. 1. 1961, Chap. 1, "The Electrical Double Layer and its Influence on the Rates of Electrode Reactions," Parsons, R.; Chap. 2, "Hydrogen Overvoltage and Adsorption Phenomena," Frumkin, A. N.; Chap. 4, "Semiconductor Electrode Reactions," Gerischer, H.; Chap. 5, "The Study of Fast Electrode Reactions," Delahay, P.; Vol. 3, 1963, Chap. 3, "Hydrogen Overvoltage and Adsorption Phenomena," Frumkin, A. N.; Chap. 4, "Electrocrystallization and Metal Deposition," Fleischman, H. M., and Thirsk, H. R.; Chap. 5, "Anodic Films," Vermilyea, D. A.
6. CHARLOT, G., BADOZ-LAMBLING, J., AND TREMILLON, B., "Electrochemical Reactions (Electrochemical Methods of Analysis)," Amsterdam, Elsevier, 1962.

ROGER PARSONS

Cross-references: *Corrosion, Electrochemical Kinetics; Electrode Double Layer; Exchange Current; Tafel Lines; Transfer Coefficient.*

ELECTRODES, MICRO-. See MICROELECTRODES.

ELECTRODES, PLATINIZED. See PLATINIZED ELECTRODES.

ELECTRODEPOSITION entries—see pages 409–411.

ELECTRODIAGNOSIS

The primary purpose of electrodiagnostic techniques, which include electromyography (EMG) and electrostimulation, is to help in differentiating diseases of the "lower motor neuron" (extending from the anterior horn of the spinal cord down to the neuromuscular junction) from those of the upper motor neuron (originating in the brain) and hysteria, as well as those of either the muscle itself, or of the neuromuscular junction. The present development of these methods suggests that they may be used in the exploration of sensory systems, reflex action, and the voluntary control of movements.

Equipment

Fig. 1 shows typical EMG equipment.

Electrodes. In addition to surface electrodes, analogous to EEG (electroencephalography, q.v.) electrodes, *monopolar* or *bipolar* needle electrodes are used.

Amplifiers. The frequency response of the amplifiers used in EMG should be much broader than that of the EEG equipment, particularly insofar as the high frequencies are concerned. The frequency-response curve should be flat from 10 to 5000 c/sec.

Recorders. Although ink recorders may be used for the study of voluntary movements, in general cathode ray oscillographs must be used. In most applications, a single channel is sufficient. However, some investigators use several channels simultaneously.

Tape Recorders and Loud Speakers. Inasmuch as some of the sounds produced in a loud speaker by EMG potentials (fibrillations; myotonic responses) are characteristic, tape recorders and loud speakers are often used. The tape recorder may also be used in conjunction with the inkwriter; with this technique the electromyogram is recorded with a high speed tape, and played back into an electroencephalograph with a speed approximately 20 times as slow.

Photographic Cameras. In most applications, the camera is used to photograph a cathode-ray oscillogram.

Memoscope. A cathode ray oscilloscope with a storage device is increasingly used in EMG. This instrument permits one to inspect a great deal of sampled potentials before a permanent record is made. It is also useful for the determinations of conduction velocities, which may be determined without photography.

Averaging Devices. Different types of averaging devices are used in order to record the potential of extremely low amplitude (see EEG).

Stimulator. Square wave stimulators are

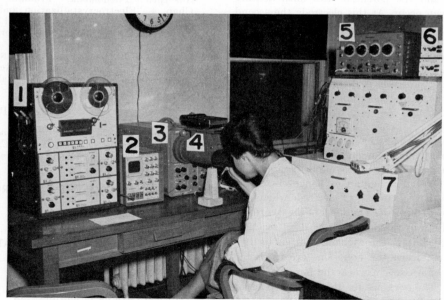

FIG. 1. (*1*) Tape recorder; (*2*) averaging computer; (*3*) memoscope; (*4*) photographic camera; (*5*) stimulator; (*6*) isolation unit; (*7*) electromyograph.

usually employed for determination of strength-duration curves and chronaxies. The range of the pulse duration should be between 0.1 and 300 msec. They may be used also for determining conduction velocities and recording evoked potentials. D-C stimulators, isolated from ground, may be used for activation of fibrillations. Currents with progressive onset of electric pulses may also be used.

Integrated EMG Equipment. This equipment permits one to record a summated electrogenesis with surface electrodes applied over the belly of a muscle.

Isometric Myograph. This equipment may be used to record mechanical contractions of the muscle.

Neuromuscular Excitability and Conduction

Excitability. *Galvanic tonus and strength duration curve.* When a direct current of prolonged duration (galvanic current, d-c) is applied to a nerve, directly or through the skin, a twitch is observed with a *threshold* stimulation in a muscle supplied by this nerve. This minimal threshold current is called "rheobase." If, as is the practice of electrodiagnosis, a monopolar method is applied (small active electrode over a nerve or a muscle; large dispersive electrodes located on the chest for example), this threshold will be higher for the anodic current (positive active electrode), than for the cathodic current (negative active electrode). The threshold will also be different in case of the closure of the circuit (the "make" of the current) than in the case of the opening of the current (the "break" of the current). Rheobase is lower with the "make" at the cathode, and with the "break" at the anode. During the constant flow of current, no muscle effect is observed, unless the stimulus reaches a relatively high level. In this case, a repetitive nerve discharge is observed resulting in a tetanus of the muscle (galvanic tetanus or galvanic tonus). When the duration of the d-c pulse falls below a certain liminal value (of the order of 10 msec), the current has to be increased to elicit a threshold contraction. This liminal, critical value is called "utilization time." If the pulse duration is decreased still more, the current has to be correspondingly increased. The relationship between the threshold current and the pulse duration is expressed by the "strength duration curve."

The pulse duration corresponding to the threshold current equal to twice the rheobase is called "chronaxy." Chronaxy, in general, is brief (below 1 msec) for the motor nerves. It is much more difficult to interpret the results of chronaxy determinations in the case of a muscle. Indeed, in a normal muscle, the intramuscular nerve endings may have a lower threshold than the muscle fibers themselves; therefore, the chronaxy determined by muscle stimulation may be that of the intramuscular nerve endings. This is particularly true of the stimulation at the motor point (see below).

Progressive current. If the stimulus is established progressively instead of an instantaneous onset, the processes of accommodation of the muscle to the stimulus may prevent a normal muscle from responding to the stimulation below a certain limit of intensity. This is not so for denervated muscle fibers which, therefore, may be stimulated selectively by "progressive currents."

Conduction velocity. In the large motor and sensory fibers of the mixed nerves, conduction velocity is of the order of 50 to 60 meters/sec, although generally, and particularly in a hospital population, slightly lower values are found. Moreover, conduction velocities determined for the nerves of the lower extremity are slightly lower than those determined for the nerves of the upper extremities. To determine the conduction velocity of a nerve, the following procedure is used: a nerve is stimulated at a proximal point and the latency time, L_P, is determined, elapsing from the time of stimulation to the emergence of the electric potential recorded from a muscle supplied by this nerve. Then a distal nerve point is stimulated and the latency, L_D, is determined in the same way. $L_P - L_D$ indicates the time necessary for the impulse to travel from the proximal to the distal nerve point. The distance, d, separating these two nerve points is then measured. Conduction velocity is then equal to $d/(L_P - L_D)$. If $L_P - L_D$ is determined in milliseconds, and d in millimeters, then $d/(L_P - L_D)$ will indicate directly velocity in meters per second. Indeed, if one multiplies the numerator and the denominator of a ratio by the same number (by 1000 in this case), its value remains the same.

Sensory conduction velocity. Three ways have been opened for determining sensory conduction velocities.

1) Direct recording from the nerve trunks by needle or surface electrodes following stimulation of the fingers or toes. In some cases, an averaging computer may be necessary in order to record these potentials. This, however, is not the case for recording with surface electrodes from the median and ulnar nerve at the wrist. All normal individuals, at least those below 60 years of age, exhibit potentials of 10 to 70 microvolts under such conditions. The normal latencies are below 4 msec.

2) Indirect determination by recording reflex responses initiated from proximal and distal nerve points (H and F responses, see below). The principle of this recording is essentially the same as in the case of a motor fiber conduction velocity determination, although the reflex time is obviously shorter when the stimulus is applied to a more proximal nerve point (located closer to the spinal cord). Conduction velocities determined in this way are slightly below those of the motor fibers, but only within 10 per cent of the higher value.

3) Indirect determination through the cerebral potentials evoked from the distal and proximal nerve point. This method is still in a research stage.

Character of muscle contraction. As mentioned above, a normal muscle is most easily stimulated at its motor point; i. e., the projection over the skin of the intramuscular nerve ending. Beyond this point, the stimulating current has to be increased in intensity in order to elicit a muscle twitch. In other words, a normal muscle is characterized by an excitability gradient which is the highest at the motor point. Its contraction is brisk and so is its decontraction.

Reflex Studies. *Monosynaptic reflexes.* A stimulus applied to a mixed nerve is followed not only by a short latency, motor (M) direct response, but also by a longer latency (in the order of 30 msec.) reflex (H or F) response. H-reflexes were discovered by Hoffman in 1922. They are present in every normal individual in the soleus muscle. There, it can be elicited by a stimulus of lower voltage than that necessary to elicit a direct (M) response. With the increase of the stimulus, the amplitude of M-response increases and that of the H-response decreases. With a supra maximal stimulation, H-reflex cannot be elicited because of a traffic jam in the centripetal direction (antidromic blocking). Indeed, a stimulus applied to a motor fiber gives rise to a nerve impulse travelling in both direc-

tions: centrifugal (toward muscles) and centropetal (toward the anterior horn). Inasmuch as the simultaneously travelling sensory impulses arrive at the synapse at about the same time, and the central delay being very short, the reflex impulse would meet head on the antidromic motor impulse, unless the excitability of the sensory fibers is higher than that of the motor ones.

However, in many instances of mixed nerves, a higher amplitude is necessary to elicit a reflex than a direct (M) response. These reflexes are called F-reflexes. It is interesting to find that in pathological conditions, namely, in patients with pyramidal lesions (sensitization of spindles), F-reflexes acquire the characteristics of H-reflexes. At times they become polyphasic and are much more constant in appearance than under normal conditions.

Spinal cord inhibition. If one asks an individual to contract voluntarily a muscle, for instance abductor pollicis brevis, and if during this contraction one applies a brief stimulus to the median nerve, the voluntary activity after a period of facilitation at the time of the F-reflex will be suspended or decreased for about 100 msec.

This "silent period" is a function of the intensity of the voluntary contraction. The more intense the latter, the briefer the silent period is. It seems to be somewhat increased in Parkinsonian patients.

Polysynaptic reflexes. The following polysynaptic reflexes are revealed:

1) Blink reflexes. Electric percutaneous stimulation of the supraorbital and infraorbital nerves elicits bilateral blink response with a dual component: the first of about 10 msec latency and the second of about 40 msec latency.

2) Trunk reflexes. A painful electric stimulus applied to the abdominal wall during a contraction of the erector spinae produces a reflex in the abdominal muscle with reciprocal inhibition of the erector spinae. The opposite relationship is found following the stimulation of the skin of the back. The general characteristic of this reflex is a movement away from the stimulus. Repeated application of a relatively weak stimulus leads to habituation. Reactivation of the reflex occurs following a strong stimulus. Thus, processes of learning and conditioning may be studied on this model.

3) Lower limb reflexes. A painful stimulus to the ball of the big toe elicits reflex contractions

of the extensor hallucis longus and brevis with dorsiflexion of the toe withdrawing from the stimulus. A stimulus to the hollow of the foot produces on the contrary plantar flexion of the toes. A stimulus to the heel also produces a plantar flexion but it is associated with an extended ankle. The famous Babinski reflex characteristic of the pyramidal tract lesion appears as an extension of all these receptive fields.

4) A linguo-maxilar reflex is an interesting

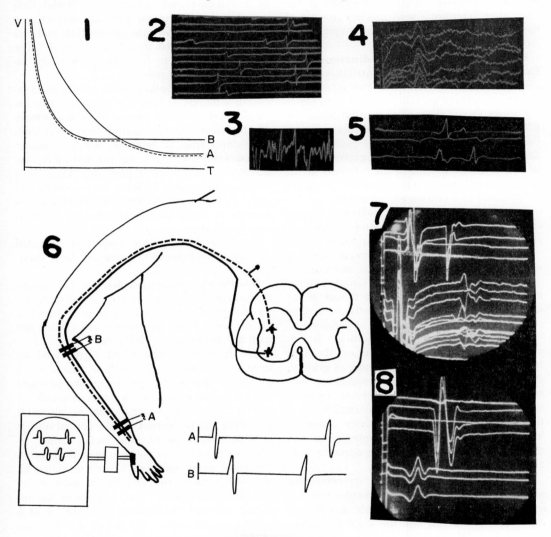

FIG. 2. (1) Strength duration curves. A: Abnormal muscle fibers; B: normal muscle fibers; dotted line: experimentally obtained complex curve in a muscle with a partial denervation. (2) Fibrillation potentials (time scale: 25 msec). (3) Interference pattern (time scale: 100 msec). (4) Median nerve potentials recorded through the skin (time scale: 5 msec). (5) Motor unit potentials (time scale: 25 msec). (6) Principle for determining the motor and sensory conduction times. A and B: stimulating electrodes; recording from a muscle of the hand. The insert shows the direct and reflex potentials. (7) Actual determination of the motor and sensory conduction velocities. The upper group of tracings is obtained by stimulating the distant nerve point; the lower set of tracings is obtained by stimulating the proximal nerve points. (time scale: 50 msec). (8) Determination of the motor conduction velocity in the motor fibers. Upper tracings: stimulation of the distant nerve points; lower tracings: stimulation of the proximal nerve points. (time scale: 25 msec). Horizontal line at the bottom of the figure indicates the time scale for above recordings.

one. When a subject voluntarily contracts his jaws, the temporal muscles and the masseter show appropriate activity. Following a brief stimulus applied unilaterally to the tongue, the voluntary activity is suspended for 50 msec or more bilaterally. In cases of lesions of the brain stem interfering with midline crossing of the fibers involved in this bilateral spread, the reflex becomes unilateral.

Posture, Voluntary Coordination, and Exercises. EMG obviously contributes to the identification of the muscles participating in posture, voluntary movements, and exercises.

Posture. One of the major contributions of the EMG study of posture is the limited active participation of the muscles in erect posture. Only muscles of the calves (soleus and gastrocnemius) as well as some segments of the extensors of the spine (erector spinae) participate in the active maintenance of a relaxed erect posture.

Gaits. Normal locomotion involves a considerably more extensive participation of the muscles. However, here again the organism makes use of the passive forces of gravity, inertia, and elasticity in the best possible way. Most muscle activity is observed to slow down initiated movements or to stop them. Thus, the flexors of the knee (hamstrings) are used mostly to accomplish this decelerating function: dorsiflexion of the ankle (for example tibialis anticus) is also used preponderantly for preventing the foot from "dropping" under the influence of gravity, etc. Muscles of the calf (gastrocnemius) and extensor of the knee (quardiceps) are the most constantly used muscles during normal locomotion. They alternate in their activity in such a way that when one of them contracts on one side, the other contracts on the opposite side, and vice versa.

Voluntary movements. The overwhelming complexity of voluntary movements requires coordinating mechanisms of muscle innervation which are bewildering for the mind to understand. Some of the reasons for this bewilderment are the necessity for the central nervous system to readjust its innervation pattern on an instant order when the movement aimed to reach a certain point in space with a segment of an extremity is made under variable conditions of speed and load, involving a complete and sudden change in the inertia involved in these movements.

A recent contribution to EMG is the analysis of "tonic" and "phasic" innervation of the voluntary muscles. It appears from this analysis that there are motor units specialized in high-frequency discharge of short duration, followed by a well-developed "silent period" (inhibition, see above). Other motor units are subject to a more sustained slow-rate innervation and are only rarely observed in a "silent period." The latter are proved to be those particularly involved in a stretch reflex.

Exercises. A voluntary static (tonic) contraction of a muscle without any resistance (for example, making a big biceps) does not involve all the motor units no matter how strenuously the subject tries. If, however, the same muscle is activated voluntarily against resistance, the number of active units increases. There is a continuous interplay between the voluntary and reflex mechanisms; the latter sensitize the motoneurons and make them more receptive to voluntary innervation.

These mechanisms are responsible for the efficacy of progressive-resistive and brief maximal isometric exercises.

Needle electromyography. Electrodiagnostic procedures involving electric stimulation and recording surface electrodes have been discussed above. Most EMG procedures are carried out with the use of needle electrodes.

The basis for needle EMG is provided by three assumptions which have been demonstrated to a large degree, at least within the practical clinical requirements. a) A normal muscle at rest is "silent." In other words, no electrical potentials can be derived from a normal muscle at rest, despite its obvious "tonic" state. b) When activated either voluntarily or electrically, the whole motor unit (see above) including all the muscle fibers supplied by an axon is involved simultaneously. The duration of the resulting recorded "motor unit potential" is of 5 to 12 msec. However, this is not the duration of individual motor fiber potentials (which may be of 1 to 2 msec). The relatively long duration of the motor unit potential is a result of statistical superimposition of the fiber potentials, travelling along the individual muscle fibers with a speed of about four meters a second. The form of the "motor unit potentials" will be affected by the geometry of the relationship between the tip of the electrode and the dispersed motor "unit." In fact, the motor unit potential may be monophasic, biphasic, or triphasic; bear a spike at the tip of one of its waves, etc. Its voltage will also vary as a function of the vicinity of most of the travelling individual potentials between 75 and 2000 microvolts.

During voluntary contractions, motor unit potentials of different form and voltages will be recorded. When the patient is asked to contract his muscle as little as possible, a single unit will be recorded, with a frequency of 10 per second. This frequency will be increased to 20 to 50 per second as the effort is increased. However, in the same process other motor units will be involved as the muscle fibers belonging to different motor units interlace in the muscle fascicles. The result will be a considerable interference between the individual motor unit potentials. The latter will no longer be recognizable in the confusing mesh of the "interference pattern."

A repeat electrical stimulation of the nerve at a frequency of 3 c/sec elicits potentials of the same amplitude despite a prolonged stimulation. If a brief period of tetanization is interposed, a post-tetanic facilitation may be observed, but no depression (characteristic of myasthenia gravis). Recent studies have shown that some muscle fibers respond only to paired stimuli.

References

1. BUCHTHAL, FRITZ, "An Introduction to Electromyography," Copenhagen, Scandinavian University Books, Gyldendalske Boghandel, Nordisk Forlag, 1957.
2. LIBERSON, W. T., Editor, *Bulletin*, American Asso. of Electromyography and Electrodiagnosis, Hines, Illinois, Vols. 7–10, 1960–1963.
3. ROSSELLE, N., Editor, "Electromyography," Belgium, Univ. of Louvain, 1962, 1963.
4. LIBERSON, W. T., "Monosynaptic Reflexes and their Clinical Significance," *Electroenceph. clin. Neurophysiol.*, Suppl. 22, pp. 79–89, 1962.
5. LIBERSON, W. T., "Report on the Standardization of Reporting and Terminology in Electromyography," *Electroenceph. clin. Neurophysiol.*, Suppl. 22, pp. 167–172, 1962.
6. LICHT, SIDNEY, "Electrodiagnosis and Electromyography," New Haven, Connecticut, Elizabeth Licht, publisher, 1961.
7. MARINACCI, A. A., "Clinical Electromyography," Los Angeles, San Lucas Press, 1955

W. T. LIBERSON

Cross-references: *Electrocardiology; Electroencephalography; Electrophysiology; Membrane Potentials.*

ELECTRODIAGNOSIS—ABNORMAL EMG

One of the most important applications of electromyography is the diagnosis of abnormal conditions, including denervation, regeneration, primary muscular diseases, mytonias, and diseases of the end plate.

Denervation

Nerve stimulation. The earliest sign of total denervation is an impossibility to elicit muscle contractions when the stimulating current is applied above the nerve injury. In the case of a partial denervation, the maximum evoked muscle contraction will be weaker in proportion to the degree of the lesion.

Muscle excitability at motor point. Later, other signs will appear with the total picture of denervation approximately three weeks after the day of injury: the motor point disappears, the gradient between the excitability at the motor point and the rest of the muscle being either suppressed or reversed.

Response to direct current. At the beginning a denervated muscle becomes hyperexcitable to galvanic (d-c) current. It is only after a relatively long period of time (a year or more) that a denervated muscle may become hypoexcitable. Polar formula may be modified so that the muscle may become more excitable at the make of the anodal stimulus than at the make of the cathodal stimulation.

Galvanic tetanus ratio. The muscle may contract continuously during the entire period of stimulation (galvanic tonus or tetanus). This may be seen even with a rheobasic current, at least for part of the muscle, or more often, for a current of less than twice the rheobase. Thus, the galvanic tetanus ratio, (Threshold for Galvanotonus/Rheobase), is low. It is equal to three or more in normal muscles.

Increase of chronaxies. The muscle does not respond to brief stimuli; therefore, its chronaxy increases. In a slightly involved muscle, it is of 1 to 5 msec. In a totally denervated muscle, the chronaxy may be more than 100 times as high as normally. In a partially denervated muscle, the chronaxy also serves as an indicator of the pathological process.

Responsiveness to progressive current. Denervated muscle fibers may be selectively stimulated by currents with progressive onset as they respond to the constant current whatever the characteristic of its establishment.

Characteristics of muscle contractions. The contraction becomes slow, particularly the decontraction. In advanced cases, the contraction is so slow that it appears vermicular.

Fibrillations. In the case of total reaction of degeneration, nerve endings disappear and the axon is no longer able to integrate the activity of the scores of individual muscle fibers which previously belonged to the same motor unit (see above). Moreover, denervated muscle fibers become over-sensitive to all sorts of mechanical, and biochemical stimuli. The result of this over-sensitivity is an apparent spontaneous activity of the denervated muscle fibers at rest. Because of the lack of synchronization of the activities of individual fibers without the unifying influence of the missing nerve impulse, the duration of the recorded potentials will be of the order of 1 msec. Occasionally, however, some synchronization will occur either by chance or by mutual influence of the electric fields around the activated muscle fibers. In this case, the duration of summated potentials will be of the order of 2 to 3 or even 4 msec.

This brief electrical activity of relatively low amplitude (limited or absent summation) is called *fibrillation*. In the case of a partial denervation, fibrillation may occur, but to a lesser degree. On the other hand, the motor unit potential, or the potential evoked by electric stimulation may show a complex configuration which includes "evoked fibrillations." This may be due to a differential involvement of different terminal nerve endings or proximal nerve fibers.

Positive sharp waves. In addition to fibrillations, a denervated muscle may generate peculiar waves which have been called "positive sharp waves." These are sharp waves with a sudden onset and a progressive decay followed by a slow phase of opposite polarity. The duration of this wave may be from 10 to 50 msec. They are attributed to injury phenomena.

High-frequency responses. In a denervated muscle bursts of high frequency potentials were also reported. The genesis of these potentials is poorly understood.

Poor interference pattern. If a patient with advanced partial denervation is asked to elicit a maximal voluntary contraction, relatively high-amplitude individual nerve motor unit potentials will be recorded, instead of complex patterns found under the same conditions in a normal individual (interference pattern).

Slowing of conduction velocities. In cases of a partial reaction of degeneration, particularly when the myeline sheath is involved in the early pathological process, conduction velocity may be modified without a complete interruption of the nerve conduction. Values below 35 msec may be observed (and as low as 5–15 m/sec) particularly in certain disease entities, such as Marie Tooth disease or Guillan-Barré syndrome. In the diseases of the lower motor neuron located to the anterior horn, conduction velocities are much less affected, if at all. In certain polyneuropathies, such as alcoholic and diabetic ones, conduction velocities may be also slowed down. In some cases, sensory fibers are involved before the motor ones. In such cases nerve potentials may not be recorded from the median or ulnar nerves. The same findings may be observed in cases of compression of the median nerve in the carpal tunnel. Motor conduction velocity in these cases are characteristically increased.

Complex evoked potentials. As mentioned before, potentials evoked by electric pulses applied to the nerve trunk may become complex because of repetitive discharges, and differentially modify conduction velocity in the nerve and muscle fibers. If the potentials are recorded under such conditions by surface electrodes, their duration is abnormally increased.

Fasciculations. Where there is anterior horn involvement, spontaneous contractions of limited bundles of muscle fibers may be observed. They occur usually with a lack of regularity. Contrary to fibrillations, these fasciculations are visible on inspection and are able to move the overlying skin. Although fasciculations occur most frequently in patients with involvement of the anterior horn cell, it is not always so. In pathological cases the fibrillations are associated with fasciculations.

It should be repeated that electrodiagnostic signs of denervation appear a certain length of time after the injury, usually three weeks insofar as fibrillations are concerned.

Regeneration

Regeneration is characterized by a regression of the signs of denervation. EMG is the sole method which allows the detection of the early regeneration. The latter is expected to be 1 mm of the nerve per day.

These are some of the signs of regeneration.

Effects on rheobase and galvanic tetanus ratio. Rheobase and the galvanic tetanus ratio (see above) may suddenly rise at the time of regeneration.

Potentials of complex configuration. This type of potential may be recorded in the regenerated muscle. These seem to be due to the sprouting of nerve fibers and a reconstruction of a large, widely distributed motor unit. At first these potentials are of low amplitude (nascent potentials). Later, these potentials increase considerably (giant potentials).

Primary Muscle Disease

Muscle dystrophies. *Electrodiagnosis by stimulation.* The electrical excitability of muscle fibers decreases, but the chronaxy is rarely elevated above 2 msec. The muscle contraction is not abnormally slow. The conduction velocity remains normal.

Electrodiagnosis by recording. In muscular dystrophies, the motor unit is affected but not necessarily destroyed in its entirety. Therefore, a part of the muscle fibers belonging to a motor unit continues to respond to the axonal activation. The partial destruction of the motor unit will result in lower amplitude motor unit potential, with a complex configuration of very brief duration. The interference pattern is still observed despite the considerably decreased muscle strength, but it is made of brief and complex low amplitude potentials. Because muscle fibers are degenerated before the involvement of the nerve fibers, no fibrillations may be observed usually. However, in some cases, they occur, presumably, because of an intramuscular strangulation of nerve endings resulting from the connective tissue proliferation.

Evoked nerve potentials. Evoked potentials following stimulation of the nerve trunk, fingers, and toes are recorded with normal amplitudes.

Muscle contractions. They decrease in amplitude, but no obvious slowing is observed usually.

Reflexes. These are not modified as long as muscles respond to nerve stimulation.

Myositis. A mixed picture may be observed. Fibrillations occur more frequently than in muscular dystrophies and muscle contractions may become sluggish.

Myotonias

Electrical stimulation. Normally, the galvanic current elicits contractions at the make (cathode) and at the break (anode). In a case of a denervated muscle, the muscle contracts, at least partially, during the entire duration of the stimulation. A myotonic muscle shows a contraction beyond the time of current flow; it persists for a certain time after the break of the current. Correspondingly, a voluntary contraction persists even though the patient tries to relax the muscle.

EMG. The muscle exhibits characteristic discharges with usually brief potentials of progressively increasing and decreasing intervals and amplitudes. This produces, through a loud speaker, the characteristic sound of a "dive bomber"—a sad reminder that EMG rapidly developed during World War II.

Myotonic reaction is observed in both myotonia congenita (Thomsen's disease) and myotonia dystrophica (Steinert's disease). In the latter case, other signs of muscle dystrophy may be observed (see above).

Myotonic or pseudomyotonic reactions are also observed in peripheral neuropathies, myositis, etc.

Diseases of the End Plate

Myasthenia Gravis. Myasthenia gravis is characterized by a decrease in amplitude of muscle contractions and motor unit potentials after voluntary contraction or tetanization.

Stimulation. Jolly reaction constitutes a classical test, showing a rapid and progressive decrease of muscle contraction with a tetanizing current.

EMG. The EMG test may be conducted in several ways. A test based on the phenomena of "post-tetanic exhaustion" characteristic of myasthenia gravis may be applied. In this test, the nerve is stimulated with a frequency of 3/ sec; then the tetanizing current of 30/sec is applied for 10 sec followed again by 3/sec stimuli. At first the amplitude of muscle potentials may increase due to an initial transitory post-tetanic facilitation. The latter is followed by a decrease of muscle potentials which may last for several minutes.

W. T. LIBERSON

ELECTRODIALYSIS

Electrodialysis is an electrochemical process in which composition and concentration changes are effected on solutions containing electrolytes as a result of electrical transfer of ions through membranes. Whereas in dialysis the driving force is a concentration gradient, in electrodialysis it is an imposed electromotive force (d-c), and ion transport is usually effected against a concentration gradient at the expenditure of electrical energy. Electrodialysis is analogous to ion exchange in that both processes involve the transfer of ions between a solution phase and a resin phase. The membranes used in electrodialysis and the beads used in ion exchange are similar in chemical structure. However, the driving force in ion exchange is the chemical potential. The energy consumed in ion exchange is energy stored in the chemicals, whereas in electrodialysis it is electrical energy.

Electrodialysis was confined to the laboratory from the turn of the century until the early 1950's. Membranes had been used in two- or three-compartment electrodialysis cells until 1940, when Meyer and Strauss suggested multicompartment cells with repeating units between two electrodes.[1] Practical permselective membranes which could be used in multicompartment cells were not available until 1950 when synthetic cation and anion permeable membranes of low electrical resistance were developed.[2,3] The history of electrodialysis in its early stages has been reviewed by Tuwiner[4] and Wilson.[5]

In the last decade, electrodialysis has developed into a commercial process for desalting of saline waters to produce potable waters, for de-ashing of whey to be used in infant formulas, and for the concentration of sea water to produce salt. Other applications are in the laboratory and pilot plant stages. Among these are: de-ashing of sugars, corn syrup, gelatin, and other food products; the recovery of valuable chemicals from waste streams in the paper and steel industries; the decontamination of milk and water contaminated by radioactive fallout; the removal of carbon dioxide from the atmosphere of submarines and spacecraft; and applications to electrochemical cells. (See **Electrodialysis Applications** and **Demineralization by Electrodialysis**.)

Electrodialysis membranes and technology are also being applied to fuel cells and batteries.

Membrane Properties

The membranes used in commercial electrodialysis are made of thin sheets of synthetic ion exchange resin. Cation permeable membranes permit the passage of cations selectively and anion permeable membranes permit the passage of anions selectively. In dilute solutions of electrolytes the transport number approaches unity for cations and anions in cation and anion permeable membranes, respectively. The permselectivity decreases as the concentration of the electrolyte increases and dissolved electroyte is less strongly excluded from the resin phase. If t_+^c is the cation transport number in cation permeable membranes and t_+^s is the cation transport number in the solution in equilibrium with the membrane, the permselectivity, P, of the membrane is defined[6] as:

$$P = \frac{t_+^c - t_+^s}{1 - t_+^s} \qquad (1)$$

The electrical conductivity is another important property of membranes for electrodialysis. In dilute solution the conductivity of the membrane is due to the mobility of the counterion associated with the fixed ion exchange groups. As the external concentration increases, the conductivity of the membrane increases because of the increase in the concentration of electrolyte in the resin. The increase in conductivity with concentration is related to the decrease in permselectivity. Both effects are caused by Donnan sorption of electrolyte by the resin phase.

Rosenberg, et al,[7] have reported on several properties, including the transport number and electrical conductivity of a commercial cation membrane, Ionics Nepton CR61, in KCl, BaCl$_2$, LaCl$_3$, and ThCl$_4$ up to a concentration of 1 eq/l. Some of these data are given in Fig. 1. In KCl the K$^+$ transport number varies from 1.0 to 0.6 and the specific conductivity varies from 10 to 30 mmho/cm (or 8 to 2.7 ohm-sq cm for a membrane 0.8 mm thick) as the external concentration increases from 0 to 1N. The transport number and the conductivity decrease with increasing valence of the counterion.

Of less importance in most water desalting applications, but often of critical importance in industrial applications is the electroosmotic water transport which generally takes place in the direction of motion of the counterion. Water transport is usually under 0.5 liter/Faraday. Data from Rosenberg, et al, on water transport are also given in Fig. 1. It decreases with increasing external concentration and with increasing valence of the counterion. It is generally less for anion membranes than for cation membranes. The water transport per Faraday for a given salt solution is proportional to the voltage gradient across the membrane; therefore, it decreases in inverse proportion to the membrane conductivity when the external concentration increases.

Membranes also exhibit some selectivity for ions of like charge. For cation membranes the order of selectivity for transfer of alkali metal ions is: Cs, Rb, K, NH_4, Na, and Li; and for alkaline earth ions in general it is: Sr, Ba, and Ca. Hydrogen ions and hydroxyl ions are transferred at a faster rate than other ions.

Other desirable properties of synthetic membranes are: low permeability to the passage of water under a hydrostatic pressure gradient and low permeability to the diffusion of both electrolytes and nonelectrolytes under a concentration gradient. To be practical, membranes must have good physical and chemical stability.

More detailed discussion of the physical chemistry of membranes and of preparation methods may be found in the books by Helfferich,[8] Nachod and Schubert,[9] Tuwiner,[4] and Wilson.[5]

The Electrodialysis Process

In multicell electrodialysis stacks, a large number of repeating cells (cell units) are placed between two electrodes. The electrode voltages become an insignificant fraction of the total voltage. Thus, except for electrolytic cells with membranes, the electrode voltage is not a significant factor in the calculations of energy consumption, total voltage, and production capacity. Depending on the particular application, a cell unit may consist of two to four membranes and two to four associated compartments. The common water desalting cell unit consists of a cation membrane, an anion membrane, and a diluting and a concentrating compartment. (See Fig. 2.) It is usually called a "cell pair." The voltage, V, of a membrane "stack" is the total of the voltages of all the cell units, n, in the stack, nV_p, and the water production capacity, F_d, is proportional to the number of cell units in the stack.

The common desalting configuration will be used to illustrate the calculation of the important parameters governing the performance of the cell.

The coulomb or current efficiency, Γ, is defined as the net equivalents transferred per Faraday of current passed. It depends on the transport numbers of the membranes.

$$\Gamma = t_+{}^c - (1 - t_-{}^a) \tag{2}$$

$$\Gamma = t_+{}^c - t_+{}^a \tag{2a}$$

The relationship between the current and the demineralization capacity for an electrodialysis stack is:[10]

$$F_d C_{di} f = \frac{i A_p \Gamma n}{1000\mathbf{F}} = \frac{I \Gamma n}{\mathbf{F}} \text{ g-eq/sec} \tag{3}$$

where

F_d = flow rate, liters/sec
A_p = area per cell pair, sq cm
i = current density, ma/sq cm
I = current, amp
$\mathbf{F}$ = Faraday's constant, 96,500 coulomb/g-eq
n = number of cell units
f = fraction of electrolyte transferred
C_{di} = initial electrolyte concentration, g-eq/l
Γ = current efficiency

For a batch demineralization the left-hand side of Eq. (3) becomes $-V_d C_{di}\left(\dfrac{df}{d\theta}\right)$ where $\dfrac{df}{d\theta}$ is the fraction of electrolyte transferred per unit time, based on the initial batch.

The expression for the minimum energy, W_m, required per unit volume of dilute effluent is given by Wilson[5] and by Spiegler.[11]

$$W_m = 2RT(C_{di} - C_{do})\left[\frac{\ln\gamma}{1 - \gamma} - \frac{\ln\beta}{1 - \beta}\right] \tag{4}$$

where

γ = $\dfrac{C_{di}}{C_{do}}$;

β = $\dfrac{C_{di}}{C_{co}}$;

C_{do} = final electrolyte concentration, diluted solution; and

C_{co} = final electrolyte concentration, brine.

The major assumptions made in the derivation of Eq. (4) are the absence of concentration polarization, electroosmosis, and diffusion of electrolyte through the membranes, and that the ratio of dilute to brine activity coefficients remains constant. Normally major energy losses result from the ohmic resistance of the solutions and the membranes, from transport numbers less than unity in the membranes, and from diffusion of electrolyte from the brine to the dilute solu-

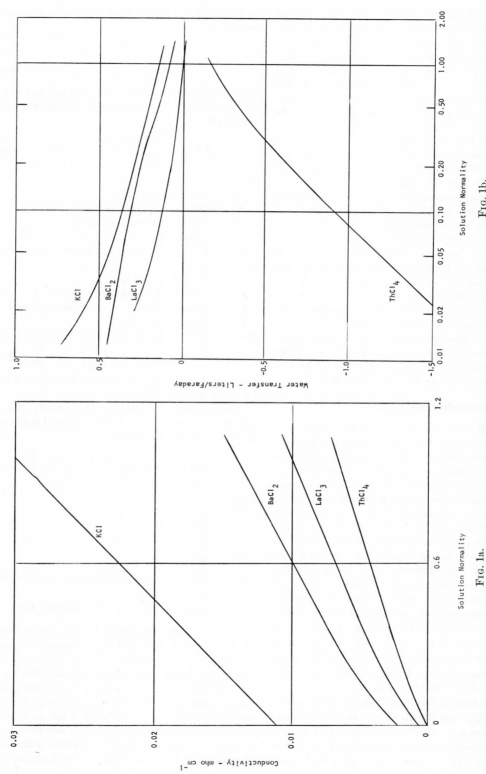

FIG. 1b.

FIG. 1a.

FIG. 1. Characteristics of a commercial cation exchange membrane (Ionics Nepton™ CR61) vs solution normality for various metallic chlorides: 1a, conductivity; 1b, water transfer; 1c, transport number.

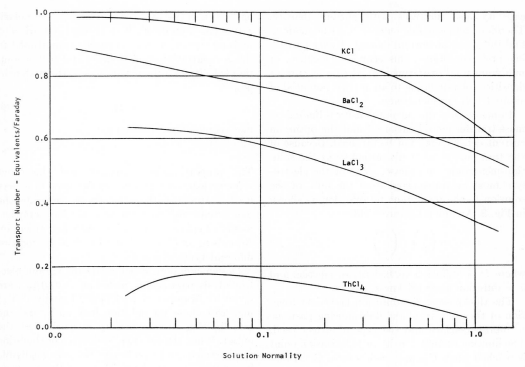

FIG. 1c.

tion. The electrode overpotential and concentration polarization potential in multicell stacks are not significant.

The apparent electrical resistance of a membrane stack can be expressed as the sum of the ohmic and polarization terms. The electrode overpotential voltage can be added to the voltage calculated from the apparent stack resistance, r_s.

$$r_s = (r_d + r_c + r_m + r_p)n \qquad (5)$$

where r_d, r_c = electrical resistance of the dilute and brine compartments, respectively, in a cell unit; r_m = electrical resistance of the membranes in a cell unit; and r_p = electrical resistance as a result of polarization in a cell unit.

The energy consumption per unit of solution demineralized can be calculated according to Mason and Kirkham:[10]

$$E_1 = \frac{0.00105 \, I^2 \, r_s}{F_d} = \frac{0.00105 \, i^2 \, A_p^2 \, r_s}{10^6 \, F_d} \qquad (6)$$

where E_1 is in kilowatt hours per 1000 gallons of solution treated. Combining Eqs. (3) and (6):

$$E_1 = \frac{0.00105 \, i \, A_p \, r_s \, C_{di} \, f\mathbf{F}}{1000 \, \Gamma n} \qquad (7)$$

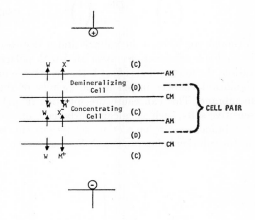

CM = CATION PERMEABLE MEMBRANE
AM = ANION PERMEABLE MEMBRANE
M⁺ = CATION
X⁻ = ANION
W = WATER, ELECTRO-OSMOTIC

FIG. 2. Desalting stack configuration.

The energy consumption per unit of water desalted, or per unit of electrolyte removed, is proportional to the current density. The production capacity also increases with current density. Therefore, an economic balance must be made to find the optimum current density. Under prevailing price conditions, this economic balance, or minimum total operating cost, occurs at current densities corresponding to an applied potential of about 1 volt per membrane.

In many cases the current density is limited by mass-transfer considerations,[12] and the optimum current density may not be attained. Because of the transport number discontinuity at the solution-membrane interphase, some of the electrolyte must be transported from the bulk of the solution to the membrane by diffusion as shown in Fig. 3. An anion balance yields:

$$(t^a - t^s)\left(\frac{i}{\mathbf{F}}\right) = \left(\frac{D}{\delta}\right)(C_d - C_{id}) \qquad (8)$$

where D = diffusion coefficient, sq cm/sec, and δ = diffusion layer thickness, cm.

The thickness of the diffusion layer is a function of the velocity of the fluid flowing past the membrane surface and the type of spacer used. The limiting current density or polarization point is reached when C_{id} approaches zero. Rearranging Eq. (8):

$$\left(\frac{i}{C_d}\right) = \frac{(D\mathbf{F})}{(t^a - t^s)}\left(\frac{1}{\delta}\right) \qquad (8a)$$

Although an increase in voltage and a decrease in coulomb efficiency are associated with polarization, the most serious effect is the occurrence of significant changes in pH in the vicinity of the membrane. This can cause precipitation of pH-sensitive salts, such as calcium carbonate, on the membranes or can have other deleterious effects on the solution being processed. Various methods

have been devised for the measurement of polarization based on its effect on voltage and pH. The limiting current density is nearly proportional to the concentration of electrolyte and to the solution velocity past the membranes to the six-tenths power.

$$i_{lim} = kC_d v^{0.6} \qquad (9)$$

more commonly expressed as:

$$(i/C_d)_{lim} = kv^{0.6} \qquad (9a)$$

The proportionality constant and the exact velocity exponent depend on the type of spacer used, tortuous path or screen, to separate the membranes and to form the solution compartments. Typical polarization data are given by Rosenberg and Tirrell[12] and by Wilson[13] for two different types of spacer.

Design equations which relate the various electrodialysis parameters, including $(i/C_d)_{lim}$, are given by Mason and Kirkham.[10] Usually (i/C_d) increases along the solution flow path, and the safe limiting current density is reached at the outlet. When the electrical resistance of the brine compartment and membranes becomes negligible in comparison with the resistance of the desalting compartment, (i/C_d) approaches a constant along the flow path. In this case:

$$\frac{\Gamma A_p (i/C_d)_{avg}}{F_d \mathbf{F}} = {}^r 1{,}000 \ln \frac{1}{1 - f} \qquad (10)$$

In most water desalting cases, this equation would not be more than 10 to 15 per cent in error and, thus, is convenient for design approximations.

References

1. MEYER, K. H., AND STRAUSS, W., *Helv. chim. acta*, **23**, 795 (1940).
2. JUDA, W., AND McRAE, W. A., *J. Amer. Chem. Soc.*, **72**, 1044 (1950).
3. KRESSMAN, T. R. E., *Nature, Lond.*, **165**, 568 (1950).
4. TUWINER, SIDNEY B., "Diffusion and Membrane Technology," ACS Monograph No. 156, p. 237, New York, Reinhold Publishing Corp., 1962.
5. WILSON, J. R., "Demineralisation by Electrodialysis," London, Butterworths Scientific Publications, 1960.
6. WINGER, A. G., BODAMER, G. W., AND KUNIN, R., *J. Electrochem. Soc.*, **100**, 178 (1953).
7. ROSENBERG, N. W., GEORGE, J. H. D., AND POTTER, W. D., *J. Electrochem. Soc.*, **104**, 111 (1957).
8. HELFFERICH, F., "Ion Exchange," Chapters 7 and 8, New York, McGraw-Hill Book Company, Inc., 1962.

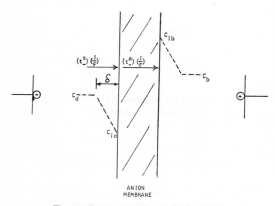

FIG. 3. Concentration polarization.

9. NACHOD, F. C., AND SCHUBERT, J., (Eds.) "Ion Exchange Technology," Chapter 6 by Spiegler, K. S., New York, Academic Press Inc., 1956.
10. MASON, E. A., AND KIRKHAM, T. A., "Design of Electrodialysis Equipment," *CEP Symposium Series No. 24*, **55**, 173–189 (1959).
11. SPIEGLER, K. S., *Trans. Faraday Soc.*, **54**, 1408 (1958).
12. ROSENBERG, N. W., AND TIRRELL, C. E., "Limiting Currents in Membrane Cells," *Ind. Eng. Chem.*, **49**, 780 (April, 1957).
13. WILSON, J. R., "Depolarisation in Electrodialytic Demineralisation," *Trans. Inst. Chem. Engrs.*, **41**, No. 1 (1963).

EDGARDO J. PARSI

Cross-references: *Demineralization by Electrodialysis; Electrodialysis Applications; Ion Exchange Resins; Ion Exchange Membranes; Ion Transport across Charged Membranes; Membranes, Electrolytic; Membrane Equilibrium; Membrane Potentials.*

ELECTRODIALYSIS APPLICATIONS

According to the function performed, electrodialysis applications can be classified in general groups. Different cell configurations or membrane arrangements are used for different functions, but sometimes the same cell configuration may perform different functions. The various functions performed are:

(1) Dilution or concentration of electrolytes (see Fig. 1);

(2) Separation of electrolytes and nonelectrodialyzable solutes or suspensions (see Fig. 1);

(3) Concentration of nonelectrodialyzable solutes or suspensions by electroosmosis (see Fig. 1);

(4) Displacement of ions to modify the cationic or anionic composition (see Fig. 2A);

(5) Metathesis or chemical conversion without electrode reactions (see Fig. 2B);

(6) Ionic fractionation (see Fig. 3); and

(7) Chemical conversions with electrode reactions (electrochemical cells with membranes) (see Fig. 4).

The most widely used cell configuration is shown in Fig. 1. It can be used to desalt water; to concentrate salt, such as in the concentration of sea water for the recovery of salt; to decontaminate water contaminated with radionuclides; and to concentrate nonelectrolytes or nonelectrodialyzables by electroosmotic removal of water.[1]

Other applications include the separation of acids, bases, and salts from nonelectrolytes, weakly ionized electrolytes, or suspended solids in solution, for example, whey, cane sugar solutions, dextrose solutions, gelatin and glycerin solutions.[2, 3] The permeability of the membranes to the nonelectrolytes is important. Unless the membrane is relatively impermeable to the nonelectrolyte, it will be transferred through the membrane by diffusion and along with the water transferred electrically. For example, in the deashing of sucrose solutions some sucrose is lost, but not enough to render the process unattractive.

The cell configurations shown in Fig. 2A can be used to modify the cationic or the anionic composition of solutions. The anion system is analogous to the cation system, and anion membranes are used in place of cation membranes. These cell configurations have been used to decontaminate milk contaminated with radionuclides. The contaminants can be purged out of the milk electrically without changing the salt composition of the milk. Referring to Fig. 2A, the milk is flowed through Compartment 2, a make-up salt solution containing the chlorides of the cations normally found in milk is flowed through Compartment 1, and the cationic con-

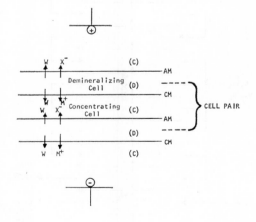

CM = CATION PERMEABLE MEMBRANE
AM = ANION PERMEABLE MEMBRANE
M⁺ = CATION
X⁻ = ANION
W = WATER, ELECTRO-OSMOTIC

FIG. 1. Desalting stack configuration.

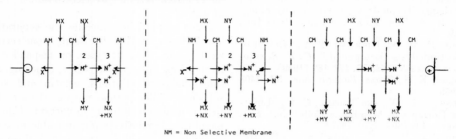

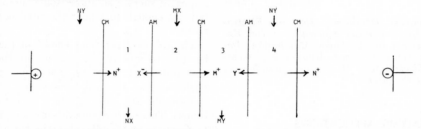

FIG. 2. Electrodialysis cell configurations for (A) displacement of ions, and (B) metathesis or chemical conversion.

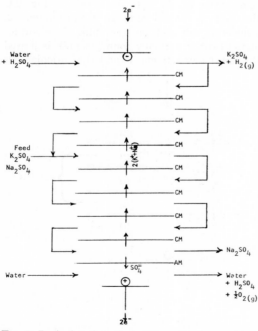

FIG. 3. Ionic fractionation still—cation separation.

taminants are flushed out from Compartment 3 as chlorides in solution admixed with chlorides of other cations displaced from the milk. The equation for displacement of a cation, N^+, by a cation or cations, M^+, when N^+ is a small fraction of the total cations is:

$$f = 1 - \exp\left(\frac{\alpha \Gamma I}{C F \mathbf{F}}\right) \qquad (1)$$

where

C = total concentration in Compartment 2 in gram equivalents per liter

f = fraction of N^+ displaced in one passage through Compartment 2

F = flow rate in *each* Compartment 2 in liters per second

$\mathbf{F}$ = Faraday's Constant, approximately 96,500 ampere-seconds per gram equivalent

I = current through *each* Compartment 2 in amperes

α = selectivity of membrane for N^+ over other cations in Compartment 2

Γ = membrane coulomb efficiency defined as the net equivalents of *cations* transferred per Faraday of current passed.

It is possible to use a nonselective membrane instead of the anion membrane in the cation system or even to eliminate this membrane, but this allows leakage of the ion displaced back into Compartment 2 unless the ion is complexed, precipitated, or otherwise removed from solu-

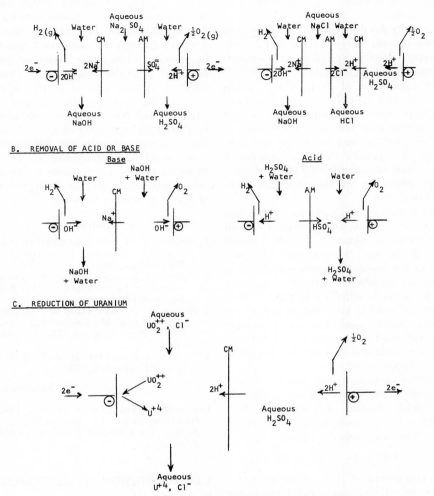

FIG. 4. Electrochemical cells using electrodialysis.

tion in Compartment 3. An application of displacement could be softening of water where sodium replaces the calcium and magnesium. The most efficient application of this system is where the ion, M+, entering the solution, is complexed, or otherwise removed from solution as an ion, so that it cannot escape with the displaced ion, N+. This is the case when a precipitate or insoluble gas is formed, when a weak acid or a weak base is formed, or when a base is neutralized by hydrogen ions or an acid by hydroxyl ions in the anion displacement system. An example of an application where a precipitate is formed is in the preparation of photographic emulsions.[3] Silver bromide is formed by displacement of ammonium ions from an ammonium bromide solution by silver ions from a silver nitrate solution.

The cell configuration shown in Fig. 2B can be used to effect a "double decomposition:"

$$N^+Y^- + M^+X^- \rightarrow M^+Y^- + N^+X^-$$

It is not necessary that phase changes or complexing of any of the ions take place, although this type of cell has been used in the preparation of photographic emulsions, where AgBr is formed from NH$_4$Br and AgNO$_3$.[3] For example, caustic soda can be made from slaked lime and salt[3] in this cell.

Ions of like change, such as alkali metal cations, can be separated by using the "ionic fractionation still" shown in Fig. 3.[4] It is analogous to a vapor fractionating tower and the mathematical approach is similar, with membranes as theoretical plates.

The selectivity for different ions of like charge is a function of ionic species, nature of the membrane, current density, agitation, and solution concentration and composition.

Another application of electrodialysis membranes is in electrolytic cells. The membrane can serve various functions: separation of the products of electrode reaction; prevention of side reactions or the undoing of an electrode reaction at the opposite electrode; control of pH, composition, or concentration of the electrolytes; and protection of the electrodes from electrochemical attack.

The preparation of acid and base from a salt is illustrated in Fig. 4A. In the case of sodium chloride a cation membrane is used to prevent oxidation of the acid to chlorine. The acid generated at the anode is transferred efficiently by the cation membrane with no significant effect on the aqueous sulfuric acid anolyte. This anolyte arrangement is also used to isolate the anode when lead is used. For the generation of caustic and chlorine the salt can be fed into the anode compartment of a two-compartment cell with a cation membrane.

The removal of acid or base can be effected in the two-compartment cells shown in Fig. 4B. The electrolytic reduction of uranium has been carried out in the two-compartment cell shown in Fig. 4C. The main cathodic reaction is:

$$UO_2^{++} + 4H^+ + 2e^- \rightarrow U^{+4} + 2H_2O$$

Hydrogen ions generated at the anode are transferred into the catholyte cell through the cation membrane. Other similar cells have been proposed for the recovery of iron and acid from spent pickle liquor.[2] Various other possible cell arrangements and applications are given by Wilson.[1] In recent years there have been a number of applications of membranes to fuel cells and batteries.

In addition to the applications discussed above, some ingenious and less conventional applications of electrodialysis have been proposed which take advantage of concentration polarization (q.v.). In one case the acid and base are generated by using "bipolar" membranes and in another, gravitational effects are utilized to separate the concentrated and diluted films which form at the membrane-solution interphase.[1]

Some applications of permselective membranes to water desalting which are related to electrodialysis are "reverse osmosis" and the "osmionic" process. In "reverse osmosis" water is driven through the membranes under hydraulic pressure, while in the "osmionic" process the electrical potential generated by solutions of different activity is used as the driving force for desalting in a specially arranged multicompartment cell. In this process a "brine" must be flowed through some of the cells to provide the necessary concentration differences.

No doubt new applications will be developed as better membranes continue to become available commercially and as electrodialysis comes of age in chemical processing.

References

1. WILSON, J. R., "Demineralisation by Electrodialysis," London, Butterworths Scientific Publications, 1960.
2. FARRELL, J. B., AND SMITH, R. N., "Process Applications of Electrodialysis," *Ind. Eng. Chem.*, **54,** 29–35 (June, 1962).
3. MASON, E. A., AND JUDA, W., "Applications of Ion Exchange Membranes in Electrodialysis," *Chem. Eng. Progress*, **55,** No. 24, 155–162 (1959).
4. DEWEY, D. R., AND GILLILAND, E. R., U. S. Patent 2,741,591 (March 2, 1951).

EDGARDO J. PARSI

Cross-references: *Concentration Polarization; Demineralization by Electrodialysis; Electrodialysis; Ion Exchange Membranes; Membranes, Electrolytic.*

ELECTRODIFFUSION. See ELECTROMIGRATION.

ELECTROENCEPHALOGRAPHY

Electroencephalography (EEG) is a study of brain electricity (synonym: brain waves). In England, Caton, 1874, was the first to register brain electricity. He was followed by several Russian investigators. Pravdich-Neminsky, 1913, from Kieff, Russia was the first to identify alpha and beta waves (respectively, primary and secondary waves) of the dog's EEG. Berger, 1924, the German psychiatrist, was the first to succeed in making a record of the human EEG by using scalp electrodes. His findings constitute the basis of all that is known at present of clinical EEG. However, the use of EEG techniques has gone beyond the limits of clinical application and now constitutes one of the major tools of the objective studies of the psychophysiology of the brain. The basic mechanism of the EEG is still unknown. It is related to the electrical pulsations of the membranes of the brain cells and their processes synchronized by a variety of mechanisms.

Technique

Intradermic needles, silver discs (generally applied with electrode paste, bentonite and collodion), fluid (silver in saline) electrodes are used. An international (10 to 20) system has been developed for the standard placement of electrodes. For a *monopolar method*, a reference electrode (ear, nose, chin, neck, etc.) is used. This method breaks down in some clinical applications, as the ear electrode becomes an "active" one in deep temporal lesions. In certain cases, the reference grids of the amplifiers are connected through standard resistances to all the scalp electrodes (average electrode technique).

Bipolar technique is preferred by many, as it permits one to better localize lesions by "phase reversal," triangulation, etc. In this technique both grids of a differential amplifier are connected to the "active electrodes."

Intracerebral electrodes. These are either macro- or microelectrodes. The macroelectrodes are wires insulated to their tips, or silver and graphite discs. Microelectrodes (q.v.) are made either of metal or glass (micropipettes) of a small diameter (0.5 to 20 microns). The smallest ones may be inserted in an individual cell.

Equipment

Amplifiers. Both steady (d-c) and transient potentials may be recorded from the brain. In most clinical applications, a 0.1 to 1 second time constant is used with a frequency response flat to 60 c/sec. Simultaneous recordings from several regions of the brain may be done. Most clinical EEG machines have eight channels, but 16 and more channel equipment is becoming increasingly more popular.

Frequency analysis. Automatic frequency analyzers have been developed for detection of latent changes in brain wave frequency.

Recording devices. The usual EEG inkwriter machine is used in clinical practice and cathode ray oscilloscopes are used in physiological studies.

Spaciographs. The usual EEG technique permits one to follow changes of brain potentials as a function of time (as in EKG, electrocardiology, q.v.). However, it may be of interest to consider the instantaneous gradient of brain potential as a function of space, this display changing continually with time. Thus, stable or moving foci may be followed by the examiner.

Averaging devices. Electroencephalograms may exhibit transient changes following a sensory stimulus (electric stimulation of the nerve, clicks, light flashes, etc.). These evoked potentials may be recorded using ordinary equipment with an intracerebral technique. They are generally of too low amplitude to be picked up on the scalp. Averaging devices have been developed recently to "extract" the evoked potentials from the resting brain activity and the amplifier's noise.

Fig. 1 shows typical EEG equipment.

Characteristics of the Alert Adult Scalp Electroencephalogram

Examples of EEG patterns are shown in Fig. 2.

Normal EEG's present a great variety of patterns. Only a superficial outline is presented, and this only in regard to the scalp EEG.

Frequency. All frequencies may be observed from 0.5 to 30 c/sec. However, some of these frequencies usually reach a higher amplitude than others under certain conditions. *Delta waves* (0.5 to 4 c/sec) are seen during normal sleep. *Theta waves* (5 to 7 c/sec) are seen during drowsiness and certain ill-defined mental states (in the anterior regions of the head with scalp to ear leads). *Alpha waves* (8 to 13 c/sec) constitute the most important component of the adult resting EEG (with eyes closed). They predominate in the occipital regions. *Spindles* (14–15 c/sec) are seen during light sleep. *Beta waves* (16 to 25 c/sec) are increased with stress; they predominate in the frontal and central leads. *Gamma waves* (above 25 c/sec) occur under the same conditions as beta waves, but are less common.

Amplitude. The wave amplitude ranges from 5 to 200 μv; average: 50 μv.

Regularity. The wave regularity increases with rest.

Continuity. Expressed by a per cent of occurrence in a unit of record.

Symmetry. Usually symmetrical, but may be

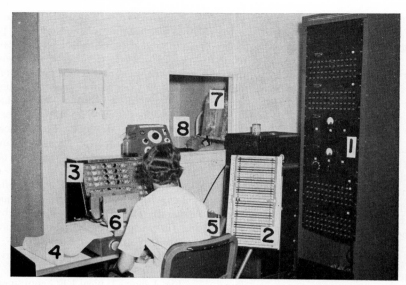

Fɪɢ. 1. (1) Automatic frequency analyzer; (2) electrode selecting board; (3) 16-channel EEG machine; (4) EEG record; (5) EEG pens; (6) analyzer pens; (7) stroboscope lamp; (8) patient inside a shielded room.

of lower amplitude on the left than on the right occipital region.

Special waves. *V-waves* occur with phase reversal over the vertex following a stimulus under resting and alert states; they constitute a regular component of a sleep record (4 to 7 c/sec). *F-waves* are slower waves often of higher amplitude in the frontal regions (occur during deep sleep). *K-complex* consists of an F-wave followed by "spindles." It occurs in response to a stimulus perceived during sleep. *Lambda waves* occur in the occipital region; they have a triangular or sharp configuration, and are associated with normal visual attention; they occur during sleep with no definite correlation. *Kappa waves* are of 7 to 10 c/sec; they occur in the fronto-temporal regions and increase with intellectual activity. *Rhythm in arceau* are waves of 8 to 10 c/sec recorded in the central regions; they are blocked by voluntary effort.

Sleep

There is an intense and diversified brain wave activity during drowsiness and sleep. When the slightest drifting of the consciousness occurs, there is a concomitant change in the EEG. This stage merges into sleep characterized by the "spindle phase" with V-waves becoming slower and spindles (14 c/sec waves) invading the vertex, frontal and later parieto-occipital region. At that time eye movements stop altogether. As sleep deepens, larger amplitude delta waves (0.5 to 2 c/sec) appear in both frontal and vertex regions. At first they appear sporadically ("K complexes"), being activated by external stimuli. Then delta activity becomes more or less continuous, appearing all over the head, including the parieto-occipital region. They may become slower in the posterior than the anterior regions of the head.

It is after this stage that often and for a relatively brief period of time delta activity disappears; the EEG may become flat except in the vertex-ear electrodes where some theta activity is still recorded while the biocular leads show rapid eye movements, which present, at times, very disorganized and bizarre patterns. This stage is called "paradoxical sleep." The latter is also observed in animals and seems to be controlled by some pontile centers. It has been found that during this paradoxical stage, the incidence of dreams is relatively high, although dreams may be reported at any stage of sleep with the exception of that characterized by high amplitude and very slow delta activity. The following are less usual sleep patterns.

"Microsleep." Brief (1 to 3 sec) bursts of sleep waves predominating in the vertex region. They arise without any transitory drowsy stage, being preceded and followed by alpha rhythm. This pattern may be produced in normal individuals by sleep deprivation.

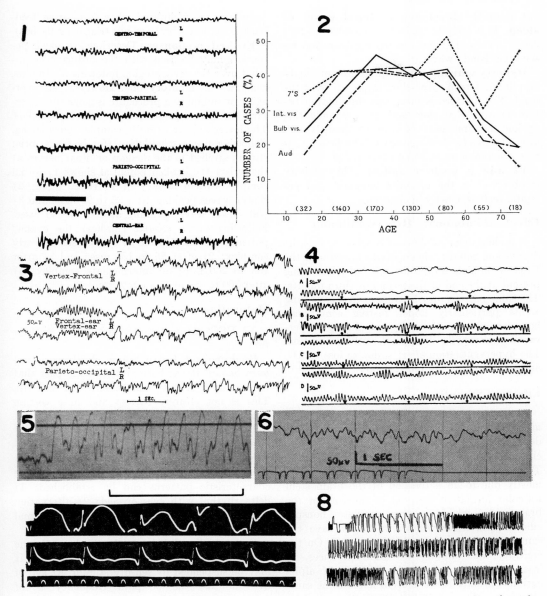

FIG. 2. (1) Example of normal EEG. (2) Frequency of alpha blocking response as a function of age. The numbers in parentheses represent the number of patients in the same age group; 7's: "100-7 test"; int. vis.: visual stimulus; bulb vis: motor response to visual stimulus; aud. vis.: auditory stimulus. (3) EEG of light sleep. (4) Different subjects (A-D) responding in different ways to intermittent flashes produced every two seconds and indicated by dots. (5) Bursts of wave-and-spike formations showing a shift in the baseline (d-c potential) at the beginning. Line = 2 secs. (6) Driven responses to pairs of flashes repeated four times a second. (7) Spike-and-wave formation recorded from the hippocampus of the guinea pig. (8) Beginning of an epileptic discharge recorded in the hippocampus of a guinea pig.

"**Rapid onset.**" A sudden onset of delta rhythm of sleep preceded by alpha rhythm. This pattern is observed primarily in elderly individuals.

"**Occipital onset.**" The appearance of 4 to 7 c/sec activity in the parieto-occipital region prior to the onset of V-waves. This pattern is mostly observed in mid-aged individuals.

Unusually developed occipital waves of sleep. This occipital activity (frequency 4 to 7 c/sec) shows at times a sharp configuration resembling lamda waves.

Hypersynchrony. The presence of high-amplitude 4 to 5 c/sec slow waves all over the head. This pattern is often seen in children before (paroxysmal slow activity predominating during the first year of life) or (mostly) on arousal (steady slow activity). The latter pattern predominates at 3 to 4 years of age.

14 and 6 positive spikes. This activity is observed in the posterior-temporal and occipital regions, mostly in children.

Effects of Pulmonary Hyperventilation

If a child or an adolescent is asked to breathe deeply and rapidly, slow activity appears in the EEG with high-amplitude delta rhythm being present at the end of the second or third minute. The same pattern may be present in some young adults particularly under fasting conditions; however, usually slow rhythm during hyperventilation rapidly disappears with maturation. The hyperventilation effect is due to loss of CO_2 and is fostered by low blood sugar.

Effects of Stimuli

Changes in the resting EEG. *Visual stimuli* (heterogenous visual field; opening of eyes) depress alpha activity, particularly in the occipital regions after a latency of 0.3 seconds. This alpha blocking effect is now considered as mostly due to an activation of the brain stem reticular formation (located in the core of the brain stem) which, in turn, activates nonspecific cortical areas. *Auditory stimuli* have the same effect when they are not expected. On the contrary, an auditory attention produces, at least in certain individuals, increase of alpha activity. *Mental concentration* induces the same changes in the occipital alpha rhythm; it may induce kappa waves (see above) in the anterior leads. *Anxiety* produces alpha block together with an increase of beta activity.

Driving. Repeated flashes of light (with eyes closed) at a frequency of 1 to 30 c/sec may induce "driven" rhythms in the EEG. Sometimes the basic frequency is completely replaced by the induced one; at other times only episodic driven responses are observed. In some subjects no driven frequency response is observed. Driven responses are facilitated when a positive feedback is induced (brain waves triggering flashes).

Evoked responses. Occasional evoked potentials may be seen with the ordinary equipment over the vertex region following a stimulus, generally an auditory one. However, an averaging or summating procedure is generally necessary to elicit representative evoked potentials. The latter appear as quite complex phenomena. Following *nerve stimulation* (for instance, brief stimuli applied to the median or ulnar nerves at the wrist) the evoked potential shows 1) initial complex with a latency of 10 to 20 msec; 2) slower waves peaking after 35 to 90 msec and 3) still slower waves peaking at 100 to 300 msec. Following *visual stimuli* (flashes) the evoked potential shows 1) after 35 to 85 msec an early complex; 2) after 85 to 135 msec and 3) after 135 to 260 msec an intermediate complex; 4) after 260 to 350 msec a late complex.

Maturation

All EEG parameters are subject to maturation.

Background brain wave rhythms. *Newborn babies.* It has been stated in the past that no organized activity can be recorded at birth. This is not entirely correct and in a certain number of neonates even 8 to 10 c/sec may episodically be recorded. However, poorly bilaterally synchronized theta and delta activities predominate. It is difficult to correlate their presence with either alert or sleep states. Some characteristic patterns can be established: 1) delta rhythm with eyes opened; 2) alternation of delta rhythm and flat records; 3) paroxysmal bursts of fast activity.

Early childhood. Prior to the third month, the dominant brain wave frequency is 2 to 4 c/sec. It may be suspended by sensory stimuli. At age of five months, the occipital frequency is of 4 to 6 c/sec. It reaches the frequency of 7 c/sec at age 3 and the adult rhythm at age 8. In fact, there are considerable individual differences, and it may be more important to consider the whole spectrum of brain wave frequencies (as seen in the analyzer's tracing) than only the dominant rhythm. During sleep spindles, V-waves appear very early during the first months of life. The 14 c/sec central spindles may be seen at birth, and their incidence increases with age, particularly after the first year of life. The 12 c/sec frontal spindles appear at age 3 and decrease during adolescence. Hypersynchrony, particularly at arousal, constitutes the most striking characteristic of the child's sleep record.

Adult maturation. EEG maturation processes do not stop at puberty. In fact, they are present during the whole adult life. During the "teens," theta activity often predominates in the central and lateral areas of the head (for instance, in the vertex-ear electrodes) and decreases in the twenties. However, this process is highly individualized and may constitute an important psychophysiological personality parameter to be further investigated. The most striking changes with age are those of the reactivity of alpha rhythm to the sensory and emotional stimuli. The available data suggest that reactivity to stimuli increases until the age of 30; then it remains at a plateau until the age of 40 to 50; it decreases more or less rapidly afterwards.

Involution. During the age of involution and senescence, a dual tendency appears in the population of patients; some show an increase of fast activity; others slowing of the alpha rhythm. In addition, the following patterns may be observed at this age: 1) "occipital onset" of sleep, characterized by 5 to 7 c/sec activity appearing instead of flattening of the occipital alpha rhythm, and 2) "microsleep" (period of very brief sleep pattern).

Abnormal EEG

In the following article EEG abnormalities are discussed.

References

1. *Electroencephalography and Clinical Neurophysiology Journal*, Amsterdam, Elsevier Publishing Company, 1949 to present.
2. GLASER, GILBERT H., "EEG and Behavior," Basic Books, Inc., 1963.
3. HILL, DENIS, AND PARR, GEOFFREY, "Electroencephalography," New York, The Macmillan Company, 1963.
4. LIBERSON, W. T., "Electroencephalography" in "Review of Psychiatric Progress," *Am. J. Psychiatry*, yearly from 1949 to date.

W. T. LIBERSON

Cross-references: *Electrocardiology; Electrodiagnosis; Electrophysiology; Nerve Impulse Transmission.*

ELECTROENCEPHALOGRAPHY, ABNORMAL

Electroencephalographic abnormalities may be related to changes of brain waves in *frequency, amplitude, form, and spatial distribution.* In general, it may be stated that the abnormal rhythm may be excessively slow or fast. In practice most of the abnormal records show abnormally slow rhythm (with the exception of barbiturate intoxication, the beginning of a grand mal seizure, and of epileptic spike discharges).

Abnormal Form of Brain Waves

Wave-and-spike formations. When their frequency is of 3 c/sec and if they persist all over the head for more than 10 seconds they are diagnostic of "petit mal epilepsy." However, any form of epilepsy may be associated with the incidence of wave-and-spike formation.

Wave-and-spike variants. They are of slower frequency, generally 1.5 to 2 c/sec. They are also characteristic of epileptic disorders, particularly in children. When their amplitude reaches very high values, they are called hyposorhythmic, indicating a very severe cerebral involvement in childhood.

Spikes. Single spikes may be observed, or groups of spikes. Their duration is of about 70 milliseconds. They also indicate an epileptic process.

Sharp waves. These are "slow spikes" of about a ⅓ to ⅕ second duration.

Spatial relationships. Normally the EEG patterns are symmetrical on both sides of the head. Two exceptions to this rule may be seen. a) Parieto-occipital alpha activity may be of lower amplitude on the left than on the right occipital region, particularly in some tense individuals. b) Sleep spindles may not be perfectly synchronized. In contradistinction to this, abnormal patterns may be localized to one particular region, or predominate over one hemisphere.

In general, one should distinguish four types of abnormality:

Continuous and generalized. Such abnormality may be seen in diffuse arteriosclerotics, metabolic or toxic encephalopathies, or in any other diffuse encephalopathy. Occasionally, it may be observed in patients suffering from epilepsy or head trauma.

Continuous and localized abnormality. This is characteristic of a great number of focal lesions, such as tumors, hematomas, brain traumas, embolisms, or thrombosis. Continuous or localized abnormalities are generally seen in relatively superficial lesions.

Episodic and generalized abnormality. This type of abnormality is seen in deeply seated lesions, particularly those involving the mid fossa of the cranium or near the midline of the brain. They may be of either epileptic or non-epileptic nature.

Episodic and localized abnormalities. These are in general the patterns of traumatic lesions or epileptic foci; also some tumors may be expressed at the beginning by this type of localized transitory brain waves.

In clinical practice, EEG is most useful in tumors, epilepsy, and post-traumatic states.

Brain tumors

The following general remarks should be made. Subtentorial tumors may easily escape the EEG diagnosis or they are detectable at a late stage of their development. Even then they may give rise to a false localization; namely, bursts of frontal waves (distant effects) instead of the occipital abnormality. Among the supratentorial tumors, meningiomas are much less detectable by EEG than other types of brain tumors. Also pituitary tumors may remain undetected. In general, episodic synchronized delta waves, easily depressed by stimuli and showing some predominance over the frontal regions, are often due to distant effects and, therefore, have much less localizing significance than lower amplitude, irregular delta waves present over a more limited region of the scalp and having a much greater continuity. Moreover, one should be aware of the following: focal delta activity is not a sign of a tumor. It may be observed in a great variety of conditions: vascular lesions, post-traumatic foci, brain atrophy or porencephalopathy, etc. When rapidly increasing over a short period of time, the probability of a brain tumor increases.

Post-traumatic abnormality

Here again a great variety of patterns may be observed. More or less diffuse delta activity may be seen during the period immediately following the trauma, particularly in the case of open cranial lesions. Subdural hematoma is classically expressed by a depression of activity over a more or less extensive area of the scalp. In many cases, continuous delta activity is recorded instead. Chronic EEG abnormalities following trauma are very diverse. Their incidence is higher in open than in closed injuries and is particularly observed in cases with a post-traumatic loss of consciousness. Serial examination will help to detect formation of an epileptic focus in a certain number of cases.

Epilepsy

The presence of positive findings may considerably abbreviate diagnostic workup and an early start of appropriate therapy. It will also contribute immeasurably to the diagnosis of the type of epileptic disorder.

Activating techniques have been devised to reveal hidden epileptic abnormalities. The simplest activation technique should be used first or exclusively.

Sleep. The incidence of epileptic abnormalities increases during sleep. This particularly is true in children and in cases of temporal foci and spike-and-wave generalized activity. The natural sleep is the best activator; if not, the use of seconal or other narcoleptics is of current practice.

Hyperventilation is another *must*. Only the presence of a focal or specific abnormality should be considered as diagnostic.

Flicker. Exaggerated driven rhythm should not be considered as diagnostic for epilepsy. Only the emergence of more or less independent discharge is diagnostic.

Metrazol. Injection of metrazol may elicit epileptic discharges. Unfortunately, this may occur in normal individuals; therefore, this test should not be advised as a routine procedure. Only when the diagnosis of epilepsy is certain and one wishes to better localize the epileptic focus or to observe the seizure is it justified to use this drastic test.

Effects of Drugs

Electroencephalography is easily modified by neuro- and psychotropic drugs. The first observations were made on the effects of alcohol, mescaline, and anesthetics. The latter affect the EEG in different ways at different stages of anesthesia. The final stages are characterized by slow delta activity, alternation of bursts of activity and "silences" (burst-suppression pattern), and, ultimately, a flat record. At some early stages, fast activity may be observed. The latter stage is not the same with various anesthetic agents. Effects of anesthetics have been compared to that of anoxia or hypoxia. The latter is characterized by an initial alert hyperactivity which is considered as due to a reactive process, initiated in the reticular formation. EEG helps to monitor anesthesia, particularly during cardiac surgery, which may involve severe anoxia.

Early research showed that ingestion of a limited amount of alcoholic beverage by a subject with a "flat record" (no alpha activity) activates electrogenesis, presumably by its sedative effect. The same amount of alcoholic beverage would elicit little effect on the EEG with an abundant alpha rhythm. Conversely, mescaline, an hallucinogen, decreases significantly the continuity of alpha rhythm. These findings led to a hypothesis postulating the existence of two kinds of agents: the "synchronizers" and the "desynchronizers" of the alpha rhythm. More recent research has shown that "tranquilizers," such as phenothiazine and reserpine, stabilize and regularize alpha rhythm in a subject showing poor alpha activity, while little effect is observed with the same moderate dosage of the drug in a subject with an abundant EEG. Using a higher dosage, a slowing of alpha rhythm is observed, together with a depression of fast activity and, in certain cases, the emergence of paroxysmal epileptic-like phenomena. Conversely, the energizers (used to treat depression) seem to decrease the continuity of alpha rhythm and increase the incidence of fast activity, particularly when the latter pre-existed in the pre-drug record.

A great number of drugs have a more drastic effect on the EEG. For instance, metrazol elicits slow rhythm and convulsive activity; insulin decreases background frequency; barbiturates elicit at first fast activity, then theta and delta rhythms.

Behavioral Diseases

It has been a great disappointment for EEG'ers to find that neuroses and major functional psychoses are not associated with diagnostic EEG patterns. Yet, undoubtedly EEG findings help the psychiatric diagnosis.

a) A patient considered as suffering from a functional psychosis may be found in the light of an EEG test to have a brain tumor, a toxic state, an epileptic pattern, or a diffuse arteriosclerosis.

b) A patient considered as organically involved may show no EEG abnormality and,

therefore, justifies a more painstaking consideration of a possible functional mental condition.

W. T. LIBERSON

ELECTROFORMING

Electroforming is a method of producing or reproducing articles by electroplating. The electroplated materials may be pure metals, such as copper, iron, nickel, silver, and less commonly gold or platinum; alternate layers of pure metals; or, in some cases, alloys. In general the thickness range of electroplating employed is from 0.005 to 0.5 inch. Most frequently, though, the thicknesses will be between 0.005 and 0.1 inch. It is also common practice to "back up" the electroform with casting materials, or by soldering to a backing plate. This is done where additional rigidity or heat-transfer properties may be required.

One of the distinguishing features of the use of electroplating for electroforming as contrasted to its use in most other applications is that in electroforming the deposit is ultimately separated from the basis material. Thus, while most electroplaters strive to attain maximum adhesion to the basis metal, the electroformer is concerned with having only sufficient adhesion to prevent premature separation of the electrodeposit from the object being coated.

A second distinguishing feature is that the thicknesses of electroplating employed in electroforming are from ten to fifty times as thick as in most plating applications.

The types of plating baths employed in both cases are similar, however. The reader may therefore obtain this information from books dealing with electroplating. Excellent coverage is also given in the ASTM "Symposium on Electroforming—Applications, Uses, and Properties of Electroformed Metals," STP No. 318, 1962.

Operations for Electroforming

The sequence of operations will vary widely depending upon the nature of the article to be produced or reproduced, the quantity of electroforms required, and the cost factor. A few examples will serve to illustrate these points.

If a cowhide texture is desired for embossing thin vinyl plastic material which will ultimately be used to make ladies' purses or men's wallets, the following sequence of operations might be employed.

(1) Select a cowhide of desired size and texture.

(2) Treat to preserve and waterproof.

(3) Place on suitable frame.

(4) Metallize one side to make surface conductive.

(5) Electroplate a heavy deposit of nickel (0.01 to 0.03 inch) over the metallized surface.

(6) Separate leather from electroform.

(7) Strip thin metallized film from nickel.

(8) "Flash" chromium plate the nickel surface.

(9) Attach electroform to a roll by soldering or other suitable means.

In the above case a nonconductor (the cowhide) is utilized as a matrix to produce a metal embossing plate or roll. If the volume of vinyl sheet to be embossed is such that one roll will suffice, no further processing is involved. However, if a number of embossing rolls are desired, several approaches are then available:

A. Treat the proper number of cowhides as outlined in steps (1) through (9) above.

B. Repeat steps (4) through (9) using the original cowhide each time.

C. Using the nickel "master" from step (7), passivate the surface and make a negative by depositing 0.01–0.030 inch of nickel against it. Separate the "master" and negative (sometimes referred to as a "mold") and use the negative to electroform further embossing rolls.

As indicated above, the choice of A, B, or C will ultimately be governed by the economics involved and perhaps the quality required.

The phonograph record industry has used each of the above sequences (A, B and C) to produce stampers for pressing records.

As a second example, assume it is desired to electroform venturi tubes from nickel. Again, several possible approaches exist.

A. Turn a mandrel from plastic or wood. After suitable waterproofing, metallize the mandrel to make it conductive or use graphite for this purpose. Electroform the nickel over the mandrel, and withdraw the mandrel.

B. Cast the mandrel from a low-melting alloy using an existing venturi as a mold. Electroform the nickel over the casting, then melt out the casting or withdraw it.

C. Turn a metal mandrel from steel or stainless steel to the desired internal dimensions of the venturi. Chromium plate the steel to facil-itate its release from the electroform. Electroform the venture onto this mandrel and separate by withdrawing the mandrel.

In the above cases it has been assumed that the venturi has a continuous draft in one direction, thus permitting the withdrawal of the mandrel. If a reverse draft does exist, the problem is obviously more complicated.

Mandrels, Masters or Matrices Employed for Electroforming

All of the above terms have been used to describe the materials upon which the electroforms are deposited. Graham has divided these materials into three catagories; 1) expendable conductors, such as low-melting alloys, aluminum, and zinc; 2) permanent conductors, stainless steel, nickel, Invar, Kovar, nickel plated brass; 3) semipermanent nonconductors, such as glass, plastic, and wood.

Bottomley's classification for matrices is based upon whether the electroform 1) can be separated laterally as in electroformed phonograph record stampers, graining plates, and surface texture replicas; 2) completely surrounds the matrix except for one or both ends, so that the matrix can be withdrawn; 3) completely surrounds the matrix or madnrel, necessitating melting or dissolving of the matrix material after electroforming. Thus, it is clear that the geometry of the article being produced or reproduced plays an important part in the choice of a mandrel or matrix material. Other considerations are: tooling costs for permanent versus an expendable mandrel, rate of production, dimensional accuracy and surface finish requirements, and compatability of the mandrel material with "grow-on" parts, such as inserts, flanges, etc.

The design of the mandrel for electroforming should allow extra length so that nodular deposits which tend to build up at the ends of the electroform may be trimmed off. Generous radii rather than sharp corners should also be utilized. Permanent mandrels must be free from undercuts or reverse taper where possible. If this is not possible, several sections may be bolted or fitted together to facilitate their removal. However, great care must be taken in making these joints to prevent weakness of the electroform.

Since the electroform is a faithful reproduction of the mandrel, every effort should be made to eliminate imperfections and to obtain the necessary finish on the mandrel. Frequently subsequent mechanical finishing of the electroformed part can be minimized or eliminated by careful preparation of the mandrel. This is particularly important on internal surfaces that are inaccessible on the finished part.

Properties of Electroformed Materials

The physical and mechanical properties of electroformed metals and alloys are to a large extent determined by: 1) type of solution employed, 2) operating conditions, such as temperature and current density, 3) addition agents, and 4) subsequent heat treatment. Specific coverage of these areas is given in the above-mentioned ASTM Symposium.

The ranges of hardness obtainable from electrodeposited metals are shown in Fig. 1. In addition, typical mechanical properties of deposits obtained from copper, iron, and nickel plating solutions are given in Table 1. This table indicates the variation in properties that may be obtained by changing solution composition and operating conditions. Unfortunately, similar data are lacking for other metals useful for electroforming.

From a practical standpoint control of stress in the electroform is highly important. Excessive stresses can cause exfoliation or premature separation of the deposit.

Efforts to enhance the high-temperature capabilities of electroformed materials in the missile and space vehicle fields have led to some recent developments in alloy plating of nickel-tungsten, cobalt-tungsten, and cobalt-nickel-tungsten. Other alloys having good high-temperature properties will doubtless be developed.

Applications for Electroforming

Numerous applications have been described in literature. Only a few of the more important will be mentioned here. Probably the largest volumes of electroforming are done for the phonograph

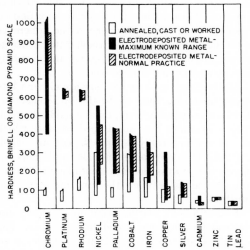

Fig. 1. Relative hardness of electrodeposited metals. (From Ref. 1, by permission.)

TABLE 1

Plating Solution	Typical Mechnical Properties			
	Stress, psi	Hardness	Tensile Strength, psi	Per cent Elongation in 2 inches
Copper sulfate	0–5000	250–275 DPH	35,000–42,000	5–25
Copper fluoborate	—	44–74 Rockwell 15T	17,000–32,000	3.2–14.5
Copper pyrophosphate	10,000 compressive	150–200 DPH	60,000	
Ferrous chloride	15,000–40,000	215–270 Brinell	50,000	40
Ferrous fluoborate	—		—	—
Watt's Nickel—low pH bath	15,000–30,000 Without stress-reducing agents	140–160 Vickers	50,000	30
Hard nickel	40,000–45,000	350–500 Vickers	152,000	5–8
Chloride nickel	40,000–50,000	230–260 Vickers	98,000	21
Fluoborate nickel	16,000–26,000	183 Vickers	75,000	16–17
Sulfamate nickel	1500–10,000	140–190 DPH	105–110,000	15–20

Data from article "Modern Electroforming Solutions and Their Applications" by M. B. Diggin contained in ASTM "Symposium on Electroforming—Applications, Uses, and Properties of Electroformed Metals." STP No. 318, 1962.

record, the electrotyping, and the gravure industries. Texture replicas and graining plates also account for a large quantity of electroforming.

The automotive industry has made extensive use of electroformed paint-spray masks, plastic molds for sun visors, arm rests and floor mats. In addition, electroformed molds for other products, such as rubbers and boots, have been produced from iron and nickel for many years.

The electronics industry has made use of gold, silver, and copper electroforming for wave guide components, slip rings, and miscellaneous parts.

Coronet, trombone, and trumpet bells, and mouthpieces for musical instruments have been electroformed from copper. They have superior tonal qualities over those made by spinning techniques.

Relatively few applications for commercial aircraft and allied areas have been reported. Pitot tubes, deicer protective strips for helicopter blades and searchlight reflectors are among the most common mentioned.

Recently the aerospace industry has taken a new look at the use of electroforming, and such varied components as nozzles, venturi-type wind tunnels, pressure vessels, heat sinks for nose cones, hyperbolic paraboloid sandwich panels, and other structural assemblies have been electroformed.

References

1. ASTM "Symposium on Electroforming—Applications, Uses and Properties of Electroformed Metals," STP No. 318, 1962.
2. GRAHAM, A. K., Editor, "Electroplating Engineering Handbook," New York, Reinhold Publishing Corp., 1962.
3. LOWENHEIM, F. A., Editor, "Modern Electroplating," New York, John Wiley & Sons, Inc., 1963.

HAROLD J. WIESNER

Cross-references: *Alloy Electrodeposition; Barrel Plating;* entries with *Electroplating* titles; specific metals, *Electroplating* or *Plating.*

ELECTROGALVANIZING

Zinc coatings are generally applied to steel because of their protective power against atmospheric corrosion. It has been said that per dollar of coating cost, zinc coatings confer more protection to iron and steel than any other coating. However, there are instances where zinc is applied to steel or other metals because it can

be easily treated by a chemical conversion coating to transform the surface into a better base for paint. Very light coatings of zinc are adequate for this purpose.

Zinc coatings have been applied by hot-dipping processes for a longer period of time than by electrodeposition. The coating thickness obtained by hot-dipping is generally in excess of one mil, and the coating is apt to be rough and nonuniform. Unless special precautions are taken, as in continuous strip coating, adherence can be a problem, especially if the coated area is postformed. On the other hand, zinc coatings applied by electrodeposition can be any desired thickness; the uniformity is good and adherence is excellent. As a result, electrodeposited coatings of zinc are in some cases less costly and give better service than hot-dipped coatings.

Electrodeposited zinc coatings are either white matte in appearance or bright and reflective. They are essentially pure, ductile, and adherent. This is in contrast to hot-dipped coatings which are characteristically spangled, contain small amounts of many other metals, and, depending on the process, contain a significant layer of iron-zinc alloy between the zinc and the steel substrate.

Two types of plating solution are used for electrodepositing zinc: acid and alkaline. The acid type includes the sulfate, chloride, fluoborate, and combinations of these anions as electrolytes. The most common alkaline electrolyte is the cyanide, although ammoniacal, pyrophosphate and zincate solutions are being used. There are many proprietary alkaline electrolytes in use, chiefly where it is desired to produce bright zinc deposits. Preparation for plating is simple, provided heavy oxide films and layers of grease or lubricating oils are not present. If these are present, they can be removed by commonly employed treatments prior to plating. Most metal substrates over which zinc is commonly plated require no other preparation for plating.

Wire and Strip Plating

Wire and strip are the principal products which are plated with zinc. Steel wire is coated with zinc in thicknesses ranging from 0.5 to 5 mils. Wire diameters range from about 9 to 20 mils. Strip steel as wide as 60 inches is plated with zinc in thickness range extending from 0.013 mil to 0.170 mil, and there is no technical reason why coatings as heavy as 1.0 mil cannot be applied to a wide steel strip. As a matter of fact, one of the advantages of the electrogalvanizing process is its versatility. Thus, if the equipment is designed properly, strip can be coated with zinc on one or both sides or with one coating thickness on one side and a different coating thickness on the opposite side. In most zinc plating lines the strip moves horizontally through the plating cells, permitting anodes to be placed opposite either side.

While cyanide baths are sometimes used for plating strip, the most common baths for either wire or strip are acid, and the most common anion employed is the sulfate. There are several reasons for using acid baths instead of alkaline. First, while acid baths have poor throwing power compared to alkaline, this is not as important in wire or strip plating as it is in plating formed or cast parts. Second, a considerable investment is required to build a large strip or wire plating unit, and it is essential that a high production capacity be obtained. This requires plating zinc at a high rate of speed, and the acid baths have the greatest potential here.

The Chloride Bath

The all-chloride type of plating bath has the highest conductivity and thus, for a given plating voltage, permits the highest current density. A typical high-conductivity, high-current density zinc chloride plating bath which can be used for strip plating has the following composition:

$$ZnCl_2 , 18 \text{ oz/gal}$$

$$NaCl, 31 \text{ oz/gal}$$

$$AlCl_3 \cdot 16H_2O, 3 \text{ oz/gal}$$

$$pH, 3.0 \text{ to } 4.0$$

This bath is easy to control and for strip moving at 100 to 150 ft/min, a current density of 500 amp/sq ft can be obtained. It should be operated between 100 and 140°F. The aluminum chloride helps to maintain the pH of the bath. When plating steel strip, iron goes into solution and must be continuously removed by filtration. Because of the amount of iron that is generally present in the bath, the deposits are not as white as desired, and this may prove to be objectionable.

The cathode efficiency in a properly operating bath ranges between 95 and 100 per cent. However, the anode efficiency may easily exceed 100 per cent because of the chemical attack of the solution on the anodes. In normal operation this is no problem because there is a certain amount of solution lost as dragout which tends to maintain the metal ion concentration of the bath.

Various modifications of the bath have been made to improve it. Additions of other anions, such as sulfate, acetate, and fluoride, have been proposed to make it less corrosive, both to the equipment and to the zinc anodes. The acetate especially tends to buffer the solution and prevent wide variations in pH. The chemical attack on the zinc anodes may be minimized by alloying the metal with aluminum or aluminum and mercury, although when the anodes are located above the strip, mercury may fall on the strip and cause black spots to form.

In spite of the high conductivity of the bath, which permits high current density plating at low voltages, the all-chloride bath has not been widely used. The chloride ion renders it extremely corrosive to surrounding equipment and supporting structures, and these must be protected constantly.

The Sulfate Bath

The sulfate bath is used most widely in large industrial installations for either wire or strip plating. At present distinctly different processes employing essentially the same solution are used, depending on whether wire or strip is being plated.

In wire plating, an insoluble anode is used, and the zinc metal ion is replenished by chemical recovery from zinc-bearing materials, principally zinc ores. Thus, except for the fact that the cathode is a plurality of wires moving at constant speed, this process has many of the elements of an electrowinning process. A process patented by U. C. Tainton is a good example of the type in general use. Extremely high current densities up to 5,000 amp/sq ft have been reported, although a range of from 1,000 to 3,000 amp/sq ft is most common. Special alloys of lead are used almost exclusively as anodes. This is the most common insoluble anode material.

In the operation of this process zinc is, of course, plated out on the wire which is the cathode. However, instead of zinc going into solution at the anode, oxygen is liberated. The net result is that the pH of the bath decreases as sulfuric acid is regenerated. The plating solution is recirculated through the zinc recovery system where the excess sulfuric acid (33 ounces per gallon) reacts with the zinc-bearing materials to increase the zinc metal ion concentration in the solution and to increase the pH. This solution must first be purified before it can be returned to the plating cells. After purification it is added to the recirculating plating cell solution to maintain the concentration at about 29 ounces per gallon zinc sulfate.

While the sulfate solution is most widely used for plating wire, a zinc ammonium chloride solution has found some application. This bath is not strictly an acid bath, but since it employs an insoluble anode, it is mentioned at this point. High conductivity and the possible use of chloride-bearing zinc waste materials seem to be its chief advantages. Instead of the pH decreasing as noted above in the sulfate process, it increases as zinc is plated out and ammonia is regenerated. In the recovery system the excess ammonia is consumed to form zinc ammonium chloride.

In most strip plating operations where the sulfate solution is used, soluble zinc anodes of high purity are used. The anodes, therefore, furnish the zinc metal ions which are plated out on the strip. There is no necessity for a recovery and purification plant, although the solution is recirculated continuously through filters to remove the iron which accumulates.

A typical strip plating sulfate type bath has the following composition:

$ZnSO_4$, 50 oz/gal

Metallic zinc, 11.5 oz/gal

Na_2SO_4 , 9.5 oz/gal

$MgSO_4 \cdot 7H_2O$, 8.0 oz/gal

pH, 3.0 to 4.0

The purpose of the sodium sulfate is to improve conductivity. Magnesium sulfate tends to whiten the zinc deposit. The solution operates well within a temperature range of from 130 to 150°F. Within this range it is possible to obtain from 250 to 400 amp/sq ft using from 8 to 12 volts.

Because of the limitations of current density and the relative size of the strip compared to wire, it has not been possible to attain the high speeds and heavy coating thicknesses which are common in wire coating operations. This has been a deterring factor in the development of the processs, in spite of its versatility,

as compared to the continuous-strip, hot-dip galvanizing operation. Thus, considerable capital investment has been made in equipment for producing hot-dip galvanize.

Preparation for Plating

In both wire and strip plating operations it is essential that all oils and metal oxides be removed before plating; otherwise, poor adherence and blistering will occur. Rolling oils are generally removed on continuous lines by a combination soak in a fairly strong alkaline solution, mechanical scrubbing, and finally electrolytic cleaning in a more dilute alkaline solution composed of the same chemicals. Alkaline silicated cleaners are usually sodium silicates or phosphates combined with sodium hydroxide or sodium carbonate to which is frequently added certain proprietary wetting agents. Formulated mixtures ranging from 2 to 8 ounces per gallon are used, the concentration depending on the type and amount of oil to be removed. In electrolytic cleaning, the strip may be cathodic, anodic or alternately cathodic and anodic at current densities as high as 100 amp/sq ft. Solution temperature should be between 180 and 200°F. Agitation during electrocleaning is beneficial.

After thorough rinsing, the strip or wire is pickled. Both immersion and anodic pickling are used. The amount of scale or oxide present may determine the pickling process selected. It is essential, to avoid hydrogen embrittlement, that the pickling time be held to a minimum. Sulfuric acid is most often used for pickling in a concentration range of 2 to 10 per cent, although anodic pickling solutions may be as high as 16 per cent. In immersion pickling a satisfactory solution temperature is 150°F. Pickling inhibitors are frequently added to minimize the attack of the solution on the areas where the oxides have been removed. Anodic pickling is more often conducted at temperatures as low as 100°F. Thorough rinsing following pickling is essential. Oxide removal may also be carried out by pickling in hydrochloric or phosphoric acid solutions.

Rack and Barrel Plating

Plating processes used for zinc coating small cast or fabricated parts are generally alkaline and almost exclusively employ the cyanide type bath. In plating these articles, throwing power is important to insure that the zinc coating is deposited in the recesses of the part to be plated. Another matter of considerable importance is brightness. Frequently it is an advantage to be able to produce a bright zinc deposit. There are many brighteners available for the cyanide zinc plating bath which are incorporated in a number of different proprietary processes.

The major constituents of the cyanide zinc plating bath are zinc cyanide, sodium cyanide and sodium hydroxide. The ratio of sodium cyanide to zinc has a direct bearing on the performance of the bath. As the metal ion concentration is increased, the cathode efficiency increases for a given current density. Also, as temperature and sodium hydroxide concentration are increased, the current efficiency increases. However, as the current density increases, the current efficiency falls. Good results in both rack and barrel plating can be obtained if the total sodium cyanide to zinc metal ratio is maintained between 2.0 and 3.0. Where brightening agents are used, the supplier of the plating solution should be consulted for specific recommendations.

A typical straight cyanide bath from which white zinc deposits can be produced has the following composition:

$ZnCl_2$, 8–11 oz/gal

NaCN, 2.5–10 oz/gal

NaOH, 10–15 oz/gal

Metallic zinc, 4.5–6.0 oz/gal

Operating conditions vary depending on whether rack or barrel plating is being done. If the bath temperature is maintained at 100°F and the cathode current density at 25 amp/sq ft, the resultant cathode efficiency will generally exceed 90 per cent over quite a wide range of concentration of bath constituents.

Unless specific conditions permit the use of "Intermediate" or "Prime Western Grade" anodes, it is recommended that high-purity zinc anodes be used. Zinc goes into solution chemically and electrochemically in cyanide baths. Thus, it is necessary to exercise some control over the solution of the anodes or the metal concentration will tend to increase. Magnesium, calcium, and aluminum in combination with mercury reduce the anode efficiency. Another method for controlling zinc concentration is to use a small number of stainless steel anodes. However, if the anodes are immersed in the plating solution during down periods, zinc will

go into solution rapidly because of the couple effect which exists between zinc and iron.

As in acid zinc plating, it is essential to have a clean surface upon which to plate. Oils tend to be cleaned off because of the alkaline nature of the solution, but this well lead to contamination or possibly excessive foaming. The same procedures are, therefore, recommended for cleaning articles to be zinc plated in alkaline solutions as were recommended for acid solutions.

References

1. MATHEWSON, G. H., "Zinc:The Science and Technology of the Metal, Its Alloys and Compounds," New York, Reinhold Publishing Corp., 1959.
2. GRAHAM, A. K., "Electroplating Engineering Handbook," Second Edition, New York, Reinhold Publishing Corp., 1962.
3. LOWENHEIM, F. A., "Modern Electroplating," New York, John Wiley & Sons, Inc., 1963.

EDWIN J.. SMITH

Cross-references: *Barrel Plating;* entries with *Electroplating* titles; specific metals, *Electroplating* or *Plating; Zinc and Cadmium Electrovinning.*

ELECTROGRAPHIC PRINTING

Electrographic printing is an electrochemical method for evaluating voids, such as porosity and cracking, in protective-coating systems. This method makes use of an applied direct current to transfer ions from the basis metal to a chemically treated dye-transfer paper through discontinuities in the applied coating. A pressure device is employed during passage of the current to hold the material firmly against the treated paper.

The protective coating can be either metallic or nonmetallic but the basis metal is always metallic. In the electrographic technique, a piece of dye-transfer photographic paper soaked in a dilute electrolyte solution is pressed firmly against the surface to be examined. A potential of 1.5 to 6.5 volts direct current is applied for several seconds to a few minutes across a "sandwich" formed by the test part as anode and a suitable metal cathode separated from the photographic paper by blotter paper soaked in dilute electrolyte. At pores or cracks in the protective coating, cations from the underlying metal are formed under the influence of the applied potential. They diffuse into the gelatinized surface of the dye-transfer paper where they react with appropriate chemicals to form colored precipitates or soluble complexes. Cracks are shown on the print as colored lines, while pores appear as colored dots. Thus, mirror images of the crack patterns or pore sites are produced. Considerable enlargement of pore sites is achieved by this technique. For instance, pores impractical to locate with a microscope are easily discernible because of the lateral diffusion of the colored reaction products on the paper.

The cations reacting with the chemicals in the dye-transfer paper sometimes can be composed of two or more different components in which case the cation reacting to form the predominant color will dominate if it is present in significant quantities. A good example is 50–50 cobalt-nickel alloy. When the reagent is dimethylglyoxime, cobalt gives a light brown color; nickel a blood-red color. However, the 50–50 electrodeposited alloy under chromium gives a red color.

Room temperature solutions are employed for preparing electrographic prints. The electrolytic current starts at 4 to 10 ma/sq in., depending on the voltage, and falls rapidly to a steady 2 to 4 ma/sq in. after several seconds. Little or no

0.0002-inch-thick chromium plate was produced. The cross-section area developed increases proportionately to the printing time. Four and one-half minutes printing time in the above example was exceptionally high. Printing times of 30 to 120 seconds normally suffice.

The magnification of pores and cracks that is achieved by electrographic printing depends on the thickness of the outermost coating, the size of the pores and cracks, the applied voltage during printing, and the printing time and pressure. Pores are magnified from 28 to 60 times. The magnifying effect for narrow cracks has been reported to be about 300 times. Pores as small as 0.00005 inch have been detected and cracks 0.000003 inch wide have been resolved.

Accurate pore and crack counts can best be achieved when flat specimens and pressure platens are employed. In order to evaluate discontinuities in coatings on objects having irregular shapes, a low-pressure technique can be employed satisfactorily. The equipment required in the latter technique differs from the former, in that molding clay is substituted for platens and hand pressure is used. Aluminum foil is used as the cathode contact.

Examples of color reactions produced by metal ions and selected indicators are as follows:

Metal Detected	Coating Being Evaluated	Reagent	Color Reaction
Chromium	Nickel	S-diphenyl carbazide in alcohol	Violet
Cobalt	Chromium	Dimethylglyoxime in alcohol	Light brown
Copper	Chromium	Same as cobalt	Green
Iron	Tin, organic, phosphate	Potassium ferricyanide	Blue
Nickel	Chromium	Same as cobalt	Blood red

attack on the surface coating occurs during electrographic printing if the proper chemicals are selected, if dilute solutions are adopted, and if the proper current, time, and pressure conditions are applied. The most satisfactory conditions should be determined for each composite. Dissolution of the surface coating has occurred under unusual circumstances, such as in one instance when excess electrolyte was pressed from the blotter pads onto an area of the coating not in the sandwich.

Electrochemical corrosion of the basis metal always occurs when the electrolyte penetrates through discontinuities in the coating. For example, after 4.5 minutes printing at voltage setting of 7.5 volts, a 0.00018-inch-deep, 0.00031-inch-wide cavity in the nickel under a crack in

An excellent source book for determining indicator reagents for specific uses is F. Feigl, "Spot Tests in Organic Analysis."

In summary, it can be said of electrographic printing that it has many attributes as a tool for determining the presence and quantity of pores and/or cracks. Some attributes are (a) it gives a high degree of magnification of pores and particularly cracks, (b) the printing technique is applicable to field work and contour shapes, (c) it can be employed as a research tool for determining the continuity of coatings before and after specific tests, and (d) it gives a permanent visual record of defects and permits rapid comparisons.

Historically, electrographic printing has been employed to locate flaws in metals. Later it was extended to identify coatings and evaluate coating continuity of electroplated hardware, porosity in organic films, porosity in tin, and phosphate coatings. One group of investigators has employed it for rapidly comparing the experimental results from chromium plating baths using selected operating conditions. Evaluation of chromium plate continuity before and after heating is another specific use. It has also been employed for determining the presence of suspected impurities on surfaces.

References

1. Miller, H. R., and Friedl, B., "Developments in Electrographic Printing," *Plating*, **47**, 520–527 (1960).
2. Ogburn, F., and Ernst, D. W., "The Nature, Causes and Effect of Porosity in Electrodeposits," (AES Project No. 13), *Plating*, **46**, 831–833 (1959); **48**, 491–497 (1961).

Hugh R. Miller

ELECTROKINETIC POTENTIALS

The Four Fundamental Phenomena

Electrokinetic potentials (which often are called, following H. Freundlich, ζ potentials) have been introduced by H. Helmholtz[1] to account for the four phenomena in which movement of electricity and of two phases parallel to their interface takes place. These phenomena are (1) *electroosmosis*, i.e., movement of a liquid along a solid in an electric field; (2) *electrophoresis* or cataphoresis, i.e., movement of a solid suspended in a liquid in an electric field; (3) *streaming potential*, i.e., formation of a potential difference between the upstream and the downstream ends of a liquid vein streaming past a solid; and (4) *sedimentation potential*, i.e., formation of a potential difference between the top and the bottom of a vessel in which a solid powder suspended in a liquid gradually falls down.

All these effects can be understood if it is assumed that the liquid surface layer next to the solid is electrically charged, the charge being equal and opposite to that present in the solid surface. When the system is placed in an electric field, the opposite charges are pushed in the opposite directions, and electroosmosis or electrophoresis occurs depending on which phase is mobile; and, if the two phases are displaced relative to each other by a mechanical force, this displacement of matter involves displacement of charge which results in streaming or sedimentation potentials.

When the above model is treated quantitatively, it is found that the measurable effects are proportional to a potential difference (ζ) rather than to a charge; Helmholtz' equations are

$$u = \frac{D\zeta}{4\pi\eta}\,Y \qquad (1)$$

for electroosmosis and electrophoresis and

$$E = \frac{D\zeta P}{4\pi\eta\kappa_0} \qquad (2)$$

for the two potentials. In them, u means the linear velocity (cm/sec) of the liquid relative to the solid (or of the solid relative to the liquid), D is the dielectric constant of the liquid, Y the intensity of the electric field parallel to the liquid-solid interface, η the viscosity of the liquid, E the streaming or sedimentation potential, P the pressure causing the shift along the solid-liquid boundary, and κ_0 the electric conductivity of the liquid if κ_0 of the solid is infinitely small. Of course, all quantities should be expressed in one set of units. If ζ is given in volts and Y in volt/cm, then the numerical factor of Eq. 1 is 2.78×10^{-6} rather than $\frac{1}{4}$; thus, with $D = 80$ and $\eta = 0.01$ g/cm sec, as water, the linear velocity in unit field (i.e., 1 volt/cm) is 7.08×10^{-4} cm/sec when $\zeta = 0.1$ volt. In Eq. 2, pressure, P, is equal to $gM\,[1 - (\rho_0/\rho)]$ for sedimentation; g is acceleration due to gravity, M the mass of powder descending per sq cm of the cross-section of the vessel in a liquid of density ρ_0, and ρ is the density of the powder.

Introduction of ζ establishes correlation between the measurable magnitudes, u and E. If Eq. 2 is combined with Eq. 1, relation

$$\frac{\kappa_0 E}{P} = \frac{u}{Y} \qquad (3)$$

is obtained, which contains only experimental quantities; a confirmation of Eq. 3 can be found, for instance, in Ref. 2.

Surface Conductance

Unfortunately, use of Eqs. 1 and 2 is not as simple as it appears to be. Doubts as to the values of D and η in them are mentioned in other articles (*Electroosmosis, Streaming Potential*). The values of Y in Eq. 1 and of κ_0 in Eq. 2 are

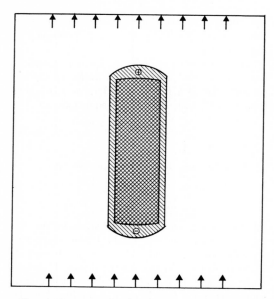

Fig. 1. A nonconducting particle surrounded by a highly conducting surface layer in a liquid of medium conductivity.

affected by surface conductance or induced asymmetry of the ionic atmosphere. It is clear that Y is the local, rather than macroscopical, field strength. Consider, e.g., an insulating rod-like particle in a liquid, as indicated in Fig. 1. The electric field far from the particle (and, consequently, the motion of the positive ions) is directed from the bottom to the top of the figure. If the conductivity of the (lightly shaded) space around the particle (dark shade) is greater than that of the surrounding liquid, there will be accumulation of positive charges near the upper end, and of negative charges near the lower end, of the particle. The field which determines the particle motion is the sum of the external field and that produced by the just described polarization. Quantitative treatment leads to the equation[3]

$$Y = \frac{Y_1}{1 + \frac{\chi\Omega}{\kappa_0 S}} \qquad (4)$$

in which Y_1 means the macroscopic field intensity, χ is surface conductivity (measured in ohm^{-1}), Ω the perimeter, S the cross-section of the particle or the pore, and κ_0 the bulk conductivity of the solution. According to Ohm's law, the macroscopic field strength in a pore is $Y_1 = I/\kappa_0 S$, I being the current strength; thus,

$$Y = \frac{I}{\kappa_0 S + \chi\Omega}; \qquad (5)$$

this equation may be easier to use than Eq. 4. As follows from Eq. 4, Y is smaller than Y_1 as long as χ is positive.

Surface conductivity has two causes and two components, at least one of which always is positive.[4] (1) The ionic composition of the liquid next to the solid is different from the composition in the bulk of the solution. In a dilute solution of a binary uni-univalent electrolyte whose bulk concentration is C moles/cc, the concentration of the cations in the electric double layer (q.v.) near the wall is greater (say, αC) and that of the anions is smaller (say, βC) than C if the wall is negatively charged. The product $\alpha\beta = 1$ everywhere in the double layer; hence, the total concentration of ions in it, equal in every point to $(\alpha + \beta)C$, is greater than that (equal to $2C$) far from the wall (because the value of $\alpha + (1/\alpha)$ has a minimum at $\alpha = 1$). Hence, also the electric conductivity of the liquid near the wall usually is greater than κ_0.

(2) Conductivity is proportional to $C(v_+ + v_-)$ in the bulk and to $\alpha Cv_+ + \beta Cv_-$ in the surface layer, if v_+ and v_- are the mobilities of the cations and the anions, respectively. If the whole liquid moves relatively to the electrodes (as in electroosmosis) with velocity u, the mobilities recorded become $v_+ + u$ and $v_- - u$ so that the effect on κ_0 is nil. Near the wall, conductivity becomes proportional to $\alpha C(v_+ + u) + \beta C(v_- - u)$; as α is $>\beta$, electroosmosis renders conductance greater.

The sum of the above two terms often is of the order of magnitude of $\chi = 10^{-9}$ ohm^{-1}. It is approximately proportional to $C^{0.5}$, i.e., varies with concentration, C, less than the bulk conductivity, κ_0. Therefore, when C decreases, the ratio $\chi\Omega/\kappa_0 S$ increases and the local field intensity, Y, becomes a smaller fraction of the macroscopical intensity, Y_1, see Eq. 4. This effect seems to explain[4] many instances of the decrease of ζ, calculated from Eq. 1 or 2, on diluting the solution (past a maximum value of ζ).

Swelling

Another factor, which makes ζ calculated from the original expressions too small, is swelling. Consider electroosmosis in a narrow capillary whose cross-section is S_2 before and S_1 after swelling; $S_2 > S_1$. As swelling usually has little effect on v_+ and v_-, the S in Eq. 5 is equal to S_2.

However, liquid flow is possible only over the cross-section, S_1. Thus, the volume flow rate, V (cc/sec), of electroosmosis is

$$V = \frac{D\zeta}{4\pi\eta} \cdot \frac{IS_1}{\kappa_0 S_2 + \chi\Omega}, \qquad (6)$$

i.e., smaller than expected by Helmholtz. Analogously, the streaming potential

$$E = \frac{D\zeta P}{4\pi\eta} \cdot \frac{S_1}{\kappa_0 S_2 + \chi\Omega} \qquad (7)$$

"Shear Surface" and Surface Roughness

The potential, ζ, calculated from any of the above equations is different from the usual "transverse" electrostatic or electrochemical potentials. Consider a semi-infinite volume of a solution in contact with a solid electrode. The electrostatic or electrochemical potential difference between the two phases is the work needed to move a unit charge from the middle of one to the middle of the other phase. Without an additional theory, this potential difference can be obtained only relative to another potential. On the contrary, ζ potential is obtained in absolute units but represents only the work required to bring a unit charge from the bulk of the solution to the "immobile" layer of this solution next to the wall. The hypothetical boundary between the "immobile" and "mobile" strata is often referred to as "shear surface."

Probably, however, no true "shear surface" exists. Movement of liquid along a solid wall is retarded by the surface roughness of the solid (see Ref. 3, p. 417); if h_{av} is the average height of hills covering the wall, the flow of liquid is hindered *as if* a liquid layer, approximately h_{av} cm thick, remained stagnant when the rest is taking part in laminar motion. The value of h_{av} usually ranges from 100 Å for exceptionally well-polished, to 20,000 Å for visibly rough surfaces. Thus, it is greater than the common range of the thicknesses of the equivalent double layer; as the capacity of this layer in aqueous solutions, as a rule, is between 10 and 100 μF/sq cm, it corresponds to capacitor thicknesses between approximately 70 and 7 Å. Consequently, the major part of the charge in a diffuse double layer is confined to valleys in which laminar flow is obstructed. Hence, a considerable part of the charge is inactive, as far as electrokinetic phenomena are concerned, and ζ derived from experimental data is only a fraction of the potential difference between the solid-liquid interface and the bulk of

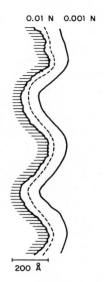

0.01 N   0.001 N

200 Å

Fig. 2. Comparison of surface roughness with the thickness, δ, of the equivalent double layer, $h_{av} = 200$ angstroms. The calculated δ is shown for $C = 0.001\ N$ and $C = 0.01\ N$.

the liquid. Common values of ζ are between $+0.1$ and -0.1 volt while "transverse" potentials easily exceed 1 volt.

Surface roughness supplies a satisfactory explanation for the long-known fact that the four main electrokinetic effects become negligible in concentrated solutions. The values of h_{av} generally are independent of C, while the thickness of the equivalent double layer is smaller the greater C; thus, the higher the ionic concentration, the greater is the fraction of the charge almost immobilized in the cracks and valleys of the surface, see Fig. 2. The depression of ζ by high electrolyte concentrations is perhaps the most striking part of the difference between ζ and the "transverse" electrochemical potentials.

The Electrolyte

The value of ζ depends on the nature and the concentration of the electrolyte. If the solid is negative in most dilute aqueous solutions, the nature of the cation is more important than that of the anion; and the opposite is true for preferentially positive surfaces. For instance, the streaming potential, E, in a glass capillary (negatively charged) may be identical for dilute solutions of potassium chloride, potassium sulfate, and potassium ferrocyanide, while less than a micromole per liter of aluminum chloride, thorium chloride, and other tetravalent cations will reverse the sign of E.

Ions of higher valency generally are more effective than those of lower valency. In a particular experiment, the potential of aqueous phase (in electroosmosis) was lowered to 0.025 volt, the solid being negative, by adding 27 milliequivalents potassium chloride, or 3 milliequivalents barium chloride, or 1.5 milliequivalent aluminum chloride per liter. If the wall is positive, the effects are analogous. For instance, a constant lowering of the ζ potential of a positive FeO(OH) sol was achieved by 0.115 millimol $[Au(CN)_4]^-$, 0.055 millimol $[Pt(CN)_4]^{2-}$, 0.026 millimol $[Cu(CN)_4]^{3-}$ and 0.0085 millimol $[Fe(CN)_6]^{4-}$, all with potassium salts in one liter.

Hydrogen, hydroxyl, and some large or heavy ions are more effective than their valency would indicate. In particular, substances of amphoteric nature readily suffer change of sign when hydrogen is displaced by hydroxyl or vice versa. Large organic monovalent cations may depress a negative, or enhance a positive, ζ potential (of the solid) as much as the tervalent aluminum cation does.

As far as the concentration, C, of the solution is concerned, ζ often increases with C to a maximum and then decreases to almost zero; the probable causes of this behavior have been indicated above.

If a nonaqueous solvent is substituted for water, the ζ potential is not fundamentally altered as long as the solvent has a high dielectric constant and gives rise to well conducting solutions. For instance, ζ in nitrobenzene solutions is not very far from the ζ in aqueous media, a negative As_2S_3 sol in nitrobenzene can be made positive by $FeCl_3$, etc. However, liquids of small D, which permit but little electrolytic dissociation, usually give low ζ values by Eqs. 1 and 2; this may be accounted for by surface conductance. When κ_0 is very small, as in hydrocarbons, the ratio $\chi\Omega/\kappa_0 S$ is likely to be very large; thus, ζ of Eq. 1 or 2 is only a small fraction of the ζ of Eq. 6 or 7.

The Solid

The sign of the ζ potential depends on the nature of the solid as much as on that of the liquid. If the solid is acidic, i.e., tends to emit hydrogen ions into the solution, the ζ of the solid usually is negative; cellulose may serve as an example. Many solids, or at least their surface layers, readily act as ion-exchangers, and their ζ consequently greatly depends on the solution they are in contact with, as mentioned in the preceding section. For instance, clay in water generally is negative because the polymer silicate anions are not soluble, while the common cations (Na^+, K^+ and so on) are; but when the alkali metal cations are displaced by the poorly soluble methylene blue cation, the clay becomes positive.

Barium sulfate precipitated in the presence of an excess of barium chloride is positive, while it is negative when sodium sulfate was in excess; presumably, the crystals in the first instance contain an excess of Ba^{2+} and in the second, an excess of SO_4^{2-}. Analogous experiments have been performed with AgCl precipitated either with excess $AgNO_3$ or with excess NaCl.

In many other instances, the sign of the solid is difficult to predict. Electrophoresis is observed also with liquid drops or gas bubbles suspended in an immiscible liquid, and the sign of these drops and bubbles also is not always predictable; in some instances it may be determined by the rate of diffusion of various ions present.[5]

Importance of Electrokinetic Potentials

Electrokinetic potentials influence many other phenomena in addition to the four basic effects and surface conductance. Thus, the bulk electric conductance of a colloidal solution may be expressed as a function of ζ or of χ which depends on ζ.[6,7] Let a colloidal particle carry n unit charges and have a velocity, relative to the electrodes, equal to u. The n compensating univalent ions in the diffuse double layer may have an inherent mobility, v_+. If the particle and the ions could move independently of each other, the contribution of the (particle + counterions) complex to the bulk conductivity would have been $n(u + v_+)$. In reality only a fraction of the compensating ions can break loose from the particle in unit time, and this fraction is determined by ζ. The majority of the counterions move, at any instant, with the particle so that this transports a much smaller charge than n. Electric conductance of many colloidal solutions in a constant field is due chiefly to ions not intimately connected with the sol particles.

The situation is different in alternating fields and also when the dielectric constant is determined. Each particle depicted in Fig. 1 acts as a dipole whose moment depends on the value of ζ;[7,8] when there are many large particles in unit volume, the dielectric constant at low frequencies may reach and exceed 1000.

The apparent viscosity of a liquid flowing in a narrow capillary (or a capillary system) or of a colloidal solution depends on ζ; this is the electroviscous effect (q.v.) discovered by M. Smoluchowski. Consider a capillary as an example. When liquid flows through it, streaming potential is established between the ends of the tube; this streaming potential gives rise to electroosmotic movement of the liquid; this movement is opposite to the initial flow; hence, the rate of flow is lowered and an abnormally high viscosity simulated. Analogously, particle sedimentation is retarded by the sedimentation potential and viscosity of colloids is enhanced by their electrokinetic potentials; see, e.g., Ref. 9.

Stability of colloids, suspensions and emulsions, as a rule, is affected by the mutual repulsion of the electric double layers surrounding the particles. It is not clear whether the ζ potential or the electrochemical potential is of greater importance in this respect; examples of both types are known. It was noticed many years ago that rapid coagulation of colloidal solutions occurred at a "critical potential," namely, when ζ (in electrophoresis) was 0.025 to 0.030 volt. Apparently, the rate of coagulation depends on ζ also when the former is slow.[10] It has been claimed that the "critical potential" was independent not only of the nature of the particle and the electrolyte but also of that of the solvent.

Electrokinetic potentials presumably are of importance in many biological[11] and industrial processes. A partial list of the latter follows:

Adhesion of powders to solids (especially that of phosphors to glass), detergence, electric drying, electrodeposition, electrodialysis, flotation, mordanting and dyeing, paper formation, purification of sugar juice, setting of clay, and swelling.

References

1. HELMHOLTZ, H., *Ann. Physik*, [3], **7**, 337 (1879). An English translation was published as Engineering Research Bull. No. 33 (1951) of University of Michigan, Ann Arbor, Mich.
2. BIEFER, G. I., AND MASON, S. G., *J. Colloid Sci.*, **9**, 20 (1954).
3. BIKERMAN, J. J., "Surface Chemistry," 2nd ed., p. 418, New York, Academic Press, 1958.
4. BIKERMAN, J. J., *Kolloid-Z.*, **72**, 100 (1935).
5. DUKHIN, S. S., AND DERYAGIN, B. V., *Koll. Zhur.*, **20**, 705 (1958).
6. BIKERMAN, J. J., *J. chim. phys.*, **32**, 460 (1935).
7. O'KONSKI, C. T., *J. Phys. Chem.*, **64**, 605 (1960).
8. BIKERMAN, J. J., *J. chim. phys.*, **32**, 285 (1935).
9. HARMSEN, G. J., SCHOOTEN, J. VAN, AND OVERBEEK, J., TH. G., *J. Colloid Sci.*, **8**, 64 (1953).
10. GHOSH, B. N., AND BANDYOPADHYAY, *J. Indian Chem. Soc.*, **39**, 314 (1962).
11. BIER, MILAN, Ed., "Electrophoresis," New York, Academic Press, 1959.

J. J. BIKERMAN

Cross-references: *Elecrode Double Layer; Electroosmosis; Electrophoresis; Electrophoretic Deposition; Electroviscous Effect; Streaming Potential.*

ELECTROLUMINESCENCE

Electroluminescence is luminescence excited by electric fields or currents in the absence of bombardment or other means of excitation. Several different types of electroluminescence can be distinguished.

The first observation of what is known as "recombination or injection electroluminescence" was made in 1923 by Lossew, who found that when point electrodes were placed on certain silicon carbide crystals and current passed through them, light was often emitted. Explanation of this emission has been possible only with the development of modern semiconductor theory. If minority charge carriers are injected into a semiconductor, i.e., electrons are injected into p-type material or "positive holes" into n-type material, they recombine spontaneously with the majority carriers existing in the material. If some of these recombinations result in the emission of radiation, electroluminescence results. Minority-carrier injection may occur not only at point contacts but also at broad area rectifying junctions; in this case the junction must be biased in the forward or "easy-flow" direction, and the electric field in the junction is lower when the voltage is applied than in its absence.

The recombinations in this type of electroluminescence may occur directly between energy bands of the host material ("recombination radiation" or "edge emission") or by means of impurity or activator centers. In general, the emission intensity is a linear function of the injected current; the emission is "current controlled." This type of emission has now been observed in a wide variety of materials, including SiC, diamond, Si, Ge, CdS, ZnS, ZnO, and many of the so-called III-V compounds, such as AlN, GaSb, GaAs, GaP, InP, and InSb. The emission of many of these materials lies in the infrared region of the spectrum. In some cases the efficiency is also very low, values of one emitted quantum per million injected carriers often being observed. However, in some materials (particularly GaAs) the efficiency is high and approaches one emitted photon for each carrier passing across the junction. In GaAs (and presumably other materials in the future) sufficient radiation intensity may be obtained to cause stimulated rather than normal (spontaneous) emission, resulting in an electrically-excited solid-state laser (q.v.).

Another kind of electroluminescence was first observed in 1936 by Destriau. He observed the emission of light from a specially prepared zinc sulfide phosphor suspended in an insulating oil and subjected to an intense alternating electric field by means of capacitor-like electrodes; the emission is "field controlled." Today the phosphor powder is usually embedded in a solid organic (plastic) or inorganic (glass) medium. Thin films of tin oxide or of metal are used to provide transparent electrically conductive electrodes. Such "cells" can be made with a base of glass, metal, or flexible or rigid plastic material.

This type of electroluminescence, which has been called the "Destriau effect" or "acceleration-collision electroluminescence," has also been observed in ZnSe, Zn_2SiO_4:Mn, $BaTiO_3$, TiO_2, BN, and some organic materials. The best electroluminescent phosphors, however, are still ZnS and related materials; copper is the most common activator, although ZnS:Cu,Mn is also used. The emission or recombination process in these materials is the same as for excitation by ultraviolet radiation or by cathode rays. The excitation process, however, is quite different. It has been found that to prepare good electroluminescent phosphors it is necessary to make the material very nonuniform electrically by introducing, on the surface or in defects in the interior of the ZnS particles, segregations of a relatively good conductor, such as ZnO or Cu_2S. The local electric field strength in the neighborhood of these segregations may be a hundred or more times the applied field strength, which is already of the order of 10^4 to 10^5 v/cm. It has been commonly assumed that, under the action of these intense local fields, electrons are liberated and accelerated to acquire considerable energy from the field; some of these energetic electrons may collide with and excite or ionize the activator or luminescence centers. However,

the mechanism of electroluminescence in ZnS is still not completely understood. Minority carrier injection may also be important in this material.

If a p-n junction is reversed to the opposite direction, which results in high internal field strength, other types of emission can occur. For example, the presence of energetic ("hot") carriers can result in emission at energies greater than the forbidden band gap of the material; this has been called "avalanche emission." In this way visible radiation can be generated in germanium or silicon. Emission at energies less than the band gap can also occur. This is attributed to intraband transitions; it is therefore "deceleration radiation" resulting from a change in kinetic energy of the carriers. The efficiency in this case is expected to be quite low.

If metal electrodes, such as Al or Ta, are immersed in suitable electrolytes and current passed between them, light emission may also be observed. This "galvanoluminescence" is often electroluminescence in a thin oxide layer formed on the electrode by electrolytic action.

Electroluminescence in ZnS

The intensity of electroluminescence in ZnS increases rapidly as the applied alternating voltage is increased, and also increases slightly less than linearly as the frequency is increased until a region of saturation is approached at frequencies of the order of 100,000 cps. Very high brightness may be achieved (2500 ft-lamberts or more at 20,000 cps). Maximum efficiency is not achieved at the same conditions as maximum brightness. The efficiency of electroluminescence (2.5–3.0 per cent) is yet low compared to other light sources. Some comparative figures are: electroluminescence, 10 lumens/w; incandescence, 16 lumens/w; fluorescent lamp, 70 lumens/w. Electroluminescence, however, is an area source of light, in contrast to an incandescent lamp, which is essentially a point source, or a fluorescent lamp, which is a line source. Electroluminescent lamps may be made only a fraction of an inch in thickness and of any size or shape. Some electroluminescent phosphors also exhibit a change in emission color as the frequency of the applied voltage is varied.

Another feature of electroluminescent ZnS phosphors of practical importance is the decrease in output during operation. This deterioration is strongly influenced by humidity, temperature, and operating frequency. High temperature and high frequency greatly accelerate the deterioration; the time required to produce a given loss is usually inversely proportional to the frequency. Moisture must be carefully excluded. Lamps have been made with an initial output of 100 ft-L and a life to 50 per cent of this value of 1000 hours (operation at 1000–3000 cps). The time required for the output to "buildup" after application of a sinusoidal voltage is of the order of a few cycles and hence decreases as the frequency is increased; this time may be decreased by application of a d-c bias. The decay time after excitation is independent of frequency.

Phosphors with controlled brightness-voltage characteristics may be prepared for specialized electronic applications. In addition to powder phosphors, continuous films of ZnS a few microns thick may be prepared. These films operate on a-c as well as d-c and at comparatively low voltage (of the order of 20 v). Superposition of a-c and d-c can lead to interesting interaction and control of output by small signals.

In electronic applications electroluminescent phosphors ("electroluminors") may be advantageously used in conjunction with other solid-state components, such as nonlinear resistors, photoconductors, magnetic devices, and ferroelectrics, for voltage distribution and control. Uses range from single-element control circuits to complicated logic circuits, multielement storage devices, shift registers, light and x-ray image amplifiers and storage panels, and thin large-area image display devices for radar or television. Specially segmented lamps for display of numerical, alphabetical, or other types of information are also available.

Electrophotoluminescence

In addition to electroluminescence proper, other interesting effects occur when electric fields are applied to a phosphor which is concurrently, or has been previously, excited by other means. Such effects are usually termed electrophotoluminescence. One such phenomenon is the "Gudden and Pohl effect," discovered in 1920. Here the phosphor is first excited (by ultraviolet radiation, for example) and then an electric field is applied during the afterglow or phosphorescence, or even after the emission has decayed below the limit of detection. A burst of emission is observed with some materials, even those which do not exhibit electroluminescence.

In this case the field acts on electrons in traps that are responsible for the phosphorescence.

Most phosphors, if continuously excited by ultraviolet radiation, x-rays, or cathode rays, show a decrease in emission if an electric field is simultaneously applied. This "field quenching" was first observed by Déchêne in 1935. In 1954 Destriau discovered that some ZnCdS:Mn phosphors excited by x-rays show the opposite effect; i.e., their emission is increased by the application of an electric field. Since that time a similar enhancement effect has been observed for excitation by light, ultraviolet radiation, cathode-rays, and α-particles. These effects may find application in radiation converters, light amplifiers, and particle detectors.

References

1. HENISCH, H. K., "Electroluminescence," New York, Pergamon Press, 1962.
2. IVEY, H. F., "Electroluminescence and Related Effects," New York, Academic Press, 1963.

HENRY F. IVEY

Cross-references: *Fluorescence; Lasers; Luminescence; Phosphorescence; Phosphors; Semiconductors.*

ELECTROLYTIC CAPACITORS. See CAPACITORS, ELECTROLYTIC.

ELECTROLYTIC CONDUCTIVITY. See CONDUCTIVITY, ELECTROLYTIC.

ELECTROLYTIC CONDUCTIVITY MEASUREMENT See CONDUCTIVITY (ELECTROLYTIC) MEASUREMENT.

ELECTROLYTIC HYDROGEN PEROXIDE. See HYDROGEN PEROXIDE.

ELECTROLYTIC POLISHING: THEORY

Electrolytic polishing is the production of a nearly specularly reflecting surface on a metal by anodic dissolution. It consists of two processes operating conjointly: *leveling* or *smoothing* giving a macroscopically smooth surface and *brightening* giving lustre. The two effects can occur separately, but must be conjoint to give polishing. Electrolytic polishing was first noted

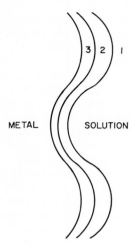

FIG. 1. Successive stages, 1. 2. and 3. in leveling by uniform dissolution normal to the local surface.

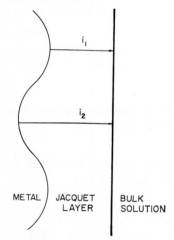

FIG. 2. Jacquet layer set up by diffusion-convection conditions at dissolving anode. Current density, $i_1 > i_2$, assisting leveling.

in the mid-nineteenth century in certain silver-plating anodes, but was first examined scientifically and developed by Jacquet from 1930 onwards.

In ordinary anodic dissolution at fairly low current density, most metals and alloys dissolve uniformly but with the production of an etched surface. This consists of large numbers of small facets, usually of close-packed planes, and is formed because the most easily dissolving atoms on the surface are those forming the edges

or especially corners or kinks of the planes of closest or nearly closest packing.

Any kind of dissolution gives some degree of leveling. Thus, the low-relief on a coin disappears during acid dissolution, and the molding on a bar of soap is soon lost in the bathtub. This can be simply explained by the model of Edwards (Fig. 1). If the surface of the hills and valleys of an irregular surface dissolves uniformly, normal to the local surface, then the depth removed in unit time from a hill must be greater than that from a valley, from purely geometrical considerations. Edwards showed theoretically and demonstrated practically that the removal of a total depth some ten times that of the surface irregularity can produce a nearly level surface by this mechanism.

However, in most cases leveling by dissolution is achieved more readily, because the dissolving material forms a layer of solution next to the metal surface, of which the outer boundary is nearly plane (Fig. 2). Through this liquid layer, demonstrated by Jacquet, the anodic reactant from the solution side has to arrive, and the dissolution product has to deposit, by diffusion-convection: where the layer is thin, over the hills, arrival or departure is faster than where it is thick, over the valleys, and consequently it contributes largely to the leveling effect. It may frequently provide the rate-determining stage of the overall dissolution process: a limiting current-density of an anodic dissolution process (Fig. 3) may be set by the rate of arrival of anodic reactant through the diffusion-convection layer. It is, however, not an *essential* condition for good leveling that the overall dissolution process should be so limited. Often, viscous solutions provide the best leveling because in them the

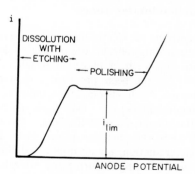

FIG. 3. Current/potential relationship, showing limiting current density in polishing range.

outer surface of the Jacquet layer is the most sharply defined and plane, but again, solution viscosity is not an essential factor for leveling.

To produce *brightening*, the production of the small etch facets has to be suppressed so that these surface irregularities are small compared with the wavelength of light. Hoar and co-workers have shown that in ordinary electrolytic polishing in aqueous solutions, dissolution takes place *through* a compact solid film very similar to that producing passivity (q.v.), except that it has the property of dissolving rapidly at its outer surface as fast as it forms at the metal/film interface (Fig. 4). Then, the rare and *random* arrival or production of cation vacancies or other defects at the metal/film interface dictates which metal atoms leave the metal interface at any instant, so that random dissolution occurs, rather than etch figures dictated by the metal lattice; the surface becomes bright, like a random liquid metal surface. The compact solid film has been demonstrated in several ways to be present *during* electrolytic polishing: thus, mercury does not wet a polishing (or brightening) anode, although it readily amalgamates with an etching one, or one on which the film is allowed to dissolve without reforming; the a-c capacitance of anodes that are brightening is much lower, and the a-c resistance much higher, than those of anodes that are undergoing etching; and brightening anodes show the effects in the reflection of polarized light that are to be expected on a reflecting surface carrying an invisible transparent surface film. Finally, under special conditions with little or no convection, the Jacquet layer may be developed to great thicknesses, and then the solid film also thickens sufficiently to develop characteristic interference colors; since with the thick layer and thick film the anodic current density falls to very low values, this demonstration may require several days.

A very similar randomization of dissolution, leading to brightening, can sometimes be produced by anodic dissolution into a *molten* salt. Here, the medium in contact with the metal lattice consists of positive and negative ions only, with no solvent. Although the short-range order of such ionic liquids is not so nearly perfect as that of a solid ionic film, it is sufficiently good to make the occurrence of cation vacancies next to the metal rare enough to lead, as with the solid films, to random dissolution.

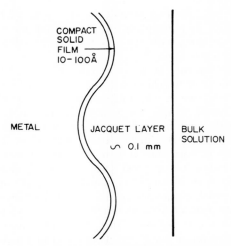

FIG. 4. Complete conditions for polishing, showing solid film and Jacquet layer (schematic).

"Chemical" polishing can often be produced with solutions containing vigorous cathodic reactants, such as nitric or chromic acids. Here, the cathodic reduction occurs on the outside of the solid film, and random anodic removal of metal from the lattice at the metal/film interface, as in electrolytic polishing. No external cathode or emf is needed.

References

1. HOAR, T. P., "Anodic Behaviour of Metals," in "Modern Aspects of Electrochemistry," No. 2., Ed. J. O'M. Bockris, pp. 262–342. London, Butterworth, 1959.

T. P. HOAR

Cross-reference: *Electropolishing*.

ELECTROLYTIC POLYMERIZATION. See POLYMERIZATION (ELECTROLYTIC) OF VINYL MONOMERS

ELECTROLYTIC RESTORATION OF ANCIENT METALS

The word "patina" was originally used to describe the tarnish appearing with age on bronze objects. Many art collections were originally formed, not primarily for their historic or metallurgical importance, but for the attractiveness of the patinas. In the last decade, a greater interest has been aroused in the study of the nature and corrosion of ancient metals and alloys along with the study of the metallurgy and fabrication.

In the case of many metals and alloys, the forming of a tarnish is due to a primary stage of corrosion in which an oxide or a sulfide film of simple composition is produced. When sufficiently uniform, this patination film protects the metal from further attack and is the first stage of corrosion. It is due to this protective corrosion film in great part that works of art have been preserved for great periods of time. External appearance and color of the patina will vary considerably. Oftentimes one finds a bronze with a very smooth patina caused by oxidation in dry burial conditions. Other ancient bronzes, when rich in copper, are often covered with green or blue carbonates whose formation is brought about by carbon dioxide. When rich in tin or lead, the patina appears gray or black. In some cases, the corrosion film is a crust which is thick and warty.

Upon examination, one finds in general, the stable corrosion products to be true minerals. The corrosion of an alloy will vary as to its constituents and will have individual characteristic ways of corroding. The speed of corrosion in the ground is influenced by many variable factors, such as acidity, alkalinity, and the presence of soluble salts. All have effect on the rate of corrosion, especially when the soil is porous and the object is subjected to periodic moisture. For convenience, several types of corrosion processes, such as direct chemical or uniform surface corrosion, pitting, galvanic, concentration cell, parting, and dezincification (the actual plating out of the noble metal), are referred to in the study of corrosion. In restoration work, one defines corrosion as essentially an electrochemical action, and deals with the galvanic type. By arranging the metals in order of their normal electrode potentials, a galvanic series (q.v.) of the metals in order of their nobleness is obtained.

GALVANIC SERIES OF METALS

(anodic, or least noble)

Potassium
Sodium

Calcium

Magnesium
Aluminum

Zinc
Iron

Tin
Lead

HYDROGEN

Copper
Mercury
Silver

Platinum
Gold
(cathodic, or most noble)

Gold and platinum are found at the bottom of the list while silver, copper, tin, and iron follow toward the anodic or least noble end of the scale. The noble metals are more easily reducible but are not easily corrodable. They stand at the cathodic end of the scale.

The reactive metals, reducible with difficulty and easily corrodable, stand at the top or anodic end of the scale. If an alloy, consisting of a solid solution of one metal in another, is subjected to anodic treatment under conditions of potential which would allow the more reactive metal to pass into the ionic state, it would leave the more noble metal undissolved. The behavior of the alloy will depend on the proportions in which the two metals are present. Under certain circum-

FIG. 1. Ancient bronze which has an original, uncorroded area in the center, surrounded by a heavy incrustation of green malachite.

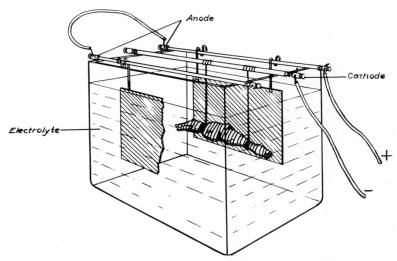

FIG. 2. Schematic electrolytic cell for restoration of art objects. The object to be restored is the cathode.

FIG. 3. An Egyptian bronze aegis of the 22nd Dynasty (950–730 B.C.) before electrolysis.

FIG. 4. The aegis of Fig. 3 after restoration by electrolysis.

stances, "parting" takes place as the result of the reactive metal passing into solution and the most noble metal remaining. The presence of the nobler metal hastens the corrosion of the baser one (by electrochemical action). In cleaning corroded metal artifacts, on occasion, one finds alloys of silver and copper. When the copper has migrated to the surface and formed a green

FIG. 5. Another bronze aegis of the 22nd Dynasty before electrolytic restoration.

The fundamental idea is to replace cathodically the metal that has passed into the crust, rather than to completely eliminate the crust with its metal content, by corrosive acids or by mechanical means. In developing the electrolytic process, Fink tried various electrolytes used by earlier workers, including Finkener's electrolyte of 2 per cent potassium cyanide, KCN, which were found not satisfactory. A 2 per cent solution of caustic soda, NaOH, was finally decided upon as the safest electrolyte to use.

Without any preliminary cleaning, the object to be treated is hung as a cathode into a 2 per cent caustic soda solution and a low-amperage direct current is applied. Very low current densities are preferred. Fine, annealed copper wire is wrapped around the object, one or two turns per inch, and electrical connections are made with the ends of the wire (Fig. 2). The action of the electrolysis is to evolve hydrogen at the cathode and to reduce the crust to finely-divided or spongy copper.

corrosion product, malachite, it conceals the silver beneath, the presence of which was unsuspected and only revealed by cleaning.

It has generally been observed that ancient copper objects survive under burial conditions better than bronze. This is to be expected when a single metal is concerned and an electrochemical action not realized. The phenomena of electrochemical action can often be observed when a bright, original uncorroded area in a bronze has entirely survived corrosion but is surrounded by a heavy warty incrustation of green malachite (Fig. 1). Such a condition can be explained if the mixture was not uniform at the time of casting and such an area, from its composition, was in a condition of nobleness in contrast to the surrounding metal.

A method of electrolytic cleaning, first published by Finkener and described in detail by Rathgen in 1905, and further developed by Fink in 1925 with refinements made by other workers in the field, has proved, for general application, to be a safe and practical method of restoration.

FIG. 6. The aegis of Fig. 5 after electrolysis.

For relatively small objects, two to twelve square inches of surface, a bath is connected in series with a rheostat in a direct current circuit, so as to allow from 0.1 to 0.5 amperes through the circuit. Anodes are hung on either side of the object—iron, nickel and platinum anodes have been used. Copper, bronze, silver, and iron have successfully been treated by the electrolytic method with very gratifying results.

The use of too strong an electrolyte or high current densities will cause excessive gassing at the cathode with detrimental results. Complete reduction is indicated by a free evolution of gas at the cathode. The object is then removed from the bath, soaked in several changes of warm water to remove all traces of the caustic soda, followed by drying in an oven at 40 to 60°C.

Figs. 3 and 4, and 5 and 6 are "before and after" photographs of Egyptian bronzes of the 22nd Dynasty (950–730 B.C.) which show the remarkable results obtained by electrolytic restoration.

References

RATHGEN, FRIED, "The Preservation of Antiquities," (Trans.) Cambridge, University Press, 1905.

ROCCHI, FRANCESCO, "Experimental Sciences in Art and History," *Rassegna d'Arte*, **7**, 1920.

FINK, C. G., AND ELDRIDGE, C. H., "The Restoration of Ancient Bronzes and other Alloys," First report Metropolitan Museum, New York, May, 1925.

FINK, C. G., AND POLUSHKIN, E. P., "Microscopic Study of Ancient Bronze and Copper," Technical Publication No. 693-E.209, American Institute of Mining and Metallurgical Engineers, Feb., 1936.

GARLAND, H., AND BANNISTER, C. O., "Ancient Egyptian Metallurgy," London, Ch. Griffin & Co., 1927.

GETTENS, R. J., "Mineralization, Electrolytic Treatment and Radiographic Examination of Copper and Bronze Objects from Nuzi," *Tech. Studies Field of Fine Arts*, **1** (1933).

EVANS, U. R., "Corrosion of Metals," London, Edward Arnold Co., 1926.

CUSHING, DANIEL, "Corrosion and Corrosion Products of Ancient Non-Ferrous Metals." "Application of Science in Examination of Works of Art," Museum of Fine Arts, Boston, 1958.

PLENDERLIETH, H. J., "Technical Notes on Chinese Bronzes with Special Reference to Patina and Incrustations," *Trans. Oriental Ceramic Society*, **16**, (1938–39).

YOUNG, W. J., "Examination Works of Art Embracing the Various Fields of Science." "Application of Science in Examination of Works of Art," Museum of Fine Arts, Boston, 1958.

W. J. YOUNG

Cross-references: articles bearing *Corrosion* headings; *Cathodic Protection*.

ELECTROMACHINING

In electrochemical machining, the workpiece (any electrically conductive material to be modified) is the anode, connected to the positive terminal of a d-c power source. The tool (conductive material that has the three-dimensional contour needed to generate the desired shape in the workpiece) is connected to the negative terminal. In between is a conducting solution that can support electrolysis according to Faraday's Laws.

In operation, electrons under the driving force of the applied emf flow from the workpiece (anode) and away from it through the external circuit and power source to the tool (cathode). The least strongly bound electrons in the workpiece are those of its surface atoms. These electrons move away and into the electronic circuit. The surface atoms are left behind in near-ionic state. The net result is, these atoms leave the surface in accordance with Faraday's Laws, by a reaction represented by:

surface metal atom + anion(s) →

$$\text{metal salt* + electron(s)} \quad (1)$$

This reveals the electrolytic source of electrons that move into the electronic circuit.

An excess of electrons reaches the cathode. And, if electric current is to flow, a comparable and counterreaction must take place at the tool (cathode) surface—to use up those electrons as follows:

$$\text{cation + electron(s)} \rightarrow \text{atom} \quad (2)$$

In electrolytic machining, the cations are H_3O^+ and the discharged atoms are hydrogen. The current flow-path is completed by ionic conductance in the electrolyte.

If the atom removal rate is fast enough, by Eq. 1, the metal surface is removed at a rate that can do practical machining. However, more than this is required. The action according to Eq. 1 requires an ample supply of anions to be on hand to accept the metal atoms as ions. Therein lies the key to ECM.

Consider the example of a part to be made

* One will recognize that this could be a hydroxide or an oxide according to the anion involved.

of pure iron by ECM, using an acid chloride electrolyte. Eq. 1 will then be:

$$Fe + 2Cl^- \rightarrow FeCl_2 + 2 \text{ electrons}$$

The $FeCl_2$ is in the electrolyte right at the surface that the Fe atoms just left. Because the electrolyte can accept only a finite amount of $FeCl_2$, the rate of the iron dissolving process is controlled by the rate at which the $FeCl_2$ leaves the area of the work surface. In a still electrolyte, $FeCl_2$ diffuses away because of the concentration gradient from workpiece (anode) face to the bulk of the electrolyte.

Electroplating and electropolishing experience shows that such diffusion-controlled electrolyte conductance can support anode current densities of 50 to 1440 amperes per square foot (up to 10 amperes per square inch.) The higher value can be maintained if the temperature is high enough.

At a current density of 10 amp/sq in., iron dissolves at 100 per cent current efficiency, according to Faraday's Laws, at a rate equivalent to 0.00135 inch per minute. However, this is impractically slow for machining and shaping metals. Therefore, much higher amperage is

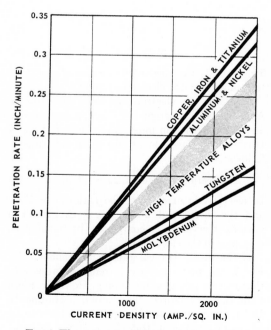

FIG. 1. The rates at which the electrochemical-machining process penetrates typical metals. As shown, the penetration rate is also affected by the current densities used.

needed and much faster rate of salt removal from the anode face is required.

A penetration rate of 0.125 inch per minute is practical; 0.25 inch has been achieved; and even 0.004 inch is worth while. These rates, respectively, require theoretical current densities of 925, 1850, and 30 amp/sq in. All three are well beyond the level that can be maintained by diffusion-controlled electrolysis. Thus, rapid flow of electrolyte is essential for ECM if salt removal from the workpiece face is to be kept ahead of salt build-up at that point.

But this, too, is only a part of the story. The electrolyte must fill the space between the tool and workpiece in uniform and rapid flow. The electrolytic current distribution must be controlled so as to generate the desired work surface contour. At the same time, the cathode process (Eq. 2) must not be impeded by accumulation of hydrogen gas. Thus, the electrolyte flow must be effective at the tool face as well as at the work face.

Special tooling design and electrolyte flow at the surface speeds in the range of about 2,000 to 15,000 linear feet per minute (23 to 170 miles per hour) are required to satisfy the condition. The pressure needed to circulate the electrolyte at these speeds, which is dictated by the space available between tool and workpiece, has no electrochemical significance on action according to Eq. 1. However, pressure, by compressing gas bubbles, may decrease overvoltage associated with action by Eq. 2. If so, the effect would be to lower the applied emf needed. Local turbulence must be avoided so that there is no hydraulic effect to distort the electrolytic current flow needed for accurate shaping.

Thus, the conditions for practical ECM are supplied by rapid, controlled electrolyte passage that can support current densities in excess of 30 amp/sq in. The graph, Fig. 1, shows the relationship between current density and penetration rate for several metals. The limiting penetration rate (stock removal rate) depends on the ability of the electrolyte to carry away the salt formed with the metallic ions and on the heat generated. This is an important relationship because of the small gap between the tool and workpiece.

The resistance of the electrolyte is an important and controlling factor in the operation. The effective electrolysis regions are thin films (less than 0.001 inch thick) on the workpiece and on the tool. Only a very small amount of material dissolved from the work is needed to change the electrochemical activity of the film at the work surface. A small increase in the amount will slow down the stock removal rate. Fast and accurate metal removal depends primarily on the rapid, effective, and continuous replacement of the used film with fresh electrolyte.

To achieve removal, the "effective gap" between the tool and workpiece must be in the range of 0.001 to 0.020 inch. This is the width of the electrolysis cell. Thus, current must flow at first only from the point of the tool nearest to the work.

As the tool advances toward the workpiece, other areas attain the required gap width and electric current flow increases proportionately, at the constant low applied emf. Soon all surfaces are at the same gap distance and current flow is uniform over the entire contour. The desired surface will then have been generated.

When proper tooling, electrolyte composition, and flow of electrolyte are provided, electric current passage at the start of ECM is largely from the region of the tool nearest the work face. Indeed, it would be desirable for the current at that point to be 100 times greater than at the point where tool and work face are farthest apart. For example, if the distance dif-

ferential between parts of the workpiece and tool is 250 mils (0.25 inch), the final shape of the workpiece will have been achieved when the farthest penetration has been 0.253 inch and the least penetration 0.0025 inch. An oversize envelope (metal beyond the size of the finished product) of at least 0.0025 inch would be needed.

A typical ECM fixture is shown in Fig. 2. It provides for rapid continuous removal and replacement of electrolyte in the machining zone (i.e., in the gap). The distribution of electric current at the start of ECM is illustrated schematically, Fig. 3. The density of lines between tool and metal part represents density of current. The current flows first from the nearest surface, "a," on the tool to "b" region of the metal part. At the completion of stock removal (in the illustration, a cavity), the form of the tool is reproduced as shown in the lower illustration. The dimensions shown in the illustration are actual measurements for an electrochemical machining operation. The electrolyte flows in the 0.005-inch gap in a closed hydraulic circuit.

Obviously, at the start of electrolysis any local turbulence in the electrolyte in the gap would change the pattern of current flow at the initial ECM zone, a → b. Also after appreciable tool advance, local turbulences that alter the flow pattern of electric current and electrolyte are to

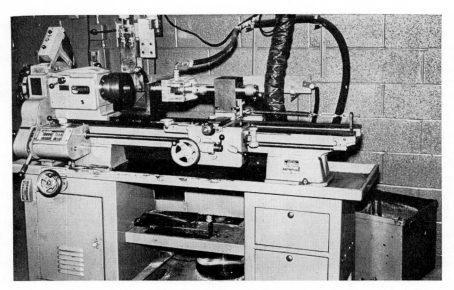

FIG. 2. Representative electrochemical machining equipment. The cubical fixture (center) holds the tool and the part to be machined. The attached hose carries the electrolyte into the fixture at the required rate of flow.

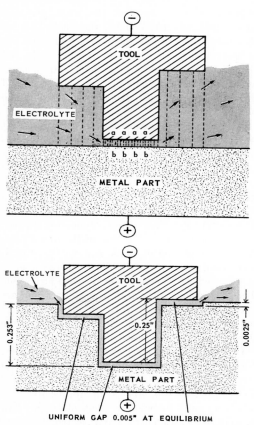

FIG. 3. As electrochemical machining begins, the electric current flows almost entirely from a to b (top). Only in that area is the gap small enough for the current to pass at the applied emf. As the machining proceeds, the shape is formed at the equilibrium gap as shown in the cross-sectional sketch of the tool and metal part (bottom). Electrolyte must flow through the gap at high velocity during entire operation.

be avoided. Otherwise, the contour generated will match the electrolyte-flow pattern and not the tool-face contour as designed for the job. Knowledgeable selection of electrolyte, voltage, and current density is important to the achievement of desired results.

ECM operates with constant applied voltage (2 to 18 volts). The size of the power supply is determined by the area to be machined and the required metal removal rate. With a 1000-ampere supply and 50-square-inch maximum surface area, the maximum penetration rate for iron is 0.0027 inch per minute. A significant point is that the ECM tool moves only a distance equal to the amount of the penetration. One motion cuts the whole surface. If penetration

is to be 0.5 inch, the tool moves 0.5 inch. In contrast, an abrasive belt or wheel in generating contour may travel many feet before reaching 0.5-inch penetration in producing a shaped surface. ECM works on the entire surface. Chip-by-chip removing tools work only on a small fraction of the total surface at any one instant.

In summary, ECM should be recognized for several unique and highly practical features. Briefly stated they are:

(1) There is no contact between tool and workpiece, hence, there is no tool pressure on the workpiece. Hard-to-cut metals can be shaped and ultrathin metals can be electro-machined as easily as heavy sections.

(2) Because there is no pressure, there are no burrs at cut edges. Hence, there is no deburring cost and no burrs at inaccessible points. Indeed, the edges are naturally broken and are not sharp.

(3) Because there is no contact and no pressure, the operation of electrolytic shaping and cutting is noiseless. Hence, there are no sparks, no chatter, no crunch, and no dust.

(4) Once fixturing and tooling are designed, electroshaping is simple to operate.

References

1. FAUST, CHARLES L., AND SNAVELY, CLOYD A., "Electroshaping: New Process Speeds Metal Removal," *The Iron Age*, **185** (November 3, 1960).
2. "Electroshaping," *Metal Industry* (London), **98**, 63 (January 27, 1961).
3. FAUST, CHARLES L., "Sculpturing Hard Metal," *Industrial Science & Engineering* (February, 1961).
4. CRAWFORD, J. H., "Electrolytic Machining Powers Its Way Through Exotic Metals," *SAE Journal*, **70**, 90 (June, 1962).

CHARLES L. FAUST

ELECTROMETRIC TITRATIONS

The titration procedure, whereby an unknown quantity of a specific substance is determined by adding to it a standard reagent (the titrant), which reacts with it in a definite and known proportion, is well established as one of the most precise, accurate, rapid, and simple methods of quantitative analysis. Many titrants have been found which react rapidly and quantitatively either directly with a large number of sought-for constituents or with their products from prior quantitative reactions, thereby providing wide applicability. Of course, even with a good available reaction, whether it be acid-base, precipitation, redox or complexation, a reliable method of determining the end point is required; i.e., an experimental method which indicates to the chemist the *quantity of titrant* just sufficient to be chemically *equivalent* to the unknown quantity of sought-for constituent. For example, if a Ce (IV) solution is used as a titrant and added to an unknown quantity of Fe (II) solution it is necessary to have some method of signaling when the cerric titrant has quantitatively oxidized the ferrous iron. The experimentally observed signal that indicates the completion of the titration reaction is called the *end point*.

The end point should be coincident with the equivalence point. In other words, the unknown amount (equivalents) of a sought-for constituent should be equal to the equivalents of titrant delivered to some experimentally observed signal. However, good accuracy can be obtained if there is a small reproducible difference (*titration blank*) between the equivalence and end points. Unfortunately, there is not any one end-point system universally applicable for all the useful titration reactions. Consequently, many different end-point systems have been developed and applied to provide good precision and accuracy for specific titration problems. In fact, one of the common classifications of titrations is according to the method of end-point detection. Hence, a *potentiometric titration* is a titration in which the end point is determined by measuring changes of electrode potential during the titration reaction; a *conductometric titration* is one in which the end point is obtained through conductance measurements. In an *amperometric titration* the end point is determined by measuring changes of current. Sometimes end points are determined by controlling the currents through various electrode pairs and measuring potential changes, or vice versa, and these methods are referred to as *voltammetric titrations*. Descriptions of the principles, techniques and applications of potential, current or resistance (conductance) measurements to detect the end points in titrations comprise most of the literature under the general topic *electrometric titrations*.[2-6]

Coulometric Titrations

Another major topic that comes under the general heading of electrometric titrations is called *coulometric titrations*.[4] It is not related to the method of end-point detection, but instead this topic focuses attention on the titrant. It refers to the number of *coulombs* or electrons necessary to oxidize or reduce, either directly or indirectly, an unknown amount of a specific sought-for constituent.

If a current exists between two electrodes immersed in a solution, oxidation of some specie(s) must occur at the anode and reduction of another specie(s) at the cathode. The product formed at either the anode or the cathode might be used as the titrant for a coulometric titration. For example, it is possible to generate iodine by electrolytic oxidation of iodide ions at a platinum anode; the iodine could then serve as a titrant to react with some sought-for reducing constituent such as thiosulfate. In this example iodine can be generated directly in the presence of a solution containing an unknown concentration of thiosulfate and a large excess concentration of iodide. Therefore, the chemical reaction can occur immediately between the thiosulfate and the generated iodine. Since the reduction product at the cathode is not important in this titration and might interfere, the cathode is chemically but not electrically isolated by a suitable compartment.

The iodine could also be generated externally in a small tube and flowed into the titration vessel.[4] In the case of either internal or external generation and assuming 100 per cent efficient generation of iodine at the anode, the quantity of iodine generated up to the end point is directly proportional to the charge (coulombs) used from the start to the end of the titration.

In most applications a constant current source is used so that the product of current, i, in amperes (coulombs per second) multiplied by the time, t (seconds), required to reach the end point provides a measure of the charge, Q (coulombs), necessary to generate the iodine equivalent to the thiosulfate; i.e., $Q = it$. Therefore, the number of equivalents of thiosulfate is equal to $Q/\mathbf{F}$, where $\mathbf{F}$ is the Faraday constant (96,494 coulombs per equivalent).

There are several advantages to coulometric titrations. The preparation and storing of titrants and the filling of burets for controlling and measuring titrant are eliminated. Unstable reagents can be generated for on-the-spot use. Microquantities of titrant can be accurately delivered by using an accurate low-current source and timer (a 1 ma current for 10 seconds

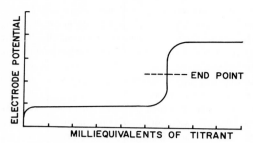

FIG. 1. Potentiometric titration curve.

would be equivalent to adding 0.1 ml. of a 0.001N titrant). Also, the ease of starting and stopping the current with a relay lends itself to the automation of various titrations. It is necessary, of course, to use an end-point detection system that is sufficiently sensitive and precise for each specific titration. Amperometric end-point detection has been a common choice for use with coulometric generation of titrant. The coulometric generator electrodes sometimes interfere with potentiometric end-point detection.

The potentiometric, conductometric, and amperometric methods of end-point detection are considered in more detail in the subsequent sections.

Potentiometric Titration

The potentiometric detection of an end point requires two electrodes. One electrode (the reference) should maintain a constant potential throughout the titration; the other electrode (the indicator) must undergo a significant change in potential that is related to the change in concentration of the species involved in the titration reaction. In general, a plot of the measured voltage between the indicator-reference pair versus milliequivalents of added titrant provides a *titration curve* that has a sigmoid shape, as shown in Fig. 1.

The shape of a potentiometric titration curve results from the logarithmic relationship between potential and concentration (Nernst equation) and the nature of the titration procedure. The sigmoid shape indicates that the relative concentration changes of the reacting species are very large in the region of the equivalence point when the solution changes from one with a small remaining amount of the titrated substance to one with a slight excess of titrant. Reaction and electrode equilibria in the region of the equivalence point are, therefore, important in establishing the end point.

By definition the potentiometric end point is the *inflection point* of the sigmoid curve. Theoretically, the inflection point is coincident with the equivalence point for symmetrical titration curves wherein the reaction at the indicator electrode is reversible and one mole or ion of the titrant reacts with one mole or ion of the substance titrated. In the case of asymmetrical curves (resulting from nonreversible indicator-electrode reactions or when the number of molecules of the titrant and titrated substance are unequal) there is a small difference between the inflection point and the equivalence point.

The type of indicator electrode depends on the specific reactants that undergo concentration changes during the titration. For acid-base titrations the pH changes greatly, and an electrode that responds rapidly to pH changes is used. The most common indicator electrode for acid-base titrations is the glass electrode (q.v.).

For redox titrations a platinum wire electrode is the most common indicator electrode; for halide titrations with silver ion titrant a silver wire or silver-silver chloride wire is used as an indicator electrode. In most cases a calomel electrode that is isolated from the titration media by a saturated KCl salt bridge is used as the reference electrode (q.v.).

Many techniques of potentiometric end-point detection have been published.[4] Some of the most commonly-used techniques are: (a) the end point is taken from the titration curve which is manually plotted from the potential readings that are obtained after the addition and mixing of each small increment of titrant; (b) the titration curve is automatically plotted by using a self-balancing potentiometric strip-chart recorder that has the chart-drive synchronized with the titrant delivery system—and again the end point is read from the curve; (c) the addition of titrant is continued until a preset end-point potential is observed and then the delivery of titrant is terminated. (This is usually a null point obtained by comparing the potential difference of the electrode pair with a potential source that is set at a value equal to the end-point potential); (d) the method is the same as (c) except that the seeking of the preset end-point potential and termination of titrant delivery are automatically performed; (e) the delivery of titrant is automatically terminated at the inflection point of the titration curve by utilizing an electronically computed second-derivative signal of the potentiometric titration curve.

Each of the above potentiometric titration methods has advantages and disadvantages. The complete titration curves that are obtained by methods (a) and (b) can provide information about the titration reaction as well as the end-point values. The automatic method of plotting has the obvious advantage of speed with the disadvantage of more expensive equipment. For obtaining only end-point values the (a) and (b) methods are generally more time-consuming and cumbersome than methods (c), (d), or (e). Methods (c) and (d) are similar in principle to many of the classical visual end-point methods; i.e., the titrant delivery is terminated at some absolute end-point potential rather than at some specific indicator color. Both the manual and automatic methods in (c) and (d) have the disadvantages of requiring knowledge about the absolute end-point potentials for each specific titration. Therefore, the potential of the reference electrode must be known and remain stable, junction potentials must be small, and the indicator electrode must come rapidly to its equilibrium values. The second-derivative signal that is necessary for method (d) is automatically computed by a simple electronic device and is shown in Fig. 2. The inflection point is the point at which the second derivative signal rapidly crosses the zero axis after a brief voltage swing prior to the end point.[5] The brief voltage pulse sets a relay that trips as the signal travels through zero. The relay automatically terminates the titrant delivery at the zero (inflection) point. This second derivative method has the advantages of not requiring reference electrodes of known potential or indicator electrodes that come to specific equilibrium values. Therefore, the choice of electrode pairs is often greatly simplified. For example, a graphite pencil lead and a platinum alloy wire serve as good reference and indicator electrodes, respectively, for both aqueous and nonaqueous acid-base titrations. The graphite lead remains at nearly constant potential during the short period prior to termination of titrant delivery although it drifts slowly throughout the titration. The indicator Pt-Rh wire undergoes a maximum rate of potential change at or close to the equivalence point, even though the absolute potential in

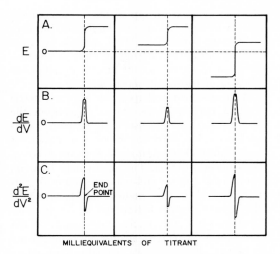

FIG. 2. Potentiometric titration curves showing (A) ordinary curve of voltage *vs* meq. of titrant, (B) first derivative curve, (C) second derivative curve.

similar solutions shifts with use. Also, it is not necessary to know and set any end-point values with the second-derivative method. The major disadvantage is that the titration reactions must be relatively rapid to provide a useful second-derivative signal.

Conductometric Titration

The conductometric detection of an end point requires an electrode and measurement system which provides a readout value that is a simple function of conductance. The most-used system is an a-c Wheatstone bridge (q.v.) which has for the unknown arm of the bridge a pair of platinum electrodes immersed in the titration media. When the bridge is balanced to a null point the value read from the dials is generally the resistance of the solution between the two electrodes. However, it is possible to design the bridge so the readout value is conductance. This is an advantage in plotting a conductometric titration curve because conductance is proportional to concentration. (See **Conductivity, Electrolytic; Conductivity (Electrolytic) Measurement**.)

The electrical conductance of a solution is a summation of contributions from all the ions present. Therefore, electrolytes that do not enter into the titration reaction provide a "background" conductance. The conductance changes that result from changes in the specific reacting ions are observed on top of this "background." This is one of the serious limitations of conductometric titrations. Many samples contain large quantities of electrolytes that are not involved in the titration but greatly decrease the precision of end-point detection.

There are many shapes for conductometric titration curves. These shapes depend on the specific reactions because each measured conductance value depends on the summation of conductance changes for all ions involved in the titration reaction. The ideal conductometric titration for precise end-point detection is generally one where the conductance changes rapidly in one direction before and in the opposite direction after the equivalence point. When conductance is plotted against milliequivalents of titrant there are two straight lines intersecting at a sharp angle. Therefore, the end point (point of intersection of the two lines) can be precisely determined.

For a conductometric titration curve with two straight lines, it is not necessary to obtain data in the region of the equivalence point. A few conductance measurements can be obtained near the beginning and a few after the equivalence point. Straight lines are then drawn through the plotted points and extrapolated so they intersect to provide the end point. In this way solution equilibrium in the region of the equivalence point is not important in establishing the end point.

Conductometric titrations are seldom used for routine determinations because the background conductance for most practical samples is too high for good precision. However, useful information about new chemical reactions can be obtained from studying the shapes of conductometric titration curves.

An increase in sensitivity for conductometric titrations is often possible by using the so-called *high-frequency titration methods*.[4] In these methods the electrodes are attached to the outside walls of a vessel that contains the titration solution. By making the vessel a part of a high-frequency oscillator circuit, it is possible to measure changes of current, voltage, or frequency that are related to the solution conductance. Because the electrodes are on the outside of the vessel they are not contaminated by solution particles and micro air bubbles that cling to the surface and change the electrode area and the measured conductance. The nonlinear response between readout value and conductance somewhat limits the application of the high-frequency methods.

Amperometric Titrations

The detection of end points by current measurements is related to the principles and techniques of polarography (q.v.) and voltammetry.[2] A voltage is applied between a reference and microelectrode (q.v.) so that at least one specific constituent that is involved in the titration reaction undergoes either oxidation or reduction at the surface of the microelectrode, and either before or after the equivalence point. Because of the small area of the microelectrode, a limiting current is obtained that is proportional to the concentration of the specific species undergoing electrode reaction. A sensitive current-measuring device is put in series with the cell.

To illustrate the shape of typical amperometric titration curves assume that an unknown concentration of Pb^{++} is titrated with a chromate ($CrO_4^{=}$) titrant to form insoluble $PbCrO_4$ precipitate. The applied voltage is adjusted so that both lead ions and chromate ions are reduced at the microelectrode. Before the equivalence point the lead ion concentration is decreased by precipitation with chromate titrant, and the limiting

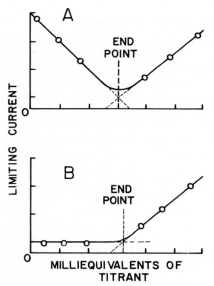

Fig. 3. Amperometric titration curves: (A) Titration of lead ions with chromate ions at an applied voltage when both reactant and titrant give limiting currents. (B) The same titration as in (A) except that at the applied voltage only the chromate titrant gives a limiting current.

current decreases until the equivalence point is reached; then the limiting current increases as the concentration of chromate increases with the addition of excess titrant, as shown in Fig. 3A.

If the applied voltage between the reference and microelectrode is set so that only chromate and not lead ions are reduced at the microelectrode, the amperometric titration curve would be as in Fig. 3B. Since there is no electrode reaction prior to the equivalence point, the current is essentially zero; but after the equivalence point (when the Pb^{++} is quantitatively precipitated), the excess chromate provides a limiting current proportional to its concentration.

For amperometric titration curves, such as in Figs. 3A and 3B, the end points are obtained by extrapolation of two straight lines to the point of intersection. Therefore, amperometric endpoint detection has the advantage of requiring data only away from the equivalence point, as is the case for conductometric titrations. Amperometric end-point detection can be made rather specific because measured currents can be obtained from selected electroreducible or electroxidizable constituents involved in the titration reaction. The specific species to undergo reaction at the microelectrode are selected by adjusting the applied voltage to the cell.

One disadvantage of amperometric titrations is that oxygen must be removed from solution (usually by bubbling in nitrogen for a few minutes) for many useful titrations. The oxygen, if present, undergoes reduction at the same applied voltages that are applicable for many other substances involved in many practical titrations. The reduction of oxygen provides a large variable background current.

There are hundreds of specific procedures that utilize amperometric end-point detection.[3]

References

1. BARD, A. J., Anal. Chem., **34**, 57R (1962).
2. DELAHAY, P., "New Instrumental Methods in Electrochemistry," New York, Interscience Publishing Co., 1954.
3. LAITINEN, H. A., Anal. Chem., **34**, 307R (1962).
4. LINGANE, J. J. "Electroanalytical Chemistry," 2nd Ed., New York, Interscience Publishing Co., 1960.
5. MALMSTADT, H. V., Record of Chemical Progress, **17**, 1 (1956).
6. MURRAY, R. W., AND REILLEY, C. N., Anal. Chem., **34**, 313R (1962).

HOWARD V. MALMSTADT

Cross-references: *Chronoamperometry; Chrono-* *potentiometry; Conductivity, Electrolytic; Conductivity (Electrolytic) Measurement; Electrode Potentials; Faraday's Laws; Glass Electrode; Nernst Equation; Polarography; Reference Electrodes.*

ELECTROMIGRATION IN LIQUID METALS

Definition, Description by Transport Numbers

Electromigration is any mass motion in solids or liquids caused directly by the presence of an imposed electric field. The definition includes all electrolytic phenomena, but not thermal diffusion in current heating or effects due to container walls and electrode surfaces.

The term *electrolysis*, used where a mixture of chemical species, such as a salt or an alloy, is separated into its components by a current, is sometimes also applied to current-induced demixing of the isotopes in a chemically pure metal (*isotope transport* or *Haeffner effect*). Electromigration also includes the motion in a pure metal of activated ions under the influence of an electric field (*self-transport*).

Alternate terms for electromigration in metals, often used in literature, are *electrotransport* and *electrodiffusion*. The latter word stresses the connection of the effect with diffusion as a rate-governing factor. In qualitative analogy with diffusion, electromigration is by several orders of magnitude greater in liquid than in solid metals, and much less temperature dependent. Quantitatively, *transport numbers* is a satisfactory description. In a conducting mixture, where the i-th component, z_i unit charges, has the concentration c_i ($\Sigma c_i = 1$) and migrates with the velocity v_i, in a certain reference frame, the transport number is defined by

$$U_i = \frac{c_i z_i v_i}{\Sigma c_i z_i v_i},$$

with the sign convention of all velocities positive towards the cathode. Accordingly, $\Sigma U_i = 1$, if one includes electrons and other charge carriers as components. A suitable reference frame in solids is the crystal lattice. In liquids a meaningful reference system is not so obvious. The container is rather unsatisfactory, as the electrolyzed melt may move under the influence of factors other than electromigration. However, even in a melt the great majority of atoms is at any moment stationary with respect to its neighbor, in a close-range order. Electromigration velocity can, therefore, be taken with reference to the bulk of the melt, in analogy with solids, regardless of whether experiments show absolute transport to be meaningful or not.*

In metals, only a very small share of the current will be carried by the ions. Consequently, $U_i \ll 1$, and for all practical purposes

$$U_i = -\frac{c_i z_i v_i}{c_e v_e}$$

(index e referring to electrons). Most experiments give only the migration velocity of one component relative to another, and most data in literature yield *relative* transport numbers, in the form

$$U_{jk} = -\frac{c_j z_j v_j - c_k z_k v_k}{c_e v_e},$$

independent of any reference system.

Brief Survey of Experimental Work

As early as 1861 it was observed that, after electrolysis in the molten state, a Pb-Sn alloy was soft at one end and brittle at the other, and that a Na-Hg amalgam only decomposed water at one end[1] (electromigration in solid alloys, with transport numbers smaller by at least 3 powers of 10, eluded observation for another half-century). The first quantitative results were obtained in Austria and Germany in the early 1920's. Many investigations of liquid alloy systems were carried out throughout the next two decades, notably by R. Kremann and K. E. Schwarz (for a valuable survey, see a monograph by the latter[2]). Most of the early measurements suffered from great experimental inadequacies, and though the list of results is large, it has not been very helpful in furnishing a basis for a quantitative theory.

New interest in electromigration was stimulated by the discovery (Swedish Atomic Energy Company, Stockholm, 1953) of the Haeffner effect, i.e., the isotope separation effect caused by direct current flowing through liquid metal. First detected in Hg at 50°C, the effect and its temperature dependence have since been investigated in molten In, Li, K, Rb, Sn, Zn, Cd, and in a Rb-K alloy (Chalmers University of Technology, Gothenburg, Sweden), in Ga (C. E. N. Saclay, France), and again in Hg (Ukrainian Acad. of Sciences, Kiev, USSR), and Ga (Rensselaer Polytechnic Institute, Troy, N. Y.). For a survey, see Refs. 3 and 4.

Liquid alloy electromigration has been taken up in several laboratories in the USA and the USSR during the last decade, sometimes with considerable experimental improvements on earlier work. Dilute amalgams have been investigated at the University of Chicago.[5, 6] At the University of Michigan, dilute sodium amalgams and Bi-alloys have been studied, as well as the Bi-Sn system at different concentrations and temperatures. Workers at the Mendeleev Inst., Moscow, USSR, have electrolyzed dilute alloying components in K and Na at 100°C and dilute solutions of Ag and Au in different solvents. At the Steel Institute, Moscow, USSR, several other dilute binary systems of Bi, Se, Ca, Zn, Cd, Sn, Pb, Ag have been studied. A recent thesis by Verhoeven[1] offers a very good survey of latest alloy work.

Basic Measurements in Capillary Cells

The experimental set-up in liquid metal electromigration is governed by two main practical considerations: a) ohmic heat development, and b) convection.

a) The derived migration velocities require current densities of 10^3 to 10^4 amps/sq cm, corresponding to a field of the order 10^{-1} volts/cm. In a cylindrical cell of 1 cm radius the heat dissipation would thus be something like 1 kw per cm length. To avoid excessive heating, cooling by temperature baths or otherwise is necessary, and the cell diameter is kept small; usually capillaries of 0.2–1 mm diam. are used, reducing the heating to the order of 1 w per cm length. The cells are in principle capillary arms with their ends closed by fused-in electrodes to prevent bulk motion and atmosphere contamination, and to facilitate filling by vacuum methods. The glass cell shown in Fig. 1[3] is rather typical. Some workers have used bent capillaries to lessen heat convection. Others, where composition changes could be measured resistometrically, without sacrificing the cell after each run for chemical analysis, have used permanent cells with auxiliary electrodes, permitting simultaneous resistivity and diffusivity measurements.[5] Cell material varies with corrosion consideration.

---

* The meaning of absolute transport numbers, as measured in liquid salts, has generally been somewhat obscured by the presence of container walls. The above notion of absolute U-values seems, however, experimentally justified by the Haeffner effect (See **Fused Salt Transport Numbers**).

The length of the cell is decided by the desired separation on one hand, diffusion and convection on the other. In electrolysis the composition change begins at the electrodes and spreads towards the middle of the cell, where it arrives after a *critical time*

$$\tau = \frac{L^2}{\pi D_{eff}} \qquad (1)$$

where L is the cell half-length, and $D_{eff} = D + D'$, D being the true self-diffusion coefficient and D' a convection term (for detail, see Ref. 3, Chap. 1). The length,

$$z_{eff} = \sqrt{\pi D_{eff}\, t},$$

can be called the *practical separation range* for an experiment of duration, t. For $t > \tau$, the composition quickly approaches a steady state. Considering two components, j and k, with a velocity difference $\Delta v = v_j - v_k$, in the steady state the concentration everywhere in the column (length coordinate, z) will be governed by

$$\frac{\partial(\ln c_k/c_j)}{\partial z} = \frac{\Delta v}{D_{eff}}. \qquad (2)$$

On the other hand, Δv can be determined for $t = t' < \tau$, *without* having to know D_{eff}, from

$$\Delta v = \left(\frac{N_k}{(N_k)_0} - \frac{N_i}{(N_j)_0} \right) \frac{z'}{t'} \qquad (3)$$

where

$$\sqrt{\pi D_{eff}\, t'} < L,$$

and N, N_0, respectively, are the mole amounts between $z = 0$ and $z = z'$ after and before the experiment.

Most experiments reported in literature have been of the steady-state type ($t > \tau$), and suffered from the uncertainty in D_{eff}, sometimes to the extent of rendering the results very doubtful. The other kind of experiments (for $t < \tau$) has to satisfy the condition that there is a constant composition at one end of the analyzed volume throughout the run; it is otherwise independent of diffusion and of cell shape. Though the latter kind of setup may sometimes require longer capillaries and correspondingly greater power dissipation, such experiments are generally more reliable.†

† In steady state techniques capillary arm lengths of the order of a few cm are usually ample for both alloy and pure metal work. In "long capillary" techniques 10 cm may do for the alloys

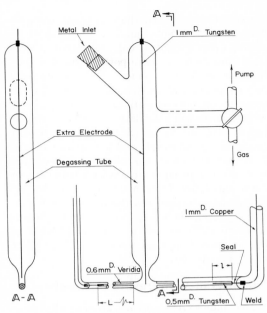

Fig. 1. Schematic diagram of simple capillary cell.

In some cases[3] both methods have been used in parallel, thus obtaining D_{eff}. Inasmuch as D' can be assessed or eliminated, this affords a new method for measuring diffusion in liquid metals.

Convection Effects

The convection term, D', thus causes errors in results, or impairs current economy. It is due to one or several of the following factors:

Thermal Convection. This is normally limited by using small capillary diameters. In alloys the cells are sometimes arranged vertically with slightly higher temperatures at the top, in pure metals horizontally.

Intermittent Vibrations or Temperature Changes. Here the main problem, solidification after the experiment, is avoided in permanent cells and its effect can be assessed in others.

Specific Gravity Differences in Alloys. The heavy component has a tendency to "get under" the light one, causing gravity flow. This has been tackled[2] by making sharp bends in the capillaries in the vertical plane, or by letting the light component migrate upwards. Again, reducing the capillary diameters has proved most efficient.

Nonlinear Flow Profiles. Electroosmosis (i.e., a net force on the liquid in a thin layer near

(using about 1000 amps/sq cm), and 15 to 20 cm for the pure metal (with some 3000 amps/sq cm).

the capillary wall) and the compensating back-flow give the whole liquid a parabolic flow profile, with consequent convective mixing. A related effect, with a fourth-power-curve flow profile, is caused by the Lorentz force of the current, in combination with small deviations from ideally constant capillary cross-section. According to a recent calculation,[7] this latter kind of stirring is proportional to $I^4 r_0{}^2$, where I and r_0 are, respectively, the (total) current and the capillary radius. It is much the largest contribution to convection at ca 3000 amps/sq cm in precision-bore 0.6 mm diam. capillaries. In even thinner capillaries, although cross-section irregularities may get relatively greater, the electroosmosis effect (proportional to $I^2 r_0{}^{-2}$) as well as thermal effects may become more important than the stirring effect of the Lorentz force.

Summary of Main Qualitative Results

Here only a cross-section is given of what seem to be the more distinct tendencies. A good detailed review is presented by Ref. 1.

Self-transport. Absolute transport numbers, as deduced (see below) from the Haeffner-effect isotope mass-effects, are of the order -10^{-4} to -10^{-3}.† In *all* liquid metals so far investigated, the mass transport goes to the *anode*. The transport numbers increase with temperature, faster in fact than do the corresponding self-diffusion coefficients, especially at high temperatures.

Alloy Electrolysis. The data are very heterogeneous. The relative transport numbers are of the order 10^{-5} to 10^{-3} and can be either positive or negative. The temperature dependence is not strong, certainly smaller than that of diffusion; $|U|$ may either increase or decrease as temperature goes up. The signs and magnitudes of transport depend on component concentrations as well as on temperatures. At some concentrations or temperatures, in certain alloys, reversals of directions may occur. The relative transport directions seem connected with the alloy's resistivity increment per added component atom. An atom's "differentness" from its environment, such as chemical dissimilarity or dilution, usually increases relative transport. In alloying partners with different valences, the statistical tendency (with many exceptions, however) is for the higher valence component to concentrate at the cathode.

† At about 3000 amps/sq cm this corresponds to isotope abundance changes of some 10 per cent at the electrodes after a few days' run.

Another tendency is that for the dilute component of a binary to concentrate at the anode.

Besides these trends, much other information has been reported in the many papers on alloy electrolysis, but it is difficult to draw safe conclusions of a general nature. The measure of cross-agreement in different laboratories on theoretically relevant points has not been great. The reader is referred to the individual reports (see survey Ref. 1).

Elements of Theory

Though the importance of *electron friction* in metal electromigration was suggested already during World War I (by Skaupy in Germany), in most subsequent theories (see Ref. 2) it was neglected. No real headway was, therefore, made until Klemm's successful attempt in 1954 (in Germany) to explain qualitatively the Haeffner effect. Since then theoretical contributions towards the problem of liquid metal electromigration have been made by several workers, in France, Germany, Sweden, the USA, and the USSR. At the present stage, the theory is by no means complete, but in several instances good qualitative agreement with the more reliable experiments has been achieved. Here only the main points of view will be sketched and controversies if possible avoided. The main objectives of study are similar as in the field of solid metals; see the article by H. B. Huntington in this volume.

Force Acting on an Activated Ion. In a current-carrying metal, an ion is subjected to the force

$$F_i = Ee(z_{eff})_i = Ee\bar{z}(\xi_i - \varphi_i). \qquad (4)$$

Here E is the field, e the electronic charge, $(z_{eff})_i$ can be referred to as the *effective valence* of the ion, $\bar{z}$ the number of free electrons per atom (the mean valence of the melt atoms), $\xi_i \bar{z}e$ the true charge of the atom i, and $\varphi_i \cdot \bar{z}Ee$ the *electron friction* force, due to the scattering of the charge carriers. The factor ξ_i accounts for screening and ionization. The sign of φ_i can be negative, if positive holes are charge carriers. As evidence, however, indicates that all liquid metals are good electron conductors (see below), here charge carriers will be referred to as "electrons."

The bulk of the metal is electroneutral and there must be no net force. In a perfect array of identical atoms $\xi_i = \varphi_i$. In a real metal, however, there will be impurity atoms, as well as atoms which are near greater-than-average density fluctuations or in a greater-than-average degree of disorder. Such atoms will be referred to as *activated*. They have, beside greater mobility, greater-than-average electron scattering cross-sections, and may have different true charges from more stationary atoms. In alloys, moreover, different species will have different cross-sections and charges. Thus, ξ_i and φ_i will not in general cancel.

The ion receives migration velocity, $v_i = F_i B_i$ (where B_i is its mobility), which can be determined chemically, resistometrically or mass-spectrometrically in experiments as discussed above.

Isotope Transport and Self-transport. The Haeffner effect gives an enrichment of the light isotope at the anode. The order of magnitude is expressed by the *mass-effect*, $\mu \approx 10^{-5}$ to 10^{-4}, where

$$\mu = \frac{\Delta v / (-v_e')}{\Delta M / M}$$

(v_e' is the electron cloud velocity on the arbitrary assumption of one free electron per atom; Δv is the velocity difference of two isotopes of mass number difference, ΔM, mean mass number, M). The effect could not be explained by isotope differences in ξ or φ in an otherwise uniform medium. All such calculation predicted a cathode-directed migration of the light isotope, and too small by far. The first plausible explanation (Klemm, 1954[8]) rests on the notion of activated atoms in a pure metal (see above) giving rise to self-transport. In the transport motion, the light isotope will be more mobile than the heavy one and so be enriched at the electrode towards which the self-transport is directed.

Assuming for simplicity just one activated state (i.e., zero mobility of nonactivated ions), the bulk velocity relative to the electron cloud can be written:

$$w = v - \bar{z} v_e = c^* B^* F^* - v_e' \qquad (5)$$

(v is the self transport velocity, and v_e the electron velocity, stars denoting activated ions, sign conventions as above). Differentiating w with respect to isotope mass and dividing it by itself,

$$\frac{\partial(\ln w)}{\partial M} = \frac{1}{w} \cdot \frac{\partial v}{\partial M} = \frac{v}{w} \frac{\partial(\ln v)}{\partial M}$$

$$= \frac{v}{w} \frac{\partial \ln (c^* B^* F^*)}{\partial M} \qquad (6)$$

But this, considering that $w \simeq -v_e'$, gives for

the mass effect (with U and μ defined as above) $\mu = U \cdot a / \bar{z}$ where

$$a = \left(\frac{\partial c^*}{c^*} + \frac{\partial B^*}{B^*} + \frac{\partial F^*}{F^*} \right) \frac{M}{\partial M} \qquad (7)$$

is the isotope term and U the transport number. In the bracket, the force term can probably be neglected,† and the other two, denoting the isotope difference in diffusion, should, by comparison with evidence from isotope electromigration in liquid salts make $a \simeq -0.1$. This factor should very slowly decrease as temperature rises.

Thus, the mass-effect being $\mu \approx 10^{-5}$, the self-transport numbers are $U \approx -10^{-4}$, in good agreement with the magnitude of relative transport numbers measured in alloys. The direction, always towards the anode, indicates that φ dominates safely over ξ, and that the liquid metals are good electron conductors. This latter has been confirmed by several recent Hall effect measurements.

Temperature Dependence of φ. If the electron scattering cross-section of an activated ion is σ^* and the mean scattering cross-section of the ions is $\bar{\sigma}$, then $\bar{\sigma}$ will be responsible for the resistance, ρ, and σ^* will represent an atomic resistivity increment, $\Delta \rho^* / c^*$. By definition of mean free path, l, and of scattering cross-section, the force $Ee\bar{z}\, \varphi^* = Ee\, n\, l\sigma^*$ (n is the number of electrons per unit volume), and $Ee\bar{z} = eE\, n\, l\bar{\sigma}$, so that $\varphi^* = \sigma^* / \bar{\sigma} = \Delta \rho^* / c^* \rho$, and the effective valence is‡

$$z_{eff}^* = \bar{z} \left(\xi^* - \frac{\Delta \rho^*}{c^* \rho} \right). \qquad (8)$$

Temperature Dependence of Self-transport. The transport number will be given by

$$U = \frac{c^* B^* F^*}{-c_e v_e} \cdot \frac{\bar{z}}{1 + \bar{z}}$$

which by simple calculation reduces to

$$U = \bar{z} \rho e^2 z_{eff}^* \frac{D'}{f' k T} \qquad (9)$$

(D' is the self-diffusion coefficient, f' a Bardeen-Herring correlation factor, and k is Boltzmann's constant).

† According to simple considerations by the author, to be published.
‡ Lines of reasoning leading to expressions of this form were published independently by workers in Russia, Sweden, and the USA in 1959 and 1960.[9, 10, 11]

The experimental fact that the Haeffner effect self-transport numbers, U, despite the negative temperature characteristic of $\rho z^*_{eff}/T$ (approx. $\sim T^{-1}$) grow considerably faster with the temperature than does the self-diffusion coefficient, D, seems to indicate $D' > D$, i.e., that the mechanism governing liquid electromigration is not identical with that of main diffusion and has higher "activation energy." This could possibly be attributed to ring-exchange of diffusing atoms or to rotation of clusters.

Alloys. Continuing on the above model for qualitative predictions in alloys, not only scattering cross-sections and ionization degrees of activated components should be known, but also their mobilities. A further complication is that (see above) it is possible that not all diffusing ions partake of electrotransport. Assuming, however, identical mechanisms, the transport numbers should have the form

$$U_{ik} \sim \frac{1}{kT}[(\xi^*_j D_j - \xi^*_k D_k) - (\varphi^*_j D_j - \varphi^*_k D_k)] \quad (10)$$

As the φ^*'s are inversely proportional to resistances, then, if electron friction predominates, the transport numbers will show a rather mild temperature dependence, the approximately exponential rise of the D's being balanced by T^{-2}. At higher temperatures the electron friction terms, from having dominated, may become smaller than the coulomb force terms, in which case the transport direction reverses. By some workers the observed reversals have been tentatively attributed to solvation bonds disappearing at higher temperatures.

Mangelsdorf[6] has considered in some detail the correlation between φ and the atomic resistivity increment of added solute. He has also proposed a refinement to the concept of electron friction by separating it into two parts, one acting on the central ion due to "impurity scattering" and proportional to the square of the valence difference, the other on the immediate environment of the ion.

Too little experimental evidence is yet available and the great number of parameters in formula 10 makes it difficult to verify. The diffusion coefficients have only in exceptional cases been measured concurrently with electromigration. The φ^*'s are not necessarily related to the component resistivity increments unless the solutions are very dilute and so each atom is "activated." The screening factors of activated atoms, ξ^*, have scarcely been studied. Many electro-

migration workers at present consider binary liquid alloys as a simple mixture of chemical components. Others, as here, speak in terms of activated and nonactivated species in each component, and treat the relative motion as caused by composition-dependent differences in electron-scattering cross-sections and in degrees of ionization of the activated components. The correctness of any view is very much subject to future experimental test.

References

1. VERHOEVEN, J. D., "Electrotransport in Some Liquid Metal Alloys," Ph.D. Thesis, University of Michigan 1963. Obtainable from University Microfilms, Ann Arbor, Michigan; survey published in *Met. Reviews*, **8**, No. 31 (1963).
2. SCHWARZ, K. E., "Elektrolytische Wanderung in Festen und Flüssigen Metallen," Leipzig, J. A. Barth, 1940; also, Edwards Bros., Ann Arbor, Michigan, 1945.
3. LODDING, A., "Isotope Transport Phenomena in Liquid Metals," Gothenburg Stud. Phys. 1, Stockholm, Almquist and Wiksell, 1961.
4. LODDING, A., *J. chim. phys.*, **60**, 254 (1963).
5. MANGELSDORF, P. C., JR., *Metallurgy Soc. Conf. AIME*, **7**, 428, Interscience Pub., 1961.
6. MANGELSDORF, P. C., JR., *J. Chem. Phys.*, **30**, 1170 (1959).
7. LODDING, A., AND KLEMM, A., *Z. Naturforschg.*, **17a**, 1085 (1962).
8. KLEMM, A., *Z. Naturforschg.*, **9a**, 1031 (1954).
9. FIKS, V. B., *Fiz. Tver. Tela*, **1**, No. 1 (1959), or *Sov. Phys. Sol. State*, **1**, No. 1, 14 (1959).
10. LODDING, A., *Z. Naturforschg.*, **14a**, 934 (1959).
11. HUNTINGTON, H. B., AND GRONE, A. R., *J. Phys. Chem. Solids*, **20**, 76 (1961).

A. LODDING

Cross-reference: *Electromigration in Solid Metals and Alloys; Isotopes-Electrochemical Separation.*

ELECTROMIGRATION IN SOLID METALS AND ALLOYS

Definition of Title

The term electromigration as used in this article is defined to apply to those situations where mass transport occurs in the solid by virtue of the application of electric fields (and currents). In such studies the directly measured quantities are the transport numbers of the constituents of the solid. The transport numbers give the fractional molar number for each constituent that flows for every Faraday of charge conducted through the specimen. The transport numbers are necessarily less than unity, and this treatment will be concerned primarily with metals and alloys for which the transport numbers are small compared with one. Electromigration, involving large transport numbers (comparable to unity), occur in situations involving ionic conductivity, such as the decomposition of salts by electric current. Such solid state electrolysis will not be treated here. Consideration of electromigrations in liquid metals is given in an adjacent article in this Encyclopedia by Dr. Alexander Lodding.

History

Although scientific investigators have speculated for over fifty years on the possible nature of mass transport in solid and liquid metals under the influence of electric forces, it has only been recently that the topic has started to take logical shape and some sort of pattern has begun to emerge for the conceptual framework. A good many of the basic measurements still have to be made. It seems fair to state that the field as a whole is in an adolescent stage. In the 1930's considerable experimental activity took place, located largely in Germany. Reviews of this period have been written by Schwarz,[1] Jost,[2] and Seith.[3] The studies included the observations of the motion of interstitial atoms, such as hydrogen, boron, nitrogen, and carbon. Additional studies were made of some substitutional systems including copper and palladium in gold and polonium in silver.

The really modern period in the development of this subject came around 1953–55 with the work of Seith[4] and Wever.[5] For one thing they were the first to incorporate the use of moving markers on specimens in which electromigration was occurring. Formerly all work had been done in alloy systems and the experiments had consisted in measuring the relative transport of the various elements within the specimen. With the new technique it was then possible to observe a possible net transport of both constituents with respect to the lattice. It was but a step from this type of measurement to extend the studies to pure metals and to observe for them also net transport under the influence of electric fields.[6] Because in many of these experiments the motion of the metallic ion seemed to go in the direction opposite to that expected from the influence of the electric field alone, momentum exchange with the charge carriers of the system appeared operative. Although such

electron drag effects had been postulated for nearly twenty years, nevertheless this was the first really conclusive evidence. In addition Seith and Wever found by investigating a series of Hume-Rothery alloys across their phase diagram that the sign of the momentum transfer seemed to change with the sign of the charge carrier. For example, in those intermetallic compounds for which the current was largely conducted by holes, the charge-carrier momentum exchange was directed toward the cathode.

During the last ten years electromigration has been vigorously pursued in many different laboratories.[7] In Germany there have been active programs at Münster, Berlin, and Mainz. Investigators in the Soviet Union have been particularly busy. There have been theoretical and experimental studies in Leningrad and Moscow and very active experimental programs at Kiev. Electromigration studies, particularly in liquids, have been pursued in Gothenburg, Sweden. In the United States there has been active interest at the Universities of Chicago and Michigan, and at Rensselaer Polytechnic Institute. For a comprehensive and scholarly review of the state of the field up to the beginning of 1963 one is referred to the thesis of John Daniel Verhoeven.

Theoretical Concepts

There have been several recent theoretical treatments of the nature of electromigration originating in various countries (Germany, the United States, Russia, and France) and proceeding from rather different viewpoints to nearly common conclusions. The picture that emerges is that electromigration in metals takes place from the motion of activated atoms subjected to conflicting forces. One of these is the field force itself which acts in a purely electrostatic manner to draw the ions of the metal in one direction. Usually opposed to this force is that of the aforementioned "electron friction," by which is meant the force evolving from the momentum exchange with the charge carriers. For the most part it appears that the latter predominates. It is difficult to make quantitative estimates of the magnitude of these forces from first principles, although one has a good qualitative feeling as to what should be the relative sizes. It is also hard to resolve the effects separately.

It may seem strange that the field force is not directly calculable, but the difficulty arises from the fact that the moving metal ion is to some extent shielded by the surrounding electric charge, so that it is probably an overestimate to assume that it carries its nominal valence value. In fact, there is one extreme theoretical point of view which maintains that the ions of the metal are so completely shielded that they are not subject to an electrostatic force.

In treating the electron friction all the theoretical treatments so far have been forced to introduce some empirical constant to embody the interaction. The exact way in which this constant is introduced depends on the viewpoint of the theorist. It is the interaction of the metallic ion at the activated complex for diffusion with the charge carriers that is the unknown quantity. The commonest way to present this interaction is to speak of the activated ion as having acquired a particular charge. An alternate formulation is to introduce a particular cross section for scattering the charge carrier. A more macroscopic formulation of the phenomena is couched in terms of an ion-charge carrier mutual friction. Still another approach borrows the nomenclature of irradiation damage to speak of the ion as having a certain specific resistivity per per cent. Irrespective of the particular formulation of this interaction constant, its quantitative calculation with any degree of confidence seems to be only remotely possible at this time. As a result several questions as to its nature are somewhat unresolved. Specifically, one would like to know how it depends on the valence of the mobile atom, on the density of charge carriers, on the current density, on the sign of the charge carrier, and on the temperature.

Intuitively one feels that the interaction should be independent of current density and so it appears to be for most of the careful studies which have been carried out for pure metals. However, there exists some evidence that in the case of alloys the opposite is true and that the electromigration from carrier drag falls off at higher concentration. Some further experimental investigation of this point is perhaps needed.

There seems to be no clear reason why the interaction between the activated ion and charge carriers should be temperature independent. Since the mobile ions must compete with the rest of the lattice for the charge-carrier momentum and since normal resistivity increases (linearly) with temperature, T, in this region, one would expect the electron-wind force

to decrease inversely with T. In general the observed results indicate a somewhat more rapid fall-off. Particularly remarkable is the case of copper where two independent observers agree that the direction of electromigration reverses with increasing temperature around 1000°C. At this time there appears to be no convincing explanation for this phenomenon.

One would expect that the scattering power of the mobile ion might vary as the square of its valence, somewhat according to the picture originally put forward by Mott for the treatment of impurity resistivity. For several reasons this treatment is not quantitatively applicable here. For one thing the nature of the valence of the mobile defect at the activated configuration is not a quantity susceptible to direct calculation or even perhaps to direct interpretation. Also, the actual mechanism for mobility introduces certain particular considerations. For example, if one visualizes a vacancy mechanism, then for the mobile atom poised halfway between two semivacancies the cross section for effective scattering of electrons depends in a very crucial way on the configuration not only of the moving atom itself but also of its neighbors. In addition the direction of the incoming electron can have some bearing.

The number of effective charge carriers is reasonably established in the case of a monovalent metal, but the situation becomes much more complicated when one deals with a polyvalent metal for which both electrons and holes contribute to the conductivity. Most of the theoretical work relies heavily on the simplified picture of the free electron sphere, whereas it is known in the case of the polyvalent materials the complexity of the Fermi surface can give rise to holes and electrons of widely different effective masses.

This last point leads perhaps to the most subtle and disturbing aspect of the whole question of mobile ion-charge carrier interaction, namely, to what extent does the sign of the interaction depend on the sign of the charge carrier. The experimental evidence is somewhat obscure and the direct theoretical approach does not give unequivocal results. In some quarters it has been stressed that the intrinsic inertial property of the electron, as indicated by $m°$, is the crucial quality in determining the momentum exchange as is the case in the Einstein-De Haas effect and also the Barnett effect. On the other hand if the charge carriers, as they approach the mobile defect, experience an interaction which can be described completely in terms of an electric field, then the mutual interaction between the two can take place by virtue of a change in the pseudomomentum, hk (h is Planck's constant divided by 2π; k is 2π divided by the wavelength of the electron wave function). Moreover, in polyvalent materials the sign of the Hall effect is the resultant of several conflicting contributions from electrons of different m^*. Here these various contributions are averaged according to the square of their respective mobilities. In the same way the electromigration effect in polyvalent metals is also the resultant of electrons of various different m^*, but the averaging is done in a somewhat different way than in the Hall measurement.

Experimental Results

As for the electromigration of interstitials, the more recent studies have shown that the oxygen atom diffuses toward the anode in β-titanium, zirconium, and yttrium. On the other hand, the diffusion of carbon has been widely studied in the ferrous alloys and is found by the

Russian workers uniformly to move in the direction of the cathode. It would be interesting to carry out a careful series of experiments on the electromigration of different interstitial impurities in the same matrix. Presumably the electron friction force should be similarly directed for all interstitials, but of course the field force would vary from one impurity to another.

Since the pioneer work of Seith and Wever[4, 5] there has been a considerable number of investigations of electromigration in substitutional alloys of all kinds. Refractory metals and transition metal alloys have been particularly extensively studied. A Soviet team in the Ukraine has used radioactive isotopes widely to observe the electromigration in alloy systems. Few systematic tendencies are apparent.

Electromigration studies in semiconductors have been particularly interesting. Because of the very large mobility of certain impurities, such as lithium in germanium and silicon, and as copper in germanium, such experiments give substantial results. In some cases checks with the Nernst-Einstein relation have shown clearly a predominance of the field force. In other cases,

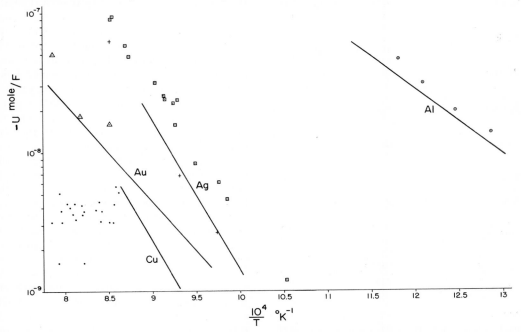

Fig. 1. Comparison of Self-Transport Measurements in Thermal Gradient with Those under Isothermal Conditions. The transport number, U, is plotted against the reciprocal of the absolute temperature times 10^4.

Solid lines best average fit for measurements with thermal gradient, except in case of copper at high temperature, for which symbol of individual measurement is $\cdot$. For isothermal measurements;

$$Cu = \triangle \quad\quad Ag = \boxdot \quad\quad Au = + \quad\quad Al = \odot$$

TABLE 1. SELF-TRANSPORT PARAMETERS
FOR PURE METALS*

Metals	Conditions		$-U \times$ 10^9 mole/F.	$D \times 10^9$ sq cm/ sec	$\rho\mu\Omega$-cm	e^*/e
	I or G	T/T_m				
Aluminum	G	0.90	39	2.1	9.6	11.2
	I		43			12.4
	G	0.95	72	6.8	10.3	6.3
	I					
Cadmium	I	0.88	13.9	1.1	13.2	5
Copper	G	0.90	4.5	.83	8.1	8.2
	I		18.1			18
	G	0.95	~0	2.4	8.5	0
	I		56.0			22
Gold	G	0.90	16.4	2.0	9.9	6.6
	I		90.0			32
	G	0.95	32.8	6.2	10.4	5.5
Indium	G	0.9	2.76	.08	13.6	10.2
		0.95	8.90	.28	15.1	9.2
Iron	G	0.88	−65	.45	126	−9
Lead	I	0.9	9.2	.037	40.1	46
		0.95	32	.13	43.1	45
Nickel	G	0.9	8.4	.56	58	1.9
		0.95	20	1.72	60	1.6
Platinum	G	0.9	−1.4	.20	61.3	−0.28
		0.95	−4.9	.78	64.7	−0.32
Silver†	G	0.90	9.6	.43	7.0	7.6
	I		34			27
	G	0.95	42	2.9	7.4	10
	I		91			22
Tin	I	0.91	3.3	.01	21	216
Zinc	I	0.90	26.6	2.2	13.5	4

* The notations in the column headings have the following meanings:
    I for isothermal conditions; *G* with thermal gradient T_m for melting temperature.
    Moles per Faraday for the unit of the transport number, *U*; micro-ohms centimeter for the unit of resistivity. The last column gives the effective charge, e^* in units of the electron charge.
† Preliminary results

sometimes called self-transport, is a field of particular interest. As remarked earlier, the first of these experiments was carried out by Wever on copper. Since then measurements have been made on gold,[8] silver, iron,[9] nickel,[9] platinum, zinc, cadmium, lead, indium, tin, and aluminum. In every case it is necessary that the specimen be marked in some way. Beyond this common feature, there are two rather different techniques employed.

In one case data are obtained over a wide temperature range by observing the motion of a sequence of marks distributed along the length of a current-carrying specimen whose ends are force cooled.[8] The motion of these marks is in the opposite direction from that of the mass flow, but their velocity is not necessarily equal to that of the average atomic motion under the influence of the electric field, because the motion is the result of the creation (or annihilation) of point defects in the regions of the temperature gradient. The change in the dimensions of these regions of growth or collapse may be either uniaxial or isotropic. In the event that the change is uniaxial in the direction of length, then the marker motion is equal to that of the average atomic velocity. If, on the other hand, hand, the dimensional changes are isotropic, the marker motion is only one-third of that of the average atom velocity. Experiments on such motions in aluminum specimens have shown that the crucial criterion in determining whether uniaxial or isotropic conditions prevail depends on the dimensions of the specimens. The thinner, more elongated specimens give rise to the conditions of isotropic dimensional change.

The alternate procedure employed by some Soviet workers[10] in the Ukraine has relied on radioactive tracers sandwiched in between the butt ends of a pressure-welded specimen. By measuring the net displacement of the center of radioactivity with respect to the original interface, used as a marker, they are able to carry out a truly isothermal measurement. A serious concern in this method is the soundness of the weld between the two halves of the specimen. A comparison of the results of the two methods is shown in the adjoining figure. It can be seen that in one or two cases such as aluminum the results agree rather well. However, for the most part the results of the isothermal measurements appear to be considerably higher, and perhaps more erratic, than those obtained from the study of multiple markers.

however, it is found that the direction of impurity migration reverses itself in the higher temperature regime. Apparently this effect is associated with the dominance of the electron wind force, since it is favored by increasing the number of charge carriers.

A study of electromigration in pure metals,

In Table 1 a compilation has been made of several significant parameters in self-transport from extant measurements on pure metals. The values have been chosen for the most part at $T = 0.95\ T_m$ and $0.90\ T_m$ (T_m is the melting temperature) to give a common basis for comparison. The letters I and G mean, respectively, under isothermal conditions[10] or in a temperature gradient.[8, 9] The transport number, U, is given in the fourth column. In the final column e^*/e is given. The quantity e^* is the effective charge on the moving ion which one would deduce from a straightforward application of the Nernst-Einstein relation to the observed mobility. The symbol e represents the magnitude of the electronic charge.

One of the most interesting recent developments has been the work of investigators in Moscow and Leningrad who have been able to isolate the influence of the field force alone. They have done this by studying electromigration in specimens in a magnetic field. The direction of motions studied is that of the Hall voltage, thereby eliminating the electron drag effects. The initial work in this area has revealed that iron ions in germanium appear to carry a positive valence of three from application of the Nernst-Einstein relation. A similar study of radiocarbon deposited on an iron film shows it to have a positive valence. Where applicable, this technique should allow investigators to separate clearly the influence of the electrostatic force from that of the electron friction effect.

References

1. SCHWARZ, K. E., "Electrolytic Migration in Liquid and Solid Metals," Ann Arbor, Michgan, Edwards Brothers, 1945.
2. JOST, W. "Diffusion in Solids, Liquids and Gases," New York, Academic Press, 1952.
3. SEITH, W., "Diffusion in Metals," Berlin, Springer, 1955.
4. SEITH, W., AND WEVER, H., Z. Elektrochem., 57, 891 (1953).
5. WEVER, H., AND SEITH, W., Z. Elektrochem., 59, 942 (1955).
6. WEVER, H., Z. Elektrochem., 60, 1170 (1956).
7. VERHOEVEN, J. D., "Electrotransport in Some Liquid Metal Alloys," Ph.D. Thesis, University of Michigan 1963. Obtainable from University Microfilm, Ann Arbor, Michigan; survey to be published in Met. Reviews.
8. HUNTINGTON, H. B., AND GRONE, A. R., J. Phys. Chem. Solids, 20, 76 (1961).
9. WEVER, H., "Electrolytic Transport and Conduction Mechanism in Iron and Nickel," Vol. 1, Paper 2L, London, Her Majesty's Stationary Office, 1959.
10. KUZ'MENKO, P. P., Ukr. Fiz. Zhur., 7, 117 (1962).

H. B. HUNTINGTON

Cross-references: *Electromigration in Liquid Metals; Hall Effect; Semiconductors.*

ELECTROMOTIVE FORCE AND HALF-CELL POTENTIALS

The *electromotive force* (*emf*) between two points is usually defined as *that force which causes a flow of current* (or as the tendency for a current to flow) between the points; *quantitatively* the *unit of emf* may be defined as the *potential difference* which requires *one unit of work* to be done in moving *one unit of charge* between the points (against the potential difference). The *sign* (i.e., *direction*) of the emf is defined such that *a positive charge will tend to flow spontaneously from a higher to a lower potential.* This definition may be applied to a galvanic cell by defining the *emf* as the *electrical potential equal in sign and magnitude to the electrical potential of the metallic conducting lead of the electrode on the right when that of the similar lead (same metal) of the electrode on the left is taken as zero, the cell being open.* However, an emf measured in this manner is useful for thermodynamic calculations *only* if the two electrodes are *reversible* and if the assumed cell reaction is indeed the reaction which is occurring; otherwise the measured voltage may have little or no relation to the thermodynamic properties of the constituents involved in the assumed reaction. The term *reversible* is used here in its thermodynamic sense, i.e., the measurements must be made on such a cell and under conditions such that an infinitesimal change in conditions (e.g., counter potential) will reverse the current and the cell reaction Measurements on a reversible cell must necessarily be made under conditions of potentiometric balance (or nearly so with *very* small current flowing).

The function E is defined as the measured *emf* of a *reversible cell* of known cell reaction. In this case the measured emf is equal to E and may be readily related to or calculated from the free energy change ΔF of the cell reaction according to Eq. (1).

$$\Delta F = -n\mathbf{F}E \tag{1}$$

where n is the number of moles of electricity per

mole of cell reaction and $\mathbf{F}$ is the Faraday constant. While E was defined as a measured emf for a *reversible* cell, a value of E for an assumed cell reaction may be calculated from other thermodynamic data by the use of Eq. (1) whether or not a reversible cell involving the reaction can be constructed. Although an emf may be defined for any cell, in the following discussion only reversible cells will be considered (whether or not they are feasible in practice) and hence the term emf will be equal to E.

The free energy and cell potential of Eq. (1) have their standard values $\Delta F°$ and $E°$ if all gases involved in the reaction are at unit fugacity (approximately one atmosphere pressure) and all solutes at unit activity; pure solids and pure liquids are taken as unit activity by convention. If $E°$ is known, the value of E at any other conditions may then be determined by use of the Nernst equation.

Any oxidation-reduction reaction may be divided into two *half reactions* or *couples* and at least conceptually the corresponding cell emf can be divided into two (half-cell) *electrode potentials* or into two *oxidation potentials*. The tabulation of half-cell standard potentials allows a concise presentation of thermodynamic data since any two half-cell reactions may be combined and the standard free energy for the resulting reaction readily obtained. The experimental determination of the absolute emf of any couple or half-cell is a difficult problem, but since any chemical reaction involves only the difference between two couples, the absolute values are not necessary. For this reason it is customary to assign an arbitrary value to some reference couple and then evaluate all others relative to this reference. The reference couple so chosen is the hydrogen gas-hydrogen ion couple (at unit fugacity and activity) and the assigned value is zero

$$H_{2(g)} \rightarrow 2H^+ + 2e^- \qquad E° = 0 \qquad (2)$$

There are two suggested conventions for the reference couple: (a) that $E° = 0$ at all temperatures, and (b) that $E° = 0$ only at 25°C. According to convention (a), for the half-reaction (2) $\Delta F° = 0$ at all temperatures [by Eq. (1)] as does the standard entropy change $\Delta S°$ and enthalpy change $\Delta H°$, since

$$\left(\frac{\partial \Delta F°}{\partial T}\right)_P = -\Delta S°$$

and

$$\left(\frac{\partial \Delta F°/T}{\partial T}\right)_P = -\frac{\Delta H°}{T^2}$$

(This is the convention used in the section on "EMF Measurements in Aqueous Solutions at High Temperatures".) Convention (b), however, is preferred by some chemists since it allows an arbitrary choice to be made on the value of $\Delta S°$ (and hence on the partial molal entropy of the hydrogen ion) at each temperature.

Conventions Regarding Sign

In principle three different systems regarding sign and meaning have been suggested for half-cells: the so-called "American" system involving *oxidation potentials* or *reduction potentials*; the Gibbs or "European" system involving *electrode potentials*; and a system proposed by J. B. Ramsey involving *electron chemical potentials*. The two in widest use are (1) the "American" system in which tables are given in terms of oxidation potentials, i.e., the half-cell reactions involve an oxidation process, and (2) the Gibbs or "European" system in which (half-cell) electrode potentials are given the sign and magnitude which they would show externally (if reversible) when compared to a standard hydrogen electrode ($E° = 0$).

The oxidation potentials in the "American" system are equal in magnitude but opposite in sign to the reduction potentials, which are equal to the Gibbs electrode potentials V in both sign and magnitude.

The "American" system is used by most American physical chemists. The "European" system is used by most European chemists and some American analytical chemists, electrochemists, biochemists and metallurgists.

Consider the cell reaction

$$Zn + 2Ag^+ \rightarrow Zn^{++} + 2Ag$$
$$\Delta F° = -72 \text{ kcal/mole} \qquad (3)$$

for the cell

$$Zn, Zn^{++} \| Ag^+, Ag \qquad E°_{(cell)} = 1.562 \text{ volts} \qquad (3a)$$

where the $\|$ represents a salt bridge or a porous plate separator to keep the Ag^+ from contacting the Zn electrode where it would react and short-circuit the cell.

Both "American" and "European" systems give the same $E°_{(cell)}$; both involve a positive $E°_{(cell)}$ if the reaction goes spontaneously with positive electricity going from left to right inside the cell. Both systems involve a change in sign if the cell and reaction are reversed; thus

$$2Ag + Zn^{++} \rightarrow 2Ag^+ + Zn$$

$$\Delta F° = +72 \text{ kcal/mole} \quad (4)$$

for the cell

$$Ag, Ag^+ \parallel Zn^{++}, Zn \quad E°_{(cell)} = -1.562 \text{ v} \quad (4a)$$

Besides the agreement on the $E°_{(cell)}$ and the reference cell $E°$ (hydrogen-hydrogen ion) $= 0$, there still remains an arbitrary assignment of sign (not of magnitude) for the various half-cells. Once the sign convention is established for the half-cells, then the method of combining (adding or subtracting $E°$ values or $V°$ values) in conformity with the above $E°_{(cell)}$ convention is fixed.

Since it is not always made clear which system has been used in a tabular compilation of $E°$ values the following simple test may be of value. In the "American" system the oxidation potentials (for $M \rightarrow M^{+n} + ne^-$) are positive for all metals which will reduce H^+, e.g., the alkalis, the alkaline earths, Zn, etc., while they are negative for all metals the ions of which are reduced by hydrogen, e.g., copper, silver, etc. Both the reduction potentials (for $ne^- + M^{+n} \rightarrow M$) in the "American" system and the electrode potentials $V°$ of the "European" or Gibbs system have the reverse signs.

The "American" System

Cell reaction (3) may be broken into the following two half-reactions with the corresponding assigned signs

$$Zn \rightarrow Zn^{++} + 2e^- \quad E° = 0.763 \text{ v} \quad (5)$$

$$Ag \rightarrow Ag^+ + e^- \quad E° = -0.799 \text{ v} \quad (6)$$

Such half-cell potentials are called *oxidation potentials* since they are the potentials (compared to the $E°$ reference (Eq. (2)) for the half-cell oxidation reactions. According to the conventions involved in Eqs. (2), (5), and (6), the reduced side of any couple is capable of reducing the oxidized side of any couple with an algebraically lower $E°$. Thus Zn will reduce H^+ (with a potential of 0.763 volts) and Ag^+ (with a potential of 1.562 volts) spontaneously. H_2 will reduce Ag^+ (with a potential of 0.799 volts) but not Zn^{++} unless a counter voltage greater than 0.763 v is applied. It should be borne in mind however that these conclusions based upon $E°$ tables hold only when all constituents are in their standard

states. The E values may vary significantly from the $E°$ values in any practical case (according to the Nernst Equation) if one or more of the activities of solute or gaseous constituents deviates from unity by a large multiplicative factor.

In combining any two half-cell oxidation potential reactions into a net reaction, the one with the algebraically higher $E°$ value is left unaltered while the one with the lower $E°$ value is reversed and the sign of its $E°$ value is changed. After multiplying the entire half-reactions (but not the $E°$ values) by whatever factors are necessary so that the number of electrons on each side will cancel, the resulting equations are added. The $E°$ values (after the above reversal of sign) are added algebraically to get the cell $E°$; since the potentials are always on a per electron (or per mole of electricity) basis no correction should be made if more than one e^- is involved. In calculating the free energy change (which is on a per mole basis) from $E°$ values, however, a correction should be made as indicated (by n) in equation (1).

Thus in combining oxidation potentials and half-reactions to get the $E°_{(cell)}$ and cell reaction for the cell (3a):

$$Zn \rightarrow Zn^{++} + 2e^- \quad E° = 0.763 \text{ v}$$

$$2e^- + 2Ag^+ \rightarrow 2Ag \quad E° = 0.799 \text{ v}$$

$$\overline{Zn + 2Ag^+ \rightarrow Zn^{++} + 2Ag \quad E°_{(cell)} = 1.562 \text{ v}}$$

An alternative approach under the "American" system is to write all half-cell reactions in the inverse order with a change in sign of all $E°$ values. These might be called *reduction potentials*; e.g.,

$$2e^- + Zn^{++} \rightarrow Zn \quad E° = -0.763 \text{ v} \quad (7)$$

$$e^- + Ag^+ \rightarrow Ag \quad E° = 0.799 \text{ v} \quad (8)$$

In calculating $E°_{(cell)}$ for cell (3a) and reaction (3) in this case, it is (as before) the equation with the (algebraically) lowest $E°$ value which must be reversed (with change in sign of $E°$) before balancing the number of electrons and adding.

The "European" or Gibbs System

Consider the cell

$$Zn, Zn^{++} \parallel H^+, H_{2(g)}Pt$$

in which all constituents are in their standard state and where two wires of the same material are attached one each to the Zn and Pt electrodes. Let the emf between these two wires be measured. According to the usual electrostatic conventions (i.e., that the electron be defined as negative and that a positive charge move spontaneously from a higher to an algebraically lower potential), the wire attached to the Zn electrode will be more negative than the Pt (hydrogen) electrode by 0.763 v or will be relatively -0.763 v. Similarly the wire attached to the silver electrode in the standard cell

$$Ag, Ag^+ \| H^+, H_{2(g)} Pt$$

is $+0.799$ v compared to the wire attached to the Pt (hydrogen) electrode. The Gibbs or "European" system assigns as the *electrode potential* of any electrode in its standard state the value and sign of the external potential of this electrode compared to a standard hydrogen reference electrode in the same cell. The sign is always the negative of that given in tables of *oxidation potentials* for half-cells (and the same as that given in a table of *reduction potentials*).

To distinguish between the two widely accepted systems, the "American" *oxidation potentials* and "European" (or Gibbs) *electrode potentials*, the symbol for the latter will be V or $V°$ (for non-standard and standard conditions, respectively) after Gibbs' original notation, although E and $E°$ are often used in textbooks.

In combining two electrode potentials to get a cell emf in the Gibbs system, the one on the left is subtracted from the one on the right, i.e., for cell (3a)

$$E°_{(cell)} = V°_{(right)} - V°_{(left)}$$
$$= V°(Ag, Ag^+) - V°(Zn, Zn^{++})$$
$$= +0.799 - (-0.763)$$
$$= +1.562 \text{ v}$$

For the reverse cell (4a)

$$E°_{(cell)} = V°(Zn, Zn^{++}) - V°(Ag, Ag^+)$$
$$= -0.763 - (+0.799)$$
$$= -1.562 \text{ v}$$

The distinctions in using the two major systems in half-cell calculations will be given below after brief mention of a third system suggested by J. B. Ramsey.

The Electron Chemical Potential

The *electron chemical potential* ϵ has been defined by Ramsey as the partial molal free energy (electrochemical potential) of the electrons in a metallic phase divided by the Faraday constant, $\mathbf{F}$. It is opposite in sign to the Gibbs potential V.

Application of "American" and "European" Systems to Half-Cells

There is general agreement on the emf of a (complete) cell in both the "American" and "European" systems, and therefore Equation (1) and the Nernst Equation may be applied to cells and cell reactions with little or no ambiguity. In either case a positive $E_{(cell)}$ means the assumed cell reaction should occur spontaneously as written.

In the "American" system the sign in Eq. (1) and in the Nernst Equation (see section on *Nernst Equation*) are the same for half-cells as for (complete) cells. In the "European" system since the Gibbs V has the same sign regardless of which way a half-reaction is written, care must be taken as to sign in using these equations.

For half-reaction (5)

$$\Delta F = -n\mathbf{F}E_{ox} = +n\mathbf{F}V$$
$$\Delta F° = -2\mathbf{F}(+0.763 \text{ v}) = +2\mathbf{F}(-0.763 \text{ v})$$
$$= -1.526 \text{ v } \mathbf{F} = -35.05 \text{ kcal}$$

and

$$E = E°_{ox} - \frac{RT}{2\mathbf{F}} \ln a_{Zn^{++}}$$

while

$$V = V° + \frac{RT}{2\mathbf{F}} \ln a_{Zn^{++}}$$

For the reduction reaction (7)

$$\Delta F = -n\mathbf{F}E_{red} = -n\mathbf{F}V$$
$$\Delta F° = +1.526 \text{ v } \mathbf{F}$$
$$E = E°_{red} - \frac{RT}{2\mathbf{F}} \ln \frac{1}{a_{Zn^{++}}}$$

while

$$V = V° + \frac{RT}{2\mathbf{F}} \ln a_{Zn^{++}}$$

where $E_{ox} = -E_{red}$ while the V's are unchanged and $V = E_{red}$.

Classification of emf cells

Cells for experimental measurements may be classified as follows:

A. Cells with liquid junctions
  1. Different electrodes
     $$Zn \mid Zn^{++} \rightarrow Cu^{++} \mid Cu$$

2. Concentration cells
   Pt-H_2 | $HCl_{(m_1)} \rightarrow HCl_{(m_2)}$ | H_2-Pt

B. Cells with liquid junction practically eliminated by means of a salt bridge (indicated by the sign ‖).
   1. Different electrodes
      Zn | Zn^{++} ‖ Cu^{++} | Cu
   2. Concentration cells
      Pt-H_2 | $H^+_{(m_1)}$ ‖ $H^+_{(m_2)}$ | H_2-Pt

C. Cells without liquid junction
   1. Different electrodes
      Pt-H_2 | HCl | Cl_2-Pt
   2. Concentration cell of metal
      (Hg + 10% Cd) | Cd^{++} | (Hg + 1% Cd)

Cells with liquid junctions between *different* electrodes cannot be given an exact thermodynamic treatment and should be avoided if possible. In the determination of hydrogen ion activity, however, cells in which the liquid junction potentials have been practically eliminated are widely used.

References

1. LEWIS, G. N., AND RANDALL, M., "Thermodynamics," 2nd Edition, revised by K. S. Pitzer and Leo Brewer, Chap. 24, New York, McGraw-Hill Book Co., 1961.
2. International Union of Pure and Applied Chemistry, "Manual of Physico-Chemical Symbols and Terminology" (conventions adopted at Stockholm 1953 Meeting), London, 1959, Butterworths Scientific Publications.
3. LICHT, TRUMAN S., AND DEBETHUNE, ANDRE J., *J. Chem. Ed.*, 34, 433 (1957).
4. LATIMER, W. M., "Oxidation Potentials," 2nd Edition, Chap. 1, New York, Prentice-Hall, Inc., 1952.
5. RAMSEY, J. B., *J. Electrochem. Soc.*, 104, 255 (1957).

M. H. LIETZKE AND
R. W. STOUGHTON

Cross-references: entries bearing *Electrode Potential* titles; *EMF Measurements in Aqueous Solutions at High Temperatures; Electromotive Series; Nernst Equation; Nomenclature, Remarks on; Tension, Cell and Electrode.*

EMF MEASUREMENTS IN AQUEOUS SOLUTIONS AT HIGH TEMPERATURES

Because of the success of the emf method at and near 25°C in establishing standards of reference and in providing useful thermodynamic data, the method has been used recently in fundamental solution studies at elevated temperatures —and with equal success. The usefulness of the Ag, AgCl; the Ag, AgBr; the Ag, Ag_2SO_4; the

Hg, Hg_2Cl_2; the Hg, Hg_2SO_4; and the glass electrodes has been investigated to 200°C or higher; while the useful range of the quinhydrone electrode has been extended to 55°C. Activity coefficients of HCl have been measured to 275°C and of HBr to 200°C by the use of the hydrogen electrode. An operational pH scale has been defined to 275°C. Above 100° aqueous emf studies involve high pressure bombs, and methods have been devised for inserting insulated leads through metallic bomb walls.

Electromotive Force Measurements

Any electrolytic cell involves two electrodes: the *cathode* where electrons are dissipated into the solution or associated solid and the *anode* at which electrons are transported from the solution or associated solid, i.e., the electrode at which oxidation takes place. The sum of the two electrode reactions (an oxidation and a reduction process) constitutes the cell reaction and the algebraic difference between the two electrode potentials is equal to the cell potential. The potential of an electrode is the difference in potential between the electrode and the solution in contact with it. Both electrode reactions must be reversible if reproducible and reliable potential measurements are desired. In devising a cell for making suitable emf measurements it is often convenient to think of one of the electrodes as a reference electrode and the other as an indicator electrode.

Reference Electrodes. A reference electrode must show a steady, reproducible potential during the course of a measurement. Its potential must not vary because of side reactions that may occur as the external conditions within the solution change, e.g., hydrolysis of the electrode components as the temperature is raised or the acid concentration is decreased. If the reference electrode is bridged into the solution, then the junction potential between the salt bridge and the solution in which the indicator electrode is functioning, as well as the junction potential between the salt bridge and the solution in the electrode compartment, must be taken into account. If a temperature gradient exists in the salt bridge, the Soret potential due to the temperature gradient must be considered. Impurities (particularly occluded gases) present in varying amounts may have a considerable effect on the electrode potential by introducing other reactions at the electrode-solution interface.

Indicator Electrodes. An indicator electrode

must respond in a reproducible way to varying conditions in the solution. The choice of an indicator electrode is dictated to some extent by the type of solution in which the measurements are to be made. For example, the hydrogen electrode cannot be employed in the presence of certain "poisons," materials that inhibit the reversibility of the electrode process. Some of these are CN^-, H_2S, arsenic compounds, and the cations of metals more noble than hydrogen. Some anions interfere with the functioning of the hydrogen electrode; e.g., NO_3^- may be reduced to NH_4^+ in strongly acid solutions. Many organic compounds may also be reduced by hydrogen. Other indicator electrodes, such as metal-metal oxide electrodes, are sensitive to the method of preparation. Both the condition of the metal and of the oxide may have some influence on the behavior of the electrode. Moreover, metal-metal oxide electrodes are sometimes easily polarized, making it necessary to use a device of high input impedance, such as a vibrating reed electrometer, in making the measurements. The very useful glass electrode exhibits an error (correlated with changes of the water activity of the solution) in strongly acidic solutions and a "sodium error" in alkaline solutions containing sodium and other cations.

If proper account is taken of the difficulties mentioned above, it is possible with suitable electrodes to determine at elevated temperatures, for example, the same types of solution properties that can be determined by means of electrodes at room temperature; namely, activity coefficients of electrolytes; partial molal heat contents and heat capacities; and equilibrium constants of reactions, including dissociation, hydrolysis, and solubilities of salts.

In order to determine the usefulness of electrodes for making high temperature measurements it is necessary to combine two in a cell and compare the calculated and observed emf values over the desired temperature range. Emf values may be calculated over a range of temperatures if the emf, E, or the free energy change, ΔF, and the enthalpy change, ΔH, for the cell reaction are known at any one temperature and the heat capacities of all species involved in the reaction are known over the desired range.

In the case of saturated electrode combinations where all the substances appearing in the chemical reaction are solids, all heat capacities as a function of temperature are usually expressed in the form

$$C_{p_i} = a_i + b_i T + c_i T^{-2} \qquad (1)$$

where a_i, b_i, and c_i are sets of constants characteristic of each substance. Hence, the total heat capacity change per mole of cell reaction becomes:

$$\Delta C_p = (C_p \text{ products} - C_p \text{ reactants})$$
$$= (\Delta a) + (\Delta b)T + (\Delta c)T^{-2} \qquad (1a)$$

where (Δa), (Δb), and (Δc) are the algebraic sums of the individual heat capacity coefficients a_i, b_i, and c_i. Eq. (1a) may be substituted into Eq. (2) and the integration performed:

$$\Delta H = \Delta H_0 + \int \Delta C_p \, dT. \qquad (2)$$

ΔH represents the enthalpy change per mole for the cell reaction, ΔH_0 is an integration constant and T is the absolute temperature.

Then by the use of Eq. (2) and the integration of Eq. (3):

$$\left[\frac{\partial(\Delta F/T)}{\partial T} \right]_p = \frac{-\Delta H}{T^2} \qquad (3)$$

Eq. (4) is obtained for the free energy per mole of reaction as a function of temperature:

$$\Delta F = \Delta H_0 - (\Delta a)T \ln T$$
$$- \frac{(\Delta b)}{2} T^2 - \frac{(\Delta c)}{2T} - KT \qquad (4)$$

The integration constants, ΔH_0 and K, can be computed from a knowledge of ΔH and ΔF at one temperature, e.g., 25°C. Hence, ΔF can be calculated at any desired higher temperature by means of Eq. (4). Then the emf, E, of the cell can be calculated for that temperature by means of the relationship between free energy and electromotive force (i.e., $-\Delta F = nFE$, where n is the number of moles of electricity per mole of reaction and F is the Faraday constant). In the case where all reactants and products are solids the ΔF obtained is the standard value ΔF° as is the corresponding emf or E°.

After the emf of the cell combination has been calculated at several different temperatures in the range of interest, a plot of emf versus temperature can be made. In Figs. 1 and 2 are shown plots of emf versus temperature for two pairs of reference electrodes which have been studied.

The Silver, Silver Sulfate-Mercury, Mercury(I) Sulfate Electrode System

Fig. 1 shows the emf values obtained with this system as a function of sulfuric acid concentration and temperature. The emf values as measured

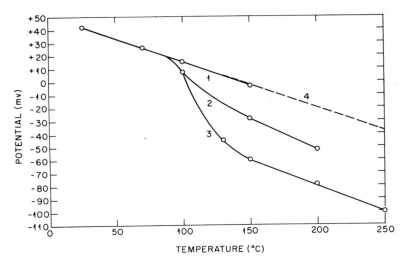

FIG. 1. The emf of the Ag, Ag$_2$SO$_4$ and Hg, Hg$_2$SO$_4$ electrode system as a a function of temperature. Line (1) = electrodes in 0.5 m H$_2$SO$_4$, (2) = electrodes in 0.2 m H$_2$SO$_4$, (3) = electrodes in 0.05 m H$_2$SO$_4$, and (4) = calculated emf with no hydrolysis.

in 0.5 m H$_2$SO$_4$ correspond almost exactly with the plot of E versus T calculated for the cell reaction.

$$2Hg + Ag_2SO_4 \rightleftharpoons 2Ag + Hg_2SO_4 \qquad (5)$$

As the acid concentration is decreased the emf values become more negative than expected, indicating the occurrence of side reactions. It has been shown that this is consistent with a mechanism involving disproportionation and hydrolysis of the mercury(I) sulfate at higher temperatures according to the reaction

$$Hg_2SO_4 + H_2O \rightleftharpoons Hg + HgO + H_2SO_4$$

If this is so, the cell reaction becomes in the limit,

$$Hg + Ag_2SO_4 + H_2O \rightleftharpoons 2Ag + HgO + H_2SO_4 \quad (6)$$

$\Delta F°$ for this reaction is about $+12,560$ calories, which gives a value for the emf of the cell of -272 mv at 25°C. $\Delta S°$, the standard entropy change for the reaction, is -41.0 entropy units at 25°C; hence, the temperature coefficient of the emf is -0.9 mv/deg (since $(\partial E/\partial T)_p = \Delta S/n\mathbf{F}$). If the emf of the cell is determined by Eq. (5), the temperature coefficient is about -0.4 mv/deg at 25°C.

Examination of Eq. (6) indicates that higher sulfuric acid concentrations will tend to repress this reaction and hence favor the reaction given by Eq. (5), as observed experimentally. It is probable that as the temperature is raised, Eq.

(6) is approached as a limit in dilute sulfuric acid solutions after perhaps several stages of basic salt formation.

It appears that the mercury(I) sulfate electrode can be used as a reference electrode at least up to 150°C, provided the solution is about 0.5 molal in sulfuric acid to repress hydrolysis of mercury(I) sulfate. It has been shown that silver sulfate solutions are stable at least up to 250°C even with no excess sulfuric acid. Hence, the silver sulfate electrode is a suitable reference electrode, even in very dilute sulfuric acid solutions, to at least 250°C.

The Silver Chloride-Calomel Electrode System

Fig. 2 shows the emf values obtained with the silver chloride electrode measured against the calomel electrode as a function of temperature and hydrochloric acid concentration. The emf values measured in 1 m HCl follow the values calculated for the reaction:

$$Ag + \tfrac{1}{2} Hg_2Cl_2 \rightleftharpoons AgCl + Hg \qquad (7)$$

up to about 240°C. As the acid concentration is decreased the emf values become more positive than expected at the higher temperatures. Even in 1 m HCl above 240°C the observed emf values are more positive than those calculated.

Just as in the case of the Hg$_2$SO$_4$, calomel disproportionates and hydrolyzes at higher temperatures and low acid concentrations. In this case

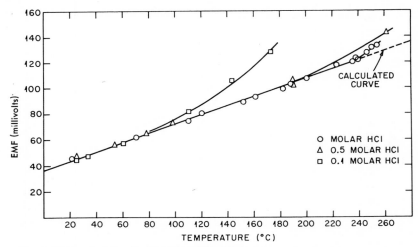

FIG. 2. The emf of the Ag, AgCl and Hg, Hg$_2$Cl$_2$ electrode system as a function of temperature.

○ = 1.0 molal HCl; △ = 0.5 molal HCl; and □ = 0.1 molal HCl.

the cell reaction becomes in the limit:

$$2Ag + HgO + 2HCl \rightleftharpoons Hg + 2AgCl + H_2O. \quad (8)$$

If the emf of the cell were determined by Eq. (8), an $E°$ value of 703 mv would be observed at 25°C and a value of 780 mv at 250°C. Hence, the deviations in emf observed experimentally are consistent with a mechanism involving the approach of Eq. (8) as a limit at the higher temperatures and lower acid concentrations, after perhaps several stages of basic salt formation.

The experimental results indicate that the calomel electrode can be used as a reference electrode up to about 80°C in 0.1 m HCl, to 180°C in 0.5 m HCl, and to about 240°C in 1 m HCl. Since there is no evidence for the decomposition of silver chloride by water, it appears that the silver chloride electrode can be used as a reference electrode to above 200°C even in very dilute acid solutions.

It should be obvious that the foregoing emf measurements were made with the electrodes and solution sealed in a bomb under the vapor pressure of the solution at each temperature. In carrying out the theoretical calculations of emf, the pressure coefficient was neglected since the cell reactions involve only solid materials, the compressibilities of which are small.

The Cells: Pt-H$_{2(p)}$ | HX$_{(m)}$ | AgX-Ag and Thermodynamic Properties of HX(X = Cl, Br.

Each of the above cells involves two electrodes, each of which could be used as a reference elec-

trode, with the Ag, Ag salt electrodes being useful over a wider range of acidity. Of course, each of the electrodes just discussed could be used as an indicator electrode in the proper cell system. However, of the possible indicator electrodes that might be used to study solution phenomena above 100°C, the hydrogen electrode is perhaps the most important. In conjunction with a suitable reference electrode, the hydrogen electrode can be used to determine the thermodynamic properties of many electrolyte solutions over wide ranges of temperature and concentration. Moreover, the hydrogen electrode can be used to calibrate other indicator electrodes, such as metal-metal oxide or special glass electrodes, for use in systems not compatible with the hydrogen electrode.

The cell

$$Pt - H_{2(p)} \mid HCl_{(m)} \mid AgCl\text{-}Ag$$

has been studied over the concentration range 0.005 to 1.0 m HCl, the temperature range 25 to 275°C and at hydrogen pressures of about one atmosphere. The $E°$ values for the Ag-AgCl electrode and the thermodynamic properties of hydrochloric acid have been determined, based on a standard state of one atmosphere of hydrogen and on the convention of $E° = 0$ at all temperatures for the hydrogen electrode. The hydrogen pressure was obtained by subtracting the vapor pressure of the solution from the observed total pressure read on a precision Heise gauge. Corrections were applied for the presence of the HCl in solution by Raoult's law and for the effect of the presence of hydrogen on the vapor pressure of the solution.

A similar study has been made of the cell:

$$\text{Pt} - \text{H}_{2(p)} \mid \text{HBr}_{(m)} \mid \text{AgBr-Ag.}$$

Because the Ag-AgBr electrode was not as stable as the corresponding chloride electrode, especially at elevated temperatures, the study was terminated at 200°C.

In Table 1 are shown comparative values of the standard electrode potentials of the silver-silver halide electrodes and the activity coefficients of the hydrohalogen acids.

An important conclusion from this work is that the Debye-Hückel equation in extended form is found to be entirely applicable over the range of temperatures studied. The extended equation for the natural logarithm of the mean activity coefficient may be written as:

$$\ln\gamma_{\pm} = -\frac{S\sqrt{\rho_0 I}}{1 + A\sqrt{\rho_0 I}} + BI + CI^2 + \cdots, \quad (9)$$

where S is the limiting slope; ρ_0 is the density of water; I is the ionic strength; and A, B, and C are adjustable parameters. When this equation is put into the Nernst equation at unit hydrogen pressure, the new potential function, $E^{\circ \prime\prime}$, may be obtained after rearrangement

$$E^{\circ \prime\prime} \equiv E + \frac{2RT}{F}\left[\ln m_{\pm} - \frac{S\sqrt{\rho_0 I}}{1 + A\sqrt{\rho_0 I}}\right]$$

$$= E^{\circ} - \frac{2RT}{F}[BI + CI^2 + \cdots] \quad (10)$$

where $m_{\pm}$ is the mean molality of H^+ and Cl^- ions and the other terms have their usual significance. The values of $E^{\circ \prime\prime}$ for both cells at all

temperatures are linear in I to about 0.1 m and quadratic in I to 1.0 m.

The relative partial molal heat content, $\bar{L}_2$, and heat capacity, $\bar{J}_2$, are given by:

$$\bar{L}_2 = -4.606\,RT^2\left(\frac{\partial \log \gamma_{\pm}}{\partial T}\right)_{m,p} \quad (11)$$

$$\bar{J}_2 = \left(\frac{\partial \bar{L}_2}{\partial T}\right)_{m,p} = -9.212\,RT\left(\frac{\partial \log \gamma_{\pm}}{\partial T}\right)_{m,p}$$

$$-4.606\,RT^2\left(\frac{\partial^2 \log \gamma_{\pm}}{\partial T^2}\right)_{m,p} \quad (12)$$

Values of the relative partial molal heat content and partial molal heat capacity of HCl in aqueous solution are shown as a function of concentration and temperature to 200°C in Table 2.

It is interesting that the $\bar{L}_2$ and $\bar{J}_2$ values at elevated temperatures when plotted as function of the square root of I show deviations from the limiting slope on the high side at low concentrations and vice versa in a manner similar to that observed in dioxane-water mixtures at room temperature at comparable values of the dielectric constant. This behavior indicates that the dielectric constant or the DT product is perhaps more important than the exact nature or temperature (*per se*) of the solvent in causing such deviations.

The experimental error in the HBr measurements is substantially larger than in those involving HCl, causing appreciably greater uncertainty in the change of the activity coefficient with temperature. For this reason the relative partial molal heat content and heat capacity were not calculated for HBr.

TABLE 1. E° VALUES FOR THE CELL: Pt, $\text{H}_{2(p)}$, $\text{HX}_{(m)}$, AgX, Ag AND $\gamma_{\pm}$
VALUES FOR HX *vs.* TEMPERATURE

t (°C)	E° X = Cl	E° X = Br	$\gamma_{\pm}$ HCl at m =				$\gamma_{\pm}$ HBr at m =			
			0.01	0.1	0.5	1.0	0.01	0.1	0.5	1.0
25	0.2223	0.0716	0.9044	0.7972	0.7540	0.8061	0.905	0.794	0.808	0.873
60	.1968	.0501	.899	.776	.728	.762	.901	.789	.819	.852
90	.1696	.0251	.893	.758	.692	.713	.896	.781	.751	.773
125	.1330	−.0048	.884	.744	.655	.653	.886	.773	.708	.717
150	.1032	−.0312	.876	.720	.621	.608	.878	.750	.662	.653
175	.0708	−.0612	.869	.714	.591	.560	.870	.731	.618	
200	.0348	−.0951	.860	.694	.554	.514	.863	.715	.580	
225	−.0051		.846	.663	(.572)					
250	−.054		.82	.58	(.54)					
275	−.090		.82	.62	(.53)					

TABLE 2. THE RELATIVE PARTIAL MOLAL HEAT
CONTENT AND HEAT CAPACITY
OF HYDROCHLORIC ACID

t (°C)	0.005 m	0.01 m	0.05 m	0.1 m	0.2 m	0.5 m	1.0 m
$\overline{L}_2$ (cal)							
25	30.8	55.1	152	246	306	416	565
60	66.0	92.1	205	321	418	587	839
90	107	133	260	397	534	767	1130
125	167	193	334	498	693	1020	1550
150	221	246	395	580	825	1230	1900
175	283	306	462	669	972	1470	2310
200	355	374	537	767	1140	1730	2770
$\overline{J}_2$ (cal/degree)							
25	0.83	0.90	1.4	2.0	2.9	4.3	6.8
60	1.2	1.2	1.7	2.4	3.6	5.5	8.8
90	1.5	1.5	2.0	2.7	4.2	6.5	10.8
125	2.0	1.9	2.3	3.1	5.0	7.9	13.2
150	2.3	2.2	2.6	3.4	5.6	8.9	15.1
175	2.7	2.6	2.8	3.8	6.2	10.0	17.2
200	3.1	2.9	3.2	4.1	6.9	11.2	19.4

Other Electrodes Involving Acid Activities

Since the hydrogen electrode is incompatible with many systems because of its reducing properties, a number of others have received attention with varying success. These include the glass, various metal-metal oxide, the quinhydrone and the $PbSO_4$-PbO_2 electrodes.

The Glass Electrode. By the use of the very high-impedance vibrating reed or other high-impedance electrometer the glass electrode may be used to measure acidities in a rather larger intermediate pH range even at elevated temperatures. If the temperature is maintained constant in a flowing system and if an accuracy of only ±0.1 pH unit is required, as in certain industrial plants, the glass electrode can be used for at least many days at a time to 200°C. For this purpose the Beckman amber glass high-temperature electrode is more satisfactory than the general-purpose glass instrument. The electrode will not stand thermal cycling to elevated temperatures, however. For example, the amber glass electrode fails to give the correct pH response after one to three cycles between 25° and 150°C.

In isothermal static systems at elevated temperatures the corrosion of the glass involves a problem. While the corrosion of the pH-sensitive glass (Beckman Glass Electrode) does not appear to be significant, the lead glass shell (of which most glass electrodes seem to be made) does show considerable corrosion, especially above about 100°C. The resulting corrosion products of the lead glass can markedly change the pH of a solution which is below about 10^{-2} m in acid in a relatively short time (which depends on the temperature). If the solution and electrode inside the glass electrode are dilute-HCl, AgCl, Ag, the corrosion inside becomes a problem too. However, two satisfactory procedures have been used to obviate problems of corrosion on the inside: (1) the use of a buffered (e.g., a phosphate buffered) solution containing chloride, or (2) placing an amalgam (e.g., a Pb amalgam) instead of an aqueous solution inside the glass electrode tube.

Three of the most common reference electrodes used with the glass electrode at elevated temperatures are (a) a Ag-AgCl electrode maintained at the same temperature; (b) another glass electrode in contact with some reference solution and separated from the solution in question by means of a fritted glass plate; and (c) a calomel electrode maintained at room temperature and connected to the solution of interest with a KCl bridge using asbestos wicks to restrict the solution flow. With any of these reference electrodes it is necessary to calibrate the glass electrode at each temperature with known solutions.

It appears that with sufficient precautions and cross-checks a glass electrode system can be used to give moderately accurate results at elevated temperatures. However, a thoroughly satisfactory accurate glass electrode system for this purpose has yet to be developed.

Nevertheless, a rather thorough study of the hydrolysis of U(VI) has been made in nitrate media at 94°C by the use of a glass electrode: the principle species reported being UO_2OH^+, $(UO_2)_2(OH)_2^{++}$ and $(UO_2)_3(OH)_5^+$. The study has been extended to 148°, but corrosion of the glass so far has obscured precise results.

Metal-metal Oxide Electrodes. Of the metal-metal oxide electrodes perhaps the one receiving the most attention at and near room temperature is that involving Sb-Sb_2O_3. This electrode has not been generally found reliable for accurate work, although if no great accuracy is required and if oxygen is excluded it gives a response over a wide pH range near neutrality, especially if it is recalibrated regularly. It has not been studied at elevated temperatures.

Both niobium and tantalum electrodes have been suggested as titration indicator electrodes. It was found that both the niobium and tantalum electrodes showed a linear response to pH over a wide range at short exposure times. However, a series of measurements of the niobium and tantalum electrodes against the Ag, AgCl electrode in dilute HCl solutions both at room temperature and above 100° did not come to constant efm values within a few days.

The Quinhydrone Electrode. The quinhydrone electrode with a Ag-AgCl reference electrode has been used to measure HCl activity coefficients to 55°C. This temperature is not necessarily an upper limit to which reproducible measurements can be made.

The PbO_2-$PbSO_4$ Electrode. Emf measurements have been made on the cell

$$Pt, PbO_2 , PbSO_4 \mid H_2SO_4(m) \mid Ag_2SO_4 , Ag$$

to 140°C and with 0.3 to 2.0 m H_2SO_4. This cell behaves in a reproducible manner under proper conditions as to preparation of electrodes and gives a measure of the ratio of activities of H_2O to H_2SO_4. Because of the increasing stability of the HSO_4^- ion with temperature and the consequent increasing solubility of Ag_2SO_4 in H_2SO_4 media, however, this activity ratio is obtained not in a H_2SO_4 solution but in a H_2SO_4-Ag_2SO_4 mixture of comparable concentrations at elevated temperatures. The increasing stability of the HSO_4^- ion with temperature represents a limit on the usefulness of the Ag-Ag_2SO_4 electrode.

References

1. GREELEY, RICHARD S., et al., *J. Phys. Chem.*, **64**, 652, 1445, 1861 (1960).
2. GREELEY, RICHARD S., *Anal. Chem.*, **32**, 1717 (1960).
3. BATES, ROGER G., "Electrometric pH Determinations," New York, John Wiley and Sons, 1954.
4. HARNED, H. S., AND OWEN, B. B., "The Physical Chemistry of Electrolytic Solutions," Third Edition, New York, Reinhold Publishing Corp., 1958.
5. KRAUS, KURT A., HOLMBERG, ROBERT W., AND BORKOWSKI, C. J., *Anal. Chem.*, **22**, 341 (1950).
6. BAES, C. F., JR., AND MEYER, NORMAN J., *Inorg. Chem.* (scheduled for November 1962 issue).
7. FOURNIE, R., LeCLERC, P., AND SAINT-JAMES R., *Silicates Industriels*, **27**, No. 1, 33 (January 1962).
8. INGRUBER, O. V., *Pulp Paper Mag. Can.*, **55**, 124 (1954).
9. HAYES, JOHN C., AND LIETZKE, M. H., *J. Phys. Chem.*, **64**, 374 (1960).
10. VAUGHEN, J. V., AND LIETZKE, M. H., *J. Am. Chem. Soc.*, **79**, 4266 (1957).
11. LIETZKE, M. H., AND STOUGHTON, R. W., *J. Chem. Ed.*, **39**, 230 (1962).

M. H. LIETZKE AND
R. W. STOUGHTON

Cross-references: *Activity and Activity Coefficient;* entries bearing *Electrode Potential* titles; *Electromotive Force and Half-Cell Potentials; Electromotive Series; Glass Electrode; Nernst Equation; Reference Electrodes; Soret Potential.*

EMF MEASUREMENTS IN FUSED SALTS. See FUSED SALT ELECTRODE REACTIONS; FUSED SALT ELECTROMOTIVE FORCE SERIES.

ELECTROMOTIVE SERIES

An oxidation-reduction (redox) reaction may be divided into two half-reactions or redox couples which indicate the electron transfer process. For example, the reaction where metallic zinc is oxidized by a solution of copper sulfate,

$$Zn + Cu^{++} \rightarrow Zn^{++} + Cu \qquad (1)$$

may be divided into the two half-reactions,

$$Zn \rightarrow Zn^{++} + 2e \qquad (1a)$$

$$Cu \rightarrow Cu^{++} + 2e \qquad (1b)$$

The conversion of zinc (or copper) to zinc ions (or copper ions) is an oxidation reaction and the reverse process a reduction reaction. Each half-reaction is an oxidation-reduction (redox) couple.

These half-reactions may be treated as electrode reactions, each taking place at one of the electrodes of the cell:

$$\overset{-}{Zn} \mid Zn^{++} \parallel Cu^{++} \mid \overset{+}{Cu} \qquad (A)$$

When the two electrodes are connected by a wire, which is the *external circuit*, electrons will flow *spontaneously* from the zinc electrode through the wire to the copper electrode. The reactions inside the cell will correspond to reaction (1a), an oxidation, at the zinc electrode (anode) and reaction (1b) in the reverse direction, a reduction at the copper electrode (cathode).

The electromotive force, emf, of the cell, E_{cell}, is equal to the cell voltage as measured by a potentiometer in a "null" circuit. E_{cell} is the driving force of the reaction and is related to the decrease in the Gibbs free energy of the total reaction as follows:

$$-\Delta G = n\mathbf{F}E_{cell} \qquad (2)$$

where n is the number of electrons transferred per molar unit of reaction, $\mathbf{F}$ is the Faraday and G the Gibbs free energy.

When all the substances concerned are at unit activity, the emf is called the standard emf of the cell, E°_{cell}. This may be considered a result of the two half-reaction emf's, $E^{\circ}_{Zn,Zn^{++}}$ and $E^{\circ}_{Cu,Cu^{++}}$.

It follows that the relative values of the two half-reaction emfs indicate the *spontaneous* direction of the total reaction and their algebraic difference will give E°_{cell}, which is proportional to the free energy change for the reaction.

The half-cell emf of a couple, which may be designated as a redox potential, is therefore a relative measure of the couple's oxidizing (or reducing) strength. A list of the standard redox potentials of the chemical elements, arranged in the order of increasing oxidizing strength is known as the *electromotive series*. In much of the literature these redox potentials may be designated oxidation-potentials or standard electrode potentials. The potentials are relative values which are based on an arbitrary scale where the standard potential of the hydrogen gas-hydrogen ion couple potential is arbitrarily and by convention set equal to zero at all temperatures. An oxidizing component of any given redox couple has a tendency to oxidize the reducing component of any redox couple which is above it in the series. For example, any metal has a tendency to be displaced from its solution by a metal above it in the series.

Sign Conventions

Total Cell Emf. Eq. (2) states that the decrease in free energy when reaction (1) occurs in the *spontaneous* direction is equal to the maximum electrical energy which may be supplied to an external circuit. Therefore, a positive value of E°_{cell} should correspond to the spontaneous direction of the cell reaction. The following convention and rules may be used to obtain the proper sign.

1. The diagrammatic description of the cell is written, e.g.,

$$\overset{-}{Zn} \mid Zn^{++} \mid Cu^{++} \parallel \overset{+}{Cu} \qquad (A)$$

2. If in a closed circuit electrons flow from the left-hand electrode to the right-hand electrode in

an *external wire*, the sign of E°_{cell} is taken as *positive*. Conversely, if electrons flow in the reverse direction, E°_{cell} is taken as negative.

3. The total reaction is written in the direction *it would occur* if electrons flowed from the left-hand electrode to the right-hand electrode in the *external* wire of the cell as written.

For cell A, the reaction and E°_{cell} are:

$$Zn + Cu^{++} \rightarrow Zn^{++} + Cu; \quad E^{\circ}_{cell} = +1.10 \text{ v}$$

and according to Eq. (2) the free energy *decreases* when the reaction proceeds from left to right.

On the other hand, if the cell is written as

$$\overset{+}{Cu} \mid Cu^{++} \parallel Zn^{++} \mid \overset{-}{Zn} \qquad (B)$$

the cell reaction and E°_{cell} are:

$$Cu + Zn^{++} \rightarrow Cu^{++} + Zn; \quad E^{\circ}_{cell} = -1.10 \text{ v}$$

and the free energy *increases* when copper is oxidized by zinc ions. The correct direction for the spontaneous reaction is obtained for either cell diagram provided the chemical reaction is written so that it corresponds to the cell current as given by rule 3.

Half-Cell Potentials. There are two conventions for determining the sign of the half-cell or couple potential. The one which is sometimes referred to as the American or thermodynamic convention uses the concept of the emf produced by the half-cell reaction. According to this scheme the half-cell reaction may be expressed as an oxidation reaction and written as the Eqs. (1a) and (1b) with the electrons as a product of the reaction. The redox potentials above hydrogen in the series have a positive sign while those below hydrogen have a negative sign. The total cell reaction and cell emf are obtained by the algebraic subtraction of the half-cell reactions and potentials. For example:

$$Zn \rightarrow Zn^{++} + 2e \qquad E_{Zn,Zn^{++}} = +0.76 \text{ v}$$

$$Cu \rightarrow Cu^{++} + 2e \qquad E_{Cu,Cu^{++}} = -0.34 \text{ v}$$

$$Zn + Cu^{++} \rightarrow Zn^{++} + Cu \qquad E_{cell} = 1.10 \text{ v}$$

According to this convention, if E° of a redox couple is positive, then the reduced member of the couple is a better reducing agent than hydrogen. If E° is negative, then the oxidized member of the couple is a better oxidizing agent than hydrogen ion.

The electromotive series of the elements, according to this American convention, is shown in Table 1.

OXIDATION POTENTIALS OF ELEMENTS
Values, in Volts, Referred to the Hydrogen – Hydrogen Ion Couple as Zero, are for Unit Activities and Temperature of 25°C.

Element	Reaction	$E^O ox$	Element	Reaction	$E^O ox$
Li	$Li \rightarrow Li^+ + 1e$	+ 3.045	Nb	$Nb \rightarrow Nb^{+++} + 3e$	ca + 1.1
K	$K \rightarrow K^+ + 1e$	+ 2.925	S	$S^{--} \rightarrow S + 2e$	+0.92
Rb	$Rb \rightarrow Rb^+ + 1e$	+ 2.925	Se	$Se^{--} \rightarrow Se + 2e$	+0.78
Cs	$Cs \rightarrow Cs + 1e$	+ 2.923	Zn	$Zn \rightarrow Zn + 2e$	+0.763
Ra	$Ra \rightarrow Ra^{++} + 2e$	+ 2.92	Cr	$Cr \rightarrow Cr^{+++} + 3e$	+0.74
Ba	$Ba \rightarrow Ba^{++} + 2e$	+ 2.90	Ga	$Ga \rightarrow Ga^{+++} + 3e$	+0.53
Sr	$Sr \rightarrow Sr^{++} + 2e$	+ 2.89	Te	$Te \rightarrow Te^{++} + 2e$	+0.51
Ca	$Ca \rightarrow Ca^{++} + 2e$	+ 2.87	Fe	$Fe \rightarrow Fe^{++} + 2e$	+0.44
Na	$Na \rightarrow Na^+ + 1e$	+ 2.714	Cd	$Cd \rightarrow Cd^{++} + 2e$	+0.403
La	$La \rightarrow La^{+++} + 3e$	+ 2.52	In	$In \rightarrow In^{+++} + 3e$	+0.342
Ce	$Ce \rightarrow Ce^{+++} + 3e$	+ 2.48	Tl	$Tl \rightarrow Tl^+ + 1e$	+0.336
Nd	$Nd \rightarrow Nd^{+++} + 3e$	+ 2.44	Co	$Co \rightarrow Co^{++} + 2e$	+0.277
Sm	$Sm \rightarrow Sm^{+++} + 3e$	+ 2.41	Ni	$Ni \rightarrow Ni^{++} + 2e$	+0.250
Gd	$Gd \rightarrow Gd^{+++} + 3e$	+ 2.40	Mo	$Mo \rightarrow Mo^{+++} + 3e$	ca + 0.2
Mg	$Mg \rightarrow Mg^{++} + 2e$	+ 2.37	Sn	$Sn \rightarrow Sn^{++} + 2e$	+0.136
Y	$Y \rightarrow Y^{+++} + 3e$	+ 2.37	Pb	$Pb \rightarrow Pb^{++} + 2e$	+0.126
Am	$Am \rightarrow Am^{+++} + 3e$	+ 2.32	D_2	$1/2 D_2 \rightarrow D^+ + 1e$	+ 0.003
Lu	$Lu \rightarrow Lu^{+++} + 3e$	+ 2.25	H_2	$1/2 H_2 \rightarrow H^+ + 1e$	0.000
H	$H^- \rightarrow H + 1e$	+ 2.25	Cu	$Cu \rightarrow Cu^{++} + 2e$	- 0.337
$H_{(g)}$	$H \rightarrow H^+ + 1e$	+ 2.10		$Cu \rightarrow Cu^+ + 1e$	- 0.521
Sc	$Sc \rightarrow Sc^{+++} + 3e$	+ 2.08	I_2	$2I^- \rightarrow I_2 + 2e$	- 0.536
Pu	$Pu \rightarrow Pu^{+++} + 3e$	+ 2.07	Hg	$2Hg \rightarrow Hg_2^+ + 2e$	- 0.789
Th	$Th \rightarrow Th^{++++} + 4e$	+ 1.90	Ag	$Ag \rightarrow Ag^+ + 1e$	- 0.7991
Np	$Np \rightarrow Np^{+++} + 3e$	+ 1.86	Rh	$Rh \rightarrow Rh^{+++} + 3e$	ca - 0.8
Be	$Be \rightarrow Be^{++} + 2e$	+ 1.85	Pd	$Pd \rightarrow Pd^{++} + 2e$	- 0.987
U	$U \rightarrow U^{+++} + 3e$	+ 1.80	Br_2	$2Br^- \rightarrow Br_{2(L)} + 2e$	- 1.066
Hf	$Hf \rightarrow Hf^{++++} + 4e$	+ 1.70	Pt	$Pt \rightarrow Pt^{++} + 2e$	- 1.2
Al	$Al \rightarrow Al^{+++} + 3e$	+ 1.66	Cl_2	$2Cl^- \rightarrow Cl_2 + 2e$	- 1.36
Ti	$Ti \rightarrow Ti^{++} + 2e$	+ 1.63	Au	$Au \rightarrow Au^{+++} + 3e$	- 1.50
Zr	$Zr \rightarrow Zr^{++++} + 4e$	+ 1.53		$Au \rightarrow Au^+ + 1e$	ca - 1.68
Mn	$Mn \rightarrow Mn^{++} + 2e$	+ 1.18	F_2	$2F^- \rightarrow F_2 + 2e$	-2.85
V	$V \rightarrow V^{++} + 2e$	ca + 1.18			

(Reproduced by permission from "Handbook of Chemistry and Physics," Chemical Rubber Publishing Company, Cleveland, Ohio, 44th Edition, 1962–1963.)

The other convention, usually referred to as the European Convention, is used extensively in America as well as abroad. The rules for determining the sign of the whole cell emf, E°_{cell}, are identical as those given above. The difference occurs in determining the sign of the half-cell potentials. According to this convention the half-cell potentials are interpreted as electrical potentials, and designated as single electrode potentials, E°, or sometimes, V. These electrode potentials have a sign which is the opposite of those assigned by the American convention. Thus, the couples above hydrogen in the series are negative while those below hydrogen are positive.

The rule for obtaining the total cell emf is algebraically to subtract the single electrode potential of the *right* electrode *from* that of the *left* electrode. For example, for the cell

$$\overset{+}{\text{Zn}} \mid \text{Zn}^{++} \parallel \text{Cu}^{++} \mid \overset{-}{\text{Cu}}$$
$$(1) \qquad\qquad (2)$$

$$E^{\circ}_{cell} = E_2^{\circ} - E_1^{\circ} = E^{\circ}_{Cu,Cu^{++}} - E^{\circ}_{Zn,Zn^{++}}$$

$$E^{\circ}_{cell} = (+0.34) - (-0.76) = +1.10$$

or

$$\overset{+}{\text{Cu}} \mid \text{Cu}^{++} \parallel \text{Zn}^{++} \mid \overset{-}{\text{Zn}}$$
$$(1) \qquad\qquad (2)$$

$$E^{\circ}_{cell} = E_2^{\circ} - E_1^{\circ} = E^{\circ}_{Zn,Zn^{++}} - E^{\circ}_{Cu,Cu^{++}}$$

$$E^{\circ}_{cell} = (-0.76) - (+0.34) = -1.10 \text{ v}$$

Applications

The electromotive series is very useful in physical chemistry, analytical chemistry, and for the interpretation of electrode reactions in electrolysis, voltaic cells, and corrosion. The standard redox potentials are basically thermodynamic quantities and, therefore, give only the tendency for the reactions to occur. The rates of a predicted reaction may be very low in some cases. For example, in the electrolysis of an acid solution of zinc sulfate, it would be expected that the reduction of hydrogen ions should occur preferentially. Due to the slowness of this reaction on zinc, the zinc ions in solution are reduced at a high efficiency, however.

In practical cases where the activity of the substances differ from unity the redox potential for the given conditions may be obtained by the following expression at 25°C.

$$E_M = E_M{}^{\circ} - \frac{0.0591}{n} \log Q \qquad (3)$$

where Q is the product of the activities of the resulting substances divided by the product of the activities of the reacting substances, each activity raised to that power whose exponent is the coefficient of the substance in the reaction, and $E_M{}^{\circ}$ is the standard potential. In the case of metal-metal ion couples the expression is simply:

$$E_M = E_M{}^{\circ} - \frac{0.0591}{n} \log (M^{n+})$$

There are many cases in practice where the rates of the half-reactions are too slow for the establishment of a reversible potential. The electrode may then exhibit a mixed potential (q.v.) and the behavior expected from the reversible values in the series may not be observed. This is particularly the case in many corrosion and electrolysis problems.

References

1. LATIMER, WENDELL M., "Oxidation Potentials," Englewood Cliffs, N. J., Prentice-Hall, Inc., 1952.
2. CREIGHTON, H., AND KOEHLER, W. A., "Electrochemistry," New York, John Wiley & Sons, Inc., 1935.
3. CONWAY, B. E., "Electrochemical Data," New York, Elsevier Publishing Co., 1952.
4. CHARLOT, G., "Oxidation-Reduction Potentials," New York, Pergamon Press, 1958.
5. KORTÜM, G., AND BOCKRIS, J. O'M., "Electrochemistry," New York, Elsevier Publishing Co., 1951.

See for Sign Conventions

6. LINGANE, JAMES J., "Electroanalytical Chemistry," New York, Interscience Publishers, Inc., 1958.
7. LICHT, T. S., AND DE BETHUNE, ANDRE J., *J. Chem. Education*, **34,** 433 (1957).
8. LEWIS, G. N., AND RANDALL, M., "Thermodynamics," Revised by K. S. Pitzer and Leo Brewer, 2nd Edition, New York, McGraw-Hill Book Co., 1961.

J. V. PETROCELLI

Cross-references: *Electrode Potentials; Electromotive Force and Half-Cell Potentials; Galvanic Series; Nomenclature, Remarks on.*

ELECTROMOTIVE SERIES IN FUSED SALTS. See FUSED SALT ELECTROMOTIVE SERIES

ELECTROMYOGRAPHY. See ELECTRODIAGNOSIS

ELECTRON

The electron is the elementary unit of negative electrical charge, the value of which has been found to be 4.803×10^{-10} e.s.u. The electron has the smallest mass of any of the stable elementary particles—9.1066×10^{-28} gm. Electrons appear to revolve around the nucleus of an atom in more or less well defined orbits, the number of electrons in each orbit being governed by the

Pauli exclusion principle. Thus, there are allowed 2 electrons in the innermost orbit or shell, 8 in the second, 18 in the third, and in the nth orbit $2n^2$.

The number of electrons surrounding the nucleus of a neutral atom is equal to the atomic number of that atom. The tendency for atoms to form complete shells accounts for the valence of that atom. For instance, sodium, which has atomic number 11, normally has its 11 electrons distributed with 2 electrons in the first shell, 8 in the second and 1 in the third. When the outermost electron is removed, the atom is said to be *ionized*. This leaves the atom with a positive charge of one unit and accounts for the valence of +1 in the case of sodium.

Similarly, fluorine has its 9 electrons arranged with 2 in the first orbit and 7 in the second. Its tendency is to accept one more electron to complete the second shell, giving the atom a charge of −1. Therefore, fluorine is said to have a valence of −1. All the halogens have a shortage of one electron to form a closed shell, but they also could get rid of seven electrons and thereby form a closed shell. This accounts for the valence of +7 in such a compound as $KClO_4$.

As one goes up in the Periodic Table, the various shells are not necessarily filled to completion before the next shell is started. For instance, calcium has 2 electrons in the first shell, 8 in the second, only 8 in the third, and 2 in the fourth shell. The next few elements in the table keep the 2 electrons in the fourth shell while filling the remaining ten vacancies in the third shell, thus accounting for the ten elements in what is called the first transition group. These elements can form closed shells in a variety of ways, thus accounting for the multiple valencies of such elements as chromium and manganese.

Similarly, the rare earths form a group which begins with only 18 electrons in the fourth shell where there is room for 32, even though these elements have 8 electrons in the fifth shell and 2 in the sixth. Thus, this group consists of 14 elements all behaving much alike chemically because of the similarity in the structure of the fifth and sixth shells and differing only in the degree to which the fourth shell is filled. This shell, being so far in the interior of the atom, has little influence on the chemical behavior of the element.

Electrons can be removed from metal or other surfaces in various ways such as heating the surface (thermionic emission), allowing light of appropriate wavelength to strike the surface (photoelectric effect), placing the surface in a strong electric field (field emission), or bombarding the surface with charged particles (secondary electron emission or positive ion bombardment).

Although the name "electron" is usually reserved for a particle carrying a negative charge, there can be produced, by gamma rays of sufficient energy, pairs of electrons, one of which is an ordinary electron while the other is similar in all respects except that it carries a positive charge. These positive electrons, or *positrons*, have only a momentary existence, after which they combine with a negative electron to form a pair of gamma rays.

Because of their small mass, moving electrons have very small inertia and thus are easily controllable in vacuum tubes. In such devices the electrons are emitted from a heated filament and then accelerated by various combinations of electric and magnetic fields. They may also be accelerated in special devices such as betatrons and synchrotrons, and their speed has been reported to approach closely the speed of light under such conditions.

R. T. ELLICKSON

ELECTRON BEAM MELTING

Electron beam melting of metals has recently become an important process for industry and for research. Marcello von Pirani first produced homogeneous ingots of tantalum and other metals by electron beam melting early in this century. The realization of the electron beam melting process on a large scale was shown for the first time by Smith and his team from Temescal Metallurgical Corporation in the late 1950's. This long delay was due to the specific requirements of electron beam melting technology which could not be fulfilled until many industrial advances were achieved in these years.

Equipment

The requirements of a system for electron beam melting and casting can be summarized as follows:

(a) An adequate electron beam source, i.e., electron guns and auxiliary electron optical focussing system.

(b) Suitable controls and protective devices for the electron beam source.

(c) A vacuum system capable of maintaining adequate dynamic low-pressure condition during melting.

(d) A suitable mold assembly, usually a retractable, water-cooled copper receptacle.

(e) Convenient arrangements for introducing feed material into the work chamber.

There are two ways to carry out electron beam melting of metals:

1. Drip melting—the beam impinges on consumable electrode of the crude metal which, upon melting, collects in a water-cooled copper crucible. (See Fig. 3.)

2. Pool melting—small pieces or compacts of the crude metal are fed into the molten metal pool in the crucible to build up the ingot, and the pool is kept molten by focussing the beam on it. (See Fig. 2.)

Electron Source

In electron beam melting and casting furnaces, the electron gun may be work-accelerated (that is, the work piece is the anode) or self-accelerated (the work piece is not the anode but is placed in the path of the electron beam, the anode being located elsewhere in the system). There are two types of electron beam sources: those utilizing annular rings, and those producing a columnar beam from remote guns. Furnaces equipped with an annular cathode are used for zone refining and floating zone single crystal growth, as well as for drip melting of refractory metals. Melting by remote electron guns has recently begun to find wide application in both drip melting and pool melting.

Electron beam melting furnaces with annular cathodes have been used successfully in the refractory metal industry for a few years, largely due to the effort of Smith and his team at Temescal Metallurgical Corporation. In a furnace designed by Smith, the feedstock (anode) is fed through an annular cathode and drip-melted into a retractable water-cooled crucible. Furnaces with power output in the range of 50 to several hundred kw have been in use. These close-coupled, work-accelerated guns are simple to construct and capable of producing ingots with excellent as-cast surfaces. However, they are susceptible to pressure variations in the melt area and subject to contamination from condensed stock vapor.

Electron beam melting furnaces with classical electron guns were first mentioned by Candidus, et al, at National Research Corporation. Instead of an annular gun, the emission system produces a column beam that is directed to the work piece. For large production furnaces, several guns can be combined into a sturdy and compact unit. The guns are arranged systematically to the axis of the crucible by vertical mounting in the common and separating gun chamber. A magnetic focussing and beam deflecting system is used to direct the beam to the molten pool. By a system of multiguns the problem of energy shadow with the use of a consumable electrode in drip melting is overcome. Guns of 100 kw or more have been built and furnaces with output over 500 kw have been in practical use. The megawatt-class electron beam melting and casting furnace at Temescal is described in detail by Smith, et al.[4] A photograph of this furnace is shown in Fig. 1.

Considerations in the design of electron beam system for heating have been discussed by Smullin[5] and Morley[5] and other books on electron optics.

Several advantages of the remote gun sys-

FIG. 1. Overall view of megawatt electron beam melting furnace. (*Courtesy Temescal Metallurgical Corp.*)

tem in comparison with the ring beam systems are as follows:

(a) One common beam system can be used for various crucible diameters and also for drip melt and pool melt.

(b) The relatively long distance from the guns to the molten pool offers good protection of the cathode against splashes and metal vapors.

(c) Melting is performed in a configuration held at ground potential to minimize ion current and occurrence of glow discharges during outgassing.

(d) Differential pumping can be employed in the gun chamber to obtain high stability of the electron beams and long cathode life time.

Vacuum System

The difficulty in early furnaces was the electrical instability caused by outgassing of the feed metal or its surroundings, and the resultant breakdown of the system. To solve this problem, a hard vacuum, below 10^{-4} Torr, (1 Torr = $\frac{1}{760}$ of a standard atmosphere) is maintained in the furnace even at high melting rates at which gases evolve very rapidly from the feed, sometimes even in bursts. This vacuum is obtained with diffusion pumps of very large capacity to maintain the 10^{-4} Torr and below in the furnace, backed up with an oversized oil booster pump to keep 10–300 microns of mercury pressure, and large fore vacuum pumps.

Pumps with large pumping capacity are needed because the melt stock usually contains a considerable amount of gaseous impurities, such as nitrogen, oxygen, and carbon (a fraction of a per cent in weight), which, during melting, evolve in the form of N_2 and CO; the remainder of the oxygen forms metal suboxide, which is condensable. At a melt-rate of ten or twenty pounds per hour, a few grams of permanent gases per hour are generated. At a vacuum of 1×10^{-4} Torr, it is necessary then to remove a total gas load of the order of 10,000 liters per second, assuming a constant gas generation rate. Baffles and traps are often not used in the vacuum system, since the losses in pumping efficiency they introduce are more serious than the contamination that may occur without these arrangements. In practice, the melting rate must be matched to the existing capacity of the vacuum system. The gas loads for a melting process are usually not predictable. Since there are always spurts of gas evolution, the electron guns are protected either by differential pump-

ing or shielding. Shielding will also minimize any possible condensation of metal vapor on the guns or the migration of pump fluid. The vacuum conditions are monitored during operation at convenient locations throughout the system. Ionization gauges are used for the hard vacuum; thermistors and thermocouple gauges are used on the higher pressure portions of the system.

Control System, Power Supplies and Material Handling

In addition to a highly effective vacuum system, the operation requires the maintenance of a steady voltage condition, even through transient local discharges, by limiting the maximum circuit current (for instance, by means of a cathode emission limiter in the power supply). Other suitable controls and protective devices for the power supply are needed: filament emission temperature control and circuit protection devices. These devices can all be conveniently incorporated into a controller. An electron beam melting furnace is essentially a low-voltage, high-power heating device. The power supplies are usually designed to operate at the maximum voltage consistent with avoidance of x-ray hazard levels in the furnace. Typical operating voltage is in the range of 15 to 18 kv.

Material handling for a large size production furnace is a very important problem since the high vacuum must be maintained. Various interlocks which can be pumped down rapidly must be used in the feeding and withdrawal of ingot. The withdrawal of hot ingots adds to the design problem of this furnace. However, these difficulties have been overcome and continuous furnace operation has been achieved.

In Figs. 2 and 3 are schematics of complete electron beam melting and casting furnaces of the pool and drip type, respectively, given to illustrate the essential parts.

Electron Beam Melting—Special Features and Advantages

Several unique factors in combination constitute the electron beam process.

(a) The melt surface is exposed to high vacuum and electrons are chemically clean.

(b) The melt is cast in a noncontaminating water-cooled mold.

(c) The melt may be constantly observed visually.

(d) The melt can be precisely controlled both

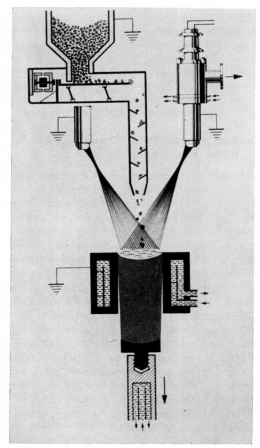

Fig. 2. An electron beam melting furnace of the pool melting type. Upper left, melt stock feeding mechanism; upper right, one of two electron guns; center, electron beams focused on molten pool of metal; below this pool is the solidified metal ingot held in a water-cooled crucible; bottom, ingot withdrawal mechanism. (*Courtesy of Heraeus Hanau*)

with regard to residence time, material addition, and withdrawal.

(e) The melting can be carried out at a very high temperature, not attainable by conventional processes.

Vacuum melting is necessary for processing highly reactive metals, such as zirconium and titanium. In electron beam melting, because of its unique features, impurities of oxygen, nitrogen, and carbon left in the metal from ore reduction can be removed. Absence of a gas ambient prevents absorption of oxygen, nitrogen, and hydrogen in the metal which will cause embrittlement.

Major advantages of electron beam melting are the following.

(a) The combination of high vacuum and high temperature makes it feasible to melt and cast very reactive and refractory metals.

(b) The purification process is very effective. Major contaminants in electron beam melted metals are generally carbon due to back-streaming of diffusion pump oil and tungsten which is used as filament material, but levels of contamination are very low.

(c) There is no chemical reaction between melt and crucible since the conventional refractory or graphite crucibles are replaced by water-cooled copper ones.

(d) The process is very flexible because close and independent control is possible over melting rate, residence time in the pool, degree of superheat and solidification rate, etc.

Electron beam melting makes possible the production of reactive refractory metals of low impurity content, superior microstructures, and excellent surface smoothness. These, in turn, provide easier fabricability, greater metal yield after fabrication, and possible elimination of conditioning and machining usually needed prior to working.

Mechanism of Metal Purification in Electron Beam Melting

The degree of purification of electron beam melting achievable depends on the type and concentration of contaminants. Several types of contaminants are found in as-reduced feed metals. Interstitial gaseous contaminants include nitrogen, oxygen, and possibly hydrogen and other gases. Oxygen may also exist in the form of oxides of the base metal or other contaminants. Metallic impurities may be present. Several nonmetallic impurities, such as carbon, sulfur, or silicon, may also occasionally be found.

In electron beam melting of metals, purification is achieved largely by a mechanism of volatilization or evaporation. The efficiency of this volatilization process with respect to any specific impurity is a function of several variables: level of vacuum, residence time of metal in the molten state, amount of superheating above melting, and intensity of mixing in the liquid. In many cases, transfer of the impurity from interior of the molten metal to the surface is the rate-limiting step of the purification process.

The rate of purification of an impurity by

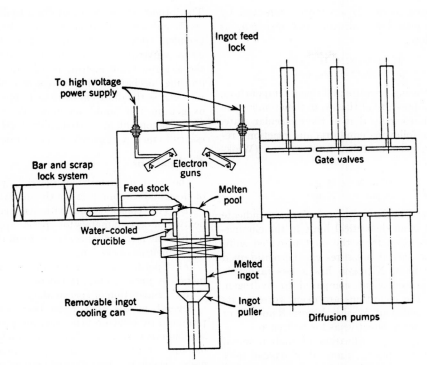

FIG. 3. Electron beam melting and casting furnace of the drip melting type. (Reprinted with permission from R. Bakish, Ed., "Introduction to Electron Beam Technology," copyright 1962 by John Wiley & Sons, Inc.)

volatilization is determined in a molten metal of uniform composition by the distribution co-efficient. If the ratio of partial pressure of this impurity to its concentration in the molten me-dium is less than the distribution coefficient, volatilization will proceed. Unfortunately, for many metals of interest in electron beam melt-ing, the values of these distribution coefficients are not known. A general rule used as a guide is that these reactions proceed at economically rapid rates in electron beam melting until the theoretical equilibrium vapor pressure of the particular species is about 10^{-5} atmosphere.

The removal of metallic impurities from a molten metal medium by volatilization can be complicated by physical phenomenon, such as formation of an intermetallic compound. For example, consider the removal of copper and silicon from iron (this is a rather awkward ex-ample, but the metallurgy of iron is well known, whereas with refractory metals little is known in detail). Copper has low affinity to iron and, hence, tends to segregate. Its vapor pressure at elevated temperatures is about one order of

magnitude higher than that of iron. Therefore, it is relatively simple to estimate the efficiency of copper removal from iron by electron beam melting.

With an impurity like silicon in an iron-based alloy, the situation is quite different. Silicon has great affinity to iron and forms intermetallic compounds. As a result, the vapor pressure ratio of silicon to iron becomes very unfavorable with decreasing silicon concentration. Gradual en-richment of silicon may occur at low silicon level in molten iron-based alloy. Occasionally, in prac-tice, however, a reduction in silicon content is found, due probably to an entirely different mechanism, e.g., the formation of volatile silicon monoxide.

In the case of evaporation of alloy constitu-ents from a melt, standard vapor pressure data corrected for known intermetallic bonding effects and estimated solution effects can be used with good reliability to predict tendencies of alloys to change in composition.

Gaseous impurities are removed in electron beam melting by several mechanisms. Hydrogen and nitrogen in metals are mostly removed by forming molecular hydrogen and nitrogen, as shown below:

$$H \text{ melt} \rightarrow \tfrac{1}{2} H_2 \text{ gas}$$
$$N \text{ melt} \rightarrow \tfrac{1}{2} N_2 \text{ gas}$$

With decreasing pressure and rising temperature, the partial pressure of the gas in the atomic state exceeds increasingly that of the molecular state, so that the following equilibria and reactions, respectively, must be taken into account (Winkler, 1960).

$$H \text{ melt} \rightarrow H \text{ gas}$$
$$N \text{ melt} \rightarrow N \text{ gas}$$

With these mechanisms, calculations indicate that there is no theoretical limit to the elimination of hydrogen from the melt provided sufficiently low partial pressures can be maintained above the melt. Nitrogen has a less favorable distribution coefficient compared to hydrogen. In reality the conditions are even worse as its diffusion coefficient is also lower. Removal of nitrogen is not as effective as for hydrogen.

In the case of purification of molten metal from oxygen impurity, removal of oxygen may proceed by one or all of the following mechanisms, including, of course, the evolution of molecular or atomic oxygen,

$$O \text{ melt} \rightarrow \tfrac{1}{2} O_2 \text{ gas}$$
$$O \text{ melt} \rightarrow O \text{ gas}$$

the evaporation of dissolved oxide, such as TiO_2 or BeO,

$$BeO \text{ melt} \rightarrow BeO \text{ gas}$$

and the formation of a volatile reaction product, for example, oxidation of carbon,

$$O \text{ melt} + C \text{ melt} \rightarrow CO \text{ gas}$$

The extent of removal by each mechanism is determined by the thermodynamics involved. In the case of oxidation phenomena, a theoretical approach, based on thermodynamic properties of metal suboxides, has provided a surprisingly good basis for estimating oxidation tendencies of all metals processed thus far.

Some nonmetallic impurities are removed by similar mechanisms. For instance, with an element such as sulfur, its removal may proceed by the following reactions:

$$S \text{ melt} \rightarrow \tfrac{1}{2} S_2 \text{ gas}$$
$$FeS \text{ melt} \rightarrow FeS \text{ gas}$$
$$C \text{ melt} + 2S \text{ melt} \rightarrow CS_2 \text{ gas}$$

The important factor, in addition to distribution coefficient, is the transport of the different chemical species in the liquid phase and in the gas or vapor phase. It has been reported[4] that in the electron beam melting of niobium, the rate-limiting mechanism in the removal of CO and nitrogen is the diffusion of carbon, nitrogen, and oxygen in the liquid niobium. To reduce the nitrogen content to a satisfactory level, it is necessary to melt it at greatly reduced rate.

Applications

The most important commercial applications of electron beam melting are the following.

(a) The consolidation with associated purification of certain metals for special applications.

(b) The recovery of scraps to form cast ingots in one melting operation.

(c) Up-grading low-grade lots of refractory metals by prime metal producers.

(d) Preparation of special alloys.

Several metals that have been successfully produced by electron beam melting processes on a commercial scale are beryllium, molybdenum, niobium, tantalum, tungsten, zirconium, hafnium, rhenium, nickel, and titanium. Many other metals and alloys prepared by similar processes are forthcoming. Some properties of electron beam melted metals have been discussed by Rexer and by Lawley. Wah Chang Corporation has reported that its quadruple electron beam melting of molybdenum produces 3 inch diameter ingots with a total interstitial content below 40 ppm. This is at least an order of magnitude lower than that obtainable by any other technique. At Temescal, the megawatt furnace has turned out product ingot $6\tfrac{1}{2}$ ft long by 20 in. in diameter. Besides tantalum and similar refractory metals, it has been producing nickel-base superalloys. Presently the limitation of this process is largely economical. With further scaling up, however, the cost of this process can be reduced considerably and many new applications are predicted.

References

1. SMITH, H. R., JR., "Electron Bombardment Melting Techniques," Chapter 14 in "Vacuum Metallurgy," R. F. Bunshah, Editor, New York, Reinhold Publishing Corp., 1958.
2. SMITH, H. R., JR., "Electron Beam Melting," Chapter 7 in "Introduction to Electron Beam Technology," R. Bakish, Editor, New York, John Wiley & Sons, Inc., 1962.
3. KRAMS, T., AND WINKLER, O., "The Reactions

Occurring in Electron Beam Melting of Metals," Chapter 6 in "Introduction to Electron Beam Technology," New York, John Wiley & Sons, Inc., 1962.

4. SMITH, H. R., *et al*, "1961 Transactions of the Eighth Vacuum Symposium and Second International Congress," p. 708, Oxford, London, and New York, Pergamon Press, 1962.
5. BAKISH, R., Editor, "Proceedings Third Symposium on Electron Beam Technology 1961," Cambridge, Mass., Alloy Electronics Corp., 1961, Smullen, p. 8, and Morley, p. 26.
6. BAKISH, R., Editor, "Proceedings Fourth Symposium on Electron Beam Technology 1962," Cambridge, Mass., Alloy Electronics Corp., 1962.
7. Anonymous, *Steel*, pp. 2–5 (June 4, 1962).
8. PIERCE, J. R., "Theory and Design of Electron Beams," New York, D. Van Nostrand Co., 1954.

PEI WANG

ELECTRON BEAM WELDING

Electron beam welding is a metal joining technique where a highly collimated electron beam is used as a controlled heat source to achieve weldments in a good vacuum. As an industrial practice, it is still in its infancy. However, it offers the following advantages over other metal joining techniques.

(a) Low total energy input to the work piece for a given job.

(b) Great controllability of process.

(c) Exceptionally clean environment and least contamination to work piece.

(d) Very high power densities available.

These specific features of electron beam welding techniques make it possible to do many jobs difficult or even impossible by any other metal joining technique.

Specific Properties of Electron Beam Welding Techniques

Low Total Power Input. The low total power input obtainable in this technique is dependent on the ability to focus electrons and produce a collimated beam of high power density. The fusion penetration of such a beam into the work piece does not depend on the thermal conductivity of the material. High-energy electrons, accelerated by a strong electric field, penetrate deeply into the material and release energy when they hit lattice atoms. The con-

version of beam energy into heat is nearly 100 per cent. In this manner, a large amount of heat can be concentrated in a very small region, allowing relatively little thermal conduction to take place. The deep penetration of an electron beam to generate heat instantly in a three-dimensional, almost cylindrical fashion, achieves the high depth-to-width fused-zone ratio. This highly efficient energy conversion in a three-dimensional fashion with minimum heat loss (due to conduction) allows the weldment to be made with a very low total power input. This narrow fused zone greatly minimizes deformation of the work piece, and the microstructure of the unwelded material adjacent to the weldment is little affected. Since the operation does not cause excessive distortion in the work and only minimum changes in its properties, this technique performs the joining of heat-treated metals or alloys. This eliminates the requirement for heat treatment of the complete structure which is often very difficult.

Controllability. In electron beam welding, the electron beam is controlled by the design of the gun and the associated electron optics. Great controllability is possible as to beam power, spot size (or area of application of energy) and spot position. The beam can be pulsed (used quite extensively in electron beam milling), or the heating time can be controlled by adjusting the travel of the work piece. By moving the parts to be welded at a suitable speed under the beam, a continuous weldment can be made. The harsh starts common to other welding processes are not encountered because of the smooth heat build-up to the material melting point. All these process variables are not affected by the work piece material or shape. The low total power input and the controllability combined allow little time for strength reducing grain growth and/or diffusion processes. This means strong and reliable weldments.

The great controllability of this technique also permits the heat treatment of the weldment and its adjacent areas by passing the electron beam under a different but favorable condition a second time over the joined areas. This heat-treating will not cause change in the base material.

Purity. In the electron beam welding, the work piece is not contaminated. No mobile foreign atoms are produced during the welding operation. Electrons are chemically pure and nonreactive. The process takes place in a high

TABLE 1. ENERGY DENSITIES AND MINIMUM CROSS SECTIONAL AREAS OF VARIOUS HEAT SOURCES IN WELDING

Heat Source	Minimum Area, sq in.	Approximate maximum power density, watts/sq in.
Welding flame	32×10^{-4}	6.5×10^4
Electron arc	65×10^{-6}	6.5×10^5
Laser beam (ruby laser)	est. 10^{-6}	est. 10^7–10^8
Electron beam	32×10^{-8}	1×10^{10}

vacuum (1×10^{-4} mm Hg or better). Concentrations of undesirable gas species, such as oxygen, water vapor, carbon dioxide, etc., in such a high vacuum are several orders of magnitude below those normally found in inert gases available. The high purity of the process and the nonreactive ambient atmosphere permit the welding of reactive materials with minimum contamination.

The welding operation sequence, including the outgassing during pump-down of the welding chamber, and in some cases an after-heat treatment, removes a considerable amount of volatile and gaseous contaminants. Therefore, a certain degree of purification may be obtained.

High Power Density. One specific feature of electron beam welding is the high temperature attainable because of the high power density of the electron beam. Temperature rises of 10,000°C/sec are possible, for example, when an electron beam of 10 ma current at 100 kv is focussed on an impingement area 0.1 in. diameter on a molybdenum plate ¼ in. thick.

In Table 1 a comparison is given of the possible power densities of several welding techniques. Although a laser beam can have very high power density, photons in a laser beam cannot be accelerated as can electrons in an electron beam. Furthermore, photons do not possess the high penetrating capability of electrons. Advantages of a laser beam are obvious; it does not have x-ray hazards, and it can be seen (for ruby lasers). The power densities attainable by other welding techniques are not comparable to electron beam welding.

Equipment and Performance

Historically, electron beam welding equipment has fallen into two somewhat arbitrary divisions. High-voltage welding utilizes equipment of the 70,000 to 150,000 volt range, while low-voltage welding utilizes equipment of the 15,000 to 30,000 volt range. The most important parameters of an electron beam welder are the beam power density and voltage.

Beam power density is defined as

$$D = IV/A$$

where I = beam current, V = accelerating voltage, and A = area of beam impingement on work piece. The low-voltage systems operate at around 10 kw with power densities of the order of 200,000 watts/sq cm. The high-voltage systems operate at power levels of 1 to 3 kw and power densities exceeding 1,000,000 kw/sq cm.

Electron optics physics shows that power density is proportional to beam current and voltage as follows: (7)

$$D \sim I^{1/4} \, V^{7/4}$$

The spot size is also proportional to voltage and current as follows:

$$d \sim \left(\frac{I}{V}\right)^{3/8}$$

At any power level, a combination of high voltage and low current produces high power density and small spot size. Deep penetration is achieved by high voltage, variations in current having relatively little effect in the weld penetration.

Spot sizes can be focussed to as low as 0.001 in. diameter in high-voltage machines, and to about 0.010 in. diameter in low-voltage machines. Fusion-zone width-to-depth ratio in materials with favorable parameters—low melting point, low thermal conductivity and low volatilization loss—can be about 25:1 in high-voltage machines, and about 8:1 in low-voltage machines.

Since at higher voltages the beam can be focussed better and deeper penetration of the beam into work piece can be obtained, high-voltage units offer better fusion-zone depth-to-width ratio and better controllability. On the other hand, low-voltage units are much more economical and are relatively free of x-ray hazards. Therefore, for many jobs, considerations of financial and operational factors are in favor of the low-voltage systems. Generally, self-accelerated electron guns are used in both types of equipment. The high-voltage welders use the telefocus gun (Steigerwald 1949) to produce an electron beam which converges quite slowly and has a long focal length. Low-voltage welders usually are equipped with electron guns of Pierce type.

In any electron beam process, a good vacuum chamber is a definite requirement. Care must be taken to assure a leak-tight chamber. Under the dynamic conditions of electron beam welding minute leaks can introduce sufficient gas contaminants to seriously degrade the properties of materials such as zirconium or titanium alloys. The dynamic vacuum, or pumping capacity, but not the ultimate vacuum attainable, is the important consideration. Although the outgassing problem in electron beam welding is not as severe as in electron beam melting, spurious outgassing from the work piece is likely and must be taken care of by suitable design of the vacuum pumping system.

To minimize arc-over, the electron gun assembly can be located in a separate chamber and the beam passed through an entrance hole into the work chamber. Differential pumping can be utilized to maintain a better vacuum in the electron gun chamber. The equipment can be extremely versatile. The same machine can be used to deliver almost kilojoule energy for deep welding of tungsten, etc., or to deliver pulsed input of 1×10^{-5} kilojoule for welding transistor lead wires of 0.001 in. diameter to metallized ceramic wafers.

In addition to the vacuum system, a good welder is provided with a suitable work piece transport mechanism such that continuous welds can be formed for different objects. An optical sighting facility is also provided for visual observation of the operations. A schematic of electron beam welding arrangement is given in Fig. 1.

Mechanism of Electron Beam Welding

The mechanism of electron beam welding is still not quite clearly understood. Considerable amounts of work have been carried out in the study of the nature of weldment as functions of welding operation variables and properties of material being welded. It has been shown that penetration is a function of accelerating voltage (Barton and Frankhouse, 1959). Fusion-zone width increases with increasing current. Plots of fusion-zone depth-to-width ratio versus electron beam current have maxima, as a minimum applied current is required to begin melting and excess current causes more spreading than deep-

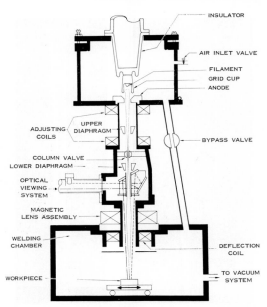

FIG. 1. Schematic Hamilton Zeiss electron beam machine. (*Courtesy, Hamilton Standard Division, United Aircraft Corp.*)

ending of the beam. Meier[4] has shown a similar increase in penetration with increasing voltage and amperage, as well as power. His work was done in stainless steel, and there is no maximum in a similar plot. He does show, however, that penetration is an inverse function of welding speed. His work on welding zone properties on thermal conductivity does not give a clear-cut relationship. In most cases, fusion depth increases with decreasing thermal conductivity, but it is not the only controlling factor. For instance, at identical settings the penetration in AISI 4340 low-alloy steel is roughly double that observed in pure niobium; yet, the thermal conductivities of the two materials are almost equal. Other material properties must also play important roles in fusion-zone properties. Properties, such as melting point, density, and lattice parameters, may all have an influence. The relation of material physical properties to weld-zone characteristics is definitely in need of continued detailed study.

In electron beam welding, the electron beam strikes the surface of the work piece and heats part of it. The volume that is heated will depend on the penetration of the electrons into the material, on the thermal properties of the material, and on the time cycle of the electron beam. Generally, if the electron beam energy

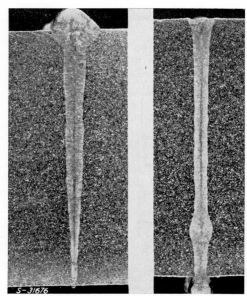

Fig. 2. Electron beam weldments on type 18-8 stainless steel 1 in. thick (vertical distance in photo). (*Courtesy of Hamilton Standard Division, United Aircraft Corp*)

is of the order of kilovolts and if the beam is switched on and off with an active period of the order of milliseconds, then the depth of this heated zone might be measured in microns.

When sufficient energy is available in the beam, the material of the work piece is melted and evaporation takes place. The molecules of the material as they evaporate will travel upward with a significant momentum, which will exert a downward force on the liquid. The electron beam, therefore, will dig a cavity in the work piece, the liquid material being pushed aside. This cavity will then move around the work piece under the beam, the liquid material flowing from the hotter to the colder side as the electron beam moves across the work piece. In a typical case the effect of the vapor momentum will be found to be of the order of ten times greater than the effect of electron pressure. Only a small material loss is necessary to account for the weld cavity sizes that are observed.

With the welding process in progress, this cavity is allowed to fill up again behind the beam to give a deep, narrow weld. The quantity of material lost from the work piece by evaporation will, in a practical case, be much smaller than the volume of the metal that is melted.

On the upper surface of the material there is sometimes a raised ridge formed by the molten material pushed upward by the pressure of the evaporating material while on the surface of the material adjoining the hole there are sometimes refrozen globules of materials from the hole. The shape in which the liquid resolidifies is determined partly by surface tension. The high energy of the electrons necessary to achieve a deep weld is therefore required not only so that an adequate power density may be obtained, but also, at least in part, so that the electron beam may penetrate the vapor without excessive scatter. Such a weld is shown in Fig. 2.

Properties of Electron Beam Welded Joints

Due to its low total power inputs, process controllability and cleanliness, an electron beam weldment usually has good ductility and microstructure. In general, there is little structural change or loss of strength in the base metal adjacent to the weld. For welds in stainless steel of thickness up to 1 inch, for instance, with depth to width ratio of 25 to 1, the transverse shrinkage is less than 0.002 inch. This low degree of distortion is of specific importance for work where close tolerance is imperative. Fusion-zone mechanical strengths are a function of grain size and heat-treatment and, therefore, are dependent on welding conditions.

Mechanical properties of weldments of various metals have been discussed extensively in several publications. Brief discussions will be given on several specific examples for illustration. With titanium fusion-zone strengths may match or exceed unwelded base-plate values and are unrelated over wide limits to interstitial content. Fusion-zone strengths are also essentially independent of joint width, but depend primarily on its grain size. Fusion-zone impact resistance values are similar to or higher than those of base plates and increase as weld width increases. This may be due to hydrogen outgassing.

For both molybdenum and tungsten, very thin (0.02 inch width) fusion zones apparently cause metallurgical notches and considerably lower tensile strength than base plates. Wide welds (0.32 inch) in molybdenum are almost of the same strength as unwelded material. Similarly, wide welds in tungsten are apparently lower in strength than unwelded material but higher than that of thin welds. Wide molybdenum fusion zones have substantially more impact resistance than thin fusion zones or unwelded base plate.

Electron beam welded joints of high strength still are very ductile, due probably to loss of the gaseous interstitial contents, e.g., of nitrogen and oxygen. The extremely high local heating may destroy the strengthening effect of cold rolling in the immediate vicinity of the weld. The welds generally are free of cracks or voids. Tensile strength and fatigue data of weldment are about equal to that of the base plates.

For beryllium, electron beam welding does not appreciably change ductility. Impact resistance at lower temperatures is the same in the fusion zone and in base metal (either pressed and sintered or hot-rolled). At higher temperatures, weldments offer increased impact resistance. Extensive studies of mechanical and structural properties of weldments in metals and alloys have been carried out. Since this is a relatively new field, much improvement can be expected.

Application and Limitations

Electron beam welding is now being widely applied, especially in nuclear, aerospace and similar industries. It can produce reliable, strong joints, some of which cannot be achieved by any other technique. However, it must be made clear that the technique cannot change the basic metallurgy. The phase diagram of the components dictates what phases are formed in the weld. If brittle intermetallic phases occur in the system chosen, the weld may be brittle. A favorable material combination is the first requirement for welded joints of desirable properties. Nevertheless, this technology has been successfully used to form welded joints for refractory metals and between dissimilar material, for instance, molybdenum to tungsten, tungsten to graphite, and ceramic to metals.

Metals which sublime in vacuum at high temperatures cannot be welded. Metals having very high vapor pressures are not suited to electron beam welding.

Readily weldable: Be, Co, Au, Hf, Fe, Nb, rare earths, Re, Ag, Ta, Ti, V, Zr

Weldable with evaporation loss: Al, Cu, Mo, Pt metals, Th, W

Not weldable: Cd, Cr, Mg, Mn, Zn

The electron beam travels on a line of sight. Therefore, obstructed joints, the interior tubes in a cluster, for example, are almost impossible to weld. Also, since the work must be manipulated through vacuum seals that permit either straight-line or rotary motions, joints with compound curvatures cannot be welded conveniently. High-voltage equipment when used for welding volatile metals may produce excessive "boiling," and as a result weldment porosity may occur.

A new area of interest is the utilization of electron beam welding to microelectronics. Main advantages are (a) better and more reliable electrical contact, particularly between different materials, (b) less contamination to the system being welded, (c) reduction in hazard of thermal damage to components, (d) improved structural rigidity, and (e) better process control. Interested readers may find more detailed information in the references.

References

The following general references contain many interesting articles, both original publication and reviews, on electron beam welding:

1. WHITE, S. S., AND BAKISH, R., "Introduction to Electron Beam Technology," R. Bakish, Editor, Chapter 9, New York, John Wiley & Sons, Inc., 1963.
2. BAKISH, R., Editor, "First Symposium on Electron Beam Technology," Cambridge, Mass., Alloyd Electronics Corp., 1959.
3. BAKISH, R., Editor, "Second Symposium on Electron Beam Technology," Cambridge, Mass., Alloyd Electronics Corp., 1960.
4. BAKISH, R., Editor, "Third Symposium on Electron Beam Technology," Cambridge, Mass., Alloyd Electronics Corp., 1961.
5. BAKISH, R., Editor, "Fourth Symposium on Electron Beam Technology," Cambridge, Mass., Alloyd Electronics Corp., 1962.
6. BAKISH, R., Editor, "Fifth Symposium on Electron Beam Technology," Cambridge, Mass., Alloyd Electronics Corp., 1963.
7. SCHWARTZ, H. J., "Electron Beam Processes at Different Voltages," 2nd International Vacuum Congress, Oct. 1961.

The following journals publish a considerable number of papers concerning electron beam welding technology: *Welding Journal, Welding and Metal Fabrication, Welding Engineer, Metal Working, Metal Progress, Product Engineering, Engineers Digest* (in particular, the paper by Barton and Frankhouse, **20,** pp. 441, 467, 1959), *Vacuum Metallurgy Conf. Transaction.*

PEI WANG

ELECTRON PARAMAGNETIC RESONANCE IN STUDIES OF ELECTRODE PROCESSES

The use of electron paramagnetic resonance (EPR) as a tool in investigation of free radicals has become well established. The literature contains many papers dealing with the techniques and theory involved. Wertz[1] has written an excellent review dealing with the subject. A more recent book by Ingram[2] also deals with the subject. The use of an electrode as a selective reducing agent is rather attractive in that no extraneous reagents are introduced to the system and the reduction potential can be controlled. In this way, one-electron reductions or oxidations leading to free radicals can be brought about. The marriage of these two techniques has been brought about recently by Geske and Maki. This union promises to be a fruitful one.

Apparently the first experiments involving electrolysis in an EPR spectrometer were carried out by Galkin[3] *et al* who observed a resonance absorption when an electric current was passed through a solution of sodium chloride in liquid ammonia. Austin[4] *et al* generated aromatic radical ions electrochemically. These, when introduced into an EPR cavity, showed characteristic radical spectra. This report, however, is limited to work in which the radicals are generated within the microwave cavity.

Geske and Maki[5] in their study of the nitrobenzene anion radical used an all glass electrochemical cell contained in the microwave cavity of an EPR spectrometer. A mercury pool with an exposed area of 25×10^{-2} sq cm was placed at the bottom of a 3 mm O.D. Pyrex tube. Electrical connection was made through a platinum wire sealed through the bottom of the tube. This tube was connected by a standard taper joint to a larger vessel which made contact with an aqueous saturated calomel electrode through a soft glass-Pyrex Perley seal. The resistance of the cell circuit with the solutions investigated was approximately 20×10^{3} ohms. During electrolysis, nitrogen was run into the cell through a saturated glass disk. Prior to a run, preliminary degassing was accomplished by running nitrogen through this disk as well as through a fine glass capillary extending through a pin hole in the top of the cell to within one mm of the mercury pool. The cell assembly was positioned along the axis of a cylindrical resonance cavity with the surface of the mercury pool slightly below the vertical center of the cavity. The appropriate potential for electrolysis could be determined by taking a pool polarogram.

The spectrometer was a conventional X-band apparatus with a cylindrical reflection cavity operating in the TE_{011} mode. The klystron oscillator (Varian X-13) was stabilized by immersion in a large bath of mineral oil and locking its frequency to that of the sample cavity by means of a modified Pound feedback circuit operating at 100 kc. The microwave circuit contained a calibrated reflection cavity wavemeter used for the measurement of the sample cavity resonance frequency for each experiment.

The Varian V 4007 and V 2200A 6 in electromagnet and power supply gave a magnetic field homogeneity of better than 0.1 gauss over the sample volume and about 0.2 gauss on the probe volume of the proton magnetic resonance spectrometer used for magnetic field calibration. The magnet gap of 2.75 inches allowed the microwave cavity and the proton resonance probe to be simultaneously inserted and allowed a precise determination of the magnetic field at the sample point. The magnetic field was swept by a steadily varying d-c potential applied to the magnet power supply. The field was also simultaneously modulated at 280 cps by means of modulation coils around the pole pieces. The signal was detected by a crystal, amplified by a narrow band audio amplifier, phase detected, and applied to a graphic recorder to produce a trace of the first derivative of the absorption.

Using the apparatus, Geske and Maki were able to observe the 54 hyperfine components which may be expected from the nitrobenzene anion radical ($C_6H_5NO_2$). They were able to calculate a spectrum which fitted their experimental data well using the following coupling constants (gauss): nitrogen, 10.32 ± 0.03; ortho proton, 3.39 ± 0.02; meta proton, 1.09 ± 0.01; para proton, 3.97 ± 0.02. These constants can be rationalized with reasonable electronic structures.

Maki and Geske[6] extended this work in an impressive study of a series of substituted nitrobenzene negative ions, using both the EPR technique and polarographic methods. Comparison of the nitrogen coupling constant of the nitro group with the polarographic half-wave potential of the para substituted nitrobenzenes showed a decrease in the coupling constant accompanied by an increasing ease of reduction.

A comparison of modified sigma values[7] with the nitrogen coupling constant shows that electron repelling substituents cause an increase in the coupling constant, while electron attracting ones cause the reverse effect.

A plot of the coupling constant for the ortho protons (a_o) *vs* that of the meta protons (a_m) for the various para substituted nitrobenzenes gives a rather impressive straight line. Assuming the spin density on the meta carbon to be negative, and that on the para positive, the line can be expressed as: $a_o + a_m = 2.30 \pm .04$ gauss. This suggests that the total electron spin in the proton containing ring orbitals of the para substituted nitrobenzenes is independent of the nature of substituents.

They were able to calculate the apparent spin density (P_c) on the aromatic atom adjacent to the proton using the following semiempirical equation: $a_H = 22.5 \, P_c$ gauss where a_H is the proton coupling constant. Measurement of the F^{19} coupling constant of p-fluoronitrobenzene anions supported the earlier suggestion[8] that a similar relation held for the interaction with fluorine containing molecules.

An additional bit of information uncovered included evidence for hindered rotation of the aldehyde group about the carbon to carbon bond in p-nitrobenzaldehyde.

In a logical extension of their work Maki and Geske[9] investigated the EPR spectra of the mononegative ions of the three isomeric dinitrobenzenes and some of their deuterium substituted analogues. These were generated in acetonitrile by controlled electrolysis within the microwave cavity. Some polarographic work was also included in this study. The experimental setup was similar to that described previously. In this case the reference electrode was an aqueous saturated calomel electrode connected through a salt bridge. In this study, they observed the hyperfine structure due to the isotropic interaction of the unpaired electron with both the nitrogen and ring proton nuclear moments. From the hyperfine structure, they were able to calculate coupling constants. For nitrogen, the coupling constants were 4.68, 3.22, and 1.74 gauss for the meta, ortho, and para anions, respectively. These were identical for the two nitrogens in a given radical. The larger nitrogen coupling constant for the ortho isomers can be explained on the basis that some s character should exist in the π orbitals of the nitrogen atoms, since steric effects will not allow the nitro group to be coplanar with the ring. The ring proton coupling constants of meta-dinitrobenzene anions (as well as the earlier observed anions) are consistent with the picture of alteration of positive and negative electron spin density on the ring. This is not the case in the ortho and para cases, since alternating positions can be shown to be equivalent. The proton coupling constant for these isomeric anions range between 0.42 and 4.19 gauss.

TABLE 1. COUPLING CONSTANTS FOR ANION RADICALS OF METHYL SUBSTITUTED NITROBENZENES

Methyl position	Coupling constants		(absolute value in gauss)	
	a_N	a_o	a_m	a_p
—	10.32	3.39	1.09	3.97
4	10.79	3.39	1.11	3.98
3, 5	10.6	3.29	1.08	3.92
2	11.0	3.12	1.04	3.91
2, 3	11.7	2.91	0.99	3.3
2, 6	17.8	0.87	—	1.44
2, 3, 5, 6	20.4	—	—	—

That the ortho and para dinitrobenzene anions show a considerable smaller hyperfine width than the meta dinitrobenzene anions is explained by the existence of negative spin density in the meta species, as well as by the possibility of quinoid resonance in the ortho and para variety. This quinoid resonance would place unpaired electron density in the oxygen nonbonding orbitals.

An interesting study on steric effects of a series of methyl substituted mono- and dinitrobenzene anions has been carried out by Ragle and Geske.[10] They generated the anions by electrochemical reduction, in the microwave cavity of millimolar solutions of the parent molecules dissolved in acetonitrile. They used an homodyne balanced mixer X-band spectrometer using bolometer detection and 400 cycle modulation. Their data is presented in the following table:

Here a_N is the nitrogen coupling constant, and a_o, a_m, and a_p are the coupling constants for the positions ortho, meta, and para to the nitro group. No differences are observed between the coupling constants for ring protons and those for methyl protons on the same position.

The authors conclude from the nitrogen coupling constants that sterically induced decoupling of the nitro group π electron system from the aromatic π electron system exists. They were also able to conclude that the inductive effect of the methyl group is not of much importance in determining the distribution of spin density, but that the steric effect of ortho methyl groups tends to localize unpaired electron density on the nitro group.

Piette, Ludwig and Adams[11] have carried out similar work using aqueous solutions. Prior to this, there was reason to believe one could not generate appreciable concentrations of anion radical ions in a proton rich solvent, since it seemed likely that a rapid irreversible protonation would occur. This would be followed by further reduction. They have observed both anion and cation radicals. The EPR spectrometer used was a Varian V-4500 X-band instrument with 100 kc field modulation. The radicals were generated electrochemically, using modified Varian V-5496 sample cells in the cavity. They used both mercury pool cells and platinum gauze cells for anodic studies. The supporting electrolytes used were 0.1 M lithium perchlorate, 0.5 M potassium chloride or buffers. They also used propanol or methanol to enhance solubility or to influence the spectra. This work has demonstrated the general utility of combining polarographic and EPR studies. The mononegative anions of o-, m-, and p-nitroaniline; o-, m-, and p-nitrophenol; p-nitroanisole; p-nitrodimethyaniline; and nitrobenzene were observed. In an aqueous system the nitrogen coupling constants are 3 to 4 gauss larger than in acetonitrile. When the electrolysis current was turned off, the radicals' decay was first order, with a half life of about 2 sec. This seems to indicate that the radical ions react with the solvent rather than with other ions. The spectra of a series of mononegative ions of aliphatic compounds (C_2 to C_4). showed a very strong nitrogen coupling (22 to 25 gauss) and coupling of the unpaired electron with the proton on the adjacent carbon. In these cases, there is no aromatic system to allow delocalization.

In their studies with nitroaromatic anion radicals they found it was necessary to work in solutions whose pH was above 7 to 8. Success in unbuffered solutions was ascribed to hydrogen ion consumption in the overall reduction, leading to a basic solution in the area where the measurements were made. This does indicate that protonation of negative ions in an aqueous media can be significant. The aromatic nitroanion radicals had somewhat longer half lives than did the aliphatic, presumably because of the delocalization of the odd electron in the ring.

These investigators were able to observe the spectrum of the p-phenylenediamine positive ions in acidic aqueous solutions of p-phenylenediamine which had been anodically oxidized. The importance of this observation was largely the demonstration that the radical ion exists as an intermediate in the electrolysis, whereas the polarographic result is ambiguous. The coupling constants observed in the aqueous systems, pH 4.8, are compared below with those observed by Melchior and Maki[12] in acetonitrile.

	a_n	$a_H NH_2$	a_H ring
pH 4-8 buffer	5.12 gauss	5.67	2.10
acetonitrile	5.24	5.88	2.13

The differences are surprisingly small, and there is little reason to doubt that essentially the same radicals are involved. They observed an enhancement of the spectrum in the presence of methanol. Their study also includes several other nitrogen containing molecules.

This work was extended to include investigation of positive radical ions by Melchior and Maki[12] who generated the monopositive radical ion of p-phenylenediamine by controlled potential electrolysis at a polarizable platinum electrode in the cavity of the microwave spectrometer. They used acetonitrile as a solvent, along with sodium perchlorate as the supporting electrolyte. The spectra of several substituted ions were investigated and employed in making the assignments. The spectra led to the following coupling constants for the p-phenylenediamine positive ion: nitrogen, 5.29; amine proton, 5.88; and ring proton, 2.13 gauss.

Recently Lee and Adams[13] have combined voltammetry with EPR in a study of the isomeric phenylenediamines. They demonstrated that chemical interaction following the electrolysis of a mixture of the isomers makes the practical analysis of mixtures of these isomers by stationary electrode voltammetry not feasible.

Whenever paramagnetic ions are generated *in situ*, they are generated in a medium relatively rich in their parent molecules. Under these conditions, interaction between the radical ions and the parent molecules are likely. Ludwig and Adams[14] have studied the situation with benzonitrile negative ions, obtained by controlled potential electrolysis of benzonitrile in acetonitrile or dimethyl formamide containing tetraethyl ammonium perchlorate. They showed that in dimethylformamide the spectra can be varied between the expected 54 line pattern (nonexchange case) to a simple narrow line by varying the concentration. A similar situation exists using acetonitrile, except that even in dilute cases the spectrum is not as well resolved as it is in dimethyl formamide. They estimated that the bimolecular rate constant is about 10^8 liter mole^{-1} sec^{-1}.

While most of the work reported to date has involved organic compounds, Maki and Geske[15] demonstrated rather early the existence of the free radicals in lithium or sodium perchlorate in anhydrous acetonitrile which had been subjected to electrooxidation within the cavity of an EPR spectrometer. Most likely the spectrum observed is that of the perchlorate radical ($\cdot ClO_4$). Hopefully the next several years will see investigations involving free radicals derived electrochemically from a large number of inorganic compounds.

The existence of good commercial EPR spectrometers and accessories which lend themselves well to this kind of work, coupled with recent appearance of advertisements extolling the virtues of these techniques, lends support to the hope that the work of Maki, Geske, Adams, *et al*, described here, has laid foundations for the rapid growth of these techniques.

References

1. Wertz, J. E., *Chem. Rev.*, **55**, 829 (1955).
2. Ingram, D. J. E., "Spectroscopy at Radio and Microwave Frequencies," London, Butterworths, 1955.
3. Galkin, A. A., *et al.*, *J. Exptl. Theoret. Phys. (USSR)*, **32**, 1581 (1957).
4. Austin, D. E. G., Gwin, J. H., Ingram, D. J. E., and Peover, M. E., *Nature*, **182**, 1784 (1958).
5. Geske, D. H., and Maki, A. H., *J. Am. Chem. Soc.*, **82**, 2671 (1960).
6. Maki, A. H., and Geske, D. H., *J. Am. Chem. Soc.*, **83**, 1852 (1961).
7. Van Bekkum, H., Verkade, P. E., and Wepster, B. M., *Rev. Trav. chim.*, **78**, 815 (1959). Taft, R. W., Jr., and Lewis, I. C., *J. Am. Chem. Soc.*, **81**, 5343 (1959).
8. Anderson, D. H., Frank, P. J., and Gutowsky, H. S., *J. Chem. Phys.*, **32**, 196 (1960).
9. Maki, A. H., and Geske, D. H., *J. Chem. Phys.*, **33**, 825 (1960).
10. Geske, D. H., and Ragle, J. L., *J. Am. Chem. Soc.*, **83**, 3532 (1961).
11. Piette, L. H., Ludwig, P., and Adams, R. N., *J. Am. Chem. Soc.*, **83**, 3909 (1961), and *Anal. Chem.*, **34**, 916 (1962).
12. Melchior, M. T., and Maki, A. H., *J. Chem. Phys.*, **34**, 471 (1961).
13. Lee, H. Y., and Adams, R. N., *Anal. Chem.*, **34**, 1587 (1962).
14. Ludwig, P., an Adams, R. N., *J. Chem. Phys.*, **37**, 828 (1962).
15. Maki, A. H., and Geske, D. H., *J. Chem. Phys.*, **30**, 1357 (1959).

Albert W. Jache

ELECTRON SPIN RESONANCE SPECTROSCOPY. See ELECTRON PARAMAGNETIC RESONANCE IN STUDIES OF ELECTRODE PROCESSES

ELECTRON TRANSFERS AT ELECTRODES

An electrode immersed in a solution containing oxidizable or reducible ions or molecules will acquire electrons from or donate electrons to them. These electron transfers occur at suitable collisions of the species with the electrode, and the probability that such an electron transfer will occur depends on factors such as various differences in the chemical structures of the oxidized and reduced forms, the electrode-solution potential difference, the electrode material, the temperature, and the nature of the electrolyte medium, e.g.[1, 2]

In typical systems the net rate of electron transfer occurring per unit area of electrode is $p_1 Z_1 c_1 - p_2 Z_2 c_2$, where c_1 and c_2 are the concentrations of the oxidized and reduced species very near the electrode, Z_1 and Z_2 are collision frequencies (i.e., numbers of collisions of these species with unit area of electrode per unit time when their concentrations are unity), and p_1 and p_2 are the probability factors just mentioned.[1, 3, 4] When several types of oxidizable and reducible species undergo electron transfer with the electrode, terms for each similar to the above should be added.

The measurement of the rate constants, $k_1 (= p_1 Z_1)$ and $k_2 (= p_2 Z_2)$, and the understanding of their magnitudes are subjects of principal interest here. These k's normally depend exponentially on the electrode-solution potential difference and, thereby, on the cell potential, E:[3]

$$k_1 = k_1' \exp\left[-\alpha n \mathbf{F}(E - E')/RT\right]$$

$$k_2 = k_2' \exp\left[(1 - \alpha)n \mathbf{F}(E - E')/RT\right]$$

where k_1' is the value of k_1 when E equals any particular value of E, E'; n is the number of electrons transferred per collision with the electrode, T is the absolute temperature, α is the transfer coefficient (the slope of the Tafel plot), $\mathbf{F}$ and R are universal constants, the Faraday and the gas constant.

The net current, written cathodically, is i_c.

$$i_c = n\mathbf{F}A(k_1 c_1 - k_2 c_2)$$

where A is the electrode area. By setting i_c equal to zero at equilibrium, one obtains a kinetic derivation of the Nernst equation, $E = E^{\circ\prime} + (RT/n\mathbf{F}) \ln c_1/c_2$, with $E^{\circ\prime}$ (the formal potential) equal to a term independent of concentration, $E^\prime + (RT/n\mathbf{F}) \ln k_1^\prime/k_2^\prime$. If $E^\prime$ is selected to be $E^{\circ\prime}$, $k_1^\prime$ evidently equals $k_2^\prime$ and one denotes their corresponding value by $k^\prime$. (The Nernst equation (q.v.) itself can be derived more rigorously on thermodynamic grounds alone, of course.)

Determination of these all-important constants, k_1 and k_2, from the experimental data requires some information about c_1 and c_2. When the migration of oxidized and reduced species to and from the electrode is sufficiently fast, their concentrations equal those in the bulk of the solution and there is no difficulty from this source. But often this migration is not fast enough and a variety of techniques is used to overcome this obstacle.[3, 5—9]

Methods used to study the rates of electrode processes include (1) those designed to speed up the migration (rotating electrodes or rapid flow of solution past electrode), (2) those employing pulsed or alternating currents or potentials, (3) those using stationary or dropping electrodes and direct current techniques, and (4) various combinations of these.

Sometimes, the ion or molecule actually undergoing electron transfer is not one of the initial reactants but is formed from it by homogeneous chemical reaction. This case of consecutive processes, coupled with migration, can be handled formally, and in favorable cases in practice, by solving the appropriate differential equations. Such kinetic studies provide detailed knowledge of the reaction mechanism, its intermediates, and its various rate constants.

Conditions are simpler when these additional homogeneous reactions are highly reversible chemical equilibria. Consider, for example, the following system:

$$xA + yB \underset{\text{rapid}}{\rightleftharpoons} C_1 \xrightarrow[\text{electrode}]{ne} C_2$$

where A and B are two of the major constituents in the solution, x and y describe the stoichiometry, and C_1 and C_2 are the oxidized and reduced species. c_1 then equals $Ka^x b^y$, K being the chemical equilibrium constant and a is the concentration of A near the electrode. The net rate of electron transfer now equals $k_1 Ka^x b^y - k_2 c_2$. Appropriate measurements in which a and b are varied then yield values of x and y (the "reaction orders").

The establishment of the rate law provides detailed insight into the overall mechanism. The measurement of electrochemical reaction orders has been described in detail.[10]

The electron transfer step sometimes involves no rupture of chemical bonds. Sometimes, however, it is accompanied by rupture and simultaneous transfer of an atom between this reacting species and the electrode. The atoms or free radicals then undergo subsequent reactions. One example is the reduction of H_3O^+ ions to form hydrogen atoms adsorbed on the electrode and, eventually, to form hydrogen molecules.[11] Often, ruptures are slow compared with the pure electron transfers, but notable exceptions exist.

The vigorous development of techniques for the study of fast electrode reactions has permitted the study of many rapid electron transfers. Several related compilations of the data in this expanding field exist.[1b, 5, 12] Principally, values of α, i_0 (the exchange current density), and of the temperature coefficient of i_0 are listed. i_0 is the value of $n\mathbf{F}k_1 c_1$ measured at $E = E^{\circ\prime}$ and at local electrochemical equilibrium. It is readily shown to be $n\mathbf{F}k^\prime c_1 (c_2/c_1)^\alpha$. The value at unit concentration, $n\mathbf{F}k^\prime$, is of particular interest. Very recently a comparison of these $k^\prime$'s for a series of reactions with the rate constants of intimately related homogeneous electron transfer reactions (ones involving "isotopic exchange") has been made using a theoretically based equation, with encouraging results.[1b, 13] Again, the coefficients α are often about 0.5 for these "simple" electron transfers, in accordance with theoretical expectations when double layer penetration effects are small.[1b]

The actual mechanism of electron transfer, both in the presence and absence of bond ruptures, has been discussed from the fundamental modern viewpoint of quantum and statistical mechanics. In each type of transfer the electrochemical process is accompanied by a change from a fairly stable arrangement of the atoms of the entire initial system (oxidized species, surrounding medium, electrode) to a fairly stable atomic arrangement of the final system (reduced species, etc.). In the purely electron transfer type of process,[1] this change of atomic configuration (i.e., of atomic position) occurs inside and outside the inner coordination shell of the reacting species. Each bond in the reacting species will have a somewhat different equilibrium length in the oxidized and reduced forms of the species. Since the ionic charge also differs (by n electronic charges) the average degree of orientation of solvent molecules in the vicinity differs for the two forms, as does the average degree of proximity of other ions of the medium. Accordingly, changes of bond lengths, reorientation of solvent molecules, and some adjustments of ion atmosphere must occur during the reaction.

Fluctuations in these bond lengths, orientations, and ionic positions occur continually. Thereby, an arrangement of the atomic positions that is a fairly stable one for the final reacting system (reduced molecule, the electrolyte medium, plus charged electrode) can be formed from one which is a fairly stable arrangement for the initial system (oxidized molecule, electrolyte medium, electrode). This fluctuation can cause an electron transfer only if a sufficiently strong coupling of the electronic orbitals of the reactant with those of the electrode exists. This coupling is in fact negligible when the reactant is far from the electrode. For appreciable coupling their distance apart should be no more than a molecular diameter or so. Accordingly, a suitably close approach of the species, coupled with the other fluctuations listed above, can cause an electron transfer.[1]

Statistical mechanical calculation of the probabilities of these fluctuations occurring, plus quantum mechanical calculation of the electronic coupling and appropriate combination of these ingredients, then yields an expression for the electron transfer rate. For convenience, assumptions are usually made analogous to those of absolute reaction rate theory.[1, 14]

In the case of electron transfers accompanied by simultaneous bond rupture[10] the major fluctuation of interest is in the position of the atom being transferred from reactant to electrode (or vice versa). Theoretical descriptions of these rupture-type electron transfers have focused attention on this particular fluctuation; an improved approximation would take cognizance of the other, less important, fluctuations, too. Analogous remarks apply to electrode processes involving deposition of metal cations.

The probability of finding a reactant or product near the electrode is influenced by interaction of the species with the charges in the electrode double layer (q.v.). The interaction also alters the relative stability of the two forms of the electrochemically active species there, and provides a second effect on the rate of formation of one from the other. Some detailed studies have been made of the influence of the double layer and interpreted largely on the basis of the Frumkin equation.[2, 6] There is therefore a considerable connection between the extensive studies of double layer phenomena at interfaces and those of salt effects on electron transfer rates at the electrode.

When the electron transfer is of the bond rupture-atom transfer type, it is expected to be a sensitive function of the electrode material, for this affects the strength of the metal-atom bond. At any given current, the hydrogen overpotential (q.v.) depends markedly on the electrode material, for example. On the other hand, in the case of electron transfers not involving bond ruptures the theoretical prediction has been made that the exchange current density should be relatively insensitive to the electrode material, provided specific adsorption and electric double layer effects, surface contamination and the presence of oxide layers can be avoided or the data suitably corrected for such phenomena.[1b]

In any field as rapidly expanding as the present one, divergent points of views of authors may often be found. The true experimental test comes as widely different techniques yield similar values for the same rate constants. From the point of view of the developing theory of these processes, any approach should be examined in the light of deductions from quantum and statistical mechanics. Often in treatments of these complicated systesm *ad hoc* assumptions are unwittingly introduced, without being examined from more basic points of view. Fortunately, the ensuing controversies have often given way to profitable clarification of the concepts.

References

1. (a) Cf. MARCUS, R. A., "A Theory of Electron Transfer Processes At Electrodes" in Ref. 2, p. 239; (b) *J. Phys. Chem.*, **67,** 853 (1963), and references cited therein; (c) Abstracts, 145th National ACS Meeting, New York City (1963).
2. Cf. articles in "Trans. Symposium Electrode Processes, Philadelphia, Pa., 1959," E. Yeager, Ed., New York, John Wiley & Sons, Inc., 1961.
3. E.g., articles in "Modern Aspects of Electrochemistry," Vol. 1, J. O'M. Bockris, Ed., New York, Academic Press, 1954.
4. The equation is based on a first order rate equation for the elementary step of electron transfer. (One instance of a second order equation which has been reported and listed in Ref. 5 is for $2I^- \rightarrow I_2 + 2e$.) Adsorption effects can complicate the law and a measurement of the adsorption isotherm is then needed.
5. JORDAN, J., AND STALICA, N. R., "Handbook of Analytical Chemistry," L. Meites, Ed., p. 38, New York, McGraw-Hill Book Co., 1963.

6. Cf. articles in "Advances in Electrochemistry and Electrochemical Engineering," Vol. 1, P. Delahay, Ed., New York, Interscience, 1961.

7. GERISCHER, H., *Ann. Rev. Phys. Chem.*, **12**, 227 (1961).

8. LEVICH, V. G., "Physicochemical Hydrodynamics," Englewood Cliffs, N. J., Prentice Hall, Inc., 1962.

9. REINMUTH, W. H., in "Advances in Analytical Chemistry and Instrumentation," Vol. 1, C. N. Reilley, Ed., p. 241, New York, Interscience, 1960.

10. VETTER, K. J., "Elektrochemische Kinetische," Berlin, Springer-Verlag, 1961.

11. E.g., HORIUTI, J., in Ref. 2; GLASSTONE, S., LAIDLER, K. J., and EYRING, H., "The Theory of Rate Processes," New York, McGraw-Hill Book Co., 1941.

12. TANAKA, N., AND TAMANUSHI, R., "Kinetic Parameters of Electrode Reaction," a report to I.U.P.A.C., 1961; copies obtainable from H. Fischer, Dept. of Electrochemistry, Inst. of Technology, Karlsruhe, Germany.

13. See SUTIN, N., *Ann. Rev. Nuclear Sci.*, **12**, 285 (1962) for a recent review of the data on homogeneous electron transfer reactions.

14. For references to theoretical work of Hush and of Levich and Dogonadze, see *Trans. Faraday Soc.*, **57**, 557 (1961) and *Collection Czechoslov. Chem. Communs.*, **26**, 193 (1961) (O. Boshko, translator, University of Ottawa, Ont.).

R. A. MARCUS

Cross-references: *Electrode Double Layer; Electrode Reactions, Kinetics; Exchange Current; Nernst Equation; Overvoltage; Tafel Lines; Transfer Coefficient.*

ELECTRO-ORGANIC CHEMISTRY

Electro-organic chemistry is the borderline field between electrochemistry and organic chemistry in which reactions of organic compounds are carried out by means of electrolysis. In the past and today electro-organic processes have been attractive for specific advantages offered. Thus, they have been particularly useful for reactions which cannot be easily carried out by other methods, for example, currently, the fluorination of hydrocarbons (q.v.) and anodic or cathodic coupling reactions or, previously for several years, the reduction of sugar to sugar alcohols (q.v.), which was a commercial process until a catalytic method was developed. A second major advantage of the electrolytic method is the precise control of reaction con-

ditions, notably temperature, time of exposure of the organic reactants in the reaction zone, electrode material and potential, and composition of electrolyte. Perhaps the third major advantage of electro-organic technique is the relative ease of recovery of pure products. For example, in preparing reduction products which are difficult to separate from metal salts, the electrolytic method provides a means of effecting reduction with substantially no contamination of products by metallic reductants.

Experimental apparatus for carrying out electro-organic reactions is very simple, a cell containing two electrodes immersed in the electrolyte, usually with means of agitation and of preventing contact of the products formed at one electrode with the opposite electrode. The electrode at which the reaction is to take place should either be surrounded by the other electrode and equidistant from it at all points, as a cylindrical cathode around a rod anode, or be placed between two electrodes of opposite sign, as a working electrode in the form of a sheet or plate, between two nonworking plates. Agitation is most simply effected by a stirrer within the cell; the electrode may itself be used as stirrer. Such an arrangement is particularly advantageous when stirring at high speeds is desired. Use of a stationary porous electrode, through which electrolyte can be passed into or out of the cell, is equivalent to stirring and sometimes is more effective than simple agitation. In most reductions it is necessary to prevent the products from making contact with the anode at which they may be reoxidized. Commonly this is accomplished by separating the anode and cathode with a porous diaphragm, often Alundum or similar ceramic. On the other hand, the reduction of an oxidation product may be prevented simply by using an inactive cathode, or by setting the current density at a level such that the compound is not reduced. In reactions involving the use of inorganic intermediates, such as hypohalites, reduction may be prevented by the use of calcium or chromium salts which form hydroxides at the cathode. These precipitates behave as diaphragms.

A variety of organic reactions can be carried out electrolytically. Thus, organic compounds themselves may be electrolyzed to form coupled products at the anode as in the case of some salts of aliphatic acids, $2RCOOM + 2F \rightarrow R—R + 2CO_2$ (Kolbe synthesis), or to form metal salts, if the anode is soluble. Similarly, certain compounds may undergo electrolysis to give coupled products at the cathode, methylmercuric acetate, $2CH_3COOHgCH_3 + 2\mathbf{F}$ to form dimethylmercury with free mercury, $2CH_3Hg \rightarrow (CH_3)_2Hg + Hg$, for example. In general, an organic compound does not carry current itself. It may react at either electrode with a substance resulting from the electrolysis of another conductor, at the anode, oxygen, halogens, thiocyanogen, etc., and at the cathode, hydrogen. Further, it may itself react at the anode or cathode to form a product which will undergo further reaction.

Still another type is the reaction of an organic compound with an inorganic compound as an intermediate. Thus, a hypobromite from the electrolysis of a bromide may react with acetone to give bromoform or may oxidize the aldehyde group of a sugar to form an aldonic acid. A reversible oxidizing agent such as ceric sulfate, or reducing agent such as stannous chloride, formed at the anode or cathode, will react with the organic compound, the resulting higher valent or lower valent salt returning to the anode or cathode to complete the cycle. Reactions may also take place through the concentration of substances at either electrode. Thus, the diazotization of amines may be carried out at the anode by nitrous acid, resulting from the electrolysis of a nitrite. If a coupling agent is present, an azo dye may be prepared. An example of such a reaction at the cathode is the saponification of an ester by the alkali which is formed by the loss of hydrogen from the aqueous electrolyte containing sodium salt.

A few organic reactions are electrochemically reversible, for example, quinone ⇌ hydroquinone and nitroso ⇌ hydroxyl amine systems. However, most are irreversible and take place through several mechanisms. The compound may give up an electron to the anode or receive an electron from the cathode, or it may react with substances formed at either electrode in atomic or molecular form. Thus, at the anode, oxidations may take place through OH radical, atomic oxygen or molecular oxygen formed by the discharge of OH^-. Substitutions may take place through the formation of an atomic or molecular species after the discharge of an ion, thus: $Cl^- \rightarrow Cl \rightleftharpoons Cl_2$. It will be noted that while oxidations and substitutions may be selective. they are not necessarily so. For example,

organic compounds may be oxidized quantitatively to carbon dioxide, water, and residual material. At the cathode, reducible groups may accept electrons, after which the resulting intermediate may react with H^+, or they may react with atomic hydrogen or molecular hydrogen.

In electrolytic reactions polarization or the back electromotive force developed when voltage is applied to the electrodes in solution plays an important part. To carry out an electrolysis it is necessary to apply an electromotive force exceeding the back electromotive force to cause current to flow through the solution. Theoretically, the minimum back electromotive force is developed by a cell with electrodes of platinum black. Other systems will develop higher voltages. The difference between the value of the back electromotive force of these systems and the theoretical value is called the polarization voltage. The polarization voltage may be subdivided into the overvoltages at the electrodes. Thus, it may be seen that gases will be more easily evolved at certain electrodes than at others. In addition to relationship with the electrode material, the overvoltage increases with the current density and decreases with increasing temperature.

Reactions at the electrodes may take place considerably below the point of gaseous evolution or near it. In the first case the compound entering the reaction prevents the polarization voltage from being reached and is, therefore, said to behave as a depolarizer. As an illustration, a compound at a cathode may accept electrons at a potential lower than that for their acceptance by H^+. As long as sufficient depolarizer is present the potential will remain below that for hydrogen evolution. Similarly, compounds may lose electrons to the anode considerably below the potential for oxygen evolution. When reactions take place near the potential of the discharge of the electrolytically formed reactant, the reaction may or may not take place through electron transfer.

The potential is also important in controlling reactions which take place in steps. Thus, by maintaining a low potential at the cathode it is possible to obtain phenyl hydroxylamine, C_6H_5NHOH, in the sequence $C_6H_5NO_2 \rightarrow C_6H_5NO \rightarrow C_6H_5NHOH \rightarrow C_6H_5NH_2$.

To obtain the maximum yield in an electrolytic reaction certain conditions must be obeyed.

In the first place the electrode material must be chosen carefully. In potential-controlled stepwise reactions, the low potentials necessary for obtaining intermediates are obtained more easily at cathodes of low minimum overvoltage. In general at cathodes of high overvoltage the reaction will be more rapid and complete. There are, however, notable exceptions, making necessary a study of the relationship between the structure of the compound entering the reaction and the electrode material. Furthermore, the type of reaction will determine the nature of the latter. Thus, for example, cathodes of low hydrogen overvoltage apparently behave as catalysts for the hydrogenation of olefins, which are not reducible at cathodes of high hydrogen overvoltage at which the mechanism of reduction is by electron transfer or atomic hydrogen.

In the case of reductions which take place only at cathodes of high hydrogen overvoltage, the character of the cathode material may be of more importance than the overvoltage. Thus, a typical aliphatic amide has been shown to be reducible only at a cathode of lead and not at other cathodes of high hydrogen overvoltage. Not only the electrode material itself, but also its physical structure are of importance. Benzoic acid, C_6H_5COOH, in aqueous sulfuric acid is not reduced at a smooth cadmium surface, but is reduced to benzyl alcohol, $C_6H_5CH_2OH$, at a surface which has been macroetched. It is likely that the crystal orientation plays an important part. Cathodic reactions are much more easily controlled than anodic reactions, particularly oxidations, because of the wider choice of electrode material. There are too few anodes which are not corroded, and some of these are expensive, i.e., the platinum metals. Furthermore, it is sometimes difficult to prevent the combustion of an organic compound. The choice of anodes in acid solution has been restricted to the platinum metals, lead peroxide, and carbon. A few others, such as nickel and iron, may be used in alkaline solution. On the other hand, many metals may be used as cathodes, also carbon and possibly certain other nonmetals.

Another deciding element is the electrolyte, not only its pH but its kind. The course of a reaction is often decided by the pH of the electrolyte. Thus, aromatic nitro compounds are usually reduced to amines in acid solution and to azoxy, azo, and hydrazo compounds in alkaline solution. Sulfuric acid is preferable to hydrochloric acid in many reductions because it is less corrosive with certain cathodes. The concentration of conductor in the electrolyte is also important. Higher yields will often be obtained at higher concentrations. In aqueous solution the usual conductors are the commoner acids, bases, and salts. The field is not limited to aqueous electrolytes, however. Reactions have been carried out in the lower alcohols, ethylene glycol, glacial acetic acid, acetonitrile, and dimethylformamide, for example. Nonaqueous media may be advantageous in solving the problem of the insolubility of many organic compounds. When no intermediate reagent, such as a hypohalite, enters the reaction, an organic compound must make contact with an electrode. In an aqueous electrolyte this may be accomplished by adding a blending agent, such as ethyl alcohol, to increase the solubility of the organic compound or by emulsification either by stirring alone or in the presence of an emulsifier.

Another very important factor is the current density, except in reactions which are not potential controlled. The optimum current density will depend on the rate of reaction at the electrode and on the rate of diffusion to the electrode of the compound undergoing reaction. It is obvious then that normal stirring will often increase the optimum current density.

The temperature will also influence the current density by its effect on the diffusion. The higher the temperature, the greater is the diffusion. As in chemical reactions in general the rate may also increase with temperature. In certain reactions an increase in the temperature may have no influence and in others even have an adverse effect, probably by disturbing the layer immediately adjacent to the electrode, as in the Kolbe synthesis mentioned previously. The current concentration, or number of amperes per volume of solution, may be of importance. Too high a current concentration will cause an increase in the temperature.

For high yields it is often necessary to allow more than the theoretical amount of current to pass through the solution because of the low efficiencies of some reactions. The cost of current for an electrolytic operation will be at a minimum when the electrolyte is an excellent conductor, if a diaphragm is unnecessary and if the compound entering the reaction is a good depolarizer.

Historically the progress of electro-organic chemistry from the experimental level to commercial application has been determined by the requirements and difficulties peculiar to the technique. Thus, in general, organic compounds either as solute or solvent are not good conductors. Further, many of them are insoluble or of limited solubility in water. Also, such factors as diverse possibilities for oxidation or reduction, stepwise or otherwise, complicated reactions, sensitivity to overexposure to electrode conditions, etc., although no more serious than similar factors in catalytic chemistry, have required solution before commercial application could be achieved. Finally, and perhaps most important, continuity of process has been required to compete with the convenience and economy of catalytic processes which normally are continuous.

To meet special requirements of certain electro-organic processes the use of nonaqueous solvents and unusual aqueous electrolytes has received much attention and has met with some success. Thus, aqueous solutions of salts of aromatic sulfonates are good conductors and are capable of dissolving high concentrations of many organic compounds. Amides and nonaqueous inorganic solvents, as sulfur dioxide and ammonia, are good ionizing media and fair solvents for organic depolarizers. Success of these efforts has been limited largely by cost or the need for closed cells operating at superatmospheric pressures, as well as by introduction of complications into recovery procedures. Similarly, the use of mercury as electrode material has received wide attention, even reached commercial application, because of its high potential and the possibility of circulating or stirring the liquid electrode, thus keeping fresh surface at the electrode face. Its application has been limited due to cost and the inefficiency of stirring a large mercury pool.

Most progress, particularly in the direction of continuous electro-organic processes, has been made with aqueous electrolytes. By more efficient means of stirring or circulation of electrolyte past the working electrode face good yields are obtained even with suspended organic solids that are substantially insoluble in the electrolyte. For example, upwards of 60 per cent material yield of reduced product from a suspension of powdered brown coal recently has been reported. Stirring by rapid rotation of the working electrode itself is particularly effective. Not only does this technique agitate the bulk of the electrolyte, preventing concentration gradients, but also sorbed layers in the immediate vicinity of the electrode face are disrupted, promoting efficient depolarization at relatively lower concentrations of depolarizer. Use of porous electrodes even without mechanical stirring, is another procedure for promoting depolarization. Electrolyte can be introduced into a cell or withdrawn from a cell through a working porous electrode. Additionally, continuity of process is obtainable, since withdrawn electrolyte contains reduced or oxidized product in relatively high concentration undiluted by the bulk of the electrolyte in the cell. Further, the use of a diaphragm sometimes can be avoided since the products of the electrode reaction are immediately withdrawn through the electrode countercurrently to the direction of diffusion to the opposite electrode.

In recent years electro-organic chemistry has received favorable impetus from the development of a variety of new materials useful as diaphragms and electrodes. Formerly, little was available for diaphragm material except ceramics that are frangible, difficult to shape, and with porosity characteristics only crudely controlled. Recent advances include, for example, resin-impregnated paper, developed chiefly for battery separators and fuel filters. These are stable to high acid concentrations and are available in a wide range of controlled pore size and pore volume. Importantly, also, the resin-paper materials can be prepared in a partially cured state, then shaped and further cured to retain the shape desired in an electrolytic cell. Also available are all-resin sheet materials which are flexible, resistant to acids and bases, and available in a variety of controlled porosity characteristics ranging from coarse down to molecular sieves (q.v.) (See **Membranes, Electrolytic.**)

Similarly, new electrode materials have made their appearance. Silicon carbide, with sufficient conductivity for use as electrodes, now can be used as an anode in strong acids where formerly only expensive platinum anodes were suitable. Advances in the field of metal sintering and plasma spraying have made available in porous form such metals as tantalum, titanium, and tungsten, as well as the ordinary metals, and control of type and size of metal powders has made possible a range of about 200 fold in pore size and about 10 fold in pore volume.

In the carbon field also, with incentive supplied largely by current interest in fuel cells, and to some extent by the requirements for atomic pile graphite, an even wider range of porous carbon and graphite electrode materials (q.v.) is being produced. In many of these, high surface area, as well as uniform macro-porosity, is provided. In general for the purposes of electro-organic chemistry, exceptions being some reactions involving gas depolarization, it is relatively coarse materials of low surface area which are best suited. Usually electrode reactions do not proceed on internal pore surface much below the apparent active face of the electrode. While even this slight penetration may furnish an increase of several fold in effective area, the optimum pore size for liquid phase depolarization usually will be found in the micron range rather than in the very fine structure characteristic of high area materials.

At the present time there is one large electro-organic operation, namely, fluorination of organic compounds (q.v.). In addition, and just as important, continuous research is being carried out on other processes, and in a number of instances development has reached the pilot plant stage.

References

Books

1. SWANN, S., JR., Chapter on "Electrolytic Reactions in Technique of Organic Chemistry," Vol. II, "Catalytic, Photochemical and Electrolytic Reactions," 2nd Ed., Edited by Arnold Weissberger, New York, Interscience Publishers, 1956.
2. ALLEN, M. J., "Organic Electrode Processes," New York, Reinhold Publishing Corp., 1958.

Review Articles

1. IZGARYSHEV, N. A., *Trudy Soveshchaniya Elektrokhim., Akad. Nauk. SSSR, Otdel. Khim. Nauk.*, **1950**, 8 (1953).
2. YAMAGUCHI, Y., *Kagaku to Kogyo*, **6**, 492 (1953).
3. UDUPA, H. V. K., AND DEY, B. B., *Bull. Centr. Electrochem. Res. Inst. (Karaikudi)*, **1**, 20 (1954).
4. UDUPA, H. V. K., AND DEY, B. B., Proc. 6th Meeting Intern. Comm. Electrochem. Thermodyn. and Kinet., p. 87, 1955.
5. KNUNYANTS, I. L., AND GAMBARYAN, N. P., *Uspekhi Khim.*, **23**, 781 (1954).
6. KOCHERGIN, S. M., *ibid.*, **24**, 779 (1955).
7. IZGARYSHEV, N. A., and FIOSHIN, M. YA., *ibid.*, **25**, 486 (1956).
8. ODO, K., *Denki Kagaku*, **24**, 673 (1956).
9. MIZUGUCHI, J., *Yuki Gosei Kagaku Kyokai Shi*, **15**, 129 (1957).
10. AIKAZYAN, E. A., AND PLESKOV, YU. V., *Zhur. Fiz. Khim.*, **31**, 205 (1957).
11. KHOMYAKOV, V. G., FIOSHIN, M. YA., AND KRUGLIKOV, S. S., *Khim. Nauka i Prom.*, **3**, 432 (1958).
12. STENDER, V. V., *ibid.*, 418.
13. KHOMAKOV, V. G., AND TOMILOV, A. P., *Khim. Prom.*, (1959) 566.
14. POPP, F. D., AND SCHULTZ, H. P., *Chem. Revs.*, **62**, 19 (1962).

N. M. WINSLOW AND SHERLOCK SWANN, JR.

Cross-references: *Adiponitrile Electrosynthesis; Electrolytic Polymerization of Vinyl Monomers; Fluorocarbons, Electrochemical Production; Glucose, Electrochemical Reduction; Kolbe and Related Reactions; Polarography, Organic.*

ELECTROOSMOSIS

The term "electroosmosis" is used for any motion of a liquid in an electric field, relative to a fixed solid. Usually the solid is a porous system, such as a glass capillary, a bed of soil, or an organic membrane. The *electroosmotic permeability*, k_e, is the volume rate of transfer per unit area by an electric field of one volt per unit length. The transfer rate per ampere is k_i. Illustrative values are presented in Table 1. In all examples given, the liquid moves toward the cathode. Motion toward the anode is uncommon.

Strictly speaking, electroosmosis is restricted to the convection of liquid by moving space charge, but this component of the motion is difficult to differentiate from transfer by solvated ions.

Theory

The basic concept is a solid with an immobile surface charge and a liquid with an equal and opposite space charge of counterions that move under the influence of an applied electric field,

TABLE 1. ELECTROOSMOTIC COEFFICIENTS

Physical System	k_e cm^2 sec^{-1} volt^{-1} × 10^4	k_iF cm^3 faraday^{-1}
Aqueous electrolyte, $10^{-1} N$ in glass capillary	1	1000
Ditto, $10^{-4} N$	10	10^7
Aqueous electrolyte, $1 N$ in highly cross-linked cation-exchange membrane	0.5	100
Ditto, $10^{-2} N$	0.1	100
Pure acetone in glass capillary	15	10^{10}
Mercury in glass capillary	25	0.025
LiCl, $1 N$ in open vessel	0.5	50
Ditto, $10^{-4} N$	0.00005	50

tangential to the surface. The electrical force is balanced by a viscous force. For porous systems two models have been developed, representing opposite extremes in the values of δ/a, where δ is the average thickness of the mobile-charged layer and a is a measure of pore size.

Macroporous Model.[8] In the classical theory of Helmholtz and Smoluchowski, δ/a is negligibly small. Charge is replaced by potential, using Poisson's equation, and the result is

$$k_i = \zeta D/4\pi\eta \ \kappa_p = \zeta D/4\pi\eta\kappa_m\bar{J}$$
$$k_e = \zeta D/4\pi\eta\bar{J}$$

where ζ is the potential at the shear boundary due to immobile charge, D is dielectric constant, η is viscosity, κ_p is specific conductivity in the pore, κ_m is the specific conductivity of the porous system, and $\bar{J}$ is the conductivity cell constant per unit area and length of the system. In cgs and practical electrical units there is a factor 1.113×10^{-5} on the right side of the equation. In rationalized mks units.

$$k_e = \zeta D/\eta\bar{J} \times 8.854 \times 10^{-12}$$

The classical formulas are widely used and are fairly successful in correlating electroosmotic data with other colloidal phenomena in lyophobic systems for which a is of the order of microns. Physical systems may depart from the model in several ways:

(1) It is probable that the strong electric field normal to the pore wall causes a decrease in D and an increase in η affecting the mobile charge. Because of the uncertainties in revising the model to account for this, conventional values of ζ are calculated with normal values of D and η.

(2) Fluid flow is not purely viscous in very wide or very short pores, and such pores do not obey the classical equations.

(3) A significant fraction of the conductance may occur very close to the pore wall. It is possible to correct for this "surface conductance" by using measured variations in $\bar{J}$ in cases where the shear boundary is everywhere parallel to the axis of flow, as in right circular capillaries. However, this procedure is not valid for random pores. With such systems, it has been found as a good approximation that the expressions for k_e and k_i must be divided by $(1 + B\chi/a\kappa)$ where B is a parameter depending on pore shape, χ is specific surface conductance, and κ is conductivity of the external liquid.[2] A linear decrease in electrokinetic effects,

proportional to $1/a$, has been found experimentally in aqueous electrolytes.

(4) The value of δ, which is approximately equal to the Debye-Hückel radius, increases in dilute solutions, and in the smaller pores δ/a may no longer be negligible. A refinement of the classical theory multiplies the expressions for k_e and k_i by $(1 - C\delta/a)$, where C is a shape factor. This effect is difficult to distinguish from that of surface conductance in aqueous electrolytes where δ is a fraction of a micron and χ/κ attains the order of 10^{-4}. Deviations from the classical theory in low-conductivity organic liquids have been attributed to the size of δ, which in this case can be of the order of millimeters.

Microporous Model.[9] The model for large δ/a consists of a uniform distribution of counterions in the interstices of a network of the solid, regarded as an immobile electrolyte. An idealized analysis, disregarding interionic forces, leads to

$$k_e = \mathbf{F}Ak/\eta; \qquad k_i = \mathbf{F}Ak/\eta\kappa_m$$

where $\mathbf{F}$ is the Faraday, A is the concentration of mobile charge in equivalents per unit pore volume, and k is the specific hydraulic permeability (dimensions l^2). The simple form of this theory has qualitative value in explaining deviations from the classical theory for lyophilic systems with fine pores of indefinite geometry, such as biological membranes. All the parameters are capable of independent measurement, and it is not surprising that quantitative agreement is rare.

Phenomenological Equations.[5] The methods of irreversible thermodynamics are useful for formulating the connection of electroosmosis with other electrokinetic effects and with ordinary osmosis, to have a more comprehensive basis for devising models. The basic equation for transport of the ith of n components, when transport is linear, is

$$J_i = \Sigma_k L_{ik} \ \text{grad} \ \bar{\mu}_k$$

where J is flux density, L's are mobilities relative to the porous solid, and the $\bar{\mu}$'s are total chemical potentials. For flow at uniform temperature and concentration, when grad $\bar{\mu}$ consists only of an electric field and a pressure gradient, experimental coefficients can be expressed in terms of the mobilities by

$$k/\eta = \Sigma_{ik} L_{ik} v_i v_k$$
$$\kappa_m = \Sigma_{ik} L_{ik} z_i z_k$$

$k_e = \Sigma_{ik} L_{ik} v_i z_k$ (also equals coefficient of streaming current)

where v's and z's are, respectively, the partial volumes and charges per mole (or any other unit mass).

A more useful formulation is in terms of *friction coefficients* defined by

$$X_{ik} = f_{ik}/(u_i - u_k)$$

where f_{ik} is the force of friction between components i and k, per mole of i; u's are velocities. The X's can be related through the basic transport equations to data of diffusion, transference, and electroosmosis, by use of the relation $c_i u_i = J_i$, where c_i is the volume concentration of component i, and remembering that grad $\bar{\mu}_i$ must balance all the friction forces, including that with the solid. Friction coefficients reflect the physical conditions in a porous medium in a more penetrating way than mobilities. In case of a negatively charged solid (s), and water (w) dissolving a single electrolyte, $X_{+,s}$ is larger than $X_{-,s}$ because of the relative distribution of the ions near the solid. In microporous systems $X_{-,s}$ is nearly zero. Abnormal values of $X_{+,w}$ have been interpreted as indicating tortuous flowlines, or excess viscosity within the pores.

Observed Characteristics of Electroosmotic Permeability[6, 8, 9, 10]

The coefficients k_e and k_i are very sensitive to the state of the interface and, in addition, are influenced by the experimental conditions imposed.

Electrolyte. In hydrophobic systems the charge on the solid is strongly influenced by specific adsorption of "potential determining ions;" polyvalent counterions reduce or even reverse the charge. These fairly clear-cut effects become less distinct as systems become more lyophilic. In Table 1 there is a marked difference between a glass capillary and a cation exchange membrane in their response to concentration. The glass capillary behaves like the classical model, for which an increase of concentration compresses the mobile charge layer, and consequently reduces ζ. The membrane behaves more like the microporous model, for which an increase of concentration would have no first-order effect on k_e. The membrane also behaves like simple hydration transfer, for which concentration has little effect on k_i. This resemblance is more striking when it is observed that the amount of water transferred through a membrane per equivalent of various

counterions goes up and down with their hydration numbers in free solution. For a cation exchange membrane that virtually excludes anions from its pores, the expression for electroosmosis in terms of friction coefficients can be simplified to

$$k_i F \approx 1/(c_+ + c_w(X_{ws}/X_{+,w}))$$

The finer the pores, the more dominant the second term, because of X_{ws}. Therefore, those cations that carry more hydration water in free solution (normally large $X_{+,w}$) will produce greater transport in fine pores. When the first term predominates, water transport depends on concentration within the pores and not on specific ion properties. Thus, with membranes less highly linked, an increase of electrolyte concentration brings a decrease in k_i along with a decrease in water content.

Pore Size. The effect on k_e (or k_i) of decreasing pore size already discussed for the classical model is the beginning of a transition to the properties of the microporous model. In synthetic membranes k_e and k_i decrease with diminishing water content, often proportionately, and with increasing cross linking. This corresponds with the fact that the coefficients are proportional to k, and hence roughly proportional to the square of pore size. When there is a variation in pore size along the direction of flow, the overall behavior of either a macroporous system or a microporous system tends to be determined by the properties of its finest pores.

Current Density. With well-defined macroporous systems, k_e and k_i are constant over wide voltage ranges, provided secondary effects of the current are avoided, such as heating or electrodialysis. There is some indication of an increase of k_e for organic liquids with hundreds of volts per cm applied. In microporous systems, there are regular variations that can be explained in terms of membrane polarization due to passage of current across the membrane boundary where conductivity, transference numbers, and concentrations change abruptly. The most prominent variation is a decrease in k_i as current density exceeds a certain value, which ranges from a few μa to a few ma per sq cm, depending on the electrolyte concentration and membrane type. Other variations less well understood have been observed, even including inversions or oscillations of flow with steady current through soils and membranes under certain conditions.

Temperature. The variation of k_e with temperature is largely determined by viscosity changes, while with k_i the viscosity effect is compensated by conductivity changes. In some cases $k_e\eta$ and k_i show a small increase with rising temperature.

Quasi-Electroosmotic Phenomena

Liquid Metals.[3] Transfer is due to inelastic scattering of current carriers at the pore wall. It is proportional to (mean free path)$^2/\eta$. The nature of the wall has no influence.

"Alternating Current Electroosmosis."[4] Unidirectional motion of liquids through porous media can be produced by alternating high fields, when the field is made nonuniform either by geometrical asymmetry or by gradients of dielectric constant. This is chiefly a process of *dielectrophoresis* (q.v.), which is proportional to the square of the field, and hence indifferent to its polarity.

Experimental Methods[1, 8]

Electroosmotic measurements rarely achieve a precision closer than a few per cent. Three distinct techniques have been used:

Velocity. In open rectangular or cylindrical cells, electroosmosis causes motion along the wall that is compensated by a return flow in the middle. A velocity profile is obtained by observing the motion of suspended particles at various levels under the microscope. The geometry determines in a known way the level at which there is no flow. The motion of the particles at this level gives a correction for their electrophoretic movement. The electroosmotic velocity is evaluated by extrapolating the corrected profile to the wall.

Total Flow or Pressure. The flow is usually measured by observation of the meniscus in a capillary, preferably horizontal to prevent pressure changes. If k_i is desired, current can be regulated with an electronic stabilizer or measured with an ammeter or coulometer. Irreversible electrodes are used when contamination is a problem, and reversible electrodes have the advantage of not forming gas. In either case the volume change of the electrode reaction must be taken into account. Alternatively, the pressure necessary to prevent flow can be measured and used to evaluate k_e through the phenomenological equations.

Acoustical Measurements. A porous system subjected to alternating current in the low audio-frequency range will generate alternating pressure waves. Measurements of this effect by acoustical techniques give a measurement of electroosmosis that is relatively free from such defects as polarization. As pressure and flow are varying together, the phenomenological equations are used to get k_e, which is understood to refer to constant pressure. The data must be extrapolated to zero frequency. As the method requires a reasonable hydrodynamic impedance, it does not work with ordinary glass capillaries.

Applications

Scientific Applications. Electroosmotic data give values of ζ, which are valuable in interpreting stability and rheology of colloids. They have been used to study adsorption and the kinetics of corrosion, to distinguish polysaccharide from protein surfaces, and to characterize carbonate rocks of different genesis and composition. Electroosmosis is important in interpreting membrane phenomena and may play a significant role in physiology.

Technical Applications. The value of k_e for most soils is close to 0.5×10^{-4} despite variations in hydraulic permeability by a factor of 10^7. Therefore, electroosmosis is effective in removing water when natural drainage is prohibitively slow. It has been used to stabilize soil in railroad cuts, U-boat pens, and tunnel approaches, and to strengthen the bond between soil and foundations.

Clay is purified and dewatered by a combination of electrophoresis and electroosmosis. About 25 kwh is required to produce a ton of clay with 35 per cent water. In the formation of ceramic articles, clay is prevented from sticking to dies by the application of -200 volts that attracts water by electroosmosis, a process known as "electric lubrication."

Paint films and rubber are sometimes tested for electroosmotic activity. Anticorrodent paints should have a negative charge that tends to dehydrate the more corrosive anodic portions of a metal surface. Rubber blends that show electroosmosis must be avoided in insulation for ships' cables.

Drying of peat, industrial wastes, and sewage by electroosmosis has been investigated, but has not been made economically successful. Electrical tanning of leather, in which tannin is driven into the pores by electroosmosis much faster than by diffusion, suffers from the anodic oxidation of the tannin.

References

1. COOKE, C. E., JR., *J. Chem. Phys.*, **23**, 2299 (1955).
2. GHOSH, B. N., CHOUDHURY, B. K., AND DE, P. K., *Trans. Faraday Soc.*, **50**, 955 (1954).
3. KLEMM, A., *Z. Naturforsch.*, **13a**, 1039 (1958).
4. LASZLO, Z., *Acta Phys. Acad. Sci. Hung.*, **10**, 79 (1959).
5. MACKAY, D., AND MEARES, P., *Trans. Faraday Soc.*, **55**, 1221 (1959).
6. MACKAY, D., AND MEARES, P., *Kolloid-Z.*, **176**, 23 (1961).
7. MANTELL, C. L., "Electrochemical Engineering," 4th Ed., New York, McGraw-Hill Book Co., Inc., 1960.
8. OVERBEEK, J. TH. G., in KRUYT, H. R., "Colloid Science," Vol. 1, Chap. 5, Houston, Elsevier Publishing Co., 1952.
9. SCHMID, G., *Z. Elektrochem.*, **55**, 229 (1951).
10. TOMBALAKIAN, A. S., BARTON, H. J., AND GRAYDON, W. F., *J. Phys. Chem.*, **66**, 1006 (1962).

PHILIP B. LORENZ

Cross-references: *Electrokinetic Potentials; Electrophoresis; Streaming Potential.*

ELECTROPHORESIS

The development of electrophoresis dates back to an observation recorded by Reuss in 1807. He observed that when electricity was passed through a glass tube containing a suspension of clay in water, clay particles moved toward the positive electrode. Decades later, it was shown that any negatively-charged particles in solution or suspension moved toward the positive electrode and positively-charged particles in the opposite direction. Moreover, particles were found to move at differing speeds, depending on their net electrical charge, size, and shape, thus opening up the way to use electrophoresis as a means of separating particles from a mixture. The electrical charges borne by particles of colloidal size may arise from charged atoms or groups of atoms that are part of the structure of the particle itself, from ions which are adsorbed from the liquid medium, and from other causes. As the knowledge of the behavior of colloidal particles and of ions in an electrical field increased, it became evident that they differed only in degree rather than in kind. Although a colloidal particle is much larger than an ion, it may also bear a much greater electrical charge, with the result that the movement in an electrical field may be about the same, varying roughly from 0–20×10^{-4} cm per second in a potential gradient of 1 volt per cm.

Suppose, for simplicity, that a nonconducting particle, spherical in shape, of radius, r, and bearing a net charge of Q coulombs is immersed in a conducting fluid of dielectric constant, D, and having a viscosity of η poises. Suppose, further, that the particle moves with a velocity of v cm/sec under the influence of an electrical field having a potential gradient of χ volts per cm. The force causing the particle to move, namely, $Q\chi \times 10^7$ dynes, is opposed by the frictional resistance offered to its movement by the liquid medium. From Stokes' law, the latter is given by $6\pi\eta r v$. Under steady-state conditions and introducing the electrophoretic mobility, $u = v/\chi$, rearrangement yields the expression $u = Q \times 10^7/6\pi\eta r$. It is evident that if the electrophoretic mobility of a particle can be measured, it should be possible to determine Q, the net charge on the particle. More rigorous treatment of the problem must take into account such complicating factors as the actual size and shape of the moving particle, the electrolyte concentration in the solvent medium, and the conductivity of the particle itself.

Three techniques for measuring electrophoretic mobilities are currently available. The oldest is usually referred to as microscopic electrophoresis. The migration of particles is observed in a solution contained in a glass tube placed horizontally on the stage of a microscope. Only relatively large particles, such as bacteria and blood cells, are readily investigated by this method. Some protein molecules have been studied by introducing tiny spheres of glass, quartz, or plastic into the protein solutions. The protein molecules are adsorbed on the surface of the spheres which then respond to the electrical field in terms of the charge on the protein. The method is not often used today.

In the moving-boundary method of electrophoresis, the movement of the boundary of a *mass* of particles is measured, thus obviating the necessity of seeing the particles. The material to be studied is poured into the bottom of a U-tube, and on top of it, in each arm of the U-tube, a buffer solution is carefully laid so as to produce sharp boundaries between the two solutions. Electrodes, inserted in the top of each arm of the tube, are attached to a d-c electrical source. If the material under study is a protein, bearing an excess of negative charges on its molecular surface, the boundary will move toward the positive electrode. Since the net electrical charge on the protein molecule varies with the acidity of the buffer solution, the charge on the molecule, and hence its mobility, may be varied by varying the acidity of the buffer. As the acidity of the buffer is progressively increased (lowered pH), the mobility of the protein is reduced until finally a point on the pH scale is reached at which it fails to move (isolectric point). If the pH is further reduced, the protein will acquire a net positive charge and will move toward the negative electrode. Other important factors which affect the mobility include the concentration of the buffer solution (more specifically, its ionic strength), the temperature, and electroosmosis.

A group of scientists in Sweden, especially Tiselius and his colleagues, were responsible for many of the developments which have helped to make moving-boundary electrophoresis such a discriminating and exact technique. These developments include the use of straight-sided tubing, instead of the conventional round kind, for the U-tube. The tubing has a narrow rectangular cross section which provides for better cooling of the solution. The U-tube is immersed in a water bath held at the temperature of the maximum density of the solution (approximately 2.8°C for a 0.1 normal sodium acetate solution.) At this point a change in temperature produces the least change in density and therefore minimum convection. The lowered temperature also increases the resolving power of the apparatus. The apparatus is equipped with a cylindrical lens system to render the boundaries visible as shadows (or schlieren) from which the technique is known as the *schlieren method*. The method is based on the fact that at a boundary between two transparent materials of different density the light rays are refracted, thus casting shadows which mark the place of refraction. The instrument produces a photographic diagram wherein the abscissas represent the refractive index gradients which can be related to concentration gradients. The areas under the curves are, therefore, proportional to the concentration of the various components.

The third technique for carrying out electrophoretic separations is known variously as ionography, zone electrophoresis, electrochromatography, etc. It lends itself equally well to the study of electromigration of ionic or colloidal materials. Under favorable conditions substances are not only separated totally from mixtures but

may be recovered almost completely. The restrictions on the temperature, current, and composition of the solutions are largely removed if the electrophoresis is carried out in a solution stabilized with a material, such as paper, cellulose acetate, starch, polyacrylamide gel, or agar. Adaptations of the technique provide for continuous operation, thus permitting the separation of relatively large quantities of substances. In one form or another it is now by far the most widely-used technique of electrophoresis.

Normally, a small zone of the mixture to be separated is placed near the midpoint of a horizontal column of buffer solution which saturates the stabilizing agent, e.g., a narrow strip of paper, and a controlled d-c source of electric potential is applied to the ends of the column. The substances under study, the migrants, begin to move, and each rapidly reaches a constant velocity of electromigration through the stabilizing structure. The velocity depends, among other factors, on the potential gradient, the charge on the substance, the ionic strength of the solution, the temperature, the barrier effect interposed by the stabilizing agent, the wetness, electroosmosis, and mechanical movement of the solvent through the stabilizing structure. In general, as the electromigration proceeds, the original zone breaks up into several discrete zones having different specific electromigration velocities. The distance of each separated spot or zone from the area where the mixture was originally placed is a measure of the mobility of the particles making up that spot, and the density and area of the spot provide an index to the quantity of that material in the mixture. See Fig. 1. If the substances separated are colorless, the spots may be brought out by the use of suitable dyeing reagents.

The most important applications of electrophoresis are to the analysis of naturally-occurring mixtures of colloids, such as proteins, lipoproteins, polysaccharides, and nucleic acids. Some form of electrophoresis often offers the only available method for the quantitative analysis and recovery of physiologically active substances in a relatively pure state. It provides the most convenient and dependable means of analyzing the protein content of the body's fluids and tissues and provides an important tool in most hospital laboratories. The marked differences between normal and pathological serum samples are useful in the diagnosis and

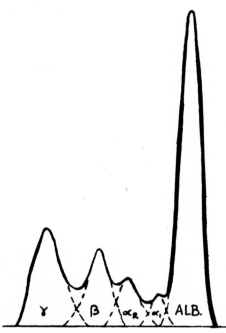

FIG. 1. A densitometer reading of an ionogram (optical density versus distance of migration along the ionogram) for normal human plasma. The major peak represents the albumin fraction; the lesser peaks represent the α_1, α_2, β, and γ globulin fractions.

understanding of disease. Such changes in the electrophoretic diagrams of the blood serum or urine are evident in multiple myeloma, nephrosis, obstructive jaundice, liver cirrhosis, and other diseases.

The electrophoretic diagram is not to be interpreted as specific for a given disease but rather as an index to the physiological condition of the patient. If the electrophoretic pattern of a patient's blood plasma shows an excess of gamma globulin, the inference is that the body is suffering from an infection since most of the antibodies evoked by the presence of infectious microbes are gamma globulin-like proteins. An increase in the alpha globulin, a result of the breakdown of tissue proteins, is likely to herald a fever-producing disease, such as pneumonia or tuberculosis. When the blood shows a decrease in albumin, the clinician looks to the liver as a possible seat of the disease because it is the main factory for albumin production. When the liver fails, other tissues try to make up for the lower albumin level, it is believed, by pouring out an excess of globulins.

References

1. BIER, M., Editor, "Electrophoresis; Theory, Methods and Applications," New York, Academic Press, 1959.
2. McDONALD, H. J., "Ionography; Electrophoresis in Stabilized Media," Chicago, Year Book Publishers, 1955.
3. McDONALD, H. J., "Theoretical Basis of Electrophoresis and Electrochromatography," Chap. 9, in "Chromatography," edited by E. Heftmann, New York, Reinhold Publishing Corp., 1961.
4. RIBEIRO, L. P., MITIDIERI, E., AND AFFONSO, O. R., "Paper Electrophoresis," New York, Elsevier Publishing Co., 1961.
5. STERN, K. G., "Electrophoresis and Ionophoresis," Vol. II, "Physical Techniques in Biological Research," edited by Oster, G. and Pollister, A. W., New York, Academic Press, 1956.

HUGH J. McDONALD

Cross-references: *Electrochromatography; Electroosmosis; Electrophoretic Deposition.*

ELECTROPHORETIC DEPOSITION

Electrophoretic deposition is the process by which electrically charged particles, suspended in a liquid, are deposited on an electrode. In contrast is electroplating, which involves the deposit of ions dissolved in a liquid to form a hard, crystalline, tightly adherent coating on the electrode. Electrophoretic deposition is not as widely used as electroplating because electrophoretic deposits are loosely adherent coatings of powder which normally require further treatment before their final use. However, electrophoretic deposits have advantages which have led to their use in specialized industrial applications. Among these advantages are the following: (1) practically any powdered material may be deposited on any electrically conducting substrate; (2) electrophoretic deposits are very uniform in thickness even on complicated shapes; (3) the deposit thickness can be controlled precisely; (4) coatings as thick as $\frac{1}{8}$ in. are easily applied; (5) codeposits can be made of two or more materials in desired proportions; and (6) deposits are made in a very short time, usually of the order of seconds.

History and Applications

Even though electrophoresis, the movement of electrically charged particles suspended in liquid under the influence of an external electric field, has been known and investigated for over 150 years, the first published application of electrophoretic deposition was a British patent issued to Thos. Cockerill in 1908 for the separation of rubber from latex by electrophoretic deposition. In 1922–23, Klein in Hungary and Sheppard and Eberlin in the United States independently discovered that sulfur, fillers, and vulcanization accelerators could be codeposited with the rubber, making a commercially usable process for the production of objects, such as rubber gloves, by electrophoretic deposition on a suitable form. By the 1930's several investigators independently discovered that electrophoretic deposition was much more useful if organic liquids were made the suspending medium, rather than the water of naturally-occurring latex, because gas-forming electrode reactions were eliminated in these organic liquids. Perhaps the most important application then developed was the deposition of powdered barium and strontium compounds on electrodes to form the oxide-coated cathodes widely used in electron tubes.[2] By a similar process, alumina insulation is deposited on tungsten wires, also for use in electron tubes. Other present day applications range from the coating of the inside of tin cans with a thin layer of lacquer[9] or even wax to the deposition of boron on the surfaces of counters used to measure neutron fluxes.

Theory

There is no satisfactory theory which fully explains all the aspects of electrophoretic deposition. The velocities at which the particles move have been the subject of many experimental and theoretical investigations by workers in the field of electrophoresis, and may be said to be well understood. However, these velocities are unimportant for electrophoretic deposition, and the crucial problem becomes the mechanism by which a deposit forms and adheres when the particles reach the electrode.

The theories which have been advanced to explain the formation of a deposit in electrophoretic deposition may be divided into two classes. The first of these assumes that the electrically charged particle arrives at the electrode and is neutralized or that the deposit is formed in a manner analogous to the sedimentation which takes place in a stable suspension when the electrically charged particles settle to the bottom of a container under the influence of

gravity.[5, 6, 10] The force of gravity is replaced by the electrical force which causes the particles to move to the electrodes. These theories fail to explain the fact that the particles in two suspensions may have identical electrophoretic velocities, and yet one will form a deposit while the other will not.

The second class of theories assumes that a secondary process takes place at the coating electrode which liberates ions in the vicinity of that electrode.[1, 7] These ions then cause flocculation of the suspension very near the electrode and the discharged particles remain on the electrode. These theories satisfactorily explain the induction time which is sometimes observed as the time after the current begins to flow before any deposit is formed. They do not explain why the inert or noncoating electrode is observed to have an effect on this induction time.[4]

Methods

The optimum size of the particles for electrophoretic deposition ranges from about one to twenty microns. This range is intermediate between sieve sizes, which are usually greater than 40 microns, and true colloidal sols in which the particle sizes range between about one millimicron and one-half micron. This desired particle size is most easily achieved by ball milling a liquid suspension of a powder which has already been classified by sieves into a convenient starting range of particle sizes. It is important that no foreign ions be introduced into the powder during this grinding because they make the later electrophoretic deposition difficult or impossible. For example, iron, both metallic and ionic, is added to the suspension from iron balls and containers; for very hard powders tungsten carbide rods in polyethylene containers are much more satisfactory. Isopropyl alcohol is a suitable suspending agent, but nitromethane decomposes during grinding and causes the suspension to flocculate. After grinding, a suitable range of particle sizes may be selected by allowing the particles in the suspension to settle for the correct length of time as calculated from Stokes' Law. The powder may be separated by centrifuging from the liquid in which it was ground and resuspended in another liquid for deposition. The particles acquire their electric charge spontaneously when they are mixed with the suspending liquid.

Alternatively, a colloidal precipitate may be

formed in a suitable liquid, and then deposited directly from that liquid. This method has been used in the past by Patai and Tomaschek[8] to deposit barium carbonate, and by Feinleib[3] to form deposits of vinyl plastics.

Many organic solvents, such as acetone, and methyl, ethyl, and isopropyl alcohol, have been used as suspending media. Special solvents may be used when binders are codeposited with the powders, for example, dimethyl ketone is useful with nitrocellulose and nitromethane is useful because it is a solvent for zein, a corn protein. Small amounts of ionic additives, such as ammonium hydroxide, citric acid, and benzoic acid, frequently help in the formation of an adherent deposit.

The concentrations of the suspensions used in electrophoretic deposition vary widely; a typical suspension of a metal powder in isopropyl alcohol would have a concentration of about 5 milligrams per cubic centimeter. The concentration of the suspension may be varied to allow one to coat an object of known area with a coating of a prescribed thickness, by plating to depletion, i.e., until all the particles have been deposited and only clear solvent is left. The time required for depleting a typical suspension is only a minute or so. Codeposits of two or more materials may be made from a mixed suspension of their particles. Usually the particles will deposit on the electrode in the same proportions that exist in the suspension.

Voltages of the order of 15 volts are used when electrophoretic deposition is done from water suspensions, as in latex, for example. However, when the suspending medium is an organic liquid, much higher voltages, from hundreds of volts up to 2,500 volts, are used to minimize deposition times. Current densities are usually about 1 milliampere per square centimeter (about 1 ampere per square foot). In general, deposits are formed on the anode, but the coating electrode must be determined experimentally for each material because the particles acquire their charge spontaneously when mixed with the solvent. Further, this charge may be reversed with suitable ionic additives.

Before their final use, electrophoretic coatings are usually heat-treated at temperatures high enough to sinter the powder, or occasionally the coating is melted to form a bond with the underlying material. Isostatic pressing increases the density of the coating, and sometimes will form a suitable bond without a subsequent heat treatment. It is possible to produce a hard, tightly adherent coating for immediate use with no further treatment by electroplating one material at the same time that another material is deposited electrophoretically.

References

1. BEAL, C. L., *Ind. Eng. Chem.*, **25,** 609 (1933).
2. BENJAMIN, M., AND OSBORN, A. B., *Trans. Faraday Soc.*, **36,** 287 (1940).
3. FEINLEIB, M., *Trans. Electrochem. Soc.*, **88,** 11 (1945).
4. GUTIERREZ, C. P., MOSLEY, J. R., AND WALLACE, T. C., *J. Electrochem. Soc.*, **109,** 923 (1962).
5. HAMAKER, H. C., *Trans. Faraday Soc.*, **36,** 279 (1940).
6. HAMAKER, H. C., AND VERWEY, E. J. W., *Trans. Faraday Soc.*, **36,** 180 (1940).
7. KOELMANS, H., AND OVERBEEK, J. TH. G., *Discussions Faraday Soc.*, **18,** 52 (1954).
8. PATAI, E., AND TOMASCHEK, Z., *Kolloid-Z.*, **75,** 80 (1936).
9. SUMNER, C. G., *Trans. Faraday Soc.*, **36,** 272 (1940).
10. TROELSTRA, S. A., *Philips Tech. Rev.*, **12,** 293 (1951).

CONRADO P. GUTIERREZ AND JOHN R. MOSLEY

ELECTROPHOTOLUMINESCENCE. See ELECTROLUMINESCENCE.

ELECTROPHYSIOLOGY

Electrophysiology is the investigation and attempted explanation of the electrical properties of living cells and intracellular substances, and the correlation of these with physiological functions.

This discipline arose in the early 18th century.[23] That muscle and nerve could be electrically stimulated and that certain eels and rays could duplicate these effects was well known before the Galvani-Volta discussions during and after 1791.[13] Galvani demonstrated more clearly than the others that living tissues could produce electricity. Some aspects of electrophysiology, such as alternating current impedance (Schwan, 1959), thermal effects of imposed currents, and steady state membrane potentials can be studied in any cell. Variation of the membrane potential upon stimulation, however, has been investigated mostly in nervous tissue, muscle (striated, cardiac, smooth), and glands; these are the so-called excitable tissues. There is no cell whose membrane potential cannot be modified, so the term excitable is relative. In excitable cells a response may be obtained by light (retina), mechanical stimuli (cochlea, Pacinian corpuscle, stretch receptor, the axon itself), temperature variation (thermal receptors), chemicals, and electrical stimuli. The electrical variations may trigger additional events, such as muscular contraction or glandular secretion. Electrophysiologists may therefore study (1) passive electrical properties, not necessarily of a linear nature, (2) electrical membrane phenomena, (3) electrical field effects of masses of cells (electrocardiography, electroencephalography), (4) response to electrical stimulation, and (5) effects of drugs and other chemicals. It is not possible even in summary to discuss the many fields of study, so discussion must be limited to the basic mechanisms. Instruments and circuit diagrams can not be treated here.

Studies on many types of animal and plant cells have revealed surprising uniformity of electrical parameters. All cells have a physiologically active surface membrane of about 5 to 10 millimicrons in thickness across which a steady-state potential difference of 50 to 100 millivolts is maintained, with the inside negative to the outside. One sq cm of membrane has a resistance between 1,000 and 10,000 ohms, and a capacitance of about 1 microfarad. The resistivity is thus about 10^9 to 10^{10} ohm-cm, the dielectric constant is approximately 5, there is an electrical phase angle of about 75°, and there is a potential gradient of about 100,000 volts per cm.

Conceptual advances have been linked with advances in instrumentation. Workers prior to Galvani used crude instruments which were insensitive and slowly reacting. Both Galvani and Volta used the electroscope for physiological experiments. They were not able to locate the site of production nor the magnitudes of biological voltages. Volta discovered that stimulation of a motor or sensory nerve elicits the proper function of the nerve. Nobili (1827) designed the astatic needle galvanometer and was able to measure the current of injury the year after Ohm published his definition of resistance. Matteucci (1838) showed that a difference of potential exists between an excised frog's nerve and its damaged muscle, but it was du Bois-Reymond who (1843) described the decrease in injury current (its negative variation) during contraction of muscle. He also proved the negative variation in nerve. These observations were important even though made on injured muscle. Although Helmholtz measured the speed of conduction of a nerve in 1852, and Bernstein by 1871 had demonstrated the presence of an action potential, the magnitude and time course were not known. Two additional advances were yet needed—faithfully responding recording equipment and the use of intracellular electrodes. Sensitivity was increased with invention of the galvanometer by Sweigger in 1811 and the mirror galvanometer by Gauss and Weber in 1837. Speed of response was successively increased by Lippmann's capillary electrometer (1872), Einthoven's string galvanometer (1901), Matthews' magnetic oscillograph (1928), and the application of both vacuum tube amplification and the cathode ray oscilloscope by Gasser and his colleagues (1921 and later).

Many of the fundamentals of electrophysiology were established in the 19th century by du Bois-Reymond, Helmholtz, Gotch, and others, but recently there have been equally rapid advances. With better equipment, Gasser, Erlanger, and Bishop made many new discoveries concerning the properties of vertebrate nerve, but these were made with extracellular electrodes. Both Osterhout and Blinks inserted a capillary tube into algae to record from the sap vacuole. Hodgkin and Huxley (1939), and Curtis and Cole (1940) used smaller capillaries to record intracellularly from the giant axon of the squid. They demonstrated the magnitude of the steady-state membrane potential and showed for the first time that the negative internal potential does not merely fall to zero upon stimulation of the nerve but that the interior becomes positive. The positive overshoot of 30 to 50 millivolts has been shown to be a sodium concentration potential and follows closely the Nernst or Planck potential as calculated from the observed Na ratio (outside to inside) of 10 to 20:1. Graham and Gerard (1942) used truly microelectrodes of the capillary type to record intracellularly the membrane potential of muscle. Many types of metallic microelectrodes have been described. However, the theoretical aspects of the use of microelectrodes are difficult, because the magnitude of the junction potentials of the electrode with cytoplasm of the cell are unknown. Gesteland et al (1959) have given an excellent discussion of the properties of microelectrodes, and Burns (1961) and Fatt (1961) have reviewed their use for recording. In practice, the microelectrode is placed in the fluid near the external surface of the cell and a potential reading taken as a reference potential. The microelectrode is advanced through the membrane and there is a sudden jump to a more negative potential which is called the membrane potential. But the junction potential between microelectrode and extracellular fluid may not be the same as junction potential between the same microelectrode and cytoplasm. By whatever magnitude the junction potential changes, the measured membrane potential will be in error. Since it is thermodynamically impossible to measure the junction potential alone, it is likewise impossible to measure the membrane potential alone. By making certain assumptions about ionic mobilities at the junction, the error of ascertaining the membrane potential can probably be reduced to a few millivolts. A pipette with less than 1 micron tip diameter may have a resistance of 10 to 50 megohms. To prevent distortion of voltage changes occurring in a few microseconds, the input capacitance of the amplifier must be very small. With the recent development of compensated negative-capacity amplifiers of very high input resistance, amplifier distortion is not now a problem.

The Steady-state Membrane Potential

To maintain voltages and currents in a dissipative (resistive) system requires energy, and interference with metabolic energy production leads to loss of the membrane potential. After energy production has been blocked, the decline of membrane voltage may require many minutes or hours, and, if the block is removed, may be reversible. Such a dissipative system is obviously not in thermodynamic equilibrium. The nature of the coupling by which energy is utilized to maintain disequilibrium, and thus an emf, is currently being studied. It is accepted that metabolic energy is utilized to maintain the integrity and function of the membrane itself and to transport ions through the membrane against electrochemical gradients. Almost all ions which have been analyzed chemically in the cell have been found to differ in concentration inside and out. But to find a difference does not mean the ion is actively transported. It may be mechanically or electrically constrained. The constraint of even one type of ion will tend to cause redistribution of the freely diffusible ions by a Gibbs-Donnan mechanism.

(See **Membrane Equilibrium**). In a Donnan equilibrium, the electrochemical potential is the same on both sides, and electrical energy can not be extracted from the system.

Bernstein in 1902 proposed that the membrane potential was a potassium concentration potential. Prior to this (1890), Planck had treated theoretically the potential difference at a diffusion boundary of aqueous phases with different electrolyte concentrations, and subsequently (1911) Donnan examined the case of phases separated by a membrane with at least one nondiffusible ion. The K concentration inside most cells is about 30 to 50 times that outside. The Planck equation for a single monovalent cation is

$$E = \frac{RT}{\mathbf{F}} \ln \frac{[\mathrm{K}]_i}{[\mathrm{K}]_0} ;$$

and K ratios usually encountered give a calculated membrane potential of 90 to 100 mv. In most cases this is higher than the observed potential by several millivolts. For this and other reasons, a growing number of investigators believe K passively distributes itself in an electrochemical gradient set up by another mechanism (Lorente de Nó, Stämpfli, Eyring, Grundfest, Ling, and others). Every cell has been found to transport actively at least one ion, usually sodium, and many cells transport more. The transport of two ions may be coupled, so that interference with the transport of one will affect transport of the other. In one cell or another, almost every one of the light molecular weight ions has been shown to be transported actively but only a limited number in any one cell. Since cells transport sodium actively toward the outside, many workers have identified the "sodium pump" with the source of emf. Eyring has shown that such an ion transport mechanism would be a source of emf and would maintain a membrane potential of the observed magnitude; he states that any ion which in the steady state does not obey the Nernst equation is obviously being pumped. The mechanism which serves as the ion "carrier" and the manner in which energy is injected into the carrier system remain to be demonstrated. Many believe that energy is contributed directly to the transport mechanism by adenosine triphosphate. The carrier is coupled to the ion, diffuses to the opposite membrane surface, unloads the ion, and diffuses back to recycle. Hokin believes the carrier to be phosphatidic acid.

Enzymes necessary for the loading and unloading process are known to exist. Since the membrane is a double layer of lipid covered by a layer of protein or other nonlipid on each surface, it has the correct properties for such activity. The low dielectric constant of the membrane would permit the carrier-sodium complex to be nonionized, and a lipid soluble carrier could move freely through the membrane. Historically, Osterhout seems to have first suggested energy requiring active transport of ions.

Pumping out of sodium from the cell leaves the inside negatively charged, and there will be a tendency for positive ions to diffuse inward and negative ions outward. Such ionic conductances have been measured for many tissues by Hodgkin and Huxley, Curtis and Cole, Keynes and many others. For squid giant axon the K:Na:Cl conductances are in the ratio of 1:0.04:0.45. Since these are the ions which carry the majority of the current for nerve and muscle, Hodgkin and Huxley have developed a formula, based on one by Goldman, for the relation between membrane potential, ionic conductances, and ionic activities

$$E = \frac{RT}{\mathbf{F}} \ln \frac{Pk[\mathrm{K}]_i + Pna[\mathrm{Na}]_i + Pcl[\mathrm{Cl}]_0}{Pk[\mathrm{K}]_0 + Pna[\mathrm{Na}]_0 + Pcl[\mathrm{Cl}]_i}$$

where Pk is membrane permeability (conductance) for K, and $[\mathrm{K}]_i$ is inside K activity, etc. Although Goldman developed his theoretical treatment on the assumption of a constant electrical field within the membrane, and this was adopted in the Hodgkin and Huxley development, Harris has shown that the equations are correct for an arbitrary field distribution. Eyring has shown further that if the field is initially a series of potential jumps, ions diffusing through the membrane will accumulate in such a manner at the jumps as to produce a more nearly constant potential gradient.

For those ions moving under passive transport only, the fluxes of the various types may be different. These differences can be partly explained on a mechanical basis by assuming that the membrane has aqueous channels or pores of the same order of size as hydrated ions. Hydrated ions vary in size, and diffusion rates will differ in a constricted channel. In addition there may be fixed electrical charges near or in the pores which will repel ions of like charge and favor those of unlike charge or even cause mechanical changes in pore size.[33] This is discussed at length also by Ussing, Teorell, Sollner, and others.

Cole has remarked that for a membrane resistivity of 10^9 ohm-cm, the pores must constitute a very small fraction of the surface area, perhaps only 0.1 per cent. In pores of ionic dimensions, diffusion of one ion type may modify the free diffusion of others.

Stimulation of the cell Membrane

A membrane may respond primarily to chemical stimuli and be electrically inexcitable (electroplaque of the eel, subsynaptic membrane of some neurons, muscle membrane of motor end plate region; see Grundfest*), others may respond to many types of stimuli. The response may be a simple local graded change in membrane potential which is proportional to the stimulus and subsides without spread to the rest of the membrane. It may vary from a millisecond for nerve to many seconds in algae. A phylogenetically newer type of response is found in some membranes, but is always superimposed on the graded local response; this is a nongraded, all-or-none, propagated response of 70 to 130 mv which spreads to all areas of the membrane and is the type which is used to transmit impulses along nerve axons.

There is a very large literature on electrical excitability of nerve and muscle[26] and empirical formulae relating excitation to duration and strength of the stimulus have been developed by Nernst, Hill, Lapicque, Blair, Rashevsky, Monnier, and others; but the studies of Hodgkin and Huxley lead to more basic formulae. The latter workers in 1952 summarized studies on ionic movements in membranes. These studies, and similar ones by Cole, used the method of Marmont (1949) of electrically clamping the membrane and studying the resulting changes in ionic fluxes. If the inside of the membrane is made more positive, there is a surge of current into the membrane capacity requiring about 20 microseconds. Then an inward flow of sodium ions rises to a peak in a few hundred microseconds, but quickly falls again to a low value. This decrease occurring with membrane depolarization maintained is called sodium inactivation. About 0.5 msec after the initial voltage change, an outward current of potassium ions begins, rises to a peak more slowly than the sodium, and remains at a high level as long as depolarization is maintained. The potassium flux de-

* Entries on **Bioelectrogenesis** and **Electric Organs.**

pends on membrane voltage alone, and not on the concomitant sodium flux.

Since the rate of change of current during Na inactivation and during the rise of K conductance is proportional to the voltage change, the proportionality factor can be called an inductance.[11] Rather than being an inductance in the sense of energy storage in a magnetic field, Mauro (1961) has shown that it is a result of the time-variant resistance of the cell membrane. It amounts to as much as 0.4H in squid axon, but is temperature and voltage dependent. It increases three-fold for a 10°C fall in temperature and decreases rapidly as membrane potential is increased. These changes depend on membrane potential only and are not affected by the current.

Hodgkin and Huxley developed one formula for membrane current density at a specific membrane potential and another for the current associated with a propagated action potential. Na conductance may be increased e-fold (2.7) by a membrane voltage change of 4 mv, while for K the figure is 5 to 6 mv. Using the formulae mentioned, almost all known functional properties of nerve can be calculated and predicted. It can be shown that weak stimuli which cause less than an 8 to 15 mv change in membrane potential will cause only a local graded response, but if the membrane changes by a little more the process is regenerative and complete depolarization with positive internal overshoot results, provided, of course, that the membrane is of a spike supporting type. During an all-or-none response the total membrane conductance may increase 40 fold, Na conductance may increase 500 fold, and the total current may reach 3 ma/sq cm.

In a membrane (such as that of striated muscle underneath the motor end plate) which is not electrically excitable, membrane potential and conductance can be altered in a local graded manner by chemical transmitters (such as acetylcholine). If the membrane becomes sufficiently depolarized, it will electrically excite the surrounding muscle membrane, which is of a different nature, and a propagated all-or-none response spreads over the muscle fiber. Synaptic transmission of many neurons is of this type.

Conductance change during alteration in membrane potential implies either structural changes or changes in electrical charges in the membrane. Since each mv change in potential changes the voltage gradient of the membrane by some 1,000 to 2,000 v/cm, structure can be physically altered and fixed electrical charges modified. Debye has discussed the high-gradient field effects. Membrane thickness seems to be unaltered, for capacitance remains constant. Some workers (Nachmansohn) believe the initial event is chemical release (such as acetylcholine) which alters membrane structure, and conductance changes follow.

This discussion can only hint at the complexity of electrophysiology. Electrical studies have been made of heart, brain, smooth muscle, cornea, ureter, gastric mucosa, uterus, skin, ganglia, and salivary gland, among others, and discussions of these are to be found in the review articles listed below. An adequate description of any one of these areas would exceed this one, but the basic electrical properties discussed here apply to most living systems.

References

1. ADRIAN, E. D., "The mechanism of nervous action," Philadelphia, Univ. Pennsylvania Press, 1932;
2. BARRON, E. S. G., Ed., "Modern trends in physiology and biochemistry," New York, Academic Press, 1952;
3. BASS, A. D., Ed., "Evolution of nervous control," Washington, Amer. Assoc. Adv. Sci., 1959;
4. BERNSTEIN, J., "Untersuchungen zur Thermodynamic der bioelektrischen Ströme," *Pflüg. Arch. ges. Physiol.*, **92**, 521–562 (1902);
5. BRAZIER, M. A. B., "The electrical activity of the nervous system," 2nd edit., New York, Macmillan, 1960;
6. BURNS, B. D., Ed., "Electrical recording from the nervous system," *Methods in Med. Res.*, **9**, 343–432 (1961);
7. BUTLER, J. A. V., Ed., "Progress in biophysics and biophysical chemistry," London, Pergamon, Vols. (1) 1950, (2) 1951, (6) 1956;
8. BUTLER, J. A. V., Ed., "Electrical phenomena at interfaces," New York, Macmillan, 1951;
9. CLARKE, H. T., Ed., "Ion transport across membranes," New York, Academic Press, 1954;
10. Cold Spring Harbor Symposia on Quantitative Biology, 17. "The neuron," Cold Spring Harbor, New York, The Biological Laboratory, 1952;
11. COLE, K. S., "The advance of electrical models for cells and axons," *Biophys. J.*, **2**, (No. 2, Part 2), 101–119 (1962);
12. DAVSON, H., AND DANIELLI, J. F., "Permeability of natural membranes," 2nd edit., Cambridge, The University Press, 1952;
13. DIBNER, B., "Galvani-Volta," Norwalk, Burndy Library, 1952;
14. ECCLES, J. C., "The physiology of nerve cells," Baltimore, Johns Hopkins Press, 1957;
15. ERLANGER, J., AND GASSER, H. S., "Electrical

signs of nervous activity," Philadelphia, Univ. Pennsylvania Press, 1937.

16. GESTELAND, R. C., et al, "Comments on microelectrodes," Proc. IRE, **47**, 1856–1862 (1959);

17. GLASSER, O., Ed., "Medical Physics," Chicago, Year Book Publ., Vols. (1) 1944, (2) 1950, (3) 1960;

18. GOLDMAN, D. E., "Potential, impedance, and rectification in membranes," J. Gen. Physiol., **27**, 37–60 (1943);

19. GRENELL, R. G., AND L. J. MULLINS, Eds., "Molecular structure and functional activity of nerve cells," Washington, Amer. Inst. Biol. Sci., 1956;

20. HECHT, H. H., Ed., "The electrophysiology of the heart," Ann. N. Y. Acad. Sci., **65**, 653–1146 (1957);

21. HODGKIN, A. L., AND HUXLEY, A. F., "A quantitative description of membrane current and its application to conduction and excitation in nerve," J. Physiol., **117**, 500–544 (1952);

22. HODGKIN, A. L., "Ionic movements and electrical activity in giant nerve fibers," Proc. Roy. Soc., **B148**, 1–37 (1958);

23. HOFF, H. E., "Galvani and the pre-Galvanian electrophysiologists," Ann. Sci., **1**, 157–172 (1936);

24. HOKIN, L. E., AND HOKIN, M. R., "Phosphatidic acid metabolism and active transport of sodium," Fed. Proc., **22**, 8–18 (1963);

25. JOHNSON, F. H., et al, "The kinetic basis of molecular biology," New York, John Wiley & Sons, Inc., 1954;

26. KATZ, B., "Electric excitation of nerve," Oxford, Clarendon Press, 1939;

27. KEYNES, R. D., "The ionic fluxes in frog muscle," Proc. Roy. Soc., **B142**, 359–382 (1954);

28. KLEINZELLER, A., AND KOTYK, A., Eds., "Membrane transport and metabolism," New York, Academic Press, 1961;

29. KROGH, A., "The active and passive exchanges of inorganic ions through the surfaces of living cells and through living membranes generally," Proc. Roy. Soc., **B133**, 140–200 (1946);

30. LING, G. N., "The interpretation of selective ionic permeability and cellular potentials in terms of the fixed charge-induction hypothesis," J. Gen. Physiol., **43** (No. 5 Suppl.), 149–174 (1960);

31. LORENTE DE NO, R., "A study of nerve physiology," Studies from the Rockefeller Inst. for Med. Res., **131**, 1–496, **132**, 1–548 (1947);

32. MAURO, A., "Anomalous impedance, a phenomenological property of time-variant resistance," Biophys. J., **1**, 353–372 (1961);

33. MULLINS, L. J., "An analysis of conductance changes in squid axon," J. Gen. Physiol., **42**, 1013–1035 (1959);

34. MURPHY, Q. R., Ed., "Metabolic aspects of transport across cell membranes," Madison, Univ. Wisconsin Press, 1957;

35. NACHMANSOHN, D., Ed., "The physico-chemical mechanism of nerve activity," Ann. N. Y. Acad. Sci., **57**, 375–602 (1946); ibid., "The

second conference- - -," ibid., **81**, 215–510 (1959);

36. NACHMANSOHN, D., "Chemical and molecular basis of nerve activity," New York, Academic Press, 1959;

37. NASTUK, W. L., AND HODGKIN, A. L., "The electrical activity of single muscle fibers," J. Cell. Comp. Physiol., **35**, 39–74 (1950);

38. Proc. IRE, "Biomedical Issue," **47**, 1813–2053 (1959);

39. SHANES, A. M., Ed., "Electrolytes in biological systems," Washington, Amer. Physiol. Soc., 1955;

40. SHANES, A. M., Ed., "Biophysics of physiological and pharmacological actions," Washington, AAAS, 1961;

41. SHEDLOVSKY, T., Ed., "Electrochemistry in biology and medicine," New York, John Wiley & Sons, 1955;

42. Symposia of the Soc. Exp. Biol., No. 8, "Active transport and secretion," New York, Academic Press, 1954;

43. TASAKI, I., "Nervous transmission," Springfield, Thomas, 1953;

44. TOWER, D. B., et al, "Properties of membranes," New York, Springer, 1962.

FRANK HARRISON

Cross-references: *Bioelectrogenesis; Biological Transducers; Electric Organs; Electrocardiology; Electrodiagnosis; Electroencephalography; Ion Transport Across Charged Membranes; Membrane Equilibrium; Membrane Potentials; Microelectrodes; Nerve Impulse Transmission.*

ELECTROPLAQUES. See ELECTRIC ORGANS.

ELECTROPLATING. See SPECIFIC METAL; ALSO ELECTRODEPOSITION ENTRIES.

ELECTROPLATING, AUTOMATIC. See ELECTROPLATING MACHINES, AUTOMATIC.

ELECTROPLATING, BARREL. See BARREL PLATING.

ELECTROPLATING, CLEANING BEFORE

Electroplating consists of depositing one metal upon the surface of another by passing a direct electric current through a water solution containing ions of the metal to be deposited.

Fabricated metal products are finished by electroplating to make them look better or last longer, to decorate them, to add saleability, to make basis metals more corrosion resistant, and to make the surface of softer metals harder so they wear better. Electroplating is an economical method to upgrade the properties of low-cost basis metals.

The basis metal is often plated in the as-fabricated condition, that is, without special mechanical finishing treatment, for example, television chassis that are zinc plated to resist corrosion. When the purpose of the finish is decorative, it is common practice to mechanically polish or buff the basis metal before plating, to brighten it. An example of this latter practice is lipstick cases that are to be finished to make them more saleable.

Metal parts that are to be electroplated must first be cleaned. Soils commonly found on such parts vary widely depending upon previous fabricating and finishing processes and include carbon or metallic smuts from pickling and rolling operations, oxides resulting from atmospheric conditions; metal filings from machining operations, shop dirt and fingerprints resulting from handling, and buffing compound which is frequently embedded in the recesses of mechanically finished or polished metal parts. These soils must be removed if the plated coating is to adhere properly and give the desired service life.

To insure thorough removal of fabricating and finishing soils, the following basic cleaning process is usually employed: (1) preclean and rinse (optional), (2) electroclean and rinse, (3) acid dip and rinse, and (4) electroplate and rinse. The character and extent of the soils on the parts will help determine the choice and desirability of the precleaning method.

Precleaning

If soils consist primarily of grease, which binds other soils to the surface, solvent precleaning may be recommended. Vapor degreasing, a common form of solvent cleaning, consists of suspending parts above a boiling chlorinated hydrocarbon solvent whose vapors then condense on the metal and dissolve the grease. Solvent cleaning, in diphase water emulsions of hydrocarbon solvents, is also used to remove heavy soil deposits. In most cases, solvent emulsion cleaning is followed by alkaline washing to remove solvent residues and prevent contamination of the electrocleaning solution by non-miscible solvents from a precleaning stage.

For average soils, the most economical precleaning is done with alkaline or detergent solutions. These may be applied either by immersion or by spray, or by combinations of these. Immersion cleaning can be accomplished with a lower capital equipment investment, but takes longer; spray cleaning is faster, and for many purposes, more efficient, particularly where large volumes of work are processed.

Ultrasonic precleaning, using high frequency sound waves to agitate solutions, has proved particularly useful for the removal of buffing compounds and solid soil from threads, knurls, filigree designs, or intricately shaped or highly decorated parts.

Soils which have been allowed to dry on surfaces are particularly difficult to remove. For this reason, precleaning should be done as soon as possible after fabrication, polishing, or buffing. Recent work on precleaning has developed the fact that some soils respond more readily to electrocleaning if treated with acid solutions after precleaning. This is true, for instance, of carbon smuts commonly found on steel surfaces, that may not be readily removed by conventional alkaline electrocleaning. Hence, the following process is frequently used to preclean steel parts: (1) alkaline preclean by immersion or spray, (2) rinse, (3) pickle in 30 per cent hydrochloric acid for 1 minute, and (4) rinse.

The parts then go through the regular electrocleaning process. This precleaning process, which when coupled with the regular electrocleaning process results in a tandem cleaning process, is obviously more expensive than simpler forms of precleaning. Its use will depend upon the quality standards set for the parts processed.

It is not always necessary to use acids to remove smuts, scale, and oxides from steel. A relatively new advance is the development of chelated alkaline compounds which remove these as well as the usual alkaline-susceptible soils. One advantage of such solutions is that there is no need for separate operations for soil and oxide removal. Other advantages, however, may be even more important. There is no danger of hydrogen embrittlement of the parts, as there is when strong acid pickling reagents are used. There is less possibility of dimensional change, or damage to threads or other machined surfaces. The chelated alkaline compounds are somewhat slower acting; hence, they may make a longer treatment time necessary. The advantages, however, often outweight this disadvantage.

It can be seen that a variety of precleaning methods is available. As in electroplating itself, the best method for any production run will depend on the metal, the soil conditions, and the quality of the plate desired.

Electrocleaning

With some exceptions, electrocleaning is generally recommended for the final cleaning before plating. Electrocleaning augments the normal detergent action of the cleaner and provides valued insurance that a good bond will be developed between the basis metal and the plated metal.

Electrocleaning consists of making the part to be cleaned either the anode (positively charged) or the cathode (negatively charged) electrode in a water solution of alkaline salts through which a direct electric current is passed. Not only is the cleaning solution agitated by the hydrogen or oxygen gas liberated by the electrolytic decomposition of the solution, but the gas generated at the work surface under the soil, which has been penetrated by the cleaner, exerts a lifting action on the soil and speeds its removal.

Electrolytic effects of electrocleaning are also important. During cathodic cleaning, positively charged hydrogen, metal ions, or colloidal particles migrate to the cathode. While beneficial in electroplating, this action is generally undesirable in electrocleaning. Should the cleaning solution become contaminated with metal as a result of parts falling into the cleaning tank, plating of the dissolved metal onto the part may occur during cathodic cleaning.

Conversely, metal may be dissolved from the surfaces of parts during anodic cleaning. If properly controlled, this is a beneficial action because it assures intimate contact between the basis metal and the metal to be deposited. Hence, anodic cleaning generally assures that the deposited metal will adhere.

Cathodic cleaning liberates hydrogen gas on the part's surface. Some of these hydrogen atoms may penetrate into a steel surface during cleaning and remain there through the plating process, emerging later to cause blisters and failure of the plate, or embrittlement of the steel. The disadvantages of cathodic cleaning are clearly demonstrated. Why then is cathodic cleaning ever used?

Nonferrous metal may be tarnished or etched if prolonged anodic cleaning is used. Thus, the jewelry industry, which deals in bright basis metal finishes and thin-plated highly decorative coatings, generally prefers cathodic cleaning because it develops little or no oxide or tarnish on the work. In addition, a few other metals, such as lead, stainless steel, and nickel, are activated by cathodic cleaning while anodic cleaning passivates them.

For most industrial plating applications, anodic cleaning is favored, at least for the final step in cleaning. The inherent advantages of anodic cleaning are: (1) better cleaning due to deplating action, (2) prevention of deposition of metals dissolved in the electrocleaner, (3) prevention of hydrogen embrittlement of steel, and (4) higher tolerance for chromic acid contamination.

Acid Dip

After electrocleaning and rinsing, the parts to be plated are generally dipped in a mild acid solution and rinsed thoroughly. This is especially important when the subsequent electroplating solution is an acidic solution. Secondly, and more important, the acid dip serves the function of activating the cleaned metal surface so that maximum adhesion of the plated coating to the basis metal is obtained.

If the plating solution is alkaline, for example, cyanide zine plating solution, sometimes a solution of sodium cyanide is employed as an alternate to the acid dip. If good precleaning has been accomplished, this is feasible, and it has the advantage of carrying a compatible residue into the cyanide plating solution.

Typical Electrocleaning Processes

Different metals react in different ways to cleaning solutions. It is not possible to recommend any particular treatment that will achieve the best results under all conditions. A consideration of electrocleaning experience with the metals most used, however, may be of some help.

Steel. Steel is the most commonly used basis metal. It is plated for both corrosion resistance and decorative purposes. Because of its hardness, steel is seldom buffed to full luster. Generally, it is uneconomical to do so. Buffing compounds, then, seldom present a problem in electrocleaning steel; the troublesome soils are usually carbon or other smut. The following is a good basic process for precleaning and electrocleaning steel for plating:

(1) Soak clean with highly alkaline compound in solutions of 8 to 14 oz/gal of water at 180 to 200°F for 2 to 4 minutes.

(2) Cold water running rinse, 30 seconds.

(3) Pickle in 30 per cent by volume hydrochloric acid, 60 seconds.

(4) Cold water running rinse, 30 seconds.

(5) Anodic electroclean with highly alkaline compound in solutions of 10 to 14 oz/gal of water at 180 to 200°F for 1 to 2 minutes, at a current density of 50 to 100 amperes per square foot.

(6) Cold water running rinse, 30 seconds.

(7) Acid dip in 5 per cent by volume hydrochloric acid for 30 seconds.

(8) Cold water running rinse, 30 seconds.

Brass. Brass, generally used where its better forming properties are needed or on goods that are finished to a high luster, is generally plated for decorative applications. It is relatively easy and economical to buff brass, so the cleaning problem is usually the removal of buffing compound without tarnishing the highly polished surface. The cleaning of brass can be greatly simplified by controlling the deposit of soils at the buffing wheel.

Electrocleaning processes for brass vary almost as widely as the buffing compounds used. The following is typical, however:

(1) Soak in soap or synthetic detergent solution, concentration 4 to 6 oz/gal, 160 to 180°F, for 3 to 10 minutes.

(2) Cold water running rinse.

(3) Cathodic electroclean in moderately alkaline buffered solution at 6 oz/gal of water at 180 to 200°F for 20 to 30 seconds at a current density of 40 amp/sq ft.

(4) Anodic electroclean in similar solution at 6 oz/gal of water at 180 to 200°F for 5 to 10 seconds at 40 amp/sq ft.

(5) Cold water running rinse.

(6) Acid dip in 5 per cent sulfuric acid.

(7) Cold water running rinse.

Where parts consist of high-nickel alloys or leaded brass, the electrocleaning may be done with only cathodic current at 50 to 100 amp/sq ft for 30 to 120 seconds, at temperatures of 180 to 200°F. In this case, the electrocleaning solution should be replaced frequently. This is followed by rinsing, then a dip in a 10 to 15 per cent by volume water solution of hydrochloric or fluoboric acid. Fluoboric, or acetic acid is preferred for leaded brass. Another rinse in running water completes the cleaning process.

Zinc Die Castings. Die casting is a high-volume technique for producing intricate parts at a cost not otherwise possible. Plated zinc die castings are found on practically every appliance, automobile, and other commodity. Because it is soft and can be buffed economically, zinc is finished to a high luster.

It is highly reactive, however, discoloring or even corroding in normal atmospheric conditions. Consequently, most zinc die castings must be plated for both appearance and resistance to corrosion.

Zinc surfaces are sensitive; they may be etched or darkened by alkaline cleaning solutions. The problem, then, is to remove buffing compounds without affecting the surfaces. Modern processing equipment has made this possible; it has also shortened the time and improved the efficiency of high-volume cleaning. Here is a typical process:

(1) Soak for 5 minutes in a diphase solvent emulsion or mild alkaline detergent with water at 140°F.

(2) Spray wash with a mild alkaline solution at ½ to 1 oz/gal, 160°F, for 30 to 60 seconds.

(3) Cold water spray rinse.

(4) Cold water spray rinse.

(5) Anodic electroclean with moderately alkaline solution at 6 oz/gal of water at 165 to 200°F, 20 to 60 seconds at 40 amp/sq ft.

(6) Cold water running rinse.

(7) Pickle, 20 to 60 seconds in a ½ per cent by volume solution of sulfuric acid.

(8) Cold water running rinse.

Good Electrocleaning Practice

Here are some good things to remember for greatest efficiency in electrocleaning:

(1) Preclean the work to remove the bulk of the soil. Precleaning pays off in dollars and quality.

(2) Skim contamination from the surface of all cleaning and electrocleaning solutions. Modern practice includes skimming of acid pickling solutions, too.

(3) Should parts fall into the cleaning bath, remove them promptly.

(4) Do not use one electrocleaning tank for both cathodic and anodic electrocleaning.

(5) Avoid chromic acid contamination of the electrocleaning solution. Keep rack coatings in good condition.

(6) Check solution concentration daily.

(7) Keep work and electrode bars clean and free of corrosion.

(8) Be sure to use adequate current.

References

1. "ASTM Standards On Electrodeposited Coatings," 3rd Edition, Philadelphia, American Society for Testing Materials, 1961. (a) "Recommended Practice for Preparing Low Carbon Steel for Electroplating," ASTM Designation B-183-49. (b) "Recommended Practice for Preparing Zinc Base Die Castings for Electroplating," ASTM Designation B-252-53. (c) "Recommended Practice for Preparing Copper and Copper Base Alloys for Electroplating," ASTM Designation B-281-58. (d) "Tentative Recommended Practice for Cleaning Metals Prior to Electroplating," ASTM Designation B-322-58T.
2. DuRose, A. H., "Typcal Processing and Operating Sequences," in "Electroplating Engineering Handbook," 2nd Edition, p. 190, New York, Reinhold Publishing Corporation, 1962.

MARTIN F. MAHER

ELECTROPLATING, COMPLEX IONS IN. See COMPLEX IONS IN ELECTROPLATING.

ELECTROPLATING FOR DECORATION AND PROTECTION

Copper, nickel, and chromium, or nickel and chromium are electroplated on many kinds of hardware and other consumer items to perpetuate a pleasing appearance.* The popular expression "chrome plate" actually refers to a very thin layer of chromium over a much thicker layer of nickel to provide resistance to wear, abrasion, and corrosion. Because completely porefree and dense chromium is difficult to electroplate and because chromium lacks good ductility, a porefree and continuous undercoat of a more ductile metal is needed as a corrosion barrier. Nickel meets this need better than any other feasible-to-plate metal or alloy. Copper is electroplated first on zinc die castings and occasionally on steel to prepare them for nickel plating. For electroplating for decoration and

* Zinc, cadmium, and other electroplates applied solely for corrosion protection are described in other sections of the Encyclopedia.

protection, the annual consumption of copper, nickel, and chromium is approximately 5,000, 30,000, and 10,000 tons, respectively.

Hundreds of metal products are protected with bright, decorative nickel and chromium electroplate. Some common examples are as follows:

Steel Stampings
   Automobile bumpers
   Builders hardware
   Metal furniture
   Vending machine panels
   Process equipment components
   Lighting fixtures
Zinc Alloy Die Castings
   Automobile door handles, head lamps, grilles, and nameplates
   Appliance housings and nameplates
   Marine hardware
   Bathroom fixtures
   Office equipment
   Cabinet door pulls
   Display fixtures
Brass and Bronze Stampings and Castings
   Plumbing fixtures
   Nameplates
   Marine hardware
   Kitchen appliances
   Ferrotype (photo printing) plates

Some small appliances fabricated from aluminum alloy are being electroplated to improve their durability. More extensive use of electroplating on aluminum has been held back because of the difficulty of preparing aluminum surfaces for plating.

Nickel and Chromium Electroplating Practices

The electroplating of nickel with highly reflective, mirrorlike surfaces is an advanced art not equaled with other bright plating processes. This characteristic is important for minimizing costly mechanical polishing or buffing for inducing specularity. Chromium electroplate duplicates the reflectivity of bright nickel, when the thickness of the chromium is in the range of 0.00001 to about 0.0002 inch. Thicker chromium is not so bright and is rarely employed because it is difficult and costly to plate on complex-shaped parts.

Changes in practices during the period of 1958 to 1962 reflect the influence of the thickness of nickel on the durability of electroplated parts.

For outdoor service, a minimum of 0.0012 to 0.002 inch of nickel is customary at the present time by comparison with only 0.0005 to 0.001 inch in 1956 and 1957. This increase in thickness is necessary to prevent perforation of the nickel by corrosion under pores in the chromium or under cracks introduced during service.

Shape is a limiting factor for parts electroplated for corrosion protection. The natural distribution of electric current results in thick deposits on edges, corners, and other protuberances. Holes, grooves, and other recesses receive less than their share. Thus, purchaser specifications refer to minimum thicknesses in recesses, to insure satisfactory corrosion protection. Table 1 lists minimum thicknesses for typical parts.

The process of electroplating nickel with mirrorlike specularity introduces inclusions of sulfides originating from the decomposition of sulfur-containing organic brightening agents. Because these sulfide inclusions lower the corrosion resistance of the nickel, the bright nickel layer frequently is limited in thickness to 0.0002 or 0.0003 inch. For outdoor applications requiring more nickel, sulfur-free, semibright nickel is plated prior to the bright nickel. Combined with 0.00001 inch of chromium, this duplex or multilayered nickel composite furnishes more corrosion protection than the same thickness of bright nickel. Semibright nickel is more ductile than bright nickel electroplate. For these reasons, composites of duplex nickel and chromium have become very popular for parts exposed outdoors.

If 0.000025 to 0.0001 inch of chromium is deposited under conditions that induce a large number of intersecting cracks, the nickel corrosion rate under an individual crack is a small fraction of the rate under an isolated pore or crack in other kinds of chromium plate. Thus, corrosion characteristics are greatly improved by a chromium plate with a large number of cracks too close together to be resolved with the unaided eye. Such electroplate is termed microcracked chromium. In practice, microcracked chromium is induced by electroplating the chromium in two layers. The cracks in the outer layer are propagated through the nonductile, highly stressed inner layer.

Brass, Bronze, Gold, and Silver

Brass or bronze alloy is electroplated on wire goods, cabinet hardware, and other items for special color effects. (See **Alloy Electrodeposition**.) As a rule, the part is first plated with 0.0002 to 0.0005 inch of bright nickel to provide a smooth and bright base for the color plate. Bright plating baths for the brass and bronze alloys eliminate or minimize mechanical buffing. The thickness of these plates usually is in the range of 0.0001 to 0.0003 inch.

Bronze—an alloy containing 90 per cent

TABLE 1. MINIMUM THICKNESSES OF COPPER, NICKEL, AND CHROMIUM

Application	Substrate	Copper, inch	Semibright Nickel, inch	Bright Nickel, inch	Total Copper and Nickel, inch	Chromium, inch
Ext. automotive	Steel	0.0005[a]	None	0.0008	0.0015	0.00001 or 0.00003
Ext. automotive	Steel	None	0.0012	0.0003	0.0015	0.00001
Ext. automotive	Zinc alloy	0.0003	0.0009	0.0003	0.0015	0.00001
Ext. automotive	Zinc alloy	0.0003	None	0.0008	0.0015	0.00003
Ext. automotive	Brass	None	None	0.0005	0.0005	0.00001
Int. automotive	Steel	Optional	None	0.0005	0.0005	0.00001
Int. automotive	Zinc alloy	0.0002	None	0.0005	0.0007	0.00001
Boat hardware	Zinc alloy	0.0003	0.0010 or 0.0012	0.0002	0.0015 or 0.0018	0.00001
Int. appliance	Steel	Optional	None	0.0003	0.0003 or 0.0005	0.00001
Int. appliance	Zinc alloy	0.0002	None	0.0003	0.0005 or 0.0007	0.00001
Plumbing fixtures	Zinc alloy	0.0002	0.0005	0.0002	0.0008	0.00001
Plumbing fixtures	Zinc alloy	0.0002	None	0.0003	0.0005	0.00001
Cabinet hardware	Steel	None	None	0.0003	0.0003 or 0.0005	0.00001
Cabinet hardware	Zinc alloy	0.0002	None	0.0003	0.0005	0.00001

[a] One purchaser permits 0.0003 inch, maximum, of white brass alloy over 0.0003 inch, minimum, of copper.

copper and 10 per cent tin—is more resistant to corrosion than brass, which contains 70 per cent copper and 30 per cent zinc. Nevertheless, bronze as well as brass electroplate usually is lacquered to prevent tarnishing in humid atmospheres.

Gold is electroplated on costume jewelry, fountain pens, watch cases, musical instruments, and laboratory apparatus to protect against tarnish and corrosion. For most of these applications a thickness of 0.00001 to 0.0001 inch is deposited over bright nickel plate. Mirrorlike, bright gold sometimes is alloyed with a very small amount of nickel or cobalt, which hardens the electroplate and improves its resistance to wear.

Silver electroplate is common for flat ware and hollow ware, which are made from alloys of nickel, zinc, and copper. Silver also is plated on musical instruments fabricated from copper or brass. A thin nickel layer sometimes is plated on these parts before the silver, which usually is in the thickness range of 0.0001 to 0.0015 inch. As a rule, a satin or butler finish is applied by mechanical buffing. Hollow ware and instruments handled infrequently usually are lacquered to protect the silver from tarnish.

Plating Procedures

Many high-volume production parts are processed automatically on conveyors through cleaning and electroplating solutions by machines costing $50,000 to $500,000, each. (See **Electroplating Machines, Automatic**.) Small-volume production generally is handled manually in small shops. In each case, the parts are affixed with spring-like members to racks made of copper for carrying large electrical currents up to 2000 amperes each. The racks are suspended from or connected to cathode bars and are insulated with plastisol coatings except for the spring tips carrying current to the parts to be plated. In automatic machines, sliding brushes transmit the current from the cathode bar to the plating racks. A row of anodes on each side of the racks completes the electrical circuit from motor generator sets or direct-current rectifiers, which supply the energy for reducing metal ions to metal at cathode surfaces. The voltage output of these direct-current sources usually is set in the range of 10 to 24 volts, depending on the conductivity of the cleaning and plating solutions and the cathode current density selected for the electrocleaning or electroplating operation.

Metal surfaces sometimes must be smoothened before plating. Scratches, pit, and other surface irregularities are visible after plating, even though copper and nickel electroplates partially level surface imperfections. In general, the surface must have a finish with a roughness of 5 to 6 rms microinches, or less, to be acceptable for decorative plating. Steel products usually are polished on wheels or belts coated with abrasive. Three to six operations with successively finer abrasives may be needed to eliminate deep irregularities. For producing automobile bumpers, flat steel blanks are polished automatically with a succession of 6 to 8 operations, prior to fabrication under presses. Other steel parts are polished with conveyorized equipment after fabrication. In each case, polishing wheels rotating at 1800 to 3600 rpm are pressed against the steel surfaces while the parts are moved on conveyors.

After the parting lines of zinc alloy, aluminum, and brass die castings are polished to remove fins, the parts often are buffed to smoothen surfaces to a finish of 1 to 2 rms microinches. The buffing usually is automated with conveyorized equipment. Some very complex-shaped parts must be buffed manually, however, to smoothen the surfaces in recessed areas. Brass and aluminum stampings are usually buffed either automatically or manually before plating.

Cleaning prior to plating (See **Electroplating, Cleaning Before**) is very important because the performance of the plated part is critically dependent upon the adherence of the electroplate. Copper and nickel can be attached to steel, zinc alloy, and other substrates with a bond strength that is at least equal to that of the electroplated metal or the substrate metal, whichever is the weaker. To accomplish this, all foreign matter, including grease, oil, dirt associated with polishing and buffing, oxides, or other metallic compounds, and fragmentary or highly stressed metal must be removed from the substrate surface.

Good cleaning requires a succession of three to five operations, as shown in Fig. 1. Each step must be controlled carefully to insure good adherence of the electroplate. To prevent accumulation of excessive amounts of grease, oil, or

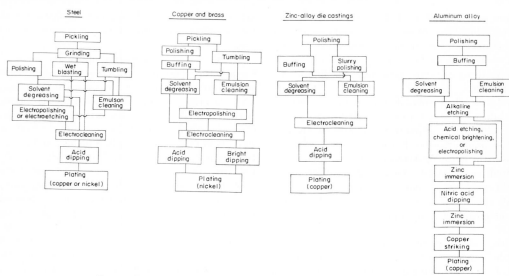

FIG. 1. Sequence of operations in preparing metals for plating.

dirt, cleaners and acid dips must be dumped and replaced at frequent intervals.

Electrocleaning and acid dipping invariably follow racking to avoid handling after cleaning, prior to plating. Thorough rinsing after cleaning and again after acid dipping is accomplished by a succession of two or three operations including water spray forced through nozzles and/or immersion in air-agitated water tanks. In areas where the water supply contains high concentrations of impurities, plating plants install deionizer units to supply high-purity water for rinsing. As a rule, cleaning and rinsing take 10 to 15 minutes.

A typical cycle for electroplating zinc alloy die castings with copper, nickel, and chromium includes many operations, such as the following:

(1) Rack (manual)—2 to 5 minutes
(2) Soak clean or emulsion clean—2 to 5 minutes
(3) Rinse with hot water spray
(4) Electroclean in hot, alkaline solution—2 to 5 minutes
(5) Rinse by immersion in hot water solution—1 to 2 minutes
(6) Rinse with hot water spray
(7) Dip in solution of sulfuric, hydrochloric, or other acid—2 minutes
(8) Rinse in air-agitated water tank
(9) Rinse with cold water spray
(10) Electroplate copper in a low-concentration copper cyanide solution (a copper strike—2 to 5 minutes)

(11) Electroplate copper in a high-concentration, high-temperature copper cyanide or copper pyrophosphate solution—5 to 10 minutes
(12) Rinse in hot water
(13) Rinse with hot water spray
(14) Dip in solution of hydrochloric, sulfuric, or other acid—1 or 2 minutes
(15) Electroplate in semibright nickel bath—20 to 40 minutes
(16) Electroplate in bright nickel bath—8 to 20 minutes
(17) Rinse in air-agitated water tank
(18) Rinse with water spray
(19) Electroplate in chromium bath—4 to 10 minutes
(20) Rinse in chromium reclaim tank with water spray
(21) Rinse in air-agitated water solution
(22) Rinse in air-agitated hot water solution
(23) Dry with forced air
(24) Unrack.

The copper plating steps (10, 11, 12, and 13) sometimes are omitted for steel and brass parts. However, steel is frequently electropolished (q.v.) or electroetched, after cleaning and before plating, to remove foreign matter embedded in its outer surface layer. A nickel strike solution with a very high acid concentration sometimes is employed to insure good adherence of nickel to steel.

Two important factors that must be carefully controlled to insure smooth and bright electroplate are temperature and current density. Current density is the current in amperes divided by the cathode area, usually expressed in square feet. Representative temperatures and current densities are as follows:

Plating Bath	Solution Temperature, °F	Cathode Current Density, amp/sq ft
Copper strike	110 to 125	15 to 40
Copper plate	150 to 170	20 to 45
Semibright nickel	130 to 140	40 to 100
Bright nickel	130 to 145	40 to 100
Chromium	105 to 130	150 to 300
Brass	85 to 100	5 to 10
Silver	75 to 85	5 to 15
Gold	100 to 130	3 to 6

The metal ion concentrations in the solutions are maintained by metal dissolved from the anodes, in the case of copper, nickel, brass, and silver. Insoluble anodes of lead alloy are employed for chromium plating. The chromic acid concentration of chromium plating baths is maintained by making regular additions of chromic acid. For solution formulations, see **Copper Electroplating, Nickel Electroplating**, and **Chromium Plating**.

Filtration of copper, nickel, brass, and silver plating solutions is important to remove dirt fall-out from the air, dirt carried in by the parts to be plated, and insoluble anode particles. For this reason, many plating baths are filtered continuously at a rate equal to two to three times the volume of plating solution, every hour. Activated carbon usually is added to the filter bed, to remove organic impurities, such as grease, oil, and organic brightener decomposition products. Nickel solutions are electrolytically purified either continuously or at frequent regular intervals to remove small concentrations of copper or zinc, which tend to darken the electroplate and reduce its corrosion resistance. Electrolytic purification with a current density of 2 to 5 amp/sq ft on dummy cathodes removes these impurities efficiently. Any iron that is dissolved in nickel plating baths must be removed by treating the solution with nickel carbonate to increase its pH and precipitate the iron.

Equipment

The power sources that supply the direct current needed for electroplating machines range in size from 5,000 to 50,000 amperes, depending on the capacity of the installation.

Plating baths range from 2,000 to 30,000 gallons. In manually operated shops, the plating baths are as small as 500 gallons, which are operated by 500 or 1,000-ampere direct-current rectifiers.

Many different materials are used to make electroplating equipment. Some important items of equipment are made with the following materials:

Item	Material
Alkaline cleaning tanks	Steel
Plating tanks	Rubber-lined steel, reinforced fiberglass
Plating racks	Plastisol-coated copper
Bus bars	Copper or aluminum
Filters and pumps	Stainless steel and rubber-lined steel
Heat exchangers	Stainless steel, iron-silicon alloy, carbon, tantalum
Conveyors	Steel
Air agitators	Plastic pipe and tubing
Fume vents	Plastic-coated steel or asphalt-coated steel
Anode baskets	Titanium

Small parts are handled in bulk by plating them in barrels that are rotated at 3 or 6 rpm to keep the parts slowly turning. (See **Barrel Plating**.) The barrels range in diameter from 6 to 36 inches and in length from 15 to 40 inches and carry from 100 to more than 500 amperes per load. Current is transmitted to the work by dangling cables in horizontal barrels that are moved through the normal succession of cleaning, acid-dipping, and plating solutions. The entire cleaning, plating, rinsing, and drying cycle ranges from 45 to 90 minutes. For cleaning and for plating copper, nickel, brass, silver, and gold, plastic barrels are perforated with small-diameter holes that allow solution and current to be transmitted from anodes placed outside of the barrel. Specially constructed barrels with "internal" anodes are required for chromium plating.

Plating Costs

Costs for electroplating copper, nickel, and chromium or nickel and chromium generally range from about 20 to 80 cents/sq ft, depending on the shape and complexity of the parts being plated, the need for mechanical finishing before plating, and the volume of production. These cost ranges include labor, material, power, equipment depreciation and maintenance, and overhead. Small-lot jobs sometimes cost more than 80 cents/sq ft. Finishing costs usually are lower for large-lot parts that can be plated in rotating barrels.

References

1. BLUM, W., AND HOGABOOM, G. B., "Principles of Electroplating and Electroforming," Third Ed., 436 pages, New York, McGraw-Hill Book Co., 1949.
2. GRAHAM, A. K., Editor, "Electroplating Engineering Handbook," Second Ed., 774 pages, New York, Reinhold Publishing Corp., 1962.
3. LOWENHEIM, F. A., Editor, "Modern Electroplating," Third Ed., sponsored by The Electrochemical Society, New York, John Wiley and Sons, Inc., 1963.
4. "ASTM Standards for Electrodeposited Metal Coatings," Third Ed., 149 pages, Philadelphia, American Society for Testing Materials, 1961.
5. BLOUNT, E. A., "Introduction to Electroplating," 20 pages, Newark, American Electroplaters' Society, 1962.

W. H. SAFRANEK

Cross-references: *see specific metals; Addition Agents; Alloy Electrodeposition; Barrel Plating; Brightening Agents; Electrical Currents, Effects on Electrodeposition of Metals; Electroplating, Cleaning Before; Electroplating Machines, Automatic; Electroplating Terms; Manual Plating; Periodic Reverse Plating; Throwing Power.*

ELECTROPLATING MACHINES, AUTOMATIC

Automatic electroplating machines provide the means of cleaning, preparing, electroplating, and otherwise finishing large quantities of metal parts or basic metal in a uniform manner under precisely controlled sequences and conditions. They are designed to transport the work three-dimensionally to and from a series of stations at which the various treatments are applied, and to provide the required time and special conditions (and their variants) for each of these successive operations. First appearing soon after World War I, the early automatic electroplating machines, crude and naive, have evolved from basic single drive conveyors into a broad variety of highly specialized types.

Single or Double File Elevator Machines

Up to now the most widely seen, these machines use "return" or racetrack shaped conveyors, fitted with vertical-lift elevator mechanisms. A horizontal framework raises plating racks or plating barrels progressively in and out of the successive cleaning and preparation treat-

ments, through the extended plating tanks, and, subsequently, in and out of rinsing and final treatments. The tanks are all grouped around a central framework and drive units. All single-station work carriers are raised at once and indexed forward one space and lowered into the next station. At multiple station tanks (such as plating tanks) the work is not raised, and the forward index (movement) is in the immersed position.

The treatment time is controlled basically through the number of stations per tank, and by a "dwell" timer which can be set to vary the immersion period.

This type of machine is always used for rack-mounted fabricated or individual workpieces and may combine several successive electroplating steps, such as copper, nickel, and chrome.

The separate elevating and indexing drives are sequentially controlled by limit switches, and the range of operating sequences, the weight and size of workpieces, the height of lift, the tank sizes, and the possible finishes are virtually limitless. Production can be as high as 200 racks per hour for a double file unit or half of that for a single file machine.

Pivoted Arm Machines

This subtype of the return-type elevator machine omits the elevator framework and drive as such, and in its place a cammed rail raises the carrier arms, pivoted at their inboard ends, through an arc, thus lifting the work rack or part prior to the forward index. This type of machine is generally used for light loads or for cupped parts which must be spilled and filled and for relatively shorter lifts; as such, it is less costly. Production limits are in the area of 60 to 75 small racks or loads per hour. Open top oblique barrels can be handled on heavy-duty pivoted arm machines.

Recent developments now permit "square" transfer on these units with consequent space savings.

Continuous Process Machines

These are usually laid out in straight lines, and are used to plate, clean, or anodize any width of strip, wire, chain, foil, electronic connectors or terminals (in strip form), wire cloth, wire fence, conduit, or pipe.

General practice has been to enter and exit treatment tanks in an up-hill and down-hill configuration using deflector and "sink" rolls, but a more efficient concept is to use a level "pass-line" and recirculate the end-of-tank spillage which is collected in overflow sumps. Individual treatments are confined to separate tanks; plating is split up into several "cells," and skipping while rare, is possible.

Terminal Equipment, such as pay-off and take-up reels, is required, except for conduit or pipe. Drive means can be selected from towing bridles, "S" rolls, multiple-helper drive rolls, driven wringer rolls, or, for short or light-duty lines, the take-up reel or spool may be driven itself. In pipe and conduit lines, 10 ft lengths are carried across the line of travel on paired conveyors, raised and lowered over tank barriers, and rolled through electrified treatments.

Strip plating or anodizing can be done on one or both sides. Selective plating thicknesses are feasible, and finished strip can be finish-roller coated, sprayed, dyed, or interleaved with paper, as desired. The thickness of a strip can range from foil to as much as 0.200 inch, and the width is almost unlimited, with steel-mill lines handling strip up to 6 feet wide. In such applications the strip must be steered at one or more points to insure edge registry on the finished coil.

Controlled depth or selective-coverage precious metal plating is now coming into use on continuous process lines for electronic components in strip form.

Productive capacity in this general type of machine is extremely high since multiple strands can be handled, as in narrow strip or in wire plating, where up to 40 strands can be run at once.

Practical speed ranges of continuous process machines are as follows:

Plating wide and/or thick strip	10 to 200 ft per minute
Plating narrow or thin strip	10 to 400 ft per minute
Cleaning strip	to 3000 ft per minute
Scrubbing strip	to 2000 ft per minute
Anodizing strip or wire	5 to 30 ft per minute
Plating wire	10 to 1000 ft per minute
Conduit or pipe plating (Exterior Only)	up to 24,000 ft per hour (in 10 ft lengths)
Plating chain	3 to 20 ft per minute
Plating wire fence or cloth	up to 50 ft per minute

"Educated Hoists"

This new concept utilizes floor- or ceiling-supported, self-propelled, small bridge cranes with inbuilt raise-lower drives. Each crane can be preprogrammed to sequentially select from several predesigned treatment cycles. Since each individual treatment tank (or multiple plating cell) has its own timer, one can vary individual immersion times independently, within practical limits dictated only by "traffic" conditions. Modular control circuits can be adapted to changing needs; tanks can be added or eliminated, and any desired combination of skips can be arranged without "hold-outs." One or more "hoists" can operate on a given structure, and these units either remain *with* a load, as in cleaning or rinsing treatments, or, after depositing a load in a plating cell, *leave* it and remove another load that has "timed out." Automatic load and unload stations can be put at either end, or both at one end.

Due to the cell-type principle, several different plating solutions can be employed, or various kinds of agitation or circulation, etc., can be used simultaneously in different cells. In addition, different current densities can be applied simultaneously to opposite sides of a rack load in a given plating cell. Solution volumes are substantially reduced in this type of automatic plater, while mechanisms and horsepower are used more economically.

Miniature or "Table-top" Pivoted-Arm or Cam Automatics

Producing up to 500 carriers per hour, with as little as 3 to 4 seconds transfer time, these extremely precise and versatile plating machines have been developed recently to meet the exacting specifications called for in the precision plating of electronic parts and space age components. Particularly interesting for controlled-depth precious metal plating on switch contacts, these machines are also ideal for specification plating on items like watch cases, transistors, and the like.

Chain Transfer Machines

Straight-line. Using essentially elevatorless conveyors, the work is hung on hooks which in turn are attached to cross bars on two parallel endless chains running on multiple sprockets at each side of the parallel frameworks. The chains, driven by a common drive, alternately raise and lower the work over the tank barriers and move forward for multiple station tanks. Rack carrier return is overhead by a high-speed conveyor.

Automatic loading and unloading is achieved from and to plant monorail conveyors. These are used mainly for simple plating jobs, such as zinc and cadmium, where production is very high and space is at a premium, and where cycle variations are not required. Individual elevators can be substituted for the drive chains when treatments must be varied.

Cell-type Units. While similar to the straight-line chain transfer units, these generally employ an elevator mechanism combined with a chain-type or pusher forward drive for applications where conforming anodes must be used, as in automobile bumper plating. Here a carrier is advanced until the first *empty* cell is reached, at which point it is lowered. The cell-select principle, of course, is used in multiple cells (plating or similar operations).

Walking Beam Machines

Also "straight line," these machines almost invariably are used where all the treatment times are uniform. The loads are transferred from cell to cell simultaneously via lateral crank-operated lifting beams which, running the full length of line, impart a "square" motion: "Up, forward, down and return," thus accomplishing the transfers. The machines are excellent for simple cycles, and can handle light to moderate work loads.

Special Procedures, motions or treatments that are difficult, impractical, or not sufficiently uniform for manual operation, but frequently needed in automatic plating, can be accomplished on elevator machines or educated hoists. These may be grouped under a single heading and are briefly described.

Two-speed drives are used on hoist or elevator automatics for unusually fast transfer speeds, or with very long carrier arms, or both, culminating in a high peripheral speed "around the end." Normally, 55 ft/min at the outside rack on elevator-type units is considered maximum. Higher speeds produce sway if in the "up" position, or solution drag if immersed (as in the case of "J" or "U" shaped tanks). A two-speed drive provides slow stopping and starting, especially important at the tangent point. Equally useful are controllable electric clutches and brakes for smooth starting and stopping of high-speed drives.

Auxiliary elevators are useful for revamps, such as inserting a rinse in a long bright-nickel tank, when changing to duplex nickel, etc. It is not practical to extend an existing elevator very far; it is easier to add a short auxiliary elevator at that point, hanging it on a column, for example.

Automatic cycle selection is feasible via tabs or flags mounted either on racks or on carriers. These tabs or flags can be made in many configurations, such as common butt hinges, in which one butt is fixed to the rack and the other half either extended to contact a limit switch, or folded flat so as to "miss." A selectively notched "comb," or series of pins, may be carrier mounted, or a punched card may be used (in a holder) to activate photoswitches. These all may be remotely operated, if desired, to provide an infinite number of skip combinations, etc.

Rack drain or filling devices are used for hollow ware (coffee makers, for example). Rack-tilt devices are available to drain retained solution. Also, parts can be mounted upside down and filled by means of vent pipes or tubes built into the rack and via automatic siphons. These last are often used with shell cases.

Ultrasonic cleaning is feasible for relatively small tanks, and is applied to work pieces with easily entrained buffing compounds, etc., such as jewelry with filigree work, watch bands, electronic components, etc. Ultrasonic generator-transducer packages are often applied to cleaning or rinsing treatments on small elevator automatics, pivoted arm types, "tabletops," or continuous wire or connector lines.

Solvent drying is also practical, though less frequently used for "spotless" drying, such as water-displacing dips and hot trichlorethylene dips. This can be applied to "Educated Hoist" machines or elevator automatics.

Sprays, fog sprays, blow-offs, etc. are all more or less self-explanatory—to get extra rinsing, or to keep work wet, or to blow off droplets to avoid spotting. Top sprays, fogs, and blow-offs can be made automatic and would operate only on elevator motion or forward index, via limit switches.

Automatic unracking, via rack "dumping." This is acceptable only on certain kinds of work and can be done by raising the rack mechanically and tilting it until the work falls off onto a belt or into a hopper or tote box.

Automatic racking is occasionally (repeat, only occasionally) feasible for uniform parts like shell cases, flashlight cases, cylindrical fittings, pistons, and similar items. Also, it must be noted that a great deal of engineering, controls, and equipment would be involved.

Delayed set-down is a method of lowering an elevator automatic-carrier arm individually via an auxiliary elevator, *belatedly,* so as to provide a shorter immersion period.

Advance pick-up is the reverse of *delayed set-down.*

Skip is a device for selectively skipping, or avoiding, a given treatment station or multiple stations, and the control may be either manual, automatic, or selective. If manual control is used, it is appropriate for long or protracted runs with a given cycle. If frequent batches requiring different treatments occur, the skip should be automatic, via a solenoid actuation, or push-button controlled. If a more sophisticated approach is required, such as a multiple choice skip or skips, signal tabs may be attached to either the carrier arm or the rack, so as to select the cycle via decoding limit switches.

Inside anodes require bipolar carriers, racks, anode and cathode rails, and separate polarity collectors for the carriers. The inside anode feature may be provided with a disconnect plug (manual) for intermittent or occasional use on hollow or deeply recessed parts.

Selective treatments are means of selecting an optional lift, or selective "up" or "down" position at a given station. Similar to skipping, a rack may be automatically unloaded from one position, or retained if in the other position, as for inspection or for secondary processing elsewhere.

Work oscillation or solution agitation is accomplished in several ways:

(1) Clean air, via submerged perforated pipes on tank floors.

(2) Mechanical up and down motions: a) alternately raising and lowering either the carrier arm, or b) the cathode rail, or c) moving a pivoted yoke on the arm (for multiline units) or d) eccentric rollers, or cam rails.

(3) Recirculation of solutions through pumps and appropriate piping.

Grease traps are usually used on cleaner tanks having an overflow weir into a sump, a recirculation pump, and a "skimmer" tube which "sweeps" the solution surface.

Automatic load-unloads are usually referred to as "loaders" and are applied to educated-hoist type, straight-line machines, and either single-line or multiline automatic elevator conveyors. They will transfer "finished" racks from the plater to a plant monorail and "raw" racks from the plant monorail to the plater in either single or double file. Single-file units are simpler and less expensive, mainly in the controls, while automatic unloading and loading of hoist or straight-line type units is the simplest and least expensive. Loaders are usually desired for handling heavy work and for substantial labor savings because no operators are necessary. Fully automatic sequenced controls as well as safety interlocks with plater and monorail must be provided to prevent collisions or jam-ups. Loaders may be overhead, floor-supported, or combinations of them.

Other features, such as automatic proportioning of additive chemicals or precious metals, pH control, electropurification, etc., may be applied to conventional automatic plating or metal processing machines with cost the only limiting factor.

Special Processes

Obviously, many highly specialized processes that exist on the fringes of the plating industry, but which are quite properly electrochemical in nature, are applicable to most of the machine types described.

Electroless plating, or deposition of metal by chemical reduction; and

Immersion plating by actual metallic exchange at the interface, are both widely used. There is no other satisfactory way, for example, in preplating printed circuits, to deposit copper in the holes or to get thin tin deposits on aluminum pistons. In the case of printed circuits, with complex treatment sequences, "educated hoists" are successfully employed, while the latter task would be assigned to elevator, pivoted-arm, or chain-transfer automatic machines.

Electropolishing, at high current densities in complex acid baths is now coming into its own for inexpensive smoothing and leveling of steel, aluminum, and stainless steels. High production rates and heavy parts, such as appliance and auto trim, sinks, and stove parts, etc., can be handled economically on automatic elevator machines under conditions that would ordinarily rule out manual production. Similarly, strip or wire can be electropolished continuously at fairly high speeds.

Electroforming of complex shapes, such as wave guides, stepped or tapered tubes, and unmachinable precision parts, is being done by actual thick, precision deposits on mandrels.

Such operations are not practical unless mechanized, as the work-piece must be revolved or moved continuously during the deposition process. Phonograph record strike masters are made in this way, with a reproducibility that is otherwise impossible. After the buildup to the desired thickness of metal (nickel, gold, silver, etc.) is completed, the mandrel is either parted off or dissolved out.

Virtually without exception, automatic plating machines have been regarded almost solely as labor-saving tools. This is a gross error, as more and more attention must now be paid to highly sophisticated electrochemical processes whose quality control standards, part repeatability, large masses, or special processing defy human capabilities. Particularly significant in the automotive, defense, space, computer, and communications industries, automatic plating machines must be regarded ultimately as job generators rather than labor eliminators, in terms of products or processes otherwise unobtainable or uneconomic.

References

ARNOLD, PETER, "Tanks and Tank Linings," paper given at Empire State Region, Tech. Session, American Electroplaters' Society, May 24, 1962.
ARNOLD, PETER, "How and When to Automate," paper given at Dixie Region, Tech. Session, American Electroplaters' Society, Feb. 9, 1962.
ARNOLD, PETER, *Iron Age*, **180**, 108–110 (Oct. 25, 1962).

PETER ARNOLD

Cross-references: *Barrel Plating; Manual Plating.*

ELECTROPLATING, MANUAL. See MANUAL PLATING.

ELECTROPLATING TERMS

The following glossary of electroplating terms is taken from a larger list prepared by a committee of electroplating specialists for the American Society for Testing Materials and published as ASTM Designation B374–62T (1962). They are reprinted here by permission of the ASTM.

Addition Agent. A material added in small quantities to a solution to modify its characteristics. It is usually added to a plating solution for the purpose of modifying the character of the deposit. (See entries on *Addition Agents* and on *Brightening Agents*.)

Anode. The electrode in electrolysis, at which negative ions are discharged, positive ions are formed, or other oxidizing reactions occur. (See entry on *Anode*.)

Barrel Plating. Plating in which the work is processed in bulk in a rotating container. (See entry on *Barrel* Plating.)

Brightener. An addition agent that leads to the formation of a bright plate, or that improves brightness of a deposit. (See entry on *Brightening Agents*, also entry on *Addition Agents*.)

Bright Plating. A process that produces an electrodeposit having a high degree of specular reflectance in the as-plated condition.

Buffing. The smoothing of a surface by means of a rotating flexible wheel to the surface of which fine, abrasive particles are applied in liquid suspension, paste, or grease stick form.

Burnt Deposit. A rough, noncoherent, or otherwise unsatisfactory deposit produced by the application of an excessive current density and usually containing oxides or other inclusions.

Cathode. The electrode in electrolysis at which positive ions are discharged, negative ions are formed, or other reducing actions occur. (See entry on *Cathode*.)

Cleaning. The removal of grease or other foreign materials from a surface. (See entry on *Electroplating, Cleaning Before*.)

Alkaline Cleaning. Cleaning by means of alkaline solutions.

Anodic or Reverse Cleaning. Electrolytic cleaning in which the work is the anode.

Cathodic or Direct Cleaning. Electrolytic cleaning in which the work is the cathode.

Diphase Cleaning. Cleaning by means of solutions that contain a solvent layer and an aqueous layer. Cleaning is effected both by solvent and emulsifying action.

Direct Current Cleaning. See *Cathodic* or *Direct Cleaning.*

Electrolytic Cleaning. Alkaline cleaning in which a current is passed through the solution, the work being one of the electrodes.

Emulsion Cleaning. Cleaning by means of solutions containing organic solvents, water, and emulsifying agents.

Immersion Cleaning. See *Soak Cleaning.*

Reverse Current Cleaning. See *Anodic* or *Reverse Cleaning.*

Soak Cleaning. Cleaning by immersion without the use of current, usually in alkaline solution.

Solvent Cleaning. Cleaning by means of organic solvents.

Spray Cleaning. Cleaning by means of spraying.

Ultrasonic Cleaning. Cleaning by any chemical means aided by ultrasonic energy.

Composite Plate. An electrodeposit consisting of two or more layers of metal deposited successively.

Corrosion. (1) Gradual solution or oxidation of a metal. (2) Solution of anode metal by the electrochemical action in the plating cell.

Current Density. Current per unit area.

Electroforming. The production or reproduction of articles by electrodeposition upon a mandrel or mold that is subsequently separated from the deposit. (See entry on *Electroforming.*)

Electrotyping. The production of printing plates by electroforming.

Energy Efficiency. The product of the current efficiency and the voltage efficiency for a specified electrochemical process. (See entry on *Energy Efficiency.*)

Free Cyanide. (1) *True.* The actual concentration of cyanide radical, or equivalent alkali cyanide, not combined in complex ions with metals in solution. (2) *Calculated.* The concentration of cyanide, or alkali cyanide, present in solution in excess of that calculated as necessary to form a specified complex ion with a metal or metals present in solution. (3) *Analytical.* The free cyanide content of a solution, as determined by a specified analytical method.

Note. The true value of free cyanide is rarely known with certainty and is therefore usually only dealt with in discussions of theory. The calculated or analytical value is usually used in practice.

Hard Chromium. Chromium plated for engineering rather than decorative applications; not necessarily harder than the latter. (See *Chromium Plating.*)

Leveling Action. The ability of a plating solution to produce a surface smoother than that of the substrate.

Rack, Plating. A frame for suspending and carrying current to articles during plating and related operations.

Shield, *n.* A nonconducting medium for altering the current distribution on an anode or cathode.

Shield, *v.* To alter the normal current distribution on an anode or cathode by the interposition of a nonconductor.

Strike, (1) *n.* A thin film of metal to be followed by other coatings. (2) *n.* A solution used to deposit a strike. (3) *v.* To plate for a short time, usually at a high initial current density.

Throwing Power. The improvement of the coating (usually metal) distribution over the primary current distribution on an electrode (usually cathode) in a given solution under specified conditions. The term may also be used for anodic processes for which the definition is analogous. (See entry on *Throwing Power.*)

CLIFFORD A. HAMPEL

ELECTROPOLISHING

Electropolishing might be viewed as the reverse of electroplating. The work is made the anode in an electrolytic solution, and metal is dissolved from the surface. Brightening results because microroughness (asperities less than one microinch) is eliminated. Although such a surface is very lustrous, it may still not be smooth, in the sense of optical flatness. Removal of about 0.001 inch of surface by electropolishing reduces roughness by about one-half. For example, a surface initially 30 rms microinch before would show about 15 rms microinch according to a profilometer after electropolishing. Removal of another 0.001 inch takes the surface to about 7 to 8 rms microinch. The ultimate attainable with wrought and cast metals is in the range of 2 to 5 rms microinch.

There is no mechanical work performed on the metal during electropolishing. So, electropolished surfaces have properties that are unique and advantageous relative to surfaces finished by the cutting, tearing, and smearing action of abrasives and cutting tools. Because of these differences, electropolishing is not another method for producing the burnished appearance attained by polishing, buffing, and coloring with abrasives. It is a method for achieving new surface qualities and appearance that are outstanding in many applications.

Electropolishing produces a surface with good

properties for: receiving electroplates having better smoothness, better appearance, and, because of fewer voids, better corrosion protection; resisting corrosion when there is no plate or other coating; more uniform anodizing, phosphating, black oxidizing, and other conversion coatings; greater reflectivity of light and heat; better emissivity in electronic tubes; and wear against other metal surfaces without loose metal fragments to cause fretting.

The principal limitations of electropolishing are: the process cannot smear over and cover up defects, such as seams and nonmetallic inclusions in metals; multiphase alloys in which one phase is relatively resistant to anodic dissolution are usually not amenable to electropolishing; heavy, orange-peel, mold-surface texture on castings, and rough scratches are not removed by a practical amount of electropolishing and require "cutting down" first, just as needed before buffing and coloring. This last situation can be reversed, and electropolishing is used as a "roughing operation" before color buffing on wheels.

Seams and nonmetallic inclusions impose a limitation. In showing up such conditions, electropolishing is a good inspection tool. Although unpassable by established inspection habits, an electropolished and plated surface can be superior in performance.

Methods

All the commercially feasible electropolishing processes and baths are covered by patents. Included is an article claim covering electropolished stainless steel. The details of the processes have never been published except in the issued patents, many of which have expired. Details and operating experiences are available from holders of the patents or from authorized distributors.

Perchloric-acetic acid baths have the widest applicability to electropolishing different metals. They are not recommended for the customary metal-finishing shop because of the explosion hazard. Refs. 1 and 2 discuss the hazards in detail.

Nonhazardous baths are known for most of the common metals, except for lead and tin and alloys of the two. They can be electropolished only in the perchloric-acetic acid type of electrolyte. Phosphoric acid, saturated with chromic acid, has almost as wide utility as perchloric-acetic acid. Sulfuric-phosphoric acid solutions are next most widely used in the range of ratios 15/63 to 41/45 sulfuric-phosphoric. All others are more or less specific for certain metals or alloys.

TABLE 1. ITEMS COMMERCIALLY ELECTROPOLISHED

Type of Metal	Kind of Part or Field of Application	Size Range of Part
Stainless steel, steel, brass	*Automotive Components:* hubcaps, escutcheons, dash panels, horn buttons, exhaust deflectors, lamp doors, fender trim, moldings, piston rings, gears, shafts, bearing backings, bumpers, ash tray fronts, handles.	1 sq in. to 5 sq ft
Stainless steel, high-temperature alloys	*Aircraft Components:* gears, pins, compressor blades, turbine buckets, piston rings.	1 sq in. to 1 sq ft
Stainless steel, steel, brass, aluminum, silver	*Appliances:* Refrigerator—trim items, trays, shelves, handles, escutcheons, bin frames; Stove Items—escutcheons, heating elements, shields, name plates, door and drawer handles, burner heads; toaster—covers, waffle-iron grids; Tableware—cooking utensils and kitchen ware; cutlery. Sink strainers.	1 sq in. to 3 sq ft
Stainless steel, brass	*Jewelry:* costume, wrist-watch bands, earrings, pins, necklaces, lighters.	¼ to 8 sq in.
Steel	*Tools:* wrenches, saws, sockets, and other mechanics' items.	3 sq in. to 2 sq ft
Steel, brass, stainless steel	*Hardware:* plumbing fixtures, lock plates, door knobs, and other builders' items; architectural trim items; molding; tubular furniture.	1 sq in. to 4 sq ft
Brass, aluminum	*Miscellaneous:* band instruments, camera parts, electric instrument parts, reflectors.	

Operating Factors

Different methods do not necessarily give the same result as to appearance, brilliance, and color on the same metal or part. Nor are they equal in cost, in simplicity of the control factors, nor in breadth of applicability and in throwing power.

Temperature for electropolishing baths is usually in the range of 110 to 250°F.

Current density is usually in the range of 100 to 500 amp/sq ft for decorative and surface preparation uses. For electrodeburring, current densities are in the range of 50 to 200 amp/sq ft and for supersurfacing and electromachining are in the range of 500 to 3000 amp/sq ft.

Time of electropolishing generally is 1 to 15 min for decorative finishing and preparation for plating or other finishing. Ampere-minutes of treatment are more definitive, being a direct measure of the treatment accomplished. Thus, at higher current density, shorter time is used and throwing power is improved. Tank capacities remain the same, voltages are higher, but the time can be enough shorter to offset the cost of higher voltage. For electrodeburring, 2 to 15 min cover the usual range of practical treatment. For supersurfacing at very high current density, the time is ½ to 1½ min, and for machining is 1 to 10 min.

Voltage for electropolishing is 6 to 25 volts, depending on work shape, anode-to-cathode distance, and kind of bath. Most commonly used is 12 to 17 volts at the direct current source.

Control

The metal dissolved from the work must be removed from commercial electropolishing baths to keep them operating. This is done in some baths by electrodeposition on the cathodes. It is done in most through precipitation (sludging) of insoluble salts. In others, the metals neither plate out nor precipitate, but remain dissolved, reaching a concentration at which good electropolishing ceases. Then, a portion of the "aged" bath is discarded and replaced with fresh bath. This procedure of regular "decanting" maintains good electropolishing composition. Normal dragout of electropolishing baths is replaced with fresh bath, or with maintenance solution.

Operations in electropolishing are analogous to those in plating. The work is racked and conveyed (or carried) through the following sequence of operations:

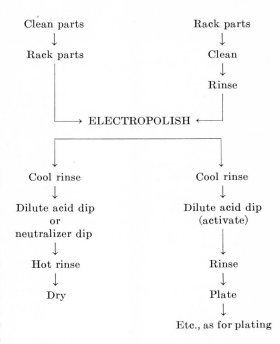

Equipment for Electropolishing

Most electropolishing equipment uses standard materials of construction. The electropolishing installation has the same outward appearance as a plating setup, but electropolishing has a few special requirements.

(1) Because of higher current density, the bussing and the rack structure must be heavier, and the contact from rack to work and from rack to rod must be firm and positive.

(2) Tank bracing for the polishing bath must be heavier, because the bath usually weighs much more than plating baths.

(3) Contamination and impurities are much less of a problem than in plating.

(4) The work bar is connected to the positive d-c terminal, and the other electrodes are cathodes.

(5) Bath conductivity is usually less, so that voltages are higher and heating effects are greater. These effects are offset by higher operating temperatures.

(6) Before final decision on equipment, the plan should be checked with distributors of the electropolishing process to be used.

For additional details, see "Electroplating Engineering Handbook," 2nd Edition, edited by A. K. Graham, Reinhold Publishing Corp., New York, 1962.

References

1. HERR, F. A., *Metal Finishing*, **45**, 72–73, 107 (1947).
2. JACQUET, P. A., *Metal Finishing*, **47**, 62–69 (1949).
3. BRUNE, FRED G., "Practical Electropolishing of Stainless Steel," *Metal Finishing*, **48** (October, 1950).
4. RILEY, MALCOM W., "When and Where to Use Electropolishing," *Materials & Methods*, **39** (June, 1954).
5. FAUST, CHARLES L., "Smoothing by Chemical and Electropolishing," *Proc. Am. Electroplaters' Soc.*, **37** (1950).
6. FAUST, CHARLES L., AND GRAVES, E. E., "Industrial Electropolishing," *Proc. Am. Electroplaters' Soc.*, **35** (1948).
7. FAUST, CHARLES L., "Surface Preparation by Electropolishing," *J. Electrochem. Soc.*, **95**, 62C (1949).

CHARLES L. FAUST

Cross-reference: *Electrolytic Polishing Theory.*

ELECTROREFINING

Electrorefining is an electrolytic process for the removal of impurities from metals. The process is carried out in an electrolyzing cell containing a suitable electrolyte in which the electrodes are suspended and through which the electrolyzing direct current flows, from anode to cathode. The passing of the current causes metal to be dissolved from the anode and deposited on the cathode. The purpose of the process is to deposit only the one desired metal at the cathode, thus eliminating all of the impurities present in the anode material. Such perfection is never achieved, but some remarkably fine results have been obtained.

The process is of commercial importance in the production or the reclaiming of bismuth, copper, gold, indium, lead, nickel, silver, tin, and titanium. In addition to the commercial market for these metals, an increasing demand has been developing for these and other metals in special grades of exceptionally high purity. A number of these high-purity metals have been produced on a laboratory or a pilot plant scale by adaptations of the electrorefining process.

The metal which is to be refined contains various impurities, many of which are present in sufficient quantity to warrant their recovery. In general, the values in the by-products make the electrorefining operation commercially feasible. In some cases these by-products become the chief source of supply of various essential elements.

Cells

The cells used in electrorefining in no way differ from those used in electrowinning or in electroplating. They can vary greatly in size, from 300 or 400 cubic feet for the cells in a copper refinery down to beaker size for some of the rarer metals. As the electrolytes are of a corrosive nature, the cells must be constructed of, or lined with, suitable corrosion-resistant materials. If the material happens to be a conductor of electricity, such as a lead lining, it becomes necessary to insulate the conductor to prevent leakage of current to ground or to other cells in the circuit. The importance of proper insulation will be apparent when it is realized that the circuit voltage may be as high as 200 or 300 volts. Potentials of this magnitude are required when a large number of cells are placed in series electrically. As the anodes in the refining cells by definition will be soluble anodes, the voltage drop across each cell will be quite low. In the case of a copper refining cell the drop will be around 0.2 to 0.3 volts, indicating that a series circuit with 500 cells will require 100 to 150 volts.

Most cells are designed for installation of a number of anodes and cathodes, electrically in parallel, with a positive bus bar along one wall with which the anodes make electrical contact and with a negative bus bar along the opposite wall providing the cathode contact. The end electrodes may both be anodes, or both cathodes, or there may be an end anode at one end and an end cathode at the other. As the electrodes are electrically in parallel, an equal distribution of current will not be possible unless all of the electrodes are also parallel to each other with equal current gaps or solution gaps from one electrode to the next. A further requirement is that all of the electrode faces should be centered along the center of the cell to prevent crowding of current along one edge of an electrode with resulting low current density along the opposite edge. Finally, the cathode deposition area is generally made larger than the corresponding anode area. The reason for this is that the current does not travel in straight lines but in curves similar to the familiar pattern of iron filings around a magnet. With electrodes of equal size this can cause a very objectionable crowding of current along the vertical edges and the bottom of the deposit. The result will be welts, rolls, or trees of metal along the edges of the cathode, inviting trouble from short circuits and increasing the danger of inclusion of impurities in the refined metal.

Anodes

The anodes are prepared from the impure metal that is to be refined, generally in the form of castings. As in the case of the cells, the anodes will vary greatly in size, the weight varying from several hundred pounds for copper down to what can be accommodated in beakers in the case of some rarer elements.

The impurities in the anode do not behave alike in the refining cell. One group of impurities will remain in contact with the anode, forming an adherent slime blanket. Part of this material will tend to drop to the bottom of the cell and remain there, while another part will become suspended as solid particles in the electrolyte, eventually settling in the cell itself or in pipes, launders or tanks in the external solution circuit. A small part of the slimes in suspension will find its way to the cathode face, thus making it possible for solid particles of slime to adhere to the cathode and become a contaminant of the refined metal.

Another group of impurities will dissolve in the electrolyte. Depending upon their position in the electromotive series, they will either be deposited as impurities in the refined metal, or they will remain in the electrolyte. In the latter case, they may continue to concentrate in the solution until the saturation point is reached, after which they will tend to crystallize out at the low-temperature points in the solution circuit. This can become most annoying and necessitate a periodic cleanout cycle. Some soluble impurities achieve concentrations, below saturation, at which they lower the solubility of the metal to be refined. All told, the soluble impurities frequently demand some means of electrolyte purification. Discussion of the procedures used will be found in the chapters regarding the individual metals.

Electrolyte

The electrolyte used will vary according to the metal being refined. Lead, for instance, is refined in a fluosilicic acid bath and copper in a sulfuric acid bath, these electrolytes being of an acid nature. Other electrolytes may be alkaline or about neutral. The choice of electrolyte will depend upon a number of factors, such as the solubility of the metal to be refined and of the impurities to be left behind, the resistivity of the solution, and the electrical efficiency to be expected.

The composition of the electrolyte must be maintained within the limits that have been established for each particular application of the electrorefining process. The composition will affect the cell voltage, which should be low because it directly affects the power cost. The concentration in solution of the metal being purified must be controlled; if too high, the cell voltage will be high and it may be difficult for the anode to dissolve; if too low, there may not be sufficient ions available for deposition at the cathode face. The purity of the electrolyte will also be a matter of concern that will be dealt with in the chapters on the individual metals. It should be realized that the electrolyte represents a capital investment in the process and that it can not be discarded just because the concentration of some impurity has become excessive. For this reason a great deal of effort is justified in the developing of procedures for purification of the electrolyte.

The refining cell electrolyte must be capable of dissolving the anode metal to permit refining to take place. The metal to be refined will enter into solution at the anode face and it will be removed from solution at the cathode face. In consequence, the solution density will increase at the anode and decrease at the cathode. There is a definite tendency for the solution to move downward in front of the anode and upward in front of the cathode. There will, however, also be a tendency for some of the heavier solution to drop to the bottom of the cell into the stagnant pool below the bottom of the electrodes. Similarly, there is a tendency for the lighter solution to form a layer at the top of the cell. The net result is the establishment of layers of solution of varying metal concentration. As it is generally desired to avoid such layering effects, it is necessary to provide means of mixing. In laboratory cells this can easily be done by stirring, but in plant practice it is more practical to circulate electrolyte through the cells to a reservoir from which it is returned to the cells in a continuous stream.

Circulating of the electrolyte has other advantages as well. There are definite limits to the composition of the electrolyte, and it is much simpler to sample and control one circulating bath of nearly uniform composition than it is to do the same for a large number of individual cells. The optimum cell electrolyte temperature will have been established for each plant, and it is clear that the single bath of uniform temperature will be the easier to control.

Deposits

The refined metal is deposited at the cathode. The cathode may be a thin sheet of the same metal or it may be a thicker sheet of some different material. The thin sheet in the former case is called a starting sheet, and it becomes part of the refined metal and will not be recovered as a starting sheet. The thicker sheet in the latter case is called a starting blank, or simply a cathode. The deposit will, eventually, be separated from the blank, and the blank will be returned to the cell again. The metal may be shipped in the form of cathodes, or it may be melted and cast into shapes as demanded in commerce.

The cathodic deposit is crystalline, and the crystal structure may be coarse or fine; the surface may be smooth or rough, and the deposit may be tight or open with a number of voids. A relatively smooth surface is desirable, as it is a tight structure with a minimum of voids. Smoothness makes it more difficult for solid particles of slimes to become attached to the deposit, and it also effectively decreases the number of metal-to-metal short circuits between anode and cathode, thereby increasing the current efficiency. Elimination of voids is important because they will introduce electrolyte with its dissolved impurities into the refined metal.

Addition agents are used extensively in order to promote a smooth surface and a dense structure of the deposit.

References

1. BUTTS, A., "Copper—The Science and Technology of the Metal, Its Alloys and Compounds," New York, Reinhold Publishing Corp., 1954.
2. HAMPEL, C. A., "Rare Metals Handbook," New York, Reinhold Publishing Corp., 1961.
3. NEWTON, J., "Extractive Metallurgy," New York, John Wiley & Sons, Inc., 1959.

G. D. STENDAHL

Cross-references: see specific metals; Electrowinning.

ELECTROREFINING IN MOLTEN SALTS

The development of superior alloys to withstand high temperatures and severe environmental changes has created new demands for pure alloying raw materials free of carbon, oxygen, and nitrogen, regarded as the prime noxious elements to inherent ductility. Refining techniques, such as electron beam melting, solid state electrolysis, molten salt electrorefining, etc., have been used to minimize these interstitial elements in the reactive and refractory metals, most of which have a great affinity for oxygen. Electrorefining in molten halides has also proved successful in the laboratory for preparing high-purity metals with a minimum contamination, particularly of oxygen and nitrogen. By selecting proper materials for cell feed and construction, electrolyte components, operating conditions, and using an inert gas atmosphere, control of oxygen, carbon, and nitrogen in the cathode deposit is effected.

Basically, electrorefining consists of the transfer of the metal ions from the anodic electrode through the molten salt electrolyte to the cathode where the high-purity product is deposited. The electrolyte chosen must be nonvolatile and stable, be an ionic conductor, be able to support in solution the metal ions to be electrolyzed, and be inert to the container and atmosphere. The electrolyte must also have limited solubility for contaminating elements in the presence of the respective metal to be electrolyzed.

To produce metals of high-purity, selectivity is necessary in the deposition of the various ion species available in the electrolyte. This requires careful choice of electrolyte constituents. If the deposition potentials of the metal ions in the solution are fairly close together, their activities or concentration in electrolyte must be different to prevent codeposition of the metals. To illustrate this point,[10] the decomposition potential of divalent titanium in a chloride-electrolyte at 850°C is 1.83 volts as compared to the decomposition potential of sodium chloride, 3.21 volts. Sodium ions are, therefore, not codeposited with titanium in the titanium electrorefining cell, provided the titanium ions are of significant concentration near the cathode. In the selection of the electrolyte cations, consideration must also be given to the alloying effects of the metals. If the metals tend to form solid solutions, it is practically impossible to inhibit their codeposition.

In electrorefining in halide melts, the impurities collect in the anode residue. As the impurity content builds up, the activity of the metal to be refined decreases, and the anode material becomes passive. For these reasons, it is necessary that the anode material fed to the cell be relatively pure, especially with respect to the interstitial impurities. The rate of solution at the anode depends on the surface area of the feed material as well as the ionic concentration in solution of the metal being electrorefined.[11] Most of the metals concerned in this discussion have multivalent states with little difference in the electrochemical stability between states. As a result, the two separate valence species coexist in the electrolyte.

In general, the reactive metals, such as beryllium, titanium, vanadium, chromium, manganese, zirconum, hafnium, uranium, thorium, molybdenum, cerium, and plutonium, have been amenable to electrorefining in molten halide electrolytes. The electrolytes that have been shown to be effective in removing oxygen and other interstitial and metallic contaminants are: alkali chlorides, bromides, and fluorides containing the respective metal halide in concentration of about 6 to 10 mole per cent.

The halide melts are readily hydrolyzed by air and moisture and contaminated with nitrogen; therefore, provision must be made to operate the cell in a controlled atmosphere of high-purity inert gas.

The essential features of the cell design are shown in Fig. 1. Provision is made to remove the solid cathode deposits from the cell to the inert gas air lock by a slide gate valve, thus protecting the cell atmosphere. Modifications have been made in the basic cell design for depositing molten metals such as cerium and plutonium. In most electrorefining cells, the solid anode material, offgrade metal, alloy scrap, machine trimmings, etc., is fed directly to the crucible bottom, and sufficient electrical contact is obtained to supply the necessary potential for dissolving the respective metal. For the metals beryllium, titanium, hafnium, and zirconium, iron crucibles are sufficient. Vanadium, chromium, manganese, thorium, and cerium require graphite liners, and quartz crucibles are satisfactory for molybdenum electrorefining.

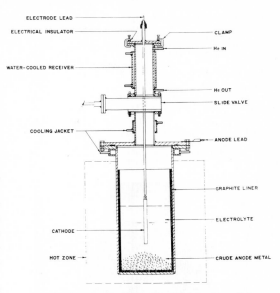

FIG. 1. Electrorefining cell with graphite liner.

Many industrial[5, 6, 7, 8] and government[13, 14] laboratories have studied electrorefining of the reactive metals with the objective of developing processes for the production of high-purity metals from offgrade or scrap materials.

More intensive research has been made on refining titanium (q.v.) than on the other reactive metals, and the process development can be exemplified by the Bureau of Mines work.[1, 9, 14, 16, 12]

The electrolyte found to be most satisfactory consists of a molten sodium chloride solution that contains 12 weight per cent titanium dichloride. Titanium trichloride also is present in quantities slightly above the equilibrium value calculated from the titanium and titanium subchloride reaction.[11] The cell, during optimum operation, contains about 1.5 per cent titanium trichloride. Offgrade titanium is used as feed material. The cathodes made from mild steel, stainless steel, or titanium are satisfactory. The operating voltage on small cells ranges from 0.3 to 0.8 volt with a cathode current density of approximately 70 amperes per square decimeter. The operating temperature is 850°C. As expected, the coarseness of the metal deposit is somewhat dependent on the current density, concentration of the metal chloride in the electrolyte, and availability of reactive anode material.

The most critical operating conditions are

TABLE 1. COMPARATIVE ANALYSES OF TITANIUM*

Element	Cell feed, per cent	Cell product, per cent	Element	Cell feed, per cent	Cell product, per cent
Fe	0.40	<0.005	C	0.026	0.010
Cr	.02	<.005	V	.07	<.005
Mg	.12	<.001	Cu	.01	<.006
Si	.02	<.005	H	.005	.002
Mn	.04	.02	N	.210	.001
Al	.02	<.03	O	.268	.011

* Brinell hardness values are as follows: 314, for cell-feed titanium; 63, for cell-product titanium.

FIG. 2. Titanium deposit from 10,000 ampere cell.

adequate control of the cell atmosphere and the salt purity. The slightest leak to the atmosphere causes fine crystals of poor quality to be deposited. Significant leak rates cause a precipitate of metallic material throughout the electrolyte, and the deposit does not adhere to the cathode. When there is an insufficient supply of readily soluble metal at the anode, such as titanium, oxidation of the electrolyte takes place, causing an increase in higher valence state metal chloride, such as $TiCl_3$. Titanium trichloride and other higher valence state chlorides are much more volatile than the divalent species, and excessive volatilization takes place. Also, increased $TiCl_3$ content of the bath apparently has the tendency to cause greater reaction with the anode impurities and corrosion of the cell crucible. These impurities are transferred to the cathode, causing increased contamination.

As an example of the extent of purification by electrorefining in chloride melts, Table 1 compares the purity of titanium metal fed to the cell with that of the refined product.

Many aspects of the titanium refining processes have been investigated, and the cell has been successfully operated at 10,000 amperes.[9] The operating conditions of the cell are similar to the small cells, except that a voltage of 2.5 volts is generally used. Internal heating, by passing alternating current between two mild steel electrodes submerged in the electrolyte, is also used. Internal heating has the advantage of reducing the overall power required for cell operation and allowing the outside cell structure to operate at a lower temperature, thus decreasing the corrosion of the cell. The uniformity of the deposit obtained from the large cell is shown in Fig. 2. The chemical purity, quantity, and screen size of the metal are uniform over the entire cathode surface.

The laboratory technique described for titanium refining has been successfully applied to other meals with modifications as follows. Electrolysis in potassium chloride-lithium chloride eutectic[17] to which had been added 7 to 10 mole per cent beryllium chloride, $BeCl_2$, was successful in preparing high-purity beryllium from material that contained 3.3 per cent oxygen and 2.7 per cent magnesium. The cathode impurities are each less than 0.05 per cent. The utilization of the potassium-lithium chloride eutectic permits the cell operation to be performed at a temperature of 450 to 500°C. A mild steel cell has been operated successfully with beryllium without corrosion to the cell structure.

The main alteration for vanadium electrorefining[4] is the use of a graphite liner to minimize the transfer of iron from the anode and cell structure to the cathode deposit. The electrolyte, operating at a temperature of 850°C, is molten sodium chloride containing about 12 per cent vanadium chloride, essentially as VCl_2.

FIG. 3. Rolled sheet of vanadium metal.

Feed materials refined consisted of offgrade vanadium and a product obtained from aluminum reduction of vanadium oxide. The offgrade vanadium is very hard and brittle and, therefore, easily crushed to obtain large surface area anode material. The product is removed from the cathode and leached in a dilute hydrochloric acid solution. To demonstrate the ductility of the metal, the vanadium crystals were melted into a button in a nonconsumable electrode arc furnace. This as-cast button was easily cold-rolled, in excess of 80 per cent, to a thin sheet which is shown in Fig. 3. Even with this amount of reduction, there is very little edge cracking in the metal.

Chromous chloride is added to sodium chloride for electrorefining of chromium metal,[3] and again the operating temperature is approximately 850°C. Iron is a much greater problem with chromium than with either vanadium or titanium. A cell design that prevents any contact between the electrolyte components and any heated iron materials is necessary. Graphite liners prove quite satisfactory, but special precautions are required to prevent molten electrolyte from diffusing through the graphite crucible to the steel container. It should be noted that transport of impurities, through the vapor phase, represents a major source of contamination of the electrolyte. Chromic chloride vapor, produced at the anode by the oxidation of the chromous chloride, volatilizes from the surface of the bath and, if it contacts hot steel, produces ferric chloride vapor. This vapor, in turn,

can contaminate the electrolyte and codeposit iron with chromium.

Hafnium[7, 15] and zirconium[2] electrorefining procedures (q.v.) are essentially similar to those described for titanium and vanadium.

Utilization of quartz as a structural material for a cell for electrorefining of molybdenum has been successful because molybdenum is not as reactive with respect to oxygen as titanium and other reactive metals. The lower valent chlorides of the reactive metals will attack quartz at any appreciable temperature to produce an alloy mirror on the immersed quartz surface. As a result of this reaction, oxygen compounds are formed in the salt and contaminate the cathode deposit. The following equations can be used to represent the reactions that take place if titanium were the metal being electrorefined:

$$7TiCl_2 + SiO_2 \rightarrow 2TiOCl + 4TiCl_3 + Ti(Si)$$

The above reaction takes place at the container wall, and at the titanium cathode the following reaction would take place:

$$2TiOCl + Ti \rightarrow TiCl_2 + 2Ti(O)$$

where Ti(O) designates a titanium alloy. Therefore, oxygen-containing structural materials cannot be used indiscriminately in the various electrorefining cells.

An exception to the oxygen contamination by ceramic materials is that of the production of liquid plutonium[13] metal by electrorefining. Electrorefining has proved successful in producing high-purity plutonium in the liquid state in stabilized oxide crucibles to contain the liquid plutonium anode and the refined product. The operating temperature for this cell ranges from 700 to 800°C.

Electrorefining of cerium is very similar to that of titanium and vanadium, except that a potassium chloride-barium chloride electrolyte is used. Because of the high free energy of formation of cerium trichloride, an electrolyte must be prepared composed of 64 per cent $BaCl_2$, 17 per cent KCl, and 19 per cent LiCl with 2 to 3 weight per cent $CeCl_3$ added to this composition. Because cerium melts at 800°C, an operating temperature of 700°C is chosen. Impure cerium metal is suspended in the electrolyte from an anode lead and refined onto a solid molybdenum cathode. This technique has proved very satisfactory in decreasing the impurities by an order of magnitude.

References

1. BAKER, D. H., JR., AND NETTLE, J. R., "Titanium Electrorefining: Cathode Studies and Deep Bath Deposition," *BuMines Rept. of Inv.* **5481,** 1959, 11 pp.
2. BAKER, D. H., JR., NETTLE, J. R., AND KNUDSEN, H., "Electrorefining Zirconium," *BuMines Rept. of Inv.* **5758,** 1961, 12 pp.
3. CATTOIR, F. R., AND BAKER, D. H., "Electrorefining Chromium," *BuMines Rept. of Inv.* **5682,** 1960, 15 pp.
4. —, "Fused-Salt Electrorefining of Vanadium," *BuMines Rept. of Inv.* **5630,** 1960, 11 pp.
5. DEAN, R. S., "Electrolytic Titanium," 35 pp. Riverdale, Md., Chicago Development Corp., 1957.
6. DEAN, R. S., GULLETT, W. W., AND McCAWLEY, F. X., "Electrorefining of Titanium, Zirconium, Hafnium, Vanadium, Chromium, and Molybdenum," presented at Electrochemical Society meeting, Ottawa, Canada, Abs. a76, October 1958, 14 pp.
7. GUCCIONE, EUGENE, "Here's Hafnium: Hardest Element to Isolate," *Chem. Eng.,* **70,** 128–130 (Feb. 18, 1963).
8. GULLETT, W. W., "Refining Titanium Alloys," U.S. Patent 2,817,631 (Dec. 24, 1957).
9. HAVER, F. P., AND BAKER, D. H., JR., "Development of a 10,000-Ampere Cell for Electrorefining Titanium," *BuMines Rept. of Inv.* **5805,** 1961, 42 pp.
10. HENRIE, T. A., AND BAKER, D. H., JR., "Mechanism of Sodium Reduction of Titanium Chlorides in Fused Salts," *BuMines Rept. of Inv.* **5661,** 1960, pp. 15–24.
11. HENRIE, T. A., KLEESPIES, E. K., AND BAKER, D. H., JR., "Reaction Rate of Titanium and Titanium Subchlorides in Molten Sodium Chloride," *BuMines Rept. of Inv.* **6162,** 1963, 20 pp.
12. LEONE, O. Q., NETTLE, J. R., AND BAKER, D. H.,

13. MULLINS, L. J., LEARY, J. A., MORGAN, A. N., AND MARAMAN, W. J., "Plutonium Electrorefining," Los Alamos Scientific Lab. of the Univ. of Calif., Los Alamos, N. Mex., June 22, 1962, 70 pp.
14. NETTLE, J. R., BAKER, D. H., JR., AND WARTMAN, F. S., "Electrorefining Titanium Metal," *BuMines Rept. of Inv.* **5315,** February 1957, 43 pp.
15. NETTLE, J. R., HIEGEL, J. M., AND BAKER, D. H., JR., "Hafnium Electrorefining," *BuMines Rept. of Inv.* **5851,** 1961, 18 pp.
16. NETTLE, J. R., HILL, T. E., JR., AND BAKER, D. H., JR., "Electrorefining of Titanium From Binary Alloys," *BuMines Rept. of Inv.* **5410,** 1958, 11 pp.
17. WONG, M. M., CAMPBELL, R. E., AND BAKER, D. H., JR., "Electrorefining Beryllium, Studies of Operating Variables," *BuMines Rept. of Inv.* **5959,** 1962, 14 pp.

JR., "Electrorefining Titanium, Using an Internally Heated Cell," *BuMines Rept. of Inv.* **5494,** 1959, 20 pp.

D. H. BAKER, JR. AND
T. A. HENRIE

Cross-references: *Aluminum Electrorefining; Fused Salt* entries; *Hafnium, Electrolytic Preparation; Titanium, Electrolytic Preparation; Zirconium, Electrolytic Preparation.*

ELECTROSTATIC COATING PROCESSES

The development of electrostatic coating processes began about 1920. The first commercial applications of electrocoating processes were to apply grit on abrasive paper and to apply flock on paper and textiles. Electrostatic spray coating methods came into use shortly after 1940, and by 1950 an electrostatic method was available to apply continuous uniform coatings on web products.

All electrostatic coating and deposition processes are based on the fact that electrical fields exert forces on charged particles. Strictly speaking, none of the coating processes is literally electrostatic. Alternating fields often are used. Charge movement almost always occurs on particles of coating and often in the form of ions that are generated in the coating process. The charge movement is small, however, in comparison to current flow in low-resistance electrical circuits. Hence, it is useful to refer to them as electrostatic.

For electrostatic processes, the coating material is prepared in the form of fine powders, granules, chopped fibers, or droplets, and is charged electrically, while being dispersed in a suitable manner to be applied uniformly on the surface to be coated. Although air is the most commonly used dispersion medium, because it offers low resistance to movement of the coating material, other gases and dielectric liquids have been used also. Electrostatic fields are applied to deposit the material from the dispersed state onto the substrate to be coated. Processes differ in the method of supplying the coating material, the method of charging the material, the method of establishing the depositing field, and the environment in which the coating is applied. These factors determine the type of materials that can be applied in each process, the type of base material that can be coated, and the type of coating that is produced.

Theory

When a particle of radius, a, is placed in an electrical field, a force, F_e, is exerted on the particle in the direction of the electrical field. The magnitude of the force is determined by the field intensity, E, and the charge, Q, on the particle.

$$F_e = EQ$$

The movement of the particle is opposed by the viscous force, F_d, of the surrounding medium.

$$F_d = 6\ \pi\mu a v$$

where μ is the viscosity and v is the velocity of the particle. These two forces determine the terminal velocity, v_t, of the coating particle, which is reached almost instantaneously in air.

$$v_t = EQ/6\ \pi\mu a$$

The terminal velocity and the speed at which the material is being carried into or through the coating area determine the length and space geometry of the electrodes necessary to precipitate the coating efficiently.

The electrical forces can be used to great benefit in applying coatings of very finely-ground or finely-atomized materials that are necessary to prepare thin uniform coatings. Small particles do not impact on surfaces or settle readily because the gravitational forces and centrifugal forces are small. For example, in an electrical field of 600 volts per centimeter, the electrical force on a 200-micron-diameter particle (dielectric constant 2, unit density, and maximum electrical charge) is 15 times as great as the gravita-

tional force. For a 20-micron particle, the electrical force is 150 times as great as the gravitational force and 1500 times as great as the gravitational force on a 2-micron particle.

Charging Processes

Although there are at least six methods of producing charge, only two charging processes are used commonly in electrostatic coating processes, induction charging and ion bombardment. Induction charging is accomplished by applying an electrostatic field so as to cause electrical charge to flow to or from a droplet or particle while it is in contact with a conductive body. The only current involved in coating processes using inductive charging is the charge carried by the coating material. To be charged inductively, the material must be somewhat conductive but not necessarily as conductive as a metal. Resistivity less than 10^{10} ohm-centimeters generally is sufficient for inductive charging at practical rates. The ultimate charge attained is a function of the surface area of the particle.

Ion bombardment can be used to charge particles or droplets of any conductive or non-conductive material that is suspended in an air stream. High ion concentrations are produced by corona from fine wires or needles at high electrical potentials. The ions collide with and charge any particles that pass into the electrical fields. The maximum quantity of charge, Q, that can be produced by ion bombardment is a function of the dielectric constant, D, of the material, the electric field intensity, E, and the particle radius, a.

$$Q = \left[1 + 2\,\frac{(D-1)}{(D+2)} \right] E a^2$$

When the ion density is high, this charge is attained in a fraction of a second. Although larger than induction currents, corona-charging currents are still very small.

Electrostatic Spray Coating

Several types of electrostatic spray coating processes are widely used to apply liquid and powder coatings. One or more high-voltage electrodes are placed in or near the atomizing nozzles so as to charge the coating material by induction or ion bombardment, depending on the coating application. Liquid coating materials generally are charged by induction; however, ion bombardment can be used by placing emitting electrodes around the nozzle. The charged droplets are sprayed toward the objects to be coated and are attracted to the object by image forces or by externally applied electrical fields that drive the particles to the surface to be coated.

Various spray heads, such as two-fluid, airless, and disk atomizers, are suitable for atomizing liquids. Air movement is a minimum in the latter two atomizers which is an advantage because air currents tend to create flow pattrens and can carry away some of the coating material. Powder spray systems require a small amount of air to elutriate the powder.

The electrostatic spraying processes generally are operated with rectified voltages in the range of 50 to 150 kv. Nevertheless, power requirements are low because very little current is consumed.

Many types of commercial coatings, including paints, plastics, and ceramics, are applied by electrostatic spray processes. Most of the coatings only require drying to evaporate the small amount of solvent used to atomize the material. Advantages of electrostatic spraying are the reduction of overspray, better over-all coverage, and increased production with less labor. Because electrostatic fields cause the spray to wrap around objects, simple spray setups can be used to coat complex objects that otherwise would require multiple spray applications to cover all surfaces. The degree of control attained with electrostatic spray techniques has made possible automation of many coating operations and the elimination of much of the manual control formerly required.

Electrocoating of Abrasives and Flock

Practically all abrasive papers and flock-coated papers are made by the electrocoating process. The process is a web-coating operation in which the abrasive or flock is charged inductively, oriented electrically, and imbedded in an adhesive layer.

The basic apparatus consists of a pair of electrodes, one grounded and one at a high electrical potential. The high-voltage electrode usually is covered with a resistive coating or belt to prevent arcs. The electrodes are spaced from less than 1 inch up to several inches apart. Rectified or alternating potentials of 70 kilovolts or more can be used, but alternating potentials are preferred to avoid chain formation in the coating material between the electrodes.

A belt carries the coating material over one of the electrodes, generally the electrode at high potential, into the electrical field. Charge flows through the belt onto the coating material, and the electrical field then moves the charged material from the belt to a web passing over the other electrode. To prevent the grit or flock from changing polarity and returning to the belt, it is imbedded in a tacky adhesive on the web.

In addition to depositing the grit and flock on the adhesive, the electrical field orients irregular and elongated materials parallel to the electrical lines of force. The particles are deposited with the long axis perpendicular to the surface of the adhesive. The "end-on" orientation of grit maximizes the cutting power of abrasive papers. Also, the end-on orientation produces excellent flock coatings with fiber densities up to 300,000 fibers per square inch.

Electrostatic Coating of Webs

The first commercial application of an electrostatic process for coating webs was made in 1960 in applying remoistenable adhesives on paper. In this process, the coating material is prepared in powder form, suspended in air, charged electrically, and deposited on the base material with strong electrical fields.

In electrostatic units for coating webs, the coating material is circulated in a closed system. A blower breaks up powder agglomerates, suspends the powder uniformly in the air, and circulates the powder into the coating chamber. The powder is charged electrically by corona from wires at high electrical potential and is deposited on the paper which passes over a grounded coating drum. Slightly reduced air pressure in the coater prevents dust leaks. The process is used with rectified potentials in the 10- to 25-kilovolt range. Current output of the charging wires is less than 2 milliamperes in a machine that coats 60-inch webs at speeds up to 250 ft/min.

Although the process currently is being used only to apply adhesives on paper, the same apparatus has been used to apply resins, plastics, pigments, or ceramic coatings on paper, textiles, metals, and other types of web products. Once the powder coating is deposited, the coating is fixed by heating or by exposure to solvent vapor to activate the coating material or suitable binders in the coatings. Calendering generally is used to smooth the coating and improve the bond to the base.

Other Electrostatic Coating Processes

A great number of patents have been issued concerning electrostatic processes for applying coatings on specific products. These include application of coatings inside molds, coating glass tubes, applying oil on sheet metal, depositing antioffset powders on printing presses, and many others. All of these processes use the basic principles and techniques described in electrostatic spraying, electrocoating, and electrostatic coating of webs, but are limited to specific products.

Although no commercial applications are known, electrophoretic and dielectrophoretic processes have been proposed for applying coatings from dielectric liquids. An electrical field will cause charged particles to move through a dielectric liquid. Dielectrophoretic forces in nonuniform electrical fields can be used to move polarized particles through dielectric liquids although the particles are not charged. However, motion of polarized particles in nonuniform fields is slow compared to the motion of charged particles. Moreover, the movement of particles in liquids is much slower than in air because the viscous drag is much greater in a liquid than in air.

General Considerations

The use of electric fields to deposit charged particles makes it possible to control the movement of the coating materials. This results in more efficient deposition of sprayed coating material, more uniform application of the coatings, and application of coatings on complex surfaces with relatively simple equipment. Orientation of the coating material in the electrical field is an added benefit that is useful in making products, such as abrasive papers or flocked coatings. The fact that like-charged particles repel one another can be used to enhance coating uniformity and to limit the amount of coating applied. Elimination of expensive solvents through the use of air to transport the coating material can provide a substantial saving in the cost of making some products. Higher speeds, more efficient use of materials, and in some cases, automation of otherwise complex coating operations have been achieved with electrostatic processes to actually produce better products at low cost.

Some limitations are inherent, however. For example, most of the processes require that the substrate to be coated must be relatively conductive. This is particularly true when ion-charging processes are used because charge accumulation on the substrate limits the quantity and adversely affects the uniformity of the coating applied. To do an effective job of coating on insulating materials, the ratio of coating material to charge applied should be high. In addition, surface treatments must be used to drain off the charge deposited with the coating or the charge must be neutralized periodically. Alternating the polarity of the charge reportedly has been used with some success.

Other considerations are involved in fixing the coatings. Evaporation of solvents applied with sprayed systems often is sufficient. On the other hand, powder coatings require exposure to solvent vapors or processing at temperatures that are sufficient to fuse the coatings. Also, although powder coatings have a cost advantage in eliminating solvents, the coating materials must be grindable or otherwise available in powder form. Grinding can be an expensive operation on many desirable types of coating materials, and limits the materials that can be applied.

Other factors make electrostatic coating processes unique in special cases. Because the coatings are deposited without contacting the substrate, coatings can be applied on hot substrates that would damage conventional coating equipment or on tacky or delicate surfaces that would be damaged by contact. Electrostatic forces also are sufficient to hold fine powders on surfaces until fusing can be completed so that temporary binders that often are used with ceramic coatings can be eliminated. Another use is making coatings of materials that are not soluble enough for solvent application or stable enough for hot-melt application.

References

1. AMSTUZ, JOHN O., "Electrocoating," *The Rubber Age*, **49**, No. 1, 19–22 (April, 1941).
2. REIF, R. B., "An Electrostatic Process for Applying Dry Coatings on Paper," *Tappi*, **38**, No. 10, 607–609 (October, 1955).
3. WHITE, H. J., "Particle Charging in Electrostatic Precipitation," *AIEE Trans.*, **70**, 1186–1191 (1951).
4. HOLT, F. W., LORENZ, C. H., AND REIF, R. B., "Electrostatic Coating Process for Making Flat Gummed Paper," *Tappi*, **44**, No. 1, 54–57 (January, 1961).
5. RIDDICK, THOMAS M., "Zeta-Potential: New

Tool for Water Treatment," *Chem. Eng.*, **68**, No. 14, 141–146 (July 10, 1961).

6. POHL, H. A., "The Motion and Precipitation of Suspensions in Divergent Electric Fields," *J. Applied Physics*, **22**, 869–871 (1951).

7. PENNY, G. W., "Electrostatic Precipitation of High-Resistivity Dust," *AIEE Trans.* **70**, 1192–95 (1951).

8. SITTEL, Karl, "Electrostatic Deposition Processes," *Elec. Eng.*, **79**, No. 4, 288–293 (April, 1960).

ROBERT B. REIF

Cross-references: *Dielectrophoresis; Electrophoretic Deposition.*

ELECTROSTATIC POTENTIALS—EFFECT ON FRICTION AND HARDNESS

An electrostatic potential can be established between a metallic conductor and its environment if an excess charge (electrons) is added to or withdrawn from the metal. When the metallic conductor is immersed in a medium in which ions exist (e.g., an electrolyte), the potential can be static (quasi-static) or dynamic. In the first case only small amounts of (net) charge, if any, cross the boundary between metal and solution, whereas in the latter an appreciable current is required to maintain the desired potential.

A close consideration of the nature of the metal-solution interface reveals that oppositely charged species, for example, electrons on the metal side and cations on the solution side of the interface, form an electrical double layer (q.v.).[1] It is reasonable, therefore, to inquire how the physical properties of the surface atoms, or possibly the bulk of the metal, are affected by such an accumulation of charge.[2] Also, how does the adsorbed layer of ions influence these properties?

By observing variations of the logarithmic decrement, $d \log a/dt$, of the amplitude (a) of the swing of a Herbert pendulum as a function of metal-solution potential, Rehbinder, *et al*[3,4] concluded that the bulk hardness of the metal is controlled by this potential and consequently by the adsorption of polar species present in the contacting solution. Bockris and Parry-Jones[5] repeated some of Rehbinder's experiments and suggested that the variations in the logarithmic decrement with applied potential, which re-

semble the variations of surface tension of mercury with applied potential,[6] perhaps reflect surface friction and surface "hardness," and that these changes are brought about by the presence of the adsorbed species and the electronic charges at the interface.

Staicopolus[7] recently devised an apparatus sensitive to variations in friction between a metal test surface and a nonconductor and showed that the frictional properties of copper and Type 304 stainless steel are governed by the magnitude of the applied electrode potential and by the nature of the adsorbed polar species. In this respect, this work supports similar experiments by Bowden and Tabor,[8] who studied the effect of applied potential on the friction between a wire and a nonconductor immersed in a variety of electrolytes. The conclusions drawn in Staicopolus' work suggest that the Bockris and Parry-Jones interpretation of the Rehbinder experiments is the more likely. Thus, it appears that the adsorbed polar species and the associated hydration sheath about each adsorbed ion form a lubricating layer, which is more or less tightly held between the metal and the nonconductor (glass). The "friction maximum," corresponding to the electrocapillary maximum,[6] is thus the result of an absence of preferred adsorption of either the cation or the anion, and, therefore, of an absence of any substantial "lubricating" layer.

In Rehbinder's work, the method of study depends partly on friction and partly on the surface hardness of the substrate. It is, therefore, difficult to decide to what extent each contributes toward the end result. It appears, however, that the response of the pendulum in the Rehbinder "hardness" experiments cannot be due to bulk hardness. Bulk hardness variations, as detected by any indenter type of instrument, including the pendulum in Rehbinder's experiments, depend on the freedom of motion and on the number of dislocations existing or created at the surface during indentation. It is conceivable that the nature of the adsorbed species at a charged metal-solution interface can alter the ease with which dislocations can be created and propagated. Once, however, a small surface area has been deformed by the indenter, that part of the substrate becomes work-hardened, and the dislocations are trapped in the bulk of the deformed metal. The release of such dislocations and, therefore, softening is normally brought about by thermal annealing. It is therefore not obvious how, by changing the potential and the extent and nature of the adsorbed species, the bulk hardness of a metal can reach a maximum and then decline without annealing. At any rate, considerable hysteresis in the hardness versus potential relationship should be expected when the hardness maximum is approached from either side. The time dependence of such measurements should be governed by the ability of the test metal to undergo room-temperature annealing as it is being stressed. This behavior, however, has not been demonstrated by the pendulum experiments.

In their consideration of the response of the pendulum upon hardness variations of the substrate, Rehbinder, et al,[4] assumed that a plastic deformation of the asperites on the metal surface is caused by high loads on the support of the pendulum (glass sphere). They also observed a more pronounced effect when the surface of the glass sphere was rough. A circumstance of this sort, however, should have a transient effect and not necessarily a continuous effect on $(d \log a/dt)$ as was observed, since any such deformation is not reversible.

Triboelectric potentials often are developed when a substance is rubbed against another. To what extent these potentials influence the frictional properties has not been elucidated, nor have any useful applications of such potentials been disclosed.

References

1. STERN, O., Z. Elektrochem., **30,** 508 (1924).
2. Proceedings of the 2d International Congress of Surface Activity (III), "Electrical Phenomena and Solid-Liquid Interface," New York, Academic Press Inc., 1957.
3. REHBINDER, P. A., AND WENSTRÖM, E. K., Acta Physicochim., **19,** 36 (1944) and J. Phys. Chem., **26,** 1847 (1952).
4. WENSTRÖM, E. K., LICHTMAN, B. I., AND REHBINDER, P. A., Akademii Nauk S.S.S.R. Doklady, **107,** 105 (1956).
5. BOCKRIS, J. O'M., AND PARRY-JONES, R., Nature, **171,** 930 (1953).
6. LIPPMANN, G., Pogg. Ann., **149,** 547 (1873); Ann. chim. phys., (5) **5,** 494 (1875).
7. STAICOPOLUS, D. N., J. Electrochem. Soc., **108,** 900–904 (1961).
8. BOWDEN, F. P., AND TABOR, D., "Properties of Metallic Surfaces," London, Inst. of Metals, 1953.

D. N. STAICOPOLUS

ELECTROSTRICTION

Electrostriction is a form of elastic deformation or strain induced in dielectric matter by an electric field: specifically, those components of strain which are unchanged by reversal of the field direction. Electrostriction is a property of all dielectric substances and is to be distinguished from the converse piezoelectric effect (see **Piezoelectricity**), a linear field induced strain occurring in certain solids which changes sign when the field is reversed.

The electrostrictive effect depends on the square of the electric field strength and is quite small for most materials, but becomes sizable for some ferroelectric crystals or ceramics which have been used for electromechanical transducers.

Mathematical Formulation

The elastic strain, S, is a function of a stress, T, and electric displacement, D, at constant temperature and may be expanded in a power series: $S = S(T,D) = sT + gD + NT^2 + QD^2 + 2MT \cdot D + \cdots$ cubic and higher terms, where $s = (\partial S/\partial T)_D$ is the elastic compliance, $g = (\partial S/\partial D)_T$ is the piezoelectric voltage constant (which vanishes for nonpiezoelectric materials), $N = \frac{1}{2}(\partial^2 S/\partial T^2)_D$ is the nonlinear (quadratic) elastic compliance, $Q = \frac{1}{2}(\partial^2 S/\partial D^2)_T$ is the electrostrictive constant, and $M = \frac{1}{2}(\partial^2 S/\partial D \partial T)$ is a piezoelectric-elastic cross term. The preceding terms may be expressed as matrices or tensors of ranks $1(D)$, $2(S,T)$, $3(g)$, $4(s,Q)$, $5(M)$, and $6(N)$, respectively.

From the previous definitions,

$$Q = \frac{1}{2}(\partial g/\partial D)_T,$$

and from thermodynamics one can show that $g = -(\partial E/\partial T)_D$, where E is the electric field. Thus,

$$Q = -\frac{1}{2}(\partial/\partial D)_T(\partial E/\partial T)_D$$
$$= -\frac{1}{2}(\partial/\partial T)_D(\partial E/\partial D)_T.$$

But, $(\partial E/\partial D)_T = \beta = 1/\epsilon$, where β and ϵ are the dielectric impermeability and permittivity, respectively. Then,

$$Q = -\frac{1}{2}(\partial\beta/\partial T)_D = -\frac{1}{2}(\partial\beta/\partial S)_D(\partial S/\partial T)_D$$
$$= -\frac{1}{2}s(\partial\beta/\partial S)_D.$$

For most materials $(\partial\beta/\partial S)_D$ is positive, so electrostriction results in a contraction or negative strain when a field is applied.

In addition to the uniform electrostriction, unbalanced electrical forces can arise whenever nonuniform polarization occurs, e.g., at inhomogeneities or surfaces where permittivity or field gradients exist. These forces can distort or accelerate the dielectric and may be expressed by the divergence of the Maxwell stress tensor, $T_m = (\widehat{DE} - \frac{1}{2}D \cdot E)$, where $\widehat{DE}$ represents the matrix product of D and E. Thus, $T_{ij} = D_i E_j - \frac{1}{2}(D \cdot E)i \cdot j$.

General Properties

The maximum electrostrictive strain or deformation which can be developed before dielectric breakdown occurs seldom exceeds a few parts per million for ordinary dielectrics. Larger strains (parts per thousand) can be achieved with materials for which the product QD^2 can assume a high value; for example in barium titanate where the displacement, D, may exceed $\frac{1}{4}$ coulomb/sq meter, or in rubber or other elastomers where the compliance, s, may exceed 10^{-6} sq meter/newton. Electrostriction is not confined to solids, but also occurs in liquids for which the tensile strain is usually defined as $-\Delta\rho/3\rho$, where ρ is the density. The only remaining stress is hydrostatic pressure, and the compliance becomes compressibility. This quantity becomes very large as one approaches the critical point where the electrostrictive effect can become appreciable.

Commercial applications of electrostriction are largely limited to ferroelectric crystals or ceramics (see **Ferroelectricity**).

Reference

FORSBERGH, P. W., JR., "Piezoelectricity, Electrostriction, and Ferroelectricity," "Encyclopedia of Physics," Vol. XVII, Berlin, Springer-Verlag, 1956.

ROBERT D. WALDRON

Cross-references: *Ferroelectricity; Piezoelectricity.*

ELECTROTINNING. See TIN ELECTRODEPOSITION.

ELECTROTRANSPORT. See ELECTROMIGRATION.

ELECTROVISCOUS EFFECT

In the classical sense, the viscosity increase experienced with many colloidal suspensions is termed an "electroviscous effect." This phenomenon, an inherent property of the colloid, is usually encountered in very dilute concentrations with such diverse examples as suspensions of clays, silica, silicon carbide, proteins and other polyelectrolytes.

The magnitude of the electroviscous effect depends on a number of complex factors. A few of the most important are: size of the suspended particles, concentration of the suspension, and dielectric constant of the solvent or suspending medium. The Einstein viscosity equation was modified and expanded in the first theoretical expression of this phenomenon by von Smolchowski, and later by Krasny-Ergen. The final and most widely accepted derivation was made without the limiting assumption that the (Helmholtz) double layer is thin compared to the radius of the suspended particle. Thus, Booth derived the Einstein equation as a power series in terms of the charge on the particle or the electrokinetic (zeta) potential of the double layer.

More recently some attention has been given to the effect of an externally-applied electric field on the viscosity of nonaqueous fluids. Both nonpolar (e.g., benzene) and polar (e.g., chlorobenzene, chloroform) organic liquids have been examined. The viscosity increase observed also has been termed "viscoelectric effect" to differentiate it from the classical concept and to indicate that the effect occurs only while the voltage is applied.

This phenomenon was first described by Andrade and Dodd, who subjected the liquids to alternating currents across narrow gaps (e.g., 500–600 volts at frequencies up to 10,000 cycles/sec across gaps of about 0.005–0.008 in.). An equation describing the effect was derived from the works of Onsager and Debye. The first rigorous theoretical expression was given by Eisenschitz and Cole. Their interpretation of the effect was made by considering the intermolecular forces which are induced by an electric field and their contribution to the flow of momentum. The electric field gives rise to intermolecular forces that are proportional to the square of the field strength. Because of these forces there is a change in the radial distribution function. From this, the interaction of the molecules in an electric field is derived for steady flow conditions. Then, based on the Debye equation for dipole moment and polarizability, the interaction is derived for thermal equilibrium. In both cases the single assumption is made: the molecules interact with central forces on which the forces of a molecular dipole can be superposed.

The practical import of this phenomenon would be in its potential industrial application to various types of mechanical energy transducers. This would require that the difficulties of large current demand and very small gap width be resolved in a practical and economical manner.

References

1. BOOTH, F., *Proc. Roy. Soc.* (*London*), **A203,** 533 (1950).
2. EIRICH, FREDERICK R., "Rheology," Vol. 3, Chap. 3, New York, Academic Press, Inc., 1960.
3. KRUYT, H. R., "Colloid Science," Vol. 1, p. 348, New York, Elsevier Publishing Co., 1952.
4. ANDRADE, E. N. DAC., AND DODD, C., *Proc. Roy. Soc.* (*London*), **A204,** 449 (1951); **A187,** 296 (1946).
5. EISENSCHITZ, R., AND COLE, G. H. A., *Phil. Mag.,* **45,** 394 (1954).

LAWRENCE U. BERMAN

ELECTROWINNING

Electrowinning is a procedure by which metals are recovered from solution by electrolysis. The electrolyte is an aqueous one in the winning of antimony, cadmium, chromium, cobalt, copper, gallium, indium, manganese, thallium, and zinc, while a fused salt electrolyte is used for aluminum, beryllium, calcium, cerium and other rare earth metals, magnesium, lithium, sodium, and other alkali metals. Insoluble anodes are used with both types of electrolyte, with the result that the cell voltage is relatively high. Metal is deposited at the cathode and the corresponding anion is liberated at the anode.

One type of process has been developed for use with the aqueous electrolyte. This type differs widely in fundamental aspects from the processes in which the fused electrolytes are used and in which the operating conditions of necessity are entirely different.

Electrowinning from Aqueous Solution

Feed to Process. The feed material to this process can be an ore, a concentrate, or a metallurgical by-product from which desired elements can be leached. Regardless of its source, its content of the metal to be recovered must be soluble in the electrolyte used in the process. If it is not already soluble, it must be rendered so by appropriate treatment prior to the leaching step. An example of such a preliminary treatment is the roasting of a zinc sulfide concentrate to convert the zinc sulfide to zinc oxide which is readily soluble in the sulfuric acid electrolyte used in the zinc plants.

During the extraction leach the solution will generally dissolve other constituents of the feed in addition to the sought metal. As a result the solution will require a purification treatment to remove objectionable impurities. This will be followed by a clarification step which then yields a rich purified solution that is suitable for cell feed solution.

Cells. The cells used with aqueous electrolyte are rectangular open-top boxes that are constructed of materials that protect against corrosion and against stray currents. The threat of corrosion is a serious one, particularly in the case of strongly acid electrolytes. The problem of stray currents can not be ignored either, especially in the larger plants where the circuits may operate at many hundreds of volts.

Anodes. The anodes used in all electrowinning operations must, to all practical purposes, be insoluble in the electrolyte to which they are exposed. In consequence, the cell voltage tends to be high. The product released at the anode is predominantly oxygen and this gas is vented to the atmosphere. If solid materials are also deposited at the anode, the anodes or the cells will require periodic cleaning, depending upon whether the solids adhere to the anode or fall to the bottom of the cell. The anodes may last for several years, but they must eventually be replaced as the result of slow chemical attack and of repeated cleaning.

Cathodes. The cathode sheet may be made of the same metal that is being recovered in the cell, in which case it is used only once, or it may be of some different metal. In the latter case the deposited metal will be stripped from the cathode sheet at intervals and the sheet returned to the cell. The edges of the sheet are frequently protected against deposition of metal by suitable means to facilitate the removal of the deposit. This removal could become nearly impossible if the deposit were allowed to grow around the vertical edges. Some deposits are so brittle that they can be dislodged by hammering on the sheet.

Electrolyte. Some cells are operated at a

constant pH and a constant concentration of metal in the electrolyte. This is done by continuously adding strong purified solution at the required rate. Other cells are operated within a wide range of pH and metal concentration, a relatively large volume of electrolyte being diverted to the leaching step at intervals, the removal being followed at once by the addition of the corresponding volume of strong purified solution.

The purity demanded of the electrolyte varies greatly with the type of operation. Some impurities can be tolerated in some electrolytes in concentrations of 10 to 30 grams per liter. In other electrolytes some impurities can spell disaster in concentrations of only a few micrograms per liter.

Addition Agents. Electrowinning deposits tend to become rough as the deposit increases in thickness. It has been found that this effect can be reduced considerably by the addition to the electrolyte of substances that are classed as addition agents. A large number of compounds and of complex mixtures have been suggested, and a number of explanations have been offered to show the manner in which the addition agents work. It is probably safe to say that there is much yet to be learned in this area and that the use of these addition agents is an art rather than a science at this time.

A special use for addition agents has been the development of a controlled froth blanket to reduce the misting in the air of a cell room. The oxygen that is liberated at the anode and the hydrogen that represents loss of efficiency at the cathode rise to the surface in minute bubbles. Droplets of electrolyte are propelled into the atmosphere as these bubbles burst, and the resulting mist can become a health hazard in addition to creating highly unpleasant working conditions. In some cases the addition of a small quantity of a suitable material will cause a froth blanket to be formed at the solution surface. The small bubbles break inside the blanket and only the resulting larger bubbles of the blanket burst in the air, thus materially lowering the number of droplets of electrolyte that become air-borne.

A third function of addition agents is to reduce the harmful effect of various impurities upon the current efficiency. Too little is known about the reactions that are involved in bringing about these results.

Temperature. The temperature of the electrolyte in the cell will affect the resistivity of the solution, hence the cell voltage and the power consumption. This leads to a wish to operate at as high a temperature as possible. On the other hand, the higher temperature will increase the heat losses and will also tend to increase the harmful effect of those impurities that lower the current efficiency. In this manner the selected operating temperature is decided upon as a result of a compromise. Cooling of the electrolyte is required in some cases.

Electrowinning from Fused Salts

The metallurgical importance of the process of electrolyzing of molten salts is apparent from the fact that all of the primary aluminum of commerce is produced in this manner.

Feed to Cell. The nature of the hot molten electrolyte is such that the feed material is added directly to the cell, rather than to a circulating electrolyte in an external circuit. There is no opportunity to purify the melt in the cell, and it is not economically practical to discard it continuously. In consequence, the feed material to the cell must be substantially free of such impurities as would tend to concentrate in the electrolyte.

Cells. The cells that are used in electrowinning from fused salts are specifically designed for each process. Among the factors that must be considered are resistance to corrosion by the molten salts, insulation against losses of heat and current leakage, and exclusion of air to prevent oxidation or to permit recovery of gas that is liberated at the anode.

Electrolyte. The electrolyte consists of a molten solution of metal salts. The electrolyte should, preferably, have a low melting point to save heat, a low resistivity to lower the power cost, a low viscosity to ease the escape of gas and to promote mixing in the cell, and a high solubility for the salt of the metal that is being recovered. Salt mixtures that approach eutectic composition are frequently used.

Anodes. The anode used in electrowinning from fused salts is made of some form of carbon or graphite. The anode arrangement will depend upon whether the electrolyte is lighter or heavier than the metal being produced. If the metal sinks to the bottom of the cell, then the anode will be introduced through the top of the cell. If the metal floats on top of the molten salts, then the anode will enter through the bottom or side of the cell.

Deposits. The cathode deposit is generally in the form of molten metal, and it will be tapped or ladled from the cell as required. Special precautions must be taken to protect the metal against oxidation in some instances. The anode product may or may not be recovered, depending on the type of material that is fed to the cell. In the case of aluminum the oxide is used, and the anode product will be oxygen that reacts with the carbon content of the anode. If the cell feed is a chloride, then chlorine will be liberated at the anode, and this gas must be recovered because the economics of the process are based upon such recovery.

References

1. EDWARDS, J. D., *J. Electrochem. Soc.*, **99**, 298C (1952).
2. GILBERT, H. N., *J. Electrochem. Soc.*, **99**, 305C (1952).
3. HAMPEL, C. A., "Rare Metals Handbook," New York, Reinhold Publishing Corp., 1961.
4. HUBBARD, D. O., *J. Electrochem. Soc.*, **99**, 307C (1952).
5. LOONAM, A. C., *J. Electrochem. Soc.*, **99**, 295C (1952).
6. LOOSE, W. S., *J. Electrochem. Soc.*, **99**, 304C (1952).
7. NEWTON, J., "Extractive Metallurgy," New York, John Wiley & Sons, Inc., 1959.

G. D. STENDAHL

Cross-references: *see specific metals; Addition Agents; Electrorefining; Electrorefining in Molten Salts;* entries with *Fused Salt* titles.

ENERGY EFFICIENCY

Energy efficiency is the fraction in percentage form, expressed by the theoretically necessary energy divided by that actually consumed in an electrolytic cell for electrochemical production, refining, electrowinning, electroforming, electroplating, etc. The energy efficiency is always less than 100 per cent. The losses within the cell may be considered to be of five-fold origin:

(1) ohmic resistance of the electrodes;
(2) ohmic resistance of the electrolyte;
(3) polarization of electrode surfaces;
(4) current inefficiency;
(5) decomposition voltage.

In principle, the first two may be made as small as is feasible, the first by adequate dimensioning of electrodes and associated cell circuitry (external circuitry and generating equipment are not considered here). The second may be reduced to negligible magnitude by reduction of anode-cathode distance, and by lowering the ohmic resistance of the electrolyte by adjustments of concentration, temperature (in aqueous electrolytes), pH, addition agents, and other external physico-chemical interference. In some cases this may be precluded by other technical considerations, but these do not concern us here.

Under the term "polarization" are lumped together all phenomena associated with modification of electrode surface behavior excluding overvoltage phenomena. The latter are connected with choice of electrode material, which may in some cases be restricted. In general, polarization causes an increase of resistance to passage of current. Sometimes this may be advantageous in that it prevents undesirable departures from uniformity of current distribution which might cause unwanted secondary products to appear at the electrode surfaces. Hence its reduction, although to some extent controllable by external interference such as addition agents, pH adjustments, and the like, may also be severely limited. Polarization is therefore frequently a necessary energy sink dictated by technical or other commercial considerations.

The fourth source of energy inefficiency does not arise in certain aqueous electrolytes if the purpose is the production of hydrogen and oxygen. In other cases limited control may be exerted by chemical interference, adjustment of temperature, current density adjustment, or a combination of these.

The last source of energy loss is irreducible below a certain minimum, namely that determined by the energy of formation of the compound being dissociated by electrolysis, and the law of conservation of energy.

The mathematical expression for the energy consumed per unit time in a cell is $EI = I^2R$, where E is the total voltage drop through the cell, I is current in amperes, and R the "effective" resistance in ohms obtained by adding the voltage drops due to the five sources enumerated. The formula then represents the loss in watts per unit time. If $E = E_0 + E_d$, where E_0 is the total voltage drop due to ohmic resistance and polarization, and E_d the decomposition voltage, then E_d for a given cell with a given electrolyte has a value that cannot be reduced below a certain minimum, by chemical interference, or temperature or pressure modifications. The first equation now states: total energy consumed equals $(E_o + E_d)I$, from which it is evident that the energy efficiency depends on the current efficiency.

In the case of aqueous electrolytes it should not be thought that the decomposition voltage represents a force (electrostatic or other) that acts to separate the ions liberated at the electrodes. These ions in theory are already separated as a consequence of the dissolution of the chemical in water. The decomposition voltage serves to *liberate* the ions over a potential barrier at the electrode surfaces. The barrier is a characteristic which varies with electrode material and physical surface constitution (and sometimes also with the character of the solution). There is, however, at least one choice of electrode material and electrolyte composition for which the liberation voltage is a minimum: this is the decomposition voltage.

Generally speaking, the decomposition voltage may be determined theoretically for any cell by means of the Gibbs-Helmholtz equation (q.v.) and by the Nernst equation (q.v.), but this will not be pursued here.

An example of computation of decomposition voltage from experimental data is given by the case of hydrogen and oxygen production. The standard free enthalpy of hydrogen burned in oxygen is $-56,690$ g-cal per mole or $-237,190$ joules per mole. One mole of hydrogen is deposited by $2 \times 96,500$ coulombs, and the energy required is at least E_d times this. Hence, the decomposition voltage is found to be 1.229 volts. (See **Water Electrolysis.**) This agrees with measured values using platinized platinum electrodes which for this case exhibit the lowest electrode potential. Most other electrodes require a higher voltage due to the hydrogen and oxygen overvoltage. This is another way of saying that the decomposition voltage must exceed or at least be equal to the sum of the electrode potentials in the cell. Hence, the energy efficiency for a hydrogen-oxygen producing cell is the number 1.229 divided by the actual voltage across the cell, and the quotient multiplied by the current efficiency.

In electrochemical production of chemicals, in electrowinning, and in electrorefining the energy efficiency of the cell is of prime importance and may mean the difference between industrial success or failure compared with other methods of production. In electroforming and electroplating energy efficiency is rarely considered; if it is, the reason is usually only because some undesirable property is acquired by the product if the energy efficiency falls below a certain minimum. Thus, in these processes the energy efficiency is an *indicator* of technical *quality* rather than of financial profit or loss. An example is given by nickel plating for corrosion protection: the energy efficiency as such is of little importance because the energy costs are negligibly small compared with other processing costs connected with this industrial operation. On the other hand, if the energy efficiency is reduced as a consequence of decreased current efficiency, hydrogen embrittlement may progress to a point where the deposit is without value.

Some examples of typical industrial energy efficiencies can be cited.

In diaphragm-type chlor-alkali cells (q.v.) the theoretical decomposition voltage is 2.3 volts, but in industrial cells the voltage drop is much higher. In typical 30,000 amp cells the voltage is about 3.9 volts, while the current efficiency is about 96 per cent. The energy efficiency is then $96 \times 2.3/3.9 = 56.5$ per cent.

The cathode reaction is different in mercury cathode chlor-alkali cells and the theoretical decomposition voltage (reversible cell voltage) is 3.07 volts. A typical 150,000 amp cell operates at 4.35 volts and a current efficiency of 95 per cent. This results in an energy efficiency of 67 per cent. (See **Chlorine Production in Mercury Cells.**) The energy efficiency can also be calculated another way. The electrochemical equivalent for chlorine is 0.36743 mg per coulomb (685.834 kiloampere-hours per ton). Multiplying this by 3.07 volts gives a theoretical power requirement of 2100 kwh per ton at 100 per cent current efficiency. The actual power consumption is 3100 kwh per ton, so the energy efficiency is 2100/3100 or 67 per cent.

When fused salt electrolysis is involved and the current serves to keep the bath at desired temperature, the energy efficiency is much lower than for aqueous solution electrolyses. For example, sodium and chlorine are produced in the Downs cell (see **Sodium Production**) by the electrolysis of fused $NaCl-CaCl_2$, whose theoretical decomposition voltage is about 3.48 volts. The commercial cell operates at 6.9 volts and a current efficiency of 83 per cent. Thus, the energy efficiency is 42 per cent.

For the electrowinning of aluminum by the Hall-Heroult process the theoretical reversible potential is 1.15 volts. The large industrial cells operate at 4.7 volts and a current efficiency of 87 per cent (see **Aluminum Electrowinning**). The energy efficiency is then 21.3 per cent.

In electrowinning of copper (q.v.), energy efficiencies of 50 to 60 per cent may be reached but are often less because of rising anode or cathode potentials due to colloidal addition agents in the solution. These increase the ohmic resistance of the electrolyte, but above all increase the polarization layer on the electrodes and thereby increase the total voltage drop through the cell. The beneficial effect is improvement of surface appearance of electrodes, especially the cathode, and uniformizing of dissolution of anodes.

In commercial chromium plating (q.v.) the energy efficiency is about 3 or 4 per cent, while in silver electroforming 100 per cent is closely approximated.

JOHN KRONSBEIN

Cross-references: *Current Efficiency; Current Distribution; Electrode Potentials; Polarization.*

ENTHALPY OR HEAT CONTENT

The enthalpy, H, of a substance is an extensive thermodynamic quantity; hence, its value is a function only of the state and amount of the substance and not of its previous history. While absolute values are not known, changes in H are readily measured; and these are sufficient for most purposes.

The *enthalpy* has been defined as the *internal energy*, E, *plus* the *product* of the *pressure*, P, *times* the *volume*, V, of the substance in question

$$H = E + PV$$

With this definition, ΔH becomes equal to the heat absorbed, q, (hence the name *heat content*) in a reaction at *constant pressure* in which *no work* is done *except mechanical (pressure-volume) work against the atmosphere*. This can be seen from the fact that $\Delta E = q - w$, where w is the work done by the system, and that at constant pressure, $\Delta P = 0$; i.e.,

$$\Delta H = q - w + P\Delta V + V\Delta P = q$$

since $P\Delta V = w$.

Thus, for processes at constant pressure in which only mechanical work against the atmosphere is done, ΔH is equal to the *heat absorbed*. While it is equal in magnitude to the *heat of reac-*

tion for such processes, ΔH is always *negative* if heat is *evolved*. Unfortunately there is no such consistency in tabulated "heats of reaction." Usually the heat of reaction refers to the heat evolved. The heat of vaporization or of fusion refers to the heat absorbed in the process. In the case of heat of solution usage varies. In order to avoid this confusing inconsistency it is recommended that enthalpy changes, rather than the more ambiguous "heat of reaction" changes, be reported.

The usual convention in tabulating ΔH values is to take the pure elements under one atmosphere pressure at 25°C as the standard states. Then the $\Delta H°$ (of formation) for these at 25° is zero and the $\Delta H°$ value for any compound is its enthalpy of formation per mole from the elements. (In cases of solids of more than one crystalline form, one of them must be taken as the standard and the others will have slightly different values).

It is useful to tabulate values of $\Delta H°$ of formation with respect to standard states for various substances. These then may be added (or subtracted) algebraically to calculate various enthalpy changes, ΔH, for reactions of interest. The following examples will illustrate calculations of enthalpy of reactions.

$$C_{(graphite)} + O_{2(g)} \rightarrow CO_{2(g)}$$

$$\Delta H°_{(reaction)} = \Delta H°_{(CO_2)} - \Delta H°_{(C)} - \Delta H°_{(O_2)}$$

$$= -94.05 - 0 - 0$$

$$= -94.05 \text{ kcal/mole at } 25°C$$

$$CO_{(g)} + \tfrac{1}{2}O_{2(g)} \rightarrow CO_{2(g)}$$

$$\Delta H°_{(reaction)} = \Delta H°_{(CO_2)} - \Delta H°_{(CO)} - \Delta H°_{(O_2)}$$

$$= -94.05 - (-26.42) - 0$$

$$= -67.63 \text{ kcal/mole at } 25°C$$

$$H^+_{(aq)} + OH^-_{(aq)} \rightarrow H_2O_{(l)} \quad \text{(in aqueous soln)}$$

$$\Delta H° = \Delta H°_{(H_2O)} - \Delta H°_{(H^+)} - \Delta H°_{(OH^-)}$$

$$= -68.32 - 0 - (-54.96)$$

$$= -13.36 \text{ kcal/mole at } 25°C$$

(Since by convention $\Delta H°_{(H^+)}$ is set to zero at unit hydrogen ion activity the value for $\Delta H°_{(OH^-)}$ is also at unit activity.)

In work at other temperatures some investigators prefer to define the standard state (in a manner similar to that at 25°C) at each temperature. Others prefer to take the standard state as the pure substance at 25°C. The choice should depend upon the purpose of the investigation.

Values of enthalpy change at any temperature may be computed from a knowledge of the free energy change, ΔF, or of the heat capacities of the substances involved in a reaction as a function of temperature. Thus,

$$\left(\frac{\partial \frac{\Delta F}{T}}{\partial T} \right)_P = -\frac{\Delta H}{T^2} \quad (1)$$

and

$$\Delta H_{T_2} = \Delta H_{T_1} + \int_{T_1}^{T_2} \Delta C_p \, dT \quad (2)$$

In the latter case the value of ΔH at temperature, T_1, must also be known. Alternatively, if ΔH is known as a function of temperature, the variation of the free energy change, ΔF, with temperature can be calculated by integrating Eq. (1).

References

1. KLOTZ, I. M., "Chemical Thermodynamics," Chapts. 4 and 5, New York, Prentice-Hall, Inc., 1950.
2. LEWIS, G. N., AND RANDALL, M., "Thermodynamics" (2nd Edition), revised by K. S. Pitzer and Leo Brewer, Chapt. 6, New York, McGraw-Hill Book Co., 1961.
3. LATIMER, W. M., "Oxidation Potentials" (2nd Edition), New York, Prentice-Hall, Inc., 1952.
4. KELLEY, K. K., *U. S. Bur. Mines Bulls.* **476** (1949); **584** (1960); and **477** (1950).

M. H. LIETZKE AND
R. W. STOUGHTON

ENTROPY

Definition and Evaluation

The entropy change of a process was first defined by R. J. E. Clausius who expressed the *differential entropy change* as the *heat absorbed in a reversible process*, dq_{rev}, divided by the absolute temperature, T.

$$dS = \frac{dq_{rev}}{T} \quad (1)$$

The *reversible process* referred to in this definition is one in which heat is added from an immediate environment only slightly higher in temperature, so that the flow could be reversed by an infinitesimal change in temperature.

If suitable data are available, e.g., values of heat capacity *vs* temperature, Eq. (1) may be integrated to obtain a finite ΔS for a process not at constant temperature. In heat capacity measurements, small increments of heat are added to a well insulated system and the increase in temperature of the system measured. Under these circumstances, where essentially no work is done by the system, all the added heat energy goes into raising the temperature; and the initial and final state are independent of the exact procedure involved. In this case the heat absorbed is equal to the reversible heat, δq_{rev}, which in turn is equal to the heat capacity, C, times the increase in temperature, δT. For measurements at constant (e.g., atmospheric) pressure, in view of Eq. (1),

$$S_{T_2} = S_{T_1} + \int_{T_1}^{T_2} C_p \frac{dT}{T} \quad (2)$$

A similar calculation could be made for the entropy increase for measurements at constant volume, if such were available.

Unlike the thermodynamic energy functions, E, H and F, absolute values of entropy, S, are defined and tabulated by virtue of the third law of thermodynamics, which in effect states that *if the entropy of each element in some crystalline form is taken as zero at the absolute zero of temperature, then every perfect crystalline compound has zero entropy at the absolute zero of temperature.* Since careful heat capacity measurements may be made to very low temperatures and since general analytical expressions for heat capacity *vs* temperature at low temperatures are known, absolute values of the entropy of substances may be calculated by the use of Eq. (2).

Another very important approach to the calculation of entropies (particularly of gases) involves the methods of statistical mechanics. From thermodynamics it follows that the equilibrium state of an isolated system is the one of maximum entropy. According to statistical mechanics, such a system goes to a state of maximum probability. It therefore seems reasonable to expect that there should be some relation between entropy and probability. Indeed the entropy may be expressed in terms of the logarithm of the "thermodynamic probability" which is a measure of the number of different energy states which a given molecular configuration can occupy. The greater the number of possible states, the less certain can one be of the configuration and the greater the entropy of the system. At absolute zero in a perfect crystal all the molecules are in the same energy state; hence, the probability of being in this state is unity and the entropy, which is proportional to the logarithm of the probability, is zero. At any higher temperature other energy states become possible, and the entropy is greater than zero. Because there are a number of experimental methods available (particularly those of spectroscopy) for evaluating atomic and molecular energy states, statistical mechanics provides a very useful tool for the calculations of entropies of a number of systems. The procedure is essentially that of calculating the "entropy of mixing" of the various energy states in a manner analogous to calculating the entropy of mixing when forming solutions from pure substances.

Thus, in the case of mixing n_1 moles of one substance with n_2 moles of another to form a perfect solution, the entropy of mixing is given in terms of the mole fractions, N_i, by

$$\Delta S_{mix} = -R(N_1 \ln N_1 + N_2 \ln N_2)$$

where

$$N_i = \frac{n_i}{n_1 + n_2}$$

and R is the gas constant. (In most practical cases there are additional entropy terms when solutions are formed due to the interactions of the molecules.) Since N_1 and N_2 are both <1, their logarithms are negative and, hence, the entropy change is positive.

The Meaning of Entropy

An idea of the importance of the concept of entropy regarding naturally occurring phenomena may be obtained by considering certain irreversible processes: diffusion of a solute in solution is always from a higher to a lower concentration; a gas always diffuses from a higher to a lower pressure; a clock always runs down (until rewound by an external agent); heat always flows from a hot to a cold body; etc. While such processes may be reversed, this requires external work by an external agent; and the total net effect (including that to the agent) involves a "running down," a rendering unavailable of some of the energy of the universe. Thus, (with the possible exceptions of certain processes in living matter and certain submicroscopic phenomena) the observed universe is "running down," is tending toward a final state of equilibrium, as far as can be determined experimentally to date. Although the energy of the universe is constant according to the first law of thermodynamics, it is becoming less and less available for "useful" purposes according

to the second law of thermodynamics. The entropy change in any reaction (including the consequent change in the environment) gives a quantitative measure of this general process of degradation of *availability of energy*, and for any naturally occurring process the net ΔS for all systems involved is *positive*. Interestingly enough, some scientists have pointed to this increase in entropy and its ramifications as the most convincing evidence for the unidirectional passage of time. Without this increase in entropy many natural processes, e.g., the rotational movements of heavenly bodies, might be "purely" periodic with the beginning of any cycle indistinguishable from that of any other.

In view of the foregoing, the value of the entropy change for a process has been considered as a criterion of spontaneity, i.e., if ΔS is positive, the process should occur spontaneously and not otherwise. However, to use this criterion it is necessary to evaluate all entropy changes including those in the environment (which are generally not known). Hence, as a test of spontaneity of a particular reaction the entropy change of the constituents involved is not very useful; for such a test the free energy function, F, is most useful.

Entropy Calculations

Perhaps the most useful purpose served by tabulations of entropy data is in the calculation of free energy changes, ΔF. Thus, if the entropy change, ΔS, and enthalpy change, ΔH, are known for a given reaction or can be calculated from heat capacity data, the free energy change can be calculated from Eq. (3).

$$\Delta F = \Delta H - T\Delta S, \text{ at constant } T \qquad (3)$$

If only ΔS is known, then Eq. (4) may be used to evaluate the temperature variation of the free energy change.

$$\left(\frac{\partial \Delta F}{\partial T}\right)_P = -\Delta S \qquad (4)$$

Methods of calculating entropies from experimental data may be summarized as follows.[5]

Entropy from Low Temperature Heat Capacity Data. Eq. (2) can be used between any two temperatures if sufficient heat capacity data are available in the temperature range. Although measurements cannot be made to absolute zero, most substances have heat capacities following the equation

$$C_p = aT^3 \text{ or } C_p = aT^3 + bT$$

(the linear term being required if metallic electrons are involved). Hence, with the evaluation of a and b theoretically or experimentally from the measurements above the lowest experimental temperatures, Eq. (2) can be used to evaluate the increase in entropy from absolute zero to the temperature of lowest measurement.

Entropy from Spectroscopic Data. Spectroscopic data may be interpreted in terms of energy states and relative molecular populations of these states. As mentioned above, these results may be used to evaluate entropies of systems; at present such calculations are limited to gaseous substances.

Entropy from Molecular Constant Data. This method is a simplified version of method (2), applicable at lower temperatures (e.g., near 25°C) and applied to systems on which detailed spectroscopic data have not yet been obtained.

Entropy from "Residual-Ray" Data. In some cases energy states of solids can be ascertained by measurements of so-called "residual-ray" wavelengths. These can be interpreted in terms of heat capacity *vs* temperature functions, which may be inserted into Eq. (2).

Entropy Changes for Reactions. If the standard free energy change, $\Delta F°$, and the enthalpy change, $\Delta H°$, for a reaction are known, the standard entropy change may be evaluated at any temperature by the use of Eq. (3).

$$\Delta S° = \frac{\Delta H° - \Delta F°}{T}$$

The free energy change for a reaction may be expressed in terms of an equilibrium constant, K, or (in some cases) in terms of the standard emf, $E°$, of a *reversible* galvanic cell involving a particular chemical reaction, i.e.,

$$\Delta F° = -RT \ln K \quad \text{or} \quad \Delta F° = -n\mathbf{F}E°$$

where R is the gas constant, n is the number of equivalents of electricity involved per mole of cell reaction, and $\mathbf{F}$ is the Faraday constant. Hence, if either K for the reaction or $E°$ for the pertinent cell is known as a function of temperature, the entropy change may be evaluated by the use of Eq. (4)

$$\left(\frac{\partial \Delta F°}{\partial T}\right)_P = -\Delta S° = -R\left(\frac{\partial T \ln K}{\partial T}\right)_P$$

or

$$= -n\mathbf{F}\left(\frac{\partial E°}{\partial T}\right)_P$$

This method gives the entropy change per mole of reaction. In order to get the $S°$ for any one reactant or product, the values of $S°$ for all the other constituents must be evaluated by independent methods.

References

1. LEWIS, G. N., AND RANDALL, M., "Thermodynamics" (2nd Edition), revised by K. S. Pitzer and Leo Brewer, Chaps. 7-12 and 27, New York, McGraw-Hill Book Co., 1961.
2. KLOTZ, I. M., "Chemical Thermodynamics," Chap. 7, New York, Prentice-Hall, Inc., 1950.
3. DANIELS, F., AND ALBERTY, R. A., "Physical Chemistry" (2nd Edition), Chaps. 5 and 19, New York, John Wiley & Sons, Inc., 1961.
4. FOWLER, R. H., AND GUGGENHEIM, E. A., "Statistical Thermodynamics," Cambridge, England, Cambridge University Press, 1952.
5. KELLEY, K. K., *U. S. Bur. Mines Bulls.* **477** (1950); **476** (1949); and **584** (1960).

M. H. LIETZKE AND
R. W. STOUGHTON

EXCHANGE CURRENTS

Two dissimilar phases, in contact with each other, may establish a chemical equilibrium of dynamic character. The condition for such an equilibrium to occur is that there is a continuous chemical exchange of at least one constituent common to both phases.

Consider, for example, a metal phase in contact with an electrolyte phase containing the corresponding metal ions. There will be a certain probability that metal ions will leave the crystal lattice of the solid metal and dissolve into the electrolyte. In turn, there is a probability that dissolved metal ions will deposit onto the metal surface and enter the metallic lattice. For an electrode of silver in contact with a solution containing silver ions, the following reaction will thus take place

$$\text{Ag(metal)} \underset{b}{\overset{f}{\rightleftarrows}}$$
$$\text{Ag}^+\text{(aq. solution)} + e^-\text{(metal)}$$

(1)

Thus, the reaction in the forward direction produces electrons and silver ions, and the backward reaction consumes electrons and silver ions. If the two reactions proceed at exactly the same speed, no *net* production or consumption of electrons or ions occurs; the system is at equilibrium. The electrons produced by the forward reaction are consumed by the backward reaction. Since the reactions involve electrons, they may be written in terms of a current. The currents of the forward and backward reactions become identical at equilibrium and are termed *exchange currents*.

The concept of a dynamic equilibrium established by a forward and backward reaction is common in chemical kinetics. In applying it to a single electrode, however, a difficulty is introduced in that one is dealing now with charged species, electrons or ions, and it is thermodynamically impossible to assess the free enthalpy of these individual ions.

The energetic state of such species must, however, be estimated in some manner because it enters directly into the theory of reaction rates. Rates of chemical reactions are normally described by the Arrhenius equation, which for a first order reaction takes the form

$$-\frac{\partial C_i}{\partial t} = k_i C_i \exp(-E/RT)$$

where $\partial C_i/\partial t$ is the number of moles reacting per unit time and volume, k_i is the rate constant, C_i the concentration of the reacting species, E the activation energy, R the gas constant, and T the absolute temperature. The activation energy is the energy difference per mole of reacting species in the activated state, E^*, and in the initial state, μ°. Thus

$$E = E^* - \mu^\circ$$

Unfortunately, E and μ° for individual ions are not accessible to determination by experimental measurement in an exact and absolute way.

In this dilemma it is important to consider that, although the energetic states of the individual ions are impossible to determine thermodynamically, the local microscopic chemical and electric forces acting on one particular species must be balanced somehow on a microscopic scale that a state of equilibrium is established. For instance, the chemical affinity of the silver ions in solution to the solid silver surface might tend to favor deposition of silver ions, but the positive charge of the silver surface might electrostatically repel the silver ions such that no net transfer occurs at equilibrium because the probabilities for forward and backward reaction have become identical.

Generally, one writes for a chemical reaction involving the reactants A, B, and C

$$A \rightleftharpoons B + C \tag{2}$$

At equilibrium, the forward and backward reactions proceed at equal rates. At the same time the free enthalpy of the reaction becomes zero

$$\Delta G = \mu_C + \mu_B - \mu_A = 0 \tag{3}$$

where the μ's are the partial molal free enthalpies, or the Gibbs free energies, or the chemical potentials of the constituents. In applying this thermodynamic concept to the individual electrode reaction given above one must again consider that the exchange involves a charge transfer across a heterogeneous phase boundary. In this interface between the electrode and the electrolyte there exists an electrical double layer causing strong electric fields and an electric voltage difference between the two phases. The silver ion moving from the solution into the interface will experience strong electrostatic forces and will thus acquire a certain electrostatic potential energy. The sum of the average electrostatic potential energy and its "purely chemical" free energy must remain constant if equilibrium exists throughout the interface.

To deal with the energetics of an individual ion and the reaction on a single electrode, one has, in the past, introduced the so-called electrochemical potentials, $\bar{\mu}$.

$$\bar{\mu}_i = \mu_i + Z_i \mathbf{F} \psi \tag{4}$$

where μ_i is the chemical free enthalpy and $Z_i \mathbf{F} \psi$, should represent the average electrostatic energy of the species, i, with valency, Z_i, and where $\mathbf{F}$ is the Faraday number. Here, ψ represents the so-called inner electric potential at the location of the particle, i. This type of separation between electric and chemical energy terms is physically without justification. It does by no means represent the true energetic behavior of an individual ionic species because ψ has no precise physical meaning. A much sounder approach would be to estimate the actual local electrostatic energy content of a particle from a simple model and to relate this electrostatic energy to the electric potential difference across the phase boundary. In this manner a proper kinetic equation could be set up to describe the forward and backward reaction.

If one uses Eq. (4) formally to express the total free enthalpy of individual charged species, then applying it to reaction (1) one obtains

$$\mu_{e^-} - \mathbf{F}\,\psi_{metal} + \mu_{Ag^+} + \mathbf{F}\,\psi_{soln} - \mu_{Ag} = 0$$

or

$$\mu_{e^-} + \mu_{Ag^+} + \mathbf{F}(\psi_{soln} - \psi_{metal}) = 0 \tag{5}$$

This then would be the condition required for equilibrium. However, one must remember that no physical meaning can be attached to the individual terms of this equation. Nevertheless, it has in the past been the basis for deriving the dependence of the rate of electrode reactions on the electrode potential as shown below.

Treating Eq. (1) as a first order reaction, the number of moles transformed per unit of surface area and per unit time is

$$\frac{-\partial N_{Ag}}{\partial t} = \frac{\partial N_{Ag^+}}{dt} = k_f C_{Ag} - k_b C_{Ag^+} \qquad (6)$$

where the C's are concentrations and the k's are called formal rate constants in the forward and backward direction. The k's include the exponential activation energy terms. The k's are expressed in cm sec^{-1} because they refer to a heterogeneous process, whereas conventional first order rate constants are expressed in sec^{-1}.

It is recognized that any chemical reaction must overcome an energy barrier known as the activation energy. This principle is applicable to any type of reaction, but at an electrochemical interface the effect of the electric field has to be taken into account. This field favors the reaction in one direction and hinders the reaction in the other direction. Erdey-Gruz and Volmer first suggested that the activation energy of the forward and backward electrochemical reactions depends on the electrode potential as follows:

$$E_f = E_f{}^\circ - \alpha \mathbf{F} \psi$$
$$E_b = E_b{}^\circ + (1 - \alpha)\mathbf{F}\psi \qquad (7)$$

where α is the so-called *transfer coefficient* (q.v.), ψ the electrode potential, $\mathbf{F}$ the Faraday number, and E° the activation energy in absence of the electric potential difference, ψ.

Because electrochemical reaction rates involve charge transfer they may be written as currents per unit area. Since each mole of reactant carries the charge, $Z_i\mathbf{F}$, across the phase boundary per unit time where $\mathbf{F}$ is the Faraday number and Z_i the number of electrons involved in the charge transfer, the currents become for $Z_i = 1$

$$i_f = \mathbf{F}C_{Ag}\, k_f{}^\circ \exp[\alpha \mathbf{F}\psi/RT] \qquad (8)$$
$$i_b = -\mathbf{F}C_{Ag^+}\, k_b{}^\circ \exp[-(1-\alpha)\mathbf{F}\psi/RT] \qquad (9)$$

For the total current density one obtains

$$i = i_f + i_b \qquad (10)$$

In this manner the chemical reaction rates may be expressed in terms of current densities (amp/sq

cm). At equilibrium, the electric potential assumes the value $\psi = \psi_e$, and the current densities in the forward and backward direction become equal, $i_f = -i_b = i_0$. The value of i_0 is termed *exchange current density*.

The exchange current density may be used to write Eqs. (8) and (9) in the simpler form; by introducing at the same time the overvoltage

$$\eta = \psi - \psi_e \qquad (11)$$

One then derives

$$i_f = i_0 \exp[\alpha \mathbf{F}\eta/RT] \qquad (12)$$
$$i_b = -i_0 \exp[-(1-\alpha)\mathbf{F}\eta/RT] \qquad (13)$$

The total current, i, flowing through the electrode is the sum of i_f and i_b. The dependence of the experimental current dependence on overvoltage may be represented with fair accuracy by the sum of Eqs. (12) and (13).

At equilibrium, $i_f + i_b = i = 0$; hence from (8) and (9)

$$\frac{C_{Ag} k_f{}^\circ}{C_{Ag^+} k_b{}^\circ} = \exp[-\mathbf{F}\psi_e/RT]$$

or

$$\psi_e = \frac{RT}{\mathbf{F}} \ln \frac{k_b{}^\circ}{k_f{}^\circ} + \frac{RT}{\mathbf{F}} \ln \frac{C_{Ag^+}}{C_{Ag}}$$

This is precisely the Nernst equation for the electrode potential, whereby the standard potential is expressed by the term involving the formal rate constants, $k_f{}^\circ$ and $k_b{}^\circ$. Concentrations, rather than activities appear in the last term because the influence of the activity coefficients is included in the formal rate constants.

From (8) and (9) one also readily derives the equations

$$\left(\frac{\partial \ln i_0}{\partial \psi_e}\right)_{Ag} = \frac{\alpha \mathbf{F}}{RT}$$

and

$$\left(\frac{\partial \ln i_0}{\partial \psi_e}\right)_{Ag^+} = -\frac{(1-\alpha)\mathbf{F}}{RT}$$

An example how the total current, i, is composed of the individual currents of the forward and backward direction is shown in Fig. 1. The current, i, is the algebraic sum of cathodic and anodic current. Currents are given in units of 10^{-3} ampere, and potentials in volts referred to the equilibrium constant. Fig. 1 refers to the following conditions: $T = 298.1$, $n = 1$, $C_i = 10^{-6}$ mole/cc, $\alpha = 0.5$, $i_0 = 0.166$ ma/sq cm.

By comparison of (8) and (9) one derives for the relationships between exchange currents and rate constants the equations:

$$i_0 = \mathbf{F}C_{\mathrm{Ag}}\,k_f{}^\circ\,\exp\,[-\alpha\mathbf{F}\psi_e/RT]$$

$$i_0 = \mathbf{F}C_{\mathrm{Ag}^+}\,k_b{}^\circ\,\exp\,[+(1-\alpha)\mathbf{F}\psi_e/RT]$$

It is important to remember that the exchange currents are concentration dependent.

At very small overvoltage values, one can expand the exponential terms of (12) and (13) and then derive

$$i = \frac{i_0\,\eta\mathbf{F}}{RT}$$

This provides an independent method to determine exchange currents and is thus a check on the validity of (12) and (13) at small overvoltage.

Exchange currents have been measured for many electrode reactions. For the hydrogen evolution reaction, for example, exchange currents range from 10^{-15} to 10^{-3} amp/sq cm. Higher exchange currents have been observed, e.g., metal deposition and dissolution reactions on amalgam electrodes where the exchange current may exceed 10^{-1} or even 1 amp/sq cm. For measurements on systems with such extreme reversibility, experimental difficulties arise with respect to concentration polarization (q.v.) in the solution as well as in the electrode. The measurements must thus be made using so-called transient or pulse techniques, avoiding any changes in the solution or on the electrode. Current-step or voltage-step methods are widely used. Another way of measuring the kinetics of an electrode without interference by concentration polarization is to use high-speed rotating disc electrodes.

It should be pointed out that exchange currents determined from experiments involving a study of current-voltage relationships are in a strict sense just parameters to fit a mathematical equation to the measurements. The true physical meaning of these parameters is at present still not fully understood. Physically more transparent are experiments concerning the exchange between a heterogeneous phase boundary with the help of isotopes. Here, the exchange is clearly interpretable as a dynamic equilibrium, brought about by a forward and a backward reaction, proceeding in opposite directions at exactly the same rate.

Exchange currents determined by extrapolation to the equilibrium potential, of logarithmic cur-

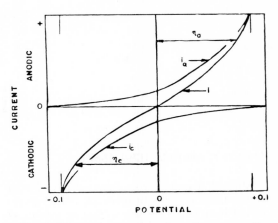

FIG. 1. Schematic representation of current-voltage curves for the forward (anodic) reaction and the backward (cathodic) reaction. The exchange currents correspond to the values of i_a and i_c at the equilibrium potential, which is arbitrarily set at zero.

rent-voltage plots, on the other hand, may not represent a physical quantity descriptive of the equilibrium state. The structure of the electrochemical interface at high anodic or cathodic overvoltages may be entirely different from that corresponding to the equilibrium potential. "True" exchange currents obtained, e.g., by radioactive tracer exchange measurements at equilibrium may thus have values completely different from those obtained from extrapolated logarithmic current-potential curves.

References

1. DELAHAY, P., "New Instrumental Methods of Analysis," p. 32, New York-London, Interscience Publishers, Inc., 1954.
2. IVES, D. J. G., AND JANZ, G. J., "Reference Electrodes," p. 14, New York-London, Academic Press, 1960.
3. GLASSTONE, S., LEIDLER, K. J., AND EYRING, H., "The Theory of Rate Processes," p. 581, New York-London, McGraw-Hill Book Company, Inc., 1941.
4. VETTER, K. J., Z. Elektrochemie, 59, 596 (1955).
5. BOCKRIS, J. O'M., "Modern Aspects of Electrochemistry," p. 180, London, Butterworths Scientific Publications, 1954.
6. PARSONS, R., Trans. Faraday Soc., 47, 1332 (1951).
7. RUETSCHI, P., J. Electrochem. Soc., 110, 1120 (1963).

PAUL RUETSCHI

Cross-references: *Electrode Double Layer; Electrode Reactions, Kinetics.*

F

FARADAY, MICHAEL (1791–1867)

Michael Faraday was born at Newington Butts, England, on September 22, 1791, and received little or no education. During a term as apprentice to a bookbinder, he read a few scientific works and became so interested in science that he applied to Sir Humphry Davy for some scientific occupation. Davy appointed him to the staff of the Royal Institution in 1813, where Faraday spent the next 54 years. In contrast with his humble birthplace, he died in London, August 25, 1867, at Hampton Court, where he was residing at the invitation of Queen Victoria.

The one hundred and sixty-three published papers of Michael Faraday demonstrate a wide range of interests in chemistry, electrochemistry, metallurgy, and physics. Faraday's major contributions to chemistry include the discoveries of benzene, nitrobenzene, o- and p-dichlorobenzene, hexachlorobenzene, hexachloroethane, naphthalene mono-sulfonic acid, butylene, and chlorine derivatives of butylene, and a systematic study of the liquefaction of gases. In electrochemistry, Faraday proved the identity of electricity derived from different sources; investigated the source, quantity, and intensity of the electricity of the galvanic battery; expounded the theory and mechanism of electrochemical decomposition, first using the terms anode, cathode, electrolyte, etc.; established the First Law of Electrolysis "that the chemical power of a current of electricity is in direct proportion to the absolute quantity of electricity which passes", and the Second Law of Electrolysis that "electrochemical equivalents coincide, and are the same, with ordinary chemical equivalents". To test the First Law under all varieties of conditions, and for the establishment of the Second Law, Faraday constructed an instrument which measured the current passing through it, which he called a Volta-electrometer, later known as a voltameter.

With Stodart, Faraday published two papers on alloys of steel. A vast field was covered, and a large number of alloys of iron with carbon, chromium, nickel, copper, silver, gold, platinum, rhodium, palladium, and silicon were prepared and evaluated. This work represents the true beginning of research on alloy steels. During these experiments, Faraday made a contribution to chemistry which is often overlooked, namely, the production of graphite from charcoal.

In terms of practical consequences, Faraday's experiments reached a peak in 1831, when he discovered that an electric current is generated by moving a magnet into and out of a coil of wire, and thereby made possible the invention of the induction coil, and the electromagnetic machines that led to the modern dynamo. Other noteworthy accomplishments include the discoveries of electromagnetic rotation of the plane of polarized light (Faraday Effect), terrestrial electromagnetic induction, and diamagnetism.

Faraday's work was done entirely at the Royal Institution, first, as lecture and laboratory assistant, and, later, as Director of the Laboratories, and Fullerian Professor of Chemistry. In 1826, he started the renowned Friday evening discourses, which have been continued ever since.

Faraday's labors were characterized by great number, thoroughness, exactitude of results, and originality. They were guided by marvellous intuition, brilliant imagination, and mastery of experimental technique. Above all, he was an experimentalist. His imagination was guided by judgement and principle, but restrained and directed by experiment.

Possessed of a love of truth, and wishing always to remove the "doubtful knowledge" that is "the early morning light of every advancing science", he was nevertheless more or less directed by preconceived ideas; whether true or false, these led him into new roads, where most frequently he found what he sought, sometimes what he did not seek, but where he constantly made some important discovery.

A guiding and stimulating principle in Faraday's work was his belief in the unity of nature—that "the various forms under which the forces of matter are made manifest have one common origin; or, in other words, are so directly related and mutually dependent that they are convertible, as it were, one into another, and possess equivalents of power in their action".

Faraday's genius for finding the correct solution through the maze of mysteries he was investigating has rightly given him a leading place among scientific investigators.

At the time of his death Faraday was one of the best-known men in England in the field of science, both because of his many discoveries and because of his very popular lectures on science. He received over one hundred honors, medals, degrees, orders, etc. during his lifetime and was a member of the chief learned and scientific societies of Europe and America.

WILSON LYNES

FARADAY SOCIETY

The Faraday Society was originally founded in 1903 "to promote the study of electrochemistry, electrometallurgy, chemical physics, metallography, and kindred subjects." Then, as today, there were dangers, both financial and otherwise, in creating yet one more society and one more journal, but despite this the project made a good start under the presidency of Sir Joseph Swan, supported by such eminent men as Professor Crum Brown, Professor F. G. Donnan, Lord Kelvin, Sir Oliver Lodge, Dr. Ludwig Mond, Lord Rayleigh, Sir James Swinburne, and others. It was no contradiction that in 1951 the objects of the Society were redefined as: "to promote the study of sciences lying between chemistry, physics, and biology," for the founders had wisely included the indefinite phrase "and kindred subjects."

The Faraday Society never held regular meetings devoted to the reading of papers on unrelated topics, but sought a new approach to the technique of scientific discussion: to secure a survey of the topic under discussion from the varied points of view of scientists working along different lines of attack, to focus general interest in a subject with the object of extending its

development or applications; to afford an opportunity of bringing forward new facts and theories for criticism and appreciation; and finally to map out possible new lines of investigation. All papers are published in full as preprints three weeks or so before the meetings, so that they may be studied at leisure. The Society has been fortunate in obtaining the constant support of overseas contributors, and the meetings are truly international in character.

The success of the *Discussions* depends primarily on the choice of subject and timing. Looking back to the time when the theory of strong electrolytes represented a new powerful approach to replace the classical theory of dissociation, scarcely a name is missing from the 1921 *Discussion* which one would expect to see there, and how aptly was the time chosen. The Debye-Hückel theory appeared in 1923 and Onsager's extension three years later, but their work was still hotly debated. It is no exaggeration to attribute the general acceptance of these theories and the opening up of the modern attack on the problem of short-range forces in solution to this meeting.

In 1921 on the subject of chemical kinetics, there was the first suggestion by Lindemann (afterwards Lord Cherwell) of the modern concept of the nature of unimolecular reactions; this led to the well-known Hinshelwood-Lindemann theory and sounded the approaching doom of the old radiation theory. But, almost as if it were in compensation, after the destructive criticism of an application of radiation theory in one *Discussion* there appeared in a later one a concept of major importance in guiding the spectroscopist and the photochemist in a memorable contribution by J. Franck containing the first enunciation of that broad generalization, the Franck-Condon Principle. Again, although the Society did not publish the original concept, the first application of chain reactions to hydrocarbon reactions was given in the 1926 general discussion on "Photochemical Reactions" by Prof. H. S. Taylor (now Sir Hugh Taylor) of Princeton University. At a meeting seven years later, Rice proposed his chain mechanism of the thermal cracking of hydrocarbons. Although this has now been modified and extended, the immense value of this one contribution to many industrial developments is hard to assess.

The history of the Society has shown that one of its important services has been to promote the development of physical chemistry at its most promising growing points. The original bias towards electrochemistry, metallography and metallurgy in its more technical aspects has changed, but this interest has been taken over by the Institute of Metal Finishing (formerly the Electrodepositors' Technical Society) which might almost be termed a daughter society. Similarly the Colloid Committee, which was formed in 1934, inspired by Sir William Hardy and sustained by the continuing efforts of Sir Eric Rideal, later developed into the Colloid and Biophysics Committee of the Faraday Society. In 1960 the Society gave its blessing and financial support to the formation of the British Biophysical Society which developed naturally out of the Colloid and Biophysics Committee.

The Society has been fortunate in possessing amongst its Presidents men of great renown from the Founder President, Sir Joseph Swan, down to the present day. The Society is governed by a Council consisting of a President, Vice-Presidents, Treasurer, Ordinary Members of Council and the Secretary. The general administrative business of the Society is in the charge of the Secretary and the Assistant Secretary, acting under the direction of the Council.

The Society is represented on a number of joint committees of other organizations, such as the National Committees for Chemistry and Biophysics of the Royal Society, various committees of the Chemical Society, the Chemical Council, and the Parliamentary and Scientific Committee. The Society is also represented on the Editorial Board of the Journal of Physical Chemistry (now published under the auspices of the American Chemical Society).

The Society is self-supporting, apart from occasional special grants from other bodies, and relies on its revenue from membership subscriptions, sales of publications, and investments. The present membership is about 2,500, nearly half of which is overseas.

The publications of the Society comprise the monthly *Transactions* and the twice-yearly *Discussions*. It is not a condition of publication that papers be written or communicated by members; the only stipulation being that they are up to the required standard and are of sufficient interest to the majority of the readers.

Each year the Society invites two lecturers from overseas to give the Bourke Lectures at universities in Great Britain on some subject or subjects of their own choosing, with the two-fold object of enabling younger scientists to visit

Great Britain and of enabling university centers to hear lecturers who might otherwise not be available to them. The lectures are named after Lt.-Col. J. J. Bourke, one of the Society's benefactors. The Spiers Memorial Lecture is given approximately every two years in memory of the first Secretary, Mr. F. S. Spiers, usually as the general introduction to one of the general discussions.

The Marlow Medal and Award, instituted in 1957 in memory of Mr. G. S. W. Marlow, Secretary of the Society from 1927 to 1948, is awarded annually to a Member under the age of 33 in respect of publications (not necessarily in the *Transactions*) over the preceding 3 years on any subject normally published in the *Transactions*.

The Society has always favored co-operation with other scientific societies. Almost from the beginning, it has had a mutually helpful relationship with the Electrochemical Society of the United States and in later years with the Société de Chimie Physique of France, the Deutsche Bunsengesellschaft of Germany, and the Koninklijke Nederlandse Chemische Vereniging of Holland.

F. C. TOMPKINS

FARADAY'S LAWS

The bases for electrochemical theory and technology are *Faraday's Laws of Electrolysis*, so called in honor of Michael Faraday (1791 to 1867) who first discovered and stated them in 1833 and 1834. As usually stated, these laws are: (1) The amount of chemical change produced by electrolysis is proportional to the total amount of charge passed through the cell; and (2) the amount of chemical change produced is proportional to the equivalent weight of the substance undergoing chemical change.

The chemical change produced by electrolysis may be the electrodeposition of a metal, the evolution of a gas, the oxidation or reduction of a species in solution, or in fact, any reaction that involves the transfer of charge across an electrode interface. If the reaction is electrodeposition, then the amount of change is usually expressed as weight of the deposit, and Faraday's Laws may conveniently be summarized by the following formula:

$$W = \frac{ItA}{Fz} \tag{1}$$

In Eq. 1, W is the weight in grams of the deposit, I is the current in amperes, t is the elapsed time in seconds, A is the atomic weight of the substance which is being electrodeposited, and z is the number of charges involved in the elementary reaction. The product, It, is thus the total charge passed, and A/z is the equivalent weight. If the current, I, is not constant during the electrolysis, then the product, It, must be replaced by the integral.

$$\int_{t_1}^{t_2} I \, dt.$$

The constant, $\mathbf{F}$, is called the *Faraday*, and inspection of the formula shows that $\mathbf{F}$ must be equal to the charge contained in one equivalent. It has the value 96,493.5 coulombs/equivalent (based on the chemical scale of atomic weights), and for all but the most accurate calculations is rounded to 96,500 coulombs/equivalent.

The following example illustrates the use of Faraday's Laws. During the electrodeposition of copper from a solution of cupric sulfate, two electrons neutralize each double-charged, positive copper ion. The charge number, z, is therefore two, and the atomic weight is 63.54. If a current of 0.1 amperes flows for 10 minutes or 600 seconds, then the number of grams of copper deposited will be given by

$$W = \frac{0.1 \times 600 \times 63.54}{96,500 \times 2} = 0.0198 \text{ gram.}$$

The determination of the Faraday may be accomplished in two ways. Eq. 1 can be rearranged as follows:

$$\mathbf{F} = \frac{ItA}{Wz} \qquad (2)$$

If, therefore, a substance of known equivalent weight is electrolyzed, the Faraday can be determined if the current, elapsed time, and weight are accurately determined. This is usually done by passing a precisely known current though a cell containing silver nitrate and weighing the resulting deposit of silver. Alternately, the cell reaction may be the oxidation of iodide ion and the reduction of iodine. In this case a two compartment cell is used so that the solutions around the cathode and the anode are not mixed. A solution of iodine in potassium iodide is placed in the cathode compartment, and the reaction is $I_3^- + 2e \rightarrow 3I^-$. The anode compartment contains concentrated potassium iodide solution, and the reaction is $3I^- \rightarrow I_3^- + 2e$. The Faraday is determined by measuring the changes in concentration of iodine dissolved in the anode and cathode compartments by titration with arsenious acid. The Faraday can also be determined from Avogadro's number and the charge of an electron. According to the atomic theory, one gram-atom of an element contains 6.023×10^{23} atoms (Avogadro's number). If the charge on each ion is z, then it is evident that it will take $z \times 6.023 \times 10^{23}$ electrons to deposit one gram-atom, or it will take

$$\frac{z \times 6.023 \times 10^{23}}{z} = 6.023 \times 10^{23}$$

electrons to deposit one equivalent of the substance. To obtain the number of coulombs in a Faraday, it is necessary to multiply 6.023×10^{23} by 1.602×10^{-19} coulombs, the charge of an electron. The fact that these two methods of measuring the Faraday yield the same result is a striking and satisfying confirmation of the atomic theory.

It is clear from the above discussion, that Eq. 1 can also be used to determine the amount of charge passed in a circuit. If Eq. 1 is rearranged, then it is found that the charge $= It = (W\mathbf{F}z/A)$. The determination of the charge passed in a given circuit can conveniently be determined by placing in the circuit a cell similar to those described above for use in determining the value of the Faraday. The determination of the weight of the silver or the number of equivalents of iodine produced will permit the charge to be determined. When used in this manner, such an instrument is called a *coulometer*. A particularly convenient but less accurate coulometer is the gas coulometer, in which the amount of gas evolved by a current is measured volumetrically. Faraday himself constructed and used such a coulometer.

If Faraday's Laws are tested experimentally, apparent deviations are frequently found. Electrochemists, therefore, use the terms *current yield* or *efficiency* and define these terms as the per cent of the total charge which is effective in carrying out the desired reaction. A common cause of efficiencies less than one hundred per cent is the occurrence of extraneous electrode reactions during the electrolysis. Thus, in the deposition of metals on platinum, if the potential of the electrode is cathodic enough, a certain amount of hydrogen evolution will occur. Other causes of lowered efficiency are recombination of the products of electrolysis, dissolution of the electrodes, and reaction of the primary products of electrolysis with the solvent, electrodes, or environment. All of these effects will tend to lower the amount of the desired product and thus lower the efficiency from 100 per cent. Faraday was well aware of these effects, and it was just these effects which prevented many of his contemporaries and predecessors from arriving at the correct laws of electrolysis. These effects are of extreme importance to the industrialist who uses electrolysis in the manufacture of his product. A difference of a few per cent in efficiency may be the difference between a competitive or a noncompetitive product.

It is difficult for modern scientists to appreciate the importance of these laws to the development of modern physical science, for most students are already familiar with atomic theory when Faraday's Laws are first encountered. These laws are almost self-evident once the atomic and ionization theories are known. However, during Faraday's experimentation in 1834, none of the modern theories of chemical bonding, valence, ionization, etc., were known, and many conflicting and erroneous theories of chemical bonding were extant. In fact, a correct scale of atomic weights had not yet been generally accepted. Faraday discovered these laws only after a long series of ingeniously conceived and carefully executed experiments with the relatively crude apparatus of the early nineteenth century. That his deductions were correct establishes him as one of the greatest of experimental scientists. It was of extreme importance to the development of chemistry that he established a fundamental connection between the then unrelated fields of chemistry and electricity. Faraday realized this connection and speculated upon the nature of the chemical bond in his papers. Readers interested in these speculations and in the accounts of his experiments and conclusions regarding electrolysis can refer to his diary which has been published[1] and to his "Experimental Researches in Electricity."[2]

References

1. "Faraday's Diary," Vol. I–VII, 1820–1862, London, G. Bell and Sons, 1932–1936.
2. FARADAY, M., "Experimental Researches in Electricity," London, J. M. Dent and Sons, 1914.

ROBERT E. MEYER

FATIGUE CORROSION. See CORROSION FATIGUE.

FERROALLOYS

Ferroalloys are alloys of iron and another metal or metals used in the production of steel to introduce alloying elements or to aid in the cleansing, deoxidation, or desulfurization of steel. Their annual United States production is about 2,000,000 tons. They are made principally in electric arc furnaces which provide the high temperatures needed to reduce the refractory oxides of the alloying metals. Ferroalloy production uses over 2.6 per cent of the electrical energy consumed in the United States.

Among the more than 100 grades and types of ferroalloys made in electric furnaces are ferrochromium, ferromanganese, ferrosilicon, ferrocolumbium, ferroboron, silicomanganese, ferrovanadium, ferrotungsten, ferrotitanium, and silicon.

Carbon is the chief reducing agent, but low-carbon ferroalloys of chromium, manganese, and vanadium are obtained by the use of silicon or silicides as the reducing agent. The concentration of iron in ferroalloys is controlled by the amount of iron added in the charge to the furnace.

Carbon reduction is typified by the reaction for the production of ferrosilicon:

$$SiO_2 + 2C + Fe \rightarrow FeSi + 2CO$$

while silicon reduction is typified by the reaction for the production of low-carbon ferrochromium:

$$3Si + 2Cr_2O_3 + 4Fe \rightarrow 4FeCr + 3SiO_2$$

(Here, FeSi and FeCr indicate the alloys and are not intended to indicate compounds or stoichiometric relationships.)

In the second example a two-stage operation is used. First, the silicon or silicide is made in the furnace, and the reduction then conducted by adding it with the metal ore or oxide to the second-stage furnace where the final ferroalloy is obtained. This is a development pioneered by F. M. Becket (q.v.).

With the exception of the ferroalloys with very high melting points which preclude tapping them in molten condition, such as ferrotungsten whose 80 per cent alloy melts at 1900°C, the ferroalloys are made in furnaces operated continuously and tapped at intervals. For ferrotungsten-type products the furnace is allowed to cool and the ferroalloy removed as a button by knocking down the furnace for each batch.

Raw Materials

The source of the alloying metal may be ores, concentrates, or compounds, but careful selection is indicated since most of the metallic elements present may appear in the ferroalloy product due to the extremely high temperature in the reaction zone and the vigorous reducing conditions which exist in the furnace. Further, stoichiometric quantities of reactants are used in the charge to the furnace to avoid the presence of undesired elements in the product. Slagging materials may or may not be used, depending on the particular product being made. In ferrosilicon production, for example, no slagging materials are added, and the aluminates in the quartz or quartzite and the ash in the coke are kept at a minimum because aluminum would be formed from them and be found in the product. When silicon is the reducing agent, lime is sometimes added to the charge to form a calcium silicate slag.

The iron can be added as scrap iron, mill scale or iron ore, and the carbonaceous reducing agent is usually high-grade coke, although charcoal and other carbon sources may be used.

Furnaces

In general the furnaces used for ferroalloy production are similar to those used for calcium carbide, phosphorus, and other smelting processes described in specific articles in this book. Single- or three-phase power is used and capacities range from 500 to 20,000 kw. Very little application is made of two-phase furnaces. Single-phase furnaces may be operated with a single electrode with a carbon bottom in the furnace acting as the other electrode, or they may use two electrodes with the current passing from one electrode through the charge and out the other electrode.

The vertical electrodes may be arranged in a line or in a triangular configuration. They may operate with submerged arcs, also called smothered arcs in that the arc passes through the molten slag or metal, or with open arcs. Ferrosilicon, ferrochromium (high-carbon), ferromanganese, and other alloys made by carbon reduction are usually made in submerged-arc type furnaces. Those alloys made by silicon or silicide reduction are made in open arc furnaces.

The hearth linings of the furnaces using carbon reduction are usually constructed of carbon blocks backed up with firebrick or other refractories, and the furnaces using silicon reduction usually are basic-lined, e.g., magnesite.

In this country prebaked carbon electrodes are employed almost entirely, while in Europe the Söderberg self-baking electrodes are the predominant type. See **Electric Smelting Furnaces** and **Söderberg Electrodes in Electric Furnaces**. Electrodes are fed into the furnace through rather elaborate devices located above the furnace at a rate equal to their consumption. New sections are attached to the upper end of the electrode when it reaches a certain level, the current to that electrode being shut off just long enough to make the attachment. Electrode consumption varies widely, depending on the specific product and installation, ranging from 30 to 40 lb/ton of product for 50 per cent ferrosilicon, to 50 to 70 for ferrochrome, to 70 to 100 for ferromanganese.

The carefully weighed and correctly proportioned and sized charge is fed from bins through chutes and swinging spouts into openings in the furnace roof located near the electrodes. A burden of charge is kept on the molten bath in furnaces that are continuously operated. The product is tapped at intervals at the hearth level into ladles or directly into pans or molds on the ground floor.

Voltages range from 85 to 200, with the variation in a given furnace being much closer, say, 160 to 200 for a large ferrosilicon furnace. Power consumption depends on the product being made, as well as on many other factors which affect heat losses. For silicon metal it may be 7 kwh/lb of Si and for 50 per cent ferrosilicon made in the same furnace it may be 5 kwh/lb Si. The current density values for most ferroalloy operations are 35 to 70 amp/sq in., with 40 to 50 being the most common.

Operating Conditions

For specific details on ferroalloy production the reader is referred to the annual *Electric Furnace Conference Proceedings*, published by the American Institute of Mining, Metallurgical and Petroleum Engineers, 345 East 47th St., New York 17, N.Y. Mantell[1] gives a good summary of the subject, and an illustrated description of ferrosilicon production has been prepared by Thum.[2] Information about the electric furnaces which can be used for ferroalloy preparation is found in other articles in this book: **Calcium Carbide; Electric Smelting Furnaces** (three articles); **Phosphorus, Electrothermal Production; Söderberg Electrodes in Electric Furnaces;** and **Steel Making in Electric Arc Furnaces.**

References

1. MANTELL, C. L., "Electrochemical Engineering," New York, McGraw-Hill Book Co., Inc., 1960.
2. THUM, E. J., "Ferrosilicon Manufacture at Marietta," *Metal Progress*, **70**, 1–8 (Oct., 1956).

CLIFFORD A. HAMPEL

FERROELECTRICITY

Ferroelectricity is a reversible spontaneous dielectric polarization occurring in certain piezoelectric materials. (See **Piezoelectricity**.) Certain crystals belonging to the pyroelectric group of piezoelectric crystals, such as barium titanate, $BaTiO_3$, or Rochelle salt, $NaKC_4H_4O_6 \cdot 4H_2O$, possess a polar axis which can be reversed by the application of an electric field. These crystals may be cycled repeatedly and display an electrical hysteresis (see Fig. 1a) analogous to the magnetic hysteresis of ferromagnetic materials, hence the name.

Ferroelectric materials have found widespread use in electromechanical transducers owing to their high conversion efficiencies and power levels attainable. Other applications include dielectric materials for capacitors and experimental devices, such as information storage elements and dielectric amplifiers.

The Ferroelectric State

The electrical reversibility of the polar axis in ferroelectric crystals implies an equivalent atomic configuration for each direction of spontaneous polarization. In addition, the energy barrier for interconversion cannot exceed the electrostatic energy available at field strengths approaching dielectric breakdown. This relative ease of electrical (and atomic) motion leads with few exceptions to high dielectric and piezoelectric constants and a strong temperature dependence of these properties resulting from changes in interatomic distances and thermal motions of the atoms (Fig. 1b). As the temperature is raised, the spontaneous polarization drops to zero; this defines the Curie

point, $T = T_c$, so named because the susceptibility, χ, above this temperature follows the Curie-Weiss law: [$\chi(T - T_c) =$ constant] similar to ferromagnetic materials. In this region the material is no longer ferroelectric, having usually transformed to a structure of higher symmetry.

A similar high-temperature dielectric behavior occurs for some materials which, however, fail to develop spontaneous polarization or dielectric hysteresis on cooling below the Curie temperature. These materials are antiferroelectric and consist of lines or planes of polarized atoms whose polar axes alternate in regular fashion so that no net polarization occurs. For certain materials, such as $NaNbO_3$, both ferroelectric and antiferroelectric phases exist depending on the temperature.

Domain Structure

Ferroelectric samples ordinarily possess a domain structure similar to magnetic materials. This consists of small regions of uniformly polarized material separated from adjacent regions having different polar axes by domain walls a few atom layers thick. Reversal of polarization usually proceeds by motion of domain walls which requires less energy than simultaneous reversal throughout the volume.

In Rochelle salt where only two directions of polarization are possible, the structure consists of needle shaped domains parallel to the polar axis. Barium titanate has six possible directions for spontaneous polarization and adjacent domains may have polar axes separated by either 90 or 180 degrees. The domain walls lie in planes which minimize free charge accumulation or mechanical strain. Thus, 180° domain walls are parallel to polar axes and 90° domain walls bisect the axial directions.

Representative Properties

The following table lists the spontaneous polarization, Curie temperature, and dielectric constants for some typical ferroelectric and antiferroelectric materials.

The coercive field, E_c, varies considerably for different samples of the same material depending on crystal perfection, residual strains, etc. For barium titanate at room temperature, E_c is about 5×10^4 v/m while for lead titanate the coercive force exceeds 10^6 v/m at room temperature.

Strain and Electrostriction

The spontaneous polarization of ferroelectrics leads to a spontaneous strain or deformation with respect to a hypothetical state of zero polarization. (The reference state may be obtained by extrapolation of the properties of the nonferroelectric phase above the Curie point.) For BaTiO₃ the spontaneous strain consists of an elongation about ¾ per cent along the polar axis and a lateral contraction of about ¼ per cent. Since reversal of the polar axis does not change the strain, this quantity is an even (symmetric) function of the polarization or electric displacement, and represents electrostriction. The electrostrictive coefficient, $Q = \frac{1}{2}(\partial^2 S/\partial D^2)$, has a value

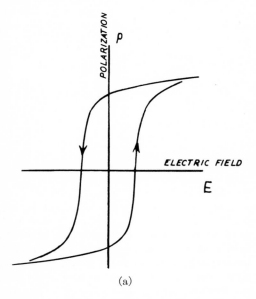

(a)

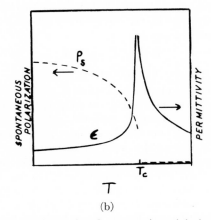

(b)

Fig. 1. Ferroelectric properties; (a) ferroelectric hysteresis, polarization *vs* electric field; (b) dielectric response, temperature *vs* spontaneous polarization (on left) and temperature *vs* permittivity (on right); $T_c =$ Curie temperature.

$Q_{12} = -4 \times 10^{-2} \ m^4/c^2$ for transverse fields in barium titanate.

A polycrystalline or ceramic transducer can be operated in either an unbiased or polarized state. In the former case the coupling is purely electrostrictive with the strain being proportional to the square of the displacement or polarization resulting in vibration at twice the frequency of the electrical field. The latter case involves piezoelectric coupling with the strain a linear function of displacement and vibration occurring at field frequency. The polarization is achieved by either a biasing field or using the remanent polarization of materials with high coercive fields. Most commercial applications have favored the use of polarized ceramics.

Applications

The important commercial applications of ferroelectric materials depend on either their piezoelectric or dielectric properties without regard to hysteresis. The former group is discussed under **Piezoelectricity** (see reference) while the latter group includes capacitor materials. The large temperature coefficients are a disadvantage in some cases.

Considerable experimental work has been done to utilize the nonlinear dielectric properties (hysteresis) of ferroelectrics. Various laboratory devices, such as computer memory storage elements, frequency modulated oscillators, and dielectric amplifiers, have been tested. Three major problems have prevented widespread commercial development of these devices: lack of satisfactory square loop materials, dielectric leakage in the presence of internal fields, and switching speed limitations.

References

1. VON HIPPEL, A., Ed., "Molecular Science & Molecular Engineering," Chapts. 16, 17, New York, John Wiley & Sons, 1959.
2. KAENZIG, W., "Ferroelectrics and Antiferroelectrics," Vol. 4, "Solid State Physics," New York, Academic Press, 1957.
3. FORSBERGH, P. W., JR., "Piezoelectricity, Electrostriction, and Ferroelectricity," "Encyclopedia of Physics," Vol. XVII, Berlin, Springer-Verlag, 1956.
4. SHIRANE, G., JONA, F., AND PEPINSKY, R., "Some Aspects of Ferroelectricity," *Proc. IRE* (now IEEE), 43, 1738 (1955).
5. JAYNES, E. T., "Ferroelectricity," Princeton, Princeton University Press, 1953.

ROBERT D. WALDRON

Cross-references: *Electrostriction; Piezoelectricity.*

PROPERTIES OF FERROELECTRICS AND ANTIFERROELECTRICS

Substance	Spontaneous Polarization (10^{-2} coulomb/sq m)	Curie Temperature (°K)	Dielectric constants	
			ϵ_x/ϵ_0 ϵ_z/ϵ_0	
			(Room temp.)	
			κ_x	κ_z
A. Ferroelectric				
1. Barium titanate	26	$\begin{cases} 393 \\ 273 \end{cases}$	~5000	~100
2. Guanidinium aluminum sulfate hexahydrate, GASH	0.35	$-H_2O$, 380	5	6
3. Lead titanate	>50	763		
4. Lithium tantalate	23 (723°K)	>723		~40
5. Potassium dihydrogen arsenate, KDA	5.0	97	62	22
6. Potassium dihydrogen phosphate, KDP	4.95	123	42	21
7. Potassium niobate	>26	707		~500
8. Rochelle salt	0.24	$\begin{cases} 297 \\ 255 \end{cases}$	4000	
B. Antiferroelectric				
1. Ammonium dihydrogen arsenate, ADA		216	75	12
2. Ammonium dihydrogen phosphate, ADP		148	56	15.5
3. Lead zirconate		506	80	
4. Sodium niobate		$\begin{cases} 911 \\ 64 \end{cases}$	76	670

FIGURE OF MERIT

In the analysis of the operating characteristics of a thermoelectric cooling or power generating unit, it can be shown that the efficiency of such a device depends on three factors: (1) the Carnot efficiency, $(T_h - T_c)/T_h$, where T_h and T_c are the temperatures of the hot and cold junctions, respectively; (2) the dimensions of the device; and (3) a combination of physical parameters of the material from which the device is fabricated. This last factor is referred to as the *thermoelectric figure of merit*, is denoted by ZT, and is expressed as

$$ZT = \frac{\alpha^2 T}{K\rho}$$

where α = thermoelectric power,
T = absolute temperature,
K = total thermal conductivity, and
ρ = electrical resistivity.

To make the efficiency of a particular (single-element) device as large as possible, it is necessary to maximize this combination of parameters.

The particular combination of parameters which is defined above arises in an interesting fashion in the theory of the measurement of basic transport properties of materials, particularly semiconductors. It can be shown that when an electrical current flows through a material, there is an accompanying flow of thermal energy and that the two are most simply related by the following expressions:

$$E = \rho j + \alpha \, dT/dx$$
$$w = \alpha T j - K \, dT/dx$$

where E = electric field strength,
w = thermal current density,
j = electrical current density, and
dT/dx = temperature gradient along sample.

The isothermal resistivity is defined as $\rho_i = E/j$ under the condition that $dT/dx = 0$. Hence, by inspection, it follows that $\rho_i = \rho$. On the other hand, the adiabatic resistivity, ρ_a, is measured under conditions where no total heat flow occurs in the specimen. Hence, $\rho_a = E/j$ with $w = 0$. Eliminating dT/dx in the above equations and solving for E/j, one finds

$$\rho_a = \rho + \alpha^2 T/K$$
$$= \rho_i(1 + ZT).$$

In the measurement of the resistivity of most metals and semiconductors, it is usually not necessary to take into account the difference between ρ_i and ρ_a since ZT is a very small factor. However, the correction factor, ZT, will be on the order of unity for materials used in applications for thermoelectric devices. Furthermore, whereas no particular care must be taken regarding the boundary conditions in the measurement of other parameters (such as Hall coefficient, magneto-resistance, etc.) in common materials, serious errors may arise in the measurement of these same parameters in the semiconducting thermo-electric device materials. It should be noted in passing that the measurement of both ρ_a and ρ_i is one of the standard techniques utilized in the determination of the figure of merit.

The maximization of ZT for particular classes of materials in definite temperature ranges constitutes a major undertaking. There are several competing mechanisms which must be considered. In the first place, a standard technique for improving the figure of merit of a given material employs doping of the material with a controlled density of impurities. If these impurities are ionized at the temperature of interest, there will be a decrease in the resistivity due to the increased carrier density. There will also be a decrease in the lattice contribution to the thermal conductivity, since the periodicity of the lattice has been disturbed and phonons are scattered more readily. Each of these factors contributes to increased values of ZT.

On the other hand, the increased carrier density decreases the thermoelectric power, (which goes to zero for a completely degenerate electron gas) and increases the electron contribution to the thermal conductivity. Each of these factors decreases the value of ZT, thereby competing with the mechanisms cited above.

Several elegant theoretical techniques have been forwarded which permit the prediction of the maximum value of ZT obtainable from a given material when properly doped. These methods require only that the individual parameters of one specimen of the material be determined. Graphical solutions of optimizing equations then permit a close estimate of the best possible value of ZT for this one material.

The discussion in the preceding paragraphs has been confined to the figure of merit for devices which make use of the Seebeck and/or Peltier effects (q.v.) and, henceforth, the thermoelectric figure of merit will be referred to as $Z_{SP}T$. Recently, interest has been aroused in the use of thermomagnetic effects for cooling or power generation. In particular, when a temperature gradient, dT/dx, is established along a specimen and a magnetic field, H_z, is impressed, the Nernst or Nernst-Ettingshausen effect gives rise to a transverse electric field, E_y, which is given by

$$E_y = BH_z \, dT/dx$$

where B is referred to as the Nernst or Nernst-Ettingshausen coefficient. It can be shown that, as in the previous case, the efficiency of such a generator is related to several thermodynamic and dimensional parameters, as well as to the thermomagnetic figure of merit,

$$Z_{NE}T = \frac{(BH)^2 T}{K_H \rho_H}$$

where K_H = thermal conductivity and ρ_H = electrical resistivity, both being measured in the magnetic field of strength, H, and the other factors have their usual connotation.

Although the development of thermomagnetic materials and devices is not nearly so far advanced as the thermoelectric counterparts, there are two features which are quite interesting at the present. In the first place, thermomagnetic devices require only one type of semiconducting material (either n- or p-type) while thermoelectric devices require one of each type for maximum efficiency. Thus, it is anticipated that the materials development problem will be somewhat simpler for the former class of applications. Secondly, it has been shown that the ratio $Z_{NE}T/Z_{SP}T$ may be sufficiently great that large-scale, efficient operating modules may be possible. At the present, considerations have not been given to the theoretical optimization techniques as previously described for thermoelectric materials.

References

1. HARMAN, T. C., CAHN, J. H., AND LOGAN, M. J., *J. Appl. Phys.*, **30**, 1351 (1959).
2. SIMON, R., *Advanced Energy Conversion*, **1**, 81 (1961).
3. SIMON, R., *J. Appl. Phys.*, **33**, 1830 (1962).
4. HARMAN, T. C., AND HONIG, J. M., *J. Appl. Phys.*, **33**, 3178, 3188 (1962).

JULES J. DUGA

Cross-references: *Peltier Effect; Seebeck Coefficient; Thermoelectric Power; Thermoelectric Power Generation.*

FINK, COLIN GARFIELD (1881–1953)

Dr. Colin Garfield Fink was known for his extensive research in electrochemistry and for his active membership of over 40 years in the Electrochemical Society.

He was born in Hoboken, New Jersey, on December 31, 1881, in a German-American community. His father (the founder of Lehn & Fink) later moved the family to Manhattan.

After graduation in 1903 from Columbia University, Fink studied and taught at the University of Leipzig in the Ostwald Research Laboratories. In 1907, he received his doctorate degree "summa cum laude superato" for his thesis on "Kinetic der Kontak Schwefelsäure."[1] After his return to the United States in 1907, he joined the staff of the General Electric Company.

Two major inventions came out of his career at the Schenectady research center. Fink is the originator of the ductile tungsten lamp filament[2] and the copper-clad nickel-steel leading-in wire substitute for platinum. These inventions revolutionized the lamp industry. Fink was next assigned to G.E.'s Lamp Works Laboratory in Harrison, New Jersey. Here, in the period 1910–1917, he helped supervise the introduction of his developments to practice.

In 1917 he moved from Harrison, New Jersey, to uptown New York City to become head of the new research laboratories in the Chile Exploration Company, N. Y. His invention of the insoluble "Chilex" anode was an immediate success when introduced at the great plant at Chuquicamata, Chile. It is still being used in the electrowinning of copper (see **Copper Electrowinning**).

In 1921 he became Secretary of the Electrochemical Society, a post he held until 1947. In 1922 he was called to head the Division of Electrochemistry of Columbia University. In addition to a large graduate-teaching and research load, Dr. Fink managed the affairs of the Electrochemical Society as secretary, office manager, editor-in-chief, symposium and convention planner, etc. Previously, he had served as president (1917) and in other offices of the Society. During the 1930's he kept the Society going almost singlehanded. Many industrial friends were persuaded to take out company memberships in this period.

Dr. Fink became an abstracter for *Chemical Abstracts* in 1907. As Assistant Editor in 1909, he took charge of the section on Electrochemistry until 1950.

His 28 years at Columbia University, until 1950 when he became professor emeritus, led to a continuous series of basic publications and inventions, a few of which are mentioned below.

Field	Research Developments
Electrodeposition	Chromium, tungsten, rhenium, rhodium, and tin.
Art and Archeology	Restoration of ancient bronzes; preservation of stones; identification of Egyptian method of antimony plating on copper.
Historical	Authentication of the Drake Plate.
Metal Cladding	Aluminum-alloy coatings for ferrous and other metals.
Electrowinning of Ores	Manganese, tungsten, iron, zinc, gold; insoluble anodes.
Corrosion	Acid-resisting alloy, protective coatings, high-temperature alloy, etc.

During this intensive research period, he usually had the able assistance of several research associates and three or more graduate students. The importance of his basic chromium-plating patent, developed during 1923–1925, was immediately recognized when granted in 1926, and the process was widely applied to practice.[3] His "Al-plate" invention of the early '30s was finally patented in 1937.[4] Other patents followed in later years. The process involved taking steel wire or strip and prepacking it with hydrogen at 1000°C. The steel was immediately introduced into a cooler, molten aluminum-alloy bath. Any tendency to form aluminum oxide on the surface was eliminated by the evolution of nascent hydrogen from the steel surface. Fink established the principle involved to obtain an adherent coat. He was ahead of his time in visualizing the wide range of applicability for aluminum-coated steel.[5]

During his active career of 15 years in industrial research and 28 years at Columbia University, he published 216 papers and patents. Dr. Fink obtained considerable pleasure in training graduate students and young assistants in research. He was much in demand as a lecturer. He also particularly enjoyed his work on artistic and archeological matters. With his associates, he used his broad technical knowledge to develop techniques for the verification of ancient materials, such as old coins, bronzes, artifacts, paintings, etc.

In 1933, Dr. Fink received the Acheson Medal, followed shortly in 1934 by the Perkin Medal. At the celebration in 1936 at Oberlin College, Ohio, of Hall's invention of the electrolysis process for aluminum, Dr. Fink gave the keynote address and was awarded an honorary D.Sc. degree. He was the American plenary lecturer at International Conference on Chemistry, Luzerne, Switzerland, in 1936, and in 1938 he was a delegate at the International Union of Chemistry meetings in Rome, Italy. Tau Beta Pi and other honorary societies included him as a member.

After a long illness, Dr. Fink died on September 16, 1953, in Red Bank, New Jersey. In the *Chemical Abstracts* obituary he was referred to as "Mr. Electrochemistry."

References

1. FINK, C. G., *Z. physik. Chem.*, **60**, 1–69 (1907).
2. FINK, C. G., *Trans. Am. Electrochem. Soc.*, **17**, 229 (1910).
3. DUPERNELL, GEORGE, *Plating*, **47**, 35–53 (January 1960).
4. U. S. Patent, 2,082,622, issued in 1937 to C. G. Fink.
5. *Aluminum and Magnesium*, **2**, No. 2 (November 1945).

Biographical References

1. *Trans. Electrochem. Soc.*, **92**, 3–9 (1947).
2. *Ind. Eng. Chem.*, **26**, 232–239 (February 1934).
3. *Trans. Electrochem. Soc.*, **64**, 2–6 (1933).
4. *J. Electrochem. Soc.*, **108**, 229C–231C (October 1961).
5. *J. Electrochem. Soc.*, **100**, 317C (November 1953).

FREDERICK W. FINK

FLADE POTENTIAL

The Flade potential is best defined by reference to the experiments which first showed it to be a well-characterized feature of the transition of certain metals between the passive and active states. In 1911 Flade reported experiments in which he polarized an iron electrode to a noble potential in sulfuric acid of different concentrations and then observed the potential as a function of time after opening the circuit. The potential fell rapidly at first, then more slowly, until, at a rather reproducible value, it again fell very rapidly and the electrode lost its passivity.[3] The characteristic potential at which activation of the metal set in was subsequently called the *Flade potential*.

The experimental determination of the Flade potential may be made most satisfactorily by a potentiostatic procedure in which the entire polarization curve is established. It has been observed also as a brief arrest in the oscillographic trace of polarization curves in certain systems, the arrest being detectable on both falling and rising potentials. It is also seen as an arrest in potential-time curves when iron is passivated in an inhibited medium under oxidizing conditions and then activated by addition of electrolytes that nullify the effect of the inhibitor.[2] The potentiostatic measurements show that the transition between passive and active states is not accomplished instantaneously at a sharply defined potential, but spreads over an appreciable interval both of time and of potential. The change is sharpest in strongly acidic media, such as 1 N H_2SO_4 or concentrated HNO_3.

The Flade potential has been investigated most extensively with iron; for this metal in numerous electrolytes the numerical value at 20° is given by $E_f = 0.58 - 0.058$ pH, referred to normal hydrogen electrode.[4] Polarization curves or charging curves have been determined also for gold,[9] palladium,[9] nickel,[1] chromium,[5, 7] titanium,[8] and various ferrous alloys with chromium or chromium and nickel.[6] These exhibit sharp changes in current density at potentials which resemble Flade potentials. The potentials also have a pH dependence like that of iron, though the transitions are generally less sharp.

There have been various efforts to give a theoretical interpretation of the Flade potential. The potential of the passive iron electrode cannot be treated simply as that of a metal-metal oxide system with conventional free-energy values for the known oxides in bulk form. Attempts have been made to relate its value to the heat of adsorption of oxygen on the metal (Uhlig), or to the potential of a metal-metal oxide-aqueous system, having an equilibrium potential between the surface and aqueous phases and a potential drop through the film (Vetter). Efforts have been made also to base an explanation on the properties of a single-phase film having a defect structure or a two-phase "sandwich" type of film involving a potential drop across the interphase. Kolotyrkin considers passivity not to derive from the presence of a film at all, but rather, from kinetic effects of the electrical state of the metallic surface which results from adsorption of solute species. None of the theories can be considered adequate, however. A film is demonstrably present; it definitely reacts with components of the solution to which it is exposed; and these interactions certainly alter the energetics and kinetics of electrochemical processes occurring across the interface. It is, therefore, understandable that no simple explanation of the Flade potential is at hand.[10]

References

1. ARNOLD, K., AND VETTER, K. J., *Z. Elektrochem.*, **64**, 407 (1960).
2. CARTLEDGE, G. H., AND SYMPSON, R. F., *J. Phys. Chem.*, **61**, 973 (1957); cf. UHLIG, H., AND KING, P. F., *J. Electrochem. Soc.*, **106**, 1 (1959) and Discussion, *ibid.*, p. 1074.
3. FLADE, FR., *Z. physik. Chem.*, **76**, 513 (1911).
4. FRANCK, U. F., *Naturforschg.*, **4a**, 378 (1949).
5. KOLOTYRKIN, Y. M., *Z. Elektrochem.*, **62**, 664 (1958).
6. OLIVIER, R., Dissertation, Leiden (1955); PRAŽÁK, M., *Werkstoffe u. Korrosion*, **9**, 517 (1958).
7. ROCHA, H. J., AND LENNARTZ, G., *Arch. Eisenhüttenw.*, **26**, 117 (1955).
8. STERN, M., AND WISSENBERG, H., *J. Electrochem. Soc.*, **106**, 755 (1959).
9. VETTER, K. J., AND BERNDT, D., *Z. Elektrochem.*, **62**, 378 (1958).
10. For a general discussion, see VETTER, K. J., "Elektrochemische Kinetik," pp. 603–608, Berlin, Springer-Verlag, 1961; YOUNG, L., "Anodic Oxide Films", pp. 227–240, Academic Press, New York, 1961; and papers presented at the First International Colloquium on the Passivity of Metals, Heiligenberg, Germany, 1957, published in *Z. Elektrochem.*, **62**, 619–827 (1958). The papers presented at the Second International Symposium (Toronto, 1962) appeared in *J. Electrochem. Soc.*, **110**, 596–703 (1963).

G. H. CARTLEDGE

Cross-references: *Corrosion Inhibition; Passivity; Polarization.*

FLUORESCENCE

Fluorescence and phosphorescence are two of the most important terms used in conjunction with the more inclusive phenomenon of luminescence. Many substances, inorganic and organic, gaseous, liquid, and solid, emit light following the absorption of energy. This absorbed energy may for different substances be in the form of electromagnetic radiation (ultraviolet light) high energy particles (high energy elec-

trons, α particles), ultrasonic sound waves, chemical energy, and others. The process of energy absorption by such materials is called excitation, and the light emitted during excitation is called *fluorescence*. The light emitted after excitation has ceased is called phosphorescence. The dividing line between the two phenomena may be taken at about 10^{-8} seconds after excitation has ceased, this time being the average lifetime of excited atoms in the gaseous state (for allowed transitions). The latter process obviously results from some storage in the fluorescent material of part of the excitation energy which is released, more or less slowly, in the form of light.

The term fluorescence had its origin in the light emitted by natural fluorites when they were excited by ultraviolet light. It is now known that this fluorescence results from the presence of small traces of certain metallic impurities in these natural fluorites. Most solid inorganic fluorescent materials either of natural or synthetic origin owe their fluorescence to the presence of minute traces of various types of impurities. These materials, commonly called phosphors, find wide application in fluorescent lamps, television and cathode ray tube screens, scintillation counters, and many other devices.

Fluorescence is observed also in gases which can be excited by electric discharge or the absorption of light of an appropriate wavelength from an external source. The sodium vapor lamp and high-pressure mercury arc lamp used in highway lighting, as well as the low-pressure mercury lamp (germicidal) and fluorescent lamps, make use of gaseous fluorescence. In the last mentioned case, the ultraviolet fluorescence of the excited mercury atoms (2537Å) is used in turn to excite the fluorescence of the solid inorganic phosphor powder coated on the wall of the tube. Fluorescence can occur in gaseous molecular as well as atomic systems.

In organic compounds, liquid or solid, fluorescence is observed also. Brilliant fluorescence is associated particularly with compounds having phthalein structures and also with aromatic structures containing several benzene rings, such as anthracene and naphthalene.

More details regarding fluorescence and related phenomena can be found in the articles on *Electroluminescence, Luminescence, Phosphorescence, Phosphors*, and *Scintillation Counters*. The most recent and exciting application of fluorescent phenomena in solids, liquids, and gases is discussed in some detail in the article on *Lasers*.

References

1. GARLICK, C. F. J., "Handbuch der Physik," edited by S. Flügge, Vol. XXVI, Berlin, Springer-Verlag, 1958; article on "Luminescence," pps. 1–128.
2. LEVERENZ, H. W., "Introduction to Luminescence of Solids," New York, John Wiley and Sons, Inc., 1950.
3. PRINGSHEIM, P., "Fluorescence and Phosphorescence," New York, Interscience Publishers, Inc., 1949.
4. KROGER, F. A., "Some Aspects of the Luminescence of Solids," New York, Elsevier Publishing Co., Inc., 1948.
5. KLICK, C. C., AND SCHULMAN, J. H., "*Solid State Physics*," edited by F. Seitz and D. Turnbull, Vol. 5, p. 97, New York, Academic Press, Inc., 1957.

J. S. PRENER

FLUORINE PRODUCTION

Fluorine, the first member of the halogen family, is the most electronegative of all the elements. Its atomic number is 9, and it has only one isotope, with an atomic weight of 19.00. At ordinary temperatures it is a gas; it can be liquefied at $-188.1°C$. The most important source of fluorine chemicals is fluorspar, CaF_2, a mineral that is widely distributed in nature, with many very rich accumulations in the United States. It is also found in deposits of commercial importance as cryolite, Na_3AlF_6, in Greenland. Fluorapatite, $CaF_2 \cdot 3Ca_3(PO_4)_2$, is a common mineral and is an important source for fluorosilicic acid and the fluorosilicates.

Fluorine, with a normal electrode potential (fluoride-fluorine couple) of -2.87 volts, is substantially more reactive than chlorine, its nearest halogen neighbor, whose potential is -1.36 volts. Fluorine forms compounds with nearly all of the other elements; even the inert gases, such as xenon and radon, have been found to react with it.

No chemical methods have ever been found to liberate fluorine from its stable compounds. The energy required to release fluorine from hydrogen fluoride can be supplied through electrolysis and by ionizing radiation. The only free fluorine reported in nature is said to be released by radiation from uranium-bearing fluorspar. Although fluorine is easily released by these methods, its extreme reactivity made it very difficult for the early workers to prepare sufficient amounts to study. It reacts with incendiary violence with many materials. Some of the resulting compounds are almost as reactive as fluorine itself, while others are outstandingly inert. As will be shown later, the inertness of many of the fluorides make the generating and handling of fluorine possible on an industrial scale.

Ampere, in 1812, recognized that the gas he prepared by treating fluorspar with sulfuric acid contained a new element which he called fluor, and suggested that it could be liberated by electrolysis. Sir Humphrey Davy electrolyzed hydrofluoric acid in 1813 but failed to isolate fluorine. Fremy, while passing an electric current through a molten fluoride, noted a pungent gas which attacked water to form hydrofluoric acid, and liberated iodine from iodides. This experiment was done in 1856 and was probably the first preparation of fluorine. However, Henri Moissan is usually given credit for the preparation of fluorine some 30 years later, when on June 26, 1886, he succeeded in isolating fluorine in sufficient amount to study its chemical and physical properties. This classical electrochemical preparation was done in a U-shaped vessel made from a platinum-iridium alloy. Electrodes, also made from the same alloy, were sealed in each arm of the vessel, using supports cut from large fluorspar crystals. The electrolyte was a solution of potassium fluoride in anhydrous hydrogen fluoride. The vessel containing the electrolyte and electrodes was cooled to about $-25°C$ by means of a liquid methyl chloride bath. When current was passed, fluorine was liberated at the anode in one arm of the U, and hydrogen at the cathode in the other arm. The gases were conducted out of the vessel through cooled platinum tubes. The hydrogen fluoride vapors swept out of the cell along with the fluorine were removed by passing the mixture through two platinum tubes containing sodium fluoride, where the hydrogen fluoride combined with sodium fluoride to form a complex salt, $NaF \cdot HF$, leaving pure elemental fluorine.

During the fifty years following Moissan's classical preparation there were only a few who worked in this difficult field. However, substantial improvements were made in the design of the electrolytic cell. In 1919 Argo and Mathers described a fluorine cell using graphite anodes

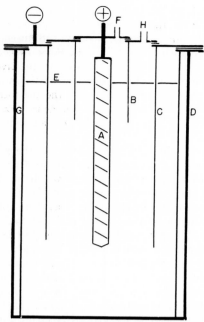

FIG. 1. Typical arrangement of parts in a fluorine cell. A, carbon anode; B, gas barrier; C, iron cathode; D, steel tank; E, electrolyte level; F, fluorine outlet; G, heating jacket; and H, hydrogen outlet.

with potassium bifluoride at 250°C as electrolyte. In 1925 Lebeau and Damiens produced the element by the electrolysis of molten $KF \cdot 3HF$ at 100°C using nickel anodes. But perhaps the greatest contributions to fluorine cell design during this period were made by George Cady. Working between 1934 and 1942 he developed a cell which used an electrolyte with the approximate composition $KF \cdot 2HF$ that operated at 100°C and used carbon anodes. He also demonstrated a method of regenerating the electrolyte in situ using liquefied HF from a cylinder. These developments of Cady made the large-scale production of fluorine possible.

The United States Atomic Energy Commission's need for elementary fluorine on an industrial scale for the manufacture of uranium hexafluoride resulted in a sudden acceleration in fluorine cell development after 1940. The story of this wartime development was told at a symposium of fluorine chemistry held during the 110th Meeting of the American Chemical Society in 1945.[3]

All modern commercial fluorine cells use an electrolyte with a composition of approximately $KF \cdot 2HF$ (38 to 43 per cent HF) at a tempera-

ture of about 100°C. Carbon is used as anode material and iron as cathode. When current is passed through such a cell, the hydrogen fluoride is decomposed. Hydrogen is generated at the cathode and is liberated in the form of small bubbles that break away from the cathode surface and rise to the top of the electrolyte; at the anode fluorine is formed and is liberated as a thin film that rises along the anode face to the surface of the electrolyte. Since the fluorine does not penetrate into the electrolyte, no diaphragm is needed between the anode and cathode to keep the hydrogen and fluorine from mixing in the electrolyte. The two gases are kept from mixing above the electrolyte by a metal "skirt" around the top end of the anode which dips a few inches into the electrolyte. The "skirt" or gas barrier is attached to the lid of the cell and is electrically insulated from both the anode and the cathode. The arrangement of these various parts is shown in Fig. 1.

Fluorine cells using carbon anodes suffer from a peculiar phenomenon called "polarization." When this effect occurs in an operating cell, current suddenly ceases to flow, unless the applied voltage to the cell is raised many volts. Polarization generally occurs a short time after start-up. It can be overcome by raising the cell voltage to about 50 volts; as current starts to flow, the cell voltage is adjusted to keep the current within safe limits. After a short electrolysis at the higher potential, the cell operation returns to normal. It is also possible to overcome polarization by replacing the carbon anode with nickel anodes for a short period, after which the carbon anodes will operate without polarization. In Great Britain forms of carbon have been developed which do not show this polarization phenomenon.

In the early stages of fluorine cell development, considerable difficulty was experienced in finding material that would withstand the action of hydrofluoric acid and fluorine. Fluorine is violently incendiary with most organic materials, water, and silicates, including concrete and asbestos. Fortunately, the ignition temperature of bulk metals in fluorine is well over 300°C; this appears to be due to a protective self-healing film of metal fluoride on the metal surface. Iron, nickel, copper, aluminum, and magnesium have all been used for fluorine cell construction. Finding suitable electrical insulators and gasket material was a more difficult task. Here again fluorine played a part. Polytetrafluoroethylene, a very stable fluorine-containing plastic material, was found to be sufficiently resistant to fluorine at moderate temperatures that it could be used as insulation and gasket material providing precautions are taken to expose a minimum of the plastic surface to the gas.

A high-capacity, long-life commercial fluorine cell has been developed by the Union Carbide Nuclear Company. This cell operates at 90°C using a fused salt electrolyte of potassium bifluoride (60 per cent KF·40 per cent HF) and can produce 135 pounds of fluorine per day. Anodes are made of carbon and cathodes of steel. The electrolyte is held in a Monel-lined steel tank 89 in. long, 32 in. wide, and 39 in. high. The tank is surrounded by a steel jacket for cooling and heating.

The cell cover is made from a one-inch steel plate. The gas separation skirt is made of Monel and is welded to the cover and dips a few inches into the electrolyte. The cover and the skirt are insulated from the cell body. The anode assembly, consisting of 32 carbon blades arranged in four rows, is supported by the cell cover but electrolytically insulated from it by polytetrafluoroethylene. The cathode assembly, made from ¼ in. steel plates (which are suspended from the cell cover) surrounds each row of anodes.

This cell has a diaphragm made from 6-mesh Monel screen placed between the anode and the cathode, just below the skirt. This diaphragm prevents broken carbon from causing a short circuit between the anode and cathode. It also must keep some of the stray hydrogen bubbles from entering the anode chamber, since the cell current efficiency is improved a few per cent with the screen diaphragm in place. Not all commercial fluorine cells use such a diaphragm.

The operating characteristics of this cell are shown in Table 1.

On start-up the electrolyte is first treated with fluorine, after which it is put in the cell, which is then operated at normal current density until the cell polarizes. Cell voltage is then raised until normal current passes, but is kept under 50 volts. The cell is operated in this manner until the polarization is overcome. This usually takes less than ten minutes.

The fluorine from the cell, containing about 10 per cent HF, is passed through copper coils cooled with dry ice, where about half of the hydrogen fluoride is removed. The gas is then passed over sodium fluoride pellets, heated to

TABLE 1. OPERATING CHARACTERISTICS OF THE UNION CARBIDE NUCLEAR COMPANY'S FLUORINE CELL

	Operating Characteristics at 4000 amp	Operating Characteristics at 6000 amp
Operating potential, volts	8–12	9–12
Cell temperature, °F	190–220	190–220
HF concentration, per cent	40–42	40–42
Effective anode area, sq ft	42	42
Anode current density, amp/sq ft	94	140
Anode number	32	32
Life, amp-hrs	16×10^6	15×10^6
Current efficiency, per cent	96	96

420°F, where the hydrogen fluoride concentration is reduced to about 2 per cent. A typical product analysis is:

Fluorine	97%
Hydrogen fluoride	2%
Oxygen	0.5%
Nitrogen	0.5%

Five cells of the type described above are used at the Oak Ridge Gaseous Diffusion Plant to generate 600 pounds of elemental fluorine per day. The purified fluorine from the five cells is compressed to about 75 psi pressure by a specially modified piston-type compressor using no oil. The fluorine is stored in steel tanks at room temperature. The pressure of the fluorine is reduced from the storage pressure to ten psi for pipeline distribution in the plant.

Fluorine can be shipped as a compressed gas at 400 pounds pressure in steel cylinders or as a liquid in zero-loss containers maintained below the boiling point of fluorine by a jacket of liquid nitrogen held in a conventional vacuum insulated vessel. Such a container permits shipment and storage of liquid fluorine at costs comparable with that for shipment and storage of liquid oxygen.

Elemental fluorine is toxic to humans. However, it can be detected by its odor at concentrations of 3 ppm, at which level it can be tolerated for several hours without harmful effect. The maximum concentration allowable for continuous exposure has been set at 0.1 ppm.

Elemental fluorine is used to make uranium hexafluoride, sulfur hexafluoride, and chlorine trifluoride. Increasing amounts of fluorine are being used in rocket research.

Large fluorine generation units are operated in the United States by the Union Carbide Nuclear Company and by General Chemical Division, Allied Chemical Corporation. In Great Britain, Imperial Chemical Industries, Ltd., operates a plant.

References

1. Moissan, H., "Le Fluor et Ses Composes," Paris, Steinheil, 1900.
2. Cady, G. H., Rogers, D. A., and Carlson, C. A., "Preparation of Fluorine," *Ind. Eng. Chem.,* **34,** 443 (1942).
3. March, 1947 issue of *Industrial and Engineering Chemistry.*
4. Simons, J. H., "Fluorine Chemistry," Vols. 1 and 2, New York, Academic Press, 1950 and 1954.
5. Rudge, A. J., "The Manufacture and Use of Fluorine and Its Compounds," London, Oxford University Press, 1962.
6. Vavalides, S. P., Cable, R. E., Henderson, W. K., and Powell, C. A., "High-Capacity, Long-Life Fluorine Cell," *Ind. Eng. Chem.,* **50,** 178 (1958).
7. Dykstra, J., Thompson, B. H., and Paris, W. C., "A 25-Pound per Hour Fluorine Plant," *Ind. Eng. Chem.,* **50,** 181 (1958).

Henry C. Miller

FLUOROCARBONS, ELECTROCHEMICAL PRODUCTION

The electrochemical process for the production of fluorocarbons was not generally known until after the end of World War II, despite the fact that it was discovered prior to 1941. The need for the fluorocarbons in the atomic bomb project caused a manuscript describing the essential features of this process to be withdrawn for security reasons. It had been accepted for publication in the Journal of the American Chemical Society in April 1941. The process was disclosed to officials of the United States Government; but it was not used during the war years, because it was considered too speculative by these officials.

The raw materials used in this process are hydrogen fluoride and a compound of carbon which is usually but not necessarily an organic substance. The hydrogen fluoride is kept in the liquid state and is made electrically conducting either by the presence of the organic compound or by the addition of a third substance.

The products are hydrogen gas and carbon compounds containing fluorine. If the raw materials contain oxygen or nitrogen, the fluorides of these elements also are found in the products. The exit gas from the electrochemical cell is chiefly hydrogen. It contains some hydrogen fluoride, most of which is returned to the cell after being condensed by refrigeration. It also contains a low concentration of the fluorides of oxygen and nitrogen, but in most operations these are minimized. It will also contain any gaseous or low-boiling fluorocarbon or fluorocarbon derivatives, such as CF_4, C_2F_6, or CF_3COF. When desired these can be removed by various forms of stripping or scrubbing. Liquid products are usually more dense than the electrolyte and insoluble in it. They are removed from the bottom of the unit. Some products are soluble in the electrolyte. If these are desired, the electrolyte is removed from the cell for suitable processing.

The producing unit is an electrochemical cell with interleaving plate electrodes. There are no separators or diaphragms between the electrode plates. The anodes are nickel and the cathodes nickel, iron, or copper. The cell body is usually iron, but any metal resistant to hydrogen fluoride could be used. The distance between the electrodes is determined by the mechanical design of the unit and the size of the plates. It is a small fraction of an inch. Its particular value is not significant in regard to the chemical or electrical efficiency of the unit.

Small-sized laboratory cells consume between one and one hundred amperes, and a convenient temperature of operation is the freezing point of water. Industrial production units consuming up to ten thousand amperes have been constructed. These usually operate at or near atmospheric pressure and at the temperature at which the cell liquid boils. A potential below 7 volts is usually employed and this gives a current density in the 0.02 to 0.05 amp/sq cm range.

Among the essential auxilliary equipment for the producing unit are the following: (a) a power supply to provide constant potential current, (b) adequate refrigeration equipment to maintain the cell temperature, condense hydrogen fluoride from the exit gas stream for return to the cell, and strip from this gas stream any desired product, (c) a raw material storage and supply system with all necessary valves, pumps, and metering devices, (d) a product recovery and purifying system, and (e) adequate instrumentation and recording devices.

The process variables are voltage; temperature; pressure; and the concentrations of raw materials, intermediates, additives, and impurities. Except for the initial charge, the values of these concentrations are determined by the rate of operation, the quality of the feed stocks, and their rate of supply. In some cases the duration of the operation is also significant. It is not possible at this time to specify the exact values of these variables for good operations, because they vary greatly for optimum operation, depending on the specific raw material and its purity and also on the product or products desired. For example, certain processes for designated products are favored by lower concentrations within limits, whereas others are favored by higher ones. In a similar manner the preferred voltage, either higher or lower, is different for different raw materials or for different products from the same raw material. The process variables need to be adjusted by trial for each operation.

The chief products desired from this process have been the fluorocarbons and oxygen- and nitrogen-containing fluorocarbon derivatives, such as

$$C_nF_{2n+2}, \; C_nF_{2n+1}OC_mF_{2m+1},$$
$$C_nF_{2n+1}C_mF_{2m+1}NC_pC_{2p+1},$$
$$C_nF_{2n+1}COF, \text{ and } C_nF_{2n+1}SO_2F.$$

Hydrogen-containing products can and have been made, such as fluoroform and fluoropyridine. Hydrogen-containing compounds are also produced as impurities in most operations. As hydrogen-free products are chiefly desired, the process is usually operated in a manner to reduce the production of hydrogen-containing compounds; and purifying steps are employed to remove them from the products. At any time that hydrogen-containing products are desired the process variables can be changed in a manner to increase their production.

Because any particular raw material can and does produce a variety of products in this process and also because a desired product can be obtained from a variety of raw materials, choices must be made. These are based upon convenience in laboratory operations and upon economic factors in industrial processing. The particular product and its fractional yield of the total products in any specific operation depend on the values of the process variables. For example, if it is desired to produce trifluoroacetic acid as the final product, trifluoroacetyl

fluoride will be the substance obtained from the cell. It will be stripped from the gaseous cell products by water, alkali, or other means. The raw material other than hydrogen fluoride will be acetic acid, acetic anhydride, and acetyl halide (preferably the fluoride), or any other acetyl compound. The process variables will be adjusted to increase the yield of CF_3COF and reduce those of CF_4, CF_3H, and other products.

For products containing a number of carbon atoms in the molecule, it might be expected that the preferred raw material would be an organic compound with a carbon skeleton the same as that of the desired product and hydrogen atoms in the places to be occupied by fluorine atoms in the product. Very frequently this is not the case. A raw material having a different structure usually is preferred. In many cases the analogous organic compound will not produce the desired product in significant yields. The proper choice of raw material is made upon the basis of trial and experience. The state of the art has not advanced to the point of establishing a set of rules. It is known, however, that rearrangements, cyclizations, bond breaking, coupling, and similar changes of structure are to be expected.

It is not correct to call this a process of electrolysis, as it is one of synthesis rather than of decomposition. Emphatically it is not a fluoroination process, as the element is neither formed nor is it an intermediate in the process. It has been determined that the process can continue at an electrical potential below that required for the discharge of elementary fluorine, F_2. Obviously, it cannot be a fluorination by atomic fluorine, because the discharge of fluorine atoms requires about one and one-half volts more than that needed to discharge F_2.

It seems futile at this time to do more than speculate upon the mechanism of the chemical reactions involved in this process. There are no quantitative data upon which to base the verification of any proposed theory of mechanism. The operation of laboratory units under as near as possible identical operating variables do not give identical results. One unit will operate successfully under a set of conditions which will not provide for continuous operations of a duplicate unit. Until duplicate results can be obtained in different experiments, it is obvious that sufficient knowledge of the details of the mechanism of operation is not available. In this process many chemical reactions must occur in a very short time in a limited region either on the electrodes or in the electrolyte, because there is a great amount of chemical change in making a fluorocarbon derivative from an organic compound. Some of these reactions must be very fast and must be greatly influenced by small concentrations of impurities, by-products, or intermediates, and also by the process variables. Experience indicates that there are parallel sets of reactions that occur simultaneously.

Prior to the discovery of this process, it was quite reasonable for one to consider it to be impossible, because of the following facts. Organic compounds, particularly those containing oxygen, nitrogen, or sulfur, are in general quite soluble in liquid hydrogen fluoride to form electrically conducting solutions. The organic molecule combines with a proton from the solvent to form a positive ion and leaving a more or less solvated negative fluoride ion. For example, ethyl ether undergoes the following reaction:

$$(C_2H_5)_2O + HF \rightarrow (C_2H_5)_2OH^+ + F^-$$

During the passage of electric current through the solution, the fluoride ion will move toward one electrode, and the organic substance will move in the opposite direction toward the other electrode. It is difficult to visualize a reaction between these ions and to determine its exact location. Experimental attempts to isolate the site of the chemical reactions by means of diaphragms or other devices in the cells have been unsuccessful.

Despite the lack of knowledge of the details of the mechanism, the process operates very satisfactorily on a large industrial scale. The larger the unit the more satisfactory becomes the operation. Commercial units function better than those in the laboratory. This is probably because the process variables are more constant in the larger units.

The process is very excellent from an engineering point of view. It operates continuously for long periods of time, years if desired, with continuous feed and product removal. Once the process variables are set, very little attention is required. It has an excellent volume efficiency, as one cubic foot of all electrode pack can produce about fifty pounds of product per day. The cell body lasts indefinitely, and the cell pack is almost as durable under optimum operating conditions. The equipment is very versa-

tile, and a large variety of products can be produced in it without structural changes. To change from one product to another the only changes required are in feed stock and operating variables. For example, the fluorocarbon carboxylic acids from CF_3CO_2H to $C_{13}F_{27}CO_2H$ have been produced with cyclic, branched, or straight chain structures. Dibasic acids have also been produced. These products have been obtained from a variety of both aromatic and aliphatic raw materials.

References

The following references contain pertinent published information about this process.

1. Simons, J. H., and Coworkers, "The Electrochemical Process for the Production of Fluorocarbons," *J. Electrochem. Soc.*, **95**, 47 (1949).
2. Simons, J. H., "Electrochemical Process of Making Fluorine Containing Carbon Compounds," U. S. Patent 2,519,983 (1950).
3. Simons, J. H., "Electrochemical Preparation of Fluorine Compounds from Organic Compounds," Canadian Patent 466,200 (1950).
4. Simons, J. H., Editor, "Fluorine Chemistry," Vol. I, p. 414, New York, Academic Press, 1950.
5. *Ibid*, Vol. II, p. 350, 1954.
6. *Ibid*, Vol. V in press.

JOSEPH H. SIMONS

FRANKLIN, BENJAMIN (1706-1790)

Born in Boston on January 17, 1706, Benjamin Franklin, the youngest of fifteen children, received formal instruction until the age of ten and, at twelve, was apprenticed to his brother James, a printer. Franklin ran away from home and, at the age of seventeen, arrived in Philadelphia, penniless. Six years later he was the owner of his own printing shop and publisher of the *Pennsylvania Gazette* and for the next twenty years was a successful publisher, printer, and writer.

Franklin's scientific career in electricity began in 1746, when, while on a visit to Boston, he viewed the experiments of Adam Spence and discussed electricity with him.

Peter Collinson, a personal friend of Franklin and London agent for the Philadelphia Library, sent Franklin a three-foot long electric tube—a substitute for the glass tube as a generator. Purchasing equipment similar to Spence's and aided by his ingenuity in making his own equipment, Franklin began his experiments.

Electricity, though the most talked-about topic of the day, was regarded generally as a subject of amusement and mystery. Scientists did know that electricity could be conducted by some substances and not by others, that some charged substances were attracted and others repelled, and was thought to be a fluid, vitreous or resinous, that could be gathered in an insulated conductor, for example, a musket barrel suspended by silk threads. In 1745, Von Kleist and Von Mussenbroek independently discovered the Leyden jar.

Franklin's account of his experiments and observations were contained in letters to Collinson beginning in 1748. Collinson had the letters read before the Royal Society, where they were received with a mixture of skepticism and interest. Franklin never wrote accounts of his experiments; his letters to Collinson were published as *Experiments, Observations,* and *Transactions.* In 1751, Collinson had the collection published under the title *Experiments and Observations on Electricity.*

In his first letter to Collinson, Franklin indicated that the years 1746–48 had been spent in most fruitful experiment. Franklin discussed his observations of electricity as a single-fluid theory and called the fluids negative and positive.

Franklin's one-fluid theory was based on the belief that electricity was positive only. An object with a normal amount of electricity, he considered neutral, one with more than this amount was positive, one with less, negative. His theory was based on experiments with the tube, testing attraction and repulsion.

Franklin studied the electrical properties of metallic points and repeated the experiments of Mussenbroek and Wilson. He suggested erecting a pointed iron rod on an exposed tower or hill and testing it regularly with a conductor to see if it had become electrified.

Buffon verified Franklin's thesis about electricity and in May, 1752, in separate experiments, the French scholars, Dalibard and DeLor performed Franklin's experiment with the lightning rod or "electrical conductor" as it was called, and corroborated the theory. Louis XV of France witnessed the experiment and wrote Franklin a congratulatory letter.

In June, 1752, during a storm, Franklin, accompanied by his son, flew a silk kite to which a sharp pointed wire had been affixed at the crosspiece. A key had been attached at the junction of twine and silk ribbon and this key, following the experiment's conclusion, was found to be electrically charged. The now-famous kite experiment proved to the world and scientists generally, with dramatic force, that electricity and lightning had the same characteristics. Lightning was the same "stuff" made in static electricity machines and stored in the Leyden jar.

An account of the experiment was read before the Royal Society in 1753 and was published in the *Transactions* of the year. That same year, Franklin was awarded the Copley Medal by the Royal Society and in 1756 was admitted to fellowship without being required to request election or pay the usual fees. The French Academie des Sciences elected Franklin one of its eight foreign associates. William and Mary, Harvard, and Yale granted him honorary degrees.

The position of post master general of Philadelphia, delegate to the Albany convention, and his other well-known Revolutionary and post-Revolutionary diplomatic and governmental activities took Franklin from further full-time experimentation in electricity. His interest in nature and the philosophy of scientific inquiry never lagged, however, and it became a part of his notably well-rounded character.

Franklin's one-fluid theory has been disproven and his observations about the nature of electricity have been greatly refined. His contributions became part of science in general, but his influence on the study of electricity was far reaching and permanent. As a major worker in static electricity, Franklin was the first great name in American science. Internationally famed for this and other activities, Franklin died April 17, 1790 in Philadelphia.

References

1. Donovan, Frank, The Benjamin Franklin Papers," New York, Dodd, Mead, 1962.
2. Hindle, Brooke, "The Pursuit of Science in Revolutionary America, 1735–1789," Chapel Hill, University of North Carolina Press, 1956.
3. Moulton, F. R., and Schifferes, J. J., "The Autobiography of Science," Garden City, N.J., Doubleday, 1960.
4. Van Doren, Carl, "Benjamin Franklin: A Biography," New York, Viking, 1956.

Elizabeth A. Hampel

FREE ENERGY

There are two free energy functions in common use: The *Gibbs free energy*, F, (also called *free enthalpy* and also designated as, G)

$$F \equiv H - TS \qquad (1)$$

and the *Helmholtz free energy*, A, (sometimes designated as F)

$$A \equiv E - TS \qquad (2)$$

where H is the enthalpy (or heat content), E is the internal energy (not to be confused with the electrical potential, E), S is the entropy and T is the absolute temperature. As will be seen below, the Gibbs free energy, F, is the more useful quantity for isothermal reactions at constant pressure while A is the more useful one for those at constant volume. Since it is more common to work at constant (e.g., atmospheric) pressure than at constant volume, it is customary among American experimental chemists to use simply the term "free energy" for the Gibbs free energy and "Helmholtz free energy" for the A function. On the other hand those working in the field of statistical mechanics usually refer to the A function as the "free energy." Hence, it is well to refer to the actual definition used when the term "free energy" is seen in the literature.

The relation between F and A can easily be seen, since H is defined as the internal energy, E, plus the pressure-volume product, PV

$$H \equiv E + PV \qquad (3)$$

Substitution of Eq. (3) into (1) gives

$$\begin{aligned} F &= E + PV - TS \\ &= (E - TS) + PV = A + PV \end{aligned} \qquad (4)$$

Either free energy function (a) provides a criterion of spontaneity of a reaction, (b) predicts the maximum yield obtainable in a reaction (in which the products are not immediately removed), and (c) gives a measure of the maximum work which may be obtained from a particular transformation. After a discussion of spontaneity of a reaction and of equilibria, examples of items (b) and (c) will be given.

Criterion of Spontaneity

In any differential process the change in the internal energy, E, is defined as the heat absorbed, dq, less the work done by the system, dw, i.e.,

$$dE \equiv dq - dw \qquad (5)$$

If Eq. (3) is differentiated and Eq. (5) is inserted into it,

$$dH = dq - dw + PdV + VdP \qquad (6)$$

A differential process will now be considered which is *reversible* (i.e., one in which an infinitesimal change in one of the variables will reverse the process) and in which the only work done is steric mechanical (pressure-volume work against the atmosphere). By the definition of entropy, $dq_{rev} = TdS$ for a reversible process. If only steric mechanical work is done, $dw_{rev} = PdV$. Now if Eq. (6) is substituted into the differential of Eq. (1)

$$\begin{aligned} dF &= (dq_{rev} - PdV) + PdV \\ &\quad + VdP - TdS - SdT \\ &= VdP - SdT. \end{aligned} \qquad (7)$$

The corresponding equation for dA may be obtained by differentiating Eq. (4), inserting the result on the left side of (7) and simplifying:

$$dA = -PdV - SdT \qquad (8)$$

At equilibrium the (forward and backward) processes are *reversible*; that is, an infinitesimal change or stress can force the reaction to go in one way or the other. Hence, according to Eq. (7) for an isothermal process ($dT = 0$) at constant pressure ($dP = 0$), the equilibrium condition is

$$dF = 0, \text{ at constant } P, T \qquad (9)$$

or for any finite transformation

$$\Delta F = 0, \text{ at constant } P, T \qquad (10)$$

(Actually it is not necessary that the pressure and temperature be kept constant throughout the process but only that the final pressure and temperature be the same as the initial values for the process under consideration.) Similarly, according to Eq. (8) at equilibrium

$$\Delta A = 0, \text{ at constant } V, T \qquad (11)$$

Eqs. (10) and (11) provide a means of determining or calculating the equilibrium condition. Qualitatively it can be stated that if ΔF for an isothermal reaction at constant pressure is negative it will occur spontaneously; if ΔF is positive it will occur spontaneously in the reverse direction. Thermodynamics gives us no idea, however, about the rate of a reaction; it may occur so slowly as to be imperceptible. A similar qualitative statement can be made concerning ΔA for an isothermal process at constant volume.

Equilibrium and Maximum Extent of Reaction

Although absolute values of free energy are not known, free energy changes are sufficient for most purposes. Consequently, the free energy of any substance is defined in terms of that in the standard (or reference) state $F°$, and an activity or "thermodynamic concentration" as

$$F = F° + RT \ln a \qquad (12)$$

where R is the gas constant and T the absolute temperature. Pure solids or pure liquids are taken as the standard states at any temperature; for gases the standard state is taken as the gas at unit fugacity (approximately one atmosphere pressure), while for solutes in solution it is taken as a hypothetical solution of unit activity with heat capacity and enthalpy equal to the values at infinite dilution.

For a typical chemical reaction

$$bB + cC \rightarrow mM + nN \qquad (13)$$

ΔF is the algebraic sum of the free energies of the products less the sum for the reactants

$$\Delta F = \Delta F(products) - \Delta F(reactants)$$

$$= \Delta F° + RT \ln \frac{a_M{}^m \, a_N{}^n}{a_B{}^b \, a_C{}^c} \qquad (14)$$

At equilibrium $\Delta F = 0$, each activity is equal to its equilibrium value, and the activity quotient becomes equal to the equilibrium constant, K, or

$$\Delta F° = -RT \ln K \qquad (15)$$

Thus, from tabulated values of standard free energy changes the activities of the various constituents can be calculated, and these can be evaluated, at least approximately, in terms of concentrations (or pressures).

As an example of the calculation of the maximum extent to which a reaction can be made to go under equilibrium conditions, the direct synthesis of ammonia from nitrogen and hydrogen will be considered at 800°K (527°C) in the presence of a catalyst (without which the rate would be immeasurably slow). This is known as the Haber process, the chemical equation for which is

$$N_{2(g)} + 3H_{2(g)} \rightarrow 2NH_{3(g)} \qquad (16)$$

The equilibrium constant for this reaction may be expressed as

$$K = \frac{a_{NH_3}^2}{a_{N_2} \, a_{H_2}^3} = \frac{f_{NH_3}^2}{f_{N_2} \, f_{H_2}^3} \simeq \frac{p_{NH_3}^2}{p_{N_2} \, p_{H_2}^3} \qquad (17)$$

where a represents activity which for a gas is equal to the fugacity, f, which in turn is approximately equal to the partial pressures, p, (the approximation being better, the lower the pressure and the higher the temperature). From tables of thermodynamic data the free energy change for the reaction can be seen to be about 18.4 kcal per mole of N_2 reacting at 800°K. Use of Eq. (15) gives a K value equal to 9.1×10^{-6}. If the initial partial pressures of N_2 and H_2 are 1 and 3 atmospheres, respectively, then at equilibrium in terms of the partial pressure of NH_3 set equal to $2x$,

$$K \simeq \frac{(2x)^2}{(1-x)(3-3x)^3} \qquad (18)$$

according to the stoichiometry of the chemical equation. Since x is small compared to unity under the above conditions

$$(2x)^2 \simeq (9.1 \times 10^{-6})(1)(3)^3 \simeq 2.46 \times 10^{-4} \quad (19)$$

or

$$p_{NH_3} = 2x \simeq 1.57 \times 10^{-2} \text{ atm.} \qquad (20)$$

Hence, the fraction of reaction = $N_{2(reacted)}/N_{2(initial)} = x/(1) = 0.008$, or 0.8 per cent of the N_2 will have reacted. The thermodynamic meaning of this calculation is that no more than 0.8 per cent of the N_2 can react (until the product NH_3 is removed, e.g., by condensation in a "cold-trap" or by solution in H_2O). Then, of course, the reaction can be made to proceed again to the same extent.

This reaction can be made to be more efficient by increasing the total pressure. For example, at 50 atm of N_2 and 150 atm H_2 (which are reasonable industrial conditions) use of Eq. (17) shows that $p_{NH_3} \simeq 23$ atm, or 23 per cent of the N_2 can react at best, until the product is removed and the process repeated.

Example of Maximum Available Work

Consider the process in which a piece of zinc metal reacts with an acid solution. The zinc may be dissolved directly in a vessel of acid in which no work is done except the steric mechanical (pressure-volume) work of the evolved hydrogen against the atmosphere

$$Zn + 2H^+ \rightarrow Zn^{++} + H_{2(g)} \qquad (21)$$

This process is a highly irreversible one. Alternatively, the zinc may be used as an electrode of a galvanic cell with a standard hydrogen electrode, in a thermostat with the two electrodes connected to a motor. As the cell reacts, the zinc dissolves with the evolution of hydrogen at the other electrode and the resulting electrical energy runs the motor, performing useful work. The amount of useful work obtained depends on the efficiency of the experimental equipment, being greater the more nearly reversibly the process is carried out. The ultimate in work obtainable in addition to the mechanical (pressure-volume) work of the hydrogen against the atmosphere with perfect efficiency (i.e., with a reversible arrangement) is given by the value of $-\Delta F$ for reaction (21). Thus, $-\Delta F$ gives a measure of the maximum available energy or "free energy." The amount of heat absorbed from the thermostat will increase with the quantity of work obtained.

$-\Delta A$ for reaction (21) gives a measure of the maximum work available *including* the steric mechanical work against the atmosphere, in agreement with Eq. (4).

Equations for Evaluating Free Energy Changes

In addition to Eq. (15) for expressing free energy in terms of ordinary measurable quantities, ΔF may be expressed in terms of the electrical potential of a reversible galvanic cell, E, as

$$\Delta F = -n\mathbf{F}E \qquad (22)$$

where n is the number of equivalents of electricity per mole of the cell reaction and $\mathbf{F}$ is the Faraday constant. It may also be expressed in terms of the enthalpy change, ΔH, and the entropy change, ΔS, as

$$\Delta F = \Delta H - T\Delta S \qquad (23)$$

(for an isothermal process).

The variation of free energy with temperature and pressure may be given by

$$\left(\frac{\partial \frac{\Delta F}{T}}{\partial T} \right)_P = -\frac{\Delta H}{T^2} \qquad (24)$$

$$\left(\frac{\partial \Delta F}{\partial T} \right)_P = -\Delta S = -n\mathbf{F}\left(\frac{\partial E}{\partial T} \right)_P, \qquad (25)$$

and

$$\left(\frac{\partial \Delta F}{\partial P} \right)_T = \Delta V, \qquad (26)$$

where ΔV is the overall change in volume.

References

1. LEWIS, G. N., AND RANDALL, M., "Thermodynamics," 2nd Edition, revised by K. S. Pitzer and Leo Brewer, Chaps. 13–15 and Appendix 7, New York, McGraw-Hill Book Co., 1961.
2. KLOTZ, I. M., "Chemical Thermodynamics," Chaps. 8–10, New York, Prentice-Hall, Inc., 1950.
3. LATIMER, W. M., "Oxidation Potentials," 2nd Edition, New York, Prentice-Hall, Inc., 1952.
4. KELLEY, K. K., *U. S. Bur. Mines Bulls.* **477** (1950); **476** (1949) and **584** (1960).

M. H. LIETZKE AND
R. W. STOUGHTON

FRETTING CORROSION

The term fretting corrosion is applied to a particular type of wear caused by minute reciprocating sliding motion between adjacent machine parts. It is usually accompanied by rapid oxidation of the surfaces at the interface, hence the use of the word corrosion. The term fretting is also used to designate a grinding type wear where pulverized debris is formed under the same conditions without chemical reaction. Fretting corrosion commonly occurs in press fits, bolted assemblies, and other load-bearing surface contacts where repeated mechanical straining due to vibration or mechanical movement takes place.

Many theories have been advanced to explain the phenomenon. Although differing somewhat, there is general agreement on the fact that the shearing action of the mechanical motion, although quite small, removes minute particles of both already formed oxide surfaces as well as some base material which may subsequently oxidize. The actual points of contact of the surfaces deform plastically, weld, shear off, and perhaps reweld many times during the course of the reciprocating motion. The grinding action of the debris which forms may also contribute to the removal of more debris. The only theoretical attempt to separate the mechanical and chemical contributions to the total wear product has been proposed by Uhlig *et al*[8, 9] in the empirical equation for the fretting of steel parts,

$$W(\text{total}) = (k_0 L^{1/2} - k_1 L)C/f + k_2 dLC$$

where

W is specimen weight loss, mg
L is the load, psi
C is the number of cycles
f is the frequency, cps
d is the length of a single stroke, inches
k_0, k_1 and k_2 are constants.

The values obtained by Uhlig for steel on steel are

$$k_0 = 5.05 \times 10^{-6}, \quad k_1 = 1.51 \times 10^{-8},$$

$$k_2 = 4.16 \times 10^{-6}$$

Fretting corrsion wear is affected by many variables, such as amount of motion, normal pressure, the number of cycles, frequency, hardness of surfaces, temperature, coefficient of friction, lubrication, humidity and other environmental conditions such as inert atmospheres or vacuum. These effects are also interrelated in that high pressure may reduce motion or cause high local temperature. The geometry of the surfaces may cause different effects. Rough surfaces may produce high surface elasticity or provide cavities for the escape of debris or pockets for lubricant. Conversely, the geometry may cause entrapment of the debris.

Motion is necessary for fretting corrosion to occur. Mild evidence of corrosion can be found with as little as 6.5×10^{-8} inches reciprocating movement. Practically, motions as large as 20 to 50 microinches can be tolerated without serious effect. Larger motions are usually damaging with the amount of wear being roughly a linear function of the length of the cyclic stroke. Fretting corrosion can be completely eliminated if sliding does not occur. A thin rubber film or other elastic media between the fretting parts can absorb the motion elastically and stop fretting corrosion.

Increased pressure will often prevent motion and thereby prevent damage, but doubling the pressure with the same motion will result in nearly twice the damage. Pressures that will break protective oxide surface films will always produce fretting corrosion when accompanied by the necessary motion.

Tens of thousands of cycles are required for significant fretting damage unless pressures or motions are quite high. The first 50 to 100 thousand cycles produce somewhat erratic results but continued uniform reciprocating motion will result in a uniform or slowly diminishing wear rate.

The frequency of the cyclic slip is generally of little importance unless it is fairly low, well below 1000 cpm. If sufficient time is allowed, naturally formed oxides in air cause the damage per cycle to be greater at low frequencies, but the total damage is only mildly increased.

Hard materials tend to be less susceptible to fretting corrosion. Hard surface treatments also reduce fretting damage; chrome plating, shot peening, nitriding, etc., are often used to prevent excessive fretting. Hard oxide particles which are broken loose usually cause more severe wear. The harder nonmetals, such as ruby, quartz, and glass, have better fretting resistance than the softer ones, such as lucite or mica.

Temperatures below the freezing point of water cause increased fretting damage when the environment is atmospheric. Higher than room temperatures tend to increase fretting corrosion rates also but the effect is quite mild unless coupled with low frequencies.

High atmospheric humidity in contrast to its effect on steel parts in causing rust will reduce fretting corrosion. Apparently the water acts as a lubricant. High humidities are not recommended because of their chemical corrosive effect, but this relationship does point up the difference in the two corrosive processes.

Reducing the coefficient of friction between parts which are subject to fretting motion will reduce fretting regardless of how the reduction in friction is accomplished. Oils and greases, dry lubricants, or plastic films with inherent low coefficients of friction on metal parts all can greatly reduce fretting corrosion. Various surface treatments which produce such an effect, such as phosphating, are also helpful in reducing fretting corrosion.

Fluid lubricants also protect against fretting by surrounding the surfaces with a film which limits the supply of oxygen to the corroding surfaces. The rate of wear in a vacuum or inert atmosphere is less than one tenth the value for fretting corrosion in air. The corrosion rate due to fretting action in a water or oil bath is also greatly reduced such that a mechanical wearing or grinding action predominates.

There is no positive way to identify fretting corrosion. It may be possible by x-ray diffraction to differentiate between rust and fretting debris in that rust usually has combined with it a certain amount of water, while fretting corrosion debris usually does not. However, after sufficient time fretting debris may also combine with the moisture in the air. Although the red Fe_2O_3 is usually formed, Fe_3O_4 and FeO may also be formed with limited oxygen supply. The possibility of motion or actual indications of wear tracks with motions in the order to 3 to 4 mils are the most positive means of identifying fretting action as the cause for corroded surfaces.

References

1. ALMEN, J. O., "Lubricants and False Brindling of Ball and Roller Bearings," *Mechanical Engineering*, **59**, 415–422 (1937).
2. GODFREY, DOUGLAS, "Investigation of Fretting Corrosion by Microscopic Observation," *NACA Technical Note No.* **2039**, February, 1950.
3. GODFREY, DOUGLAS, AND BISSON, EDMOND E., "Effectiveness of Molybdenum Disulfide as a Fretting Corrosion Inhibitor," *NACA Technical Note* **2180**, September, 1950.
4. HALLIDAY, J. S., AND HIRST, W., "The Fretting Corrosion of Mild Steel," *Proc. Roy. Soc.*, **A236**, No. 1206, 411–425 (August 2, 1956).
5. McDOWELL, J. R., "Fretting Corrosion Tendencies of Several Combinations of Materials," *ASTM Special Technical Publication No.* **144**, June, 1952.
6. SAKMANN, B. W., AND RIGHTMIRE, B. G., "An Investigation of Fretting Corrosion Under Several Conditions of Oxidation," *NACA Technical Note No.* **1492**, June, 1948.
7. TOMLINSON, G. A., THORPE, P. L., AND GOUGH, H. J., "An Investigation of Fretting Corrosion of Closely Fitting Surfaces," *Proc. Inst. Mech. Eng.*, **141**, p. 223–249 (1939).
8. UHLIG, H. H., FENG, I. M., TIERNEY, W. D., AND McCLELLAN, A., "Fundamental Investigation of Fretting Corrosion," *NACA Technical Note* **3029**, December, 1953.
9. UHLIG, H. H., TIERNEY, W. D., AND McCLELLAN, A., "Test Equipment for Evaluating Fretting Corrosion," *ASTM Special Technical Publication No.* **144**, June, 1952.
10. WATERHOUSE, R. B., "Fretting Corrosion," *Inst. Mech. Eng.*, **169**, No. 59, 1157–1172 (1955).
11. WRIGHT, K. H. R., "An Investigation of Fretting Corrosion," *Proc. Inst. Mech. Eng.*, **1B**, 556–574 (1952–53).

J. R. MCDOWELL

FUEL CELLS

A fuel cell is a device for continuously converting chemicals into electricity through electrochemical reactions. The name, fuel cell, is sometimes applied to an entire system in which the reaction products are regenerated outside the cell by an external energy source such as heat, light, radioactivity, or chemical reactor, and are then recycled.

Historically, the fuel cell was thought of as a means to decrease the cost of electrical power by direct electrochemical conversion of the energy of solid fuels such as coal. Downgrading of the energy content of fuel (coal to carbon monoxide) to arrive at a workable fuel cell defeated the historical purpose. An upgraded fuel such as water gas was acceptable. In 1896, as today, the popular press pictured the fuel cell as a device which could be placed in the basement of homes to furnish current for the household. The picture has not materialized. And, whereas the same desires remain, the aims have broadened to include other than conventional and upgraded fuels. Thus, while some descriptions still limit fuel cells to those which use low cost fuels directly, others now place no cost limitation upon the fuel. Cells using fuels directly are called *direct fuel cells*. Cell systems that use an intermediate fuel derived from fossil fuels or regenerated from a primary energy source, such as the sun or wind, are called *indirect fuel cells*. The two types of cells are illustrated in Fig. 1. Batteries with replaceable electrodes also have been called fuel cells.

All fuel cells, like batteries, produce direct current eletricity. The voltages generally are less than 2.0 volts per cell and voltages less than 1.0 volt per cell are common. Fuel cells are connected electrically in series to attain desired voltages. They might look like automobile batteries or like laboratory furnaces if they were commercialized. However, first uses have been for military applications and up to 500-watt sizes have been used in space vehicles. To demonstrate future possibilities, a farm tractor was equipped in 1959 with fuel cells and an electric motor in place of the ordinary gasoline engine. It pulled a plow successfully but has not since been put on the market.

How It Works

A fuel cell uses many of the principles of batteries (q.v.) wherein all fuel, oxidant, and reaction products are contained internally. As with batteries, a fuel cell requires two electronic-conductor electrodes separated by an ionic-conductor electrolyte. The negative electrode is the anode. The positive electrode in the

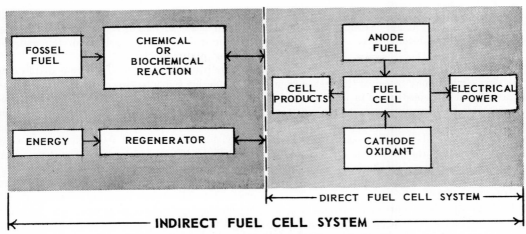

FIG. 1. Illustration of direct and indirect fuel cells.

cathode. Fuel is oxidized at the anode giving electrons to an external circuit, while the oxidant accepts electrons from the anode and is reduced. Simultaneously with the electron transfer, an ionic current in the electrolyte completes the circuit. The sum of the electrochemical reactions at the anode and cathode constitutes the cell reaction. For example:

Anode: $H_2 + 2OH^- \rightarrow 2H_2O + 2$ electrons
Cathode: 2 electrons $+ \frac{1}{2}O_2 + H_2O \rightarrow 2OH^-$
Fuel Cell: $H_2 + \frac{1}{2}O_2 \rightarrow H_2O$

The anode and cathode assume a difference of potential derived from the free energy (q.v.) of the overall reaction. Both the quantity (Faradays, F, or coulombs) and intensity (reversible potential, E, in volts) of the cell output are contained in the molar free energy, ΔG, of the cell reaction:

$$\Delta G = -nFE = -E \times I \times t,$$

where n is the number of electrons per molecule of fuel that is oxidized and I is the average current in amperes derived for t seconds of time. The quanitity of electricity ($I \times t$) is proportional to the weight of chemical consumed: one Faraday, or 26.8 ampere-hours per gram-equivalent weight. Fuel cells differ from batteries in two major ways:

(1) Structural details of the fuel cell must permit continuous movements of fuel, oxidant, and reaction product into and out of cells. This is an important difference that has impeded the development of fuel cells compared with battery development.

(2) Fuels and oxidants for fuel cells often require a catalyst or high temperature to speed the electrochemical reactions. This too is an important difference, as chemicals in convential batteries are consumed rapidly even at ambient temperatures without a catalyst.

Specific operating details are given for various kinds of fuel cells described below.

Advantages for Fuel Cells

Popular articles on fuel cells list such advantages as: high efficiency, no moving parts, low maintenance, noiseless operation, absence of noxious fumes, large power output per unit weight or volume, low cost, use of waste products, portability, versatility, and convenience. Unfortunately, no fuel cell should be expected to combine all these proposed advantages.

High efficiency is one of the most commonly cited virtues. A Russian writer, for example, has noted that fuel cells might be twice as efficient as a steam-generator plant for the production of electricity. Since his country is not overabundant in fossil fuels, he reasoned that a successful fuel cell would double, in effect, his country's supply of natural fuel.

The present era of fuel cell technology is based on modern power demands and on needs for special-purpose power supplies rather than on efficiency alone. This divides advantages of fuel cells between convenience or performance and low energy cost, or between need and cost. Convenience overrides low cost of energy for specialty cells having military and space applications. This situation reverts to the historical demand for low-cost energy in the case of central-station d-c power for the electrochemical industry. Both low cost and convenience are important for industrial applications, such as lift trucks and electric locomotives.

History

A device which may be called the first oxygen-hydrogen cell was constructed in 1839 by Grove. He was able to draw current from the setup involving two platinum electrodes, one saturated with hydrogen and the other with oxygen. In 1854 he proposed the idea of a fuel cell as an electrochemical device for direct conversion of the heat of combustion of coal and fat into electrical energy.

In 1855 Becquerel obtained current from a cell made from a carbon and a platinum electrode immersed in fused nitrate. Jablochkoff used a similar cell in 1877 but employed cast iron instead of platinum. These cells placed carbon in direct contact with an oxidizing agent resulting in a nitrite-nitrate concentration cell with very low power output.

An improvement of the Becquerel-Jablochkoff cell was made in 1897 by Jacques. He designed a cell in an iron pot containing fused caustic soda (positive) into which a carbon rod (negative) was inserted. Air was bubbled through the fused bath during production of current. Jacques claimed a current of 150 amperes at 1 volt. A test by Stone & Webster reported that the cell operated with 82 per cent of the theoretical efficiency. This cell received considerable attention as a potential device to furnish current in homes. Haber and Brunner, however, declared that it was not a proper carbon/oxygen cell because the electromotive element at the carbon pole is really hydrogen produced indirectly between carbon and sodium hydroxide. Further, sodium hydroxide was transformed to carbonate during production of the hydrogen and the hydroxide had to be regenerated or replaced.

The term fuel electrode (Brennstoffetement) probably can be credited to Borchers who devised a carbon-oxygen fuel cell in 1894, patented in 1896.

Mond and Langer, around 1889, designed a hydrogen-oxygen cell possessing many features still being considered today. The electrodes consisted of thin platinum sheets perforated with some 1,500 small holes per square centimeter. The sheets were coated with platinum black. The electrolyte was dilute sulfuric acid absorbed in a porous diaphragm against which the electrodes were clamped. Currents of 2 to 2.5 amperes at 0.73 volt could be obtained from a cell with an active surface of 700 square centimeters, containing 0.35 gram of platinum foil and 1.0 gram of platinum black.

Taitelbaum, in 1910, used a porous diaphragm to divide his cell into two compartments. Manganese dioxide was added to the positive side. Carbon and iron electrodes were immersed in molten sodium hydroxide at 370 to 390°C. The cell yielded a current of 0.020 ampere at 0.53 volt. The addition of sawdust as a depolarizer resulted in 0.100 ampere at 0.50 volt.

Beutner, in 1911, employed platinum tubes as electrodes. The tubes contained hydrogen and oxygen separately and were closed at the ends with thin palladium foil. Diffusion of the gases through the palladium into the fused potassium fluoride and sodium chloride proved too slow.

Baur and Ehrenberg, in 1912, designed a direct fuel cell using fused borax as an electrolyte, a carbon rod as anode, and silver saturated with air as the cathode. The cells gave 0.95 volt on open circuit.

In 1913, Siegl improved the Mond-Langer cell by depositing platinum black on small grains of carbon 3 mm in diameter instead of supporting the platinum black on thin sheets of platinum. This cell gave an emf of 0.90 volt.

The use of fused carbonates as electrolytes is shown in descriptions of an early cell by Bauer, Treadwell, and Trumpler and another cell by Von Rhorer, both in the early 1920's. Bauer's cell consisted of a carbon anode and a magnetite-ferric oxide cathode separated by a magnesium oxide diaphragm, immersed in a melt of sodium and potassium carbonates. Estimated capacity was 470 watts per cubic meter at 800 to 900°C. Von Rhorer's cell operated at 900°C. The electrolyte consisted of sodium and potassium carbonates with additions of barium carbonate, magnesium oxide, and aluminum oxide. Carbon anodes were used along with cathodes of platinum, silver, copper, or iron. The open-circuit voltage was around 1.2 volts.

The recent history of fuel cells commences with the invention of highly efficient hydrogen-oxygen cells. Inventions by Bacon, Kordesch, Grubb, and Justi, for example, have brought about a renewed and vigorous interest in all fuel cell concepts.

Biochemical fuel cells have a separate history. Although the electrochemical behavior of biochemical systems has been a subject of continual research interest, the idea of deriving electrical power from such systems had been suggested by only a few authors between 1911 and 1931. In the last few years directed research has begun in this area and appears to be promising.

References for further reading and cross-references appear at the end of the following article.

JOHN McCALLUM and
LESLIE D. McGRAW

FUEL CELLS—CLASSIFICATION

All known fuel cells use solid electrodes as electronic conductors. The fuel can be gaseous, liquid, or solid. Only liquid or solid electrolytes are known. Gaseous or liquid oxidants may also be used. If fuel cells are classified according to phases at the fuel electrode, there are only four kinds of fuel cell. They are:

Electrode	Fuel	Electrolyte	Examples
Solid	Gas	Liquid	Pt, H_2, KOH solutions
Solid	Liquid	Liquid	Fe, Na in Hg, NaOH solutions
Solid	Solid	Liquid	Zn, Zn, KOH solutions
Solid	Gas	Solid	Pt, H_2, CaO in ZrO_2

Literally hundreds of materials and chemicals have been used in fuel cells. "How the cells work" has led to many names to describe various kinds of fuel cells.

Gas-diffusion fuel cells require diffusion of gases through a liquid electrolyte. Porous electrodes are used to provide a large number of contact areas between gaseous fuel, liquid electrolyte, and solid electrode. Gas is fed into one side of an electrode while liquid is retained in the other side by capillary forces within the pores. The products are sometimes removed by diffusion out of the cell into an excess of one of the gas streams. Sometimes products are moved by circulation and treatment of the electrolyte.

Gas pressures have to be adjusted so that liquid electrolyte does not *flood* the pores and gas does not *blow through*. To assist in this pressure regulation, the porous electrodes are made in special ways. A *two-layer electrode* is often used with a layer having small pores on the electrolyte side backed up with a layer having larger pores on the gas side. Gas pressure can then be regulated to maintain gas in the large pores and liquid in the small pores. A *graded-porosity electrode* is made sometimes from compacted powder so that the pore sizes

become progressively smaller across the electrode. Large pores are placed towards the gas phase, and liquid is held by capillarity within the smaller pores. A double-skeleton electrode is also used in which a supporting electrode having large pores is partially filled with finely divided material such as Raney nickel. Such a structure is sometimes called a *DSK* electrode because the inventor, Justi, used that abbreviation.

Electrolyte is sometimes kept from *flooding* the pores by placing a retaining material between the electrodes. This *electrolyte retainer* has pores smaller than those in the electrodes. Capillarity then retains the liquid in the smaller pores. Asbestos fibers or papers are used as electrolyte retainers for low-temperature fuel cells. Porous magnesia disks are used as electrolyte retainers for molten carbonates in fuel cells at high temperatures, or a *pasty electrolyte* will serve the same purpose. All these *quasi-solid electrolytes* contain liquid electrolyte which wets the electrodes and transports gaseous fuel and oxidant to the electrodes by diffusion.

Electrolyte penetration in pores is sometimes controlled by *wet-proofing* the porous electrodes. Thin coatings of paraffin, fluorocarbons, or other materials are spread through all pores so that capillary forces are largely eliminated. The process is also called *controlled wetting* because with complete wet-proofing the three phases lose contact with one another.

Gas-diffusion fuel cells require catalysts for activation of the incoming gases. The most common catalysts are platinum at the fuel electrode and silver at the oxidant electrode. The entire electrode may be constructed with these precious metals, in which case they are electronic conductors and supporting structure as well as catalyst. More often electrodes are porous carbon, porous nickel, or porous alloys on which thin coatings of catalyst are placed. Gas molecules are adsorbed on the catalytic surface, thereby speeding the electrochemical reactions. Nickel, palladium, cobalt, iridium, and a few other metals and alloys have also been reported as useful catalysts.

The most successful fuel cells to date use hydrogen and oxygen with KOH electrolyte. Platinum or palladium are used as catalysts for hydrogen and silver is the most common catalyst for oxygen. Current densities of 10 to 100 ma/sq cm are quite easily attained at room temperature. By pressurizing the cells and operating them at higher temperatures, current densities in excess of 1000 ma/sq cm can be achieved. Water is produced at the hydrogen electrode through the reaction

$$H_2 + 2OH^- \rightarrow 2H_2O + 2\epsilon \qquad (1)$$

The theoretical voltage for a hydrogen-oxygen cell is 1.23 volts at room temperature. However, the oxygen is not directly reduced to hydroxyl ions but first makes perhydroxyl ions:

$$O_2 + H_2O + 2\epsilon \rightarrow HO_2^- + OH^- \qquad (2)$$

the perhydroxyl ions are catalytically decomposed:

$$HO_2^- \rightarrow OH^- + \tfrac{1}{2}O_2 \qquad (3)$$

and the net cell reaction is the combination of Eqs. (1), (2), and (3):

$$H_2 + \tfrac{1}{2}O_2 \rightarrow H_2O \qquad (4)$$

However, because of the intermediate perhydroxyl at the oxygen electrode, the cell voltage is governed by perhydroxyl equilibria:

$$H_2 + O_2 + OH^- \rightarrow HO_2^- + H_2O \qquad (5)$$

Observed voltages are, therefore, always less than the 1.23 volts predicted for Eq. (4). Open-circuit voltages between 1.0 and 1.1 volts are commonly observed in accordance with Eq. (5).

Another gas diffusion cell of great interest uses molten carbonate electrolytes at 600 to 800°C. These *molten carbonate fuel cells* can use carbonaceous fuels because the electrolyte can reject carbon dioxide. Alkali metal carbonates, such as Na_2CO_3, can be used but, to lower the melting point, eutectic mixtures of carbonates are usually desired. At the anode, fuel and carbonate ions interact to release electrons. For example,

$$CO + CO_3^{--} \rightarrow 2CO_2 + 2\epsilon$$

Carbonate ions have to be reformed at the cathode. This requires addition of carbon dioxide to the incoming oxygen (or air):

$$\tfrac{1}{2}O_2 + CO_2 + 2\epsilon \rightarrow CO_3^{--}$$

Molten-carbonate fuel cells are still in the laboratory stage of development. Their greatest promise seems to be for central stations, industrial processes, or home power requiring electricity where low-cost fuels are necessary. The cells require long periods of heating for start-up. Presently reported batteries of molten carbonate fuel cells are bulky. They require several cubic feet per kw. But more compact batteries down to

tenths of a cubic foot per kw seem to be possible. Their main problem is cell life, as the high temperature molten carbonate system corrodes electrodes and other cell parts. Laboratory cells last from 1 to 100 days. An assured life in excess of one year is required for practical application. Since reaction products, such as carbon dioxide and steam, evolve at relatively high temperature, these cells hold promise particularly where the waste heat can be used.

"Hydrox" fuel cells and **"Carbox" fuel cells** are copyrighted names applied to hydrogen-oxygen fuel cells and to cells using carbonaceous fuel gases with oxygen or air, respectively.

Solid electrolyte fuel cells are made by placing porous electrodes over the solid electrolyte. There is no wetting of the electrode. Electrochemical action occurs at the electrode-electrolyte contacts. Because these contact areas are a small percentage of the total electrode area, the cells have a contact resistance several times larger than the electrolyte resistance.

Early fuel cells used solid mixtures of alkali metal carbonates with rare earth oxides (monazite) and tungstic oxide. These electrolytes changed in composition and electrical properties as they were used.

Solid electrolytes of zirconium phosphates can be used with catalyzed surfaces and screen electrodes as current collectors at temperatures less than 100°C. Their behavior is similar to organic ion-exchange membranes and cells using them are sometimes called *inorganic ion-exchange fuel cells*.

Solid mixtures of CaO in ZrO_2 conduct at high temperatures (760°C) by movement of oxide ions. Fuels consume the oxide ions to release electrons while oxygen reacts at the other side to make oxide ions by receiving electrons. The net effect is that of an *oxygen concentration cell* across the solid electrolyte.

Ion-exchange-membrane fuel cells use organic ion-exchange membranes (q.v.) as electrolytes. Finely divided platinum, palladium, silver, or other catalyst is spread as electrodes over the membrane. Gases are fed to each side of the membrane and water is formed on one of the electrodes. Electroosmosis (q.v.) tends to cause drying out of the membranes on the opposite side. This creates what is called the water balance problem. Two membranes with electrolyte between them lessens the water balance problem which normally requires elaborate engineering design. The electrode reactions are similar to those for gas-diffusion electrodes.

Ion-exchange membranes are sometimes called *quasi-solid electrolytes* because they seem to be solids but operate as though they were liquids. That is, the membranes must be thoroughly wetted including wetted contacts with the catalyzed electrodes. The gases must diffuse through these wetted contacts making the cell, in reality, a gas-diffusion fuel cell. Ionic conductor sites are held within the organic structure so that flooding, when it occurs, is with water. Other gas diffusion types of cells, if they flood, do so with electrolyte rather than water.

Both cationic and anionic membranes (q.v.) can be used. The membranes are generally 5 to 50 thousandths of an inch thick, permitting thin cells. Batteries have been made that give a few kw per cubic foot. Ion-exchange-membrane batteries are in an advanced stage of development. They have been used in space vehicles and as portable power sources for military application.

An ion-exchange-membrane cell is also the easiest to make for demonstration purposes. The membranes are available from several manufacturers and numerous detailed descriptions for cell construction are available for students or amateur scientists who want first-hand experience with the construction and operation of a model fuel cell.

Regenerative fuel cells is the name applied to a closed system having a fuel cell plus an external energy source. The external energy is used with an external reactor to put the fuel and oxidant back into their original forms for reuse. The same "fuel" is used over and over with none being added to, or taken from, the system.

The **lithium hydride fuel cell** is a lithium-hydrogen fuel cell. Its molten electrolyte, containing lithium hydride, is circulated; external heat dissociates the hydride into lithium metal and hydrogen gas outside the cell. Lithium becomes the fuel that is returned to the anode and oxidized to Li^+, and hydrogen becomes the oxidant that is returned to the cathode and reduced to H^-. The molten lithium flows over a steel anode while the hydrogen is used at a gas diffusion type of cathode. This is a *thermal regenerative fuel cell*. Other examples of this type of cell are based on thermal decomposition of inorganic materials, such as PCl_5 to PCl_3 plus Cl_2 or $SnCl_4$ to $SnCl_2$ plus Cl_2. Light-sensitive materials susceptible to oxidation or reduction

by sunlight lead to *solar regenerative fuel cells*. Radioactive energy is used also as part of suggested regenerative fuel cell systems. Either the heat would be used for thermal regenerations, or charged particles emitted from the radioactive source would be used to reduce or oxidize fuel cell products for recycle.

Sometimes regenerative fuel cells are referred to as *energy-converter systems* because they convert one kind of energy into electrical energy.

Redox fuel cells use an intermediate fuel that is oxidized in the fuel cell and chemically reduced externally by the primary fuel. An early, and still attractive, fuel cell concept is to use CO as fuel at about 800°C. The CO_2 formed in the fuel cell by electrochemical oxidation is recycled over a fossil fuel, such as coal, at about 700°C. The coal reduces the CO_2 to CO which is then fed back to the fuel cell to complete the cycle. Such a fuel cell conceivably can provide 100 per cent thermal efficiency for converting coal to electricity even though the fuel cell possesses electrochemical inefficiencies.

Polyvalent ions, such as Fe^{++}-Fe^{+++} or Ce^{+++}-CeO^{++}, have been used in redox fuel cells. The ions are reduced externally by a primary fuel and are oxidized in the fuel cell. The cathode can also use polyvalent ions that are oxidized externally by air or oxygen. Bromine is sometimes used as an oxidant, and the bromide ions are subsequently reoxidized by air to reform the bromine which is cycled.

Redox fuel cells generally require circulation of electrolyte through the external reactor. However, the intermediate fuel may be contained between the electrodes. Then a separator is placed in the electrolyte to prevent mixing of intermediate fuel and oxidant. A high concentration of the oxidized form is maintained around the cathode, and a high concentration of reduced form is maintained around the anode.

Redox fuel cells are distinct from regenerative fuel cells. Redox fuel cells use chemical reactions between external chemicals and fuel cell products for regeneration; regenerative fuel cells use the energy of some external source to put the cell products into their original form.

Consumable-electrode fuel cells use an active metal anode, such as zinc or magnesium. Usually the cell is designed for batch operation with intermittent replacement of electrodes and electrolyte. However, rods of fuel can be inserted continuously; or powdered or pelletized fuel can be added continuously to porous inert tubes. Spent electrolyte can also be replaced continuously. When the cells are designed for batch operation, many technologists prefer to call them batteries or primary cells rather than fuel cells.

Zinc-oxygen fuel cells with KOH electrolyte have been used to power small racing cars. They can deliver energy at a high power density (several kw per cu ft) but are relatively expensive because the zinc is costly compared with gasoline.

Early consummable electrode fuel cells visualized carbon rods as electrodes.

Liquid metal fuel cells use highly reactive metals, such as sodium or potassium, dissolved in another metal, such as mercury, tin, or lead.

The **amalgam fuel cell** uses mercury as the metal solvent. Dissolved sodium or potassium is the fuel. Aqueous alkaline solution is the electrolyte. The amalgam can provide up to several hundred amps per sq ft with little polarization. In one fuel cell scheme, elemental sodium is added to mercury. The amalgam flows over a steel electrode and the sodium is oxidized by electrochemical reactions. The steel anode is coupled with a gas-diffusion oxygen cathode to form sodium hydroxide solution as the fuel cell product. The mercury is recycled for continuous addition of sodium and spent electrolyte is continuously replaced. In another scheme, the alkali metal is added continuously to anode mercury and is removed by deposition of metal into pure mercury at the cathode. The result is a *metal concentration fuel cell* whose potential is governed by the different concentrations of alkali metal in the mercury at the two cell electrodes.

Dissolved-fuel fuel cells provide fuel to the cell as a solution in the electrolyte. This dissolved fuel diffuses to the electrode surface, or is circulated through electrode pores or over an electrode surface. Alcohols dissolved in alkaline or acid solutions have been used this way. A simple demonstration fuel cell is made by using platinum and silver electrodes (platinum and silver coatings on nickel will suffice) immersed in caustic solution. Alcohol and hydrogen peroxide solution is added to the electrolyte. Oxidation of the alcohol is catalyzed by the platinum but not by the silver electrode. The peroxide is reduced more readily at the silver electrode. The net result is that a potential of several tenths of a volt develops between the electrodes. An alternative to specific catalysts,

which do not permit oxidation of fuel at the cathode, is the use of a mechanical separator between anolyte and catholyte. Hydrazine dissolved in caustic has been used as a dissolved fuel.

Biochemical fuel cells use biological materials, such as bacteria, enzymes, plants, algae, etc., in a fuel cell system. Various names have been coined for such cells: *Biological Fuel Cells, Bio-Fuel Cells, Biobatteries,* and *Biosolar Cells* are some of the more common names. All such cells use some aspect of a biological system to help derive electricity from low cost or abundant fuels.

In one scheme, the living organism breaks down a complex organic compound into molecules that exhibit electrochemical activity. Hydrogen sulfide from sulfur-containing organic compounds, or from dissolved inorganic sulfates is an example.

Some organisms consume complex organic materials and evolve oxygen which is then used at the fuel cell cathode. Some bacteria create enzymes which then act as catalysts at the electrode to permit electrochemical oxidation of organics. Best performance is usually attained when the living organisms are on the electrodes.

Electrochemists find biochemical fuel cells intriguing for several reasons: they can use cheap fuels, such as cellulose, or even sewage; there are many combinations of biological systems, each with unique properties; they suggest new uses for vast forces of nature that heretofore have never been utilized. The entire Black Sea, for example, has been suggested as a gigantic oceanic fuel cell. Desulfovibrio bacteria towards the bottom of the sea create large amounts of hydrogen sulfide as they obtain their oxygen from sulfates in the water. At the sea surface, algae, combined with photosynthesis, create large amounts of oxygen in the sea water. Electrodes at the top and bottom of the sea therefore, might permit electrochemical reactions of hydrogen sulfide at the bottom with oxygen at the surface. Feasibility of the scheme has been demonstrated, but only in test tubes.

References

1. "Fuel Cells," Edited by G. J. Young, New York, Reinhold Publishing Corp., 1960.
2. "Fuel Cells: Power for the Future," Research Associates, Harvard University, (October 1960).
3. YEAGER, ERNEST, "Fuel Cells," *Science,* **134,** 1178–1186 (October 20, 1961).

4. LIEBHAFSKY, HERMAN A., "Fuel Cells," *International Science and Technology*, **1**, 54–62 (January 1962).
5. AUSTIN, LEONARD G., "Fuel Cells," *Sci. American*, **201**, 72–78 (September 1959).
6. EISENBERG, M., "Electrochemical Auxiliary Power Sources for Missiles and Space Flight," *Elec. Eng.*, **79**, (1), 58–63 (January 1960).
7. "Target: More Versatile Fuel Cells," *Chemical Week*, 43–46 (May 27, 1961).
8. CAIRNS, ELTON J., "Build Your Own Working Model. Ion-Exchange Fuel Cell," *Science and Mechanics*, 106–109 (December 1960).
9. McGRAW, L. D., "How a Fuel Cell Operates," *SAE Journal*, **68**, 74–79 (December 1960).

JOHN McCALLUM AND
LESLIE D. McGRAW

Cross-references: *Batteries; Biochemical Fuel Cells; Bioelectrochemistry; Membranes, Electrolytic; Nickel Electrodes for Fuel Cells and Batteries; Platinized Electrodes; Porous Carbon; Solar Energy Converter; Space Power.*

FUEL CELLS, BIOCHEMICAL. See BIOCHEMCAL FUEL CELLS.

FURNACES, CONSUMABLE ELECTRODE. See FURNACES, INERT ATMOSPHERE AND VACUUM ARC.

FURNACES, ELECTRIC SMELTING. See ELECTRIC SMELTING FURNACES.

FURNACES, ELECTRIC STEEL. See STEEL MAKING IN ELECTRIC ARC FURNACES.

FURNACES FOR HOT-PRESSING

Most hot-pressing operations are done in two general types of furnaces: resistance heated and high-frequency induction heated. Temperatures range from 1500 to 2650°C, while pressures may vary from 1000 to 10,000 psi. Practically all refractory materials can be hot-pressed in equipment capable of operating within the above limits. Notable exceptions, however, are synthetic diamond and cubic boron nitride which require very specialized techniques and equipment.

Graphite-tube Resistor Furnaces

One of the most practical furnaces of this type is the horizontal furnace described in U.S. Patent 2,125,588 (R. R. Ridgway). See Fig. 1. The graphite heater tube is 5.25 in. ID by 6.50 in. OD by 64 in. long equipped with water-cooled copper clamps at each end. The tube is thermally insulated on the outside by 8 in. of carbon black enclosed in a cast aluminum shell having a wall thickness of 0.75 in. The shell is split vertically and one half is insulated electrically from the other half. Flexible copper cables connect the clamps at each end of the furnace tube to the respective halves of the furnace shell. An interlaced bus system connects the furnace shell to a low-voltage induction regulator of 15,000 amp capacity having a continuously variable secondary voltage from 0 to 30 volts.

The interlaced bus system and the furnace connections give noninductive conditions which result in a power factor of 98 per cent for 25-cycle operation, and 91 per cent for 60-cycle use. A power input of 100 kw at 15 volts is sufficient to bring the furnace to a temperature of 2000°C in approximately 35 minutes. The efficiency of the insulation is such that a temperature of 2200°C can be maintained at a power input of 8 kw and 5 volts.

The graphite dies used for hot-pressing are 5.125 in. OD and up to 18 in. long. They may have single or multiple cavities, depending on the size of the article to be fabricated and the strength of the graphite. The loaded die is placed in the central part of the furnace so uniform heating conditions will be maintained. Graphite furnace bars hold the die in place. One of the bars is held stationary by a positioning screw, while the other bar contacts the plunger on a pneumatic ram. The ram is double-acting and is controlled by a directional valve as well as a pressure reducing valve which is supplied with 100 psi air.

The movement of the ram forces the furnace bars to push the projecting plungers into the die. The movement of the furnace bars indicates the contraction of the powder being hot-pressed. Pressure is increased in conjunction with temperature until the required hot-pressing conditions have been met. The temperature is observed with an optical pyrometer sighted through a graphite tube extending through the shell, insulation and resistance tube and focused on the central part of the graphite die. See Fig. 2.

This type of furnace is applicable to the hot-pressing of articles up to 4 in. in diameter, the length being limited in this case due to the relatively thin walls of the die. Smaller diameter

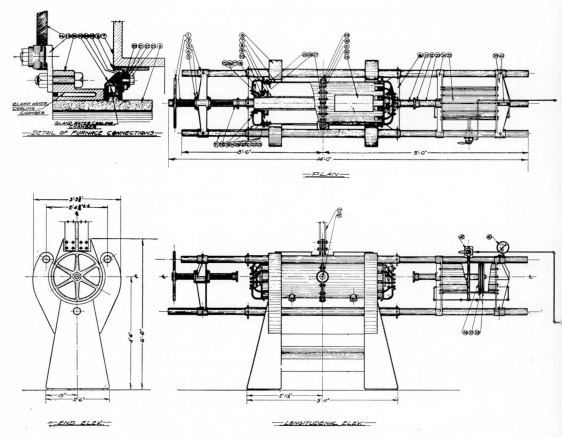

Fig. 1. Ridgway graphite-tube resistor furnace.

articles may be hot-pressed in multiple or tandem according to the strength of the graphite used in the die. Bursting (tensile) stresses of the graphite govern die design.

High-Frequency Induction Furnaces

Furnaces of this type can be designed to fabricate a wide range of sizes, ranging from articles of 1 in. diameter and smaller to large pieces of 15 in. diameter and perhaps larger. The small-scale work requires a power supply of about 15 kva at 30,000 cycles. Large-scale work will require 300 kva at 1000 cycles. Coils and tuning condensers are usually custom-designed to cover the required scale of operations.

This type of furnace is operated most efficiently in a vertical position, because the installation of a coil in the clear opening of a hydraulic press is easily done, and because more efficient thermal insulation can be maintained

in vertical use. Concentricity of the coil, susceptor, and die can be kept to close tolerance in this position. See Fig. 3.

The furnace consists of a water-cooled helical coil of copper tubing, of the required diameter and height, equipped with suitable connections to the high-frequency power source. A layer of sheet mica or asbestos paper is placed inside the coil to hold the granular insulation in place. The coil is placed on zirconia bricks resting on the platen of a suitable hydraulic press. Provision must be made for the lower ram of the press to engage the lower die plunger if "double-end" hot-pressing is planned.

A graphite tube, having a slightly larger bore than the OD of the hot-pressing mold, is centered within the coil. This tube usually has sufficient wall thickness to allow from 1 to 3 in. of granular insulation to be placed between it and the coil. The granular insulation may be

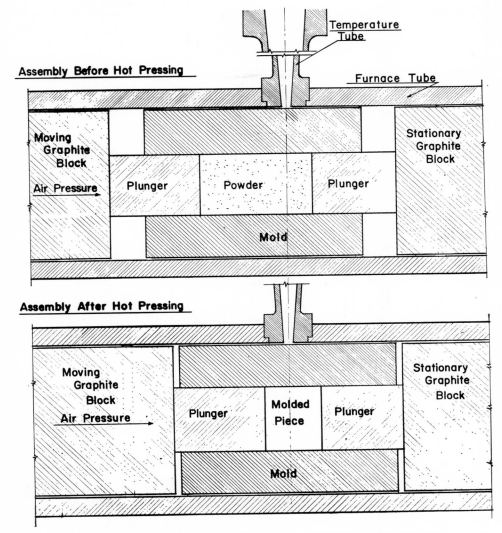

FIG. 2. Hot-pressing die assembly for use in graphite-tube resistor furnace.

carbon black, but a preferred material is a bubble-type of fused stabilized zirconia. It is an excellent thermal insulator at high temperatures and is also nonoxidizing as well as clean to handle.

The loaded graphite die is centrally located in the furnace tube with the bottom plunger contacting a graphite cylinder of suitable length. This cylinder is thermally insulated from the lower ram or platen with zirconia bricks. A similar graphite cylinder engages the top plunger and is thermally insulated from the ram with zirconia bricks.

Power is applied at a high rate similarly to the resistance furnace procedure, but it must be cut back well in advance of the desired temperature, as it is quite easy to exceed the temperature limit. The temperature is measured by an optical pyrometer sighted onto the die wall through a thin-walled graphite tube. This tube extends from the space between turns of the coil through sheet insulation, granular insulation, and furnace tube into the central portion.

Pressure is applied gradually while the temperature is rising, until the required hot-pressing conditions are obtained. Plunger movement in

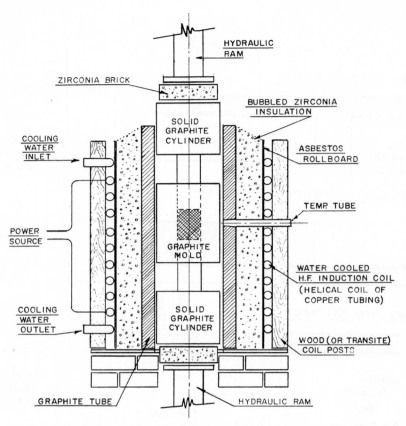

FIG. 3. Vertical, graphite-tube, high-frequency, induction hot-pressing furnace.

the die is indicated by a scale pointer connected to each ram. Full contraction can be obtained on small sections (¼ in. dia. by ½ in. long) in about 10 minutes after the power is turned on. This is much faster than resistance furnace practice. Large sections (12 in. OD by 12 in. long) require several hours for hot-pressing, e.g., a power input of 200 kw will give 2200°C on a 30 in. dia. coil set-up within 2.5 hours. Total time for a run of this nature is approximately 8 hours, and approximately 90 kw is required to hold the temperature constant at 2200°C.

Practically all refractory carbides, borides, nitrides, silicides, oxides, etc. can be hot-pressed in these furnaces. Many different shapes may be produced, providing the length to diameter ratio does not become too large. Re-entrant angles cannot be molded properly as a general rule.

A limitation of the resistance furnace is the constant temperature zone in the central portion. This seldom exceeds a length of 12 in. The "hot-zone" or constant temperature section within a high-frequency induction coil extends approximately ¾ of the coil length if the assembly is efficiently insulated.

References

1. CAMPBELL, I. E., "High Temperature Technology," pp. 271–277, New York, John Wiley & Sons, Inc., 1956.
2. RIDGWAY, R. R., AND BAILEY, B. L., U.S. Patent 2,150,884 (Mar. 14, 1939).
3. KNOWLTON, J. W., AND FETTERLEY, G. H., U.S. Patent 2,522,046 (Sept. 12, 1950).
4. WATSON, G. R., U.S. Patent 2,535,180 (Dec. 26, 1950).

D. T. LAPP

FURNACES, INERT ATMOSPHERE AND VACUUM ARC

Robert Hare, M.D., circa 1839, may be regarded as the originator of the idea for the "cold" crucible or mold arc furnaces. A furnace of this type developed by von Bolten represents the first such furnace to be used for the production of ductile vacuum-melted metal. Later O. H. Simpson developed the "cold" crucible furnace for vacuum melting tantalum for use as lamp filaments, dental and surgical instruments.[1] The Hopkins or "electric ingot" process first used commercially about 1937, although employing a slag cover instead of an inert gas cover or vacuum, finds continued and expanding use today in the production of high-quality steels.[2] The impetus to present day applications was largely provided by Kroll, Beall, Wood and coworkers at the Bureau of Mines Station, Albany, Oregon, who established the basic melting practices and furnace designs used today for melting titanium, zirconium, and other reactive materials.[3]

The "cold" crucible arc furnace process may now be regarded as one of the standard methods of melting materials when high purity and superior ingot quality are paramount. The relatively small furnaces used to melt titanium and zirconium in 1952 have rapidly grown in size and range of applications to the extent that in 1962 vacuum-melted steel ingots 60 inches in diameter and weighing 50 tons or more have been produced with a single consumable electrode.

Comparison between vacuum arc melting and vacuum induction melting plants reveals that the former possesses a net advantage for the production of iron- or nickel-base alloys. There is no limit to the weight of the ingot and the melting costs are substantially lower than in induction melting.[4]

Process Description

Inert or vacuum "cold" crucible furnaces utilize water-cooled copper crucibles to contain the liquid metal and the arc. In essence the melt is contained within a thin frozen envelope of the material being melted supported by the water-cooled copper crucible. This latter feature, combined with the release of heat from the arc at the top central region of the molten pool, allows material to be melted without contamination from the crucible. Impurities that might otherwise be introduced from the atmosphere are excluded by conducting the melting under inert gases and high vacuum. High-vacuum melting permits further purification by removal of gases from the electrode and melt. The introduction of carbon to the melt may further reduce impurities in some metals (e.g., tantalum) by combining with the oxygen to form carbon monoxide which is pumped out of the furnace.

Two main processes are in general use.

Consumable Electrode Process

Vacuum arcs are normally used for melting with consumable electrodes to obtain the benefits of vacuum melting, namely, degassing of the melt and removal of volatile impurities. The theory of vacuum melting and its application to "cold" crucible melting practice is thoroughly reviewed by Winkler.[4]

This process utilizes consumable electrodes fabricated either by welding together pressed compacts of powder or granular metal or by melting and casting the material to be melted into electrodes for subsequent remelting. The fabricated or cast electrodes are generally fastened to a water-cooled feed rod. Electrodes may be fed into the furnace by means of feed rolls, or a combination of feed rolls and a welding process for continuous joining.[5] These are melted into primary or first-melt ingots which may be joined together, either in a specially constructed inert atmosphere welding box or within the furnace itself by fusion welding of the ends of the two ingots. Titanium and zirconium sponge and metals and alloys prepared from compacted powder and granular particles are normally remelted to give secondary ingots for processing into fabricated forms. Double melting enhances the purity and homogeneity of the final ingot. A typical vacuum arc furnace with consumable electrode feed is shown in Fig. 1.

A skull casting furnace employing both consumable and nonconsumable electrodes in which the molten pool is subsequently cast into shapes by tilting the crucible is shown in Fig. 2. A comprehensive review of vacuum arc melting furnaces is given by Gruber.[5]

The phenomena which occur under optimum vacuum conditions during the melting of a titanium sponge electrode have been depicted in

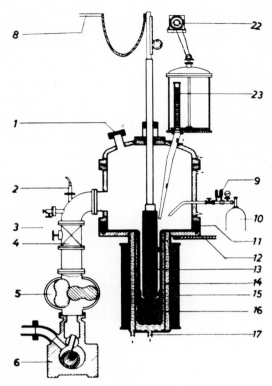

the diagram in Fig. 3 taken from a review by Winkler.⁴

The energy input to the cathode consists of the energy imparted by the impact of positive ions; by radiation, conduction, and convection from the anode, surrounding surfaces, gases, and plasma; and the I^2R losses in the electrode itself.

Fine drops of metal spray off the face of the cathode tip into the anodic pool of molten metal. The anodic pool receives heat from impinging electrons by radiation, conduction, and convection from the arc plasma, cathode, surrounding gases and plasma, and the superheated cathode material striking the bath.⁴, ⁷

Most of the heat received at the anode is transmitted to the coolant through the narrow zone around the upper edge of the pool in inti-

mate contact with the mold wall. Below this, heat is lost by radiation across a gap formed as a result of shrinkage of the ingot. At high melting rates the pool may extend deeply below the surface of the pool and occupy as much as 50 per cent of the total ingot volume.⁹

Gas is evolved mainly at the face of the cathode, the surface of the anodic bath, and to a lesser degree from the surface of the droplets of metal falling into the melt. Slag inclusions in steel primary and secondary electrodes cannot be fully decomposed or reduced during the short residence time between the cathode and anode. Inclusions in steels accumulate as slag on the surface of the bath and possible harmful affects from the remaining slag are reduced by dispersion in the metal as very fine particles. Ingot

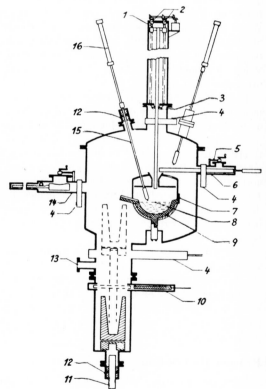

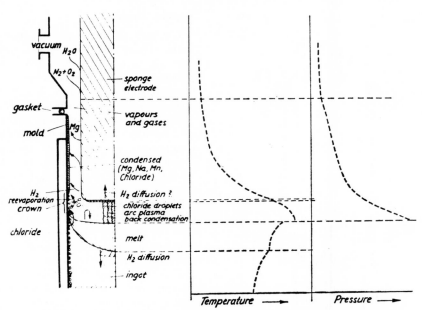

FIG. 3. Schematic diagram of the arc zone in vacuum melting with a consumable electrode. (Kroll[8] and Rossin[7])

quality is high due largely to purification and freedom from segregation. Grain size may be reduced by magnetic stirring coils, ultrasonic vibration, and other means.

Work by Butler and Morgan indicates that by using an open arc technique a purity level in niobium, tantalum, and tungsten equivalent to that obtained by standard electron beam processing can be achieved.[10, 11]

Nonconsumable Electrode Process

The nonconsumable or permanent electrode process has been largely replaced by the consumable electrode process in large melting plants. Nevertheless, it still has widespread application in research laboratories for preparing small melts of materials. It is also used for melting materials not amenable to fabrication into electrodes or which are nonconducting at low temperatures. The design of a typical small laboratory furnace is shown in Fig. 4. The batch of material to be melted may be introduced through the top before securing the cover. Another port (not shown) may be used to feed material while melting is progressing.

The nonconsumable electrode arc furnace is similar to the consumable electrode process in design and operation in most respects. The electrode consists of a water-cooled copper electrode with a short length of high-melting point con-

ductive material fastened to the tip. Thoriated tungsten is the most suitable material for electrode tips, but graphite and graphite coated with a refractory carbide are also suitable depending on the nature of the material being melted and the degree of carbon contamination that can be tolerated.

Material is introduced into the furnace either in powder or granular form from a feeding device which allows the feed material to fall into the crucible close to the crucible wall at a controlled rate. The arc is usually moved over the surface of the molten bath by rotational movement of an offset electrode tip thereby insuring complete fusion of the charge materials. In small research furnaces, complete fusion and homogeneity are achieved by moving the arc about with a magnet and by repeated remeltings of the button, either turning the melt over or cutting it up into smaller pieces for remelting. Usual practice is to operate at a pressure of 100–200 mm Hg of inert gas.[4] The heat losses in the electrode, side walls, and bottom of the mold have been reported to be approximately 10, 86 and 4 per cent of the electrical power input, respectively. Approximately 40 to 50 per cent of the energy dissipated in the mold is conducted through the ingot to the mold wall while the remainder enters the mold walls by radiation, convection, and gas conduction.[13]

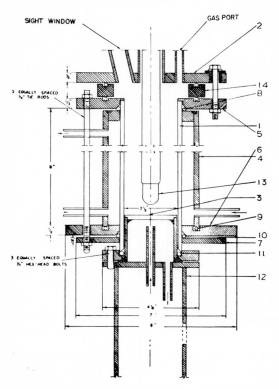

FIG. 4. Small laboratory nonconsumable inert atmosphere arc furnace. (Kuhn[10]) (*Courtesy Electrochemical Society, Inc.*) 1. water-jacketed copper crucible 2. cover 3. water-cooled bottom plate 4. 4-inch diameter steel pipe 5. upper flange 6. lower flange or base plate 7. pressure ring 8. O-ring 9. O-ring 10. O-ring 11. O-ring 12. 3½-inch steel pipe support 13. tungsten tip 14. fiber insulation.

This process is unsuitable for melting material that, because of moisture or highly volatile substances, spatters onto the electrode and drips back into the melt carrying sufficient dissolved electrode material to contaminate the melt.

Design and Operation of Vacuum Arc Furnaces

In the design of any melting plant two main considerations are involved: the engineering of the system for safe, efficient, convenient, and reliable operation, and the positional behavior of the arc as influenced by environment, electrode materials, and crucible geometry. System design is dependent on the specific requirements of the application. Positional behavior of the arc determines the safety, reliability, and efficiency of operation and the ingot quality.

System Design

The basic system employing consumable electrodes consists of (1) a "cold" crucible melting unit, (2) a power supply, (3) equipment for preparing consumable electrodes, and (4) materials handling equipment. A large vacuum arc furnace installation is shown in Fig. 5.

The "cold" crucible vacuum melting unit consists essentially of a vacuum chamber to which is connected a high-vacuum pumping system, a "cold" mold crucible, and the electrode with its support and electrode feed mechanism and control.

The crucible is generally made of thick-walled copper (between 10 and 50 mm depending on size) to dissipate the heat at hot spots and thereby minimize burn-through. The interior mold walls should have a fine finish to facilitate removal of the ingot. Detachable mold bottoms and replaceable molds are commonly employed with cooling jackets designed to accommodate two or more mold sizes. The consumable electrode is generally attached to a water-cooled feed rod or "stinger" which slides freely through vacuum-tight seals at the top of the furnace. Water-cooled cables are attached to the top of the electrode. Direct current power is commonly supplied via germanium or silicon rectifiers.

Data on power requirements for several metals is given in Table 1 taken from a paper by Ham and Sibley.[15]

Rectifier power supplies and control systems have been reviewed by Borrebach.[16] Arc-voltage regulator types of arc length control have been discussed by Gruber and found to be inadequate for arc melting in vacuum.[4] Precise automatic regulation of arc length with a short-circuit frequency type of arc length control is described by Johnson.[17] Stability is promoted by incorporating reactance or using high open-circuit rectifiers. The polarity of the molten pool for high-melting point metals is normally anodic but may be cathodic with some low-melting point metals and under special circumstances.

Positional Arc Behavior

Efficient and safe operation of the "cold" crucible arc furnace depends greatly on the positional stability of the arc. Inherent in "cold" crucible melting is the danger that the arc will penetrate the wall, causing molten metal to contact water from the water jacket. Under such circumstances the arc may simply extinguish

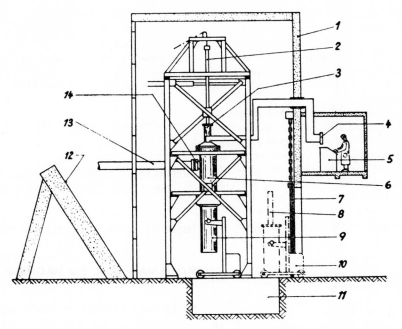

FIG. 5. Large vacuum arc furnace with protective wall for the operators and an optical viewing system. (Gruber[5]) (*Courtesy of the Institute of Metals*) 1. concrete wall 2. feeder rod. 3. dynamic vacuum seal 4. teleoptic screen 5. control desk 6. furnace chamber 7. steel safety door 8. consumable electrode 9. water-cooled mold 10. charging trolley 11. furnace pit for charging electrode 12. deflection wall 13. duct for released gases 14. pressure-release valve.

and contaminate the ingot or with reactive metals may occasionally result in a serious explosion. Engineering approaches to overcome this problem include the use of a coolant other than water, such as liquid sodium and gases. It is important that the arc remain anchored to the bottom of the electrode, or more specifically that the cathode spot remain at the bottom of the electrode and the anode spot on the surface of the pool. Above 30 mm Hg the anode becomes positionally unstable, and, combined with the positional instability of the cathode, the arc can easily wander away from the pool well up the side of the electrode and crucible wall. This gives rise to the "glow discharge" arc, which does not melt the electrode but heats the crucible wall.[18]

At pressures below about 0.4 mm Hg the anode remains positionally unstable, but the cathode becomes positionally stable at the electrode tip. This is the region of the "vacuum" arc characterized by uniform heating at both arc terminals and a much lower voltage gradient than for higher pressure arcs. At short arc lengths, the electrode consumption rate is quite high, and heat is concentrated at the melt sur-

TABLE 1. DATA REGARDING COLD-MOLD CONSUMABLE-ELECTRODE ARC MELTING[15]*

Metal	Electrode Cross-Section, in²	Mould Dia., in.	Amperes	Volts	Pressure, mm Hg	Kwh/lb
Ti	28	10	9000	30	30 A	0.50
Fe	3.1	5	850	45	760 A	0.32
Zr	3.9	9	4450 a-c	41	0.008	0.2
Mo	3.9	9	6000 a-c	65	0.025	0.43
Hf	5.0	4	2400	32	63 A-63 He	.42
W	0.2	1.5	1650 a-c	21	0.025	0.39
Ta	0.3	2	2000 a-c	36	0.025	0.80
U	4.9	4	2300	27	190 A-190 He	0.15
Zr-base	1.5	4	1200	35	0.1	0.22
Ni-base	1.2	4	1800	30	0.003	0.30
Co-base	1.1	4	1400	30	0.005	0.23
Ti-base	1.2	4	940	31	0.06	0.27

* d-c electrode negative except as noted.

face. At long arc lengths, the electrode is consumed relatively slowly and the anode heat is directed at the side walls. For this reason the short-circuit frequency type of arc length control is most effective. In the intermediate range between about 30 and 0.4 mm the positional instability is considered to be a consequence of both the anode and cathode terminals being positionally unstable.

The studies of Johnson and Wood should be consulted for additional details on this important subject.[17, 18, 19] With reverse polarity Johnson has shown that the cathode spots are on the pool surface and the crucible wall while the anode terminal remains anchored in the electrode tip. Electrode consumption may then occur at currents as low as 250 amperes, well below that possible with straight polarity (pool cathodic).

References

*1. KUHN, W. E., "Arcs In Inert Atmospheres and Vacuum," Ed., W. E. Kuhn, pp. 1–7, New York, John Wiley and Sons, Inc., 1956.
2. McKEEN, W. A., JOSEPH, L. G., AND SPEHAR, D. M., *Metal Progress*, **82**, No. 3, 86 (September, 1962).
3. ROBERSON, A. H., *J. Inst. Metals*, **86**, 1 (1957–1958).
*4. WINKLER, O., *Metallurgical Reviews (Institute of Metals, London)*, **5**, No. 17, 1–117 (1960).
5. GRUBER, H., "Arcs in Inert Atmospheres and Vacuum," pp. 118–148, New York, John Wiley and Sons, Inc., 1956.
*6. HAM, J. L., "Vacuum Metallurgy," edited by R. F. Bunshah, New York, Reinhold Publishing Corp., 1958.
7. ROSSIN, P. C., *ibid.*
8. KROLL, W. V., *Metall.*, **11**, 1 (1957).
9. BEALL, R. A., BORG, V. O., AND WOOD, F. W., *U. S. Bur. Mines Rep. Invest.* **No. 5144**, 1955.
10. BUTLER, T. E., AND MORGAN, R. P., *J. of Metals*, **14**, No. 3 (March, 1962).
11. BUTLER, T. E., AND MORGAN, R. P., *J. of Metals*, **14**, No. 6 (June, 1962).
12. KUHN, W. E., *J. Electrochem. Soc.*, **99**, 89–96 (March, 1952).
13. KUHN, W. E., *J. Electrochem. Soc.*, **99**, 97–108 (March, 1952).
14. GRUBER, H., AND SCHEIDIG, H., *Z. Metallkunde*, **47**, 149 (1956).
15. HAM, J. L., AND SIBLEY, C. B., *J. Metals*, **9**, 976 (1957).
16. BORREBACH, E. V., "Vacuum Metallurgy," edited by R. F. Bunshah, p. 121, New York, Reinhold Publishing Corp., 1958; also Ref. 5, p. 87.
17. JOHNSON, E. W., AND ITOH, R., "Positional Instability Behavior of Low Pressure D.C.

Arcs," paper presented at meeting of the Electrochemical Society, Inc., Ottawa, Canada, September 28–October 2, 1958 (to be published).

18. JOHNSON, E. W., AND ITOH, R., Ref. 5, p. 19.
19. WOOD, F. W., AND LOWERY, *U. S. Bureau of Mines Rep. Invest.* **No. 5749** (1961).

W. E. KUHN

Cross-references: *Electric Arc Properties; Electron Beam Melting; Vacuum Arc Properties.*

FURNACES, VACUUM ARC. See FURNACES, INERT ATMOSPHERE AND VACUUM ARC.

FUSED ALUMINA. See ALUMINA, FUSED.

FUSED MAGNESIA. See MAGNESIA, FUSED.

FUSED SALT CHRONOPOTENTIOMETRY

Chronopotentiometry is rapidly becoming a very useful electroanalytical technique; the theory and the applications of this technique are discussed elsewhere in this volume. Because of its versatility, chronopotentiometry is particularly suited to the study of fused salt systems. Measurements are fairly simple to obtain, and since large indicator electrodes can be used, electrode construction is simplified. In melts of a corrosive nature chronopotentiometry is probably the only useful technique. This application was first suggested by Delahay.[1] The first actual fused salt chronopotentiometric experiment was performed by Laitinen and Ferguson,[5] who showed that in the fused LiCl-KCl eutectic at 450°C cathodic chronopotentiometry could be used to analyze for bismuth (III), cadmium (II), silver (I), and copper (I). They also were able to analyze mixtures of bismuth (III) and silver (I) or bismuth (III) and copper (I). The accuracy of their method was ±3 per cent. The indicator electrodes used in this work were either platinum wire sealed in glass, flush-ground or projecting, or platinum foil; the reference electrode was a Pt(II)-Pt electrode and a large platinum counterelectrode completed the three electrode circuit. The reference and the counterelectrode were isolated in separated fritted glass compartments. They found that the basic equation of chronopotentiometry was obeyed.

---

* General literature references.

$$i\tau^{1/2} = \frac{n\mathbf{F}\pi^{1/2} D^{1/2} C}{2}$$

where i is the current density in amperes per square centimeter, τ the transition time in seconds, n the number of electrons transferred, $\mathbf{F}$ the Faraday, D the diffusion coefficient in square centimeters per second, and C the concentration in moles per cubic centimeter. They showed that for transition times of 2 to 5 seconds, semi-infinite linear diffusion prevailed for all electrodes except flush-ground electrodes of small areas. In this case, hemispherical diffusion was approached. Plots of $i\tau^{1/2}$ vs C gave straight lines for all ions studied, and from the slope of these plots diffusion coefficients for the ions were calculated. Extrapolation to zero concentration yielded a "residual transition time" in every case, which they attributed to electrochemically active impurities in the fused LiCl-KCl solvent. It was further shown that at transition times greater than 5 seconds, errors were introduced by convection currents in the salt phase due to the existence of temperature gradients. Laitinen and Ferguson emphasized that the well-defined diffusion conditions of chronopotentiometry make it the best method for evaluating diffusion coefficients in fused salts. Solid electrode polarography has the disadvantages of poorly defined diffusion conditions, the possibility of dendritic growths changing the electrode area and geometry, and the difficulty of measuring accurately the electrode area and thus the current density. A dropping electrode such as the bismuth electrode developed by Heus and Egan[3] presents the most accurate way of measuring polarographically diffusion coefficients.

Laitinen and Gaur[6] extended the study initiated by Laitinen and Ferguson. By using an oscillographic technique they were able to measure transition times less than 1 second. They studied the cathodic chronopotentiometry of cadmium (II), cobalt (II), lead (II), and thallium (I) in the LiCl-KCl eutectic at 450°C. In an exhaustive manner, they studied the constancy of the "chronopotentiometric constant," $i\tau^{1/2}/C$, for these ions at a series of electrodes, concentrations, and current densities. Diffusion coefficients were evaluated, and theoretical curves were calculated for the concentration gradients set up at an electrode surface during the constant current electrolysis of a cadmium (II) solution in the chloride eutectic.

Other chronopotentiometric investigations have been successfully conducted in fused salts. Wood[11] has studied the cathodic chronopotentiometry behavior of iron (II) in fused $CaCl_2$-NaCl at 600°C in the concentration range of 0.02 to 9.4 mole per cent. By using an oscillographic technique he was able to determine transition times as low as 0.001 second. Delimarskii[2] and co-workers determined diffusion coefficients of lead (II), zinc (II), silver (I), nickel (II), and cadmium (II) ions in an equimolar mixture of KCl and NaCl at 710°C.

Van Norman[10] determined zinc and lithium in their respective liquid bismuth alloys by anodic chronopotentiometry at a liquid bismuth pool, stripping the metals into the LiCl-KCl eutectic at 450°C. Diffusion coefficients of lithium and zinc in liquid bismuth were calculated.

Liu[7] studied the cathodic and anodic chronopotentiometric behavior of copper (I) dissolved in the Li_2SO_4-K_2SO_4 eutectic at 625°C. He found that copper (I) could be determined by cathodic chronopotentiometry at platinum foil electrodes with an accuracy of ±3 per cent. The reproducibility of anodic chronopotentiograms was only ±15 per cent, attributed by Liu to the possible formation of an oxide film on the platinum electrode in the sulfate melt. The diffusion coefficient of the copper (I) ion in the sulfate melt was also calculated.

Inman and Bockris[4] applied chronopotentiometry to the following molten systems: $PbCl_2$ in the LiCl-KCl eutectic, $AgNO_3$ in $NaNO_3$, AgCl and NaCl in $NaNO_3$, $AgNO_3$, $PbCl_2$, $Pb(NO_3)_2$, $AgNO_3$-KCN and $Cd(NO_3)_2$ in $NaNO_3$-KNO_3, all at various temperatures. They confirmed the reversibility of the reaction $Pb^{2+} + 2e^- \rightarrow Pb$ at a liquid lead electrode in the LiCl-KCl eutectic at 400°C by plotting $\log(\tau^{1/2} - t^{1/2})$ vs E, the cathode potential. A straight line was obtained with a slope of 69 mv, in good agreement with that predicted from the equation

$$E = E° + \frac{RT}{n\mathbf{F}} \ln \frac{2i}{n\mathbf{F}\pi^{1/2} D^{1/2}} + \frac{RT}{n\mathbf{F}} \ln (\tau^{1/2} - t^{1/2}).$$

By plotting $\log \tau^{1/2}$, obtained from chronopotentiograms at a platinum electrode vs the ratios of concentration of NaCl and $AgNO_3$, C_{NaCl}/C_{AgNO_3}, for a series of mixtures in $NaNO_3$ at 330°C, Inman and Bockris calculated a concentration solubility product, K_s, for AgCl in $NaNO_3$. They obtained a value of 2.2×10^{-4}

TABLE 1. DIFFUSION COEFFICIENTS OF CADMIUM (II) AND LEAD (II) IN FUSED SALTS

Ion	Solvent System	$D \times 10^5$ sq cm/sec	Method	Ref.
Cadmium (II)	LiCl-KCl, 450°C	1.7	chronopotentiometry	5
	"	2.08	"	6
	"	1.8	polarography at a dropping bismuth electrode	3
	KCl-NaCl, 710°C	3.7	chronopotentiometry	2
	NaNO₃-KNO₃, 262°C	0.51	"	4
	LiNO₃-KNO₃-NaNO₃, 160°C	0.15	polarography at a dropping mercury electrode	8
Lead (II)	LiCl-KCl, 450°C	2.18	chronopotentiometry	6
	"	1.7	polarography at a dropping bismuth electrode	3
	KCl-NaCl, 710°C	7.0	chronopotentiometry	2
	NaNO₃-KNO₃, 263°C	2.3	"	4
	LiNO₃-KNO₃-NaNO₃, 160°C	0.18	polarography at a dropping mercury electrode	8

moles² per 1000 g $NaNO_3$. In the presence of cyanide ion, the deposition potential of silver (I) in $NaNO_3$-KNO_3 was shifted approximately 400 mv, indicating the formation of complexes.

Utilizing a hanging mercury drop as an indicator electrode they observed conventional chronopotentiometric behavior for the reduction of lead (II) and cadmium (II) in molten $NaNO_3$-KNO_3. The mercury was employed to lower the activity of deposited metal since both pure cadmium and lead are oxidized by the nitrate melt. A plot of E vs $\log(\tau^{1/2} - t^{1/2})/t^{1/2}$ had a slope corresponding to the predicted value of $2.303\ RT/n\mathbf{F}$.

Topol and Osteryoung[9] studied the Bi-BiBr₃ system chronopotentiometrically as well as polarographically. The chronopotentiometrically determined diffusion coefficient of the subhalide species formed in this system agreed with that estimated polarographically.

Of all the electroanalytical techniques used in fused salts, chronopotentiometry offers the most accurate way for the evaluation of diffusion coefficients. Diffusion coefficients of cadmium (II) and lead (II) in different media as determined by the different methods are summarized in Table 1.

References

1. DELAHAY, P. S., "New Instrumental Methods in Electrochemistry," p. 214, New York, Interscience Publishers, 1954.
2. DELIMARSKII, IU. K., GORODYSKY, A. B., AND KUZMOVIC, V. V., *Coll. Czech Chem. Comm.*, **25**, 3056 (1960).
3. HEUS, R. J., AND EGAN, J. J., *J. Electrochem. Soc.*, **107**, 824 (1960).
4. INMAN, D., AND BOCKRIS, J. O'M., *J. Electroanal. Chem.*, **3**, 126 (1962).
5. LAITINEN, H. A., AND FERGUSON, W. S., *Anal. Chem.*, **29**, 4 (1957).
6. LAITINEN, H. A., AND GAUR, H. C., *Anal. Chim. Acta*, **18**, 1 (1958).
7. LIU, C. H., *Anal. Chem.*, **33**, 1477 (1961).
8. STEINBERG, M., AND NACHTRIEB, N. H., *J. Am. Chem. Soc.*, **72**, 3588 (1950).
9. TOPOL, L. E., AND OSTERYOUNG, R. A., *J. Phys. Chem.*, **66**, 1587 (1962).
10. VAN NORMAN, J. D., *Anal. Chem.*, **33**, 946 (1961).
11. WOOD, J. M., Paper presented at 111th Meeting, Electrochemical Society, Washington, D. C., 1957.

JOHN D. VAN NORMAN

Cross-references: *Chronopotentiometry; Polarography.*

FUSED SALT CONDUCTANCE. See FUSED SALT ELECTROCHEMICAL PROPERTIES.

FUSED SALT CORROSION

The field of corrosion by fused salts has been little studied in comparison with corrosion in aqueous systems or by high-temperature gases. The major stimulus for research in this field has come from the possible use of fused salts in nuclear reactors as heat-transfer and fuel-bearing agents. Most of the work has been done with halides, so this review will treat corrosion by molten halides primarily.

As with any type of corrosion, the driving force for the reaction of a metal with a fused salt can be related to the free energy change of the reaction. The corrosion of a metal by aqueous or gaseous systems is in many cases hindered by the accumulation of corrosion products on the surface of the metal. No such effect seems to occur in corrosion by fused halides, presumably because the corrosion product halides are relatively soluble in the melt. Therefore, the reaction of a metal with a fused halide will proceed rather rapidly towards the equilibrium conditions, and a good estimate of the amount of reaction to be expected can be obtained from a calculation of the equilibrium.

Equilibrium Considerations

When a metal is exposed to the fused halide of another metal, the direct replacement reaction

$$M + M'X \rightarrow M' + MX$$

will occur until the equilibrium quotient

$$K = \frac{a(M')a(MX)}{a(M)a(M'X)}$$

is satisfied, or nearly so. In this equation the a's represent the thermodynamic activities of the components. To obtain a rough approximation one may assume (1) the activities of the two salts are equal to their mole fractions in the melt, and (2) the activities of the metals are unity (i.e., pure metal M' precipitates).

The equilibrium constant, K, is related to the standard free energy change for the reaction, ΔF^o, by the relation $\Delta F^o = -RT \ln_e K$. Values of ΔF^o for most halide replacement reactions can be obtained by proper addition of ΔF^o of formation of the halides, which are generally available in tables of thermodynamic data.

Table 1 lists the free energies of formation of a few chlorides of interest. The order is one of increasing free energy (per gram-atom of chlorine) so that a metal higher on the series will replace a lower one from its molten chloride almost completely. However, it should be noted that any pure metal will react to some extent when exposed to the salt of another metal. Thus, if silver is placed in molten sodium chloride at 800°C, the reaction

$$Ag + NaCl \rightarrow AgCl + Na$$

will occur until the equilibrium quotient ($K = 5 \times 10^{-12}$) is satisfied. If one assumes the activities of metals are unity and those of the salts are equal to their mole fractions, then one

TABLE 1. STANDARD FREE ENERGY OF FORMATION OF SOME LIQUID CHLORIDES AT 800°C

Chloride	$-\Delta F^o$, kcal/equivalent
½ BaCl$_2$	(81.7)
KCl	79.3
½ SrCl$_2$	(80.0)
LiCl	79.7
½ CaCl$_2$	76.6
NaCl	74.7
⅓ LaCl$_3$	69.1
½ MgCl$_2$	56.7
⅓ UCl$_3$	(52.6)
¼ UCl$_4$	45.5
½ CrCl$_2$	(31.2)
½ FeCl$_2$	25.8
⅓ CrCl$_3$	25.7
CuCl	22.4
½ NiCl$_2$	20.2
AgCl	19.0
PtCl	~ 0
AuCl	~ -5

Notes: 1) ΔF^o is the free energy change for the reaction: ½ Cl$_2$(g) + (1/x)M(s, l) $\rightarrow$ (1/x) MCl$_x$ (l), i.e., per equivalent of Cl.

2) Numbers in parentheses are extrapolated from higher temperatures for salts that melt above 800° C.

calculates the AgCl mole fraction to be 5×10^{-12}, which for most purposes is low enough.

If the activity coefficients of the salts in the melt are known and if information is available about the state of the metal formed by the reaction, a more reliable estimate of the degree of corrosion can be made. The activity coefficients listed in Table 2, when multiplied by the mole fraction of the halide, give its activity. The activity coefficients tend to be smaller than unity, presumably because of complex ion formation in the melt. As a result, a larger mole fraction of the halide must be formed in the melt to attain equilibrium. In the example above, since the ac-

TABLE 2. ACTIVITY COEFFICIENTS OF CHLORIDES IN NaCl-KCl MELT (AT 700°C)

Chloride	Activity Coefficient
AgCl	1
NiCl$_2$	0.3
CuCl	0.27
CrCl$_3$	0.041
ZnCl$_2$	0.015
CrCl$_2$	0.011
MnCl$_2$	0.010
FeCl$_2$	0.006
CuCl$_2$	0.003

tivity coefficient of silver chloride is unity, then its mole fraction is correct as calculated.

The state of the metal formed as a corrosion product can have an effect on the extent of the corrosion reaction. If the metal formed by the displacement reaction alloys with the parent metal, the activity of the metal formed can be much less than unity, and corrosion greater than that estimated on the assumption of unit activity must occur.

If the metal formed is soluble in the salt melt, it will be formed at an activity less than unity, and again a greater concentration of corrosion product halide will be formed. In the case of the silver-sodium chloride reaction, it is known that sodium dissolves in molten sodium chloride and the corrosion reaction goes further than estimated above. The best estimate that can be made at the present time includes all these effects: the equilibrium constant is 5×10^{-12}; the activity coefficient of AgCl in NaCl is unity; Na is soluble in NaCl, so its mole fraction is equal to that of the AgCl; (the activity coefficient of Na in NaCl is unknown but it can be estimated to be of the order of 10); the activities of Ag and NaCl are essentially unity. Thus

$$5 \times 10^{-12} = \frac{a(\text{Na})a(\text{AgCl})}{a(\text{Ag})a(\text{NaCl})} = \frac{(10 \times \text{Na})(1 \times \text{AgCl})}{(1) \quad (1)}$$

and with $X(\text{Na}) = X(\text{AgCl})$; then $X(\text{AgCl}) = 0.7 \times 10^{-6}$. Therefore, the fact that Na is soluble in NaCl gives rise to a manyfold increase in the amount of corrosion.

Quite a few metals are soluble in their own molten salts. Although the evidence is not conclusive, it appears that metals are not soluble in salts of other metals except by the oxidation mechanism illustrated for Ag-NaCl. The metals that are known to be soluble in their own molten halides are the alkali metals, the alkaline earth metals, the rare earths, and certain others, such as Cd, Bi, Ni, and Hg. In each group the miscibility of the metal and molten halide increases with increasing atomic weight of metal so that lithium is almost insoluble and cesium completely miscible. The miscibility decreases in going from the alkalis to the alkaline earths, to the rare earths, for the same approximate atomic weight. Not much is known about the solubilities of the transition metals.

Effect of Impurities

Impurities in the fused salt can lead to corrosion beyond that considered above, which assumed pure substances at constant temperatures. Water presents probably the greatest problem as an impurity. It is readily absorbed from the atmosphere and is very difficult to remove from fused salts. Even melting under vacuum is not sufficient to remove water completely from a salt. In halide melts water acts like hydrogen halide and readily oxidizes most construction metals with the liberation of hydrogen. Oxygen dissolved in a melt will, of course, corrode most metals to oxides. In the presence of fused salts, oxygen and air are more corrosive than in the absence of the salt. The salt tends to dissolve or flux away the oxides layer which might otherwise protect the metal.

The corrosion of metals by fused salts with oxyanions (i.e., SO_4^{--}, NO_3^{-}, CO_3^{--}) has not been studied extensively. In general, metals react with such salts to form oxides. The other element of the oxyanion may also react with the metal (to form sulfides or carbides), but information on this aspect is very meager. There is some tendency for an oxide scale to form on the metal surface and hinder the progress of the corrosion.

State of Metal

The principles outlined above have considered the chemical nature of the process and assume the metal to be a uniform chemical substance. The physical and metallurgical properties of the metal are important, but again have been little studied.

The corrosion of some alloys, especially Ni, Cr, and Fe alloys, has been somewhat investigated. Of these metals, Cr is markedly more electropositive than Fe or Ni and is thus preferentially leached from the surface of the metal by a fused halide. Also, the salt is found to contain a higher concentration of Cr than Fe or Ni. In addition to its selective removal from the metal surface, Cr is found to diffuse from subsurface regions, since fused salt temperatures are high enough for diffusion processes to occur in the alloy. In such alloys, Cr diffusion is more rapid along the grain boundaries of the metal so that Cr is selectively lost in the grain boundary regions. This grain boundary attack penetrates into the metal to depths that are many times that of the simple surface corrosion by the fused salt. Also, in Ni, Cr, and Fe alloys the Cr diffuses out more rapidly than the other constituents can diffuse in to replace it. As a result, voids form in the metal below its surface.

Mass Transfer

A possible use of fused salts may be as heat-transfer media. In this application they absorb heat at high temperature, as in a nuclear reactor, and discharge it at some lower temperature. Thus, the salt will continually circulate from the high to the lower temperature. A mass-transfer type of corrosion can occur under these conditions. Metal is dissolved in the salt at the high temperature by a corrosion reaction and deposited in the cold part of the system by a reversal of the corrosion reaction. The reversal occurs because of a shift of the metal-salt equilibrium in accord with its temperature coefficient. Failure of the heat transfer system can occur because of the penetration of the metal at high temperature or by plugging of the pipes from the deposit at the low temperature.

The mechanisms of mass transfer by fused salts can be illustrated by a specific example. Inconel (15 Cr, 7 Fe, 78 Ni) can be used to contain a possible nuclear reactor salt: $NaF-ZrF_4-UF_4$. In the high temperature region Cr is dissolved from the Inconel by the reaction

$$Cr + 2UF_4 \rightarrow CrF_2 + 2UF_3$$

A small concentration of CrF_2 and UF_3 is produced in the melt. In the low temperature part of the cycle, the equilibrium is shifted to the left. As a result Cr precipitates in the cooler regions. (In some cases Cr-Fe alloy has precipitated.)

Mass-transfer corrosion is also observed when liquid metals are used as coolants. The nature of the corrosion process is essentially the same: at the higher temperature the greater solubility of the container metal in the liquid metal results in its precipitation in the cooler regions. The mechanism of the solution process in liquid metals, however, differs from that in fused salts.

References

1. GRIMES, W. R., AND CUNEO, D. R., "Corrosion of Structural Materials" in "Reactor Handbook—Materials," Vol. 1, p. 457 ff, 2nd Ed., New York, Interscience Publishers Inc., 1960.
2. LITTLEWOOD, R., AND ARGENT, E. J., First International Congress on Metallic Corrosion, London, Butterworths, 1961.
3. MANLY, W. D., et al, "Metallurgical Problems in Molten Fluoride Systems," Proc. Second U. N. International Conf. on Peaceful Uses of Atomic Energy, Vol. 7, 1958.
4. KOCHERGIN, V. P., AND CO-WORKERS, series of papers in Russian literature. See *Chem. Abstracts*, **55**, 24486d, 22055h, 20787i, 8262i, **72216i, and earlier papers.**
5. SUSSKIND, H., et al, "Corrosion Studies for a Fused Salt-Liquid Metal Extraction Process for the Liquid Metal Fuel Reactor," **BNL 585,** 1960.

DANIEL CUBICCIOTTI

Cross-reference: *Corrosion by Liquid Metals;* other entries with *Fused Salt* headings.

FUSED SALT COULOMETRIC TECHNIQUES. See COULOMETRIC TECHNIQUES IN HIGH TEMPERATURE SYSTEMS.

FUSED SALT DIFFUSION COEFFICIENTS. See FUSED SALT POLAROGRAPHY.

FUSED SALT, ELECTROCHEMICAL PROPERTIES

One of the distinguishing features of fused salts is their relatively high electrical conductivity. The conductivity is primarily ionic, as shown by the fact that Faraday's laws are obeyed during electrolysis. That is, when current is passed through a fused salt, electrochemical reactions occur at the electrodes. The current, which is carried by electrons in the metal electrodes, is then carried by ions in the melt. Thus fused salts are composed at least in part of mobile ions.

The relative values of conductivity in various fused salts provide a rough idea of the proportion of ions to neutral species. The highly conducting alkali halides are presumed to be almost completely ionized into alkali metal ions and halide ions. In contrast, very poorly conducting fused salts, such as mercuric chloride or zinc chloride, are only slightly ionized. However, the conductivity depends on both the concentration of ions and their mobilities. The mobilities of ions depend not only on their own nature but also on the nature of the melt itself and the other ions that constitute it. Therefore, the conductivity of a pure fused salt does not give a direct measure of its degree of ionization. Still, the large differences in conductivities of pure fused salts do indicate differences in their degrees of ionization, because ionic mobilities are not believed to have a large enough range of values to account for the great range of conductivity.

Other properties of fused salts substantiate the evidence from conductivities regarding the degree of their ionic nature. Boiling points

TABLE 1. EQUIVALENT CONDUCTANCES, FREEZING POINTS, AND BOILING POINTS OF SOME FUSED CHLORIDES

LiCl		BeCl$_2$			BCl$_3$		CCl$_4$		
183		0.088			0		0		
610		440			−107		−23		
1380		(550)			13		190		

NaCl		MgCl$_2$			AlCl$_3$		SiCl$_4$		
150		35			15		0		
808		714			192		−68		
1465		1418			160		58		

KCl	CuCl	CaCl$_2$	ZnCl$_2$	ScCl$_3$	GaCl$_3$	TiCl$_4$	GeCl$_4$		
120	94	64	0.02	15		0	0		
772	430	782	275	939		−23	−50		
1407	1690	(2000)	732	967		137	84		

RbCl	AgCl	SrCl$_2$	CdCl$_2$	YCl$_3$	InCl$_3$	ZrCl$_4$	SnCl$_4$	NbCl$_5$	MoCl$_5$
94	118	69	58.5	9.5	14.7	0.85	0	2×10^{-7}	1.8×10^{-6}
717	455	875	568	700	586	437	33	194	194
1380	1564	2480	970	(1510)	498	908	113	250	268

CsCl	AuCl	BaCl$_2$	HgCl$_2$	LaCl$_3$	TlCl$_3$	HfCl$_4$	PbCl$_4$	TaCl$_5$	WCl$_6$
86		77	3×10^{-2}	29	3×10^{-3}		2×10^{-5}	3×10^{-7}	2×10^{-6}
645		962	277	870	25		−15	211	275
1300		(1830)	304	(1750)			(140)	240	337

Numbers under each compound are its equivalent conductance (ohm^{-1} cm sq equivalent^{-1}) near the melting point, the melting point (°C), and boiling point (°C) in that order. Values in parentheses are estimated.

provide one such indication. The evaporation of a fused salt at moderate temperatures produces gaseous molecules, not ions. Those fused salts whose intermolecular forces cause them to be molecular (nonionized) liquids will evaporate more readily to the gaseous molecules than highly ionized ones. Therefore, the boiling points of less ionized salts will be lower than those of completely ionized salts. A similar correlation tends to hold for their melting points. A comparison of conductivities with boiling and melting points is made in Table 1 for some chlorides. The correlation is fairly good but there are exceptions.

The structure of the solid form of a salt can give indications of the degree of ionic nature of the fused salts. Those salts that crystallize in layer lattices and molecular lattices tend to give poorly ionized melts, while the more ionic solids with higher coordination number and higher symmetry give highly ionized melts.

Conductance

The electrical conductivity of fused salts is generally determined by measuring the resistance of a sample between fixed metallic electrodes by a-c methods. The geometry of the cell is determined indirectly by measuring the resistance of a reference liquid. The specific conductance can be calculated from the relation,

$$R = \frac{1}{\kappa} \frac{\ell}{A},$$

which relates the specific conductance, κ, (ohm^{-1} cm^{-1}) to the measured resistance of the cell, R, (ohms) and the cell geometry factors: ℓ, the distance between electrodes (cm) and A, the effective cross section of the electrodes (sq cm). The specific conductance is the conductance (the reciprocal of the resistance) of the material between two electrodes with one sq cm cross section separated by one cm.

For comparisons of chemical properties and theoretical treatments, the equivalent conductance is considered to be of more fundamental significance. The equivalent conductance, Λ, (ohm^{-1} sq cm equiv^{-1}), is defined by the relation $\Lambda = \kappa V_e = \kappa(E/\rho)$, in which V_e is the volume of one gram equivalent of salt, ρ the density of the fused salt, and E the gram equivalent weight of the salt. The equivalent conductance represents the conductance of one equivalent of salt between electrodes one cm apart and of sufficient cross section to include all the salt. For mixtures, the average equivalent weight $\overline{E}$ is used instead of E. For binary mixtures it is defined by $\overline{E} = f_1E_1 + f_2E_2$, in which the f's are the equivalent fractions of the salts in the mixture. (The equivalent fraction of a component is the ratio of the number of its equivalents to the total equivalents of salt.)

Values of Conductance. The equivalent conductances of a number of molten chlorides are shown in relation to the position of the cation in the periodic table in Table 1. There is a general trend to lower conductivity in going from the ionic chlorides, on the left, to the covalent ones, on the right. The incompleteness of the table tends to indicate the present state of our information. Data on the transition metal halides, for example, are quite sparse. Values for the alkali halides, which are the most ionic and tend to have the highest conductances, have been carefully examined. For a given anion the equivalent conductances of the alkali halides decrease with increasing size, or atomic number, of the cation. Among the alkaline earth halides the reverse is true. The effect of anion for given cation is less clearly defined. The order of decreasing conductance seems to be chloride, bromide, iodide for both alkali and alkaline earth cations.

Salts with anions other than halides have been less well investigated. Scattered information on alkali nitrates, nitrites, sulfates, and carbonates indicates that they are generally good conductors in the molten state. There is a tendency for these salts of oxyanions to decompose to the oxide and gaseous oxide parent of the anion at higher temperatures. Fused lithium hydride is an interesting salt. It is a good ionic conductor and, on electrolysis, yields hydrogen at the anode.

Effect of Temperature. The conductivities of fused salts almost invariably increase with temperature from their melting points to tempera-

tures as high as they have been investigated. If a decrease occurs, the behavior is considered abnormal and special explanations are sought. To represent the temperature effect, the conductivity is generally fitted to an Arrhenius-type equation such as:

$$\Lambda = A \exp (-\Delta E_\Lambda/RT)$$

$$\kappa = B \exp (-\Delta E_\kappa/RT)$$

In these equations R is the gas constant, 2 cal per mole degree, A and B are constants or vary only slowly with temperature; and ΔE_Λ and ΔE_κ are called activation energies for conduction. The values of ΔE_Λ and ΔE_κ are not equal for a given salt but are related through the volume expansivity of the salt.

The activation energy usually is almost constant with increase in temperature from somewhat above the melting point to the highest temperatures measured. Values of E_Λ for the alkali halides range from about two to four kcal per mole and for the alkaline earth halides (except Be) from four to six kcal per mole. Certain salts, e.g., $ZnCl_2$ and $BeCl_2$, show a large decrease of ΔE as temperature increases. This is believed to be due to a dissociation of large molecular complexes into smaller ones and into ions.

Mechanism. The present ideas as to the constitution of fused salts are still incomplete and are changing rather rapidly. They have been derived from such information as conductances, x-ray structures of fused and solid salts, and other properties. In general, it is believed that the good fused salt conductors are largely ionized into simple positive and negative ions. In a uni-univalent salt these ions are symmetrically arranged around one another so as to minimize the potential energy associated with their ionic and overlap repulsive forces. In the liquid it has been found that the average distance between positive and negative ions is *smaller* than in the solid; however, the average number of ions immediately surrounding a given ion—i.e., the coordination number—is smaller in the liquid. The net result is that in the liquid the ions are packed more loosely than in the solid, and their constant jostling motion, due to thermal energy, leads to a much greater mobility. There is no net motion of the material, but each individual ion will wander throughout the sample of material in the course of time. When an electric field is applied, there is a tendency for the ions to move towards the oppositely charged electrode, but this directed motion is only a small addition to the thermal motion. An ion will drift only slowly towards the electrode, with many backward and sidewise excursions. As the temperature of the system is increased, the mobilities of the ions increase primarily because the volume of the system increases.

The poorer conductors are presumed to consist primarily of neutral molecules only slightly dissociated into ions while intermediate cases of partial ionization can occur (i.e., $MCl_2 \rightarrow MCl^+ + Cl^-$). In these cases increase in temperature increases the degree of dissociation into ions as well as the individual mobilities of the ions.

Mixtures. The equivalent conductivities of mixtures of simple molten salts (e.g., alkali halides) tend to be slightly smaller than values calculated from the formula Λ (mixture) = $f_1\Lambda_1 + f_2\Lambda_2$. In other salt mixtures the deviations from simple additivity are generally larger and can be positive or negative. In many cases, the negative deviations are taken to indicate complex ion formation. Thus in the potassium chloride-cadmium chloride system there is a pronounced minimum in the conductance at 50 mole per cent KCl. There is also a solid compound shown by the phase diagram at that composition. These data are taken as evidence that the complex ion $CdCl_3^-$ is formed in that system. The potassium chloride-lead chloride system shows similar evidence for the complex $PbCl_4^{--}$. Other such systems are: $AlCl_3$-NaCl, $ZrCl_4$-NaCl, and ZrF_4-NaF.

An interesting class of mixtures is found in so-called metal-salt solutions. Certain metals are miscible with their own molten salts. The heavier alkali metals, for example, are quite miscible with their molten halides, the heavier alkaline earth metals are somewhat less miscible, and the rare earths still less so. These mixtures have conductances that are greater than those of the pure salts and that increase rapidly with increasing metal content. The increased conductance over that of the pure salt is electronic. When current is passed through such a mixture, the electronic part of the conductance does not give rise to electrochemical reactions at the electrodes. Thus, Faraday's laws of electrolysis would not hold for the total current passed in these cases since only a fraction of the conductance is ionic.

Transference Number

Transference numbers in ordinary solutions relate the amounts of each type of chemical matter carried through a solution by the electrical current. In such systems the solvent provides a frame of reference, on the molecular scale, relative to which the transport of chemical material can be measured. For a pure fused salt there is no such frame of reference. Measurements of transference numbers of pure fused salts reported in the literature use a macroscopic body, such as the walls of the container or porous plug in the cell, as a frame of reference. Transference numbers obtained in this way do not have the same significance as those obtained in ordinary solutions, and it has been questioned whether such measurements have any meaning relative to the intrinsic properties of the pure fused salts. See **Fused Salt Transport Numbers.**

For mixtures of fused salts, however, the transference number of one species relative to another of like sign does have meaning. This relative transference number should be used with the emf of fused salt cells with transference to evaluate the thermodynamics of the reactions occurring.

References

1. Blomgren, G. E., and Van Artsdalen, E. R., "Fused Salts" in "Annual Review of Physical Chemistry," Vol. II, Palo Alto, California, Annual Reviews, Inc., 1960.
2. Delimarskii, Iu. K., and Markov, B. F., "Electro-Chemistry of Fused Salts," transl. by A. Peiperl and R. E. Wood, Washington, D. C., Sigma Press, 1961.
3. Bloom, H., and Bockris, J. O'M., "Molten Electrolytes" in "Modern Aspects of Electrochemistry," Vol. 2, London, Butterworths Scientific Publ., 1959.
4. "Molten Salts" in *Annals of the New York Academy of Sciences,* **79,** Article II, 761–1098 (1960).
5. "The Structure and Properties of Ionic Melts," *Discussions of the Faraday Society,* No. **32,** 1961.

Daniel Cubicciotti

Cross-references: other entries with *Fused Salt* headings.

FUSED SALT ELECTRODE POTENTIALS. See FUSED SALT ELECTRODE REACTIONS; FUSED SALT ELECTROMOTIVE FORCE SERIES.

FUSED SALT ELECTRODE REACTIONS

Electrochemical cells containing molten salts as electrolytes, were described by Davy[1] in 1807, in his classical experiment on the electrolysis of fused potassium and sodium hydroxides. Faraday,[2] in 1833 was the first to investigate systematically the decomposition potentials of a large number of fused salts and to obtain a comparative electromotive force series of the elements. From his investigations, he was able to establish the fundamental laws of electrolysis that bear his name. In spite of such promising results, the field was not further exploited to any significant extent, and only in the early 1900's, Lorenz[3] and later Drossbach, Klemm, and many others of the European school, demonstrated the feasibility of precise electrochemical measurements in molten salts. From these studies, the ionic nature of melts was established.

Interest was revived recently, and since the 1950's the properties of the molten ionic state have been the object of many systematic investigations. Reasons for this revival may be sought in recent developments in nuclear technology and in the various attempts to produce the reactive metals of the transition series, Ti, Zr, Th, etc., by fused salt electrolysis. It is worth mentioning that the more conventional metals, aluminum, sodium, potassium, lithium, and most of the magnesium, are produced today by fused salt electrolysis. However, the techniques in these operations are more art than science, as the mechanism of the electrode reactions in the more complex electrolytes is far too little understood.

This article will be concerned with recent developments in the subject of the reversible reactions that occur in electrochemical cells employing molten electrolytes. For a complete coverage on the literature, the reader is referred to the recent review articles[4] and monographs[5, 6, 7] published on this subject.

Equilibrium Potential Measurements in Molten Salts

An electrochemical cell for equilibrium potential measurements, employing molten salts as the electrolyte, is very similar to its counterpart in the more conventional aqueous systems. It consists of two metal electrodes, or a metal and a nonmetal electrode, each in contact with a melt, that could be either a pure molten salt, or a mixture of molten salts, containing the ionic species of the electrode material. The main difference between the electrochemical cells in molten salts and the similar cells in aqueous solutions lies in the nature of the electrolyte.

In molten salts of electrochemical interest, the medium is ionic and the oppositely charged particles, anions and cations, are in intimate contact. The positive and negative charges are distributed in a manner that satisfies the conditions of overall electrical neutrality. The forces which are acting between the charged particles in the melt are mainly the short range type of electrostatic interactions, and it is virtually impossible to differentiate in a mixture between solutes and solvent on the basis of their differences in the type of bonding. It is usual to refer to the salt in excess as the solvent, while all the other components in the mixture represent the solutes.

The classical thermodynamic treatment of electrochemical cells is also applicable to molten salts. The experimentally measured potential of the cell provides an excellent direct method for calculating the free energy change, ΔG, of the overall cell reaction. Unfortunately, with the exception of relatively few and rather simple reactions, the chemical processes that occur within a cell are not too well understood. This is particularly true in cells employing molten salt mixture where the state of the ions in solution is entirely unknown. In this case, by choosing a convenient state as the "standard" state of the components in the mixture, the potential measurements may be used to calculate deviations from ideality in terms of activity coefficients. Activity coefficients having values well below unity are usually interpreted as indicating the formation of complex species in the melt. The actual values of the activity coefficients and of the other thermodynamic functions which are used to describe the complexes in solution, will depend entirely upon the definition of the noncomplexed, or "ideal" state.

The methods of calculating activities in molten salts from emf measurements and the electrochemical cells that have been most widely used will be presented in the following.

Formation Cells without Transference. The simplest type of formation cell consists of a pure molten binary salt as the electrolyte and of two electrodes which are reversible to each of the ionic species in the melt. For example, the cell:

$$\begin{array}{c|c|c} \text{Ag} & \text{Ag}^+\text{Cl}^- & \text{Cl}_2\,(1\text{ atm}) \\ & \text{(liq)} & \text{graphite} \quad \text{Cell A} \\ (-) & & (+) \end{array}$$

may be constructed by immersing a solid silver electrode and a graphite electrode saturated with chlorine gas at one atmosphere pressure into a melt of pure liquid silver chloride.

The overall cell reaction is readily found by considering the most probable electrode reactions, and the experimentally obtained polarities of the electrodes. Thus, at the negative electrode, $Ag^\circ \rightarrow Ag^+ + e^-$, and at the positive electrode, $\frac{1}{2}Cl_{2(1\text{ atm})} + e^- \rightarrow Cl^-$, the overall cell reaction being

$$Ag^\circ + \tfrac{1}{2}Cl_{2(1\text{ atm})} \rightarrow Ag^+Cl^-_{(liq)} \qquad (1)$$

Cells of this type are known as "formation" cells because the overall reaction is the formation of a pure compound.

For an amount of cell reaction corresponding to stoichiometric quantities of reactants and products, the quantity of electricity required is $z\mathbf{F}$ coulombs, where z is the number of electrons required in either electrode reactions ($z = 1$ in the case of silver chloride) and $\mathbf{F}$, is the Faraday constant (23,060 cal).

The cell potential, E°, is related to the standard free energy of reaction 1, by the well-known relationship,

$$\Delta G^\circ = -E^\circ z\mathbf{F} \qquad (2)$$

where, E° is the measured reversible cell potential, z is the number of electrons taking part in the reaction, and $\mathbf{F}$ is the Faraday constant.

The next simplest type of formation cell is a multicomponent cell that consists of a homogeneous molten mixture of two or more salts having a common ion, one of which should contain the ions to which the electrodes are reversible. The cell:

$$\begin{array}{c|c|c} \text{Ag} & \text{Ag}^+\text{Cl}^-\ (m) & \text{Cl}_2\,(1\text{ atm}) \\ & \text{K}^+\text{Cl}^-\ (n) & \text{graphite} \quad \text{Cell B} \\ (-) & & (+1) \end{array}$$

serves as an example. m and n represent here the number of moles of AgCl and KCl in the mixture, respectively, and the electrolyte composition is defined by the mole fraction,

$$X_{\text{AgCl}} = \frac{m}{m+n}$$

The overall cell reactions may be found as follows: At the negative electrode,

$$Ag^\circ + [m\ Ag^+ + n\ K^+ + (m+n)Cl^-]_{liq} \rightarrow$$
$$[(m+1)\ Ag^+ + mK^+ + (m+n)Cl^-]_{liq} + e^-$$

and at the positive electrode,

$$\tfrac{1}{2}Cl_{2(1\text{ atm})} + e^-$$
$$+ [mAg^+ + mK^+ + (m+n)Cl^-]_{liq} \rightarrow$$
$$[mAg^+ + nK^+ + (m+n+1)Cl^-]_{liq}$$

where the quantities in parentheses describe the solution as an ionic mixture.

The overall cell reaction is obtained by adding these two equations

$$Ag^\circ + \tfrac{1}{2}Cl_{2(1\text{ atm})}$$
$$+ [(Ag^+Cl^-)_m + (K^+Cl^-)_n]_{liq} \rightarrow \qquad (3)$$
$$[(Ag^+Cl^-)_{m+1} + (K^+Cl^-)_n]_{liq}$$

The free energy change, $\overline{\Delta G^\circ}$, associated with reaction (3) is equal to the partial molar free energy of silver chloride in its state as a solute, in a solution of a given composition. This quantity may be calculated from the experimentally measured potential, E, of Cell B, by using the familiar expression:

$$\overline{\Delta G^\circ} = -Ez\mathbf{F} \qquad (4)$$

It should be noted that while the potential, E°, of Cell A is only a function of temperature, the potential, E, of Cell B depends upon both the temperature and the composition of the electrolyte.

Subtracting Eq. (1) from (3) and rearranging, the following equation is obtained:

$$(Ag^+Cl^-)_{liq} + [(Ag^+Cl^-)_m + (K^+Cl^-)_n]_{liq} \rightarrow$$
$$\qquad\qquad\qquad (5)$$
$$[(Ag^+Cl^-)_{m+1} + (K^+Cl^-)_n]_{liq}$$

For the thermodynamic treatment it is necessary to assume m and n as representing large numbers of moles of AgCl and KCl, respectively. Then Eq. (5) would represent the process of isothermal mixing of one gram-mole of silver chloride with a solution of a given constant composition, and the free energy, $(\overline{\Delta G_m})_{\text{AgCl}}$, for this reaction should be by definition the partial molar free energy of mixing of silver chloride, its standard state being also defined as pure liquid silver chloride at the temperature of the experiment.

According to classical thermodynamics, the partial molar free energy of mixing is related to the activity of silver chloride in the mixture (a_{AgCl}) by the well-known equation:

$$(\overline{\Delta G_m})_{\text{AgCl}} = RT\ln a_{\text{AgCl}} \qquad (6)$$

By combining Eqs. (2), (4), and (6), and remembering that Eq. (5) has been derived by subtracting Eq. (1) from (3), the general relationship is obtained:

$$E = E^\circ - \frac{RT}{z\mathbf{F}} \ln a_{AgCl} \qquad (7)$$

which represents the Nernst equation for cells of this type.

The activity of silver chloride in the mixture, (a_{AgCl}) is related to its mole fraction (X_{AgCl}) by the usual relationship,

$$a_{AgCl} = x_{AgCl} \cdot \gamma_{AgCl} \qquad (8)$$

where γ_{AgCl} represents the activity coefficient.

Formation cells have been used rather extensively to determine the thermodynamic properties of pure molten salts, and the partial molar properties of mixtures. In addition to chlorine electrode for chloride melts, bromine electrodes for bromide melts, and even oxygen electrodes for oxide melts, have been used with a varying degree of success.

Hildebrand and Salstrom[8] were the first to obtain precise emf data on metal-metal chloride systems, and more recently, several similar measurements have been made by various other investigators.[9-12, 14]

The many other types of electrochemical cells in molten salts may be thought to arise by various combinations of cells of Type A and Type B, respectively. Thus, a concentration cell may be assembled by combining two identical cells of Type B where only the solute electrolyte is present at two different concentrations. A chemical cell may also be assembled by the combination of two cells of either Type A or Type B having different electrode systems.

Reference Electrodes and Cells

Single electrode potentials cannot be measured experimentally as any measurement of this type would involve the coupling of two electrodes, neither of which could have a zero value. It is possible, however, to observe changes in single electrode potentials if it is so arranged that one of the electrodes in the cells retains a constant potential during the time of observation. This constant potential electrode is known as the *reference* electrode and may be assigned arbitrarily a zero value.

The reader should not attempt to compare the universally accepted standard electrode in aqueous solutions to a reference electrode in molten salts. In the former, the standard reference is a hydrogen electrode with hydrogen gas at 1 atm, and unit activity of the hydrogen ions in solution. In molten salts a universal reference cannot be found as the choice of the electrode material would depend entirely on the chemical composition of the electrolyte.

For example, in any of the cells so far described, either of the two electrodes could serve as a reference, provided that the composition and temperature of the electrolyte would not change during the time of observation.

In chemical or concentration cells with transference, or generally in any case where the occurrence of secondary processes between the two electrode systems is suspected, it is necessary to separate the two half-cell compartments by means of a suitable diaphragm. The separating medium should allow the electrical migration of ions, and prevent diffusive or convective mixing. The diaphragms used so far should be classified as the membrane type, permeable to all ions present, the semipermeable membrane, and the salt bridge type.

The former are represented by the various sintered refractory discs, tightly packed asbestos plugs,[12] and even glass joints wetted with the melt. An improved type of asbestos diaphragm was used by the author and consisted of an asbestos fibre flame sealed into Pyrex or silica capillaries. The Pyrex modification was most suitable for cells operating at temperatures below 500°C[13] while silica could be used for temperatures as high as 1000°C.[14]

The type of junction established by the permeable membrane type of diaphragm is not too well-defined. A porous membrane is the equivalent of a bundle of fine capillaries of all possible shapes and of varying orifice. It should be expected that some diffusion should take place from both ends so that the composition of an interface at any cross-section of the diaphragm would change continuously. Under these conditions any theoretical calculation of the junction potential should be extremely difficult, if not impossible. Fortunately, the junction potential becomes negligibly small when using dilute solutions in the same molten salt solvent, on both sides of a junction.

Semipermeable diaphragms are represented by the various types of glasses or porcelains and will be described in connection with the corresponding electrodes.

The salt bridge type of diaphragm was used by Pletenev and Rosov.[15] The electrical contact between the two independent electrode compartments was established by means of a suspended asbestos wick. The wick was impregnated with molten potassium chloride and was dipping into the two solutions at each end.

Fig. 1 illustrates a galvanic cell equipped with a silver-silver chloride reference electrode, and the asbestos diaphragm described above.

Recent investigations have shown that solutions of metals in molten salts, as well as some metal oxides and sulfides,[16] exhibit electronic rather than ionic conduction. Therefore, the standard free energy of formation of compounds such as Cu_2O and Ag_2S cannot be obtained from emf measurements of the corresponding formation cells. Even in the case of typical ionic conductors, such as solid AgBr or AgI, electron hole conduction becomes appreciable at higher halogen partial pressures, and, therefore, the simple relations given in Eq. (4) are no longer valid. It is evident that the type of conduction in the melt should also be carefully considered before attempting any measurements.

The main reference electrodes in molten salts are now described briefly.

Gaseous Electrodes. These include the various halogen and oxygen electrodes. A halogen electrode consists of a porous graphite rod saturated with halogen gas at a given constant pressure, preferably 1 atmosphere. The electrode is immersed in a molten electrolyte containing the corresponding halogen anions. Of the halogens, chlorine has been used the most, although bromine and iodine electrodes have also been reported. Fig. 2 illustrates a cell equipped with the chlorine electrode described above.

It should be noted that the potential of the chlorine electrode is a function of the pressure of the chlorine gas, as well as of the activity of the chloride ions in the melt. Thus, for the electrode reaction,

$$Cl^-_{(a_{Cl^-})} \rightarrow \tfrac{1}{2}Cl_{2(P)} + e^-$$

the electrode potential should obey the equation:

$$E_{Cl^-/Cl^\circ} = E^\circ_{Cl^-/Cl^\circ} - \frac{RT}{F} \ln \frac{P^{1/2}_{Cl_2}}{a_{Cl^-}} \quad (9)$$

where $E^\circ_{Cl^-/Cl^\circ}$ is the "standard electrode" potential at 1 atm pressure, and unit activity of the chloride ions in the melt. By considering the two formation cells, such as

$$\underset{\text{liq}}{Ag/AgCl/Cl_2} \text{ (1 atm)},$$

and

$$\underset{\text{liq}}{Pb/PbCl_2/Cl_2} \text{ (1 atm)},$$

it is evident that the activities of the chloride ions in the melt of AgCl and $PbCl_2$, respectively, are different. Chlorine electrodes, therefore, should not be considered as a universal reference electrode for *all* chloride melts.

Oxygen electrodes[17] are similar to the chlorine electrodes in that the electrode potential should reflect the reaction,

$$\begin{pmatrix} O^{2-} \\ a_{O_2-} \\ \text{in melt} \end{pmatrix} \rightarrow \tfrac{1}{2}O_2 + e^- \quad (P_{O_2} \text{ in gas}) \quad (10)$$

Metal Electrodes. Of the metal electrodes, silver has been found to be the most suitable. The metal has only one stable valence state and forms an oxide, Ag_2O, that decomposes rapidly

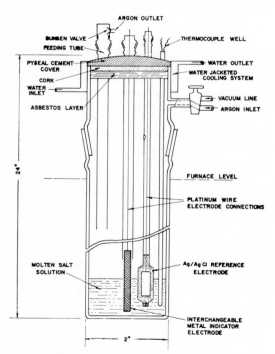

ARGON OUTLET

BUNSEN VALVE
FEEDING TUBE
THERMOCOUPLE WELL
PYSEAL CEMENT COVER
WATER OUTLET
CORK
WATER JACKETED COOLING SYSTEM
WATER INLET
ASBESTOS LAYER
VACUUM LINE
ARGON INLET

24"

FURNACE LEVEL

PLATINUM WIRE ELECTRODE CONNECTIONS

MOLTEN SALT SOLUTION
Ag/Ag Cl REFERENCE ELECTRODE

INTERCHANGEABLE METAL INDICATOR ELECTRODE

2"

Fig. 1. Cell for cmf measurements against a silver-silver chloride reference electrode:

M	MCl_n	AgCl	Ag.
	KCl+NaCl	KCl+NaCl	

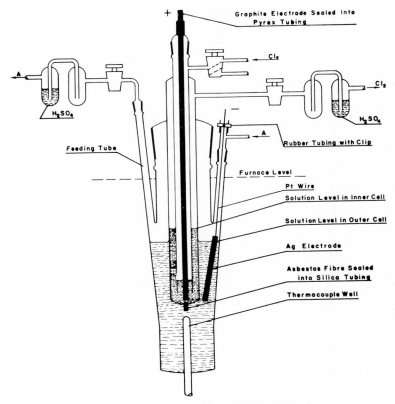

Fig. 2. Cell equipped with a chlorine electrode:

AG	AgCl	‖	KCl + NaCl	C (graphite)
	KCl + NaCl	‖		Cl_2 (1 atm).
−				+

above 300°C. Its solubility in molten salts is negligibly small, if it exists at all.

The reaction: $Ag° \rightarrow Ag^+ + e^-$ has been found reversible for all systems investigated, and the equilibrium potential of the electrode is established almost instantaneously.

Of the other metals, platinum immersed in a chloride melt containing Pt^{2+} ions has also been used as a reliable reference electrode. The Pt^{2+} was generated coulometrically *in situ*, with a one hundred per cent current efficiency at low current densities.[18] This electrode, however, could be used only at low temperatures, as the $PtCl_2$ solutions become unstable above 500°C.

Glass Electrodes. Electrodes with glass diaphragms have also been reported mostly by Russian investigators. At high temperatures, glass may be described as an ionic conductor, the type of conductance depending upon its chemical composition and temperature.

A sodium glass electrode may be constructed by introducing sodium metal or sodium alloy in a glass ampule, which is then immersed in a melt containing sodium ions. The glass should be thin but not porous.

Electrodes of the type: M-Na/Na-Glass/Na^+ in melt, where M is Hg or Sn, have been investigated extensively by Delimarski,[19] Skobets and Kavetski,[20] and by Lengyel and Sammt.[21]

More recently Bockris[22] and Littlewood[23] operated silver-silver chloride electrodes equipped with suitable glass diaphragms. Electrodes employing porcelain diaphragms have also been proposed by Labrie and Lamb.[24]

References

1. DAVY, H., *Phil. Trans.*, **25**, 98 (1808).
2. FARADAY, M., "Experimental Researches in Electricity, I, 1831–38," 2nd Ed., London, Richard and John Edward Taylor, 1949.
3. LORENZ, R., AND KAUFLER, F., "Elecktro-

chemie geschmolzener Salze" in "Handbuch der angewandten physikalishen chemie," G. Bredig, Ed. Vol. 11, Part 1, Leipzig, Barth, 1909.

4. BLOMGREN, G. E., AND VAN ARTSDALEN, E. R., "Annual Review of Physical Chem.," Vol. 11, Fused Salts, p. 273, 1960.

5. DELIMARSKI, IU. K., AND MARKOV, B. F., "Electrochemistry of Fused Salts," translation edited by R. E. Wood, Washington, D. C., The Sigma Press Publishers, 1961.

6. IVES, D. J. G., AND JANZ, G. J., Eds., "Reference Electrodes," "Electrodes in Fused Salts," by R. W. Laity, p. 524, New York, Academic Press, 1961.

7. BLOOM, H., AND BOCKRIS, J. O'M., "Modern Aspects of Electrochemistry," No. 2, Bockris J. O'M. ed., New York, Academic Press, 1959.

8. HILDEBRAND, J. H., J. Am. Chem. Soc., **51**, 66 (1929); HILDEBRAND, J. H., AND SALSTROM, E. J., ibid, **52**, 4650 (1930); SALSTROM, E. J., ibid, **53**. 1794, 3385 (1931); **54**, 4252 (1932); HILDEBRAND, J. H., AND SALSTROM, E. J., ibid, **54**, 4257 (1932).

9. SENDEROFF, S., AND MELLORS, G. W., Rev. Sci. Instr.,, **29**, 151 (1958).

10. STERN, K. H., J. Phys. Chem., **62**, 385 (1958).

11. MARKOV, B. F., DELIMARSKI, IU. K., AND PANCHENKO, I. D., J. Polymer Sc., **31**, 263 (1958).

12. SENDEROFF, S., MELLORS, G. W., AND BRETZ, R. I., Ann. New York Acad. Sc., **79**, 878 (1960).

13. FLENGAS, S. N., AND RIDEAL, ERIC, Proc. Roy. Soc. A., 233–443 (1956).

14. FLENGAS, S. N., AND INGRAHAM, T. R., J. Electrochem. Soc., **106**, 714 (1959).

15. PLETENEV, S. A., AND ROSOV, W. N., Zhur. Fiz. Khim., **9**, 854 (1954).

16. KIUKKOLA, K., AND WAGNER, C., J. Electrochem. Soc., **104**, 308 (1957).

17. FLOOD, H., AND FORLAND, T., Disc. Far. Soc., **1**, 302 (1947).

18. LAITINEN, H. A., AND LIU, C. H., J. Am. Chem. Soc., **80**, 1015 (1958).

19. DELIMARSKI, IU. K., AND KHAIMOVICH, R. S., Ukrain. Khim. Zhur., **15**, 77 (1949); and Kolotii, A. A., ibid, **16**, 438 (1950).

20. SKOVETS, E. M., AND KAVETSKII, N. S., Zhur. Obschei. Khim., **10**, 1858 (1940).

21. LENGYEL, B., AND SAMMT, A., Z. physik. Chem., **181**, 55 (1937).

22. BOCKRIS, J. O'M., HILLS, G. J., INMAN D., AND YOUNG, L., J. Scien. Instrum. **33**, 438 (1956).

23. LITTLEWOOD, R., Electrochem. Acta, **3**, 270 (1961).

24. LABRIE, R. J. AND LAMB, V. A., J. Electrochem. Soc., **106**, 895 (1959).

S. N. FLENGAS

Cross-references: other entries under *Fused Salt* headings.

FUSED SALT ELECTROMOTIVE FORCE SERIES

The establishment of an electromotive force series in molten salts will depend entirely upon the nature of the electrolyte. A series may be established based on the free energy of the pure electrolytic phase, the phases being of similar type, such as chlorides, bromides, iodides, hydroxides, etc. These values may be measured directly with formation cells of Type A (see **Fused Salt Electrode Reactions**), or may be calculated from the available thermodynamic data. The potentials would correspond to the decomposition voltages of the molten electrolytes, assuming that the products are formed in their standard states, and that the cells contain no ohmic voltages or electrode polarization. Furthermore, as they may be calculated from the standard free energies of the pure compounds, they should be referred to as "standard potentials."

Standard potentials for about 95 metal chlorides have been calculated recently by Hamer et al.[1] The values for some of the more important metals are given in Table 1, and may be used in calculating the activities of molten metal chloride mixtures by the methods outlined previously.

It should be noted that a series of this type should not be considered as an electromotive force series, since it was not based on individual half-cell reactions measured against a common reference electrode. As already mentioned, chlorine electrodes in the various pure molten metal chlorides are not comparable. A thermodynamically acceptable electromotive force-series may be obtained from potential measurements with chemical cells in the following manner

Take the reaction:

$$U + 3Ag^+ \text{ (in 1/1 mole KCl, NaCl)}$$
$$\rightarrow U^{3+} \text{(in 1/1 mole KCl, NaCl)} + 3Ag$$

in the molten mixture of KCl and NaCl as the supporting medium. This system has been investigated rather extensively,[2, 3, 4] using cells of the type:

U (−)	UCl₃ (X₁) (in 1/1 mole KCl, NaCl or the KCl, LiCl eut.)	AgCl (X₂) (in 1/1 mole KCl, NaCl, or the KCl, LiCl eut.)	Ag (+)

The electrode to the right is the reference electrode, and is separated from the indicator

TABLE 1. REVERSIBLE DECOMPOSITION POTENTIALS OF PURE METAL CHLORIDES CALCULATED FROM THERMODYNAMIC DATA[1]
(Standard Potentials)

| Metal Chloride | M.P. (°C) | B.P. (C°) | $E°$ (volts) | | | | | | | |
| | | | 400 | 450 | 500 | 550 | 600 | 800 | 1000 | 1500 |
			t (°C)							
KCl	790	1500	3.854	3.805	3.755	3.707	3.658	3.441	3.155	2.598
BaCl$_2$	962	1560	3.888	3.848	3.808	3.768	3.728	3.568	3.412	3.079
CsCl	645	1300	3.791	3.739	3.692	3.645	3.599	3.362	3.078	2.667
RbCl	715	1390	3.795	3.745	3.695	3.645	3.595	3.314	3.001	2.428
SrCl$_2$	873	—	3.757	3.720	3.684	3.648	3.612	3.469	3.333	2.977
LiCl	614	1360	3.722	3.684	3.646	3.608	3.571	3.457	3.352	3.122
NaCl	800	1413	3.615	3.566	3.519	3.471	3.424	3.240	3.019	2.366
CaCl$_2$	772	1600	3.607	3.570	3.534	3.498	3.462	3.323	3.208	2.926
LaCl$_3$	872	—	3.277	3.241	3.205	3.170	3.143	2.997	2.876	2.607
CeCl$_3$	800	—	3.229	3.193	3.157	3.121	3.086	2.945	2.821	2.540
MgCl$_2$	714	1418	2.760	2.720	2.680	2.641	2.602	2.460	2.346	1.974
ZrCl$_2$	— dec.	—	2.629	2.594	2.560	2.526	2.508	—	—	—
UCl$_3$	835	—	2.566	2.530	2.494	2.458	2.423	2.280	2.162	1.886
ThCl$_4$	765	922	2.546	2.509	2.472	2.435	2.399	2.264	2.208	—
ZrCl$_3$	— dec.	—	2.540	2.509	2.492	—	—	—	—	—
UCl$_4$	590	—	2.217	2.181	2.146	2.111	2.078	1.974	1.953	—
MnCl$_2$	650	1190	2.032	1.999	1.967	1.935	1.902	1.807	1.725	1.649
TiCl$_2$	1035	—	2.006	1.975	1.945	1.914	1.885	—	—	—
TiCl$_3$	(730)	—	1.886	1.852	1.836	—	—	—	—	—
VCl$_2$	—	—	1.828	1.794	1.761	1.727	1.695	1.566	1.441	1.269
TlCl	429	816	1.660	1.629	1.606	1.583	1.561	1.473	1.470	—
ZnCl$_2$	283	732	1.655	1.629	1.603	1.577	1.532	1.476	—	—
CrCl$_2$	815	1300	1.600	1.568	1.537	1.505	1.474	1.352	1.262	1.137
CdCl$_2$	568	960	1.481	1.442	1.403	1.364	1.331	1.193	1.002	—
InCl	255	608	1.465	1.439	1.414	1.389	1.364	1.360	—	—
CrCl$_3$	subl.	945	1.412	1.374	1.336	1.299	1.261	1.113	1.006	—
PbCl$_2$	501	954	1.345	1.307	1.271	1.243	1.215	1.112	1.039	—
SnCl$_2$	247	652	1.373	1.346	1.320	1.295	1.270	1.259	—	—
FeCl$_2$	677	1026	1.327	1.297	1.267	1.237	1.207	1.118	1.050	1.041
COCl$_2$	740	1025	1.203	1.171	1.140	1.109	1.079	0.977	0.900	0.881
NiCl$_2$	subl.	987	1.139	1.104	1.070	1.036	1.003	0.875	0.763	—
CuCl	422	1366	1.050	1.035	1.024	1.013	1.003	0.970	0.943	0.862
AgCl	455	1550	0.935	0.911	0.896	0.883	0.870	0.826	0.784	0.665
PtCl$_2$	— dec.	—	0.328	0.299	0.270	0.242	0.225	—	—	—

electrode by a suitable diaphragm of the asbestos type. The cell potential is given by:

$$E_{cell} = E°_{UCl_3} - E°_{AgCl} - \frac{RT}{3F} \ln \frac{a_{UCl_3}}{a^3_{AgCl}} \quad (1)$$

where the experimentally measured emf,* E_{cell}, is always a positive quantity, and $E°_{UCl_3}$ and $E°_{AgCl}$ are the reversible decomposition potentials of the corresponding pure metal chlorides given in Table 1, and a_{UCl_3} and a_{AgCl} are the activities of UCl$_3$ and AgCl, respectively, in the dilute solutions. Experimental studies have shown that the cell potential varies linearly with the logarithmic term in Eq. (1) when the mole fractions for the metal chlorides become less than 10^{-2}.

* Corrected for the thermoelectric potential.[5]

For the concentration below this value, the activity coefficients become constant as the system follows quite closely Henry's law.

Eq. (1) may then be written as:

$$E_{cell} = E°_{UCl_3} - E°_{AgCl} - \frac{RT}{3F} \ln \frac{X_{UCl_3} \gamma_{UCl_3}}{(X_{AgCl} \cdot \gamma_{AgCl})^3} \quad (2)$$

where X is the mole fraction, and γ the activity coefficient.

The activity coefficient of AgCl in the equimolar mixture of NaCl-KCl is unity,[5] hence, Eq. (2) is also written as:

$$E_{cell} = \left[E°_{UCl_3} - E°_{AgCl} - \frac{RT}{3F} \ln \gamma_{UCl_3} \right]$$
$$- \frac{RT}{3F} \ln \frac{X_{UCl_3}}{X^3_{AgCl}} \quad (3)$$

TABLE 2. FORMAL ELECTRODE POTENTIALS IN EUTECTIC LiCl-KCl, AT 450°C[6, 7] AGAINST THE Pt, Pt²⁺, Ag, Ag⁺ AND Cl⁻, Cl° REFERENCE ELECTRODES

(Mole Fraction Scale)

	Pt, Pt⁺², volts	Ag, Ag⁺¹, volts	Cl⁻¹, Cl₂°, volts
Li⁺¹	−3.410	−2.773	−3.626
Mg⁺²	−2.580	−1.943	−2.796
Mn⁺²	−1.849	−1.212	−2.065
Al⁺³	−1.797	−1.160	−2.013
Zn⁺²	−1.566	−0.929	−1.782
V²⁺	−1.533	−0.896	−1.749
Cr⁺²	−1.425	−0.788	−1.641
Tl⁺¹	−1.370	−0.733	−1.586
Cd⁺²	−1.316	−0.679	−1.532
Fe²⁺	−1.171	−0.534	−1.387
Pb⁺²	−1.101	−0.464	−1.317
Sn⁺²	−1.082	−0.445	−1.298
Co⁺²	−0.991	−0.354	−1.207
Ga⁺³	−0.88	−0.243	−1.096
V³⁺, V²⁺	−0.854	−0.217	−1.070
Cu⁺¹	−0.851	−0.214	−1.067
In⁺³	−0.835	−0.198	−1.051
Ni⁺²	−0.795	−0.158	−1.011
Sb⁺³	−0.670	−0.033	−0.886
Ag⁺¹	−0.637	0	−0.853
Cr⁺³, Cr⁺²	−0.631	+0.006	−0.847
Bi⁺³	−0.588	+0.049	−0.804
Hg⁺²	−0.5	+0.137	−0.716
Pd⁺²	−0.214	+0.423	−0.430
Fe³⁺, Fe²⁺	−0.020	+0.617	−0.236
Pt⁺²	0	+0.637	−0.216
Cu⁺², Cu⁺¹	+0.045	+0.682	−0.171
Cl°, Cl⁻	+0.216	+0.853	0
Au⁺¹	+0.311	+0.948	+0.095

The quantity in brackets is a constant of the system and may be obtained experimentally by plotting the cell potential, E_{cell}, versus log X_{UCl_3}/X_{AgCl}^3 and extrapolating the resulting straight line to zero log-term.

The potential thus determined is the:

$$E_f{}^\circ = E_{UCl_3}^\circ - E_{AgCl}^\circ - \frac{RT}{3F} \ln \gamma_{UCl_3} \qquad (4)$$

and may be called the "formal potential" or "apparent standard potential" of the cell.

The formal potential, by the method of its derivation, defines a hypothetical standard state in which "the solute has a mole fraction of unity, but in all respects has the thermodynamic properties of a solution at infinite dilution."

Once $E_f{}^\circ$ has been determined in this manner, Eq. 4 may be rewritten as:

$$E_{cell}^\circ = E_f{}^\circ - \frac{RT}{3F} \ln \frac{X_{UCl_3}}{X_{AgCl}^3} \qquad (5)$$

and may be used to calculate the cell emf for any given mole fraction of the two solutes for which the linear function was found to be valid. The temperature dependence of the measured cell potentials and of the calculated formal potentials is linear over a wide temperature range. Formal potentials for a number of metal-metal chloride systems, obtained in this manner, are thermodynamically comparable and may be tabulated as an electromotive series.

Tables 2 and 3 show tabulations of this type.[2, 5, 6, 7, 8, 11]

Although the experimentally measured cell emf is always a positive quantity, the values listed in Tables 2, 3, and 4 have negative signs to conform with the IUPAC-Stockholm[9] convention. These negative values would then correspond to the opposite reactions.

From measurements of the cell:

Ag (−)	AgCl (X) (1/1 mole KCl, NaCl)	1/1 mole of KCl, NaCl	Cl₂ (1 atm) graphite (+)

at various temperatures, the data of Table 2 may be converted to values referred to a standard chlorine electrode as the "zero potential" reference.

The converted values would then correspond to the emf of the formation cell.

(U) (−)	UCl₃ (X) (1/1 mole KCl, NaCl)	Cl₂ (1 atm) graphite (+)

and to an overall cell reaction,

$$U + \tfrac{3}{2}\ Cl_2\ (1\ atm) \rightarrow$$
$$UCl_3\ (in\ 1/1\ mole\ KCl,\ NaCl)$$

By adding the values of the silver-silver chloride electrode to the potentials given in Table 3, formal potentials with respect to the chlorine scale are readily calculated and given in Table 4.

For example, the formal potential of UCl_3, in the chlorine scale should be given by the equation:

$$E_f{}^\circ = E_{UCl_3}^\circ - \frac{RT}{3F} \ln \gamma_{UCl_3} \qquad (6)$$

and the reversible decomposition potential of UCl_3 in solution in the equimolar mixture of KCl and NaCl at various concentrations, would be given by:

$$E_{cell} = (E_f{}^\circ)_{UCl_3} - \frac{RT}{3F} \ln X_{UCl_3} \qquad (7)$$

TABLE 3. FORMAL ELECTRODE POTENTIALS OF METALS IN FUSED 1/1 KCl-NaCl, AS CALCULATED AGAINST A SILVER-SILVER CHLORIDE REFERENCE ELECTRODE[2,5,8,11]

System	Negative Electrode Reaction in Molten KCl-NaCl	Overall Cell Reaction in Molten KCl-NaCl	Formal Potentials in Volts $(E_f°)^M$					
			670°C	700°C	750°C	800°C	850°C	900°C
Th, Th^{4+}	Th $\to$ Th^{4+} + e$^-$	Th + 4Ag$^+$ $\to$ Th^{4+} + 4Ag	−1.655	−1.643	−1.624	−1.605	−1.586	
U, U^{3+}	U $\to$ U^{3+} + 3e$^-$	U + 3Ag$^+$ $\to$ U^{3+} + 3Ag	−1.563	−1.554	−1.535	−1.519	−1.501	−1.485
U, U^{4+}	U $\to$ U^{4+} + 4e$^-$	U + 4Ag$^+$ $\to$ U^{4+} + 4Ag	−1.293	−1.285	−1.270	−1.252	−1.238	−1.223
Mn, Mn^{2+}	Mn $\to$ Mn^{2+} + 2e$^-$	Mn + 2Ag$^+$ $\to$ Mn^{2+} + 2Ag	−1.211	−1.206	−1.195	−1.190	−1.181	−1.172
Ti, Ti^{2+}	Ti $\to$ Ti^{2+} +2e$^-$	Ti + 2Ag$^+$ $\to$ Ti^{2+} + 2Ag	−1.115	−1.106	−1.095	−1.076	−1.062	−1.046
Ti, Ti^{3+}	Ti $\to$ Ti^{3+} + 3e$^-$	Ti + 3Ag$^+$ $\to$ Ti^{3+} + 3Ag	−1.046					
Ti^{2+}, Ti^{3+}	Ti^{2+} $\to$ Ti^{3+} + e$^-$	Ti^{2+} + Ag$^+$ $\to$ Ti^{3+} + Ag	−0.910					
Zn, Zn^{2+}	Zn $\to$ Zn^{2+} + 2e$^-$	Zn + 2Ag$^+$ $\to$ Zn^{2+} + 2Ag	−0.868	−0.860	−0.850	−0.835	−0.822	−0.810
Cr, Cr^{2+}	Cr $\to$ Cr^{2+} + 2e$^-$	Cr + 2Ag$^+$ $\to$ Cr^{2+} + 2Ag	−0.764	−0.758	−0.750	−0.740	−0.732	−0.726
Ti, Ti^{4+}	Ti $\to$ Ti^{4+} + 4e$^-$	Ti + 4AgCl + 2KCl $\to$ K$_2$TiCl$_6$ + 4Ag	−0.697					
Tl, Tl$^+$	Tl $\to$ Tl$^+$ + e$^-$	Tl + Ag$^+$ $\to$ Tl$^+$ + Ag	−0.665					
Cd, Cd^{2+}	Cd $\to$ Cd^{2+} + 2e$^-$	Cd + 2Ag$^+$ $\to$ Cd^{2+} + 2Ag	−0.632	−0.620	−0.600	−0.580		
Fe, Fe^{2+}	Fe $\to$ Fe^{2+} + 2e$^-$	Fe + 2Ag$^+$ $\to$ Fe^{2+} + 2Ag	−0.523	−0.520	−0.516	−0.510	−0.504	−0.498
U^{3+}, U^{4+}	U^{3+} $\to$ U^{4+} + e$^-$	U^{3+} + Ag$^+$ $\to$ U^{4+} + Ag	−0.494	−0.483	−0.473	−0.459	−0.449	−0.437
Cr, Cr^{3+}	Cr $\to$ Cr^{3+} + 3e$^-$	Cr + 3Ag$^+$ $\to$ Cr^{3+} + 3Ag	−0.437	−0.425	−0.405	−0.385	−0.364	−0.345
Pb, Pb^{2+}	Pb $\to$ Pb^{2+} + 2e$^-$	Pb + 2Ag$^+$ $\to$ Pb^{2+} + 2Ag	−0.394	−0.390	−0.385	−0.376	−0.365	−0.355
Sn, Sn^{2+}	Sn $\to$ Sn^{2+} + 2e$^-$	Sn + 2Ag$^+$ $\to$ Sn^{2+} + 2Ag	−0.375	−0.370	−0.360	−0.354	−0.346	−0.340
Co, Co^{2+}	Co $\to$ Co^{2+} + 2e$^-$	Co + 2Ag$^+$ $\to$ Co^{2+} + 2Ag	−0.336	−0.319	−0.310	−0.300	−0.287	−0.275
Cu, Cu$^+$	Cu $\to$ Cu$^+$ + e$^-$	Cu + Ag$^+$ $\to$ Cu$^+$ + Ag	−0.260	−0.256	−0.260	−0.256	−0.260	−0.260
Ni, Ni^{2+}	Ni $\to$ Ni^{2+} + 2e$^-$	Ni + 2Ag$^+$ $\to$ Ni^{2+} + 2Ag	−0.140					
Ag, Ag$^+$	Ag $\to$ Ag$^+$ + e$^-$		0	0	0	0	0	0
Cu, Cu^{2+}	Cu $\to$ Cu^{2+} + 2e$^-$	Cu + 2Ag$^+$ $\to$ Cu^{2+} + 2Ag	+0.167	+0.170	+0.175	+0.180	+0.187	+0.192
Cr^{2+}, Cr^{3+}	Cr^{2+} $\to$ Cr^{3+} + e$^-$	Cr^{2+} + Ag$^+$ $\to$ Cr^{3+} + Ag	+0.223	+0.246	+0.280	+0.321	+0.362	+0.396
Ti^{3+}, Ti^{4+}	Ti^{3+} $\to$ Ti^{4+} + e$^-$	Ti^{3+} + Ag$^+$ + 2KCl + 4Cl$^-$ $\to$ K$_2$TiCl$_6$ + Ag	+0.350					
Cu$^+$, Cu^{2+}	Cu$^+$ $\to$ Cu^{2+} + e$^-$	Cu$^+$ + Ag$^+$ $\to$ Cu^{2+} + Ag	+0.590	+0.596	+0.601	+0.611	+0.620	+0.628

It should be noted that similar relations may be developed for bromides, iodides, fluorides, oxides, or any other anion for which reversible electrodes may exist.

Eq. (6) is most useful in calculating metal-salt equilibria for various displacement reactions, while Eq. (7) may be used to obtain the reversible decomposition potentials of metal chlorides in

Table 4. Formal Electrode Potentials of Metals in Fused 1/1 KCl-NaCl As Calculated Against A Chlorine Reference Electrode[5, 8, 11]

System	Negative Electrode Reaction in Molten KCl-NaCl	Overall Cell Reaction in Molten KCl-NaCl	Formal Potentials in Volts ($E_f°$)					
			670°C	700°C	750°C	800°C	850°C	900°C
Th, Th^{4+}	Th → Th^{4+} + 4e$^-$	Th + 2Cl$_2$ → ThCl$_4$	−2.507	−2.488	−2.456	−2.425	−2.393	
U, U^{3+}	U → U^{3+} + 3e$^-$	U + $\frac{3}{2}$ Cl$_2$ → UCl$_3$	−2.415	−2.399	−2.365	−2.339	−2.309	−2.280
U, U^{4+}	U → U^{4+} + 4e$^-$	U + 2Cl$_2$ → UCl$_4$	−2.147	−2.130	−2.100	−2.072	−2.046	−2.018
Mn, Mn^{2+}	Mn → Mn^{2+} + 2e$^-$	Mn + Cl$_2$ → MnCl$_2$	−2.063	−2.051	−2.025	−2.010	−1.989	−1.957
Ti, Ti^{2+}	Ti → Ti^{2+} + 2e$^-$	Ti + Cl$_2$ → TiCl$_2$	−1.967	−1.951	−1.925	−1.896	−1.870	−1.841
Ti, Ti^{3+}	Ti → Ti^{3+} + 3e$^-$	Ti + $\frac{3}{2}$ Cl$_2$ → TiCl$_3$	−1.898					
Ti^{2+}, Ti^{3+}	Ti^{2+} → Ti^{3+} + e$^-$	TiCl$_2$ + $\frac{1}{2}$Cl$_2$ → TiCl$_3$	−1.762					
Zn, Zn^{2+}	Zn → Zn^{2+} + 2e$^-$	Zn + Cl$_2$ → ZnCl$_2$	−1.720	−1.705	−1.680	−1.655	−1.630	−1.605
Cr, Cr^{2+}	Cr → Cr^{2+} + 2e$^-$	Cr + Cl$_2$ → CrCl$_2$	−1.616	−1.603	−1.580	−1.560	−1.540	−1.521
Ti, Ti^{4+}	Ti → Ti^{4+} + 4e$^-$	Ti + 2Cl$_2$ + 2KCl → K$_2$TiCl$_6$	−1.549					
Tl, Tl$^+$	Tl → Tl$^+$ + e$^-$	Tl + $\frac{1}{2}$Cl$_2$ → TlCl	−1.517					
Cd, Cd^{2+}	Cd → Cd^{2+} + 2e$^-$	Cd + Cl$_2$ → CdCl$_2$	−1.484	−1.465	−1.430	−1.400		
Fe, Fe^{2+}	Fe → Fe^{2+} + 2e$^-$	Fe + Cl$_2$ → FeCl$_2$	−1.375	−1.365	−1.346	−1.330	−1.312	−1.293
U^{3+}, U^{4+}	U^{3+} → U^{4+} + e$^-$	UCl$_3$ + $\frac{1}{2}$Cl$_2$ → UCl$_4$	−1.346	−1.328	−1.303	−1.279	−1.257	−1.232
Cr, Cr^{3+}	Cr → Cr^{3+} + 3e$^-$	Cr + $\frac{3}{2}$ Cl$_2$ → CrCl$_3$	−1.289	−1.270	−1.235	−1.205	−1.172	−1.140
Pb, Pb^{2+}	Pb → Pb^{2+} + 2e$^-$	Pb + Cl$_2$ → PbCl$_2$	−1.246	−1.235	−1.215	−1.196	−1.173	−1.150
Sn, Sn^{2+}	Sn → Sn^{2+} + 2e$^-$	Sn + Cl$_2$ → SnCl$_2$	−1.227	−1.215	−1.190	−1.174	−1.154	−1.135
Co, Co^{2+}	Co → Co^{2+} + 2e$^-$	Co + Cl$_2$ → CoCl$_2$	−1.184	−1.164	−1.140	−1.120	−1.095	−1.070
Cu, Cu$^+$	Cu → Cu$^+$ + e$^-$	Cu + $\frac{1}{2}$Cl$_2$ → CuCl	−1.112	−1.101	−1.090	−1.076	−1.068	−1.055
Ni, Ni^{2+}	Ni → Ni^{2+} + 2e$^-$	Ni + Cl$_2$ → NiCl$_2$	−0.992		−0.			
Ag, Ag$^+$	Ag → Ag$^+$ + e$^-$	Ag + $\frac{1}{2}$Cl$_2$ → AgCl	−0.852	−0.845	−0.830	−0.820	−0.808	−0.795
Cu, Cu^{2+}	Cu → Cu^{2+} + 2e$^-$	Cu + Cl$_2$ → CuCl$_2$	−0.685	−0.675	−0.655	−0.640	−0.640	−0.603
Cr^{2+}, Cr^{3+}	Cr^{2+} → Cr^{3+} + e$^-$	CrCl$_2$ + $\frac{1}{2}$Cl$_2$ → CrCl$_3$	−0.629	−0.597	−0.555	−0.499	−0.499	−0.399
Ti^{3+}, Ti^{4+}	Ti^{3+} → Ti^{4+} + e$^-$	TiCl$_3$ + $\frac{1}{2}$Cl$_2$ + 2KCl → K$_2$TiCl$_6$	−0.502					
Cu$^+$, Cu^{2+}	Cu$^+$ → Cu^{2+} + e$^-$	CuCl + $\frac{1}{2}$Cl$_2$ → CuCl$_2$	−0.262	−0.249	−0.229	−0.209	−0.188	−0.167

Table 5. Electrode Potentials of Metals in Various Complex Electrolytes at 700°C, Calculated Against the Sodium Glass Electrode as the Zero Potential* Reference.[10]

Electrode System	In, NaCl-SrCl$_2$-KCl, + 10 mole % MCl$_n$	In, NaCl-AlCl$_3$, + 5 mole % MCl$_n$	In, NaBr-KBr + 10 mole % MBr$_n$	In, NaBr-AlBr$_3$, + 5 mole % MBr$_n$	In, NaI-AlI$_3$ + 5 mole % MI$_n$	In NaI	In NaF
Na, Na$^+$	0	0	0	0	0	0	0
Li, Li$^+$	—	—	—	—	—		0.29
Zn, Zn^{2+}	1.83	1.90	1.60	1.73	—	1.36	0.75
Mn, Mn^{2+}	1.41	1.77	1.26	1.40	—	0.98	0.67
Be, Be^{2+}	1.33	1.43	1.33	1.40	—	1.24	—
Al, Al^{3+}	1.65	1.58	1.66	1.60	1.61	1.64	0.81
Tl, Tl$^+$	1.71	1.79	1.42	1.49	—	1.16	—
Cd, Cd^{2+}	1.99	2.01	1.70	1.77	1.63	1.50	0.93
Sn, Sn^{2+}	2.27	2.11	2.06	2.07	1.76	1.70	—
Cu, Cu$^+$	2.31	2.41	2.16	2.07	1.82	1.72	—
Ag, Ag$^+$	2.47	2.38	2.08	2.14	1.66	1.68	—
Hg, Hg^{2+}	2.51	2.49	2.34	2.26	2.08	2.10	—
Pb, Pb^{2+}	2.19	2.17	2.06	2.07	1.76	1.70	1.19
Co, Co^{2+}	2.35	2.42	2.00	2.19	2.10	1.82	1.19
Ni, Ni^{2+}	2.37	—	2.22	2.27	2.16	2.06	1.33

* Potentials given in this table represent the difference,

$$E = E°_{Na, Na^+} - E°_{M, M^{n+}}$$

as in Table 6. Accordingly the potential, $E°_{M,M^{n+}}$, which may be calculated from the data is the decomposition potential of the corresponding metal chloride in solutions having the stated compositions.

solution. Equilibrium potential data may also be used to calculate the conditions for the simultaneous discharge of several ions at a cathode or the preferential deposition of one of the metal cations in the electrolyte. For example, it may be predicted from the data in Table 3, that titanium metal should be recovered by the electrolysis of titanium tetrachloride dissolved in alkali chloride solvents by a process involving two main stages.

In the first stage, at about 1.5 volts, the tetravalent titanium ions should be reduced to a mixture of di- and trivalent titanium ions in solution, and in the second stage the metal should be recovered from this solution at a potential of about 2.5 volts. Recent experimental

TABLE 6. ELECTRODE POTENTIALS OF METAL-METAL HALIDE SYSTEMS AT 700°C, CALCULATED AGAINST THE SODIUM GLASS ELECTRODE AS THE "ZERO POTENTIAL" REFERENCE[10]*

Electrode System	ΔE (volts)			
	F^-	Cl^-	Br^-	I^-
Na, Na^+ (as NaCl)	0	0	0	0
Li, Li^+	+0.56	−0.02	−0.05	−0.14
Sr, Sr^{2+}	−0.40	−0.15	−0.06	−0.13
Rb, Rb^+	—	−0.23	—	—
K, K^+	+0.22	−0.14	−0.18	−0.17
Ba, Ba^{2+}	−0.47	−0.23	−0.27	−0.01
Cs, Cs^+	—	−0.29	—	—
Ca, Ca^{2+}	−0.29	+0.01	+0.10	+0.18
Mg, Mg^{2+}	+0.56	+0.78	+0.77	+0.80
La, La^{3+}	—	+0.22	—	—
Th, Th^{4+}	—	+1.17	—	—
Be, Be^{2+}	—	+1.47	—	—
Mn, Mn^{2+}	—	+1.51	+1.52	+1.37
Al, Al^{3+}	—	+1.78	+1.78	+1.72
Tl, Tl^+	—	+1.92	+1.66	+1.40
Zn, Zn^{2+}	—	+1.96	+1.85	+1.54
Cd, Cd^{2+}	—	+2.11	+1.89	+1.62
Pb, Pb^{2+}	—	+2.27	+2.07	+1.82
Sn, Sn^{2+}	—	+2.31	+2.22	+1.78
Ni, Ni^{2+}	—	+2.36	—	—
Co, Co^{2+}	—	+2.42	+2.30	+2.24
Hg, Hg^{2+}	—	+2.53	+2.44	+2.18
Ag, Ag^+	—	+2.55	+2.25	+1.74
Cu, Cu^+	—	+2.65	+2.29	+1.98
Bi, Bi^{3+}	—	+2.75	+2.54	+2.14
Sb, Sb^{3+}	—	+2.90	+2.56	+2.30

* Potentials shown in this table represent the difference

$$E = E^{\circ}_{Na,Na^+} - E^{\circ}_{M,M^{n+}}$$

where the sodium electrode potential, E°_{Na,Na^+}, is the decomposition potential of pure sodium chloride at 700°C, i.e., $E^{\circ}_{Na,Na^+} = 3.39$ volts. The potential, $E^{\circ}_{M,M^{n+}}$, which can be calculated from the data in the table, represents the decomposition potential of the corresponding pure metal halide.

evidence has indicated the correctness of the proposed mechanism.

The electrode potentials of various metal-metal halide systems, with respect to a sodium glass electrode as a zero potential reference, have also been calculated by Delimarski[10] and are given in Tables 5 and 6.

The calculations were based on the experimentally measured decomposition potentials, and accordingly the values listed herein should be considered only as approximate.

References

1. HAMER, W. H., MALMBERG, M. S., AND RUBIN, B., *J. Electrochem. Soc.*, **103**, 8 (1956).
2. FLENGAS, S. N., *Can. J. Chem.*, **39**, 773 (1961).
3. GRUEN, D. M., AND OSTERYOUNG, R. A., *Ann. N. Y. Acad. Sc.*, **79**, 897 (1960).
4. BOCKRIS, J. O'M., *Can. J. Chem.*, **37**, 1161 (1961).
5. FLENGAS, S. N., AND INGRAHAM, T. R., *J. Electrochem. Soc.*, **106**, 714 (1959).
6. LAITINEN, H. A., AND LIU, C. H., *J. Am. Chem. Soc.*, **80**, 1015 (1958).
7. LAITINEN, H. A., AND PANKEY, J. W., *J. Am. Chem. Soc.*, **81**, 1053 (1959).
8. FLENGAS, S. N., *Ann. N. Y. Acad. Sc.*, **79**, 853 (1960).
9. LICHT, T. S., AND deBETHUNE, A. J., *J. Chem. Educ.*, **34**, 443 (1957).
10. DELIMARSKI, IU. K., AND MARKOV, B. F., "Electrochemistry of Fused Salts," translated by R. E. Wood, Washington, D. C., The Sigma Press Publishers, 1961.
11. SRINIVASAN, R., AND FLENGAS, S. N., *Can. J. Chem.* (in press).

S. N. FLENGAS

Cross-reference: other entries under *Fused Salt* headings; *Titanium, Electrolytic Preparation.*

FUSED SALT OVERVOLTAGE MEASUREMENTS

In previous entries the methods of measuring the equilibrium electrode potentials in molten salts, and the significance of the measurements have been presented. It has been explained that the thermodynamic treatment and the various forms of the Nernst equation for a cell potential are valid only when the electrode reactions occur reversibly, in which conditions no net reaction takes place in the cell.

Unfortunately, reversible reactions cannot be realized in practice, as any useful electrolytic process should also be irreversible by definition. Thus, when it is attempted to carry out a reaction at an electrode at an appreciable rate, the potential of the electrode should be changed in a direction that would sustain the flow of current. The degree of reversibility is measured by the departure of the electrode potential from the reversible value, under the same conditions of temperature, pressure, and concentration of the electrolyte.

The applicability of Faraday's law to molten salt electrolysis has been well established by various investigators. Reduced current efficiencies in certain operations can only indicate secondary reactions in the cell. These should include: solubility of the metals in the molten electrolyte, stepwise reductions at the cathode, anodic reoxidation, volatility of the electrolysis product, formation of metallic deposits in the form of fine powders, simultaneous discharge of several ions, electronic conductance in the molten electrolyte, anode effect, etc. However, the detailed discussion of each of these effects is beyond the scope of this article.

The potential of a polarized electrode in molten salts may be measured by techniques which are similar to these developed for aqueous systems. That is, the potentials of a working electrode are measured during electrolysis against a suitable reference electrode. The geometric arrangement of the two electrodes in this case is quite important as the body of the reference electrode should not shield the exposed surface area of the working electrode, and the measured changes in the electrode potential should not include any of the IR drop in the electrolyte.

The conditions for reliable overvoltage measurements and their interpretation have been discussed recently by Piontelli.[1] Owing to the many technical difficulties at high temperatures and to the nonavailability of reliable reference electrodes, until recently, very few accurate data on overvoltage measurements in molten salts have been made available. However, it appears from the information that is available, that the activation overvoltage during cathodic metal deposition is negligibly small.

Solid metals deposit from fused salts with a small activation polarization that could also be accounted for by the experimental error of the measurements. Thus, the overvoltage reported for the deposition of Ag from fused $AgNO_3$, or AgI, at a current density of 5 amp/sq cm is only 1.5 mv. With AgCl and AgBr under the same conditions, the overvoltage is 4–5 mv and

in the electrolysis of Cu_2Cl_2, it is only 1 mv. According to Drossbach[2] in the electrolysis of the system $NiCl_2$-KCl-NaCl containing 21 weight per cent $NiCl_2$, the overvoltage of the nickel electrode is only 11–16 mv. Polarization measurements by Piontelli, on the electrode systems:

$Pb_{(l)}/PbCl_{2(l)}$, $Pb_{(l)}/PbCl_2 + KCl$, $Cd_{(l)}/CdCl_2 + KCl$, $Sn_{(c)}/SnCl_2 + KCl$, $Zn_{(l)}/ZnCl_2 + KCl$, $Mg_{(l)}/MgCl_2 + KCl$, $Al_{(s)}/AlCl_3 + KCl$, $Ni_{(s)}/NiCl_2 + KCl$, and $Cu_{(s)}/CuCl_2 + KCl$

at temperatures up to 750°C have indicated the absence of activation polarization. Piontelli points out that the vanishing of electrode overvoltage in chloride melts appears to be a property that is shared at high temperatures by all metals, i.e., metals whose overvoltages are small in aqueous solutions at ordinary temperatures, and by metals like nickel which are characterized by high overvoltages.

According to Delimarski,[3] at the interface between a metal and a melt, the exchange currents are quite large and of the order of several amperes per sq cm. Recent work by Nanis[4] has also confirmed the existence of such large exchange currents. As long as the polarizing current is smaller than the exchange current, an appreciable polarization of the electrode is not likely to occur. With solid electrodes, the situation is more complicated as passivation might also take place by a chemical action of the electrolyte, or because of oxygen or water impurities in the melt. Thus, Piontelli has observed that a nickel electrode immersed in melts containing nitrate ions became coated with compact uniform layers of the oxide, NiO.

Data on anodic overvoltage are even more scarce. It is characteristic of the lack of information in this field that the behavior of carbon anodes during the production of aluminum by the well-known Hall-Heroult process is still open to discussion.

The cathodic reaction in cryolite, $3NaF \cdot AlF_3$, containing 2–7 per cent Al_2O_3, is primarily

$$2Al^{3+} + 6e^- \rightarrow 2Al \qquad (1)$$

while some sodium metal is also codeposits. Both Drossbach[5] and Piontelli[6] found that the cathodic overvoltage on aluminum cathodes is negligibly small.

The anodic reaction, however, appears to be more complicated. The anode consists of a carbon electrode, and the oxygen which is primarily deposited reacts chemically with the carbon producing carbon dioxide, and to a smaller extent, carbon monoxide.

The overall anodic reaction may be represented by either of the following equations:

$$3O^{--} - 6e^- \rightarrow 3[O] \qquad (2)$$

$$3[O] + 3C \rightarrow 3CO \qquad (3)$$

or

$$6[O] + 3C \rightarrow 3CO_2 \qquad (3a)$$

The overall cell reaction may be found by adding Eqs. (1), (2) and (3), as:

$$Al_2O_3 + 3C \rightarrow 2Al + 3CO \qquad (4)$$

or

$$2Al_2O_3 + 3C \rightarrow 4Al + 3CO_2 \qquad (4a)$$

Welch and Richards[7, 8] considered the carbon reference electrode as an oxygen electrode, where the oxygen pressure is determined by the equilibrium:

$$CO + \tfrac{1}{2}O_2 \rightleftharpoons CO_2 \qquad (5)$$

Carbon in this case behaves as an inert electrode and does not take part in the electrode reaction. The overall cell reaction may be found by adding Eqs. (1), (2) and (5), as:

$$Al_2O_3 + 3CO \rightarrow 2Al + 3CO_2 \qquad (6)$$

where the CO/CO_2 ratio defines the equilibrium oxygen pressure.

At 1000°C, the calculated reversible potential, corresponding to an overall cell reaction given by either Eqs. (4) or (4a), is of the order of 1 volt, while that represented by reaction (6), at a P_{CO_2}/P_{CO} ratio equal to 3, is of the order of 1.4 volts. Welch and Richards measured the reversible potential corresponding to reaction (6) and obtained values of the order of only 1.0 volt. The discrepancy was explained in terms of the nonreliability of the aluminum cathode reaction.

It is of interest to note that the decomposition potential in an aluminum cell operating with a current density of about 1 amp/sq cm is about 1.7 volts.[9]

Recent experimental work by Thonstad and Hove[10] indicates that the reversible cell reaction is best represented by Eqs. (4) and (4a), and that reaction (5) is too slow to influence the oxy-gen equilibrium. Thus, the voltage in excess of the reversible potential represents an anodic activation overvoltage that follows the Tafel equation. The origin of this overvoltage is not yet too well understood, and appears to increase with decreasing chemical reactivity of the carbon anodes.

Overvoltage measurements on graphite anodes, during the electrolysis of chloride melts, i.e., KCl-MgCl₂ at 750°C, by Piontelli[1] indicated the absence of any significant overvoltage.

"Concentration polarization" has not been included in the present discussion. The term is significant only in the electrolysis of molten mixtures, as concentration gradients cannot exist in one-component melts. Concentration polarization appears only at high current densities, with electrodes of relatively small surface area, and in cells that should be free of any kind of convection.

It may be concluded that deposition or decomposition potentials in simple molten salts may be calculated with sufficient accuracy from the corresponding data on the equilibrium potentials. Equilibrium potential data may also be used to calculate the conditions for the simultaneous discharge of several ions at a cathode or the preferential deposition of one of the metal cations in the electrolyte. With complex electrode systems, the information available at present is insufficient to allow for any generalizations. It is evident that more experimental work is required in this field.

References

1. PIONTELLI, R., *Ann. N. Y. Acad. Sc.*, **79,** 11, 1025 (1960).
2. DROSSBACH, P., *Z. Electrochem.*, **56,** 23 (1952).
3. DELIMARSKI, IU. K., AND MARKOV, B. F., "Electrochemistry of Fused Salts," trans. by R. E. Wood, Washington, D. C., The Sigma Press Publishers, 1961.
4. NANIS, L., "Electrode Kinetics in the System Ag-AgNO₃," paper presented to the XVIIIth Congress of Pure and Applied Chemistry, Montreal, August 1961.
5. DROSSBACH, P., *Z. Elektrochem.*, **42,** 65 (1936).
6. PIONTELLI, R., Atti simposia electrolisi sali fusi e produzione metalli speciali in Italia, Milano, 1960.
7. WELCH, B. J., AND RICHARDS, N. E., AIME International Symposium on the Extractive Metallurgy of Aluminum, New York, 1962.
8. RICHARDS, N. E., "Studies of anode overpotential in an aluminum reduction cell," Part I; "Development of a Reference Electrode," Project No. 2-8-003-1, Reduction

Research Laboratory, Reynolds Metals Company, Listerhill, Alabama, June, 1961.
9. PORTER, E. C., "Electrochemistry," p. 322, New York, MacMillan Co., 1961.
10. THONSTAD, J., AND HOVE, E., "The anodic overvoltage in aluminum electrolysis," *Can. J. Chem.* (in press).

S. N. FLENGAS

Cross-references: *Aluminum Electrowinning;* other entries with *Fused Salt* headings.

FUSED SALT POLAROGRAPHY

Polarographic techniques developed for aqueous solutions have been successfully extended to the study of high-temperature fused salt systems. Polarographic studies in fused salts have been characterized by the variety of techniques used and by the wide range of fused salt systems studied. Polarography in fused salts has not been confined to simple problems of analysis but has been employed as a tool for the study of problems of a fundamental nature, such as complex ion formation, kinetics of electrode processes, evaluation of diffusion coefficients, subhalide formation in metal-metal salt systems, characterization of oxidation states, and studies of the structure of fused salts.

Delimarskii and Markov,[2] in their chapter on fused salt polarography, have pointed out the wide range of solvent systems which have been investigated. These range from the lower melting nitrate, bisulfate, perchlorate, and formate systems to the higher melting ones, such as halides, sulfates, borates, phosphates, and oxides. Indicator electrodes employed in these studies include dropping metal electrodes, i.e., mercury in the low melting nitrates, bismuth in the higher melting chlorides, and solid microelectrodes which include electrodes flush-ground to the seal, needle electrodes, rotating electrodes, and dipping or bubbling electrodes.

As in aqueous polarography, the reference electrodes used in fused salt polarography should be nonpolarizable or at worst only slightly polarizable and can be considered to fall into two types: (1) a nonpolarizable electrode with a nondefined potential, best represented by a large metal foil or pool in direct contact with the fused salt solution corresponding to the mercury pool used in aqueous polarography; (2) a nonpolarizable electrode of a well defined potential, such as a gas electrode, e.g., the Cl_2-Cl^-

electrode, or a metal in contact with a solution of its ion in the fused salt. An example of the latter is the Pt(II)-Pt electrode used by Laitinen, Liu, and Ferguson.[8] This type of electrode must be separated from the main solution with electrolytic contact through some type of salt bridge. Decomposition potentials of pure and mixed fused salts and half-wave potentials of metal ions are generally measured against a reference electrode of the second type.

Polarograms obtained in fused salts are very similar to those obtained in aqueous polarography. Polarographic waves for a number of fused salt systems have been characterized with regard to the wave height, shape, and half-wave potential. Steinberg and Nachtrieb[10] used the dropping mercury electrode in the $LiNO_3$-$NaNO_3$-KNO_3 mixture at 160°C to study the cathodic polarograms of cadmium (II), nickel (II), lead (II), and zinc (II). The polarograms obtained were very similar to those obtained in aqueous nitrate solutions. Plots of log $i/i_d - i$ vs E, applied potential, gave slopes within 4 per cent of the theoretical value predicted from the equation

$$E = E_{1/2} - \frac{RT}{nF} \ln \frac{i}{i_d - i}.$$

They also found that plots of log $i_d - i/i$ vs E for anodic polarograms of cadmium and lead in a dropping cadmium or lead amalgam electrode yielded slopes in fair agreement with theory.

Black and De Vries[1] studied the cathodic polarography of nickel (II), cobalt (II), and lead (II) in the LiCl-KCl eutectic at stationary and rotating platinum microelectrodes. Slopes of the plot of log $i_d - i$ vs E for these ions at a stationary platinum microelectrode were in fair agreement with those predicted from the equation

$$E = E_M^0 - 2.3 \frac{RT}{nF} \log \frac{K_s}{f_s} + 2.3 \frac{RT}{nF} \log i_d - i$$

where f_s is the activity of the metal ion and K_s is a proportionality constant. They also showed that the polarographic wave height at a rotating platinum electrode depends on the mole fraction of the electroactive species, the rate of rotation, the rate of polarization, the electrode area, and the temperature. The change of half-wave potential as a function of concentration was found in agreement with theory. They reported that in the stepwise reduction of CrO_4^{--} to Cr (III) then to Cr (II) the ratio of the wave heights was in the predicted ratio of 3:1.

Laitinen et al[8] found that the stepwise reduction of chromium (III) to chromium (II) then to the metal in the LiCl-KCl eutectic at 450°C, the ratio of the first wave's height to the total wave height was the theoretical 1:3. They also showed that the plot of $i_d - i$ vs E was a straight line with the predicted slope for both cadmium (II) and bismuth (III). Polarograms of copper (II), copper (I), indium (III), gallium (III), lead (II), thallium (I), mercury (II), and aluminum (III) were also obtained in the chloride eutectic.

Use of polarography in fused salts for the study of complex ions was first made by Christie and Osteryoung.[4] They were able to determine polarographically the formation constants of the metal-chloro complexes of lead (II), cadmium (II), and nickel (II) in the $LiNO_3$-KNO_3 eutectic at 160°C by measuring the shift of the half-wave potential of these metal ions as a function of chloride ion concentration. It was shown that the electrode process was diffusion controlled; a plot of log i_d vs log h, height of the mercury column, had a slope close to the theoretical value of 0.500.

Another interesting electrode used in fused salts is the dipping platinum electrode developed by Flengas.[6] He achieved a periodic dipping and isolation of a platinum electrode by a bubbling arrangement. For the reduction of silver (I) in a KNO_3-$NaNO_3$ mixture it was found that the product of the diffusion current, i_d, and the square root of the bubbling time was a constant.

Diffusion coefficients of ions in fused salt media have been determined polarographically. Steinberg and Nachtrieb[10] evaluated diffusion coefficients of heavy metal ions in fused $LiNO_3$-$NaNO_3$-KNO_3. Heus and Egan[7] determined diffusion coefficients of lead (II) and cadmium (II) in the LiCl-KCl eutectic at 450°C using a dropping bismuth electrode. The use of these electrodes minimized many of the problems inherent in the use of solid microelectrodes for diffusion coefficient studies, i.e., poorly-defined electrode areas, dendrite formation, and deviation from linear diffusion conditions at a small electrode.

Although cathodic processes have been the main subject in fused salt investigations some studies of anodic processes have been performed. Lialikov and Novik[9] using a platinum indicator electrode studied the anodic behavior of bromide, iodide, and nitrite ions in fused nitrates, and found evidence that the oxidation was irreversible. Egan[5] used the anodic wave of excess lead dissolved in its chloride to show that Pb_2^{++} ion was formed in the molten Pb-$PbCl_2$ system.

There are of course many other applications of polarography to the study of fused salt systems. Several should be mentioned to further demonstrate the scope of the technique. Chovnyk[3] applied derivative polarography in the $AlBr_3$-$NaCl$ system at 245°C. He studied the reduction of cadmium (II), cobalt (II), lead (II), and Cu (I), and reported that he could achieve better resolution and higher sensitivity than with a conventional polarographic technique. Delimarskii[2] and coworkers have studied the polarography of metal oxides dissolved in borax and metaphosphate melts.

References

1. BLACK, E. D., AND DE VRIES, T., Anal. Chem., **27**, 906 (1955).
2. DELIMARSKII, IU. K., AND MARKOV, B. F., "Electrochemistry of Fused Salts," Chapter 8, Washington, D. C., The Sigma Press, Translation 1961.
3. CHOVNYK, Doklady Akad. Nauk. SSSR, **95**, 599 (1954).
4. CHRISTIE, J. H., AND OSTERYOUNG, R. A., J. Am. Chem. Soc., **82**, 1841 (1960).
5. EGAN, J. J., J. Phys. Chem., **65**, 2222 (1961).
6. FLENGAS, S. N., J. Chem. Soc., 534 (1956).
7. HEUS, R. J., AND EGAN, J. J., J. Electrochem. Soc., **107**, 824 (1960).
8. LAITINEN, H. A., LIU, C. H., AND FERGUSON, W. S., Anal. Chem., **30**, 1266 (1958).
9. LIALIKOV, M. S., AND NOVIK, R. M., Uch zap. Kishineuskogo Univ., **27**, 61 (1957).
10. STEINBERG, M., AND NACHTRIEB, N. H., J. Am. Chem. Soc., **72**, 3558 (1950).

JOHN D. VAN NORMAN

Cross-references: Chronopotentiometry; Polarography.

FUSED SALTS, ELECTROREFINING IN. See ELECTROREFINING IN MOLTEN SALTS.

FUSED SALT TRANSPORT NUMBERS

Concepts and Principles

The transport or transference number of an ionic species in any electrolyte is defined as the fraction of the total current carried by that species during electrolysis. Thus,

$$t_i = z_i J_i / \sum z_k J_k ,$$

where z refers to ionic charge and J to flux (gram formula wt/sq cm-sec), the summation being taken over all ionic species. But since $J_i = c_i v_i$ (concentration times velocity), the magnitude of the flux and, hence, that of the transport number, depends on a frame of reference. The choice of reference for ionic velocities in any electrolyte is arbitrary. Most systems of interest, however, contain one that is natural or logical—a neutral solvent present in large excess, or even the set of lattice points on a crystal. No such obvious frame of reference exists in a fused salt. It is this fact which has led to considerable confusion in the past, and which forms the basis for much of the following discussion.

The suitability of a given reference depends on the purpose for which transport numbers are required. The uses to which they have been put can be divided into two categories. (a) Transport numbers provide a means of correlating the results of different types of experiments involving ionic motion in a given electrolyte. Obvious examples are the different experiments by which they can be measured (to be discussed below). (b) An individual ionic conductance λ_i, or mobility $\mu_i = \lambda_i/\mathbf{F}$ (sq cm/volt sec), can be assigned to each species on the basis of its transport number and the equivalent conductance, Λ, of the electrolyte: $\lambda_i = t_i \Lambda$. Such quantities are useful in predicting the conductivities of systems containing various combinations of ions, and provide an experimental basis for theories of conductance that treat the motion of each species separately.

When the need for transport numbers in a fused salt falls into category (a), the problem of finding a suitable reference reduces to that of making sure the same reference is employed in all experiments to be correlated. This does not necessarily put restrictions on experimental procedures, since it is usually possible from the results of a particular transference experiment to calculate transport numbers relative to any reference frame of interest. If the ionic velocity relative to a reference, r, is employed in determining the transport number, t_{ir}, then the value of t_{is}, the transport number relative to a new reference, s, is given by

$$t_{is} = t_{ir} + z_i c_i v_s / \sum z_k J_k$$

where v_s is the velocity at which s moves with respect to r during the experiment. If r consists, for example, of the walls of the cell, and s is the

center of the mass of the liquid, then

$$\frac{v_s}{\sum z_k J_k} = \frac{1}{\rho} \sum_k \frac{t_{kr} M_k}{z_k}$$

where M_k is the gram formula weight of species k, and ρ is the density of the melt. (Note that since $\sum z_k J_k$ is equal to the total current density, the reference for J_k in the expressions above is arbitrary).

The reference in a given experiment is not always obvious. When electrolysis is carried out in a U-tube, ionic velocities relative to the tube are subject to the gravitational requirement that the hydrostatic pressures in both arms of the tube remain equal. In the case of a binary fused salt this means that transport numbers are completely determined by the relative diameters of the two arms, the equivalent volume of the salt, and the nature of the electrode reactions. Now, if a temperature gradient is established along the tube, the same electrodes (assuming they are reversible) can be used to measure the thermoelectric power of the system. To interpret the results of this measurement in terms ionic "heats of transport" requires a knowledge of the transport numbers relative to the thermal gradient. Since this has been fixed relative to the walls of the tube, it might appear that the transport numbers defined by electrolysis in the same tube are appropriate. This is not the case. When current is passed through the cell, the velocities of ions relative to the tube are determined initially by their interactions with its walls. Any motion that tends to produce an accumulation of ions in one arm, however, will lead to an opposing gravitational force. Even in a 1 mm bore capillary U-tube a steady state will quickly be established at normal current densities in which the two liquid levels are not noticeably different. By employing a much finer capillary, however, or a large-bore tube with arms separated by a porous plug (max. pore diameter about 1μ), it is possible to observe the motion of the liquid due to ionic interaction with the walls before the gravitational effect becomes significant. The transport numbers determined by such an experiment are the relevant quantities in the interpretation of thermoelectric power, since the current flowing during an emf measurement is too small to produce a significant "head" in the liquid. In principle, these transport numbers could depend on the diameter of the pore or tube, as well as on its chemical composition and surface condition. Transference measurements on several molten salts using a variety of porous separators have given evidence to the contrary, however, as has the observed indifference of thermoelectric power in molten silver nitrate to the presence of a porous diaphragm in the thermal gradient.

The situation is more straightforward in another type of emf measurement requiring transport numbers for its interpretation. Whenever there is an isothermal junction between two electrolytes of dissimilar composition, the resulting "junction potential" can be related to individual ionic contributions as follows:

$$E_{l.j.} = \frac{RT}{\mathbf{F}} \int \sum \frac{t_i}{z_i} \, d \ln a_i \qquad (1)$$

The integration extends from one electrolyte composition to the other, and the summation is taken over all species in the junction. The magnitude of this sum is independent of the reference selected for the transport numbers, so that *any* self-consistent set of t_i is adequate. At the junction of two pure salts having one ion in common, for example, it is convenient to choose the common ion for reference. Its transport number is then equal to zero throughout the entire range. The transport numbers of the two like-charged species can be determined as functions of concentration by methods to be discussed below.

It is the attempt to use transport numbers in fused salts as a basis for defining useful ionic mobilities (category (b)) that has encountered the greatest difficulty. Conductivity data show that it is impossible to assign to each species a unique mobility that is preserved from one fused salt to another. Although not a surprising result, this rules out use of the ion mobility concept for fused salts in one way that has been of primary importance in other electrolytes.

The possibility of using experimentally determined ion mobilities as a guide in developing the theory of electrolytic conductance in fused salts has presumably been the major objective in attempts to devise a suitable method for transport numbers. There has been a tendency for many workers to regard this as an experimental problem resulting from the inapplicability of conventional methods designed for determining mobility relative to an inert solvent. Thus, the numerous reports of transport number determinations in the literature must be examined with care to ascertain the nature of the reference

in each case. Sometimes it is completely trivial, like the walls of the large-bore U-tube discussed above. Most commonly, however, it corresponds more nearly to the fine capillary or porous plug. Since this latter type of reference seems to have gained some popularity currently as a basis for assigning ion mobilities in fused salts, its significance bears further examination here.

A satisfactory interpretation of fused salt transport numbers measured relative to an adjacent wall in the absence of bulk flow of the liquid has yet to be presented in the literature. Phenomenologically, transport of an electrolyte through a porous diaphragm by application of an electric field is called *electroosmosis* (q.v.). Experimental results for aqueous electrolytes were known as far back as the time of Helmholtz, who provided a theoretical analysis based on the inhomogeneous distribution of charge at the solid-liquid interface (the electrical double layer). The Helmholtz treatment thus predicts that the electroosmotic behavior of a given electrolyte will depend on the nature of the solid material with which it is in contact. This is found to be the case in dilute electrolytic solutions, and the theory is generally accepted. In a pure fused salt, however, there can be no significant changes of concentration near a solid surface, so that the nature of the double layer must be very different. The experimentally-observed lack of dependence of electroosmotic transport on the nature of the porous diaphragm indicates that a property of the salt, rather than the salt-solid interface, is being measured. (This is analogous to the measurement of viscosity, in which the rate of flow is independent of the nature of the wall past which a fluid is flowing). It would seem to justify using a name like "transport number" to distinguish this operationally defined property of a fused salt from phenomena familiarly identified with interfacial properties. Mobilities calculated from such transport numbers have been called "external mobilities" in a recent article by Klemm.[1]

Even though the significance of ion mobilities based on electroosmotic transport has not been elaborated, some workers have identified the frame of reference as "the bulk of the liquid," implying that this remains fixed relative to the cell wall in the absence of viscous flow. The nature of the "bulk" in a system composed of two types of particles moving in opposite directions has not been further specified. Experiments on a substantial number of systems show that in general it is *not* identical with the center of mass of the liquid, as was suggested by one worker when the only reliable data available were the results for pure $PbCl_2$. A microscopic picture of ionic motion forms the basis for an interpretation that has appealed to a number of workers. Each ion of the liquid is assumed to spend most of its time at potential energy minima defined by the positions of surrounding ions, much like lattice points of an ionic crystal. Transport is effected by the occasional jumps between such minima that occur when the ion acquires sufficient thermal energy. For a mechanism of this type the reference frame of interest is the immediate environment of the ion as it jumps. The assumption that this remains fixed relative to the walls of a porous plug (as it would in a crystal) thus leads to a microscopic interpretation of experimental results. This viewpoint can be questioned, however, on the ground that there is no lattice in a liquid. There is not even a restriction on the motion of the environment of a moving cation relative to that of a moving anion. Thus, unless such a restriction is incorporated into the model, there may be more than one microscopic reference frame. Transport numbers are no longer required to total unity, and a single macroscopic reference of any kind is inadequate.

In view of the foregoing, future attempts to develop the theory of conductance in fused salts may be forced to focus on mobilities of ionic species relative to other species in the same melt. Klemm has proposed the name "internal mobilities" for such quantities.[1] In a pure salt the mobility of either ion relative to the other is calculated directly from the equivalent conductance: $\mu_{+-} = \Lambda/\mathbf{F}$. In a mixture there is one μ_{ik} for each pair of ionic species present, but they are not all independent. For this reason the "interionic friction coefficients," a set of phenomenological coefficients developed from equations of irreversible thermodynamics,[2] may offer some advantage. Still another approach is to use "diffusional" mobilities, determined by means of ionic tracer-diffusion experiments, as a basis in defining electrical mobilities. For the former quantities the choice of reference frame is unequivocal. The potential usefulness of such definitions depends on similarity of the microscopic mechanisms of diffusion and migration processes. Experimental results show that they cannot be identical, but some workers have assumed this is due to factors that can be taken into account in the definition. Two different proposals in the literature lead to the same expression for transport numbers in a pure binary salt.[3]

$$t_i = 0.5 + \frac{\mathbf{F}^2}{2RT\Lambda}\left(\left|z_i\right|D_i - \left|z_j\right|D_j\right) \qquad (2)$$

Here $\mathbf{F}$, R and T have their usual significance, while D_i and D_j are the tracer diffusion coefficients of the two oppositely-charged species. Although Eq. (1) provides an operational definition, its usefulness is yet to be established.

Experimental Methods

Three of the different bases for assigning fused salt transport numbers discussed above are of particular interest: (1) the reference for t_i is a porous diaphragm or other external substance; (2) an ionic constituent of the melt serves as reference; (3) values of t_i are calculated from coefficients of tracer diffusion and conductance as in Eq. (2). Experimental methods appropriate to each will be considered briefly.

There is not as yet a "standard" method for comparing the rates at which ions move relative to a porous diaphragm, although several approaches have proved satisfactory in specific systems. When the melt is a pure salt, the quantity to be determined is the change in the *amount* of salt in an electrode compartment whose boundary is defined by the position of the diaphragm. Both weight and volume change measurements have been employed. Making suitable allowance for the corresponding change in electrode material, either can be converted to change in number of equivalents of salt. The ratio of this quantity to the number of faradays fixes the values of the transport numbers, provided bulk flow of the liquid is negligible. Cell designs aimed at minimizing such flow have been described in the literature.[1] If there is appreciable flow, transport numbers can still be determined in two ways: (1) In a series of runs, electrolyze at a fixed current for varying lengths of time. Plot the observed ratios (equivalents of salt gained or lost per faraday) as a function of time, and extrapolate to zero. (2) Employing electrode reactions that produce no change in the total quantity of salt, continue electrolysis at constant current until a point is reached at which the quantity in each compartment no longer changes. Measure the steady-state difference in liquid levels of the two compartments and divide this by the current (faradays/sec). In a separate experiment, determine the rate at which the liquid flows through the diaphragm (equiv./sec) per unit difference in levels when no current is flowing. The product of these two ratios gives the transport number of the ion not involved in the electrode reactions.

When a mixture of salts is being studied, it is necessary to analyze the contents of one compartment after electrolysis to determine the number of equivalents of each species transferred through the diaphragm. The same data can be used to evaluate transport numbers with respect to ionic constituents of the melt, as discussed below.

If one of the ions is taken as reference, the concept of transport number in a pure binary salt is trivial. The value for the reference ion is zero; that for the other ion is unity and no measurement is required. When more than two species are present, however, the restriction on the "moving" ions applies only to the sum of their transport numbers. To determine individual values for each requires a transference experiment analagous to one of those used for transport numbers in aqueous solution. Hittorf, moving boundary, and concentration cell methods (see *Transference Numbers in Solvents*) have all been applied to mixtures of two binary salts with one ion in common. In the Hittorf method a known quantity of electricity is passed through the cell, resulting in a change in the initially uniform composition of electrolyte around each electrode. The boundary of either compartment is specified by the number of equivalents of salt removed for analysis. As in aqueous solutions the transport numbers calculated by comparison of initial and final compositions do not depend on the size of the sample, so long as it includes all the melt of changed composition. Porous plugs are often used to confine this to a relatively small quantity by preventing convective mixing. It is assumed that a diaphragm with sufficiently large pores will not affect the relative mobilities of ions passing through. The effect of pore size has not been studied carefully, however, and discrepancies among a number of results in the literature suggest this factor may be more important than has been realized in the past.

In the moving boundary method the velocity of an interface between two melts of differing composition is measured during electrolysis at a known current, just as in aqueous solutions. Here, however, the change in composition is defined by concentration ratios of like-charged ions. The common ion serves as reference, corresponding to the water in the aqueous solution measurement. Conditions for establishing suitable boundaries have been discussed by Klemm.[1]

To obtain transport numbers from emf measurements it again is necessary to establish a junction between melts of differing compositions. The boundary need not be sharp, however, and a porous plug may be used. Electrodes reversible to any of the ionic constituents are then placed on either side of the junction, and the potential difference is measured. To calculate transport numbers from such data, thermodynamic information about the system is also needed.[4] This is best provided by measurements on cells without transference, when electrodes reversible to more than one ionic constituent are available. By comparing the results for pure salt "formation cells" with those for the mixtures it is easy to calculate the required thermodynamic activities as functions of composition. If the activities in Eq. (1) are set equal to concentrations, it is interesting to note that the junction potential is equal to zero when like-charged ions have equal mobilities.

Methods have been developed for both the conductivity and tracer-diffusion measurements needed to calculate fused salt transport numbers from Eq. (2). Equivalent conductance of a pure salt is obtained from specific conductance, κ, and density: $\Lambda = \kappa E/\rho$, where E is the equivalent weight. Conventional a-c bridge methods are used for κ. The significant difference from determinations in aqueous electrolytes is in the conductivity cell. Due to the very small resistivity of fused salts, a correspondingly large cell constant is desirable. This can be effected by constricting part of the conducting path to the cross-section of a small capillary tube (1 or 2 mm ID) submerged in the melt. One electrode (sometimes both) is housed in a tube of larger bore joined to the top of such a capillary below the liquid surface. A separate calibration experiment with an electrolyte of known conductivity is used to obtain an accurate value for the cell constant, which is almost completely determined by the capillary dimensions. Conventional methods can also be used for the measurement of density, one of the simplest being based on the relative weights of a platinum bob *in vacuo* and suspended in the melt.

Tracer- or "self"-diffusion coefficients have been obtained most accurately in fused salts by the open-ended capillary technique. A small capillary tube with one end sealed is filled with a sample of salt in which one ion is isotopically labeled. This tube is carefully immersed in a vessel containing a large quantity of the same salt unlabeled. While diffusion is gradually causing the labeled ions in the capillary to be replaced by unlabeled, the concentration of labeled ions at the open end is effectively kept at zero by constantly stirring the salt in the outer vessel. After a suitable time lapse the capillary is removed. Its contents are analyzed for total quantity of labeled ion remaining. The tracer-diffusion coefficient is calculated from the ratio of initial to final isotopic content.

In concluding this section it is appropriate to mention transport number determinations in which the progress of a labeled ion is followed during electrolysis. The labeling here simply serves as an analytical tool to detect movement that is substantially identical with that of unlabeled ions. Thus, it may find use in either of the first two categories discussed in this section as an alternate to measurement of mass or volume changes, or as a means of determining changes of composition. Except in the indirect approach through tracer-diffusion coefficients, labeling does not, as some workers have implied, provide a method for transport numbers with respect to the "bulk liquid" distinct from methods involving unlabeled species only.

Results of Transport Number Measurements

A recent survey by Klemm[1] has presented a comprehensive compilation of fused-salt transport data. Some typical results will be reproduced here

TABLE 1. TRANSPORT NUMBERS IN PURE FUSED SALTS[3]

Salt	Temp. °C	t_+	
		Porous diaphragm reference	Calculated from Eq. (2)
NaCl	860	0.62	0.73
$PbCl_2$	518	0.24	0.53
$LiNO_3$	350	0.84	0.80
$NaNO_3$	350	0.71	0.66
KNO_3	350	0.60	0.53
$AgNO_3$	350	0.72	0.66

for each of the three types of transport numbers considered in the preceding section.

For pure binary salts it is of interest to compare transport numbers measured relative to a porous diaphragm with those calculated from conductance and self-diffusion results via Eq. (2). A comparison is given in the Table 1, where it is seen that available data indicate some parallel tendencies for the values of the two quantities. In fact, for each of the salts except $PbCl_2$ the two numbers listed can probably be considered equal within experimental error. A correlation of this type enhances the potential value of fused salt transport numbers as a means of assigning theoretically useful ion mobilities.

Transport numbers with respect to an ionic constituent are useful for comparing relative mobilities of like-charged ions in the same melt. For a mixture of two salts with an ion in common, the latter species can be taken as reference to permit assignment of numerical values to each of the other ions. A recent survey[5] of such figures has noted some substantial disagreements among workers who have reported results of Hittorf-type measurements on the same systems. For a surprising number of systems, however, there has been at least one recent report indicating that relative mobilities of like-charged ions differ by less than 10 or 15 per cent over a wide range of concentrations and conductivities. The list includes $AgNO_3$-$NaNO_3$, $LiNO_3$-KNO_3, $AgNO_3$-$AgCl$, and $LiCl$-KCl. This behavior is consistent with that indicated by reports of emf measurements on at least six other systems of this type: $AgCl$-KCl, $AgBr$-KBr, $AgBr$-$NaBr$, $AgBr$-$PbBr_2$, KCl-$PbCl_2$. In every case the liquid junction potentials are equal to zero within experimental error, implying mobility differences no greater than a few per cent. Since there are still systems for which the only available data show much greater mobility differences (as much as 140 per cent in $LiCl$-$PbCl_2$, determined by the moving boundary method), it is perhaps too early to generalize about the characteristics of ionic transport in such systems.

References

1. KLEMM, A., "Transport Properties of Molten Salts," in "Selected Topics in the Physical Chemistry of Molten Salts," Edited by Milton Blander, New York, Academic Press, John Wiley & Sons, in press, 1963.
2. LAITY, R. W., "Interionic Friction Coefficients in Molten Salts," *Ann. N. Y. Acad. Sci.,* **79,** 997 (1960).

3. LAITY, R. W., "Formalisms and Models for Ionic Transport," *Disc. Faraday Soc.*, **32**, 172 (1962).
4. LAITY, R. W., "Electrodes in Fused Salt Systems," in "Reference Electrodes: Theory and Practice" Ed. by Ives, D. J. G. and Janz, G. J., New York, Academic Press, 1961.
5. LAITY, R. W. AND MOYNIHAN, C. T., "Relative Mobilities of Like-Charged Ions in Fused Salts," *J. Phys. Chem.*, **67**, 723 (1963).
6. SINISTRI, C., "Transference Numbers in Pure Fused Salts," *J. Phys. Chem.*, **66**, 1600 (19.62)

7. LAITY, R. W., "Electrochemistry of Fused Salts," *J. Chem. Ed.*, **39**, 67 (1962).
8. REDDY, T. B., "The Electrochemistry of Molten Salts," *Electrochem. Technol.*, 1, 325 (1963).

RICHARD W. LAITY

Cross-references: *Electromigration in Liquid Metals; Electromigration in Solid Metals and Alloys;* entries with *Fused Salt* titles; *Irreversible Electrochemical Processes, Thermodynamics of; Transference Numbers.*

G

GALLIUM ELECTROCHEMISTRY

Gallium (Ga^{+++}) has an electrode potential of −0.52 volt ($H_2 = 0.0$ volt—National Bureau of Standards nomenclature) and an electrochemical equivalent (Ga^{+++}) of 0.24083 mg/coulomb.

Electrowinning

All of the processes for electrowinning gallium have been from caustic solutions. Only two raw materials have been discussed in the literature: (1) a by-product from lead-zinc recovery and (2) sodium aluminate liquor from the Bayer process.

The by-product from lead-zinc ores, containing about 1 per cent gallium, is dissolved in 10 per cent caustic soda solution and after clarification the solution is electrolyzed in a stainless steel container with stainless steel electrodes at about 6.5 volts. Gallium, zinc, and lead are deposited as a sponge on the cathode from which it is periodically scraped off. Electrolysis is continued until deposition ceases; removal of the gallium from solution is not complete. Few details are available for this process.

One process for recovery of gallium from sodium aluminate solutions (from the Bayer process) involves selective precipitation by acidic substances of the gallium (and part of the aluminum). The precipitate is redissolved in strong caustic soda solution and the liquor is electrolyzed using stainless steel anodes and cathodes. This cell is reported to be operated at a cathode current density of 0.8 amp/sq cm and 10 volts at a temperature of 80°C.

In another process for sodium aluminate liquor from the Bayer process, the gallium content of the liquor is allowed to increase until it is sufficient for recovery. At this stage, the sodium aluminate liquor is electrolyzed, using a mercury cathode with continuous agitation. Gallium is deposited on the cathode. After electrolysis, the sodium aluminate liquor is returned to the alumina recovery system. The mercury, containing the gallium, is leached with hot sodium hydroxide solution. The gallium is dissolved by the caustic solution; the mercury is separated and returned to the cathode. The electrolysis is carried out at 40–50°C and about 4 volts with a cathode current density of approximately 0.5 amp/sq dm. Anode current density is from 20 to 60 amp/sq dm. Electrical consumption is reported to be 80 watt-hour per gram of gallium.

The described processes for electrowinning gallium produce only impure metal which requires further processing. Removal of the bulk of these impurities is essential, since one major use of gallium is as a constituent of electronic material which must be of very high purity.

Electrodeposition

Crude gallium precipitates or solutions are usually purified and almost invariably the end product is a relatively pure solution of gallium in caustic soda. Some further purification of the gallium is obtained in the electrodeposition step but if electronic grade gallium (99.999 per cent) is desired, considerable effort is made to start with the purest possible solution.

A 10 per cent caustic soda solution, containing the gallium, is electrolyzed at 5.5 volts with current density of 0.5 amp/sq cm for the anode and 0.33 amp/sq cm for the cathode. Platinum is used for the anode; for the cathode, platinum is used for very high purity, although copper can be used for lower purities. Pyrex glass containers are usually employed. At these current densities, the cell temperatures are well above the melting point of gallium (30°C). The tip of the cathode is placed over a porcelain or Pyrex crucible (which rests on the cell bottom). As the gallium is electrolyzed, the liquid metal drips into the crucible.

Cathode efficiency is about 35 per cent until the concentration of the gallium falls below 2 gpl. Below this concentration, efficiency decreases rapidly and electrolysis is usually terminated. The residual gallium in solution is returned to the production circuit.

Electrode spacing is 3 to 5 cm depending on the size of the cell. Gassing is heavy during deposition and provides adequate circulation for the electrolyte except at the bottom of the cell. This is corrected by occasional stirring.

The electrodeposited liquid gallium is washed with distilled water, dilute hydrochloric acid and dilute nitric acid. The drosses formed are skimmed off; when no further dross is formed during the acid wash, chemical treatment is considered complete.

To obtain ultrapure gallium, it is necessary to take elaborate precautions with the starting solution and the equipment. Containers must be kept covered and extreme care must be used to avoid contamination at all stages.

References

1. MUSGRAVE, J. R., "Gallium," chapter in "Rare Metals Handbook," 2nd edition, edited by C. A. Hampel, New York, Reinhold Publishing Corp., 1961.
2. DE LA BRETEQUE, PIERRE, "Gallium," Marseille, l'Institut de Recherches de la Société Francaise Pour L'Industrie de L'Aluminum, 1962.

JOHN R. MUSGRAVE

GALVANI, LUIGI (1737–1798)

The man whose name is immortalized in one of the basic concepts of electrochemistry, Luigi Galvani, was born September 9, 1737 in Bologna, Italy, where he spent all of his life. He studied medicine and was appointed lecturer in anatomy at the University of Bologna in 1762, advancing to a professor in 1778. Galvani became well-known for his researches on the organs of hearing and the genitourinary tract of birds, about which he published treatises.

His wife was the highly intelligent daughter of Galeazzi, a medical professor under whom he had studied, and she worked with him in his anatomical researches. It was she who observed that a scalpel which had been in contact with an electric machine produced remarkable muscular contractions when it was touched to the body of a skinned frog. Galvani instituted a series of experiments using a device made of iron and cop-

per whereby one metal in contact with a dead frog's nerve and the other with a muscle resulted in the contraction of the muscle. He ascribed this result to electricity (correctly), but erroneously assumed that the electricity had been generated by the frog's tissue. These studies began in 1786 and in 1791 Galvani published an account of them in his work, "De viribus electricitatis in motu musculari commentarius." It might be mentioned that Galvani's interpretation of "animal electricity" may have been derived from his observations of the electric fish, *Torpedo*, which does generate an electric current (see *Electric Organs*).

Galvani's publication came to the attention of Volta, who deduced that the current noted by Galvani resulted from the two dissimilar metals in contact with an electrolyte, the cell solution of the frog's tissues. A celebrated controversy then arose between Volta and Galvani, which stimulated Volta to conduct the experiments which resulted in his correctly interpreted and epochal discovery of the production of electricity by the electrochemical reactions between two dissimilar metals in an electrolyte in his "pile and crown of cups," the voltaic pile.

The latter years of Galvani's life were affected by the death of his beloved wife in 1790 which left him inconsolable. In 1797 he was relieved of his professorship when he refused to swear allegiance to the newly created Cisalpine Republic, and he refused to resume the chair later when the government offered to allow him to do so unconditionally because of his fame. He died at Bologna December 4, 1798. It is his name, of course, that is perpetuated in the terms galvanic, galvanism, galvanometer, etc.

CLIFFORD A. HAMPEL

Cross-references: *Electric Organs; Electrophysiology; Volta, Alessandro.*

GALVANIC CORROSION

Galvanic corrosion is defined as the acceleration of the rate of attack of one metal as a result of its being joined by means of an electronic conductor to another metal while both are in contact with a corrosive environment capable of permitting passage of an electric current by ionic conduction. In such combinations, the corrosion of the second metal or metals in the couple is reduced. This discussion excludes instances where the galvanic corrosion of the more attacked metal is arranged deliberately so as to achieve protection of another metal, e.g., cathodic protection by such galvanic anodes as aluminum, magnesium, or zinc, discussed elsewhere.

This discussion also excludes galvanic action involving phases, compounds, and enriched or depleted zones which exhibit a difference in electrical potential as related to an alloy in which they exist. These second phases may have either detrimental or beneficial effects and may be introduced deliberately for this latter purpose, e.g., palladium in titanium. Also excluded are cases where differences in potential arise from such phenomena as passivity or concentration cell effects (q.v.).

The extent of accelerated corrosion resulting from galvanic action is affected by the following factors:

1. The difference in potential between the metals in the couple.

2. The resistance of the electrical circuit.

3. The drift in potentials towards each other as a result of the passage of the galvanic current (anodic and cathodic polarization).

The distribution of galvanic corrosion, e.g., as a function of distance from the point or line of contact, is determined by:

1. The operating potential of the galvanic couple.

2. The conductivity of the electrolyte.

3. The effects of polarization and insulating films or deposits formed as by-products of anodic or cathodic reactions.

4. The geometrical relationships of the metals in the couple.

The several factors that influence the magnitude and distribution of galvanic action will be discussed in turn.

Potential Difference

Any metal or alloy in contact with an electrolyte will exhibit an irreversible potential that

can be measured. Such measurements are usually made between the metal or alloy and an appropriate reference electrode using an instrument that does not permit passage of enough current to cause any appreciable polarization while the measurement is being made. Common instruments are potentiometers, vacuum tube voltmeters or conventional voltmeters having a very high resistance, e.g., at least 20,000 ohms per volt. In some cases, the difference in potential between dissimilar metals may be measured directly. It is generally preferable to make the measurements with reference to some standard of potential or reference electrode (q.v.). The potentials of some reference electrodes relative to the standard hydrogen electrode at 25°C (77°F) are given in Table 1.

The saturated calomel electrode is used more frequently than the other calomel electrodes. The copper:copper sulfate electrode is used principally in connection with cathodic protection of buried materials. The potential of a metal or alloy is influenced by the chemical nature of the environment, by temperature, by velocity, by oxidizing or reducing constituents of the environment, and by films (oxides or other corrosion products) that may exist or develop on the metal surfaces. Most corrosion product films cause a shift in potential in the more noble direction. For these reasons, metals and alloys do not have a galvanic potential that is independent of the nature of the corrosive environment, the incidental conditions of exposure in terms of factors that normally influence corrosion and the conditions of the metal surface.

For the reasons cited, the potential relationship of one metal to another may shift not only in magnitude but in direction from one environment to another and in the same general environment at different temperatures. Iron can be anodic (less noble than) copper in salt water and cathodic (more noble than) copper in a cyanide solution. Zinc can be anodic to iron in certain waters when they are cold and cathodic in the same waters when they are hot. Stainless steels can be anodic to copper in hot unaerated sulfuric acid and cathodic to copper in the same acid when it is aerated and cold.

It is not possible, therefore, to arrange metals and alloys in a galvanic series in the invariable positions occupied by metals in the standard electromotive series (q.v.). Strictly speaking there could be as many galvanic series as there are different environmental conditions. How-

TABLE 1. REFERENCE ELECTRODE POTENTIALS

Electrode	Potential vs Hydrogen Electrode
Saturated calomel	0.2415
Normal calomel	0.2800
$\frac{1}{10}$ Normal calomel	0.3337
Silver: silver chloride	0.2222
Copper: copper sulfate (sat.)	0.316

ever, it is possible to set up a practical galvanic series without values of potentials of the several metals and alloys and which can be used as a fair guide to the probable direction of galvanic effects in the absence of data related specifically to a particular set of environmental conditions. Such a galvanic series will be discussed in the following article. An example of a galvanic series related to a specific environment is based on measurements of open circuit potentials in aerated sea water flowing at a velocity of 13 ft per sec at 25°C (77°F) as shown in Table 2.

Electrical Resistance

The acceleration of corrosion of the anode associated with galvanic action is directly proportional to the amount of current that flows in the galvanic circuit in accordance with Faraday's Law:

$$W = (tM/\mathbf{F}n)\ I$$

where W is the weight in grams of metal dissolved in generating the galvanic current, t is the time in seconds that the current flows, $\mathbf{F}$ is the Faraday constant (96,501 coulombs), M is

TABLE 2. OPEN CIRCUIT POTENTIALS IN SEA WATER FLOWING AT 13 FT PER SEC AT 25° C (77° F)

Metal	Potential Negative to Saturated Calomel Half Cell
	Volts
Zinc	1.03
Aluminum (commercially pure)	0.79
Low carbon steel	0.61
Brass (70% Cu 30% Zn)	0.36
Copper	0.36
Bronze (88% Cu 10% Sn 2% Zn)	0.31
Cupro nickel (10% Ni)	0.28
Cupro nickel (30% Ni)	0.25
Nickel	0.20
Titanium (commercially pure)	0.15
Silver	0.13
Monel nickel copper alloy (70% Ni)	0.08
Stainless steel (18% Cr 8% Ni)	0.08
Stainless steel (18% Cr 12% Ni 3% Mo)	0.05

the atomic weight of the metal, n the charge of the metal ions formed, and I is the galvanic current in amperes.

The magnitude of the current, I, in amperes is determined in accordance with Ohm's Law:

$$I = E/R$$

where E is the working potential of the galvanic cell (open circuit potential minus the sum of anodic and cathodic polarization potentials) in volts and R is the resistance in ohms of both the internal and external electric circuits including any films or deposits on the electrode surfaces.

It is evident that the higher the resistance introduced from any source the lesser will be the galvanic action. When the external current is interrupted by the introduction of a perfect insulator so that R becomes infinite the galvanic effect will be zero. For similar reasons, galvanic action can be expected to be greater in environments that are good ionic conductors, such as acid, alkaline, and salt solutions, e.g., sea water, than in poor conductors, such as tap water or distilled water. Likewise, galvanic couples immersed in a large volume of solution will produce a greater effect than when the electrolyte exists as a film, e.g., on surfaces exposed in the atmosphere that become wet occasionally by thin films of rain water or dew.

Polarization

For the purpose of this discussion, polarization is defined as the shift in potential of the anode towards that of the cathode and of the cathode towards that of the anode as a result of the flow of the galvanic current.

Depending on the nature of the metal and the incidental conditions of exposure, the polarization effect can be predominant on the anode or the cathode or about the same on both. In some instances there may be no polarization of either electrode. In such cases the magnitude of the galvanic effect will be determined entirely by the open circuit potentials and the resistance of the circuit. These possible situations are shown diagramatically in Fig. 1.

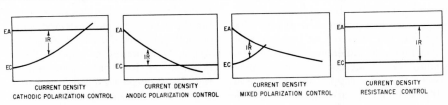

FIG. 1. Effects of polarization and resistance on galvanic currents.

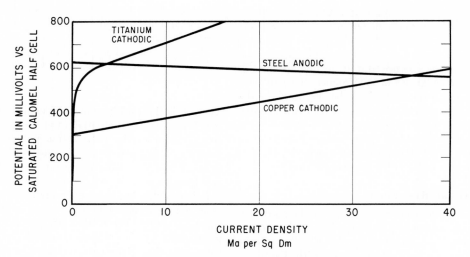

FIG. 2. Cathodic polarization of different metals.

Included in the diagrams in Fig. 1 is an indication of the effects of resistance superimposed on polarization effects. With zero resistance the maximum galvanic current would be determined by the intersection of the polarization curves. With some resistance, the galvanic current will be that which, when multiplied by the resistance of the circuit, will equal the difference between the polarized potentials as shown in the diagrams. The larger the resistance the less will be the current when equilibrium has been reached.

Anodic and cathodic reactions do not proceed with equal facility on all metal surfaces. In galvanic corrosion, the cathodic reaction is frequently most important. This can be hydrogen evolution or reduction of an oxidizing substance, e.g., dissolved oxygen.

Metals having high hydrogen overvoltages will have steeper cathodic polarization curves and cause less galvanic corrosion than metals of lower hydrogen overvoltage (q.v.). Similarly, metals having a high oxygen reduction overvoltage (q.v.) will have steep cathodic polarization curves and be less aggressive in galvanic couples. This is illustrated by the polarization curves in Fig. 2 based on tests of galvanic couples of steel with copper and with titanium in flowing aerated sea water. It will be observed that titanium polarized as a cathode much more readily than did copper. In spite of the fact that, on open circuit, the potential difference between steel and titanium was about 200 millivolts greater than between steel and copper, the galvanic effect of the titanium as accounted for by the polarization curves, was only about one-seventh

as great when the weight losses of the steel specimens in the galvanic couples were compared.

It is necessary, therefore, to pay as much attention to polarization phenomena as to potential differences in estimating the possible extent of galvanic corrosion on the basis of measurements of potential differences or relative positions in a galvanic series.

Area Effects

As indicated in Fig. 1, the extent of polarization is a function of current density. When the action is under a substantial degree of cathodic control, with relatively little anodic polarization, a combination in which the area of the anode is small and the area of the cathode is large will bring about very little cathodic polarization and thus permit a severe galvanic effect, aggravated further by the high anodic current density at the small anode. Conversely, when the area of the cathode is small and the area of the anode large the galvanic effect may be negligible. For example, steel rivets in a copper plate immersed in sea water were practically destroyed while there was little visible evidence of accelerated corrosion of steel plates in the vicinity of copper rivets exposed under the same conditions and for the same time as illustrated in Fig. 3. As a general rule one should avoid galvanic couples where the immersed area of the anodic material is much less than that of the more noble material. In atmospheric exposures where the electrolyte exists as a thin film, the area of each metal participating in the galvanic action is

FIG. 3. Area effect shown by rivet and plate assemblies.

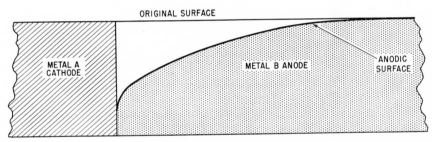

FIG. 4. Distribution of galvanic corrosion from line of contact in a poorly conducting electrolyte (schematic).

likely to be about the same, irrespective of differences in their overall dimensions.

The area effect principles extend as well to efforts to control galvanic corrosion by applying protective coatings. Insulating coatings should never be applied to the anodic metal alone. The cathodic surfaces should be coated as well or the anodic surfaces should be left bare. The presence of bare spots in a coating on an anodic material will result in concentration of the galvanic action on such small areas leading to an intensity of localized attack that will be much greater than if no coating had been applied.

Distribution of Effects

As mentioned previously, the extent to which galvanic effects will extend, e.g., from a line of contact, will depend principally on the operating potential, the conductivity of the electrolyte,

and the volume of the electrolyte as this will influence the resistance of the electrolyte portion of the circuit. Everything else being the same, the galvanic action will extend over a larger distance for a couple immersed in the ocean than for the same couple immersed in a vessel just large enough to contain the couple and enough water to cover the assembly. Where the electrolyte resistance is high the galvanic action will be most severe at the line of contact and will decrease exponentially as the distance from the line of contact increases, as shown diagramatically in Fig. 4.

Observations of galvanic couples in a marine atmosphere, e.g., between bare magnesium and bare steel, have shown that the galvanic action does not extend more than about 1/4 inch from the line of contact.

If the anodic member of the couple is coated

with an insulating film the galvanic action may spread for much larger distances than when the metal is bare. For example, on steel pipe specimens coated with an insulating tape with bare spots at different distances from the line of contact with a large bronze cathode the intensity of the galvanic effect at a bare spot thirty feet from the line of contact was almost as intense as a bare spot only a few inches from the line of contact. The effect of such coatings in extending the distribution of galvanic action will vary with the resistance of the electrolyte. With thin films of electrolyte associated with atmospheric exposures the spreading effect may be slight.

Secondary Effects

There may sometimes be secondary effects of galvanic action that may be of considerable importance. In electrolytes, e.g., aerated salt water in which the principal cathodic reaction product will be hydroxyl ions, the cathodic member of the couple may also suffer accelerated corrosion as a result of galvanic action if the cathodic metal is vulnerable to alkalis. For example, if equal areas of aluminum (cathode) and magnesium (anode) are coupled and immersed in sea water, both metals in the couple will be destroyed. The magnesium will suffer accelerated corrosion as the anode of the couple while the aluminum will be attacked by the alkali generated at its surface acting as a cathode.

Similarly, a coating used on the cathodic member of a galvanic couple should be resistant to alkaline attack.

Simple galvanic corrosion may become complicated by the corrosion-aggravating effects of corrosion products of one metal which may accelerate attack on the other metal in the couple. For example, aluminum will corrode more in the atmosphere in galvanic contact with copper and copper alloys which yield corrosion-accelerating corrosion products than in contact with austenitic stainless steel which does not release such corrosion products. It should be noted, also, that such effects of soluble corrosion products do not require that the metals be in electrical contact so long as they are located relative to each other so that the accelerating corrosion products can wash over the surfaces of the susceptible metal. Copper may deposit onto the aluminum from such corrosion products and set up secondary galvanic action. This may also occur in liquids into which copper corrosion

products may be released upstream of aluminum or other less noble metal surfaces.

In galvanic couples in environments where hydrogen is released on the cathodic surfaces, the hydrogen may have a harmful effect on the cathodic material if it is subject to hydrogen embrittlement or hydrogen blistering. Such harmful effects have been observed on hardened martensitic stainless steel self-tapping screws used to fasten aluminum in corrosive atmospheres. The stainless steel screws failed by spontaneous cracking after hydrogen embrittlement from the galvanic action. Austenitic stainless steels are not similarly affected.

References

1. Evans, U. R., *J. Soc. Chem. Ind.*, **47**, 73T (1928).
2. Evans, U. R., *J. Franklin Institute*, **208**, No. 1, 52 (1929).
3. Evans, U. R., and Hoar, T. P., *Proc. Royal Soc. (London)* A, **137**, 343 (1932).
4. Evans, U. R., "Metallic Corrosion, Passivity and Protection," p. 513, London, Edward Arnold & Co., 1937.
5. Brown, R. H., and Mears, R. B., *Trans. Electrochem. Soc.*, **74**, 502 (1938).
6. Uhlig, H. H., *Metals Technology*, **6** (1939).
7. Wesley, W. A., *Proc. Am. Soc. Testing Materials*, **40**, 690–702 (1940).
8. Mears, R. B., and Brown, R. H., *Ind. Eng. Chem.*, **33**, 1010 (1941).
9. Copson, H. R., *Trans. Electrochem. Soc.*, **84**, 71–81 (1943).
10. Tomashov, N. D., *Comptes rendus de l'academie des sciences de l'U.R.S.S.*, **52**, 601 (1946).
11. Fontana, M. G., *Ind. Eng. Chem.*, **39**, 7, 85A–86A (1947).
12. Sub-Committee VIII Committee B-3 ASTM, *Proc. Am. Soc. Testing Materials*, **48**, 167 (1948).
13. Delahay, P., *J. Electrochem. Soc.*, **97**, 6, 198 (1950).
14. LaQue, F. L., "Corrosion Handbook," Edited by H. H. Uhlig, p. 415, New York, John Wiley and Sons, Inc., 1948. Wesley, W. A., and Brown, R. H., *ibid.*, p. 481. Sample, C. H., *ibid.*, p. 1002.
15. Paige, H., and Ketcham, S. J., *Corrosion*, **8**, 413 (Dec., 1952).
16. Haller, H. D., *J. Electrochem. Soc.*, **97**, 271, 272, 453, 461 (1950); **98**, 252 (1951).
17. LaQue, F. L., *Proc. Am. Soc. Testing Materials*, **51**, 495 (1951).
18. Waber, J. T., *J. Electrochem. Soc.*, **101**, 271 (1954); **102**, 344 (1955); **102**, 420 (1955); **103**, 64 (1956); **103**, 138 (1956); **103**, 567 (1956).
19. Teeple, H. O., *ASTM STP #175*, p. 89, 1956.
20. Compton, K. G., and Mendizza, A., *ASTM STP #175*, p. 116, 1956.

21. GODARD, H. P., *Materials Protection*, **2**, 38 (June, 1963).

FRANK L. LaQUE

Cross-references: *Cathodic Protection; Concentration Cells;* entries with *Corrosion* titles; *Electromotive Series; Overvoltage; Passivity; Polarization; Reference Electrodes.*

GALVANIC SERIES

In the general discussion of galvanic corrosion it was pointed out that the potential relationship that exists between metals and alloys depends on the nature of the corrosive environment and the incidental conditions of exposure. The open circuit potential exhibited by an alloy is influenced also by surface films. The most important examples of such effects are found in alloys, e.g., stainless steels that may be either active or passive.

In their active condition, e.g., in hot concentrated hydrochloric acid, the stainless steels may exhibit an open circuit potential about the same as that of carbon steel. In their passive condition, e.g., in strong nitric acid, the same stainless steels may exhibit a potential about as noble as that of gold or platinum.

The possibility of encountering environments in which stainless steels may exhibit borderline passivity or suffer localized loss of passivity in active pits, or in crevices where corrosion may be occurring, makes it impossible to assign a single position for a stainless steel in a general galvanic series which may be used as a rough guide to the probable direction of galvanic effects in the absence of more specific data. Similar behavior is sometimes observed with other chromium alloys. Consequently, in arranging metals and alloys in order in such a general galvanic series it is necessary to indicate two positions for such active or passive alloys.

A general purpose galvanic series is shown in Table 1.

It will be noted that the metals and alloys have been arranged in groups. Under many circumstances it is safe to combine metals within a group especially when their exposed areas are approximately equal or where the area of the metal towards the top of a group is larger than that of the metal towards the bottom. Greater caution is recommended where the opposite area relationship exists and where the environment is known to be appreciably corrosive to the metal higher in the group.

TABLE 1. GALVANIC SERIES OF METALS AND ALLOYS

Corroded End (anodic, or least noble)

Magnesium
Magnesium alloys

Zinc

Aluminum 1100

Cadmium

Aluminum 2017

Steel or Iron
Cast Iron

Chromium-iron (active)

Ni-Resist

18-8 Chromium-nickel-iron (active)
18-8-3 Chromium-nickel-molybdenum-iron (active)

Lead-tin solders
Lead
Tin

Nickel (active)
Inconel (active)
Hastelloy C (active)

Brasses
Copper
Bronzes
Copper-nickel alloys
Monel

Silver solder

Nickel (passive)
Inconel (passive)

Chromium-iron (passive)
18-8 Chromium-nickel-iron (passive)
18-8-3 Chromium-nickel-molybdenum-iron (passive)
Hastelloy C (passive)

Silver

Graphite
Gold
Platinum

Protected End (cathodic, or most noble)

These same general precautions apply to combinations of metals from different groups.

In the case of alloys, such as the stainless steels shown in two positions in the table, it is prudent to assume that in environments where some loss of passivity may occur, they will occupy their active position when their exposed area is relatively small and their passive position when their exposed area is relatively large.

The other factors involved in galvanic corrosion as discussed previously should be considered when estimating the danger of harmful galvanic effects by reference to the galvanic series.

References

1. Edwards, J. D., and Taylor, C. S., *Trans. Am. Electrochem. Soc.*, **56,** 27 (1929).
2. Gatty, O., and Spooner, C. R., "Electrode Potential Behaviour of Corroding Metals in Aqueous Solutions," p. 241, Oxford University Press, 1938.
3. Latimer, W. M., "Oxidation Potentials," New York, Prentice Hall, Inc., 1938.
4. Whitmore, M. R., and Teres, J., *Ind. Eng. Chem.*, **31,** 608 (1939).
5. Geller, W., *Korrosion und Metallschutz*, **15,** 298 (1939).
6. LaQue, F. L., and Cox, G. L., *Proc. Am. Soc. Testing Materials*, **40,** 670–689 (1940).
7. Huston, K. M., and Teel, R. B., *Corrosion*, **8,** 251 (1952).

Frank L. LaQue

GALVANIZING. See ELECTROGALVANIZING.

GALVANOMETERS

The simplest device available for detecting and measuring current or voltage is the galvanometer. It is admirably suited for use in portable instruments or equipment. The galvanometer was originated by Oersted in 1819, but the "Moving Coil" galvanometer, which is widely used today, was first described by Sturgeon in 1836 and improved by d'Arsonval in 1882. The current to be measured flows through a coil of one or more turns, usually rectangular in form and arranged to move in a uniform radial horizontal magnetic field. Fig. 1 shows such an arrangement. The coil may be pivoted (usually in jewels) or held in position by a fine wire suspension of gold or copper. When the coil is suspended, the turning torque of the suspension produces the restoring force to bring the system

to its normal balanced position when no current is flowing through the system. In a pivoted instrument a restoring spring supplies the restoring force. When current flows through the coil, a torque is produced which tends to turn the system against the restoring torque, and rotate it from its balanced position. Suspension galvanometers are usually more sensitive and accurate than pivot instruments. A pointer is fastened to the coil to indicate the deflection of the system from its normally balanced position. Where greater sensitivity is required, a mirror is fastened to the coil and a reflected light beam indicates the deflection from the zero position. Fig. 1 shows the fundamental system. These types of systems have sensitivities with light beam indication down to 0.003 microampere per millimeter or 0.05 microvolt per millimeter with periods less than eight seconds. Fig. 2 shows some typical galvanometers employing d'Arsonval systems.

Definitions

There are three major definitions of interest concerning the operation of a galvanometer. They are:

1. Sensitivity
2. External Critical Damping Resistance
3. Period

Sensitivity. There are various ways of expressing galvanometer sensitivity. Each involves a statement of the electrical conditions necessary to produce a standard deflection. This

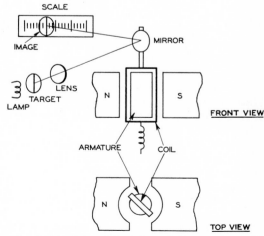

Fig. 1. Fundamental system of the moving coil galvanometer. (N and S are poles of the magnet.)

standard deflection in galvanometers having attached scales is assumed to be one division. In galvanometers not equipped with scales, the standard deflection is usually assumed to be one millimeter, with a scale distance of one meter.

Current Sensitivity. This is the current required to give the standard deflection. All other expressions of galvanometer sensitivity are derived from the current sensitivity.

Voltage Sensitivity. This is the voltage that must be impressed on the circuit made up of the galvanometer coil and the external critical damping resistance to produce the standard deflection. The voltage sensitivity equals the product of the current sensitivity and the total circuit resistance.

Megohm Sensitivity. This expresses the resistance in megohms which must be placed in series with the galvanometer so that an impressed emf of one volt shall produce the standard deflection. Neglecting the resistance of the galvanometer coil itself, the number representing the megohm sensitivity is the reciprocal of the number representing the current sensitivity.

Ballistic Sensitivity. This is the quantity of electricity that must be discharged through the galvanometer to produce the standard deflection. When critically damped, the sensitivity of a ballistic galvanometer is about a third of its undamped sensitivity.

External Critical Damping Resistance. This is the external resistance in the galvanometer circuit necessary to produce the critical damped condition.

The advantage of the critical damped condition rests chiefly in the fact that it aids in rapid work since the galvanometer system, when critically damped, returns more promptly to rest than when in an undamped or overdamped condition. Another advantage is that when approximately critically damped, the system is prevented from passing much beyond its position of rest upon its return, and, therefore, the zero or null position is rendered more stable. Practically, it is best to work with a galvanometer just slightly underdamped. This permits the galvanometer to slightly overshoot its balanced position, thus making it easier to determine that the galvanometer has reached its balanced position.

Period. The period usually stated for a galvanometer is the full undamped period, which is the time in seconds elapsing between two successive passages in the same direction through the position of rest. It is customary to take the period of a critically damped galvanometer as equal to its undamped period, for while the critically damped period is theoretically infinite, practically, a critically damped deflection is within about 1.5 per cent of its final position in the undamped periodic time.

Galvanometer Constants

There are two sets of constants used in designing galvanometers. They are:

Intrinsic Constants	Working Constants
K = Moment of inertia	A = Current sensitivity
G = Dynamic or displacement constant	P = Voltage sensitivity
U = Torsion constant	S_c = Ballistic sensitivity
D = Damping constant	R_c = Total critical damping resistance
g = Galvanometer resistance	R' = External circuit resistance for critical damping
ϵ = Base of natural logarithm	T = Period

G, the dynamic or displacement constant, is the displacing torque due to unit current, and is denoted by the equation, $G = HF$, in which H is the strength of the magnetic field and F is the area of the coil face times the number of turns of wire.

The following equations give the relations between working and intrinsic constants and enable the user to predict the result of changing intrinsic constants.

$$A = \frac{G}{U}$$

$$P \propto \frac{T}{G} \quad \text{or} \quad \frac{T}{HF}$$

$$P \propto \frac{1}{G}\sqrt{\frac{K}{U}} \quad \text{or} \quad \frac{1}{HF}\sqrt{\frac{K}{U}}$$

$$P \propto \sqrt{\frac{T^3}{KR_c}}$$

$$P \propto \sqrt{\frac{T}{UR_c}}$$

$$S_c = \frac{2\pi}{T\epsilon} A \quad \text{or} \quad \frac{2\pi G}{T\epsilon U}$$

$$R' = \frac{G^2}{2\sqrt{KU}} - g \quad \text{or} \quad R_c - g$$

$$R_c = \frac{G^2}{2\sqrt{KU}} \quad \text{or} \quad \frac{(HF)^2}{2\sqrt{KU}}$$

$$T = 2\pi \sqrt{\frac{K}{U}}$$

It should be noted that changing intrinsic constants to produce a new working constant will change the other working constants unless a second counteracting change is made.

Precautions in Using A Galvanometer

In setting up a galvanometer it is important to follow the directions of the manufacturer.

Zero shift in galvanometers may be caused either from hysteresis in the suspension or from magnetic foreign impurities in the suspended system. It is more prevalent in the more sensitive units.

Thermoelectromotive power may be present in the galvanometer or its circuit and may be detected by noting whether a deflection results when the galvanometer circuit is closed without a known emf being in the circuit. Better galvanometers reduce the thermal emf's within the galvanometer to a negligible amount by making the circuit, including the suspension binding posts and leads, entirely of copper.

A change in temperature will change the coefficient of rigidity of the suspension, the strength of the magnet field and the resistance of the galvanometer. In instruments for current measurements this last change may be ignored; the first two changes tend to compensate each other, but only partially. If the temperature coefficient of the current sensitivity is known, the coefficient of the voltage sensitivity usually can be calculated from a knowledge of the materials composing the circuit.

Ballistic Galvanometer

A galvanometer is said to be used ballistically when, instead of being deflected to a definite angular position by a steady current, the coil is subjected to an electromagnetic impulse of short duration by the passage through it of a quantity of electricity. This results in an excursion through an angle, from which it immediately returns. Theoretically, any moving coil

galvanometer can be used ballistically but, practically, only galvanometers with periods of several seconds are so used. There are two reasons for the desirability of a long period: (a) the observer must have time to read the turning point on the scale; (b) the flow of electricity must end before the coil has had time to turn through an appreciable angle. If the impulse is not instantaneous in comparison with the period of the galvanometer, an error in measurement results.

It can be shown that the angular throw of a ballistic galvanometer is proportional to the quantity of electricity discharged through it when the discharge is completed before the coil has moved appreciably. Hence, having calibrated the galvanometer by observing the throws produced by known quantities of electricity, the ballistic galvanometer can be used to measure discharges of electricity of short duration which are passed through it.

While it is true that an undamped ballistic galvanometer is more sensitive than a critically damped one, the latter is much more convenient to use. When critically damped, the ballistic sensitivity, S, is $1/\epsilon$ of the undamped sensitivity and $2\pi/T\epsilon$ of the current sensitivity ($\epsilon = 2.72$).

A-C Galvanometer

The a-c galvanometer resembles very closely the d-c galvanometer. Its distinguishing feature is the substitution of an electromagnet for the permanent magnet of the d-c instrument, the electromagnet being energized from the same a-c source that supplies the current to be measured or detected. It is not useful for any but rough measurements of currents because of the numerous variables which affect its sensitivity. It is intended primarily for use as a detector in balancing impedance bridges energized by power frequencies, usually 50 or 60 cycles.

The general form of the equations of motion of the suspended system of the a-c galvanometer is much the same as that for the d-c galvanometer, but includes additional terms which take account of phase relationships, wave forms, etc.

Phase selectivity is an important characteristic of the a-c galvanometer when used as a detector of a-c bridge unbalance. The a-c galvanometer has its greatest sensitivity when the current in the moving coil is in phase with the a-c field produced by the electromagnet and is entirely insensitive when it is out of phase by 90 degrees. The current energizing the electro-

FIG. 2. Typical galvanometers employing d'Arsonval systems: (upper left) high sensitivity d-c reflecting galvonometer; ((upper right) high sensitivity d-c self-contained galvanometer; (lower left) medium sensitivity d-c self-contained galvanometer; (lower right) d-c pointer galvanometer.

magnet may be supplied through a phase-shifter which can continuously adjust the phase of the flux with respect to that of the current to be detected. Alternatively, the phase shift may be made in the input to the moving coil with the same result.

Vibration Galvanometer

The vibration galvanometer, which is used to measure a-c, operates with its coil in the field of a permanent magnet so that the coil deflects, first in one direction and then in the other for each cycle of an alternating current which is passed through it. If the period of the galvanometer is adjusted to equal $1/f$, where f is the frequency of the alternating current, a condition is reached at which the current in the coil reverses in unison with the swings of the coil and large oscillations may result.

If an image of a spot of light reflected from a mirror on the vibrating system is received on a screen, it is spread out by the oscillation into a band of light, the length of which is proportional to the magnitude of the alternating current in the coil. At zero current the band is a spot. The galvanometer is suited for use as a detector of small a-c currents, such as in the balancing of a-c bridges.

Conclusion

The galvanometer is a relatively simple, inexpensive detector suitable for use in making d-c or a-c measurements. Special forms of galvanometers used to obtain greater sensitivity have not been discussed herein due to space limitations, but the references given provide this information. It has become common practice to use galvanometers with electronic amplifiers to obtain good sensitivity with ruggedness of operation.

References

1. STEWART, O. M., *Phys. Rev.*, **16**, 158 (1903).
2. WHITE, WALTER P., *Phys. Rev.*, **19**, 305 (1904).
3. PIERCE, B. O., *Proc. Amer. Acad. of Arts & Sciences*, 283 (1909).
4. WENNER, FRANK, *Natl. Bur. Standards Bull.*, **6**, 347 (1909).
5. WENNER, FRANK, *Natl. Bur. Standards Sci. Paper*, **273** (1916).
6. WEIBEL, E., *Natl. Bur. Standards Bull.*, **14**, 23 (1918).
7. HILL, A. W., *J. Sci. Inst.*, **11**, 309 (1934).
8. LAWS, FRANK A., "Electrical Measurements," p. 1, New York, McGraw-Hill Book Co., 1938.
9. STOUT, M. B., "Basic Electrical Measurements," p. 160, New York, Prentice-Hall, Inc., 1960.
10. Leeds & Northrup Company, Notes on Moving Coil Galvanometers, ED 2 (1), 1950.
11. HARRIS, F. K., "Electrical Measurements," p. 43, New York, John Wiley & Sons, Inc., 1952.

W. R. CLARK

GASEOUS DIELECTRICS. *See* **DIELECTRICS, GASEOUS.**

GASES, ELECTRICAL CONDUCTANCE AND IONIZATION

An article so brief as the present one cannot adequately cover the entire subject including its theoretical aspects. A list of important reference books is therefore appended.

Although gases, under certain conditions, have in common with electrolytic solutions the ability to transmit electrical current, the nature of their conductance is so different from that in electrolysis as to require a somewhat detailed comparison of the two. They have in common the property of being able to bring about chemical reaction associated with the discharge or neutralization of their respective ions, but this must be further differentiated. While ions carrying positive or negative charge are necessary in both cases, their nature and mode of generation are widely different. Electrolytic ions are produced at once when an electrolyte is dissolved in a medium capable of dissociating it. Both positive and negative ions with single or multiple charges are produced. They may be drawn to oppositely charged electrodes as soon as a field is applied. When the ions reach the electrodes they are neutralized (if the voltage is sufficient) and chemical action ensues, which may produce a new soluble substance, cause evolution of a gas, or precipitation of a solid. The amount of reaction produced is proportional to the current passing; the proportionality factor may be considered as the electrolytic or current yield.

On the other hand, gases require a source of energy, such as radiation, alpha (α), beta (β), or gamma (γ) rays, to produce positive and negative ions by removal of one or more electrons (e^-) from a gas molecule. The energy of the bombarding particle or of the quantum of electromagnetic radiation must, of course, exceed the ionization potential (IP) of the given molecule struck (see below). If an external γ-ray source is employed, the gas (or gases) should have a sufficient pressure to successively absorb the energy until it is reduced below the ionization potential. A sufficient internal source may be radon mixed with the gas to be radiated, or alpha or beta radiation from a radioactive solid.

But if a gas is to conduct continuously by current flow or by discharge from an internal voltage source, it must be retained at a low pressure (small fractions of an atmosphere). The initial voltage source should be high enough to give a current by successive ionization of the molecules it energizes on collision by detaching electrons, thus leaving positively charged molecules or charged fragments.

Gas ions produced by either method may undergo chemical reaction, either of dissociation, of association, or of combination of fragment ions with molecules or with other fragments. But, for reactions of association to occur in gaseous discharge, the pressure must not be so low as to prevent sufficient collisions.

With the foregoing introduction let us consider some specific cases, first a few in electrical discharge. In the simple element, oxygen, radiation can produce ozone by the reaction: $O_2 + (\alpha, \beta,$ or $\gamma) \rightarrow O + O^+ + (-)$, succeeded by the following steps: $O_2 + (-) \rightarrow O_2^-$, at once followed by $O_2^- + O_2 \rightarrow O_4^- \rightarrow O_3 + O^-$ and $O_2 + O^+ \rightarrow O_3^+ \vdots + O^- \rightarrow O_3 + O$; $O_2 + O \rightarrow O_3$.

Ozone is better measured in a rapid flow of ionized oxygen than in a static system. The decomposition of ozone once formed is a long-chain reaction as shown by Lewis.[1] Hence, the unequal competition of low-yield ozone synthesis with the long-chain decomposition means that the ion yield of the former can never rise above $+M_{O_3}/N_{O_2} =$ ca. 2, no matter how fast the flow to avoid decomposition. In ozone formation by irradiation of air its yield may also be depressed by charge exchange with the NO_2 simultaneously formed.

In methane the reaction is simpler since there is no affinity of CH_4 for electrons and hence no negative ions by attachment. Therefore, the following reactions: (1) CH_4 + ionizing agent $\rightarrow$ $CH_4^+ + (-)$; $CH_4^+ + CH_4 \rightarrow (CH_4)_2^+$; $(CH_4)_2^+ + (-) \rightarrow C_2H_6 + H_2$. Or some would prefer a different mechanism: (2) $CH_4^+ + CH_4 \rightarrow CH_5^+ + CH_3$ and $CH_5^+ + CH_4 + (-) \rightarrow 2CH_4 + H$; and $H + H + $ 3rd body $(M) \rightarrow H_2 + M$ or $H + CH_3 + (M) \rightarrow CH_4 + (M)$.

In a mixture of hydrogen and nitrogen, ammonia is formed by irradiation with an ionizing source (Rn). Here again there is no attachment of thermal electrons except to neutralize the final (or intermediate) products. Not only is ammonia formed, but it is also decomposed, thus giving the equilibrium: $N_2 + 3H_2 \rightleftharpoons 2NH_3$. The theoretical yield of ammonia synthesis is about 0.32 NH_3 per ion pair, while the corresponding yield of NH_3 decomposition would be

0.68 or equilibrium at 13.8 per cent of the stoichiometric mixture $N_2 + 3H_2$. However, the actual equilibrium found by experiment (D'Olieslager and Jungers[2]) was only 4.7 NH_3 by volume. This depression of the equilibrium below 13.8 per cent, that calculated from initial concentrations of H_2 and N_2, is to be explained as follows. Both H_2 and N_2 have higher ionization potentials than that of the product, NH_3. Therefore, charge exchange from ions of either component to NH_3 produced will occur: $H_2^+ + NH_3 \rightarrow H_2 + NH_3^+$ and $N_2^+ + NH_3 \rightarrow N_2 + NH_3^+$. Thus, the ionization and chemical activation of NH_3 is increased at the expense of its synthesis and the equilibrium is depressed from theory down to 4.7 per cent NH_3 by volume.

In mixtures of oxygen and nitrogen (air, for example) irradiation produces various oxides of nitrogen: N_2O, NO, N_2O_3, NO_3, N_2O_5. Dmitriev and Pshezhetsky[3] have made extensive studies of the oxidation of nitrogen under ionization by 200 kev electrons. They found the reaction to be second order with yield proportional to the concentration of nitrogen. With 20, 50 and 80 per cent oxygen, electrons reacted at a rate proportional to the current and to the thickness of gas layer. At 50 per cent O_2, $G = 2$; in air $G = 1.3$ (G is the yield of product per 100 electron volts). They reported results on the fixation of N_2 by ionizing irradiation of mixtures of N_2 and O_2 at various pressures, temperatures, dosage and gas composition using Co^{60} and $\bar{e}$'s. Up to $\bar{e}$ impact of 100 ev, the ionization and excitation of N_2 is about ten times more probable than its dissociation. The most important reactions of fixation of nitrogen they found to be:

$$N_2^+ + O_2 \rightarrow NO^+ + NO$$

$$N_2^+ + O_2 \rightarrow NO_2^+ + N$$

$$N + O_2 \rightarrow NO + O$$

$$N + O_2 + M \rightarrow NO_2 + M.$$

Although gases ionized by radiating agents, such as α, β or γ rays and high energy fragments of nuclear disruption, are electrical conducting media by means of their free positive and negative ions, little consideration has been given them as conductors, as already stated. This being the case, it only remains to mention some of the commonest systems that could be so employed.

The carriers in gaseous conduction are the

positively and negatively charged molecular or atomic ions produced by the various ionizing agents, positive, negative, or neutral. Collision of two particles, one often being a neutral molecule and the other an ion (+ or −) or an electron, is essential for reactions of radiation chemistry. Heavy particles (ions and also neutral molecules and atoms), produce in a single collision both ionization and excitation only when their kinetic energy is very great.

Under conditions of low ionization, due either to a dilute gas medium or to sparse ionizing agents, collision between ions and electrons is rare, hence recombination, which would also require a third body, is almost negligible. Recombination of ions accompanied by emission of radiation is rare, and conversion to kinetic energy is impossible.

In excitation and ionization by $\bar{e}$ collision with neutral gas atom or molecule, assuming thermal equilibrium of all particles, the average kinetic energy, $(m/2)\bar{v}^2 = (M/2)\bar{V}^2$, in which m and $\bar{v}$ are the mass and velocity of the electron, and M and $\bar{V}$ of the molecule. The ratios of their velocities are between 65 for H_2 and 605 for Hg.

Miscellaneous

An apparatus to measure electron attachment to O_2 in mixtures of oxygen in argon has been described by Bortner and Hurst[4] and applied to the study of ozone formation.

Charge transfer in ion-molecule reactions by α-radiolysis of various hydrocarbons has been determined in the mass spectrograph by Rudolph and Melton.[5]

Hirschfelder[6] considered ortho-para conversion of H_2, using the previously measured reactions $H_2 + Br_2$ and $2CO + O_2$ as examples.

The reactions of nitrogen activated by *glow discharge* were investigated by Varney.[7] Active nitrogen formed NO or N_2O_3 with O_2 downstream, and NH_3 with H_2. But N ions do not react as such. Passing O_2 or N_2 through the glow and then admitting to N_2 gave no reaction. (See also: Knewstubb, P. F.. and Tickner, A. W., *J. Chem. Phys.*, **37**, 2941-9 (1962)). In CO, carbon was deposited on the *anode*, indicating no such reaction as

$$CO + CO^+ \rightarrow C^+ + CO_2 .$$

Morinaga[8] examined the reaction produced by silent electrical discharge in $H_2 + O_2$ mixtures and found H_2O_2 as a product. The effect of fre-

quency on the formation of O_3 was studied by Morinaga and Suzuki[9] and the effect of packing by Morinaga[10] in the ozone reaction, and in $H_2 + O_2$.[11]

The dissociation of large hydrocarbon molecules was investigated by Gur'ev[12] and others. From $C_{24}H_{50}$, for example, they found C_4 compounds in maximo and others in the proportions shown below:

$$C_4 \ (100), \ C_3 \ (83), \ C_5 \ (58.5),$$

$$C_6 \ (40), \ C_2 \ (21), \ C_7 \ (10),$$

and C_8 to C_{24} trailing off from (6) to <(1).

The ion-molecule reactions:

$$CH_4^+ + CH_4 \rightarrow CH_5^+ + CH_3 \text{ and}$$

$$D_2^+ + D_2 \rightarrow D_3^+ + D,$$

demonstrated by V. L. Tal'roze and A. K. Lyubimova[13] in the mass spectrograph, are said to be the first cases of extraction and addition ever reported.

References

1. LEWIS, BERNARD, *J. Phys. Chem.*, **37**, 533 (1933).
2. D'OLIESLAGER, J. F., AND JUNGERS, J. C., *Bull. soc. chim. Belg.*, **40**, 75 (1931).
3. DMITRIEV, M. T., AND PSHEZHETSKY, S. Y., Moscow Conf. on Radiation Chemistry (1957), A.E.C. Translation, p. 2925; *Atomnaya Energiya*, **3**, 350 (1957); *Int. J. Appl. Radiation and Isotopes*, **5**, 67 (1957).
4. BORTNER, T. E., AND HURST, G. S., *Health Physics*, **1**, 39 (1955).
5. RUDOLPH, P. S., AND MELTON, C. E., *J. Chem. Phys.*, **32**, 586 (1963).
6. HIRSCHFELDER, J. O., *J. Phys. Chem.*, **52**, 447 (1948).
7. VARNEY, R. N., *J. Chem. Phys.*, **23**, 866 (1955).
8. MORINAGA, K., *Bull. Chem. Soc. Japan*, **35**, 345 (1962).
9. MORINAGA, K., AND SUZUKI, M., *Ibid.*, **35**, 204 (1962).
10. (*Ibid.*, **35**, 429 (1962)).
11. (*Ibid.*, **35**, 625 (1962)).
12. GUR'EV, M. V., TIKHOMIROV, M. V., AND TUNITSKII, N. N., *Bull. Acad. Sci. U.S.S.R.*, *Phys. Series*, **24**, 977 (1960).
13. TAL'ROZE, V. L., AND LYUBIMOVA, A. K., *Dokl. Akad. Nauk S.S.S.R.*, **86**, 909 (1952).

Literature References

1. PENNING, F. M., "Electrical Discharges in Gases," New York, Macmillan, 1957.
2. SLEPIAN, J., "Conduction of Electricity in Gases," East Pittsburgh, Pennsylvania, Educational Department, Westinghouse Electric Co., 1933.
3. WHEATCROFT, E. L. E., "Gaseous Electrical

Conductors," Oxford, Clarendon Press, 1938.

4. Emeleus K. G., "The Conduction of Electricity through Gases," 3rd Ed., London, Methuen, 1951.

5. Massey, H. S. W., and Burhop, E. H. S., "Electronic and Ionic Impact Phenomena," Oxford, Clarendon Press, 1952.

6. Loeb, L. B., "Basic Processes of Gaseous Electronics," Berkeley, University of California Press, 1955.

7. Thomson, Sir J. J., and Thomson, G. P., "Conduction of Electricity through Gases," Cambridge, Cambridge University Press, 1933.

8. Flügge, S., "Handbuch der Physik," Band XXI, XXII, Berlin, Springer, 1956.

9. Wien, W., and Harms, F., "Handbuch der Experimental Physik," Band XIII, 2. und 3. Teil, Leipzig, Akademische Verlagsgesellschaft M. B. H., 1928, 1929.

10. von Engel, A., "Ionized Gases," Oxford, Clarendon Press, 1955.

11. Darrow, K. K., "Electrical Phenomena in Gases," Baltimore, The Williams and Wilkins Co., 1932.

12. Geiger, H., and Scheel, K., "Handbuch der Physik" Band XIV, Berlin, Springer, 1927.

13. Druyvesteyn, M. J., and Penning, F. M., "Mechanism of Electrical Discharges in Gases of Low Pressure," Rev. Mod. Phys., 12, 87 (1940).

14. Francis, V. J., and Jenkins, H. G., "Electrical Discharges in Gases and their Applications," Report Prog. Phys., 7, 230 (1940).

15. Lind, Samuel C., "The Chemical Effects of Alpha Particles and Electrons," A. C. S. Monograph Series, New York, Chemical Catalog Co., 1921; Revised Ed., 1928.

16. Glockler, George, and Lind, S. C., "The Electrochemistry of Gases and Other Dielectrics," New York, John Wiley & Sons, 1939.

17. Lind, Samuel C., with Hochanadel, C. J., and Ghormley, J. A., "Radiation Chemistry of Gases," A. C. S. Monograph No. 151, New York, Reinhold Publishing Corp., 1961.

S. C. Lind

Cross-references: *Acetylene by Electric Discharge; Air Ion Generation; Dielectrics; Glow Discharge Electrolysis; Nitrogen Fixation by the Arc Process; Ozone; Vacuum Arc Properties.*

GAUSS, KARL FRIEDRICH (1777–1855)

Johann Karl Friedrich Gauss, born in Braunschweig, Germany, on April 30, 1777, has long been called the Prince of Mathematicians and ranks with Archimedes and Newton in the class of the very great. His birth to poor parents in a miserable cottage and early life under the upright, uncouth, harsh man who was his father gave little indication of the extraordinary individual who was to come. The line of descent of Gauss' genius was from his mother's side and was encouraged in the boy by his uncle, Friederich, who was clever and able to rouse the boy's amazing logic by his philosophy and observations. Gauss' mother was a woman of sharp intellect and good sense and realized early that the boy had outstanding talent. She took his part against her obstinate husband so the boy would have opportunities and not remain as ignorant as his father. She lived to be 97 and her old age was serene and happy under the protection of her famous son. Gauss' precocity as a child was astounding, and he showed his caliber before he was three years old. In later life he enjoyed the joke that he knew how to reckon before he could talk.

When he reached the age of seven Gauss entered his first school, run by a brute named Büttner whose ideas of teaching were based largely on thrashing the students into insensibility. Here, at the age of ten, Gauss first came in contact with arithmetic. His ability astounded the teacher to such an extent that he actually bought the best textbook on arithmetic and presented it to the boy. Fortunately, Büttner realized the boy was way beyond his capabilities and permitted a close association between Gauss and his assistant (Johann Martin Bartels) who had a passion for mathematics. The friendship continued throughout Bartels' life. It is out of this early work that the one of the dominating interests of Gauss' career developed. He quickly mastered the binomial theorem and, dissatisfied with what he found in his book, he made a proof. This initiated him into mathematical analysis. The correct use of infinite processes is the very essence of analysis, and the work thus begun was to change the whole aspect of mathematics. Gauss was a revolutionist and applied the same critical spirit to elemental geometry. At twelve he was examining the foundations of Euclidean geometry and by sixteen started to glimpse non-Euclidean geometry.

Bartels, fortunately, was acquainted with some of the influential men of Brunswick and made it his business to acquaint these men with the genius under his wing. The favorable attention of Carl Wilhelm Ferdinand, Duke of Brunswick, assured the youth of his continued education. At the Collegium Carolinum in Brunswick he made great headway in the classical languages and the Duke subsidized a two-year course at the Gymnasium where his lightning mastery of the classics astounded all. During his three years at the Caroline College, Gauss began those researches in the higher arithmetic which were to make him immortal. It is at this time that his amazing powers of calculation came into play.

At the age of 18 he left the Caroline College for the University of Göttingen and was still undecided whether to follow mathematics or philology as a life work. Fortunately, he decided in favor of mathematics. The turning point occurred in March 1796 when Gauss set forth the first advance in Euclidean constructions that had occurred in over 2000 years. Up until the time he entered the university he had displayed amazing mathematical powers in criticizing the foundations of Euclidean geometry, recognizing convergence, and giving proof of the binomial theorem. At 17 he had discovered the flaw in Adrien M. Legenre's attempted proof of the law of quadratic reciprocity and shortly thereafter devised his own proof. He was granted his doctor's degree at the University of Helmstedt in 1799 for a dissertation giving the first proof of the fundamental theorem of algebra. It was a masterpiece in logical rigour.

In 1807 he was made professor of mathematics and director of the observatory at Göttingen, positions he held until his death. Here he conducted his famous measurements of terrestrial magnetism and published his works on the mathematical relations of electricity and magnetism. For his experimental work he developed the magnetometer, the heliotrope for transmitting light signals, and one of the earliest telegraphs (1834). To honor Gauss' application of absolute units of length, mass, and time to magnetic fields, as well as his other outstanding contributions to the understanding of magnetism, his name has been given to the value of the intensity of a magnetic field.

The scope of his work is so vast and his abilities in both pure and applied mathematics so extensive that it would be impossible to cite his tremendous contributions to mathematics and electromagnetism. His astounding calculative powers enabled him to do in weeks what might have taken others years to accomplish; he was the veritable computing machine of his day. Gauss died at Göttingen February 23, 1855.

CARMEN W. WALSH

GENERATION OF AIR IONS. See AIR ION GENERATION.

GIBBS, JOSIAH WILLARD (1839–1903)

Josiah Willard Gibbs was born February 11, 1839, the son of J. W. Gibbs, professor of sacred literature at the Yale Divinity School. He entered Yale in 1854. Gibbs' doctoral thesis was presented in 1863. Three years later Gibbs went to Europe and studied at Paris, Berlin and Heidelberg. In 1871 he was appointed professor of mathematical physics at Yale, a position he held until his death on April 28, 1903. His studies in physical chemistry led to the publication of "Graphical methods in the thermodynamics of fluids, 1873". His most important work "On the equilibrium of heterogeneous substance", 2 vols., 1876–1878 is a classic in physical chemistry, and although little recognition was given to this work in the U. S., a German translation by Ostwald assured it a large audience in Europe. In 1900 Gibbs was awarded the Copley Medal of the Royal Society "For the first to apply the second law of thermodynamics to the exhaustive discussion of the relation between chemical, electrical and thermal energy and capacity for external work." Gibbs' name is associated with the Gibbs-Helmholtz equation and the celebrated phase rule. His publications include "Multiple algebra, 1886", and "Elementary principles in statistical mechanics, 1902". His correspondents included Maxwell, Boltzmann, Kelvin and Ostwald. The practical applications of his work are manifold. In the metallurgical industry, especially the compounding of alloys, and in the chemical industry, phase studies with the aid of Gibbs' formulas have been of tremendous value. It may be said that Willard Gibbs was the father of modern thermodynamics.

BERNARD JAFFE

GIBBS-DONNAN EQUILIBRIUM. See MEMBRANE EQUILIBRIUM.

GIBBS-HELMHOLTZ EQUATION

If a chemical reaction can be carried out reversibly in an electrochemical cell, then the measurement of the cell electromotive force (emf) as a function of temperature allows the free energy, enthalpy, and entropy changes of the reaction to be determined. The free energy change (ΔF) depends upon the cell emf as shown in Eq. 1

$$\Delta F = -n\mathbf{F}E \tag{1}$$

where E is the cell emf, $\mathbf{F}$ is the Faraday constant (96,493.5 coulombs/equiv. or 23,062.3 cal/volt-equiv.), and n is the number of electrons or equivalents transferred in the cell reaction as it is written. The computation of the enthalpy of the reaction is made possible by Eq. 2, which is called the *Gibbs-Helmholtz* equation after the two scientists, J. Willard Gibbs (1839–1903) and H. von Helmholtz (1821–1894) who contributed to its derivation.[1, 5]

$$\Delta H = \Delta F - T\left(\frac{\partial \Delta F}{\partial T}\right)_P. \tag{2}$$

Eqs. 1 and 2 may be combined to give the form of the Gibbs-Helmholtz equation most useful to electrochemists.

$$\Delta H = -n\mathbf{F}E + n\mathbf{F}T\left(\frac{\partial E}{\partial T}\right)_P \tag{3}$$

Thus, the free energy change may be evaluated using Eq. 1, the enthalpy change using Eq. 3, and the entropy change from the familiar equation

$$\Delta F = \Delta H - T\Delta S \tag{4}$$

or directly from Eq. 7 which is given below.

The Gibbs-Helmholtz equation may be derived according to the methods of Gibbs (1) from his expression

$$dF = -SdT + VdP \tag{5}$$

Taking the derivative of F with respect to T at constant P

$$\left(\frac{\partial F}{\partial T}\right)_P = -S \tag{6}$$

and for a process

$$\left(\frac{\partial \Delta F}{\partial T}\right)_P = -\Delta S \tag{7}$$

Eq. 7, when combined with Eq. 4, gives the Gibbs-Helmholtz equation directly.

As an example, consider the cell

$$\text{Pt-Cl}_{2(p)} \mid \text{HCl}_{(m)} \mid \text{AgCl-Ag}$$

with the cell reaction

$$\text{AgCl} \rightarrow \text{Ag} + \tfrac{1}{2}\text{Cl}_2 .$$

For the case where all substances are in their standard states (unit activity), the cell potential is -1.1362 volts, and the temperature coefficient of the cell is 0.595 millivolts/degree. Using Eq. 1,

$$\Delta F = -1 \text{ equiv.} \times 23,062 \text{ cal/volt-equiv.}$$

$$\times (-1.1362) \text{ volts} = 26,203 \text{ calories.}$$

From Eq. 3,

$$\Delta H = 26,203 \text{ cal} + 1 \text{ equiv.} \times 23,062 \text{ cal/volt-}$$

$$\text{equiv.} \times 298 \text{ deg} \times 0.595 \times 10^{-3} \text{ volts/deg}$$

$$= 30,292 \text{ calories.}$$

The value determined calorimetrically is 30,090 calories. The difference between these two values is within normal experimental error.

Several precautions must be kept in mind in the use of the Gibbs-Helmholtz equation. Eq. 2 is quite general and applicable to both reversible and irreversible processes. On the other hand, Eq. 3, which contains the cell emf and is derived using Eq. 1, is strictly applicable only to reversible cells of known cell reactions. Therefore, it is not at all valid to apply Eq. 3 to a cell potential unless it is shown that the reaction is carried out reversibly. Strictly speaking, this treatment is applicable only to cells without liquid junction potentials, although approximate results might be obtained if the junction potential is small. In this connection, it is useful to remember that junction potentials are on the order of magnitude of millivolts and that a one millivolt error in E causes an error of 23 calories if $n = 1$.

It must also be remembered that the use of the derivative of the cell potential poses severe requirements on the accuracy of the data. Since the temperature coefficient of the cell is of the order of fractions of millivolts per degree, it is evident that a rather high degree of accuracy is required in the measurement of the cell emf, for an error of 10 microvolts per degree in the temperature coefficient corresponds to an error of about 70 calories at 298°C for $n = 1$.

Although in principle the determination of the thermodynamic properties of a cell reaction is relatively simple, in practice the determinations require extremely careful experimental techniques. In addition, the treatment of the experimental data involves specialized functions and extrapolation procedures for obtaining the standard cell emf and the correct temperature coefficient. These techniques, along with the Gibbs-Helmholtz equation, are especially suitable to the determination of the relative partial molal heat content and the relative partial molal heat capacity of electrolytes, and a large amount of work has been carried out for this purpose. Further information on these techniques may be obtained from the reference list below, especially reference 2.

References

1. Gibbs, J. W., *Transactions of the Connecticut Academy of Sciences*, **2**, 309, 328 (1873); **3**, 108, 343 (1875–1878). "Scientific Papers of J. Willard Gibbs," Vol. I, New York, Longmans, Green and Company, 1906. "The Collected Works of J. Willard Gibbs," Vol. I, New York, Longmans, Green and Company, 1928.
2. Harned, H. S., and Owen, B. B., "The Physical Chemistry of Electrolytic Solutions," New York, Reinhold Publishing Corp., 1958.
3. Ives, D. J. G., and Janz, G. J., "Reference Electrodes, Theory and Practice," New York, Academic Press, 1961.
4. Lewis, G. N., and Randall, M., "Thermodynamics" (2nd ed. revised by K. S. Pitzer and Leo Brewer) New York, McGraw-Hill Book Co., 1961.
5. Wheeler, L. P., "Josiah Willard Gibbs," p. 97, New Haven, Yale University Press, 1952.

Robert E. Meyer

GLASS, ELECTRIC MELTING OF

It is well-known that glass is an electrical insulator at room temperatures. Not so well-known is that glass becomes a conductor of electricity when it is hot. This change of properties is gradual from room temperature to melting temperatures, say 2600°F, and is almost entirely due to the change in viscosity. At room temperatures, glass is a solid. The resistance is about 100,000,000 ohms between faces of a one-inch cube. At 1200°F, glass is about as stiff as unchewed chewing gum. The resistance has dropped to 1,000 ohms. At melting temperature,

2600°F, the viscosity is about the same as table syrup. The resistance has dropped further to a few ohms.

The change in resistance with temperature of several kinds of glass is shown in Fig. 1.

This change in resistance can be demonstrated very simply by the following experiment. Fasten two pieces of ordinary iron wire 12 in. long to a horizontal insulating board so that the wires hang down and are insulated from each other. Bend hooks in the ends of the wires and position them one inch apart. Place a two inch piece of soft soda-lime glass (soft glass tubing or rod, a fragment of a bottle, or a strip of windowglass) across the hooks. Support a brick touching the hooks from below to catch the glass when it melts. Connect the upper ends of the iron wire through a ten ampere fuse to 120 volts house current. Heat the glass with a Bunsen burner to make the glass conductive. After the glass has reached a strong red heat, electric heating will take over and the glass will be quite hot. An ammeter in the circuit can be used to follow the increase in current flow. It is likely that the fuse will blow.

Electrical conductivity in glass is electrolytic in character. Glass contains sodium ions, which behave in the same way as sodium ions in a salt or sodium hydroxide solution in water. Ordinary glass contains about 15 per cent Na_2O, and is a nonconductor at room temperatures only because the ions are immobile. As soon as the glass is heated to permit the ions to be mobile, they begin to conduct.

Polarization effects are also easy to demonstrate. A fireclay crucible is filled with broken bottle glass and heated by a gas flame in a simple brick enclosure. After the crucible is up to a bright red temperature, say 1500°F, iron rods are lowered through the roof into the glass, but separated from each other. A six-volt battery is connected across the outer ends of the rods through a one-ampere ammeter. At the first contact, the reading will be quite high but will drop swiftly to about one-seventh of the initial reading. This drop is due to polarization whereby sodium ions are congregated at one electrode and silica ions at the other electrode. When the current is removed, depolarization occurs quickly.

In the foregoing experiment, the iron rods can be connected to a heavier variable transformer, and the glass in the crucible can be kept hot solely by the heat generated by the passage

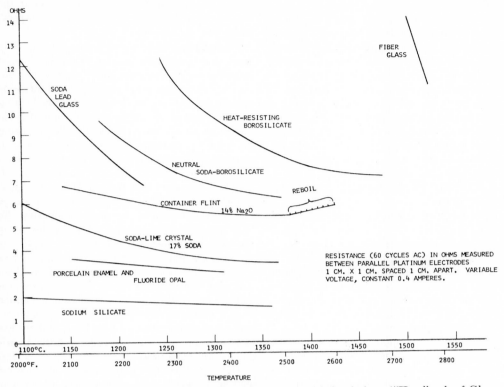

Fig. 1. Change in resistance with temperature of several kinds of glass. ("Handbook of Glass Manufacture," Vol. II p. 259, New York, Ogden Publishing Group)

of the electric current through the glass bath serving as the resistor. The resistance between electrodes will be in the order of 1–10 ohms, depending on the temperature.

Polarization can cause changes in the glass composition, resulting in dark streaks arising from electrodes. This is particularly the case with graphite electrodes, since the wetting of glass to graphite is poor and hence the contact resistance is high. Evidently high temperatures arise at the interface, even approaching incipient arc conditions, so that some reactions can take place that would not normally be expected in a glass bath. For example, graphite electrodes under conditions of loading higher than 3 amp/ sq in. can cause discoloration which is believed to be due to colloidal silicon reduced from silica.

The use of a-c power decreases the difficulty due to polarization, although under conditions of high current density, the discoloration effects mentioned above the respect to graphite can also occur against molybdenum electrodes.

The conductivity of glass at high temperatures has been known in patent literature since

1902. The first furnaces to use this principle used graphite and iron electrodes to contact the bath from opposite sides, but encountered quality difficulties due to the reaction of these electrode materials with the glass itself. Polarization and chemical reactivity cause discoloration and bubbles.

With the availability of large molybdenum rods for use as electrodes, electric melting of glass became more convenient to install, since a molybdenum rod 1-¼ in. diameter can replace a graphite rod 12 in. in diameter. The molybdenum-electrode process has been widely applied throughout the world since that time, mostly in boosting but with an increasing application to all-electric furnaces.

The traditional glass furnace is a large room made of brick, say 15 ft wide by 30 ft long by 6 ft high. Molten glass fills the lower half, leaving the upper half for fuel combustion space. Batch, consisting of silica sand, sodium carbonate, and limestone, is fed in continuously at one end and finished glass is continuously removed from the other end. The electric booster melting process consists of inserting molybdenum electrodes through the sidewalls of the basin to make contact with the glass and passing a large current at moderate voltage through the bath itself. The resistance between the electrodes is in the order of 0.1 ohms, so that 100 volts will cause a current of 1,000 amperes to flow. The resulting 100 kw of electric power is sufficient to melt an additional five tons of glass per day above the normal output of the furnace. Booster installations range from 100 to 2,000 kw. In the above furnace example, the normal fuel-fired glass output would be 90 tons per 24 hours. With a booster of 600 kw, the output can be increased to 120 tons.

The efficiency of applying electric heat to an existing furnace is very high, since the heat is liberated almost entirely within the glass itself.

Sixty-cycle alternating current is used in most commercial applications, although higher frequency up to 10,000 cycles is used with platinum electrodes to prevent colloidal disintegration of the platinum which would cause the glass to have a foggy appearance.

Some glasses contain potassium oxide as the flux instead of sodium oxide. Potassium glasses have a conductivity only about half as high as sodium glasses of the same weight per cent of the oxide, partly because there are fewer potassium ions per gram and also partly because of the larger diameter of the potassium atom which impedes its mobility. Potassium glasses are usually higher in viscosity than sodium glasses, even though the alkali is present in the same molar per cent.

Glasses of the heat resisting type called borosilicate contain about 4 per cent sodium oxide. They are several times higher in resistance than normal bottle glasses. Borosilicate glass can be melted electrically, using a higher voltage to overcome the higher resistance.

Some glasses contain practically no alkali. They are very high in resistance even at elevated temperatures. One such glass, however, contains 22 per cent $CaO + MgO$, and above 2800°F it becomes a very satisfactory conductor. In this case, the alkaline earth ions carry the current.

One particular glass used in polished thick blocks for atomic radiation shielding windows consists of 79 per cent PbO and 21 per cent SiO_2. The melting temperature of this glass is low at 1800°F, but because of the high lead ion content and the low viscosity, the electrical conductivity at melting temperatures is about the same as soda-lime glass at much higher temperatures.

Some glasses have volatile components such as boric oxide or sodium fluoride. Opal glasses used for cosmetic jars contain about 5 per cent fluoride as the opacifying agent. The fluoride is volatile, which can be demonstrated by heating a small piece of such glass in a platinum crucible for about one hour at 1800°F. The resulting glass will lose its opacity because of evaporation of the fluoride. All-electric melting is very beneficial for such glasses, since the powdered batch floats on the surface of the bath while the glass below is kept hot by the Joule-effect heating. A fire is used to make the glass conductive the first time when starting such a furnace, but after the glass is sufficiently conducting, the fire is turned off. Floating batch covers the entire surface. The volatile components, such as fluoride, are cooled in the batch as they evaporate and are returned to the bath in the same manner as in a reflux condenser. This reflux action prevents loss of the volatile ingredient, and results in a uniform percentage of the volatile ingredient in the glass product.

Another favorable application of electric melting of glass is in the melting of colored glasses which are generally opaque to thermal radiation. Instances have been known with dark glasses used for sun glasses where the surface glass was 2750°F and the glass only eight inches below was so cold that it was solid. In such applications, electric heat can be applied to the bath so that the bath temperature is the same from the surface to the floor of the furnace.

In a practical electric glass furnace, the resistance of the bath goes down as the temperature goes up. If the electrodes are connected to a fixed-voltage transformer, the power input will be correct at only one temperature. If the temperature is colder, the power input will not be sufficient and the glass will become cooler. Its resistance will rise and the power input will be even less until the furnace becomes completely cold. Conversely, if the temperature is above the critical temperature, the power input will be too high and will become even higher until the furnace is destroyed. The system is known as "self-deregulating." Accordingly, such furnaces have power-control systems based on transformers with many taps or with voltage control devices such as saturable reactors.

All-electric melting of glass is gaining importance today and will be even more important in the future as fossil fuels are depleted and atomic energy becomes available in the form of electric power.

References

1. VOELKER, A., U.S. Patent 702,081 (June 10, 1902). In Germany, applied for June 28, 1900.
2. BOREL, E. V., "Practical Aspects of Electric Melting of Glass," *J. Soc. Glass Tech.*, **34**, 160 (October, 1950).
3. PENBERTHY, L., "Current Status of Electric Booster Melting," *Glass Industry*, **36**, (12), 635 (1955).
4. HOROWITZ, I., "Electrical Glass Melting," *Glass Industry*, **34**, (2), 65; (3), 132; (4) 204 (1953).
5. PENBERTHY, L., U.S. Patent 2,693,498, (Nov. 2., 1954).
6. PENBERTHY, L., U.S. Patent, 2,749,378, (June 5, 1956).
7. SNELL, R. G., "Electrical Properties and Uses of Glasses," *Glass Industry*, **43**, (9), 484 (1962).
8. MOREY, G. W., "The Properties of Glass," New York, Reinhold Publishing Corp., 1954.

LARRY PENBERTHY

GLASS ELECTRODE

A glass electrode cell chain is a pH-sensitive electrolytic cell which serves as the basis for the most common means of measuring pH. The pH-sensitive element in this combination is a thin bulb or membrane of glass which, when in contact with a solution of a given hydrogen ion concentration, or pH, will develop a difference of potential between its inner and outer surfaces which is linearly proportional to the pH. This difference of potential is additive to an invariant potential difference which is a function of the means of contacting the other surface of the glass and also depends on the history of the membrane.

A common construction for the glass electrode of the cell chain takes the form of a thin-walled glass bulb, usually of a soft glass known as Corning 015, joined to a tubular stem of non-sensitive glass, such as lead glass. The bulb is filled with a buffer solution and a stable reference electrode, such as a silver-silver chloride electrode, is immersed in the buffer. The other electrode of the cell chain is a reference electrode (q.v.), usually a calomel half-cell, isolated for protection by a liquid junction; these will be described later. The electrodes are held in a suitable mechanical mounting and arranged so that they can easily be immersed in the solution

whose pH is to be measured. Connecting leads with excellent insulation and shielding, necessitated by the high electrical resistance of the glass bulb, attach the cell chain to the pH meter which measures the voltage of the cell chain and reads it out as pH.

The possible shapes and forms of the glass electrode are limitless. The most commonly used form is a bulb about one-quarter inch in diameter whose resistance at ordinary room temperature is of the order of 200 megohms. This regular glass electrode is commonly used for pH's up to 9 or 10 when made of "015" glass. Above 10 pH an error increasing with pH becomes important when sodium ion is present in the sample. For accurate pH determination in highly alkaline solutions the electrode is made of one of several sodium-free glasses which do not exhibit this sodium error. When measurements are to be made habitually in solutions at high temperature, 80 to 100°C, the bulb may be made with a heavier wall or of a more resistant glass to minimize failure of the bulb by solution in the hot sample. In the former case advantage is being taken of the rapid reduction of bulb resistance as temperature rises. Several kinds of glass electrodes are shown in Fig. 1.

In any of the above glasses, bulbs may be made in many shapes for special purposes ranging from capillary tubing for micro samples through pointed, strong-walled bulbs for plunging into meat. Special electrodes have been made to be swallowed for gastric work; tiny bulbs

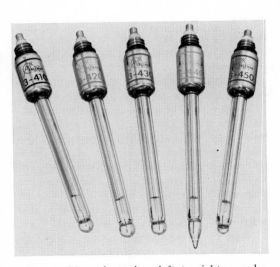

FIG. 1. Glass electrodes; left to right: regular, high-alkalinity, high-temperature, penetration, and heavy-duty screw base types.

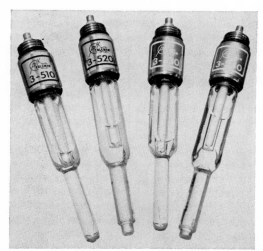

FIG. 2. Reference electrodes; left to right: calomel with capillary liquid junction, calomel with plunger liquid junction, silver-silver chloride with capillary liquid junction, and silver-silver chloride with plunger liquid junction; all with screw bases.

have been embedded into teeth for dental investigations.

The most commonly used reference electrodes are the calomel half-cell and the silver-silver chloride half-cell. Other types, such as chloride-free half-cells, have been used for special purposes. Because of the danger of contaminating the reference cell, it is not normally immersed directly into the sample but rather into a liquid junction reservoir filled with saturated potassium chloride. Connnection is made from the reservoir to the sample by means of a liquid junction. Fig. 2 illustrates typical reference electrodes for use with glass electrodes for pH measurement.

The liquid junction may be several porous fibers, such as asbestos, sealed through the wall of the reservoir. These give an electrical connection between the reservoir and the sample and at the same time permit a slow seepage of the saturated potassium chloride out of the reservoir to keep the junction clean. Another type of junction is the ground joint. This joint is a snugly fitted ground-glass plug and socket which permits the necessary seepage and conductive path for the junction. The older types were likely to freeze, the newer sliding junction avoids this. Rough rubber tubing snapped over a hole in the side of a tubular reservoir has been much used to form a junction. For some purpose pastes or gels containing the electrolyte have been used,

especially where renewal must be frequent or where contact must be made to the skin, as in vaginal or nasal investigations.

In most pH work the two electrodes are mounted in a clamp either attached to the pH meter or to a separate stand. Remote installations are possible if suitable shielded cabling is used between the electrodes and the meter. However, because of the high resistance of the cell chain, the use of long runs of cable may slow down significantly the response of the pH meter to changes in pH, and flexing of the cable, unless specially treated, may introduce fluctuation into the reading of the meter because of voltages generated in the cable. The inherent response of the glass electrode to pH changes is extremely rapid; sluggishness in reaching equilibrium is usually due to excessive cable length, a slow pH meter, or failure to keep the electrode surface clean.

References

1. DOLE, M. "The Glass Electrode," New York, John Wiley & Sons, Inc., 1941.
2. BATES, R. G., "Electrometric pH Determinations," New York, John Wiley & Sons, Inc., 1954.
3. IVES, D. J. G., AND JANZ, G. J., "Reference Electrodes," Chapters 3 and 5. New York, Academic Press, 1961.
4. BATES, R. G., Chapter 10 in KOLTHOFF, I. M., AND ELVING, P. J., "Treatise on Analytical Chemistry," New York, Interscience Encyclopedia Inc., 1959.
5. PERLEY, G. A., Chapter 1 in BOLTZ, D. F., Ed., "Modern Instrumental Analysis," Englewood Cliffs, N.J., Prentice-Hall, Inc., 1952.

JOHN J. J. STAUNTON

Cross references: *pH; pH Meter; Reference Electrodes.*

GLOW DISCHARGE. See VACUUM ARC PROPERTIES.

GLOW-DISCHARGE ELECTROLYSIS

Glow-discharge electrolysis is achieved by passing an electric discharge to a conducting solution from an electrode situated in the gas space above the surface. As generally practiced, the electrode above the surface is the anode, while the cathode is immersed in the electrolyte; at reduced pressure, the discharge once initiated can be maintained at voltages of 500 v upwards, and substantial currents can be passed to the surface, bringing about remarkable chemical reactions in the liquid phase. The technique was first used as a method of carrying out electrolysis without a solid electrode in contact with the electrolyte [Gubkin (1887), Klüpfel (1905), Makowetsky (1911)].

Extensive studies by Klemenc and co-workers (1914–53) showed, however, that the chemical effects produced could be far in excess quantitatively of those expected from Faraday's Laws. Recent fundamental investigations by Hickling and associates (1950–62) have shown that charge transfer plays only a minor part in the process. The current is carried by positively-charged gaseous ions which are accelerated in the cathode fall near the liquid surface and enter the solution with energies of about 100 ev. They can bring about dissociation of solvent molecules by collision, as well as discharge of ions by charge transfer, and the chemical effects are analogous to the radiolysis produced by ionizing radiations, particularly low-energy α-particles. Each gaseous ion entering the solution can give a substantial yield of radicals from solvent molecules, and the chemical changes produced arise from the reactions of these radicals. Quantity of electricity is still an important factor since it determines the total number of gaseous ions entering the liquid, but we have now a new kind of electrochemistry based on energy transfer in addition to the charge transfer of conventional electrolysis.

Experimental Technique and Discharge Characteristics

The experimental cell can take many forms; one convenient type is shown in Fig. 1. It consists of two cylindrical glass vessels, forming the anode and cathode compartments, joined by a side tube containing a filter paper or sintered glass plug to prevent mixing of anolyte and catholyte. The compartments are closed by ground glass caps or rubber stoppers carrying the cell components. The anode may be a platinum wire attached to a tungsten rod sealed into a glass holder; the nature of the cathode is immaterial, but on a small scale a platinum foil electrode is convenient. It is sometimes useful to have the anolyte stirred, and this can be done by a magnetic stirrer. The anode and cathode compartments are connected to a vacuum line in which a constant pressure in the range 25 to 200 mm is maintained. Considerable heat is dissi-

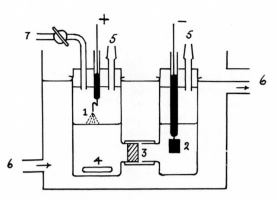

Fig. 1. Electrolytic cell: (1) glow-discharge anode; (2) cathode; (3) porous plug; (4) magnetic stirrer; (5) connections to vacuum line; (6) cooling water; (7) gas supply.

pated in the discharge and the cell is therefore almost completely immersed in a bath through which tap water is passed.

Current is best supplied from a rectifier of adjustable voltage (0–1500 v) through an ammeter and suitable ballast resistor; this last is necessary to maintain a stable discharge and should give a voltage drop of 100–200 v. To initiate the discharge, a pulse from an induction coil or high-voltage transformer can be used, or the anode may be brought momentarily into contact with the liquid surface. Once started, the discharge is very steady, and currents in the range 0.02–0.2 amp can readily be used with the anode at distances of up to 1 cm from the surface.

The discharge takes the form of a sharply-defined cone between the tip of the anode and a circular glow-spot in the electrolyte surface. Its color depends upon the nature of the vapor present; with aqueous electrolytes in air it is pinkish-blue. The area of the glow-spot increases with rise of current and decrease of pressure; at a given pressure the change of area with current is often such that the current density in the spot is approximately constant. Experiments with probe electrodes show that the major part of the voltage drop in the discharge occurs over a distance of less than 0.05 cm from the liquid surface, and this cathode fall, which is 415 v for aqueous solutions, is independent of most experimental variables. It is the presence of this considerable field near the electrolyte surface which gives rise to the characteristic chemical effects in the liquid phase.

If the electrode above the surface is made a

cathode instead of an anode, most of the voltage drop occurs near it and there is only a relatively small anode fall close to the liquid surface; as would be expected, therefore, the chemical effects produced in the solution are small with this arrangement, and the metal electrode becomes white hot and may melt. Alternating current can be used for glow-discharge electrolysis, most of the chemical reaction then occurring during the half cycles in which the electrode above the surface is positive.

A method has recently been discovered of effecting glow-discharge electrolysis at atmospheric pressure with very simple apparatus. In this method, which is termed "contact glow-discharge," the anode is a thin wire which is immersed to a few centimeters depth in the electrolyte. On passing a small current, conventional electrolysis occurs. If the current is gradually increased, a point is reached at which the electric power dissipated near the electrode surface is sufficient to vaporize the solvent locally. The anode than becomes enveloped in a sheath of vapor through which glow-discharge occurs. The chemical effects produced are closely analogous to those obtained with the more usual arrangement, and the discharge is automatically initiated and maintained. The overall voltage which has to be applied is minimized by the absence of external resistance and may be as low as 500 v.

Results and Interpretation

With aqueous solutions of inert electrolytes, such as sodium phosphate or sulfuric acid, the main product of glow-discharge electrolysis in the solution is hydrogen peroxide. This is initially formed in amount proportional to the quantity of electricity passed, and the yield may be as high as 2 equivalents/faraday; the excess oxidation over that possible from charge transfer is balanced by an equivalent amount of hydrogen liberated into the gas phase. As the hydrogen peroxide accumulates in the solution, a decomposition reaction due to the glow-discharge sets in and ultimately a stationary concentration is reached when the peroxide is decomposing as fast as it is formed.

It may be supposed that in the discharge gaseous ions travel towards the liquid in the gas phase and are accelerated through the cathode fall near the electrolyte surface; they are, thus, likely to enter the solution with sufficient energy to bring about dissociation of

several water molecules per particle. Thus, in the primary reaction zone in the glow-spot in the liquid there may be dissociation akin to radiolysis which, in the simplest case, may be represented as:

$$H_2O \rightsquigarrow OH + H.$$

In addition, transfer of charge may yield 1 equivalent of OH/faraday, according to:

$$H_2O - \epsilon \rightarrow OH + H^+.$$

The chemical products formed will therefore be determined by interaction of the radicals among themselves, and formation of hydrogen peroxide is probably due to dimerisation of OH radicals:

$$2OH \rightarrow H_2O_2$$

in competition with the back reaction:

$$OH + H \rightarrow H_2O.$$

Subsequent decomposition of hydrogen peroxide may then arise by its reaction with further OH radicals. By using oxidizable substrates in the solution, such a ferrous, azide, and cerous ions, it is possible to scavenge the OH radicals formed and by extrapolating to very high substrate concentrations, to estimate the initial radical yield. This works out to be some 7–8 OH radicals per unit positive charge entering the solution.

With liquid ammonia as a solvent and solutes such as ammonium nitrate, glow-discharge electrolysis produces hydrazine as the main product in solution. The initial yield is approximately 2.5 moles/faraday, and this falls off slowly as hydrazine accumulates in the liquid, but stationary concentrations as high as $2M$ can be reached. The results conform to a reaction scheme, analogous to that for aqueous solutions, with a primary process leading to NH_2 radicals, such as:

$$NH_3 \rightsquigarrow NH_2 + H.$$

Hydrazine formation may then arise by the dimerisation:

$$2NH_2 \rightarrow N_2H_4,$$

in competition with the back reaction:

$$NH_2 + H \rightarrow NH_3.$$

The cathode fall with ammonia is 390 v, similar to that of 415 v observed with water, and the initial yield is about 12 NH_2 radicals per unit positive charge entering the liquid phase.

Applications

Glow-discharge electrolysis gives us a method of producing very high local concentrations of radicals formed from the break-up of solvent molecules in the liquid phase. It may thus provide a new route to products which are otherwise difficult to obtain. Anhydrous hydrazine can readily be obtained experimentally by glow-discharge electrolysis of conducting solutions in liquid ammonia followed by distillation of the resulting mixture, and there appears to be no fundamental difficulty in scaling-up the process. The economics of such a method must, however, be largely governed by the cost of the considerable electric power involved; the essential feature of glow-discharge electrolysis is the existence of a cathode fall of potential of *ca* 400 v and thus any operating voltage must exceed this figure. Little work has yet been done in applying the technique to organic systems, although a synthesis of oxamide by glow-discharge electrolysis of formamide in acid solutions has recently been reported. It seems certain that the use of organic ionizing solvents and mixed organic-aqueous systems will be a fruitful field of study.

References

No general review of glow-discharge electrolysis is available, but the following recent papers give details of current views and will serve as a guide to the earlier literature.

1. BROWN, E. H., WENDELL, D. W., AND ELMORE, K. L., *J. Organic Chem.*, **27**, 3698 (1962).
2. DEWHURST, H. A., FLAGG, J. F., AND WATSON, P. K., *J. Electrochem. Soc.*, **106**, 366 (1959).
3. HICKLING, A., AND DENARO, A. R., *J. Electrochem. Soc.*, **105**, 265 (1958).
4. HICKLING, A., AND NEWNS, G. R., *J. Chem. Soc.*, 5177, 5186 (1961).

A. HICKLING

Cross-references: *Gases, Electrical Conductance and Ionization; Vacuum Arc Properties.*

GLUⅭ SE ELECTROCHEMICAL REDUCTION

The purpose of this article is to review, briefly, the electrolytic reduction of glucose. The Atlas Powder Company (now Atlas Chemical Industries, Inc.) used the process for about 12 years to produce sorbitol, mannitol, and a non-crystallizing syrup of polyols. The electrolytic process has been replaced by a catalytic hydrogenation process which produces these materials at a lower cost.

The development of the electrolytic process and the chemistry of the reactions have been reported by Creighton,[1, 2] who pioneered in the work. In reporting their studies of the electrolytic reduction of hexoses, Parker and Swann[8] review the relevant literature and patents. The plant built in 1937 by Atlas Powder Company has been described by Killeffer[6] and by Taylor.[11] The problems attendant to the operation of electroorganic processes have been discussed by Swann.[10] Sanders and Hales[9] have described the performance of electrolytic cells used commercially for the reduction of glucose.

Commercially, the electrolytic reduction of glucose was performed in a batch reaction system. The catholyte was an aqueous solution of glucose rendered electrically conductive by sodium sulfate. The anolyte was dilute sulfuric acid. The two solutions were separated by a porous ceramic diaphragm. The anode was lead and the cathode was amalgamated lead or amalgamated zinc.

When reduction of a batch of catholyte was completed, the catholyte was removed from the cell system, neutralized, and evaporated almost to dryness. The sodium sulfate crystallized during the evaporation step. The residue in the evaporator was digested by hot aqueous ethanol to dissolve the polyols. The slurry was filtered to remove the sodium sulfate. If mannitol was present, the filtrate was cooled. The mannitol crystallized and was separated from the ethanolic solution of sorbitol. The ethanol was separated from the sorbitol by distillation. The still residue was an aqueous solution of sorbitol. This solution was treated to remove color and other impurities, then adjusted to the desired concentration for packaging. The mannitol was purified by recrystallization from water.

The reduction equipment consisted of a cell box which contained the electrodes and the diaphragm boxes, an external reservoir for the catholyte, a catholyte cooler, and a pump to circulate the catholyte from the reservoir through the cooler and thence to the cell. The catholyte flowed by gravity from the cell box to the catholyte reservoir.

The original commercial cell was a rectangular steel box 13 feet (3.96m) long, 6 feet (1.83m) wide, and 2 feet (0.61m) deep which was lined

TABLE 1

Current density	1 to 2 amp/sq dm
Catholyte temperature	68° to 75° F
Ratio of cathode area to catholyte volume	0.8 to 2.5 sq dm/l
Alkalinity of catholyte	zero to 20 g NaOH/l
Initial sugar concentration	300 to 500 gpl
Sodium sulfate concentration	70 to 100 gpl

with rubber. The diaphragms were ceramic boxes with open tops. Their outside dimensions were: length 24 inches (61 cm), height 24 inches (61 cm), width 3 inches (7.6 cm). Each cell contained 36 cathodes, 35 anodes and 70 diaphragms. The diaphragms were set in 35 rows of two each, and baffles directed the flow of catholyte back and forth across the cell past groups of diaphragms. The anolyte was contained in the diaphragm boxes. Each anode had 2 skirts and served a row of 2 diaphragms. The cathodes hung between the rows of diaphragm boxes.

It is necessary to have the cathodes as close to the diaphragms as possible in order to reduce the power consumption of the cell. This restriction results in a cell with small holding capacity for catholyte. The purpose of the external reservoir for catholyte is to permit use of the desired ratio of cathode area to catholyte volume and to take care of the increase of volume of catholyte during a run.

The heat evolved in the reduction of glucose to sorbitol is about 110 BTU per pound. This and the heat equivalent of the electrical energy supplied to the cell must be removed by the catholyte cooler. The catholyte cooler consisted of glass pipes which were jacketed by steel pipes through which cooling water flowed.

A flow sheet of the process and photographs of the plant, the cells, the catholyte reservoirs, and the coolers appear in the paper by Creighton.[1]

The nature of the product is extremely sensitive to operating conditions. Glucose, fructose, and mannose in alkaline aqueous solution undergo conversion into each other, the Lobry deBruyn rearrangement.[7] Glucose reduces to sorbitol, fructose to a mixture of sorbitol and mannitol, and mannose to mannitol. Furthermore, alkali causes the sugars to undergo other structural changes, and the products so formed reduce to polyols other than sorbitol and mannitol. The action of alkalies on sugars is sum-marized by Evans.[4] Wolfrom and co-workers[12] have isolated D-L-glucitol, 1-desoxy-D-mannitol (D-rhamnitol), 2-desoxy-D-mannitol (2-desoxy-sorbitol), allitol, a 2-desoxy-hexitol of undetermined configuration, and a pentitol of unknown structure from the products of the electrolytic reduction of glucose. Goepp and Soltzberg[5] have demonstrated the presence of a substance having a branched chain.

Table 1 presents a list of the variables involved in the reduction process and the usual ranges of their values.[9]

The current density is determined by economic considerations and by the nature of the desired reduction products. There is a limiting current density which is proportional to the concentration of glucose and which increases with increasing temperature. Use of a current density greater than the limiting value results in a waste of electric power. Use of a current density less than the limiting value increases the time required to reduce a batch of catholyte, and hence permits transformation of the glucose to other sugars and to degradation products and so results in a lower concentration of sorbitol in the product.

The rate of reduction is proportional to the current density until the concentration of sugar in the catholyte drops to such a value that the limiting current density equals the current density being used. After that point, the rate of reduction is proportional to the concentration of sugar in the catholyte. This latter period can be shortened by increasing catholyte temperature to increase the limiting current density.

In the reduction of dextrose, the alkalinity of the catholyte affects the nature of the products. The effect of increasing temperature is to increase the limiting rate of reduction and the rate at which alkali, if present, alters the nature of the reduction products. Increasing current density increases the rate of reduction, thus shortening the time the catholyte is exposed to the effects of alkali. Increase in current density, therefore, tends to compensate for increases in concentration of alkali and in temperature.

Increase in the ratio of cathode area to volume of catholyte shortens the time required to reduce a batch of catholyte, so like increase in current density tends to offset the effects of increasing alkali concentration and temperature.

It was found by Creighton and Hales[3] that for any specified degree of alkalinity of catholyte, the composition of the reduction product is a function of Co/RD and the temperature of the catholyte.

Co = initial concentration of glucose in the catholyte, gpl

R = ratio of cathode area to volume of catholyte, sq dm/l

D = current density, amp/sq dm

The dimension of the group Co/RD is grams of sugar per ampere.

Magnesium acts as a cathode poison.

Reference to most of the patents relating to the electrolytic reduction of glucose will be found in the articles referred to in the bibliography.

References

1. CREIGHTON, H. J., *Trans. Electrochem. Soc.*, **75**, 289 (1939).
2. CREIGHTON, H. J., *Can. Chem. Process Ind.*, **26**, 690 (1942).
3. CREIGHTON, H. J., AND HALES, R. A., U. S. Patent 2,458,895 (Jan. 11, 1949).
4. EVANS, W. L., *Chem. Revs.*, **6**, 281 (1929); also *J. Am. Chem. Soc.*, **48**, 2665 (1926); **50**, 1496 and 2543, (1928).
5. GOEPP, R. M. JR., AND SOLTZBERG, S., paper presented before the Division of Sugar Chemistry and Technology, American Chemical Society at Cincinnati, Ohio, April 11, 1940.
6. KILLEFFER, D. H., *Ind. Eng. Chem., News Ed.*, **15**, 489 (1937).
7. LOBRY DEBRUYN, C. A., AND VANEKENSTEIN, W. A., *Rec. Trav. Chem.* **14**, 203 (1895).
8. PARKER, E. A., AND SWANN, S. JR., *Trans. Electrochem. Soc.*, **92**, 343 (1947).
9. SANDERS, M. T., AND HALES, R. A., *Trans. Electrochem. Soc.*, **96**, 241 (1949).
10. SWANN, S. JR., *Ind. Eng. Chem.*, **29**, 1339 (1937).
11. TAYLOR, R. L., *Chem. Eng.*, **44**, 588 (1937).
12. WOLFROM, M. L., AND CO-WORKERS, *J. Am. Chem. Soc.*, **68**, 122, 578, 1443 and 2342 (1946).

MARSHALL T. SANDERS

GOLD PLATING. See PRECIOUS METAL ELECTROPLATING.

GRAPHITE ELECTROLYTIC ELECTRODES. See CARBON AND GRAPHITE ELECTROLYTIC ELECTRODES.

GRAPHITE, ELECTROTHERMIC PRODUCTION

Commercial graphite is produced by heating amorphous or turbostratic carbon to high temperatures in electric furnaces. The basic process was discovered by E. G. Acheson in 1896, and the fundamentals have remained the same with improvements in production technology, raw materials, and manufacturing techniques.

Carbon is composed of a mixture of small, perfect graphite-like layers and disoriented material. At the lower temperatures of carbonization, the graphite-like layers are arranged in groups of 2 planes per group. X-ray analysis shows that the spacing between layers is 3.7 Å, whereas the true graphite spacing is 3.354 Å. As the temperature is increased, the layers grow in diameter at the expense of the disoriented material at the same time that there is an increase in the number of layers in parallel per group. As the number of layers in parallel grows, the distance between layers diminishes until when 5 or more layers are in parallel, the spacing has dropped to 3.44 Å. The maximum number of parallel layers formed in carbon is about 12, with layers having a diameter of approximately 20 Å. The carbon shows only 2-dimensional order as the layers are parallel to each other, but are not mutually oriented.

When the disoriented carbon is consumed in the formation of larger graphite-like layers, this is probably an atom-by-atom process or, at most, in small fragments until only a few carbon atoms remain to link with neighboring layers or crystallites.

At this stage of the graphitizing process, there are two theories to explain how additional crystallization and growth takes place. One school of thought believes that further growth occurs by a gradual movement or rotation of whole layers or groups of layers, and, as the size of the groups of layers increases, the additional energy of higher temperatures is required to move them. A later theory is that the final 3-dimensional ordering proceeds by the movement of boundaries or arrays of dislocations, and that the range of energies required is due to the many kinds of imperfections in the structure of carbon.

When the 3-dimensional order begins, the spacing between the layers again decreases. The ordered 3-dimensional spacing of graphite has a layer spacing of 3.354 Å. Thus, there are 2 basic spacings of the layers, 3.44 Å for the completely carbonized layers with 2-dimensional order, and 3.354 Å for the 3-dimensional graphite layers. This information can be used to determine the degree of graphitization of a particular material as intermediate values for spacing are due to a mixture of carbon and graphite.

On a tonnage basis, by far most of the synthetic graphite made today uses as raw materials petroleum coke with coal tar pitch as a binder. After a mixing at a temperature high enough to melt the pitch, shapes are extruded or molded and baked at 800–1200°C to convert the binder to carbon. After the baking operation, the shapes are converted to graphite by heating in electric furnaces. Much of this type of graphite is used as electrodes for electric furnaces in metallurgical applications and anodes for electrochemical processes. The production of chlorine, caustic soda, sodium, chlorates, magnesium, titanium, zirconium, and special alloys depend upon the employment of graphite. Other uses are for heat exchangers, reaction towers, atomic power reactors, and space age applications.

A very valuable use of electrographite is in the production of electric brushes for electric machines of all sizes and importance from small fractional horsepower motors used in home appliances and electronic controls to large generators, motors, and synchronous condensers used by industry. This type of electrographite is derived from lampblack and coal tar pitch which results in a carbon that is not completely converted to graphite. An indication of this is given in Graph 1 which illustrates the relative change in electrical conductivity of the usual petroleum coke base material and the lampblack base material used in electrical brushes.

The conversion of carbon to graphite by high temperature produces a considerable reduction in hardness and electrical resistance, and a large increase in thermal conductivity. It is interesting to note that these changes begin to occur at about 2000°C and transformation is quite fast above this temperature, as indicated by the slope of the curves in Graph 1. It has been shown by x-ray diffraction that this corresponds to the temperature where crystal size increases rapidly. Typical properties of carbon and graphite are given in the following table:

	Carbon	Graphite
Final bake temperature (°F)	1800	5000
Scleroscope hardness	70	35
Electrical resistivity (ohm-inch)	0.0015	0.00035
Transverse strength (psi)	5000	3000
Apparent density (g/cc)	1.55	1.57
Thermal conductivity (Btu-ft/ hr ft²°F)	3	85
Threshold oxidation temperature (°F)	600	800

Batch Graphitizer

The oldest type of graphitizing furnace is the batch type. The principle has remained the same for nearly 70 years, but many refinements in design, operation, equipment, and considerable increase in sizes have resulted.

Typical modern furnaces are from 30 to 60

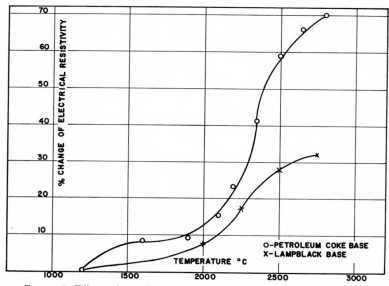

GRAPH 1. Effect of graphitizing temperature on electrical resistance.

feet long and 18 to 30 feet wide, with the shell of the furnace constructed of reinforced concrete. The bed of the furnace is built up of 18 inches of insulator mix on top of a fire brick bottom. A ¾ inch layer of sawdust covers the insulator mix and separates it from a layer of 4 inches of resistor mix. The baked carbon pieces are then placed horizontally on the bed and the spacing between pieces adjusted according to the sizes to be graphitized. Good loading practice requires geometric balance of the charge in all directions. The spaces between the baked carbon pieces and an additional 4 inches on top are filled with resistor mix. Side walls of the furnace are built up of concrete blocks about 2 feet away from the resistor pack, and the space between is filled with insulator mix. An extra 2 feet of insulator mix is placed on top of the pack. Water-cooled graphite electrodes are used for electrical connection to the pack through holes or slots in the reinforced concrete heads.

Fresh insulator mix consists of sand and coke in the proportions required for the formation of silicon carbide with the addition of 10 per cent of sized sawdust. The silicon carbide formed during the graphitizing process is crushed and reused for insulator mix by adding sawdust. Chemical analysis controls the addition of either sand or coke to the insulator mix.

The resistor mix consists of a mixture of graphitized and ungraphitized coke particles, mostly sized in the ¼ to ⅛ in. mesh range.

Graphite fines are tamped in the area around the head for good connection.

With packing completed, electrical connections are made to the graphite electrodes by means of copper bars, and a low-voltage, high-amperage current flows through the resistor.

A complicated system of transformers, switches, and breakers is required to control the heating rate of the furnace as the resistance varies with temperature and the degree of graphitizing of the material. Currents from 30,000 to 100,000 amperes are used.

Each furnace is fired according to a predetermined schedule which specifies rate of power application and total energy input. The heating cycle lasts from 2 to 4 days, and the end point is determined by the number of kilowatt hours consumed. The total energy input may vary from 2 to 4 kwh per pound of material graphitized, depending upon the size of the pieces, size of the furnace load, and quality required.

Electrodes up to 60 inches in diameter and up to 20 feet in length have been graphitized in this type of furnace.

Continuous Graphitizer

The second unit used in the production of graphite is the continuous graphitizer. It essentially is an electric resistance furnace employing a carbon tube as a heating element through which material to be processed is passed. With proper design and maintenance procedures, this unit can compete economically with the widely-used batch graphitizer. Its advantages are speed and uniformity of product, whereas its inability to handle larger sizes constitutes its chief disadvantage.

The furnace makeup is a carbon tube, preferably rectangular in shape, suspended by electrodes within an airtight metallic shell. The tube is extended on both sides through the ends of the shell and contained in metal housings which serve as coolers. Along its length, the tube is divided into two sections through which material travels in opposite directions to effect a thermal balance, (i.e., incoming cold material is heated by hot exit material and vice versa). Lampblack powder is used to thermally insulate the shell from the tube. Heating of the furnace is accomplished by simply passing electric current through the middle portion of the tube via the suspending electrodes. A centrally located opening provides an exit for the volatiles.

Figs. 1 to 4 show various furnace views.*

The power supply for the oven consists of a single-phase induction regulator capable of regulating the primary of a 200 kva stepdown transformer (2850–12v) to deliver 6 to 14.5 volts to the furnace electrodes. Temperature level is controlled by manually adjusting the voltage or automatically doing the same through use of a controller with a temperature-sensing device (i.e., photocell). Unlike the batch graphitizer, material can be processed at any temperature level with a total variation of less than 100°C (i.e., 1900, 2400, 2800°C). This permits production of materials with properties that excel on specific applications. Power required to fully graphitize carbon ranges from 1.0 to 2.5 kwh per pound, depending on size and shape of the material with correspondingly lesser amounts for the lower temperature levels.

Size limitations for the continuous furnace are pieces approximately 3 in. thick by 9 in.

* For detailed information, see patent reference.

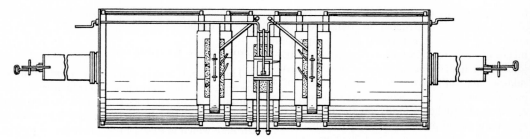

Fig. 1. Top view of continuous graphitizing furnace.

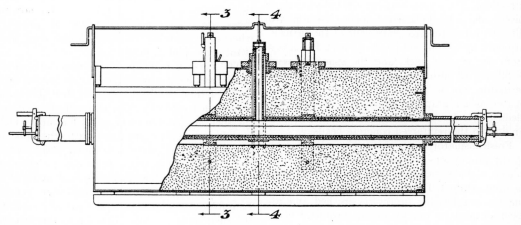

Fig. 2. Side elevation of furnace with a cross-section view of the central two-way tube for holding articles to be graphitized and vertical stack for escape of gases.

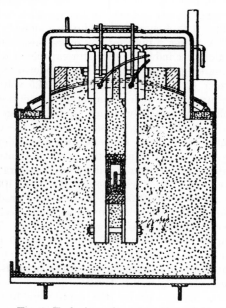

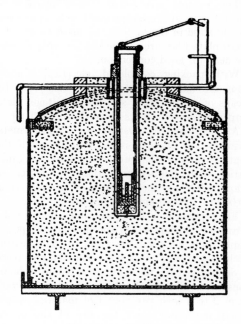

Fig. 3. End view of cross-section of furnace along line 3-3 of Fig. 2, showing vertical electrodes on each side of small central graphitizing tube.

Fig. 4. End view of cross-section of furnace along line 4-4 of Fig. 2, showing vent stack for graphitizing tube.

wide by 60 in. long. Material is pushed through the unit in both directions at a rate of five feet per hour. With this speed, the total cycle is about 4 hours. A protective atmosphere is not essential. Here, air in the tube reacts with carbon to form carbon monoxide which significantly reduces the rate of further oxidation. Normal life of the furnace is two to three weeks, after which time the entire insides are rebuilt.

The versatility of carbon as a construction material can be seen to some extent by examining the design and operation of the continuous graphitizer.

The carbon material heated from room temperature to 5000°F in less than 2 hours shows no cracking or spalling which demonstrates its ability to withstand thermal shock. The high thermal insulation property of lampblack powder is shown by the fact that the outside shell temperature is less than 400°F, whereas 2 feet away, the tube is at 5000°F. On the other hand, the excellent thermal conductivity and high emissivity coefficient of graphite within the tube itself effect a heat exchange between incoming and outgoing material that permits less kwh per pound than with the batch graphitizer. The lubricity of graphite is shown by the little power required to push material through the furnace and the near absence of mechanical wear on either the tube or material. The combination of low thermal expansion and increase in strength at high temperature preclude breakage of the electrodes or tube at 5000°F operating temperature.

References

1. "Proceedings of the Fourth and Fifth Conference on Carbon," New York, Pergamon Press, 1960, 1962.
2. "Industrial Carbon and Graphite—London Conference," London, Society of Chemical Industry, 1958.
3. MANTELL, C. L., "Industrial Carbon," New York, D. Van Nostrand Co., 1947.
4. "Carbon & Graphite," *Catalog 40C*, Stackpole Carbon Company, St. Marys, Pa., 1960.
5. SANDERS, V. H., (to Stackpole Carbon Co.). U. S. Patent 1,969,478 (Aug. 7, 1943).

WALTER G. KRELLNER AND
PAUL SMISKO

H

HAEFNER EFFECT. *See* ELECTROMIGRATION IN
LIQUID METALS.

HAFNIUM, ELECTROLYTIC PREPARATION

The metal hafnium is always closely associated with zirconium due to both its natural occurrence with zirconium ores and the very similar chemical characteristics of the two metals.
The historical development of these metals is
also parallel in most respects. Processes that are
applicable to zirconium are, in most cases, also
applicable to hafnium.

Since the advent of the nuclear reactor, emphasis on hafnium technology has been increased
due to the unique properties possessed by hafnium qualifying it as a control rod material
(high neutron absorption cross section). This
has necessitated development of commercial
procedures for limited production of the metal.
In the course of this development, it is logical
that electrolytic methods would be considered.
Development of electrolytic methods has advanced to the point where an electrolytic refining method is now being used commercially,
in place of the iodide refining operation.

Hafnium, like zirconium, is also a highly oxygen-sensitive metal. It is thus not amenable to
processing in aqueous or moisture-containing
systems. All reported successful electrolytic procedures have been based on molten salt processing.

Electrowinning

Extensive work has not been reported on
molten salt electrowinning procedures for hafnium. It is known that hafnium can be electrodeposited from K_2HfF_6 and $HfCl_4$ dissolved in
alkali or alkaline earth chlorides. Hafnium with
apparent ductile characteristics can be deposited
from 30 wt per cent K_2HfF_6 in NaCl at about
850°C. Process parameters for hafnium deposi-

tion would appear to be quite comparable to
conditions employed for analogous zirconium
work. In all probability hafnium compounds are
reduced directly from the 4+ state to the metal
as a single-step process.

There is considerable doubt concerning the
existence of reduced hafnium halides. Thus, in
the use of $HfCl_4$ as a source electrolyte, it would
be necessary to provide a suitable complexing
agent to stabilize the melt. This would not be
accomplished, as in the case of $TiCl_4$, by reduction to the 3+ state. If such a material were not
suitably complexed, excessive volatilization losses
would occur.

Hafnium electrowinning methods would also
require use of inert atmosphere cells. Cell design
characteristics described for titanium and zirconium would also apply to hafnium.

Further development of electrowinning processes for hafnium largely depends on process
development for related metals. If electrolytic
procedures should be instituted for titanium
offering profound cost or purity advantages over
existing magnesium or sodium reduction methods, these would likely be extended to hafnium.
Otherwise independent developments specifically
for hafnium are unlikely in light of the relatively
small production tonnage concerned.

Electrorefining

The greatest interest in electrolytic processes
for hafnium is in the area of electrorefining. This
is directly due to existing requirements for high-
purity grades of material used in nuclear applications.

The U. S. Bureau of Mines and Carborundum
Metals Co. have carried out extensive studies
in this area. One process is commercially employed for preparation of high-purity hafnium
using magnesium-reduced metal as a feed material.

Electrorefining of hafnium is directly analogous to related methods for titanium and zir-

TABLE 1. HAFNIUM ELECTROREFINING

Material	Hardness BHN	O ppm	C ppm	H ppm	Mg ppm	Na ppm	Fe ppm	Si ppm	Mn ppm	Al ppm	Cr ppm	Other ppm
Anode feed (Hf turnings)	268–323	1750			1250		50	100	560	400	800	Cu-500
Electrolytic product	148–158	390			90	50	10	100	150	—	<10	Cu-340
Iodide crystal bar	160–240	240	32	28								N-15 W-10

conium. Electrolytic cells devised for one metal are equally useful for the other two. Hafnium work has been carried out using cells of graphite or steel. Cathodes of steel have been generally employed. Cells operate in an atmosphere of argon or helium.

A variety of electrolytes might be employed provided they possess the necessary characteristics of chemical stability and good electrical conductance and contain a hafnium-based carrier species. The carrier salt requirement has been met by use of K_2HfF_6, and also by in situ production of a carrier by chlorination of Hf metal. In the latter case, it is difficult to maintain the requisite concentrations of $HfCl_4$ due to its loss by sublimation. This tendency is reduced somewhat by use of 2-component solvent systems, such as NaCl-KCl or NaCl-LiCl, as opposed to NaCl alone.

Specifically the following electrolytes have produced good electrorefining results:

95 wt per cent NaCl—5 wt per cent KCl containing 5.1 wt per cent of Hf in solution. Electrolysis at 840°C and 0.3v.

45 wt per cent NaCl—55 wt per cent KCl containing 4.5 wt per cent of Hf in solution. Electrolysis at 700°C and 0.3v.

Operation is conducted with an initial cathode current density of about 20 a/sq dm. Efficiency is 85 to 95 per cent based on a four-electron change.

Commercial processing is reported carried out in a solvent of NaCl, KCl or LiCl. The carrier species is not specified, but temperature control is considered important in terms of product purity. Specific figures on product characteristics are not available, but since the process replaces the iodide dissociation method, competitive purity and hardness would be assumed.

Earlier results for hafnium electrorefining are given in Table 1. The feed material is compared with the electrolytic product and with available data for iodide-produced metal. It is apparent that electrolytic refining is quite effective in re-

moval of oxygen, magnesium, iron, chromium, and probably also carbon and nitrogen.

Electrorefined hafnium is deposited in the form of coarse dendritic crystals. Deposits are generally treated in a vacuum furnace for removal of residual salts. Aqueous recovery procedures could also be employed as for zirconium.

Extensive further development in hafnium electroprocessing is not likely in consideration of present requirements for the metal. Annual production rates are of the order of 50 tons/yr while capacity is 4 to 5 times this figure. Increased usage of electrorefining at present production levels seems probable since an equivalent or superior product and an appreciable cost reduction are reported as compared to iodide refining.

References

1. BLUE, D. D., AND BAKER, D. H., Intl. Conf. for Peaceful Uses of Atomic Energy, p. 698ff, Geneva, 1958.
2. MARTIN, D. R., AND PIZZOLATO, P. J., Chap. 12 in "Rare Metals Handbook," Hampel, C. A., Ed., 2nd Ed., New York, Reinhold Publishing Corp., 1961.
3. PASCAL, P., Ed., "Nouveau Traite de Chimie Minerale," Vol. 9, pp. 825–863, Paris, Masson et Cie, 1963.
4. THOMAS, D. E., AND HAYES, E. T., "The Metallurgy of Hafnium," p. 119ff, Washington, U.S. Atomic Energy Commission, 1960.

MERLE E. SIBERT

Cross-references: Electrorefining in Molten Salts; Titanium, Electrolytic Preparation; Zirconium, Electrolytic Processing.

HALF-CELL POTENTIALS. See ELECTRODE POTENTIALS; ELECTROMOTIVE FORCE AND HALF-CELL POTENTIALS.

HALF-WAVE POTENTIALS. See POLAROGRAPHY.

HALL, CHARLES MARTIN (1863–1914)

The name of Charles Martin Hall is inseparably connected with aluminum in America. In 1886, just eight months after graduating from Oberlin College, Hall discovered the process of making aluminum which is still in use today. This young inventor was born in Thompson, Ohio, on December 6, 1863, and died in Daytona, Florida, on December 27, 1914. In this too-short span of life, Hall and his associates raised aluminum from a semi-rare metal to an everyday metal.

Hall first became interested in aluminum as a schoolboy and during college years made a number of unsuccessful experiments seeking a low-cost method of producing the metal. Aluminum made by the chemical method, using metallic sodium to reduce aluminum chloride, was then selling for about $8 a pound. Eventually Hall reached the conclusion that an electrolytic method offered the most promise for his purpose but it would have to operate in the absence of water. After deciding that aluminum oxide would be the best and cheapest compound to work with, he set out to find a molten solvent for the oxide.

Hall set up home-made equipment and batteries in the family woodshed attached to the kitchen of his Oberlin home. After numerous discouraging tests, on February 23, 1886, he dissolved some alumina in molten cryolite and passed direct current between two carbon electrodes for several hours. The run was successful, for he produced several small pellets of aluminum. After some further experimentation with the process, he filed a patent application. In a few months a patent interference was declared and Hall was surprised to find that Héroult, in France, had made substantially the same discovery. However, after proving the date of his discovery, Hall was awarded the United States patent.

Hall had no means for promoting his process and sought people with venture-money to back him. After several discouraging adventures in this search, he was introduced to Alfred E. Hunt in Pittsburgh. With several associates, Hunt formed The Pittsburgh Reduction Company and a small pilot plant was erected. The first aluminum was produced on Thanksgiving Day in 1888.

The Pittsburgh plant was followed by a larger one at New Kensington, Pa., and in 1895, the works were moved to Niagara Falls. By 1900, the Company was making 5,000,000 pounds of aluminum a year and had reduced the price to 33 cents a pound.

In 1907, the Company's name was changed to Aluminum Company of America. Research and development by Hall and his associates introduced technologic improvements in the operation. Users of the metal gained experience in fabricating, joining and casting processes, and numerous new applications were developed. The demand for aluminum made substantial progress. Hall's contributions to electrometallurgy were given international recognition when he was presented with the Perkin Medal in 1911.

Hall's activities in later years were handicapped by illness but his fertile mind kept working on the Company's problems to the very end of life. In 1915 his Company produced over a hundred million pounds of aluminum.

Hall received generous treatment from the founders of The Pittsburgh Reduction Company, and he husbanded his stockholdings through panics and boom days. Hall never married and left the bulk of his fortune to the cause of education. To his Alma Mater—Oberlin College he gave a trust endowment which eventually amounted to twenty million dollars.

The amazing coincidence between the lives of Hall and Héroult (q.v.), which extends to the dates of their birth and death, as well as their interest in aluminum, is most notable.

JUNIUS D. EDWARDS

Cross-references: *Aluminum; Castner, Hamilton Y.; Héroult, Paul L. T.*

HALL EFFECT

The Hall effect is the most important of the six thermo-galvano-magneto-electrical effects which can be observed with direct current. This current goes lengthwise through a rectangular conductor body which has two additional side contacts located symmetrically and at equal distance from the ends. Between these side contacts an electric voltage is produced when a magnetic field is applied in a direction rectangular both to the main flow of the current in the conductor and to the connecting line of the side contacts. The sign and the magnitude of this "Hall voltage" depends on the current and on the shape, size, and nature of the conductor. Remarkable is the great variety of the size and of the polarity of the Hall effect in the different electrical conductors. It is especially large in some compounds, e.g., indium antimonide. The Hall effect in this and similar materials has found practical applications in watt meters, multipliers, d-c to a-c converters, or function generators.

The other five effects, together with the Hall effect, in which a magnetic field acts on a current are shown in the table. Also shown are the names of the discoverer or investigator who is connected with a particular effect.

Magnetic Field	Electric Current	
transversal	ΔV transversal Hall	ΔT transversal Ettinghausen
transversal	ΔV longitudinal	ΔT longitudinal Nernst
longitudinal	ΔV longitudinal	ΔT longitudinal

This table shows the six effects which occur when a magnetic field acts on the current. (Six analogous effects can be observed if a magnetic field acts on the temperature gradient field.)

See **Semiconductors** for a mathematical treatment of the Hall Effect.

E. K. Weise

Cross-references: *Conductivity; Semiconductors.*

HEART, ELECTRICAL ACTION OF. See ELECTROCARDIOLOGY.

HEAT CAPACITY

The *heat capacity* of a substance may be defined as *the quantity of heat* required to raise the temperature of *one mole* of the substance by *one degree*. Since the heat capacity varies with the temperature, the exact value at any point of temperature is a derivative, i.e., a ratio of infinitesimals of the quantity of heat added (per mole) to the temperature rise. The heat capacity also varies with the other state variables (e.g., pressure and volume), and there are two different heat capacities in general use: that for a temperature rise at constant volume, C_V, and that for a temperature rise at constant pressure, C_p. These may be expressed as derivatives of the internal energy, E, (not to be confused with the electrical potential, E) and the enthalpy, H:

$$C_V = \left(\frac{\partial E}{\partial T}\right)_V \quad \text{and} \quad C_p = \left(\frac{\partial H}{\partial T}\right)_P.$$

C_p is usually the more useful quantity since most reactions are carried out at atmospheric pressure. Above room temperature C_p is usually expressed in terms of the absolute temperature, T, as

$$C_p = a + bT + \frac{c}{T^2}$$

where a, b and c are adjustable parameters. Values of these parameters may be found in tabulated form in the literature.

With the heat capacities of the reactants and products of a reaction known as a function of temperature the

$$\Delta C_p = C_p(\text{products}) - C_p(\text{reactants})$$

for the reaction can be integrated to obtain the variation of enthalpy and entropy changes of the reaction with temperature. Thus,

$$\Delta H_{T_2} = \Delta H_{T_1} + \int_{T_1}^{T_2} \Delta Cp \, dT$$

and

$$\Delta S_{T_2} = \Delta S_{T_1} + \int_{T_1}^{T_2} \Delta Cp \, d\ln T$$

Then from the relation

$$\Delta F = \Delta H - T\Delta S$$

and the relation

$$\left(\frac{\partial \frac{\Delta F}{T}}{\partial T}\right)_P = -\frac{\Delta H}{T^2}$$

the free energy and its variation with temperature can be evaluated.

References

1. Klotz, I. M., "Chemical Thermodynamics," Chapts. 4 and 5, New York, Prentice-Hall, Inc., 1950.
2. Lewis, G. N., and Randall, M., "Thermodynamics" (2nd Edition), revised by K. S. Pitzer and Leo Brewer, Chapt. 6, New York, McGraw-Hill Book Co., 1961.
3. Kelley, K. K., *U. S. Bur. Mines Bulls.* **476** (1949); **584** (1960); and **477** (1950).

M. H. Lietzke and R. W. Stoughton

HEAT CONTENT. See ENTHALPY OR HEAT CONTENT.

HEAT TRANSFER CORROSION. See CORRO-SION UNDER HEAT TRANSFER CONDI-TIONS.

HEAVY WATER-ELECTROLYTIC PRODUCTION

Definitions

Ordinary water is a mixture of 18 distinct kinds of molecules, formed by the combination of the three hydrogen isotopes, having relative masses of 1, 2, or 3, with the three oxygen isotopes of masses 16, 17, or 18.

The three hydrogen isotopes are called *protium, deuterium* and *tritium.* Of these nuclides only tritium is radioactive. In ordinary water, approximately one hydrogen atom out of every 7000 is deuterium. As to tritium, its natural abundance is so small (less than one atom in 10^{17}) that it can be neglected in the following considerations.

Usually, protium and deuterium are designated with the symbols H and D, respectively. Accordingly, the term *heavy water* is generally assumed to mean pure *deuterium oxide*, D_2O, irrespective of the relative abundance of the three oxygen isotopes in the compound.

History

Soon after the discovery of deuterium by Urey,[15] the same author, in collaboration with Washburn,[18] proved that, when ordinary water is electrolyzed, protium is preferentially discharged at the cathode, so that the water remaining in the electrolytic bath becomes enriched in deuterium oxide. Until 1943 this was the universal method of making heavy water.[10] As soon as its properties as a moderator in nuclear reactors were recognized, more efficient manufacturing methods were developed under the Manhattan Project, covering the scientific and engineering activities which had as their objective the utilization of atomic energy for military purposes.[12] One of these methods was based on the combination of the electrolytic process with steam-hydrogen catalytic exchange (see hereunder); it was adopted for the first time at the Trail Plant in British Columbia. By 1945, this plant was producing 1,100 lb of 99.8 per cent heavy water per month.

At present, whenever heavy water is obtained as a coproduct in the industrial manufacture of electrolytic hydrogen, water electrolysis performs in this respect only the function of a preenrichment step, which is always associated with or followed by another nonelectrolytic process, such as catalytic exchange or hydrogen distillation.

Electrolytic Separation Factor

This factor, also called *instantaneous fractionation factor* (see **Isotopes-Electrochemical Separation**), is defined as the ratio

$$\alpha = \frac{(H/D)gas}{(H/D)water}$$

where H and D indicate the atom fractions of the two isotopes.

When ordinary water is fed to the electrolytic process, as well as in the following preenrichment stages, in which the relative deuterium abundance is still small, the statistically prevalent species among the molecules coexisting in gas and liquid phase are H_2O, HDO, H_2 and HD. Accordingly, if no electrochemical reaction were proceeding, the isotopic interchange would be controlled by the following purely chemical reaction:

$$H_2O \text{ (liq)} + HD \text{ (gas)} \rightleftharpoons HDO \text{ (liq)} + H_2 \text{ (gas)}$$

At the normal operating temperatures of the electrolysis bath (60 to 70°C) the equilibrium constant of this reaction is about 3.[8]

$$K = \frac{(HDO)_l \, (H_2)_g}{(H_2O)_l \, (HD)_g}$$

Under reversible equilibrium conditions for the chemical interchange, as well as for the electrochemical discharge of protium and deuterium, their relative abundances, or atom fractions, in the two phases would be determined by the equilibrium constant, which would therefore coincide with the separation factor (indeed, the two expressions for α and K are formally quite similar). It ensues that, if the cathode metal were to act only as a catalyst in respect of chemical interchange, the separation factor for a definite reaction rate, that is away from reversibility, could never exceed a value of about 3.

The fact that in practice it is possible to obtain separation factors with substantially higher values than the equilibrium constant may at first seem paradoxically against the principles of thermodynamics. However, the reason for this becomes clear when one considers that cathodic discharge is not a spontaneous process but is sustained by a supply of energy from an external source; consequently, some thermodynamic restrictions, proper to spontaneous reactions, are removed.

The range of values that are actually observed for the separation factor (sf) is very wide, especially depending on the cathode metal employed; the lower and the higher limit can be approximately set, for practical purposes, at 3 and 10, respectively. The possible paths that can be followed by the cathodic process, so as to determine its controlling and selective action on proton and deuteron discharge, have been investigated experimentally and theoretically by several authors.[2, 9, 13, 17] Without approaching any closer to this debated matter, it will suffice to mention that the separation factor is not necessarily connected with the "overall" hydrogen overvoltage, as measurable on a certain cathode material under simultaneous discharge of both protons and deuterons; however, it is certainly to be related to the difference between protium overvoltage and deuterium overvoltage, as was proved, for instance, by Heyrovsky and others.[17]

Aside from any kinetic details, the cathodic process may be visualized as a competition taking place mostly between the two following reactions:

$$H_2O + HDO + 2e^- \rightarrow H_2 + OH^- + OD^-$$
$$H_2O + HDO + 2e^- \rightarrow HD + 2OH^-$$

This sort of broad scheme does not show the variety of possible intermediate steps through which cathodic reduction proceeds from water molecules to final products. However, one or more of these steps seem to be determinant for the preferential discharge of protium over deuterium.

For any given cathodic material, the separation factor tends to increase with current density; on the other hand, it is approximately inversely proportional to absolute temperature.[14] Furthermore, it is markedly affected by the state of the surface and by any presence of absorbed impurities, such as oxygen or poisoning substances that in general also tend to increase the overvoltage. The following table gives an in-

dication of the approximate ranges within which the H-D sf has been determined under different conditions.

Metal	Sep. Factor
Fe	6–9
C	7–8
Cu	5.5–6.5
Ag	5–6
Ni	4–6
Pt (blank)	5–7
Pt (platinized)	3.5–4.5
Pb	3–4
Hg	3–4.5

This table shows that iron, beside being a particularly suitable cathode material in other respects (see **Water Electrolysis**) also classifies first as regards the H-D sf. In industrial electrolyzers it is seldom as high as 6.5; however, in finishing cells of special design, for raising to highest concentrations the preenriched heavy water solutions, the process is carried out with special precautions and at relatively low temperature, so that it is possible to obtain a value of 8 or higher; this can be further increased by ultrasonic agitation.[14]

Technology

In an industrial electrolyzer the holdup volume must be kept constant, so as not to change the current density and other operating conditions. This means that the water decomposed into hydrogen and oxygen, plus the quantity leaving as vapor saturating the gases, is continuously replaced with a corresponding input of feed water. It is thus evident that in the electrolysis unit the heavy water concentration cannot increase up to 100 per cent, but will take a theoretically infinite time to reach a content equal to the mole fraction in feed water times the separation factor. Indeed, on attainment of these conditions, the deuterium content in hydrogen gas will be the same as in feed water and cannot rise beyond this limit for obvious reasons of conservation of matter.

As already mentioned, a portion of the enriched water is in most cases continuously withdrawn from the electrolyzer (usually in the form of vapor with the gases) to be processed in a subsequent stage. Consequently, steady state conditions will be reached at an even lower concentration than would result from simply considering the electrolytic separation factor.

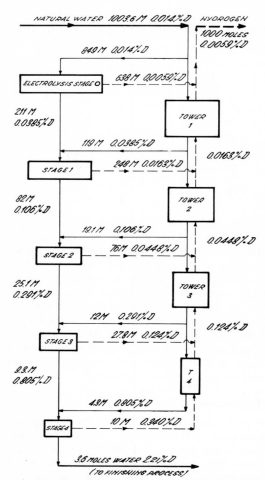

NATURAL WATER 1003.6 M 0.014% D HYDROGEN

1000 MOLES 0.0059% D

849 M 0.014% D

ELECTROLYSIS STAGE 0   638 M 0.0059% D

TOWER 1

211 M 0.0385% D

119 M 0.0385% D

248 M 0.0163% D   0.0163% D

STAGE 1

82 M 0.106% D

TOWER 2

191 M 0.106% D

76 M 0.0448% D   0.0448% D

STAGE 2

25.1 M 0.291% D

TOWER 3

12 M 0.291% D

27.8 M 0.124% D   0.124% D

STAGE 3

9.3 M 0.805% D

T 4

4.3 M 0.805% D

10 M 0.940% D

STAGE 4

3.6 MOLES WATER 2.21% D
(TO FINISHING PROCESS)

FIG. 1. Typical cascade for catalytic exchange
—electrolytic process.

Indeed, under said assumption, it is necessary
to apply the *effective separation factor*, as given
by the following equation:

$$\alpha_{eff} = \frac{(n_1 + fN_1)N_2}{(n_2 + fN_2)N_2}$$

where n_1 and n_2 are the atom fractions of H and
D in the hydrogen gas, N_1 and N_2 the corresponding fractions in feed water, and f is the
molar quantity of water evaporated for each
mole of water electrolyzed.

The electrolytic batteries forming the plant
are subdivided into several *stages*, and the number of electrolysis units in each stage decreases
from one to the next. All the units in any one
stage are operated in parallel as regards input
and output streams of materials, while the

stages are connected in series, thus forming a
cascade. The most efficient subdivision of a given
number of units in several stages requires the
solution of a rather involved mathematical problem.[4]

Since the electrolysis process still leaves in
the hydrogen gas a substantial amount of deuterium, especially in the higher stages, the yield
of the process would be too low and, therefore,
uneconomic, if heavy water production were
based simply on the residues left behind by electrolysis. Accordingly, the first thought might be
to burn the gas and feed it back as enriched
water to the preceding stages. This, however,
would imply the destruction of the results obtained by the expenditure of relatively costly
electricity, so that such a procedure would be
economically prohibitive. In fact, electrolytic
production of heavy water is remunerative only
if the hydrogen is made available for other industrial purposes, so that the combustion
method, whenever used, is limited only to a
very small fraction of the hydrogen product, to
provide a backward flow of isotopic material in
the finishing section of the plant, handling small
quantities of highly concentrated water.

To increase the yield of heavy water per unit
of electric energy, the electrolytic process is always combined with some other nondestructive
operations on the hydrogen gas.

To this purpose several methods have been
investigated and proposed since the inception
of this industry.[12] The following description will
be confined to the two best-known procedures
that have found commercial application.

Steam-Hydrogen Catalytic Exchange

A typical and simplified arrangement is schematically illustrated in Fig. 1. The hydrogen gas,
saturated with water vapor, leaving each stage
following the first one, is passed through a catalytic exchange tower countercurrent to liquid
water; the following process is achieved nearly
as far as equilibrium:

H_2O (vapor) + HD (gas) →

HDO (vapor) + H_2 (gas)

HDO (vapor) + H_2O (water) →

HDO (water) + H_2O (vapor)

Since the equilibrium constant of the reaction
in vapor phase decreases with temperature, this
is conveniently kept not higher than 75°C; the

corresponding value of the equilibrium constant is 2.88.

The tower consists of several sections and each section contains a catalyst bed and a set of bubble trays (Fig. 2). Catalysts made of platinum or nickel-chromium are particularly effective. Since the catalytic action is hindered if the catalyst is wet, a heating system prevents condensation from taking place on it, although the gas is constantly kept steam-saturated by passing it through the bubble trays upstream and downstream of each bed, thus allowing the less concentrated stream of liquid water, flowing downward and countercurrent to the gas phase, to increase its HDO content by physical equilibration with the richer vapor.

The first industrial installation reported to operate on this principle was set up at Trail, B.C. by the Consolidated Mining and Smelting Company of Canada Ltd. It consisted of a primary plant and a secondary plant. The primary plant was composed of more than 3000 cells of unipolar design, with a rated current capacity of 10,000 amp,[11] cascaded into four stages. Each stage included its own catalytic-exchange tower, reboiler, cooler, condenser, and evaporator. The rated daily output of the primary plant was 2000 lb of water containing 3.5 per cent HDO.

The secondary plant consisted of 150 finishing cells of special design,[11] with a rated capacity of 1000 amp. They were arranged in a three-stage cascade and operated batchwise. This cascade received the output water from the primary plant, which was causticized to approximately 2.5 per cent KOH. The feed in the cells was electrolyzed to about one-seventh of its volume.

The water obtained by recombustion of hydrogen with oxygen was fed back to a preceding stage. The liquid remaining in the cell was withdrawn and treated with CO_2 to convert the KOH to K_2CO_3, in order not to leave any deuterium bound in the hydroxide group. The solution was then evaporated, and the condensate was sent to the following stage. The output from the last stage had a concentration of 99.8 per cent D_2O.

The steam-exchange process is adopted also in a plant at Rjukan, Norway, belonging to Norsk Hydro Co. The electrolysis plant supplying the hydrogen consists of Pechkranz electrolyzers of the bipolar type.

A new catalytic exchange method between water in liquid phase and hydrogen gas at high pressure (200 atm) has been recently developed

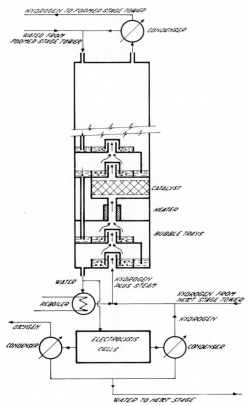

FIG. 2. Catalytic tower for steam-hydrogen exchange.

by F. Uhde GmbH in Germany.[1, 10] The catalyst is circulated throughout the reaction tower as a liquid suspension of 25 g carbon per liter and a weight ratio platinum/carbon = 0.1.

Hydrogen Distillation

The separation of deuterium from protium by distillation is possible owing to the fact that at the hydrogen boiling point (20.4°K) the vapor pressures of D_2, HD, and H_2 are in the same ratios as 1, 1.7, and 2.98, respectively.

One major industrial plant, in which fractionation is combined with water electrolysis, has been installed by the Fertilizer Corp. of India Ltd. at Nangal (Punjab).[5, 6, 7] The electrolytic plant consists of 60 de Nora filter-press units; each unit assembles 108 bipolar elements. At the rated capacity of 10,000 amp through each unit, the plant output is 27,000 cu m STP of hydrogen per hour.

The 60 electrolyzers are arranged in a cascade of 3 stages, including 30, 18 and 12 units, respectively. The water vapor recovered as condensate from the gases leaving the first stage provides the process water to the second stage, which in turn supplies its condensate output to the third stage. The heavy water concentration thus building up in the latter is such that the HD content in the hydrogen is 0.09 per cent. This gas stream only is sent to distillation before joining with the other two streams from the preceding stages, which are directly sent to the ammonia synthesis plant.

In the distillation equipment, supplied by Gesellschaft für Linde's Eismachinen A.G. (Germany), fractionation is carried out in three columns of the plate type. Of these, the primary column consists of three sections, which, in the order from bottom to top, operate at 3, 2 and 1 atm, respectively. In each section a fraction of the hydrogen stream is enriched in HD and thence is sent to the next section above. The bottom stream of the top section, at 4 per cent HD, is fed to the top plate of a secondary column for further enrichment to 90 per cent HD. This concentrated mixture is then passed through a battery of heat exchangers and enters at ambient temperature a catalytic converter, where the following reaction occurs:

$$2HD \rightarrow H_2 + D_2$$

The equilibrium constant of this reaction is 3.26 at 298°K.

After conversion, the H_2-D_2 stream is cooled again through the heat exchangers down to fractionation temperature and passed through a final distillation column. The bottoms, at 99.7 per cent D_2, are passed through a catalytic reactor together with an equivalent stream of electrolytic oxygen, so as to obtain 99.8 per cent D_2O. The rated capacity is 15 tons/year. The estimated energy requirement for distillation is 2000 kwh per kg D_2O, whereas the corresponding consumption, using the catalytic exchange process, would be 6000 kwh.

A somewhat different procedure than that described above has been developed by Sulzer Bros. Ltd. in Switzerland.[3]

Instead of submitting the rectified HD stream to catalytic conversion before burning, it is immediately sent to combustion, so that the final rectification step is carried out on the H_2O-D_2O mixture thus formed. For the first rectification step on hydrogen, as well as the second on water, use is made of Kuhn rectifying columns, specially designed to obtain a high separation

efficiency, as required when handling liquids with boiling points as close as in the present case.

References

1. BECKER, E. W., HÜBENER, R. P., AND KESSLER, R. W., *Chem. Ing. Tech.*, **30**, 288 (1958); **34**, 105 (1962).
2. BUTLER, J. A. V., *Z. Elektrochem.*, **44**, 55 (1938).
3. CHOPEY, N. P., *Chem. Eng.*, **68**, 118 (Feb. 20, 1961).
4. COHEN, C., AND MURPHY, G. M., "The Theory of Isotope Separation," New York, McGraw-Hill Book Co., Inc., 1951.
5. EDITORS, *Chem. Eng.*, **66**, 64 (Feb., 1959).
6. GAMI, D. C., GUPTA, D., PRASAD, N. B., AND SHARMA, K. C., "Proc. U.N. Intern. Conf. Peaceful Uses of Atomic Energy," 2nd, Geneva, p. 534, 1958.
7. GUPTA, D., LEHMER, W., BALDUE, W., AND MAGUIRE, W. J., *Chem. Eng.*, **66**, 68 (Feb. 23, 1959).
8. KIRSHENBAUM, I., "Physical Properties and Analysis of Heavy Water," New York, McGraw-Hill Book Co., Inc., 1951.
9. KORTUM, G., AND BOCKRIS, J. O'M., "Textbook of Electrochemistry," Vol. 2, p. 436, Amsterdam, Elsevier Publishing Co.
10. LEWIS, G. N., AND MACDONALD, R. T., *J. Chem. Phys.*, **1**, 341 (1933).
11. MANTELL, C. L., "Electrochemical Engineering," p. 313, 317, New York, McGraw-Hill Book Co., Inc., 1960.
12. MURPHY, G. M., UREY, H. C., AND KIRSHENBAUM, I., "Production of Heavy Water," New York, McGraw-Hill Book Co., Inc., 1955.
13. PASCAL, P., AND VIALLARD, R., "Nouveau Traité de Chimie Minérale," Vol. 1, p. 690, Masson et Cie, Editeurs, Paris, 1956.
14. SMITH, H. A., THOMAS, C. O., AND POSEY, J. C., *J. Electrochem. Soc.*, **106**, 516 (1959).
15. UREY, H. C., BRICKWEDDE, F. G., AND MURPHY, G. M., *Phys. Rev.*, **40**, 1 (1932).
16. WALTER, S., NITSCHKE, E., AND BODE, C., *Chem. Ing. Tech.*, **34**, 7 (1962).
17. WALTON, H. F., AND WOLFENDEN, J. H., *Trans. Faraday Soc.*, **34**, 436 (1938).
18. WASHBURN, E. W., AND UREY, H. C., *Proc. Nat. Acad. Sci. U.S.*, **18**, 496 (1932).

PATRIZIO GALLONE

Cross-references: *Isotopes-Electrochemical Separation; Water Electrolysis.*

HELMHOLTZ, HERMANN L. F. (1821–1894)

Hermann Ludwig Ferdinand Helmholtz was born on August 31, 1821, at Potsdam. His father was a professor at the Gymnasium, teaching German, philosophy, Latin, Greek, and, for several years, mathematics and physics. These interests were shared with Hermann and his sisters and brother, along with an appreciation of music and art. Entering the Gymnasium in 1832, Hermann proved to be a commendable pupil. The curriculum was largely languages, philosophy, philology, and history. Mathematics and science were introduced after the third year and fascinated Hermann, who went on to try new ideas and experiments on his own. His knowledge seemed to be almost intuitive, and mathematics became a form of relaxation.

Since an education as a physicist was too expensive for the family's modest means, a scholarship was obtained to the Friedrich-Wilhelm Institute for Medicine and Surgery, where he was to be trained as a doctor with the obligation of serving for ten years after graduation as an army surgeon. Here he came under the influence of Johannes Müller, professor of physiology, who interested him in seeking out physicochemical explanations for biological processes. His first scientific contribution, his thesis, disclosed the connections between nerve fibers and ganglion cells, a fine contribution to minute anatomy.

After receiving his degree in 1842 and serving some time as house surgeon at the charity hospital, Helmholtz was sent to the Royal Hussars at Potsdam as assistant surgeon. There he was able to set up a small laboratory, building apparatus from miscellaneous materials with the ingenuity which was to characterize all his future teaching and experiments. The question of "vitalism" inspired him. His theory was that bodily processes were simply physical and chemical processes that could occur in inorganic nature also; the vitalists contended that bodily processes were controlled by some imponderable vital force or soul. Extensive experiments were run, and the problem grow beyond the bounds of physiology. Based on a few theoretical premises of the atomic and molecular nature of matter, the law of the conservation of energy emerged in 1847. Helmholtz was not the first to formulate this law—J. R. von Mayer and James Joule had preceded him. His many experiments, his exact mathematical presentation of the implications, and his explanations of the relationships among kinetic and potential energy, chemical, electrical, and heat energy, etc., exerted great and lasting influence in the fields of physics and chemistry, as well as physiology. His work provided foundation stones for the structure of thermodynamics, and in later additions and

developments the beginnings of the concept of entropy appeared.

Recognition of his talents as a scientist followed, and he was released from his obligations as an army surgeon and appointed lecturer at the Berlin Academy of Arts. A year later he went to Königsberg as professor of physiology, remaining there for six years and beginning his great works on the origin of human knowledge. In 1855 he went to Bonn, and in 1858 to Heidelberg.

One of the masterpieces of 19th century science, *Handbuch der physiologischen Optik*, published in three parts between 1856 and 1867, resulted from experiments begun at Königsberg. In it he studied the lenses, the nerves, the interpretation by the brain, functions of eye muscles, and all the ramifications of sight. The physics of color in light and pigment, color vision, and color blindness were covered. As in all of his work, extensive, imaginative, and exact experimentation underlay his conclusions. Starting from experiments upon a small problem, he worked in ever widening areas, crossing the boundaries of scientific disciplines with ease, and built important and enduring theoretical structures. During this period, while preparing a class demonstration on the anatomy of the eye, he invented the ophthalmoscope.

His attention turned next to hearing and sound, and he covered the field as thoroughly as he had others. Musical scales, harmony, the physics of sound, vibrations of organ pipes and violin strings, and, of course, the physiology and functions of the ear were studied and experimented upon. Helmholtz included a primarily psychological discussion of the relation between external objects and the perception or sensation of them in the brain. *Die Lehre von den Tonempfindungen* was published in 1863.

In 1871 his outstanding abilities in physics and mathematics were rewarded by his appointment to the chair of physics at Berlin. In 1883 hereditary nobility was conferred on him, contributing the "von" to his name. The Physikalisch-Technische Reichsanstalt was established in 1887, and Helmholtz was invited to be its first president and chief organizer.

While working on the law of the conservation of energy Helmholtz had performed experiments involving electricity and chemical reactions. He had derived formulas which are still useful concerning the interrelationships of electrical energy and heat obtained during electrolysis. More experiments in this field occupied him after 1870, and in 1881 he gave the Faraday Memorial lecture before the Chemical Society. Although he subscribed to the dualistic theory of electricity (both positive and negative) and thought that the particles of a compound in solution were atoms, he was able, by developing Faraday's theories and including work done more recently, to strengthen those theories and to announce that the forces of chemical affinity are electrical in character, that each element has a definite affinity for one kind of electricity (positive or negative), and that work is involved in removing the electric charge from the atom, either by electrolysis or by chemical reaction (strain hypothesis).

He also made significant contributions to Maxwell's theory on the nature of light and to Hertz's work on radio waves.

In 1893 Helmholtz made his only journey to America, when he was honorary president of the International Electrical Congress at the Columbian Exposition, Chicago. On the return trip he suffered a bad fall down the companion way of the ship, a fall from which he never wholly recovered. He died on September 8, 1894.

References

1. GRUBER, H., AND GRUBER, V., *Sci. Monthly*, **83**, 92 (August 1956).
2. HELMHOLTZ, H., *J. Chem. Soc.*, **39**, 277 (1881).
3. KOENIGSBERGER, L., "Hermann von Helmholtz," translated by Frances A. Welby, Oxford, Clarendon Press, 1906.

ELIZABETH S. BENFORD

HÉROULT, PAUL LOUIS TOUSSAINT (1863–1914)

Paul Louis Toussaint Héroult was born at Thiery-Harcourt, Normandy, on April 10, 1863. He was educated at the Lyceum at Caen, but spent several years with his grandfather in England. While attending Ste. Barbe College in Paris, he became acquainted with the book which influenced his life and that of Charles Martin Hall, Henri Sainte-Claire Deville's work on aluminum. Héroult then studied at l'École des Mines at Paris, interrupted his education for a turn in the army, returned to school, but left to take over the family tannery on the death of his father in 1885.

At the tannery he found an old steam engine. Using this to run a dynamo, he set up an electric furnace to experiment with aluminum. While attempting to electrolyze cryolite, he added sodium aluminum chloride to lower the temperature. The carbon anode was attacked! Realizing that he must be dealing with an oxide, he investigated and found that the chloride had been exposed to moisture and contained hydrated alumina. It was the dissolved alumina that was being electrolyzed.

In 1886 Héroult applied for his first patents, describing a furnace in which the charge was both heated and electrolyzed by the current passing between the carbon anode and the carbon bottom. The charge was alumina dissolved in molten cryolite, and the product was pure aluminum.

There seemed no immediate market for pure aluminum, so Héroult's second patent covered the production of aluminum bronze by the electrolysis of fused alumina with a liquid copper cathode.

Several successful commercial enterprises followed, developing the European market for aluminum and aluminum alloys, while Charles Martin Hall developed the American market. Héroult experimented with several other uses for his furnace, among them the production of steel.

His first steel furnace was similar to the aluminum furnace. Later, realizing that steel with a very low carbon content would be advantageous, he modified his furnace, devising one with a nonconducting bottom lined with magnesite. Carbon electrodes in series dipped into the slag on the top, but not into the steel itself. Various slags were used in succession depending upon the impurities which needed to be removed. The first furnaces were single phase, the later ones three phase. Commercial operation was started at La Praz, France, in 1899, and the first shipment made in 1900.

Héroult described the metallurgy and uses of the electric furnace process for the production of steel to the American Electrochemical Society at St. Louis in 1904. From that time on he and his family spent much time in the United States. In 1905–6 he set up a shaft furnace at Sault Ste. Marie, Ontario, using the native magnetic ore and charcoal, but it was not a commercial success. A plant was built at Syracuse, N.Y., in 1906, the first such arc furnace installation in the United States. In 1907 he went to Shasta County, Calif., to the town named for him, and set up a successful furnace.

Within a few years many more were built, and the Héroult furnaces were producing the largest percentage of electric steel in Europe and the United States.

Many instances exist in chemistry of the simultaneous discovery of a law or a process by two or more persons. However, no examples may be found that are more remarkable than the lives of Héroult and Charles Martin Hall. Both men were born in 1863 into families of moderate means. Both were precocious children and at the same age were inspired by the same book to seek their fortunes in aluminum. They set to work in improvised laboratories at the end of their college careers and in February 1886 discovered their processes.

Héroult and Hall eventually met in 1911, when Hall was awarded the Perkin Medal for his discoveries. Despite amazingly similar lives, the two had developed very dissimilar personalities. However, they became good friends, comparing notes on past successes and future experiments. Neither man was given much longer to experiment, however. Ill health soon forced Héroult back to France, where he died from typhoid fever on May 9, 1914. The remarkable parallel was finished with Hall's death on December 27, 1914.

References

1. Bloom, M. R., Science Digest, 30, 81 (Dec. 1951).
2. Cowles, Alfred, "The True Story of Aluminum," Chapter 7, Chicago, Henry Regnery Co., 1958.
3. Kershaw, J. B. C., "Electro-thermal Methods of Iron and Steel Production," New York, D. Van Nostrand Co., 1914.
4. Met. Chem. Eng., 12, 382 (1915).

Elizabeth S. Benford

Cross-references: *Aluminum Electrowinning; Castner, Hamilton Y.; Hall, Charles M.; Electric Smelting Furnaces; Steel Making in Electric Arc Furnaces.*

HITTORF, JOHANN WILHELM (1824–1914)

Johann Wilhelm Hittorf was born March 27, 1824, at Bonn. He studied there and at the University of Berlin, and in 1846 he received his doctorate in mathematics from the University of Bonn. Receiving the post of Privat-Dozent, he went to the Academy of Münster, where he was destined to spend the rest of his long life.

Later the Academy became the University of Münster, and Hittorf became professor of physics and chemistry and, in 1879, the director of the physical laboratories.

Between 1853 and 1858, much of his time was spent studying the migrations of ions during electrolysis. He disagreed with the then current belief that equality (in terms of equivalents) of the substances released at the electrodes during electrolysis was a result of equal velocities of the ions. Devising his own apparatus, he demonstrated the difference in the concentrations of the solute at the two poles, and explained the differences in terms of the relative velocities of the ions (transport or transference number).

The effects of temperature changes and current changes were studied and found to be negligible. Changes in concentration, however, produced changes in transport numbers, although the numbers tended to remain constant at low concentrations. By drawing off samples and testing them, Hittorf was able to deduce the composition of complex ions such as the ferrocyanides. He found that many compounds produced one anion in a concentrated solution and a different anion in a dilute solution.

Hittorf's work was not well received by his contemporaries; they found his ideas revolutionary and his arguments difficult to follow—a not surprising fault since this took place thirty years before Arrhenius announced the theory of ionization. Except for criticism he was neglected and felt his isolation keenly. A religious controversy occupied some of his energies also and hampered publication of his work. He received his first honor in 1880, a corresponding membership in the Göttingen Academy of Science. Later many honors, memberships, and degrees were accorded him, including membership in the Chemical Society in 1908.

Between 1860 and 1890 several other researches occupied his attention. While studying the spectra of gases in Geissler tubes he found that one element could have several different spectra, depending on temperature and current. He discovered "metallic" phosphorus and the allotropes of sulfur and selenium. With Plücker he investigated cathode rays and described several of their properties.

In 1879, because of ill health, he retired from active teaching. Rest restored his health, fortunately, and he enjoyed another decade as productive as his earlier period. Returning to the study of electrolysis, he investigated the passivity of metals, the behavior of complex salts, and the determination of transport numbers under various conditions. He found that some diaphragms modify the velocity of the ions to a significant extent and that some can prevent the passage of either solvent or solute. A series of very accurate determinations of transport numbers brought his scientific career to a close in 1903.

Hittorf lived quietly in Münster for ten more years, enjoying the honors which had been so late in coming. He died on November 28, 1914.

References

1. GLASSTONE, S., "An Introduction to Electrochemistry," Chapter 4, New York, D. Van Nostrand Co., 1942.
2. HEYDWEILLER, A., *Physik. Z.*, **16**, 161 (1915).
3. J. W., *J. Chem. Soc.*, **107**, 582 (1915).

ELIZABETH S. BENFORD

HOFER-MOEST REACTION. See KOLBE AND RELATED BROWN-WALKER AND HOFER-MOEST REACTIONS.

HOT-PRESSING FURNACES. See FURNACES FOR HOT PRESSING.

HYDROCHLORIC ACID ELECTROLYSIS

Processes for producing chlorine from hydrochloric acid are of interest because:

(1) An excess of HCl is available in much of the world as a by-product of organic chlorination operations, where essentially half the chlorine used is combined with its molecular equivalent of hydrogen.

(2) The demand for hydrochloric acid has not kept pace with that for chlorine.

Although many means are theoretically available for extraction of chlorine from HCl, all are quite practically limited by available materials of construction for this corrosive material, and/or by the high capital cost of the equipment which is suitable. Another limiting factor which has seriously retarded development of these processes is the relatively cheap source of chlorine in salt, which is widely available in appreciable quantities near the earth's surface.

One process which has proved economical in

areas of plentiful HCl supply, and where electrical power is low priced, is the direct electrolysis of HCl in water solutions. The reactions are shown as follows:

$$HCl \rightarrow H^+ + Cl^-$$

with hydrogen released at the cathode

$$2H^+ + 2e \rightarrow H_2 \uparrow$$

and chlorine at the anode

$$2Cl^- - 2e \rightarrow Cl_2 \uparrow$$

The electrolysis of HCl takes place in an electrolytic cell in which the evolved gases are separated by a diaphragm of suitable material. Graphite electrodes are used. Theoretically 2.72 coulombs of electrical current are required per mg of chlorine recovered. Practically only 92 to 96 per cent of this current flow is effective in dissociating hydrochloric acid, the balance being lost in leakage and thermal losses. An extremely small quantity is lost in electrolysis of other compounds in a well-designed cell.

The driving force required for electrolysis, or the voltage drop required for effective release of the elements, is made up of the following components:

Components of Typical Voltage Drop in HCl Electrolysis

Chlorine discharge potential	1.02
Hydrogen discharge potential	0.28
Chlorine overvoltage on graphite	0.2
Hydrogen overvoltage on graphite	0.5
IR Drop—electrolyte, etc.	0.3
	2.30

These typical potential drops are from industrial operating units, and depend quite heavily on proper cell design and the manner of operation.

HCl dissociates readily into its respective ions at room temperature. Consequently, it has a high conductivity and low resistance to flow of electrical current. However, by going from room temperature to 94°C, for instance, the specific conductivity can be almost doubled. Also, benefiting from a better temperature selection is the hydrogen overvoltage, which for graphite is as high as 0.9 volts at 18°C.

Another factor important in HCl electrolysis is the migration velocity of hydrogen versus chlorine ions. The mechanics of electroendosmosis (migration of H_2O molecules to the cathode) has little effect in such a highly dissociated electrolyte. However, the migration rate of hydrogen ions through the diaphragm to the anolyte is about 5 times as great as that of the chlorine ions. In a static cell such a phenomena results in quite high concentration of HCl in the catholyte and rapid depletion of the anolyte. Since low anolyte concentrations result in increasing rates of H_2O electrolysis and oxygen evolution, the industrial electrolysis cell design must be carefully handled to compensate for this natural law.

Industrial research in electrolysis has done a creditable job in meeting this challenge.

History

Although some work started before 1930 in the United States, the real beginning of development of commercial aspects of HCl electrolysis took place in Germany in the 1930's. After the Second World War, the work of G. Messner and collaborators for I. G. Farbenindustrie at Bitterfeld came to light. These scientists had operated early units made up of several frames of solid graphite, clamped together in a single electrolyzer. The graphite plates were held apart by insulating gaskets, with void spaces between filled with hydrochloric acid, and separated by diaphragms.

With publication of the FIAT reports by the Allies after the war, several companies took up this work and have evolved present-day HCl electrolyzers.

The Modern Electrolyzer

Today direct electrolysis of HCl is carried out in units consisting of thirty to fifty electrolytic cells. These cells are formed by assembling thirty-one to fifty-one electrode sections, called electrolyzer elements, in the form usually associated with plate and frame filter presses. The end elements act as anode and cathode, respectively, to the electrolytic cells at the ends of the units. All other (intermediate) elements contain bipolar electrodes for the individual cells (Fig. 1).

Electrical connections, through plated copper rods, are made to the electrodes in the end elements. Current passes from each cell to the next within an electrolyzer, via the bipolar graphite electrodes.

The elements of the modern electrolyzer consist basically of the graphite electrode mounted in a corrosion-resistant frame of reinforced synthetic resin, rubber-lined steel, or the like. To this frame, the diaphragm is usually attached. It is usually made of woven synthetic resin fibers. The diaphragm may alternately be mounted in its own frame and sandwiched between the assembled elements. Some electrolyzers use sacrificial graphite, either in lumps or in removable plates, but always on the anode side of the bipolar electrodes. Others use solid electrodes, where graphite consumption is known to be low. The electrodes are grooved vertically on the active surfaces, except where

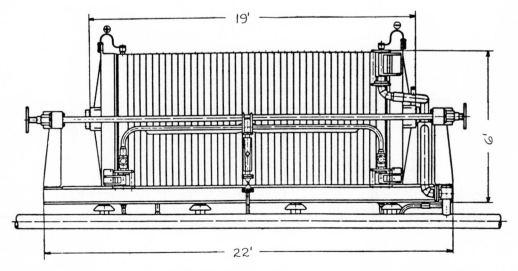

Fig. 1. DeNora 3500 ampere HCl electrolyzer (*Courtesy Oronzio deNora Impianti Elettrochimici*)

lump graphite is used against a smooth anode surface of graphite.

A modern HCl electrolyzer may typically produce 5.65 tons of chlorine per day operating at 3500 amps. Such a unit is the deNora type 260D-50C which occupies a floor space of 360 sq ft including working area.

This deNora unit is assembled with 50 electrolytic cells (51 elements) and has an operating voltage drop of approximately 115 volts d-c. One such unit is the equivalent of a 175,000 amp diaphragm or amalgam chlor-alkali cell in production capacity.

Hydrochloric acid solution of 30 to 33 per cent HCl is fed to the bottom of the electrolyzer, through channels made by drilled holes through each element. Acid is admitted to each electrolytic cell from this feed channel through a single distributor hole in each frame. The feed is to the anolyte side of each cell.

Hydrogen and chlorine gases rise in the cells and pass out through similar but larger channels at the top of the electrolyzer. The channel on one side is connected by outlets drilled into the anode chamber and on the other by holes drilled to the cathode side.

Depleted acid leaves the electrolyzer by overflowing through the gas outlets described above. About 45 per cent of the entering HCl is electrolyzed. The balance leaves the cells at a con-

centration of 15 to 20 per cent HCl. This permits operation at lowest voltage drop since the conductivity of HCl solutions is highest at a concentration of 18 per cent. This acid is reconcentrated by absorption of HCl gas, and is then fed back to the cells.

Industrial Application

An HCl electrolysis plant would typically consist of a number of electrolyzers, connected in series, up to a total circuit voltage compatible with safe operation and with economical a-c to d-c conversion equipment. This might mean 4 to 8 units in series, depending on economics. As many parallel circuits could be used as required. The flow of materials in such a plant might appear as schematically shown in Fig. 2. Acid for the plant would come from an HCl absorber at 30 to 33 per cent HCl concentration. It would be filtered to remove solids, and should be free of separate organic liquid phases. The gases would be cooled and scrubbed by recirculation of the condensate and would then be delivered to standard gas handling equipment. Depleted acid would be returned directly to the absorber for further enrichment with HCl.

Performance of HCl electrolysis equipment is dependent on many factors, all of which can be satisfactorily controlled in the operating plant. The purity of gases normally evolved is typi-

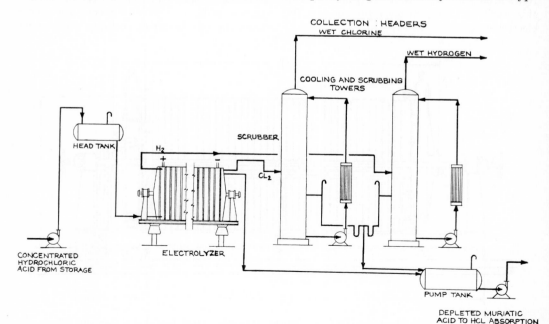

FIG. 2. Hydrochloric acid electrolysis flow sheet.

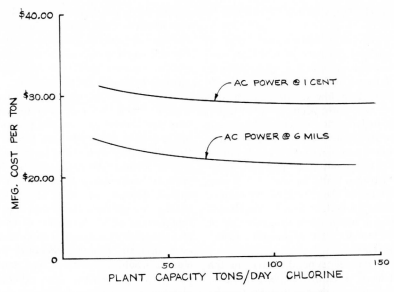

FIG. 3. Chlorine production costs from HCl electrolysis.

cally as follows:

Chlorine Gas

CO_2	approx. 0.05%
H_2	0 to 0.10%
O_2	0 to 0.01%

Hydrogen Gas

Cl_2	0 to 0.10%

Organics appear in the gases only to the extent that they enter with, and are evaporated from, the feed acid.

Consumption of graphite from the electrode surfaces is extremely small. In many instances, this consumption amounts to only ⅒ to ½₀ of that used in electrolyzing NaCl brine solutions. This phenomena derives from the high dissociation of HCl in 18 per cent solutions, and the resulting low electrolysis of H_2O in these cells. It also results in surprisingly low CO_2 evolution with the chlorine gas.

The economics of HCl electrolysis are predominantly determined by 1) the cost of electrical power, 2) the amortization of relatively large capital costs and 3) the value assigned to the feed acid. Using feed acid at no value, chlorine produced from HCl may range from 50 to 60 per cent of the cost of the equivalent amount of chlorine and its associate product (NaOH), when obtained by electrolysis of NaCl. For pro-

ducers in areas where NaOH has low value, this process becomes quite attractive.

Plant costs now range from $20,000 to $25,000 per daily ton of chlorine capacity. Production costs of liquid chlorine, run from $22 to $32 per ton produced, depending on size of plant and the price of electrical energy (Fig. 3).

References

1. MANTELL, C. L., "Electrochemical Engineering," Fourth Edition, New York, McGraw-Hill Book Co., 1960.
2. CREIGHTON, H. J., "Principles and Applications of Electrochemistry," Vol. 1, Third Edition, New York, John Wiley and Sons, Inc., 1935.
3. SCONCE, J. S., "Chlorine, Its Manufacture, Properties, and Uses," New York, Reinhold Publishing Corp., 1962.
4. Fiat Final Report No. 832, June 19, 1946.

JACK H. NICHOLS

Cross-references: *Chlorine Industry; Chlorine Production* entries.

HYDROGEN ELECTRODE. See REFERENCE ELECTRODES.

HYDROGEN, ELECTROLYTIC PRODUCTION. See WATER ELECTROLYSIS.

HYDROGEN EMBRITTLEMENT

Many rather diverse phenomena are often included in the general category of hydrogen embrittlement. A definition widely accepted among metallurgists is found in the *ASM Metals Handbook*: "a condition of low ductility in metals resulting from the absorption of hydrogen." Obviously this includes the effects of hydrogen that may come from any kind of natural source or industrial operation, whether it be metallurgical, chemical, mechanical, or physical. Conceivably the hydrogen could be occluded during the very first stages of the extractive techniques used in producing a metal, or during a corrosion process by which a metal failed in service, or in the course of any event that might occur in between these extremes.

Of the several possible general sources of the hydrogen that leads to embrittlement, the metallurgical and chemical varieties are by far the most important. Hydrogen may be produced in and absorbed by the metal in two principal metallurgical processes, namely, smelting (or refining) and welding. In both instances the hydrogen comes from the thermal decomposition of water (with or without reactions with the metal) that is always present in the atmosphere and is often a contaminant in raw materials for metal production or in welding-rod coatings. Usually it is impractical to do very much to reduce hydrogen absorption during metal production except for drying of excessively wet raw materials. Vacuum treatments of the final liquid metal or vacuum pouring are now being used for production of premium-quality steels with low hydrogen concentration. Proper storage of welding rods to keep the coatings dry should eliminate them as a hydrogen source.

Processing operations involving chemical reactions or electrochemical procedures are by far the most potent sources of hydrogen. Any chemical process involving hydrogen as a reactant or in which hydrogen is produced as a by-product on a metal surface is a possible source of hydrogen contamination. Atomic hydrogen is produced in pickling, cleaning, and stripping operations during metal finishing, but the degree of absorption is influenced by a multitude of factors too numerous and complex to present here. The same complexities prevail for electrochemical hydrogen generation; the circumstances and chemical variables are more important than the total amount of generated hydrogen in determining how much hydrogen will be absorbed compared to that which is harmlessly evolved. Plating, electrolytic pickling (cathodic), stray-current electrolysis, and electrochemical corrosion in aqueous media are common sources of possible hydrogen contamination.

If the form in which hydrogen can exist within a metal were limited to a single mode, both the theoretical and the practical problems of hydrogen embrittlement would be greatly simplified. Unfortunately, hydrogen may occur as an atomic, interstitial, solute element; as trapped molecular gas in holes, rifts or other spatial defects; or as a chemical compound, usually a hydride. It would be remarkable, therefore, if all of the effects of hydrogen could be explained by a single, simple mechanism; or even that the physical effects of hydrogen occlusion would fall into a well-defined, limited pattern of phenomena. The experimental complexities have led to much controversy among investigators, not only on theoretical considerations but even on the meaning and validity of experimental data.

Most of the material presented here is concerned with interstitial hydrogen, for it is occlusion of this species that leads to the striking and often catastrophic failure of stressed metals. Within this broad category two principal modes of failures are encountered. Some materials fail by cracking or by complete fracture immediately after they are loaded or deformed in excess of a certain amount or even during a processing operation, such as plating. The cracking of plain carbon steels falls in this category. On the other hand, a great many materials that contain a damaging amount of hydrogen and are loaded to some specific stress level will sustain the load for days, or even weeks, and then fail suddenly. This is called delayed fracture and is by far the most insidious form of hydrogen embrittlement. Most of the research on hydrogen embrittlement has been concerned with delayed failures, and most of what follows in this article pertains to the problems, testing, and mechanisms of delayed failures.

There are no nondestructive tests by which susceptibility to failure by hydrogen embrittlement may be evaluated. Unfortunately, there is no good agreement on what kind of destructive testing should be used on specially prepared specimens, either with respect to the general character of the test or the details that are involved for a particular problem. Three principal kinds of tests are in use: bend, tensile, and stress rupture.

Bend tests of a variety of kinds are popular because of their simplicity, speed, and ease of specimen preparation. They seem to work well for embrittlement problems that involve fracture that occurs during processing or immediately that the workpiece is loaded. On the other hand, they are far less useful in the delayed-fracture field or for any kind of work that involves mathematical analysis of the stress-strain relationships that prevail in the test.

The ordinary tensile test is not well adapted to the detection of embrittlement of the delayed-fracture type, simply because the expensive machine used for the test cannot be tied up for the length of time required to develop delayed fractures. Severe embrittlement may be detected in short-time tensile tests on notched specimens, but the more dangerous borderline type will not be revealed.

Leading workers in the field are agreed that the stress-rupture test is by far the best technique for determining susceptibility to delayed fractures. Occasionally the method is called the static-load test or the static-fatigue test. Notched specimens resembling ordinary tensile specimens are loaded in simple devices by means of springs or by dead weights plus levers to the desired tensile stress, and the time to failure is determined. Although the method is quite expensive, the cost is far less than that involved in using tensile-testing machines for long periods of loading.

Another vexing testing problem is the determination of the hydrogen content of both laboratory specimens and of samples of materials that have failed in service. The amounts of hydrogen that are involved are exceedingly small and their determination is a serious and difficult problem. This situation is bad enough, but to it must be added the problem of distinguishing analytically between the interstitial hydrogen, which causes embrittlement, and other hydrogen that is innocuous because of either its form or its distribution. Variations of vacuum-fusion analysis are currently the only techniques of consequence.

Relatively little is known about the mechanism of hydrogen occlusion as far as actual entry from a specific environment into a metallic lattice is concerned. Because most hydrogen embrittlement arises from metal-finishing operations, entry from solutions has received the most

attention in the work that has been done. Barton[1] has summarized rather systematically the experimental and theoretical work that has been published in this field.

It is well established that there is no simple relationship between the amount of hydrogen discharged at a metal surface and the quantity that is occluded. This means, in other words, that the efficiency of an electrolytic process or the rate of hydrogen evolution in a chemical process is not a significant factor in determining whether embrittlement will occur. What is really important is the fraction of hydrogen that remains in the atomic state during a surface reaction or process and can in this form enter the metallic body; the evolved gas, being molecular and not occludable at the temperatures encountered in aqueous solutions, is of no consequence as far as embrittlement is concerned. Although many factors must in one way or another influence the ratio of absorbed to evolved hydrogen, the area of "clean" metal surface must be a highly significant factor. It appears that substances that encourage embrittlement when added to pickling solutions are those which by adsorption effectively screen a large portion of the metal surface and prevent the ready migration of discharged hydrogen ions (atoms). Thus, they cannot readily combine to form molecules and instead, enter the metal in the atomic form.

In the case of electroplating solutions, it appears that the anions perform the same role as poisons in pickling solutions. Thus, in general, cyanide solutions, wherein the free cyanide ions are absorbed on the metal surface, are more prone to cause hydrogen occlusion than a simpler solution, such as an acid-sulfate bath. This mechanism accounts for the lack of correlation between embrittling effects and efficiency, for it is the way in which the gas is produced rather than the amount that is significant. The actual quantity required for embrittlement is so small that sufficient hydrogen is produced even in a high-efficiency bath. Embrittlement will ensue in such baths if the conditions for adsorption are favorable.

Once hydrogen has penetrated the metal lattice its passage through the metal becomes a matter of diffusion and is governed by the usual diffusion laws. Owing to the difficulty of measuring diffusion rates of hydrogen at the temperatures that prevail in metal-finishing operations, relatively little work has been done in this field.

An admirable summary of both experimental and theoretical material has been prepared by Hill.[2]

The total passage of hydrogen through a metallic body is called permeation and involves, of course, adsorption on one surface, diffusion through the body of metal, and desorption from a second surface. As far as rates are concerned, the diffusion process is much the slowest; hence, permeation measurements on reasonably thick specimens can provide data on diffusion rates. Lawrence[3] has described suitable equipment.

Steps that are taken to avoid hydrogen embrittlement problems fall into two categories: techniques that are designed to avoid the occlusion of hydrogen and those that are pointed toward the removal of hydrogen from contaminated work pieces (baking). The first group is complicated and uncertain of success; the second is simple and reliable, but time consuming.

Some interesting work has been done recently on the prevention of hydrogen embrittlement arising from corrosion or stray-current electrolysis. The workpiece or structure of interest is protected either by alloying with it something which will cause evolution rather than absorption of hydrogen or by connecting to it a cathode at which the hydrogen will be harmlessly evolved.

Hydrogen that is absorbed during chemical processing treatments, such as pickling, can be reduced or perhaps eliminated by judicious selection of conditions, reagents, or additives. There is, however, no systematic way in which the right combination may be found and resort must be had to empirical evaluations.

In electroplating and other electrolytic processes, three approaches to the problem of avoiding hydrogen absorption have been employed. Each of the three has not received an equal amount of attention, and from time to time popularity of investigation in each of the fields has varied considerably.

The most popular approach to the elimination of embrittlement has involved the search for processing solutions that are not very different from those currently employed but at the same time are not embrittling. It has been hoped that embrittlement could be eliminated without major change in processing and without sacrificing proved desirable properties of certain kinds of deposits. Most of the work has involved attempts to devise high-efficiency solutions or to avoid those containing cyanides. The

results have not been very satisfactory. Some of the reported processes have appeared to be satisfactory in the laboratory, but difficulties of control or other problems have mitigated against industrial use of the processes. Most of the suggested techniques or treatment cycles have been so sensitive to operating variables that the processors cannot trust their operations as far as reliable production of embrittlement-free workpieces is concerned. The up-shot of this has been that a baking operation is almost always used at the end of the treatment cycle. It is probable that very often the baking operation is the most useful part of the entire process.

Many investigators have reported work on unusual baths in which no hydrogen can be generated at the cathode. One group of solutions comprises those that contain no water but are based upon organic solvents having no labile hydrogen. Although experimental work indicates that many of these baths are nonembrittling, they have not been used industrially. Several problems arise. Among them are the difficulties of excluding water from the bath and the prevention of the decomposition of the solvent or other components at the anode. Many of the solutions that have been suggested require very high voltages for practical current densities; both power consumption and heat effects become troublesome. Not the least of the problems faced by the promoters of organic baths is a strong industrial prejudice against such solutions. The other kind of solution in which hydrogen formation is suppressed involves an ordinary plating bath to which a strong oxidizing agent has been added. The idea here is that hydrogen will be consumed by the oxidizing agent before it can enter the metal workpiece. Sodium nitrate in a cadmium cyanide bath has been used industrially, as described by Hamilton and Levin.[4] As they have found, the simple addition of a nitrate is not enough; other additives are required, thereby making the bath moderately complex.

As the third technique for preventing hydrogen from entering the metal, some use has been made of a barrier layer of a metal deposited from a nonembrittling solution. The barrier metal, having been selected for its impermeability to hydrogen, prevents hydrogen occlusion from a solution that is normally embrittling. Little or no use appears to have been made of this procedure in industrial work.

Prevention of embrittlement by baking the

processed parts is a widely accepted industrial technique. Although specifications differ somewhat, a popular treatment for ferrous workpieces is 375°F for 23 hr. This is so efficacious that many manufacturers are content to rely on baking for hydrogen removal, and they do not worry too much about the quantity of gas picked up during processing. An obvious limitation would be those cases where fracture of the workpiece occurs before it can be put into the baking oven.

References

1. BARTON, R. J., "Hydrogen Embrittlement in Metal Finishing," edited by H. J. Read, pp. 20–46, New York, Reinhold Publishing Corp., 1962.
2. HILL, M. L., *ibid*, pp. 46–81.
3. LAWRENCE, S. C., JR., *ibid*, pp. 97–109.
4. HAMILTON, W. F., AND LEVINE, M., *ibid*, pp. 166–183.

HAROLD J. READ

HYDROGEN PEROXIDE

In 1818 Thenard discovered "oxygenated water" by treating barium peroxide with nitric acid. Hydrogen peroxide remained more or less a laboratory chemical until 1908 when the first electrolytic cells were invented. Pietzsch and Adolph, among others, determined that the electrolysis of ammonium bisulfate to ammonium peroxydisulfate, followed by various methods of hydrolysis, would yield a stable solution of hydrogen peroxide. The Loewenstein or Riedel process used an electrolysis cell working on a dual electrolyte and added a novel hydrolysis step which improved hydrogen peroxide recoveries and reduced labor costs. The Weissenstein process electrolyzed sulfuric acid to peroxydisulfuric acid which was hydrolyzed to hydrogen peroxide. Of these electrolytic processes, only the Loewenstein or Riedel process remains in commercial use in the United States. It is the most economical, having high hydrolysis yields, good cell efficiency, and low labor costs. This process will be described in greater detail.

The two reactions which are used in the manufacture of hydrogen peroxide are:

Electrolysis: $2NH_4HSO_4 + 2F$
$$\rightarrow (NH_4)_2S_2O_8 + H_2 \uparrow$$

Hydrolysis: $2H_2O + (NH_4)_2S_2O_8$
$$\rightarrow 2NH_4HSO_4 + H_2O_2$$

Adding these two reactions shows that the raw materials are electric power and water, to give hydrogen gas and hydrogen peroxide.

$$2H_2O + 2F \rightarrow H_2 \uparrow + H_2O_2$$

A single cell consists of a platinum anode, a porous ceramic diaphragm or separator, a lead cathode, appropriate anolyte and catholyte solutions, and necessary coolers. The standard oxidation-reduction potential for the reaction is:

$$2HSO_4^- \rightarrow S_2O_8^{--} + 2H^+ + 2e$$
$$E° = 2.18 \text{ volts}$$

The anode must have a smooth, shiny surface, or current efficiency is decreased due to the formation of oxygen. The shape of the anode is such that it meets the requirements of minimum costs, high current density, and effective coverage of the diaphragm and cathode areas. Cells have been operated with anodic current densities from 0.3 to 1.5 amperes per square centimeter and corresponding cell voltages of 4.8 to 5.5 volts. The cathode is electrolytic lead. It is designed to accomplish two objectives: first, to provide maximum hydrogen release area with minimum possibilities of gas binding and, second, to provide sufficient area so the cathodic current density will range between 0.08 and 0.40 amperes per square centimeter.

The tank portion of the cell can be made of a variety of materials which are corrosion-proof to the acid electrolyte. In the past, chemical porcelain, stoneware, glass, hard rubber, or lined steel tanks were used, but with the coming of the Plastic Age, polyvinyl chloride, certain polyesters, and polypropylene are in use. The plastic tanks have many advantages over the stoneware tanks—weight, dimensional stability, and more flexibility in cell design features.

The necessity for coolers becomes apparent with a look at the various cell voltage drops. There are the two electrode overvoltages, plus voltage drops contributed by the diaphragm and the solution. The usual cell voltage is from 4.8 to 5.5, but the chemical voltage to form peroxydisulfate is only 2.2 volts. The heat developed by the difference between these voltages, multiplied by the current flowing, must be removed, or temperatures will rise to levels that cause excessive peroxydisulfate decomposition into bisulfate and oxygen. Normal operating temperatures range from 20 to 40°C. Coolers must be made of acid-compatible materials such as lead, plastic, or glass.

The porous ceramic diaphragm serves the purpose of maintaining a barrier between the anolyte and catholyte solutions which have different concentrations of sulfuric acid and ammonium sulfate. The diaphragm is not a barrier to the flow of ions and current. Pore size and diaphragm thickness must be carefully controlled. In addition, diaphragm electrical resistance is held to a minimum, consistent with physical strength, corrosion resistance, and cell design features. The diaphragm is secured in the tank by various sealing techniques using waxes or gaskets.

The above paragraphs have described the fundamental requirements for a single electrolytic cell. A designer can satisfy these requirements in many ways which are only limited by his ingenuity and the availability of the cell components. Usually a commercial battery tank consists of multiple cells in combinations of series-parallel electrical and solution circuits. As more cells are included in a battery tank, the solution piping becomes complex because each cell must still have its two solutions. However, these must not provide an electrical leakage path to the next cell which is operating at a different voltage level. In multiple units, anodes are connected to cathodes in the next cell so solutions are electrically isolated by various means using long flow paths. Cooling water connections may be for one individual battery tank, anode and cathode coolers in series or parallel, or several tanks connected in series. These connections depend on the temperature of the available cooling water, its cleanliness, and the heat transfer characteristics of the coolers. The ultimate shape, size, and arrangement of a battery tank is fixed only by fulfilling the physical and electrochemical requirements. Some tanks are large —three feet square and three feet deep. A tank of this size is one cell as far as voltage drop is concerned, but has many separate electrodes and diaphragms. Other tanks have three or four cells in solution and electrical parallel, with two or three cells in solution and electrical series. The final production cascade arrangement will depend on available floor space and the rectifier operating voltage. Solutions flow by gravity from cell to cell and tank to tank so the tanks are arranged in stairstep cascade. The voltage above ground where the solution enters and exits the cascade must be considered to prevent stray current corrosion at some remote location. Ventilation of the tank is required for good housekeeping and safety. If the hydrogen from the cathode is not to be recovered, the entire surface of the tank can be covered and sufficient air drawn over the cell to dilute the hydrogen to a safe level. The same air will remove any traces of vapors from the anolyte compartment. The ventilation ducts are made of compatible materials. These discharge the vapors outside the building. If pure hydrogen is desired, the design of the cell must allow for no possible air leakage into the free space above the cathode. The hydrogen can be collected thru appropriate ducts. The anolyte surface must have a separate duct system.

The product of electrolysis is active oxygen in the form of ammonium peroxydisulfate. The next process step is the hydrolysis of ammonium peroxydisulfate to hydrogen peroxide. This is accomplished by increasing the acid concentration and the temperature while maintaining conditions of minimum decomposition. Vacuum distillation is used. The feed solution is reduced in volume by about two-thirds with the evaporation of water. The hydrogen peroxide forms in the liquid phase, but, as it has a lower boiling point than the acid, it vaporizes. However, an equilibrium exists between the vapor and the liquid such that one-quarter of the original active oxygen remains in the liquid. For efficient operation, this amount of hydrogen peroxide is recovered by stripping the liquid with steam. The final electrolyte contains less than two per cent of the feed active oxygen. The hydrogen peroxide-water vapor is rectified in a tower to a liquid product of 20–35 per cent concentration. The overhead stream is water which is condensed and returned to the electrolyte to maintain the proper acid concentration.

The design of a hydrolysis still requires knowledge of materials of construction, heat transfer characteristics, mass transfer rates, and an understanding of the chemistry involved. Evaporators can be made of impregnated graphite, tantalum, or lead. The major vessels must be corrosion-proof to concentrated boiling acid. Therefore, chemical stoneware and porcelain are used. All solution piping is stoneware or glass. The product, hydrogen peroxide, contains traces of electrolyte which may corrode aluminum or stainless steel, but a correct choice of alloys minimizes this problem. The condensers are usually aluminum for high heat transfer rates and minimum contamination of the water.

The hydrogen peroxide obtained by hydrolysis could be used, but a further purification step gives a more concentrated solution which has very stable storage characteristics. The hydrogen peroxide is distilled under vacuum in a manner that allows the impurities to remain in the liquid phase and only pure vapors are sent to a rectification tower. A single stage of distillation can yield a stable product up to 70 per cent concentration. If higher concentrations and fewer impurities are required, additional stages of distillation are required to attain up to 90–95 per cent concentration. Special distillation or other techniques consistent with safety can be used to approach anhydrous hydrogen peroxide.

An important step in the manufacture of hydrogen peroxide is the purification of the electrolyte. The solution picks up inorganic impurities as it travels thru the plant. The majority of these are decomposition catalysts which affect hydrolysis yields. The usual purification requires a ferrocyanide precipitation of impurities, so any residual active oxygen must be destroyed before the ferrocyanide addition is made. The precipitate is removed on porous carbon or stoneware candles.

The previous process steps suggest a cyclic process. Although two solutions are required for electrolysis, they are really the same carrier electrolyte at different ratios of ammonium sulfate to sulfuric acid. Imagine a figure-eight flow pattern with the cross over point being the electrolysis cell. Start at the anode side of the cell for the production of ammonium peroxydisulfate. From this point, the flow goes to the hydrolysis still for the actual production of hydrogen peroxide. The spent electrolyte from the still flows to the cathode side of the cell. The catholyte outlet stream goes to solution purification on the other side of the figure-eight. The purified solution goes back to the anode side of the cell, completing the cycle. Thus, the electrolyte is the carrier in which electric power and water are reacted to produce hydrogen peroxide.

Hydrogen peroxide can be stored for long periods of time in pure aluminum tanks. Most shipping containers, drums, tankcars, and trailer trucks are aluminum. Each container must have one essential part for safety. Hydrogen peroxide is safe and easy to store and ship, yet it decomposes slowly, so provisions must be made to release the oxygen from the container. These vents are made to allow gas to escape, but will not let dirt or other contaminants get inside the container.

Hydrogen peroxide is thermodynamically unstable. Many things act as decomposition catalysts—iron rust, dirt, most metallic oxides, and some organic compounds. Therefore, cleanliness is extremely important in everything connected with the manufacture, the transportation, and the use of hydrogen peroxide.

The major uses of hydrogen peroxide are not well known, although almost everyone knows of the 3 per cent drug store variety. In 1962 approximately one hundred million pounds of 100 per cent hydrogen peroxide were produced and consumed. The bleaching of textiles consumed a large proportion of this quantity. High-quality papers are brightened with hydrogen peroxide. Unusual applications are the preparation of straws and felts for hats, the bleaching of cherries, and the brightening of hardwood bats for the baseball world. The plastic industry uses hydrogen peroxide to make organic peracids and intermediate compounds. The transistor industry finds it can improve its product by using etching techniques with hydrogen peroxide. The insecticide field has areas of application. A new cheese-making procedure uses a special grade of hydrogen peroxide. It is used as a raw material in the manufacture of inorganic peroxides and perhydrate compounds.

The military and space applications require high-strength, pure hydrogen peroxide in rockets and manned vehicles. The attitude control system in the Mercury Capsules and the X-15 aircraft rely on thrust from decomposing hydrogen peroxide.

Thenard's "oxygenated water" has progressed a long way and has become a most interesting, useful, and necessary chemical.

References

1. SCHUMB, W. C., SATTERFIELD, C. N., AND WENTWORTH, R. L., "Hydrogen Peroxide," New York, Reinhold Publishing Corporation, 1955.
2. MACHU, W., "Das Wasserstoffperoxyd und die Perverbindungen," Second Ed., Vienna, Springer-Verlag, 1951.
3. WOOD, W. S., Chemistry and Industry, 1953, 2.
4. BRETSCHGER, M. E., CREWSON, G. G., AND CUSHING, R. E., P. B. Report 17331 (1946).
5. U. S. Department of Commerce, P. B. Reports 45252, 33489, 74329.
6. BRETSCHGER, M. E., AND SHANLEY, E. S., J. Electrochem. Soc., 99, 311 (1952).
7. FLACH, D. O., AND GARVER, R. E., U. S. Patent 2,899,272 (August 11, 1959).
8. SHANLEY, E. S., J. Chem. Educ., 28, 290 (1951).

REED E. GARVER

Cross-reference: Peroxygen Chemicals.

I

IMMERSION (DISPLACEMENT) PLATING

A piece of steel dipped in copper sulfate solution becomes coated with copper although no external current is supplied. Such immersion deposits are formed by many metals, with the basis metal dissolving in quantities chemically equivalent to the deposit. This example may be formulated: $CuSO_4 + Fe \rightarrow FeSO_4 + Cu$, or in ionic terms: $Cu^{++} + Fe \rightarrow Fe^{++} + Cu$. The iron is said to *displace* copper from its solution.

Displacements depend on the relative activities (q.v.) not only of the metals but also of their ions in solution, as formulated in the electromotive series (q.v.). With metals in the order of decreasing activity, each metal displaces all those below it.

The phenomenon is explained by the observed electrode potentials (q.v.). In 1 M Cu^{++} solution, a copper surface establishes a potential of 0.35 v (*vs* NHE) across the metal-solution interface; if the potential is made more negative, Cu^{++} accepts electrons and is deposited as metal. An iron surface in 1 M Fe^{++} establishes a potential of -0.44 v, which is therefore quite negative enough to cause copper to deposit if its ions are present. After the initial deposit, an iron-copper couple or local cell (see **Corrosion**) exists in which the iron surface, in accordance with its potential, functions as anode, releasing Fe^{++} to the solution and liberating electrons within the metal. These flow to the copper and shift its potential to more negative values, so that the electrons are transferred to Cu^{++} in the electrolyte and cause copper to be plated out. This couple acts, therefore, as a voltaic cell (q.v.) short-circuited at the iron-copper interface. Initially, inhomogeneities on the iron surface give rise to copper deposition at cathodic regions.

Immersion deposition is essentially electrodeposition by currents generated internally at local cells. Compared to electroless plating, it is distinguished by the use of the basis metal rather than an added chemical reagent to effect reduction and deposition.

Action continues until the entire surface is covered by deposit and the anode regions disappear, unless the supply of depositing ions becomes exhausted. Usually the deposit reaches a thickness of about 2 to 10 microinches. (Because these thin deposits are quite porous, basis metal is still exposed to electrolyte, but polarization within the pores shifts the anode potential towards that of the cathode until local cell action virtually ceases.)

The nature of the deposit is governed by the factors which operate in ordinary electroplating (q.v.). Local cell currents may become quite large; for iron in a copper solution, the net driving force is $0.35 - (-0.44) = 0.79$ v, and is even greater before Fe^{++} accumulates in the electrolyte, whereas in the short-circuited local cell, electrical resistance is minimal. Accordingly, deposits are frequently burned and poorly adherent. Undercutting of the basis metal by anodic dissolution may also interfere with adhesion. The deposit is usually not a satisfactory basis for subsequent electrodeposits. Since steel or zinc surfaces dipped into a copper sulfate plating bath receive immersion deposits, the initial copper deposit must be made from a cyanide bath to avoid them (see **Copper plating**).

If the copper sulfate bath is dilute in copper and strongly acidified, the immersion coating is sufficiently adherent to serve as lubricant in drawing steel wire or shapes. The bath is not suitable for electroplating, and the adhesion of the coating may not be adequate for holding further electrodeposits. In this bath, deposition ceases before loose, bulky deposits accumulate. Large quantities of steel are treated in this way; sometimes copper-tin deposits are applied.

On zinc surfaces, the absence of immersion deposits from cyanide copper baths is the consequence of shifting the copper potential to a more negative value than that of zinc, by the complexing (q.v.) action of cyanide. With iron, the shift does not reverse the order of metal potentials, and failure to form an immersion deposit is the result of exceptionally slow kinetics of iron dissolution. (Because the reaction is so slow, its potential cannot be measured, but must be calculated.)

Immersion deposits of tin from stannate baths on aluminum are sufficiently adherent to protect pistons against "scuffing" during the running-in of an internal combustion engine, but they are not tight enough for satisfactory electroplating over them nor for a satisfactory bond for soldering. However, immersion deposits of zinc from zincate baths on aluminum provide a good basis for subsequent copper plating from cyanide baths; afterwards other plated coatings may be applied. These processes are in extensive use.

The ordinary attack by acids on active metals is actually immersion or displacement deposition of hydrogen; it is limited to metals more active, that is, higher than hydrogen in the activity series, but here, too, kinetic factors are often controlling. For example, extremely pure zinc scarcely dissolves in dilute sulfuric acid, even though the driving force exceeds 0.76 v, because of the exceptionally large hydrogen overvoltage (q.v.) on zinc. The presence of a metallic impurity (e.g., copper or lead) on the surface permits electrons originating in the zinc to reach hydrogen ions in the electrolyte at the surface of the impurity, where hydrogen overvoltage (kinetic hindrance) is low; the cathode reaction (hydrogen evolution) then proceeds at a good rate, and correspondingly zinc dissolves rapidly from the anode regions. (Less active metals than hydrogen dissolve in acids if an oxidizing agent is present; the diffusion of atmospheric oxygen permits a slow attack on copper, for example.)

Accordingly, conclusions drawn from the activity series may be profoundly influenced by complexing or by kinetic factors. Nickel and iron, for example, which are characteristically sluggish in electrode reactions, often do not display the expected displacement behavior. Furthermore, passivation (q.v.) causes metals to act with diminished activity.

Immersion ("wash") deposits of tin, gold, platinum, and palladium on such metals as silver and brass are applied for decorative purposes. As ions of the basis metal accumulate in the bath at the reacting surfaces, they may redeposit as an alloy with the noble metal. (See articles under the individual metals.)

The purification of zinc plating baths (q.v.) by means of zinc dust depends on immersion deposition of impurities, chiefly lead and copper, on the zinc particles, which are then removed. The method has the advantage of not adding unwanted ions to the bath. Zinc anodes often accumulate coatings of displaced metal impurities in regions which are shielded from the plating current.

On very active metals, such as magnesium, ordinary plating baths form immersion deposits which are spongy and burned, not only because of high local current densities, but also because they include metal hydroxides precipitated as a result of the rise in pH caused by displacement of hydrogen ions and consequent evolution of hydrogen at the metal surface. Aluminum offers somewhat similar problems after the protective oxide film is removed.

The Preece test for galvanized coatings depends on the displacement of copper by the zinc coatings immersed in a sulfate solution. The spongy black immersion deposit is removed by wiping at regular intervals; when the coating is penetrated, bright, adherent copper is deposited on the steel exposed, and marks the end of the test. Unfortunately, the rate of attack on the zinc depends sharply on a number of uncontrolled factors, and the test is not generally reliable.

References

1. STRAUMANIS, M. E., AND FANG, C. C., *J. Electrochem. Soc.*, **98**, 9 (1953).
2. JOHNSON, R. W., *J. Electrochem. Soc.*, **108**, 632 (1961).
3. RHODA, R. H., *Plating*, **50**, 307 (1963).

ERNEST H. LYONS, JR.

INDIUM ELECTROREFINING

Indium is a soft, silvery metal with the following physical constants:

Atomic number	49
Atomic weight	114.82
Melting point	156.61°C
Boiling point	2000.0°C
Density	7.31 (g/cc, 20°C)
Resistivity	8.37 (microhm-cm, 6°C)

The metal has quite varied uses, from providing corrosion resistance in bearings to semiconductors and other solid-state devices.

The metal price is somewhat more than that of silver, making it a semiprecious metal. The metal is, however, too soft for ornamental jewelry, limiting its usefulness to industrial applications.

Indium metal has some characteristics similar to zinc and cadmium, as well as tin and lead. It has other characteristics which are quite unique, such as the low melting point, but very high boiling point (see above).

Indium is generally associated with zinc blende which is a major source of the indium of commerce. Several producers of zinc, therefore, recover indium as a by-product. Some operate complete recovery and purification electrolytic processes, others sell some concentrated form to other processors. Still other electrolytic purification systems operate on scrap-recovered indium. Each source has individual characteristics and impurities which necessitate development of suitable chemical and electrolytic techniques.

In the electrolytic refining of indium, the electrochemical rather than physical properties become the most important. The following metal-metal ion potentials show the values of indium with other metals of the same group for acid solutions.

$$Al \rightarrow Al^{+++} + 3e = +1.67 \text{ volts}$$
$$Ga \rightarrow Ga^{+++} + 3e = +0.52 \text{ "}$$
$$In \rightarrow In^{+++} + 3e = +0.34 \text{ "}$$
$$Tl \rightarrow Tl^{+++} + 3e = -0.719 \text{ "}$$

While these values are of general interest, the important potentials, if electrorefining is to be effective, are the potentials of metals close to indium, as follows:

(signs according to Latimer convention)
$$Zn \rightarrow Zn^{++} + 2e = +0.76 \text{ volts}$$
$$Ga \rightarrow Ga^{+++} + 3e = +0.52 \text{ "}$$
$$Fe \rightarrow Fe^{++} + 2e = -0.44 \text{ "}$$
$$Cd \rightarrow Cd^{++} + 2e = -0.40 \text{ "}$$
$$In \rightarrow In^{+++} + 3e = -0.34 \text{ "}$$
$$Tl \rightarrow Tl^{+} + e = -0.33 \text{ "}$$
$$Co \rightarrow Co^{++} + 2e = -0.27 \text{ "}$$
$$Ni \rightarrow Ni^{++} + 2e = -0.23 \text{ "}$$
$$Sn \rightarrow Sn^{++} + 2e = -0.14 \text{ "}$$
$$Pb \rightarrow Pb^{++} + 2e = -0.12 \text{ "}$$

It will be noted from these potentials that the elements from cadmium down the list are possible impurities that may codeposit with indium. Some, fortunately, are not normally associated with sources of indium, others may be controlled by electrolytic conditions or removed chemically or by pyrometallurgy from the indium refining system. As would be expected from these potential values, cadmium will be most difficult to control during electrorefining. As a matter of fact, at the cathode potential of indium, i.e., −0.34 volts, a large number of metals would codeposit, if present in the electrolyte.

Electrolyte

Polarographic studies dating back to 1924[1] indicate the irreversible nature of the indic ion potential in many electrolytes. A summary of such effects is presented by Moeller and Hopkins;[2] also included is a large bibliography. The desirability of operating electrorefining processes from chloride systems is made evident by this polarographic work. Accordingly, the refining processes described will use chloride or chloride-containing electrolytes.

The operating characteristics of a typical electrolytic refining indium cell are described in the literature[3] and given as follows:

Indium (as chloride or sulfate)	40–60 gpl
Sodium chloride	90–100 gpl
pH 2.0–2.5	
Temperature, less than 40°C	
Current density	10–20 amps/sq ft
Addition agent, glue	1.0 gpl
Anodes, bagged (cotton)	
Tanks, rubber-lined steel	
Cathode purity	99.98%

Most of the concentrations are not critical, but sufficient chloride ion must be available to insure the reversible potentials of anode and cathode. The best cathode current efficiency appears to be in the pH range given. The temperature should not be above 40°C to maintain the best cathode efficiency. The current density could be increased considerably if adequate circulation and cooling were provided. The deposited indium exhibits "spike" type growths which have a tendency to short to anodes. Glue appears to be helpful in controlling the rate of growth toward the anodes and rounding off the projections. Purification of the electrolyte during electrolysis is generally done by circulating, either continuously or intermittently, over or through indium sponge. This is usually prepared by precipitation of indium by galvanic action of aluminum, from an indium solution containing chlorides.

Anodes

As previously mentioned, metal impurities in the electrolyte must be controlled by either continuous purification of the electrolyte by galvanic or chemical action, or by limiting the metals other than indium in the anodes. Actually, both methods of control may be necessary.

Anodes of less than 99.5 per cent purity would not be considered suitable to produce cathodes of 99.98 per cent purity. The methods by which the anode purity is attained are many and varied, depending on the source of the indium to be refined. This, of course, is different with each producer. The methods may involve pyrometallurgical, chemical, and galvanic precipitation of impurities. A typical example of purification procedures for anode material is given in the previously cited reference.[3] It is not possible to give in detail all of the various methods used by different producers, most of which are not published and are generally classified as confidential.

The "bagging" of the anodes is of considerable importance, since the impurities which do not dissolve in the electrolyte are very finely-divided particles which would contaminate the cathode metal by mechanical inclusion in the deposit.

Cathodes

Indium metal of good purity is rolled into sheets of about 0.005 to 0.010 inch thickness. This sheet is used as the cathode "starting" material. These sheets are looped over a "header" bar connected to the negative bus bar of the power supply. Many types of attachment devices are used. The entire cathode deposit, including the rolled sheet, is melted down at the end of the deposition period. The cathodes generally are melted down under a sodium hydroxide solution as a cover. Analysis of this cathode material would be about as follows:

> Pb 0.007%
> Sn 0.007%
> Cu <0.001%
> Fe <0.001%
> Cd <0.001%

High Purity Indium

The requirements of the solid-state technologies have created a demand for extreme purity in many of the metals, including indium. In some instances, depending on available facilities, the users of such metal prefer to do their own purification. However, most consumers expect the primary producer to prepare suitable high-purity indium.

The usual procedure in improving the purity of the 99.98% cathode indium is by re-electrolysis. The cathode metal is melted and recast as anode slabs. These are bagged and re-electrolyzed much as in the primary electrorefining. However, certain precautions are taken in the process to minimize impurities. The rolled indium cathode starting sheets are of higher purity. Electrolyte purification is more critical, involving close analytical control of the impurities and maintenance of rigid tolerances. The bagging of the anodes is more effective by wrapping with finer textured materials than cotton, such as "hard" grades of filter paper. By such precautions cathode metal of 99.995 per cent or better may be produced. Where still higher purity is required, vacuum baking for removal of such impurities as cadmium, zinc, and others may be employed. The high boiling point and relatively low vapor pressure of indium make this technique suitable for purification. Zone refining may also be employed. Purities of the order of 99.9999 per cent may be attained. This means a total of all impurities below 1 part per million, a rather severe requirement. Analysis of cathode metal from the above process, without benefit of vacuum baking or zone refining methods, is about as follows:

> Pb 0.0001% (1 ppm)
> Sn 0.0001%
> Cd 0.0001%
> Cu <0.0001%
> Tl <0.0001%
> Bi <0.0001%
> Ag <0.0001%
> Mg <0.0001%
> Si <0.0001%

The electrorefining of indium is widely practiced and has been quite efficient. Unfortunately, no specific, unvarying procedure can be described in detail, owing to the differences of impurities encountered in the range of crude indium-bearing materials to be processed. However, the basic principles and examples of electrolytic conditions and cathode purities required for successful operation have been described.

References

1. HEYROVSKY, J., Compt. rend., **179**, 1044, 1268 (1924).

2. MOELLER, T., AND HOPKINS, B. S., *Trans. Electro-chem. Soc.*, **93**, 84–93 (1948).
3. MILLS, J. R., HUNT, B. G., AND TURNER, G. H., *ibid.*, **100**, 136–140 (1953).
4. MILLS, J. R., KING, R. A., AND WHITE, C. E. T., chapter on "Indium," pp. 220–238, "Rare Metals Handbook," Ed., C. A. Hampel, New York, Reinhold Publishing Corp., 1961.

ROBERT P. YECK

INDUCTION HEATING

For induction heating, eddy currents are set up in the work material by means of a varying magnetic field. The induced current flowing through the electrical resistance of the work causes heating. The work is usually placed inside or adjacent to an inductor coil and subjected to an alternating magnetic field set up by the inductor coil current. The magnitude and frequency of the coil current are calculated to provide the desired concentration and degree of heat in the work. The magnetic field of the coil induces currents to flow around closed paths in the work, and the resultant resistive losses raise the work temperature.

This heating method has a broad range of use in the metal working industry. Brazing, soldering, annealing, melting of ferrous and of non-ferrous metals, sintering powdered metals, and surface hardening are all handled with facility. Some of its advantages are: the instantaneous control of heat input, with no thermal lag time on or off; the freedom of physical contact between the coil and the work, which makes the method ideal for a continuous process; accuracy and repetitiveness of heat control, considered to be better than with any other known heating method; the generation of heat in regions of the work defined by the shadow of the coil on the work and by the depth of current penetration, to provide heat selectivity and to restrict heating to given areas and limited depths of the work; the high rate of power input means a short heat time and minimum oxidizing of the work; the provision of clean heat, with no contamination from the heating source; controlled atmospheres can be used for heating reactive metals and other materials.

The latter features are most important in zone refining (q.v.), where silicon, germanium, and certain metals that are to be highly purified are refined in vacuum through a large number of progressive melting-resolidification operations. As the material is melted and resolidified progressively from one end to the other, a percentage of certain impurities is removed from the solid state, held in the liquid state, and concentrated near the end of the refined piece.

The most important features of high-frequency induction heating involve the ability to apply enormous quantities of energy to a restricted portion of a work piece with fine control. Parts are heated in seconds to the desired temperature, with excellent reproducibility of product.

Current in the inductor coil sets up flux linking the coil only, linking the air gap between the coil and work, and linking the work piece. Since only the flux linking the work piece does any useful work, it is then important to make this flux density as high as possible, and to keep the part to be heated close to the coil to cut down on air gap losses. The flux linking the work piece causes eddy currents to be set up at right angles to the direction of flux. The density of this current is greatest near the surface of the work, and becomes smaller for points farther from the surface. The current distribution is further affected by its tendency to flow in the portions of the work closest to the coil. Power input varies as the square of the current, so that the greatest amount of heating takes place close to the work surface and in the shadow of the coil on the work.

The use of the value δ, depth of current penetration, is widespread through the industry and permits the use of several simple formulas in design estimation. The value δ is selected so that if all the current in the work were uniformly distributed from the surface to the depth, δ, the magnitude of this uniform current density would be the same as actually occurs at the surface of the work. This value is a function of the magnetic field frequency. Table 1 shows the depth of current penetration for magnetic steel.

TABLE 1

Frequency, cps	Current Penetration, Inches	
	Below Curie temp.	Above Curie temp.
60	0.500	2.60
960	.120	.65
3,000	.060	.39
10,000	.030	.20
450,000	.005	.03

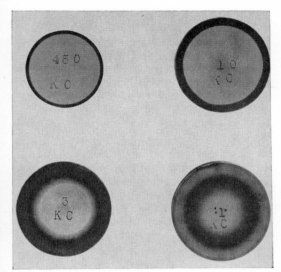

FIG. 1. Effect of frequency on depth of current penetration in the hardening of a 1041 steel by induction heating, showing the results with 450, 10, 3 and 1 kilocycle frequency.

Most of the heating power (about 87 per cent) is developed within the depth δ below the surface. Fig. 1 shows how high-frequency operation restricts the heating to the surface of the work, in accord with the information of Table 1. Thus, high frequencies are ideal for surface hardening, and low, less costly frequencies are ideal for through heating.

For a work piece of given composition and size, there is an optimum frequency at which through heating should be accomplished. At frequencies higher than this optimum figure the power input to the work drops slowly. For lower frequencies the power drop-off is rapid. For this reason, the chosen frequency preferably should be higher rather than lower than the optimum figure.

As a rough approximation, the desired frequency for through heating a piece should be such that

$$\text{Diameter or Thickness} = 3.0\ \delta$$

Coil efficiency may vary from 35 per cent to 60 per cent for long helical coils. For heating magnetic steels below the Curie temperature, about 1400°F, (the steel at this temperature changing from magnetic to nonmagnetic) the coil efficiency will be closer to 80 per cent. For short coils, or pancake or hairpin coils where the material lies beside rather than being enclosed by the coil, the efficiency may be as much as 50 per cent less. Obviously the design of the coil is a most important factor in determining the economics of this heating process.

Frequencies employed in induction heating are 60 cycle (line frequency); 180 cycle (static frequency tripler); 960, 3000, and 9600 cycles (motor-generator set); 20,000 to 100,000 cycles (spark gap oscillator); and up to 450,000 cycles with vacuum tube oscillators (RF generators).

The type of induction heating that has been discussed so far is called longitudinal flux heating; for, as in the case of a coil surrounding a cylinder, the flux passes longitudinally through the coil opening and the cylinder. Another type of induction heating is called transverse flux heating and has importance in heating of thin nonmagnetic moving strips, since the process can be carried out with good efficiency with low-frequency power. For longitudinal flux heating the operation would require a very high frequency, and the efficiency would be extremely low. For transverse flux heating, a number of pole structures are set up on either side of the strip so that the flux set up by the poles passes transversely through the strip. The eddy currents set up by this flux form zoned patterns based on the size and spacing of the pole structures. These zoned patterns would cause nonuniform heating of the strip if the strip were stationary. Application of this type of heating requires constant movement of the strip to insure that each incremental length of the strip is uniformly heated.

References

1. CURTIS, F. W., "High-Frequency Induction Heating," New York, McGraw-Hill Book Company, 1950.
2. STANSEL, N. R., "Induction Heating," New York, McGraw-Hill Book Company, 1949.
3. BROWN, G. H., HOYLER, C. N., AND BIERWIRTH, R. A., "Theory and Application of Radio-Frequency Heating," New York, D. Van Nostrand Company, 1947.
4. SIMPSON, P. G., "Induction Heating," New York, McGraw-Hill Book Company, 1960.

E. J. BORREBACH

Cross-reference: *Zone Refining.*

INHIBITION OF CORROSION. See CORROSION INHIBITION; CORROSION INHIBITION BY PERTECHNETATE ION; CORROSION INHIBITORS.

INSTRUMENTS. See CONDUCTIVITY (ELECTROLYTIC) MEASUREMENT; CONTROLLERS, AUTOMATIC; CORROSION DETECTION DEVICES; ELECTRICAL UNITS AND STANDARDS; GALVANOMETERS; GLASS ELECTRODE; MICROELECTRODES; MICROVOLTMETERS AND MICRO-MICROAMMETERS; pH METER; POTENTIOMETERS; POTENTIOSTATS; RADIATION PYROMETRY; RECORDING INSTRUMENTS; REFERENCE ELECTRODES; RESISTANCE THERMOMETERS; SCINTILLATION COUNTERS; SOLION; THERMOELECTRIC THERMOMETRY; WHEATSTONE BRIDGE.

INSULATION, CERAMIC. See CERAMIC INSULATION.

INSULATION, GASEOUS. See DIELECTRICS, GASEOUS.

INSULATION, LIQUID. See DIELECTRICS, LIQUID.

INSULATION MATERIALS. See DIELECTRIC MATERIALS; DIELECTRICS, LIQUID; CERAMIC INSULATION; ORGANIC ELECTRICAL INSULATION.

INSULATION, ORGANIC. See ORGANIC ELECTRICAL INSULATION.

INTERGRANULAR CORROSION

Metals and alloys generally consist of agglomerations of variously oriented, individual crystals. At the boundaries between these crystals, lattices of different orientations meet and zones of less perfect structure are formed whose properties depend, in part, on the relative orientations of the adjacent grains. Two properties of these boundary zones are of particular importance in corrosion. Small amounts of impurities in solid solution in metals and alloys may segregate at grain boundaries while remaining in solid solution, equilibrium segregation.[1] In addition, precipitates, which form during heat treatments in some alloys, frequently nucleate more readily in the boundaries. Thus, as a result of structural imperfections, the chemical composition and, consequently, the electrochemical properties and the corrosion resistance of grain boundaries may be appreciably different from those of the interior of grains. It is apparent that metal surfaces are planes intersecting this three-dimensional structure and consist of a two dimensional network of grain-boundary zones which surrounds sections through variously oriented grain interiors of greater structural perfection.

Intergranular attack on these surfaces may range from light etching of grain boundaries, which merely outlines the granular structure, to rapid penetration, which may lead to loss of mechanical strength or a heap of completely separated grains. Whether corrosion is predominantly by intergranular or by general attack depends on the difference between the rate of corrosion of the grain-boundary zones and that of the grain faces. This difference in rates is determined not only by the metallurgical structure and composition of the boundary but also by the characteristics of the corroding solution.

Surprisingly, even in cases of pronounced intergranular attack, the rate of grain-face corrosion plays an important role. The grain-boundary zone along which there is rapid intergranular penetration is usually very narrow. As a result, even though grain boundaries have all been dissolved, the grains tend to remain hooked together and do not drop out of the surface of the metal. However, if there is also some appreciable grain-face corrosion, the narrow groove formed by intergranular penetration is gradually widened by corrosion of the grain faces making up the walls of the grooves and grains drop out readily. In addition, the size of the grains determines how much time is required to undermine and dislodge a grain. Small grains drop out sooner than large grains. Because of these factors—the ratio of intergranular to grain-face corrosion and grain size—the results of quantitative measurements of intergranular corrosion depend not only on the type of solution that causes intergranular attack, but also on the method used.

Measurements of changes in electrical resistance clearly show the reduction in effective cross-section of the corroding metal, even when the undermined grains remain in place. In contrast, weight-loss determinations depend entirely on undermining and dropping-out of grains. Therefore, the two methods provide identical results only on metals corroding in solutions in which there is sufficient grain-face corrosion to lead to ready removal of undermined grains. Specific examples of various types of intergranular corrosion and of different techniques of measurement are described below.

The effect of grain-boundary imperfections on intergranular attack is illustrated by the attack of hydrochloric acid on high purity (99.998 per cent) aluminum, Fig. 1. Corrosion varies with the curvature of the boundary. There may also be some intensification of corrosion by equilibrium segregation of traces of iron and/or copper impurity in zones in the boundary of highest concentration of imperfections. Corrosion of aluminum in hydrochloric acid is increased by a factor of 1000 in the presence of 0.03 per cent iron.[2]

Intergranular corrosion associated with precipitates is clearly observed on 18Cr-8Ni stainless steels. Upon heating in the range of 1000 to 1700°F. (sensitization), a precipitate of chro-

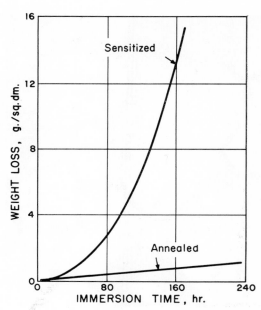

FIG. 2. Corrosion of stainless steel in ferric sulfate-sulfuric acid solution. Effect of carbide precipitation in 18 Cr-8 Ni steel on corrosion in boiling 50 per cent sulfuric acid containing ferric sulfate inhibitor. Sensitized: chromium carbide precipitate at grain boundaries. Annealed: no intergranular precipitate, all carbides dissolved in solid solution.

mium carbide forms preferentially at grain boundaries in steels containing 0.02, or more, per cent carbon. Its presence can be readily detected by metallographic examination. Because of the industrial importance of these steels, their susceptibility to intergranular corrosion has been investigated extensively, and several rapid methods for detecting susceptibility to intergranular attack have been developed.[3, 4, 5]

A solution of boiling 50 per cent sulfuric acid containing ferric sulfate as a passivating inhibitor is used for one of these evaluation tests. Typical weight-loss data obtained on two specimens of the same 18Cr-8Ni steel are plotted in Fig. 2. One of these specimens is free of chromium carbides and has a low, constant rate of corrosion. In contrast, the corrosion rate of the other specimen, which was previously heated to produce profuse precipitation of chromium carbides at grain boundaries, increases rapidly because of intensive dropping of grains. An early phase of this intergranular attack is shown in Fig. 3.

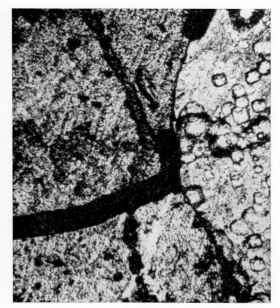

FIG. 1. Intergranular attack on pure aluminum (250X). Attack of 20 per cent solution of hydrochloric acid at room temperature on 99.998 per cent aluminum specimen.

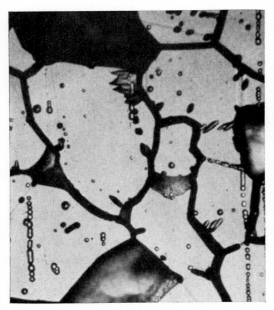

FIG. 3. Intergranular attack on stainless steel (500X). Initial stages of corrosion in boiling 50 per cent sulfuric acid containing ferric sulfate. Steel was sensitized and shows some grain face corrosion and rapid intergranular attack which has undermined and dislodged several grains.

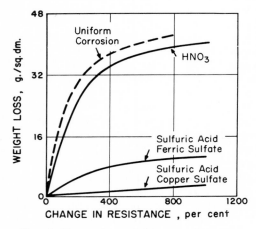

FIG. 4. Comparison of intergranular corrosion in various acid solutions. Measurement of weight-loss and change in electrical resistance on sensitized stainless steel corroding in boiling 65 per cent nitric acid, and boiling sulfuric acid solutions containing cupric or ferric sulfate. Specimen: 0.15x0.60cm in cross-section.

Differences in the type of intergranular corrosion produced on identical, sensitized specimens of 18Cr-8Ni steel in various acid solutions are shown in Fig. 4. Measurements of

weight loss and of the corresponding change in electrical resistance are plotted for intergranular corrosion in three boiling solutions: (1) sulfuric acid containing ferric sulfate inhibitor, (2) sulfuric acid containing copper sulfate inhibitor, and (3) nitric acid. The dotted line shows the relationship of weight loss and change of resistance on a specimen corroding uniformly (no intergranular attack). For a given change in resistance (i.e., penetration of intergranular attack) the weight loss is lowest in the copper sulfate-sulfuric acid solution and highest in the nitric acid solution. As expected, in all cases the weight loss is lower than on a uniformly corroding metal because some of the grains adhere even though they have been undermined. The reason for these differences is that the ratio of intergranular penetration to grain-face corrosion is different for each solution. It is highest for the copper sulfate-sulfuric acid solution because of the very low rate of grain-face corrosion and lowest in nitric acid because of the high rate of grain-face corrosion.

Electrochemical measurements[5] show that in nitric acid and in sulfuric acid solutions inhibited with cupric or ferric salts the grain faces and the grain boundaries containing chromium carbide precipitate are both passive. This passive state is a dynamic condition in which there is continual dissolution (breakdown) and re-formation (repair) of a protective, passive film by a reaction between the dissolving metal and the corroding solution. The weight of stainless steel dissolved in sulfuric acid-ferric sulfate solutions is electrochemically equivalent to the weight of ferric ions reduced. There is no evolution of hydrogen gas, even on rapidly corroding grain boundaries. However, at these boundaries the corrosion current (metal dissolution) required to keep the film in repair, and, thereby, to polarize the boundaries to the same passive potential as the grain faces, is much greater (Fig. 5). The reason for this is that precipitation of chromium carbides ($Cr_{23}C_6$) at grain boundaries greatly depletes the metal adjacent to this precipitate, and thereby increases the rate of dissolution of the film at depleted regions.

Variations in the composition of grain boundaries of 18Cr-8Ni stainless steels containing 2 to 3 per cent molybdenum may also be caused by precipitation of sigma phase, a chromium- and molybdenum-rich constituent. This precipitate forms during heating in the range of 1000 to 1600°F. and may not be visible in the

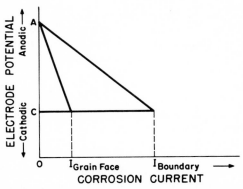

FIG. 5. Local cell polarization on grain faces and boundaries of corroding stainless steel. In ferric sulfate-sulfuric acid solutions grain faces and grain boundaries are both polarized to the oxidation-reduction potential of the solution. The corrosion current at corroding boundaries is greater than that on grain faces.

microstructure.[6] Nevertheless, such steels are rapidly attacked at grain boundaries by nitric acid, even in the absence of any chromium carbides. Since no other solutions are known which corrode these steels intergranularly and sigma phase is not visible in the microstructure, exposure to nitric acid solution is a simple, and perhaps the only, method whereby this change in metallurgical structure may be detected.

References

1. McLean, D., "Grain Boundaries in Metals," Oxford, The Clarendon Press, 1957.
2. Roald, B., and Streicher, M. A., J. Electrochem. Soc., **97**, 283 (1950).
3. Huey, W. R., Trans. Am. Soc. Steel Treating, **18**, 1126 (1930).
4. Monypenny, J. H. G., "Stainless Iron and Steel," Vol. I, p. 99, London, Chapman & Hall, Ltd., 1951.
5. Streicher, M. A., J. Electrochem. Soc., **106**, 161 (1959).
6. Binder, W. O., and Brown, C. M., ASTM STP No. 93, "Symposium on Evaluation Tests for Stainless Steels," 146 (1949).

Michael A. Streicher

ION ASSOCIATION

The subject of ion association verges on being one of definition. From the experimental point of view, ions must be regarded as associated when a solution containing them does not behave in the way that a solution of normal type is ex-

pected to behave. Thus, if the conductance of a salt solution is lower than expected for similar solutions containing ions of the same charge type, and otherwise under similar conditions, then the ions are regarded as associated. From a theoretical point of view, such anomalies must be accounted for in terms of a model of fairly general applicability. If the theory is successful, then one presumes to understand what is responsible for the anomalous behavior.

To the extent that the ions of wholly ionized electrolytes interact with each other, they might be regarded as associated, but since this interaction is expected and can be accounted for in terms of the successful Onsager theory of conductance, for example, they are not exceptional, and thus, as defined above, not associated. Unfortunately, however, the guidance offered by theory is limited to dilute solutions and to simpler valence types because of mathematical complexities. Fig. 1, adapted from Harned and Owen,[1] illustrates how the measured conductances of solutions of various electrolytes behave with respect to the theoretical calculations over a range of concentration and valence type. Zinc sulfate deviates markedly, the conductance being always too low; thus, this salt may be regarded as associated. To a lesser degree, the conductance of potassium nitrate falls below the theoretical prediction. The positive deviations of barium and lanthanum chlorides at the higher concentrations are the expected deviations

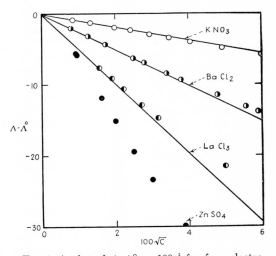

FIG. 1. A plot of $\Lambda-\Lambda°$ vs $100c^{\frac{1}{2}}$ for four electrolytes. The solid lines are theoretical computations made with Eq. (1); the points are experimental data. (Adapted from Ref. 1.)

resulting from simplifications in the theory. No experimental example has yet been found of a 2-2 electrolyte which approaches the theoretical straight line from above. The theoretical curves are plots of the equation

$$\Lambda = \Lambda^\circ - (\alpha^*\Lambda^\circ + \beta^*)\, c^{1/2} \qquad (1)$$

where α^* and β^* are factors accounting for the ionic field (interionic attractions) and electrophoresis (ion movement through a moving medium) effects; Λ and Λ° are the conductances at finite and infinite dilution; and c is the concentration.

A variety of approaches has been used to interpret these deviations. One interprets the conductance deficiency, e.g., for zinc sulfate, as due to incomplete ionization and introduces an ionization constant for an equilibrium between ions and unionized components. A second assumes complete ionization and attempts to account for all departures in terms of more elaborate theoretical treatments which include higher terms of mathematical expansions; attempts more precise arithmetic approximations; or assumes mean distances of closest approach between the ions in the physical model. A third adds purely empirical terms to the conductance equation to force agreement between experiment and a mathematical expression with incomplete and imperfect theoretical significance. Several of these approaches are critically reviewed in Ref. 1.[2] This article will refer briefly to examples of the first two approaches.

It should not be assumed that conductance is the only experimentally measurable phenomenon affected by ion association, nor that the experimental variables which give rise to association are limited to concentration and valence type. Electrical conductance is a particularly sensitive measure of the number and kind of ions present, but other phenomena dependent on these factors in whole or in part will also be affected, as for example, freezing point depressions and sound absorption. As will be seen below from the equations employed, temperature; ion size; solvent character, i.e., viscosity and dielectric constant; and a variety of kinds of specific interactions are also significant.

As noted in connection with Fig. 1, deviations of the conductance results above the theoretical curve are to be expected, while those below can be attributed to incomplete dissociation. An expression stating the relation of the equilibrium

constant, K, for dissociation of a binary electrolyte to the activity coefficient, $y_\pm$, the degree of dissociation, α, and the concentration, c, may be written

$$K = \frac{(y_\pm \alpha)^2 c}{(1 - \alpha)} \qquad (2)$$

Making an approximation which is correct at extreme dilutions, one may write

$$1 - \alpha \simeq c/K \qquad (3)$$

Since the decrease in conductance due to ionic association is $\Lambda(1 - \alpha)$ or $\Lambda^\circ(1 - \alpha)$ at infinite dilution, one may write

$$\Lambda = \Lambda^\circ - (\alpha^*\Lambda^\circ + \beta^*)\, c^{1/2} - c\Lambda^\circ/K \qquad (4)$$

This equation is subject to serious limitations. It applies only in the range of concentration in which Eq. (1) from which it is derived correctly represents the conductance of completely dissociated electrolytes, while reference to Fig. 1 will show that real electrolytes deviate above the theory while associated ones deviate below. Onsager (Ref. 1, p. 204) suggests one way out of this dilemma: assume that the curve for potassium chloride represents a normal deviation from theory; then the difference $(\Lambda_{\text{observed}} - \Lambda_{\text{theory}})_{\text{KNO}_3}$ subtracted from the corresponding difference for potassium chloride, at identical concentrations would be the "conductance deficiency," Δ, due to ionic association in the nitrate salt. Then

$$\frac{\Delta}{\Lambda_{\text{observed}}} = 1 - \alpha \qquad (5)$$

To evaluate K from Eq. (2), the activity coefficient is required, but this may be had conveniently from freezing point depression studies, which yield the quantity desired, $(y_\pm \alpha)$.

If such a procedure is applied to the data for potassium nitrate, an average dissociation constant of 1.59 is obtained. The entire procedure, however, hinges on a choice of behavior for a hypothetical completely unassociated electrolyte, here potassium chloride. Since, for higher valence types there is seldom, if at all, available such a real reference electrolyte, the physical interpretation of values of K thus obtained is in doubt. For those cases where a reasonable interpretation can be made, Davies[3] has tabulated the dissociation constants of a variety of complex valence-type salts.

The situation is much improved if a way can

be found to avoid determining K at finite concentrations. Extrapolation functions of Fuoss and of Shedlovsky permitting both K and Λ° to be evaluated simultaneously at infinite dilution are discussed in Ref. (1).[4] Both require a knowledge of activity coefficients, which for the very same kinds of complex valence-type electrolytes for which K's are sought are neither so numerous nor so accurate as for simpler salts.

It is to resolve this situation that more elaborate theoretical approaches than thus far outlined become necessary.

Two recent approaches should be mentioned. That of Guggenheim[5] undertakes an accurate numerical solution of the Poisson-Boltzmann equation which underlies the Debye-Hückel theory. The latter authors made mathematical approximations to integrate the differential equations; these approximations Guggenheim seeks to avoid through the use of electronic computation techniques. He offers also a critical summary of other mathematical extensions of the Debye-Hückel theory and of the validity of the combination of the Poisson and Boltzmann equations. The immediate result of his work is a statement of the ion distributions, and hence of the forces between the ions. These may be incorporated into other theoretical approaches along the lines suggested previously.

Recently, Fuoss and Onsager[6] have presented new expressions for the conductance of symmetrical electrolytes based on more refined mathematical approaches, one particular result of which is to bring into the theory as a natural consequence of the mathematical development what was formerly an *ad hoc* hypothesis of ion pairing controlled by a mass action equilibrium.

In some cases, however, it is still convenient to make just such an arbitrary hypothesis. In Bjerrum's approach[7] instead of attempting (as do Guggenheim, Fuoss, and Onsager) to deal with all the aspects of the forces between ions and the distribution of ions which results, the probability that an ion, i, is a distance, r, from another ion, j, is approximated. If the ions are of opposite signs, the probability has a minimum at a distance, q, such that

$$r(min) = q = \frac{\epsilon^2 z_1 z_2}{2DkT} \tag{6}$$

where ϵ is the electronic charge, the z's are the valences, D is the bulk solvent dielectric constant, k is the Boltzmann constant, and T is the

absolute temperature, from which it can be seen that q is the distance at which the energy of separation of the ions is $2kT$. For 1-1 electrolytes at 18°, $q = 3.52$ Å so that ions of this valence type in a solution where the mean distance of approach is less than 3.5 Å will form ion pairs (Eq. 7), according to this theory. The theory is not adequate for weak electrolytes, as CA in Eq. (7), but is essentially valid in media of low dielectric constant and for ions having a sufficiently large mean distance of closest approach.

In the equation

$$C^+ + A^- \rightleftharpoons [C^+A^-]^\circ \rightleftharpoons CA \tag{7}$$

the reaction of the ions C^+ and A^- to form $[C^+A^-]^\circ$ represents just such an ion pair formation, the pair being held together by coulombic forces only. In contrast, CA is a molecule joined by electronic interactions, to which Bjerrum's approach is not applicable.

Further reactions which will also remove ions from solution are possible, as

$$[C^+A^-]^\circ + A^- \rightleftharpoons [A^-C^+A^-]^- \tag{8}$$

$$[C^+A^-]^\circ + C^+ \rightleftharpoons [C^+A^-C^+]^+ \tag{9}$$

and others leading to more complex aggregates such as

$$\begin{bmatrix} C^+A^- \\ A^-C^+ \end{bmatrix}^\circ$$

Fuoss and Kraus[8] have developed theories for ion association into such triple ions and quadrupoles.

References

1. HARNED, H. S., AND OWEN, B. B., "The Physical Chemistry of Electrolytic Solutions," 3rd ed., New York, Reinhold Publishing Corp., 1958.
2. *Ibid.*, pp. 203–217.
3. DAVIES, C. W., *ibid.*, pp. 205–206.
4. *Ibid.*, pp. 206–207, Chapters 7, 11, 13.
5. GUGGENHEIM, E. W., *Trans. Faraday Soc.*, **55**, 1714 (1959); **56**, 1152, 1159 (1960); **58**, 86 (1962).
6. FUOSS, R. M., AND ONSAGER, L., *J. Chem. Phys.*, **66**, 1722 (1962); **67**, 621 (1963); **67**, 628 (1963).
7. HARNED, H. S., AND OWEN, B. B., *op. cit.*, pp. 70–74.
8. *Ibid.*, pp. 74–76.

ANDREW PATTERSON, JR.

Cross-references: *Activity and Activity Coefficient; Dissociation; Stability Constants of Metal Complexes; Wien Effect.*

ION EXCHANGE MEMBRANES

Late in the nineteenth century biochemists became aware that the only explanation for many biological phenomena was the existence of natural membranes around cells which permitted the passage through them of cations but not anions, or vice versa. To investigate these phenomena further, many of the workers utilized actual membranes from cells, such as the giant axon (portion of a nerve cell) of the squid, or other natural membranous structures such as fruit skins. As these materials were seldom readily obtainable and not very easy to work with, some biochemists began making "models" of such substances by introducing ion exchange groups into cellulose films, for example. These films had the same "permselective" properties (permitting passage of one species of ion while excluding the other) as exhibited by natural membranes.

Preparation of Ion Exchange Membranes

Much later it became apparent that such membranes could have more than academic utility provided they were sufficiently strong and durable and contained a high concentration of functional groups. Two important types have been developed. One type (heterogeneous) is made by intimately dispersing finely ground ion exchange resins throughout a thermoplastic ma-

trix. In the case of a cation-permeable membrane the resin is a sulfonated styrene-DVB type, and in the case of an anion-permeable membrane it is of the quaternary type. The matrix may be of polyethylene, polyvinyl chloride, polyvinylidene chloride, natural or synthetic rubbers. The other type (homogeneous) is made by condensation processes using sulfonated phenol and formaldehyde or nitrogen-containing compounds and formaldehyde. The condensates are laid out in thin sheets, with or without supports such as paper or plastic screen, before final gelation to an insoluble form. Other homogeneous membranes have been prepared by the graft polymerization of polyethylene and styrene following the soaking of a film of polyethylene in styrene monomer. The film is then converted to a cation exchange membrane by sulfonation and to an anion exchange membrane by chloromethylation and subsequent amination.

Both types of membrane are primarily used in electrochemical processes rather than in conventional ion exchange applications. They improve the efficiency of electrochemical processes by permitting the ready migration of either cations or anions, but not both, between the electrodes, and by preventing diffusion of the products formed at each electrode toward the other electrode.

Properties of Ion Exchange Membranes

From a chemical and physical chemical viewpoint, these materials are quite similar to conventional ion exchange resins (q.v.). They have the ability to exchange ions in the way that ordinary ion exchange resin granules and beads do, but their chief applications are in the field of electrochemistry. They may be prepared as homogeneous or heterogeneous sheets as large as 20 by 50 in. and in thicknesses from 5 to 40 mils.

Physical and Chemical Properties. The physical properties of two typical ion exchange membranes, an anion and a cation membrane, are given in Table 1.

It is evident from these data that membranes of excellent physical properties can be prepared. When dry, most films are less flexible, but they may be repeatedly desiccated and hydrated without damage to physical or chemical properties. Films of this type should be hydrated by soaking several hours before they are rigidly

TABLE 1. PHYSICAL AND CHEMICAL PROPERTIES OF TWO TYPICAL HYDRATED ION EXCHANGE MEMBRANES

Property	Cation Exchange Membrane	Anion Exchange Membrane
Tensile strength	370 lb/sq in.	370 lb/sq in.
Bursting strength[a]	25.2 lb/sq in.	13.3 lb/sq in.
% Elongation	29	16
% Swelling from dry to hydrated state	56	42
% H_2O, hydrated state	34	28
Total exchange capacity, meq/dry gram	3.0	1.5
Fixed ion concentration, eq/liter imbibed water	5.7	3.9

[a] Measured on Mullen Burst Strength Tester; appartus similar to that described in ASTM D774.

clamped into position. However, in salt, acid, and alkali solutions of ordinary concentration, these membranes shrink only slightly and will not crack when changing solutions. Membranes of this type are highly resistant to passage of water under a hydrostatic head, a square foot of the membrane, 25 mils thick, permitting leakage of 10 to 25 milliliters per hour under 1 atmosphere pressure.

The chemical stability of several commercial membranes is excellent. The films are resistant to strong acid and alkali solutions and solutions containing free halogens. They are unaffected by many common solvents and can be used at temperatures up to about 95°C.

Electrochemical Properties. The permselectivity of these ion exchange membranes may be determined by a measurement of the concentration potentials when they are employed in cells of the following type:

| Hg, Hg₂Cl₂ | KCl (saturated in agar) | KCl(C₂) | Membrane | KCl(C₁) | KCl (saturated in agar) Hg₂Cl₂ , Hg |

Saturated calomel electrodes, whose equivalence is first checked, are used as reference electrodes and the measurements made at $25 \pm 0.5°C$, using a potentiometer. Membrane conductivity is measured in a conventional manner on membranes equilibrated with solutions of varying ionic strength. Both the permselectivities and conductances of typical membranes are summarized in Table 2.

Applications

The commercial availability of permselective membranes possessing good electrochemical properties, physical properties, and chemical stability has suggested their use in many potential industrial processes.

From the study of a number of these applications, it has become evident that the ion exchange membranes are particularly suited to many electrochemical processes in which the object is to produce pure chemicals. For example, instead of adjusting the pH of solutions by the addition of acids or bases, it is a simple matter to cause the proper ions (either cations or anions) to migrate through a membrane when a voltage is applied. The electrical power involved is frequently less than the cost of chemical agents which would otherwise be required. At the same time, the solution being treated does not suffer from the introduction of a salt, which often complicates subsequent operations such as crystallization and distillation. In addition, in most cases a useful by-product, such as an acid or base, is recovered in the other electrode compartment, and it may even be worthwhile to collect the gases—hydrogen, oxygen, and chlorine—which are liberated at the electrodes.

Two-Compartment Cells. The first type is called a two-compartment cell and is simply an anode and cathode compartment separated by either an anion-permeable or cation-permeable membrane. If, for example, a pure acid is to be prepared from a corresponding sodium salt, a cation membrane would be employed and the solution of the salt fed into the anode chamber.

A specific example of the use of the cation exchange membrane is the preparation of sebacic acid from its sodium salt. Current practice involves the addition of sulfuric acid to a water solution of sodium sebacate so as to form sodium sulfate and free sebacic acid, the latter of which precipitates. The organic acid is filtered, washed, and dried. The electrochemical process is carried out in a two-chamber cell in which the electrode chambers are separated by a cation exchange membrane. The anolyte is the solution of sodium sebacate, and the catholyte is a dilute sodium hydroxide solution. Under an

TABLE 2. ELECTROCHEMICAL PROPERTIES OF TYPICAL ION EXCHANGE MEMBRANES

	Cation Exchange Membrane	Anion Exchange Membbrane
Thickness (in.)	0.020–0.030	0.020–0.030
Specific conductance (ohm⁻¹ cm.⁻¹ × 10³)		
in distilled water	0.46	0.46
" 0.01 N NaCl solution	0.545	0.511
" 0.1 N NaCl solution	1.06	0.844
" 1.0 N NaCl solution	3.32	1.90
Resistance of unit area (ohm/sq ft) in 0.1 N NaCl soln.	0.051–0.076	0.064–0.095
Permselectivity		
in 0.03 N NaCl solution	0.97	0.99
" 0.1 N NaCl solution	0.95	0.96
" 1.0 N NaCl solution	0.78	0.76

impressed potential, sodium ions migrate readily through the cation-permeable membrane out of the anode chamber into the cathode chamber, and at the anode hydrogen ions are produced and oxygen is liberated. As the acidity of the anolyte increases, sebacic acid settles out as a soft, white precipitate. The concentration of caustic in the cathode compartment meanwhile increases. Migration of hydroxyl ions toward the anode is substantially impeded by the perm-selective cation exchange membrane.

There are, thus, three advantages in the electrolytic process as compared with the conventional method: no additional chemical agent (sulfuric acid) is required; the desired product is not contaminated by added salts; and sodium hydroxide is recovered for re-use in the treatment of castor oil to produce sodium sebacate.

On the other hand, the preparing of a free amine from its hydrochloride could be accomplished with an anion-permeable membrane with the chloride ion being passed through the membrane.

A specific example of the use of the anion exchange membrane is the liberation of ethylenediamine from its hydrochloride. Normally, sodium chloride so introduced creates a considerable operational problem in the subsequent recovery of the free amine by distillation. The electrolytic process can be carried out in a two-chamber cell, the separating membrane in this case being an anion exchange membrane. The catholyte is the ethylenediamine hydrochloride solution, and the anolyte is dilute hydrochloric acid. Chloride ions migrate from the cathode chamber through the anion-permeable membrane into the anode chamber. Hydroxyl ions are formed and hydrogen is liberated at the cathode; the free amine is left in the cathode chamber. Migration of hydrogen ions from the anode chamber into the catholyte is prevented by the permselective nature of the anion exchange membrane. Chlorine is liberated at the anode, if the hydrochloric acid solution is sufficiently concentrated, and can be collected.

Here again the saving in additional chemical reagents, the liberation of the amine in a solution uncontaminated by salt, and the recovery of a useful by-product are advantages of the electrolytic process.

Many similar applications involving the use of a single ion exchange membrane separating two electrode chambers have been examined. Space permits mentioning only a few, such as the recovery of sodium hydroxide and sulfuric acid from waste sodium sulfate, production of caustic by the electrolysis of brine, precipitation of magnesium hydroxide from sea water, and the reclamation of waste sulfuric acid iron pickle liquor.

Three-Compartment Cells. A solution can be depleted of its salinity by electrolysis in a three-compartment cell employing both a cation- and an anion-permeable membrane of the following type:

Cathode	Cation-permeable membrane	Salt solution	Anion-permeable membrane	Anode

By passing an electrolyte between the membranes of such a cell, the electrolyte will be removed by the passage of cations into the cathode chamber to form alkali and of anions into the anode chamber to form acids.

Three-chamber cells, using two membranes, have been used to advantage in several cases. For example, sodium hydroxide and sulfuric acid have been produced from sodium sulfate in a cell made up according to the scheme:

Cathode: dilute NaOH: cation exchange membrane: sodium sulfate solution: anion exchange membrane: dilute H_2SO_4: anode.

A three-compartment cell consisting of either two anion or two cation membranes is sometimes used in cases when it becomes necessary to either protect an electrode from a particular electrolyte or an electrolyte from an electrode reaction. For example, during the electrolysis of sodium acetate in a single-compartment cell to form sodium hydroxide and acetic acid, the acetic acid formed in the anode compartment may be oxidized, thereby lowering the yield. This can be avoided by employing another cation membrane placed between the sodium acetate and the anode. The anode chamber is filled with dilute sulfuric acid and fed with water. During the electrolysis, sodium ions migrate from the center chamber containing sodium acetate and enter the cathode chamber to form alkali. Simultaneously, hydrogen ions migrate from the cathode chamber into the center chamber to form acetic acid. By operating in this manner, salts of organic acids may be electrolyzed without any danger of oxidizing the organic acid formed. The sulfuric acid initially charged to the cathode chamber is not consumed, since only H_2 and O_2 leave the chamber. The loss in volume is due only to a water loss which is compensated for by feeding water to this chamber.

This three-compartment cell employing two cation membranes is useful for many other applications. For example, in the electrolysis of electrolyte solutions containing some chlorides, lead anodes are not practical since the liberated chlorine destroys the electrode quite rapidly. However, by placing a cation membrane between the anode and the chloride-bearing solution and dilute sulfuric acid in the anode chamber, the electrode may be protected. The same three-compartment cell is most useful for the conversion of salts that are normally difficult to prepare. For example, the preparation of copper acrylate from sodium acrylate may be readily conducted in the following cell:

where the odd-numbered membranes are anion permeable and the even-numbered and the nth membranes are of the cation-permeable type. With electrolysis, electrolyte will be depleted in chambers a and c and will be enriched in b and d, etc. By this means, it is then possible to deionize solutions at high ampere efficiencies and at low kilowatt-hour consumption. The use of these multicompartments has been widely considered for the treatment of brackish water, and they are now employed for the treatment of such waters on a municipal scale.

Miscellaneous Membrane Applications

There are many other possible applications for the permselective membranes in the realm of electrochemistry. These include such applications as the production of silicic sols, precipitation of $Mg(OH)_2$ from sea water, oxidation or reduction of organic compounds, precipitation of uranium, recovery of viscose, sulfuric acid and zinc, treatment of nuclear feed wastes, de-

Anode, $CuSO_4$ (+) (1)	Cation membrane	Na acrylate (2)	Cation membrane	NaOH, cathode (−) (3)

With electrolysis, as sodium ions migrate from chamber (2) into chamber (3), copper ions migrate from chamber (1) into chamber (2), converting the sodium acrylate into copper acrylate.

Multicompartment Cells. Membrane cells employing a multiplicity of membranes between the electrodes have been found useful for several applications. In particular, an arrangement of alternating anion-permeable and cation-permeable membranes between an anode and cathode has been most useful for deionizing electrolyte solutions but with a minimum expenditure of current. A cell of this type has been called the multiple ion exchange membrane electrodialysis (MIEME) cell and is basically of the following type:

ashing of sugar sirups, production of alkali and chlorine, etc.

References

1. KUNIN, R., "Ion Exchange Resins," New York, John Wiley & Sons, Inc., 1958.
2. HELFFERICH, F., "Ion Exchange," New York, McGraw Hill Book Co., Inc., 1962.
3. SPIEGLER, K. S., "Salt Water Purification," New York, John Wiley & Sons, Inc., 1962.
4. WILSON, J. R., "Demineralization by Electrodialysis," London, Butterworths Scientific Publications, 1960.

ROBERT KUNIN

Cross-references: *Electrodialysis*; entries bearing *Membrane* titles; *Electrophysiology*.

Anode	Solution 1	Solution 2	Solution 3	Solution 4	···	···	···	Cathode
	a	b	c	d	e	f	n	

ION EXCHANGE RESINS

The widespread interest during the past decade in ion exchange and its general utility is a direct result of the development and commercial availability of stable and high-capacity ion exchange resins. The first ion exchange resins were developed in England by Adams and Holmes in 1935 as a result of experimentations, during their lunch period, with ground phonograph records at the Central Research Laboratory. The work of Adams and Holmes was soon followed by studies in both the United States and Germany, and rapid commercial development of these new resins was soon realized. The resins of this period were primarily phenolic types. The typical cation exchange resins were reaction products of phenol, formaldehyde, and sodium sulfite, and the typical anion resins were derived from a phenol, formaldehyde, and some polyamine. Although these resins were found to be of considerable interest and utility, they failed to live up to expectations because of low capacity and chemical and physical instability.

Newer Ion Exchange Materials

Shortly after World War II, a considerable effort along synthetic lines led to commercial availability of higher capacity, more versatile, and more durable ion exchange resins (see Table 1). The outstanding developments have been the synthesis of a sulfonated styrene-divinylbenzene copolymer (Formula 1), quaternary and weak base resins based upon the amination of the chloromethylated styrene-divinylbenzene copolymer (Formulas 2 and 3), and acrylate carboxylic divinylbenzene copolymers (Formula 4). These synthetic achievements led to the establishment of ion exchange resins in the water conditioning field (water softening and deionization) and in the chemical process industries.

Considerable effort has also been devoted to the synthesis of resins showing high specificity for particular ionic species and also of resins of special physical form and shape. Although these studies are in the early stages of development, interest remains high.

Some successful laboratory attempts have been made in Great Britain and the United States on the synthesis of resins having some similarity to the well-known complexing agent, ethylenediaminetetracetic acid. The British have made these resins by allowing the chloromethylated and subsequently aminated cross-linked polystyrene copolymer to react with chloroacetic acid, and by allowing the chloromethylated cross-linked polystyrene copolymer to react with iminodiacetonitrile, followed by hydrolysis.

TABLE 1. TYPICAL COMMERCIAL ION EXCHANGE RESINS

Resin Type	Functional Group	Exchange Cap.		Moisture Content, %	Trade Names	Manufacturer
		meq/g dry	meq/ml			
Cation exchanger, strong acid (sulfonated cross-linked polystyrene)	$-SO_3H$	4.5	1.9–2.0	44–48	Amberlite IR-120 Dowex 50 Permutit Q Duolite C-20	Rohm & Haas Co. Dow Chemical Co. The Ionac Co. Diamond Alkali Co.
Cation exchanger, weak acid (cross-linked polymethacrylic acid)	$-COOH$	10	3.5	44–45	Amberlite IRC-50	Rohm & Haas Co.
Anion exchanger, strong base (quaternized chloromethylated cross-linked polystyrene)	$-N(CH_3)_3^+$	3.5–4.3	1.2	40–50	Amberlite IRA-400 Dowex 1 Permutit S-1	Rohm & Haas Co. Dow Chemical Co. The Ionac Co.
Anion exchanger, weak base (aminated chloromethylated cross-linked polystyrene)	Primary and secondary amines	5–6	2.0	35–40	Amberlite IR-45 Dowex-3	Rohm & Haas Co. Dow Chemical Co.

Sulfonic acids cation exchange resin
Formula 1

Strong base anion exchange resin
Formula 2

Weak base anion exchange resin
Formula 3

Carboxylic cation exchange resin
Formula 4

Resins having a beta diketone structure have a very high affinity for copper. A resin based upon n-methylglucamine having high specificity for boron has also been synthesized. As yet, no commercial utility has been found for these highly specific resins. Resins capable of entering into reversible oxidation-reduction reactions have been synthesized and studied. These polymers have been called redox or electron exchange resins.

Most attempts to synthesize highly selective resins have been along the lines of incorporating functional groups usually found in the selective organic analytical reagents. These attempts have been somewhat abortive in that resins containing these groups have lost the degree of freedom (rotation) that the selective reagents have in true solution. In other words, the ability to form the bond angles necessary for chelation has been lost.

Conventional ion exchange resins are essentially homogeneous cross-linked polyelectrolyte gels with the exchange sites of gel distributed statistically throughout the entire particle. Most ion exchange equilibrium and kinetic data are consistent with such a model. It is difficult to speak of porosity and pore size with such polyelectrolyte gels, since the distances between cross links and chains of such gels vary considerably depending on such factors as electrolyte concentration, nature of solvent, nature of mobile and immobile ions, and temperature. The pore structure of such gels can only be considered as an apparent molecular-type pore structure, and the average porosity of such structures is dependent on the distances between polymer chains and cross links under any particular set of conditions.

The flexibility offered by the styrene-divinylbenzene system for controlling the above type of porosity has been useful during the past decade for many ion exchange applications. However, several limitations have become apparent. For example, if the degree of cross-linking is decreased to accommodate larger ionic species, a considerable volume change is encountered during the exchange process and during changes in ionic strength, resulting in poor physical properties and in operational difficulties, particularly in chromatography. In those systems featuring low degrees of cross-linking, the rates of chemical degradation processes are accelerated. Further, the porosity associated with the conventional styrene-divinylbenzene copolymer is solely dependent on the swelling characteristics of the gel structure. Therefore, in nonaqueous, nonpolar systems, these resins have but a negligible pore structure. These deficiencies of conventional ion exchange resins in certain applications have been apparent for several years.

Recently a series of ion exchange resins has been prepared by a new polymerization technique that yields a cross-linked ion exchange structure entirely different from the conventional homogeneous gels and having a rigid macroporous structure similar to those of conventional adsorbents, such as alumina, silica, and the carbons, which is superimposed on the gel structure. In contrast to the conventional ion exchange resins, these resins have been designated as a macroreticular (MR) ion exchanger. A comparison of these macroreticular resins with the gel-type resins is given in Table 2. These resins have high surface areas and porosities and are quite useful for ion exchange and catalysis in nonpolar media.

Theory

Kinetics. Although the understanding of the equilibrium and kinetics of ion exchange has been enhanced during the past few years, an adequate theory that is of use for quantitative purposes is still lacking. However, qualitative application of the theory of ion exchange is most satisfactory. Kinetically, all ion exchange reactions are diffusion controlled. At low concentrations (below 0.001 N), the rate-controlling step is normally the rate of diffusion of ions across a thin hydrodynamic film around the ion exchange particle. At high concentrations (above 0.3 N), the rate-controlling step is usually the rate of diffusion of ions in the ion exchange particle itself. For film diffusion, the overall rate varies inversely as the radius of the particle. For particle diffusion it varies inversely as the square of the radius. Unfortunately, since most of the ion exchange reactions encountered in practice are in a concentration range 0.001 to 0.3 N, the rate of most ion exchange reactions is influenced by two rate mechanisms, film and particle diffusion. With respect to factors other than those of the solution phase, the particle size and the degree of crosslinking of the resin are the most important variables from a kinetic point of view.

Equilibrium. From an equilibrium point of view, the most important advances have been in the realm of ion selectivities. The term ion selectivity is a nonthermodynamic expression and may be defined as

$$K_D = \left(\frac{M_1}{M_2}\right)_r \left(\frac{M_2}{M_1}\right)_s$$

where the M's refer to the number of cations, M_1 and M_2 (univalent), in the ion exchange particle and solution phases and the subscripts, r and s, mean resin and solution, respectively. The selectivity coefficient, K_D, varies with the

TABLE 2. COMPARISON OF PHYSICAL PROPERTIES OF CONVENTIONAL AND MACRORETICULAR ION EXCHANGE RESINS

Resin	Form	Moisture Holding Capacity, % H₂O	Surface Area sq meters/g of dry resin	Apparent Density,[a] g/ml	True Skeletal Density,[b] g/ml	Porosity (P), ml/ml	Av. pore diam., Å
Amberlyst 15	Na+	50	42.5	1.012	1.512	0.319	288
Amberlite IR-120	Na+	46	<0.1	1.489	1.518	.018	—
Amberlite XN-1001	Cl-	60	62.9	0.559	1.136	.508	645
Amberlite IRA-400	Cl-	45	<0.1	1.136	1.140	.004	—

[a] Mercury displacement.
[b] Helium displacement.

degree of resin crosslinking, degree of resin saturation, concentration, etc. The simplified thermodynamic expression for the ion exchange equilibrium is $RT \ln [K_D (\gamma_1/\gamma_2)]r = \pi (v_2 - v_1)r$, where the γ_1/γ_2 is ratio of the cation activity coefficients in the resin phase, v_1 and v_2 are the hydrated molar volumes of the cations in the resin, and π is the osmotic pressure. The difficulty with this expression is the difficulty, at present, in evaluating $(\gamma_1/\gamma_2)r$. Although Glueckauf and Soldano have had some success in this direction, further progress must await new advances in the field of the electrochemistry of concentrated solutions of simple and polyelectrolytes. Until such progress is made, one must depend to a large extent on the rules of thumb. Tables 3 and 4 summarize ion exchange selectivity data of several ion exchange resins for the common anions and cations.

Applications

In general, the major applications of ion exchange may be classified according to the following categories: (a) separations, (b) concentrations, (c) removal of ions, (d) catalysis.

Separations by means of ion exchange materials may involve two or more ionic species, a mixture of an ionic and nonionic species, or two or more nonionic species. The separation of two or more ionic species by means of ion exchange resins is now classic; the separations of amino acids and of rare earth mixtures are well-known examples. The mixture is usually adsorbed at the top of a column of an ion exchange resin, and the separation is achieved by eluting slowly with a solution of some electrolyte. Good separations can be best achieved by operation close to equilibrium conditions. If the ions differ in valence or size, the separation is quite simple; however, if the ions are of the same valence and similar in size, the separation is more difficult.

The separation of a mixture of a nonionic and an ionic species can be performed by one of two ways with an ion exchange material. By passing the mixture over a column of the proper ion exchange material, the ionic species can be adsorbed by exchange with ions present in the exchange complex, and the nonionic species can be rinsed out with water or other suitable solvent. The separation may also be achieved by means of the ion exclusion principle.

Sargent and Rieman have recently found it possible to separate a mixture of closely related

TABLE 3. SELECTIVITY SCALE OF CATION EXCHANGE RESINS
(Sulfonated Styrene-Divinylbenzene Copolymers)
(K_D relative to $Li^+ = 1$)

Cation	Per cent Divinylbenzene		
	4	8	16
Li^+	1.00	1.00	1.00
H^+	1.30	1.26	1.45
Na^+	1.49	1.88	2.23
NH_4^+	1.75	2.22	3.07
K^+	2.09	2.63	4.15
Rb^+	2.22	2.89	4.19
Cs^+	2.37	2.91	4.15
Ag^+	4.00	7.36	19.4
Tl^+	5.20	9.66	22.2

TABLE 4. ANION EXCHANGE SELECTIVITIES OF QUATERNARY AMMONIUM RESINS
(K_D relative to $Cl^- = 1$)

	RN^+ $(CH_3)_3$	RN^+ $(CH_3)_2$ C_2H_4OH
Salicylate	32.2	32.2
Perchlorate	10.0	10.0
Iodide	8.7	8.7
Phenolate	5.4	7.3
Bisulfate	4.1	6.1
Nitrate	3.8	3.3
Bromide	2.8	2.3
Cyanide	1.6	1.3
Bisulfite	1.3	1.3
Nitrite	1.2	1.3
Chloride	1.0	1.0
Bicarbonate	0.32	0.65
Dihydrogen phosphate, $H_2PO_4^-$	0.25	0.53
Formate	0.22	0.34
Acetate	0.17	0.22
Aminoacetate	0.10	0.18
Hydroxide	0.09	0.13
Fluoride	0.09	0.10

nonionic species on an ion exchange resin. Their technique involves elution chromatography, employing the principles of ion exclusion and "salting in." Normally, a mixture of nonelectrolytes will not separate when eluted from a column with water; however, these investigators have found that when an ammonium sulfate solution was used as the eluant, a complete separation is readily achieved. A series of related alcohols can readily be separated in this manner.

Concentration of an ionic species by ion exchange is another important general application of ion exchange. By virtue of their high capacity and selectivity, ion exchange resins are ideally suited for concentrating a dilute solution of an ionic species. For example, extremely dilute solutions of metals may be concentrated from 10–1000-fold by passage of the solution over a column of an ion exchange resin and subsequent elution with a concentrated eluant. This technique has been used quite extensively for the recovery of metals from dilute hydrometallurgical liquors and for the concentration of extremely dilute solutions in analyses for traces of metals. Practically all of the uranium now used in the atomic energy field has been recovered and purified by means of ion exchange resins.

Removal of ionic constituents from various solutions may be differentiated from the other general applications not by principle but by purpose. For example, water softening (removal of calcium and magnesium in exchange for sodium) and water deionization (removal of all ionic constituents) are applications of ion exchange that involve separation of ionic constituents and concentration of ionic substances. Applications of this category, however, are considered separately since they involve a difference in purpose, i.e., the removal of ions that are undesirable in a product.

Catalysis by means of ion exchange materials is a field of general application that, although intriguing in nature, has not developed too rapidly. The acid and basic forms of any ion exchange substance can catalyze most reactions that can be catalyzed by most common acids and bases. The advantage of this type of catalysis over the homogeneous type are several-fold. First, they introduce no acid or base into the reaction products that must later be removed. Second, the occurrence of side reactions is usually less than with the soluble catalysts. Third, catalyst consumption is also lessened.

The most well-known ion-exchange-catalyzed reaction is the cracking of petroleum stocks to form gasoline. This is accomplished by means of the hydrogen or acid form of the aluminosilicate cation exchangers. Inversion of sucrose, the hydration of ethylene oxide, and the epoxidation of oils are examples in which the acid form of the sulfonic acid cation exchange resin is most effective. Anion exchange resins have been found effective for aldol condensation and hydrolysis reactions; however, resin stability is a problem. Macroreticular resins have proved themselves to be most effective catalysts, particularly in nonpolar media.

Water Treatment. This is still the major application of ion exchange materials. Of recent interest has been the large-scale use of the mixed bed or Monobed technique for deionization of water. As a result of the demand on a large industrial scale for water of extremely high purity by such industries as the power utilities, synthetic fibers, television tube, condenser paper, ice manufacture, and sugar refining, the deionization of water by means of a single pass through a mixture of a cation and an anion exchange resin has achieved a prominent role in ion exchange technology. It is most interesting to note that these industries are now able to produce water of the quality of conductivity water (10^7 ohm-cm) at a rate of millions of gallons per day at a cost of but a few cents per 1000 gal.

Atomic Energy. Ion exchange as a unit operation is not only of importance to those industries allied with the atomic energy programs, but it is an important link throughout the entire chain of operations within the atomic energy programs—from the recovery and purification of the natural uranium to the analyses of the fission products contained in the radioactive fallout after a nuclear bomb detonation.

At the present time, a large fraction of the uranium mined in the United States, Canada, Republic of the Congo, South Africa, and Australia is processed into a high-grade concentrate by means of quaternary ammonium anion exchange resins. Low-grade uranium ores are first leached with sulfuric acid and the resulting solution passed over a bed of the above resin. In solutions of this type, the uranium exists primarily as an anionic sulfate complex that is strongly adsorbed by an anion exchange resin. The bulk of the impurities, iron, aluminum, magnesium, calcium, silica, etc., is not adsorbed. The uranium which is concentrated on the resin is eluted with either acidified sodium chloride or ammonium nitrate as a highly concentrated and purified solution from which a high-grade U_3O_8 product can be precipitated with ammonia or magnesium oxide.

Sugar. Ion exchange has been of interest to the sugar industry ever since the first inorganic gel zeolites were available commercially. These materials were first used to remove calcium to reduce scale formation during the evaporation of the sugar juices and sirups. With the availability of the synthetic ion exchange resins, a considerable interest developed in the use of such materials for the deionization of sugar juices to obtain higher yields of crystalline, white sugar. Although ion exchange technology has not replaced conventional sugar refining practices, it has become an important part of sugar refining, particularly in conjunction with conventional refining techniques. Porous quaternary ammonium anion exchange resins are now being used in the decolorizing operation and Monobeds of carboxylic acid cation exchange resin and the above anion exchange resin are being employed for the production of high-grade liquid sugar sirups used in the beverage, confectionery, and related industries.

Pharmaceutical Applications. In the pharmaceutical field, the use of a carboxylic cation exchange resin for the recovery and purification of the antibiotic streptomycin has been quite spectacular. In this application, the antibiotic is adsorbed from the filtered fermentation broth onto the salt form of the carboxylic cation exchange resin and is eluted, highly purified and at a high concentration, with a dilute mineral acid. This application is of extreme interest because of the high capacity and selectivity of the resin for streptomycin, the purity of the streptomycin eluted from the resin, and the fact that the resin has been used in many installations for more than 1000 cycles without any apparent loss in activity. Neomycin is also recovered and purified with a carboxylic cation exchange resin in essentially the same fashion as for streptomycin. Ion exchange resins play a most important role in the laboratory and pilot plant for many new antibiotics now under experimental study.

Biochemistry and Medicine. The work initiated by the late Edwin Cohn and being continued by his associates at Harvard on the use of ion exchange in blood collection, preservation, and fractionation is of considerable importance. This work has led to a newer and more efficient method for isolating the critically needed gamma globulin as well as a safer plasma solution. These studies involve the removal of calcium and magnesium from the blood, immediately after collection, by passing the blood through a column of the sodium form of a carboxylic or sulfonic acid cation exchange resin. This step stabilizes the blood from coagulation and avoids the addition of acid citrates formerly used for this purpose. Studies are now in progress on the use of ion exchange resins as artificial kidney devices.

Other developments in the field of medicine include the continued use of weak base anion exchange resins in the treatment of stomach disorders, and the use of cation exchange resins for the treatment of edemas and for the measurement of stomach acidity. The use of these resins as drug carriers for sustained release of various drugs has been widely accepted.

References

1. GLUECKAUF, E., *Endeavor*, **14**, 54 (1955).
2. HELFFERICH, F., "Ion Exchange," New York, McGraw Hill Book Co., Inc., 1962.
3. "Ion Exchange and Its Applications," London, Soc. Chem. Ind., 1955.
4. KITCHENER, J. A., "Ion Exchange Resins," London, Methuen & Company, 1957.
5. KUNIN, R., "Ion Exchange Resins," New York, John Wiley & Sons, Inc., 1958.
6. NACHOD, F., "Ion Exchange," New York, Academic Press, Inc., 1949.
7. NACHOD, F., AND SCHUBERT, J., "Ion Exchange Technology," New York, Academic Press, Inc., 1957.
8. OSBORN, G., "Synthetic Ion Exchangers," 2nd Ed., London, Chapman & Haas, 1961.
9. REICHENBERG, D., AND MCCAULEY, D., *J. Chem. Soc.*, **2741** (1955).
10. SAMUELSON, O., "Ion Exchangers in Analytical Chemistry," 2nd Ed., New York, John Wiley & Sons, Inc., 1962.

ROBERT KUNIN

Cross-reference: *Molecular Sieves.*

IONIC EQUILIBRIA

The principles of chemical equilibria and the mass law may be applied to a number of reactions in which ions are generated in solution in small concentrations. Examples are usually chosen for aqueous solutions, although the principles are as valid for other solvents in which small ionic populations can be maintained. Each ionic constituent is assumed to contribute its own chemical potential to the free energy of the reactants or products in these reactions, and the thermodynamic criterion of equilibrium at constant temperature and pressure leads to the familiar constant equilibrium quotient for the activities of the several constituents. The only problem is that no method exists for unambiguously determining activities for single ionic species. All experimental methods lead to an activity of the complete electrolyte and hence to a mean activity coefficient, $f_\pm$.[1] To assign a value to the activity or activity coefficient of a single ion requires some assumption, in consequence of which all values for these quantities must be treated as estimates only. (See **Activity and Activity Coefficient.**)

Two methods of estimating ionic activity coefficients are in common use. One is to assign equal weight to the contribution of anionic and cationic species to the mean activity coefficient; in the case of a 1:1 electrolyte

$$f_+ = f_- = f_\pm = (f_+ f_-)^{1/2}$$

The other method is to employ the Debye-Hückel equation or some extension of this to estimate f for a particular ion. For use at any appreciable concentration these equations contain adjustable constants which are assigned on the basis of experiments utilizing the complete electrolyte, so that once again to assign a single ionic activity coefficient requires the exercise of discretion.

Because of these limitations, rigorous application of the mass law to ionic equilibria is frequently not possible. In carefully controlled physico-chemical experiments, where allowance for activity coefficients has been made, it has been shown that the mass law does apply in cases such as the four examples given below. However, to apply equilibrium constants as determined in such studies to systems with appreciable concentrations of electrolytes requires some care in estimating the effects of ionic strength on the various activity coefficients involved.

Case 1. The Self-Ionization of Water

This process may formally be treated as a dissociation of the water molecule ($H_2O \rightleftharpoons H^+ + OH^-$), although it should better be considered as a proton transfer from one water molecule to another ($H_2O + H_2O \rightleftharpoons H_3O^+ + OH^-$). For either representation, thermodynamic reasoning leads to a constant ionic product for water

$$a_{H^+} a_{OH^-} = \text{constant} \times a_{H_2O} = K_W$$

The limiting values of K_W, i.e., those extrapolated to zero ionic strength, for selected temperatures are given below; for additional values refer to Harned and Owen.[2]

Temperature, °C	$K_W \times 10^{14}$
0	0.1139
20	0.6809
25	1.008
30	1.469
60	9.614

The dependence of K_W on temperature is greater than for other ionic equilibria and should be kept in mind when applying K_W or the pH scale at temperatures other than 25° for which the commonly remembered value of $K_W = 10^{-14}$ is valid.

In applying the principle of the constancy of the product, $a_{H^+} a_{OH^-}$, in dilute aqueous solutions it is important to remember that the value of K_W includes the activity of the water in such solutions. The latter can be defined as unity for pure water, but will depart from this value for solutions containing any appreciable concentration of solute. The effect of various electrolytes on the ionic activity coefficient product, $\gamma_H \gamma_{OH}/a_{H_2O}$, and, hence, on the ionic concentration product, $m_H m_{OH}$, is given by Harned and Owen. For instance, the concentration product at 25°C reaches a maximum ($\sim 2K_W$) in sodium or potassium halides at about 0.5 M, and falls off again at higher salt concentrations.

Case 2. The Ionization of Weak Electrolytes

The mass law has been found applicable to the ionization of weak electrolytes. Most of the weak electrolytes of interest in this connection are weak acids and bases, for which the ionizing reaction is a proton-transfer process involving the solvent.

$$HA + H_2O \rightleftharpoons H_3O^+ + A^-$$

$$B + H_2O \rightleftharpoons BH^+ + OH^-$$

In such proton-transfer reactions it is customary to speak of A^- or OH^- as the conjugate bases of HA or H_2O, respectively, or of H_3O^+ or BH^+ as conjugate acids of H_2O or B, respectively.

The conventional ionization constants for weak acids and bases do not show the activity of the solvent. Thus, for the above reactions

$$\frac{a_{H^+} a_{A^-}}{a_{HA}} = K_a \quad \text{and} \quad \frac{a_{BH^+} a_{OH^-}}{a_B} = K_b$$

A conjugate acid-base pair may be assigned two ionization constants, one referring to the dissociation of BH^+ as an acid, the other to the reaction of B with solvent to form BH^+. It can easily be shown that the product of these two ionization constants is the ionic product of the solvent (for aqueous solutions, K_W).

Although the mass law applies strictly to activities of the various constituents in solution, it is sometimes practically useful to neglect, or to compensate for, activity coefficients, and to apply the principle to concentrations. The equilibrium quotient for the concentrations in a solution of a weak acid, for instance, is

$$\frac{[H^+][A^-]}{[HA]} = K_a \frac{f_{HA}}{f_H f_A} = K_a \frac{f_{HA}}{f_\pm^2} = K_a'$$

K_a' may be called a concentration constant for the acid and is related to the thermodynamic constant by the approximate relationship

$$pK_a' \sim pK_a + 2 \log f_\pm$$

This assumes that f_{HA} may be treated as unity, an approximation that is permissible up to moderate concentrations of the acid. Since $f_\pm$ is capable of being estimated by the extended Debye-Hückel relationships, a reasonable estimate of K_a' for a particular medium is possible.

A variation of the preceding rearrangement yields what is sometimes called a Brönsted ionization constant, K_a''

$$\frac{a_{H^+}[A^-]}{[HA]} = K_a \frac{f_{HA}}{f_{A^-}} = K_a''$$

$$pK_a'' \sim pK_a + \log f_{A^-}$$

The justification for the introduction of this quantity is that conventional pH measurements yield what is believed to be a close estimate of $-\log a_{H^+}$ under favorable conditions. Hence, a_{H^+} can be estimated from a measurement of pH, and Brönsted ionization constants determined by measurements of $[A^-]$ and $[HA]$.

In inorganic and analytical chemistry many measurements of ionic equilibria are made in solutions contrived to be of constant ionic strength by the addition of some indifferent electrolyte such as sodium perchlorate. The constancy of ionic strength is believed to result in essentially constant values of $\log f_\pm$ or $\log f_{A^-}$, so that practically constant values of the equilibrium quotient are obtained. These latter are sometimes called "conditional" equilibrium constants, and the justification for their use is that they permit comparisons of related compounds, they indicate the position of equilibrium under

practical conditions, and by appropriate correction or extrapolation they may lead to true thermodynamic constants.

The relationship between pH and the ratio of concentrations of a conjugate acid-base pair is given by the Henderson equation

$$pH = pK_a'' + \log \frac{[base]}{[acid]}$$

This relationship may also be written as

$$pH = pK_a'' + \log \frac{\alpha}{1 - \alpha}$$

in which α represents the fraction of the acid converted to the conjugate base at the stated pH. The variation of α with pH can then be portrayed graphically as in Fig. 1 (a). From this it is evident that in the middle range of values, α can be varied somewhat with relatively little change in pH. For instance, in passing from $\alpha = 0.5$ to $\alpha = 0.4$ or 0.6 the corresponding change in pH is only 0.18. This is the basis of buffer action displayed by all solutions of conjugate acid-base systems; appreciable amounts of acid or alkali may be added to these without greatly altering the ratio, $[base]/[acid]$.

Polyfunctional acids and bases ionize in stages with successive ionization constants

$$H_2A + H_2O \rightleftharpoons H_3O^+ + HA^-$$

$$HA^- + H_2O \rightleftharpoons H_3O^+ + A^{2-}$$

$$\frac{a_{H^+} a_{HA^-}}{a_{H_2A}} = K_{a1} \qquad \frac{a_{H^+} a_{A^{2-}}}{a_{HA^-}} = K_{a2}$$

and so on. From electrostatic considerations it follows that the second ionization constant should be smaller than the first, and so on. For acids of the type $XO_m(OH)_n$, the successive ionization constants usually decrease by 10^4 or 10^5. The effect of one stage of ionization on the next is much less when the functional $-OH$ groups are on separated atoms as, for instance, in organic dicarboxylic acid or pyrophosphoric acid.

Equilibrium among the various constituents in solutions of dibasic or polybasic acids can be portrayed graphically by plots similar to Fig. 1 (a). Representative values are shown in Fig. 1 (b) carbonic acid, (c) tartaric acid. A vertical line at any selected pH is divided into lengths by the field of each constituent, which are proportional to the fraction of that constituent.

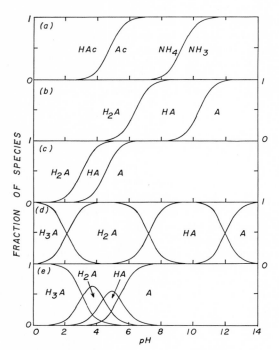

FIG. 1. Representation of the distribution of constituents derived from weak acids in aqueous solution at 25°C as a function of pH: (a) acetic acid and ammonium ion, (b) carbonic acid, (c) tartaric acid, (d) phosphoric acid, (e) citric acid.

Another kind of representation may be illustrated for the case of a tribasic acid; for any solution derived from such an acid there is a conservation or totality relationship, viz.,

$$[H_3A]_T = [H_3A] + [H_2A^-] + [HA^{2-}] + [A^{3-}]$$

By appropriate substitutions in the mass-law expressions, the respective concentrations of the constituents on the right-hand side of this equation can be shown to be in the ratios

$$a_{H^+}^3 : a_{H^+}^2 K''_{a1} : a_{H^+} K''_{a1} K''_{a2} : K''_{a1} K''_{a2} K''_{a3}$$

These proportions will vary as a_{H^+} or pH varies, and the fraction of each species may be represented as functions of pH. Typical cases are represented in Fig. 1 (d) phosphoric acid, (e) citric acid.

Case 3. Hydrolysis of Ions

What has formerly been described as hydrolysis of salts is now more appropriately regarded as hydrolysis of one or both ions in the particular salt solution. The anion of any salt of a weak acid will undergo hydrolysis according to the equation

$$A^- + H_2O \rightleftharpoons HA + OH^-$$

The ion A^- is functioning as a base, with the ionization constant for this reaction being more commonly called a hydrolysis constant. From the principle mentioned in Case 2 above, the equilibrium constant is given by the ratio, K_W/K_a, since A^- is the conjugate base of the acid HA whose ionization constant is K_a. Hydrolysis in these cases produces alkaline solutions unless some other hydrolytic process takes precedence.

The cation of a weak base similarly undergoes hydrolysis to produce an acidic solution.

$$BH^+ + H_2O \rightleftharpoons B + H_3O^+$$

The hydrolysis constant here is K_a for BH^+, or K_W/K_b where K_b is the ionization constant of the weak base.

A large number of metallic cations, indeed most of those bearing charge $+2$ and all those bearing higher charge, undergo some hydrolysis. A simple case, namely hydrolysis of the ferrous ion, produces a simple complex ion, viz.,

$$Fe^{2+} + 2H_2O \rightleftharpoons FeOH^+ + H_3O^+$$

This may be regarded as a proton transfer from one of the water molecules in the hydration mantle of the aqueous ion to a solvent molecule

$$Fe(H_2O)_6^{2+} + H_2O \rightleftharpoons Fe(H_2O)_5OH^+ + H_3O^+$$

In agreement with this mechanism, increased hydrolysis is favored by higher charge and smaller radius of the cation, resulting in a higher proton-repelling field. However, recent work by Sillén and co-workers[3] has shown that the majority of metallic cations hydrolyse to di- or polynuclear species which presumably arise from condensation of the mononuclear species produced as in the above equation. The principal product of hydrolysis of the ferric ion is $Fe_2(OH)_2^{4+}$, with smaller proportions of $FeOH^{2+}$ and $Fe(OH)_2^+$. Polynuclear species of varying complexity have been inferred for other metal ions undergoing hydrolysis; representative species include $Be_3 \cdot (OH)_3^{3+}$, $Sn_3(OH)_4^{2+}$, $Bi_6(OH)_{12}^{6+}$, etc.

The methods that have permitted deduction of the formation of such complex products of metal cation hydrolysis have also yielded information on the formation of isopoly anions. The condensation reactions by which these are formed are really the reverse of hydrolysis, e.g.,

$$2CrO_4^{2-} + 2H_3O^+ \rightleftharpoons Cr_2O_7^{2-} + 3H_2O$$

By analysis of the pH changes during titrations

in such systems Sillén and his associates have deduced the formulae of the principal species resulting from such condensations. As an example, the pervanadyl ion, VO_2^+, is converted by increase in pH mainly to $H_2V_{10}O_{28}^{4-}$, which on further raising the pH liberates one and then both hydrogen atoms by proton transfer to the solvent.

Case 4. The Solubility of Sparingly Soluble Electrolytes

In considering the equilibrium attainable in a saturated solution of an electrolyte, if one rules out weak electrolytes and solutions concentrated enough for ion-pair formation to become appreciable, the following represents the process with respect to which equilibrium may exist:

$$M_xA_y(s) \rightleftharpoons xM^{y+} + yA^{x-}$$

In such cases, at a fixed temperature the activity product, $a_M{}^x a_A{}^y$ will be constant. It is often more useful to apply the solubility product principle to the concentration of the ions in a saturated solution. For the simpler case of a 1:1 salt, MA,

$$[M^+][A^-] = \frac{K_s}{f_+f_-} = \frac{K_s}{(f_\pm)^2}$$

The solubility of MA will generally be lower in a solution containing a second electrolyte having an ion in common with MA. This phenomenon is known as salting out and is one example of what is often called the common-ion effect. The increase in concentration of the common ion is greater than the usual decrease in $f_\pm$ at low concentrations, with the result that the concentration of the other ion must be lower in the saturated solution. On the other hand, the solubility of MA may often be slightly increased by the addition of a soluble electrolyte having no ion in common. This is called salting in, and depends on the usual decrease in $f_\pm$ that occurs as the ionic strength of solutions increases from very small values. Quantitative calculations based on these effects are advisably restricted to electrolytes whose initial solubility is low, since it is only with such solutions that the changes in the activity coefficient may reliably be estimated or, for less rigorous purposes, ignored.

Some apparent exceptions to the solubility product principle can be traced to competitive processes. For instance, the solubility of silver

chloride is much increased in aqueous chloride solution, but this has been shown to be due to formation of a complex ion, $AgCl_2^-$, accompanied by considerable lowering of the silver ion activity. The true equilibrium to be considered in this case is

$$AgCl(s) + Cl^- \rightleftharpoons AgCl_2^-$$

for which the equilibrium constant is K_sK_f, where K_f is the formation constant of the complex ion.

References

1. MacInnes, D. A., "The Principles of Electrochemistry," New York, Dover Publications Inc., 1961.
2. Harned, H. S., and Owen, B. B., "The Physical Chemistry of Electrolytic Solutions," 3rd Edition, New York, Reinhold Publishing Corp., 1958.
3. Sillén, L. G., *Quarterly Reviews*, **XIII**, 146 (1959).

W. A. E. McBryde

Cross-references: *Acidimetry and Alkalimetry; Activity and Activity Coefficient; Dissociation; pH; pH Titration Curves; Stability Constants of Metal Complexes.*

IONIZATION. See DISSOCIATION; IONIC EQUILIBRIA.

IONIZATION IN GASES. See GASES, ELECTRICAL CONDUCTANCE AND IONIZATION.

IONIZED GASES. See PLASMA.

IONS, GENERATION OF AIR. See AIR ION GENERATION.

ION TRANSPORT ACROSS CHARGED MEMBRANES

The transport of ions across charged membranes is a special, somewhat complicated case of the transport of molecules across membranes. It is actually simpler to consider the general case. The treatment must be limited to small gradients of the displacements from equilibrium.

We are interested in the flow of each species and of heat. We define j_k as the number of moles of species k passing through unit area of surface of the membrane in unit time. The corresponding flows of mass, volume and electricity are $j_k M_K$, $j_k \bar{V}_K$ and $j_K Z_k$ $\mathbf{F}$, if M_k is the molecular weight, $\bar{V}_K$ the partial molal volume, and Z_K the valence, negative for an anion, of species k, and $\mathbf{F}$ is the Faraday. The total flows of mass, volume, and electricity are

$$j_M = \sum_i j_i M_i$$

$$j_V = \sum_i j_i \bar{V}_i$$

$$j_e = I = \mathbf{F} \sum_i j_i Z_i$$

Similarly we will denote the heat flow as j_q.

These flows depend upon the difference between the two bulk phases on the two sides of the membrane in composition, pressure, temperature, electrical potential, and certain other potentials, such as gravitational, which usually differ so little that they may be neglected. These flows also depend upon the properties of the membrane, which themselves depend more or less on those of the two bulk phases. Often the properties of the membrane must be determined from the flows themselves, but we will consider first those which can be determined from a study of the membranes.

It is extremely difficult not to picture a membrane as a bundle of circular pores, and most of the names applied to membrane properties come from this picture. A real membrane may be a thin film of a liquid which is insoluble in either of the bulk phases, but most of those which are important in ion transport resemble a sandpile or a randomly piled fishnet. The important difference of any of these membranes from a bundle of capillaries is that each passage branches into two or three and each branch joins with two or three others, all within a distance about the same as the width of the passage. Two reasons for the persistence of the capillary picture is that the other structures are more difficult to treat mathematically and cannot be pictured in two dimensions so that each of the phases appears continuous.

For a practical membrane the mechanical properties of tensile strength, rigidity, and compressibility and the chemical property of stability are important. The strength and rigidity are roughly proportional to the thickness, but so is the resistance to flow. Therefore, the thickness is an important property. If all the material flow is in one direction, the screening can be done in a very thin face on a backing which is much less resistant to flow. Otherwise, a compromise must be reached.

The next most important properties are the ratio of open volume to the total volume of the membrane, usually called the porosity; the ratio of the open volume to surface area between this open volume and the membrane skeleton, or the grain size, usually called the pore size; and the sign and density of electrical charge fixed upon the membrane skeleton.

The porosity of a membrane used with liquid solutions may be determined by weighing the surface-dried membrane in equilibrium with the solvent, evaporating out the liquid, and weighing the dried membrane to determine the weight, and therefore the volume, of the liquid by difference. The total volume is determined from the area and thickness.

The surface area may sometimes be measured by gas adsorption. Half the ratio of the open volume to the surface is often called the pore size because this ratio is the radius for a right circular pore. In some cases the open volume, skeletal volume, and surface area at the external surface may be measured from a microphotograph as the open area, skeletal area, and the perimeter between the two areas. The ratio is more often determined from the viscosity and the volume flow of solvent by Poiseuilles' law. For circular pores perpendicular to the outer membrane surface

$$r^2 = 8 L^2 \eta j_V / \Delta P V$$

in which r is the radius of the pore, L is its length, j_V / V is the ratio of the volume flow to the open volume, and ΔP is the pressure difference. For real membranes each method of measurement gives a different value, but their ratios are usually not too far from unity. The property of greatest practical importance is $j_V / \Delta P$, which is called the permeability of the membrane to the solvent.

The distribution of "pore size" may sometimes be determined from a photomicrograph of the surface as the distribution of sizes of the free areas, or it may be determined from the rate of gas flow down through the membrane into the solvent. If the "pores" are all the same size, there is no gas flow until the pressure reaches the value $2\,\sigma/r$, if σ is the surface tension. For higher pressures the flow is proportional to the pressure. If there is a variation in pore size, each pore will open at its proper pressure and the distribution can be calculated from the relation of flow to pressure. The method can be extended by replacing the gas with a liquid which is immiscible with the solvent and does not wet the membrane. Fortunately the pore-size distribution is much less important for a real membrane than for a bundle of capillaries unless there is a "pinhole," a very large passageway going through the membrane.

The fixed charges in a membrane may be determined by direct titration. If they are anions, the membrane is equilibrated with acid, rinsed thoroughly with solvent to remove any mobile anions and the equivalent hydrogen ions, and then titrated with base, usually with the addition of the salt of the acid and base to hasten equilibrium between the membrane and the solution. If the fixed charges are cations, the acid and base are interchanged. The number of fixed charges is sometimes expressed as the surface charge density on the internal surface between the open volume and the skeleton. It is usually expressed, however, as moles per total volume of membrane in liters or as moles per kilogram of solvent within the membrane.

The relative rates of diffusion of two non-electrolyte solutes or of a solute and solvent appear to be nearly the same in a membrane as in the solvent unless the pores are almost small enough to exclude one of the solutes. When pressure is applied, the filtrate has approximately the composition of the solution inside the membrane, and the permeability, $j_V/\Delta P$, is nearly proportional to the reciprocal of the viscosity.

For electrolyte solutions and a charged membrane the situation is more complicated because the concentration of mobile anions is very different from that of the cations. One method of treating these cases is to consider the fixed charges in solution. This solution must be electrically neutral so that $m_R Z_R + m_G Z_G + m_C Z_C = 0$, if R refers to fixed ions, G to gegenions or counterions and C to co-ions. Then $Z_R = \pm 1$, Z_G has the opposite sign to Z_R and Z_C the same sign as Z_R. We will consider only the case where Z_G and Z_C are also ± 1. At equilibrium with the bulk phase

$$m_G m_C = m_C(m_R + m_C) = G m_W^2$$

in which G is a ratio of activity coefficients, usually of the order of unity, and m_W is the concentration of either ion in the bulk solution. If m_R/G is much larger than m_W, m_C will be much smaller than m_W and very much smaller than m_R or m_G.

Although the diffusion or the permeation of the co-ion will be speeded up because of the much greater concentration of gegenion, it cannot be changed much. The filtrate concentration will be only a little larger than that of the co-ion in the membrane. Diffusion will be a little faster than that corresponding to the diffusion constant of the salt and the concentration of the co-ion. For other than univalent ions, or for mixtures, the mathematics is more complicated, but the principles are the same.

We may learn something about a membrane from its electrical resistance, but the transport of molecules in an electrical field is the important electrical property. There are two ratios which are important,

$$t_k = j_k/(E/\mathbf{F}) = j_k/\sum_i j_i Z_i$$

and

$$\tau_k = j_k Z_K/\sum_i j_i Z_i .$$

They have the same sign for cations, usually positive. They have the opposite sign for anions, τ_k is usually positive and t_k negative. For neutral molecules τ_k is always zero but t_k is usually not. It may be positive or negative. t_k is considered more important because it is more important to know direction than speed, but largely because it is not zero for nonelectrolytes. For example, the membrane potential, E, is given by

$$E = - \sum_i t_i \Delta\mu_i/\mathbf{F}$$

in which $\Delta\mu_i$ is the difference in intrinsic or chemical potential on the two sides of the membrane.

In a charged membrane j_1 for the solvent may be much larger than that for either ion. This has been explained by the solvation of the gegenion and by electroendosmosis. The first is probably responsible for some, the second is giving a name not explaining it. Let us consider the solvent as standing still and the membrane moving. The two mobile ions may be expected to have about the same mobility relative to the solvent as in a bulk phase of the same total concentration. The behavior of soap micelles and similar molecules indicates that the mobility of the membrane should be the same as though it were cut up into univalent pieces, i.e. about the same as that of toluene sulfate ion for the usual ion-exchange membrane. In water this value is about half that of chloride ion. The transference number of the membrane would then be a third for KCl, which corresponds to a transference number of the solvent, t_1, of $\pm 0.30/0.018\ m_R$ if the membrane is fixed. We should expect the water transfer to be greater with slower moving gegenions, and expect it to decrease with increasing concentration of the co-ion.

We know almost nothing about transport through membranes due to differences in temperature. In the absence of a membrane most salts in water solution are more concentrated at the low temperature than at the high. From theory we know that the effect should depend upon $\sum_i Q_k^* j_k$ with Q_k^* defined as

$$Q_k^* = (j_q/j_k + T\bar{S}_k)$$

at constant temperature.

For the quantitative discussion of transport we will give a very brief summary of the results of Kirkwood (Ref. 2, p. 119). He starts with the usual differential treatment,

$$j_k = -\sum_i L_{ki} d\bar{\mu}_i/dx - L_{kq} d \ln T/dx \qquad (1)$$

$$j_q = -\sum_i L_{qi} d\bar{\mu}_i/dx - L_{qq} d \ln T/dx \qquad (2)$$

in which x is the distance across the membrane and $\bar{\mu}_i$ is the total potential of species, i. With the limitations we made earlier it is the electrochemical potential, $\mu_i + Z_i \mathbf{F} \Phi_e$. Then

$$\begin{aligned} d\bar{\mu}_i dx = \bar{V}_i dP/dx - \bar{S}_i dT dx \\ + d(RT \ln a_i)/dx + Z_i \mathbf{F} d\Phi_e/dx \end{aligned} \qquad (3)$$

if $\bar{S}_i$ is the partial molal entropy of x and a_i its activity.

For the steady state, with each j_K independent of x, Kirkwood derives the equations

$$j_k = -\sum_i \lambda_{ki} \Delta \bar{\mu}_i + \lambda_{kq} \Delta \ln T \qquad (4)$$

$$j_q = -\sum_i \lambda_{qi} \Delta \bar{\mu}_i + \lambda_{qq} \Delta \ln T \qquad (5)$$

in which $\Delta \bar{\mu}_i$ and $\Delta \ln T$ are the differences in $\bar{\mu}_1$ and $\ln T$ in the bulk phases at either side of the membrane. They are thermodynamic functions and so are independent of the membrane. The properties of the membrane, including the solution within it, are given by the λ's. Like the L's they obey the Onsager reciprocal relations

$$\lambda_{ki} = \lambda_{ik}, \qquad \lambda_{kq} = \lambda_{qk} \qquad (6)$$

provided that all potential gradients are small. If there are n species in the bulk phases, there

are $n + 1$ flows to be considered and $(n + 1)(n + 2)/2$ λ's.

To determine the coefficients we may vary the conditions. We may easily make j_V or I zero, or fix ΔT, ΔP or $\Delta \Phi_e$ at zero or some other value, and we may easily fix the composition of solutions A and B by renewing the solutions rapidly. So, in simple cases we may fix each $\Delta \bar{\mu}_i$.

We have already discussed some cases, but let us consider a few of them formally

For a one-component system

$$j_1 = -\lambda_{11} \Delta \mu_1 - \lambda_{1q} \Delta \ln T \qquad (7)$$

$$j_q = -\lambda_{1q} \Delta \mu_1 - \lambda_{qq} \Delta \ln T \qquad (8)$$

At constant temperature

$$\lambda_{1q}/\lambda_{11} = j_q/j_1$$

For $j_1 = 0$

$$\lambda_{1q}/\lambda_{11} = -\Delta \mu_1/\Delta \ln T \qquad (9)$$

If the temperature difference is small enough so that $\bar{V}_1$ and $T\bar{S}$ may be regarded as constant enough to be given their average values,

$$\Delta \mu_1 = \bar{V}_1 \Delta P - T\bar{S}_1 \Delta \ln T$$

and

$$\bar{V}_1 \Delta P/\Delta \ln T = -(\lambda_{1q}/\lambda_{11} + T\bar{S}_1) = Q^* \qquad (10)$$

This is probably the most direct way of determining Q^*. Since the heat conductivity of the membrane is usually of the same order as that of the liquid, however, it is not easy to determine $\Delta \ln T$ precisely.

For a two component system if the solute is also a nonelectrolyte

$$j_1 = -\lambda_{11} \Delta \mu_1 - \lambda_{12} \Delta \mu_2 - \lambda_{1q} \Delta \ln T \qquad (11)$$

$$j_2 = -\lambda_{12} \Delta \mu_1 - \lambda_{12} \Delta_{22} - \lambda_{2q} \Delta \ln T \qquad (12)$$

$$j_q = -\lambda_{1q} \Delta \mu_1 - \lambda_{2q} \Delta \mu_2 - \lambda_{qq} \Delta \ln T \qquad (13)$$

If the membrane is impermeable to 2, λ_{12}, λ_{22}, and λ_{2q} must each be zero. Then Eqs. (11) and (13) are reduced to (7) and (8), but

$$\Delta \mu_1 = \bar{V}_1 \Delta P - T\bar{S}_1 \Delta \ln T + \Delta RT \ln a_1$$

If $\Delta \ln T = 0$ and $j_1 = 0$

$$-\Delta RT \ln a_1 = -RT \Delta \ln a_1 = \bar{V}_1 \Delta P \qquad (14)$$

and ΔP is the osmotic pressure.

If $\Delta P = 0$ and $j_1 = 0$

$$\Delta RT \ln a_1 = \Delta \ln T(\lambda_{1q}/\lambda_{11} - T\bar{S}_1)$$
$$= (\Delta \ln T)Q^* \qquad (15)$$

and the ΔT corresponding to $\Delta \ln T$ is the osmotic temperature. It differs from the osmotic pressure in that it does not correspond to equilibrium because heat is flowing from the hot to the cold side of the membrane. The term "steady state" is often applied to this case of $j_k = 0$ for all species, rather than to the more general one we have used $(dj_k/dx = 0)$.

If the membrane is permeable to both components and $\Delta \ln T = 0$, the pressure may be adjusted to make either $\Delta\mu_1 = 0$ or $\Delta\mu_2 = 0$. If $\Delta\mu_1 = 0$,

$$\lambda_{12} = -j_1/\Delta\mu_2 , \qquad \lambda_{22} = -j_2/\Delta\mu_2 ,$$
$$\lambda_{2q} = -j_q/\Delta\mu_2 \tag{16}$$

If $j_2 = 0$,

$$\lambda_{12} = -j_1/\Delta\mu_1 , \qquad \lambda_{12} = -j_2/\Delta\mu_1 ,$$
$$\lambda_{1q} = -jq/\Delta\mu_1 \tag{17}$$

A difference between the two values of λ_{12} would indicate a change in the properties of the membrane with pressure.

For an electrolyte we will denote the cation by 3 and the anion by 4. We have the conditions that each bulk phase and the membrane must be electrically neutral, and the flow equations

$$j_1 = -\lambda_{11}\Delta\mu_1 - \lambda_{13}\Delta\bar{\mu}_3 - \lambda_{14}\Delta\bar{\mu}_4 - \lambda_{iq}\Delta \ln T \tag{18}$$

$$j_3 = -\lambda_{13}\Delta\mu_1 - \lambda_{33}\Delta\bar{\mu}_3 - \lambda_{34}\Delta\bar{\mu}_4 - \lambda_{3q}\Delta \ln T \tag{19}$$

$$j_4 = -\lambda_{14}\Delta\mu_1 - \lambda_{34}\Delta\bar{\mu}_3 - \lambda_{44}\Delta\bar{\mu}_4 - \lambda_{4q}\Delta \ln T \tag{20}$$

$$j_q = -\lambda_{1q}\Delta\mu_1 - \lambda_{3q}\Delta\bar{\mu}_3 - \lambda_{4q}\Delta\bar{\mu}_4 - \lambda_{qq}\Delta \ln T \tag{21}$$

We will consider only the case for which $\Delta \ln T = 0$, $\Delta P = 0$ and the composition of the two bulk phases are the same. Then $\Delta\mu_1 = \Delta\mu_3 = \Delta\mu_4 = 0$.

$$\Delta\bar{\mu}_3 = Z_3 \mathbf{F}\Delta\phi_e , \qquad \Delta\bar{\mu}_4 = Z_4 \mathbf{F}\Delta\phi_e$$

$$j_1 = -(\lambda_{13}Z_3 + \lambda_{14}Z_4)\mathbf{F}\Delta\phi_e \tag{22}$$

$$j_3 = -(\lambda_{33}Z_3 + \lambda_{34}Z_4)\mathbf{F}\Delta\phi_e \tag{23}$$

$$j_4 = -(\lambda_{34}Z_3 + \lambda_{44}Z_4)\mathbf{F}\Delta\phi_e \tag{24}$$

$$j_q = -(\lambda_{3q}Z + \lambda_{4q}Z_4)\mathbf{F}\Delta\phi_e \tag{25}$$

$$I = j_3Z_3 + j_4Z_4 = -(\lambda_{33}Z_3{}^2 + 2\lambda_{34}Z_3Z_4 + \lambda_{44}Z_4{}^2)\mathbf{F}\Delta\phi_e \tag{26}$$

$$t_3 = (\lambda_{33}Z_3 + \lambda_{34}Z_4)/(\lambda_{33}Z_3{}^2 + 2\lambda_{34}Z_3Z_4 + \lambda_{44}Z_4{}^2) \tag{27}$$

$$t_4 = (\lambda_{34}Z_3 + \lambda_{44}Z_4)/(\lambda_{33}Z_3{}^2 + 2\lambda_{34}Z_3Z_4 + \lambda_{44}Z_4{}^2) \tag{28}$$

$$t_1 = (\lambda_{13}Z_3 + \lambda_{14}Z_4)/(\lambda_{33}Z_3{}^2 + 2\lambda_{34}Z_3Z_4 + \lambda_{44}Z_4{}^2)$$
$$= t_3(\lambda_{13}Z_3 + \lambda_{14}Z_4)/(\lambda_{33}Z_3 + \lambda_{34}Z_4)$$
$$= t_4(\lambda_{14}Z_3 + \lambda_{14}Z_4)/(\lambda_{34}Z_3 + \lambda_{44}Z_4) \tag{29}$$

The transference number of the solvent is seen to arise from the cross terms, λ_{13} and λ_{14}, when $\Delta\mu_1 = 0$. The transference number equations may be generalized to any number of ions for nonelectrolytes as

$$t_k = \sum_i \lambda_{ki}Z_i / \sum_{ij} \lambda_{ij}Z_iZ_j \tag{30}$$

The applications of Eqs. (4) and (5) are straightforward though they may be intricate.

There are many discussions of the flow Eqs. (1) and (2) in discussions of the thermodynamics of irreversible processes. There is a great variety of symbols and none of the general treatments pay much attention to ions or membranes. A simple introduction is given in Reference (1). The other references are to symposium discussions.

References

1. Lewis, G. N., and Randall, M., "Thermodynamics," revised by K. S. Pitzer and L. Brewer, Chapter 28, New York, N.Y., McGraw-Hill Book Company, Inc., 1961.
2. Clarke, H. T., Editor, "Ion Transport Across Membranes," New York, N.Y., Academic Press, Inc., 1954.
3. Shedlowsky, T., Editor, "Electrochemistry in Biology and Medicine," New York, N.Y., John Wiley and Sons, Inc., 1955.
4. "Membrane Phenomena," General Discussion of the Faraday Society, No. 21, 1956.
5. Hamer, W. J., Editor, "The Structure of Electrolytic Solutions," New York, N.Y., J. Wiley and Sons, Inc., 1959.

GEORGE SCATCHARD

Cross-references: *Electrodialysis; Ion Exchange Membranes; Membrane Equilibrium; Membrane Potentials; Membranes, Electrolytic.*

IRREVERSIBLE ELECTROCHEMICAL PROCESSES, THERMODYNAMICS OF

As soon as a noninfinitesimal electric current passes through an electrochemical system, this passage and all accompanying phenomena are to be regarded as irreversible in the thermodynamic sense, and it is therefore evident that the thermodynamics of irreversible processes must be one of the keys to the understanding of electrochemistry. Electrochemical thermodynamics, developed according to the pattern of De Donder's chemical thermodynamics and with the other aspects of "irreversible thermodynamics" taken into account, is one of the two main foundations of electrochemical theory. The other, electrochemical kinetics, is of course essentially based on general chemical kinetics, but it can be shown to receive considerable additional power from close contact with irreversible thermodynamics.

In the present outline of the thermodynamics of irreversible electrochemical processes we are forced to limit ourselves to the bare essentials of the subject. Details are available in the writings listed in the "References."

Let us consider an electrochemical system (galvanic cell or electrolytic cell) consisting of the following phases:

Copper I/Metal 1/Solution 2//Solution

3/Metal 4/Copper II

in which the copper phases I and II represent the connections with an outside circuit or the leads to a measuring instrument; phases 1 and 2 contain the reduced form, X^-, and the oxidized form, X, of a couple (e.g.: $X^- = \frac{1}{2}$ Zn, Ag + Cl^-, $\frac{1}{2}$ H_2O, etc.; $X = \frac{1}{2}$ Zn^{2+}, AgCl, $\frac{1}{4}$ O_2 + H^+, etc.); similarly phases 3 and 4 contain the reduced form, Y^-, and the oxidized form, Y, of another couple.

If a positive current, I, passes from left to right in the system, with electrons going from I to II in the outside circuit, the following amount of electric work is done by the system during the infinitesimal lapse of time, dt:

$$dw_{el.} = I \cdot (\varphi^{II} - \varphi^{I}) \cdot dt \qquad (1)$$

φ^{I} and φ^{II} being the inner electric potentials of the copper terminals I and II. The *first law of thermodynamics* gives us then the energy balance:

$$dE = dQ - p \cdot dV - I \cdot (\varphi^{II} - \varphi^{I}) \cdot dt \qquad (2)$$

in which E is the internal energy of the system, dQ the quantity of heat received from the surroundings during dt, p the pressure, and V the volume of the system.

The reactions occurring at the various interphases are the following:

$$X^- \rightarrow X + e^-(1)$$
$$e^-(1) \rightarrow e^-(I)$$
$$Y + e^-(4) \rightarrow Y^- \qquad (3)$$
$$e^-(II) \rightarrow e^-(4)$$

with, in addition, the transfer of electrons through the outside circuit:

$$e^-(I) \rightarrow e^-(II) \qquad (4)$$

the overall reaction being:

$$X^- + Y \rightarrow X + Y^- \qquad (5)$$

whose degree of advancement ξ is such that:

$$I \cdot dt = \mathbf{F} \cdot d\xi \qquad (6)$$

in which $\mathbf{F}$ designates the Faraday. Eq. (2) can then be written as follows:

$$dE = dQ - p \cdot dV - \mathbf{F} \cdot (\varphi^{II} - \varphi^{I}) \cdot d\xi \qquad (7)$$

The *second law of thermodynamics* gives us:

$$dQ = T \cdot dS - dQ'$$

with

$$dQ' = T \cdot d_i S \geq 0 \qquad (8)$$

in which T is the absolute temperature, S the entropy of the system, dQ' the Clausius uncompensated heat, and $d_i S$ the entropy production during dt. From (7) and (8) we obtain:

$$dE = T \cdot dS - p \cdot dV - \mathbf{F}(\varphi^{II} - \varphi^{I}) \cdot d\xi - dQ'. \qquad (9)$$

On the other hand, calling A the chemical affinity of the cell reaction (5), we have:

$$dE = T \cdot dS - p \cdot dV - A \cdot d\xi. \qquad (10)$$

From (8), (9) and (10) we then obtain the fundamental condition:

$$dQ' = [A - \mathbf{F} \cdot (\varphi^{II} - \varphi^{I})] \cdot d\xi \geq 0. \qquad (11)$$

In the limiting case of reversibility, i.e., at zero or infinitesimally small current, we have:

$$A - \mathbf{F} \cdot (\varphi^{II} - \varphi^{I})_{rev.} = 0 \qquad (12)$$

or

$$(\varphi^{I} - \varphi^{II})_{rev.} + A/\mathbf{F} = 0. \qquad (13)$$

We shall call the difference of inner electric potential from I to II the *electric tension*, U, of the cell and the ratio, $A/\mathbf{F}$, its *chemical tension* or *electromotive force*, E. We then have the equilibrium condition:

$$U_{rev.} + E = 0. \qquad (14)$$

Going back to (11) and considering $d\xi$ as positive (reaction (5) then actually goes from left to right) we have:

$$U + E \geq 0 \qquad (15)$$

If, with $d\xi > 0$, we have $A > 0$ we are dealing with a galvanic cell and we have $|U| < E$; if $A < 0$ we are dealing with an electrolytic cell and we have $U > |E|$. The sum, $\mathbf{F}U + A = \mathbf{F} \cdot (U + E)$, is the *electrochemical affinity*, $\tilde{A}$, of the cell. The sum, $U + E$, is its *electrochemical tension*, A. At equilibrium these quantities are both equal to zero. We easily see that, in general, $\tilde{E} = U - U_{rev.}$.

The electrochemical tension can be shown to be equal to the sum of the various overvoltages and ohmic electric potential drops resulting from the passage of the current. We have left out of consideration in this brief presentation the effect of the irreversible diffusion at the liquid junction between solutions 2 and 3. The normally small electric potential difference at the junction can be regarded as being neglected or as having been allowed for through a suitable correction. It is, on the other hand, one of the significant achievements of the thermodynamics of irreversible processes that it provides a straightforward solution of this problem.

Let us now consider the single electrode 1/2 at which the reaction $X^- \to X + e^-$ takes place. The electrochemical affinity, $\tilde{A}$, of this reaction is related as follows to the electrochemical potentials, $\tilde{\mu}$, the chemical potentials, μ, and the electric potentials, φ^1 and φ^2:

$$\tilde{A} = \tilde{\mu}_{X^-} - \tilde{\mu}_X - \tilde{\mu}_{e^-} = \mu_{X^-} - \mu_X$$
$$- \mu_{e^-} + \mathbf{F} \cdot (\varphi^1 - \varphi^2). \qquad (16)$$

However, at equilibrium (zero current) we have:

$$\mu_{X^-} - \mu_X - \mu_{e^-} = -\mathbf{F} \cdot (\varphi^1 - \varphi^2)_{rev.} \qquad (17)$$

and we thus have:

$$\tilde{A} = \mathbf{F} \cdot [(\varphi^1 - \varphi^2) - (\varphi^1 - \varphi^2)_{rev.}] = \mathbf{F} \cdot \eta \qquad (18)$$

in which η is the *overvoltage* (or *overtension*) corresponding to a certain current, I. The rate of entropy production corresponding to this electrode process is given by:

$$d_iS/dt = (1/T) \cdot \tilde{A} \cdot (d\xi/dt) = (\eta/T) \cdot I \qquad (19)$$

which is seen to be the product of the force, η/T, and of the flux, I. In the range of very small currents and very small corresponding overvoltages we have the proportionality

$$I = L \cdot (\eta/T). \quad \text{or} \quad I = l \cdot \eta \qquad (20)$$

in which the phenomenological coefficients, L and l, can be shown to be related to the Tafel parameters. If the electrode process $X^- \to X + e^-$ obeys a rate expression of the form

$$I = I_0 \cdot [\exp(\beta_a \mathbf{F}\eta/RT) - \exp(-\beta_c \mathbf{F}\eta/RT)] \quad (21)$$

we see that, in the limiting case of very small overvoltages, we have:

$$I = I_0 \cdot (\beta_a + \beta_c) \cdot \mathbf{F}\eta/RT \qquad (22)$$

and hence:

$$L = lT = I_0 \cdot (\beta_a + \beta_c) \cdot \mathbf{F}/R \qquad (23)$$

If the electrode 1/2 is the seat of several simultaneous processes whose equilibrium electric tensions are very close to one another, a certain amount of mutual influence can be expected to take place between these processes. The partial currents are then linear functions of the overvoltages and the mutual influence coefficients obey Onsager's symmetry rule, $l_{ij} = l_{ji}$. In the case of two processes we have:

$$I_1 = l_{11} \cdot \eta_1 + l_{12} \cdot \eta_2$$
$$I_2 = l_{21} \cdot \eta_1 + l_{22} \cdot \eta_2 \qquad (24)$$

with $l_{12} = l_{21}$. The total rate of entropy production is given by

$$T \cdot (d_iS/dt) = \eta_1 \cdot I_1 + \eta_2 \cdot I_2$$
$$= l_{11} \cdot \eta_1^2 + 2l_{12} \cdot \eta_1 \cdot \eta_2 + l_{22} \cdot \eta_2^2 \qquad (25)$$

The reversible electric tensions of couples 1 and 2 being known and their self-influence coefficients, l_{11} and l_{22}, having been deduced from their separate polarizations (see (20)) the determination of the mixed electric tension at zero net current ($I = I_1 + I_2 = 0$) would make it possible to evaluate the mutual influence coefficient, l_{12}. Although linear relations such as (24) hold only for very small overvoltages (corresponding to electrochemical affinities small compared to RT) interesting qualitative considerations can be based upon an assumed linearization of polarization curves in the range of medium overvoltages. As we have suggested elsewhere electrochemical corrosion phenomena can usefully be discussed in this manner.

Prigogine's theorem on stationary states of minimum entropy production takes up a specially interesting aspect in electrochemistry. Let us still consider the two simultaneous processes for which the entropy production is given by (25) and let us maintain $A_1 = \mathbf{F} \cdot \eta_1$ constant in the course of time by suitable adjustment of the composition of the system and regulation of its electric tension. It is easily found, by differentiation with respect to η_2 at η_1 constant, that the entropy production reaches a minimum value when $I_2 = 0$, the stationary value of I_1 being then $(l_{11} - l_{12}^2/l_{22}) \cdot \eta_1$. The overvoltage, η_2, in the stationary state is $-(l_{12}/l_{22}) \cdot \eta_1$. It can be shown that this stationary state is stable with respect to small perturbations, such as a modification of the composition of couple 2 away from that corresponding to the stationary value of η_2. This self-regulation of the stationary state is similar to that exhibited by a closed system at equilibrium in accordance with the Le Chatelier principle. One may well wonder, again in the field of corrosion, if the device of maintaining one or more reactions at constant electrochemical affinities might not be used in practice to block certain destructive reactions. The continuous reduction of X_1 to X_1^- at constant η_1 would prevent the oxidation of X_2^- to X_2. Corrosion inhibition, passivation, cathodic protection, etc. are all subjects which would greatly benefit from an irreversible thermodynamic analysis.

Several other important areas within the confines of electrochemistry or across its borderlines with neighboring fields of physical chemistry, physics and even biophysics and biology benefit in a fundamental manner from the type of phenomenological analysis provided by irreversible thermodynamics. In the experimental ranges of most of these areas forces and fluxes of simultaneous processes are actually connected by linear relations with mutual influence coefficients obeying the Onsager symmetry rule. The coupling phenomena characteristic of irreversible thermodynamic theory, which in earlier treatments were overlooked, neglected or misunderstood, are now brought to the fore, providing for instance fundamental derivations and explanations of reciprocity relations, such as Saxén's relation between streaming potential and electroosmosis in the field of electrokinetic phenomena, Thomson's relation between thermoelectric power and Peltier heat in thermocouples and thermocells. Incidentally, the often misunderstood thermodynamics of the Peltier heat at isothermal junctions is now most conveniently handled. We cannot do more here than merely list topics of at least partly electrochemical character which have been treated in this manner.

The study of simultaneous diffusion of several ionic species leads to the exact formulation of the resulting electric potential gradients, solutions being provided for the problem of liquid junctions and that of concentration cells with transference. Simultaneous electrochemical, osmotic and diffusion phenomena in systems with membranes are treated systematically, with promising extensions into the field of living membranes and biological, physiological, and biochemical phenomena. Active transport, i.e., the movement of an ionic species against the gradient of its electrochemical potential occasionally observed in living systems, has received particular attention. Electrokinetic phenomena (a field not to be confused with that of electrode kinetics but also belonging definitely to electrochemistry) now has a complete thermodynamic substructure of which the already mentioned derivation of Saxén's relation is but one aspect. The theory of metallic thermocouples and of thermocells or of thermoelectricity in general has of necessity become of an irreversible thermodynamic nature since electric, thermal, and material flows exhibit couplings and obey linear laws in terms of the gradients of electric potential, temperature, and composition. The existence of nonzero mutual influence coefficients implies that of heats and entropies of transfer, quantities whose unraveling is possible only through accurate irreversible thermodynamic analysis. In the case of thermocells we have to distinguish between the problem of the initial electromotive forces corresponding to the absence of the effect of thermal diffusion (or Soret effect) and that of the final electromotive forces corresponding to the stationary state resulting from thermal diffusion. Let us mention as a last example the rapidly developing field of the electrochemistry of semiconductors which will also greatly benefit from the application of the thermodynamics of irreversible processes.

References

1. De Donder, Th., and Van Rysselberghe, P., "Thermodynamic Theory of Affinity," Stanford, Stanford University Press, 1936.
2. Prigogine, I., "Etude Thermodynamique des Phénomènes Irréversibles," Paris, Dunod, and Liège, Desoer, 1947.
3. Van Rysselberghe, P., Bull. classe sci., Acad. roy. Belg. (5) **38**, 1060 (1952).
4. Van Rysselberghe, P., J. Phys. Chem., **57**, 275 (1953).

5. Van Rysselberghe, P., "Electrochemical Affinity," Paris, Hermann, 1955.
6. Van Rysselberghe, P., *Corrosion Technology*, **5**, 49 (1958).
7. de Bethune, A. J., Licht, T. S., and Swendeman, N., *J. Electrochem. Soc.*, **106**, 616 (1959).
8. de Bethune, A. J., *J. Electrochem. Soc.*, **107**, 829 (1960).
9. Prigogine, I., "Introduction to Thermodynamics of Irreversible Processes," 2nd Edition, New York and London, Interscience—Wiley, 1962.
10. Van Rysselberghe, P., "Thermodynamics of Irreversible Processes," Paris, Hermann, 1963.

Pierre van Rysselberghe

Cross-reference: *Nomenclature, Remarks on.*

ISOTOPES—ELECTROCHEMICAL SEPARATION

Definitions and History

By the name of *isotopes* are designated the several atomic species which may be considered to belong to one same element, in that they are characterized by the same *atomic* or *charge number*; therefore, they occupy a same place in the periodic table, although they have different mass numbers, owing to different quantities of neutrons in their nuclei.

Electrochemical separation of isotopes can be achieved in two different ways, namely:

1. *electrolysis*, by which a selective transfer of the isotopic species to be separated is carried out from the electrolytic medium into another phase, so that their abundance ratios become different from those in the original state;

2. *electromigration* of isotopic ions in a countercurrent flow of electrolyte, based upon the different mobilities of the ions formed by the isotopes to be separated.

Electrochemical methods were proposed by several authors in the early decades of this century, during the first developments of isotope theory.[13, 16] The possibilities afforded by electrolysis were proved experimentally for the first time in 1932 by Washburn and Urey,[23] when they found that the electrolytic holdup in electrolyzers, after prolonged operation for producing hydrogen and oxygen, had a higher content of deuterium oxide than detectable in ordinary water (see **Heavy Water**). Countercurrent electromigration was first investigated in aqueous solutions by Brewer and coworkers[3, 4] and in molten salts by Klemm.[14]

Electrolysis Method

Let a nonreactive electrode be the seat of an electrochemical oxidation or reduction process; let the ionic species that are thus affected contain some isotopes. If the product of the electrochemical reaction separates in a different phase, for instance in gaseous form, or as an amalgam, a change in the relative abundances, or atom fractions, of the isotopes will usually ensue from the irreversible phenomena accompanying the electrode process.

If x is the atom fraction of a certain isotope in the electrolyte and y the corresponding value in the new phase, the separation process accompanying the discharge is expressed in terms of the *electrolytic separation factor*, α, defined as follows:

$$\alpha = \frac{(1-y)/y}{(1-x)/x}$$

The importance of this factor as a characteristic of the process is that it remains practically constant over a wide range of x for a given set of operating conditions, such as electrode material, current density, temperature and electrolyte composition.

If the process involves only two isotopic species, such as Cl^{35} and Cl^{37}, the above definition is identical with the following:

$$\chi = \frac{(Cl^{35}/Cl^{37})\ gas}{(Cl^{35}/Cl^{37})\ electrolyte}$$

It can also be noted that the foregoing expression is equivalent to an integrated form of a differential relationship like

$$d\log n_1 = \alpha d\log n_2$$

in which n_1 and n_2 express total quantities of the two isotopes present in the electrolyte of any stage in the process. Accordingly, if n_1^0 and n_2^0 are the original amounts and n_1 and n_2 are the corresponding amounts in any subsequent stage,

$$\log(n_2/n_2^0) = \alpha\log(n_1/n_1^0)$$

or

$$n_2/n_2^0 = (n_1/n_1^0)^\alpha$$

The logarithmic expression is very convenient in that the separation process that is carried out

TABLE 1. ELECTROLYTIC SEPARATION FACTORS

Isotopic Species	Nat. Abundance, %		Sep. Factor, α	Electrode Material	References
H^1/H^2	H^2	0.015	7.5	iron*	22
Li^6/Li^7	Li^6	7.52	1.02–1.079†	mercury	7, 11, 19, 20, 21
O^{16}/O^{18}	O^{18}	0.204	1.008	iron	10
Cl^{35}/Cl^{37}	Cl^{37}	24.6	1.0061	platinum	12
				graphite	8, 25
K^{39}/K^{41}	K^{41}	6.91	1.0054	mercury	9

* For other electrode materials see under same reference and under *Heavy Water*.
† Depending on the lithium compound used for the electrolyte.

in several stages will thus be represented by a straight line on logarithmic graph paper.

The state of affairs implied by the independence of the separation factor (sf) from the isotope concentration is not peculiar to electrolysis or to isotope exchange reactions, but is a general characteristic of a number of separation processes, such as chemical exchange, fractional distillation, and gaseous diffusion.

In Table 1 are listed the values determined for some of the best investigated isotopes. They show a remarkable regularity in the decrease of α with the increase of the element mass number. This feature provides a considerable support to the Bell-Gurney[1, 6] mechanism of isotope discharge, which is based on the application of quantum mechanics to the theory of overvoltage. According to this theory, the difference in discharge rates, as shown by two isotopes, depends on the difference in zero-point energy between their hydrated ions; this energy corresponds to the energy level in which, according to the teaching of quantum mechanics, an ion (or more generally a molecule) is still to be found above zero even at the absolute zero of temperature.

It is further to be noted that the influence exerted on the sf by electrode material, current density, and temperature becomes vanishingly small as the atomic weight increases.[9]

Beside the electrolytic separation of deuterium, which has been extensively discussed with the production of heavy water (q.v.), another typical example of this method will be afforded by a brief description of the experimental procedure adopted by Holleck[7] for the separation of lithium isotopes.

Electrolysis was carried out batchwise in three stages, using for the first two stages a horizontal *mercury cell*, having a cathode surface of 500 sq cm. The cell shape was not essentially different from the conventional design known in the chlor-alkali industry, except for the fact that, to obtain a lesser concentration gradient of amal-gamated lithium in the upper surface of the mercury layer and thus increase the current efficiency, the velocity of the mercury stream was increased from the inlet to the outlet by gradually narrowing the cell width from one end to the other. The amalgam denuder also was of horizontal type and the amalgam decomposition process was enhanced by impressing a slight anodic polarization from an external voltage source. Agitators for the electrolyte phase were provided in the electrolytic cell and in the denuder.

The starting electrolyte solution consisted of 18 liters at 38 per cent LiCl. This was electrolyzed at an average current density of 0.07 amp/sq cm, the temperature being 38 to 40°C. The total current was 30 to 40 amp, corresponding to a voltage of 5.8 to 7 v. The amalgam, which was continuously flowing in the closed circuit between the cell and the denuder, entered the latter at a concentration of 0.0025 to 0.005 per cent Li and was reacted with water to produce lithium hydroxide. Electrolysis was stopped when the solution had been depleted by one-tenth of its lithium chloride content. Ten alkaline batches were thus produced, then joined together and neutralized with hydrochloric acid, to obtain 18 liters in all at 34.3 per cent LiCl, which was the product of the first stage of the process. The second stage was performed on this batch and with the same procedure as for the first stage. The alkaline product from the denuder was reconverted into 70 g lithium chloride and this was partially electrolyzed in a smaller cell, so as to obtain a final product that after reconversion amounted to about 7 g LiCl. The atom fraction of Li^6 was 7.79 per cent in the starting solution and had increased to 12.78 per cent in the final product.

Electromigration Method

The best way of getting a first grasp of the principle underlying this method is to consider a typical example, such as the system applied by Klemm to the separation of lithium isotopes,[15] which is schematically illustrated in Fig. 1.

The electrolytic cell, shaped like a U-tube, is filled with minute granules of a chemically inert material resistant to high temperature, such as calcined steatite. The function of this packing is to avoid as far as possible any convection and consequent remixing in the molten lithium chloride that is submitted to electrolysis.

The lithium metal that separates at the cathode is continuously recombined with the chlorine gas developing at the anode, so as to provide a recirculation of electrolyte from the cathode to the anode that is countercurrent to the electromigration of the lithium cations.

The electrolyte flow rate will thus be such as to hinder the motion toward the cathode of the heavier and therefore slower Li^7 isotope, while still allowing the migration of Li^6 in the direction dictated by the electric field. By consequence, the cathodic leg of the U-shaped cell will thus become enriched in Li^6, while Li^7 will concentrate in the anodic leg, from which it can be gradually withdrawn as concentrated Li^7Cl. Rather than keeping the anode directly immersed in the lithium chloride bath, the continuity between the electrode and the electrolyte is established by means of a lead chloride bridge, so as to facilitate the separate withdrawals of chlorine and molten lithium chloride. Owing to the great difference in atomic weight between lithium and lead, there is practically no diffusion or migration of the latter outside the bridge.

The reported separation factor, as obtainable with an adequate tube length, is about 300. In this case, the definition of the separation factor applies to the relative isotope concentrations in the two phases closest to the electrodes. However, whereas for electrolytic separation this factor is independent of time, it is a time-dependent variable in the case of electromigration; therefore, when time is not specified, any value given for the separation factor should only mean its asymptotic limit.

Brewer and coworkers, who have applied the method to the separation of potassium isotopes K^{39} and K^{41} in aqueous solution,[3] give in the same paper a clear and concise outline of the theoretical aspects of the process, while Westhaver has developed its mathematical analysis.[24] Electromigration in aqueous solution has been successfully investigated also for the separation of other isotopes, such as deuterium.[17]

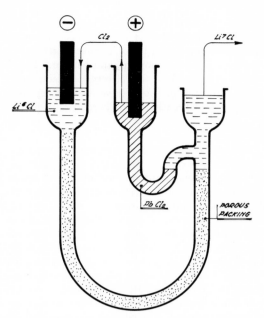

FIG. 1. Lithium isotopes separation by electromigration (A. Klemm).

Whether the process be carried out in aqueous solution or in a molten salt, the basic principle rests on an imposed countercurrent reflux of electrolyte through a packed column or a capillary system, in the direction from the cathode to the anode and at a rate just sufficient to reduce to zero the net forward transport of the cationic species including both isotopic ions as a whole. Accordingly, the mathematical concepts applicable to this problem are the same as in other conventional reflux columns. The concentrations that can be built up by this method are limited only by the number of theoretical plates that can be realized in the packing.

An important parameter characterizing the process is the *separation coefficient*, ϵ, defined as the ratio of the mobilities of the two isotopic ions. The mobility of any isotopic ion, that is, its average forward drift velocity under steady state conditions as formerly assumed, for a given temperature and for electric field intensity equal to unity, is shown by analysis to be inversely proportional to the square root of the ion mass. Consequently, the theoretical separation coefficient for hydrated potassium ion isotopes can, for instance, be calculated as follows:

$$\epsilon = \left(\frac{K^{41} \cdot 7H_2O}{K^{39} \cdot 7H_2O} \right)^{1/2} = 1.006$$

In its application to molten electrolytes, and beside lithium salts, the method has given successful results also for isotopic separation of magnesium, calcium, strontium, and barium.[18] Interesting combinations of electromigration with other physical methods have been suggested, such as centrifugation[2] and thermal diffusion.[5]

Uses

The electrolysis process has found its most important application in the recovery of deuterium and the associated production of heavy water. Nonetheless, it is of practical utility also in obtaining other stable isotopes.

The preparation of these isotopes, although in relatively smaller amounts, is of general interest for their use as indicators in physics, biology, medicine, and agriculture. Natural calcium, for example, contains Ca^{46} in the very small abundance of 0.0033 per cent. This isotope, however, can be transmuted by (n, γ)-nuclear reaction into radioactive Ca^{47} (half-life 4.7 days) which is useful as a tracer in the diagnosis of bone carcinoma. Now, enrichment of Ca^{46} by electromigration up to concentrations useful for medical purposes has been shown to be economically competitive versus electromagnetic separation.[18]

On the other hand, deuterium, heavy water, and lithium are of paramount interest in nuclear technology. The use of heavy water as a reactor moderator is well known. As to deuterium, aside from its warfare applications in thermonuclear fusion bombs, any future development allowing its exploitation as a controllable thermonuclear fuel would provide a source of energy capable of satisfying mankind's needs for all foreseeable ages to come.

Isotopes Li^6 and Li^7 are both useful in that they differ so widely from each other in their absorption cross sections for thermal neutrons (nat. mixture = 71 barn; Li^6 = 945 barn; Li^7 = 0.033 barn). By virtue of its metallic properties, Li^7 provides an excellent coolant for nuclear reactors. On the other hand, Li^6 can be transmuted into tritium and in combination with deuterium (as Li^6D) it is suitable, like tritium, as a thermonuclear explosive.

The fact that on the world market there are available large quantities of lithium salts depleted by more than 40 per cent of their natural Li^6 content is an indication that isotope separation is extensively carried out on this element. Beside the electromagnetic method, and in competition with it, electrochemical processes certainly play an important role in this respect too; indeed, their technical details are mostly kept secret.

References

1. BELL, R. P., J. Chem. Phys., **2**, 164 (1934).
2. BEYRARD, N. R., AND OSS V., C. J., German Patent DAS 1,086,213 (Aug. 4, 1960).
3. BREWER, A. K., AND OTHERS, J. Res. Nat. Bur. Std., RP 1765, **38**, 137 (1947).
4. BREWER, A. K., AND OTHERS, Science, **104**, 156 (1946).
5. CLASEN, H. (to Metallgesellschaft A.-G.), German Patent DAS 1,075,556 (Feb. 18, 1960).
6. GURNEY, R. W., Proc. Roy. Soc. (London), **A134**, 137 (1932).
7. HOLLECK, L., Z. Elektrochem., **44**, 111 (1938).
8. HUTCHISON, D. A., J. Chem. Phys., **13**, 536 (1945).
9. HUTCHISON, D. A., J. Chem. Phys., **14**, 401 (1946).
10. JOHNSTON, H. L., J. Am. Chem. Soc., **57**, 484 (1935).
11. JOHNSTON, H. L., AND HUTCHISON, D. A., J. Chem. Phys., **8**, 869 (1940).
12. JOHNSTON, H. L., AND HUTCHISON, D. A., J. Chem. Phys., **10**, 469 (1942).
13. KENDALL, J., AND ORITTENDEN, E. C., Proc. Nat. Acad. Sci. U.S., **9**, 75 (1923).
14. KLEMM, A., Z. Naturforsch., **1**, 252 (1946).
15. KLEMM, A., "Physiker Tagung Wiesbaden," p. 73, Mosbach (Baden), Physikverlag, 1956.
16. LINDEMANN, F. A., Proc. Roy. Soc. (London), **(A) 99**, 103 (1921).
17. MARTIN, H., AND RUHTZ, E., Z. Elektrochem., **56**, 560 (1950).
18. NEUBERT, A., AND KLEMM, A., Z. Naturforsch., **16a**, 685 (1961).
19. PERRET, L., ROZAND, L., AND SAÏTO, E., Proc. U.N. Intern. Conf. Peaceful Uses Atomic Energy, 2nd, Geneva, **4**, 595 (1958).
20. TAYLOR, T. I., AND UREY, H. C., J. Chem. Phys., **5**, 597 (1937).
21. TAYLOR, T. I., AND UREY, H. C., J. Chem. Phys., **6**, 429 (1938).
22. TOPLEY, B., AND EYRING, H., J. Chem. Phys., **2**, 217 (1934).
23. WASHBURN, E. W., AND UREY, H. C., Proc. Nat. Acad. Sci. U.S., **18**, 496 (1932).
24. WESTHAVER, J. W., J. Res. Nat. Bur. Std., RP 1766, **38**, 169 (1947).
25. YACOUBAN, K. V., Helm. Chim. Acta, **22**, 808 (1939).

PATRIZIO GALLONE

Cross-reference: *Electromigration in Liquid Metals, Heavy Water, Water Electrolysis.*

J

JOULE EFFECT

James Prescott Joule, an English physicist, discovered that when electricity flows through a conductor heat is produced at a rate directly proportional to the electrical resistance of the conductor and the square of the current, expressed by the familiar formula, I^2R. This heating of the conductor is an irreversible exchange of electric energy to heat caused primarily by scattering of electric charge carriers, electrons, or holes, by the atoms of the conductor. It is completely independent of the direction of the current. While in many applications resistance heating or heating by the Joule effect is very important, it is generally a waste of energy over which there is little control. Only in superconductors whose resistance disappears near absolute zero on the temperature scale is there found an absence of the Joule effect. All other materials offer a resistance to the flow of electric current.

ALBERT J. CORNISH

Cross-references: *Resistance Heating; Thermo-electricty.*

K

KINETICS OF CORROSION. See CORROSION, ELECTROCHEMICAL KINETICS.

KINETICS OF ELECTRODE REACTIONS. See ELECTRODE REACTIONS, KINETICS.

KLEIST, EWALD GEORGE VON (1700–1748)

Ewald George von Kleist, inventor of the oldest form of electric condenser, the Leyden Jar, was born on June 10, 1700, into a famous Pomeranian family of learned scholars, statesmen, generals, and poets. Among the family notables were the poets, Ewald Christian von Kleist and Franz von Kleist, and the world famous dramatist, Heinrich von Kleist. His father, Ewald Joachim von Kleist, was district president of Belgard. His mother was Hedwig Magdalene von Blankenburg from Maerkisch-Friedland.

Little is known of his education, except that he entered the Neustettin Gymnasium in 1715, the Danzig Gymnasium in 1718, and began to study law at the Leyden Academy Lugduno-Batavae in 1721.

In 1722 he acquired his cousin's prebend in Kamin, Pomerania which he controlled for twenty-five years. Though not considered a clergyman, he owned the churchly possessions and titles of the prebend, which was secularized after the Diocese of Kamin had been reformed in 1544.

He was engaged to the daughter of Otto Gustav von Lepel, a major-general and governor, but his debts prevented their marriage. On September 1, 1735, he married Magdalena Lukretia von Platen from the House of Rarfin. Their family included seven sons and one daughter.

On December 9, 1745, he reported to Professor Johann Gottlof Kruger of Halle his discovery of the Leyden Jar. This was probably the most important innovation in electricity prior to Franklin's findings. Like so many other discoveries in science, the name, Leyden Jar, is a misnomer. It ought to be called the "Kleistsche Flasche" instead of the "Leydener Flasche." In January 1746, Pieter van Musschenbroek, a renowned Dutch physicist at the University of Leyden reported the same "invention." It is not known whether the university was influenced by von Kleist's letter or not. It is also not clear why he was appointed a member of the Berlin Academy of Science on December 8, 1746, but it was undoubtedly because of his work on the Leyden Jar.

His theories were published by Kruger in his *Geschichte der Erde* (History of the Earth) in 1746 at Halle. The principle of the oldest form of electrical condenser as discovered by both men, states that a glass bottle lined inside and outside with a conducting material could be used to store some charge. The following account of von Kleist's discovery, in his own words, appears in Priestley's *History of Electricity*:

When a nail, or a piece of thick brass wire, etc. is put into a small apothecary's phial and electrified, remarkable effects follow, but the phial must be very dry or warm. I commonly rub it over beforehand with a finger on which I put some pounded chalk. If a little mercury or a few drops of spirit of wine be put into it the experiment succeeds the better. As soon as this phial and nail are removed from the electrifying glass and the prime conductor to which it had been exposed is taken away, it throws out a pencil of flame so long that, with this burning machine in my hand, I have taken sixty steps in walking about my room. When it is electrified strongly I can take it into another room and there fire spirits of wine with it. If, while it is electrifying, I put my finger on a piece of gold, which I hold in my hand to the nail, I receive a shock which stuns my arms and shoulders.

The Leyden Jar was exhibited throughout Europe. It did more to stimulate scientific interest in electricity than all previous endeavors in this field.

By order of the King on August 25, 1747, von Kleist became president of the law court of Coslin; he held this office until his death on December 10, 1748. The exact location of his tomb is unknown, but he was buried in the graveyard at Coslin.

MARY L. CHEKEWICZ

KOHLRAUSCH, FRIEDRICH WILHELM GEORG (1840–1910)

Friedrich Wilhelm Georg Kohlrausch was born on October 14, 1840 in Rinteln-on-Weser, Germany where his father, Rudolph Hermann K., was a teacher of mathematics and physics at the Gymnasium of Rinteln. Unquestionably influenced by his father's profession, he dedicated his life to teaching and research during that notable era of German history which contributed more than its share of today's scientific background. He died suddenly on January 17, 1910 in Marburg while his colleagues were preparing to celebrate his seventieth birthday.

Kohlrausch, who could easily be confused with his equally talented brother with a similar name, Wilhelm Friedrich K., is remembered for his notable work in the field of electrolytic conduction. As a physicist his contributions were also numerous in the fields of thermoelectricity, terrestrial magnetism, and elasticity. In electrochemistry his name is as common as those of his contemporaries, Nernst and Ostwald. We need only recall his work which led to the law of the independent migration of ions, his use of the a-c bridge and the telephone method of measuring conductivities, his discovery of ways of determining the solubility of difficultly soluble substances from their conductivities, and his work on the conductivity and dissociation of pure water.

After early schooling in Rinteln, Kessel-Marburg, and Erlangen, he received his doctor's degree in 1863 at Göttingen. He later returned to Göttingen in 1866 to perform his notable studies on the conductivities of electrolytes. In 1870 he left to accept a professorship at the Zürich Polytechnic Institute but resigned the next year to go to Darmstadt. He was professor of physics at Würzburg in 1875 and at Strassburg in 1888. After the death of Helmholtz in 1894, Kohlrausch was elected president of the Physikalisch-technische Reichsanstalt and remained there as its head until 1905 when ill health forced him to leave. In 1908 he received the first Bunsen medal of the Deutsche Bunsen-Gesellschaft and spent the last few years of his life as active in his investigations as ever but in the tranquility of his home at Marburg.

Kohlrausch was an influential teacher and a prolific writer. One of his books in the field of electrochemistry was "Das Leitvermögen der Elektrolyte, Insbesondere der Lösungen. Methoden resultate und chemische Anwendungen" which was coauthored by Ludwig Holborn and published in 1898. During his life, however, his more noted work was "Lehrbuch der praktischen Physik" which went through eleven editions before the author's death and was re-edited another five times until 1930 by additional authors. So highly regarded was this treatise that it has been estimated that during the first quarter of the twentieth century every German student of physics used this book at one time or another.

ROBERT E. MEREDITH

KOLBE AND RELATED BROWN-WALKER AND HOFER-MOEST REACTIONS

Although Michael Faraday in 1834[2] first noted the formation of hydrocarbon material by the electrolysis of an aqueous solution of a metal acetate, it was Kolbe fifteen years later[3] who recognized the stoichiometric character of the reaction which he represented simply as an oxidation of the carboxyl group by oxygen to give carbon dioxide and a saturated dimeric hydrocarbon:

$$2CH_3CO_2H + O \rightarrow C_2H_6 + H_2O + 2CO_2$$

This product is frequently referred to as the *Kolbe product* to contrast it with one of several other alternative products which are discussed below.

Scope. The anodic reaction to give Kolbe product proceeds with all substituted or unsubstituted carboxylic acids in aqueous, aqueous-organic, or organic media with the following exceptions:

(a) dicarboxylic acids which give olefins or acetylenes instead of Kolbe product.

(b) monocarboxylic acids with an alpha-substituent, such as alkyl, aryl, aralkyl, hydroxyl, alkoxyl, amino, acylamino, cyano, or halogeno, which tend to give predominantly olefins, alcohols and esters in water solution.

(c) monocarboxylic acids with chlorine, bromine, or iodine in any position up to about the fourth carbon atom from the carboxyl group.[4] Alcohols are usually formed rather than Kolbe product.

(d) acids with $\alpha\beta$- or $\beta\gamma$-unsaturation which give acetylenes or allenes.

(e) aromatic carboxylic acids, such as benzoic acid, which in aqueous media are unchanged, the current being used up in oxygen evolution. In organic media organic products but not of the Kolbe type are obtained (see later).

When the Kolbe reaction proceeds normally to give a dimeric product, but in a system which contains a second carboxy-ester group, the process is usually referred to as the *Brown-Walker* reaction because of its special significance in the synthesis of long chain dicarboxylic acids. If electrolysis leads to the formation of alcohol or ether by reaction with solvent, the process is usually referred to as a *Hofer-Moest* reaction. The infrequent formation of an ester carries no special designation but is a kind of mixture of Kolbe and Hofer-Moest reactions:

$$2CH_3CO_2H + O \rightarrow CH_3CO_2CH_3 + CO_2 + H_2O$$

Experimental Technique. The Kolbe reaction proceeds only at an anode of smooth platinum, iridium or, rarely, graphite.[5] In aqueous solution the reaction is strongly inhibited by added cations, such as those from silver, lead, manganese, iron, copper or cobalt, and added anions, such as ferricyanide, sulfate, chloride, phosphate, nitrate, perchlorate, hydroxyl, bicarbonate, carbonate, and fluoride, the effectiveness of inhibition being approximately in the order given.[6] In these instances instead of Kolbe product, alcohol formation with oxygen evolution predominates. Alcohol formation is usually called the Hofer-Moest reaction and has already been mentioned. It represents a type of reaction involving solvent.[7]

$$RCO_2H + O \rightarrow ROH + CO_2 + H_2O$$

Formation of Kolbe product is favored by low temperature, high acid concentration and current density, and absence of the ions listed above. Water containing enough alkali to neutralize about 10 per cent of the organic acid has been the most commonly used medium, but in recent years excess of aqueous ammonia has gained favor as an alternative. Methanol is frequently used instead of water. It is a better solvent for organic materials and the adverse influence of temperature, concentration, foreign ions, and low current density as well as certain restrictive features due to molecular structure are not so keenly felt.[8] In methanol the usual by-product is the methyl ether,[9] a type of Hofer-Moest product.

$$RCO_2H + CH_3OH + O \rightarrow ROCH_3 + CO_2 + H_2O$$

In water, and to a lesser degree in methanol, the most critical factor controlling Kolbe product is current density or the related anode potential. At low values oxygen evolution predominates, but as the potential rises past 2.1 to 2.3 v (SCE) Kolbe product appears in major amount. The current density at which this transition occurs has become known as the "critical" current density and in water at shiny platinum has a value of about 0.25 amp/sq cm. In methanol and other organic media the value is appreciably lower.

Although electrolysis is usually carried out using direct current, commercial, 60-cycle, alternating current has been used. Thus, ethane is formed from acetate in water or acetic acid containing sulfuric acid, but the yields are not quite as high as with direct current.[10]

The Fatty Acid Series. In the fatty acids the yield of Kolbe product is highest (85 per cent) with acetic acid and, surprisingly enough, lowest (8 per cent) with propionic acid. A. Moser[11] gives the figures of Table 1 for various aliphatic acids, the effect of alpha-substitution being most marked.

If the anolyte contains two different monocarboxylic acids, electrolysis will, in general, lead to a mixture of all three possible Kolbe products. For example, a mixture of palmitic (1 mole), and propionic (1½ mole) acids in

TABLE 1. PRODUCTS FROM FATTY ACIDS

Acid	Products (Current Efficiency, %)		
	Kolbe	Olefin	Ester
acetic	85	2	2
propionic	8	66	5
n-butyric	14	53	10
iso-butyric	—	62	10
n-valeric	50	18	4
iso-valeric	43	42	5
methylethylacetic	10	42	10
trimethylacetic	13	52	0
caproic	75	7	1
lauric	45		
myristic	34		
palmitic	30		
stearic	28		

aqueous-alcoholic solution at 70°C gives mainly n-heptadecane with lesser amounts of triacontane and butane:[12]

$$C_{15}H_{31}CO_2H + C_2H_5CO_2H \rightarrow$$
$$C_{17}H_{37} + C_{30}H_{62} + C_4H_{10}$$

Synthetic Applications. Electrolysis of mixtures of acids to give what may be termed cross-Kolbe products is widely applicable and has been extended to examples in which either or both acids contain various substituents. Bearing in mind the fact that the reaction is inhibited in exactly the same way as the simple Kolbe with a single carboxylic acid and that the products in general contain all three possible Kolbe products, cross-products have been isolated when one of the following substituents is present in one or both original carboxylic acids: carbonyl,[13] cyano,[14] alkyl or aryl,[14, 15] thus making possible the synthesis of unusual structures. For example, in methanolic solution at platinum, levulinic acid gives appreciable 2,7-octanedione[13],

$$2CH_3COCH_2CH_2CO_2H \rightarrow$$
$$CH_3COCH_2CH_2CH_2CH_2COCH_3$$

and a mixture of levulinic and valerianic acids gives methyl n-hexyl ketone,[13]

$$CH_3COCH_2CH_2CO_2H + CH_3(CH_2)_3CO_2H \rightarrow$$
$$CH_3CO(CH_2)_5CH_3$$

along with some octanedione and octane. The products are easily separable. In an analogous manner, 10-fluorodecanoic acid and the half ester of sebacic acid give 18-fluoroöctadecanoic (18-fluorostearic) acid in good yield:

$$F(CH_2)_9CO_2H + CH_3O_2C(CH_2)_8CO_2H \rightarrow$$
$$F(CH_2)_{17}CO_2CH_3$$

As already mentioned, the electrolysis of the half ester of a dicarboxylic acid to give the dicarboxylic acid ester of twice the carbon skeleton is usually called the Brown-Walker modification of the Kolbe reaction.[16] It may be illustrated by the reaction of the half ester of adipic acid to give suberic acid diester (62 per cent), the hydroxy-ester (17 per cent), the olefin-ester (8.5 per cent) and higher esters (6 per cent).[17]

$$CH_3O_2C(CH_2)_4CO_2H \rightarrow$$

$$CH_3O_2C(CH_2)_8CO_2CH_3 \quad 62\%$$
$$HO(CH_2)_4CO_2CH_3 \quad 17\%$$
$$CH_2{:}CH(CH_2)_2CO_2CH_3 \quad 8.5\%, \text{ etc.}$$

One of the more interesting and valuable uses of the Kolbe reaction has been to synthesize complex naturally occuring materials not otherwise easily made.[18] Thus, by a suitable choice of starting acids, stearic acid of a purity higher than that from naturally occuring material has been made[19] by electrolysis of a mixture of either (a) myristic and adipic acid half ester (C_{13} + $C_5 \rightarrow C_{18}$); (b) n-capric and sebacic acid half ester (C_9 + $C_9 \rightarrow C_{18}$) or (c) acetic acid and hexadecane-1,16-dicarboxylic acid half ester (C_1 + $C_{17} \rightarrow C_{18}$). Nervonic acid, also known as selacholic acid or cis-tetracos-15-enoic acid, which occurs in cerebrosides of brain tissue and in fats of many elasmobranch fish, and its $trans$-isomer have been synthesized by electrolysis of a mixture of methyl hydrogen suberate and either oleic (for cis-) or elaidic (for $trans$-) acid:[20]

$$CH_3(CH_2)_7CH:CH(CH_2)_7CO_2H +$$
$$CH_3O_2C(CH_2)_6CO_2H \rightarrow$$
$$CH_3(CH_2)_7CH:CH(CH_2)_{13}CO_2CH_3$$

Use in Structure Determination of Polypeptides

Electrolysis of N-acylglycines and -acyl-α-alanines in methanol gives N-methoxyalkyl-amides in excellent yield,[21] and the reaction:

$$CH_3CONHCHR.CO_2H \rightarrow$$
$$CH_3CONHCHR(OCH_3) + CO_2 \ (R = H \ or \ CH_3)$$

has been employed[22] progressively to degrade a peptide at the carboxyl end. Electrolysis replaces terminal carboxyl by methoxyl and a paper chromatogram of the fully hydrolized product quickly reveals which amino-acid has been lost in the electrolysis. The reaction is repeated:

$$-CONHCHRCO_2H \rightarrow -CONHCHR(OCH_3) \rightarrow$$
$$-CONH_2 + RCHO$$

thus chipping away the amino acids one at a time.

Mechanism. Kolbe's original vague postulate[3] of a direct oxidation of the carboxyl group by oxygen was amplified by Crum Brown and Walker[16] by the suggestion of the intermediate formation of a radical. This mechanism which could be termed the ionic discharge reaction is essentially that most favored today.

$$2CH_3CO_2H \rightarrow 2CH_3CO_2\cdot \rightarrow C_2H_6 + 2CO_2$$

Alternative proposals, most of them to accommodate the special peculiarities of aqueous media, have, in general, involved the intervention of peroxidic materials. Thus, Schall[23] and later Fichter[24] considered acyl peroxide was involved. Such an intermediate was believed to decompose either directly to give Kolbe product or through the per-acid to give alcohol (Hofer-Moest reaction).

$$2RCO_2H + O \rightarrow (RCOO)_2 + H_2O$$
$$\swarrow \qquad \searrow H_2O$$
$$R_2 + 2CO_2 \qquad RCO_3H + RCO_2H$$
$$\downarrow$$
$$ROH + CO_2$$

The proposal is supported by the fact that electrolysis of many acids at low temperatures gives rise to detectable amounts of peroxide[25] and that peroxides themselves do decompose to give products analogous to the electrolysis products, but beyond that the parallel ceases. Particularly pertinent are the gross differences in the ratio of the products produced on the one hand by electrolysis and on the other by peroxide decomposition. Electrolysis is remarkable in giving such high yields of dimeric Kolbe product. Such a fact must be explained by any acceptable hypothesis.

Restricting their thinking to aqueous media, Glasstone and Hickling[26] proposed the prior formation of hydrogen peroxide but met considerable criticism.[27]

It is now becoming more and more evident that radicals are more or less directly involved. The evidence is varied and extensive. Thus, in organic media, where oxygen evolution is suppressed, rearrangement of the carbon skeleton, frequently a characteristic of radical or cationic intermediates, has been observed. For example, cyclobutanecarboxylic acid gives some cyclopropyl carbinol:[28]

$$\square CO_2H \rightarrow \square OH + \triangleright CH_2OH$$

Further, optically active 2-methylbutanoic acid gives products containing only racemic 2-butanol, suggesting the intervention of a free, electron-deficient, intermediate.[29] In pyridine solution, electrolysis of a fatty or aromatic acid gives alkyl- or aryl-pyridines or rearrangement products.[30] The catalysis of the polymerization of vinyl monomers is known to proceed through radical and cationic initiators, and it is pertinent to observe that, in organic media, Kolbe decarboxylation is known to initiate such polymerization processes (see **Polymerization of**

Vinyl Monomers, Electrolytic). Still more convincing for the intervention of radicals in the Kolbe decarboxylation in the presence of butadiene or isoprene is the formation of compounds containing two molecules of diene linked together, with the ends of the resulting fragment terminated by the residues from acetic[31] or a dicarboxylic acid monoester.[32] For example, butadiene and ethyl hydrogen succinate give diethyl 5,9-tetradecadiene-1,14-dioate.[32]

$$2C_2H_5O_2C(CH_2)_2CO_2H + 2C_4H_6 \rightarrow$$
$$C_2H_5O_2C(CH_2)_3CH:CH(CH_2)_2CH:CH(CH_2)_3$$
$$\cdot CO_2C_2H_5$$

Finally, kinetic experiments have shown[33] that in both aqueous and acetic acid solution the electrolysis of potassium acetate involves a slow, first-order loss of carbon dioxide by the first-formed acetoxyl radical. On the other hand, ethylene formation from propionate, which is almost the exclusive reaction at 25°C is second order and strongly current-density-dependent,[33, 34] suggesting a reaction involving two propionoxyl radicals. Just as convincing is the anodic acetoxylation of anisole and furan[33] which indicates the independent existence of the acetoxyl radical, although it is a moot point whether such a radical can ever be considered really free of the anode.

References

Since the literature is voluminous, only the most pertinent and recent references are given. For a detailed bibliography the reader is referred to the books and review articles in reference (1).

1. Löb, W., and Lorentz, R., "Electrochemistry of Organic Compounds," New York, John Wiley and Sons, 1905. Arndt, F., "Elektrolytische Methoden," in Houben-Weyl, "Methoden der Organischen Chemie," Vol. II, Leipzig, Thieme, 1925. Brockman, C. J., "Electro-Organic Chemistry," pp. 11–101, New York, John Wiley and Sons, 1926. Müller, E., and Ellingham, H. J. T., "A Laboratory Manual of Electrochemistry," London, Routledge, 1931. Fichter, F., "Organische Elektrochemie," pp. 39–71, Leipzig, Steinkopf, 1942. Glasstone, S., and Hickling, A., "Electrochemical Oxidation and Reduction," pp. 312–331, London, Chapman and Hall Ltd., 1935. Müller, E., "Elektrochemisches Praktikum," Dresden, Steinkopf, 1942. Swann, S., Jr., "Technique of Organic Chemistry. Electrolytic Reactions," New York, Interscience Publishing Co., 1948. Weedon, B. C. L., *Quarterly Reviews,* **6,** 380 (1952).
Allen, M. J., "Organic Electrode Processes, pp. 96–111, New York, Reinhold Publishing Corp., 1958. Weedon, B. C. L., "Advances in Organic Chemistry. Methods and Processes," Vol. I, p. 1, New York, Interscience Publishing Co., 1960.
2. Faraday, M., *Pogg. Annalen,* **33,** 438 (1834).
3. Kolbe, H., *Annalen,* **69,** 257 (1849).
4. (a) Korsching, H., *Naturwissenchaften,* **44,** 89 (1957).
   (b) Pattison, F. L. M., Stothers, J. B., and Woolford, R. G., *J. Amer. Chem. Soc.,* **78,** 2225 (1956).
5. Kronenthal, R. L., (to Colgate Palmolive-Peet Co.), U.S. Patent 2,760,926 (1956). Matsuda, R., Hisano, T., and Kubota, D., *Bull. Chem. Soc. Japan,* **34,** 649 (1961).
6. Glasstone, S., and Hickling, A., *J. Chem. Soc.,* **1934,** 1878.
7. Hofer, H., and Moest, M., *Annalen,* **323,** 284 (1902); Kroenthal, R. L., (to Colgate Palmolive-Peet Co.), U.S. Patent 2,867,569 (1956).
8. Salauze, J., *Bull. Soc. Chim. France,* (4), **37,** 522 (1925); Fioshin, M. Ya., Girina, G. P., Vasil'ev, Yu. B., Krul'ev, M. V., Polievktov, M. K. and Artem'ev, R. G., *Dokl. Akad. Nauk, S.S.S.R.,* **140,** 1388 (1961); *Chem. Abstracts,* **56,** 12658 (1962); Offe, H.-A., (to B.A.S.F. A-g.), German Patents, 854,508 (1952), 880 289 (1953).
9. Wladislaw, B., and Ayres, A. M. J., *J. Org. Chem.,* **27,** 281 (1962).
10. Wilson, C. L., and Lippincott, W. T., *J. Electrochem Soc.,* **103,** 672 (1956).
11. Moser, A., "Die Elektrolytischen Prozesse der Organischen Chemie," Halle, 1910. See also Thiessen, G. W., *Illinois Acad. Sci. Trans.,* **43,** 77 (1950) and Brockman, C. J., Ref. 1.
12. Matsui, M., and Arakawa, S., *Mem. Coll. Sci. Kyoto,* **15A,** 189 (1932).
13. Motoki, S., and Odaka, T., *Nippon Kagaku Zasshi,* **76,** 930 (1955); *Chem. Abstracts,* **51,** 17727 (1957). Idem. Ibid., **77,** 163 (1956); *Chem. Abstracts,* **52,** 268 (1958); Tsuzuki, Y., Motoki, S., and Odaka, G., (to Ajinomoto Co.), Japan Patent 6626 (1957); *Chem. Abstracts,* **52,** 9821 (1958). Tsuzuki, Y., and Motoki, S., (to Ajinomoto Co.), Japan Patent 9458 (1956); *Chem. Abstracts,* **52,** 14656 (1958). Kimura, K., Takahashi, M., and Tanaka, A., *Yakugaku Zasshi,* **78,** 802 (1958); *Chem. Abstracts,* **52,** 16085 (1958).
14. Asano, M., Kameda, S., and Wada, T., *J. Pharm. Soc. Japan,* **64,** (8A), 25 (1944); *Chem. Abstracts,* **45,** 4302 (1951).
15. Asano, M., and Ohta, J., *J. Pharm. Soc. Japan,* **65,** (5/6A), 10 (1945); *Chem. Abstracts,* **45,** 4302h (1951).
16. Crum Brown, A., and Walker, J., *Annalen,* **261,** 107 (1891); *Trans. Roy. Soc. Edinburgh,* **36,** 291 (1891); Offe, H-A. (to B.A.S.F.A-g), German Patent 880,289 (1953).
17. Fuchs, W., and Moritz, H., *Fette, Seifen Anstrichmittel,* **61,** 1124 (1959).

18. VON MILLER, W., AND HOFER, H., *Ber.*, **28**, 2427 (1895); MEHROTA, J. K., AND DEY, A. N., *J. Indian Chem. Soc.*, **38**, 885 (1961).
19. GREAVES, W. S., LINSTEAD, R. P., SHEPHARD, B. R., THOMAS, S. L. S., AND WEEDON, B. C. L., *J. Chem. Soc.*, **1950**, 3326.
20. BOUNDS, D. G., LINSTEAD, R. P., AND WEEDON, B. C. L., *J. Chem. Soc.*, **1954**, 448.
21. HOFFE, H-A., *Z. Naturforsch.*, **2b**, 182, 185 (1947); LINSTEAD, R. P., SHEPHARD, B. R., AND WEEDON, B. C. L., *J. Chem. Soc.*, **1951**, 2854.
22. BOISSONNAS, R. A., *Helv. Chim. Acta*, **35**, 2226 (1952); *Nature*, **171**, 304 (1953).
23. SCHALL, C., *Z. Elektrochem.*, **3**, 83 (1896).
24. FICHTER, F., *Trans. Electrochem. Soc.*, **45**, 131 (1924).
25. HALLIÉ, G., *Rec. trav. chim.*, **57**, 152 (1938); DENINA, E., *Gazzetta*, **68**, 443 (1938); KHOMUTOV, N. E., AND KHACHATURYAN, M. G., *Tr. Mosk. Khim-Tekhnol. Inst.*, **1961**, No. 32, 207; *Chem. Abstracts*, **57**, 7011 (1962).
26. GLASSTONE, S., AND HICKLING, A., *Trans. Far. Soc.*, **31**, 1656 (1935); *Trans. Electrochem. Soc.*, **75**, 333 (1939).
27. WALKER, O. J., AND WEISS, J., *Trans. Far. Soc.*,

31, 1011 (1935); HAÏSSINSKY, M., *Faraday Soc. Discussion*, **1**, 254 (1947).
28. COREY, E. J., BAULD, N. L., LaLONDE, R. T., CASANOVA, J., JR., AND KAISER, E. T., *J. Am. Chem. Soc.* **82**, 2645 (1960).
29. BRENNER, J., AND MISLOW, K., *J. Org. Chem.*, **21**, 1312 (1956); DAUBEN, H. J., AND LIANG, H-T., *Hua Hsueh Hsueh Pao*, **25**, 129 (1959); *Chem. Abstracts*, **54**, 4365 (1960).
30. GOLDSCHMIDT, H., AND MINSINGER, M., *Chem. Ber.*, **87**, 956 (1954); BUNYAN, P. J., AND HEY, D. H., *J. Chem. Soc.*, **1960**, 3787; **1962**, 1360, 2771.
31. SMITH, W. B., AND GILDE, H. G., *J. Am. Chem. Soc.*, **81**, 5325 (1959).
32. LINDSEY, R. V., JR., AND PETERSON, M. L., (to DuPont Co.), U.S. Patent 2,680,713 (1954).
33. LIPPINCOTT, W. T., AND WILSON, C. L., *J. Am. Chem. Soc.*, **78**, 4290 (1956).
34. PANDE, G. S., AND SHUKLA, S. N., *Electrochim. Acta*, **4**, 215 (1961).

CHRISTOPHER L. WILSON

Cross-references: *Electro-Organic Chemistry; Polymerization of Vinyl Monomers, Electrolytic.*

L

LASER

Laser is an acronym for Light Amplification by Stimulated Emission of Radiation. The laser is usually operated as a generator of radiation rather than a pure amplifier and the name is commonly applied to devices which operate in the visible, infrared and ultraviolet regions of the spectrum. The term Optical Maser is used synonymously with laser but only occasionally, even though historically it is the original name.[1, 2, 3]

The Nature of Stimulated Emission

Fundamental to an understanding of the operation of a laser is an understanding of stimulated emission. To illustrate stimulated emission it will be assumed that an atom, ion, molecule, or crystal has only two energy states, or levels, which are separated by an energy E, as shown in Fig. 1. If the hypothetical atomic system is initially in the lower of these energy states, the "ground" state, and is left unperturbed by any outside influence, it will remain there indefinitely. If, however, the atom is placed in an electromagnetic field, it may absorb a photon from the field and subsequently be found in the upper, or excited, energy state. The atom has thus been induced or stimulated to make a transition from the lower of its two energy states to the upper state. After the transition has been made, the energy of the atom has increased by E and the number of photons in the field has decreased by one, so that the energy in the electromagnetic field has decreased by E. The probability that this transition will occur in a given time interval is proportional to the number of photons having an energy E present in the field before the transition occurs and thus is zero if none is present.

In a way which is completely analogous to absorption, an atom initially in its excited state may interact with photons having the energy E and be induced to make a transition to its ground state. The probabilities that transitions from either the ground or excited state to the other state are induced are exactly equal. A very important difference between the two, however, is that in absorption a photon is destroyed and the atom acquires its energy, whereas in stimulated emission a photon is created and the atom loses energy. Therefore, if one could prepare a number of atoms in their excited states and allow them to interact with photons having energy E, they would be stimulated to emit more photons of energy E, thus amplifying the intensity of the radiation field. Once a particular atom has made the transition to the ground state, it must be removed from the field or it may reabsorb energy. If one can continuously maintain more atoms in the excited state than in the ground state, one may continuously amplify radiation of a frequency, $\nu = E/h$, where h is Planck's constant.

The significant property of a stimulated emission amplifier is that the photons emitted in the induced transitions are coherent with those in the radiation field before the transition occurs. Thus, if all of the photons in the field have the same energy, which is close to the atom's "resonance" energy, E, the emitted photon will have the same energy as the other photons. Similarly, if all of the photons are travelling in the same direction, the added photon will travel in that direction.

Spontaneous emission is the more familiar emission process in the visible region of the spectrum, such as that in luminescence and incandescence. An atom initially in its excited state will not remain there, even in the complete absence of any perturbing field. It may spontaneously return or relax to the ground state and create a photon. This photon will have approximately the energy E, the separation of the

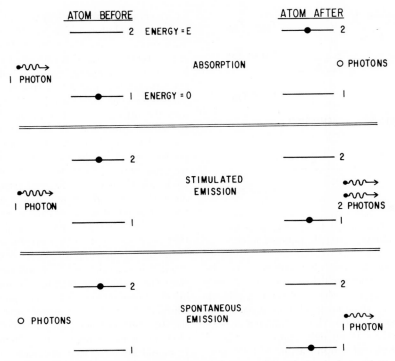

FIG. 1. A schematic representation of the meaning of absorption, stimulated emission, and spontaneous emission.

energy levels. This is never a precisely defined energy, however, and spontanously emitted radiation may have a spectral breadth, $\Delta E/E$, ranging from a few parts per million up to fifty per cent, which is to be contrasted with a stimulated transition in which the emitted radiation is precisely determined by the stimulating field. The spontaneously emitted photons may also leave the atom in essentially any direction.

The Generation of a Population Inversion

Any atomic system in thermal equilibrium will always have a greater probability of being in the lower of any two of its energy states. Thus, the number of atoms, or "population," in the lower of two states will always be larger than that for a higher lying state. Therefore, radiation which passes through matter is ordinarily absorbed. The thermal equilibrium situation is considered the normal one so the condition required for a stimulated emission amplifier, with more atoms in the upper of a particular pair of states, is called a population inversion.

The method of obtaining a population inversion that is simplest conceptually is to identify, by some means, those atoms in the excited state

and move them physically to the area where they will amplify the radiation. After they have experienced a transition to the ground state they must be removed so that they do not reabsorb radiation.

It is usually not practical to separate physically those atoms or molecules in the excited state from those in the ground state. Three more generally applicable schemes for achieving a population inversion will be outlined here. The first of these is termed optical pumping and is the most commonly-used method in solid-state lasers. Fig. 2 illustrates the energy level scheme of an idealized atomic system having four allowed energy states. Assume that it is desired to produce an inversion between levels 1 and 2 and thus amplify radiation corresponding to the energy difference of these levels. An atom, molecule, or ion is chosen which has the following properties: (1) when it is placed in energy level 3 it tends to relax into level 2 much more frequently than into levels 1 or 0, (2) when it is placed in level 2 it tends to relax to level 1 rather than 0, and (3) it relaxes from level 1 to level 0 more rapidly than it decays from level 2 to level 1.

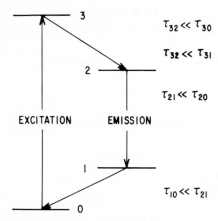

FIG. 2. The energy level scheme of an idealized 4-level optically pumped laser.

If atoms having these characteristics are excited with radiation which causes transitions from level 0 to level 3, they will tend to pile up on level 2 more than on level 1 because of the relative transition rates, thus producing a population inversion. If enough atoms are placed in level 2, sufficient amplification will be produced to make a practical amplifier. Optical pumping is practical because a number of solid materials have been found in which the transition from level 0 to 3 can be induced over a range of energies so that the spectrally broad incoherent emission from a pumping lamp can be utilized.

These broad absorption bands are not present in atomic gases so that one generally resorts to a second inversion technique, excitation with an electron current. This has the advantage that an electron need not give all of its energy to an atom so that it need not have precisely the energy difference between levels 0 and 3. This feature also has the disadvantage that the electrons can excite the atoms to nearly any level so that one tends to lose the selective excitation that is present in optical pumping. Nevertheless, gaseous lasers with this type of excitation have been made to operate at well over 100 different wavelengths. Most of these are transitions of noble gas atoms.

The third fundamental means of achieving a population inversion is the injection technique employed in the semiconductor laser. The energy levels of a semiconductor relevant to its operation as a laser form two groups, each with a very large number of closely-spaced levels. The two groups, or energy bands, are separated

by an energy corresponding to that of the visible or infrared photon which will be amplified. The semiconductor has the further distinction from the systems described earlier in that an electron in a particular energy state is not localized in the crystal but instead is free to move about. Thus, electrons may be injected from a contact into the upper of the two energy bands, travel part way across the crystal, then fall from the upper band of levels to the lower, emitting a photon. Once in the lower band the electrons continue across the crystal to the opposite electrode where they are removed from the crystal. Near the electrode which injects electrons into the semiconductor there will be more electrons in the upper energy band than in the lower so that there is a population inversion.

In the semiconductor laser one uses semiconductor material to inject and remove carriers from the amplifying region. The material which injects the electrons into the region where the stimulated transitions occur (n-type) has a slightly different composition from that of the electrode which removes the electrons (p-type). It should be noted that although the population inversion is produced in the semiconductor, the pumping, or excitation, occurs in the power supply which drives the electrons through the semiconductor.

In each of the three basic schemes for achieving a population inversion, optical pumping, electron impact excitation or electrical excitation and injection into a semiconductor, the schemes have been described only superficially here and a great many important details have been omitted.

The Construction of a Generator of Coherent Radiation

Most of the technological applications of lasers are based on their ability to generate an intense, well-collimated beam of radiation. To construct such a source an oscillator is made which oscillates in only one, or at most a few, simple modes, and a simple optical system can then easily be arranged to convert the emission into a collimated beam.

Any oscillator consists of an amplifier and some means of feeding back part of the amplifier's output to its input. As an amplifier, an ensemble of excited atoms or ions which will be contained in a tube, a crystal rod, or a variety of other forms may be used. A plane wave of radiation of the proper frequency which enters one end of the rod emerges from the opposite end with a greater intensity. If mirrors are added to the ends of the rod, a fraction of the radiation will be reflected back into the rod and be reamplified. The device will oscillate in the steady state if the amplification on one pass through the rod just makes up for the losses, such as those caused by the reflection at the mirrors, scattering, etc. To obtain a useful output from the oscillator one mirror is made partially transmitting. For the details of the actual forms that lasers assume and also for a more quantitative discussion of their operation, the interested reader is referred to Lengyel's book "Lasers,"[4] to "Advances in Quantum Electronics,"[5] and to the Proceedings of the Third International Symposium on Quantum Electronics.[6]

Applications of Lasers

A great many applications have been proposed for lasers but the areas in which lasers might be fruitfully employed will be discussed here only in very general terms. As previously mentioned, the characteristic of the laser which should prove most useful is that it emits coherently over a large portion of its radiating surface and thus its radiation can be collimated into a beam with a divergence much smaller than usually achievable. The divergence of a beam is at best limited by diffraction from the radiating aperture. The angle of divergence is then of the order of λ/D where D is the diameter of the aperture. Since light has a much smaller wavelength than the electromagnetic radiation generated by vacuum tubes, a much smaller diameter of the radiator is required to achieve a given divergence, and a much smaller device may be used to efficiently transmit a beam over large distances. This feature leads the engineer to hope that he will someday be able to construct communications links with laser transmitters, and perhaps laser receivers. Another attractive feature of the laser for this application is its very high frequency which in principle increases the amount of information which may be transmitted on one beam.

The ease with which a laser beam may be collimated also implies that the beam may be brought to a very sharp focus. The size of the focus of a collimated beam is θf, where θ is the beam divergence and f is the focal length of the lens. If $\theta = \lambda/D$, the spot size is $\lambda f/D$.

The ratio D/f is the angular aperture of the lens and is not usually greater than one so that the spot size is usually larger than λ. By using a laser source, for which λ is very small, the radiation may be concentrated into a very small area, of the order of 10^{-8} sq cm, for purposes of micromachining, welding of refractory materials, surgery, etc. Coupled with this is the fact that very large powers have been produced with relatively small laser devices. The Q-spoiled laser of McClung and Hellwarth[7] has produced powers in excess of 10 megawatts for periods of 10 nanoseconds. Geusic and Scovil[6] have described a high-power ruby amplifier which they predict may reach 10^{12} watts output in 10^{-11} second pulses.

Some of the applications proposed for lasers make use of its temporal coherence or extremely narrow spectral output. Because its emission frequency may, in some devices, be extremely accurately defined the laser may be used as a time standard, although lower frequency devices are usually more suited for this. In principle, one could use a gaseous laser to measure changes of the order of 10^{-4} inches in lengths up to 10^4 miles long.[8]

It seems certain that the laser will soon prove quite useful in the laboratory as an analytical tool. However, the large-scale commercial applications may be somewhat further in the future.

References

1. SCHAWLOW, A. L., AND TOWNES, C. H., *Phys. Rev.*, **112**, 1940 (1958).
2. SCHAWLOW, A. L., *Solid State Journal*, **2**, 21 (1961).
3. SCHAWLOW, A. L., *Scientific American*, **204**, 52 (1961).
4. LENGYEL, B. A., "Lasers," New York and London, John Wiley and Sons, Inc., 1962.
5. SINGER, J. R., Editor, "Advances in Quantum Electronics," New York and London, Columbia University Press, 1961.
6. Proceedings of the Third International Conference on Quantum Electronics, to be published by Columbia University Press.
7. McCLUNG, F. J., AND HELLWARTH, R. W., *J. Appl. Phys.*, **33**, 828 (1962).
8. JASEJA, T. S., JAVAN, A., AND TOWNES, C. H., *Phys. Rev. Letters*, **10**, 165 (1963).

J. D. KINGSLEY

Cross-references: *Electroluminescence; Fluorescence; Luminescence; Phosphorescence; Phosphors; Scintillation Counters.*

LEAD DIOXIDE ANODE

The lead dioxide anode is an electrode of massive lead dioxide in an extremely hard and dense form. It is produced by electrodeposition on a suitable base material from an aqueous lead salt bath. This form of lead dioxide is of increasing interest as an inert anode in electrochemical processes. Its many favorable properties make it a promising substitute for the platinum anode.

Other forms of lead dioxide, such as thin flash coatings which may be formed on lead anodes in sodium hydroxide solution, or the pasted lead dioxide anodes of the lead storage battery, are not included in this discussion.

Background

Platinum has long been the favored anode material for electrochemical processes because of its high oxygen overvoltage and low erosion and dissolution rates. However, platinum requires a large capital investment, and its anodic losses, while small in volume, may be significant in dollar value. Also, with rising requirements for platinum in the United States in the period after World War II, it was felt that the supply might not be adequate in times of national emergency. Therefore, interest in other inert and high current efficiency anode materials was aroused.

The production of sodium perchlorate by the electrolysis of a concentrated sodium chlorate solution is of particular interest and importance in relation to this need for inert anode material. In the period of 1951–1954, Pennsalt Chemicals Corporation under a research contract from the Office of Naval Research explored alternate anodes to replace platinum in the electrolytic oxidation of sodium chlorate to perchlorate. A lead dioxide anode made by electrodeposition of lead dioxide from a lead nitrate bath on tantalum and nickel metal cores was developed. Based on this research effort, American Potash and Chemical Corporation (Western Electrochemical Company) carried out a development study under a Navy Bureau of Ordnance contract during 1954–1956. A pilot plant cell was designed, constructed, and successfully operated for the conversion of sodium chlorate to perchlorate in which lead dioxide anodes were used. In 1962, Pacific Engineering and Production Company of Nevada was reported to be producing lead

dioxide anodes commercially and using them in electrolytic cells for the production of sodium perchlorate.

The technical literature shows a strong, continuing interest, beginning about 1934, in lead dioxide anodes and their use in electrochemical oxidations. Recent work has been concentrated on improvements in the process for electrodepositing lead dioxide and on means for increasing the anode current efficiency in process use.

Forming Lead Dioxide Anodes

Several types of baths from which lead dioxide may be plated have been proposed, including those based on alkaline lead tartrate, neutral lead perchlorate, and acid lead nitrate. The lead nitrate bath is preferred, since it may readily be controlled over long plating periods and gives a high-quality deposit over a relatively wide range of operating conditions. A typical bath composition is:

Lead nitrate, $Pb(NO_3)_2$	250–350 gpl
Copper nitrate, $Cu(NO_3)_2 \cdot H_2O$	1.5–4.0 gpl
*Surface-active agent	0.5–2.0 gpl

* Preferably a nonionic of the class of alkyl phenoxy polyoxyethylene ethanol, as for example, "Igepal CO-880" (Trademark General Dyestuff Corporation).

The addition of copper nitrate serves to suppress lead deposition on the cathode, which may be carbon, graphite, or copper. A suitable surface-active agent ensures deposition of lead dioxide of high strength, density, and surface smoothness. Other additives, such as nickel nitrate and sodium fluoride, also have been proposed. Periodic additions of 35 per cent hydrogen peroxide are claimed to aid in maintaining anode plating efficiency above 85 per cent. Regeneration of the plating bath to maintain production of high-quality lead dioxide deposits has also been effected by additions of n-amyl alcohol to used cell effluent. The n-amyl alcohol removes residual surface-active agents, and its altered products in a separated liquid layer which is decanted. A fresh amount of surface-active agent is then added to the regenerated plating solution.

Initial bath pH is about 3.5 and during anodic lead dioxide plating the pH is usually controlled in the range of 2 to 4 by the frequent addition of lead oxide. Strong, dense deposits of lead dioxide in thicknesses of 2.5 cm or more have been obtained by operating the bath at an anode current density of 0.016 to 0.032 amp/sq cm (15 to 30 amp/sq ft) and a temperature of 70°C. Impurities in the bath, such as iron or cobalt compounds, can drastically reduce the strength, density, and surface smoothness of lead dioxide deposits.

Lead dioxide deposits on iron or steel base surfaces are difficult to form in the acid nitrate bath because of dissolution of the base. This dissolution effect may be minimized by maintaining a bath pH of 4 or above. With careful control of the bath at 2 to 4 pH, nickel is a satisfactory anode base. Anode bases which are essentially independent of bath acidity are tantalum, platinum-clad tantalum, carbon, and graphite. Tantalum metal as a plating base has the further advantage that in subsequent electrolytic use of the lead dioxide anode the tantalum rapidly polarizes and then acts as an inert, noneroding filler. Other metal bases, such as nickel and steel, are gradually dissolved during electrolytic use of the lead dioxide anode.

Nodular-free deposits are most easily formed on wire or rod-form cores or bases. Where flat, rectangular anodes are desired, deposits may be formed on both sides of screen or expanded metal mesh. In this case, inert, nonconducting baffles closely spaced about the anode edges permit formation of nodular-free deposits within close dimensional tolerances.

Properties

Two modifications of lead dioxide have been reported, the orthorhombic α-PbO_2 and the tetragonal β-PbO_2. The massive form electrodeposited from the lead nitrate bath is β-PbO_2 which has a higher oxygen overvoltage than the α-PbO_2. This oxygen overvoltage is comparable to that of platinum. When dried at 80 to 90°C the water content is about 0.2 per cent. With a resistivity as low as 40×10^{-6} ohm-cm, the dense lead dioxide is a better electrical conductor than many metals and a much better conductor than carbon or graphite. Chemically it is inert to most oxidizing agents and resistant to many strong acids. While massive, electrodeposited lead dioxide is rather brittle, it has adequate strength for ordinary handling when plated in rod or plate form to thicknesses of 0.5 cm or greater. It is extremely hard, dense, and metallic in appearance with a gray to black coloration.

Current Contacts

For successful use of the lead dioxide anode, a durable, low-resistance current contact must be made. When a conventional clamp-type current contact of copper or other usual conductor metal is made directly to the lead dioxide, a high contact resistance and local heating results. This high contact resistance is also observed when current contact is made to the core when this is a metal, such as nickel, iron, or steel. However, when a thin spray coating, 0.002 cm or less in thickness, of a noble metal such as silver is first applied to the top of the lead dioxide anode, an extremely low-resistance current contact may be made by any of the usual means. Preferably, the thin silver coating is protected by a further spraying with a heavy layer of copper to form a jacket about the top end of the anode. Where the lead dioxide is plated on a carbon or graphite core, the same unplated top portion of the core may be successfully utilized as current contact in both the electrodeposition of the lead dioxide and in the subsequent electrochemical use of the lead dioxide anode.

Applications

Lead dioxide has been proposed as an insoluble anode for the electrolysis of aqueous solutions containing such anions as Cl^-, Br^-, I^-, F^-, ClO^-, ClO_3^-, ClO_4^-, SO_4^{-2}, NO_3^-, CO_3^{-2}, and $C_2H_3O_2^-$. Lead dioxide has been used in sodium chloride electrolysis for chlorine production, where it is reported to have a low chlorine overvoltage. Also, it is claimed to be efficient in very dilute hydrochloric acid, allowing chlorine formation at almost reversible potential. Lead dioxide, however, is attacked by concentrated hydrochloric acid. In the oxidation of iodic acid, HIO_3, to periodic acid, HIO_4, with an anode of lead dioxide, the current efficiency is 100 per cent as compared to only 1 per cent at smooth platinum. This is an example of the catalytic activity of the anode. The electrolytic oxidation of starch has also been carried out at a lead dioxide anode. A perchloric acid power cell from which high currents may be drawn at temperatures as low as −20°C has positive plates of lead dioxide plated on an inert conducting grid such as palladium. The negative plates of this cell are lead metal, and the electrolyte is aqueous perchloric acid.

Greatest interest for lead dioxide anode use

has been in cells for electrochemical oxidation of sodium chlorate to perchlorate. Perchlorate cells using lead dioxide anodes are very similar in structural details and operating conditions to those using platinum anodes. One striking difference is that whereas in the platinum-anode cell, 0.5 to 5 gpl of sodium dichromate is added to improve current efficiency, in the lead dioxide-anode cell presence of chromate reduces current efficiency. As a result, the mild steel cathodes in the platinum-anode cell which are protected by the chromate ion are replaced by stainless steel or nickel in the chromate-free lead dioxide cell. The most effective additives for improving current efficiency in the lead dioxide-anode cell are sodium fluoride and potassium persulfate used at concentrations of 0.5 to 2.5 gpl. Other typical cell operating conditions are:

Sodium chlorate	500–600 gpl
Anode current density	0.16–0.32 amp/sq cm (150–300 amp/sq ft)
Voltage	5–6.5
Temperature	25–40° C
pH (adjusted with HCl)	6.0–6.8

Cumulative current efficiency with suitable additive approaches that obtained with the platinum anode, being 80 per cent or better down to a chlorate concentration of 100 gpl. Below this concentration current efficiency drops rapidly with both platinum and lead dioxide anodes.

Although judgment must be made on a rather limited experience to date beyond the laboratory stage, electrodeposited lead dioxide shows promise of development to a high efficiency as an inert and insoluble anode of long, indefinite life in electrochemical processes.

References

1. GRIGGER, J. C., MILLER, H. C., AND LOOMIS, F. D., J. Electrochem. Soc., **105**, 100 (1958).
2. NARASIMHAM, K. C., SUNDARARAJAN, S., AND UDUPA, H. V. K., J. Electrochem. Soc., **108**, 798 (1961).
3. SCHUMACHER, J. C., STERN, D. R., AND GRAHAM, P. R., J. Electrochem. Soc., **105**, 151 (1958).
4. SHIBASAKI, Y., J. Electrochem. Soc., **105**, 624 (1958).
5. SUGINO, K., Bull. Chem. Soc. Japan, **23**, 115 (1950).

J. C. GRIGGER

Cross-references: *Bromates, Electrolytic Production; Perchlorates; Periodates, Electrolytic Preparation.*

LEAD ELECTROREFINING AND ELECTROPLATING

Lead Electrorefining

Electrolytes which have been studied and proposed for the electrodeposition of lead are numerous. The first attempts to refine lead electrolytically were carried out by Hampe with an acetate electrolyte. His experimental work was extended by Keith who tried to refine lead on a commercial scale by using a solution of sodium acetate in which lead sulfate was dissolved. Tommasi proposed to refine lead using an acetate solution as the electrolyte and a rotating disc of aluminum bronze as the cathode. L. Glaser made a series of tests with a number of electrolytes and claims to have secured a solid lead deposit. Leuchs was the first to electrolyze lead fluosilicate and lead fluoborate solutions.

Anson G. Betts deserves the credit for providing a practical solution for the problem of electrolytic refining of lead. In 1901 he developed and patented a fluosilicate process which had commercial application, and this process is used almost exclusively for electrolytically refined lead today.

Because Betts was the first to develop and put into commercial practice his process on an economic scale at Consolidated Mining and Smelting Company of Canada, Limited in Trail, B. C., the means of producing lead by electrolysis of its salts is commonly referred to as the Betts process. The Betts process eliminates practically all of the bismuth from the lead and makes it recoverable from the slimes. Thus, it has had a special field in refining lead bullion with high bismuth content. Successful processes have been developed for removing bismuth by pyrometallurgical methods of refining, but these are often costly when bismuth content of lead is high.

In recent years, attention has been given to a new electrolyte having a base of sulfamic acid. The use of electrolytes, consisting of the salts of sulfamic acid, was introduced in electroplating and in hydrometallurgy by L. Cambi and R. Piontelli in 1937. The process has found application in recent years.

Processes. The Betts and sulfamic acid parallel one another in many respects except for the electrolyte composition. Since the sulfamic acid process is relatively new and as yet has not found widespread commercial application, only a brief description of this process is given.

In the sulfamate process, the cells are the same as those used in the Betts process. Anodes with lead content of 95 per cent plus are used and the starting sheet is made from refined lead. The electrolyte is composed of about 80 gpl of lead and 100 gpl of sulfamic acid, H_3NSO_3H. Current density employed is 10 to 12 amps per square foot. Cell voltage ranges from 0.5 to 0.65 volts. Efficiencies of 95 per cent are reported and purity of refined lead is stated to be 99.99 per cent. The advantages claimed for the process are as follows:

1) The electrolyte (a) has high solubility of acid and its salts, (b) has strong reactivity and low toxicity, (c) is not hygroscopic, being solid, and easy to handle and store, making the bath preparation simple.

2) Tin content of anodes which passes entirely to the cathode in Betts electrolysis is harmless until the content exceeds 1.0 per cent. In addition, bismuth, copper, silver and arsenic give no trouble.

3) The corrosion of impure anodes is more regular than in the Betts process because fluosilicates are more easily hydrolyzed than the sulfamates in the slime blanket where they attain very high concentrations.

4) Electrolyte losses in the anode slimes are less significant than for the Betts process.

It is possible that the sulfamic acid process may gain more widespread attention as it becomes better known.

Betts Process. Major plants now employing the Betts process, or a modification of it, are the Consolidated Mining and Smelting Company of Canada, Limited at Trail, B. C., which was the pioneer; Cerro de Pasco Corporation in La Oroya, Peru, S. A.; U. S. S. Lead Refinery, Inc., in East Chicago, Indiana; and Montevecchio Soc. Italiana del Piombo e dello Zinco in San Gavino Monreale, Sardinia. These four major plants have a capacity for electrolytically refining 345,000 short tons of lead per year with the following individual capacities, in short tons.

Consolidated Mining & Smelting Co. of Canada, Limited	175,000
Cerro de Pasco Corporation	90,000
U. S. S. Lead Refinery, Inc.	40,000
Montevecchio Soc. Italiana del Piombo e dello Zinco	40,000

In addition to the above major refineries it is reported there are eight electrolytic lead refineries in operation in Japan with a total annual refining capacity of 64,000 short tons. The U.S.S.R. also has an electrolytic lead refinery with an annual capacity of 30,000 short tons. In 1962 there was an annual electrolytic refining capacity of approximately 438,000 short tons which amounts to about 12 per cent of the present day total installed refining capacity for lead.

Electrodes. Bullion from the lead furnace is drossed for copper by cooling. Soluble copper compounds separate from the lead and rise to the surface of the kettle from which they are skimmed. Copper content is reduced to 0.05 per cent or less. If tin is present, it must be removed. That is done by oxidation in kettles with agitation provided by high-speed stirrers. Anodes are cast in open molds on a circular casting wheel. They are cast with lugs to support them and to make electrical contact with the bus-bars on the cells. A thin anode is used in lead refining as compared with that used in copper refining. This is because during electrolysis most of the impurities cling to the anode as slime, thus increasing resistance to the current. Some slime may drop to the bottom of the cell, particularly if the lead content of the bullion refined is high. The cells must, therefore, be cleaned at periodic intervals. Through suspension, small amounts of slime may also be deposited at the cathode. Generally the anodes contain 98 per cent or more lead, the remaining percentage being bismuth, antimony, copper, arsenic, tellurium, silver, and gold. Antimony is usually the chief impurity to the extent of 1 per cent or more. At Cerro de Pasco Corporation in La Oroya, Peru, anodes containing about 96 per cent lead are used, and the resulting refined lead is of very high purity.

Cathode starting sheets were originally prepared by pouring melted electrolytic lead down an inclined cast iron plate, thus forming a sheet of lead about 1/32 in. thick. The starting sheets are still made this way, but in recent years a continuous method for casting starting sheets from molten lead has been developed by Consolidated Mining and Smelting Company, Ltd. of Canada. The cathodes are usually about 1/2 to 1 in. larger than the anodes in length and width. They are suspended from copper crossrods and are placed in the cells alternating with the anodes.

Electrolyte. Acid used in the preparation of the electrolyte can be purchased or produced at the refinery. Where it is necessary to manufacture electrolyte, the following process is used.

A mixture of fluorspar and sulfuric acid is heated in a retort or a revolving drum which produces hydrofluoric acid, according to the equation

$$CaF_2 + H_2SO_4 \rightarrow CaSO_4 + 2HF$$

Hydrofluoric acid is liberated as a gas which is absorbed in water. The resultant hydrofluoric acid is mixed with fine silica to produce fluosilicic acid as follows:

$$6HF + SiO_2 \rightarrow H_2SiF_6 + 2H_2O$$

The above results in an aqueous solution of about 33 per cent fluosilicic acid. Lead fluosilicate is made by circulating the acid through boxes containing granulated lead, litharge, or basic carbonate. To assure a deposit of good physical characteristics, addition agents, such as glue or goulac, are added. Normal electrolyte will carry about 7 to 9 per cent lead, 10 to 14 per cent combined fluosilicic acid, and 5 to 8 per cent free fluosilicic acid.

Operating Conditions. Operating conditions are similar to those used in the multiple process for the electrolytic refining of copper. In electrolytic lead refining, however, the amount of lead deposited per ampere hour at 100 per cent current efficiency is 3.8590 grams which is equivalent to 0.2042 lb per ampere day.

The electrodes are placed alternately in the cells with about 2¼ in. center to center spacing. The number of electrodes per cell varies from plant to plant. The temperature of the electrolyte is maintained between 35 and 48°C. It is circulated through cells at rates varying from 2 to 6 gallons per minute. Metals which tend to accumulate in the electrolyte are iron, zinc, nickel, cobalt, and thallium. Fortunately, these metals are not present in lead bullion to any extent or, with the exception of thallium, are removed in drossing before the lead bullion is cast into anodes. There is no tendency for impurities, except thallium, to collect in the electrolyte, and thallium is removed with lead peroxide when lead is stripped periodically from the electrolyte by means of insoluble graphite anodes.

The cells are operated at potentials of 0.35 to 0.65 volts. Lowest voltage is obtained with new anodes and the highest with the old. The voltage increases because of the resistance of the anode slime blanket. Current density employed is dependent upon impurities present in the impure bullion, but ranges from 16 to 22 amperes per square foot in the major refineries.

The life of the anode is dependent on the amount of the impurities present. Generally two cathode pulls are made for each anode change. In electrolytic refineries employing a six-to-ten day anode cycle, the anodes are taken from the cells at the end of the cathode cycle, and the slime is removed. The anodes are then reset in the cells with new starting sheets. Current efficiencies generally range from 93 to 95 per cent of the theoretical figure. The amount of return anode scrap in lead refining is much higher than in copper refining because only 65 to 75 per cent of the anode is dissolved.

An electrolyte loss of 2–5 pounds of fluosilicic acid per ton of refined lead is attributed in part to the dissociation of the acid. Definite systems for recovering acid from the anode slime are used. At Cerro de Pasco's refinery in Peru, where the slime is almost completely adherent because of the lower lead content in the anode, the slime is washed in place on the anodes by means of a counter-current wash system to eliminate acid. The slime is then removed by high-pressure water sprays in a mechanical washing machine, dewatered, and filtered prior to treatment for recovery of the metal values it contains. At other major plants, the adherent slime is removed from the anode by mechanical means. It is heated in rubber-lined steel tanks and after settling, the supernatant liquid is syphoned off and returned to holding tanks for addition to the main electrolyte circulating system. Operating data for three major refineries are tabulated in Table 1.

Melting and Casting. On removal from the cells the lead cathodes are dip washed in water. After washing, the copper cross-rods are removed from the cathodes and the cathodes melted. Cross-rods are cleaned periodically by tumbling in a drum with wood chips or by immersion in boiling water. After cleaning they are sometimes given a dip in a light lubricating oil which provides a protective coating. The cathodes are melted in welded steel kettles and removal of the very small amount of impurities which have been occluded in the deposited metal, mainly as slime or electrolyte, is then carried out. The molten lead is heated to about 500°C and air is introduced into the bath either by means of compressed air through a pipe or by a stirrer. This mixes the metal and oxidizes the minor amount of arsenic and antimony it may contain. The oxides are collected on the surface of the lead bath together with some litharge and are skimmed prior to casting the metal into pigs or other commercial shapes. In recent years a small amount of caustic has been mixed into the lead with a stirrer following the air agitation. This brings the impurity level down to a very low degree. A typical analysis by per cent of electrolytically refined lead is:

Ag	Cu	Bi	Sb	As	Sn	Fe	Pb (by difference)
0.0001	0.0005	0.0015	0.0001	0.0001	0.0001	0.0001	99.9975

Anode Slime Treatment. Insoluble impurities in lead anodes consist of bismuth, antimony, copper, arsenic, tellurium, selenium, silver, and gold. Regardless of how acid is removed from the anode slime, the slime must be dewatered and partially dried prior to melting.

The partially dry slimes are then melted, and some of the impurities volatilized pass off with the furnace gas. Metal from the first melt is treated in either reverberatory or converter type furnaces. Arsenic and antimony are volatilized as oxides. These oxides pass off with the fume gas and are collected in a baghouse or Cottrell precipitator. Fume collected contains principally antimony, arsenic, lead, and silver. All of the antimony is not recovered as fume; the last of it is collected as an antimony slag combined with considerable litharge. Slag is returned to the lead blast furnace circuit if a smelter is operated in conjunction with refinery, or can be worked up into antimonial lead. After arsenic and antimony are removed, bismuth along with some of the copper, silver, and gold is slagged. This slag is retained for recovery of the metals it contains. Metal from the oxidizing operation is treated in cupels for the recovery of silver and gold. Bismuth slags which result from the treatment of the slime are reduced to form a crude bismuth metal which can be refined either by pyrometallurgical or electrolytic methods. If copper is refined electrolytically in the same location, lead and copper slime may be treated together for the recovery of contained metal values as the addition of copper slimes to lead slimes does not change the basic process. This is done by Cerro de Pasco Corporation in La Oroya, Peru and flow sheets of the slimes treatment plant there are shown in Figs. 1 and 2.

Lead Electroplating

The appearance and properties of lead limit its commercial use largely to the field of corrosion protection. Lead has not been extensively electroplated because the low melting point of the metal (327°C) has made it possible to use a hot dipping process. For the hot dip process, lead must be alloyed with tin because lead in its pure state does not adhere readily to iron. It has been pointed out, however, that lead plating is superior to lead dipping. The deposit is less porous, and it is ductile.

Lead plating is used principally in linings for chemical apparatus, pipes, and pipe fittings employed in contact with corrosive fumes and liquids, and for nuts, bolts, and storage battery parts. It also has application in bearing alloys in the aircraft industry.

Lead has been deposited from a great number of solutions. They include nitrate, acetate, fluoborate, perchlorate, oxalate, dithionate, and sulfamate. Of the numerous baths, the fluoborate is the most commonly used. The sulfamate bath has gained wider recognition in recent years. Concentrated solutions of the fluoborate bath and sulfamate salt mixtures are marketed by several chemical manufacturers.

Lead Plating. The composition of the fluoborate bath varies depending on the thickness of the deposit. Typical bath compositions are as follows:

	Fluid oz/gallon
Lead fluoborate (50%)	24–54
Free fluoboric acid (42%)	4–8
Free boric acid	3–6
Glue-gelatin	0.02–0.04

For the dilute bath, a cathode current density of 10 to 20 amperes per square foot is used. With the concentrated bath, cathode current density is from 20 to 60 amperes per square foot. Anode and cathode current efficiencies are generally 100 per cent so there is no problem in obtaining bath balance. High-purity lead anodes are used.

In the sulfamate bath, the solution consists essentially of lead sulfamate with sufficient acid to give the solution a pH of about 1.5. The acid is stable and nonhygroscopic. Characteristics and operation of the sulfamate bath are similar

TABLE 1. Operating Data of Three Lead Electrorefineries

	Plant A	Plant B	Plant C
Cells			
Size-l. x w. x d.	9'-5" x 34" x 48"	15' x 38" x 48"	11'-6" x 30" x 48"
No. anodes-cathodes	24–25	33–34	28–29
Mtls. of constr.	Conc.-Asphalt Lined	Conc.-Asphalt Lined	Conc.-Asphalt Lined
Anodes			
Composition	Pb-98.3%, Cu-0.05% As-0.3%, Sb-1.0% Bi-0.06%, Ag-80 oz/t Au-0.101 oz/t	Pb-96.8%, Cu-0.05% As-0.15%, Sb-1.8% Bi-0.7%, Ag-113 oz/t Au-0.12 oz/t	Pb-98% Sb-1.5%
Size-l. x w. x thk.	30-⅛ x 26 x ¼" Submerged	37 x 27 x 1"	36 x 24 x 1-¼"
Weight, lb	430	330	470
Life, days	6	4	10
Per cent scrap	33	40	28
Cathodes			
Size-l. x w. x thk.	39 x 27 x 0.025"	38 x 28 x ⅛"	37-½ x 28 x 0.023"
Weight, lb (start)	12	12	11
Mode suspension	Wrapped	1 large loop	3 strips folded
Life, days	3	4	5
Weight cathode, lb	160	165	175
Electrolyte			
Pb, gpl	85	76	55
Total H_2SiF_6, gpl	155	128	100
Free H_2SiF_6, gpl	95	75	61
Temperature, °C	40–48	38	44
Circulation, gal/min	4–6	2	3–4
Reagents	Glue-goulac	Glue-goulac	Glue-goulac
Current			
Amps/sq/ft	22.3	15.0	14–16
Voltage per tank	—	0.4–0.65	0.4–0.62
Current, amps	6000	7600	5000
Current efficiency, %	93	94.5	93
Kwh/lb	—	0.084	0.092
Anode Slime Composition	—	Ag-10%, Au-0.01% Pb-16%, Sb-41% As-1.4%, Bi-16% Cu-1.2%, Te-1.0%	Ag-15%, Au-0.3% Pb-9%, Sb-50% As-2.5%, Sn-0.06% Cu-0.60%, Te-0.43%

Plant Identification
Plant A—Consolidated Mining and Smelting Company, Ltd., Trail, B. C.
Plant B—Cerro de Pasco Corporation, La Oroya, Peru, S.A.
Plant C—U.S.S. Lead Refinery, Inc., East Chicago, Indiana

to those of the fluoborate bath. With the sulfamate bath, cathode current densities range from 5 to 40 amperes per square foot and bath temperatures from 75 to 100°F. High-purity lead anodes are also recommended.

When lead is deposited on steel, the steel is prepared by usual cleaning and pickling steps. Although lead can be plated directly on iron and steel from a fluoborate bath, it has been found desirable to use a copper strike on the article to be plated. This improves the covering power of the bath. The copper strike is particularly advantageous if the steel or cast iron surface is rough.

Lead-tin Plating. The lead-tin fluoborate bath is essentially the same as the lead fluoborate bath except that a second addition agent, resorcinol, is generally used along with glue or

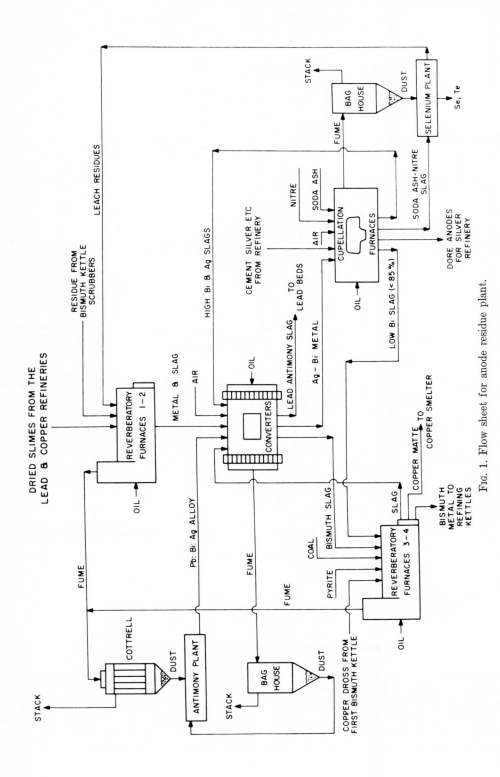

Fig. 1. Flow sheet for anode residue plant.

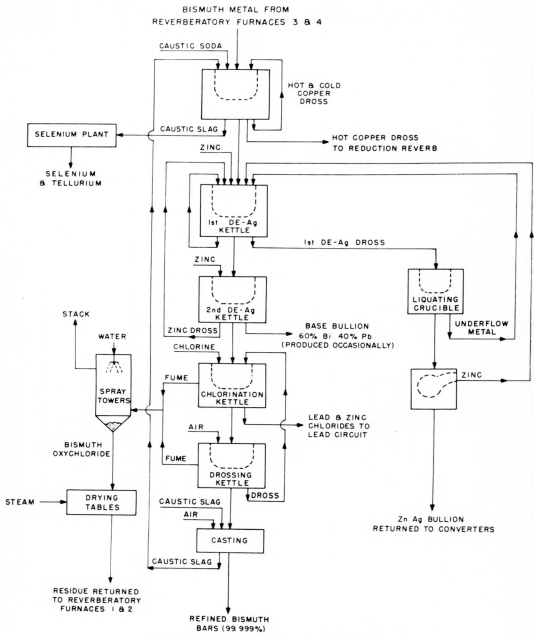

FIG. 2. Flow sheet for fire refining of bismuth.

gelatin. Operation is similar to that of the lead plating bath. As little as 2 per cent tin in electroplated lead will give it a more pleasing color than lead alone, and the plate will not darken as readily. It is stated that alloy deposits of 5 per cent tin yield better protection against corrosion of steel than either pure lead or alloys with higher tin content.

Lead-tin and lead-tin-copper alloy deposits have useful bearing characteristics, and lead-tin plating is now being used in the electronics industry for the plating of solder.

Typical bath compositions for lead-tin plating are given below:

	Fluid oz/gallon
Lead fluoborate	20–46
Stannous fluoborate	4–20
Fluoboric acid	4–6
Boric acid	2–3
Bone glue or gelatin	0.05–0.07
Resorcinol	0.05

Current densities employed range from 10 to 40 amperes per square foot and temperature of baths range from 70 to 100°F.

The Lead Industries Association has recently been conducting investigations on high-speed plating of lead. The program is directed toward the development of low-cost electroplating techniques for the deposition of lead coatings on steel sheets. The necessary thicknesses of lead plating are being determined by corrosion tests which form part of the program.

References

1. *Can. Mining J.*, **75**, No. 5 (1954). The management and staff of the Consolidated Mining and Smelting Co. of Canada, Ltd.
2. GRAHAM, A. KENNETH, Ed., "Electroplating Engineering Handbook," 2nd Edition, New York, Reinhold Publishing Corp., 1962.
3. MOHLER, J. B., AND SEDUSKY, H. J., "Electroplating For the Metallurgical Engineer and Chemist," New York, Chemical Publishing Company, 1951.
4. KIRK, RAYMOND E., AND OTHMER, DONALD F., Editors, "Encyclopedia of Chemical Technology," New York, Interscience Publishers, 1956.
5. LIDDELL, DONALD M., Ed., "Handbook of Non-Ferrous Metallurgy," Vol. II, 1st Edition, New York, McGraw-Hill Book Co., Inc., 1926.
6. RODGERS, THOMAS M., "Handbook of Practical Electroplating," New York, Macmillan Company, 1959.
7. HANLEY, JOHN W., Cerro Corporation Records and Personal Notes.
8. MANTELL, C. L., "Industrial Electrochemistry," 2nd Edition, New York, McGraw-Hill Book Co., Inc., 1940.
9. BRAY, JOHN L., "Non-Ferrous Production Metallurgy," 2nd Edition, New York, John Wiley & Sons, Inc., 1956.
10. GRAY, ALLEN G., Ed., "Modern Electroplating," New York, John Wiley & Sons, Inc., 1953; LOWENHEIM, F. A., "Modern Electroplating," Second Ed., New York, John Wiley & Sons, Inc., 1963.
11. KOEHLER, W. A., "Principles and Application of Electrochemistry," Vol. II, "Applications," 2nd Edition, New York, John Wiley & Sons, Inc., 1944.
12. BLUM, WILLIAM, AND HOGABOOM, GEORGE M., "Principles of Electroplating and Electroforming," New York, McGraw-Hill Book Co., Inc., 1949.

J. W. HANLEY

LEAD, ELECTROTHERMIC SMELTING

Electrothermic lead smelting is very unique and practised only in Sweden by Bolidens Gruvaktiebolag[1, 2] and, evidently, to some extent in Russia.[3]

Metallurgical Principles

In conventional lead smelting dead-roasted, sintered lead sulfide concentrate is reduced in a blast furnace with 8 to 10 per cent of the charge of metallurgical coke according to the reaction: $2PbO + C \rightarrow 2Pb + CO_2$. This is the basic idea of the *roast-reduction process*.

Rich concentrates with over 60 per cent Pb have to be diluted, usually by adding return slag to the sinter charge, as otherwise the sinter will smelt too soon both during sintering and in the blast furnace, thereby reducing considerably the gas permeability. To overcome this limitation of the blast furnace process for rich lead concentrates a special method, the hearth process, was developed, the Newnam modification still being used. The main idea is to mix rich lead sulfide concentrate and returned oxidic flue dust on a shallow hearth and to blow air into and over the charge. Added cokebreeze gives the necessary reaction temperature of about 800°C. The reactions follow the equations:

$$2PbS + 3O_2 \rightarrow 2PbO + 2SO_2$$

$$PbS + 2PbO \rightarrow 3Pb + SO_2$$

$$PbS + PbSO_4 \rightarrow 2Pb + 2SO_2$$

$$2PbO + C \rightarrow 2Pb + CO_2$$

This is the basic idea of the *roast-reaction process*.

The method is suited for concentrates containing over 70 per cent Pb. The hearth process gave a slag assaying around 35 per cent Pb which had to be retreated. The process was laborious, had low capacity, and gave a high load of circulating dust, around 35 per cent of the charge. Furthermore, the process was very unhygienic. Other variants of this process therefore have been developed. One is that of Lurgi,[4, 5] where the lead-forming reactions take place on an updraft sintering strand and in a short drum furnace. The process has been run for some years in Mezica in Yugoslavia. The Boliden method[6] with the roast reactions performed in an electrically heated furnace, provides another alternative.

Boliden Method, General

In the Boliden method a partially roasted lead sinter, produced according to a special method[1] without dilution of the lead-rich concentrate, is smelted and reacted in a hearth furnace by electric heat. The power is supplied by electrodes immerged into the slag. Heat is developed by the resistance which the slag provides to the electric current. Fluxes are added, preferably in the sintering step, to give the slag the desired composition and fluidity. Also, the flue dust separated in the Cottrell precipitator for furnace gas is returned mainly to the sinter charge. A small amount of coke is charged with the sinter.

As mentioned above, the roast-reaction starts at 800°C, but slag composition and necessity of a clean surface on the slag bath demand a considerably higher temperature of the furnace slag. Practice has shown that, with the present power input and heat consumption by charging and forced cooling of the furnace, the optimum temperature in the central part of the slag bath is between 1,300 and 1,400°C. As the charging rate is high and held at maximum and as the reactions occur instantaneously and are followed by evolution of SO_2 gas, it is of importance to match the power input to the charging rate.

The high bath surface temperature gives a strong evaporation of lead sulfide and zinc causing a circulation of dust amounting to around 20 per cent of the charge weight.

The slag, being relatively low in lead, is discarded. A high CaO content is the main factor in keeping down the lead loss. The lead content in the slag is decreased to a minor extent by keeping the oxidation level in the sinter low and by adding coke to the furnace charge.

Normal slag has the following analysis:

Ag	Cu	Zn	Pb	S	SiO₂	FeO	MgO	CaO
8 g/t	0.1%	10%	3.7%	1%	23%	15%	3.5%	37%

The sinter with a total sulfur content of 7 per cent has a slight surplus of sulfide sulfur, which will remain unreacted in the furnace lead, which contains 2 to 3 per cent S. An increase in addition of coke increases the sulfur content in the lead. Previous to a conventional refining of the lead, this sulfur is eliminated in a Pierce Smith converter by blowing with air.

A high sulfur content in the furnace lead has a certain disadvantage, especially as the sulfur makes the furnace lead dissolve zinc, which in the following converter operation generates drosses high in lead, which have to be returned to the furnace, where the oxidized zinc goes with the slag.

Equipment

Fig. 1 shows a section of the electric furnace transversal to its length axis with auxiliary equipment, including one of the two converters.

The furnace is rectangular with inner dimensions 13×4.5 m. The bottom is strongly curved to prevent the bricks from being pushed up by lead penetrating under them. The lining is all magnesite.

To prevent the furnace lead, the viscosity of which at 1,000°C is equal to that of water, from leaking out through the lining, the furnace walls are water-cooled up to the surface level of the slag bath. The wall-bottom lines and wall-corner lines are fitted with copper boxes for water-cooling, and under each electrode there is a cooling box on the bottom steel plate. Along the rimzone of the bottom steel plate there are additional cooling boxes.

The roof is flat and suspended which allows small repairs during short shutdowns of an hour or so. The roof is totally renewed every year, the walls every second year, and the bottom every fourth year. The electrodes are inserted through square, water-cooled copper blocks in the roof. The charging tubes end in openings in the corners of these blocks.

The charge is automatically weighed in batches of two tons, passes through a mixer to charging bins from which it is conveyed by screws to the charging tubes. The screw speed is regulated to give the proper charging rate.

The furnace is heated by four Söderberg electrodes (q.v.) connected to the transformers by a Scott's coupling (Fig. 2). The installed power is 8,000 kva. The electrodes are hung in Wisdom bands. The furnace transformers are primarily

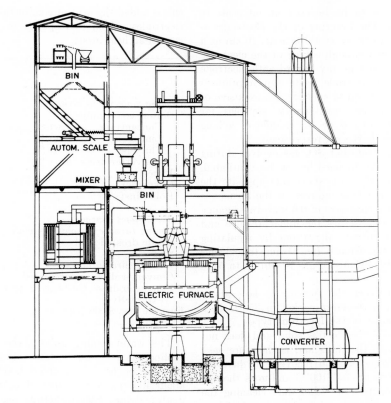

FIG. 1. Cross-section of the lead smelting furnace with auxiliary equipment.

fed with 30,000 v. A 17-step tap change provides a voltage range of 100 and 200 v between electrodes.

The furnace is equipped with manual and automatic impedance control, which controls the electrode hoists. For every level of power input the position of the electrode in the slag bath relative to the lead metal surface is controlled by choice of electrode voltage. By these means it is possible to distribute the heat between metal and slag at will.

The desired power input is manually set by adjusting the rheostats in the circuits of the impedance control and the automatic device then keeps the power input constant. The power factor, cos ϕ, is around 0.90 and the average operating power is 7,000 kw.

The electrodes have a diameter of 1 meter. Contrary to normal practice, the electrode paste is dumped into the steel cylinders as solid blocks and smelted by electrical heating elements on the outside of the electrode above the electrode clamps. To secure a good coking of the paste

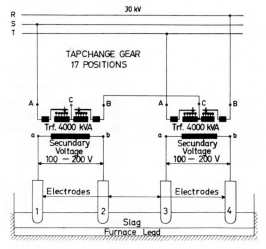

FIG. 2. Diagram of Scott connection used for the 8000 kva Boliden lead smelting furnace.

the electrodes are thermally isolated 1 meter above the roof.

The electrodes are consumed continually and,

therefore, have to be lowered at intervals in their clamps. The lowering of the electrodes is restricted to about every third hour, 10 cm at a time, to secure thorough coking of the electrode paste and to prevent any hazard with electrode breakage. The electrode paste consumption is around 8 kg per ton of cold charge, exclusive of coke. The furnace has separate tapholes for lead and slag, placed on the middle of a long side and on a short side, respectively.

Due to the fact that SO_2 gas evolves during the smelting, the furnace has to be ventilated. Gas is drawn off at the short side opposite the slag taphole. For hygienic reasons the furnace is held at an underpressure of 0.6 mm water gauge by a device that senses the underpressure and automatically corrects deviations by regulating the speed of the exhaust fan. Owing to leakages in the roof, the exhausted gas is diluted to 5–10 per cent SO_2.

The gas leaving the furnace is hot, about 1,100°C, and is therefore cooled to 350°C in a waste-heat boiler of the La Mont type.

Under 350°C the dust is solid and does not clog or stick to the walls and is therefore easy to handle. To get a good recovery of dust the gas is cooled to around 100°C and goes then to a Cottrell precipitator. After dust cleaning the furnace gas is blown to the sulfuric acid plant.

The recovered dust is transported automatically by a pneumatic batchwise system to the charge preparation in the sintering plant.

Operation

The furnace is tapped of slag only once a shift. The depth of the slag bath varies between 50 and 80 cm. The furnace lead is tapped four to five times every 24 hours. The furnace lead bath is allowed to accumulate up to 25–30 cm above the taphole. The furnace lead has a temperature of around 1,000°C when tapped.

Material Balance

As seen from the balance of material, the loss of lead in slag is about 1.5 per cent of the lead fed as new material. The circulation of dust is about 20 per cent of the charge. The energy consumption is about 1,000 kwh per ton lead or 450 kwh per ton charge. The reaction heat of the lead-forming reactions is very low, only about 5 per cent of the total heat balance. To this is added the heat of combustion of coke and electrodes, which corresponds to about 25 per cent of all heat input.

	Tons/day	% Pb
Ingoing material to furnace:		
Sinter, containing:	283	66
Concentrate 71 wt %		
Limestone 8 wt %		
Fluedust 12 wt %		
Converter dross 9 wt %		
Limestone	10	
Cokebreeze	4	
Boilerdust	29	65
Total furnace charge:	326	
Outgoing furnace & converter materials		
Crude drossed lead	140	99
Slag	59	3.7
Dust, recirculated	67	65
Converter dross, recirculated	28	65
Converter dross, Cu-bearing, treated externally	2.5	75
Furnace gas, 8,000 Nm³/h.		

The water-cooling takes about 700 kw and cooling of roof and bottom takes about 1,300 kw. The gas heat takes about 5,000 kw of which about 40 per cent is recovered as 70 tons/day of 9 atm steam. Electrothermic lead smelting is competitive with conventional blast furnace lead operation at a place where the price of metallurgical coke is high and that of electricity is low. The electric lead smelting is still in development, so further decrease in cost will be obtainable.

References

1. WALLDÉN, S. J., LINDVALL, N. B., AND GÖRLING, K. G., *Trans. Met. Soc. AIME*, **212**, 146 (1958).
2. LINDVALL, N. B., AND WALLDÉN, S., *Erzmetall*, **11**, 264 (1958).
3. LAKERNIK, M. M., LAVROV, L. G., AND FOKIN, N. A. *Cvetnye Metally*, page 32 (1956).
4. PUNGARTNIK, G., *Erzmetall*, **13**, 249 (1960).
5. SCHWARTZ, W., AND HAASE, W., *Trans. Met. Soc. AIME*, **224**, 939 (1962).
6. KALLING, B., WALLDÉN, S., AND TANNER, G., U.S. Patent 2,416.628 (1947).

BENGT RUDLING

Cross-references: *Electric Smelting Furnaces; Söderberg Electrodes in Electric Furnaces; Zinc, Electrothermic Production.*

LECLANCHÉ, GEORGES (1839–1882)

Georges Leclanché was born in 1839 in Paris. In 1860 he entered l'École centrale des arts et manufactures. Later he was employed by the Compagnies de chemin de fer (Railroad Companies) as a maker of the primary cells used in telegraphy and signaling. He also did similar work for the military forces. On May 22, 1863, he was named a member of the Société chimique de Paris and gave a paper on the spectrum of hydrogen.

Setting to work in earnest for the Railroad Companies, Leclanché produced thousands of batteries, experimenting as he built. In a brochure published in 1867 he described a primary cell he had devised, explaining the functions of the substances involved. He used a glass bottle, with a rod of amalgamated zinc for the negative electrode, and a porous jar filled with a mixture of manganese dioxide and retort carbon, centered by a graphite rod, for the positive electrode. The bottle was two-thirds filled with a solution of ammonium chloride and the top sealed with wax except for a small breather hole.

In 1877 Leclanché again explained his battery at length;[1] he had developed a new positive electrode. He combined 40 per cent coarse manganese dioxide, 55 per cent retort carbon, and 5 per cent gum lac and subjected them to a pressure of 300 atmospheres at 100°C. A little potassium bisulfate was added to the interior to dissolve the oxychlorides that tended to clog the pores, and a graphite terminal was attached to the top. With the use of this electrode he could develop enough current from one battery to redden a platinum wire and light a gas jet.

In 1878 he described another improvement consisting of plates of the pressed mixture attached to a center graphite pole.[2]

Leclanché's batteries evoked much interest throughout Europe, and many experimenters tested their current and internal resistance. Although they were not properly dry cells themselves, they contained their own depolarizer; they did not need to be taken apart when not in use since they did not function without a closed circuit; and they could be practically sealed. It remained for Gassner in 1888 to produce the first fully sealed cell with the electrolyte absorbed in a paste.

Leclanché died in Paris in 1882. He saw his cell used for telegraphy, signaling, laboratory work, and electric bells. The twentieth century brought greater importance to it, however, as a source of electricity where power is not available and particularly for portable devices.

References

1. LECLANCHÉ, G., *Ann. chim. phys.*, [5], **10**, 420 (1877).
2. LECLANCHÉ, G., *Comptes Rendus*, **87**, 329 (August 19, 1878).
3. VINAL, G. W., "Primary Batteries," p. 20, New York, John Wiley and Sons, Inc., 1950.

ELIZABETH S. BENFORD

LEWIS, GILBERT NEWTON (1875–1946)

Gilbert Newton Lewis was born near Boston on October 25, 1875, but spent most of his school years in Lincoln, Nebraska. After attending the University of Nebraska for two years, he transferred to Harvard, from which he was graduated in 1896. For a year he taught at Phillips Academy and then returned to Harvard for his graduate work, receiving his Ph.D. in 1899. An instructorship at Harvard followed, with a year spent in Germany studying with Ostwald and Nernst. Then he accepted the post of Superintendent of Weights and Measures in the Philippine Islands and Chemist in the Bureau of Science at Manila.

In 1905 he went to the Massachusetts Institute of Technology, where he was to spend seven years, starting work in the fields in which he was to make his important contributions. His first papers on thermodynamic chemistry and free energy began a series of sixty which led to the great *Thermodynamics and the Free Energy of Chemical Substances*, written with Merle Randall in 1923, the book which enabled chemists to use thermodynamics as an extremely important working tool.

Here he also began a long series of very accurate determinations of electrode potentials of various elements, including the difficult alkali metals.

When the Division of Physical and Inorganic Chemistry of the American Chemical Society was formed in 1908, Lewis became its first chairman.

In 1912 the University of California invited him to become dean of the College of Chemistry and chairman of the department. He was given freedom to choose many new members of the faculty and to organize the department according to his own ideas. New research facilities were also added. A tightly knit faculty resulted, where ideas and creativity were nourished among the staff and a rigorous training was given the students.

In 1917 he was commissioned a Major in the Chemical Warfare Service, and in 1918 was sent to France. After a brief period as observer in the front lines, he became Chief of the Defense Division of the Chemical Warfare Service, where he acquitted himself in his usual style.

Lewis' theories of valence rank in importance with his contributions to thermodynamics. His first paper, "The Atom and the Molecule," appeared in 1916, and the most extensive treatment appeared as an American Chemical Society Monograph in 1923, *Valence and the Structure of Atoms and Molecules.* He called attention to evidence of the pairing of the outer octet of electrons and the completion of these pairs not by the loss or gain of an electron, but by the sharing of a pair of electrons between two atoms, so that the atoms are bound in a nonpolar manner. He was thus able to reconcile the organic and inorganic theories of valence.

These theories led him into many related avenues of research, such as the peculiar properties of atoms with odd numbers of electrons, and the relationship between magnetic properties and electron structure. Lewis' ideas on the nonpolar bond were not immediately accepted, especially by physicists, but quantum mechanics later provided confirmation of this type of bond.

From 1933 to 1935 he spent much time isolating and determining the properties of deuterium and "heavy water." In 1938 to 1940 he worked on the question of acid-base reactions, redefining acids and bases in terms of ability to furnish or accept electron pairs. The concept of color in relation to structure was the subject for a series of papers from 1939 to 1945.

Aside from his fields of chemistry and administration, Lewis had wide interests, American prehistory, economics, and contract bridge, for example. He loved good company and was an excellent conversationalist, but was modest and uncomfortable when in the public eye.

He died in his laboratory on March 23, 1946 in the midst of further experiments on fluorescence.

References

1. HILDEBRAND, JOEL H., "National Academy of Sciences, Biographical Memoirs," Vol. 31, p. 210, New York, Columbia University Press, 1958.
2. LAMB, ARTHUR B., *Chem. Met. Eng.*, **24**, 869 (1921) and JOHNSTON, JOHN, *Chem. Met. Eng.*, **24**, 870 (1921).
3. ROBERTSON, G. ROSS, *Chem. Eng. News*, **25**, 3290 (1947).

ELIZABETH S. BENFORD

LIPPMANN POTENTIAL

The Lippmann potential[7] of a metal immersed in electrolytic solution is a null or zero charge potential; it is identical to the potential of the electrocapillary maximum as determined from electrocapillary curves of liquid metal electrodes. In the case of liquid metals (Hg, Ga, etc.), electrocapillary curves[5, 6, 9, 11] or plots of surface tension *vs* electrode potential (measured with respect to a suitable reference electrode) may be obtained by use of the Lippmann capillary electrometer. These curves are nearly parabolic in shape, and exhibit a maximum at a characteristic potential, the Lippmann potential. According to the thermodynamic theory of capillarity, the slope of the electrocapillary curve is given by the Lippmann-Helmholtz equation of electrocapillarity,

$$\frac{d\sigma}{dE} = -q_M ,$$

where σ is surface tension, E is electrode potential, and q_M is the excess surface charge density on the metal side of the electrical double layer at the interface. The slope of the electrocapillary curve is zero at the Lippmann potential (E_N), so that q_M is zero at E_N. Because of overall interfacial electroneutrality, the excess charge density on the solution side of the double layer is also zero, hence, the outer or Volta potential difference between metal and solution $(\Delta\Psi)$ is zero at E_N. The overall inner or Galvani potential difference $(\Delta\phi)$ is defined by $\Delta\phi = \Delta\Psi + \chi_M - \chi_S$,[6] where χ_M and χ_S are potential differences due to the existence of dipolar layers in metal and solution phases, respectively. Therefore, $\Delta\phi = \Delta\phi_N = \chi_M - \chi_S$ at the Lippmann potential. The surface potential, χ_M, is thought to exist even when $\Delta\Psi = 0$ because of electronic "overlap" at the surface of the metallic phase. The surface potential, χ_S, arises on the solution side of the double layer because of the presence of oriented dipoles including solvent molecules, induced dipoles, and specifically adsorbed ionic species at the interface.

Lippmann potentials may be determined by a variety of experimental techniques. (a) The classical method of determining E_N from the potential of the electrocapillary maximum is limited to liquid metal electrodes. (b) On solid metals, the angle of contact of adherent gas bubbles is a measure of the interfacial surface tension; as in the case of electrocapillary curves of liquid metal electrodes, E_N is the potential of maximum surface tension. (c) Measurements of the interfacial impedance of solid or liquid metal electrodes provide values of the differential capacity of the double layer, which is a measure of the change in excess charge density required to change the interfacial potential difference. Differentiation of the Lippmann-Helmholtz equation gives,

$$C = \frac{dq_M}{dE} = -\frac{d^2\sigma}{dE^2},$$

where C is the differential capacity. Plots of C vs E for electrodes in dilute electrolytic solutions exhibit a minimum of differential capacity at E_N. (d) Differential capacities may be determined also from the slopes of charging curves, provided the externally applied or measurable current (i_{ext}) is used essentially exclusively for changing the potential of the electrical double layer during the time of observation. In this case,

$$C = \frac{dq_M}{dE} = \frac{dq_M/dt}{dE/dt} = \frac{i_{ext}}{dE/dt}$$

(e) In the absence of appreciable faradaic current, a dropping mercury electrode ultimately attains the potential of zero charge (E_N) because any excess charge initially present in the metallic phase is removed by formation of an ionic double layer on the first few mercury droplets which emerge from the reservoir. Other methods which may be used for measuring E_N with dropping mercury electrodes include (f) the variation of drop weight with potential and (g) the variation of capacitive current necessary for formation of the electrical double layer at the interface of the expanding mercury sphere. (h) Various experimental arrangements for studying the hardness or friction properties of metals in solution show that the hardness of a metal surface is a maximum at E_N. (i) Direct measurements of the extent of adsorption of ions involved in the formation of the electrical double layer on electrodes of large surface area demonstrate minimum adsorption in the vicinity of the Lippmann potential. (j) In addition, the zeta potential or the potential of the diffuse portion of the electrical double layer is zero at the Lippmann potential, and electrokinetic properties of metals undergo a sign reversal at E_N, the potential of zero charge.

Values of Lippmann potentials in the absence of specific adsorption of ions or dipolar substances (other than the solvent) vary with the identity of the metal because of differences in the interaction strengths of various metals with the solvent. Lippmann potentials measured by a variety of techniques have been reported,[1, 8, 11] and the following is a list of certain values of E_N (in volts) vs the normal hydrogen electrode: Au, $+0.3$; Pt, $+0.11$ to $+0.27$; Ag, $+0.02$ to $+0.05$; C, -0.07 to $+0.2$; Hg, -0.190 to -0.194; Fe, -0.37; Ga, -0.61 to -0.62; Zn, -0.63; Pb, -0.62 to -0.67; Tl, -0.69 to -0.82; Cd, -0.70 to -0.90.

During the development of the science of electrocapillarity, attempts were made to interpret the Lippmann potential as an absolute potential for which $\Delta\phi = \Delta\phi_N = 0$. The modern view holds that only $\Delta\Psi = 0$ at E_N because of the absence of excess charge on either phase, and that a potential difference between phases ($\Delta\phi_N = \chi_M - \chi_S \neq 0$) surely exists, in spite of no excess charge, due to the orientation of dipole layers in each phase at the interface. The specific adsorption of ions or dipoles at the metal-solution interface affects the electrocapillary curve and causes a shift of E_N. In general, specific adsorption of anions (I^-, etc.) affects primarily the positive branch of the electrocapillary curve ($E - E_N > 0$); E_N is shifted to more negative values. On the other hand, specific adsorption of large cations ($N(C_2H_5)_4^+$, etc.) alters the negative branch of the curve ($E - E_N < 0$), and E_N shifts to more positive potentials. Specific adsorption of uncharged organic substances is often greatest in the vicinity of the Lippmann potential, and these substances may be desorbed at potentials sufficiently far from E_N in either direction because the attraction of the large surface charge density for ions then exceeds its attraction for the organic molecules.

A potential scale convenient for many purposes refers all measurements of electrode potentials to the potential of zero charge of the metal in question. The use of this "rational" scale of potentials[5] is particularly advantageous in considerations of the effect of the structure of the electrical double layer on the kinetics of electrode processes.[1, 2, 3, 4, 10] Comprehensive reviews are available on theoretical and experimental aspects of the electrical double layer and on the application of double layer theory to electrochemical kinetics.[5, 6, 9, 11]

References

1. FRUMKIN, A. N., *Z. Elektrochem.*, **59**, 807 (1955).
2. FRUMKIN, A. N., in Delahay, P., Ed., "Advances in Electrochemistry and Electrochemical Engineering," Vol. 1, p. 65, New York, Interscience, 1961.
3. FRUMKIN, A. N., in Yeager, E., Ed., "Transactions of the Symposium on Electrode Processes," p. 1, New York, John Wiley & Sons, Inc., 1961.
4. GIERST, L., in Yeager, E., Ed., "Transactions of the Symposium on Electrode Processes," p. 109, New York, John Wiley & Sons, Inc., 1961.
5. GRAHAME, D. C., *Chem. Rev.*, **41**, 441 (1947).
6. LANGE, E., in Wien, W., and Harms, F., Eds., "Handbuch der Experimentalphysik," Vol. 12-2, p. 261, Leipzig, Akademische Verlagsgesellschaft M. B. H., 1933.
7. LIPPMANN, G., *Pogg. Ann.*, **149**, 547 (1873).
8. OEL, H., AND STREHLOW, H., *Z. physik. Chem.*, *N. F.*, **4**, 89 (1955).
9. PARSONS, R., in Bockris, J. O'M., Ed., "Modern Aspects of Electrochemistry," Vol. 1, p. 103, New York, Academic Press, 1954.
10. PARSONS, R., in Delahay, P., Ed., "Advances in Electrochemistry and Electrochemical Engineering," Vol. 1, p. 1, New York, Interscience, 1961.
11. VETTER, K. J., "Elektrochemische Kinetik," Berlin, Springer-Verlag, 1961.

FRANZ A. POSEY

Cross-references: *Electrocapillary Phenomena; Electrode Double Layer; Electrode Reactions, Kinetics; Electrokinetic Potentials.*

LIQUID DIELECTRICS. See DIELECTRICS, LIQUID.

LIQUID INSULATION. See DIELECTRICS, LIQUID.

LIQUID METAL CORROSION. See CORROSION BY LIQUID METALS.

LITHIUM ELECTROWINNING

Lithium is produced by the electrolysis of fused lithium chloride in a lithium chloride-potassium chloride bath at 400 to 450°C held in a cell designed somewhat like the Dow magnesium cell or the Downs cell for sodium production so that the intermixing of the lithium metal and the chloride gas is prevented. (See **Magnesium Electrowinning** and **Sodium, Electrolytic Production**.) The LiCl-KCl mixture is approximately the eutectic mixture (about 45 per cent LiCl) whose melting point is 352°C; the melting point of LiCl is 606°C. Compared with the use of fused LiCl alone, this mixture improves operational efficiency, decreases corrosion problems, minimizes deterioration of the graphite anodes, and permits continuous operation.

The raw material is lithium chloride of high purity, particularly with respect to water and sodium content, although water can be removed to a degree from the bath by a pre-electrolysis at low amperage. Since lithium chloride is very hygroscopic, the handling of it to deter water pickup is a problem.

The physical properties of lithium and the LiCl-KCl eutectic mixture influence cell design. Lithium melts at 179°C and at 400°C has a density of 0.49 g/cc, a viscosity of 0.402 centipoises, a vapor pressure much less than 1 mm Hg, and a surface tension of about 400 dynes/cm. The eutectic mixture has a density of 1.65 g/cc at 450°C and a viscosity of 5 centipoises at 500°C. Lithium chloride has a decomposition potential of 3.684 v at 450°C calculated from theromodynamic data, and the formal electrode potential for Li^{+1} in eutectic LiCl-KCl at 450°C is −3.41 v measured against a Pt, Pt^{+2} reference electrode. (See **Fused Salt Electromotive Force Series**.)

One type of cell used commercially is constructed of a covered steel pot suspended in a firebrick heating chamber, much like the magnesium cells. Gas or oil is used to heat the cell. Top entering graphite anodes dip into the fused salt bath, and the steel cathodes are so positioned that the lithium rising from them to the surface of the bath is prevented from approaching the chlorine gas rising from the anodes. Separate collecting means are used for withdrawal of the lithium and the chlorine. The molten lithium is carefully protected from contact with air, and is withdrawn from a collecting vessel and cast into molds.

Another type of cell described recently[1] is designed much like the Downs sodium cell. It is a covered, brick-lined cylindrical pot 26 in. in diameter and 30 in. deep with a single bottom entering graphite anode 6 to 8 in. in diameter centered vertically in the pot. A steel cylindrical cathode 9 to 12 in. inside diameter and 8 to 12 in. high surrounds part of the anode, and between them is a cylindrical diaphragm of perforated, 24-gage, 316 stainless steel sheet, which keeps the chlorine rising along the anode from mixing with the lithium rising along the inside of the cathode. A vertical hoodlike nickel chlorine collector is positioned over the top of the anode, and a steel collector placed over the cathode is used to hold and guide the molten lithium to a vertical takeoff line continuously into a stainless steel holding tank. Auxiliary electric heating elements in the bath maintain the temperature.

The lithium cells hold only a few hundred pounds of bath, and the production rate from cells using 900 to 1000 amperes is in the range of 8 to 10 lb of lithium per day per cell.

Some typical operating data for commercial cells are given in Table 1.

The cell described in Ref. 1 operates at somewhat lower voltage, current density, current efficiency, and unit energy consumption, and its chemical efficiency is somewhat higher. While designed to operate at 1000 amperes, it can be operated up to 3500 amperes with no abnormal behavior.

TABLE 1. LITHIUM CELLS—OPERATING CHARACTERISTICS[2]

Current (amp)	850–900
Temperature	
°C	400–420
°F	752–788
Voltage	8–9
Anodic c.d. (amp/sq in.)	9.0
Cathodic c.d. (amp/sq in.)	13.0
Current efficiency (%)	85–90
Unit energy (kwhr/lb)	18.2
Chemical consumption (LiCl/lb Li)	7.3
Chemical efficiency (%)	83.7
Cell capacity (lb)	220

Details about cell operation and about the physical properties and electrochemical behavior of lithium and its salts are presented in Refs. 1 and 2.

The separation of lithium isotopes 6 and 7 can be effected by electrolysis in a mercury cathode cell and by electromigration techniques. Information about both methods is given in the article **Isotopes—Electrochemical Separation;** also see **Electromigration in Liquid Metals**.

References

1. MOTOCK, G. T., *Electrochem. Tech.*, **1**, 122–127 (1963).
2. LANDOLT, P. E., AND SITTIG, M., chapter on "Lithium" in "Rare Metals Handbook," C. A. Hampel, Editor, New York, Reinhold Publishing Corp., 1961.

CLIFFORD A. HAMPEL

Cross-references: *Fused Salt* entries; *Isotopes—Electrochemical Separation*; *Magnesium Electrowinning*; *Sodium, Electrolytic Production*.

LUMINESCENCE

Luminescence denotes an emission of light which is greater than could occur by temperature radiation alone. It may be observed in the gaseous, liquid, or solid state of matter. Various prefixes characterize the agent or mechanism used to excite the luminescence, such as photo-, cathodo-, electro-, thermo-, tribo-, chemi-, or bioluminescence. In all cases, the effective absorption of radiant or corpuscular exciting energy leads to a momentary increase of a material's electronic energy to an unstable excited state; the light emission then arises on the spontaneous or stimulated return of this state to the normal one.

The most noteworthy forms are photoluminescence, which occurs under excitation by light of shorter wave length than the emitted light, and cathodo- and electroluminescence, which result from electrons accelerated by external or internal electric fields. The light emission that is confined to the period of excitation is called *fluorescence* (q.v.); that which persists after excitation has ceased is *phosphorescence* (q.v.). The latter declines steadily in intensity and is observable from small fractions of a second to many hours, depending on the material.

Phosphor (q.v.) is the name given to those solid compounds capable of developing fluorescence. The fluorescent emission from inorganic compounds is associated with the presence, at very low concentrations in the host material, of impurity features called *activators*. These may be certain types of crystal defects or one or more deliberately added foreign elements. Typical activators are silver or copper at about 0.001 to 0.01 per cent in zinc sulfide, and manganese at about 1 to 2 per cent in zinc fluoride and chiefly in many of the compounds formed from the oxides of Group II elements in the periodic system (Zn, Cd, Ca, Mg, etc.) with the acid radical of oxy-acids (silicates, phosphates, borates, etc.). Other lattice disturbances may also function as activator, such as monovalent zinc atoms in zinc sulfide or perturbed groups of atoms in the self-activated tungstates or vanadates. The effectiveness of monovalent activators in the bivalent host crystal of zinc sulfide requires the simultaneous introduction of coactivators to secure charge compensation. Equivalent amounts of chlorine in place of sulfur or of aluminum in place of zinc serve this purpose. Often, the efficiency and color of luminescence depend critically upon a particular crystal modification of the host material. Thus, tin activator in alkaline earth metal phosphates of different structure can give either blue or orange emission.

The color of fluorescence ranges over the entire spectrum and depends upon the nature of the activator and the composition and structure of the host compound. In zinc sulfides, substitution of cadmium for zinc in increasing amounts shifts the color continuously from blue to red for silver activation, and from green to infrared for copper. The fluorescence due to divalent manganese ranges from green as in zinc silicate to yellow and red in different compounds. Lead, thallium, antimony and titanium activators generally give rise to fluorescence in the ultraviolet or blue. With all the common activators, the emission is in the form of a spectral band; only rarely, as with samarium or tetravalent manganese, does it occur as spectral lines of lesser or greater width.

For photoexcitation to occur, there must be an absorption band at the spectral location of the exciting radiation, and this radiation must be of such wave length that its energy equivalent is sufficient to raise the activator ions to their excited state. In the absence of such an absorption band, the phosphor may still be photoexcited if a second activator is added, the sensitizer, which introduces the needed absorption. The phosphor then emits two bands, one due to the sensitizer and the other to the activator proper. Their relative intensities depend on the concentrations of the two. The activator proper receives its excitation energy from the sensitizer by an internal resonance process. Examples are calcium silicate activated with lead and manganese, which emits in the ultraviolet and the orange, and the family of calcium halophosphates activated with antimony and manganese, which emit in the blue and the yellow.

Phosphorescence is generally of the same spectral color as fluorescence. It occurs in two stages. The first has an exponential decay, lasting generally from a few microseconds to milliseconds or even as long as a second for zinc fluoride activated with manganese. It is independent of temperature below about 100°C. The second stage of decay is of bimolecular rate, and its persistence ranges from seconds to hours, being longest for the bismuth-activated sulfides of calcium and strontium. It is strongly temperature-dependent. At low temperatures, this glow is readily extinguished or frozen in; it may then be released again on warming—the phenomenon of *thermoluminescence*. The controlled release and measurement of this stored energy gives rise to glow curves which in turn give information on the nature of traps—still other defects in solid luminescent materials which make phosphorescence possible. At high temperatures both fluorescence and phosphorescence are quenched, and the electronic energy is dissipated as heat to the crystal.

In *cathodoluminescence*, the fluorescence is excited by the impact of high-voltage electrons. The spectral emission is the same as under photoexcitation, but the bimolecular phosphorescence is greatly reduced.

A somewhat related phenomenon is *triboluminescence*, the light emitted when certain crystalline substances, notably sugar or manganese-activated zinc oxide-sulfide, are crushed. Its primary cause lies in the formation of charged cleavage surfaces which lead to luminous gaseous discharges rich in ultraviolet radiation. If the substance is a phosphor, additional luminescence may thus appear as fluorescence excited by the discharge.

Certain phosphor compositions, notably chromium or rare earth-activated compounds in form of flawless long crystals or glass rods, have gained importance in laser application where they allow the production of extremely high intensities of collimated and coherent light radiation of characteristic, very sharp wave lengths.

Industrially, the largest quantities of phosphors are used for illumination and for television, radar, and fluoroscopic screens. Fluorescent lamps utilize a low-pressure mercury discharge whose predominant emission lies in the 2537Å line. Phosphors responding to this excitation include calcium and magnesium tungstates for blue, zinc silicate for green, different calcium halophosphates for a combined blue and yellow emission leading to various shades of near-whites, and modified strontium orthophosphate phosphors for orange-red emission. Combinations of phosphors are used to give almost any color of light desired.

Electroluminescence (q.v.) is a related phenomenon. It appears when an electric potential is applied to a thin film of a suitable phosphor composed of powder particles or of evaporated continuous films. In practice, phosphor powder is suspended in an organic dielectric between two plate electrodes one of which is transparent, such as conducting glass. A-C operated lamps of this construction can be used for low brightness dial or marker illumination or as component parts for opto-electronic devices.

The light mechanism of organic phosphors is similar to that of inorganic. The more notable ones are dilute solutions of rhodamine or other fluorescent dyes in a liquid or solid medium, such as alcohol or nitrocellulose. Fluorescent paints and lacquers are generally of this type. Inasmuch as their phosphorescence is extremely brief, a suspension of a sulfide in a plastic is employed when this property is desired.

Chemiluminescence denotes the light given off in a chemical reaction. The reaction must be such that a product is formed, whether compound, radical, or ion, which is capable of exhibiting luminescence on excitation; furthermore, the reaction must release sufficient energy to excite this product. A simple example is the weak light observed in the oxidation of pyrogallol by hydrogen peroxide. More brilliant effects are given by bubbling air or oxygen through solutions of Grignard reagents, particularly parachlorphenyl magnesium bromide.

Bioluminescence is also a common and spectacular form of chemiluminescence. It is exhibited by living organisms, such as bacteria, glow worms, fireflies, and luminous fish. It is due to the admixture of two types of substances present in the organism; one of them, *luciferin*, is capable of oxidation in the presence of the second, an enzyme termed luciferase. The reaction produces an excited form of luciferase, and its return to the normal form is accompanied by the emission of light.

References

1. LEVERENZ, H. W., "An Introduction to Luminescence of Solids," New York, John Wiley & Sons, 1950.
2. GARLICK, G. F. J., "Luminescent Materials," Oxford, Clarendon Press, 1949.
3. KLICK, C. C., AND SCHULMAN, J. H., "Luminescence in Solids," "Solid State Physics," edited by F. Seitz and D. Turnbull, Vol. 5, pp. 97–172, New York, Academic Press, Inc., 1957.

G. R. FONDA

Cross-references: *Electroluminescence*; *Fluorescence*; *Laser*; *Phosphorescence*; *Phosphors*; *Scintillation Counters*.

M

MAGNESIA, FUSED

About 10,000 tons of fused magnesia are produced annually in the USA and Canada from magnesia or magnesite analyzing better than 90 per cent MgO. Four companies: Norton Company, General Electric Company, Muscle Shoals Electro-chemical Corp., and Tennessee Electro Minerals Corp. share the bulk of the production.

Practically all fused magnesium oxide is produced in an electric arc furnace of the open arc type. Because of its high melting point (2790°C) and narrow solidification range, fused MgO does not lend itself readily to a continuous casting type of operation and is therefore usually made in a batch operation.

At one time fused MgO was made in a resistance furnace similar to that used for silicon carbide. However, the open arc furnace has replaced the resistance furnace completely.

The fusion is made by placing a metal container partially filled with calcined magnesite under a set of vertically suspended graphite electrodes. On top of the charge in the furnace a bridge of carbon or graphite is placed in such a manner as to form a connection between the electrodes when they are lowered. Current passing through this bridge causes it to heat up and burn out. As it burns out it melts MgO, and by the time the bridge is all gone enough MgO has melted so that it can continue to act as a conductor between the electrodes. The furnace is filled by gradually feeding mix into the bath under the electrodes. A portion of the feed just inside the metal container walls does not fuse, but sinters to form a container for the fused material. This protects the steel container from the very high temperatures of the bath. As a further protection for the container, water is sprayed on the outside of the shell during the fusion and also during the cooling period.

After the contents of the furnace are cooled sufficiently, they are dumped out onto a breaking floor where the fused product is separated from the sintered and unfused material. These reclaims are used in subsequent fusions.

The physical appearance of fused MgO ingots (usually referred to as "pigs") depends to a considerable extent on the raw material used as feed. The higher the impurity content, the poorer the crystallinity. In general the product from a fusion is an aggregate of well-developed single crystals averaging about 8 to 10 mesh in the bulk of the product. There are zones in the pig where larger crystals often form. These crystals, which are optically clear, may range in size to the occasional 2 inch cube. Under a highly controlled process commercial quantities of crystals having one face as large as ¾ inch are produced.

Raw materials are obtained from several sources. (1) Calcined natural magnesite runs 90 to 97 per cent MgO, the balance being mostly SiO_2 and CaO with lesser amounts of Fe_2O_3 and Al_2O_3. (2) Sea water magnesia and magnesia extracted from dolomitic ores contain the same impurities but usually in lesser amounts.

Fused MgO has a number of unique properties that make it valuable both as a commercial product and as a research tool. Its resistivity and thermal conductivity at 1000°C, 10–50 megohms/in. and 0.02 cal/cm/sec/°C, respectively, combine to make it an ideal electrical insulator in stove elements, water heaters, coffee pots, frying pans, etc.

Its high melting point and chemical inertness (it resists aqueous caustic alkali, fused alkali, alkaline vapor, anhydrous HF, and corrosive iron slags) make it an excellent refractory.

MgO crystals are cubic and can be cleaved readily with a hammer and chisel in the (100) position to give perfect rectangular shapes. These crystals are relatively hard (5½–6 on Mohs' scale), compare in brittleness to glass, and will pass better than 80 per cent of infrared light up to 7 microns.

These crystals doped with minor quantities of impurities have been found ideal for studying nuclear magnetic resonance, Zeeman effect, plastic yield stress at high temperatures, dislocation and interaction in crystal structure, and many other properties.

References

1. WHITE, H. J., "Electrically Fused Magnesia," *J. Amer. Ceramic Soc.*, **17**, 216–229 (1938).
2. SEATON, MAX Y., "Production and Properties of the Commercial Magnesias," *Mining Technology*, **Tech. Pub. 1946** (July, 1942).
3. HICKS, J. C., AND DAVIES, B., "High Temperature Properties of Magnesia Refractories," *Iron Age*, **164**, 98–105, 157, 158 (August 11, 1949).
4. STRONG, J., AND BRICE, R. T., "Optical Properties of Magnesium Oxide," *J. Opt. Soc. Am.*, **25**, 207–210 (1935).
5. GANGLER, JAMES T., "Some Physical Properties of Eight Refractory Oxides and Carbides," American Ceramic Society Preprint, April 23–27, 1950.
6. CHERRY, R. M., AND FINLAYSON, F. E., "Making High-Speed Calrod Elements," *General Electric Review*, **36**, 409–410 (1933).
7. DITCHBORN, R. W., "Properties of Crystalline Magnesium Oxide," *Nature*, **136**, 70–71 (1935).

JOHN J. SCOTT

MAGNESIUM ELECTRODES, ANODIC REDUCTIONS. See ANODIC REDUCTIONS AT MAGNESIUM ELECTRODES.

MAGNESIUM ELECTROWINNING

Magnesium is a silvery-white metal with a density two-thirds that of aluminum or about one-fifth that of steel. It is not only the lightest commonly available structural metal, but finds wide use as an alloying material, a reducing agent, and as sacrificial anodes in cathodic protection systems. It is sold commercially as ingot in sizes up to 42 pounds. World production capacity in 1962, exclusive of Russia and East Germany, was approximately 145,000 tons a year, of which about 80 per cent is electrolytic. Capacity in the United States is 102,000 tons a year, of which 90 per cent is electrolytic. Production in the United States is about 80,000 tons/year.

Electrolytic magnesium is produced by the decomposition of magnesium chloride. Because the decomposition potential of magnesium chloride is approximately 2.6 volts, electrolysis must take place in a nonaqueous medium. From a practical standpoint, this leads to the selection of molten electrolytes composed of the inexpensive chlorides of metals less noble than magnesium. These are the sodium, calcium, and potassium salts. They are selected to obtain a suitable compromise between low melting point, high electrical conductivity, and compatibility with impurities in the magnesium chloride feed.

Magnesium is extremely abundant in nature. Sea water, natural brines, carnallite, dolomite, magnesite, and brucite have been the most commonly-used raw materials. The methods selected for preparation of magnesium chloride depend on the starting material and the type of equipment used for electrolysis.

Magnesium chloride crystallizes from aqueous solution as $MgCl_2 \cdot 6H_2O$. Because it is expensive to dehydrate this material completely, the two predominant commercial processes circumvent the problem. In the Dow process, see Fig. 1, cells are designed to accommodate feed with a composition approximating $MgCl_2 \cdot 1.5H_2O$. All other commercial cells use anhydrous magnesium chloride prepared by methods which avoid the aqueous phase.

The Dow Cell

The Dow electrolytic cell, based on patents by Ward[12] and described by Hunter,[8] has been the dominant type of equipment used in the United States. See Fig. 2.

The Dow cells are large, rectangular steel pots with internal dimensions of approximately 13 ft long by 4½ ft wide by 5½ ft deep. These pots hold about 10 tons of fused salt electrolyte and conduct the current to the internal steel cathodes. They are operated at 700°C. Graphite anodes are suspended into the cell from above the refractory cover. Operating range is 50,000 to 90,000 amperes. Pot lines contain up to 124 cells connected in series.

Inherent in the concept of the Dow cell is a careful balance of the economics of feed preparation and cell operation. By avoiding the expense involved in complete dehydration of magnesium chloride, certain disadvantages in the use of water-containing feed can be tolerated. The generation of large amounts of water vapor within the cell, when the $MgCl_2 \cdot 1.5H_2O$ falls onto the surface of the molten electrolyte, precludes the collection of chlorine gas in a concentrated form. This removes one of the argu-

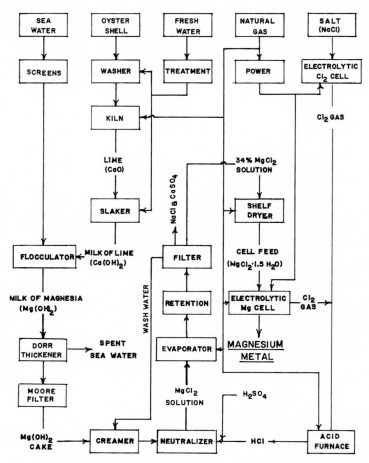

FIG. 1. Dow sea water magnesium process flowsheet.

ments in favor of separate anode and cathode compartments. The cell design, therefore, is based on bringing anode and cathode as close together as possible without undue recombination of magnesium and chlorine. This is accomplished by providing conical cathodes with a system of inverted troughs which trap the rising metal and direct it into collection sumps outside the electrolysis zone.

The following advantages are gained:

1. The steel pot permits external heating. This, in turn, permits complete power interruption for extended periods and a wide range of ampere loads.

2. More anode-cathode pairs can be fitted into a given sized container.

3. The close anode-cathode spacing permits high current density without undue penalty in power consumption.

4. The water-containing feed extends the upper limit of cell capacity by acting as a cooling agent.

Disadvantages consist of the following:

1. Final dehydration of the feed within the electrolytic chamber results in high graphite anode consumption. Labor to service the anodes is high.

2. Much of the chlorine produced at the anode is converted to HCl before it leaves the cell.

3. Large volume of cell gases diluted with water vapor and air must be handled.

4. As water is flashed from the feed, the hydrolysis of $MgCl_2$ introduces variables which can result in substantial changes in cathode efficiency. Effective operation of the cells depends to a significant extent upon the skill of the operator.

The basic design of the Dow cell has remained essentially unchanged since 1940. Development

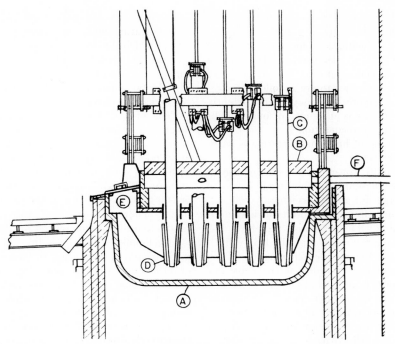

FIG. 2. The Dow magnesium cell. (*Courtesy of The Dow Chemical Co.*)
The steel container (A) is equipped with ceramic cover (B) through which
pass graphite anodes (C). The magnesium is deposited on the cathodes (D)
and is diverted as it rises into collection sump (E). The chlorine is withdrawn through vent (F).

has taken the form of minor design changes
which exploit a better understanding and control
of operating factors. Capacity of individual cells
has been increased about 30 per cent without
penalty in power consumption.

I. G. Farbenindustrie Cell

I. G. Farbenindustrie A. G. of Germany developed a successful means of producing molten
anhydrous magnesium chloride in the period
1924–1929[5] by chlorinating magnesium oxide at
high temperature in the presence of carbon.
This company also developed a cell which is the
parent design for virtually all facilities outside
the United States. Variants of this cell, with a
total capacity of 35,000 tons a year, are being
operated currently in Norway, the United
States, and Japan. They have been operated
on a large scale in the past in Germany, Canada,
and England.

Fig. 3 shows the salient features of the cell.
Fixed tabular graphite anodes are flanked on
either side by suitable steel cathodes. Refractory
dividers extend below the surface of the electrolyte and effectively direct the magnesium into

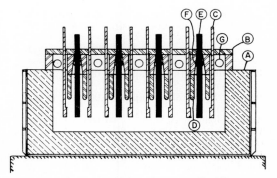

FIG. 3. I. G. Farbenindustrie type cell. (*Courtesy
of The Dow Chemical Co.*) The refractory-lined
container (A) is equipped with ceramic cover (B).
Magnesium deposited on the cathodes (C) rises
into cathode compartments formed by partitions
(D). Chlorine is released at anodes (E) and is
drawn off through vents (F). Vents (G) draw off
any gases which escape into the cathode compartment.

cathode compartments and chlorine into anode
compartments.

The largest cells of this type have internal
container dimensions of approximately 10 ft
long by 5 ft wide by 4 ft deep. Each tabular

anode is made up of seven rectangular graphite plates 4 inches thick by $7\frac{1}{2}$ inches wide by 60 inches long, which are submerged to a depth of 25 inches in the electrolyte. There are 4 anodes and 8 cathodes per cell.

Advantages of the design are as follows:

1. Cathode ampere efficiency is consistently in the 90 to 92 per cent range so long as cells are in good structural condition.

2. Dry chlorine of high concentration is withdrawn from the cell.

3. Low graphite consumption, due to use of anhydrous magnesium chloride feed, leads to low labor charges for anode servicing.

4. Use of anhydrous feed results in fewer operating variables. The cells are, therefore, less dependent on operator skill than the Dow cell.

Disadvantages include the following:

1. The refractory structure of the container and dividers puts practical limitations on size.

2. The refractory divider leads to relatively wide electrode separation. This limits the current density which can be economically tolerated and therefore the cell capacity.

3. Failure of the refractory divider, a significant operating problem, admits Cl_2 to the cathode compartment and requires shut-down of the cell.

TABLE 1. COMPARISON OF DOW AND I. G. FARBENINDUSTRIE CELLS

	DOW		I.G.F.	
1962 World installed cap., tons/yr*	80,000		36,000	
1962 U. S. installed cap., tons/yr.	80,000		11,000	
Ampere load, max.	90,000		38,000	
Voltage per cell, approx.	6.5		7.5	
Cathode efficiency, %	78		90	
D-c kwh per lb Mg	8.4		8.4	
Anode-cathode spacing, inches	1.5		5	
Operating temperature, °C	700		790	
Graphite use, lbs/T Mg	200		30	
Magnesium content of product, %	99.8		99.8	
Analyses, (a) feed; (b) electrolyte	(a)	(b)	(a)	(b)
MgCl$_2$, %	72	20	96.3	12
CaCl$_2$	0.5	20	1.4	35
NaCl	1.0	57	2.2	28
KCl		2		24
CaF$_2$		1		1
MgO	1.5		0.1	
H$_2$O	25			

* Exclusive of Russia and East Germany.

4. The fixed electrodes and absence of external heating limit the range of ampere load within which the cell can be operated.

5. Metal must be collected from each of a series of small cathode compartments.

6. Metal must be refined to remove chlorides before casting as ingot.

Cells of this type were used in the largest magnesium facility ever constructed, the Basic Magnesium Corporation plant built in 1942 at Henderson, Nevada. There were 10 pot lines of 88 cells each, designed to operate at 18,000 amperes. Design capacity of the plant was 56,000 tons a year. Two of the pot lines are still intact. They are used for captive magnesium production by a manufacturer of titanium.

Developments have been directed toward raising capacity by increasing the width and length of electrodes and by reducing anode-cathode spacing. Some effort has been made to provide cathodes which can be moved while the cell is in operation. Cells which were operated in Canada incorporated means of collecting the metal from the cathode compartments into a common sump. The advent of a reliable, thin, nonconducting material to use as a divider would be a substantial boon.

The Dow and I. G. Farbenindustrie cells are compared in Table 1.

Russia is using the I. G. Farbenindustrie type cell. Cell feed is dehydrated molten carnelite, or anhydrous magnesium chloride derived as a by-product of titanium production. The Russians have made extensive studies of electrolyte circulation, temperature profiles, and current distribution in the cells. These studies apparently form the basis for design of cells with up to 100,000 amperes capacity. Although cells of this capacity probably have been built, the author does not know whether they have reached a stage of development which would permit their use on a production basis. Russian capacity to produce magnesium has been estimated by the U. S. Bureau of Mines to be as much as 55,000 tons a year, and production in 1962 to have been 35,000 tons.

Other Electrolytic Methods

Although a variety of other cells has been operated based on the electrolysis of magnesium chloride in electrolytes heavier than magnesium,[7, 9, 11] none has found commercial application. Several processes involving the use of magnesium oxide as a feed have also been proposed,[6, 10] again without attaining commercial success.

A fundamental goal in magnesium cell design is to prevent recombination of magnesium and chlorine. One means of accomplishing this is to collect the magnesium at the bottom of the cell while the chlorine is withdrawn from the top. The use of a heavy liquid metal cathode, such as lead, has been proposed.[1, 2] Such methods have been unsuccessful, because of the expense involved in removing the magnesium from the alloy formed.

More recently, electrolytes lighter than magnesium have been developed. These are described in the patent of Williams[13] which utilizes LiCl and those of Dean[3, 4] which utilize potassium chloride or a combination of lithium and potassium chlorides.

Accumulation of NaCl or $CaCl_2$ in such electrolytes would result in an increase in density which would cause the magnesium to float. Feeds of very high purity are therefore required. In cells utilizing lithium chloride, or lithium and potassium chlorides, anhydrous magnesium chloride feed is mandatory because of the hydrophyllic nature of the bath. Such cells have the advantage of an extremely conductive electrolyte and operate at a moderate temperature of 680–750°C. Those employing KCl can tolerate a water-containing feed, but have a relatively low-conductivity electrolyte and operate at the significantly higher temperature of 825–850°C. Cells of both types have been operated for protracted periods as a part of commercial cell lines. Designs capable of operating at more than 150,000 amperes are considered practical.

Nonelectrolytic Methods

Only one nonelectrolytic method for producing magnesium has attained commercial success. This involves the reduction of dolomite with ferrosilicon. This method is attractive primarily for plants of modest size and is used in the United States, Canada, Italy, France, and Japan.

Future Development

The trend in magnesium electrolytic cell development will undoubtedly be in the direction of high individual cell capacities and close anode-cathode spacing. The latter, in turn, will prompt the development of economical cathode construction, which will maintain dimensional stability over many years of operation at 700°C and above.

Choice of cell feed and cell design will be dictated by the raw materials and economics which exist at any given location. Thus, a variety of processes may find application. It is likely, however, that those situations which offer magnesium chloride as a raw material will ultimately have the best chance of success, since two commodities—magnesium and chlorine—will be produced from the cells.

References

1. ASHCROFT, E. A., U. S. Patent 1,359,653 (Nov. 23, 1920).
2. CARTWRIGHT, B., MICHELS, L. R., AND RAVITZ, S. R. "Electrolysis of Magnesium into Liquid Cathodes from MgO-Carbon Suspension in Molten Chlorides," **R. I. 3805**, U. S. Dept. of Interior, Bureau of Mines, 1945.
3. DEAN, L. G., AND McCUTCHEON, C. W., U. S. Patent 2,950,236 (Aug. 23, 1960).
4. DEAN, L. G., OLSTOWSKI, F., AND POSEY, K., U. S. Patent 2,880,151 (March 31, 1959).
5. German Patents 450,979 (1925); 502,646 (1926); 506,276 (1928); 509,601 (1928).
6. HARVEY, W. G., Chem. & Met. Eng., **32**, 573 (1925).
7. HUNT, B. G., U. S. Patent 2,393,685 (Jan. 29, 1946).
8. HUNTER, R. M., Trans. Electrochem. Soc., **86**, 21–32 (1944).
9. HUNTER, R. M., Blue, R. D., AND NEIPERT, M. P., U. S. Patent 2,468,022 (April 26, 1949).
10. LLOYD, R. R., STODDARD, C. K., MATTINGLY, K. L., LEIGHDIGH, E. T., AND KNICKERBOCKER, R. G., Metals Technology, **T. P. 1848** (1945).
11. MacMULLIN, R. B., U. S. Patent 2,432,431 (Dec. 9, 1947).
12. WARD, L. E., U. S. Patent 1,921,377 (Aug. 8, 1933).
13. WILLIAMS, E. J., DEAN, L. G., AND McCUTCHEON, C. W., U. S. Patent 2,888,389 (May 26, 1959).

F. J. KRENZKE

MAGNETOHYDRODYNAMICS

Magnetohydrodynamics is the science of interactions between electromagnetic fields and the flow of conducting fluids in general. As such, the science would be better described as "electromagnetic fluid mechanics," because it comprises the study of the interaction between those forces which are mutually created by electric, magnetic, and electromagnetic fields on one hand and the motion of charges present within the fluid on the other. In all respects, the interactions observed in the case of fluid conductors are altogether parallel to the interactions observed between electromagnetic fields and charges moving through solid conductors. In the case of a conventional motor, galvanometer, or loudspeaker, electrical charges move in the presence of a magnetic field within a copper conductor which is solid and practically not deformable, while in the case of MHD devices, the conductor, being a fluid, is highly changeable in its geometry.

In either case, however, one may observe two general categories of devices, namely, those in which the magnetic field is fixed and the flow of charges, that is, the current, is variable, and those in which, conversely, the current flow is fixed and the magnetic field varies. Typical examples in these two categories will be given. In general, however, one should first take into consideration that, while in the case of conventional electromagnetic devices the solid conductor through which the current flows is substantially unchangeable in its geometry and the charges must in their motion substantially conform to its shape, in the case of fluid conductors, on the other hand, the forces which act upon the charges which pass through them affect the conductor itself locally rather than as a whole and, therefore, affect in turn the point-to-point shape of the conductor itself.

The conductor may, therefore, be shrunk, elongated, kinked, or choked, depending on the intensity of the forces set up by the electromagnetic interaction and depending, moreover, on the fluid mechanics forces which act on the system. This means that in addition to the effects produced by the magnetic field and by charges in the fluid which move through the field, there will be effects caused by the nature of the fluid itself, that is, its viscosity, density, the mobility of its ions and electrons, and their coupling with the neutral particles.

The science of MHD is mostly concerned with the coupling effects of the purely electromagnetic interaction of the magnetic field and the electric current in the fluid on one hand and of the purely fluid dynamics behavior of the fluid itself, which is dependent upon such characteristics as its density, viscosity, and velocity.

The coupling effects will be substantially different whether the fluid is a gas or a liquid. They will be larger as the magnetic fields' intensity increases and the ionization of the fluid becomes larger. In the case of liquids, the percentage of ionized atoms and molecules is generally low, while in the case of gases, if the density is sufficiently low or the temperature sufficiently high, full ionization is frequent. Phenomena of electromagnetic coupling are, therefore, more apparent and generally stronger in the case of gases than in the case of liquids; of the total amount of research done today, the greatest portion is carried out upon gases.

Morphologically, magnetohydrodynamic devices may be divided into two broad categories: the first where the magnetic field is variable, the second where it is fixed.

A case where the magnetic field is variable is typical of a plasma accelerator where an existing globe of ionized gas has induced within itself currents produced by a magnetic field which is both variable in time and divergent in space, which results in an acceleration of the gas in the direction of the divergence of the lines of force.

A simple device where the magnetic field is fixed comprises a permanent magnet among the poles of which a fluid is forced by a pressure gradient. If the fluid is sufficently ionized, the electrical charged particles are made to spiral by the presence of the magnetic field, thus increasing their collision rate and consequently the temperature, while the velocity of the flow will decrease, in a manner similar to that of the Faucolt disk.

There are also many devices in which both electric current and magnetic field vary. One of the oldest of these is the Poulsen singing arc. In this device, the current of an electric arc between two carbon electrodes is modulated by a microphone which is installed in the circuit of the arc itself. The current within the arc varies and so does its associated magnetic field, which results in the periodic compression and constriction of the gaseous envelope of the arc in synchronism with the current.

A more recently investigated type of device in the variable current category is the exploding wire. Here current is passed through a wire in an amount sufficient to melt it and subsequently vaporize it. The transient magnetic field generated during the blowing-up process interacts with the variable current within the vaporized metallic gas which, if the geometry is appropriate, is rapidly accelerated in a given direction. This process typically couples conventional electromechanics with MHD through a continuous transition from solid conductor to liquid to gas. While wires have exploded every time fuses have blown, yet only recently has this method been studied as a means for accelerating metallic plasmas.

The MHD effects are present on very large as well as very small scales. They were originally postulated in conjunction with the evolution of galactic shapes and the generation of cosmic rays. On the other end, the MHD effect may be observed on a microscopic scale as well.

The major practical objectives of MHD are three, namely, the compression of gases for the purpose of obtaining extremely high temperatures; the acceleration of gases, liquids, and particles, for the purpose of propulsion; and the conversion of kinetic (or thermal) energy into electrical energy.

In the first category efforts are being made toward nuclear fusion; the gas used is mostly deuterium; the geometry of the device varies greatly, the two principal ones being the toroid type and the sausage type; magnetic fields are at times parallel to the plasma body, while in other cases they are at right angles with it. In most cases, the magnetic field expands and compresses, and its lines of force act upon the plasma in the same manner in which a piston acts upon a combustible mixture. The problems of energy transfer from the magnetic field to the plasma and the associated problems of its geometrical stability are severe and at this time are being given a great deal of attention.

In the case of propulsion, the applications are mostly for space use because of the high velocities characteristic of MHD acceleration methods which permit high specific impulses and, therefore, economy of propulsive material. Conversely, the storage means of electrical energy for producing high acceleration are heavy.

In the case of the production of electrical energy through the conversion of another form of energy, such as kinetic or thermal energy, magnetohydrodynamic devices parallel in many ways the geometries and interactions of conventional electromagnetic machines. For example, ionized gases traveling within an electromagnetic field are slowed down by the interaction between the ionized particles and the field itself, and kinetic energy is translated into electrical energy. At other times, the stream does not move as a whole, and electrical energy is generated by virtue of the derandomization of the gas particles. The variety of schemes proposed for magneto-

hydrodynamic power conversion is considerable and continuously changing.

Although a great amount of research is being expended in all of the foregoing directions, practical short-ranged results are not as yet apparent at this time.

References

1. BROWN, S. C., "Basic Data of Plasma Physics," Cambridge, Technology Press of M.I.T., 1959.
2. SPITZER, LYMAN, "Physics of Ionizing Gases," New York, Interscience Publishers, 1956.

GABRIEL M. GIANNINI

Cross reference: *Plasma.*

MANGANESE DIOXIDE, ELECTROLYTIC

Manganese dioxide is the most widely used depolarizer in Leclanche type dry cels. The most battery-active forms of manganese dioxide are predominantly "gamma," "Ramsdellite," and "rho." Electrolytic deposition of manganese dioxide under specified conditions produces the "gamma" form. This battery-active manganese dioxide acts as a superior depolarizer in dry cells, contributing to extended battery life.

America's first commercially produced, electrolytic, battery-active manganese dioxide was made by the Burgess Battery Company in the late 1930's. Other producers of electrolytic battery-active manganese dioxide are or have been Bright Star Industries, National Carbon Company, Olin Industries, E. J. Lavino & Company, and American Potash and Chemical Corporation. Current production is estimated to be 7,000 tons per year, which is consumed by battery manufacturers.

The manufacturing process consists essentially of five steps, i.e., reduction of the ore, leaching of the manganese, purification of the manganese sulfate solution, deposition of manganese dioxide in electrolytic cells, and preparation of finished manganese dioxide.

Either a low-grade domestic ore containing only 20 per cent manganese or a high-grade imported manganese ore containing 55 per cent manganese can be used as the starting material for battery-active electrolytic manganese dioxide. As has been stated,[8] "The manganese ion doesn't remember its ancestry." Manganese exists in the ore as manganese dioxide and other compounds of +3 valence state. Manganese in the ground ore is reduced to the acid-soluble, 2-valence state using oil, coal, coke, or natural gas at 750°C. Reduction is 98 to 99 per cent complete. A rotary kiln is the generally accepted equipment for reduction.

Manganese is leached from the calcine with effluent from the electrolytic cell enriched with fresh sulfuric acid. The pH of the leach solution is held between 2.0 and 3.5. Leaching is commonly done either at ambient temperature or at 60 to 75°C. Higher temperature speeds up the rate of reaction, but does not appreciably increase the percentage of manganese extracted. The leach operation may be continuous or batch.

Ferrous iron resulting from reduction is also leached by sulfuric acid. The ferrous ion in solution is oxidized to the more readily removable ferric form by unreduced manganese dioxide in the ore. To be certain of complete oxidation, a small amount of finely ground raw ore is generally added to the leach circuit. After leaching is complete, the pH is adjusted to 6.5 to 7.5 with lime or calcine to precipitate iron, aluminum, and silica. Manganese sulfate solution is separated from insoluble material in a thickener. The tails may be washed in a thickener or filtered and washed on a drum filter.

The manganese sulfate solution contains various heavy metal impurities, namely, zinc, copper, cobalt, lead, and nickel, which are precipitated as sulfides using barium sulfide or hydrogen sulfide. Precipitated sulfides are removed by filtration.

A relatively pure manganese sulfate solution containing about 150 grams per liter manganese sulfate is fed to the electrolytic cell.

The overall reaction in the manganese dioxide cell is:

$$MnSO_4 + 2H_2O \xrightarrow{-2e} MnO_2 + H_2SO_4 + H_2$$

Manganese dioxide is plated on the anode. The acid concentration in the diaphragmless cell is held constant by overflow of the solution. The exact mechanism of the deposition is not completely understood. It has been suggested that the process is not electrodeposition in the conventional sense, but involves a transfer of electric charge through pores of deposited manganese dioxide—not direct contact of ion and anode.[5] H. K. Chakrabarti and T. Banerjee[3] have suggested a mechanism involving the highly reactive discharged OH ion.

$$OH^- \rightarrow OH + e \cdots$$
$$2OH \rightarrow H_2O + \tfrac{1}{2}O_2 \cdots$$

etc.

They believe that a layer of OH^- and SO_4^{--} ions remains firmly attached to the anode surface and a second layer consisting of Mn^{++} and H^+ ions forms on it.

There appears to be no generally accepted size or material of construction for an electrolytic manganese dioxide cell. A nonconducting material is used for construction, and the size and shape depend on the type of anode and cathode used. The Schumacher cells[8] used by American Potash and Chemical Corporation are converted magnesium cells that use long graphite rods as anodes and cathodes. A cell using a graphite plate anode and cathode would have a different design.

Typical operating conditions for an electrolytic cell to produce battery-active manganese dioxide are:

Temperature	90–94°C
Anode current density	5–10 amps/sq ft
Acid concentration	5–75 gpl
Manganese sulfate concentration	50–100 gpl
Voltage	2.2–2.6 volts
Cathode current density	2.5–10 amps/sq ft
Power requirements	1 kwh/lb MnO_2
Heavy metals and iron impurities in solution	<0.05%
Cathodes	graphite
Anodes	graphite
Anode-cathode spacing	1–2 inches
Current efficiency	90–95%

Deposition of manganese dioxide is generally continued until the deposit is one inch thick. If plate graphite or lead is used as an anode, the manganese dioxide is stripped from the plate by hitting it with a hammer. If a rod anode is used, it is ground with the manganese dioxide.

A decrease in cell temperature below 90°C tends to decrease the current efficiency of the cell,[3] as well as decrease the battery-active quality of the manganese dioxide deposited. Heat is supplied to a commercial cell by electric heating rods, steam coils, or live steam.

Anode current density using graphite anodes appears to be critical in the 5 to 10 amp/sq ft range. Higher current densities decrease the current efficiency of the cell and lower the battery activity of the manganese dioxide deposited.[7] There is some correlation between cell temperature, anode current density, and battery quality of the manganese dioxide produced.

Probably the cell condition that has been varied most is acid concentration. Acid concentrations from 5 to 150 grams per liter have been studied. The most economical operating condition is one in which the acid concentration in the cell is high. High acid concentration decreases the recycle of manganese sulfate and increases the acid concentration in the leach circuit. Commercial cells are operated at an acid concentration of 50 to 75 grams per liter. There is, however, some indication that low acid concentration in the cell gives a higher quality battery-active manganese dioxide.[10]

Manganese sulfate concentration in the cell tends to vary with acid concentration and degree of water removal in the process. No absolute value for manganese sulfate concentration is indicated in the literature. Of important consideration is the ratio of manganese sulfate to sulfuric acid. For production of high-quality, battery-active manganese dioxide at a high current efficiency, the minimum ratio is one to one.

Voltage across the cell is the sum of a number of components, i.e., anode and cathode reversible electrode potentials, overvoltage to deposit manganese dioxide, voltage drop through electrodes, voltage drop through solution, and overvoltage on the cathode. Both high concentration of acid in solution and high temperature favor a low voltage drop through the solution. Voltage drop through the electrodes depends on the type used and their configuration. Graphite is a better conductor than lead. Long, thin electrodes have a higher voltage drop than short, thicker electrodes. A typical voltage drop across a cell has not been discussed in detail in the literature. Latimer[6] gives a value of 1.23 volts for the reversible potential of the reaction

$$Mn^{++} + 2H_2O \rightarrow MnO_2 + 4H^+ + 2e$$

This value is about the same as the theoretical reversible oxygen electrode in acid solution. Kissin[5] estimates that the oxygen overvoltage on a graphite anode in a manganese dioxide cell is in the neighborhood of 0.3 to 0.5 volts. Steinhoff,[10] using as reference the N hydrogen electrode, reported that anode-to-solution drop was 1.30 volts; 0.13 volts was the drop across 2.5 inches of solution; and cathode-to-solution drop was 0.45 volts. The cell conditions using graphite anodes were: 30 gpl sulfuric acid, 7 amps/sq ft anode current density, and 4 amps/sq ft cathode current density at 95°C.

Cathode current density does not appear to be critical in the range between one-half to one times the anode current density.

Energy efficiency is determined by two factors: voltage drop across the cell and current efficiency, high acid concentration, good electrode conductivity, and high temperature all favor a lower energy requirement per pound of manganese dioxide produced.[3]

Cathode-anode spacing in an electrolytic manganese dioxide cell varies with cell design and type of manganese dioxide recovery employed. Because of the high conductance of the sulfuric acid-manganese sulfate solution in the cell, the effect of cathode-anode spacing on voltage is not as great as in other electrolytic cells. It is interesting to note that even when the manganese dioxide deposited on the anode touches the cathode, there is little or no effect on cell voltage.

Current efficiency in deposition of manganese dioxide is high under the best cell operating conditions. Current efficiency is lowered by decrease in temperature, impurities in the manganese sulfate solution, low manganese sulfate concentration, high acid concentration, and high current densities.

Presence of heavy metals and iron in manganese sulfate solution decreases current efficiency in the cell, as well as lowering the battery quality of manganese dioxide deposited.[2]

In commercial manganese dioxide cells, graphite is generaly used as the cathode. Other materials that have been used for cathodes are copper, lead, and stainless steel.

Because graphite as an anode is slowly consumed, research has been concentrated on finding a nondestructible anode. In Japan and Europe, lead anodes are used, but manganese dioxide produced on lead anodes always contains lead. Lead anodes have not been widely used in the United States because battery manufacturers have felt that lead in electrolytic manganese dioxide has an adverse effect on the shelf life of batteries. Also, the quality of graphite produced in the United States in the past has been superior to that available in other countries. The Japanese removed chlorides from manganese sulfate solution to decrease the attack on lead anodes. As in the case of electrolytic manganese cells, the best lead anodes in a manganese dioxide cell contain 0.15 per cent silver.[1] Titanium[4] and platinum[5] have also been used as electrodes for deposition of manganese dioxide.

To conserve heat and to decrease atmospheric pollution, the solution in the manganese dioxide cells is covered with a low melting wax. Manganese dioxide from the cells is harvested by breaking it from the anode with a hammer or by grinding the anode with the manganese dioxide. In the latter case, the graphite, after crushing of the manganese dioxide, is removed by a mechanical jig.[8] The manganese dioxide is ground until 95 per cent passes a No. 100 U.S. Standard Sieve. It is washed to remove sulfuric acid, manganese sulfate, and to bring the pH within a range of 4.0 to 7.0. Alkali metal hydroxides and ammonium hydroxide are avoided in the wash step because the cation enters the lattice of manganese dioxide[5] and lowers the battery quality of the material.

The manganese dioxide is then filtered and dried until it contains about one per cent moisture.

A typical analysis of electrolytic battery-active manganese dioxide is:

Available oxygen (as MnO_2)	89.5%
Total manganese (as Mn)	59.5%
Absorbed moisture	0.95%
Iron (Fe)	0.07%
Lead (Pb)	Nil
Silicon (Si)	0.09%
Insoluble in hydrochloric acid	1.33%
pH	5.4
Passing U.S. Standard Sieve No. 200	92.8%
Passing U.S. Standard Sieve No. 325	59.3%

Complete specifications for battery-active manganese dioxide are given in U.S. Signal Corps specifications.[9]

References

1. AITKENHEAD, W. C., *Bulletin No.* **219,** Washington State Institute of Technology, State College of Washington, June, 1953.
2. ARSDALE, G. D., AND MAIER, G. C., *Trans. Amer. Electrochem. Soc.,* **33,** 109 (1918).
3. CHAKRABARTI, H. K., AND BANERJEE, T., *J. Scientific & Ind. Res.,* **12B,** 211 (1953).
4. ISHIMO, T., TANURA, H., AND YANOKAVA, M., *Osaka Univ. Tech. Report,* **6,** 359 (1956).
5. KISSIN, G. H., *Final Report, Project No. 107-7,* Georgia Institute of Technology, State Engineering Experiment Station, July 31, 1949.
6. LATIMER, W. M., "The Oxidation States of the Elements and Their Potentials in Aqueous Solutions," Second Edition. Edgewood Cliff, New Jersey, Prentice-Hall, Inc. (1952).
7. MURAKAMI, I., AND OKAJIMA, Y., *Kogyo Kagaku Zasshi,* **64,** 137 (1961).
8. SCHRIER, E., AND HOFFMANN, R., *Chem. Eng.,* **61,** 152 (1954).
9. Signal Corps Technical Requirements--Manganese Dioxide, Military Battery Grade, SCL-3175, 28 July 1955.
10. STOREY, O. W., STEINHOFF, E., AND HOFF, E. R., *J. Electrochem. Soc.,* **86,** 344 (1944).

THOMAS W. CLAPPER

MANGANESE ELECTROWINNING

The successful electrowinning of manganese metal depends on the transformation of the thin layer of gamma metal first deposited on the cathode to fine-grained alpha metal and the subsequent deposition of macroscopic crystals of alpha manganese in order to maintain the current efficiency over extended periods. While thick deposits of gamma metal can be obtained from very pure solutions, the commercial process depends on the transformation to the alpha form by the presence of certain sulfur compounds in the electrolyte.

The flowsheets shown by Figures 1 and 2 are a good background to follow the individual steps for producing electrolytic manganese.

The ore used for producing the electrolyte is crushed to less than ¼ inch and roasted to MnO, leaving as much of the iron as possible in the form of Fe_3O_4, which is less soluble in dilute acid than the lower oxide of iron. Gas, oil, and solid fuel have all been used in the reducing roast.

Since the electrolyte used on a large scale consists of manganese ammonium sulfate, leaching in the cyclic process is performed with solutions containing $(NH_4)_2SO_4$, some $MnSO_4$, and 25 to 40 gpl H_2SO_4. The leaching step is the simplest and most standardized of the process steps. After the calcine is charged to brick-lined leach tanks equipped with stainless steel agitators, sulfuric acid is added with the leach solution to hold the pH at 2.5, and ammonium sulfate added to maintain a concentration of 135 to 140 gpl. The time of leaching is 1.25 to 1.50 hours. After completing the leach at a pH of 2.5, the solution is neutralized by NH_4OH or calcine to a pH of 6.5. An overall extraction of 98 to 99 per cent of the manganese is obtained. On neutralization, iron and aluminum are precipitated as hydroxides by neutralization of the solution, and molybdenum, arsenic, and silica are carried down with this floc. The leach liquor is pumped to a

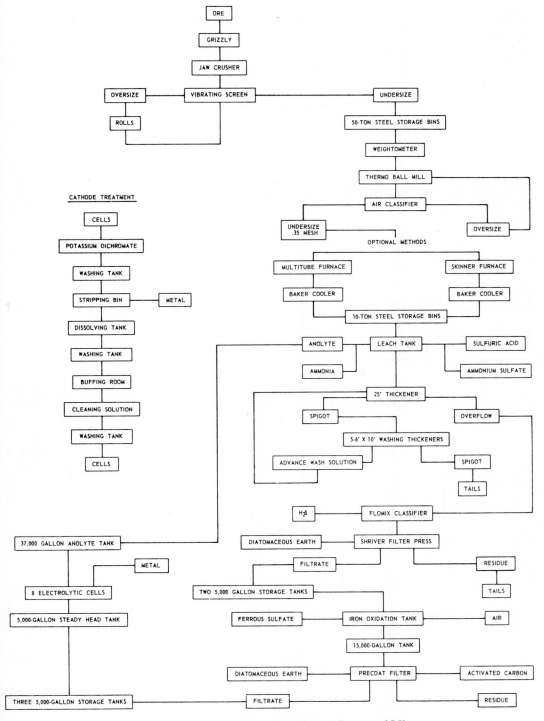

FIG. 1. Flowsheet of Boulder City Plant of Bureau of Mines.

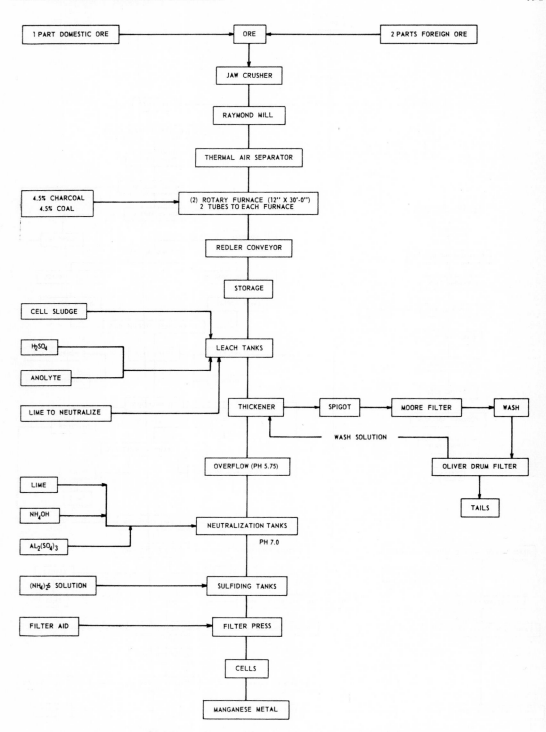

F<small>IG</small>. 2. Suggested flowsheet of Knoxville plant of the Electro Manganese Corporation.

thickener and the overflow sent to the purification step. Wash solution containing 75 to 90 gpl $(NH_4)_2SO_4$ and 16 to 20 gpl manganese flows to the leach thickeners. The leach contains 2.5 to 3 per cent solids which settle out rather slowly. The sulfuric acid consumption is approximately 0.25 lb/lb of leached manganese due to the presence of elements that form insoluble sulfates, i.e., $CaSO_4$.

Experience has shown that, in the electrowinning of metals, the presence of metals more noble than the metal being won will decrease the current efficiency. The only metals present which are less noble than manganese are aluminum and the alkali and alkaline earth metals; all others are deleterious.

The next step in the purification is to remove all the copper, zinc, nickel, and cobalt dissolved from the ore. The copper, zinc, nickel, and cobalt are quantitatively removed from the leach solution by treating with sulfide ion, either as ammonium sulfide plus charcoal or as H_2S. After filtering the solution, ferrous sulfate is added and oxidized to precipitate a ferric hydroxide floc as a carrier to free the resulting solution from metallic impurities and reduced sulfur compounds.

The magnesium dissolved by the spent electrolyte builds up in the solution, and although it has no adverse effect on the electrolysis, it will eventually separate as the triple sulfate of manganese, magnesium, and ammonium. Two methods are available for removing magnesium: (1) precipitation as magnesium fluoride, and (2) crystallization at low temperatures. The latter method is preferred, but some loss of $MnSO_4$ and $(NH_4)_2SO_4$ occurs.

The successful electrolysis of manganese from very pure solutions of $MnSO_4$ plus $(NH_4)_2SO_4$ depends on cell design, solution concentration, pH, flow rate to cells, temperature, anode and cathode composition, and treatment of the cathode. The design of the cells is described by Bacon in another encyclopedia (see Bibliography).

Manganese hydroxide formation in the catholyte takes place if the manganese content is raised above 14.5 gpl, and treeing and burning also take place. The addition of 0.10 gpl of sulfur dioxide prevents this. The deposit without the SO_2 addition is in the form of gamma metal at a current efficiency of only 42 per cent, while with SO_2, alpha metal is deposited at an efficiency of 60 per cent.

The optimum conditions for electrowinning manganese are:

1. Purified feed solution
   Mn as $MnSO_4$, gpl 30–40
   $(NH_4)_2SO_4$, gpl 125–150
   SO_2, gpl 0.10
   Glue, gpl 0.008–0.016
2. Anolyte composition
   Mn as $MnSO_4$, gpl 10–20
   H_2SO_4, gpl 25–40
   $(NH_4)_2SO_4$, gpl 125–150
3. Current density, amp/sq ft 40–60
4. Catholyte pH 6–7.2
5. Anode composition .... Pb-1% Ag
6. Cathode composition .... "Hastelloy," Type 316 stainless steel, or Ti
7. Cell voltage, volts 5.1
8. Diaphragm .... 18 oz. canvas
9. Power used per lb Mn, kwh 3.6–4.0
10. Current efficiency, % 60–65

Stripping of the cathode is important and is influenced by cathode surface treatment, gage of cathode, manganese concentration in cells, catholyte pH, smoothness of surface, and cathode material. Since it is brittle, manganese cannot be removed from the cathode in sheets, but it is removed as chips by flexing or striking the cathode with a rubber mallet.

A typical analysis of electrolytic manganese is given in the following tabulation.

Element	%	Element	%
Fe	0.0015	Sulfide S	0.0170
Cu	0.0010	Sulfate S	0.0140
As	0.0005	C	0.0020
Co	0.0025	H_2	0.0150
Ni	0.0025	Si	—
Pb	0.0025	Mg	—
Mo	0.0010	Ca	—

The hydrogen in the metal can be removed by heating at a temperature of 500°C.

Electrolytic manganese is used in the production of nonferrous alloys and some stainless steels. The price of electrolytic manganese as of early 1963 was $0.28/lb. The metal with hydrogen removed sold for ¾¢/lb premium. There is also a high nitrogen electrolytic manganese produced which is sold at $0.3275/lb.

References

1. DEAN, R. S., "Electrolytic Manganese and Its Alloys," New York, The Ronald Press Company, 1952.
2. JACOBS, J. H., et al., U. S. Bureau of Mines, Bull. 463 (1946).

3. Bacon, F. E., "Encyclopedia of Chemical Process Equipment," Editor, W. V. Mead, New York, Reinhold Publishing Corporation, 1964.
4. Carosella, M. C. and Fowler, R. M., *J. Electrochem. Soc.*, **104**, 352 (1957).

F. E. Bacon

MANUAL PLATING

Manual operation of a plating cycle involves the handling and processing by one or more operators of the parts to be plated through the various treatment tanks of the cycle. The parts may be loaded on wires or placed in racks, trays, baskets, and portable barrels.

The size of the loads is limited to what an average operator can handle with regard to weight and dimensions. The control of the cycle is dependent on the operator and thus can be very flexible, permitting varying time cycles in any of the treatment steps.

The arrangements of tanks for a manually operated plating line can be of almost any configuration, but the recommended arrangement is "U" shaped, so that the operator returns to practically his starting point after having transferred work through each step in the cycle, from preliminary cleaning through the final rinse. A straight line arrangement is also used, but this demands additional walking by the operator and the chance of increased fatigue and decreased production.

Manual operation of a cycle is not necessarily limited to one operator, since two or more may be processing work through the plating line at intervals. Also, one operator may carry work through several steps in the line to a selected point, at which a second operator may take over to process the work through subsequent steps, or to another selected point where a third operator may take over to advance the work through additional steps of the cycle. Each man is then responsible for processing of the work only through a portion of the whole sequence of steps in the plating cycle. The use of multiple manual operators is obviously dictated by the number of steps in a cycle and the total length of the treatment line.

Parts to be processed may be strung up on a single wire or on multiples of wires. The parts may be wired and the wires tied on racks in multiples, so that processing may be easily accomplished. Parts may also be held on racks of various designs to accommodate various sizes and configurations. The size of the racks will depend on the total loaded weight which an operator may handle without fatigue. Trays and baskets containing parts also should be limited in size by total weight. Portable barrels may be manually processed through a plating line, and here again total loaded weight is a consideration.

A manually operated cycle should be designed so that the flow of parts being treated does not reach a bottleneck at any point. The time of plating will probably be the longest of any step in the cycle, so this tank should be large enough to permit the removal of a load of parts of the work being plated just as a similar load leaves the rinse tank steps prior to the plating tank. Also, the use of multiple plating cells might be provided, whereby a load of parts is ready to enter a plating tank about to be unloaded. This all requires proper planning to determine the size and number of plating tanks necessary to maintain the desired flow of production.

Included in a manually operated plating line may be a sequence of plating cycles needed to effect the desired final plated finish. For example, chromium plating (q.v.) involves a copper strike, a bright nickel bath and finally a bright chromium bath.

By the use of a chain hoist and monorail or a motor-driven hoist and monorail, both manually operated, the size of the loads processed may be greatly increased, the control of the cycle still being dependent on the operator and flexible as to time for processing in each step. Careful planning of the cycle and the size of tanks is again required to insure a smooth flow of production. The use of a hoist and monorail lends itself to both the straight-line cycles and the return type. Less fatigue of the operator can be anticipated with this type of manual operation.

References

1. Graham, A. K., Editor, "Electroplating Engineering Handbook," New York, Reinhold Publishing Corp., 1962.
2. Lowenheim, F. A., Editor, "Modern Electroplating," Second Edition, New York, John Wiley and Sons, Inc., 1963.

Oscar A. Stocker

Cross-references: *Barrel Plating;* entries bearing *Electroplating* and *Electrodeposition* titles; entries for specific metals.

MARINE CORROSION

The Phoenicians, Greeks, Romans, and other ancient travelers across the Mediterranean Sea no doubt observed marine attack of the metal items that served on their ships. It is not known whether they conducted research in corrosion. With the introduction of iron and steel, the interest in marine corrosion was intensified. Seafaring nations, like the English, have been investigating marine corrosion continuously since the days of Humphrey Davy. Since sea water is a principal natural corrosive agent, marine corrosion programs are being carried out by many nations. In the United States, the marine laboratories of the Navy and The International Nickel Company are among the leaders in providing data on the behavior of metals in sea water.

Natural sea water is usually more corrosive than synthetic sea water. This is mainly because living organisms, present in the ocean water, may deposit onto metal surfaces and play a significant role in the local attack.

Corrosive Ions in Sea Water

The chloride ion is probably the most deleterious ionic constituent occurring in sea water in large quantities. Its corrosive nature probably comes from the fact that it is small and can readily penetrate some types of protective films on metals.

In addition to chloride ions, the anions found to the greatest extent in sea water are sulfate, bicarbonate, bromide, and fluoride. Lyman and Abel[1] list a typical analysis for the major constituents of a sample of northern Pacific Ocean water. Their data, tabulated below, also include the major cations present.

Cations	Per Cent	Anions	Per Cent
Na^+	1.056	Cl^-	1.898
Mg^{++}	0.127	SO_4^{--}	0.265
Ca^{++}	0.040	HCO_3^-	0.014
K^+	0.038	Br^-	0.0065
Sr^{++}	0.001	F^-	0.0001
	1.262		2.184
	H_3BO_3 (undissociated)		.003

Grand Total: 3.449%

Natural processes, operating both at the surface and at great depths, result in a continuous circulation of ocean water so that the relative proportions of dissolved salts are virtually the same everywhere, although the total salt content (salinity) may show appreciable variations with the geographical location.

The halogen ions, other than chloride, are present only in small amounts, and their corrosive effects in sea water are probably masked by the very high chloride content.

Other corrosion experience would suggest that the sulfate also contributes much less to the corrosive attack by sea water than the chloride.

While the presence of bicarbonate ions in water can help promote corrosive attack on many metals, its role in sea water is largely involved in mineral-scale formation. The pH of sea water normally ranges from 7.5 to 8.2, indicating a slight excess of hydroxyl ions.

Oxygen content varies with depth. At the surface, sea water is normally saturated with oxygen. Cold currents, originating in the Arctic, flowing over the sea bottom toward the equator, are high in oxygen. At intermediate depths, decaying organic material may consume the available oxygen.

Conductance and Salt Concentration

Since corrosive attack is dependent on electrolytic processes, it is greatly influenced by the conductivity of the solution. Sea water is a good electrolyte, so it is not too surprising that it is corrosive. Fig. 1[2] shows that the resistivity of sea water is relatively low at normal temperatures. However, it can also be seen that as the

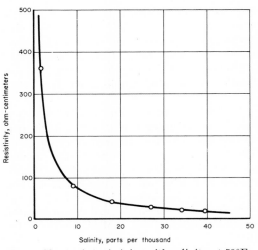

Fig. 1. Change in resistivity with salinity at 59°F.

sea water is diluted (as might occur near rivers), the resistivity is markedly increased. Accordingly, the corrosion might be expected to be somewhat less in the vicinity of rivers. Actually, the corrosive effect of varying the salinity is interrelated with some of the other variables, particularly oxygen solubility.

Oxygen and Temperature

Of the environmental factors, oxygen ranks high in degree of importance. It affects corrosion reactions by depolarizing cathodic areas and by changing corrosion-cell potentials.

An increase in temperature normally can be expected to speed up a chemical reaction. Corrosion could be expected to accelerate as the temperature is increased. The oxygen solubility, however, decreases with higher temperature. Thus, a point is reached, as one raises the temperature, where the lower oxygen content tends to slow down the reaction. If one concentrates sea water, the oxygen solubility will be reduced. For a metal such as steel, raw sea water is more corrosive than deaerated sea water.

Biological Effects

A primary factor is the presence of biological effects in natural sea water which are not present in the synthetic mixture. Marine fouling is likely to occur in all the oceans from the Arctic to the tropics, especially during the breeding periods. In northern waters, fouling occurs only during the summer months, whereas in the tropics it is practically continuous.

One effect is that fouling of the metal surface often promotes localized attack. For example, when a barnacle or mussel attaches itself to a plate of stainless steel in sea water, a differential-aeration corrosion cell is formed. Intense local pitting results, which may lead to complete perforation of the steel within a relatively short time.

A variety of animals and plants, as well as colonies of microorganisms, may deposit from natural sea water onto the surface of the metal. The life processes and decomposition products may contribute directly to corrosive attack on the metal. Fouling may obstruct flow in heat exchangers and in pipes, which will lead to such corrosive effects as are caused by overheating or by impingements at local high water velocities.

Some organisms enter a marine piping system in their larval stages, they then anchor themselves to sites such as interior tube walls. If these larvae are allowed to grow, the local turbulence may result in severe corrosion. The organisms may be killed by chlorination, by flooding temporarily with fresh water or hot sea water, or by toxic materials such as sodium pentachlorophenol. Even when the organisms are killed, their decomposing bodies may clog the sea water system and promote corrosion.

Two facts concerning the corrosion behavior of metals in sea water stand out:

1. Although there is variation in temperature, in salinity, and in content of living organisms, the rates of attack—especially for steel—are of the same order of magnitude at many different locations throughout the world.

2. The relative order of resistance of metals, as determined by their corrosion rates in natural sea water, is not readily simulated with synthetic sea water preparations in the laboratory.

Copper and some of its high-copper alloys normally are not susceptible to fouling. However, any treatment to the metal which restricts the formation of a film of ions on the surface may result in a tendency for copper to foul. Corrosive attack on some metals may actually be stifled by fouling, particularly if the coverage is complete. For many metals, localized attack can be more serious under fouled areas. At velocities of 2 to 3 feet per second or more, metals usually are not apt to foul. Once the organisms become attached to metals during a shutdown or off-period of a plant handling sea water, even extremely high initial velocities may not dislodge them at the start-up.

Corrosion behavior tends to follow much the same pattern in clean sea water everywhere. If there is pollution, it may (1) alter the pH, (2) change the marine life present, (3) decrease the dissolved oxygen, or (4) alter the chemical balance of the sea water. Normally, pollution will result in a saline water becoming considerably more aggressive to one or more metals. Specific tests must be conducted to determine the applicability of a metal in each type of polluted water. Sulfides (which are often found in polluted waters) tend to promote corrosion of both ferrous and nonferrous metals.

Materials of Construction

Ferrous-Base Metals. *Steel.* Steel finds wide use in sea water, especially as a structural material for ships, off-shore drilling towers, piling for piers and docks, and for sea walls. It is also used as piping to handle sea water. Compared with other metals, steel is one of the least expensive materials of construction.

Steel is the basic material of construction for many sea water plants. Even though it may corrode in some sections of a plant, such as a distillation unit, its low initial cost may result in lower over-all costs. However, it is essential that good design and good corrosion-control practices be followed.

The rate of attack for immersed conditions is fairly uniform in unpolluted sea water and averages about 5 mils per year. General attack, when it occurs, has been observed to be a linear function of time; that is, it usually continues at a fairly uniform rate, despite an accumulation of corrosion products or marine growth.

However, steel often is subject to pitting attack by sea water. The deepest attack on steel is reported to be about 10 to 15 mils per year. The presence of mill scale on the steel—especially when it covers a large portion of the exposed area—significantly increases the rate of pitting, and penetrations of about 20 mils per year or more can be expected. This is a result of the mill scale serving as large cathodes to the small, bare, anodic areas. Pitting attack often tapers off with continued exposure.

Wrought Iron. Wrought iron has found considerable application in marine-based structures and in piping. While wrought iron, according to some sources, appears to be more resistant than mild steel to general and localized corrosion by sea water, there is no general acceptance of this material by operators of marine plants. Advantage is sometimes taken of its directional physical properties where corrosion resistance also is needed. It should be mentioned that for the same initial cost a much thicker wall can be purchased in a cast iron or steel pipe than for one of wrought iron.

Aluminum and Its Alloys. Aluminum can be employed in sea water as a corrosion-resistant material of construction. By proper corrosion-control practices, aluminum can be used for an entire plant which processes sea water. The sea water entering the plant should be free of all heavy metal ions, especially copper or nickel. It is essential, in such a plant, that no copper-base alloys be used at all and that galvanic couples to most other metals be avoided.

To obtain longer lifetime in sea water service, aluminum-clad tubing is recommended. Properly chosen, the cladding acts as a sacrificial metal and the attack will not penetrate into the base metal until most of the cladding has been consumed by corrosion. The aluminum usually chosen for cladding is both more corrosion resistant and slightly anodic to the base alloy. The fact that a metal is more anodic than an adjacent one, in the galvanic series for sea water service, does not necessarily imply that it will corrode at a higher rate when exposed uncoupled.

Monel. Extensive use for sea water service is provided by Monel. This metal has given excellent service in heat exchangers, piping, sheathing to protect structural steel at the half-tide zone, valves, pump impellers, and fittings in general. Monel has been used in fabricating distillation units. In one type, a Monel heat exchanger "basket" can be made to flex in order that the sea water scale will drop off. This flexing service is considered much too severe for most metals. Monel shafts, such as the harder K Monel, are resistant to corrosion fatigue in sea water service. Marine experience, in general, considers Monel one of the best versatile metals for handling sea water.

Copper-Base Alloys. There is a wide range of copper-base alloys that have given good service in sea water use. Admiralty brass, 70Cu-29Zn-1Sn, plus an inhibitor such as arsenic, has found wide use as condenser tubes in marine-based plants using sea water for cooling purposes. While this metal is not so resistant as the cupro-nickels, it often seems to be preferred because of lower initial cost.

Another alloy widely used in cooling-water service is aluminum brass, 76Cu-22Zn-2Al. The aluminum content improves this metal's resistance to velocity and impingement. This alloy seems to be more susceptible to pitting than some of the other copper alloys in stagnant sea water. Arsenic is added as an inhibitor of dezincification.

Ordinary copper is not recommended for sea water plants if the water velocities are much greater than 2 feet per second. It remains to be demonstrated whether copper can be employed in contact with completely deaerated sea water at higher velocities.

Cupro-Nickels. At the present time, most marine-plant operators agree that the cupro-nickels are the most useful material of construction for sea water service. Since World War II, the 90-Cu-10Ni alloy modified with about 1.5 per cent iron has become well established. The lower nickel content results in a cost advantage over the 70Cu-30Ni alloy. Alloys containing 70Cu-30Ni or 80Cu-20Ni, each with added iron, are preferred by some designers to withstand more severe conditions.

The cupro-nickels have been widely accepted as the best available alloys for condenser tubes. There has been some favorable experience with cupro-nickel for pumps and heat exchangers for handling sea water.

Titanium. Unlike other metals, titanium normally does not pit; it is not susceptible to stress-corrosion cracking; it is free of local corrosion under fouling organisms; it is free of impingement and cavitation attack at velocities which attack copper-base alloys; it is not susceptible to sulfide attack in contaminated sea water. Experiments with water velocities at 20 to 50 feet per second show no attack on titanium.

Titanium and its alloys are said to be less susceptible to mineral scaling in sea water service than most other metals. (The rough, corroded surface on a metal, such as steel, probably helps to anchor sea scale deposits.) Although thermal conductivity is low, the over-all efficiency—taking full advantage of the very high velocities permitted—can be greater than with material used at present in sea water applications involving high rates of heat transfer.

Stainless Steel. In sea water, stainless steel has a tendency to rapid, local corrosive attack at stagnant areas at joints, crevices, or under barnacles and shell fish. A fully-quench-annealed austenitic stainless steel impeller or propeller will afford good service in sea water, provided it is properly designed and is not allowed to stand idle in service.

Magnesium and Zinc. Alloys of these metals are finding application as sacrificial anodes to provide cathodic protection to steel structures in sea water.

References

1. LYMAN, JOHN, AND ABEL, ROBERT B., "Chemical Aspects of Physical Oceanography," *J. Chem. Education*, **35**, 113–115 (March 1958).
2. "The Corrosion Handbook," edited by Herbert H. Uhlig, p. 1115, Table 6, New York, John Wiley & Sons, Inc., (also, Chapman & Hall, Limited, London, England), 1948.
3. FINK, FREDERICK W., "Corrosion of Metals in Sea Water," Research and Development Progress Report No. 46, PB 171344 (December 1960), Office of Saline Water, U. S. Department of the Interior, 157 ref. (Available at the Office of Technical Services, Washington 25, D. C.).
4. FINK, FREDERICK W., "Corrosion of Metals in Sea Water," "Saline Water Conversion," Advances in Chemistry Series 27, p. 27, Washington, D. C., American Chemical Society, 1960.

FREDERICK W. FINK

Cross-references: entries with *Corrosion* titles; *Cathodic Protection; Galvanic Series.*

MEMBRANE EQUILIBRIUM

This term is applied to a special type of osmotic equilibrium, first described in 1911 by Donnan and Harris. They were studying the osmotic pressure of saline solutions of a dye, Congo red, which is the sodium salt of a high-molecular weight sulfonic acid. The membranes of their osmometer were permeable to water and to ordinary salts, but impermeable to the dye. After osmotic equilibrium had been attained in their experiments, sodium chloride was present on both sides of the membrane, but its concentration was always higher in the external solution, which contained none of the large ions of the dye. To explain this unequal distribution, Donnan worked out a theory which he expressed in simple equations, based on thermodynamics and the laws of dilute solutions. He showed that diffusible ions tend to be unequally distributed in such a system whenever there is some constraint which prevents at least one kind of ion or charged particle from diffusing freely. Other investigators referred to the unequal distribution of ions as the Donnan effect, and called this type of equilibrium the Donnan equilibrium. After it was pointed out Donnan might have based his theory on more general equations deduced by Gibbs in 1875–1878, the term Gibbs-Donnan equilibrium came into use.

A simple type of membrane equilibrium may be illustrated by the use of a diagram.

I	II
H_2O	H_2O
$z/n\ R^{n-}$	
$y + z\ Na^+$	$Na^+\ x$
$y\ Cl^-$	$Cl^-\ x$

Here the vertical line represents a membrane impermeable to the ion, R^{n-} but freely permeable to water and to sodium chloride. The molar concentrations of ions, after equilibrium has been reached, are indicated by the small letters. The notation is consistent with the electroneutrality of each solution; z is the equivalent concentration of the anion of valence n and molar concentration z/n. According to Donnan's theory, equilibrium requires an equality of the products of the concentrations of the ions of sodium chloride in the two solutions. This may be expressed by the equation

$$x^2 = y(y + z)$$

which shows at once that x is greater than y, or that the concentration of diffusible salt is greater in the external solution, II. This unequal distribution may be very marked; for example, if z is equal to 100 y, the ratio x/y is 10.05. On the other hand, if y is equal to 100 z, the ratio x/y is only 1.005. It is characteristic of the Donnan equilibrium that a high concentration of any diffusible electrolyte tends to suppress the unequal distribution.

Equilibrium in such a case requires a difference in pressure between the two solutions, and this difference is the difference between their osmotic pressures. The observed difference, although it is often called the colloid osmotic pressure, may be largely due to the unequal distribution of diffusible ions. Donnan pointed out that it would approach that due to the ions of the whole colloidal electrolyte only if x and y were much less than z, while in the opposite extreme it would approach that due to the colloidal ions alone.

Donnan also deduced the existence of an electric potential difference between the two solutions at equilibrium. Since this is a single potential difference, it cannot be measured directly; the best that can be done is to connect identical electrodes with the solutions on opposite sides of the membrane by way of salt bridges. Many measurements of this sort were made by Loeb in his work on the colloidal behavior of proteins. It was later found that the electromotive force of such cells, of the order of 30 millivolts, was changed very little by the puncture or removal of the membrane after equilibrium had been reached.

The Donnan equilibrium in nonideal solutions has been treated mathematically by Overbeek.

The theory of membrane equilibrium has been especially useful in the study of proteins. Biological scientists have found it necessary to consider the Donnan equilibrium in trying to explain differences in ionic concentration, osmotic pressure, and electric potential across cell membranes.

References

1. BOLAM, T. R., "The Donnan Equilibria," London, G. Bell & Sons, 1932.
2. DONNAN, F. G., "The Theory of Membrane Equilibria," *Chem. Rev.*, **1,** 73–90 (1924).
3. HITCHCOCK, D. I., "Proteins and the Donnan Equilibrium," *Physiol. Rev.*, **4,** 505–531 (1924).
4. HITCHCOCK, D. I., "Membrane Potentials in the Donnan Equilibrium. II," *J. Gen. Physiol.*, **37,** 717–727 (1954).
5. LOEB, J., "Proteins and the Theory of Colloidal Behavior," New York, McGraw-Hill Book Co., 1924.
6. OVERBEEK, J. TH. G., "The Donnan Equilibrium," *Progr. in Biophys. and Biophys. Chem.*, **6,** 57–84 (1956).

DAVID I. HITCHCOCK

Cross-references: *Bioelectrogenesis; Electrophysiology; Ion Transport Across Charged Membranes;* entries with *Membrane* titles; *Nerve Impulse Transmission.*

MEMBRANE POTENTIALS

The *"membrane potential"* in the wider sense of this term is the potential which arises in all cells of the type: Electrolytic Solution (1) | Membrane | Electrolytic Solution (2), the two electrolytic solutions, in the same solvent, being of different composition. The treatment given here is elementary; a more rigorous approach is found in the quoted literature.

Membrane potentials are measured in a conventional electrochemical manner, with the same reservations and restrictions which apply to all such methods,[1] e.g., by the use of salt bridges and calomel electrodes. Membrane cells ordinarily are not equilibrium systems but degrade spontaneously; the potentials arising in them are ordinarily not equilibrium potentials; equilibrium (and quasi-equilibrium) systems represent a limiting case. In a narrower sense the term "membrane potential," refers to the specific case of the *Donnan membrane potential*,[2] *Donnan potential* for short, the equilibrium potential which arises if at least one of the solutions contains one (or more) species of strictly nonpermeable ions, *and* provided that the activities of the solvent in the two compartments are equalized, e.g., by the presence of a nondiffusible nonelectrolyte in the more dilute salt solution, or by the application of a hydrostatic pressure to the more concentrated one.

Membrane potentials arise across membranes of almost any *microporous* material, such as parchment paper, collodion, many plastic films, gels, porous silicates, plant and animal membranes, etc., also across *liquid*, "oil," *membranes* consisting of a liquid immiscible with the adjacent solutions.[3] Interphases of solid electrolytes, including the glass electrode (see **Glass Electrode**), are not treated here.

With membranes of high porosity (porous diaphragms) the membrane potentials hardly differ from the potentials which arise between the same two solutions on free diffusion in the absence of a membrane, the so-called *liquid junction* or *diffusion potentials*. With stepwise denser membranes, the membrane potentials deviate more and more from the liquid junction potentials. The close relationship of the membrane potential and the liquid junction potentials is obvious.

The sign and the magnitude of the membrane potential depend on the concentrations and concentration ratios of the electrolytes in the two solutions, their nature, and the nature of the membrane. Formally the membrane potential, ϵ, can be considered as a diffusion potential with modified ionic mobilities; the general equation for the diffusion potential is applicable to it:

$$\epsilon = - \frac{RT}{\mathbf{F}} \int_{(1)}^{(2)} \sum_n \frac{t_i}{z_i} \, d \ln a_i \qquad (1)$$

in which R is the gas constant, T the absolute temperature, $\mathbf{F}$ the Faraday constant, t_i, z_i and a_i the transport number, valency and the activity, respectively, of the ith component of the n component system. For a critical discussion of this highly involved problem, see the classical book of MacInnes,[1] particularly pages 220ff. The application of this general theoretical treatment to experimental cells is one of the central tasks of the basic electrochemistry of membranes; formidable conceptual and experimental difficulties arise. Success in this field is still confined to certain relatively simple types of cells, only a few of which can be treated here.

The physical mechanism which causes the ionic selectivity of membranes is of no concern in the validity of Eq. 1. However, from the point of view of a comprehensive theory of the electrochemistry of membranes and of their use as scientific and technological tools (see **Electrodialysis**), the mechanism of ionic selectivity is of paramount importance.[3]

The fact that the membrane potential deviates from the corresponding liquid junction potential shows unequivocally that the ratio of the contributions of the anions and cations to the transportation of electricity across the membrane is different from that in the liquid junction. Either the cations or the anions are more restricted in their diffusion across the membrane; consequently, the ions of the opposite sign have a preferred permeability across the membrane. The membrane is selectively permeable for these latter ions.

Early studies of the membrane concentration cells (cells with solution of different concentration of the same electrolyte, see below), have shown that the direction of the deviation of the membrane concentration potential from the liquid junction potential is correlated to the electrokinetic charge of the membrane. With electronegative membranes, the more dilute solution is more positive; with electropositive membranes, it is more negative than in free diffusion. With electronegative membranes, the transference number of the cation, τ_+, is larger than in solution, t_+; $(\tau_+ > t_+$; and $\tau_- < t_-)$. With positive membranes, the inverse holds true. This means that electronegative membranes are preferentially cation permeable, electropositive membranes preferentially anion permeable.

According to electrokinetic theory (see **Electrokinetic Potentials**) the electrokinetic charge of a solid in contact with a liquid is due to charges which are fixed immovably to the solid surface, forming the immovable part of an Helmholtz electrical double layer. (See **Electrode Double Layer**.) The other part of the double layer consists of an electrically equivalent number of counter-ions of opposite charge in the adjacent solution. In the microporous structure of a membrane, the charges on the pore walls are accompanied by an electrically equivalent amount of counter-ions in the pore water. Any transportation of electricity across the membrane is due to the movement of these counter-ions of the fixed charges in the pores and whatever other electrolyte, equivalent quantities of cations and anions, is present in the pores; the fixed wall charges cannot participate in the transportation of electricity. This explains the preferential, selective permeability of negative membranes for cations, and of positive membranes for anions.

With low molecular weight electrolytes as solutes, the preferential cationic or anionic selectivity of membranes has been shown by Teorell, and Meyer and Sievers to be due to the ion exchange properties of the membranes.[4] The *"fixed charge theory"* of *ion exchange membranes* developed by these authors goes a long way in explaining the electrochemical, especially the electromotive, properties of membranes. According to this theory, all common membranes carry inherently a definite, invariable number of immovable, potentially dissociable groups as part of their chemical structure: anionic (acidic) groups, such as carboxyl or $-SO_3H$ groups, in the case of electronegative membranes, and cationic (basic) groups, such as amino groups, in the case of electropositive membranes. Ordinarily, the number of these fixed charged groups in the membrane can be considered as independent of the nature and the concentration of the adjacent electrolytic solutions. The conception of membranes as ion exchange bodies has clarified their nature and mode of action and is today the cornerstone of electrochemical membrane theory. (See **Ion Exchange Membranes.**) The electrochemistry of ion exchangers can now be incorporated most profitably into the electrochemistry of ionic membranes.

All ionic processes across ion exchange, *"ionic" membranes*, such as the diffusion of ions (which generates the membrane potential) or the flow of current are due, as stated before, to the movement of the counter-ions of the charged wall groups and whatever additional diffusible *"nonexchange" electrolyte* (equivalent quantities of anions and cations) may be present in the pores. As in bulk ion exchangers, the concentration of nonexchange electrolyte in the pore system of a membrane is determined by a distribution equilibrium which depends on the width of the pore, the charge density on the pore walls, the valency of the ions in solution, and last but not least, on the concentration of the outside solutions.[4] The higher the concentration of the outside solution, the greater the concentration of nonexchange electrolyte in the pore system of an ionic membrane. In dense membranes in contact with dilute solutions, nonexchange electrolyte may be virtually absent. (In such membranes, ionic size can also become a significant factor.)

Combining the basic concepts from which the general Eq. 1 and all derivative equations for the liquid junction potential are obtained, with the conception of the membranes as ion exchange bodies, Teorell, and Meyer and Sievers[4] have developed a set of equations for the electromotive action of membranes in concentration (and other) cells. In doing so, they had to make several simplifying assumptions. The equations developed on this basis, too involved for meaningful presentation here, have not yet been tested critically over a great variety of conditions. For the limiting situations involving membranes of extreme ionic selectivity, they reduce to equations such as Eq. 3 below, which can be derived in a less elaborate manner. In spite of the still existing uncertainties and difficulties, the further development of the fixed charge theory of ionic membranes can confidently be expected to be the basis of deeper insight into the molecular details of the origin of membrane potentials in general, including membrane potentials in cells of great complexity like those in living systems. (See **Ion Exchange Membranes** and **Ion Transport Across Charged Membranes.**)

Oil membranes and the *potentials* which arise *in cells with oil membranes* are a sorely neglected field of critical and systematic physicochemical investigation.[5] They have been studied in the past primarily by physiologists because of their importance in electrophysiology (q.v.), particularly cellular and neurophysiology, many living membranes being considered to be akin to oil membranes. Much basic work on membrane potentials in cells with oil membranes is due to Beutner who treats them essentially as phase boundary potentials (see **Electrode Potentials**). Their experimental study is difficult, hindered in many instances by the extremely high resistance of such cells, and by a lack of sharp reproducibility of the results. The search for the most appropriate theoretical treatment is still in a state of flux. At present, this topic does not lend itself to a concise survey and the reader must be referred to the literature.[5]

The simplest of the membrane cells which can be discussed here are the membrane *concentration cells*, that is, cells with solutions of different concentrations of the same electrolyte. The potential arising in such cells is called *"membrane concentration potential"* or *"concentration potential."* With a given membrane and a given electrolyte, the membrane potentials which arise in cells with the same concentration ratio of the two solutions are lower at higher concentrations, due to the presence of nonexchange electrolyte (see above) in the pores; the ionic selectivity of the membrane is lower at higher concentrations. With certain membranes of rather low porosity (and therefore negligible water permeability) the concentration potential may reach the magnitude of the potential difference which would arise if the two solutions were connected

$c_1:c_2$, equiv./l	Theoret. maximum, mv	Cation exchange membr.[a] mv[c]	Anion exchange membr.[b] mv[c]
0.004/0.002	±17.31	+17.19	−17.13
0.04/0.02	±16.63	+16.52	−16.51
0.4/0.2	±15.95	+15.40	−15.30

[a] Sulfonated polystrene collodion matrix membrane.
[b] Protamine collodion matrix membrane.
[c] The sign refers to the more dilute solution.

to each other through a pair of reversible electrodes, specific either for the cations or the anions in solution, as the case may be (Table 1).

The correlation of the concentration potential, ϵ, and the transference numbers in the membrane, τ_+ and τ_-, may be expressed by the well-known Nernst equation for the diffusion potential, for 1-1 electrolytes:

$$\epsilon = \frac{\tau_+ - \tau_-}{\tau_+ + \tau_-} \frac{RT}{\mathbf{F}} \ln \frac{a_\pm^{(2)}}{a_\pm^{(1)}}, \qquad (2)$$

where $a_\pm^{(1)}$ and $a_\pm^{(2)}$ are the activities of the uni-univalent electrolyte in the two solutions, the sum of τ_+ plus τ_- being unity.[3] With membranes of virtually ideal ionic selectivity, permeable exclusively to cations or to anions and impermeable to ions of the opposite sign, the transference number of the permeable ions (cations with acidic membranes, anions with basic membranes), τ_+ or τ_- is virtually unity. In this case there is a membrane cell with a single species of potential determining ions; the membrane acts electromotively like a double-sided electrode, reversible for the permeable species of ions, and the membrane potential, ϵ, reaches the thermodynamically possible maximum value. (Compare Table 1.) Eq. 2 reduces to:

$$\epsilon = \frac{\pm RT}{n\mathbf{F}} \ln \frac{a_\pm^{(2)}}{a_\pm^{(1)}}, \qquad (3)$$

n being the valency of the permeable ion. This situation involving a membrane of virtually ideal ionic selectivity can be considered as the simplest possible case of a Donnan membrane equilibrium[2] (see below), provided the movement of solvent is negligibly slow, a condition which can be realized experimentally in many instances.

It is of interest to note here that cells with membranes of high cationic and anionic selectivities respectively, can be used as *"membrane electrodes"* for the electrometric determination of the activities of numerous cations and anions in solution including many for which classical, specific electrodes are difficult to handle or not available at all, such as F^-, NO_3^-, ClO_3^-, ClO_4^-, IO_3^-, $CH_3 \cdot COO^-$, etc.[7] (Compare also articles **Glass Electrodes** and **Reference Electrodes**.) In recent years, this easy and accurate method has been finding increasing use, and can be recommended highly as a routine laboratory procedure with single electrolyte solutions.

Membrane potentials arising in cells other than concentration cells with a single electrolyte (that means the great variety of cells with several electrolytes in solution and membranes with all gradations of ionic selectivity) have not yet been studied extensively from a strictly physico-chemical point of view. Much more attention has been paid to such cells by physiologists because of their great importance in the biological sciences, particularly cell, muscle, and neurophysiology. The cause for the lack of systematic information is undoubtedly due to their great complexity. The theoretical treatment of the interdiffusion of several electrolytes in systems with membranes of limited degrees of ionic selectivity, as are most membranes in living structures, is highly involved and beset with experimental difficulties. The numerous empirical coefficients that are needed in a systematic treatment of a single membrane pertain only to the particular membrane under investigation, while the art of reproducible preparation of membranes is still in its infancy. However, the approach of Teorell, and Meyer and Sievers, if combined with the just emerging work on the irreversible thermodynamics of membrane processes[6] (compare article **Irreversible Electrochemical Processes, Thermodynamics of**) gives hope for future progress in this most important area of the electrochemistry of membranes. Some relatively simple cases, which have already been studied experimentally in some detail, are presented in the next article below, **Membrane Potentials-Bi-ionic and Polyionic.**[8]

Finally, consider the historically first instance (Donnan, 1911) in which a membrane potential was shown to be amenable to a quantitative treatment, the *Donnan membrane potential.*[2, 9] (Compare article **Membrane Equilibrium.**) This particular membrane potential arises due to the uneven distribution of electrolyte between the two compartments of a membrane cell if (at least) one species of ions, referred to in the literature commonly as the "colloidal" ion, R^+ or R^-, cannot penetrate across the membrane, for instance due to its large size, whereas all other species of ions can permeate through it.[2,9] To simplify the presentation, the treatment given here is in the customary manner in terms of concentrations instead of activities. It is assumed that all electrolytes in the system are completely dissociated, that all ions including the R-ion are univalent, also that the volumes of the two solution compartments are the same, and that the movement of solvent is prevented.

Donnan's classical system is one in which in the initial state the membrane separates the solution of a "colloidal" electrolyte, e.g., NaR from the solution of another sodium salt, say NaCl:

Membrane

Na^+ R^-		Na^+ Cl^-
c_1 c_1		c_2 c_2
(1)		(2)

Initial State

On standing, sodium chloride diffuses through the membrane into solution (1) until equilibrium is established, the concentration of R^- remaining constant:

Membrane

Na^+ R^- Cl^-		Na^+ Cl^-
$c_1 + x$ c_1 x		$c_2 - x$ $c_2 - x$
(1)		(2)

Equilibrium State

As pointed out by Donnan,[2] the value of x is determined by the condition that in the equilibrium state the same amount of work is required to transport dn mols of Cl^- or dn mols of Na^+ from (2) to (1) as is required to transport the same amount of the two ions from (1) to (2); the change in the free energy, F, is zero:

$$dF = dn \; RT \ln \frac{[Cl^-]_2}{[Cl^-]_1} + dn \; RT \ln \frac{[Na^+]_2}{[Na^+]_1} = 0 \quad (4)$$

$[Cl^-]_1$ and $[Na^+]_1$ being the concentrations in solution (1), and $[Cl^-]_2$ and $[Na^+]_2$ those in (2). From Eq. 4 are obtained:

$$\frac{[Na^+]_1}{[Na^+]_2} = \frac{[Cl^-]_2}{[Cl^-]_1} \quad (5)$$

and

$$[Na^+]_1[Cl^-]_1 = [Na^+]_2[Cl^-]_2 \quad (6)$$

Introducing into Eq. 6 the corresponding values

from the scheme describing the Equilibrium State, one can write:

$$(c_1 + x)x = (c_2 - x)^2 \quad (7)$$

and arrive at:

$$x = \frac{(c_2)^2}{c_1 + 2c_2} \quad (8)$$

Essentially the same considerations can be extended to systems with a higher number of species of diffusible ions, with ions of different valencies, with different volume ratios of the two solutions, etc. For systems, e.g., with two additional species of diffusible ions, say K^+ and Br^-, Eq. 5 becomes:

$$\frac{[Na^+]_1}{[Na^+]_2} = \frac{[K^+]_1}{[K^+]_2} = \frac{[Cl^-]_2}{[Cl^-]_1} = \frac{[Br^-]_2}{[Br^-]_1} \quad (9)$$

For systems with a univalent and a bivalent diffusible ion of the same sign, say Na^+ and Ca^{++}, one obtains:

$$\frac{[Na^+]_1{}^2}{[Na^+]_2{}^2} = \frac{[Ca^{++}]_1}{[Ca^{++}]_2} \quad \text{etc.} \quad (10)$$

Thus, it is possible to calculate all ionic concentrations in the two solutions for any Donnan system in the Equilibrium State. In a rigorous treatment all these relationships are expressed in terms of activities and electrochemical potentials.[9]

The uneven distribution of electrolytes between (1) and (2) according to Eqs. 5 to 10 is the cause of a difference in the osmotic pressure of the two solutions. This difference is readily measured and widely used in determining the molecular weights of high molecular weight electrolytes, such as proteins and polyelectrolytes, by the measurement of the "colloid-osmotic" pressure due to the presence of the R-ions. The numerous electrochemical ramifications of this method cannot be treated here, nor the various other electrochemical aspects of the Donnan ion distribution in general, such as membrane hydrolysis,[2] the study of the activities in mixed electrolyte solutions,[3,7] etc. However, of primary importance here is the membrane potential that results from the uneven distribution of ions, the *Donnan potential*.

The equilibrium state described by Eqs. 4 to 10 (in which the concentration of Na^+ in (1) is greater than in (2), while the reverse holds for Cl^-) can be maintained only if there is established an electric force which compensates for this inequality in concentration. The electrochemical equilibrium at the membrane is characterized by the identity of the *electrochemical potential* (see **Electrode Potentials**) of the diffusible ions. This means that (in the example) solution (2) is at a higher potential, Π_2, than that of solution (1), Π_1. It can be shown readily by rigorous thermodynamic reasoning[2, 9] that the difference in potential, ϵ_{Donnan}, is given by the equation:

$$\epsilon_{Donnan} = \Pi_2 - \Pi_1 = \frac{RT}{\mathbf{F}} \ln \frac{a_{Na^+}^{(1)}}{a_{Na^+}^{(2)}}$$

$$= \frac{RT}{\mathbf{F}} \ln \frac{a_{Cl^-}^{(2)}}{a_{Cl^-}^{(1)}} . \tag{11}$$

Eq. 11 is essentially identical with Eq. 3 which was derived as the limiting case of the liquid junction potential across a membrane of ideal ionic selectivity. The membrane concentration potentials across such membranes can be considered as Donnan potentials in which one species of *small* ions acts as the nondiffusible "colloidal" ion of the classical Donnan cells.

References

1. MacInnes, D. A., "The Principles of Electrochemistry," New York, Reinhold Publishing Corp., 1939; Spiegler, K. S., and Wyllie, M. R. J., in Oster, G., and Pollister, A. W., Eds., "Physical Techniques in Biological Research," Vol. II, p. 301–392, New York, Academic Press, 1956.
2. Donnan, F. G., Z. Elektrochem., **17**, 572 (1911); Chem. Rev., **1**, 73 (1924); Bolam, T. R., "The Donnan Equilibria," London, G. Bell and Sons, Ltd., 1932.
3. Sollner, K., J. Phys. Chem., **49**, 47, 171, 265 (1945); J. Electrochem. Soc., **97**, 139C (1950); Ann. N. Y. Acad. Sci., **57**, 177 (1953); in Shedlovsky, T., Ed., "Electrochemistry in Biology and Medicine," p. 33–64, New York, John Wiley and Sons, Inc., 1955.
4. Teorell, T., Progress in Biophysics, **3**, 503 (1953); Discussions Faraday Soc., **21**, 9 (1956); Meyer, K. H., and Sievers, J. F., Helv. Chim. Acta, **19**, 649, 665, 987 (1936); Meyer, K. H., Trans. Faraday Soc., **21**, 1073 (1937); Helfferich, F., "Ion Exchange," New York, McGraw-Hill Book Co., Inc., 1962 (with numerous references).
5. Beutner, R., "Die Entstehung elektrischer Ströme in lebenden Geweben," Stuttgart, Ferdinand Enke, 1920; "Physical Chemistry of Living Tissues and Life Processes," Baltimore, Williams and Wilkins Co., 1933; in Gasser, O., Ed., "Medical Physics," p. 35–88, Chicago, Year Book Publishers, 1944; Michaelis, L., "Hydrogen Ion Concentration," Baltimore, Williams and Wilkins Co., 1926;

Bonhoeffer, K. F., Kahlweit, M., and Strehlow, H., Z. phys. Chem. (N.F.), **1**, 21 (1954); Kahlweit, M., Strehlow, H., and Hocking, C. S., ibid., **4**, 212 (1955); Kahlweit, M., Pflügers Archiv., **271**, 139 (1960).
6. Staverman, A. J., Trans. Faraday Soc., **48**, 176 (1952); Scatchard, G., J. Am. Chem. Soc., **75**, 2883 (1953); Katchalsky, A., in Kleinzeller, A., and Kotyk, A., Eds., "Membrane Transport and Metabolism," p. 69–86, London and New York, Academic Press, 1961; Katchalsky, A., and Kedem, O., Biophys. J., **2**, 53 (1962); Kedem, O., and Katchalsky, A., J. Gen. Physiol., **45**, 143 (1961); (all with numerous references).
7. Gregor, H. P., and Sollner, K., J. Phys. Chem., **58**, 409 (1954); Sollner, K., J. Am. Chem. Soc., **68**, 156 (1946); Hills, G. H., in David, D. J. G., and Janz, G. J., Eds., "Reference Electrodes," p. 411–432, New York, Academic Press, 1961.
8. Sollner, K., J. Phys. Chem., **53**, 1211, 1226 (1949); Wyllie, M. R. J., ibid., **58**, 67 (1954); Dray, S., and Sollner, K., Biochem. Biophys. Acta, **18**, 341 (1955); **21**, 126 (1956); **22**, 213, 220 (1956).
9. Donnan, F. G., and Guggenheim, E. G., Z. phys. Chem. (A), **162**, 346 (1932); Donnan, F. G., ibid., **168**, 369 (1934); Bronsted, J. N., "Physical Chemistry," New York, Chemical Publishing Co., 1938; Overbeek, J. Th. G., Progress in Biophysics, **6**, 57 (1956).

Karl Sollner

Cross-references: *Bioelectrochemistry; Bioelectrogenesis; Electrode Potentials; Electrode Double Layer; Electrodialysis; Electrokinetic Potentials; Electrophysiology; Glass Electrode; Ion Exchange Membranes; Ion Transport Across Charged Membranes; Irreversible Electrochemical Processes, Thermodynamics of; Membrane Equilibrium; Nerve Impulse Transmission; Reference Electrodes.*

MEMBRANE POTENTIALS — BI-IONIC AND POLYIONIC

The interdiffusion of several electrolytes across membranes of various degrees of ionic selectivity is a problem of great complexity which still awaits systematic study in spite of its fundamental importance in the pure electrochemistry of membranes and for electrophysiology (q.v.), that is, for the electrochemistry of living systems. The general theoretical background for the study of such cells has been treated in the preceding article on **Membrane Potentials.**[1, 3, 4, 6] Here only some relatively simple cases can be outlined.

Up to now only cells with membranes of high ionic selectivity permeable exclusively either to cations or to anions and impermeable for ions of the opposite sign (see the preceding article), have been shown to be amenable to a rather detailed experimental study. In cells with such membranes the complexity of the systems is reduced considerably by the fact that only ions of one sign of charge can participate in the transportation of electricity across the membrane and thus act as potential co-determining ions.

The simplest possible case of dynamic membrane cells with more than one species of potential determining ions of the same sign and membranes of extreme ionic selectivity[3] are the cells in which the so-called *bi-ionic potentials* arise.[8] The solutions of two electrolytes at the same concentration (or more correctly activity) with different permeable ions, A^+ and B^+, which are able to exchange across the membrane, and the same counter-ion, X^-, are separated by a membrane which is impermeable to the counterions as shown in the scheme:

A^+X^- c_1 (1)	Cation permeable anion impermeable membrane	B^+X^- c_1 (2)

Bi-ionic potentials may be as high as 150 millivolts according to the nature of the membrane and the combination of permeable ions. They are fairly constant over wide ranges of concentration.[8] The membrane has a rather unpredictable influence on the absolute magnitude of these potentials. Contrary to the situation prevailing with the concentration potential, there are no predictable lower and upper limits of the bi-ionic

potential. For some typical bi-ionic potentials, see Table 1.

The cations and anions can be arranged into two consistent sequences according to the relative magnitude of the bi-ionic potentials they cause. These sequences coincide with the so-called Hofmeister series. The sign and the magnitude of the bi-ionic potential depend on the relative ease with which the two species of critical ions penetrate across the membrane. The more readily permeable critical ions impress a potential on the other solution which is identical in sign with that of their own charge. The quantitative evaluation of the bi-ionic potential is based on the Planck-Henderson equation, which permits the interpretation of the experimental bi-ionic potential values in terms of ionic processes with a minimum of assumptions.[8] For the bi-ionic system given before, the Planck-Henderson equation yields the expression:

$$\epsilon_{BIP} = \frac{+RT}{\mathbf{F}} \ln \frac{\tau_{A^{+(1)}}}{\tau_{B^{+(2)}}} \tag{1}$$

(the sign referring to the charge of solution 2), and its analogue for cells with anion selective membranes.

To visualize in a quantitative way the differences in the behavior of various ions in the experimental cells referred to in Table 1, the ratios

$$\tau_{B^{+(2)}}/\tau_{K^{+(1)}} \quad \text{and} \quad \tau_{Y^{-(2)}}/\tau_{Cl^{-(1)}}$$

calculated from Eq. 1 are given in the fourth and last columns of Table 1. These figures may be considered as the measure of the ratio of the intrinsic competitive permeabilities of the two ions across a given membrane, when present in the same system. A reasonable but by no means flawless molecular picture which can explain the

TABLE 1. TYPICAL BI-IONIC POTENTIALS ACROSS PERMSELECTIVE MEMBRANES
($t = 25.0$ C)

Cation permeable membrane				Anion permeable membrane			
Sol. (1) 0.01M	Sol. (2) 0.01M	Bi-ionic potential, mv	$\frac{\tau_{B^{+(2)}}}{\tau_{K^{+(1)}}}$	Sol. (1) 0.025M	Sol. (2) 0.025M	Bi-ionic potential, mv	$\frac{\tau_{Y^{-(2)}}}{\tau_{Cl^{-(1)}}}$
KCl	CsCl	+8.7	1.41	NaCl	NaCNS	+32.0	3.48
KI	NH$_4$I	−6.8	1.30	NaCl	NaNO$_3$	+23.1	2.46
KCl	RbCl	−5.6	1.25	NaCl	NaI	+12.2	1.61
KCl	KCl	±0.0	1.00	NaCl	NaBr	+7.2	1.32
KCl	NaCl	+35.5	0.251	NaCl	NaCl	±0.0	1.00
KCl	LiCl	+63.7	0.084	NaCl	NaBrO$_3$	−2.2	0.918
KI	(CH$_3$)$_4$NI	+81.6	0.042	NaCl	NaIO$_3$	−45.1	0.173
KI	(C$_2$H$_5$)$_4$NI	+110.0	0.014	NaCl	NaAc	−46.2	0.165

data of Table 1 can be based on the fact that the membranes are ion exchange bodies with the two species of critical ions competing for positions as counter-ions of the fixed dissociable groups of the membranes. The relative abundance of the two species of critical ions in the pores multiplied by their diffusion velocities and valencies determine the sign and the magnitude of bi-ionic potential.

The considerations of the origin of the bi-ionic potential lead directly to an insight into the mechanisms of the origin of *polyionic potentials* in cells with membranes of high ionic selectivity. Polyionic potentials are defined as the membrane potentials which arise across highly ion selective membranes in cells with two or more species of potential determining ions of the same sign, which may be present at the two sides of the membrane in pure or mixed solutions, at the same or at different activities, according to the general scheme:

a_1 A$^+$ a_2 B$^+$ a_3 C$^+$ X$^-$ a_4 D$^+$ etc. (1)	$\longleftarrow \oplus \longrightarrow$ Cation permeable anion impermeable membrane	a_5 A$^+$ a_6 B$^+$ a_7 C$^+$ X$^-$ a_8 D$^+$ etc. (2)

The fundamental problem in dealing with such systems is the quantitative correlation of the potentials that arise with any ratio of activities of two or more species of critical ions in the two solutions, and the potential in some standard system or systems. The solution of this problem, too, lies in the use of the Planck-Henderson equation expressed in terms of transference numbers, and the assumption that the ratio of the transference numbers of any two permeable ions, say τ_{A^+}/τ_{B^+}, in the system, a_1 A$^+$X$^-$ | a_2 B$^+$X$^-$, is directly proportional to the ratio of the transference numbers of the two critical ions in the corresponding bi-ionic potential system (when the ratio of the two activities is unity) and to the ratio of the activities of the two critical ions in the two external solutions of the particular system under discussion. Thus, polyionic potentials can be calculated on the basis of bi-ionic potential measurements with the same membrane in the appropriate reference bi-ionic systems. The equations derived on this basis are too involved to be presented here.[5] Suffice it to say that excellent agreement between calculated and experimental polyionic

potentials has been found in a considerable variety of anionic and cationic systems.[5]

Analogous studies of cells having membranes of lesser than extreme ionic selectivity are enormously more complicated. In such cells both cationic *and* anionic species of ions participate in the generation of the membrane potential, and moreover to a degree which is dependent not only on the ratios of their activities in the two solutions but also on the absolute concentrations of the latter. Progress in this direction will be based on the recent development of irreversible thermodynamics as applied to membrane processes.[6]

References

The reference numbers refer to the reference list of the preceding article.

KARL SOLLNER

MEMBRANES, ELECTROLYTIC

A membrane or diaphragm is a material which contains microscopic passages through it. A membrane has the property of allowing passage of electricity when it separates two chambers containing electrolyte. Membranes divide into two general groups. Osmotic membranes allow passage of solvent from one chamber to the other. Nonosmotic membranes allow electrical flow and passage of solute only through the membrane. Membranes may be either ion selective or nonselective. Sponges and filters are similar to membranes in structure but have much larger pores. There is no sharp point at which a filter or sponge can be defined to be different from a membrane. Generally speaking, microporous materials with average pores of less than one micron have uses as membranes. Sufficient pores are necessary to permit passage of electricity when the pores are filled with electrolyte, yet small enough to prevent hydraulic flow through the membrane.

Membranes may be natural products or modified natural products. They can be made by colloidal chemical methods or physical methods. They can be made of a wide variety of materials. Physical methods are used to make membranes of both thermoplastic and ceramic materials. In both cases the base materials are ground to desired fineness and then either fired or sintered to fuse the particles into a rigid structure. The spaces left between the particles then become the effective pores. Membranes made in this manner usually have a small number of "holes" compared to solid structure. Membranes have been sintered of polyvinyl chloride, polyethylene, alumina, and a wide variety of other inorganic materials.

Membranes may be made by either a leaching or "cook-out" method. Salt and starch are most commonly used in these membrane processes. The materials are ground to the desired mesh size and then dispersed in molten plastic or a solution of plastic. The plastic solid mixture is then extruded or cast into sheet form. Salt particles are removed with hot water, starch by digestion in sulfuric acid. After digestion holes are left wherever solid particles were located previously. Microporous membranes have been made this way of PVC, polyethylene, rubber, and cellulose acetate.

Very uniform pore size membrane can be made via gelation processes. Gelatine can be made into a membrane by casting a solution on glass plates into a thin film. The water within the gel structure is removed by washing with methanol which in turn disrupts the gel walls leaving a microporous structure. The gelatine can be insolubilized by "tanning." The size of the pores is controlled by gelatine concentration. Polyvinyl alcohol and starch can be formed into membranes in a similar manner. The earliest synthetic membranes were produced by a gelation process from nitrocellulose in ether solution. This solution was evaporated and then leached with water. These nitrocellulose membranes have been used in bacteriology work since the beginning of this century. Their first use in dialysis was reported in 1855.[1] The early membranes produced were quite fragile. Zsigmondy reported methods of making nitrocellulose membranes which were stable and strong in 1918.[2] These membranes have been manufactured in Germany since that date. After World War II, a technical military mission to Germany obtained the details of techniques for production of these materials and made possible the manufacture of them in the United States. Commercial cellulose ester membranes are available as cellulose nitrate and acetate. The same basic process developed by early biological investigators is used in the manufacture of these membranes. Diaphragm materials by this process are also available in various polyvinyl alcohol derivatives (butyral, formal, chloride) and copolymers.

Cellulose can be used as a base for membranes. Parchment paper is used as a membrane in acid dialysis. The action of the acid gelatinizes the paper. Cellophane and sausage casing make suitable membrane materials. These are manufactured in a manner similar to rayon. Paper may also be treated with thermoplastic materials to form membranes.

Ion selective membranes preferentially allow the passage of cations or anions. Membranes may be made ion selective by treating them with ionically active chemicals. Ion exchange membranes are manufactured by some of the following techniques:

1. Casting plastics in sheet form and then reacting the material made to form ion exchange resin.

2. Mixing resins with other polymers to form heterogeneous ion selective membrane.

3. Coating a membrane with ion selective material.

Any of the methods used for production of membranes may be used for production of ion exchange membranes.

Natural membranes are the most common and are used in some industrial applications. The reader undoubtedly recalls natural osmotic membranes used in basic science courses. To demonstrate osmotic effects, egg membrane, pig's bladder, or other thin biological membranes are used. Cell walls, bacterial and virus walls, and tissues all are membrane materials. Wood is used as a membrane separator in some acid batteries.

Membranes have many uses in the electrochemical industry. The controlled pore sizes which can be obtained with membrane filters allow the choice of a membrane which will filter almost any size particle. Colloidal metals can be recovered from plating solutions using membrane filtration. In the production of transistors, the purity of wash waters is an extremely critical factor. Water is purified by distillation and then by treatment with ion exchange resins. To insure that none of the particles of ion exchange resin pass on into the rinse waters, membrane filtration is used.

In electrodialysis membranes are required which will pass solute but not solvent. Both ionic and nonionic membranes are used in electrodialysis. Electrodialysis can be applied for such operations as desalting. This process is used in a wide variety of operations which require the removal of salt from a liquid product. Membranes are used in electrolytic operations to separate

TABLE 1. COMMERCIAL MEMBRANE SOURCES

Trade Name	Material	Manufacturer
Nonionic		
Acropor	PVC Copolymers	Gelman Instrument Company, Ann Arbor, Michigan
Metrical	Cellulose Acetate	Gelman Instrument Company, Ann Arbor, Michigan
Mipor	Polyethylene	ESB Reeves Corporation, Glenside, Pennsylvania
Millipore	Cellulose Acetate	Millipore Corporation, Bedford, Massachusetts
Nalfilm	Divinylbenzene Copolymer	Nalco Chemical Company, Chicago, Illinois
Porvic	Polyvinyl Chloride	Pritchett & Gold, London, England
Versapor	Epoxy	Gelman Instrument Company, Ann Arbor, Michigan
Metrical Alpha	Rayon	Gelman Instrument Company, Ann Arbor, Michigan

Ion Exchange

AMF Ion Products, American Machine & Foundry, 689 Hope St., Springdale, Connecticut
Gelman Instrument Company, 600 S. Wagner Road, Ann Arbor, Michigan
Ionac Chemical Co., Div. Pfaudler Permutit Inc., Birmingham, New Jersey
Ionics Inc., 152 Sixth Street, Cambridge 42, Massachusetts
Radiation Application, Inc., 36–40 37th Street, Long Island City, New York

the two halves of the electrolytic cell and thus prevent the diffusion of both ionic and gaseous products between the two electrodes. Membranes be used to connect two electrochemical cells in the same manner as agar bridges are used. In the construction of pH electrodes, membranes may be used to isolate the electrode from the solution being measured. Membranes are also used in the production of other electrode systems, such as oxygen-sensitive electrodes. In the case of a lead-silver electrode for the measurement of oxygen concentration, a polyethylene membrane is used. This membrane prevents the dilution of the electrolyte within the electrode by the solution being measured, yet allows the oxygen to diffuse through the membrane into the measurement cell. Membranes have important uses in the production of batteries. Membranes serve to prevent the diffusion of metallic ions from one half of the battery cell to the other. Membranes for use in batteries should have low resistance and extremely high stability. Cellophane and sausage casing are used in low-cost batteries as a membrane. These membranes have a disadvantage of relatively short life. For long-life batteries, polyvinyl chloride copolymer membranes are used. Fuel cells require membranes similar to those used in batteries.

A comprehensive review has been written about diffusion and membrane technology.[3]

The table below lists some of the sources for synthetic manufactured membrane materials. Sources of supply for such membrane materials as sausage casing, cellophane, and packaging film have not been included in this table because of the large number of suppliers and general availability of these materials. Several manufacturers of ion exchange material have been omitted because their membranes are made only for use in their own apparatus.

References

1. FICK, *Pogg-Ann.*, **94**, 59 (1855).
2. ZSIGMONDY, R. AND BACHMANN, W., *Z. anorg. Chem.*, **103**, 119 (1918).
3. TUWINER, SIDNEY B., "Diffusion and Membrane Technology," American Chemical Society, Monograph Series, New York, Reinhold Publishing Corp., 1962.

CHARLES GELMAN

Cross-references: *Electrodialysis; Ion Exchange Membranes.*

MEMBRANES, ION EXCHANGE. See ION EXCHANGE MEMBRANES.

MEMBRANES, TRANSPORT OF IONS ACROSS. See ION TRANSPORT ACROSS CHARGED MEMBRANES.

MERCURY CATHODE CHLOR-ALKALI PROCESS. See CHLORINE PRODUCTION IN MERCURY CELLS.

MERCURY-MERCUROUS SALT ELECTRODES. See REFERENCE ELECTRODES.

METAL ELECTRODEPOSITION, ELEMENTARY PROCESSES

The subject of electrochemical metal deposition has not been studied and developed in the same degree of detail as, for example, other electrochemical ion discharge processes, such as the production of hydrogen and oxygen. On the other hand, the practical aspects of the field have received great attention for many years but such developments have usually not been closely associated with the fundamental and academic elucidation of kinetic steps and electrochemical mechanisms of the processes involved. In particular, the largely empirical physical chemistry which is involved in determining the morphology of electrodeposits cannot at the moment be related, except in some idealized cases, to the individual molecular kinetic steps which have been discussed in papers on metal deposition.

The purpose of the present article, which is not intended to be an exhaustive academic review of the subject, will be to describe the various possible elementary processes in metal deposition and relate them briefly to existing knowledge on some aspects of the kinetics of electrodeposition of metals. Fuller reviews of the subject of metal deposition are contained in references (9) and (16).

General Considerations

Electrolytic metal deposition, and related dissolution reactions, differ from most other electrochemical processes in that a new solid condensed phase is produced or dissolved. Many other electrochemical reactions involve either production of gases, e.g., H_2, O_2, N_2 (from azides or ammonia oxidation), hydrocarbons and CO_2 (from decarboxylation of aliphatic carboxylic acids), or oxidation-reduction reactions of soluble species in the solution, or species which can be deposited into a liquid metal phase, such as mercury or gallium. The production of a stable ordered lattice introduces new factors into the consideration of the electrochemistry of the discharge of ions, which are not involved in gas production reactions. However, the following general factors still determine, in part, the kinetics and mechanism of metal deposition processes:

(a) double layer structure[1] and adsorption of the depositing ions in the region some 2–3 Å from the metal "surface."

(b) solvation energy[2] and geometry of the solvated ion, or the nature of any complexes involved in the case of complex metal ions.

(c) the metal-solution potential difference or more particularly the overpotential, i.e., the difference of potential of the metal compared with that of a reversible electrode of the same metal in the same solution.

This overpotential will, of course, determine the current density associated with the metal deposition process and the current density-potential relationship will reflect the kinetic facility with which the metal deposition process can occur and will also be related to the mechanism of the metal crystal growth process.[4] In general, the current density of the metal deposition process will be related to the overpotential by the standard electrochemical free energy of activation for the process at the reversible potential and by a factor determining the potential-dependence of this free energy of activation.

Fundamental Factors in the Metal Deposition Process

The State of Ions in Solution. All metal ions which, as salts, are appreciably soluble in the solvent concerned interact strongly with the solvent or are complexed in other ways through strong interactions with some component of the solution, e.g., in the case of cyanide complexes of various metals, such as Ag $(Ag[CN]_2^-)$ or Cu $(Cu[NH_3]_4^{++})$ in ammoniacal solutions. In all cases, the metal ion to be deposited must be regarded as interacting strongly with either electrostatically or covalently associated solvent ligands or ligands of some other component. Hence, a considerable desolvation energy or energy of partial desolvation, (see below), is involved in transferring these ions out of their solvent environment to the growing crystal lattice.

The State of Ions in the Double layer. At any electrode, a double layer of charges in the metal (excess or deficit of electrons) and adjacent ions in the solution is set up.[1, 2] The ionic concentration in the double layer is normally not identical with that in solution and, in fact, there is a distribution of the metal ions between the surface region near the metal and the bulk of the solution determined by the standard electrochemical free energy of adsorption of the ions of the salt. Usually, for simple metal cations, this energy of adsorption

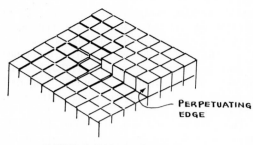

SCREW DISLOCATION

FIG. 1. Screw dislocation showing edge to which diffusion can occur and at which growth of the step can continue.

is largely electrostatic in origin and little specific adsorption effects[2] arise. The ions themselves in the double layer are hence in a physico-chemical state analogous to that in the bulk of the solution and in fact do not suffer, for example, any significant tendency to become desolvated[1] in their interaction with the metal so long as no net process of ion neutralization is occurring.

For complex metal ions, particularly anions, more specific adsorption effects can occur in the double layer; when the metal ion is a complex *anion* and has to be deposited at the negative cathode, rather specific double layer effects arise such as have been discussed by Frumkin and Nikolaeeva-Fedorovich.[3] These effects may be of practical importance in metal plating from complex anions and involve the influence of other simple *cations* present in the double layer which facilitate the adsorption of the negative metal ion at the negative electrode interface by a synergetic effect involving local ion pair formation.

Condition of the Double layer at a Real Metal Surface. Much of the study of the electrode double layer has been conducted at liquid mercury.[1, 3, 5] At solid metals, owing to the surface irregularities on an atomic and submicroscopic scale (except at atomically smooth single crystal faces), the configuration of the double layer is not as simple as it is at mercury. This introduces local geometrical effects which, among other factors (see below), lead to local heterogeneities of the kinetic rate constant for metal ion deposition, as discussed by Conway and Bockris[4] and Lorenz.[6] In addition to purely geometrical effects, the heterogeneity of real metal surfaces implies a heterogeneity of electronic work function at various

lattice planes exposed. This will result in an heterogeneity of potentials of zero-charge[1] which will lead to locally varying constitution of the double layer and, hence, to the kinetics of the metal deposition or dissolution process. This heterogeneity will be of importance in regard to the microcrystal building processes involved in a metal deposition process.

The State of the Surface. The state of the metal surface will be a basic factor in determining the kinetics of the deposition process and the morphology of resulting deposits. The population of defect sites and dislocations,[7] growth edges and kinks will determine the type of mechanism involved in the overall deposition process. In addition, the specific constitution of the double layer at the surface will influence the cation deposition process and any subsequent migration of deposited atoms ("adions")[4, 8] to crystal growth centers. Thus, the presence of certain adsorbed inorganic anions or of a variety of adsorbed organic additives or impurities can greatly modify the kinetics of the electrocrystallization process and the morphology of the deposit.[9]

Basic Mechanisms

Several types of mechanism have been proposed for the electrocrystallization process, but the basic and essential steps are as summarized below:[4, 8]

Primary Ion Discharge Step. This involves desolvation or some change in ligand coordination of the metal ion as it crosses the electrode-solution double layer potential difference. The resulting entity may or may not be regarded as a completely neutral atom owing to the difficulty of defining "electron transfer" in the case of ion deposition onto metals, in which there is usually effectively about one *"free"* electron per atom.[14] The resulting entity is then a partially neutral atom or "adion."[4, 8]

Migration of the Discharged "Adion" to Lattice Propagation Sites. This process involves surface or edge diffusion of the deposited entities to lattice growth planes. The latter are predominantly growth edges, screw dislocations with perpetuating edges (Fig. 1), or other dislocations and grain boundaries.

Decomposition of Complex Ions. In many systems, deposition from complex ion electrolytes favors smooth or bright deposits. The mechanisms of deposition under such conditions have been considered by Gerischer and others[15, 16] and in these cases a step involving decomposition of the complex ion in the double layer at the metal surface is indicated for some metals as a prior step to the actual atom or adion deposition at a lattice site.

Sequence of the Kinetic Steps

In the deposition of simple hydrated ions, the ion transfer step will be the first kinetic stage following diffusion or electrolytic migra- tion of the depositing ion into the double layer. This step is to be regarded[4, 8] as a progressive desolvation of the ion as it moves out of its hydration envelope towards the metal and becomes increasingly a metal atom associated with the delocalized system of surface orbitals at a site on the bulk metal. The transferred ion will, however, still have some ionic character owing to the partially ionic nature of the metal lattice associated with the delocalized bonds.

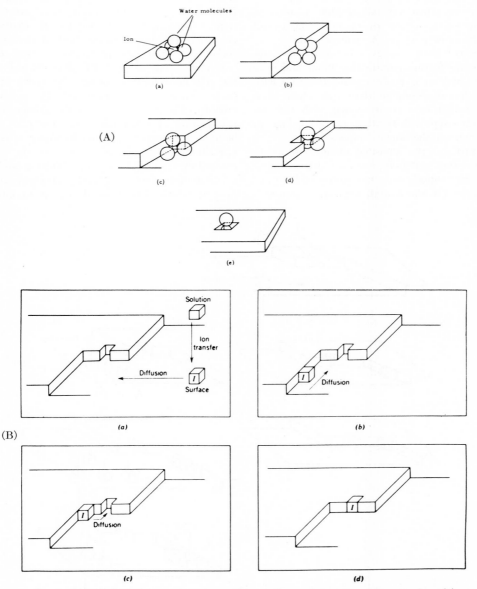

FIG. 2. (A) Hydrated ions at various sites on the metal surface prior to deposition. (B) Consecutive steps in the deposition of a metal ion on to a lattice site.

The partial ionic character ("adion") of the deposited species will allow some residual hydration to be maintained around the particle, but the energy of interaction of this hydration water with the deposited metal particle will be much smaller than that arising before the ion suffered deposition. In the deposited state, z electrons will have moved into a "surface state" at the metal interface for every ion of valency z transferred.

The sites to which the ion can be transferred will be on open crystallographic planes, at growing edges, one or several atoms high, and at kinks or corners on the growing edges.[8, 10, 11, 12, 13] Since both energy considerations and geometrical factors require that kinks and edge defects, and to a lesser extent growth edges, will be less predominant than open plane sites, the principal current associated with the ion discharge step will be that corresponding to deposition on the surface planes.

Migration of the deposited adions[8, 17] to growing edges then occurs by a surface diffusion step which may, under certain conditions, be rate-controlling for the overall deposition process.[7,] [8, 18] In the absence of growth sites (dislocations or growing steps), two-dimensional nucleation of the ad-species to form a growth center may be the rate-limiting process in the electrocrystallization.[19] The rate of the surface diffusion step will depend on the concentration gradient of adions which can be maintained at the surface between deposition points and growing edges,[20, 21] and this is analogous to the supersaturation which is normally required in the process of crystal growth from the vapor or liquid phases. In electrodeposition, this "degree of supersaturation" is essentially controlled by the electrode potential. The processes involved in the above consecutive steps are illustrated in Fig. 2.

Evidence for surface diffusion control and the role of dislocation density has been given from analysis of the form of d-c potential buildup transients obtained in the galvanostatic polarization of clean metal electrodes.[7, 18] The buildup is slower than would be expected theoretically if ion discharge alone were the rate-controlling step, so that a rate-limiting surface diffusion step involving transfer of adions from sites at which they were deposited to lattice

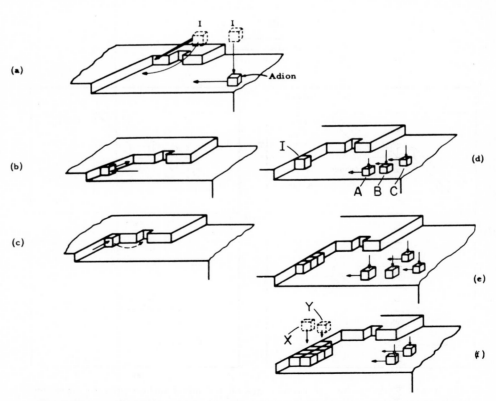

Fig. 3. The overall process of incorporation of a typical metal atom I into the lattice.

growth sites (edges, etc.) is indicated. Supporting evidence from the difference of behavior of solid and liquid gallium has been given.[17] At the liquid metal no surface diffusion process to growth steps can occur so that the overall deposition rate is solely controlled by the rate of the ion transfer step.

Hitherto, only steps associated with a single depositing particle (Fig. 2) have been considered. The whole lattice growth must involve a series of related parallel and consecutive processes involving an assembly of depositing particles. The processes involved in the overall process of building a given particle into a

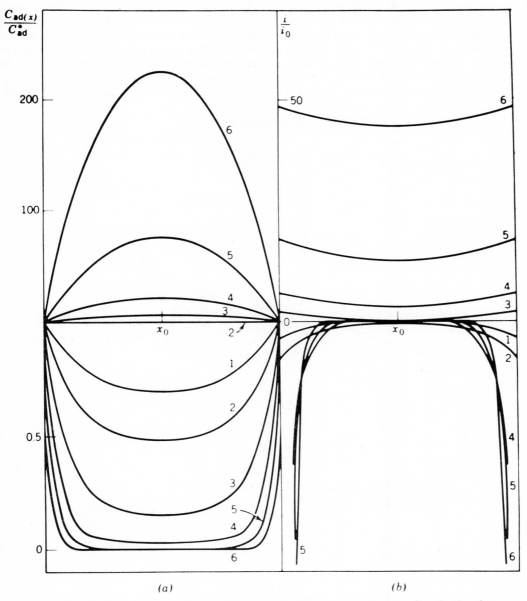

(a)   (b)

FIG. 4. Local adion concentration profiles and relative current density distribution between growth edges. (Despic and Bockris[20].) i/i_0 = local current density compared with exchange current; C_{ad}, x/C^0_{ad} = ratio of adion concentration at position x from centre line between two parallel growth edges and the concentration at this centre line. Curves given for various values of the metal overpotential (1) ±10mv; (2) ±20mv; (3) 50mv; (4) ±100mv; (5) 150mv; (6) ±200mv.

typical metal lattice element are shown in Fig. 3. Once a given representative depositing particle (I in Fig. 3) has reached a corner or kink site at a growing edge, it becomes kinetically immobile and the remainder of the process of its coordination as a typical bulk lattice atom then involves processes associated with the migration of other atoms or adions, e.g., of A, B, C ... (K, L, M) and X and Y in Fig. 3. During the steps in which the representative atom, I, is incorporated into the lattice, its energy suffers successive changes[8] due to more complete dehydration and greater degree of coordination by other atoms, until it be-

comes a typical 12- or 8 + 6-coordinated atom in the hexagonal or one of the cubic systems. Quantitative calculations of these successive energy changes have been made by Conway and Bockris[4, 8] in an attempt to examine probable rate-determining steps in metal deposition.

In the case of deposition of polyvalent ions, theoretical[8] and experimental evidence (e.g., for Cu^{++} deposition[22]) has been given that the deposition and reduction occurs in two consecutive electron transfer steps involving an intermediate ion of low valency state, e.g., Cu^+ in the deposition of cupric ions from aqueous solutions of noncomplex salts. In the case of deposi-

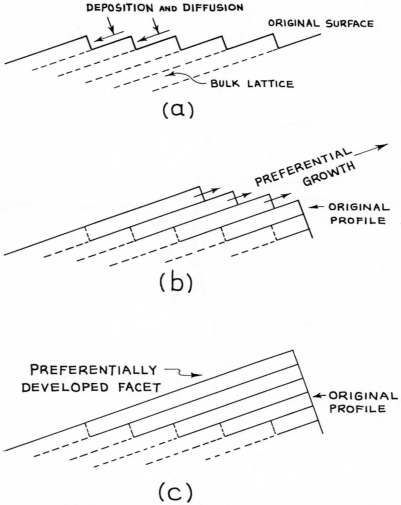

FIG. 5. Schematic diagram illustrating preferential development of certain crystal faces in electrodeposition in relation to overall morphology of resulting deposit.

tion from complex ions, dissociation of the complex ion can be an important intermediate step.[15]

Current Density Distribution

In macroelectrode systems of nonuniform geometry, the current density at the cathode is rarely homogeneous, due to shielding effects and related varying resistance of the electrolyte current path to various regions of the cathode. Similar heterogeneity of current density can also arise if the electrode has a finite and significant resistance from one extremity to another. The latter effects can arise with thin electrodes[23] and/or at high overall current

densities, e.g., in anodic machining. When either kind of effect arises, the metal deposit is nonuniform and different morphologies of the deposit may arise at various positions on the electrode owing to the dependence of deposition mechanism on current density, e.g., when a condition of diffusion control of the rate is approached and dendrite formation may set in.[24]

In addition to these macroscopic effects, the ion deposition current density may be inhomogeneous on a submicro scale near growing edges owing to the concentration gradient of adions (see Fig. 3) which is necessarily set up under steady-state conditions. These effects have been examined by Despic and Bockris,[20] and

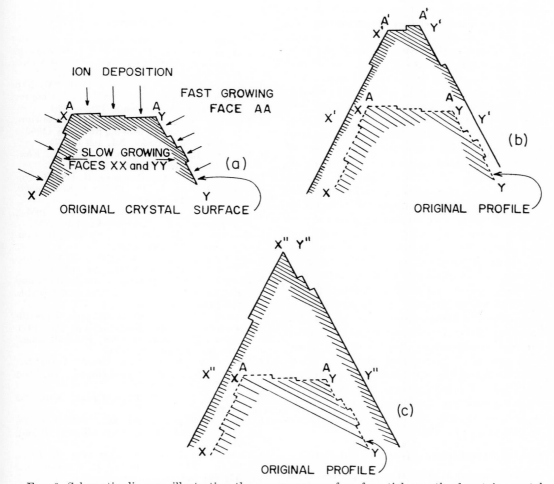

FIG. 6. Schematic diagram illustrating the consequences of preferential growth of certain crystal faces in regard to development of certain crystal habits. Faster growing face, AA, A′A′, etc., is lost at the expense of the slower growing ones, XX, YY, with resulting change of morphology of crystal unit. Diagrams (a), (b) and (c) show stages in the evolution of the pinnacle crystal habit.

typical plots of the two-dimensional adion concentration profile and the related local micro-current density distribution are shown in Fig. 4. It is clear that important variations of this current density distribution will occur with variation of electrode potential which exponentially affects the rate of the ion deposition step, and with the presence of adsorbed organic additives, e.g., levelling agents, which can interfere with the rate of the adion diffusion step and the rate of the incorporation of the diffused adion into the lattice at a growing edge or kink.

Morphology

The relation between the mechanism of individual steps in the electrocrystallization process and the resulting macroscopic morphology of a polycrystalline deposit[16] is still not well understood. However, the general kinetic principles which have been developed,[4, 6, 8, 20] and referred to briefly above, lead to an expectation of different rates of the deposition process and probably also different mechanisms under limiting conditions, e.g., at low current density,[18, 22] on faces of different crystal index. These differences arise on account of different work functions at the various faces, different energies of solvent adsorption, and different coordination energies for newly deposited atoms, as well as from any special double layer configuration effects referred to above. The resulting variations of deposition rate at various crystal faces lead to a preferential development of certain crystal facets and a resulting characteristic morphology of the deposit. Levelling agents thus probably act by diminishing marked preferential growth of certain faces by inhibition of the surface diffusion process or raising the activation energy for ion transfer at sites where preferential deposition would normally occur. The process of preferential growth of faces is illustrated in Fig. 5 from which resulting development of characteristic morphologies or crystal habits can be discerned (Fig. 6). In general, faster growing crystal faces tend to be eliminated (see Fig. 6).

Electrocrystallization from Fused Salts

Much interest attaches to the deposition from fused salts, particularly in the case of those metals which cannot easily be deposited from aqueous solutions, e.g., Ti, Ta, Al.[25, 26] Numerous studies of metal deposition from fused salts have been made in regard to the technology of metal winning, but little information is yet available on mechanisms and individual steps in these reactions. Presumably the steps will be similar except that solvent adsorption will be absent. The only mechanisms that have been examined in any detail are those involved in dendrite growth where satisfactory quantitative theories have been developed.[24] The growth of dendrites occurs under critical conditions when a condition of mass transfer control of the electrodeposition rate is approached. Study of dendrite growth is of value in development of methods for formation of thin, single crystal metals of high strength and in relation to *prevention* of dendrite growth in aqueous electrodepositions.

References

1. PARSONS, R., "Modern Aspects of Electrochemistry," Vol. 1 Chapter III, New York, Academic Press, 1954; see also Grahame, D.C., *Chem. Rev.*, **41**, 441 (1947).
2. CONWAY, B. E., AND BOCKRIS, J. O'M., "Modern Aspects of Electrochemistry," Vol. 1, Chapter II, New York, Academic Press, 1954.
3. FRUMKIN, A. N., AND NIKOLAEEVA-FEDOROVICH, G. M., *Zhur. Fiz. Khim.*, **30**, 1455 (1956); *Vestnik Mosk. Univ.*, **N4**, 169 (1957).
4. CONWAY, B. E., AND BOCKRIS, J. O'M., *Electrochimica Acta*, **3**, 340 (1961).
5. CONWAY, B. E., AND BARRADAS, R. G., *Electrochimica Acta*, **5**, 319 (1961); *J. Electroanal. Chem.*, **6**, 314 (1963).
6. LORENZ, W., *Z. Naturforsch.*, **9a**, 716 (1954); *Z. phys. Chem. (Leipzig)*, **17**, 136 (1958).
7. BOCKRIS, J. O'M., ENYO, M., AND KITA, H., *Can. J. Chem.*, **39**, 1670 (1961).
8. CONWAY, B. E., AND BOCKRIS, J. O'M., *Proc. Roy. Soc. London*, **A248**, 394 (1958).
9. FISCHER, H., "Elektrolytische Abscheidung und Elektrokristallisation von Metallen," Berlin, Springer-Verlag, 1954.
10. VOLMER, M., "Das Elektrolytische Krystallwachstum," Paris, Hermann and Cie, 1934.
11. VOLMER, M., "Kinetik der Phasenbilding," Dresden, Steinkopff, 1939.
12. KOSSEL, W., *Gott. Nachr. Math. Naturwiss.*, **K1**, 135; *Naturwissenschaften*, **18**, 901 (1927).
13. STRANSKI, I. N., *Z. Phys. Chem.*, **136**, 259 (1928).
14. MOTT, N. F., AND JONES, H., "Theory of the Properties of Metals and Alloys," Oxford, 1936.
15. GERISCHER, H., for example, see *Z. Phys. Chem.*, **202**, 309 (1953); *Z. Elektrochem.*, **57**, 604 (1953).
16. VETTER, K., "Elektrochem. Kinetik," Berlin, Springer-Verlag, 1961, e.g., see p. 525 *et. seq.*
17. BOCKRIS, J. O'M., AND ENYO, M., *J. Electrochem. Soc.*, **109**, 49 (1962).

18. BOCKRIS, J. O'M., AND MEHL, W., *J. Chem. Phys.*, **27**, 818 (1957).
19. BOCKRIS, J. O'M., *Z. Phys. Chem.*, **215**, 1 (1960).
20. DESPIC, A., AND BOCKRIS, J. O'M., *J. Chem. Phys.*, **32**, 389 (1960).
21. LORENZ, W., *Z. Naturforsch.*, **9a**, 716 (1954).
22. MATTSSON, E., AND BOCKRIS, J. O'M., *Trans. Faraday Soc.*, **55**, 1586 (1959).
23. CONWAY, B. E., AND GILEADI, E., *Can. J. Chem.*, **41**, 2447 (1963).
24. BARTON, J. C., AND BOCKRIS, J. O'M., *Proc. Roy. Soc. London*, **A268**, 485 (1962).
25. MENZIES, I. A., *et al*, *J. Electroanalytical Chem.*, **1**, 161 (1959–60).
26. INMAN, D., *et al*, *Annals N.Y. Acad. Sci.*, **79**, (11), 803 (1960).

B. E. CONWAY

Cross-references: *Electrode Double Layer; Electrode Reactions, Kinetics; Electron Transfers at Electrodes.*

METAL POWDERS, ELECTRODEPOSITION. See ELECTRODEPOSITION OF METAL POWDERS.

MICROBIOLOGICAL CORROSION

Microorganisms in soil and water may lead to increased corrosion rates by a number of processes depending on the nature of the material and the environmental situation. In general, these corrosive activities do not represent a separate or specialized form of corrosion but are merely acceleration of known corrosion reactions, such as electrolysis or even simple solution. The contribution of the microorganisms may be direct or indirect to the actual corrosion mechanism.

Anaerobic Corrosion

Theory. Anaerobic conditions in soil or water represent environments in which molecular oxygen is absent. As is well known, oxygen in aerobic conditions acts as a depolarizing agent at most metal surfaces so that corrosion continues with oxide formation. The most widely accepted theory of anaerobic corrosion of iron and steel was outlined by Von Wolzogen Kuhr and implicates the sulfate-reducing bacteria of the genus, *Desulfovibrio*, as the depolarizing agents under anaerobic conditions. The theory may be represented by the following reactions:

$$4Fe \rightleftharpoons 4Fe^{++} + 8e \qquad (1)$$

$$8H_2O \rightleftharpoons 8H^+ + 8OH^- \qquad (2)$$

$$8H^+ + 8e \rightarrow 4H_2 \qquad (3)$$

$$CaSO_4 + 4H_2 \rightarrow H_2S + 2H_2O + Ca(OH)_2 \qquad (4)$$

$$Fe^{++} + H_2S \rightarrow FeS + 2H^+ \qquad (5)$$

Eq. 1 is common to many types of corrosion, representing the anode reaction at the metal surface in which the metal is oxidized to the ferrous ion and 2 electrons are released. Likewise, Eq. 2 is simply the ionization of water related to the acidic or basic composition of the solution. The greater the activity (concentration) of the hydrogen ions, the greater is the acidity of the solution. Eq. 3 represents the reduction of hydrogen ions from water by the electrons produced in the oxidation of the metal. The product of this reaction is molecular hydrogen (H_2). Under aerobic conditions this hydrogen immediately reacts with O_2 to form water. Under anaerobic conditions, in the absence of a depolarizing agent, a film of hydrogen forms at the metal surface, slowing down and eventually stopping the loss of metal. The role of the sulfate-reducing bacteria is to act as depolarizing agents upon the hydrogen film. These bacteria oxidize the hydrogen and cause the reduction of sulfates to sulfides as indicated in Eq. 4. This reaction enables the corrosion process to continue. Further acceleration of metal loss occurs as the sulfides combine with the ferrous ion causing formation of a black insoluble precipitate of ferrous sulfide. Removal of the iron in solution shifts the equilibrium of Eq. 1 toward more active corrosion.

The key reaction according to the Von Wolzogen Kuhr theory lies in the removal of the polarizing film of hydrogen. This is brought about by an enzyme, hydrogenase, which is very active in the sulfate-reducing anaerobe *Desulfovibrio desulfuricans* shown in Fig. 1. This enzyme is present in many other bacteria. Whether these other bacteria can function in anaerobic corrosion remains one of the many unsolved problems facing research workers in this field.

The theory described in the preceding paragraphs has not been completely accepted by all corrosion workers. Some consider the bacteria as simply incidental in the process and that the sulfides or minute traces of O_2 act as depolarizing agents *per se*. Whatever the exact mecha-

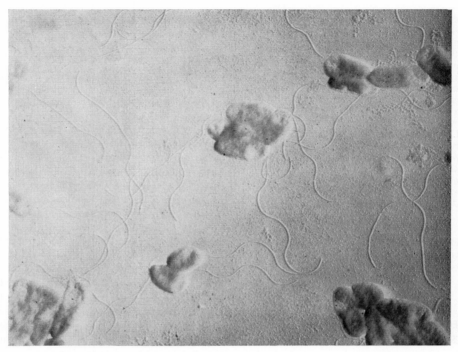

FIG. 1. Electron microscope picture of *Desulfovibrio desulfuricans*; length of bacteria in lower left corner about 1.25 microns. Magnification 8,750 × after 50 per cent reduction for printing.

nism, the practical significance of anaerobic corrosion has not been questioned.

Environmental Requirements. Since the sulfate-reducing bacteria are strict anaerobes, they grow only in the absence of oxygen. Conditions in soil which lead to anaerobiosis are excess moisture, destruction of soil structure ("puddling"), poor drainage, and organic matter that serves as food for other microorganisms which use up available oxygen in their metabolism. The anaerobic situation may be expressed in terms of the oxidation-reduction potential. It has been shown that this potential must be less than —0.150 volts (H_2 reference) for the sulfate-reducing types to grow.

Sulfates represent the only compounds reduced by the energy-yielding mechanisms of *Desulfovibrio desulfuricans*. Hence, sulfates represent an essential requirement for this bacterium. Likewise, an available source of nitrogenous compounds (ammonia, amino acids), an energy source as organic matter, and the usual mineral salts found in soil and water must be present. Marine forms may require a definite salinity while terrestial strains do not. These bacteria can grow over a wide range of acid and alkaline soils but cannot develop in very acid soils. The commonly accepted growth range is from pH 4.5 to pH 11.0.

Although the above mentioned requirements seem to be very definite, the sulfate-reducing bacteria are practically ubiquitous in nature. Literature is available showing world-wide distribution and the presence of *Desulfovibrio desulfuricans* in a wide variety of environments ranging from Antarctic muds to tropical oil field brines and from corroding casings in deepest oil wells to the fuel tanks of jet planes cruising the stratosphere. Because of the formation of the ferrous sulfide precipitate, this bacterium has assumed great economic importance in plugging the producing formations during secondary recovery of petroleum and in fuel spoilage, in addition to its role in anaerobic corrosion.

Detection of Anaerobic Corrosion. The implication of sulfate-reducing bacteria in corrosion is not always simple. The presence of the corrosion products can be identified by chemical tests for sulfides or by the typical odor of the hydrogen sulfide formed when a dilute acid solution is placed on the black iron sulfide. The surface of metal under the black precipitate usually appears a silvery gray when first exposed to air and soon changes to a brown and black appearance as the various oxides form on contact with atmospheric oxygen. Isolation and identification of the bacteria can be accomplished by proper bacteriological procedures, but quantitative methods are yet in developmental stages.

Because anaerobic soils are the site of this form of corrosion, a field survey method has been developed using the "Redox" probe. This survey device has been shown to indicate areas of low oxidation-reduction potentials which are the "hot spots" of anaerobic corrosion. However, the extreme care needed for its proper use has hindered widespread acceptance of this survey procedure by corrosion engineers.

Prevention and Control. Losses due to the activities of anaerobic bacteria can be prevented by the use of adequate protective coatings applied to the metal surfaces in contact with the soil or water environment. Common practice is to use protective coatings plus cathodic protection applied to the metallic structure. While it is theoretically possible to use cathodic protection on uncoated structures, economic considerations usually dictate the use of protective coatings. Cathodic protection used on coated metal protects poorly coated areas or breaks in the coating. Furthermore, records of current requirements in maintaining a definite potential over a period of time furnish information regarding coating performances and corrosion activities. Alteration of the physical or chemical environment, or use of disinfectants in soil or water on a large scale, such as a transmission pipeline, does not represent a practical solution to the control of microbial activities. Any man-made changes would be only temporary in nature. In a limited environment such procedures may be used although experience with chemical treatment of secondary flood waters to control *Desulfovibrio* species has proved to be an expensive and troublesome undertaking.

Other Types of Microbial Corrosion

Acid Formation. Microorganisms, other than the sulfate-reducing types, may contribute directly or indirectly to the corrosion process. Both organic and inorganic acids may accumulate as waste products. These acids may reach concentrations which significantly affect metal solubility. Organic acids, such as lactic, may ac-

cumulate by bacterial action on organic matter during anaerobic growth. Others, such as acetic and citric, may be formed by both bacteria and molds under aerobic conditions. The nature and extent of the corrosion will depend upon the organisms, the food material, moisture availability, aeration, and the type of metal. Sulfuric acid may reach concentrations greater than 5 per cent acid when sulfur or various reduced sulfur compounds, such as hydrogen sulfide or thiosulfate, are oxidized by the aerobic sulfur bacteria. The effect of this acid on iron would increase corrosion rates as the iron sulfates are soluble and could diffuse away. In contrast, if the metal is lead and the predominant anion is sulfate, a layer of insoluble lead sulfate would be deposited on the metal surface and corrosion rates would soon become negligible.

Sulfuric acid formation has been implicated in the failure of large diameter concrete sewer pipes. The air space above the flowing sewage furnishes an aerobic environment saturated with moisture and the sulfate bacteria growing on the concrete surface are constantly fed hydrogen sulfide diffusing upward from the sewage. The sulfuric acid formed converts the structurally strong calcium carbonates to the salts of the weak calcium sulfate and mechanical failure can result.

Microorganisms convert ammonia fertilizers in soil to nitrous and nitric acids. While the concentrations of these compounds do not usually reach levels to influence corrosion, the possibility remains of exceptional situations causing metallic loss.

Concentration Cell Formation. Corrosion of metals often results from the formation of areas of differential electrical potentials. Microorganisms can cause the development of cathodic or anodic zones in soil and water by several mechanisms. Probably the most common and most significant action would be the formation of oxygen concentration cells. These result in areas that are differentially aerated. Since many bacteria consume oxygen in their respiration they develop anaerobic zones in environments where organic matter is present and diffusion of air is slow. This causes the metal to be anodic in relation to the aerated sections of the structure, and metal would be lost at this point by typical electrolytic action. Because the anodic area is commonly small in relation to the cathodic portion, rapid localized loss of metal would result in pit formation.

The possibilities for other types of concentration cell formation are numerous. Differential concentrations of the acids previously discussed, carbonic acid from metabolic action, any alteration in the acid or base content of the zone adjacent to the metal surface, or changing the ionic concentrations of the environment by utilization or release of cations and anions, all represent known mechanisms by which bacteria could establish an electrical potential gradient. The significance of such activity would depend on the relative concentrations, potential differences established and maintained, electrical conductivity of the circuit (soil), polarization effects, and relative areas of the cathodic and anodic surfaces. The actual economic importance of these corrosion effects must yet be determined by extensive laboratory and field studies which will be complicated by the extremely complex interrelationships between the inanimate factors and the living organisms within the corrosive environment.

Microbial Destruction of Protective Coatings

Compared to a few years ago, relatively small amounts of unprotected metallic structures are placed in contact with natural environments whether these be soil, fresh or sea water. The use of protective coatings coupled with cathodic protection is common construction practice. The fact that these protective coatings are largely organic matter may render them susceptible to microbial deterioration. Thus, bacteria could contribute to corrosion losses in an indirect but highly significant manner.

For a number of years a research project at Kansas State University has been investigating the role of soil microorganisms in coating destruction. Laboratory investigations have established that paraffinic compounds common in asphalt and wax base coatings serve as readily available food material for many soil bacteria. Likewise, adhesive materials used in the newly developed plastics and many of the plastics themselves can be utilized by bacteria as food. In contrast, coal tar type coatings were found to be more refractory to microorganisms, substantiating numerous reports from the experience of corrosion engineers.

Field studies of the pipeline ditch have shown that this environment is favorable for microbial development. Hydrocarbon-utilizing bacteria are present in soils from "bell-hole" openings along operating oil and gas pipelines under extremes in moisture content, acid and alkaline soils, organic matter, salinity, elevation, temperature, and soil types from widely distributed areas of the United States. Significantly, the data have shown high water content of soils at pipeline depths and that aerobic conditions are common in the ditches. The presence of high bacterial populations adjacent to coated and wrapped pipes supports the hypothesis of microbial degradation. Both hydrocarbon-utilizing types and sulfate-reducing anerobes have been isolated from fluid pockets under unbonded asphalt coatings.

Although many unanswered questions remain to puzzle the research worker and the corrosion engineer, it is apparent that microorganisms can have a marked influence upon the corrosion process.

References

1. Costanzo, F. E., "Proc. Fourth Appalachian Underground Corrosion Short Course," 4, 514, University of West Virginia, Morgantown, 1959.
2. Harris, J. O., *Trans. Kans. Acad. Sci.*, 62, 46 (1959).
3. Harris, J. O., *Corrosion*, 16, 441 (1960).
4. Romanoff, M., "Underground Corrosion," National Bureau of Standards, 1957.
5. Starkey, R. L., and Wight, K. M., "Anaerobic Corrosion in Soil," Amer. Gas Assoc. Tech. Rep., New York, 1945.
6. Starkey, R. L., "Sulfate-Reducing Bacteria Science Symposium," St. Bonaventure University, N.Y., 1956.

JOHN O. HARRIS

Cross-references: *Cathodic Protection; Concentration Cells;* entries with *Corrosion* titles; *Protective Coatings.*

MICROELECTRODES

Physiologists rely heavily on microelectrodes for investigation of cellular mechanisms, functions, and organization. A microelectrode is an electrical probe with a tip diameter of 0.2–10 microns (1 micron = 0.00004 inch). They are of two types: electrolyte-filled glass pipettes, which have an open end making liquid-junction contact with the system to be investigated, and metallic probes insulated over their entire length except for the tip which makes a metal-fluid junction with the system. The signals that are of interest to the biologist fall in the frequency band from d-c to 100 kc. There is no universal microelectrode for this frequency band. The fluid-filled pipette is inherently a low-pass filter that is d-c stable, while the metallic electrode is a high-pass filter and d-c unstable.[1]

Fluid-filled Pipettes

Pipette electrodes are constructed by pulling out heated glass tubes. Usually the pulling is done with the aid of a solenoid that initially pulls gently and after the glass softens pulls harder, so that the glass suddenly necks down to a fine diameter and separates.[2] The diameter of the open end will be between 0.2 micron and 1 micron. Larger openings are made by breaking off part of the tip under a microscope. The pipettes are filled with the chosen electrolyte by immersing them tip down in the electrolyte solution in a side-arm flask. The solution should be at a temperature of approximately 80°C. Suction is applied to the flask until the solution boils moderately vigorously; then air is readmitted to the flask. Several cycles of this procedure are needed to fill the small tips. If the flask is resting on a cool surface, boiling bubbles will not come from the bottom; rather, they will originate at either the top ends of the pipettes or the solution surface and will not break off the pipette tips.

The electrolyte solution in the pipette is commonly $3M$ KCl. The high concentration of these two ions minimizes the electrode impedance. The approximately equal mobilities of the ions minimize junction potentials. The high concentration of the electrolyte in the pipette as compared with the ion concentrations in biological media causes the activity coefficient of the biological ions around the electrode tip to approach unity, so that the electrochemical potential depends solely on concentration and mobility. Other electrolytes can be used, but impedance and junction potential effects must be considered. Pipettes with very small tips develop d-c potentials because ionic diameters are not infinitesimal compared with the size of the electrolyte channel.[3] A correction for this effect must be applied to get absolute values of biological potentials with such electrodes.

Substances can be electrophoresed into cells by applying a current that will cause an ionic substance contained in the pipette to flow out, as Eccles does.[4] Pipettes of this type have an unusual use in the study of insect chemoreceptors.[5] Solutions of the particular substance for which one desires to test the receptor sensitivity are used to fill the pipette. The chemoreceptor hair is inserted into the tip of the pipette. The pipette thus supplies the stimulus, and the potential measured by the pipette indicates the response.

The impedance of a micropipette with an electrolyte core is that of a moderately large resistance shunted by a small capacitance. Contact between the electrolyte solution in the pipette and the electronic amplifier or voltmeter is made by inserting a silver-silver chloride electrode into the large end of the pipette. The area of the metallic electrode is so large compared with the area of the tip exposed to the tissue that its impedance is infinitesimal compared with that of the tip, and the silver-silver chloride is reversible and d-c stable because it is not in contact with biological fluids and because enough AgCl quickly dissolves to saturate the KCl pool. Since the impedance of a pipette is concentrated in the tip and the medium immediately around it, the distributed capacitance of the electrode can be neglected. The shunt capacitances to the grounded medium around the electrode and to ground from the connecting lead and the grid of the input vacuum tube amplifier can be lumped together. If the electrode couples to the tissue with 10-MΩ resistance, a shunt capacitance of 10 micromicrofarad will seriously attenuate all frequency components of the signal above 1 kc. It has become common practice to regenerate the signal by feeding back the output of an amplifier having an in-phase gain greater than unity to the input grid through a trimmer capacitor. This negative-capacitance circuit effectively raises the input impedance of the amplifier at high frequencies, thereby preserving the signal shape.[6] This amplifier must also have minimal grid current, if the pipette electrode is being used for d-c measurements, to avoid artifacts that are due to voltage drop across the junction impedance and to avoid damage to cells when recording from their interiors. Both the presence of a negative-capacitance circuit and the requirement for minimal grid current result in a system that has an inherently high noise figure. Usually micropipette electrodes will not be useful for recording small signals with frequency components well above 1 kc. The advantages of micropipettes are that they can have extremely small tips and hence will penetrate cells, stay inside, and do minimal damage; and they have stable d-c behavior for measuring membrane resting potentials and slow potential changes.

Metallic Electrodes

Physical chemists usually distinguish between two extreme types of ideal electrodes. The first is the reversible type in which ions from the solution are actually charged and discharged, so that a steady current is possible and the d-c potential of the electrode has a well-defined value depending on the current and the composition of the solution. The second type is the polarized electrode, in which no transformation of ions takes place, no steady current can pass, and any that does represents the charging and discharging of a double layer made up of the electrode and the ions very close to its surface. The double layer is a structure that acts as a capacitance whose value is dependent on the voltage across it. This electrode has no well-defined d-c potential; it may vary wildly under apparently identical circumstances and is enormously influenced by traces of impurities. Actual metal electrodes are always combinations of both types, and their impedance as a function of frequency shows the extent to which one or the other mechanism dominates their behavior.[7] For instance, a bright platinum electrode in spinal fluid that is rich in adsorbable compounds has an impedance very nearly proportional to ω^{-1} over the frequency range from 10 cycles to 20 kc. That is, it is nearly an ideal polarized electrode. For bright platinum in a saline solution, a more complicated behavior is observed. The electrode reaction is rapid and the current is limited by diffusion of the reacting ions and the products between the surface of the electrode and the bulk of the solution. The impedance will decline proportionally to $\omega^{-1/2}$. If the electrochemical reaction is itself slow, the impedance will be lower for small ω and higher for large ω, than for the case in which diffusion predominates. In practical cases inhomogeneities in the electrode material will spread out the band of frequencies for which the impedance declines only slowly with frequency, since the rate of the reaction is strongly dependent on the d-c potential of the electrode, and this will vary over the surface. In cases in which an insoluble reaction product covers the electrode, the multiplicity of diffusion paths of different lengths may have a similar effect. This is the case for a silver-silver chloride electrode in either a saline solution, or a saline plus gelatin

solution. It has an impedance that declines approximately proportionally to $\omega^{-1/4}$ over a wide range of frequencies. The d-c potential of the electrode can make a considerable difference in the impedance function by changing the rate or even the nature of the reaction carrying current; therefore, the balance between it and diffusion is responsible for the impedance. The real and imaginary components of the impedance of a particular electrode decline as approximately the same function of ω.

The rms noise voltage generated by a metal microelectrode in a given narrow frequency band is most easily specified in terms of an equivalent noise resistance, R_N. The relation between noise voltage and resistance is given by

$$E_{\text{rms noise}} = \sqrt{4kTR_N\Delta F}.$$

Here, k is Boltzmann's constant; T is the absolute temperature; and ΔF is the frequency bandwidth. Values of R_N determined by measuring the rms noise agree with the measured values of the real part of the impedance of several different types of metal microelectrodes. Thus, little noise, if any, in addition to the expected thermal noise is generated by a well-behaved metal electrode, and, because of the decline of impedance with increasing frequency, a metal microelectrode can provide very low-noise coupling to a signal with predominantly high-frequency components. The high impedance of metal microelectrodes at low frequencies, and hence high noise level, attenuate and obscure signals that are predominantly slowly changing. For a given tip size there is much to be gained by selecting the optimum metal electrode to record small signals.

None of the classical reversible metal microelectrodes has ever been shown to be capable of measuring reliably the d-c or thermodynamic potentials in living tissue. The Ag-AgCl electrode fails to measure Cl⁻ for a number of reasons. First, solid AgCl diffuses away from the tip of a microelectrode with great speed because the time of diffusion varies as the square of the linear dimensions of the structure, and even a sparingly soluble salt is not insoluble enough at microdimensions. Second, silver forms extremely stable complexes with organic molecules having attached amino and sulfhydryl groups that occur in places where the electrode locally damages tissue, as it must. The stability of these complexes is greater than the insolubility of AgCl. This difficulty applies to most of the heavy metals that one might hope to use: Hg, As, Sb, Bi, Pb, Cd, Cu, etc. Finally, the oxidation-reduction potential of the interior of nerve cells is low enough to reduce methylene blue; this places it below hydrogen. At this potential, AgCl is reduced to metallic Ag, and Hg_2Cl_2 to Hg, the insolubility not being adequate to the nobility of the metals. This difficulty also applies to the other heavy metals and to oxide electrodes (Sb and Bi) that are used to measure pH.

The inert or noble metal electrode should be free of these difficulties and measure the oxidation-reduction potential of the biological solution. The difficulty is that oxidations and reductions take place through enzyme-substrate complexes of high molecular weight, the activation energies being too high to permit equilibrium to be attained otherwise. The consequence is an impedance far too high to make small electrodes usable at low frequencies,—even with the best control of grid current.

The best metallic microelectrode for biological recording that has been constructed thus far is made in the following way.[7, 8] A glass pipette tip is broken off so that the pipette tip has a diameter of 2 to 5 microns. The pipette is filled with a low melting alloy, such as Cerrelow 136, by using a copper wire to extrude a slug of the alloy down the pipette as it is gently heated on a hot plate. The tip of the microelectrode is then plated with platinum black under a microscope, so that a round ball is formed on the end. (Alternatively, a little alloy can be dissolved out of the tip by using a solution of half concentrated sulfuric acid and half 30 per cent hydrogen peroxide, and the platinum black plated into the cavity thus formed. This provides a stronger tip with a glass cutting edge leading the way into the tissue.) The plating is accomplished in a cell with a platinum anode and an aqueous solution which is one per cent by weight chloroplatinic acid and 0.2 per cent agar agar. The agar agar apparently "prepoisons" the electrode, so that it will not react with tissue proteins, and greatly reduces the impedance (the reduction over a platinum black tip of the same size can be as great as a factor of 30). Plating current is initially small to deposit a thin platinum black film, then higher so that a few bubbles are evolved at the electrode tip as the ball forms.

Many other metallic microelectrodes are used,[9-11] some with improved mechanical prop-

erties, low-frequency performance, etc. For the best cases[1, 8, 11] the high-frequency impedance is always diminished by plating with Pt black. However, the electrode described has the lowest high-frequency impedance of any used thus far, and is the only electrode that has been able to record signals from the small, unmyelinated nerve fibers in vertebrates.[12] Its tip is necessarily larger than a fluid-filled micropipette, but it can pick up signals from outside nearby cells, because of its low impedance in the frequency range in which the energy of the action potential is concentrated. It is not d-c stable and must be used with a capacity-coupled amplifier or be used direct-coupled with great care taken to balance out the grid current.

Thus, the fluid-filled microelectrode is optimum for recording from inside cells from which the signals are large and for which d-c and slow potentials are of interest. The metallic microelectrode is optimum when rapidly varying signals are of interest and the amplitude of the signals is, at best, close to the noise level.

References

1. SVAETICHIN, G., "Low resistance microelectrodes," *Acta Physiol. Scan.*, **24**, Suppl. 86, 5 (1951).
2. ALEXANDER, J. T., AND NASTUK, W. L., "An instrument for the production of microelectrodes used in electrophysiological studies," *Rev. Sci. Instr.*, **24**, 528 (1953).
3. ADRIAN, R. H., "The effect of internal and external potassium concentration on the membrane potential of frog muscle," *J. Physiol.*, **133**, 631 (1956).
4. ECCLES, J. C., "The Physiology of Nerve Cells," Baltimore, p. 9, Johns Hopkins University Press, 1957.
5. HODGSON, E. S., LETTVIN, J. Y., AND ROEDER, K. D., "Physiology of a primary chemoreceptor unit," *Science*, **122**, 417 (1955).
6. AMATNIEK, E., "Measurement of bioelectric potentials with microelectrodes and neutralized input capacity input amplifiers," *IRE Trans.*, **PGME-10**, 26 (1958).
7. GESTELAND, R. C., HOWLAND, B., LETTVIN, J. Y., AND PITTS, W. H., "Comments on microelectrodes," *Proc. IRE*, **47**, 1856 (1959).
8. DOWBEN, R. M., AND ROSE, J. E., "A metal-filled microelectrode," *Science*, **118**, 22 (1953).
9. COLE, K. S., AND KISHIMOTO, U., "Platinized silver chloride electrode," *Science*, **136**, 381 (1962).
10. HUBEL, D. H., "Tungsten microelectrode for recording from single units," *Science*, **125**, 549 (1957).
11. WOLBARSHT, M. L., MACNICHOL, E. F., JR., AND WAGNER, H. G., "Glass insulated platinum microelectrode," *Science*, **132**, 1309 (1960).

12. LETTVIN, J. Y., McCULLOCH, W. S., MATURANA, H. R., AND PITTS, W. H., "What the frog's eye tells the frog's brain," *Proc. IRE,* **47,** 1940 (1959).

R. C. GESTELAND,
B. HOWLAND,
J. Y. LETTVIN, AND
W. H. PITTS

Cross-references: *Electrode Potential, Measurements; Electrophysiology; Reference Electrodes.*

MICROVOLTMETERS AND MICRO-MICROAMMETERS

Microvoltmeters generally are considered to measure voltages in the range up to 10^{-3} volt, and micro-microammeters (pico-ammeters) to measure currents in the range up to 10^{-9} ampere. The term "d-c" used to describe instruments of these classes indicates that they are capable of measuring steady or unvarying quantities, i.e., the instruments respond normally to input quantities having a range of frequencies extending to d-c. However, the instruments are not limited to d-c or slowly varying inputs; indeed, some are capable of measuring changes in input magnitude which occur in fractions of milliseconds.

Electronic microvoltmeters and micro-microammeters find extensive use in materials studies. Microvoltmeters are used for measurements of small temperature differences, relative thermoelectric power, Hall effect, and stress-strain relationships using strain gages. Microvolt signals also arise in biological and physiological investigations, and are commonly measured by these instruments. Micro-microammeters are used in research studies and industrial testing of semiconductor properties and electrical insulation. They are also used widely with photomultipliers and ionization chambers in work involving optical and radiation phenomena.

The earliest electronic micro-microammeters appear to have been developed primarily as more convenient substitutes for classical (passive) types of current measuring electrometers.[9, 10] The electronic electrometers used the very great current amplification available in a single-stage vacuum tube amplifier with a very high grid resistance. However, attempts to measure microvolt signals were hampered by the d-c voltage drifts of multistage direct-coupled amplifiers. The concept of d-c amplification using a-c modulation and carrier techniques was

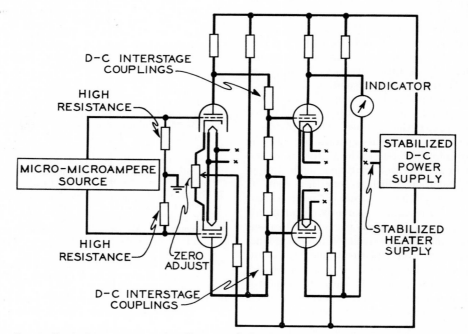

FIG. 1. Typical arrangement for direct-coupled micro-microammeter, differential type.

introduced in the early 1930's to avoid the voltage drift difficulties.[3, 6, 9]

Types

Direct-Coupled Instruments. Some modern instruments use amplifiers of the direct-coupled type. Fig. 1 shows a typical circuit of a simple instrument. Each amplifying stage is conductivity-coupled to its preceding and succeeding circuits. This form of amplifier can provide an instrument which will measure the most rapid changes of input signal magnitude as well as steady input magnitudes, i.e., the direct-coupled amplifier provides the maximum signal bandwidth.

Although simple in its basic concept, the direct-coupled amplifier suffers from instabilities which make it difficult to use for low-level inputs, particularly in the low microvolt range. Because a d-c signal at the input produces an output by changing the d-c electrode potentials of the active elements in the amplifier, any other disturbance of the d-c electrode potentials is indistinguishable from a bona fide signal. For high-level signals, the spurious disturbances are often not troublesome, but for microvolt-level signals, their effects must be suppressed.

Two general methods are used to suppress the spurious effects of electrode potential disturbances in direct-coupled instruments. Both lead to considerable circuit and design complexity. The first is stabilization of the operating conditions of the amplifier. In all cases, this includes stabilizing the supply voltages or currents for the vacuum tubes or solid-state devices, and in some severe situations, temperature stabilization of the amplifier environment must also be provided. The second method is the use of "differential" or "push-pull" circuits. This approach attempts to make a balanced bridge of each amplifier stage, so that it will be more immune to changes in supply potentials.[9, 10] Fig. 1 depicts an amplifier of this type. In this arrangement, the effect of a supply-potential change on one vacuum tube of a pair is offset in part by the effect on the other tube. Two matched vacuum tube or solid-state amplifiers are required per amplifying stage. The required closeness of match becomes greater as the sensitivity of the instrument is increased. Attempts to reach microvolt signal levels with direct-coupled instruments have combined both these methods to suppress the spurious effects.

Even with stabilization and differential amplifiers, the useful sensitivity of direct-coupled instruments is limited by disturbances generated within the low-level vacuum tubes or solid-state amplifiers. "Flicker noise" arises in vacuum tubes because of random electronic emission, and an analogous noise is produced in transistors. In these types of noise, very low-frequency components predominate, producing fluctuations in the outputs of the instruments which, because of their random nature, cannot be suppressed by differential amplifier techniques.

A variation of the direct-coupled instrument is the photoelectric-galvanometer type. This uses the very large optical amplification available from a reflecting galvanometer operating twin photocells. Some of the electronic instabilities discussed above are avoided by the large optical preamplification. Photoelectric galvanometer instruments are usually microvoltmeters.[1]

Modulated Instruments. Instruments of this type have the considerable advantage of avoiding the d-c instabilities and low-frequency noise inherent in direct coupled instruments. However, their response speed is limited by the modulation frequency, and is generally slower than that of the direct-coupled types. With careful input circuit design, instruments of this type are capable of measurements near the ultimate limit of uncertainty imposed by natural random electronic movement (thermal agitation noise).[4, 7, 12] This limit is usually at a much lower level than that imposed by low-frequency noise in direct-coupled amplifiers.

Fig. 2 shows a typical circuit for a microvoltmeter of the modulated type. The input signals are modulated by an a-c "carrier" frequency. The frequency of the modulating carrier is chosen to be higher than the highest desired frequency component of any input signal. Amplification of the input is accomplished by applying to the amplifier the alternating signal resulting from the modulation of the input. The amplifier is of the a-c type which has good inherent immunity from disturbances of supply voltages and ambient conditions. The voltage level of the selected modulated input can be raised by a transformer before application to the vacuum tubes or solid-state amplifiers, so that amplifier-generated noise does not cause significant measuring uncertainties. Further, the modulating frequency and the frequency band-

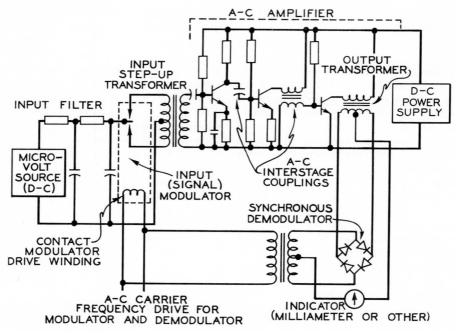

FIG. 2. Typical arrangement for contact-modulated microvoltmeter. Other forms of modulators may be used.

width of the amplifier can be chosen to avoid the region of large flicker and semiconductor noise.

Although the magnitude of the input can be determined directly from the amplified modulated signal, this method of measurement presents an ambiguity with respect to the sense of the input. The ambiguity is usually resolved by the use of synchronous demodulation of the amplified signal before the final indicating device.[3, 12]

The type of signal modulating device used in an instrument has an important bearing on its suitability as a microvoltmeter or micro-microammeter. Modulators which have been used include periodically varying resistances of the carbon granule type;[6] capacitors which are driven mechanically to produce periodically varying capacitance;[3] contacting modulators;[4, 7, 12] vacuum tubes;[2] and a number of solid-state devices.[5, 11]

Modulators using periodically varying capacitance are most suitable for micro-microammeters. Their zero errors can be 10^{-15} amperes or smaller. Typical voltage errors are more than 1000 microvolts, and change 100 microvolts per day or more.

Modulators using periodically closing contacts find their greatest use in microvoltmeters.

The metallic contacting parts and associated low-level circuits can be arranged to limit zero errors to less than 1 microvolt. High-quality units also have been built with current errors of less than 10^{-12} amperes.[8]

Magnetic modulators, particularly those of the second-harmonic type, also are useful in microvoltmeters.[14] They are rugged, and can be operated at relatively high frequencies.

Solid-state modulators are developing rapidly as a result of modern advances in solid-state physics. High-quality silicon transistor modulators show typical errors of 10^{-9} ampere and 10^{-4} volt;[8] silicon diode capacitors can be selected to have errors of less than 10^{-12} ampere and 10^{-3} volt;[14] and photoconductive modulators have shown less than 10^{-10} ampere and 10^{-6} volt. Where applicable, solid-state modulators offer the advantages of compactness and high modulation frequencies.

Chopper-Stabilized Direct-Coupled Instruments. Introduced in the late 1940's, this type of instrument combines some of the advantages of the direct-coupled and modulated types.[13] Fig. 3 illustrates a typical instrument in block form. It provides both fast response and good zero stability. A modulated amplifier, often of the contact-modulator type, is used to sense the zero error of a gain-stabilized direct-

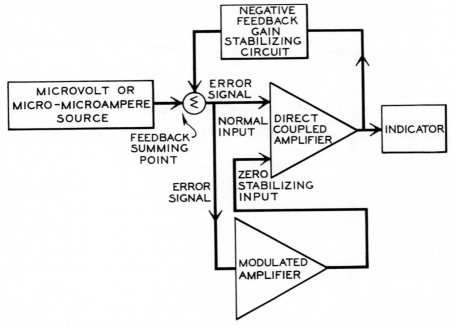

Fig. 3. Block diagram of chopper-stabilized direct-coupled microvoltmeter or micro-microammeter. The modulated amplifier maintains nearly zero error signal and correct indication of source signal in the presence of zero disturbances.

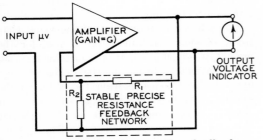

Fig. 4a. Typical series negative feedback arrangement for microvoltmeter.

$$\frac{\text{Output}}{\text{Input}} = \frac{G}{1 + G\dfrac{R_2}{R_1 + R_2}}$$

$$\cong \frac{R_1 + R_2}{R_2} \text{ when } G\frac{R_2}{R_1 + R_2} \gg 1$$

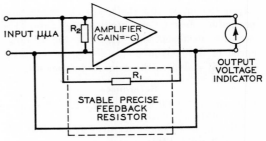

Fig. 4b. Typical parallel negative feedback arrangement for micro-microammeter.

$$\frac{\text{Output}}{\text{Input}} = \frac{-GR_2}{1 + \left(\dfrac{R_2}{R_1}\right)(1 + G)}$$

$$\cong R_1 \text{ when } G \gg 1 \text{ and } G\frac{R_2}{R_1} \gg 1$$

coupled amplifier and to provide a corrective signal to minimize this error. Although this type of instrument is usually more complex than the ordinary modulated type, the wide bandwidth provided by the direct-coupled part is a distinct advantage. Many modern microvoltmeters and microammeters use this technique.

Instruments With Negative Feedback. The foregoing discussion has indicated tech-

niques used in electronic microvoltmeters and micro-microammeters to reduce their *zero* stabilities sufficiently to make them useful for the desired low signal levels. All measuring instruments must also have a sufficient degree of *gain* stability, i.e., sufficiently constant relationship between the output indication and the input signal magnitude. Electronic amplifying devices do not possess very great inherent gain stability, so that gain stabilizing circuit arrangements are usually needed in electronic measuring instruments.

The technique of negative feedback can be applied in electronic instruments to provide nearly any desired degree of gain stability, and most modern instruments use this technique.[1, 4, 12] Fig. 3 shows schematically negative feedback applied to a chopper-stabilized direct coupled instrument, where such gain stabilization is required for success of the zero-stabilizing arrangement. Fig. 4 shows two typical simple negative feedback arrangements in greater detail. In each, a part of the instrument output is returned to the input through a network of stable resistors having precisely known values. The amplifier has sufficient gain to produce the desired output from a small difference between the input signal and the signal returned via the resistance network. Consequently, the magnitude ratio between the input and output is almost entirely dependent only on the resistances in the stable feedback network. Inherent gain variations in the amplifier caused by aging of the components, variations of power supply voltage, or changing the active tubes or solid-state devices affect only the small difference between the input and the feedback, hence have negligible effect on the input-output ratio. The negative feedback also improves the response speed of the instrument to about the same degree as it stabilizes the magnitude response.

References

1. ASSET, G., *Electronics*, **18**, 126 (February, 1945).
2. BLACK, L. J., AND SCOTT, H. J., *Proc. IRE*, **28**, 269 (June, 1940).
3. GUNN, Ross, *Phys. Rev.*, **40**, 307 (April 15, 1932).
4. HOELL, P. C., *Rev. Scientific Instruments*, **29**, *No. 12*, 1120 (December, 1958).
5. HURTIG, C. R., "Selected Semiconductor Circuits Handbook," New York, John Wiley and Sons, Inc., 1960.
6. *Instruments*, **6**, No. 11, 211 (November, 1933).
7. LISTON, M. D., QUINN, C. E., SARGENT, W. E., AND SCOTT, G. G., *Rev. Scientific Instruments*, **17**, 194 (May, 1946).
8. McADAM, W., TARPLEY, R. E., AND WILLIAMS, A. J., JR., *Proc. NEC*, **6**, 277 (1950).
9. MOLES, F. J., *General Electric Review*, **36**, 156 (March, 1933).
10. NOTTINGHAM, W. B., *J. Franklin Institute*, **209**, No. 3, 287 (March, 1930).
11. WILLIAMS, A. J., JR., EYNON, J. U., AND POLSTER, N. E., *Proc. NEC*, **13**, 40 (1957).
12. WILLIAMS, A. J., JR., TARPLEY, R. E., AND CLARK, W. R., *Trans. AIEE*, **67**, 47 (1948).
13. WILLIAMS, A. J., JR., AMEY, W. G., AND Mc-
ADAM, W., *Trans. AIEE*, **68**, Pt. II, 811 (1949).
14. WILLIAMS, F. C., AND NOBLE, S. W., *Inst. Elec. Engineers*, Paper No. **893** (December, 1949).

WILL McADAM

MIXED POTENTIAL

When an electrode is immersed in a solution and charge transfer takes place across the electrode-solution interface but the system is not in oxidation-reduction equilibrium, the measured electrode potential may be designated a *mixed potential*. Two or more different oxidation-reduction reactions occur on the electrode surface simultaneously, and a net electrochemical reaction proceeds at the steady state mixed potential. Such an electrode is sometimes called a polyelectrode.

The concept may be clarified by considering the processes involved in a given isolated metal electrode-solution system. The electrode is not connected to any external circuit, except the conventional null potentiometer circuit which measures the electrode potential with respect to a reference half cell. Under these conditions, external current cannot flow.

The solution contains ions of the metal electrode at some constant activity; and, for the present, it is assumed that only metallic ions can cross the metal-solution interface. The rate per unit area, at which ions leave the metal for the solution, may be expressed as an anodic current density, $(i_a)_M$; and the rate in the opposite direction as a cathodic current density, $(i_c)_M$.

These rates will be a function of any electrical potential difference which exists between the metal and the solution. Since the measured electrode potential includes this potential difference, the measured electrode potential, E, will be used here. The European sign convention is adopted whereby E is negative ($-$) for electrode potentials which are above hydrogen in the electromotive force series; thus, $E/_{Zn} = -0.76$ v. The two rates will equilibrate and the required equilibrium potential, E_{eq}, will be established. The functional dependence of the rates on the electrode potential is in many cases an exponential of the following form:

$$(i_c)_M = k_c a_{MS^+} \exp{[-\alpha_c \mathbf{F} E / RT]} \qquad (1)$$

$$(i_a)_M = k_a a_{ML^+} \exp{[\alpha_a \mathbf{F} E / RT]} \qquad (2)$$

Where k_c and k_a are rate constants; a_{MS^+} and

a_{ML^+} are the activity of the metal ions in the solution and in the metallic lattice, respectively; α_c and α_a are transfer coefficients (which include the symmetry factors and the number of charges transferred); $\mathbf{F}$ is the Faraday; R the gas constant and T the absolute temperature.

At equilibrium, the electrode potential is E_{eq} and

$$(i_c)_M = (i_a)_M = (i_o)_M \qquad (3)$$

where $(i_o)_M$ is the exchange current density for the metal-metal ion reaction. In the special case where a_{MS^+} and a_{ML^+} are each equal to unity, the equilibrium electrode potential is equal to the standard electrode potential, E_{eq}^0, for the system.

If the electrode potential is altered from its equilibrium value, by some means, a net current density, I_M, will flow across the interface with respect to the metal-metal ion reaction and

$$I_M = (i_c)_M - (i_a)_M \qquad (4)$$

where a positive value of I_M corresponds to cathodic polarization and a negative value to anodic polarization.

I_M may be expressed in terms of E by the use of Eqs. (1) and (2) in Eq. (4), or in terms of the overvoltage, η, where

$$\eta = E - E_{eq} \qquad (5)$$

If it is assumed that the activity of the reacting species at the interface remains constant, η may be designated the activation overvoltage. Negative values of η will correspond to cathodic overvoltage, or lower values of E, while positive values will correspond to anodic overvoltage, or higher values of E. The rates may then be given in terms of I_0 and η as follows:

$$(i_c)_M = (i_o)_M \exp\left[-\alpha_c \mathbf{F}\eta/RT\right] \qquad (6)$$

$$(i_a)_M = (i_o)_M \exp\left[\alpha_a \mathbf{F}\eta/RT\right] \qquad (7)$$

which are generally known as the Tafel relations. The net current density is

$$I_M = (i_o)_M \left[\exp\left(-\alpha_c \mathbf{F}\eta/RT\right) - \exp\left(\alpha_a \mathbf{F}\eta/RT\right)\right] \qquad (8)$$

The behavior of the system is shown schematically in Fig. 1. Curve A corresponds to the cathodic reaction as given by Eqs. (1) or (6), while curve B depicts the anodic reaction as given by Eqs. (2) or (7).

These concepts are applicable to any thermodynamically reversible electrode system, in-

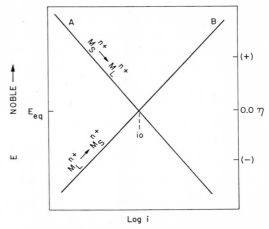

FIG. 1. Schematic polarization curves for a reversible metal-metal ion system.

cluding those which involve electron transfer, such as an inert metal electrode in a solution containing ferric and ferrous ions or hydrogen ions and hydrogen, etc.

The perturbation upon the electrode system indicated by Eqs. (4) and (8) is not possible unless some means is available to provide for the net current flow, I_M, of the metal-metal ion reaction. This can, of course, be accomplished by allowing the flow of electrons between the metal and an external circuit—a process called *external* polarization.

There is another possibility, however, and it is the one which leads to the mixed potential. If some other oxidation-reduction system which can undergo an electrode reaction is present in the solution, it will also strive to set up its own equilibrium with its characteristic electrode potential. Since only one potential can be achieved, a steady state will be reached where the electrode potential is a compromise potential, and a net electrode reaction occurs. This compromise potential is the *mixed potential*, E_{MP}.

Since a net current cannot flow in the isolated system, the sum of all the cathodic current densities will equal the sum of all the anodic current densities,

$$\sum (i_c)_n = \sum (i_a)_n \qquad (9)$$

where n designates any one oxidation-reduction system. Relations (4) and (9) lead to

$$\sum I_n = 0 \qquad (10)$$

which merely states that the net current density due to all the possible electrode reactions must be zero.

As a specific example, consider an iron electrode in a dilute solution of ferrous sulfate and sulfuric acid, saturated with hydrogen gas at 1 atmosphere pressure. There are present two oxidation-reduction systems with the following possible electrode reactions:

$$[Fe^{++}]_L + 2e\,(M) \to$$
$$[Fe^{++}]_S + 2e; \qquad (i_a)_{Fe} \qquad (10.a)$$

$$[Fe^{++}]_S + 2e \to$$
$$[Fe^{++}]_L + 2e\,(M); \qquad (i_c)_{Fe} \qquad (10.b)$$

$$H_2 \to 2(H^+)_S + 2e; \qquad (i_a)_{H_2} \qquad (11.a)$$

$$2(H^+)_S + 2e \to H_2\,; \qquad (i_c)_{H_2} \qquad (11.b)$$

Reactions (10.a) and (10.b) are the dissolution and deposition of iron ions, and (11.a) and (11.b) the oxidation and reduction of hydrogen. The two iron reaction rates will strive to equilibrate and establish the equilibrium potential of the metal-metal ion system. Simultaneously, and statistically independently, the hydrogen reactions will attempt the same for the hydrogen system.

The ensuing process may be visualized as one where reaction (11.b) polarizes the iron electrode in the positive direction relative to the metal-metal ion equilibrium potential until a steady state is reached and the mixed potential, E_{MP}, is established. Eqs. (9) and (10) become

$$(i_c)_{H_2} + (i_c)_{Fe} = (i_a)_{H_2} + (i_a)_{Fe} \qquad (12)$$

or

$$(i_a)_{Fe} - (i_c)_{Fe} = (i_c)_{H_2} - (i_a)_{H_2} \qquad (13)$$

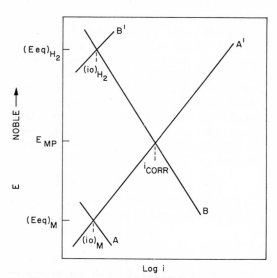

FIG. 2. Schematic mixed-potential diagram.

By use of Eqs. (4), (10), and (13) the following is obtained

$$-I_{Fe} = I_{H_2} = i_{corr} \qquad (14)$$

where i_{corr} is the rate of dissolution, or corrosion of iron.

The electrode potential of the corroding metal is, therefore, the *mixed potential* for the system and synonymous with the term *corrosion potential.*

In most practical cases, particularly in corrosion problems,

$$(i_a)_M \gg (i_c)_M$$
$$(i_c)_{H_2} \gg (i_a)_{H_2} \qquad (15)$$

so that

$$(i_a)_M \cong (i_c)_{H_2} \cong i_{corr} \qquad (16)$$

The situation whereby a mixed potential is set up is shown, schematically, in Fig. 2. The curves A and A¹ are the polarization curves for the metal-metal ion system; and curves B and B¹ are those of the hydrogen-hydrogen ion system. The two sets of curves show the mutual polarizing effect of the two oxidation-reduction systems. It is assumed that the relationships (Eq. 15) apply so that the curves A¹ and B intersect at the mixed potential, E_{MP}.

In more complex systems, several different electrode processes may occur simultaneously and independently. The general principle is the same, however. The polyelectrode will exhibit a single mixed potential, which is common to all the processes; and the sum of the rates of all the anodic reactions equals the sum of the rates of all the cathodic reactions.

The principal factors which determine the value of the mixed potential are the exchange current density, $(i_0)_n$; the "theoretical" equilibrium potential, $(E_{eq})_n$, for the existing conditions of concentrations, etc.; and the transfer coefficients, $(\alpha_c)_n$ and $(\alpha_a)_n$, which determine the slopes of the Tafel lines of the various oxidation-reduction systems present.

It should be noted that concentration changes, leading to concentration overvoltages, have been neglected. The latter may be important in some cases and should then be included.

In the case of a metal electrode in an acid solution, the smaller the ratio, $(i_0)_{H_2}/(i_0)_M$, the more nearly the mixed potential will correspond to the equilibrium metal-metal ion potential. Conversely, the larger this ratio, the more nearly the mixed potential will correspond to the equilibrium hydrogen potential.

It is of interest to note that the establishment of a mixed potential is one of the principal causes why corrosion potentials, which are found in practice, often depart from the values expected from the electromotive force series.

The concept of a mixed potential is particularly important and very useful in the interpretation of polarization curves, which are obtained by means of *external* polarization. The technique has been applied to corrosion and polarographic studies. The following example indicates the method.

When a metal such as iron is undergoing dissolution in an acid solution, the steady state condition is as previously described and shown in Fig. 2. If the metal electrode is polarized by means of an external circuit, the external current, I_{ex}, will be given by

$$I_{ex} = (i_c)_{H_2} - (i_a)_{Fe} \tag{17}$$

or

$$I_{ex} = k_{H_2} a_{HS^+} \exp\left[-(\alpha_c)_{H_2} FE/RT\right]$$
$$- k_{Fe} \exp\left[(\alpha_a)_{Fe} FE/RT\right] \tag{18}$$

Upon cathodic polarization, as the absolute value of I_{ex} increases, $(i_c)_{H_2}$ will increase and $(i_a)_{Fe}$ will decrease; until $I_{ex} \cong (i_c)_{H_2}$ and the *external* polarization curve, E versus log I_{ex} becomes equal to the E versus log $(i_c)_{H_2}$ curve.

Similarly, upon anodic polarization the *external* polarization curve becomes equal to E versus log $(i_a)_{Fe}$. Fig. 3 shows such external polarization curves, schematically, where $\overline{AB}$ and $\overline{AC}$ are the anodic and cathodic curves, respectively. If the linear portions of these curves are extrapolated to the mixed potential, E_{MP}, they will intersect at (E_{MP}, i_{corr}). This technique is applicable in many cases for obtaining i_{corr}, provided that concentration polarization does not interfere, as has been assumed above.

References

1. PETROCELLI, J. V., "The Surface Chemistry of Metals and Semi-Conductors," Edited by H. C. Gatos, p. 326, New York, John Wiley & Sons, Inc., 1960.
2. PETROCELLI, J. V., *J. Electrochem. Soc.*, **97**, 10 (1950).
3. STERN, MILTON, AND GEARY, A. L., *ibid.*, **104**, 56, 645 (1957).
4. MAKRIDES, A. C., *ibid.*, **107**, 869 (1960).
5. STERN, MILTON, *Corrosion*, **14**, 440 (1958).
6. BOCKRIS, J. O'M., "Modern Aspects of Electrochemistry," Ed. J. O'M. Bockris, p. 180, London, Butterworths Scientific Publications, 1954.

J. V. PETROCELLI

Cross-references: *Electrode Potentials; Electromotive Force; Exchange Current; Overvoltage; Polarization; Tafel Lines; Transfer Coefficient.*

MOISSAN, HENRI (1852–1907)

Born in Paris September 28, 1852, Moissan studied chemistry while working in a pharmacy. After publishing a thesis in 1876, he turned to inorganic chemistry, then in a stage of neglect. He first investigated pyrophoric iron and then after four years of work isolated the element fluorine and proceeded to do research on many organic fluorine compounds. He showed that SF_6 was almost as stable and inert as nitrogen. All this work on the highly reactive and poisonous element was done under poor laboratory conditions which Moissan felt probably would shorten his life by ten years.

In 1900, he became professor at the Faculty of Sciences at the University of Paris. He had already designed and built from quicklime in 1892 an electric oven in which he prepared calcium carbide with no thought of its industrial possibilities, but in the year of his death 165,000 tons were produced and 20 years later four times this amount. He also prepared in his fur-

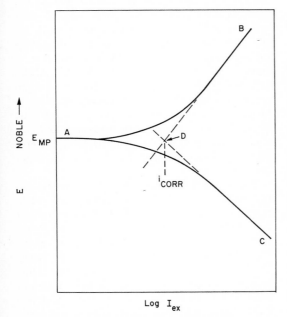

FIG. 3. Schematic external polarization curves for a corroding metal.

nace tungsten metal and steel in which boron replaced carbon. Most spectacular was the artificial production of diamonds by the rapid cooling of molten iron containing carbon, so that the hard outer shell kept the still liquid iron under high pressure while cooling. For placing at the service of science the Moissan electric furnace, as well as the isolation of fluorine, he received the Nobel Prize in 1906. In his last few years, he spent much time to the preparation of a 5-volume treatise on inorganic chemistry. Moissan died in Paris on February 20, 1907.

G. L. CLARK

MOLECULAR SIEVES

Ion exchange materials are being considered for use in fuel cells and other devices that convert heat to electricity. One such material is the so-called "molecular sieve." The use can involve not only the ion exchange capability but also the catalytic effect and the selective adsorption phenomena associated with these materials. There have been recent references to the use of these zeolites as membrane materials.

The term "molecular sieve" was originally used by McBain to describe the ability of dehydrated crystalline zeolites to selectively separate molecules on the basis of critical diameter. The term zeolite is used to define a group of molecules characterized by the presence of the SiO_2 and Al_2O_3 group, cation(s) to balance the negative charge of the aluminosilicate structure, and water of hydration. The zeolites may be crystalline or amorphous. The former types are of particular interest as the molecular sieves. The cation(s) commonly found are sodium and calcium with barium, potassium, magnesium, strontium, and iron also possible. The natural zeolites are about 25 in number with the more familiar being chabazite, gmelinite, levynite, faujasite, and mordenite. The natural zeolites have received considerable research by R. M. Barrer and his coworkers in England. These zeolites are of extreme interest from a physical chemical point-of-view. However, they are industrial curiosities due to lack of availability (hence cost) and lack of reproducibility in the physical and chemical properties.

The first commercial molecular sieves were made available by Union Carbide Corp's Linde Division during the early 1950's under the trademark "Linde Molecular Sieves." In 1959, the Davison Chemical Co., Division of W. R. Grace introduced crystalline zeolites under the trademark "Microtraps." Early in 1962, the Norton Company introduced a zeolite under the trademark "Zeolon." The physical and chemical properties of these materials are similar. In general terms, the cost varies with manufacturer and quantity and is in the range of \$1 to 2/ pound. The zeolites are available as powder, beads and pellets.

The zeolites have many uses, and the utilization of these materials is limited only by the imagination of the user. There is still much to be learned in the application of these materials. They are currently used to statically and dynamically dry gases and liquids, for selective separations based on size and polar characteristics of the molecules, as ion exchange materials, as catalysts, as chemical carriers, and as gas chromatography materials.

Physical and Chemical Properties

The Linde molecular sieves designated as Type 3A, 4A, and 5A have what is termed the A crystal structure which is cubic ($a_o = 12.32$ Å, space group $O(1/h) - Pm3m$), characterized by a three-dimensional network which has cavities 11.4 Å in diameter separated by circular openings 4.2 Å in diameter. This latter figure is the so-called pore diameter. The removal of the water of crystallization leaves an "active" crystalline zeolite that has a void volume of 45 vol per cent. Adsorption occurs in these intracrystalline voids. The Type 4A material has a chemical formula 0.96 ± 0.04 $Na_2O \cdot 1$ $Al_2O_3 \cdot$ 1.92 ± 0.09 $SiO_2 \cdot XH_2O$. Types 3A and 5A are prepared from 4A by an ion-exchange process using salt solutions which replaces 75 per cent of the Na ions present with potassium and calcium ions, respectively. The Davison Microtraps which are designated as Na and Ca types are similar to the Linde Type 4A and 5A.

The Linde Type 10X and 13X have the X-crystal structure which is also cubic, ($a_o = 24.95$ Å, space group $O(7/h) - Fd3m$), characterized by a three-dimensional net work which has intracrystalline voids separated by pores which will admit molecules having critical dimensions of 10 and 13 Å, respectively. The void volume is 51 vol per cent. The Type 13X has a chemical composition given by 0.83 ± 0.05 $Na_2O \cdot 1.0$ $Al_2O_3 \cdot 2.48 \pm 0.03$ $SiO_2 \cdot XH_2O$. The 10X is made by exchanging 75 per cent of the sodium ions in

13X with calcium. The pH of the Linde and Davison zeolites is 10 and they can be used in environments of pH 5 to 12.

The internal surface area for the Linde molecular sieves is 650 to 800 square meters per gram and the external area is 1 to 3 square meter per gram. The average volume of voids is 0.27 cc/g for the Type A and 0.38 for the Type X. The Linde and Davison materials have a specific heat of 0.23 to 0.25, a bulk density of 33 to 45 lb/cu ft which is dependent on the physical shape of the bulk materials.

Linde has a sixth zeolite designated as AW-500. This material has a pore diameter of 4 to 5 Å, is acid stable to pH 2.5. It has a bulk density of 42 lb/cu ft, a specific heat of about 0.2. It is particularly recommended for use in an acid environment.

The Norton "Zeolons" are related structurally to the natural zeolite, mordenite. There are two forms, a sodium and a hydrogen. The effective pore diameter is 9 to 10 Å. The chemical analysis of the sodium form is 71.45 per cent SiO_2, 12.05 per cent Al_2O_3, 0.52 per cent Fe_2O_3, 0.26 per cent CaO, 0.31 per cent MgO, 7.14 per cent Na_2O and 9.15 per cent H_2O. The hydrogen form is made by exchanging the sodium with hydrogen. These zeolites have a pore volume of 0.11 cc/gm, a surface area of 500 square meters/g and a porosity of 54 per cent. They are acid resistant and can be used over the entire pH range and can be heated to temperatures as high as 800°C.

Regeneration

The crystalline zeolites can be regenerated by simple heating supplemented by gas purging or evacuating. Water is removable at temperatures between 150 to 350°C. The Linde and Davison materials should not be exposed to temperatures of 800°C. The Norton materials can be exposed to temperatures of 800°C. Other materials that have been adsorbed can be removed by a water or steam flush since in general these materials have a preference for water. In general a reverse flow of purge gas is recommended during the regeneration process. Care should always be taken to avoid hazardous or explosive situations in the selection of the purge gas. In liquid processes the liquid should be drained prior to regeneration.

Adsorbent Characteristics

These zeolites as a class are characterized by the ability to adsorb molecules that have critical dimensions less than the effective pore size of the zeolite. It appears that the Linde molecular sieve Type 4A and the Davison Na type are similar and will adsorb water, carbon dioxide, carbon monoxide, hydrogen sulfide, sulfur dioxide, ammonia, nitrogen, oxygen, methane, methanol, ethane, ethanol, ethylene, acetylene, propylene, n-propanol and ethylene oxide. The Linde Type 5A and Davison Ca Type will adsorb the molecules just listed as well as propane and the n-paraffins to C_{14}, n-butene and n-olefins, n-butanol and higher n-alcohols, cyclopropane and "Freon-12." The Linde Type 10X will adsorb molecules that have a critical diameter of less than 10 Å. They will adsorb with a slightly higher capacity than 4A or 5A. The Linde Type 13X will adsorb all of the materials listed above at a slightly higher capacity than 3A, 4A, 5A and 10X. In addition, this type will adsorb the isoparaffins, isopropanol and other iso, secondary and tertiary alcohols, aromatics, cyclohexane, other cyclic compounds with at least 4 membered rings, carbon tetrachloride, hexachlorobutadiene, Freon 114 and 11, sulfur hexafluoride, and boron trifluoride. The AW-500 material will adsorb HCl, SO_2, and nitrogen oxides, molecules that have critical dimensions of about 4 to 5Å.

The Norton "Zeolon" adsorbs molecules, such as H_2O, CO_2, and H_2S. In addition, the hydrogen form adsorbs normal and cycloparaffins, and aromatics.

Drying

Because of their strong affinity for water these molecular sieve materials are extremely effective in the drying of gases and liquids in both static and dynamic applications. As a class they have good capacity; they do not deliquesce; they remain strong; they are not toxic; they are noncorrosive; and they are not explosive. In the drying of gases the synthetic zeolite can be used in drying low-humidity gases, they can be used at high temperatures, they can be used to dry gases without otherwise altering the composition, they can be used to remove selectively other impurities as well as water, they can be used to dry gases adiabatically, they are not damaged by liquid water, and they can dry gases more completely than other commercial adsorbents.

The drying of liquids can also be accomplished using the crystalline zeolites because they have a high capacity for water in liquids having only trace amounts of water; they give very dry liquids and they can dry polar liquids.

Chemically Loaded Zeolites

Linde scientists have explored the possibility of using the Linde materials as carriers for a wide variety of materials. The adsorbed chemical is released by heating or by displacement using another material such as water. The volatility, toxicity, and odor of some compounds restricts their usefulness, and the molecular sieve can be used to depress the reactivity or undesirable properties. Materials such as anhydrides, amines, ethers, organic acids, alcohols, organo-metallic compounds, aldehydes, halogens, ketones, acid gases, esters, perfumes, peroxides, and hydrocarbons have been successfully loaded on molecular sieves. In all some 200 different chemicals have been "loaded" on Linde sieves.

Ion Exchange

The crystalline zeolites can act as ion exchange materials. The ability of the commercial zeolite to undergo ion exchange is evidenced by the fact that Linde Type 3A and 5A are produced from 4A by introducing potassium and calcium for about 75 per cent of the sodium ions present. The ion exchange capacity of the Linde materials has been studied with both the A and X structures. The following cations have been introduced into the Linde molecular sieves.

Li^+	Ag^+	Ba^{++}	Ni^{++}
K^+	NH_4^+	Hg^{++}	Cu^{++}
Rb^+	Mg^{++}	Cd^{++}	Al^{+++}
Cs^+	Ca^{++}	Zn^{++}	H^+
Tl^+	Sr^+	Co^{++}	Au^{+++}

The ion-exchange capacity of the Linde molecular sieves is higher than that for the commercial zeolites and resins now being used for water softening. This ion-exchange property while in itself very useful changes the pore diameter and hence the adsorption characteristics of these materials. The sodium in Linde molecular sieve Type 13X has been replaced by Li^+, K^+, Mg^{++}, Ca^{++}, Zn^{++}, Sr^{++}, Cd^{++}, and Ba^{++}.

Although information is not directly available, the statement has been made that the "Zeolon" material can also act as an ion-exchange medium.

Catalysis

One of the potentially large uses for the molecular sieves is in the field of catalysis. They can be used as carriers for catalysts. A technique has been developed recently for use in hydrocarbon processing. The upgrading of hydrocarbons by contacting them at high temperatures with a catalyst of metal oxide on a molecular sieve support has recently been revealed. The catalyst can also be a metal or mixture of metals and compounds of the platinum group supported on a molecular sieve.

Further, the H-form of the Linde materials and Norton materials are in effect "solid" acids, due to the hydrogen ions present and with a large active surface. The hydrogen zeolon has been used as a catalyst in cracking, dehydrating, isomerization, and alkylation reactions. It has been noted that the catalytic activity exists even at temperatures of 350°C. The Linde materials act as acid catalysts. They have been used to isomerize and crack olefins and to dehydrate alcohols. The catalytic activity varies with sieve size, acidity, and composition. Generally, molecular sieves polymerize isobutylene, propylene, and ethylene in decreasing order of ease. The Type X has a greater activity than the Type A. A great deal is yet to be learned regarding the catalytic aspects of the synthetic zeolites.

Reference

HERSH, C. K., "Molecular Sieves," New York, Reinhold Publishing Corp., 1961.

C. K. HERSH

Cross-references: *Fuel Cells; Ion-Exchange Resins.*

MOLTEN SALT OR SALTS. See FUSED SALT ENTRIES.

N

NATIONAL ASSOCIATION OF CORROSION ENGINEERS

The NACE can trace its origin back to 1936, to a group of engineers interested in cathodic protection of pipelines. From 1936 until the summer of 1943, this small group of engineers, with an interest in corrosion, looked for a home in some existing association with no success. In the Fall of 1943, eleven of them met to organize an association, with corrosion control as the primary objective.

The Association was incorporated on October 8, 1945, as a non-profit corporation under the laws of the State of Texas.

In the Articles of Organization and By-Laws, eight objectives are stated. The key phrase of each is given below:

1. To promote the prevention of corrosion
2. To provide forums on corrosion prevention
3. To encourage special study and research
4. To correlate study and research on corrosion problems among technical associations
5. To promote standardization
6. To contribute to industrial and public safety
7. To foster cooperation between individual operators of metallic plants and structures
8. To invite a wide diversity of membership

NACE carries out its objectives by publishing two journals and one abstract volume, devoted entirely to corrosion science and engineering. In addition, the Association organizes and promotes short courses, maintains a sizable technical committee structure, organizes and conducts National and Regional Conferences and monthly meetings of its many sections, and supports research.

Very soon after incorporation, NACE formed a publications committee and the first journal, CORROSION, was published quarterly in March, 1945. The publication became a monthly with the September, 1946, issue and in a little over a decade developed into a technical publication of considerable worldwide statue.

In recognition of the diversity of interests among its readers, CORROSION was divided into two separate publications in January, 1962: CORROSION, a technical journal of the classical type publishing new scientific and engineering data, and MATERIALS PROTECTION, an entirely new publication carrying practical corrosion engineering information and Association activities. A new bimonthly publication titled CORROSION ABSTRACTS BULLETIN was initiated in 1962.

To develop, assemble, qualify, and disseminate data and standards useful in dealing with specific corrosion problems, NACE has a large technical committee structure. The technical committee activities began quite early in NACE's history. The first committee was designated TP-1 and, with a membership of 23, directed its efforts toward solving the corrosion problems of the oil and gas industry. From this beginning, TP-1 expanded into the Technical Practices Committee which now includes a Managing Committee, 8 Group Committees under whose direction operate 51 Unit Committees, and 151 Task Groups with a working membership of over 1000 corrosion specialists. The Group Committees are: T-1 Corrosion in Oil and Gas Well Equipment, T-2 Pipeline Corrosion, T-3 General Corrosion Problems, T-4 Utilities Industry Corrosion Problems, T-6 Protective Coatings, T-8 Refining Industry Corrosion Problems, and T-9 Corrosion of Military Equipment. The Technical Practices Committee maintains liaison with 15 other technical associations.

Through its Education Committee, the Association encourages the training of young engineers as corrosion specialists by arranging and conducting corrosion short courses in cooperation with educational institutes. NACE sponsors, co-sponsors, or participates in 11 short courses annually.

NACE is governed by a Board of Directors, composed of four officers and 19 directors. Four of the directors represent active members; five represent corporate members; and six represent regional divisions. The four ex-officio members of the board are the chairmen of the four standing committees: Regional Management, Policy and Planning, Publications, and Technical Practices. All officers and directors except those representing regions are elected by the membership. Three officers (president, vice president, and treasurer) are elected by the membership for a term of one year. The executive secretary is appointed annually by the Board of Directors and acts as the executive administrator of the Association. To assist him in performing his duties, a central office staff is maintained at the Association's headquarters, 980 M and M Building, Houston 2, Texas.

The Association is organized into 6 regions and 58 sections. The regions are: Northeast, North Central, Southeast, South Central, Canadian, and Western.

NACE holds an annual conference in a different major city each year which includes a corrosion show and a technical program. In addition, each region holds an annual meeting where technical papers are presented and Unit Committees and Task Groups meet to report on their progress. Sections hold monthly meetings.

The Association has three classes of members: active, junior and corporate. The total membership in 1962 was 7,000.

NACE makes three awards each year: The Frank Newman Speller Award, given for excellence in corrosion engineering; the Willis Rodney Whitney Award, given in recognition of outstanding achievement in corrosion science; and the A. B. Campbell Award for Young Authors, given for the outstanding paper published each year in CORROSION.

EDWARD C. GRECO

NERNST, WALTHER (1864–1941)

Born in Briesen, West Prussia on June 25, 1864, Nernst attended several universities and graduated at Würzburg in 1887 with a thesis on electromotive forces which are produced by magnetism in heated metal plates. Interest in relationships between electric and heat energies and chemical affinity were stimulated by Wilhelm Ostwald, whom Nernst joined at Leipzig. Nernst explained the potential of the electrochemical battery and derived the famous Nernst equation. In 1893 appeared his great textbook "Theoretical Chemistry from the Standpoint of Avogadro's Rule and Thermodynamics." The Nernst heat theorem based on the third law of thermodynamics was announced in 1906. The Nobel Prize was conferred in 1920 for thermochemical work. In research in physical chemistry—solutions, relations between compressibility and atomic volume, and many other principles—Nernst was quite successful, though his inventions were less so. The Nernst lamp (with a ceramic body glower) was superseded by tungsten lamps. A player piano with radio amplifiers replacing a sounding board was not well received. Nernst was professor at Berlin from 1905 on, and director of the Institute for Experimental Physics from 1924 to 1933. In this capacity he had many contacts with industry and contributed to industrial developments everywhere. He publicly stated that Röntgen, the discoverer of x-rays, would have been much wiser and would have furthered the cause of science and industry far more if he had patented his discovery. The present writer had the privilege of seeing Nernst in action along with 7 other Nobel Prize winners at a celebration in Berlin of the 80th birthday of Max Planck. Nernst died at Muskau, Germany, on November 18, 1941.

G. L. CLARK

NERNST EQUATION

Walter Nernst first introduced his noted equation in 1889 for the variation of the "potential difference metal | electrolyte," E, with the "solution pressure," P, of the metal and the "osmotic pressure," p, (by which he meant the concentration) of the n-valent metallic ions:

$$E = \frac{RT}{n} \ln \frac{P}{p}$$

where R is the gas constant (in volt-Faradays/degree) and T the absolute temperature. Since that time there have been considerable advances in precise definitions and theories pertinent to solutions; hence the Nernst equation will be discussed below in modern terms.

(Complete) Cell Electromotive Force

The electromotive force (emf) or E of a *reversible* cell depends upon the free energy change ΔF for the reaction which is assumed to take place in the cell, as expressed in Eq. (1)

$$\Delta F = -n\mathbf{F}E \tag{1}$$

where $\mathbf{F}$ is the Faraday constant and n represents the number of electrons (or moles of electricity) transferred in the cell reaction as written. If E is in volts, $\mathbf{F} = 96,494$ coulombs/equivalent if ΔF is in joules; while $\mathbf{F} = 23,062$ calories (volt-coulomb)$^{-1}$ equivalent^{-1} if ΔF is in calories. When all reactants and products are in their standard states (unit activity) Eq. (1) becomes

$$\Delta F^\circ = -n\mathbf{F}E^\circ \tag{1a}$$

The free energy, F, of any constituent is defined in terms of the standard F° and the activity, a, as $F \equiv F^\circ + RT \ln a$, where R is the gas constant in joules (or calories)/degree, depending on the units of F. The free energy change for the cell reaction is equal to the sum of the free energies for the products less the sum for the reactants, i.e.,

$$\Delta F = \Delta F^\circ + RT \ln \frac{\underset{i}{\Pi} \, a^{n_i} \,\, (products)}{\underset{i}{\Pi} \, a^{n_i} \,\, (reactants)} \tag{2}$$

which is the general expression relating free energy changes and activities of reactants and products for any chemical reaction. The exponents, n_i, are the numbers of moles of the various constituents involved in the reaction as written. For example, in the cell Pt, $H_{2(p)} \mid HCl_{(m)} \mid AgCl$, Ag the chemical reaction may be written as

$$\tfrac{1}{2}H_2 + AgCl \rightarrow HCl_{(m)} + Ag$$

and Eq. (2) becomes

$$\Delta F = \Delta F^\circ + RT \ln \frac{a_{HCl} \, a_{Ag}}{a_{H_2}^{1/2} \, a_{AgCl}} = \Delta F^\circ$$

$$+ RT \ln \frac{a_{HCl}}{f_{H_2}^{1/2}} = \Delta F^\circ + RT \ln \frac{m_{H^+}m_{Cl^-}\gamma_\pm^2}{f_{H_2}^{1/2}} \tag{2a}$$

since by convention the activities of pure solids are taken as unity and those of gases are equal to the fugacities, which in turn are approximately equal to the pressures in atmospheres at low pressures. (In the case of the hydrogen electrode an error of < 0.1 mv (or < 2 cal) results from using the pressure at 10 atmospheres at 25°C; a correspondingly smaller error would be made at lower pressures). In Eq. (2a) m_{H^+} and m_{Cl^-} are molalities of H^+ and Cl^- respectively and $\gamma_\pm$ is the mean ionic activity coefficient of HCl. (By convention the activity of an electrolyte is taken as the product of the molalities of each ion times the $\gamma_\pm$ raised to the power equal to the number of ions per molecule.)

When the substitution of Eqs. (1) and (1a) into Eq. (2) has been performed Eq. (3), the *Nernst equation*, is obtained.

$$E = E^\circ - \frac{RT}{n\mathbf{F}} \ln \frac{\underset{i}{\Pi} \, a^{n_i} \,\, (products)}{\underset{i}{\Pi} \, a^{n_i} \,\, (reactants)} \tag{3}$$

Thus, the Nernst equation relates the observed emf, E, of a reversible cell with the standard emf, E°, for the electrode system and the activities of the reactants and products of the cell reaction.

In the above example Eq. (3) becomes

$$E \cong E^\circ - \frac{RT}{n\mathbf{F}} \ln \frac{m_{H^+}m_{Cl^-}\gamma_\pm^2}{p_{H_2}^{1/2}} \tag{3a}$$

where the equation is exact if f_{H_2} is used instead of p_{H_2}.

Half-Cell Emf

While there is for the most part agreement on the sign convention regarding (complete) cell potentials, there are two systems in general use regarding half-cell potentials: the so-called "American" system involving *oxidation potentials* (or *reduction potentials*), E, and the "European" or Gibbs *electrode potentials*, V, (see entry on *Electromotive Force*).

In the "American" system Eqs. (1), (1a) and (3) also hold for half-cell reactions and values of E and E° whichever way the reactions may be written. In the "European" system, however, the *Gibbs electrode potential*, V, by definition is *sign invariant* upon a reversal of the (infinitesimal*) half-cell current, while the half-cell free energy, ΔF, is *sign bivariant*. Eqs. (1), (1a) and (3) will now be illustrated for an oxidation and a reduction process for the two systems.

* A thermodynamically meaningful emf (i.e., that of a *reversible* cell) must of necessity be made at conditions *very* close to potentiometric balance; hence the current must be *very* small.

For the oxidation

$$M^+ \rightarrow M^{++} + e^-,$$

$$E_{ox} = E_{ox}^{\circ} - \frac{RT}{n\mathbf{F}} \ln \frac{a_{M^{++}}}{a_{M^+}},$$

$$\Delta F_{ox} = -n\mathbf{F}E_{ox} = +n\mathbf{F}V$$

and

$$\Delta F_{ox}^{\circ} = -n\mathbf{F}E_{ox}^{\circ} = +n\mathbf{F}V^{\circ};$$

for the reduction

$$e^- + M^{++} \rightarrow M^+,$$

$$E_{red} = E_{red}^{\circ} - \frac{RT}{n\mathbf{F}} \ln \frac{a_{M^+}}{a_{M^{++}}},$$

$$\Delta F_{red} = -n\mathbf{F}E_{red} = -n\mathbf{F}V$$

and

$$\Delta F_{red}^{\circ} = -n\mathbf{F}E_{red}^{\circ} = -n\mathbf{F}V^{\circ}.$$

Here $V = -E_{ox} = E_{red}$ and $V^{\circ} = -E_{ox}^{\circ} = E_{red}^{\circ}$. Since V is sign invariant, for either the oxidation or reduction reaction

$$V = V^{\circ} + \frac{RT}{n\mathbf{F}} \ln \frac{a_{M^{++}}}{a_{M^+}}$$

References

1. KLOTZ, I. M., "Chemical Thermodynamics," p. 311, New York, Prentice Hall, Inc., 1950.
2. LICHT, TRUMAN S., AND deBETHUNE, ANDRE J., *J. Chem. Ed.*, **34**, 433 (1957).
3. NERNST, W., *Z. physik. Chem.*, **4**, 129 (1889); "Theoretische Chemie," 2nd German edition, pp. 665–8, Stuttgart, Enke, 1898.

M. H. LIETZKE AND
R. W. STOUGHTON

Cross-references: *Electromotive Force and Half-Cell Potentials; Electrode Potentials; Nomenclature, Remarks on.*

NERVE IMPULSE TRANSMISSION

Nerve fibers are extended processes of nerve cells. They function as the pathways along which physiological signals—nerve impulses—are exchanged between the central nervous system and the peripheral organs and tissues. The diameter of vertebrate nerve fibers (or axons) ranges roughly between 0.02 and 0.0002 mm. Giant axons approximately 1 mm in diameter are found in several species of squid. It is possible to surgically isolate a single axon and carry out various observations on it. Under experimental conditions, nerve impulses can be evoked by delivering a brief pulse of electric current between two points on the surface of an axon (see Fig. 1A) or, more directly, by passing current through the plasma membrane which constitutes the outer layer of the axon. The detection of a nerve impulse is usually done by electrical means, either by observing the flow of "action current" through the fluid medium outside the axon or by recording a variation in potential difference across the plasma membrane, namely the "action potential."

There is a time delay between stimulation of an axon and the appearance of an action potential at some distance from the point of stimulus. The velocity of propagation of a nerve impulse can be measured from such delays and depends on the chemical environment of the axon and the temperature. The largest axons in mammalian peripheral nerve carry impulses at about 100 m/sec, while lower velocities appear in smaller axons.

The nerve impulses have the following properties: (1) A nerve impulse is evoked by brief pulses of electric current in an all-or-none manner, that is to say, all pulses stronger than a certain critical value elicit action potentials of approximately the same amplitude and configuration. (2) In a normal environment, an impulse traveling along one axon does not spread to neighboring axons. (3) Following initiation of a nerve impulse, the axon goes into a "refractory period" during which a new impulse cannot be evoked or only a small, slowly propagating impulse can be elicited. (4) A nerve impulse can propagate in either direction along an axon. (5) When two impulses are evoked almost simultaneously, one at each end of an axon, they collide at a point between the two sites of stimulation. (6) Following collision the two impulses vanish due to the "refractoriness" of the axon.

The properties of a nerve impulse as stated above can be imitated by the nerve model of Ostwald and Lillie, which consists of pure iron wire immersed in concentrated nitric acid. The surface of the iron is covered by an oxide layer under these conditions and, by delivering a pulse of electric current, this layer can be reversibly removed. The process of removal and regeneration of the oxide layer spreads along the "passive" iron wire, as a nerve impulse propagates along an axon. The analogy between the nerve fiber and its iron wire model is strengthened further by the fact that in both systems the flow of electric currents between the active and passive regions play an essential role in the process of propagation. Current flow between the two regions tends to destroy the oxide layer, and if the current is strong enough, the process of activation spreads all along the surface of the wire. If the current flow is hindered by surrounding the iron wire with a narrow glass tube, the spreading of the process is either completely suppressed or the velocity of propagation is greatly reduced. Similar phenomena are known to occur in living axons of vertebrates and invertebrates.

When a nerve impulse arrives at an electrode in an axon, there is a rapid rise in the potential of the interior electrode as referred to one immersed in the surrounding fluid medium (see Fig. 1A). The amplitude of such an action potential is of the order of 0.1 volts in most of the axons studied. Since the potential in the unexcited portion of the axon is at the resting level, there is a potential difference of approximately 0.1 volts between the active and resting

zones. The resistivity of the protoplasm in the axon is roughly 30 to 120 ohm-cm. Therefore, there is a current flowing from the active region toward the resting region inside the axon. The circuit for this flow of current is closed by penetration of the current through the membrane and by flow in the outside medium in the reverse direction. In normal, functioning axons the flow of this "local current" is known to be much stronger than the critical strength of the current necessary to initiate an impulse in the resting membrane. If the electric resistance of the fluid medium surrounding an axon is raised well above the resistance of the axon interior by various means, propagation of an impulse along the fiber can be slowed down, or sometimes, completely blocked.

In large axons in vertebrate nervous systems, the mechanism of propagation of nerve impulses is complicated by the existence of the "myelin sheath," which covers the axon except at the "nodes of Ranvier." The myelin sheath has a lamellar structure and is made of layers of lipid material. At the nodes of Ranvier, which occur

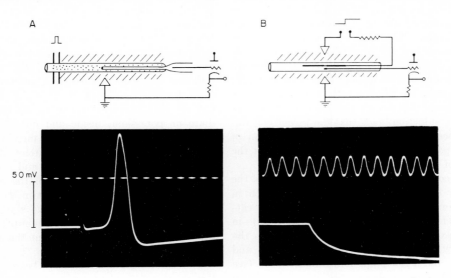

Fɪɢ. 1. A. Diagram showing the method of recording action potentials from the interior of a squid giant axon (not to scale) with a long intracellular glass pipette electrode and oscillograph record obtained by this method. The break in the continuous oscillograph trace indicates the moment at which a brief pulse of electric current is delivered to the axon near the left end of the axon in the diagram. The straight line interrupted at 2000 cycles per sec indicates the potential level before insertion of the electrode into the axon. B. Direct measurement of the membrane resistance and capacity in a squid giant axon. A constant current is delivered between a long metal electrode (indicated by the thick portion of the line in the axon) and a large electrode in the surrounding medium (sea water). The change in the membrane potential is recorded with a short intracellular electrode. From the exponential time course of the oscillograph record, the resistance and the capacity are determined. Time marker 1 kc. (From "Handbook of Physiology," Vol. 1, p. 87.)

TABLE 1. CONCENTRATION OF ANIONS AND
CATIONS IN SQUID NERVE AXOPLASM IN
MICROEQUIVALENTS PER GM AXOPLASM
From Koechlin, B. A., *J. Biophys. Biochem. Cytol.*,
1, 521 (1955).

chloride	140 ± 20	potassium	344 ± 20
phosphates	24 ± 4	sodium	65 ± 10
aspartic acid	65 ± 3	calcium	7 ± 5
glutamic acid	10 ± 3	magnesium	20 ± 10
fumaric acid⎫ succinic acid⎬	15 ± 5	organic base (by differ- ence)	84 ± 20
sulfonate 'x'	35 ± 10		
isethionic acid	220 ± 20		
total anions	509 ± 20	total base (cations)	520 ± 20

at nearly regular intervals of about 2 mm in large axons, the membrane is devoid of myelin for a distance of approximately 0.001 mm. When the intensity of electric current necessary to initiate a nerve impulse is measured with a glass capillary electrode (10 to 50 microns in tip diameter), a sharp maximum in sensitivity is found at each node of Ranvier, indicating that the myelin sheath has high resistance to penetrating electric current. Anesthetics and other agents reduce the action current of an axon only when they are applied to the nodes. The surface density of the current that flows through the myelin sheath during propagation is far smaller than the density in the naked membrane at the node. The widely accepted theory of saltatory conduction holds that the physico-chemical processes responsible for the production of action potentials are localized exclusively at the nodes of Ranvier.

The colloidal substance which constitutes the interior of an axon, or "axoplasm," is rich in potassium and poor in sodium and divalent cations. The tissue fluid (blood or lymph) in which axons are normally immersed has, on the contrary, a high concentration of sodium and calcium and a low potassium concentration (see Table 1). Using radioisotopes, it can be shown that the plasma membrane is permeable to these inorganic cations. The ability of the nerve fiber to accumulate potassium has been attributed by many biologists to a special "ion pump." A living nerve fiber is obviously an open system in which a variety of metabolic reactions constantly proceed. Probably the fluxes of these cations and metabolites through the plasma membrane are coupled with each other in the sense postulated in the thermodynamics of ir-

reversible processes. The ion selectivity of the polyelectrolytes in the axoplasm is also considered as a possible cause of potassium accumulation in the cell.

It is difficult to examine the chemical composition and the physical state of the plasma membrane because it is only of the order of 100 Å in thickness. Its properties are examined indirectly by measuring radiotracer fluxes and changes in the potential difference between the electrodes across the membrane. Electrometric measurements indicate that the plasma membrane behaves like a dielectric condenser with a parallel resistance (see Fig. 1B). The apparent capacity is estimated to be between 1 and 10 μF/sq cm and the parallel resistance 10 to 10,000 ohms-cm^2. Radiotracer measurements indicate that the membrane behaves like a thin layer of cation-exchanger.

The mechanism of action potential production is still a matter of controversy. In the sodium theory (Hodgkin and Huxley) the following assumptions are made: (1) The phases inside and outside the membrane can be regarded as dilute salt solutions (with activity coefficients close to unity). (2) Within the membrane sodium and potassium ions are carried independently of each other. (3) Ion fluxes are proportional to the deviation of the potential difference from the "equilibrium potentials" defined by $E_i = (RT/\mathbf{F})\ln(C_i'/C_i'')$. C_i' and C_i'' are the concentrations of ion species i, sodium or potassium, inside and outside of the membrane, respectively. (4) The membrane can be described by the equivalent circuit of Fig. 2, where sodium conductance, g_{Na}, and potassium conductance, g_K, are functions of the potential difference. It was postulated that in the resting state $g_K \gg g_{Na}$ and in the active state $g_{Na} \gg g_K$. On the basis of these assumptions the process of nerve excitation was mathematically treated.

The following objections have been raised to this theory: (1) There are many excitable tissues which require no sodium in the medium to maintain excitability (Nitella, crustacean muscle fiber, vertebrate spinal ganglion cells, etc.); (2) radiotracer measurements do not support the view that the resting membrane is permeable only to potassium; (3) the mathematical solutions of Nernst-Planck equations for electrodiffusion do not justify the use of the equivalent circuit postulated. Several alternative views have been proposed, stressing the importance of

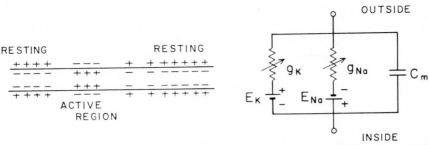

FIG. 2. The electric equivalent circuit of the squid axon membrane proposed by Hodgkin and Huxley.

the divalent ions for nerve excitation. It has been proposed that the membrane is "stable" in the state rich in calcium and also in the state rich in sodium and potassium but is unstable in the intermediate state. In this hypothesis the process of action potential production is regarded as a kind of flip-flop phenomenon.

At present, the electrical behavior of the axon is well known and some insight has been gained into the underlying mechanisms of neural transmission. There is also extensive knowledge concerning electrophysiological processes responsible for the spread of a nerve impulse from one cell to another across the specialized structures called "synapses."

References

1. FIELD, J., MAGOUN, H. W., AND HALL, V. E., Editors, "Handbook of Physiology," (prepared by the American Physiological Society), Vol. 1, Section 1, "Neurophysiology," Baltimore, William S. Wilkins, 1959.
2. HODGKIN, A. L., "Ionic Movements and Electrical Activity in Giant Nerve Fibres," (Croonian Lecture), *Proc. Roy. Soc. (London)*, **B148**, 1–37 (1957).

ICHIJI TASAKI

Cross-references: *Bioelectrogenesis, Biological Transducers, Electric Organs, Electrophysiology, Ion Transport Across Charged Membranes, Membrane Equilibrium, Membrane Potentials, Microelectrodes.*

NICKEL CONCENTRATES, ELECTRIC SMELTING. See COPPER AND NICKEL CONCENTRATES, ELECTRIC SMELTING.

NICKEL ELECTRODES FOR FUEL CELLS AND BATTERIES

Nickel exhibits a very low rate of corrosion and extremely small solubility of its corrosion product in common alkaline electrolytes, even under conditions of copious galvanic evolution of oxygen. This electrochemical behavior, together with favorable mechanical properties, good electrical conductivity, useful catalytic activity, and ready availability in suitable form and at low cost, has resulted in widespread use of nickel electrodes in alkaline storage batteries and fuel cells.

To meet requirements for high electrical conductivity and physical stability, a conductive metallic structure which is resistant to corrosion by the electrolyte is commonly used to support or contain the active material in the electrodes of storage batteries (q.v.). One of the most recently developed structures for this purpose is the "sintered" nickel plate which is extensively used in alkaline storage batteries. Although a variety of nickel powders and fibers can be used to produce such plates, they are customarily made from a special grade of nickel powder which is obtained by pyrolysis of nickel carbonyl under controlled conditions to yield largely fibrous polycrystalline particles a few microns in diameter and with a free-packing density of about one half gram to one gram per cubic centimeter. This powder is spread into thin sheet or strip form and is then heated in a nonoxidizing atmosphere to sinter it into a cohesive metallic "plaque" with good electrical conductivity but with about eighty per cent of its volume made up of interconnecting pores. Typically, the sintered nickel plaque is about a half millimeter to one millimeter thick and incorporates a layer of mesh or perforated strip to provide mechanical reinforcement and enhanced electrical conductivity. Mechanical reinforcement is especially important in stock to be used for construction of cells with coiled electrodes.

Sintered nickel plaques are converted into battery electrodes or "plates" by impregnation to partially fill the pores with electrochemically active material: nickel hydroxide for positive plates, and cadmium metal or hydroxide for negative plates in nickel-cadmium storage batteries. The resulting plates are structurally and chemically durable and, because of their low electrical resistance and the thinness and large surface area of contained active material which they expose to the electrolyte, are capable of rapid charge and discharge in either deep or shallow cycle service. In addition to containing and conducting current to and from the contained active material, nickel in the negative electrode promotes recombination of oxygen with metallic cadmium, and thus mitigates pressure rise during overcharge of sealed alkaline storage batteries which employ cadmium in the negative plate.

Unlike common primary and secondary cells which derive their energy from reaction of the electrolyte with the surface layer of the electrodes or of materials stored within them, fuel cells (q.v.) receive their reactants continuously from an external source, and the desired electrochemical reactions generally occur at or near to a three-phase interface between reactant, electrode, and electrolyte. Porous electrodes permit extending this three-phase interface, and provide an attractive means for continuously supplying reactants to it and, if desired, for removing reaction products from it.

A very large number of small pores serves to maximize the length of three-phase boundary, while maximum porosity and minimum electrode thickness compatible with adequate conductivity are sought to facilitate supplying reactant to the reaction zone, especially where reaction products must diffuse out of the electrode counter-current to reactant flow or where the reactant contains inert diluent, as in cells which employ air as the oxidant. Consequently, although such simple structures as nickel wire cloth or perforated strip have been successfully used in fuel cells employing solid or immobilized liquid electrolytes, porous nickel electrodes very similar to the plaques of sintered-plate nickel-cadmium batteries are widely preferred. For elevated-temperature operation with some fuels and electrolytes, such porous nickel electrodes provide satisfactory performance without additional catalysts. However, catalysts, such as Raney nickel or formulations based on metals of the platinum group, are commonly applied to the electrodes or electrolyte of such fuel cells for operation at lower temperatures and pressures or with less reactive fuels. Where special catalysts are used in fuel cells, some authorities reserve the term "electrode" for the catalyst formulation, and call the associated nickel member an "electrode support."

In fuel cells which employ mobile alkaline electrolytes, more complex porous nickel electrodes are widely used to supply reactants to the reaction zone, prevent their escape into the electrolyte, and control the location of the interface between reactant, electrode, and electrolyte. Such electrodes are commonly produced by sintering powders so as to obtain a thin layer with uniformly fine pores bonded to a thicker layer of material with substantially coarser pores, and often include nickel mesh or perforated nickel strip for mechanical reinforcement and improved electrical conductivity. The pores of the thin layer are made small enough so that capillary effects will ensure that they will remain flooded by the electrolyte when reactant is supplied at high enough pressure to expel at least most of the electrolyte from the thicker porous substrate, thus fixing the three-phase boundary near the junction of the two layers of the electrode. Because the pressure which the fine-pore layer can sustain without escape of reactants into the electrolyte is dependent on the dimensions of its largest single opening, and because fine pores in the substrate will remain flooded with electrolyte and thus be ineffective for supplying reactant or removing reaction product, careful control of pore size distribution is necessary in both layers of such "dual-porosity" electrodes.

The dual-porosity structure is usually produced by using powders of different sizes for the fine-pore and coarse-pore layers or, if use of powder of a single particle size is desired, either by increased compaction of the powder for the fine-pore layer or by addition of volatile expanding agents to the nickel powder for the coarse-pore layer prior to sintering. Such electrodes, made from commercial nickel powders without added special catalysts, have performed effectively with alkaline electrolytes in cells operated at intermediate temperatures and pressure with active fuels and oxidants such as hydrogen and oxygen, and at higher temperatures with less reactive fuels. However, for lower temperature operation, special catalysts are commonly used.

In one electrode which has been described for

low-temperature hydrogen-oxygen cells, the fine-pore layer is made from a mixture of elemental nickel and nickel-aluminum alloy powders so as to provide greatly increased catalytic activity when treated with caustic after sintering. A number of experimenters have also reported work with electrodes in which a catalytically active formulation of metals of the platinum group has been used to produce a fine-pore layer on a nickel substrate with relatively coarse pores. Others have reported work with dual-porosity sintered nickel electrodes in which precious metal catalysts have been deposited on the internal surfaces of the fine-pore structures.

In addition to their use in batteries and fuel cells, sintered porous nickel electrodes have also been reported effective in reducing hydrogen and oxygen overpotentials in a variety of electrolysis operations.

References

1. FLEISCHER, A., "Sintered Plates for Nickel-Cadmium Batteries," *J. Electrochem. Soc.*, **94**, 289–299 (1948).
2. COATES, A., "Development of Sintered-Plate Alkaline Batteries," *Proc. International Symposium on Batteries*, 1958.
3. COOK, C. F., *et al*, "Morphological Characteristics of Nickel Powders for Use in Sintered Plate Nickel Cadmium Batteries," *J. Electrochem. Soc.*, **105**, 154C (1958).
4. HEROLD, R., "Battery Problems Considered from the Point of View of Sintered Plate Nickel-Cadmium Cells Technique," *Proc. Second International Symposium on Batteries*, Paper No. 4, 1960.
5. BACON, F. J., "The High-Pressure Hydrogen/Oxygen Fuel Cells," *Ind. Eng. Chem.*, **52**, 301–303 (1960).
6. DOUGLAS, D. L., "Molten Carbonate Cells with Gas-Diffusion Electrodes," *Ind. Eng. Chem.*, **52**, 308–309 (1960).
7. JUSTI, E. W., *et al*, "The DSK System of Fuel Cell Electrodes," *J. Electrochem. Soc.*, **108**, 1073–1079 (1961).

A. P. EDSON

NICKEL ELECTROPLATING

Nearly all articles plated with decorative chromium are plated first with bright nickel to provide a smooth, mirrorlike base for the chromium. Nickel is also plated for resisting wear and abrasion, protecting substrates from oxidation at high temperatures, fabricating phonograph record stampers and other electroformed articles, cladding steel pipe for protecting it from

TABLE 1. THE MODIFIED WATTS NICKEL PLATING BATH

Constituent or Condition	Customary Range
Nickel sulfate, $NiSO_4 \cdot 7H_2O$, gpl	300 to 450
Nickel chloride, $NiCl_2 \cdot 6H_2O$, gpl	45 to 60
Boric acid, gpl	35 to 40
Wetting agent, gpl	0.5 to 1.0
pH	3.2 to 4.5
Temperature, °F	125 to 145
Cathode current density, amp/sq ft	50 to 80
Anode current density, amp/sq ft	20 to 40

corrosion, and for other nondecorative purposes. The amount of nickel consumed by plating exceeds the amount of any other metal.

The Watts Nickel Plating Bath

The most popular nickel plating solution is the modified Watts bath, which is prepared with nickel sulfate, nickel chloride, and boric acid. The concentrations of these constituents and conditions for operating the bath are given in Table 1. For nondecorative (engineering) purposes, ductile, porefree, and smooth nickel can be deposited from this solution without the need for addition agents. Proprietary brightening agents are consumed in appreciable quantities for plating bright nickel that requires no mechanical buffing.

A wetting agent, such as sodium lauryl sulfate, is required to prevent pitting in nickel electroplate. Its concentration is controlled by adjusting the surface tension of the solution to a value of not more than 40 dyne/cm. For reproducing high quality nickel deposits, the surface tension and the pH of the nickel bath must be controlled carefully. Inclusions and/or rough deposits will result if the pH is allowed to exceed about 5.0. A very low pH below about 2.3 causes a significant reduction in the cathode efficiency, which normally is between 92 and 95 per cent. The reduction of hydrogen ions at cathode surfaces causes a slow, gradual increase in the pH of the solution. Thus, small, regular additions of sulfuric acid are needed to maintain the pH within the recommended range of 3.2 to 4.5. Boric acid in the solution acts as a buffer and prevents large changes in the pH.

Nickel ions consumed by plating are replaced in the solution by dissolution of nickel anodes (normally with an efficiency of 100 per cent). To insure good anode dissolution, the chloride ion concentration of the solution should be no less than 10 gpl. Nickel anodes will polarize and cease to dissolve if the chloride ion concentration falls below this value. Very high chloride ion concentrations greater than about 25 gpl will, in a synergistic fashion with metallic impurities like iron or zinc, tend to cause high stress and cracking in the nickel electroplate.

A nickel sulfate ($NiSO_4 \cdot 7H_2O$) concentration of at least 300 gpl and preferably 400 or 450 gpl should be maintained to provide good conductivity and the large reservoir of nickel ions desired for plating at high current densities. Nickel sulfate, nickel chloride, and boric acid are consumed by dragout. Small additions are required at regular intervals to maintain their concentrations.

For depositing semibright nickel with leveling characteristics resulting in surfaces smoother than that of the substrate, coumarin, a coumarin derivative or another proprietary addition agent is added to the Watts bath. Mirrorlike nickel is obtained by adding two or three proprietary, patented brightening agents. In practice, no single brightener provides a broad bright plating range on complex shapes, but combinations of selected brightening agents will result in mirrorlike nickel on all areas of very complex shapes. These brighteners are organic compounds, such as saccharin, paratoluene sulfonamide, or sulfonated naphthalene combined with reduced fuchsin, allylquinolinium bromide, or sulfonated aryl aldehydes.

Hard, wear-resistant nickel sometimes is deposited in a bath containing nickel sulfate, ammonium chloride, and boric acid. Modern practice for plating hard nickel favors the modified Watts bath with an addition of coumarin or an addition of cobalt sulfate to deposit an alloy of nickel and cobalt.

The temperature of the Watts solution should be kept between 125 and 145°F, to permit the rapid plating rates obtained with cathode current densities of 50 to 80 amp/sq ft. With a lower temperature, such as 100°F, the cathode current density is limited to about 15 amp/sq ft, which deposits nickel too slowly for most purposes. A temperature above about 150°F is impractical because present-day wetting agents are ineffective in preventing pitting at such a high temperature.

Very high current densities above 80 amp/sq ft are practical if the nickel chloride concentration is increased to about 200 gpl and/or if very high agitation is supplied at cathode and anode surfaces. Solution circulation through a pump, filter, and external heat exchanger is very common for supplying agitation and heat, while removing particles that would otherwise cause rough nickel deposits.

The Nickel Sulfamate Bath

The nickel sulfamate solution has recently become popular for electroforming and for cladding substrates to protect them from high-temperature oxidation, because nickel deposited from the sulfamate solution exhibits better dimensional stability than Watts-type nickel. The low stress (less than 1000 psi) in the nickel deposited in the sulfamate bath precludes dimensional changes when the electrodeposit is separated from the mandrel employed for electroforming applications. By comparison, Watts-type nickel usually is stressed to 15,000 psi or more. Bright nickel plate sometimes is even more highly stressed (50,000 psi). Because there is less tendency for inclusions of hydrated salts, the nickel deposited in the sulfamate solution exhibits better thermal stability than Watts-type nickel.

The formulation of the nickel sulfamate solution is given in Table 2. It normally contains no chloride ions, so as to keep stress in the plate at a minimum. Because the nickel anode current density is limited to about 10 amp/sq ft in the absence of chloride ions, a small concentration of 0.5 to 1.0 gpl sometimes is added to prevent anode polarization at current densities above 10 amp/sq ft.

If anodes begin to polarize, sulfamate ions decompose, which causes considerable changes in the properties of the nickel deposit. A decrease in the pH of the plating bath during operation is indicative of anode polarization. In this case, more anodes should be added to decrease the anode current density, the temperature should

TABLE 2. THE NICKEL SULFAMATE
PLATING BATH

Constituent or Condition	Customary Range
Nickel sulfamate, gpl	400 to 450
Boric acid, gpl	30 to 35
Specific gravity	1.26
Wetting agent, gpl	0.5 to 1.0
pH	3.3 to 3.9
Temperature, °F	120 to 145
Cathode current density, amp/sq ft	15 to 40
Anode current density, amp/sq ft	5 to 10

be increased, or the agitation at anode surfaces should be increased to prevent further polarization.

The throwing power of the nickel sulfamate solution is similar to that of the Watts bath, when the cathode current density is greater than about 10 amp/sq ft. In each case, considerably more nickel is deposited on edges and other protuberances, by comparison with the metal deposited in recessed areas. Neither of the nickel baths is as good as the copper, zinc, or cadmium cyanide solutions with respect to throwing power (q.v.). When the cathode current density in the nickel sulfamate bath is kept below 10 amp/sq ft, however, throwing power is much improved, and approaches that of the cyanide solutions for copper, zinc, and cadmium.

With either the Watts or sulfamate solutions, nickel is deposited adherently on steel, copper, or brass cleaned by conventional procedures. Zinc alloy die castings should be plated first with copper, to protect them from chemical dissolution while they are being nickel plated. Stainless steel, chromium electroplate, and other metals that avidly form oxide films must be plated in a specially formulated strike solution before they are plated with Watts-type nickel or with nickel in the sulfamate solution. The strike baths contain a large concentration of acid, such as 100 gpl of sulfuric or hydrochloric acid (and about 300 gpl of nickel sulfate or nickel chloride). With this acid concentration, large quantities of hydrogen are released at the cathode surfaces and the oxide films on the substrate surfaces are reduced. After the oxide films are removed, nickel is deposited at a rate sufficient to cover the substrate with 0.000030 to 0.0001 inch of nickel in 3 to 5 minutes. The strike solutions are maintained at a temperature of 80 to 95°F. The cathode current density usually is about 100 to 150 amp/sq ft.

Anodes

The anodes in all nickel plating baths usually are bagged to prevent undissolved particles from reaching cathode surfaces and causing rough deposits. Exceptions are possible with only thin nickel deposits (less than 0.0002 inch) are being plated or when carbon-type anodes containing 0.2 per cent carbon and 0.2 per cent silicon are proved satisfactory without bags for a specific installation. The gelatinous film formed on the carbon-type anodes tends to retain undissolved particles. Best results usually are obtained when such anodes are rolled, after they are cast. Electrolytic nickel or rolled depolarized nickel create considerable quantities of undissolved particles, which must be retained in anode bags to prevent them from reaching cathode surfaces.

Trace amounts of iron and other impurities that are anodically dissolved with the nickel anodes increase stress in the plate, tend to cause pitting, and cause a reduction in the brightness of bright nickel deposited in recessed areas on complex shapes. To keep the concentration of iron and other soluble impurities such as zinc to a low, harmless level, continuous electrolytic purification is customary for large nickel plating installations. Solution pumped from the plating tank is filtered, heated, and pumped to the purification tank filled with dummy cathodes. A special current source at low voltage deposits impurities on the dummy cathodes, usually corrugated. With a cathode current density of about 3 amp/sq ft, the impurities are concentrated in the deposit, because iron, zinc, and other metals exhibit a lower deposition potential than does nickel. If steel or zinc alloy parts become detached from the plating racks while they are immersed in the nickel plating tank, any steel or zinc that is subsequently dissolved is removed by this electrolytic purification.

Auxiliary nickel anodes shaped from rolled nickel containing 0.2 per cent carbon and silicon sometimes are positioned to increase the current in recesses and other areas normally receiving less than their share of the current. Thickness uniformity is improved considerably with such anodes and much time can be saved for depositing a specified, minimum thickness. A further improvement is obtained by placing nonconducting shields over or around edges, to shield the high-current-density areas.

Properties of Nickel Electroplate

The conditions for electroplating nickel have considerable influence on its properties and characteristics. Table 3 lists properties characteristic of nickel deposited in the Watts, bright nickel and nickel sulfamate solutions as they are normally operated with good control of bath constituents and freedom from impurities. Metallic impurities that are codeposited with nickel tend to increase stress and reduce ductility. Some impurities like copper reduce the brightness of decorative nickel plate in recessed areas of complex-shaped parts. Brightener decomposition

TABLE 3. PROPERTIES OF ELECTRODEPOSITED NICKEL

Property	Watts Bath[a]	Bright Nickel Baths	Nickel Sulfamate Baths
Hardness, Vickers or Vickers equivalent	140 to 220	450 to 550	160 to 240
Tensile strength, psi	56,000 to 90,000	180,000 to 220,000	65,000 to 100,000
Elongation, per cent in 2 inches	16 to 30	2 to 5	8 to 16
Stress, psi	14,000 to 24,000[b]	−5,000 to 50,000[c]	<1,000
Youngs modulus of elasticity	24×10^6	—	—
Density, g/cc	8.9	8.7 to 8.9[c]	8.93
Density after heating to 1950°F	8.2	—[d]	8.89
Coefficient of thermal expansion, microinch/inch/°F	9.6	—	9.5
Electrical resistivity at 20°C, μohm-cm	7.8	—	—

[a] With an addition of coumarin, hardness ranges from 300 to 350 and tensile strength from 150,000, to 180,000.
[b] Dependent on impurities, especially iron.
[c] Dependent on selection of brighteners.
[d] Bright nickel plate is hot short as a result of sulfide migration to grain boundaries.

products sometimes interfere with the deposition of mirrorlike plate and/or reduce the ductility of the nickel. To keep impurity levels below harmful concentrations, Watts, bright and sulfamate nickel plating solutions are treated at regular intervals. The treatment includes the addition of nickel carbonate and/or calcium hydroxide to increase the pH to at least 5.2, which precipitates iron and other metallic impurities, and the addition of activated carbon for absorbing organic impurities. After the solution is filtered back into the plating tank, its pH is adjusted to between 3.2 and 4.5 and wetting agent and brighteners removed by the carbon are replaced. The frequency of such a treatment depends upon the rate at which impurities are introduced and the effectiveness of continuous electrolytic purification during normal operation.

Metallographic examination of Watts-type nickel and nickel deposited in the sulfamate solution reveals a columnar structure characteristic of all ductile electrodeposits. Addition agents introduced for brightening or hardening purposes invariably refine the grain size appreciably. A banded structure with grains too small for resolution by optical microscopy is characteristic of full-bright nickel plate.

References

1. LOWENHEIM, F. A., Editor, chapter on "Nickel," in "Modern Electroplating," Second Edition, sponsored by The Electrochemical Society, New York, John Wiley and Sons, Inc., 1963.
2. GRAHAM, A. K., Editor, "Electroplating Engineering Handbook," 774 pages, Second Edition, New York, Reinhold Publishing Corp., 1962.

W. H. SAFRANEK

NICKEL ELECTROREFINING

History

Electrorefining of nickel commenced in 1900 to replace existing pyrometallurgical and hydrometallurgical processes which did not recover precious metals or yield nickel of the 99.5 per cent purity produced by the electrolytic process. Commercial electrolytic production on a large scale dates from 1910. Electrolytic nickel refineries are operated in Canada by The International Nickel Company of Canada, Limited, at Port Colborne, Ontario, and Thompson, Manitoba, and in Norway by Falconbridge Nikkelverk A/S, a subsidiary of Falconbridge Nickel Mines Limited, Canada. Nickel is refined electrolytically also in Russia, Japan, Germany, and other countries.

Principle

Nickel electrorefining involves the cathodic deposition of pure nickel from crude anodes. Since the impurities also dissolve and would codeposit, it is necessary to use a divided cell wherein a porous diaphragm separates purified catholyte from impure anolyte. The impure anolyte is treated in a separate system for removal of the impurities prior to its return to the cell as catholyte.

Description

Description of the process, which follows, separates an electrolytic nickel refinery into its essential parts.

Electrical System. Electrical energy is obtained by converting alternating current to direct current by the use of rotary converters, and mercury arc or silicon rectifiers of suitable capacity for the plating cell circuitry. The room or substation housing the electrical equipment including transformers, converters, and switchboards is located at one end of the electrolytic refinery building where the bus bar system can conveniently serve the electrolytic units.

Hydroelectric energy is transformed to suitable lower voltages. Rectifying equipment produces direct current in the range of 5,500 to 10,000 amperes at 250 to 600 volts. The energy travels through copper bus bars to electrorefining cells, which are in series arrangement. Cell voltage may vary between 1.5 and 5.0 volts depending on the type and state of anode in the cell, the electrode spacing and current density, as well as on composition and temperature of electrolyte. Current from the main bus bars is distributed at each cell to the anodes and cathodes connected in electrical parallel and placed alternately in the tank. The total current is distributed to the anodes through a common bus bar of suitable cross section and shape for good electrical contact, supported on one side-wall of the tank. Cathode contact is achieved by supporting cathode suspension bars on the bus bar on the opposite sidewall. Tanks are constructed in pairs with the center bus bar acting as distributor bar for the cathodes in one tank and the anodes in the other. Ends of the electrode suspension bars opposite to the contact point rest on a capping strip of wood or other insulating material.

Cell Room. There is a walkway between each pair of cells to facilitate servicing individual electrodes. This differs from the electrolytic refining of other metals where cells are joined in a continuous line. The tanks are constructed of reinforced concrete with 6-inch thick walls lined with resistant material, such as mastic or synthetic resins. One or two rows of tanks are serviced by a bridge crane having a suitable platform from which the anodes and cathodes are handled by an auxiliary electric hoist supported on the crane. There is a work floor at one end of the cell room upon which the bridge cranes release the platforms, making them accessible to service cranes. These cranes hoist the anodes in steel racks through hatchways in the work floor, and place them on the platforms. Anode scrap and cathodes, also in racks, are removed from the platforms by the service crane and lowered through the hatchways to the narrow-gauge flat cars on tracks in the ground floor.

The number and spacing of anodes in each cell differs from one refinery to another, a typical one having 31 anodes at 6¾-inch spacing. The number of cathodes is one less than the number of anodes. Anodes used in nickel electrorefining are cast from metal produced by the reduction-smelting of crude nickel oxide, or from crude nickel sulfide.

In International Nickel Company of Canada practice at Port Colborne, Ontario, crude metal anodes containing 95 per cent nickel, 2.5 per cent copper, 0.8 per cent cobalt, 0.75 per cent iron, 0.6 per cent sulfur and 0.35 per cent of other impurities are produced by the reduction of nickel oxide in electric or oil-fired furnaces. The source of the nickel oxide is nickel sulfide separated from ore, and containing 75 per cent total of nickel, copper, iron, and cobalt, and 25 per cent sulfur, processed in fluid-bed roasters to give oxide containing about 0.5 per cent sulfur. At the refinery, the oxide and crushed petroleum coke used as the reductant are batch-weighed in the proper proportion for reduction, thoroughly mixed in a batch mixer before transporting to the furnace charging hoppers above the anode furnaces. The oil-fired furnaces are of the open-hearth, reverberatory type, 18 feet wide and 43 feet long inside. Firebrick construction consists of a low-alumina inverted arch bottom, high-alumina sidewalls to the slag line, and an intermediate-alumina brick to the skewbacks. The roof is a bonded silica brick sprung arch.

Ancillary equipment for each furnace includes a waste-heat horizontal water-tube boiler, a counterflow plate-type air preheater, and a cyclone dust collector. Effluent gases from the furnaces receive a final cleaning in an electrostatic precipitator before going to atmosphere. After the complete furnace charge of nickel oxide-coke mixture and anode scrap returned from the electrolytic refinery has been reduced and melted, the slag is skimmed, and the metal is treated to remove residual carbon. When the bath is the proper temperature of approximately 2,800°F, the melt—200 tons of anode metal—is cast into water-cooled copper anode molds arranged on a casting wheel. The anodes are removed from the casting wheel, placed in steel racks and transported to the electrolytic refinery.

Metal nickel anodes in the cells dissolve by the reaction $Ni - 2e \rightarrow Ni_{aq}^{2+}$; cathodic deposition is by the reverse reaction $Ni_{aq}^{2+} + 2e \rightarrow Ni$. The major reaction is accompanied by dissolution of other metals present in the anode below or near nickel in the electrochemical series.

The use of *sulfide anodes* in electrorefining is a unique development which eliminates the high-temperature pyrometallurgy required for the oxidation of the matte and the reduction-melting process to obtain metal anodes for electrorefining. This process is used in the refinery of the International Nickel Company of Canada at Thompson, Manitoba, which commenced operation in 1961.

As a feature of this process, converter matte is cast directly into matte anodes at about 1700°F. The anodes are cooled at a controlled rate to avoid stress and consequent breakage as a result of a phase transformation occurring at about 950°F.

Inco matte anodes contain 72 per cent nickel, 23 per cent sulfur, 3 per cent copper and 1 per cent iron in addition to other minor impurities. The mechanism of anode corrosion, whereby nickel and other metals are dissolved in the ionic state, differs between metal anodes and sulfide anodes. With sulfide anodes, instead of oxidation of elemental nickel and other metals, the anodic reaction involves oxidation of sulfide sulfur to the elemental state, with release of the metal ions to the solution. This reaction, $Ni_3S_2 - 6e \rightarrow 3Ni^{2+} + 2S$, requires an increase in anode potential from 0.2 volts for metal anodes to about 1.2 volts for sulfide anodes. Collection of the voluminous sludge containing almost 95 per cent elemental sulfur formed during sulfide anode corrosion is facilitated by bagging each sulfide anode in open-weave, acid-resistant bags, with allowance made for increase in sludge volume. Metal anodes do not require bagging, due to the much smaller volume of sludge, of which a portion drops to the tank bottom during corrosion. Anodes, after corroding for approximately 25 days, are removed from the cell, and washed free of anode slime. The uncorroded scrap is reverted to the anode furnace for remelting. The sludge or anode slime of base metal sulfides and precious metals of the platinum group and other noble metals is treated subsequently for recovery of these metals.

Starting sheets for cathodes are produced by plating a thin deposit of nickel on 1/8-inch thick stainless steel blanks. The thin nickel sheets approximately 1/32-inch in thickness are stripped from the blanks and become the cell cathodes. To provide electrical contact, straps or loops of the same material are attached to the sheets, and slipped over copper tubes for suspension in the tank. Typical cathode dimensions are 28 inches wide by 38 inches long with a final thickness of one-half inch. Growth of nickel to this thickness requires ten days at a current density of approximately 16 amperes per square foot of cathode area. Fully grown cathodes weighing about 140 pounds are removed from the cells and sheared into suitable sizes for specific applications. The larger sizes are usually shipped loose or bundled and the smaller sizes packed in drums, cartons or palletized bundles for convenient handling.

During corrosion of the impure nickel anodes, copper, iron and other impurities are also dissolved. To prevent these impurities from codepositing on the cathodes, the latter are enclosed in cotton canvas or synthetic fibre cloth-covered boxes with an open top for receiving the cathode. The cloth diaphragms fastened to both sides of a wooden frame must have the proper permeability to maintain a hydrostatic head in the boxes, ensuring a constant outward flow of catholyte through the fabric at sufficient velocity to prevent migration of the undesirable ions to the cathode. In fact, the nickel ions liberated at the anodes are not transported directly to the cathodes, but together with copper, iron, and other impurities in solution flow out of the tanks as foul electrolyte or anolyte. Thus, the nickel deposited on the cathode is supplied by purified electrolyte constantly flowing into the cathode boxes.

Nickel electrorefining is conducted in acid baths operating at pH usually below 4.0. Two reactions occur simultaneously at the cathode: namely, the discharge of nickel ions to nickel metal, and the discharge of hydrogen ions to molecular hydrogen. The discharge of hydrogen ions, at 0.5 per cent cathode current efficiency, is sufficient to raise the catholyte pH significantly. The catholyte flows through the diaphragms to the anodes where nickel and impurities from the anodes make up the metal balance. Anolyte flows from the bottom of the plating cells up through pipes built into the ends of the tanks, thence by gravity to the purification system.

Electrolyte Purification. Refinery electrolyte formerly was usually composed essentially of sulfate salts in solution. More recently, sulfate-chloride electrolyte has been generally adopted because it facilitates anode corrosion and permits higher current densities, compared with the all-sulfate electrolyte. A typical composition is 60 grams per liter of nickel as sulfate, 60 grams per liter of sodium chloride, and 15 grams per liter of boric acid.

Storage tanks located at the end of the cell room receive the impure solution discharged from the electrolytic cells. Electrolyte from these tanks is circulated through the various stages of purification by centrifugal pumps and by gravity flow in open launders. Purification elements comprise reaction tanks constructed of wooden staves or acid-resistant brick-lined concrete. Filtration for removing impure precipitates of cobalt, iron, and copper is by plate and frame presses and continuous rotary filters. Following the final purification, the purified electrolyte flow rate is controlled to the electrolytic cell system by hydrostatic head tanks connected to the main feed pipe to each cell line.

Anolyte, or impure electrolyte, from the electrolytic cells contains impurities in various amounts depending on the purity of the anode. Major elements are cobalt, copper, and iron with traces of impurities, such as lead, arsenic, and zinc. In the Port Colborne refinery, for example, removal of these impurities is in the order iron, cobalt, and then copper. The first stage is aeration for complete oxidation of the copper and nearly complete oxidation of the iron. Iron oxidation and hydrolysis are then completed in a later sequence. The reactions occurring in iron eliminations are:

(1) Copper oxidation

$$Cu_2^{++} + O + 2H^+ \rightarrow 2Cu^{++} + H_2O$$

(2) Iron oxidation

$$2Cu^{++} + 2Fe^{++} \rightarrow Cu_2^{++} + 2Fe^{+++}$$

(3) Iron hydrolysis

$$Fe^{+++} + 3H_2O \rightarrow Fe(OH)_3 + 3H^+$$

(4) Reoxidation of cuprous copper formed by reaction 2.

Cobalt, lead and arsenic are removed after the iron removal stage by oxidation with chlorine in the presence of nickel carbonate, and hydrolysis as hydrated higher valence oxides:

$$2CoCl_2 + Cl_2 + 3NiCO_3 + 3H_2O$$
$$\rightarrow 2Co(OH)_3 + 3NiCl_2 + 3CO_2$$

Copper elimination is by cementation on finely-divided active nickel powder. Reactions occurring during the cementation operation include the replacement of copper in solution by nickel and the chemical dissolution of nickel powder by the acid-bearing solution. The reactions are:

(1) $Ni^\circ + Cu^{++} \rightarrow Ni^{++} + Cu^\circ$
(2) $Ni^\circ + 2H^+ \rightarrow Ni^{++} + H_2$
(3) $Ni^\circ + 2H^+ + O \rightarrow Ni^{++} + H_2O$

The latter reaction is undesirable since it consumes nickel without beneficial effect; therefore, aeration in the system is minimized. The final copper cement is filtered from the solution. Other procedures are available for electrolyte purification, such as use of hydrogen sulfide or nickel shot and sulfur for control of copper.

The purity of electrolytic nickel exceeds 99.9 per cent.

References

1. HYBINETTE, N. V., U. S. Patents 805,555 and 805,969 (Nov. 28, 1905).
2. RENZONI, L. S., McQUIRE, R. C., AND BARKER, W. V., "Direct Electrorefining of Nickel Matte," *J. Metals,* **10,** No. 6, 414–18 (1958).
3. ARCHIBALD, F. R., "The Kristiansand Nickel Refinery," *J. Metals,* **14,** No. 9, 648–652 (1962).
4. QUENEAU, P., Editor, "Extractive Metallurgy of Copper, Nickel and Cobalt," pp. 535–544, New York, Interscience Publishers, 1961.

L. E. CUPP

Cross-references: *Copper and Nickel Concentrates, Electric Smelting; Electrorefining* and *Electrowinning of specific metals.*

NITROGEN FIXATION BY THE ARC PROCESS

History

It is well known that Sir William Crookes in 1898 asserted that the deposits of Chilean nitrate would soon be exhausted. As a result the world would starve due to lack of nitrogen fertilizers unless new permanent sources of fixed nitrogen could be detected.

This grave statement from a world known scientist was alarming and caused intensified research regarding the problem of "fixing" this resistant nitrogen gas present in such inexhaustible quantities in the air.

Priestly, as early as in 1783, made the observation that nitric oxides were formed when electric sparks passed through air. Cavendish, repeating the experiments 13 years later, came to the same conclusion. Further experiments were carried out by a number of scientists during the next century, but no process was developed which could lead to an industrial production of nitrogen oxides, and then nitric acid or nitrogen fertilizers, though some attempts were made, for example, by Mdm. Le Febre in 1859 in France and Dougal Howles in 1899 in England.

The first plant to come into operation was erected in Niagara Falls in 1902 by The Atmospheric Products Company, using a method patented by Bradley and Lovejoy. The plant was shut down in 1904 after the test periods had proved that the process could not be operated commercially. The main reasons seem to have been that the elaborate electric arc equipment was very costly and complicated, the yield per kwh was low, and the equipment was fragile which caused frequent interruptions and correspondingly high maintenance costs.

The Birkeland-Eyde Process

The two Norwegians, Birkeland and Eyde, started their research work on nitrogen fixation in 1903. Kristian Birkeland (1867–1917) was professor of physics at the University of Kristiania (Oslo). He was an outstanding scientist with a broad experience relating to magnetism, cathodic rays, etc., but he was not interested in the fixation of nitrogen. Sam Eyde (1866–1940) was educated as civil engineer. He had his own consulting office in Oslo with a relatively large staff of engineers and had won a number of international competitions for railway stations, harbor arrangements, and bridges. Eyde was at this time very interested in development of hydroelectric power based on the great water resources in Norway. He was aware of Crookes' prophecy of the coming "starvation" if Chilean nitrate not could be supplemented or replaced with synthetic nitrogen fertilizers. Was it possible that Norway's water power could be harnessed for this purpose?

Eyde met Birkeland in February 1903. He mentioned en passant his search for "concentrated" electric energy in huge quantities adopted for combination of nitrogen and oxygen in the air.

Birkeland was at this time occupied with a military problem ("the electric cannon") and during his experiments he observed a big disk-formed flame when the arc passed a magnetic field.

Now that the contact between the two was established, intensive work with the Birkeland-Eyde process started immediately. Birkeland took over the basic work regarding construction of a suitable arc furnace and Eyde had a tough job in raising the necessary money for the exploitation of the process.

The first patent application was dated February 20, 1903, and the corresponding Norway Patent 12,961 was published May 30, 1904 (U. S. Patent 772,862, Oct. 18, 1904).

The research and experimental work with the B-E process started at the University of Oslo on a laboratory scale. The continued development is recorded.

Dates	Place	H. P. utilized
July 1903	Frognerkilen	25
Oct. 1903	Ankerlökken	130
Sept. 1904	Vasmoen	1,000
May 1905	Notodden	2,500
May 1907	Notodden	42,500
Nov. 1911	Rjukan I	200,000
Nov. 1915	Rjukan II	330,000

The development period regarding the arc furnace and the absorption system was, to a large extent, finished at Notodden in 1905 and the company, *Norsk Hydro-Elektrisk Kvælstofaktieselskab*, was registered December 2, 1905.

Simultaneously with the further development of the fertilizer plant, the great dams for the water reservoirs and power stations had to be built. An idea of the difficulties encountered in this work may be given by recounting the fact that materials for the dam at Lake Mösvann had to be transported from the sea level up to 3000 feet, where no railways and practically no roads existed and had, therefore, to be built by the company itself. In this region of Norway steep hills, rivers, and lakes caused extra difficulties for establishing the transport line, where bridges and great ferryboats connecting the railway terminals on both sides of the 30 km-long Lake Tinnsjö had to be built.

In Fig. 1 a diagrammatic cross section of the B-E furnace is shown. An alternating current arc is maintained between water-cooled copper electrodes which are placed between the poles of an electromagnet, so that the direction of the

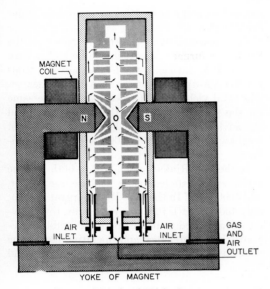

FIG. 1. Birkeland-Eyde furnace.

arc is at right angles to that of the constant magnetic field. The magnets cause the arc to spread in in circular form, appearing as a disk of flame between the fireproof bricks. The diameter of the flame-disk is about 10 feet (Fig. 2).

The capacity of these furnaces at the Rjukan Works was 4000 kw and the yield corresponded to 75 grams of HNO_3 per kwh.

The Schönherr Furnace

The pilot plant with B-E furnaces at Notodden in 1905 was in successful operation when a new arc furnace came into the picture, the *Schönherr-Hessberger furnace*, patented by Badische Co. (German Patent 201,279, 1905). A cross-section diagram of the Schönherr furnace is shown in Fig. 3. The furnace consists of four concentric iron cylinders, arranged to serve as a preheater for the entering air. A steady long arc is established in the inner cylinder between an insulated electrode at the lower part and the

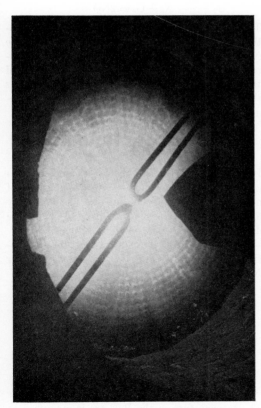

FIG. 2. Flame-disk in a B-E furnace.

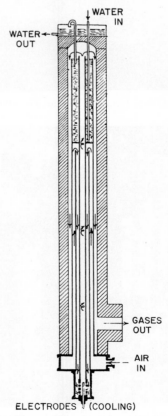

FIG. 3. Schönherr furnace.

water-jacketed upper end of the cylinder, serving as a grounded electrode. The air entering at the bottom through tangential openings is given a rapid spiral motion before arriving at the arc zone.

The Schönerr furnace was tried in a large pilot plant built at Notodden by the Badische Co. In 1910 a comprehensive series of comparisons between the Schönherr and B-E furnaces were undertaken to ascertain which type was

FIG. 4. B-E furnaces, Rjukan II (4,000 kw).

FIG. 5. Schönherr furnaces, Rjukan I (1,000 kw).

preferable in the large Rjukan plant now under construction.

The concentration of nitrogen oxides in the Schönherr furnaces was found to be higher than in the B-E furnace, which was advantageous for the absorption system, thus being cheaper. The total yield of HNO_3 per kwh was the same for the two furnaces. But the B-E furnace had the advantage that it could be built in units of 4000 kw compared with 1000 kw for the Schönherr.

In the first Rjukan plant (1911) both furnace types were installed using 3-phase a-c power, and 5000 volts. In the next Rjukan plant (1915), only 4000 kw B-E furnaces were built, these having been proved to be distinctly favorable as regards the maintenance and operating costs. The respective installations are shown in Figs. 4 and 5.

Reactions in the Arc Zone

The chemical reaction taking place when air passes the arc is:

$$N_2 + O_2 \rightleftharpoons 2NO$$

The formation of nitrogen oxide is an endothermic process, requiring 21,600 cal per mole NO. The heat absorption is practically independent of temperature as the specific heat of the components is almost constant. Pressure has theoretically no influence on this bimolecular reaction. The equilibrium is given by

$$k = \frac{(NO)^2}{(N_2)(O_2)}$$

If oxygen could be used instead of air, the concentration of NO would be, according to law of mass action, 25 per cent higher. The necessary oxygen plant, however, would have to be of huge dimensions and, hence, much too expensive.

The influence of temperature on the equilibrium concentration of NO in the air, after Nernst, is shown in the table below:

T, Absolute scale	Vol % NO
1500	0.10
2000	0.61
2500	1.79
3000	3.57
3500	5.8
4000	8.0

The temperature in the B-E arc is measured at

3300°C, corresponding to 5–6 per cent NO. The great reaction velocity, however, causes rapid decomposition back to N_2 and O_2 before it is possible to "keep" this relative high concentration obtained in the arc. The main problem is, therefore, to cool the gas mixture as soon as possible to "freeze" the yield. B-E solved this problem by immediately diluting the hot gas mixture in the arc with cold air, bringing the temperature down to about 1000°C. Further cooling of the gases, now containing 1.5–1.7 per cent NO, down to 175°C takes place in steam boilers; the generated steam is partly used in the fertilizer plant, and partly in steam turbines for regenerating electric power.

The last cooling down of the gases to 50°C is necessary for conversion of nitrogen oxide to nitrogen dioxide:

$$2NO + O_2 \rightleftharpoons 2NO_2$$

The above reaction starts at 620°C, but the reaction velocity increases as the temperature decreases. In addition, the reaction evolves heat, 14,000 cal/mole NO; therefore, efficient cooling of the gas mixture is important.

Absorption system

After a duration of 60 to 80 seconds in oxidation towers or pipelines, the gas mixture, containing about equal volumes of NO and NO_2, enters the absorption system where further oxidation occurs and nitric acid is formed:

$$3NO_2 + H_2O \rightarrow 2HNO_3 + NO$$

The new NO formed is reoxidized in the absorption towers where a great surplus of oxygen, more than 19 per cent, is present in the gas mixture leaving the last tower. To assure that as much as possible of the nitrogen oxides may be recovered, there is installed in succession to the "acid towers" one or two "alkaline towers" where the tailgases are washed with soda ash solution:

$$NO + NO_2 + Na_2CO_3 \rightarrow 2NaNO_2 + CO_2$$

The sodium nitrite is partly converted into sodium nitrate ("Chile saltpeter") by adding nitric acid:

$$NaNO_2 + 2HNO_3 \rightarrow NaNO_3 + NO + H_2O$$

The method of absorption of the diluted gases from the arc process was a complex problem. Very big absorption volume was needed, and the mixture of nitric acid and nitrogen oxides was very corrosive. It should be remembered that stainless steel did not exist at this time. Different materials were tried for the construction of the big towers. Norwegian granite proved to be acid-resisting, and towers of granite blocks with asbestos sealing and iron bandages were constructed. The 70 to 80 feet-high towers were filled with quartz lumps. (In the following years this type of tower was built in many countries for absorption of nitric oxides from ammonia-oxidizing plants.)

Nitrogen Fertilizer

The final step in the B-E process was the neutralization of the nitric acid with limestone for obtaining calcium nitrate, $Ca(NO_3)_2$. The resulting solution was concentrated by means of excess steam from the arc furnaces, dried, cooled, crushed and marketed as fertilizer, *"Norgesaltpeter," the first synthetic nitrogen fertilizer in the world*. Maximum production per year was about 220,000 tons.

Sodium nitrite and nitrate were produced as byproducts, and the ratio between them varied according to marketing possibilities.

A flowsheet of the B-E process is shown in Fig. 6.

Birkland-Eyde Plants Outside Norway

A plant was under construction in Spain (Lerida) 1914, but the work was stopped by the outbreak of the war.

In 1916 a new plant came into operation in France (Soulom, Pyrenees) for production of concentrated nitric acid and ammonium nitrate. Corresponding plants had already been built at Notodden and Rjukan. Ammonia was obtained partly from a calcium cyanamide-cracking plant at Notodden, partly from England. In the war-years of 1914–18 there was a great demand for nitrates in Europe because the shipment from Chile often failed, due to submarine activity.

Ammonia Synthesis Replaces Birkeland-Eyde method

The B-E plants in Norway were in continuous and successful operation until 1929, that is, *25 years*, but in 1927 the management of Norsk Hydro decided that the arc method should be replaced by a synthetic ammonia process to increase the company's nitrogen production. *The existing cheap hydroelectric power, on which the B-E process was based, could now, after conver-*

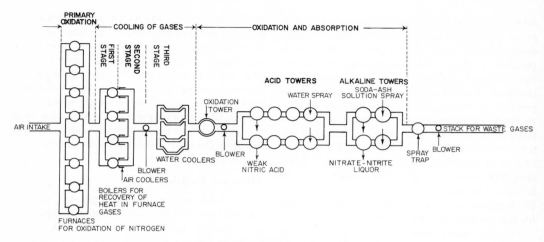

FIG. 6. Flowsheet, arc process.

sion to direct current, be used for production of electrolytic hydrogen, which is the dominating item in the cost of synthetic ammonia. The amount of power used in the B-E process would increase the company's nitrogen capacity 4 times when used for the synthesis of ammonia.

The absorption system, buildings, transportation facilities, etc. in the arc plants were of considerable value for the new process, though great capital investment was needed for erection of the new plants which came into operation in 1929.

At the present time (1963) the company's actual production via electrolytic hydrogen is 350,000 tons of ammonia per year. Calcium nitrate is still the main product, the output being more than a million tons per year. Further nitrogen products are made, such as urea, mixed fertilizers, ammonium nitrate limestone, sodium nitrate, ammonium nitrate, nitrogen solutions, and concentrated nitric acid.

Reference

1. STEINMETZ, CHARLES P., "Theoretical study of nitrogen fixation by the electric arc," *Chem. Met. Eng.,* **22,** 299–304, 353–357, 411–416, 455–462 (1920).

MIKAL FJELLANGER

NITROGEN TRIFLUORIDE

Although nitrogen trifluoride, NF_3, has been known since 1928, it has become of commercial importance only within the last few years. Ruff, Fischer, and Luft[1] prepared it first by the electrolysis of molten anhydrous ammonium bifluoride, in an electrically heated cell made of copper. The cathode was of copper, while the anode was of carbon. The electrolysis was carried out at 125°C and at 7 to 9 volts and 10 amps. The gas resulting from the electrolysis was reported to contain ozone, oxygen, nitrous oxide, hydrogen, nitrogen, hydrogen fluoride and nitrogen fluorides. It seems likely that the "ozone" may have been oxygen difluoride. The oxygen in these impurities likely came from small amounts of water in the electrolysis. Purification was accomplished by passing the gases through a copper vessel containing dry potassium fluoride, followed by another containing manganese dioxide. The resulting gases were condensed with liquid air. The NF_3 was recovered by fractionation at −160°C and allowed to stand in contact with dilute sodium hydroxide solution. Ruff later[1] reported that if the electrolyte contains 31 per cent NH_3 (pure $NH_4F \cdot HF$ contains 28.9 per cent NH_3) the product of electrolysis is nitrogen. For an electrolyte containing 28.6 per cent NH_3, the yield of NF_3 rises to 30 per cent. With less than 10 per cent NH_3, the product of electrolysis is fluorine. A patent dealing with the purification of NF_3 produced in this manner or from ammonia and fluorine has been issued to Ruff.[2] This process consists of passing the crude gases first over soda lime at 100° and then through a warm potassium iodide solution. The gas is then fractionated to free it from oxides of nitrogen.

There have since been several papers dealing with improvements on the original process. Pierce and Pace[3] prepared the gas using essentially the method of Ruff *et al*, substituting a nickel anode for the original carbon anode. This was to eliminate carbon tetrafluoride whose physical properties are quite similar to those of nitrogen trifluoride. The anode gases were passed through concentrated potassium iodide solution and then distilled from a trap surrounded by a partially frozen isopentane slush.

Jarry and Miller[4] also used a nickel anode and purified their gas by low temperature filtration and distillation. Schoenfelder[5] has recently described a device for purification of nitrogen trifluoride by filtration at low temperatures where the compound is a liquid and contaminating N_2O is a solid.

Colburn *et al*[6] have investigated the electrolysis of molten ammonium bifluoride. Ruff had reported that difluoroamine, HNF_2; fluoroamine, H_2NF; and NF_2 are also products of electrolysis. He also reported that he experienced explosions due to the decomposition of fluoroamine. Colburn *et al* report that no difluoroamine, fluoroamine, or NF_2 were observed as cell products in their work. Use of a divided cell alleviated the trouble caused by explosions when an undivided cell is used. These workers did find both cis and trans difluorodiazine, N_2F_2.

Direct burner combustion of ammonia in excess fluorine does not produce nitrogen trifluoride;[7] however, moderated reactions of fluorine with ammonia do produce some nitrogen trifluoride.[8]

Simons[9] has reported that NF_3 is a product of electrolysis of pyridine in anhydrous HF. A German patent dealing with the production of NF_3 by the electrolysis of a solution of urea in anhydrous hydrogen fluoride has been issued to Schmeisser.[10] A solution of approximately 10 per cent urea in anhydrous HF is electrolyzed at −10° C at a potential of 6 volts (approximately 20 amps). The volatile reaction products are passed through tubes containing solid potassium fluoride, for the purpose of removing HF, and are then washed with an aqueous alkaline solution to remove COF_2, CO_2, and OF_2. Water vapor is removed by a trap maintained at dry ice temperature. The resulting product is then fractionated under a high vacuum between −183 and −196° and freed from its impurities except about 1 per cent CF_4. Yields of about 50 per cent are reported.

Considerable effort has been expended investigating the physical properties of the compound. Microwave spectra[11] are consistent with a pyramidal structure with a F-N-F angle of 102°9′ and an NF distance of 1.371Å. These parameters are in reasonable agreement with those determined by electron diffraction.[12] Stark splittings of microwave lines yield dipole moments of

$$0.234 \pm 0.004 \text{ or } 0.235 \pm 0.007 \text{ Debye unit.}[13]$$

The heat of formation[14] is −29.7 ± 1.8 kcal/mole and the mean bond energy is 66.4 ± 0.8 kcal/mole. Earlier work had indicated somewhat less stability. The bond dissociation energies[15] are as follows: $D(NF_2\text{-}F) = 57.1 \pm 2.5$, and the mean of $D(NF\text{-}F)$ and $D(N\text{-}F) = 71$ kcal/mole.

Recent vapor pressure measurements include those of Pierce and Pace[16] as well as those of Jarry and Miller.[4] The vapor pressure from 86 to 144.5°K can be represented by the following equations:

$$\log P_{mm} = \frac{-673.5828}{T} + 1.869858 \log T$$

$$- 0.00783355\ T + 4.64615\ (T = °K)$$

$$\log P_{mm} = 6.77966 - \left(\frac{501.913}{T - 15.37}\right) (T = °K)$$

The vapor pressures to the critical point can be represented by:[4]

$$\log P_{atm.} = 4.27264 - \left(\frac{613.33}{T}\right).$$

Jarry and Miller[4] have also determined the liquid density of nitrogen trifluoride. The following is valid over the range −195 to −103°C:

$$d(g/cc) = 2.103 - 3.294 \times 10^{-3}T - 4.675 \times 10^{-6}T^2$$

They also determined the critical constants to be −39.36°C and 44.72 atm.

Several values have been reported for the melting, boiling, and transition points. Pierce and Pace have carefully measured the heats of these changes. They have found the following: the heat of vaporization at the boiling point (−129.01°C) is 2769 cal/mole, the heat of fusion at −206.79°C, 95.11 cal/mole, and the heat of transition at −216.54°C, 361.8 cal/mole.

The transition at −216.54°C is accompanied by a change in appearance from an opaque white solid to a transparent substance. It is surprising that the heat of this transition is remarkably greater than that of fusion. Pierce and Pace[3] have also proposed the triple point, −206.79°, as a fixed thermometric point.

Chemically, NF_3 is surprisingly unreactive. The principal characteristic is that of a strong oxidizing agent. It does not react with dry glass and is unaffected by dilute basic solutions or dilute sulfuric acid. It is somewhat soluble without reaction in water. Sparking can cause NF_3 to react with water vapor. The products are HF, NO, and NO_2. An electrical discharge will cause mixtures of NF_3 with many gaseous reducing agents (H_2S, NH_3, H_2, CH_4, C_2H_4, CO) to react explosively. Parry and Bissot[17] have reported that no compound is formed between nitrogen trifluoride and diborane and that they do not react in the vapor phase, but explosions are sometimes experienced when the reactants are in the liquid phase. Both $(PNF_2)_3$ and $(PNF_2)_4$ result[18] from the reaction of NF_3 with P_3N_5 at 710°C. Under noncatalytic conditions and at elevated temperature, nitrogen trifluoride is reported to behave as a fluorinating agent with fluorocarbon olefins, while in reactions over cesium fluoride it acts as a means of introducing =NF and —NF_2 groups into the fluorocarbons.[19]

When mixtures of nitrogen trifluoride and mercury vapor are subjected to an electrical discharge, tetrafluorohydrazine and both cis and trans difluorodiazine are found.[20] Many metals will react with NF_3 at elevated temperatures to produce tetrafluorohydrazine. These metals include stainless steel, copper, arsenic, antimony, and bismuth.[21] A typical reaction is:

$$Cu + 2NF_3 \rightarrow CuF_2 + N_2F_4$$

Rogers[22] has described a hydrogen-nitrogen trifluoride torch useful for welding, brazing, and cutting of metals. The NF_3 acts as a gaseous flux. He[23] has also investigated the suitability of nitrogen trifluoride as a gaseous dielectric. Although its ability to transfer heat is somewhat poorer than that of sulfur hexafluoride, it is superior with respect to dielectric strength.[2, 3] This superiority is more pronounced at more nonuniform fields. Obviously, the reactivity of NF_3 would be a distinct disadvantage.

In his work Rogers found that equipment designed for use with oxygen is suitable for use with NF_3. The known primary hazard of NF_3 is its strong oxidizing ability. Procedures for handling the gas are discussed in a manufacturer's data sheet.[24] Limited toxicity data are also included in this publication. A report on preliminary toxicity tests is given in the paper by Jarry and Miller.[4]

References

1. RUFF, O., FISCHER, J., AND LUFT, F., Z. anorg. Chem., **172**, 417 (1928); RUFF, O., Z. angew. Chem., **42**, 807 (1929); RUFF, O., AND MENZEL, Z. anorg. Chem., **197**, 273 (1931); RUFF, O., AND STAUB, L., Z. anorg. Chem., **198**, 32 (1931); Z. anorg. Chem., **212**, 399 (1933).
2. RUFF, O., German Patent 518,202 (1931).
3. PIERCE, L., AND PACE, E. L., J. Chem. Phys., **22**, 1271 (1954).
4. JARRY, R. J., AND MILLER, H. C., J. Phys. Chem., **60**, 1412 (1956).
5. SCHOENFELDER, C. W., J. Sci. Instr., **39**, 88 (1962).
6. COLBURN, C. B., PARKER, C. O., AND STEVENSON, K., Abstracts of Papers Presented at 138th Meeting of the American Chemical Society, New York City, September 1960, p. 30N, and private communication.
7. ARMSTRONG, C. T., AND JESSUP, R. S., J. Research Natl. Bureau Standards, **64A**, 47 (1960).
8. MORROW, S. I., et al, J. Am. Chem. Soc., **82**, 5301 (1960).
9. SIMONS, J. H., et al, J. Electrochem. Soc., **95**, 47 (1949).
10. SCHMEISSER, M., German Patent 1,052,369 (1959).
11. SHERIDAN, J., AND GORDY, W., Phys. Rev., **79**, 513 (1950); JOHNSON, C. M., TRAMBARULO, R., AND GORDY, W., Phy. Rev., **84**, 1178 (1951).
12. SCHOMAKER, V., AND CHIA-SI LU, J. Am. Chem. Soc., **72**, 1182 (1950).
13. GHOSH, S. N., TRAMBARULO, R., AND GORDY, W., J. Chem. Phys., **21**, 308 (1953); KISLIUK, P. P., J. Chem. Phys., **22**, 86 (1954).
14. MARANTZ, S., COYLE, C. F., AND ARMSTRONG, G. T., "Heat of Formation of Nitrogen Trifluoride," National Bureau of Standards Report No. 6363, Washington, D.C. (1959).
15. KENNEDY, A., AND COLBURN, C. B., J. Chem. Phys., **35**, 1892 (1961); JOHNSON, F. A., AND COLBURN, C. B., J. Am. Chem. Soc., **83**, 3043 (1961).
16. PIERCE, L., AND PACE, E. L., J. Chem. Phys., **23**, 551 (1955).
17. PARRY, R. W., AND BISSOT, T. C., J. Am Chem. Soc., **78**, 1524 (1956).
18. MAO, T. J., DRESDNER, R. D., AND YOUNG, J. A., J. Am. Chem. Soc., **81**, 1020 (1959).
19. DRESDNER, R. D., TLUMOC, F. N., AND YOUNG, J. A., J. Am. Chem. Soc., **82**, 5831 (1960).
20. FRAZER, J., J. Inorg. Nuclear Chem., **11**, 166 (1959).
21. COLBURN, C. B., AND KENNEDY, A., J. Am. Chem. Soc., **80**, 5004 (1958).
22. ROGERS, H. H., Ind. Eng. Chem., **51**, 309 (1959).
23. ROGERS, H. H., J. Chem. Eng. Data, **6**, 250 (1961).

24. Stauffer Chemical Co., Product Data Sheet "Nitrogen Trifluoride Tetrafluorohydrazine."

ALBERT W. JACHE AND
WAYNE E. WHITE

Cross-references: *Fluorine Production; Fluorocarbons, Electrolytic Production; Sulfur Hexafluoride.*

NOMENCLATURE, REMARKS ON

There has been, for far too long a period of time, a great deal of confusion in the understanding of many of the fundamental concepts of electrochemistry, in the formulation of definitions for these concepts, and even in the selection of proper terms to be associated with the concepts. The notorious difficulty with the signs of the so-called electrode potentials, electromotive forces, etc., is but one aspect of this confusion. Some of the causes of the situation are the abuse and misuse of the word "potential," the very frequent identification of electric potential difference with electromotive force, the failure to include, in the system to which thermodynamic analysis is applied, the chemically identical leads to the outside circuit—in the Daniell cell it is not the zinc electrode which is negative with respect to the copper one but the copper lead attached to the zinc, there being at this contact an increase of inner electric potential from copper to zinc of the same order of magnitude as the Volta electric potential difference of about 0.8 volt—, the closely connected lack of clarity concerning the old problem of the seat of the electromotive force of a galvanic cell, etc.

Certain international commissions have attempted to remove this confusion and to establish a logical nomenclature and a coherent set of definitions. In 1953 the Commission on Electrochemistry and that of Physico-Chemical Symbols and Terminology of the International Union of Pure and Applied Chemistry (IUPAC) prepared jointly what has become known as the Stock-

Editor's Note: Dr. Van Rysselberghe is Chairman of the Commission on Electrochemistry of the International Union of Pure and Applied Chemistry (IUPAC); and Chairman of the Subcommission on Electrochemical Symbols and Terminology. He is also Chairman of the Commission on Electrochemical Nomenclature and Definitions of the International Committee of Electrochemical Thermodynamics and Kinetics (CITCE). (See entry on **CITCE**.)

holm recommendation on the signs of electrode potentials. It can best be summarized by means of an example: the value -0.76 volt associated with the standard Zn/Zn^{2+} electrode is its standard relative electrode potential with respect to the standard hydrogen electrode. The value $+0.76$ volt may not be called electrode potential. The equilibrium (or zero current) value of the electric potential difference between a copper lead attached to the zinc and a copper lead attached to the platinum of the standard hydrogen electrode is actually -0.76 volt. Let us add, as a help towards our later discussion, that -0.76 volt is also the standard reduction potential and $+0.76$ volt the standard oxidation potential of the Zn/Zn^{2+} couple, although other names have been recommended for these quantities (see below).

Since 1953 the Subcommission on Electrochemical Symbols and Terminology of the IUPAC Commission on Electrochemistry has worked in close cooperation with the International Committee of Electrochemical Thermodynamics and Kinetics (CITCE), an organization founded in 1949 and which in recent years has been an affiliated IUPAC Commission. CITCE's Commission on Electrochemical Nomenclature and Definitions began its work in 1950 and has published since then a series of reports containing precise definitions of most of the fundamental concepts of electrochemistry, its most recent contribution being a revised set of definitions pertaining to electrode kinetics. These reports have been prepared in English and French, more recently chiefly in French on account of difficulties concerning the use in English of the language of "tensions" which the CITCE Commission strongly recommends. Translations of some of the reports have appeared in German, Italian, Japanese, and Portuguese. A complete presentation in English, with the language of "tensions" included, is to be prepared in the very near future.

We shall now briefly discuss some aspects of electrochemical nomenclature which CITCE treats in a manner different from what has been current practice, with some additional comments of our own.

It appears important to restrict the use of the term "potential" in electrochemistry to the following cases. (1) One may call, without danger of confusion, *thermodynamic potentials* the four functions of state: energy E; enthalpy H; free energy, $F = E - TS$; free enthalpy, $G = H - TS$, and their electrochemical counterparts $\tilde{E}$, $\tilde{H}$, $\tilde{F}$ and $\tilde{G}$. The expression "free enthalpy" has encountered objections but CITCE insists on its use and there is strong indication that it is becoming widely adopted in several languages. (2) The derivatives of the thermodynamic potentials with respect to mole numbers in the proper systems of variables, for instance, the derivatives of G and $\tilde{G}$ at temperature, pressure, and other mole numbers constant are called *chemical* and *electrochemical potentials*. (3) The *inner electric potentials*, φ, of the various phases of a cell whose products by the molar charges, $z_i\mathbf{F}$, are the electric potential energy terms in the electrochemical potentials, $\tilde{\mu}_i = \mu_i + z_i\mathbf{F}\varphi_i$. It is advisable to avoid the use of the term "potential" beyond these three cases. Linear combinations of μ_i's and $\tilde{\mu}_i$'s corresponding to chemical or electrochemical reactions are *chemical affinities*, $A = -\sum_i\nu_i\mu_i = -\Delta G$ and *electrochemical affinities*, $\tilde{A} = -\sum_i\nu_i\tilde{\mu}_i = -\Delta\tilde{G}$. The ratios of affinities to corresponding reaction charges, $z\mathbf{F} = -\sum_i z_i\nu_i\mathbf{F}$ are *tensions*. We thus have *chemical tensions*, $A/z\mathbf{F} = E$, *electrochemical tensions*, $\tilde{A}/z\mathbf{F} = \tilde{E}$ and *electric tensions*, $-\sum_i z_i\nu_i\mathbf{F}\varphi_i/z\mathbf{F} = U$, which are always electric potential differences between two phases (the terminal phases of a cell or the two phases of an electrode in contact with each other). In general, for a process such as a cell reaction or an electrode reaction, we have at equilibrium (or zero current), $U_{rev.} + E = 0$, and, with current passing, $U + E = \tilde{E} \neq 0$. The electric tension, U, varies from its reversible value as soon as some current is passing, while E, being a function of temperature, pressure, and composition, remains constant as long as the passage of current does not alter these state variables. The classical formula of the textbooks, $\Delta G = -z\mathbf{F}E$, can be written $\Delta G/z\mathbf{F} + E = 0$ and the ratio, $\Delta G/z\mathbf{F} = -A/z\mathbf{F}$, is seen to be the reversible electric tension of the cell, while E is its chemical tension or electromotive force. The electric tension and the chemical tension or emf balance each other at equilibrium. With current passing polarization effects or overvoltages and the internal ohmic drop of electric potential render U different from $-E$, the algebraic sum, $U + E$, being different from zero and equal to the electrochemical tension $\tilde{E}$.

Let us consider the cell

$$\text{Cu} \,/\, \text{Zn} \,/\, \text{Zn}^{++} \;//\; \text{H}^+ \,/\, \text{Pt, H}^2 \,/\, \text{Cu}$$
$$\text{I} \quad\; 1 \quad\; 2 \quad\;\; 2' \quad\; 3' \quad 3 \quad 4 \qquad\quad \text{II}$$

in which the double bar indicates the liquid junction between the two solutions. The electric tension of the cell is the difference $\varphi^{\mathrm{I}} - \varphi^{\mathrm{II}}$. Writing the cell reaction as follows:

$$\text{Zn} + 2\text{H}^+ \rightarrow \text{Zn}^{2+} + \text{H}_2$$

its chemical affinity is $A = \mu_{Zn} + 2\mu_{\mathrm{H}^+} - \mu_{Zn^{2+}} - \mu_{\mathrm{H}_2}$ and its chemical tension or emf is $A/2\mathbf{F}$. Neglecting $\varphi^{2'} - \varphi^{3'}$ or making a suitable correction we have $U_{rev.} + E = 0$. If we consider the hydrogen electrode as being in its standard state we set, conventionally, $2\mu_{\mathrm{H}^+} - \mu_{\mathrm{H}_2} = 0$ and $U_{rev.}$ becomes the standard relative electric tension of the Zn/Zn^{2+} electrode, equal to -0.76 volt at 25°C and 1 atm. The chemical tension or emf is then $+0.76$ volt, and it is seen to be the oxidation chemical tension (commonly called oxidation potential) or the *oxidation affinity per coulomb*. If the equilibrium condition is written $U_{rev.} = E' = -E$, we see that E' is then -0.76 volt, and it can be regarded as the reduction chemical tension (commonly called reduction potential) or the *reduction affinity per coulomb*. We thus have $U_{rev.} = E_{red.} = -E_{oxid.}$. As we have suggested elsewhere it seems advisable that the electromotive series be given with three columns of data: the one-signed electric tensions at equilibrium, $U_{rev.}$, the reduction chemical tensions, $E_{red.}$, and the oxidation chemical tensions, $E_{oxid.}$. When the reaction at the Zn/Zn^{2+} electrode occurs in one or the other of the two possible directions (the anodic one corresponding to $\text{Zn} \rightarrow \text{Zn}^{2+}$ or the cathodic one corresponding to $\text{Zn}^{2+} \rightarrow \text{Zn}$) the electric tension increases or decreases but remains in the neighborhood of -0.76 volt. Therefore, if an expression such as oxidation-reduction potential or oxidation-reduction tension is employed, it should refer to the electric tension and not to one or the other of the two chemical tensions. It would be dangerous, using for instance the oxidation potentials, to regard them as oxidation-reduction potentials as is unfortunately frequently done.

With current passing in the anodic direction at the Zn/Zn^{2+} electrode, we have, assuming that no polarization occurs at the hydrogen electrode, $U = E_{red.} + \eta_a + RI$, in which η_a is the positive anodic overvoltage, and with current passing in the cathodic direction we have $U = E_{red.} - |\eta_c| - RI$, in which η_c is the negative cathodic overvoltage. (See the entry on **Irreversible Electrochemical Processes, Thermodynamics of**.)

There has occasionally been a peculiar misconception about the meaning of the expressions oxidation and reduction potentials. The large positive oxidation potential of a couple has sometimes been regarded as denoting marked oxidation potentiality towards another couple, the oxidized form of the first couple oxidizing the reduced form of the other, with a similar distortion of meaning with the reduction potential. It is, of course, the exact opposite which is indicated by the large positive oxidation potential, i.e., the marked ease with which the couple undergoes oxidation. Much of this type of confusion is restricted to the English language on account of the fact that a verb like "to oxidize" can be either transitive or intransitive: H^+ oxidizes Zn to Zn^{2+}, being itself reduced to H_2, but Zn "oxidizes" (to Zn^{2+}) in the sense of "becomes oxidized."

A few words concerning the alleged conflict between so-called American and European conventions are in order. The American convention is associated with the value $+0.76$ volt for the standard Zn/Zn^{2+} couple or electrode, the European convention with the value -0.76 volt. It seems, therefore, that the Stockholm recommendation is in favor of the European convention. Actually the situation is as follows: when chemical tensions are being considered the so-called American usage has been to use oxidation chemical tensions and the so-called European usage has been to use reduction chemical tensions. Incidentally, the American preference transforms the negative sign of the free enthalpy change of the Zn to Zn^{2+} oxidation into the positive sign of the oxidation potential and this is the same change of sign as that from free enthalpy change to affinity! On the other hand, the relative standard electric tension of the Zn/Zn^{2+} electrode is always -0.76 volt, never $+0.76$ volt, and this value -0.76 volt coincides, at equilibrium, with the reduction chemical tension. It is only on account of this coincidence that the Stockholm recommendation appears to favor the so-called European convention. If one uses systematically in the electromotive series the three quantities, $U_{rev.}$, $E_{red.}$ and $E_{oxid.}$, as explained above, the distinction between the so-called American and European conventions may be completely forgotten.

References

1. CHRISTIANSEN, J. A., AND POURBAIX, M., *C. R. 17th Conf. Un. Int. Chim. pure appl.* (IUPAC), Stockholm (1953), Paris, Maison de la Chimie, 1954.

2. VAN RYSSELBERGHE, P., "Electrochemical Affinity," Paris, Hermann, 1955.
3. LANGE, E., AND VAN RYSSELBERGHE, P., *J. Electrochem. Soc.*, **105,** 420 (1958).
4. CHRISTIANSEN, J. A., *J. Am. Chem. Soc.*, **82,** 5517 (1960). (IUPAC Manual of Physico-Chemical Symbols and Terminology).
5. VAN RYSSELBERGHE, P., *Electrochim. Acta*, **3,** 257 (1961).
6. VAN RYSSELBERGHE, P., *Electrochim. Acta*, **5,** 28 (1961); *J. Electroanalyt. Chem.*, **2,** 265 (1961). (CITCE report on Electrochemical Nomenclature and Definitions).
7. VAN RYSSELBERGHE, P., *et al.*, *Electrochim. Acta*, **8,** 543 (1963); *J. Electroanalyt. Chem.*, **6,** 173 (1963). (CITCE report on Electrochemical Kinetics and Polarization).

PIERRE VAN RYSSELBERGHE

Cross-references: *Electrode Potentials, Signs;* other *Electrode Potential* entries; *Electromotive Force and Half-Cell Potentials; Electromotive Series; Irreversible Electrochemical Processes, Thermodynamics of; Tension, Cell and Electrode.*

NORTHRUP, EDWIN FITCH (1866–1940)

Known primarily as the inventor of the high-frequency induction furnace, Edwin Fitch Northrup was born February 23, 1866 in Syracuse, N.Y., where he attended public school. After graduating from Amherst in 1891, he received his Ph.D. from Johns Hopkins University in 1895, and then worked at various electric jobs in the western United States and in Mexico. He returned to Johns Hopkins in 1897 as an associate of Prof. H. A. Rowland in the development of the multiplex printing telegraph system, and became chief engineer of the Rowland Printing Telegraph Co. from 1898 to 1902.

With Morris E. Leeds he founded Leeds & Northrup Co. in 1903 and was active in that company until 1910. Here he contributed to the design of instruments, inventing the movement which made possible the automatic recording instruments known today. In the period 1910–1920 he taught physics and electrical engineering at Princeton, and did research and development work which led to the invention in 1916 of his greatest contribution, the high-frequency or coreless induction furnace, still marketed as the Ajax-Northrup furnace.

From 1916 until his death he was actively engaged in the development and application of this furnace, watching it grow from small experimental laboratory units to large industrial production units. He also invented the means of applying induction heating as a concentrated energy source for the differential surface heating of metals to effect surface hardening. This development, too, grew to have wide commercial application. At the time of his death in 1940 he was vice president and technical adviser to the Ajax Electrothermic Corp.

Northrup was an able writer and expounder of his ideas, and he published over 100 papers. As an inventor, he had more than 100 patents issued to him, and at the 1932 dedication of the new U. S. Patent Office in Washington was honored as one of the twelve leading American inventors of the day. Only two months before his death in 1940 he was cited as a "Modern

Pioneer" in a national survey honoring those who had done most to advance industry in the American way.

Northrup was a member of the Electrochemical Society, the Inventors' Guild, and the Franklin Institute, a life member of the American Institute of Electrical Engineers, and a fellow of the American Society for the Advancement of Science. Among the honors awarded him were the Medaille de Bronze, Paris Exposition, 1910; the Edward Longstreth Medal, 1912; the Elliott Cresson Medal, 1916; and the second Acheson Medal, 1931, the first having been presented to Edward G. Acheson.

He died at his home in Princeton, April 29, 1940 at the age of 74.

CLIFFORD A. HAMPEL

O

OERSTED, HANS CHRISTIAN (1777–1851)

Hans Christian Oersted, founder of the science of electromagnetism, was born August 14, 1777 at Rudkjobing, on the island of Langeland in Denmark. His father, an apothecary, transferred his own interest in electricity to Hans when the latter was still a boy. Prior to entering the University of Copenhagen to study pharmacy in 1794, Oersted succeeded in passing a strict admittance examination which he was able to do because of the tutorage of a local barber, his wife, and a baker.

In 1801, the year that Volta invented the electric battery, Oersted began a two year tour through Germany, France, and Holland, acquiring new knowledge and meeting leading scientists. These included Johann Wilhelm Ritter, who interested him in magnetism and electricity. In 1803 he returned to Copenhagen, and his private laboratory, where he conducted experiments in natural philosophy and wrote numerous scientific papers, in German and Danish, relating natural philosophy to poetry and religion. Impressed by his work, the faculty of the University of Copenhagen appointed him professor of natural philosophy in 1806.

Shortly thereafter he married Inger Birgitte Ballum, daughter of the pastor of Kjelby. Their family included three sons and four daughters.

Oersted was a simple, but devoutly religious man. Physical characteristics included a large nose, a high forehead, and long hair. Professor Hanstren, a Danish physicist, described Oersted in a letter to Faraday, as a "very happy experimenter, who could not manipulate instruments and had always to rely on an assistant with 'easy hands' to arrange the apparatus."

After thirteen years of extensive experimental research, Oersted was positive there was some relationship between electricity and magnetism. He was, however, unable to prove its existence.

In the winter of 1819 while giving a lecture to a group of students, he made his great discovery by accident. On the desk was a galvanic battery to which he had attached some platinum wire. He brought a magnetic needle in front of the battery so that the wire and needle would be parallel. But to his astonishment, the needle, which was pointing north, swung around and set at a right angle to the original direction. Saying nothing to the students, he continued his lecture. Later in his empty laboratory, Oersted repeated the experiment and reversed the direction of the current. Again the needle was deflected, but in the opposite direction. Therefore, he discovered that an electric current produced the same effect on a magnetic needle as a magnet. This discovery foretold the birth of the new science of electromagnetism.

The publication, *Experimenta Circa Efficaciam Conflictus Electrici in Acum Magneticam*, on July 21, 1820, announced this discovery to the public. In recognition of his achievement, the Royal Society of London bestowed the Copley Medal on him and the Institute of France awarded him a prize of three thousand francs.

In 1824 Oersted determined that aluminum chloride could be prepared by passing chlorine water over a hot mixture of alumina and carbon, but the credit for this discovery went to Wohler, who produced aluminum in the pure state.

Oersted's death on March 9, 1851 in Copenhagen marked the end of a somewhat colorless life; yet one that has had a definite effect on mankind. The oersted, the unit of magnetic intensity, was named in his honor.

MARY L. CHEKEWICZ

OHM, ABSOLUTE. See ELECTRICAL UNITS AND STANDARDS

OHM, GEORG SIMON (1789–1854)

A physicist, noted for his quantitative study of current electricity, Ohm was born March 16, 1789 in Erlangen, Bavaria. He was encouraged to study philosophy and mathematics by his father, a locksmith. The limited income of this trade allowed Ohm to complete a year at Erlangen Gymnasium and three terms at Erlangen University. However, after tutoring in Switzerland, he returned to the university and received a Doctor of Philosophy degree on October 25, 1811. Physics, especially the study of mechanics, light, and color, was his main interest.

Due to the Napoleonic Wars ravaging Europe, permanent teaching positions were unavailable. Foregoing military service, Ohm began to write. After publication of "Essay on Geometry" in 1817, the Jesuit High School in Cologne hired him as a teacher of mathematics and physics. Here he developed a teaching method popular today, that of dividing the class time into lecture and laboratory periods. Ohm was a successful teacher. His clearly thought out and delivered lectures were well received.

Ohm completed his major experiments during his nine and one-half years there. These experiments, showing great ingenuity as his meager funds allowed little apparatus, include: 1) the determination of the flow of electricity in metallic conductors; 2) the application of the flow of electricity in liquid conductors; 3) development of the galvanometer; 4) elucidation of Erman's experiments on unipolar conductors; 5) studies in acoustics; 6) development of a theory relating to polarized light.

These studies led to the establishment of two laws: the production of complex tones by the composition of simple vibrations (announced in 1843) and the relationship of the intensity of an unvarying electrical current, electromotive force, and resistance of a circuit, now known as Ohm's Law.

To establish the latter law, Ohm studied Gray's experiment on conduction of an electrical charge traveling along a conductor, Oersted's discovery of the relationship of magnetism to electricity, Ampere's concept of potential electricity between the ends of a wire carrying current from the terminals of a voltaic cell, Fourier's establishment of the flow of heat in a metal bar being directly proportional to the difference of temperature between the ends of the bar, and Volta's theory of the electrostatic tension of an open pile. Ohm applied the analogy of the flow of heat in a metal bar to the flow of an electric current in a conductor, using Fourier's concept of the temperature gradient and assuming that the current was distributed along the sections of a homogeneous metal ring.

He discovered the effect of length on the conductivities of different materials by using wires of the same diameters but of different lengths. Then using wires of the same materials, he studied the effect of varied cross-sectional areas on conductivity, noting it was not altered if the cross-sectional area was proportional to the length. He theorized that the wires offered a natural resistance to the passage of electrical current. His conclusion is found in his law—the magnitude of the current in a galvanic circuit is directly proportional to the sum of all the electromotive forces and inversely proportional to the whole of the reduced length of the circuit—current equals electromotive force divided by resistance.

This achievement appeared in Schweigger's Journal in 1826 entitled "Determination of the Law in Accordance with which Metals Conduct Electricity, Together with an Outline of a Theory of the Voltaic Apparatus and of Schweigger's Multiplier." It was expanded into a book, "Die Galvanische Kette," in 1827.

There was much criticism of his work, some so severe that Ohm was dismissed from his teaching position. Brokenhearted and bitter he returned to Erlangen and lived by tutoring and odd jobs for six years, while continuing his experiments.

Around 1831, Pouillet in France demonstrated the truth of Ohm's experiments. Soon others became interested and accepted his work. This acceptance led to many honors. The Bavarian government appointed him to the chair of Physics of the Polytechnic School of Nurnberg in 1833. In 1841, The Council of the Royal Society of London awarded him the Copley Medal and in 1842 made him a Foreign Associate of the Royal Society, a distinction previously won only by the German scientist, Gauss. Maximilian II, in 1849, gave him the chair of Physics at the University of Munich and the Academy of Science named him Conservator of Mathematical Physics. He also became an advisor in the development of telegraphy for the state.

Despite the many years of struggle for the recognition of truth, Ohm remained quiet, simple in taste, courteous, and generous to his colleagues. His new stature did not alter these characteristics, although it was short-lived. His health began to fail and on July 7, 1854, he died of apoplexy.

Twenty-seven years later, in 1881, The International Electrical Congress established the "ohm" as the standard unit of electrical resistance.

FLORENCE H. LARKOWSKI

ORGANIC ELECTRICAL INSULATION

Definition of Insulation and Its Purpose

The terms "insulation" and "dielectric" are commonly used interchangeably. To some the term "dielectric" denotes a medium for storing electrical energy; whereas, "insulation" refers to the wall around a conductor to control the flow of current into its useful path and to prevent its escape to ground or the surroundings.

There is no perfect dielectric or insulation unless a vacuum can be so considered. Insulators are materials in which electrons are not easily dislodged. There is no sharp division between conductors and insulators, but there is a wide range in specific conductivity between the best of each. Under changes in temperature and frequency, a conductor may become a semiconductor and insulators become conductors.

An arbitrary division of conductors and insulators has been made covering ranges as follows:

	Resistivity, Ohm-Cm	Dielectric Constant
I Conductors	$0-10^6$	30–100
II Semiconductors	10^6-10^{12}	6–30
III Good insulators	$10^{12}-10^{20}$	1–6

It is not within the scope of this entry to discuss gaseous, liquid, and solid dielectric theory and the various ways dielectrics store electrical energy. The phenomena of electronic and interfacial polarization of electric moments, absorption effects, etc., are discussed elsewhere in this book and in the references at the end of this entry. Because dielectrics are not perfect insulators, it may be sufficient to remember that

with the insulating materials being discussed, there are dielectric losses showing up as heat which become more and more important with increase in temperature, voltage, and frequency.

Major functions of electrical insulation are: to keep the current in its proper path in the conductor, or to act as a dielectric barrier or separator, as in a capacitor; to improve heat transfer and prevent overheating; to bond and strengthen the coils or windings to withstand vibration and movement under surges, shock, etc.; to cut down current leakage or withstand moisture, chemical, and oil attack, as well as the effects of corona and radiation; to protect the surface of windings from corrosive atmospheres or chemical attack; and to provide structural strength and to withstand the mechanical abuse of assembly and manufacture.

The latter is a very important consideration. The abuse of assembly has made it necessary to develop wire coatings with extreme toughness and elongation properties and to develop strong materials which maintain those properties even after being bent, hammered or scraped. This had led to very conservative engineering designs and a material may be used at only one-tenth of its capacity as a dielectric.

Surges and peaks or spikes may expose the insulation to an extremely high voltage and temperature for a microsecond of time; such exposure, if repeated often enough, can lead to early breakdown. The dielectric strength of the insulation must be sufficient to take care of these stresses.

Until the last fifteen years a favorite truism, on which discussions of the role and importance of electrical insulation were based, was that all electrical insulating materials, with the exception of glass, porcelain, asbestos, and mica, are organic in nature. They are, therefore, susceptible to thermal degradation and to chemical attack. As a consequence of their vulnerability under service conditions to decomposition and oxidation, organic insulating materials were held to be the major factor limiting the useful life of electrical equipment.

This truism still holds in the broadest sense, but developments of new resins and polymers, unforseen at the beginning of the plastic age in the early 1930's, coupled with improvements in many prewar types of insulating materials, have produced organic materials which withstand double the original Class "A" temperature level of 105°C. This level was established in 1913 from the fact that materials such as paper, cotton, and silk, begin to lose their water of composition and deteriorate at that temperature. It was not until 1957 that official recognition was given to the fact that organic materials had greatly outstripped this limiting temperature of performance. The IEEE standard ⅜1 was revised and the possibility admitted that some resins and polymers can withstand much higher hot-spot temperatures and conditions of service.[1]

The original insulating materials used were those readily at hand known to be dielectrics, poor conductors, or good insulators: cotton, linen, silk, paper, mineral oils, vegetable drying oils, and varnishes made of natural gums like shellac and copal, either alone or blended with drying oils. Because mica is such a good dielectric, but by itself difficult to apply, means were found early in electrical insulation development to split it into very thin somewhat flexible splittings. These thin splittings were laid on a backing sheet of paper or fabric with a suitable organic binder, such as shellac or asphalt, and made into flexible, rigid, or moldable sheets and tapes.

Paper made of cellulose in many forms, such as rag, Kraft, and fish paper, was used extensively until the war period. It is still being used for low-temperature rated (Class A) rotating machinery and liquid-filled transformers, capacitors, etc.

The chief function of paper is that of a separator or a carrier for resin, plastic, or varnish insulation. Untreated paper has a dielectric strength about equal to air and is very susceptible to moisture pickup. When treated or when immersed in dry oil, it becomes a useful dielectric barrier material even in large power transformers.

Fabrics are woven textiles. Cloth in the form of tapes and sheets or rolls is used to a limited extent untreated for tying and lashing. It is more frequently treated with varnish. Cotton, silk, and linen were used at first, but they have been augmented or replaced by several synthetic fabrics, such as rayon, nylon, and "Dacron."

New polymers, in the form of films and synthetic mats and woven fabrics, have replaced a large percentage of the paper and cotton universally used up to two decades ago. Fiber glass and "Dacron-"glass mats and woven cloths have also been widely substituted for cellulose derivatives, with and without a resin or varnish coating.

Synthetic Resins and Polymers

Many organic insulations used today are plastics. They are originally monomers or compounds of low molecular weight which can react with each other or with other monomers. They copolymerize or condense with or without a catalyst to form high-molecular weight polymers with properties which depend on many factors. Chief among these are time, temperature, degree of cure, and compatibility with other materials in contact in the system.

A thermosetting material is one that sets or hardens and does not again soften with heat or dissolve readily in solvents, as does a thermoplastic material. For an excellent short discussion of polymer chemistry and the formation and structure of polymers refer to Callinan and Javitz.[2]

The development of synthetic resin polymer chemistry has coincided with the equally rapid development of new understanding of dielectric behavior and with new applications for electrical insulation materials. This is not entirely a coincidence, however, but a result of an awakening to the vast possibility of these new polymers in meeting the increasingly difficult requirements of electrical and electronic design. The tailoring of insulation with specific properties to meet a need is one of the great advantages obtained when the switch from natural products to synthetics became possible.

Detailed properties of plastics and a more comprehensive discussion of their myriad uses, beyond the scope of this article, can be found in the references cited. Insulation engineering fundamentals have been discussed briefly by Graham Lee Moses and others in *Insulation Magazine* during 1956–1958, the series available as a reprint from the publisher.[11]

It is important to point out that because of the continued knowledge accumulated by the chemist, the physicist, and the engineer, design engineers are making better use of both old and new insulating materials. They can, with confidence, use materials closer to their maximum capabilities, thus cutting the traditionally very conservative factor of safety, with resultant savings in materials, labor, and size and weight of apparatus. Materials are available to give a much higher threshold at which insulation deterioration can affect the performance of equipment.

Classes of Insulating Materials

The list of important insulating materials is a long one, which cannot be covered here in detail. Invariably the adoption of a new material does not completely eliminate the old ones, so that the list grows and grows. It is difficult to classify insulating materials and their properties with complete accuracy into definite groups depending on their chemical constitution. (See **Dielectric Chemistry**.) However, such classifications have been made and are of value in screening the enormous number of materials available. They are useful as a guide in making proper choice of materials or systems for a given application, even if open to some error. The danger lies in the fact that a given family of resins or polymers, for example, the silicones or the polyesters, has become so extensive and includes so many individual materials that a wide diversity of properties is possible even in one class.

Forms of Insulating Materials

Organic insulating materials occur in many forms—as papers, resins, polymers, varnishes, elastomers, and encapsulating compounds, with and without inorganic fillers. They are also available as sheets, laminates, molded forms, coatings on wire and on metal, films, and woven and nonwoven fabrics. Most of the newer important organic materials are plastics or polymers. A polymer may be used alone as a liquid or a solid, or may be dissolved in a solvent. It may be used to impregnate or bond paper, synthetic or cellulose fabrics, glass, cloth, or mica. Insulating materials are used to coat metals, wire, cable, sleeving, and tubing, or they may be used to cement and bond laminations, laminates, coils, and windings.

Laminates are rigid or flexible composites, or insulation-sandwiches of papers, cloths, mica, films, etc., available in a great variety of combinations. Combined with fillers, such as silica, asbestos, wood, flour, and glass, polymers, varnishes, and resins are used to make putties, pastes, molding compounds, elastomer coatings, and encapsulating compounds, as well as molded parts of great diversity of form.

The purpose behind the fabrication of all these types is functional, to make them into usable forms capable of being applied easily and effectively to give maximum strength and protection, be it as a covering over a single conductor, coil insulation, ground insulation, or to separate coils from the magnetic circuit or ground. They may act as structural support or barriers, or to provide protection from electrical, thermal, chemical, or mechanical attack.

The practical combination or form may be a compromise which is not always as good as the original material in its electrical properties. The binder or impregnant may lower the dielectric strength, but give the flexibility needed for application, for example, in a mica tape, where a theoretical 3000 volts per mil material actually decreases to 500 volts per mil as used. The thermal life and electrical properties of a mica tape are both inferior to that of a sheet of mica because of the organic binder, but the mica sheet is absolutely unusable in many applications in its natural form. Many examples could be given of this kind of compromise.

Materials must have adequate service properties, but, in addition must be readily applied to the conductor, coil, transformer, or electronic device in a practical manufacturing process.

Performance of Electrical Insulation

In electrical equipment the performance of insulation depends on:

1. The inherent chemical, physical, electrical and thermal properties of the insulating materials, which are primarily the result of chemical structure and manufacturing processing.

2. Adequate designs which take advantage of the better properties of materials while minimizing or circumventing the poorer properties. All design choice is usually a compromise.

3. The assumption that the materials chosen can be applied without difficulty and that competent manufacturing procedures are established.

4. Environmental factors in service, which may have detrimental effects upon the insulating system.

Deterioration of Organic Insulation

The design engineer knows what is the useful life and reliability level of the machine or device he is designing before proceeding to a choice of an insulation system. Service life can be a matter of a fraction of a second to twenty or more years.

Chemical changes which result in insulation deterioration are usually caused by one or more of the following: depolymerization, oxidation, hydrolysis, corrosion, and electrical effects.

All of these deterioration effects are greatly accelerated by heat. Many follow at least in a practical approximation the ten degree rule of chemical reaction rates—doubling of the rate of reaction with each rise of ten degrees. This has led to wide attention being directed to the evaluation of thermal life of insulation, using accelerated test procedures and estimating life from the curve plotted from the logarithm of life in hours versus the reciprocal of the absolute temperature by extrapolation. These test procedures for compatible systems give straight lines which have been very useful in determining relative life and temperature resistance of materials and systems.[5, 6]

References

1. IEEE Standard №1 (1962) and Supplements №98 and №99, "General Principles upon which Temperature Limits are Based in Rating of Electrical Equipment and Test Procedures for the Evaluation of Insulating Materials and Systems," New York, Institute of Electrical and Electronics Engineering, 1962.
2. CALLINAN, T. D., AND JAVITZ, A. E., "Fundamental Properties of Plastics," *Electrical Manufacturing*, **64**, No. 2, 105 (August 1959).
3. CALLINAN, T. D., AND JAVITZ, A. E., "The Molecular Key to Dielectric Properties," *ibid*, **62**, No. 1, 92 (July 1958).
4. VAIL, C. R., "Molecular Behavior of Composite Insulation," *Electro-Technology*, **69**, No. 2, 73 (February 1962).
5. IEEE Publication №57 (1959), "Test Procedure for Evaluation of Enameled Wire in Air," New York, Institute of Electrical and Electronics Engineering, 1959.
6. IEEE Publication №117 (1957), "Test Procedure for Evaluation of Materials for Random Wound Machinery," New York, Institute of Electrical and Electronics Engineering, 1957.
7. SHERBURNE, A. J., *Insulation*, **6**, (Oct. 1960).
8. "ASTM Standards on Electrical Insulation," D9 ASTM (1961), Philadelphia, American Society for Testing Materials, 1961.
9. SHERBURNE, A. J., *Product Engineering*, **32**, No. 15, 41 (April 1961).
10. "Reinhold Electrical Insulation Materials," Materials and Methods Manual №137, New York, Reinhold Publishing Corp., 1957.
11. "Plastics Engineering Handbook," New York, Reinhold Publishing Corp., 1954, 1960.
12. *Insulation Magazine*, Directory/Encyclopedia Issue, **9**, No. 6, Libertyville, Illinois, Lake Publishing Corporation (May 1963).
13. "Modern Plastics Encyclopedia," New York, Plastics Catalog Corp., 1962.
14. "The Thermoplastic Selector," *Plastics Technology*, **8**, No. 9, 1 (Sept. 1962).

ARTHUR J. SHERBURNE

Cross-references: *Ceramic Insulation*, entries carrying *Dielectric* and *Dielectrics* designation.

OSTWALD, FRIEDRICH WILHELM (1853–1932)

Born in Riga, Latvia, September 2, 1853, Friedrich Wilhelm Ostwald was educated at the University of Dorpat, where he studied chemistry. In 1882 he was appointed professor of chemistry at the Riga Polytechnikum. Ostwald's interest in physical chemistry was greatly stimulated by a dissertation he read in 1884. This was Arrhenius' famous "Theory of electrolytes." Ostwald went to visit Arrhenius and a lifelong friendship resulted. Another friend of Ostwald was van't Hoff, with whom he founded in 1887 the "Zeitschrift für physikalische Chemie." It was Ostwald, who after reading Gibbs' study on heterogeneous equilibria, translated this classic into German to the great benefit of European scientists. But Ostwald's contributions were not limited to the recognition of great men and ideas; his own researches include brilliant investigations of electrochemistry, the theory of weak acids and bases, equilibria between esters and their components, the inversion of sugar, and a study of catalysis. The latter study resulted in the Ostwald-Brauer process for the catalytic oxidation of ammonia to nitric acid, a reaction of great value to German industry during the first world war. Most of his studies were made at the University of Leipzig, where, in 1887 he had accepted the chair of physical chemistry. Ostwald was awarded the Nobel prize for chemistry in 1909 "for his work on catalysis and on the conditions of chemical equilibrium and velocities of chemical reactions." In addition to his scientific interests, Ostwald wrote on philosophy, music, painting, etc. His scientific works include: "Lehrbuch der algemeinen Chemie," 2 vols., 1883–1887, "Elektrochemie," 1894–1895 and "Die Energie," 1908.

Ostwald's influence on electrochemistry in this

country was very great, since several of the outstanding American electrochemists studied under him at the University of Leipzig, among them Bancroft, Cottrell, Fink, Lind, and Whitney. After a long retirement from active scientific investigations, Ostwald died on April 4, 1932.

BERNARD JAFFE

OVERVOLTAGE, HYDROGEN

A voltage which is considerably larger than one calculates thermodynamically must be applied to an electrolytic cell to decompose water at measurable rates for the reaction

$$H_2 + \tfrac{1}{2}O_2 \rightarrow H_2O \quad \Delta G_0 = -56.96 \text{ kcal}$$

$$E_0 = -\Delta G_0/n\mathbf{F} = 1.23 \text{ volts}$$

The excess voltage over and above this decomposition voltage is usually designated with η(eta), and referred to as "overvoltage."

The overvoltage can be split into the part originating at the hydrogen evolving electrode and the part associated with the oxygen evolving electrode. Hydrogen overvoltage, then, is defined as the difference in potential between a hydrogen electrode at equilibrium and a hydrogen electrode subjected to cathodic current flow in the same electrolyte. Similarly, oxygen overvoltage (q.v.) is defined as the difference in potential between an oxygen electrode at equilibrium and one being anodized with an external current. Thus, the expression "overpotential" is sometimes used instead of "overvoltage" for individual electrodes.

Overvoltage and current density are directly related. The dependence was first described quantitatively by Tafel in 1905 by the equation

$$\eta = a + b \log i \qquad (1)$$

where i is the current density, and a and b are constants. (See **Tafel Lines.**) The fact that current and voltage of an electrode are mutually dependent on each other is observed not only for hydrogen or oxygen evolving electrodes but, in fact, for any electrode process, for example, metal dissolution, metal deposition, and electrochemical reduction or oxidation of dissolved species on redox electrodes. The general phenomena of a nonlinear current-voltage relationship is usually called "polarization" (q.v.). The terms overvoltage and polarization are therefore largely synonymous and often used interchangeably. However, overvoltage always refers to a deviation from the reversible potential of the particular reaction in question and is used with respect to the relation between current and voltage *for one single reaction only*. Polarization refers more generally to a change in potential, not necessarily from the reversible value, and not necessarily restricted to the effect of one single electrode reaction only.

Eq. (1) is obeyed for hydrogen evolution on a large number of different metals. The hydrogen discharge reaction can be written as follows:

$$H^+ + e^- \rightarrow H_{ads}$$

or, in alkaline solution

$$H_2O + e^- \rightarrow H_{ads} + OH^-$$

followed by

$$2H_{ads} \rightarrow H_2(gas)$$

Much speculation has been expended in the past on defining the discharge process more precisely. For example, the mechanisms of hydrogen discharge on a "bare" spot on the metal surface, the so-called "Volmer" discharge step, followed by recombination of discharged atoms, the so-called "Tafel" step, have been distinguished from the mechanism where a hydrogen ion is discharged onto or into the immediate vicinity of an adsorbed H atom, followed by immediate recombination therewith; this has been termed the "Heyrovsky" reaction. Physically, such distinctions are of little value without an exact description of the configuration of the activated complex, since strong interaction forces must be present which affect the adsorption energy of all reacting and discharged species. The dependence between activation energy and degree of coverage with discharged hydrogen atoms is probably approximately linear, but not of any considerable importance, since the dominant term, arising from electric dipoles of the M-H bonds, is not large for neutral discharged species. Experimental results on hydrogen overvoltage are summarized in Figs. 1 and 2.

The "a" values differ considerably from metal to metal, the "b" values are remarkably constant, about 0.120 volts. Only for very small overvoltages are smaller b values observed. However, under these conditions it is difficult to separate the cathodic reaction from the anodic (backward) reaction and from diffusion overvoltage effects

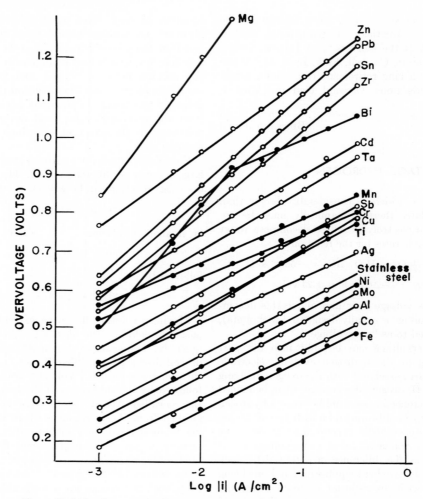

FIG. 1. Relation between hydrogen overvoltage and logarithm of current density, i, in amp/sq cm for a variety of different electrode materials in 6 N sodium hydroxide solutions at 25°C. (Data from M. D. Zhoulder and V. V. Stender, *Zhur. Priklad. Khim.*, **31**, 711 (1958)).

which become more pronounced at small overvoltages. In the immediate vicinity of the equilibrium potential, the current-voltage relations are linear.

Early investigators have noted the drastic influence of the electrode materials, and they have used the term "overvoltage" in particular to describe the influence of the metal rather than the current. In the early literature there is much discussion about the occurrence of a so-called "minimum overvoltage" for different metals, determined by such techniques as the observation of gas bubble formation. Today, it is generally accepted that there is no minimum overvoltage

but that hydrogen evolves, although at extremely small rates initially, as soon as the theoretical equilibrium value is exceeded in the cathodic direction.

Dependence of Hydrogen Overvoltage on Current Density

The theories put forward over the years to explain the logarithmic relation between current and voltage and to derive the quantitative value of the "b" constant are varied, but lack a rigorous approach. Tafel, in 1905, assumed that hydrogen atoms adsorbed on the electrode are in equilibrium with hydrogen ions in solution, and the

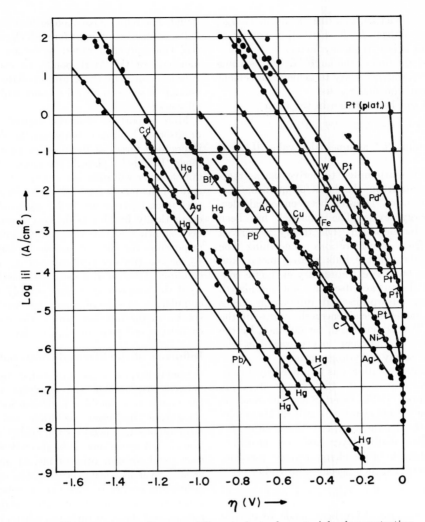

FIG. 2. Hydrogen overvoltage on different electrode materials, demonstrating the uniformity of slopes of the Tafel equation. (Data from Ref. 12 and 14.)

electrode potential thus is determined by

$$\psi = \psi_0 + RT/\mathbf{F} \ln \left([H^+]/[H]_{ads}\right) \qquad (2)$$

The current was thought to be proportional to the square of the adsorbed hydrogen atom concentration, since $H_{ads} + H_{ads} \rightarrow H_2(gas)$

$$i = kH^2_{ads} \qquad (3)$$

Combining (2) and (3) one obtains

$$\psi - \psi_0 = \eta = a - 2.303 \, RT/2\mathbf{F} \log i$$

Thus, the constant "b" in Eq. (1) assumes the value -29.6 mv at 25°C. This is a factor of four smaller than the experimentally determined value

at high overvoltages. The derivation is also unsatisfactory because it assumes thermodynamic equilibrium between electrode surface and solution.

In 1930, Erdey-Gruz and Volmer introduced a kinetic approach, using an Arrhenius-type rate equation for the forward and backward reaction. The height of the activation energy barrier was assumed to depend linearly on the electrode potential and the following rate equation was derived:

$$i = A \exp \left(-E - Z_i e_0 \eta \alpha\right)/kT \qquad (4)$$

where Z_i is the valence of the charge involved in

the transfer reaction, e_0 is the electronic charge, η the overvoltage, E the activation energy at $\eta = 0$, and A is a frequency factor.

The introduction of the factor, α, with a value of about $\frac{1}{2}$, was necessary to achieve agreement with the experimental results.

Eq. (4) can be rewritten in the form

$$\eta = a - 2.303\ (RT/\alpha \mathbf{F})\ \log i$$

The constant "b" assumes the value 0.120 if $\alpha = \frac{1}{2}$.

Gurney has attempted to derive the current-voltage relation on the basis of quantum-mechanical electron transfer between equal electronic energy levels. The approach has been expanded by Gerischer. The theory is derived entirely from considerations concerning the electronic state in the bulk phases, metal, and electrolyte, but the extraordinary energetic conditions at the surface itself are not considered. The strong adsorption and interaction forces probably create special energetic states in the interface. This is evidenced, for instance, by the dependence of hydrogen overvoltage on the adsorption energy of hydrogen atoms.

The Volmer equation was improved by Frumkin to take into account the voltage drop, ψ_1, in the diffuse double layer. Since the reacting protons are located near the so-called "Helmholtz plane" in the double layer, the voltage drop, ψ_1, in the diffuse double layer can have no direct effect on the rate of the charge-transfer reaction. The rate-equation then becomes, instead of (4)

$$i = A\ \exp\ [-E - Z_i e_0 \alpha\,(\eta - \psi_1)/kT] \qquad (5)$$

Recently, attempts have been made to modify the current-voltage equation to incorporate the effects of surface coverage. The hydrogen deposition current has been assumed proportional to $(1 - \theta)$ where θ is the surface coverage with atomic hydrogen. On the other hand, the backward reaction (ionization of H_2) has been set proportional to θ. This modification is only correct if the adsorption energy and the activation energy themselves are independent of surface coverage. There is evidence, however, that the adsorption energies are dependent on coverage. This would necessitate inserting the coverage exponentially into the rate equation, since both adsorption and activation energy must appear in the exponent. A difficulty arises from the question in relating the voltage and the surface coverage. No really satisfactory approaches have been found. The relation between surface coverage and voltage must be different for each electrode material. One approach would be to use the dipole moments of the M-H bonds, to calculate the voltage created by them, and to relate this dipole voltage in some empirical manner with the overall voltage.

More important than the mutual interaction of adsorbed hydrogen atoms are the electrostatic interaction forces of the reacting protons in the inner "Helmholtz plane." The electric field of the double layer will influence strongly the energetic state of the reacting protons. The protons do not need to partly cross the double layer to be affected energetically by this field. Very recently it has been shown that this electrostatic interaction is responsible for the appearance of the factor of $\frac{1}{2}$, or the transfer coefficient of α, in the rate equation. The factor, α, becomes exactly equal to $\frac{1}{2}$ if the overvoltage is due entirely to the accumulation of charge associated with reacting species in the interface, and if the double layer capacity is independent of potential.

Influence of the Electrode Material

Bonhoeffer, in 1924, discovered the relation between overvoltage and catalytic activity of the metals to recombine hydrogen atoms. Both electrolytic hydrogen evolution and catalytic recombination, depend on the energy of adsorption of hydrogen atoms. It has been demonstrated that the hydrogen overvoltage, in general, decreases with increasing heat of adsorption. The adsorption energy in turn can be related to the cohesion energy, or sublimation energy, of the metals, and these, in turn, to electron concentration, surface energy, interatomic distance, compressibility, melting point, and electronic work function.

Electrochemical interfaces contain species other than protons and discharged hydrogen atoms. In particular, certain metals show very strong affinity to water or oxygen, in fact, so strong that these metals cannot be plated out from aqueous solution. The discharge of hydrogen on such metal surfaces as Mo, Ta, W, Zr, Nb, Cr, and Mn, proceeds with relative difficulty because of the strong affinity of oxygen to the surface. Cathodic polarization may not remove the oxide films or adsorbed oxygen species completely. Hydrogen discharge then will take place on partially oxidized surfaces. The effect of the (theoretically high) adsorption energy of hydro-

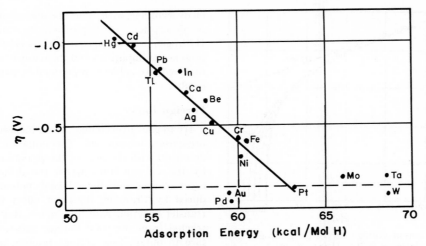

Fig. 3. Dependence of hydrogen overvoltage on electrode material at 10^{-3} amp/sq cm in 1 N hydrochloric acid at 25°C. The overvoltage in volts is plotted against the adsorption energy of atomic hydrogen. (Ref. 9).

gen on these metals is, thus, obscured by the strong affinity for oxygen. Hydrogen overvoltage thus depends on the *relative adsorption energy of protons and foreign species*. The experimental evidence for the relation between overvoltage and adsorption energy is illustrated in Fig. 3.

The Dependence of Overvoltage on pH

Changes in gas pressure and in pH will naturally shift the reversible hydrogen potential. Since overvoltage is defined here as the difference in potential between the reversible electrode and the working electrode in the same solution, at the same pressure, and at the same temperature, the overvoltage must be expressed with respect to a reversible electrode subjected to the same conditions as the working electrode. If this definition of overvoltage is used, one observes on many metals the following dependence on pH: the overvoltage first increases with increasing pH, and then decreases again in alkaline solution. The maximum overvoltage is observed at about pH 8. This is illustrated in Fig. 4 for hydrogen evolution on mercury. It should be pointed out, however, that this variation of overvoltage with pH is surprisingly small considering that the concentration of the reacting species changes by many orders of magnitude.

Dependence on H_2 Pressure

In the potential region where the Tafel relation holds, the potential of a hydrogen evolving

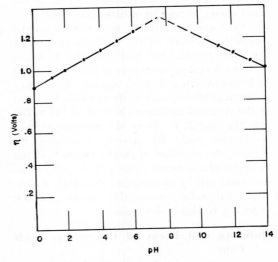

Fig. 4. Hydrogen overvoltage on mercury as a function of pH at 10^{-4} amp/sq cm. (Data from Ref. 12).

electrode is independent of hydrogen pressure. Since the reversible potential depends on pressure, so does the overvoltage:

$$\eta = (\psi - \psi_0) = \eta_0 - (RT/2\mathbf{F}) \ln p_{H_2}$$

where $\eta°$ is the overvoltage at $p_{H_2} = 1$ atm. The independence of the potential, ψ, on pressure during cathodic hydrogen is naturally expected in the region where the backward reaction can be neglected (Fig. 5).

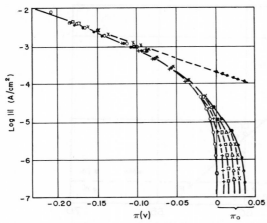

FIG. 5. Current-voltage curves for hydrogen evolution on platinum in $1N$ H_2SO_4 at 20°C and different H_2 pressures. ○ 740 mm, + 458 mm, □ 271 mm, △ 128 mm, × 70 mm, ● 35 mm. (Ref. 12).

This points to the interesting fact that, in the Tafel region, it may be of little value to express the hydrogen overvoltage with respect to the reversible electrode in the same electrolyte, at the same temperature and pressure. It might be more revealing to express the voltage of the hydrogen evolving electrode against an arbitrary constant reference, such as the calomel electrode, or the standard hydrogen electrode at pH 0, 760 mm Hg, and 25°C. Then, the influence of concentrations could be properly elucidated by keeping the potential of the hydrogen evolving electrode at a constant value with respect to this reference, and by determining the effect of concentration on the rate. In this way the reaction order can be clearly determined.

Build-up and Decay of Overvoltage with Time

At constant current the build-up of hydrogen overvoltage is linear initially and then gradually approaches a constant value. The initial slope of the charging curve is often used to estimate the "adsorption capacity." Upon interruption of current, the voltage decays logarithmically with time. The amount of desorbed gas during decay is an approximately linear function of the potential. Experiments on overvoltage build-up and decay are of interest for the determination of the degree of coverage of the electrode and of the relation between potential and the number of adsorbed hydrogen atoms and undischarged protons on the electrode surface. Slow changes

of overvoltage with time are due to adsorption, or desorption, of impurities, or "inhibitors." Hydrogen overvoltage is very sensitive to the presence of impurities and these must be carefully removed to achieve reproducible experimental results.

Foreign Ions

Hydrogen overvoltage is influenced by the presence of foreign ions. This influence is usually described with the help of the ψ_1 potential, given by the voltage drop across the diffuse double layer as discussed above. The ψ_1 potential, introduced by Frumkin, does not affect the actual transfer reaction rate and must, thus, be subtracted from the total voltage across the interface to obtain that voltage fraction influencing the activation energy. In general, specifically adsorbed anions decrease hydrogen overvoltage, specifically adsorbed cations increase hydrogen overvoltage. However, under certain conditions, adsorption of anions can instead increase hydrogen overvoltage. This is the case when the effect of the anion is not purely electrostatic, but rather chemical in nature; the adsorption of anions then decreases the covalent adsorption energy of the H atoms. Thus, a surface which is covered with anions will behave similar to a surface covered with an oxide and will exhibit a lower M-H bond energy and, thus, a higher hydrogen overvoltage.

Separation Factors

Of particular interest for the elucidation of the hydrogen evolution reaction are experiments with the hydrogen isotopes deuterium and tritium. (See **Heavy Water-Electrolytic Production.**) The separation factor is defined as the H/D ratio in the gas, divided by the H/D ratio in the electrolyte. It is characteristically dependent on the electrode material, on temperature, and, as shown quite recently, on the electrode potential.

Exchange Currents

Eq. (4) for the hydrogen evolution reaction can also be formulated

$$i = i_0 \exp\left(Z_i e_0 \alpha \eta / kT\right)$$

with the use of so-called "exchange currents," i_0. The exchange currents (q.v.) are obtained by extrapolation of the Tafel lines, as shown in Figs. 1 and 2, to the reversible hydrogen potential. The notation, exchange current, can be misleading, however. The hydrogen evolution reaction is quite irreversible on most metals and the structure of the double layer is different at the reversible hydrogen potential than at cathodic polarization and vigorous hydrogen evolution. For instance, sulfate ions become strongly adsorbed on lead in sulfuric acid, as the overvoltage decreases. This adsorption of SO_4^{--} ion increases in intensity, and progresses into the formation of lead sulfate. The potential of the $Pb/PbSO_4$ electrode is -350 mv with respect to the reversible hydrogen electrode. At the potential of the latter, lead is rapidly oxidized to lead sulfate. A lead electrode, actually held at the potential of the reversible hydrogen electrode, would probably show a much smaller exchange current for hydrogen evolution than that obtained from extrapolation of the Tafel plot.

References

1. TAFEL, J., *Z. physik. Chem.*, **50**, 641 (1905).
2. BAARS, E., *Marburger Sitzungsberichte*, **63**, 214 (1928).
3. HEYROVSKY, J., *Recueil Trav. Chim. Pays-Bas.*, **46**, 582 (1927).
4. ERDEY-GRUZ, T., AND VOLMER, M., *Z. physik. Chem.*, Abt. A., **150**, 203 (1930).
5. GURNEY, R. W., *Proc. Roy. Soc. (London)*, Ser. A., **134**, 137 (1931).
6. FRUMKIN, A. N., *Z. physik. Chem.*, **164**, 121 (1933).
7. FRUMKIN, A. N., *Acta Physicochim. U.S.S.R.*, **18**, 23 (1943).
8. HORIUTI, J., AND POLANYI, M., *Acta Physicochim. U.S.S.R.*, **2**, 505 (1935).
9. RUETSCHI, P., AND DELAHAY, P., *J. Chem. Phys.*, **23**, 195 (1955).
10. RUETSCHI, P., *J. Electrochem. Soc.*, **106**, 819 (1959).
11. GERISCHER, H., *Z. physik. Chem.*, **26**, 223 (1960).
12. VETTER, K. J., *Angewandte Chemie*, **73**, 277 (1961).
13. BOCKRIS, J. O'M., "Modern Aspects of Electrochemistry," p. 198, London, Butterworths, 1954.
14. VETTER, K. J., "Elektrochemische Kinetik," p. 476–484, Berlin-Gottingen-Heidelberg, Springer-Verlag, 1961.
15. FRUMKIN, A. N., "Advances in Electrochemistry and Electrochemical Engineering," Edited by P. Delahay, New York, Interscience Publishers, Volume I (1961) p. 65; Volume III (1963) p. 287.
16. IVES, D. J. G., AND JANZ, G. J., "Reference Electrodes," p. 71, New York-London, Academic Press, 1961.

PAUL RUETSCHI

Cross-references: *Electrode Double Layer; Electrode Reactions, Kinetics; Exchange Currents; Heavy Water—Electrolytic Production; Polarization; Tafel Lines.*

OVERVOLTAGE, OXYGEN

Oxygen overvoltage is defined as the difference in potential between an oxygen electrode at equilibrium and one being oxidized with an external current.

The oxygen evolution process can be described by the overall equation

$$2H_2O \rightarrow O_2 + 4H^+ + 4e^-$$

or

$$4OH^- \rightarrow O_2 + 2H_2O + 4e^-$$

The reversible oxygen potential is extremely difficult, if not impossible, to realize experimentally, since oxygen evolution is always associated with the formation of surface oxide, or monomolecular chemisorbed oxygen layers, which tend to be electrochemically active by themselves. The oxygen evolution mechanism involving the formation of higher metal oxides which subsequently decompose into lower oxides and oxygen according to

$$MeO_n + H_2O \rightarrow MeO_{(n+1)} + 2H^+ + 2e^-$$

$$MeO_{(n+1)} \rightarrow MeO_n + (1/2)O_2$$

has received much attention in the past. However, it is quite difficult to distinguish between higher oxides and chemisorbed oxygen species, such as O, OH, H_2O_2, or HO_2.

Relation between Current Density and Overvoltage

The oxygen overvoltage follows accurately a Tafel equation (q.v.), identical to the one for the evolution of hydrogen

$$\eta = a + b \log i$$

whereby one observes for b the value

$$b = +2.302 \, RT/0.5\mathbf{F} = 0.120 \text{ volts at } 25°C$$

for a variety of different electrode materials.

The oxygen overvoltage usually is observed to increase slowly with time. Several investigators have shown that this increase is linear with the logarithm of time. If the potential is held constant, the logarithm of the current correspondingly decreases linearly with the logarithm of time, over many hours. These slow changes of overvoltage must be connected with changes in the oxide film, such as slow chemisorption of oxygen species, increase in oxide film thickness, or by slow chemisorption of foreign anions.

Dependence on pH

Oxygen overvoltage has been found to be independent of pH if proper consideration is given to the fact that the theoretical reversible potential itself is pH dependent. This is illustrated in Fig. 1 below.

The Dependence of the Oxygen Overvoltage on Electrode Material

The discharged oxygen species, adsorbed oxygen atoms, and higher oxides, have different bonding energies to the oxidized surface depending on the nature of the metal. In general, the higher the energy of formation of the higher oxide, or the higher the adsorption bond, the lower is the oxygen overvoltage. (Fig. 2)

If the anodic currents are very high, particularly in more concentrated electrolytes, products other than oxygen might be formed, such as $H_2S_2O_8$ in sulfuric acid at concentrations between 10 and 20 moles per liter, and H_2SO_5 at concentrations above 20 moles per liter.

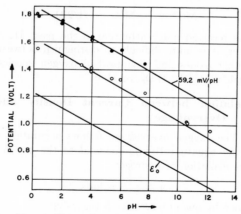

FIG. 1. Dependence of oxygen overvoltage on pH. The electrode potential during oxygen evolution for platinum (open circles) and gold (solid circles) at 5 μa/sq cm is plotted against pH at constant ionic strength. The line marked E_o is the theoretical reversible potential of the oxygen electrode. The difference between the electrode potential at 5 μa/sq cm and the reversible potential, that is the overvoltage, is independent of pH.

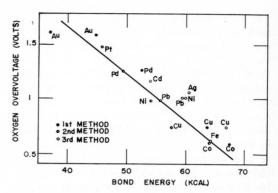

FIG. 2. Dependence of oxygen overvoltage on electrode material. Overvoltage at a current density of 1 amp/sq cm is plotted against the energy of the bond M—OH calculated by three different methods (Ref. 4).

The Cathodic Reduction of Oxygen

The reduction occurs in two steps

$$O_2 + 2H^+ + 2e^- \rightarrow H_2O_2$$
$$H_2O_2 + 2H^+ + 2e^- \rightarrow 2H_2O$$

On many electrodes, H_2O_2 can be detected experimentally. The oxygen-oxygen bond is not broken during the first reduction step. The second step, the reduction of H_2O_2, is accompanied by a considerable overvoltage on many metals. During anodic oxygen evolution one cannot detect the formation of H_2O_2. The potential of the reaction

$$H_2O \rightarrow H_2O_2 + 2H^+ + 2e^-$$

has a standard potential of 1.77 volts. Thus, only very small concentrations of H_2O_2 will be formed at potentials between 1.3 and 1.5 volts. These traces of H_2O_2 would be immediately oxidized to O_2 since the reaction

$$H_2O_2 \rightarrow O_2 + 2H^+ + 2e^-$$

has a potential of only 0.68 volts. This makes it unlikely that H_2O_2 is a *defined* intermediate in the oxygen evolution reaction.

Activity

In all cases where H_2O molecules must be considered as the reactants, for oxygen evolution in acid solution, or for hydrogen evolution in alkaline solution, the effects of electrolyte composition on the activity of water must be considered. For instance, for oxygen evolution in strong sulfuric acid, the water molecules are in a different energetic state due to hydration, and react less readily, than in dilute sulfuric acid. Similarly, sulfate additions to H_2SO_4 can influence the activity of water.

At high anodic potentials the electrodes are covered with oxide layers or adsorbed oxygen species and adsorbed anions. These species form strong dipoles with the negative pole towards the solution. The voltage drop due to these dipole layers can be an appreciable fraction of the total overvoltage. The presence of these strongly adsorbed negative charges can cause in turn an incorporation of cations into the double layer. Thus, even under extreme anodic potentials, the nature of the cations in solution, i.e., their ionic radius, may influence the oxygen overvoltage.

It has been pointed out that the term overvoltage is often used interchangeably with polarization; the expressions "concentration overvoltage," "activation overvoltage," "reaction overvoltage," "crystallization overvoltage," and "ohmic overvoltage," coined in analogy to the corresponding expressions for polarization, are covered under the heading **Polarization.**

References

1. BOCKRIS, J. O'M., "Modern Aspects of Electrochemistry," p. 198, London, Butterworths, 1954.
2. VETTER, K. J., "Elektrochemische Kinetik," Berlin-Gottingen-Heidelberg, Springer-Verlag, 1961.
3. VETTER, K. J., *Angewandte Chemie*, **73**, 277 (1961).
4. RUETSCHI, P., AND DELAHAY, P., *J. Chem. Phys.*, **23**, 556 (1955).
5. RUETSCHI, P., *J. Electrochem. Soc.*, **106**, 819 (1959).
6. BREITER, M., "Advances in Electrochemistry and Electrochemical Engineering," edited by P. Delahay, p. 123, New York, Interscience Publishers, 1961.
7. IVES, D. J. G., AND JANZ, G. J., "Reference Electrodes," p. 360, New York–London, Academic Press, 1961.

PAUL RUETSCHI

OVERVOLTAGE MEASUREMENTS IN FUSED SALTS. See FUSED SALT OVERVOLTAGE MEASUREMENTS.

OXIDATION POTENTIAL. See ELECTRODE POTENTIAL ENTRIES.

OXYGEN, ELECTROLYTIC PRODUCTION. See WATER ELECTROLYSIS.

OZONE

Ozone is a blue unstable gas that has a characteristic pungent odor. Its chemical formula is O_3, and its molecular weight is 48. Ozone can be liquefied to form a deep blue liquid that has a boiling point of $-111.9°C$ and a melting point of $-192.3°C$.

Chemically, ozone is an excellent oxidizing agent with an oxidation potential of -2.07 volts referred to the hydrogen electrode at 25°C and a hydrogen activity of one.

Ozone can be produced by several techniques. It is formed in low concentrations of a few ppm by absorption of ultraviolet radiation by oxygen. In the upper atmosphere it reaches concentrations of 15 to 20 ppm at 75,000 to 80,000 feet as a result of natural radiation in the ultraviolet range, and this accounts for its occurrence in the atmosphere. In fact, this absorption of ultraviolet radiation by oxygen at great heights prevents such radiation from harming life on the earth. The amount of ozone varies with latitude, the season of the year, and the height of the tropopause.

Microwave energy has been used to dissociate oxygen near a surface cooled by liquid nitrogen where liquid ozone condenses. This technique produces 1 to 15 g/kwh. Similar techniques utilizing a high-voltage glow discharge will also produce ozone.

Electrolytic methods based on the electrolysis of sulfuric or perchloric acid have been reported to yield concentrations as high as 50 per cent by weight, but they are still in the experimental stage.

The most common commercial process used to produce ozone in concentrations of 1 to 6 per cent utilizes an ozonator or ozonizer which gives a corona discharge when air or oxygen is passed through it. Many different generators have been used, ranging from flat plates to cylindrical tubes. In general, all ozonizers consist of a pair of electrodes, a layer of insulation, an air space, and a source of high-voltage alternating current. The discharge space must be cooled to produce ozone at a reasonable rate, and air or oxygen passes through the air space to remove the ozone as it forms. A large part of the elec-

TABLE 1. CHARACTERISTICS OF COMMERCIAL OZONE GENERATORS

	Gap, in.	Volts	Cycles/sec	Maximum Energy, watts/sq ft	Ozone, lb per kwh	Typical Production Rate, lb per hr using air
Otto Plate	0.125	20,000	500	250	0.04–0.06	4
Bloc Societe d'Operation et d'Enterprises (Brussels)	0.125	22,000	50	90	0.11	2.7
Van der Made	0.04	7–8,000	500	200	0.10	0.25
Siemens-Halske		6,000	10,000	2,000	0.11	0.25
Welsbach Type C & G	0.10	15,000	50–60	35–40	0.11–0.13	2.5 (G204)

trical energy supplied to the ozonizer or generator is released as heat. This must be removed, usually by water cooling of the electrodes, since ozone decomposition is accelerated by heat.

Some pertinent characteristics of commercial ozone generators are given in Table 1.

The interesting chemistry of ozone is described in the various references.

Ozone is highly destructive to many microorganisms, such as bacteria, fungi, and algae, and has been used for many years as a water purification agent. In concentrations of less than 1 ppm it completely sterilizes and deodorizes water, and in addition oxidizes ferrous and manganous ions to their colorless forms.

In recent months, an ozone regenerative galvanic cell has been suggested.[4] The regeneration is accomplished by means of the photosensitized reaction of oxygen to ozone. An open circuit voltage of 0.87 v at 400°K is reported, and a short circuit current density of 89 amperes per square foot is estimated. The life time of the ozone is calculated to be 154 hours at 400°K. The weight of a 28 volt (1 kw) unit is estimated to be 1200 pounds.

The toxicity of ozone should be mentioned. The odor of ozone can be detected in very low concentrations, 1 to 5 parts per hundred million. In continued exposures to several parts per million eye irritation and coughing may result. Headache, depression, nausea, and pulmonary edema are observed if the exposure is continued. The 50 per cent lethal dose for small animals ranges from 4 to 25 parts per million for three hours. The maximum allowable concentration value is 0.1 ppm for an 8-hour day, 40-hour week, as recommended by the American Conference of Governmental Hygienists in 1955. Short exposures at higher concentrations are considered to be permissible.

References

1. JAFFE, L. S., AND ESTES, H. D., "Ozone Toxicity Hazard in Cabins of High Altitude Aircraft," *Aerospace Medicine*, in print, 1963.
2. "Ozone Chemistry and Technology," Advances in Chemistry, Series 21, Washington, American Chemical Society, 1959.
3. HANN, V. A., AND MANLEY, T. C., "Ozone," "Encyclopedia of Chemical Technology," Ed. by Kirk, R. E. and Othmer, D. F., Brooklyn, Interscience Publishing Co., 1953.
4. CHU, J. C., AND LIEBERMAN, MARTIN, "Ozone Regenerative Fuel Cell," AIChE Abstract No. 70, 49th National Meeting, New Orleans, March 10–14, 1963.

CHARLES K. HERSH

P

PARTIAL MOLAL QUANTITIES

In considering changes in thermodynamic quantities associated with a chemical reaction, no difficulty in encountered in physical interpretation as long as there is only one component per phase (gaseous, liquid, or solid). In the case of solutions, however, the values of the thermodynamic quantities (volume, enthalpy, free energy, etc.) are not in general equal to the sum of the values for the pure components separately. It is therefore useful to define *partial molal quantities* which allow an assignment of the contribution of each component. For any thermodynamic property, Q, of a system, the *partial molal quantity, $\bar{Q}_i$*, of *component i* is defined as

$$\bar{Q}_i \equiv \left(\frac{\partial Q}{\partial n_i}\right)_{P,T,n_j} \tag{1}$$

where P is the pressure, T is the temperature, n represents the number of moles, and j represents all components other than i.

It follows from Euler's theorem for homogeneous functions and from the definition of $\bar{Q}_i$ that

$$Q = \sum_i n_i \bar{Q}_i \tag{2}$$

It is largely because of this fact (Eq. (2)) that the concept of partial molal quantities is so useful. If the various values of $\bar{Q}_i$ are known as a function of composition, Q may be calculated. Alternatively, if the values of all $\bar{Q}_i$ but one and the value of Q are known, the value of $\bar{Q}$ for the last component may be evaluated.

In a two component system if Q at constant P, T, and n_2 is measured and plotted as a function of n_1, the value of $\bar{Q}_1$ at any value of n_1 is equal to the slope of the curve at that value of n_1, according to Eq. (1). Values of $\bar{Q}_2$ then may be evaluated at any of these values of relative concentrations by the use of Eq. (2).

A very useful relation between the differentials

of the partial molal properties of a system, sometimes referred to as the Gibbs-Duhem relation, will now be derived. It is evident that differentiation of Eq. (2) at constant P, T gives

$$\begin{aligned} dQ &= n_1 d\bar{Q}_1 + \bar{Q}_1 dn_1 + n_2 d\bar{Q}_2 + \bar{Q}_2 dn_2 + \cdots \\ &= \sum_i n_i d\bar{Q}_i + \sum_i \bar{Q}_i dn_i \end{aligned} \tag{3}$$

On the other hand, any extensive thermodynamic property may be expressed as a function of the amounts of the constituents. Thus, the methods of calculus give for the total differential of Q

$$\begin{aligned} dQ &= \left(\frac{\partial Q}{\partial n_1}\right)_{P,T,n_j} dn_1 + \left(\frac{\partial Q}{\partial n_2}\right)_{P,T,n_j} dn_2 + \cdots \\ &= \sum_i \bar{Q}_i dn_i \end{aligned} \tag{4}$$

If the right hand sides of Eqs. (3) and (4) are set equal to each other,

$$\sum_i n_i d\bar{Q}_i = 0 \tag{5}$$

The usefulness of this equation may be illustrated by the case of a two-component system.

$$n_1 d\bar{Q}_1 + n_2 d\bar{Q}_2 = 0 \tag{6}$$

or on integration between condition a and condition b,

$$\int_a^b d\bar{Q}_2 = (\bar{Q}_2)_b - (\bar{Q}_2)_a = -\int_a^b \frac{n_1}{n_2} d\bar{Q}_1 \tag{7}$$

Thus, the variation in $\bar{Q}$ of one component (from condition a to condition b) is given by an integral of the value of $\bar{Q}$ for the other component. Much use is made of Eq. (7) in evaluating such properties as the partial molal free energy or activity of a solute from the results of measurements of thermodynamic properties of the solvent (such as vapor pressure, freezing points, etc.) as a function of concentration of the solute.

As an example of the use of the above equations, the volume of a solution, V, may be measured as a function of the number of moles, n_2, of solute added, starting with n_1 moles of the pure solvent. (On the molal scale, n_2 = molality, m, if n_1 is the number of moles in 1000 grams of solvent.) In a plot of V against n_2 the slope at any n_2 is equal to the partial molal volume of the solute $\bar{V}_2$ at that value of n_2. The partial molal volume of the solvent, $\bar{V}_1$, can be evaluated at these same points by the use of Eq. (2). In general if $\bar{Q}_2$ or $\bar{Q}_1$ is known but not obtained from values of Q (as in the determination of free energies of the solvent from vapor pressure measurements), then Eq. (7) must be used to calculate the value of $\bar{Q}$ of the other component. Hence the use of (7) will also be shown for the evaluation of $\bar{V}_1$ from values of $\bar{V}_2$. By the use of Eq. (7) the value of $\bar{V}_1$ at any n_2 is given by

$$(\bar{V}_1)_{n_2} - (\bar{V}_1)_{n_2=0} = - \int_{n_2=0}^{n_2} \frac{n_2}{n_1} d\bar{V}_2 \qquad (8)$$

where the second term on the left is simply the molal volume of the pure solvent. (Additional methods for evaluating partial molal quantities from measurements on solutions are given in the references.)

An interesting consequence of the definition of a partial molal quantity and of the fact that in partial differentiation the order of differentiating does not matter is the following. If the partial derivative of Q with respect to n_i is differentiated with respect to the number of moles of any other component n_j,

$$\frac{\partial}{\partial n_j}\left(\frac{\partial Q}{\partial n_i}\right) = \frac{\partial^2 Q}{\partial n_j \partial n_i} = \frac{\partial^2 Q}{\partial n_i \partial n_j} = \frac{\partial}{\partial n_i}\left(\frac{\partial Q}{\partial n_j}\right)$$

or

$$\frac{\partial \bar{Q}_i}{\partial n_j} = \frac{\partial \bar{Q}_j}{\partial n_i} \qquad (9)$$

Use can be made of this relation in evaluating the variation in the property of one component in a mixture from measurements of one or more other components. Surprisingly enough, while this relation has been known for several decades, relatively little use has been made of it.

In general all the thermodynamic expressions which hold for molal thermodynamic properties may be restated by replacing the quantity Q with the partial molal quantity, $\bar{Q}_i$. In any reaction the change in any quantity ΔQ is equal to $Q(products)$ less $Q(reactants)$. In the cases of pure solids, pure liquids or single component gases these refer to the molal quantities; in the

case of solutions, they refer to the partial molal quantities, $\bar{Q}$, of the constituents involved in the reaction. As an example, the reaction

$$H_{2(g)} + AgCl_{(s)} \rightarrow HCl_{(aq)} + Ag_{(s)} \qquad (10)$$

will be considered, where g and s refer to gaseous and solid materials and aq refers to aqueous solution.

$$\Delta F_{reaction} = F_{Ag} + \bar{F}_{HCl} - F_{AgCl} - F_{H_2} \qquad (11)$$

where $\bar{F}_{HCl}$ is the partial molal free energy of HCl in solution and the other values of F refer to the free energy per mole of the pure materials.

The partial molal quantities for strong electrolytes may be expressed as a sum of quantities for each ion. Thus, $\bar{Q}_{HCl} = \bar{Q}_{H^+} + \bar{Q}_{Cl^-}$. If the value for one ion is arbitrarily set to some value, then the values of $\bar{Q}$ for many different electrolytes (in which at least two have each ion in common) may be separated into $\bar{Q}$ values for each ion. Partial molal ionic entropies, for example, are often used in correlative studies.

Partial Molal Free Energy and Chemical Potential

The partial molal free energy in a solution is defined in terms of the partial molal free energy in the standard state, $\bar{F}^\circ$, and an activity, a, ("thermodynamic concentration") which gives a measure of the deviation from the standard state.

$$\bar{F} = \bar{F}^\circ + RT \ln a \qquad (12)$$

where R is the gas constant and T the absolute temperature. In solution $\bar{F}$ is often referred to as the chemical potential with the symbol μ. In liquid solutions the standard state of the solvent is usually taken as the pure liquid while that of the solute is usually taken as a hypothetical state of unit activity in which the partial molal heat content of the solute, $\bar{H}_2$, has the value at infinite dilution, $\bar{H}_2^\circ$. In the case of gaseous mixtures the activity is equal to the fugacity which is approximately equal to the partial pressure (at low pressures). The standard state of a gas is the gas at unit fugacity (approximately one atmosphere pressure).

Relative Partial Molal Enthalpy

The partial molal enthalpy (or "heat content") according to Eq. (1) is given by

$$\bar{H}_i = \left(\frac{\partial H}{\partial n_i}\right)_{P, T, n_j} \qquad (13)$$

Because the standard state of a solute is taken as the hypothetical state with the partial molal enthalpy having its value at infinite dilution, $\bar{H}_i{}^\circ$, it is convenient to define a *relative partial molal enthalpy*, $\bar{L}_i$, as

$$\bar{L}_i \equiv \bar{H}_i - \bar{H}_i{}^\circ \qquad (14)$$

The value of $\bar{L}_i$ at any concentration, m_i, is given by the equation

$$\bar{L}_i = -RT^2 \left(\frac{\partial \ln a}{\partial T} \right)_{P,m_i} \qquad (15)$$

For a nonelectrolyte the activity is expressed simply as the product of the molality m and the activity coefficient γ, i.e., $a = m\gamma$. Since the partial derivative in Eq. (15) is taken at constant molality, m, and since $\ln a = \ln m + \ln \gamma$,

$$\bar{L}_i = -RT^2 \left(\frac{\partial \ln \gamma}{\partial T} \right)_{P,m_i} \qquad (16)$$

In the case of an electrolyte which on complete dissociation gives ν_+ positive ions and ν_- negative ions per mole

$$a \equiv m_+ m_- \gamma_\pm{}^\nu \qquad (17)$$

where $\nu = \nu_+ + \nu_-$; m_+ and m_- are the molalities of the positive and negative ions, respectively; and $\gamma_\pm$ is defined as the *mean* ionic activity coefficient. For an electrolyte, Eq. (15) becomes

$$\bar{L}_i = -\nu RT^2 \left(\frac{\partial \ln \gamma_\pm}{\partial T} \right)_{P,m_i} \qquad (18)$$

Relative Partial Molal Heat Capacity

The partial molal heat capacity at constant pressure, $\bar{C}_p$, is equal to the partial derivative of the partial molal enthalpy (or heat content) with respect to temperature T

$$\bar{C}_p = \left(\frac{\partial \bar{H}}{\partial T} \right)_{P,m} \qquad (19)$$

The *relative partial molal heat capacity*, $\bar{J}$, is defined as the difference between the partial molal heat capacity at molality, m_i, and at infinite dilution

$$\bar{J}_i \equiv \bar{C}_{pi} - \bar{C}_{pi}{}^\circ = \left(\frac{\partial \bar{H}}{\partial T} \right)_{P,m_i}$$

$$\qquad (20)$$

$$- \left(\frac{\partial \bar{H}^\circ}{\partial T} \right)_{P,O} = \left(\frac{\partial \bar{L}_i}{\partial T} \right)_{P,m_i}$$

Thus, $\bar{J}_i$ in the cases of an undissociated solute and a strong electrolyte would be given by Eqs.

like (16) and (18) but with the partial derivatives replaced by second partial derivatives. Thus, for a strong electrolyte

$$\bar{J}_i = -\nu RT^2 \left(\frac{\partial^2 \ln \gamma_\pm}{\partial T^2} \right)_{P,m_i} \qquad (21)$$

References

1. KLOTZ, I. M., "Chemical Thermodynamics," Chap. 13, New York, Prentice-Hall, Inc., 1950.
2. LEWIS, G. N., AND RANDALL, M., "Thermodynamics," 2nd Edition, revised by K. S Pitzer and Leo Brewer, Chaps. 17, 25–26 and Appendix 4, New York, McGraw-Hill Book Co., 1961.
3. HARNED, H. S., AND OWEN, B. B., "The Physical Chemistry of Electrolytic Solutions," 3rd Edition, especially Chap. 1, New York, Reinhold Publishing Corp., 1958.

M. H. LIETZKE AND
R. W. STOUGHTON

PASCHEN'S LAW

Paschen's law, named after Friedrich Paschen, German physicist, states that the breakdown voltage of a gas is a function of the length of the discharge gap and the pressure of the gas. More specifically, that it is a linear function of the product of the two variables. If these variables are changed in such a way that their product is constant, the breakdown voltage will also be constant. Paschen's law in this form, $V = F(Pd)$, where P indicates gas pressure and d gap distance, assumes a constant gas temperature. If the gas pressure and gas temperature are both varied, Paschen's law may be written in the more general form, $V = F(\rho d)$, where ρ is the gas density.

Deviations from Paschen's law are found in the area of extremely low pressures (1 to 10 mm Hg $\times$ cm) where all gases exhibit a minimum breakdown voltage. At pressures lower than this, the mean free paths of charged particles become large as compared to the gap distance and the breakdown mechanism becomes independent of gas ionization. Deviations from Paschen's law have also been observed at very high gas pressure and for electronegative gases in nonuniform electrical fields.

JAMES A. BROWN

Cross references: *Dielectrics, Gaseous; Dielectric Properties of Vacuum; Sulfur Hexafluoride; Vacuum Arc Properties.*

PASSIVITY

Metals are said to be *passive* when, although exposed to an environment with which they have a thermodynamic tendency to react, they nonetheless remain substantially unchanged for a considerable period.

Schönbein and Faraday were among the first to describe the phenomenon. Faraday, noting that iron exposed to fuming nitric acid quickly ceased to evolve gas and remained apparently "passive" and unchanged, ascribed the phenomenon to an oxidized state of the surface that prevented dissolution. In recent times the oxidized state has generally been thought to be a very sparingly soluble compact film of metal oxide, although some have urged that a mere monolayer of *oxygen* is enough to produce full passivity. The isolation of films 50 to 150 Å thick from passive surfaces, their demonstration *in situ* by their stoppage of amalgamation by mercury, and their determination by ellipsometry and coulometry, show that, for full passivity, compact films at least one and usually several molecular layers thick are present.

Passivation, like corrosion, is essentially an anodic phenomenon: in the classical case of "chemical" passivation just mentioned it is now clear that the formation of the oxidized surface is brought about by the simultaneous anodic oxidation of the iron surface and cathodic reduction of the nitric acid, on one and the same area of metal. The separation of the two reactions so that the anodic reaction leading to passivation can be studied separately has been very helpful in the elucidation of the mechanism of passivation; the terms *anodic passivation* and *anodic passivity* are used to describe the phenomena at an anode whereon there is no simultaneous cathodic reaction, this taking place on a separate electrode.

When a metal is made the anode in a solution containing anions with which it forms a very sparingly soluble compound—lead in sulfate solutions, nickel in alkaline solutions—it may produce the compound in solid form on or very close to the electrode, and this solid material if coherent and adherent may produce immediate passivation. However, such layers rarely produce the most nearly complete passivation, nor, indeed, is a primary production of a very sparingly soluble product necessary for good passivation. For instance, nickel made anodic in an acid sulfate solution gives as primary product hydrated nickelous ion, by the reaction

$$Ni + xH_2O \rightarrow Ni.xH_2O^{2+} + 2e, \qquad (1)$$

without any immediate precipitation of the freely soluble nickelous sulfate. However, if the anodic polarization is increased so that the potential of the metal* is raised above the value where the reaction

$$Ni + 2H_2O \rightarrow Ni(OH)_2 + 2H^+ + 2e \qquad (2)$$

becomes thermodynamically possible, then this reaction may take over from (1). Since reaction (1) is a sluggish reaction requiring considerable *overpotential* (q.v.) to make it proceed at rapid rate, the potential for reaction (2) (Fig. 1, and see **Potential/pH Diagrams**) is quite easily reached; with other metals and other solutions, it may be even more easily reached (chromium, titanium in acid sulfate solution), or it may be very difficult to achieve (copper, silver, in nitrate solution). Once the passivating potential is reached, the passivating reaction, such as (2), is likely to be *kinetically easy* rather than sluggish, at any rate for the formation of the first monolayer; all that is needed is a transfer of protons from water molecules adsorbed all over the metal surface to water molecules in the bulk solution, followed by a pulling out of metal cations by the remaining hydroxide (or oxide) ions so as to form the first monolayer

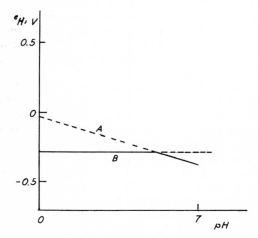

FIG. 1. Thermodynamic criterion for onset of passivation, for nickel. A. line above which $Ni + 2H_2O \rightarrow Ni(OH)_2 + 2H^+ + 2e$ becomes thermodynamically possible. B. line above which $Ni + xH_2O \rightarrow Ni.xH_2O^{2+} + 2e$ becomes thermodynamically possible.

* The over-all potential difference between the bulk metal and the bulk solution.

of metal hydroxide (or oxide). Frequently the best passivation is produced by the higher valency compounds of the metal concerned, and there is also evidence that oxide rather than hydroxide films are the more effective.

The process of anodic passivation, as of nickel in an acid sulfate solution, is very easily followed by measurement of anode current at different anode potentials, or over a period of steadily rising anode potential, applied from a potentiostat. When the potential is raised fairly rapidly, a curve such as ABCD is (in the simplest cases) obtained (Fig. 2); B represents the passivating potential and the passivating current density. When the potential is raised more slowly, a curve such as AA'B'CD is obtained. This is because the accumulation of hydrated nickelous ions near the anode is sufficient to cause precipitation of the *sulfate*, whereupon the true current density at those parts of the metal/solution interface not blocked by nickel sulfate crystals is not measured, but only the average current density, which is controlled constant by the diffusion-convection process by which nickelous ions can depart from the anode. At B', the passivating potential having been reached, passive film formation begins and spreads over the entire metal surface, dispersing the "mush" of sulfate. This mechanism, first proposed by W. J. Müller, has been confirmed by the microscopic examination of the passivation of iron in sulfuric acid.

The passivation process is never instantaneous, because it requires the passage of charge. At constant current density (galvanostatic conditions) the potential of an anode undergoing passivation rises, slowly at first and then very rapidly as the passivating film becomes complete. If high current densities are used, or if only film-forming material is produced, the passivation time, τ, (Fig. 3) is short and usually $i\tau$ is constant, because all the material produced at the anode remains there during the short period, and the conditions for passivation depend on the amount formed. At low current densities, when the initial anode product is freely soluble, $(i - i_0) \tau^{1/2}$ is often constant (i_0 being a limiting current density below which no passivation occurs), because some of the anodically produced material is leaving the anode by diffusion-convection, and only when its concentration has risen sufficiently to give saturation and precipitation can passivation proper begin. The actual amount of charge required for the

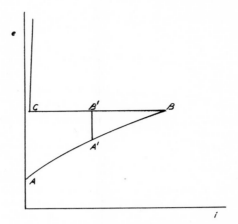

Fig. 2. Potential/current-density diagram for onset of passivation (schematic).

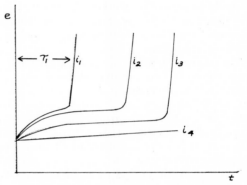

Fig. 3. Potential/time curves for passivation at constant current density (schematic); $i_1 > i_2 > i_3 > i_4$.

production of the passivating compact film itself is some 0.1 to 0.2 mC/sq cm per molecular layer; the measured passivating charge for this process usually lies in the range 0.2 to 5 mC/sq cm. The more easily soluble the initial anodic product, the more the charge required at any particular current density for the setting up of the prepassivating condition; up to several thousand mC/sq cm may be required.

The presence of chloride ion in the solution is extremely inimical to passivation; it is difficult to render iron passive in solutions containing it, and the passivation of chromium (and the stainless steels) and even of titanium is made less easy. It is probable that the strong specific adsorption of chloride ion on most metals prevents the contact of metal with the oxygen of water molecules or of oxygen-bearing anions that is necessary for the ready formation of the oxide

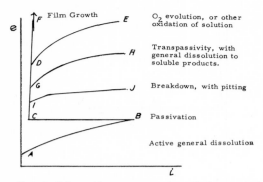

Fig. 4. Schematic representation of the several possibilities at potentials above the passivation potential.

or hydroxide films that are evidently the best passivators. However, silver and mercury are partially passivated in chloride solutions through the formation of films of their sparingly soluble chlorides; the films are not so compact and adherent as oxide films.

The current densities at passivated anodes, when these are held at potentials below that at which oxygen evolution or other anodic process can occur, are very small, usually within the range 10^{-4} to 10^{-10} amp/sq cm—the better passivating films allowing the less current density. The current is ionic, not electronic. It increases somewhat with rise of anode potential, and frequently falls with time owing to the slow thickening of the film. It may reach a steady value if the film very slowly dissolves as fast as it forms.

Passive metal surfaces may become *depassivated* or *activated* in several ways. Either mechanical removal of the film by abrasion, or chemical dissolution of the film, or electrochemical removal by cathodic reduction—which, incidentally, provides a sensitive means of estimating passive films by coulometry—can provide complete activation. A single mechanical scratch of a passive surface may lead, autocatalytically, to activation: the exposed metal acting as anode may produce cathodic reduction of the nearby film, with consequent increase of the anode area and of the rapidity of the activation. Left to itself in a solution, passive metal may *improve* in passivity if enough oxygen or other cathodic reactant is present in the solution to lead to a high anode potential and current density at any flaws in the film that may develop—but more often, it may become active as just described because a sufficient anode potential and current

density at the flaws cannot be maintained even by the cathodic reduction of the passivating film itself.

When the potential of a passive anode is raised, several possibilities arise (Fig. 4). If the passivating film is a relatively good electronic conductor (iron, nickel, platinum), oxygen may be evolved by the oxidation of water, or a solution entity such as sulfate ion may be oxidized, at the film/solution interface; the metal itself remains passive, although the current density increases along DE, Fig. 4. If the film is a very feeble electronic conductor (aluminum, tantalum), raising the potential far above that ordinarily required for oxygen evolution is possible because no electrons can move in from the film/solution interface; now, high-field ion conduction through the film may begin, DF, and the metal is no longer properly called passive since it is partaking in relatively thick film formation. The well-known "condenser" type films on aluminum and tantalum are formed in this way by anodizing in a neutral solution, such as ammonium borate or tartrate. If the film substance becomes oxidized at higher anode potentials to a higher *soluble* oxide (chromium, manganese), *transpassivity*, with the metal again dissolving actively to a soluble product, sets in, GH. Many metals and alloys can show all three effects, depending on the solution; and simultaneous film formation and oxygen evolution can occur (tin). If the solution contains chloride ion (insufficient to prevent passivation), a passive anode may often show a *breakdown potential*, I, below the potential required for oxygen evolution, film growth, or transpassivity, which is the lower the greater the chloride ion concentration; the breakdown of passivity is local only, and thus leads to *pitting* of the anode, IJ. The effect has been used as a test for pitting susceptibility in stainless steels. Finally, some passivating films can be transformed by anodic oxidation into materials that build up as thick films relatively easily, because they are much more porous then the initially formed compact passivating film (aluminum, lead, nickel).

The *self-passivation* of some metals in some solutions is of great practical importance in providing, in many cases, a means of handling solutions by metal vessels for which they have thermodynamic affinity. Although the effect with iron in fuming nitric acid, already mentioned, is of historic rather than of practical interest, that with chromium and the stainless steels in very mildly oxidizing solutions makes the chromium alloys valuable in chemical industry and in combating atmospheric corrosion. With titanium, water or hydrogen ion are strong enough oxidizing agents to provide anodically formed passivating oxides, so that titanium is self-passivating even under the acid and deoxygenated conditions that occur in crevices (see **Corrosion**).

Provided that a metal or alloy shows a reasonably wide potential range for passivity, its performance in practice can be much assisted by maintaining the potential artificially within that range by means of a potentiostat, or sometimes a crude potential-divider device, or even (in favorable cases) a simple galvanic cell. This is *anodic protection* (q.v.). Because the current demand of a passive anode is so small, anodic protection can be a very economic process; but the power source must be sufficient to give the much larger current required to *produce* passivation or to reinstate it should temporary breakdown be caused, for example, by change of the solution to which the metal is exposed.

References

Full references to the original literature will be found in:
1. HOAR, T. P., "The Anodic Behaviour of Metals," in "Modern Aspects of Electrochemistry," No. 2, Ed. J. O'M. Bockris, pp. 262–342, London, Butterworths, 1959.
2. EVANS, U. R., "The Corrosion and Oxidation of Metals," Chapter 7, pp. 219–262, London, Arnold, 1960.
3. HOAR, T. P., "Passivity and Passivation," in "Corrosion," Ed., L. L. Shreir, Vol. 1, pp. 1.116–1.129, London, Newnes, 1963.

T. P. HOAR

Cross-references: see entires bearing *Corrosion* titles: *Anodic Protection*; *Potential-pH Diagrams.*

PELTIER, JEAN CHARLES ATHANASE (1785–1845)

Jean Charles Athanase Peltier was born in Ham, department of Somme, France on February 22, 1785. He received very little formal education. He learned to read and write in school, and the local vicar taught him arithmetic and Latin. The boy was very industrious and demonstrated a unique mechanical talent early in childhood. His father, a shoemaker, arranged for an apprenticeship in watchmaking first in St. Quentin and then in Paris. Peltier developed into a very capable watchmaker, constructing many of the finest chronometers of that time. He married Mademoiselle Dufáant in 1806. In 1815 his mother-in-law died, leaving Peltier a small fortune which enabled him to retire from business and devote his life to fulfilling a number of personal ambitions. He wrote poetry, a melodrama, and several books on Latin grammar. He became intensely interested in the processes of learning, including the action of the brain. His work brought him into close association with physiologists in Paris. The relatively new phenomena of electricity was popular with this group, who were awed by Volta's experiments using electrical stimulus to cause muscle contractions in frogs' legs. In 1827 Peltier bought his first equipment to experiment with electricity. In 1830 he made his first scientific contribution, a paper discussing dry electric piles (batteries). In the fifteen remaining years of his life he succeeded in publishing papers on physiology, meteorology, microscopy, electrical phenomena, and measuring instruments. It was this rare combination of a man capable of making very delicate, sensitive instruments and a desire to measure small electric impulses that accounts for all of his scientific work.

Peltier constructed very sensitive galvanometers and observed that their deflection was proportional to force. He invented an electrometer. In 1834 he published in Vol. 26 of the *Annals of Chemistry and Physics*, Paris, his work on heating and cooling effects produced by electric currents at the junction of two dissimilar metals, the Peltier Effect. Other publications in the *Archives of Electricity*, Geneva, and *Memoirs of the Royal Academy of Science*, Brussels, deal with measuring instruments, measurement of atmospheric electricity, the production of electric currents, and other scientific phenomena. Peltier died on October 27, 1845.

ALBERT J. CORNISH

Cross-references: *Peltier Effect, Thermoelectricity, Volta.*

PELTIER EFFECT

The conversion of electric energy to heat energy when an electric (direct) current passes through the junction between two dissimilar electric conductors is called the Peltier Effect after its discoverer, Jean Charles Athanase Peltier. This phenomenon is reversible with respect to the direction of the electric current. A given junction will heat or cool depending on the direction of the current. In general, the cooling effect has been of greatest interest as it provides a means of refrigeration. The reverse of the Peltier effect, the conversion of heat energy to electric energy at a junction is called the *Seebeck Effect* and is discussed under that heading. Both the Peltier and Seebeck effects take place at junctions and not in the bulk of the material.

The rate heat is generated or absorbed at a junction by the Peltier effect is proportional to the amount of direct current passed. The proportionality constant, commonly designated as π, is called the Peltier coefficient. The units of π used may be calories per coulomb or joules per faraday. Since π is measured at a junction between two materials, subscripts are generally added to identify the different materials.

It has been shown that the Peltier effect is due to the differences between the average energies of the conduction electrons (or holes) across the junction. As electrons (or holes) pass through the junction, heat is involved or absorbed by an amount equal to this energy difference. This energy difference can be maximized by selecting a junction made up of one material with a high average conduction electron energy and another material with a low average conduction electron energy. Such a pair of materials is the p-n junction used in semiconductor diodes. However, since the amount of cooling is proportional to the amount of current passing through the junction, the semiconductors used must be heavily doped with impurity atoms to increase their electrical conductivity. It appears theoretically possible to construct a thermoelectric cooling device more efficient than the conventional compressor type refrigerating unit. However, additional research in materials and engineering will be necessary before the full benefits are achieved.

ALBERT J. CORNISH

Cross-references: *Peltier, Seebeck Effect, Thermoelectricity, Thermoelectric Power, Thermoelectric Power Generation.*

PERBORATES. See PEROXYGEN CHEMICALS.

PERCHLORATES

The present major use of perchlorate salts is as oxidizers in solid propellants. The potassium salt was first used and quickly followed by the now most important salt—ammonium perchlorate. Lithium perchlorate, which has the highest weight per cent oxygen, has been tested as an oxidizer in solid propellants, but has not found favor with propellant manufacturers.

All the important perchlorates are produced by a double decomposition reaction with sodium perchlorate:[10]

$$NaClO_4 + MX \rightarrow MClO_4 + NaX \qquad (1)$$

Generally, the chloride salt is used in the double decomposition reaction, particularly in the United States. In Europe and in other areas, the sulfate salt is used because it is less expensive[3] and because the corrosion-resistant equipment necessary for the chloride process is more expensive in Europe than in the United States.

Sodium perchlorate, the most important raw material for the preparation of perchlorate salts and perchloric acid,[8] can be produced both chemically[10] and electrolytically. Commercially, sodium perchlorate is produced in an electrolytic cell.

No one mechanism for the formation of perchlorate ion at the anode is agreed upon. Bennett and Mack[1] believe that a direct chemical oxidation by active oxygen is the mechanism involved. They suggest that perchlorate is formed at the anode at a potential below that necessary for the continuous discharge of any ion present in the solution.

Their theory is expounded by the following set of reactions:

$$H_2O \rightarrow OH^- + H^+ \rightarrow O + 2H^+ + 2e \qquad (2)$$

$$ClO_3^- + H^+ \rightarrow HClO_3 \qquad (3)$$

$$HClO_3 + O \rightarrow HClO_4 \rightarrow H^+ + ClO_4^- \qquad (4)$$

Bennett and Mack's theory appears to be consistent with the lack of variation of current efficiency with pH. Knibbs and Palfreeman[6] took exception to Bennett and Mack's theory. The high anodic potential required for the formation of the perchlorate ion is not consistent with the theory. To secure this high potential, early investigators turned to smooth platinum electrodes.

The types of cells used for the commercial production of sodium perchlorate have been discussed by Schumacher.[10] In general, the cell consists of a steel tank containing cooling coils and equipped with platinum anodes.

The sodium chlorate solution for conversion in the cells flows or is pumped from a storage tank to the cells in parallel. The solution flows through the cell, is collected, and returned to the storage tank. The operation is batch (with continuous flow through the cells) under these conditions, with a fresh storage tank being put on the line when the sodium perchlorate concentration reaches the desired concentration in the storage tank. The cells may also be arranged for continuous operation, i.e., in series. The concentrated sodium chlorate solution enters the first cell, flows from cell to cell, and leaves the last cell essentially depleted of sodium chlorate. The advantage of the series process is that the individual cells can be regulated with respect to temperature and current density for the most economical production of sodium perchlorate.

The anodes are suspended in the tank through a cover parallel to the sides of the tank and the cooling coils. The sides of the tank and cooling coils act as the cathode. The electrical connection is made to the anode above the cover. The hydrogen formed in the cell can be vented to the atmosphere through a stack at the end of the cell.

The main variation from one commercial cell to another has been the type of anode used. Most commercial cells are equipped with platinum anodes. The cost has been decreased in some cases by using platinum on tantalum or copper. The only real substitute for platinum that has proved of any real value is lead dioxide. It is reported[2] that one manufacturer of ammonium perchlorate uses lead dioxide anodes in the sodium perchlorate cell. When lead dioxide anodes are used in a perchlorate cell, stainless steel or nickel cathodes are used. Mild steel cathodes cannot be used because the lead dioxide anodes are poisoned by the chromate ions present in the electrolyte to inhibit corrosion of the mild steel.

Typical operating conditions for a commercial sodium perchlorate cell are:

Temperature	35 to 45°C
Feed rate	At least 2 gal/min
pH	6.0 to 6.8
Feed to Cell:	
Sodium chlorate	400 gpl
Sodium perchlorate	400 gpl
Sodium dichromate	5 gpl
Cathode current density	2 amps/sq in. (31 amps/sq dm)
Cell voltage	6.5 to 7.0 volts
Power consumption	1.36 to 1.60 kwh/lb d-c
Sodium dichromate concentration	2.5 to 5.0 gpl
Calcium and magnesium	As low as possible
Final sodium chlorate concentration	As high as impurity removal in recovery will permit

Temperature affects all important dependent variables in sodium perchlorate cells, and the optimum temperature must be arrived at through compromise. For example, with an increase in temperature, the current efficiency is reduced, cell voltage decreases, platinum loss increases, solubility of perchlorate increases, and the equilibrium chloride concentration increases.

The quantitative effect of electrolyte temperature on current efficiency at a current density of 0.34 amperes per square centimeter is small up to 60°C at high sodium chlorate concentration.

Sodium perchlorate cell operating temperature is controlled by the method of heat removal (coils in cell) and the voltage drop across the cell solution. Wider anode-cathode spacing results in an extra heat load that must be removed to obtain low cell temperatures.

Schumacher[11] has indicated increased platinum consumption with an increase in temperature from 40 to 65°C.

The feed solution to the cell, depending on the method of isolation of the sodium chlorate, contains sodium chlorate, sodium dichromate, sodium perchlorate, and traces of chloride, sulfate, calcium, and possibly magnesium ions.

The feed rate to the sodium perchlorate cell depends on the size and design of the cell. An adequate feed rate is important to reduce the sodium chlorate concentration gradient between the feed and effluent ends of the cell. When all the cooling is accomplished by cooling tubes within the cell tank, there is no temperature gradient across the cell. When external cooling is used, the circulation rate must be greater to aid in heat removal and to hold the temperature gradient to a minimum. There are no adverse effects of high circulation rates reported in the literature.

Agitation in the sodium perchlorate cell is obtained from the hydrogen gas evolution in the cathode area. The rate of flow through the cell contributes very little to the agitation in the cell when compared to the agitation resulting from gas evolution.

Almost without exception the electrolysis of sodium chlorate has been carried out in neutral or slightly acid solution. Knibbs and Palfreeman[6] have discussed the desirability of keeping the hydroxyl ion concentration low to minimize the loss of current efficiency that would result from anodic discharge of hydroxyl, chloride, and hypochlorite ions. They also found that acid additions are more important at elevated temperatures (50 to 60°C) than at lower temperatures (below 50°C) because of the increased mobility of the OH^-, Cl^-, and OCl^-. Karr[5] described the optimum pH range as 6.0 to 6.8, but indicated that no adverse effects are found when the pH is as low as 5.0 or as high as 9.0. His patent further teaches that perchloric acid for pH control is a better choice than the hydrochloric acid normally used. He found that much less acid is required when perchloric acid is used and that during the final one-third of batch electrolysis no acid is required.

The effect of pH on platinum losses is not reported in the literature.

The literature contains a number of references to the effects of current density on current efficiency. A review of the reports suggests that two amperes per square inch is a good choice. At high sodium chlorate concentrations and at temperatures below 50°C, current efficiency is practically independent of current density in the range of 1.0 to 2.5 amperes per square inch (15.5 to 39 amps/sq dm). In some cell designs, the upper limit of current density is apparently determined by the anode electrical connections and the cooling capacity of the cells. Anode current densities of 2.6 to 4.5 amperes per square inch (40 to 70 amps/sq dm) have been used in Europe.

Higher platinum losses at higher current density have been reported by Schumacher[11] and by Wranglen.[14]

Cathode current density is generally deter-

mined by cell design. This is particularly true when the cell body is used as the cathode. When individual cathodes are installed in a perchlorate cell, the cathode current density is generally the same as the anode current density. Literature references on the study of cathode current density are limited.

The voltage drop across the perchlorate cell depends on: (1) anode material; (2) cathode-anode spacing; (3) concentration of reagents in the cell; (4) cell temperature; (5) current density on the anode and the cathode; and (6) cathode material. Because of the high anodic potential essential for the formation of perchlorate, the voltage drop across the cell is relatively high. The voltage across the cell increases near the end of a batch process when the sodium chlorate concentration is low. Under these conditions, ozone is found in the gases from the cell.[4]

The literature reports[13] involving lead dioxide anodes in sodium perchlorate cells generally give a lower voltage drop than the 5.0 to 6.0 volts reported for laboratory cells using platinum. The reason for the lower voltage when using lead dioxide anodes appears to be the lower current density and the higher operating temperature employed.

Energy consumption for the preparation of sodium perchlorate involves all the variables discussed under voltage drop across the cell plus current efficiency. The 1.36 to 1.60 kwh (d-c) per pound discussed earlier covers the energy consumed at the cell. Schumacher[11] reported an a-c power requirement of 2.0 kwh per pound, which includes the auxiliary equipment in the process, such as pumps, centrifuges, fans, etc.

The optimum sodium dichromate concentration is difficult to establish, but is probably in the range of 2 to 5 grams per liter of sodium dichromate. The main use of dichromate is to prevent cathodic reduction. It also serves as a corrosion inhibitor. Calcium and magnesium salts have been added to the cell electrolyte to help reduce current losses through cathodic reduction. The present belief appears to be that it is not necessary to add calcium or magnesium compounds if the cell electrolyte contains an adequate amount of dichromate.

Almost without exception, all of the investigators of the electrochemical production of sodium perchlorate agree that the current efficiency is very low at low chlorate concentrations. There does not appear to be agreement in the literature on the sodium chlorate concentration at which the current efficiency starts to decrease. This is probably true because of the effect of temperature, current density, and pH, as well as the chlorate concentration, on the current efficiency.

The final concentration of sodium chlorate in the cell effluent depends, in part, on the method of isolation of the sodium perchlorate. In general, the higher the concentration of sodium chlorate in the cell effluent, the higher the current efficiency for a batch process. The effluent from a sodium perchlorate cell varies from 600 to 1,000 grams per liter sodium perchlorate, 5 to 50 grams per liter sodium chlorate. and 2 to 5 grams per liter sodium dichromate, depending on the cell design, operating conditions, and method of subsequent treatment of the sodium perchlorate solution.

Sodium perchlorate can be isolated from the cell effluent as either the hydrate or the anhydrous form. In some cases, the cell effluent can be used without isolation of the sodium perchlorate. This approach will be discussed later. Depending on the concentration of the sodium perchlorate in the solution, it is either isolated by cooling, or the solution is further concentrated by evaporation, followed by cooling. Sodium perchlorate forms the monohydrate when crystallized below about 52°C, the exact temperature depending on the amount of sodium chlorate present in the solution. Above this temperature, it crystallizes in the anhydrous form. If an evaporator is part of the isolation system, the salt is generally isolated in the anhydrous form. If no evaporator is used, the salt is isolated as the monohydrate. In either case, because of the high solubility of sodium perchlorate, the mother liquor from the isolation of the crystals contains a high concentration of sodium perchlorate. This mother liquor, after enrichment with sodium chlorate, is used as feed to the sodium perchlorate cells.

Because of the high solubility of sodium perchlorate, its isolation is avoided when it is used as an intermediate to produce other perchlorates. For example, the sodium chlorate can be destroyed by chemical treatment[9] and the dichromate removed as insoluble chromic hydroxide. This leaves a relatively pure solution of sodium perchlorate for conversion to other salts.

The manufacture of other perchlorate salts takes advantage of their lower solubilities. Potassium perchlorate is prepared by the double decomposition reaction of sodium perchlorate and potassium chloride.

$$NaClO_4 + KCl \rightarrow KClO_4 + NaCl \qquad (5)$$

Either the purified sodium perchlorate cell solution or sodium perchlorate crystals dissolved in water is treated with potassium chloride. The relatively insoluble potassium perchlorate crystallizes and is separated by centrifuging. If it is necessary to control crystal size and size distribution, the solution is first heated and then cooled.

Ammonium perchlorate is prepared by reactions similar to those used to form potassium perchlorate.[12]

$$NaClO_4 + NH_4Cl \rightarrow NH_4ClO_4 + NaCl \qquad (6)$$

The feasibility of the process lies in the mutual solubility relationship between ammonium perchlorate and sodium chloride, which permits the reaction products to be separated by fractional crystallization. The solubility of sodium chloride varies only slightly with temperature, while that of ammonium perchlorate is temperature-dependent. Thus, on cooling, ammonium perchlorate can be recovered. The mother liquor, on evaporation, deposits a crop of sodium chloride crystals which are filtered hot. The filtrate, rich in ammonium perchlorate, is then recycled.

The preparation of other perchlorate salts is similar in principle to those already described.[10] Lithium perchlorate may be produced by electrolysis of lithium chlorate or lithium chloride.[1] On a laboratory scale, other perchlorates are generally prepared by reaction of either ammonium perchlorate or perchloric acid with the desired metal oxides, hydroxides, or carbonates.

References

1. BENNETT, C. W., AND MACK, E. L., *Trans. Am. Electrochem. Soc.*, **29**, 323 (1916).
1a. BROVO, J. B., AND DELANO, P. H., U.S. Patent 3,020,124 (February 6, 1962).
2. *Chem. & Eng. News*, page 21, April 27, 1959.
3. DODGEN, J. E., "Design Study on an Alternate Method for Production of Ammonium Perchlorate," **TMR No. 190,** Naval Propellant Plant, Indianhead, Maryland, July 17, 1961.
4. HAMPEL, C. A., AND LEPPLA, P. W., *Trans. Electrochem. Soc.*, **92**, 55 (1947).
5. KARR, E. H., U.S. Patent 2,772,229 (November 27, 1956).

6. Knibbs, N. V. S., and Palfreeman, H., *Trans. Farad. Soc.*, **16**, 402 (1921).

7. Mochalov, K. N., *Trans. Butlerov Inst. Chem. Technol. Kazan*, **1**, 21 (1934).

8. Pernert, J. C., U.S. Patent 2,392,861 (January 15, 1946).

9. Ryan, J. R., U.S. Patent 2,392,769 (January 8, 1946).

10. Schumacher, Joseph C., ACS Monograph No. 146, "Perchlorates, Their Properties, Manufacture and Uses," New York, Reinhold Publishing Corp., 1960.

11. Schumacher, J. C., *Trans. Electrochem. Soc.*, **92**, 45 (1947).

12. Schumacher, J. C., and Stern, D. R., *Chem. Eng. Progress*, **53**, 428 (1957).

13. Schumacher, J. C., Stern, D. R., and Graham, P. R., *J. Electrochem. Soc.*, **105**, 151 (1958).

14. Wranglen, D. G., *Teknisk Tidskrift*, Stockholm, May 13, 1960.

Thomas W. Clapper

PERIODATES, ELECTROLYTIC PREPARATION

Periodates have been used for many years as reagents in a variety of analytical procedures for quantitative determination of both inorganic and organic chemicals. Although as chemicals they exhibit unusual versatility and specificity, their use industrially has been limited by the high cost of preparative procedures usually employed. As oxidants, the periodates rank high in strength; periodic acid has a single electrode potential of 1.7 volts.

The salts of periodic acid are believed to occur in all but one of the seven possible hydrates of iodine heptoxide. Of these, only two pertain here, the meta- and para-sodium salts. In solution, the acid is generally considered to be present as the pentahydrate of iodine heptoxide or para-periodic acid H_5IO_6. Di- and trisodium salts may be crystallized from solution at pH values of 10 and 12, respectively; trisodium paraperiodate is very insoluble at ordinary temperatures. The monosodium salt can be crystallized as either the monosodium paraperiodate or as the anhydride, sodium metaperiodate, depending on the conditions employed. Sodium metaperiodate solutions can be prepared at 25°C having concentrations of approximately 13 per cent.

Trisodium paraperiodate can be prepared by oxidizing a highly alkaline solution of sodium iodate with chlorine gas, and the resulting crystals can be washed with water with little loss. An alternative method employs another electrolytic oxidant, persulfuric acid. Neither of these methods results in a product free of contaminants and large excesses of sodium. Neutralization and recrystallization are required for the production of the pure acid or monosodium salt. Willard and Ralston[11] are credited with the first successful method of preparing either iodic or periodic acid by direct electrolytic procedures. The supporting electrolyte for iodine was a hydrochloric acid solution. No supporting electrolyte was required for the oxidation of iodic acid to periodic acid. The cell used contained a porous ceramic diaphragm, which prevented the mixing of the anolyte with the nitric acid used for the catholyte. The two reactions have distinctly different kinetics. Iodine can be oxidized to iodate at current densities of up to 11 amp/sq dm with good efficiencies with any of several anodic surfaces, such as bright platinum, carbon, and bright lead. However, lead dioxide is the only anodic surface that can efficiently convert iodate to periodate, although efficiency is not good above 5 amp/sq dm; further, the character of the anode surface materially affects efficiency.

Mehltretter,[5, 7] seeking to find a more economical method of preparing periodic acid, conceived some novel revisions of the Willard and Ralston cell. The location of the anolyte and catholyte compartments was reversed; the supporting electrolyte was sodium hydroxide and sodium sulfate; and the catholyte was sodium hydroxide. With this cell, he was able to prepare periodic acid from elemental iodine without changing either the supporting electrolyte or the anode. During the iodine oxidation stage, the anolyte was kept basic by the addition of alkali, since the sodium ions tend to migrate through the diaphragm, making the anolyte more acid. The anode was essentially lead or its basic oxides, and high current densities could be employed efficiently. After the iodide has been completely converted to iodate, the anolyte is allowed to become acidic and the current density is reduced. The proper lead oxide then quickly forms on the anode so that the following oxidation of iodate to periodate proceeds efficiently.

In the authors' work on the reuse of spent oxidant solutions from the dialdehyde starch production (q.v.), the effects of operating parameters on the efficiency of the Mehltretter process were investigated, and it was discovered that efficiencies could be improved markedly by oxidizing the iodate solutions in an annular cell of special configuration. The anode was made the outer wall of the cell, and agitation was provided by pumping the anolyte through the annular space between the anode and cylindrical diaphragm. Both agitation and spacing are critical; the preferred spacing is 0.5 inch, and the agitation that represented by a velocity of at least 5 ft per minute.

The structure of the annular cell is shown in Fig. 1. The diaphragm is a porous ceramic thimble, and the cathode is an iron rod. In the cell shown, the thimble is supported in its concentric position in the cylindrical anode by plastic spacers at the top and bottom. The cathode is supported in the thimble by a rubber stopper containing tubing through which hydrogen gas is withdrawn and water added to the catholyte.

When oxidizing anolytes containing appreciable quantities of sodium ions, the sodium hydroxide concentration can increase to the point that it crystallizes. This effect is especially noticeable if diaphragms having a low porosity are used. When using such "tight" diaphragms it is necessary to flush the diaphragms periodically to remove the excess caustic and to reduce the concentration of that remaining in the thimble. The greatest cell conductivity occurs when the sodium hydroxide concentration is between 16 and 20 g per 100 ml of solution. Diaphragms that are less "tight" permit the sodium hydroxide to diffuse back into the anolyte after it reaches some higher density, thus making it unnecessary to flush them. High-porosity diaphragms are unsatisfactory as they permit iodate to diffuse into the catholyte, where it is reduced to iodide. This iodide then, being negatively charged, migrates back toward the anode and upon returning to the acid environment of the anolyte is immediately converted to elemental iodine and is liberated from the solution if in sufficiently high concentration. This iodine is not only annoying and corrosive to the equipment, but it also reduces the efficiency of the operation. During the work it was observed that iodide or iodine, iodate, and periodate can coexist in the anolyte; contrary to findings by some investigators, periodate does not readily oxidize elemental iodine.

Obviously the selection of a diaphragm for the cell is important to operation and maintenance, and porosity is an important criterion for this selection. Simple tests of porosity can be made

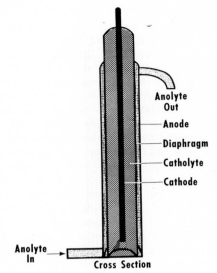

Anolyte Out

Anode

Diaphragm

Catholyte

Cathode

Anolyte In

Cross Section

FIG. 1. Cross section of annular cell.

which discriminate between ceramic bodies, but factors such as wettability and ion conductivity make it difficult to compare various materials. The material of choice is an aluminum oxide ceramic having a silicate binder. This material is available in several porosities and can be produced in a variety of forms; either hemispherical or flat-bottomed cylinders are preferred. All ceramic materials of this nature suffer from the same fault; the silicate binder is attacked by the caustic with resultant loss in tensile strength. Ceramics are low in tensile strength, inherently, and this reduction eventually decreases the strength to the point that the thimble breaks easily. They are therefore mounted in the cell in such a way that they are not under tension, being supported from below, and their alignment is maintained by retaining rings at the top. By minimizing handling these thimbles will give good service under normal conditions for approximately a year.

The anode, which is the cell wall in the annular cell, is critical for superior efficiencies. Both commercial lead and 1 per cent silver-lead alloy have been used to prepare good anodes. Proper preparation of the anode surface can be accomplished either by mechanical brushing or by electrolytic stripping in sulfuric acid; after this cleaning a thin, even film of lead dioxide is anodically formed by using a 5 per cent sulfuric acid solution for the electrolyte and a carbon cathode. The most efficient coatings result when this operation is performed at low current densities for a period of 24 hr or more. An alternative procedure is to anodize in the operating cell, making sure that the flow rates are adequate and that alkali does not contact the anode surface at any time. By this latter method, the efficiency will be poor for the first few hours of operation. Once activated, the anode exhibits a good degree of stability, with some loss of surface during operation. A good anode may be removed from operation, rinsed with distilled water, and permitted to dry without damaging the surface or efficiency of subsequent re-use. At present there is no objective method for determining anode quality other than to observe its efficiency in an actual oxidation of iodate. A good anode has a thin coat of reddish brown to black oxide. Light-colored deposits usually indicate an anode of poor quality, and these frequently cannot be regenerated without complete stripping. A chocolate brown surface usually converts to an effective anode during operation.

In anode construction, lead burning is preferred to soldering as the method of fabrication since solders may contribute to the formation of poor anodic surfaces.

In a typical oxidation, 2 lb of sodium iodate are dissolved in 3 gal of distilled water for the anolyte. This mixture is pumped through the annular space between the 2.5-inch o.d. ceramic thimble and the 3.6-inch i.d. concentric anode made of 1 per cent silver-lead alloy, at a rate of 1.25 gal per minute. Current is supplied from a 3-phase rectifier and maintained at 5 amps/sq dm by voltage control. The temperature is held at 100°F by using a cooling coil in the external circulation system. The average current efficiency to convert 80 per cent of the iodate to periodate is 61 per cent.

Efficiencies in the order of 80 per cent have been realized with carefully prepared anodes. The conversion of iodate to periodate is limited by concentration effects and by an efficiency factor that is a function of anode quality. A relationship expressing the kinetics has been derived.[3]

In making periodates industrially, the difficulties of devising a single large cell that operates efficiently are believed to be insurmountable, and thus recourse must be made to a multiplicity of smaller units, each having a diaphragm which is structurally sound. With ceramic diaphragms, a 2.5-inch o.d. by 24-inch long cylinder gives a good compromise between

strength, large surface area, and low catholyte volume; this size cylinder also requires less floor space and lower maintenance rates than other sizes. Other materials, such as synthetic fiber felts, if they could be fabricated into the desired shape and with the required porosity, might give superior performance as diaphragms.

References

1. CONWAY, H. F., AND LANCASTER, E. B., submitted to *Electrochem. Technol.*
2. CONWAY, H. F., AND SOHNS, V. E., *Ind. Eng. Chem.*, **51**, 637 (1959).
3. LANCASTER, E. B., AND CONWAY, H. F., *Electrochem. Technol.*, **1**, 253 (1963).
4. LANCASTER, E. B., CONWAY, H. F., AND WOHLRABE, F. C., to U.S. Secretary of Agriculture, U. S. Patent pending (1964).
5. MEHLTRETTER, C. L., to U. S. Secretary of Agriculture, U. S. Patent 2,830,941 (Apr. 15, 1958).
6. MEHLTRETTER, C. L., RANKIN, J. C., AND WATSON, P. R., *Ind. Eng. Chem.*, **49**, 350 (1957).
7. MEHLTRETTER, C. L., AND WISE, C. S., *Ind. Eng. Chem.*, **51**, 511 (1959).
8. MEHLTRETTER, C. L., AND WISE, C. S., to U. S. Secretary of Agriculture, U. S. Patent 2,989,371 (June 20, 1961).
9. PFEIFER, V. F., SOHNS, V. E., CONWAY, H. F., LANCASTER, E. B., DABIC, S., AND GRIFFIN, E. L., JR., *Ind. Eng. Chem.*, **52**, 201 (1960).
10. SMITH, G. F., "Analytic Applications of Periodic Acid and Iodic Acid and Their Salts," 5th ed., Columbus, Ohio, G. Frederick Smith Chemical Company, 1950.
11. WILLARD, H. H., AND RALSTON, R. R., *Trans. Electrochem. Soc.*, **62**, 239 (1932).

HOWARD F. CONWAY AND
EARL B. LANCASTER

Cross-reference: *Dialdehyde Starch Preparation.*

PERIODIC REVERSE PLATING

The PR (periodic reverse) current plating process is a major advancement in the electroplating field.[1,2] The fundamental concept of the PR plating process as described herein is the reversing of the plating current periodically for appreciable lengths of time to remove a substantial amount of previously plated metal. Heretofore, commercial plating has been accomplished mainly by the use of conventional direct current. (See **Electrical Currents, Effects on Electrodeposition of Metals.**) While much work had been done with current manipulation, such as very brief current reversal for depolarization, PR plating is distinctly different in that it removes metal and also can provide controlled anodic film formation on the plated work.[3, 5] Periodic reverse current is applicable to many plating solutions and is being used extensively at present in cyanide copper plating. Much of the detailed information usable for cyanide copper can be applied to the use of PR with any plating bath and particularly to white brass, silver, and yellow brass which are commercially plated with the PR process. Zinc, gold, cadmium, iron, nickel, and copper from the acid sulfate solution have been electrodeposited with PR current on a limited production scale.

Advantages of PR Cyanide Copper Plating

The PR plating process produces a number of outstanding results when applied to copper cyanide and other acid and alkaline metal electroplating electrolytes. The following benefits can be readily obtained in PR copper plating with normal control after the installation of properly engineered equipment.[1]

Leveling. With PR plating, consistent and substantial leveling of the base surface is possible. The leveling is reproducible and is mainly affected by the PR cycle used. It has been found that the amount of leveling can be materially increased by the use of certain inorganic and organic additives in the bath.

Uniformity of Deposit Thickness. With PR cyanide copper plating, it is possible to deposit copper on irregularly shaped objects and maintain ±20 per cent of the specified thickness over the entire surface. This uniform metal deposition can be accomplished without conforming anodes.

Higher Permissible Current Densities. The plater can greatly increase plating current densities and, thereby plate more copper in a given period despite the decrease of overall plating efficiencies caused by the reversal portion of the PR cycle. With cycles, such as 20 seconds plate and 5 seconds deplate, a thickness of 0.001 inch of copper can be commercially plated in 10 minutes. With a more sacrificial cycle, such as 60 seconds plate and 40 seconds deplate, a deposit of 0.0008 inch of copper can be plated in 14 minutes. These plating speeds are possible under certain optimum conditions.

Heavier High-Quality Deposits Obtainable. By using PR with a cyanide copper solution, it is possible to deposit smooth, uniform plating in thicknesses up to 0.050 inch and even higher without any special precaution.[4]

Electrical Equipment

Slow-Cycle PR Current. Low-voltage electrical equipment commercially used with conventional d-c plating may be modified for use with PR plating. Low-voltage d-c generators may be adapted for PR plating by the use of contactors in the field circuit, which permits reversal of the polarity of the generator field. By reversing the polarity of the generating field, the low-voltage output of the generator is reversed. If rectifiers or d-c bus systems must be modified for PR plating, low-voltage, heavy-duty contactors are required. The disadvantages of using contactors with rectifiers or with a d-c bus system is the need for large variable resistances that can vary the actual plating or deplating currents. Reversing the output of a generator by the field reversal technique is the simplest procedure, as the field currents in the largest of low-voltage d-c generators usually do not run much over 25 amperes.

With either the field reversal or low-voltage, heavy-duty contactors, an automatic recycling timing mechanism is required. This timer should be designed for independent and easy regulation of both the plating and deplating portion of the PR cycle necessary for the PR plating.

Using a d-c generator as a source of plating current, the following cycle variations can be obtained for PR plating.[1]

1. Constant cycle at fixed current.
2. Constant cycle at two different currents.
3. Two cycles at different currents.

Fast-Cycle PR Current. The use of the newly developed silicon controlled rectifier elements with the proper timing circuits should make it possible to eliminate the difficulties that have been encountered in the development of high-amperage specialized power equipment to produce a current wave form for fast-cycle PR. The use of silicon controlled rectifiers should also eliminate the need for the low-voltage contactors used with the present rectifiers to produce a slow-cycle current wave form. The amperage ratings and reliability of these low-voltage contactors to reverse the current output of a rectifier have been factors in the acceptance of slow-cycle PR current for the production deposition of metals and electrocleaning.

Fast-cycle PR current has been primarily investigated for the deposition of nickel from all of the nickel plating solutions regardless of the operating conditions. By using fast-cycle PR current, passivation will not take place during the anodic portion of the cycle. This prevents the formation of a nonadhering laminar deposit under certain bath operating conditions and reverse coulomb values. Plating from a high-sulfate nickel solution, preliminary tests with fast-cycle PR have shown that if the reverse coulombs were over 10 coulombs per square foot the deposit would be laminated.

Copper Cyanide Plating Solutions

The best results from PR plating of copper are obtained by using a potassium cyanide bath. However, the sodium and mixed sodium-potassium may also be used with good results.[1, 4]

Types of Baths.

	Optimum (oz/gal)	Limits (oz/gal)
Potassium Bath		
Cu as metal	8.0	7.5–9.0
Free KCN	1.0	0.8–1.2
KOH	6.0	5.0–7.0
Carbonates	—	Below 8.0
Temperature	185°F	180–190°F
Sodium Bath		
Cu as metal	11.5	11.0–12.0
Free NaCN	1.0	0.8–1.2
NaOH	5.0	4.0–6.0
Carbonates	—	Below 8.0
Temperature	185°F	180–190°F

Acid Copper

PR has found limited application for the deposition of copper from the acid copper sulfate solution. Russian publications claim the use of PR cycles in the range of 3 to 7 seconds cathodic and 0.3 to 1.0 seconds anodic for the deposition of copper of a uniform thickness.[9] Other publications show the use of PR cycles of 3 to 15 seconds plate and 1 to 5 seconds deplate with cycle efficiencies of 45–50 per cent.

The acid sulfate solution of the following composition is used with PR:

Copper sulfate ($CuSO_4\cdot 5H_2O$)	28.0–32.0 oz/gal
Sulfuric acid (H_2SO_4)	8.0–12.0 oz/gal
Chlorides (HCl 37%)	50–250 ml/1000 gal
Temperature	80–100°F

Foley used PR for the copper electroforming of heat sinks for missile nose cones.[7] A PR cycle in the slow-cycle range with a cycle efficiency of 50 to 70 per cent was used to obtain uniform deposits.

Nickel

The research on the application of PR current to the deposition of various metals with fast- and slow-cycle PR has been carried out simultaneously. Thus, it is only natural that the use of PR current for nickel plating and specifically bright nickel plating for the decorative field has aroused considerable attention. In the initial phase of the application of PR current to nickel plating solutions, the primary goal was to obtain bright leveled deposits with a minimum or no addition agent. Today, the organic brightener systems offered commercially for production plating with d-c give the desired brightness and leveling. However, the impairment of the physical properties of the deposit, such as ductility, internal stress, and corrosion resistance, is attributed to the organic materials added or to their oxidation or reduction breakdown products.

It has been found that in working with slow-cycle PR, using a basic Watt's solution with the normal operating pH range of 2.5 to 4.5, the nickel deposit would laminate. The lamination of the nickel deposit is caused by the passivation of the nickel deposit during the anodic portion of the PR cycle.

Basic Watt's Nickel Solution

Nickel sulfate ($NiSO_4\cdot 6H_2O$)	40.0 oz/gal
Nickel chloride ($NiCl_2\cdot 6H_2O$)	6.0 oz/gal
Boric acid (H_3BO_3)	5.0 oz/gal
pH	2.5–4.5

When nickel plating from the basic Watt's-type solution, it has been observed that if the plate and deplate times were decreased and the ratio of plate to deplate maintained at about 5:1, a semibright nickel plate could be deposited without the use of organic addition agents.

By increasing the chloride concentration of the basic Watt's-type solution or by using a nickel solution made entirely with the chloride nickel salts, the plate and deplate times of the PR cycle are not critical with regard to the lamination of the electrodeposit. Slow-cycle PR normally used for the deposition of copper, silver, zinc, and other metals could be used. Variations in the PR time cycle, pH, and temperature are not critical in plating from the high- or all-chloride nickel plating solution.

Additional work has shown that by adding

organic sulfonic acids to the standard Watt's nickel plating bath it is possible to use slow-cycle PR without the deposits laminating. Slow-cycle PR, 30 seconds plate 3 seconds deplate, has been tried in production bright nickel plating in the United States to obtain improved corrosion resistance; but due to the breakdown of the organic addition agents, other difficulties were encountered, such as decreased brightness and leveling.

Silver

Periodic reverse current has found wide application in the plating of precious metals. For instance, with PR applied to a cyanide silver plating solution, it is possible to deposit heavy, uniform silver plate. Elaborate racking and careful anode to cathode arrangements are not necessary when depositing silver with PR as would be the case when d-c is used. Thus, the deposition of silver with PR is primarily advocated for engineering application rather than decorative plating. The most important benefit obtainable with PR applied to precious metal plating is metal distribution. Due to the high cost of the metals deposited, this benefit is of prime importance. Even in the decorative plating of precious metals when plating to minimum thickness specification, any added expense of using PR is more than overcome by the savings

incurred by the reduced thickness of deposit in the high current density areas of the cathode. From Fig. 1, it is readily observed that uniform deposits can be obtained between 45 and 50 per cent reverse coulombs. When using PR cycles with over 50 per cent reverse coulombs, it is possible to obtain thinner deposits in the high current density area of the cathode; and with a reverse coulomb value in the area of 70 per cent, it is actually possible to deposit no metal in the high current density area of the cathode. The cathode is actually stripped of deposited metal in these areas.

Solution composition and operating conditions for the deposition of silver with PR are:[4]

Silver cyanide	6.0–8.0 oz/gal
Potassium cyanide (free)	6.0–12.0 oz/gal
Potassium carbonate	6.0 oz/gal maximum
Potassium hydroxide	1.0–1.5 oz/gal
pH	11.5–12.0
Temperature	80–150°F

When using PR with silver plating as is the case with copper, increased metal concentration and higher operating temperatures are often used to overcome the loss of plating efficiency due to the PR cycle. PR cycles used for silver plating will vary from 5 to 60 seconds cathodic and 1 to 60 seconds anodic. These are PR cycles very similar to those used with the copper cy-

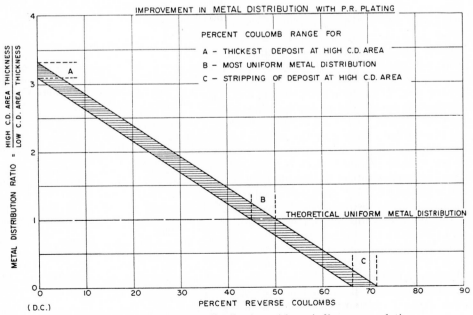

FIG. 1. Improvement in metal distribution with periodic reverse plating.

anide solution and other plating baths. The deplating current densities can be equal to, greater, or less than the plating current density. This would depend very much on the plating and deplating times. As is the case with copper plating, the PR cycles and the plating and deplating current densities would depend on the individual production requirements with hardly any two installations operating in the same manner.

White Brass

The copper-zinc alloy deposit usually referred to as white brass became of commercial interest as a nickel substitute in the early 1950's. It is still used today in one of the largest captive United States automotive bumper plants and has been used for this application since 1958. At the present, approximately one-third of all the automotive bumpers produced in the United States have a composite coating of copper, white brass, nickel, and chromium.

The solution composition and operating conditions for the deposition of the white brass alloy are as follows:

Copper	1.6–1.7 oz/gal
Zinc	2.6–2.9 oz/gal
Sodium cyanide (free)	7.6–7.8 oz/gal
Sodium hydroxide	4.6–4.8 oz/gal
Temperature	84–88°F
Cathode current density	25–50 amperes per sq ft

The PR cycles used for the deposition of the white brass, 35 to 40 per cent copper and 60 to 65 per cent zinc, are in the slow-cycle range. The plating time can vary from 10 to 45 seconds and the deplating time from 1 to 15 seconds. The PR cycle used for the production plating of the bumpers is 20 seconds plating and 2 seconds deplating. The plating current density and the deplating current density are kept the same.

Air or mechanical agitation is usually used to improve the cathode efficiency which is around 30 per cent without agitation. With such a low operating cathode efficiency even with agitation, it is impossible to use sacrificial PR cycles, that is, the PR cycles that have a cycle efficiency of less than 50 to 60 per cent.

Although carbonates are generally not a problem in the white brass plating bath, sodium cyanate is formed under certain solution operating conditions and must be maintained below 5.0 oz/gal. Sodium cyanate concentrations in the range of 8.0 to 9.0 oz/gal will precipitate out

in the plating tank and filtering system, causing considerable trouble. The white brass deposits become more brittle at the higher cyanate concentrations. Chlorides also have an adverse effect on the build-up of the cyanates, making it necessary to use deionized water for solution make-up and maintenance.

Zinc Plating

Faust, Safranek, and Miller have applied slow-cycle PR current to an acid zinc electrolyte to obtain brightness, improved surface leveling, and microfill of porosity in zinc base diecastings.[6] PR current cycles used for obtaining the bright leveling zinc deposit with good pore filling properties are in the slow-cycle range from about 15 to 60 seconds cathodic and 9 to 45 seconds anodic. The per cent leveling obtained in acid zinc solution varies from 40 to 85 per cent. Examples of plating conditions vary from higher deplating current densities to lower deplating current densities than the applied cathodic current densities.

Hammond and Bowman changed the composition of a nickel-zinc alloy by the use of slow-cycle PR current.[8] With normal d-c plating from a nickel chloride-zinc chloride plating solution, an alloy of approximately 80 to 85 per cent zinc and 20 to 15 per cent nickel is deposited.

Sample calculations and definitions relating to periodic reverse plating are given in the following entry.

References

1. GRAHAM, A. K., "Electroplating Engineering Handbook," 1st Edition, Chapter 31, 573–588, New York, Reinhold Publishing Corp., 1955.
2. (a) JERNSTEDT, G. W., "Periodic Reverse Current Electroplating," *Steel and Metal Finishing* (1947).
   (b) JERNSTEDT, G. W., "A New Tool for Electroplaters-PR Plating," *Westinghouse Engineer*, **7** (May, 1947).
   (c) JERNSTEDT, G. W., "Better Deposits at Greater Speeds by PR Plating," *Plating*, **35** (July, 1948).
   (d) JERNSTEDT, G. W., "PR Cyanide Copper Plating," *36th Annual Proceedings, AES* (June, 1949).
   (e) JERNSTEDT, G. W., "Brighter Finishes via PR Plating," *Westinghouse Engineer*, **10** (May, 1950).
   (f) JERNSTEDT, G. W., "Leveling with PR Current Plating," *37th Annual Proceedings, AES* (June, 1950).
3. TURNER, D. R., "Mechanism of Surface Leveling by PR Current in Cyanide Copper Plating,"

Electrochemical Society 102nd Meeting; *Metal Finishing*, **50,** No. 11, 70–74 (1952).

4. WALKER, P. M., BENTLEY, N. E., AND HALL, L. E., "Electroforming in Electronics Engineering," *Transactions Institute of Metal Finishing*, **32,** 349–369 (1955).

5. HICKLING, A., AND ROTHBAUM, H. P., "The Influence of Periodic Reversal of Current upon Concentration Polarization During Metal Plating," *Transaction Institute Metal Finishing*, **34,** "Cycle Electrolysis," Part I, 53, Part II, 199 (1957).

6. SAFRANEK, W. H., AND FAUST, C. L., "Improved Electroplated Finishes for Zinc Die Castings," *Plating*, **45** (October, 1958).

7. FOLEY, D. FRANK, "Copper Electroforming of Heat Sinks for Missile Nose Cones," *Plating*, **46,** 1268–1274 (November, 1959).

8. HAMMOND, MILTON B., AND BOWMAN, GLADE B., (Assignors Rockwell Standard Corporation), U.S. Patent 2,989,446 (June 20, 1961).

9. TAURIT, G. E., "Developments in Electroplating and Polishing at the Gorky Motor Car Works —Moscow," *Electroplating and Metal Finishing*, **13,** 85–88 and 90 (March, 1960).

MYRON CERESA

Cross-references: *Electrical Currents, Effects on Electrodeposition of Metals;* see *Electrodeposition* or *Electroplating* of specific metals; *Electrogalvanizing; Electroplating Terms.*

PERIODIC REVERSE PLATING CALCULATIONS

With d-c plating, the thickness of the deposit is dependent only on the time of plating, cathode efficiency, and the current density used. In PR plating, the thickness is also dependent on the cycle efficiency. Assuming 100 per cent cathode and anode current efficiency, the cycle efficiency is defined as:

$$E_c = \frac{t_p - t_d}{t_p + t_d} (100),$$

where

E_c = cycle efficiency in per cent,
t_p = plating time, and
t_d = deplating time.

Example 1: With a 20 second plating and 5 second deplating cycle:

$$E_c = \frac{20 - 5}{20 + 5} (100) = \frac{15}{25} (100) = 60\%$$

With the exception of the very short slow PR cycles such as 20 seconds plating and 5 seconds deplating, the deplating current density used is often lower than the plating current density.

The deplating current density is usually referred to as a per cent of the plating current density. For example, with a plating current density of 60 amperes per square foot and a deplating current density of 36 amperes per square foot, the deplating current density is said to be 60 per cent of the plating current density. The deplating current is also referred to as reverse current. When the deplating current density is 60 per cent of the plating current density, it is usually referred to as 60 per cent reverse current.

When the deplating current density is not the same as the plating current density, the expression then becomes:

$$E_c = \frac{t_p - t_d \dfrac{(I_r)}{100}}{t_p + t_d} (100),$$

where I_r = per cent reverse current.

Example 2: When plating for 20 seconds at 60 amp/sq ft and deplating 5 seconds at 30 amp/sq ft:

$$I_r = \frac{30}{60} (100) = 50\% \text{ reverse current.}$$

$$E_c = \frac{20 - (5)(0.5)}{20 + 5} (100) = \frac{20 - 2.5}{25} (100)$$

$$= \frac{17.5}{25} (100) = 70\%$$

Example 3: When plating for 60 seconds at 80 amp/sq ft and deplating 45 seconds at 64 amp/sq ft:

$$I_r = \frac{64}{80} (100) = 80\%$$

$$E_c = \frac{60 - (45)(0.8)}{60 + 45} (100) = \frac{60 - 36}{105} (100)$$

$$= \frac{24}{105} (100) = 22.9\%$$

For example, the high-speed cyanide copper bath operates at essentially 100 per cent anode and cathode efficiencies. All of the calculations are for a bath that is 100 per cent efficient. In production there may be a slight difference in the actual deposit weight and the calculated deposit weight, but the difference is so small that it is not considered in the calculations. For example, when the cyanide copper bath is considered to be 100 per cent efficient, it will take

8.89 ampere-hours or 533.4 ampere-minutes to deposit 1 mil (0.001 inch) of copper on one square foot of surface.

The following formula may be used to calculate the thickness of a deposit obtained with d-c plating:

$$T = \frac{tC}{533.4}$$

where

T = deposit thickness in mils;

t = total plating time in minutes; and

C = cathode current density, amp/sq ft.

When calculating the thickness of a deposit obtained with PR plating, the cycle efficiency must be considered. The formula for the thickness is:

$$T = \frac{tC}{533.4} \frac{E_c}{100}$$

Example 4: With a plating time of 15 minutes and using a PR cycle of 20 seconds plating time at 80 amperes per square foot and 7 seconds deplating time at 48 amperes per square foot:

$$I_r = \frac{48}{80}(100) = 60\%$$

$$E_c = \frac{20 - (7)(0.6)}{20 + 7}(100) = \frac{20 - 4.2}{27}(100)$$

$$= \frac{15.8}{27}(100) = 58.5\%$$

$$T = \frac{15(80)}{533.4} \frac{(58.5)}{(100)} = \frac{702}{533.4}$$

$$= 1.32 \text{ mils or } 0.00132 \text{ inch}$$

Definitions

1. *Per cent reverse coulombs*—The ratio of the deplating coulombs to the plating coulombs expressed as a per cent.
2. *Plating coulombs*—The plating current in amperes multiplied by the plating time in seconds.
3. *Deplating coulombs*—The deplating current in amperes multiplied by the deplating time in seconds. Sometimes called reverse coulombs.
4. *Deplating time*—The time of the PR cycle whenever the work is anodic, that is, the time that metal is being removed.
5. *Plating time*—The time of the PR cycle whenever the work is cathodic, that is, the time that metal is being deposited.
6. *Anodic current efficiency of the work*—The

ratio of the actual weight deplated to the weight that theoretically should be deplated during the anodic portion of the cycle expressed as a per cent.

7. *Cathodic current efficiency of the work*—The ratio of the actual weight plated to the weight that theoretically should be plated during the cathodic portion of the cycle expressed as a per cent.
8. *Per cent leveling*—The ratio of the decrease in surface roughness, as measured in microinches, of the plated metal to the original surface roughness, expressed as a per cent. This is positive when the plated metal is less rough than the base metal surface.
9. *Periodic reverse cycle (PR cycle)*—The complete cycle consisting of a plating time followed by a deplating time.
10. *PR cycle efficiency*—The net time of plating [plating time minus (deplating time × per cent reverse current)] divided by the total cycle time (assuming 100 per cent switching efficiency; that is, instantaneous switching).
11. *Plating current density*—The current per unit work area, while the work is cathodic, usually expressed in amperes per square foot (asf) or amperes per square decimeter.
12. *Deplating current density*—The current per unit work area, while the work is anodic, usually expressed in amperes per square foot or amperes per square decimeter.
13. *Metal distribution ratio*—The ratio of the thickness of metal at two specified areas of a cathode.
14. *Per cent reverse current*—The ratio of the deplating current to the plating current expressed as a per cent.
15. *Effective plating current density*—The plating current density of the PR cycle multiplied by the cycle efficiency. (Also see **Electroplating Terms.**)

MYRON CERESA

PEROXYGEN CHEMICALS

Persulfates

In the manufacture of electrolytic hydrogen peroxide (q.v.), the anodic reaction is the formation of ammonium peroxydisulfate from ammonium bisulfate. This solution can be used for either hydrolysis to hydrogen peroxide or crystallization to yield a solid product. The anolyte solution is fed to a vacuum crystallizer where the evaporation of water cools the solution sufficiently to cause half of the feed ammonium peroxydisulfate to crystallize as small particles. These are separated from the mother liquor, washed, and dried. The mother liquor can return to the electrolytic cells, or the remaining active oxygen is recovered as hydrogen peroxide.

Larger yields in quantity with better efficiency are obtained by partially evaporating the feed solution which increases the acid concentration and decreases the solubility of the peroxydisulfate, and by keeping the crystallization temperature as low as possible by using vacuums in the 5 to 80 mm Hg range. The wet solid has residual acid on its surface, so drying can only be accomplished after the solid is washed and neutralized. The final product is pure; but, being of small crystal size, caking and storage tend to be problems.

If a large crystal size is desired, a second crystallization must be accomplished. The small particles are dissolved in an aqueous solution which is maintained slightly alkaline to neutralize any acid formed by decomposition. This solution is fed to a vacuum crystallizer where large pure particles form. These are easy to separate from the circulating liquor and dry quickly.

Potassium peroxydisulfate is made by two processes. The Pietzsch cell is the electrolytic unit using a nearly neutral ammonium bisulfate solution which is saturated with potassium bisulfate. The electrolyzed solution is reacted with either potassium carbonate or hydroxide. The solid formed consists of small particles which are separated from the mother liquor, dissolved in water, recrystallized, and dried. The mutual solubilities of ammonium peroxydisulfate and potassium peroxydisulfate in the Pietzsch electrolyte will not allow a 100 per cent pure potassium peroxydisulfate solid to crystallize, and the ammonium bisulfate mother liquor will be saturated with potassium bisulfate.

When the Riedel electrolyte is used, a two stage crystallization process is necessary to attain a 100 per cent pure potassium peroxydisulfate solid and to isolate the potassium peroxydisulfate solutions from the ammonium peroxydisulfate Riedel electrolyte. The first stage crystallizer yields small ammonium peroxydisulfate particles. These are separated from the mother liquor which is returned to the Riedel hydrogen peroxide process. The particles are dissolved in an aqueous solution of potassium peroxydisulfate which is fed to the second crystallizing unit where the required amount of potassium hydroxide is added. The reaction yields a supersaturated solution of potassium peroxydisulfate. The ammonia is evaporated with the water. The crystallized product has large free-flowing particles and only traces of ammonium

peroxydisulfate. Centrifuging and drying finish the process.

Other peroxydisulfates can be produced in a manner similar to potassium, provided the cation in the carbonate or hydroxide form is alkaline enough to replace the ammonium ion. Sodium, barium, and lithium are examples of other peroxydisulfates which have been produced.

Peroxydisulfates are packaged in multiwall paper bags, and fibre drums. The uses of the compounds include polymerization catalysts, dye fixing, detergent additives, modification of starches, and desizing of textiles.

Ammonium peroxydisulfate has been used extensively in the printed circuit etching field where the advantages of easy waste disposal, no undercutting of the circuit, and rapid etching rates make it attractive.

Perborates

Electrolytic sodium perborate is made from an electrolyte of sodium tetraborate and sodium carbonate. The cell solution is cooled and solid sodium perborate crystallizes. Filtering, washing, and drying complete the process.

Currently, perborates are produced chemically using hydrogen peroxide because of improved efficiencies in hydrogen peroxide manufacture which could not be realized in electrolytic sodium perborate manufacture.

Sodium perborate tetrahydrate is the only perborate being produced in large quantities in 1963. Several raw materials can be used depending on economic factors. The boron comes either from sodium tetraborate or boric acid. Sodium hydroxide is one source of alkali, or sodium peroxide will give both alkali and active oxygen. Hydrogen peroxide is another source of active oxygen.

The raw materials may be added together, without purification, but generally a solution of sodium metaborate is formed by the reaction of sodium hydroxide and sodium tetraborate. This solution is purified. The active oxygen source is then reacted with the metaborate in various types of crystallizers. The resulting water solution of sodium perborate is cooled and the crystalline product is centrifuged and dried.

Sodium perborate is used in textile bleaching, either industrially or in home laundries. Soap manufacturers blend their detergents with sodium perborate. Quantities are used in dentifrices, cosmetic preparations, and in dyestuff development.

References

1. BRETSCHGER, M. E., CREWSON, G. G., AND CUSHING, R. E., P. B. Report 177331 (1946).
2. BRETSCHGER, M. E., AND SHANLEY, E. S., *J. Electrochem. Soc.*, **99,** 311 (1952).
3. FLACH, D. O., AND GARVER, R. E., U.S. Patent 2,899,272 (August 11, 1959).
4. MACHU, W., "Das Wasserstoffperoxyd und die Perverbindungen," Second ed., Vienna, Springer-Verlag, 1951.
5. SCHUMB. W. C., SATTERFIELD, C. N., AND WENTWORTH, R. L., "Hydrogen Peroxide," New York, Reinhold Publishing Corporation, 1955.
6. SHANLEY, E. S., *J. Chem. Educ.*, **28,** 290 (1951).
7. U.S. Department of Commerce, P. B. Reports 45252, 33489, 74329.
8. WOOD, W. S., *Chemistry and Industry*, **1953,** 2.

REED E. GARVER

Cross reference: *Hydrogen Peroxide.*

PERSULFATES. See PEROXYGEN CHEMICALS.

PERTECHNETATE ION AS CORROSION INHIBITOR. See CORROSION INHIBITION BY PERTECHNETATE ION.

pH

The pH value of an aqueous solution is a number describing its acidity or alkalinity. The usual range of pH is from about 1 for 0.1 N HCl to about 13 for 0.1 N NaOH. The pH of a neutral solution is 7.2 at 15°, 7.0 at 25°, and 6.8 at 35°C.

The pH scale was first used in 1909 by Sørensen. He defined pH as the negative logarithm (base 10) of the concentration of hydrogen ions (equivalents per liter), and he also described an electrometric method for the measurement of pH. Modern chemists have abandoned Sørensen's definition but have retained, in all essentials, his method of measurement.

The approved definition of pH is an operational one. The electromotive force, E_X, of the cell

H$_2$; solution X:

KCl (saturated): reference electrode

and the electromotive force E_S of the cell

H$_2$; solution S:

KCl (saturated): reference electrode

are measured with the same electrodes at the same temperature. The hydrogen electrode is now usually replaced by a glass electrode. The difference in pH between the unknown solution, X, and the standard solution, S, is defined by the equation

$$pH_X - pH_S = (E_X - E_S)/k$$

in which k is 2.3026 $RT/\mathbf{F}$ or 0.05916 for 25°C if E_X and E_S are expressed in volts.

To complete the definition of pH, values of pH$_S$ have been assigned to standard solutions. The National Bureau of Standards has recommended 5 solutions as primary standards (Bates, 1962). One of these, 0.05 M potassium hydrogen phthalate, has been adopted as the primary standard of pH in Great Britain and in Japan. For this solution pH$_S$ is 4.00 at 15°, 4.01 at 25° and 4.03 at 40°C (Bates and Guggenheim, 1960).

An interpretation of pH is possible in special cases. The values assigned to the standards have been chosen in such a way as to make pH$_S$ equal to $-\log C_H f_1$, where f_1 is an activity coefficient practically equal to that of sodium chloride. Approximate values of $-\log f_1$ are 0.04, 0.06, 0.09, and 0.11 for ionic strengths of 0.01, 0.02, 0.05, and 0.10, respectively. For solutions of ionic strength not over 0.1 and pH between about 2 and 12, these values may be employed in calculations involving ionic equilibria.

For example, the pH of a "standard acetate" buffer (0.1 M HC$_2$H$_3$O$_2$, 0.1 M NaC$_2$H$_3$O$_2$) is found to be 4.65. It follows that $-\log C_H$ is 4.65–0.11, or 4.54. For a 1:1 buffer the pH is equal to the pK' of the equation

$$pH = pK' + \log C_B/C_A$$

in which C_A is the concentration of the buffer acid and C_B is that of its conjugate base. The apparent constant, K', is not equal to the true constant, K, of the buffer acid because K' lacks a ratio of activity coefficients. In this case it may be assumed that $K = K'f_1$ or p$K = pK' - \log f_1$. On this basis pK (or $-\log K$) would be equal to 4.65 + 0.11, or 4.76, which is the accepted value.

A similar calculation may be made for a phosphate buffer in which the acid is H$_2$PO$_4^-$ and the base is HPO$_4^{--}$. In this case K_2 is equal to $K_2'f_2/f_1$ where f_2 is the activity coefficient of the bivalent anion. From the Debye-Hückel theory, it follows that $\log f_2 = 4 \log f_1$, and accordingly we have the relation

$$pK_2 = pK_2' - 3 \log f_1 .$$

For a buffer of 0.025 M KH_2PO_4 in 0.025 M Na_2HPO_4, the pH is 6.86 and the ionic strength 0.1. Accordingly, the value of pK_2 should be 6.86 + 0.33, or 7.19. The accepted value is 7.20. Again, the value of $-\log C_H$ is equal to pH + $\log f_1$, being 6.75 for this buffer.

References

1. BATES, R. G., "Electrometric pH Determination," Chapter 4, New York, John Wiley and Sons, 1954.
2. BATES, R. G., "Revised Standard Values for pH Measurements from 0 to 95°C," *J. Research Nat. Bur. Standards*, **66A**, 179–184 (1962).
3. BATES, R. G., AND GUGGENHEIM, E. A., "Report on the Standardization of pH and Related Terminology," *Pure and Applied Chemistry*, **1**, 163–168 (1960).

DAVID I. HITCHCOCK

Cross-references: *Acidimetry and Alkalimetry; Ionic Equilibria.*

pH METER

An instrument for the measurement of pH in terms of the potential of an electrolytic pH-sensitive cell chain is called a pH meter. Such a cell chain, to be useful for pH measurements, must develop a difference of potential across its terminals which varies in a known manner with the pH of the solution into which the electrodes of the cell chain are immersed. The most commonly used cell chain uses a glass electrode as its pH-sensitive electrode. The other electrode is a stable reference of unvarying voltage, such as a calomel half-cell or a silver-silver chloride electrode.

The glass electrode consists of a thin-walled glass bulb containing a solution-connected electrode, such as a silver-silver chloride electrode. When this bulb is immersed in a solution, a difference of potential which changes linearly with pH appears between its inner and outer surfaces. The rate of change of potential is 60 mv/pH unit at 30°C. The electrical resistance of the bulb is usually of the order of 100 to 200 megohms. The pH meter, therefore, must measure voltages of the order of several hundred

millivolts from a several hundred megohm source with an accuracy, usually better than 1 per cent, sometimes to better than 0.1 per cent. Most pH meters have either used a linear vacuum tube amplifier reading out on an accurate meter to do this, or have balanced the cell chain voltage against a known potentiometric voltage using the amplifier to drive a null indicator. The latter type of pH meter requires manual setting but is inherently capable of greater accuracy since it does not depend on the linearity of a readout meter or of the amplifier, readout being from a calibrated potentiometer.

No matter which type of readout is used, the amplifier, and especially its input stage, is a most critical part of the pH meter. Since the output of the cell chain is a low unidirectional voltage, the problems of drift and instability which are often associated with a direct current amplifier must be faced. In addition, the input impedance of the amplifier must be very high to avoid drawing current from the glass electrode, thus causing a voltage drop in the high resistance of the bulb, which would produce error. There are four approaches which have been used to this problem: (1) the direct-connected amplifier; (2) the impulse amplifier; (3) the carrier amplifier; and (4) the chopper-stabilized amplifier. All of these, as used for pH work, require that the first tube in the amplifier have a high input impedance and, especially in the case of 1 and 4, a low grid current. The direct-connected amplifier must have a very stable input tube to minimize drift; the other amplifiers are inherently drift-free or self-correcting. Both 3 and 4 have moving parts and are generally more expensive. Low-priced pH meters generally are of type 1. Fig. 1 shows a type 4 pH meter.

Certain controls or adjustments are common to most pH meters. One, always found, is the "AP" or assymetry potential control, often called the "STD" or standardize control. Since each glass electrode has a small, constant, individually different, assymetry potential in addition to its pH potential, it is necessary to immerse the cell chain in a known buffer and make an adjustment to bring the readout to the known buffer value before reading unknown pH's. This is the function of the "AP" control. Another control, the temperature compensator, is used to stretch or shrink the readout scale electrically so that it will follow pH correctly at different sample temperatures. Where this con-

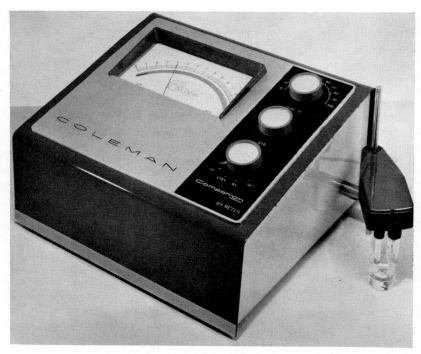

Fɪɢ. 1. Direct-reading pH meter with chopper-stabilized amplifier. Electrode assembly in beaker: glass electrode on left, reference electrode on right.

trol is not present, correction charts must be used to correct the indicated pH if the sample is not at the temperature, usually 25 or 30°C, for which the pH meter is calibrated.

Other controls may be found on the more pretentious instruments. Many instruments have a switch to change the range to read plus or minus millivolts for redox measurements or to spread a couple of pH over the whole scale for easier or closer reading. In the latter case the accuracy of pH measurement with a good instrument becomes limited by the technique with which the cell chain is employed rather than the sensitivity of the pH meter. Since the voltage per pH unit generated by a pH cell chain is a linear function of the absolute temperature, and since offsets in cell chain voltage produced by input current drawn by the pH meter, if any, will change rapidly as the resistance of the glass electrode varies with temperature, it is apparent that measurement of pH to a high degree of accuracy requires careful temperature control of the sample and buffer. Some pH meters have resistance thermometers, commonly called automatic temperature compensators, incorporated into their cir-

cuits to correct the readout for the temperature effect on the voltage generated by the glass electrode. Such a compensator cannot compensate for the effect of resistance changes of the bulb or for inherent temperature coefficients of the buffer or sample.

References

1. Bᴀᴛᴇs, R. G., "Electrometric pH Determinations," Chapter 9, New York, John Wiley & Sons, Inc., 1954.
2. Bᴀᴛᴇs, R. G., Chapter 10 in Kolthoff, I. M., and Elving, P. J. "Treatise on Analytical Chemistry," New York, Interscience Encyclopedia, Inc. N. Y., 1959.
3. Pᴇʀʟᴇʏ, G. A., Chapter 1 in Boltz, D. F., Ed., "Selected Topics in Modern Instrumental Analysis," Englewood Cliffs, N. J., Prentice-Hall Inc., 1952.

Jᴏʜɴ J. J. Sᴛᴀᴜɴᴛᴏɴ

Cross references: *Acidimetry and Alkalimetry; Glass Electrode; pH; Reference Electrodes; Resistance Thermometers.*

pH-POTENTIAL DIAGRAMS. See POTENTIAL-pH EQUILIBRIUM DIAGRAMS.

pH TITRATION CURVES

A considerable number of reactions which involve proton transfer have been studied by a careful analysis of changes in pH resulting from the addition of acid or alkali to solutions of known composition. By this procedure it is possible to derive equilibrium constants for the reactions under consideration. As they are commonly performed, some effort is made to maintain a constant ionic strength throughout the titrations so that activity coefficients of the several reacting species might be kept constant. Equilibrium constants obtained in this way are known as "conditional" constants, but they can be the basis for calculation of thermodynamic constants. (See **Ionic Equilibria**.)

The calculations involved in such studies ordinarily require that the concentration of hydrogen or hydroxide ions be known. These concentrations may be estimated from pH measurements by a judicious selection of activity coefficients for hydrogen ion in the working media, or by an empirical calibration based on measurements of pH in solutions of strong acids or bases of known hydrogen or hydroxide ion concentration.

For the titration of an acid, HA, H_2A, etc., by a base, BOH, there are relationships based upon the requirement of electrical neutrality, viz.,

$$[B^+] + [H^+] = [A^-] + [OH^-]$$

or

$$[B^+] + [H^+] = [HA^-] + 2[A^{--}] + [OH^-], \text{ etc.}$$

One may represent the course of neutralization of the acid by a quantity called the degree of neutralization, g, the number of moles of base added per mole of acid taken, i.e., $[B]_T/[A]_T$. For a strong base $[B]_T = [B^+]$, and $[A]_T$ may be represented by a conservation equation such as

$$[A]_T = [A^-] + [HA] = [A^-]\left(1 + \frac{a_H}{K_a''}\right)$$

or

$$= [A^-] + [HA^-] + [H_2A]$$

$$= [A^-]\left(1 + \frac{a_H}{K_1''} + \frac{a_H^2}{K_1''K_2''}\right) \text{ etc.}$$

These relationships may be combined to give one form of the equation for a titration curve,

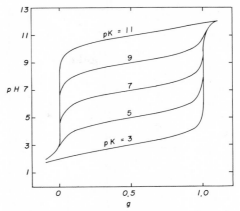

Fig. 1. Titration curves for 0.1 molar solutions of weak monobasic acids having pK's as indicated titrated by a strong base. The abscissa, g, represents the degree of neutralization.

which for a strong base and a weak monobasic or dibasic acid, respectively, is

$$g = \frac{K_a''}{K_a'' + a_H} - \frac{[H^+]}{[A]_T} + \frac{[OH^-]}{[A]_T}$$

or

$$= \frac{K_1''a_H + 2K_1''K_2''}{a_H^2 + K_1''a_H + K_1''K_2''} - \frac{[H^+]}{[A]_T}$$

$$+ \frac{[OH^-]}{[A]_T}$$

In all these expressions the values of K are shown primed (K'') to signify these are Brönsted constants (See **Ionic Equilibria**). Had concentration constants (K') been used instead, the terms derived from the mass law would have had the form $K_a'/(K'_a + [H^+])$, etc.

The titration curve is usually plotted in the form pH (ordinate) vs g (or some equivalent quantity). In the middle range of pH the second and third terms are small compared with the first, but these become significant at low and high pH, respectively. Titration curves calculated by the above for a monobasic acid are shown in Fig. 1, and show the effect of K_a on the position and shape of the curves. These reveal why acids with $pK_a > 7$ fail to give a satisfactory break in pH at the equivalence point ($g = 1$), and reveal also the factors associated with the choice of indicators for titrations of weak acids.

Titration curves of dibasic or polybasic acids

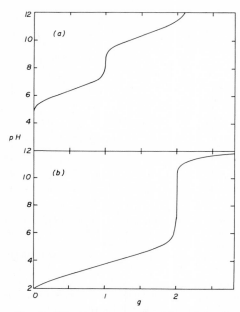

FIG. 2. Titration curves for 0.1 molar solutions of weak dibasic acids: (a) carbonic acid, (b) tartaric acid. The abscissa, g, represents the number of equivalents of strong base added per mole of acid.

may reveal more than one break in pH at $g = 1$, 2, etc., provided there is appreciable separation in K_1, K_2, etc. Thus, carbonic acid ($pK_1 = 6.5$, $pK_2 = 10.2$) gives a titration curve shown in Fig. 2 (a), while tartaric acid, ($pK_1 = 3.0$, $pK_2 = 4.1$) yields a curve in which pH rises gradually without a break until $g = 2$ as shown in Fig. 2 (b).

pH titration curves are often used to determine "conditional" ionization constants for weak acids and bases. The first term in the expressions for g given above may be called the degree of protonation, $\bar{n}_H$, of the acid; that is, the average number of protons bound per molecule of A^- or A^{--}, respectively. Thus

$$\bar{n}_H = g + \frac{[H^+]}{[A]_T} - \frac{[OH^-]}{[A]_T}$$

It is quite apparent that for a monobasic acid each estimate of $\bar{n}_H$ permits an estimate of K_a'', while each pair of estimates of $\bar{n}_H$ will yield equations which may be solved to give K_1'' and K_2'' for a dibasic acid, and so on. The technique of a titration permits a substantial number of estimates of ionization constants to be made in the course of one experiment, and a variety of devices have been suggested for obtaining the

best values of two or more constants from a series of values of $\bar{n}_H$ at different pH's.[1]

Examination of titration data can reveal considerable information concerning the hydrolysis of ions. Equilibrium constants for the hydrolysis of ions such as ammonium or carbonate are treated in precisely the same way as ionization constants of acids or bases, respectively (see **Ionic Equilibria**).

The hydrolysis of metallic ions has proved to be a slightly more complex case owing to the very common formation of binuclear or polynuclear species. The various stages of hydrolysis give rise to equilibria for which appropriate hydrolysis constants may be formulated, e.g.,

$$M + H_2O \rightleftharpoons MOH + H$$

$$\beta_1 = \frac{[MOH][H]}{[M]}$$

$$M + 2H_2O \rightleftharpoons M(OH)_2 + 2H$$

$$\beta_2 = \frac{[M(OH)_2][H]^2}{[M]}$$

$$2M + 2H_2O \rightleftharpoons M_2(OH)_2 + 2H$$

$$\beta_{22} = \frac{[M_2(OH)_2][H]^2}{[M]^2}$$

and so forth; charges are omitted in these for the sake of generality. One may measure the amount of hydroxide bound to metal in this way by the amount of hydrogen ion set free. By titrating a solution containing a strong acid and the metallic ion in known concentrations with a base of known concentration, and measuring the pH after each addition of the latter, the extent of hydrolysis at each pH can be measured. If the degree of hydrolysis, $\bar{n}_{OH}$, is defined as the average number of hydroxide groups bound per metallic atom, then it is seen that

$$\bar{n}_{OH} = \frac{[H] - [H]_T + [OH]_T}{[M]_T}$$

All quantities in this expression are known provided [H] can be related in some manner to pH values.

The degree of hydrolysis can also be formulated as

$$\bar{n}_{OH} = \frac{\beta_1/[H] + 2\beta_2/[H]^2 + \cdots + 2\beta_{22}[M]^2/[H]^2 + \cdots}{1 + \beta_1/[H] + \beta_2/[H]^2 + \cdots + 2\beta_{22}[M]^2/[H]^2 + \cdots}$$

Given that only mononuclear complexes are formed, $\bar{n}_{OH}$ is seen to be a function only of

[H] and the various hydrolysis constants for the species produced. In this case a plot of $\bar{n}_{OH}$ vs pH consists of a skew-shaped curve, quite like a titration curve, the position of which is independent of $[M]_T$. The extraction of hydrolysis constants from such a set of data becomes mathematically identical with the case of a weak acid discussed previously. More commonly, however, titrations in which different concentrations of metal are taken yield similar curves of $\bar{n}_{OH}$ vs pH but displaced from each other in fairly regular fashion along the pH axis. This is the experimental symptom of the formation of polynuclear complexes. Sillén and his co-workers[2] have developed mathematical methods for interpreting the data from systems of this sort to obtain the relevant hydrolysis constants.

The processes described in the preceding paragraphs may be encouraged by withdrawal of hydrogen ions from solution, for example, by the addition of alkali. The practical conclusion of this withdrawal of hydrogen ions is precipitation of the metallic hydroxide. There is some indication that polynuclear aggregates formed in hydrolysis may possess an ordered structure similar to that occurring in the precipitate. The model of deprotonation and condensation of hydrated metallic ions leading eventually to formation of a precipitate of hydroxide accords well with the gel-like structure of the latter which, as initially formed, often contains a considerable bulk of water. Some authors have, in fact, encouraged the use of the term hydrous oxides for these somewhat amorphous precipitates. During a titration of a metallic salt by strong alkali the pH remains moderately low until precipitation is complete owing to removal of hydroxide ions from the solution. By the mechanism suggested here these are removed by neutralization by protons stripped from the hydrated metallic ion; by an older, equivalent model they are removed by being incorporated into an insoluble compound with the metal. Immediately past the equivalence point in the titration the pH rises as the solution acquires a surplus of hydroxide ions. The course of the titration curve may not precisely follow that predicted from the solubility product constant of the metallic hydroxide, partially because of inability in some cases to allow in the calculation for all intermediate products of hydrolysis, and partially because equilibrium is not always rapidly established in the formation or dissolution of precipitates.

For a limited number of metallic ions this process of deprotonation does not stop with precipitation of the hydroxide, but further removal of hydrogen ion results in formation of one or more negative ions. This is the current interpretation of amphoteric or amphiprotic behavior on the part of metallic hydroxides. The species found in alkaline solutions of such hydroxides are formulated as hydroxy complexes, e.g., $Al(OH)_4^-$, $Sn(OH)_4^{2-}$, etc. Some indication of the extent of proton removal, or degree of hydroxylation, in such complexes may be gained by carrying a pH titration past the point of formation of the metallic hydroxide. In the case of aluminum, for instance, a second rise in pH occurs when a total of four equivalents of hydroxide has been added per mole of metal. Within the strictures suggested in the previous paragraph the pH at which this happens may be used to estimate the equilibrium constant for the process:

$$Al(OH)_3 \text{ (s)} + OH^- \rightleftharpoons Al(OH)_4^-$$

References

1. ROSSOTTI, F. J. C., AND ROSSOTTI, H., "The Determination of Stability Constants," Chapter 5, New York, McGraw Hill Book Co., Inc., 1961.
2. SILLÉN, L. G., *Quarterly Reviews*, **XIII**, 146 (1959); ROSSOTTI, F. J. C., AND ROSSOTTI, H., *op. cit.*, Chapter 17.

W. A. E. McBRYDE

Cross-references: *Acidimetry and Alkalimetry; Dissociation; Ionic Equilibria; pH; pH Titration Curves; Stability Constants of Metal Complexes.*

PHOSPHORESCENCE

All luminescent materials continue to emit light with continuously diminishing intensity for some period of time after the excitation is removed. This time may vary all the way from 10^5 seconds, as observed in diamond, down to 10^{-8} seconds or less as observed in many gases and in dilute solutions of some organic molecules such as fluorescein. This afterglow is called *phosphorescence* in contrast to the luminescence observed during excitation which is called *fluorescence* (q.v.). The dividing line between the two phenomena may be taken at about 10^{-8} seconds after excitation has ceased, this time being the average lifetime of excited atoms in the gaseous state (for allowed transitions). This definition of phosphorescence is now generally accepted, although it has also been suggested that phosphorescence be reserved only for that temperature-dependent afterglow which has a time-dependence characteristic of bimolecular processes as discussed later in this article. Phosphorescence can be due to one or more causes in a given luminescent material.

Phosphorescence will be observed when the optical transition between the excited and ground states of the luminescent system is forbidden by one or more quantum mechanical selection rules. Then the excited state of the system will have a lifetime, denoted by τ, in excess of 10^{-8} seconds. This lifetime is defined by the equation $L(t) = L(0)e^{-t/\tau}$, where $L(t)$ is the intensity of the light emitted at any time, t, after the excitation has ceased and $L(0)$ is the intensity at the moment it has ceased ($t = 0$). This is the origin of the phosphorescence observed in many solid phosphors containing small concentrations of Mn^{+2} which acts as the luminescent center. The lifetime, τ, varies depending on the solid compound which contains the manganese ion, from 10^{-1} sec for $ZnF_2:Mn^{+2}$ to 10^{-4} sec in $ZnS:Mn^{+2}$. Intermediate lifetimes are observed in $Zn_2SiO_4:Mn^{+2}$ and in $Ca_5(PO_4)_3$-$(F, Cl)Mn^{+2}$, the phosphor used in present-day fluorescent lamps. Shorter lifetimes are observed in many organic systems, such as naphthalene ($C_{10}H_8$) with $\tau = 6 \times 10^{-8}$ sec. Finally, in the phosphorescence of diamond is an example of a very forbidden optical transition with $\tau = 10^5$ sec. When the observed phosphorescence is due to a forbidden optical transition, the lifetime is determined solely by the nature of quantum states for the excited and ground configurations of the luminescent system, and its value is therefore independent of the temperature at which it is measured.

In many cases, however, it has been observed that the phosphorescent lifetime is independent of temperature at low temperatures but apparently decreases rapidly at higher temperatures. This can arise for two reasons. The higher temperatures may make available sufficient heat energy so that the luminescent system may be thermally excited to some other state from which transitions to the ground state are allowed. In other phosphors the available thermal energy may cause the luminescent system to be de-excited without the occurrence of emitted light (by so-called radiationless transitions). The

first situation occurs, for example, in many organic phosphors and in $KCl:Tl^{+1}$. The second process is the cause for the temperature-dependent phosphorescence lifetime in $Mg_2TiO_4:Mn^{+4}$.

In all the materials mentioned thus far excitation and emission occur locally whether it be in a gaseous atom, organic molecule, or impurity ion imbedded in a solid compound. There are materials, however, such as the (Zn, Cd)S phosphors containing impurities as Cu or Ag, and used in television screens, in which excitation of luminescence involves the freeing of electrons from the luminescent centers (Cu, or Ag). These electrons can travel through the solid before combining with empty luminescent centers other than the ones from which they originated. Such a process, depending on the values of the local concentrations of two different entities (i.e., electrons and empty luminescent centers), leads to an observed phosphorescence which has a time-dependence characteristic of bimolecular processes. In these materials, using the same notation as previously, $L(t) = L(0)/(1 + \alpha t)^2$, where α is a constant. During their travels through the solid the freed electrons may be trapped at various crystalline defects before they can recombine with empty luminescent centers. They can be liberated from these traps by heat and therefore it has been found that the phosphorescent decay is temperature-dependent. It is obvious from the above discussion that measurements of the time- and temperature-dependence of the phosphorescence light intensity can give much insight into the electronic processes involved in the light emission from phosphors.

Various methods have been devised for measuring the phosphorescence intensity as a function of time. The usefulness of any particular method depends on the duration time of the phosphorescence. For exponential decays with lifetimes of 10^{-6} sec or less, a device called a fluorometer has been used. Sinusoidal excitation with frequencies of a megacycle per second or greater are used and the phase shift determined between the sinusoidal light output and the excitation. For phosphorescence decay times between 10^{-5} and 10^{-2} seconds, various modifications of the Becquerel phosphoroscope have been used. Here a rapidly rotating slotted wheel placed between a steady exciting source and the luminescent material gives a square wave periodic excitation. The light output of the phosphor is then detected by a photomultiplier and displayed on an oscilloscope. Frequently a stroboscopic light source has been used for obtaining the periodic excitation instead of a slotted wheel. For decay times longer than about 10^{-2} seconds mechanical shutters can be used instead of a slotted wheel.

References

1. GARLICK, C. F. J., "Handbuch der Physik," edited by S. Flügge, Vol. XXVI, article (in English) on Luminescence, pp. 1–128, Berlin, Springer-Verlag, 1958.
2. LEVERENZ, H. W., "Introduction to Luminescence of Solids," New York, John Wiley and Sons, Inc., 1950.
3. PRINGSHEIM, P., "Fluorescence and Phosphorescence," New York, Interscience Publishers Inc., 1949.
4. KROGER, F. A., "Some Aspects of the Luminescence of Solids," New York, Elsevier Publishing Co. Inc., 1948.
5. KLICK, C. C., AND SCHULMAN, J. H., "Solid State Physics," Vol. 5, p. 97 (F. Seitz and D. Turnbull, Editors), New York, Academic Press, Inc., 1957.

J. S. PRENER

Cross-references: *Electroluminescence; Fluorescence; Laser; Luminescence; Phosphors; Scintillation Counters.*

PHOSPHORS

Phosphors are materials capable of absorbing energy from suitable sources, such as x-rays, cathode rays, ultraviolet radiation, or alpha particles, and emitting a portion of the energy as luminescence in the ultraviolet, visible, or infrared region of the electromagnetic spectrum. By definition, emission which is due only to temperature (incandescence) is excluded from luminescence. When the emission of the substance ceases immediately or in the order of 10^{-8} second after excitation, the material is said to be fluorescent. Material that continues to emit light for a period after the removal of the exciting energy is said to be phosphorescent. The half-life of the afterglow varies with the substance and may be anything from 10^{-6} second to days.

Fluorescence is observed from a large number of minerals, oils, plants, foods, dyestuffs, glasses and many organic and inorganic compounds. This property has been used in the identification of these materials. Organic fluorescent materials generally possess conjugated double bands. The luminescence, which is believed to be the property of the pure compound, can be altered by the solvent or solid media. It is estimated that probably over 3,000 inorganic phosphor materials have been prepared. Only a relatively small number of these are sufficiently efficient or stable to be used in lamps, cathode ray tubes, and other applications.

Preparation

The formulations and methods used in the preparation of inorganic phosphors have evolved largely by a trial process. The fluorescence efficiency, stability, and particle size are dependent on the purity of the ingredients, methods of mixing, and time and temperature of firing. The concentration of many of the heavy elements must be kept below 10 to 0.1 ppm, depending upon the type of phosphor. This is achieved by standard chemical methods such as recrystallization, distillation, partial precipitation, etc.

Sometimes the purified salts, such as calcium tungstate, are washed, dried, and fired to produce a phosphor. In the preparation of magnesium tungstate phosphor, it has been found that a more efficient material can be obtained by ballmilling together two moles of purified magnesium oxide and one mole of tungstic acid and firing at about 1100°C. Most other inorganic luminescent materials require one or more "impurities," called "activators" to produce a phosphor. In addition to activators, phosphors such as zinc sulfide require a flux (NaCl, NH$_4$Cl, etc.) during firing to produce maximum fluorescence.

All inorganic phosphors must be heated before they become fluorescent. Heating is required for synthesis of the material, for creating the proper type of crystal lattice, and/or for diffusion of the activator into the proper lattice sites. As an example of the second point, the low-temperature form (1100°C) of magnesium tungstate is a very efficient fluorescent material, while the high-temperature form (1350°C) is no longer a phosphor.

Application

Luminescent minerals and stones have been known from antiquity. The first recorded phosphor was reportedly made by a Bologna bootmaker and alchemist about 1603. It probably was barium sulfide activated with traces of impurities. Introduction of fluorescent lamps in 1935 had to wait for the development of the

TABLE 1. COMMON PHOSPHORS USED IN INDUSTRY

Material	Peak of Emission (Å)	Application
Zn_2SiO_4:Mn	5250	Fluorescent lamps and cathode ray tubes
$3Ca_3(PO_3)_2 \cdot Ca(F,Cl)_2$:Sb,Mn	4800 + 5850	Fluorescent lamps
$MgWO_4$	4800	Fluorescent lamps
$CaWO_4$	4200	Fluorescent lamps, x-ray screens, and cathode ray tubes
$Cd_2B_2O_5$:Mn	6200	Fluorescent lamps
$CaSiO_3$:Pb,Mn	6100	Fluorescent lamps and cathode ray tubes
$3.5MgO \cdot 0.5MgF_2 \cdot GeO_2$:Mn	6600	High-pressure Hg lamps
$(Sr,Zn)_3(PO_4)_2$:Sn	6300	High-pressure Hg lamps
$BaSi_2O_5$:Pb	3500	"Blacklight" lamps
$(Ca,Zn)_3(PO_4)_2$:Tl	3120	Sunlamps
ZnS:Ag	4400	TV tubes and x-ray screens
(Zn,Cd)S:Ag	Variable	TV tubes
ZnS:Cu	4600 + 5300	Electroluminescence
ZnS:Mn	5900	Electroluminescence
MgF_2:Mn	6100	Cathode ray tubes
ZnO:(Zn)	3900 + 5100	Cathode ray tubes
$Zn_3(PO_4)_2$:Mn	6400	Color TV tubes

low-voltage mercury-vapor discharge, as well as methods of producing large amounts of stable, efficient phosphors. The quantity of such phosphors used at the present time exceeds one million pounds per year. This is in addition to the many thousands of pounds used in television tubes, oscilloscopes, and other devices. The application of phosphors to color television, electroluminescence, high-pressure mercury lamps, and other types of detectors and light sources promises considerable activity and expansion in this field. The most important phosphors used in industry at the present time are shown in Table 1.

Organic phosphors have been extensively used in advertising and in the theater for color effects. Scintillation counters (q.v.) for the detection of nuclear particles consist of photomultiplier tubes in conjunction with solid or liquid organic or inorganic phosphors. Recently, colorless fluorescent dyes, e.g., benzoylaminostilbenes, have been used as brightening agents in textiles to replace the old "blueing" process. Natural phosphors, such as riboflavin, quinine, chlorophyll, etc., are being investigated and estimated by fluorescence. Various organic phosphors are used in the identification of infected or cancerous tissues, or as titration indicators.

Theory of Phosphors

The fundamental processes occurring in simple inorganic phosphors according to the band theory of solids are shown in Fig. 1. The activator atoms, and other impurities, introduce localized levels into the normally forbidden energy band of the pure material. Absorption of exciting radiation by the activator center causes the electron normally present in the center to be raised to the conduction band (transition 1). A return transition (6) may occur more or less immediately, giving rise to fluorescence. The electron may alternatively wander through the conduction band (2) and become localized at a trap (3). Under the action of temperature the trap can be emptied (4) at some later time. If the freed electron approaches (5) an empty activator center, recombination and resultant emission (6) of retarded radiation or phosphorescence can occur. The decay time will obviously be very dependent on the depth of the electron traps and on temperature. If the electrons are released from the traps by increasing the temperature, the emission is called thermoluminescence.

In some cases, radiation is absorbed not by the activator center, but by the host lattice itself (transition 7), in which case an electron will be raised from the valence band to the conduction band. The "positive hole" left in the valence band by this transition may diffuse (8) until it reaches the locality of a filled activator center; the electron of the center may then recombine (9) with the hole to annihilate it, leaving the center empty, just as if it had absorbed the exciting radiation initially. The subsequent stages of the process are identical to those discussed above.

It is well known that the efficiency of the luminescence process generally decreases as the temperature is increased. This is commonly ascribed to the presence of temperature-dependent competing transitions which are nonradiative. Transitions such as 10 and 11 in the figure (in conjunction with 9) fall into this category. According to Stokes' law, the energy of the emitted photon is less than that of the absorbed photon (emitted wavelength greater than absorbed wavelength). This is explained by the fact that after excitation of the center the surrounding lattice relaxes to a new position of lower energy.

The processes discussed thus far lead to motion of charged carriers in the conduction or valence bands and hence to photoconductivity. Not all phosphors exhibit photoconductivity, however. In this case, the exciting and de-exciting transitions (12 and 13) are presumed to occur within the center itself and phosphorescence may be accounted for by the lifetime of the excited state; since the excited state may be a metastable level, this lifetime may be quite long. There is also a possibility that electron traps are closely coupled to the activator centers. In some materials, called sensitized phosphors, of which $CaSiO_3:Pb,Mn$ is an example, excitation energy is transferred from one activator (Pb in this case), which can also produce emission if used alone, to another (Mn) from which most of the emission occurs.

Although most inorganic phosphors require the presence of a foreign element as an activator, the amount present must be within certain limits which vary widely for different materials; if the activator concentration is too high, the luminescent output will be reduced (concentration quenching). The presence of moderate amounts of some impurities may have little influence on the luminescence, but traces (a few parts per million) of others, commonly called "killers" or "poisons," may have disastrous effects on phosphor performance. The most common killers are Fe, Co, and Ni, although in general all the transition metals or elements with paramagnetic ions must be re-garded with suspicion. The action of killers involves interactions with electron traps and the introduction of nonradiating transitions. It may be noted that the effect on phosphorescence is generally more marked at lower killer concentrations than is the effect on fluorescence; killers may hence sometimes be used to advantage to control phosphorescence decay.

References

1. PRINGSHEIM, P., "Fluorescence and Phosphorescence," New York, Interscience Publ., 1949.
2. LEVERENZ, H. W., "An Introduction to the Luminescence of Solids," New York, John Wiley and Sons, Inc., 1950.
3. KRÖGER, F. A., "Some Aspects of the Luminescence of Solids," New York, Elsevier, 1948.
4. GARLICK, C. F. J., "Luminescent Materials," Oxford, Clarendon Press, 1949.
5. KLICK, C. C., AND SCHULMAN, J. H., "Luminescence in Solids" in "Solid State Physics," Vol. 5, p. 97, F. Seitz and D. Turnbull, Eds., New York, Academic Press, 1957.
6. KALLMAN, H. P., AND SPRUCH, G. M., Eds., "Luminescence of Organic and Inorganic Materials," New York, John Wiley and Sons, Inc., 1962.
7. HARVEY, E. N., "Bioluminescence," New York, Academic Press, 1952.
8. HARVEY, E. N., "A History of Luminescence," Philadelphia, American Philosophical Society, 1957.
9. CURIE, D., "Luminescence in Crystals," New York, John Wiley & Sons, Inc., 1963.

R. C. NAGY AND H. F. IVEY

Cross-references: *Electroluminescence, Fluorescence, Laser, Luminescence, Phosphorescence.*

PHOSPHORUS, ELECTROTHERMAL PRODUCTION

Process

This process was first used commercially in 1894, when Albright and Wilson (England) acquired the Parker-Redman-Robinson patents, and the process remains fundamentally unchanged today. Phosphate rock, which is substantially tricalcium phosphate (referred to as basic phosphate of lime, or BPL), in a suitable physical form is mixed with sufficient silica flux to give a silica-lime ratio of 0.85 and sufficient carbonaceous material, normally coke or anthracite, to reduce the phosphorus pentoxide and ferrous metal oxide content of the charge. The mixed ingredients are fed continuously or intermittently to a three-phase a-c smelting furnace

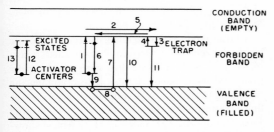

FIG. 1. Band model of a simple phosphor.

provided with a carbon-lined crucible from which molten calcium silicate slag is tapped intermittently and a mixture of phosphorus vapor and carbon monoxide gas, containing minor impurities, is evolved continuously. Any iron oxide in the charge is reduced to metallic iron, together with minor amounts of silicon, chromium, and vanadium, which combine with elemental phosphorus to give an alloy containing approximately 25 per cent phosphorus and 75 per cent iron which can be tapped separately from the slag.

Bearing in mind that phosphate ores occur in nature as fluorapatite and not as tricalcium phosphate, and neglecting the minor reactions involving reduction of ferrous metal oxides, an idealized equation for the main reaction is:

$$Ca_{10}(PO_4)_6F_2 + 9SiO_2 + 15C \rightarrow$$

$$9CaSiO_3 + CaF_2 + 15CO + 1\tfrac{1}{2}P_4$$

The evolved gases, at a temperature ranging from 200 to 600°C, are contacted with hot water in a spray tower, whereby the elemental phosphorus is condensed to a liquid immiscible with water, and carbon monoxide, approximately 90 per cent, is available as fuel.

This relatively simple scheme represents the practice of approximately 1930, when most phosphorus furnaces were in the range of 2 to 5Mw load; under these conditions reasonably coarse natural pebble rock can be used without insuperable difficulties. The problem lies in the fact that natural ores, by reason of their fines content and tendency to sinter together in the upper part of the furnace, lead, with increasing size of furnace, to the production of very hot and dirty furnace off-gas, which when scrubbed with hot water causes the production of an extremely stable emulsion of water, elemental phosphorus, and finely divided solids, largely rock dust, known as "mud."

This problem is aggravated by the fact that for reasonable crucible wear the hearth loading density in square feet per Mw can be kept constant as the size of furnace increases, and the current density carried on the electrodes can also be kept reasonably constant with increasing size of furnace, but effective area for the gas to escape in the upper part of the furnace is more nearly proportionate to the circumference than to electrode cross-section. This condition is due to the sintering together of charge in the upper part of the furnace, which often results in the

formation of a narrow annular passage largely surrounding each electrode. Hence, the filtering and heat exchanging ability of the incoming burden becomes steadily less.

The effect of all this is that with natural ore, as furnaces get larger, the off-gas will tend to get hotter and dirtier till the point is reached where the whole of the phosphorus make is produced in the form of this intractable "mud."

Today most phosphorus furnaces lie in the range of 15 to 50Mw, and, to cope with this difficulty, some or all of the following refinements will have to be added to the basic process as furnaces get larger. Improving the grade of pebble by reducing fines and selecting rock with a minimum tendency to decrepitation and sintering helps, but the limit to this improvement is probably reached at about 7Mw; increasing the depth of furnace would help in theory, but sintering in the upper part of the furnace becomes more troublesome, and in small furnaces, with small electrodes, electrode breakage becomes a problem. Increasing the amp/volt ratio will keep the electrodes deeper in the furnace and give lower off-gas temperature, but it will increase electrode consumption, power consumption, and crucible wear. In practice the only real solution to this problem, increasing furnace size, is to use a beneficiated phosphate and electrostatic precipitators. The method of beneficiating takes the form of nodulizing or pelletizing the phosphate at temperatures somewhat below the fusion point, usually around 2,200°F, which after cooling and screening the product, produces a phosphate which has been increased in P_2O_5 content by elimination of volatile impurities, rendered much coarser and more uniform in physical size, and has a sharply reduced tendency to decrepitate, abrade, and sinter. This permits a large furnace to operate with a reasonable off-gas temperature in the range of 250 to 350°C, where electrostatic precipitation is feasible, since temperatures in excess of 350° not only increase the dust loading of the gas, but also drastically decrease the efficiency of electrostatic precipitation.

A large modern furnace will therefore operate on nodulized or pelletized hardburned phosphate and will be provided with electrostatic precipitators to clean the gas before condensing the phosphorus in a wet condenser. Fig. 1 is the flow diagram of a 15 Mw furnace system, and Figs. 2 and 3 are two views of the furnace showing design features.

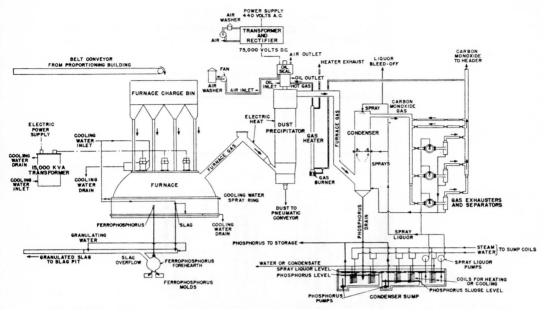

FIG. 1. Flow diagram of phosphorus furnace system for a Tennessee Valley Authority 15 Mw furnace.

Yield and Power Consumption

The chemical and energy efficiency of a large phosphorus furnace is dependent primarily on the composition and physical condition of the charge, secondarily on the electrical conditions used, and to a minor degree on the scale of the operation. It is impossible in an article of this scope to discuss this in any detail, and the following figures may be taken as applying to a large modern furnace, in the range of 15 to 50Mw load, in which the interrelated, and to some extent contradictory, features of physical layout and electrical design have been optimized.

The following tables indicate the efficiency range likely to be met in practice.

The slag loss depends partly on the phosphorus content of the ore, a rich ore giving lower slag volume and smaller losses; and partly on the depth of furnace and the amp/volt ratio, deep charge, and high amp/volt ratio permitting a greater degree of reduction without intolerable off-gas conditions.

Ferrophosphorus loss depends entirely on the iron content of the available charge materials; the off-gas loss represents the saturation pressure of phosphorus vapor in carbon monoxide at condenser temperature, together with small amounts of gaseous phosphine and suspended phosphorus.

Electrode gland losses depend on the physical nature of the charge, which affects the amount of slipping and puffing in operation, and on the adequacy or otherwise of the gas pumping and pressure control equipment. These two factors, and also the efficiency of electrostatic precipitator operation, govern the amount of the aqueous losses, which are composed partly of soluble phosphorus produced by air sucked into the furnace, and partly of suspended elemental phosphorus in the form of "mud."

Per cent net charge means the percentage of phosphorus in the rock plus flux charged to the furnace. The above figures indicate the likely range of power consumption for the two extremes of a low-grade natural rock charge of say 68 per cent BPL, and a high-grade synthetic burden based on 75–80 per cent BPL rock. Note that the process of nodulizing or pelletizing will further increase the BPL content by about 2 per cent over that of the dry-basis high-grade rock used, and that 15Mw is about the largest furnace, with electrostatic precipitator, that can be satisfactorily operated on natural rock.

As a result of the varying incidence in different locations of the chemical losses enumerated in Table 1, it is found that many phosphorus

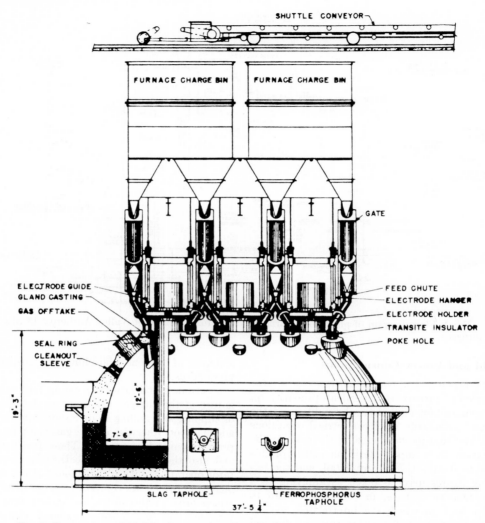

FIG. 2. Front view of 15 Mw furnace for phosphorus production designed by the Tennessee Valley Authority.

furnaces operate at approximately 87.5 per cent recovery of elemental phosphorus, particularly when fed with natural rock. It should be possible, however, in a well-designed plant operating on hardburned feed made from high-grade rock to achieve 92.5 per cent recovery. By combining Table 1 and 2, it follows that the power consumption in kwh/lb phosphorus recovered will range from 6.8 to 5.9 for these two alternatives.

While the distribution of this overall energy consumption will vary somewhat with grade of ore, size, and design of furnace, and the electrical conditions employed, a typical breakdown is as follows:

	%
Net endothermic heat of reaction at 25°C	58
Heat content of slag leaving furnace above 25°C	33
Heat content of gases, metal, and dust leaving furnace above 25°C	4
Losses, conduction, convection, radiation	5
	100

Furnace Design

For large furnaces in the range of 15 to 50Mw with charge depths and amp/volt ratios as noted below, a hearth loading density of 25 sq ft/Mw gives acceptable hearth and side-wall life. A 15Mw furnace can operate at an amp/volt ratio of about 100:1 with a charge depth of 10 to 11

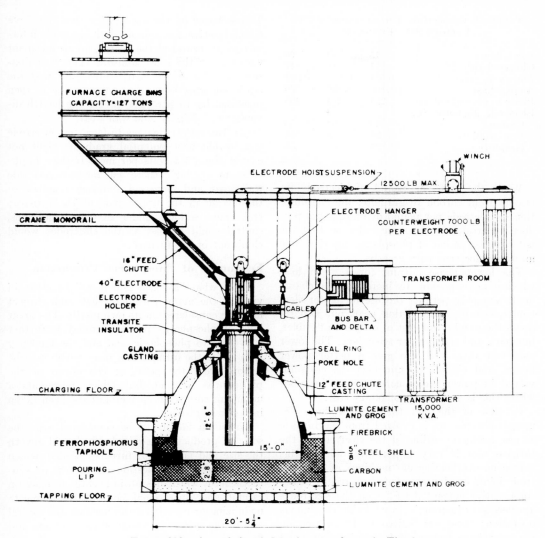

FIG. 3. Side view of the 15 Mw furnace shown in Fig. 2.

TABLE 1. CHEMICAL LOSSES, % OF PHOSPHORUS
WEIGHED INTO FURNACE

	Minimum	Maximum
Slag	2.0	5.0
Ferrophosphorus	1.5	5.0
Off-gas	0.5	0.5
Tapholes and electrode glands	0.5	1.5
Dust	1.0	1.0
Aqueous effluent	0.5	3.0
Unaccounted	1.0	1.0
	7.0	17.0

TABLE 2. POWER CONSUMPTION

Type of ore	% net charge	Kwh/lb P$_4$ at stated yield				
		100	92.5	90	87.5	85.0
Natural pebble or hard rock	10.0	6.0	6.4	6.6	6.8	7.0
Hardburned nodules or pellets	11.5	5.5	5.9	6.1	6.3	6.5

ft, whereas the same depth of charge at 50Mw would require an amp/volt ratio of about 170:1. If, however, the charge depth be increased to perhaps 16 to 17 ft, it is possible with the larger electrodes required by the higher load, to bring the amp/volt ratio back nearer to the figure of 100:1. These relationships are summarized in Table 3.

TABLE 3. OPERATING CHARACTERISTICS OF
VARIOUS SIZE FURNACES

Load, Mw	15	50	50
Charge depth, ft	11	11	17
Amp/volt ratio	100/1	170/1	100/1
Amps/phase	22,400	53,500	40,500
Phase to ground voltage	224	314	405
Electrode diameter, in.			
Carbon	40	62	53
Semigraphite	34	52	45
Graphite	28	44	38

While the cost per pound of electrode increases from carbon to graphite, the consumption of electrode per pound of phosphorus produced decreases in the same order, so that the net cost per pound of phosphorus for the three materials does not vary greatly.

The lower phase current for a given load which is made possible by increasing the charge depth not only permits the use of lighter electrodes, clamps, and hoisting gear, but also reduces the weight and cost of copper in flexibles, bus bars, and transformer secondary. The lower amp/volt ratio will also give a better power factor, and obviate or minimize the costs involved in power factor correction at locations where this is an element of power cost.

In view of the fact that the product, elemental phosphorus, is evolved from the furnace as gas, adequate sealing of the electrode in the furnace roof is very important, and for this reason no overheating or "necking" of the electrode joints can be tolerated. As a result, rather conservative current densities on the electrodes are necessary in practice for reliable continuous operation; these are limited to 18 amp/sq in. for amorphous carbon, 25 for semigraphite, and 35 for graphite.

Round furnaces, with the electrodes arranged on an equilateral triangle, are preferred to rectangular furnaces with three-in-line electrode arrangement, since they are structurally simpler, and it is easier to obtain electrical symmetry with equal power factor on each phase. If this is not done, uneven electrode consumption and hearth wear will result.

The basic layout and dimensions of a large circular phosphorus furnace can be fixed by the three following criteria, which are mutually compatible:

(1) Hearth area, 25 sq ft per Mw.

(2) Hearth diameter equal to 2.65 times the center-to-center equilateral electrode spacing.

This is based on the assumption that the three circular active zones under each electrode intersect at the center of the hearth, an arrangement which gives the most uniform energy dissipation over the whole hearth area, and that the circle circumscribing the active zones is then increased by 15 per cent to give the hearth diameter to minimize side wall wear.

(3) Interelectrode face-to-face and electrode face-to-side wall potential gradients shall not exceed about 7.5 volts per inch. If these gradients are too high, there will be increased side wall wear and increased sintering together of the charge in the upper part of the furnace; and, more serious, under extreme conditions, control could be lost as the electrodes would climb out of the furnace.

Economics of Phosphorus Production

From what has been said it will be clear, in view of the many variables, that each project must be considered on its own merits. The great bulk of phosphorus produced today is further converted to phosphoric acid and the tendency is to locate the furnace at a place which may be remote from the point of conversion of the phosphorus to acid, but which represents a minimum cost when all factors have been taken into consideration.

The main factors to be considered are: the scale of production required, which will govern the size and number of furnaces needed, which in turn poses the question of natural or synthetic feed, which has an important bearing on capital and operational cost of the project; nodulizing or pelletizing can increase the capital cost of the project by about 50 per cent and add $5 per ton to the cost of the ore. Secondly, the FOB and delivered costs of the ore, flux, and reducing agent and also their analyses, which affect the yield and power consumption, must be considered. Thirdly, the cost of electric power, and fourthly, the cost of shipping the product phosphorus to the consuming point have to be evaluated.

While it is true that large furnaces involve added capital expenditure for electrostatic precipitators and nodulizing and pelletizing equipment, against this is to be set the very considerable saving in capital and operational cost which results from the increase in furnace scale together with the saving in power consumption and raw material usage to be gained from the use of high-grade hardburned feed.

References

In spite of the fact that this process has operated for nearly seventy years, comparatively little has been published about it and much of this is of little value. By far the best source of information for those interested in the practical details of design and operation of electrothermal phosphorus furnaces are the publications of the Tennessee Valley Authority, though they are based on furnaces in the range of 5 to 15Mw; particularly *Chemical Engineering Report No. 3*, "Production of Elemental Phosphorus by the Electric Furnace Method," TVA, 1952; and *Chemical Engineering Bulletin No. 1*, "The Design of a Phosphate Smelting Electric Furnace," TVA, 1952.

R. M. O. MAUNSELL

PHOTOCONDUCTIVITY

In most materials the only observed effect of absorbed electromagnetic radiation is an increase in temperature, but in many semiconductors, dyes, and highly purified crystalline materials there are transient deviations from thermodynamic equilibrium that are of considerable interest both from the theoretical and practical point of view. To a chemist these deviations represent photochemical reactions or the complete or partial breaking of bonds. To a physicist they represent excitation to higher energy states. When these states allow increased freedom of migration of electric charge the material is called a "photoconductor." It is conceivable that the light could produce mobile ions, but in conventional photoconductors the charge carriers are electrons or empty quantum states in bond structures (holes). The mobilities of free charge carriers also may be changed by the light, but these effects are considered secondary and they will not be discussed further.

Photoconductivity probably was first observed in 1871 by Willoughby Smith, who reported the decrease in the electrical resistivity of selenium during illumination. Despite this, selenium is still one of the least understood of the photoconductors. Until 1940 the major commerical photoconductors were selenium, cuprous oxide and thallous sulfide. These and more recently developed photoconductors are listed in Table 1 with their wavelength ranges of response. As indicated in the table, some photoconductors are prepared normally as evaporated or chemically deposited films, while others are prepared as single crystals. The preparations involve considerable experience in most cases because some impurities increase or are essential for photoresponse, while others are detrimental.

Preparation of Photoconductive Materials

The preparation of most photoconductors is an art, and the success of any research program or manufacturing process largely depends on the development of this art. The following are the more common methods of preparation:

(1) *Vacuum Evaporation.* Se, PbS, PbSe, Sb_2S_3, InSb, CdS, ZnS and many other materials

TABLE 1. REPRESENTATIVE PHOTOCONDUCTORS

Material	Usual Form	Wavelength Range of Strongest Response at 300°K
Anthracene	Single crystal	3500 to 4400 Å
Cadmium selenide (doped with Cu)	Films and single crystals	0.6 to 1.0 micron
Cadmium sulfide	Films and single crystals	2000 to 6500 Å
Cuprous oxide	Films	0.5 to 1.3 microns
Diamond	Single crystal	2200 to 2400 Å
Gallium arsenide	Films and single crystals	0.8 to 1.1 microns
Germanium, pure	Single crystal	0.4 to 1.8 microns
Germanium, doped	Single crystal	1 to 40 microns
Indium antimonide	Films and single crystals	1 to 6* microns
Lead selenide	Films and single crystals	1 to 8* microns
Lead sulfide	Films and single crystals	1 to 3 microns
Selenium	Amorphous and partly crystalline films	0.4 to 0.9 micron
Silicon, pure	Single crystal	0.4 to 1.3 micron
Tellurium	Single crystal	0.4 to 4 microns
Thallous sulfide	Films	0.4 to 1.2 microns
Zinc oxide	Coatings and single crystals	3000 to 3900 Å
Zinc sulfide	Films and single crystals	3000 to 3500 Å

* Cooled to 100°K.

are prepared in this way. For binary compounds special techniques are used to maintain stoichiometry. With PbS and PbSe crystallite size and oxygen content in the condensed films are critical factors in determining infrared sensitivity.

(2) *Chemical Deposition.* The designation "chemical" is usually applied to depositions by chemical reactions from solutions (analogous to silver mirror preparation). PbS and PbSe films can be made in this manner.

(3) *Deposition of Films and Crystals from the Vapor Phase.* Crystals and films of CdS, ZnO, SiC, Ge, Si, ZnS, CdSe, PbSe, InSb and many other materials can be made by sublimations and reactions between vapors.

(4) *Sintering of Layers.* Some types of CdS and CdSe photocells are made by sintering layers of doped powders.

(5) *Crystal Growth from Melts.* There are many variations. Crystals may be grown by slowly pulling a seed crystal from a melt, by slow cooling of a melt in a closed container, or by running a liquid zone along a rod of material. (See **Single Crystals and Zone Refining.**)

The following procedure for CdS illustrates one practical method for the preparation and doping of a photoconductive material. The first step is to mix luminescent grade CdS with 0.05 per cent $CuCl_2$ and 10 per cent $CdCl_2$. After thorough milling this mixture is sintered in nitrogen at 900°C for 30 min. This operation recrystallizes and dopes the CdS, but the dark conductivity remains too high. The dark conductivity is reduced by heating the powder in sulfur vapor. The powder is mixed with a plastic binder and applied to an insulating substrate. Metal electrodes are evaporated on the layer, or for rough studies silver paint electrodes may be applied.

Mechanism of Photoconductivity

To indicate the terminology and basic mechanisms of photoconductivity, the general behavior of a photoconductor in light and the characteristics of a simple photocell will be discussed.

In the dark the conductivity, σ, of a homogeneous material may be expressed as

$$\sigma = e \ (n\mu_n + p\mu_p) \qquad (1)$$

where

e	= electronic charge;
n	= concentration of free electrons;

p = concentration of free holes; and
μ_n and μ_p = mobility of electrons and holes, respectively.

In light the increase in conductivity in the simpler cases may be written

$$\Delta\sigma = e(\Delta n\mu_n + \Delta p\mu_p). \qquad (2)$$

If the absorbed light produces q electron-hole pairs per unit volume per second, the increases in concentration of electrons and holes are related to their respective lifetimes, τ_n and τ_p, by

$$\Delta n = q\tau_n \qquad (3)$$

$$\Delta p = q\tau_p \qquad (4)$$

The lifetime of a carrier may be terminated by recombination with a carrier of opposite charge or by extraction at an electrode without renewal at another electrode. From relations (2), (3) and (4) photoconductivity may be expressed as follows:

$$\Delta\sigma = qe \ (\mu_n\tau_n + \mu_p\tau_p) \qquad (5)$$

The time during which a carrier may contribute to photoconductivity is determined by many factors. It may remain paired with a free carrier of opposite charge (as an exciton) for part of the time, or it may be trapped at a crystal defect. The free lifetime, that is, the time a carrier is free to move independently in an electric field, is often different for electrons and holes, and in sensitive photoconductors this difference may be deliberately accentuated by adding specific impurity traps. The objective is to select a trap which will have a small recombination rate with a free carrier after it has captured a carrier of the opposite charge. The trap acts as an inhibitor to the recombination of excess holes and electrons.

For recombination at impurity centers the lifetime is expressed in terms of the cross-section area, S, and concentration, N, of the centers capable of recombination by

$$\tau = (vSN)^{-1}$$

where $v = (2kT/m)^{1/2}$ = thermal velocity of the free carrier (m is its mass, k is the Boltzmann constant, and T is the absolute temperature). S varies from 10^{-12} to 10^{-22}, depending on whether the center attracts or repels the free carrier. At high light intensities the lifetime may vary considerably with q because of the variation in concentration of the empty recombination centers.

In a practical photocell, such as drawn schematically in Fig. 1, the observed photocurrent is related to the total number of hole-electron pairs generated by the light (Q) through a factor, G, called gain, as follows:

$$\Delta I = eGQ$$

where $Q = q \cdot$ (volume of the photoconductor).

The gain is related to the transit time, t, for each free carrier by

$$G = \frac{\tau_n}{t_n} + \frac{\tau_p}{t_p}$$

and

$$t = \frac{L^2}{\mu V} \text{ for each carrier.}$$

The gain corrects for the specific geometry that any practical photocell must have. If the lifetime, τ, is to be longer than the transit time, t, the excess carriers must be renewed at one electrode as they leave at the other. The transit time cannot be reduced indefinitely by increasing V because space-charge effects and breakdown occur.

The recombination processes that determine the lifetime of free carriers involve loss of excitation energy through three mechanisms: (1) by the emission of phonons (lattice vibrations), (2) by the emission of photons, and (3) by a three-body or Auger collision in which a third carrier receives the excess energy. The conditions favoring each of these mechanisms depend on imperfection and free carrier concentrations. Light emission is normally obtained only in the presence of unusually low concentrations of crystal defects. Theoretical limits to lifetimes are determined for specific materials by these mechanisms.

Applications

The photoconductive mechanism is an important part of several business copying processes, most notably the Xerox, selenium plate, and the Electrofax processes. In these and other electrophotographic mechanisms a charged plate or coating of photoconductor (ZnO in Electrofax) is exposed to a light image and the transfer of charge through the photoconductor is detected by application of a charged powder or toner. (See **Xerography.**) Photoconductive layers are

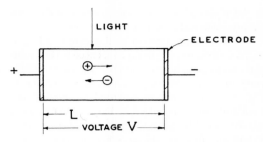

FIG. 1. Photoconductive cell.

also important parts of light amplification screens, Vidicon tubes and other image converters. Infra-red photoconductors have been used for some time in military devices. One of the most recent applications of photoconductive sensors is in cameras that automatically stop down to the correct aperture.

This discussion has touched only the highlights of the subject. More detail will be found in the following references.

References

1. BUBE, R. H., "Photoconductivity of Solids," New York, John Wiley & Sons, Inc., 1960.
2. SMITH, R. A., JONES, F. E., AND CHASMAR, R. P., "The Detection and Measurement of Infra-Red Radiation," Oxford, Oxford University Press, 1957.
3. BRECKENRIDGE, R. G., RUSSELL, B. R., AND HAHN, E. E., Editors, "Photoconductivity Conference," New York, John Wiley & Sons, Inc., 1956.

E. H. TOMPKINS

Cross-references: *Semiconductors; Single Crystals; Xerography; Zone Refining.*

PHOTOVOLTAIC EFFECT IN SEMICONDUCTOR JUNCTIONS

The conversion of energy from any form into electrical energy requires the separation of charge. Energy conversion in junctions occurs when electron-hole pairs created by photons are separated by the electric field arising from the change in conductivity type at the p-n junction. The generated minority carriers—electrons in p-type material, holes in n-type material—are mobile; they diffuse or drift to the field region and are swept to the other side. The accumulation of electrons in the n-side of the junction and holes in the p-side gives rise to a potential which can supply electrical power to a load.[1, 2, 3]

The conversion process is illustrated in Fig. 1. Light quanta whose energy, $h\nu$, exceeds the band-gap energy, Eg, are shown creating electron-hole pairs in a two-dimensional crystalline lattice in Fig. 1a. Atoms are represented by circles and covalent bonds by double lines. The vacancy left by the liberated electron is called a hole; it has an effective charge equal to that of the electron but opposite in sign. An energy-level diagram of a photovoltaic cell is shown in Fig. 1b. Only light absorption in the p-type region is shown for simplicity. The excess electrons in this region diffuse to the right while the holes are constrained by the field to remain in the p-type region.

The potential developed by the separated charge biases the p-n junction in the forward direction; hence, the junction competes with the load for the converted energy. A simplified equiva-

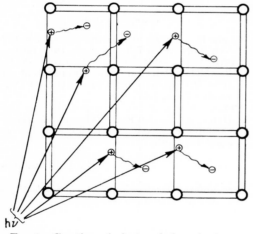

FIG. 1a. Creation of electron-hole pairs in crystalline lattice. [By permission from *RCA Review*, **20**, 373 (1959)]

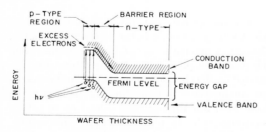

FIG. 1b. Energy-level diagram of photovoltaic cell. [By permission from *RCA Review*, **20**, 373 (1959)]

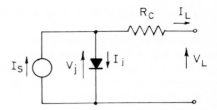

FIG. 2a. Simplified equivalent circuit of photovoltaic cell. [By permission from *RCA Review*, **22**, 57 (1961)]

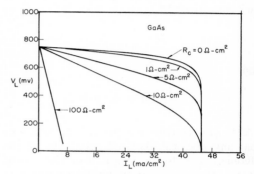

FIG. 2b. Computed photo-characteristic of GaAs solar cells. [By permission from *RCA Review*, **22**, 57 (1961)]

lent circuit of the photovoltaic cell is shown in Fig. 2a. The generated current is I_s; the junction current is I_j; and the current in the load is I_L. Series resistance is represented by R_c; shunt and distributed skin resistance are ignored.

The basic equations which govern the terminal i-v relationship of a cell are

$$I_s = I_j + I_L, \qquad (1)$$

$$I_j = I_0(e^{\lambda Vi} - 1), \qquad (2)$$

$$I_0 = Ae^{-\lambda Eg} \qquad (3)$$

and

$$V_j = V_L + I_L R_c, \qquad (4)$$

where I_0 is the reverse saturation current of the junction in the dark; A is a material constant which depends on the minority carrier lifetime, diffusion constant, density of states and doping; and $\lambda = q/kT$, q being the magnitude of the electronic charge; k, Boltzmann's constant; and T, the absolute temperature. This definition of I_0 and λ correspond to an "ideal" junction; in practice, deviations from these values are found. A computed plot of Eq. (1) is shown in Fig. 2(b) for a junction with the material properties of GaAs. The effect of series resistance, R_c, on the i-v characteristic is also illustrated. The resistance is expressed in terms of resistance times cell area (Ω-cm^2).[4]

Relationships for open-circuit voltage and current, voltage, power, and efficiency with optimum load can be derived from Eqs. (1), (2), and (4). For example, at open-circuit, $I_L = 0$ and the open-circuit voltage is given by $V_{oc} = 1/\lambda \ln [I_s/I_0 + 1]$. The effect of temperature can also be deduced from these equations. The major temperature-sensitive factor is I_0; λ and I_s are reasonably temperature independent. The current, I_0, increases exponentially with temperature, leading to an exponential increase in I_j. The net result is a decrease in open-circuit voltage by approximately 2mv/°C. A plot of the temperature variation of the i-v characteristic of an experimental GaAs cell is shown in Fig. 3. The crosses indicate the maximum power-output points.[5]

At any temperature, there is a semiconductor which, according to theory, yields the highest conversion efficiency for solar power. The optimum material shifts to high band-gap semiconductors at elevated temperatures.[5, 6] This result can be deduced as follows. The number of solar photons in the interval from a given photon energy, $h\nu$, to the upper photon energy ($\sim$5ev) is a decreasing function of $h\nu$. Since only those photons whose energy exceeds the bandgap of a given semiconductor, Eg, ordinarily participate in the conversion process, the available number of photons, and, hence, I_s, decrease as Eg is increased. On the other hand, the open-circuit voltage, V_{oc}, increases since I_0 in Eq. (3) is an exponentially decreasing function of Eg. The product, $I_s V_{oc}$, consequently has a maximum value for a particular value of Eg. Furthermore, since I_0 exponentially increases with temperature while I_s is much less sensitive, $I_s V_{oc}$ is a maximum for higher bandgap materials at elevated temperatures. For example, the optimum material has a bandgap at room temperature of 1.4 ev (GaAs), while it has a bandgap of 2.25 ev-(CdS) at 400°C. A plot of the maximum efficiency vs Eg is shown in Fig. 4 with temperature as a parameter. The case depicted is the "ideal" one mentioned above. The isothermal lines were drawn smoothly, although a smooth change is not necessarily expected since material properties other than Eg have an effect on the maximum

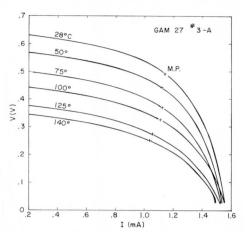

FIG. 3. Temperature variation of photo-characteristic of experimental GaAs solar cell. [By permission from *J. Appl. Physics*, **31**, 571 (1960)]

efficiency. The materials designated Y and Z are possible ternary compounds—combinations of GaAs and GaP, for example.

Important factors influencing the performance of solar cells are the collection efficiency and internal resistance. The internal resistance arises in the bulk, at the contacts or in the region (usually thin) at the surface comprising one side of the junction.[4] The effect of resistive losses was seen in Fig. 2b above. When these losses are excessive, the photo-characteristic loses its rectangular shape. They can be minimized by using low-resistance contacts and conducting grid lines on the thin surface region.

The collection efficiency, Q, is defined as the number of electrons flowing through the load per absorbed photon. Its value does not exceed unity unless multiplication occurs. Q depends on the junction depth, minority-carrier diffusion lengths, absorption constant of light, surface recombination velocity, and the magnitude of any drift-field which impels the generated carriers toward the p-n junction. Collection is facilitated generally by small junction depths, long diffusion lengths, high drift-fields in the proper direction, and low surface-recombination velocities. The influence of junction depth is shown in Fig. 5. The response of these experimental GaAs cells is enhanced at high photon energies as the junction depth is reduced. The effect of the skin and base diffusion lengths, L_s and L_B, respectively, and the surface recombination velocity is shown in Table 1 in terms of

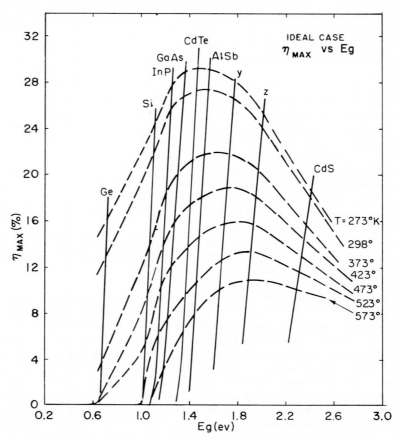

FIG. 4. Maximum efficiency of photo effect *vs* bandgap with temperature as parameter. [By permission from *RCA Review*, **20**, 373 (1959)]

an average collection efficiency for an input solar power density of 106 mw/sq cm (sunlight at air mass one). The values are computed for a Si junction with a junction depth of 1μ and a base thickness of 20 mils. Obviously, the lowest recombination velocity and longest diffusion lengths are required for a high collection efficiency.

Reflection losses are not included in the above definition of Q. These losses can amount to 25 to 30 per cent for a clean, polished surface. The net collection efficiency—response per *incident photon*—is thus reduced by this factor. Antireflection coatings of silicon monoxide or other appropriate materials can reduce the reflection loss to 5 to 10 per cent.

Photovoltaic cells have been made from a wide variety of semiconductors. The best results obtained are listed in Table 2.[7, 8] Current research is directed toward realizing efficiencies close to

the theoretical values. Effort is also being expended to fabricate cells from thin films with a consequent saving in both cost and weight, important factors as far as satellite applications are concerned. The presence of radiation belts in space has stimulated work on improving the cell's ability to deliver power for long times in the presence of high-energy particles which reduce minority-carrier lifetimes and conversion efficiency. It has been discovered, for example, that Si cells constructed from p-type material (n/p) are less sensitive to damage than those made from n-type material (p/n). Consequently, most satellite power sources are being converted to n/p Si cells. Cells made from other materials, such as GaAs, are even more radiation resistant. Furthermore, the use of drift-fields in Si cells to reduce the dependence of conversion efficiency on minority-carrier lifetime is beginning to show promising results.

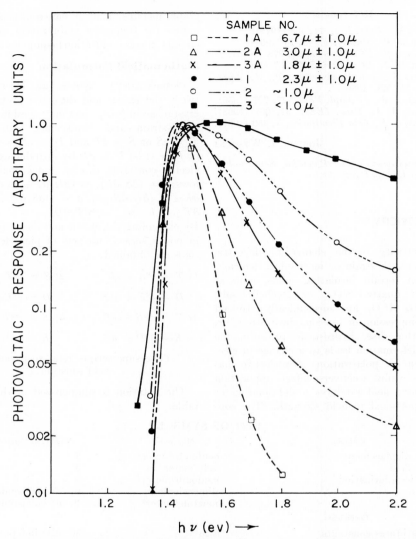

FIG. 5. Normalized spectral collection efficiency *vs* photon energy for experimental GaAs solar cells with junction depth as a parameter. [By permission from *RCA Review*, **22**, 38 (1961)]

TABLE 1. AVERAGE COLLECTION EFFICIENCY FOR Si CELL (COMPUTED)

Surface Recombination Velocity	L_B (μ)	L_s		
		10μ	1μ	0.1μ
0	100	0.73	0.67	0.52
	10	0.52	0.46	0.30
	1	0.32	0.26	0.10
∞	100	0.60	0.59	0.51
	10	0.38	0.37	0.30
	1	0.17	0.17	0.10

TABLE 2. CONVERSION EFFICIENCY OF PHOTOVOLTAIC SOLAR CELLS

Semiconductor	Highest Efficiency Reported (%)
Si	15
InP	2
GaAs	13
CdTe	6
Cu_2O	0.5
Se	1.0
GaP	<0.5
CdS	6–7

References

1. LEHOVEC, K., *Phys. Rev.*, **74**, 463 (1948).
2. CUMMEROW, R., *Phys. Rev.*, **95**, 16 (1954).
3. RAPPAPORT, P., *RCA Reveiw*, **20**, 373 (1959).
4. WYSOCKI, J. J., *RCA Review*, **22**, 57 (1961).
5. WYSOCKI, J., AND RAPPAPORT, P., *J. Appl. Phys.*, **31**, 571 (1960).
6. LOFERSKI, J. J., *J. Appl. Phys.*, **27**, 777 (1956).
7. LOFERSKI, J. J., *Proc. IEEE*, **51**, 667 (1963).
8. LOFERSKI, J. J., *Acta Electronica*, **5**, 350 (1961).

JOSEPH J. WYSOCKI

Cross-references: *Contact Potential; Semiconductors; Solar Energy Converter.*

PIEZOELECTRICITY

Piezoelectricity is the change of dielectric polarization with strain or mechanical deformation. When certain insulating solids, such as crystals of quartz, SiO_2, or Rochelle salt, $NaKC_4H_4O_6 \cdot 4H_2O$, are mechanically stressed in axial compression or tension, shear stress, or, in the latter case, hydrostatic pressure, the resultant deformation leads to a change in electric moment or polarization. Piezoelectric materials also exhibit a converse effect: application of an electric field produces a deformation or strain proportional to field strength. (The con-

graph pickups, and in electromechanical resonators for frequency stabilization of oscillator circuits in communications equipment.

Mathematical Formulation

Piezoelectricity involves an interaction between the elastic and dielectric properties of a crystal; accordingly, one may combine the usual stress-strain and displacement-field relations: $T = cS$ or $S = sT$ and $D = \epsilon E = \epsilon_0 E + \gamma P$ or $E = (1/\epsilon) D = \beta D$ by introducing the piezoelectric constants, d, e, g, and h, defined as follows: $d = (\partial S/\partial E)_T = (\partial D/\partial T)_E/\gamma$, $e = -(\partial T/\partial E)_S = (\partial D/\partial S)_E/\gamma$, $g = \gamma(\partial S/\partial D)_T = -(\partial E/\partial T)_D$, $h = -\gamma(\partial T/\partial D)_S = -(\partial E/\partial S)_D$. By expanding the elastic and dielectric variables in power series, four sets of piezoelectric equations are obtained:

1) $T = c^E S - eE$ 2) $S = s^E T + dE$

   $D = \epsilon^S E + \gamma eS$ $D = \epsilon^T E + \gamma dT$

3) $T = c^D S - hD/\gamma$ 4) $S = s^D T + gD/\gamma$

   $E = \beta^S D - hS$ $E = \beta^T D - gT$

(The superscripts refer to parameters held constant.)

The notation is summarized in the following table:

LIST OF SYMBOLS

Variables		Mks units	Number of Components
D	Electric displacement	coulomb/meter²	3
E	Electric field	volt/meter	3
P	Dielectric polarization	coulomb/meter²	3
S	Strain	dimensionless	9, (6) independent
T	Stress	newton/meter²	9, (6) independent
Coefficients			
c	Elastic stiffness constants	n/m²	36, (21) independent
d	Piezoelectric strain constants	m/volt (c/n)	
e	Piezoelectric stress constants	c/m² (n/m-volt)	18, (18) independent
g	Piezoelectric voltage constants	m²/c (m-volt/n)	
h	Piezoelectric stiffness constants	volt/m (n/c)	
s	Elastic compliance constants	m²/n	36, (21) independent
β	Dielectric impermeability	m/farad	3
γ	Geometrical factor	$\gamma = 1$ ($\gamma = 4\pi$ in cgs system)	
ϵ	Permittivity	farad/m	3

verse piezoelectric effect should not be confused with *electrostriction* (q.v.), a field-induced strain occurring in all dielectric substances which depends quadratically on the electric field strength.)

The piezoelectric effect has led to important commercial applications in pressure and vibration transducers, such as microphones and phonotion transducers, such as microphones and phono-

The dielectric variables, D, E, and P, are vectors which may be resolved into three components along appropriate coordinate axes; e.g., $D_x = D_1$, $D_y = D_2$, and $D_z = D_3$ represent the components of electric displacement along the x, y, and z axes, respectively. The elastic variables, S and T, may be resolved into six components, two along each axis; thus, S_1 and

S_4 represent the tensile and shear strains, respectively, along the x axis with S_2 and S_5 denoting the corresponding strains along the y axis and S_3 and S_6 the z axis terms. These functions may also be expressed as symmetrical tensors with nine components; the shear terms occurring twice each.

The elastic, dielectric, and piezoelectric coefficients may be represented in matrix form with m^2, n^2, and $m \times n$ components, respectively, where $m = 6$ and $n = 3$ are the number of independent components of the elastic and dielectric variables. The elastic and dielectric matrices are symmetrical which reduces the number of independent coefficients from 36 to 21 and 9 to 6 terms, respectively. The piezoelectric matrix has 18 terms, all of which are independent for crystals without symmetry. The number of independent coefficients is further reduced by crystal symmetry; e.g., isotropic (cubic) crystals have only three elastic and one dielectric constants with at most a single piezoelectric coefficient, while uniaxial crystals have two dielectric and a maximum of seven elastic constants with only one trigonal class having more than four piezoelectric coefficients. An alternative expansion of elastic, dielectric, and piezoelectric coefficients into tensors of the fourth, second, and third ranks, respectively, is sometimes employed.

The preceding coefficients may be defined at either constant temperature or constant entropy with the former (isothermal) group being applicable to low frequency or quasi-static conditions and the latter (adiabatic) group applying to high-frequency phenomena, although the distinction between isothermal and adiabatic coefficients is seldom of practical importance. The respective coefficients are functions of temperature or entropy; the derivative $p = (\partial D/\partial \theta)_E/\gamma$ where θ is the temperature defines the pyroelectric coefficient, p.

Occurrence

The symmetry of crystals governs the occurrence of piezoelectricity; specifically, crystals containing either a center of symmetry or both three- and four-fold symmetry axes are not piezoelectric and vice versa. All crystals may be grouped into 32 symmetry classes, 12 of which possess such symmetry elements and thus are nonpiezoelectric. The remaining 20 piezoelectric classes may be divided into two ten-member groups characterized by the presence or absence of symmetry elements which prevent the appearance of spontaneous polarization. [These elements, symmetry planes, or two-fold axes normal to the principal axis, z, or a mirror axis along z convert a point with coordinates (x, y, z) into an equivalent point $(x', y', -z)$.] The latter group constitutes the pyroelectric classes of piezoelectric crystals in which the spontaneous polarization is a property of the thermodynamic state of the system and thus shows a temperature and hydrostatic pressure dependence, while the former group, consisting of the nonpyroelectric classes, possesses no spontaneous polarization and cannot develop a polar axis for changes in nondirectional parameters.

Some pyroelectric crystals possess a spontaneous polarization which may be reversed by application of an electric field, a phenomenon known as *ferroelectricity* (q.v.).

Representative Properties

While many crystals are piezoelectric, the effect is seldom useful for materials in which the d constants are less than about 10^{-12} coulomb/newton (m/volt). The following table lists the piezoelectric coefficients for some typical crystals.

Strain Geometry

An electric field applied across a thin crystalline plate can induce four types of strain described as longitudinal, transverse, face shear (contour) and thickness shear (see Fig. 1). Application of an alternating voltage whose frequency coincides with a resonant vibration of the crystal will excite the vibrational mode if the polarization contains a resonant component along the direction of the applied field. Operation of crystal resonators near 200 megacycles per second has been achieved by using crystals with high elastic moduli, such as quartz, and exciting the higher harmonics of fundamental vibrational modes. For precise frequency control, the orientation of the crystal is carefully chosen to obtain an elastic modulus whose temperature coefficient vanishes at some desired operating temperature.

Nonresonant operation above 10^9 cps has recently been employed to produce strain birefringence for use in light modulators.

Conversion Efficiency

The efficiency of interconversion of electrical and mechanical energy is indicated by the elec-

PIEZOELECTRIC STRAIN CONSTANTS
(10^{-12}m/v)

Material	$d_{16(11)}$	$d_{14(15)}$	$d_{21(31)}$	$d_{22(33)}$	d_{23}	d_{25}	d_{34}	d_{36}
Ammonium dihydrogen arsenate, ADA		+41						+31
Ammonium dihydrogen phosphate, ADP		±1.5						+48-9
Barium titanate, BT (polarized ceramic)		(+270)	(−79)	(+191)				
Dipotassium tartrate, DKT	+3.5	+7.9	−0.8	+4.5	−5.3	−6.5	−12.3	−23.2
Ethylene diamine tartrate, EDT	−12.2	−10.0	+10.1	+2.2	−11.3	−18.0	−17.0	−18.4
Lead zirconate (52)-titanate (48), PZT (polarized ceramic)		(494)	(−93.5)	(223)				
Potassium dihydrogen arsenate, KDA		+23.5						+22
Potassium dihydrogen phosphate, KDP		+1.3						+21
Quartz	(−2.25)	+.85						
Rochelle salt		2000				−56		+11.8

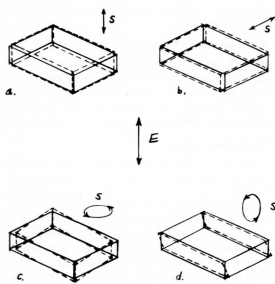

FIG. 1. Types of piezoelectric strain: (a) longitudinal, (b) transverse, (c) face shear, and (d) thickness shear, all caused by an electric field applied as indicated.

tromechanical coupling coefficient, k, defined by the equation $k = U_p^2/U_m U_e$ where U_p, U_m, and U_e represent the piezoelectric, mechanical, and electrical energy stored in the crystal. One notes that when a crystal initially in a state $S = D = T = E = 0$ is uniformly brought to a final state described by the second set of piezoelectric equations, the input mechanical energy density, $U_{im} = S \cdot T/2 = s^E T^2/2 + dE \cdot T/2$ while the input electrical energy density, $U_{ie} = D \cdot E/2\gamma = \epsilon^T E^2/2\gamma + dT \cdot E/2$.

The stored energy terms are identified with the terms $E \cdot T$, T^2 and E^2, respectively; thus, $U_p = dE \cdot T/2$, $U_m = s^E T^2/2$ and $U_e = \epsilon^T E^2/2\gamma$ and $k = \sqrt{d^2\gamma/s^E\epsilon^T}$. k also represents the square root of the ratio of energy stored to input energy and may exceed 0.7 for PZT ceramics. The maximum power density which can be transformed by a piezoelectric material depends on the peak energy densities (given by $U_{m\ max} = sT_y^2/2$ and $U_{e\ max} = \epsilon E_b^2/2\gamma$, where T_y and E_b are the yield stress and breakdown field, respectively), k^2, and the cycle rate determined by the resonant frequency (which is proportional to $\sqrt{c/\rho} = \sqrt{1/s\rho}$ where ρ is the density).

The highest outputs obtainable are derived from ferroelectric ceramics and may exceed 10^8 watt/meter³.

Molecular Theory

On an atomic scale, piezoelectricity is caused by alterations of the dipole moments (q.v.) of molecular or ionic groups by changes in interatomic distances or bond angles resulting from deformation of the unit cell of a crystal. These motions also give rise to the infrared vibrational spectra of crystals. Although no exact quantitative theory exists for predicting piezoelectric coefficients, the qualitative features of most important piezoelectric materials are well understood. Most commercially important piezoelectric crystals fall into two groups, the hydrogen-bond crystals and the ionic crystals. The former group includes the acid phosphates and arsenates, most tartrates, and various crystals with water of hydration and derives its high piezoelectric response from the displacement of hydrogen bonded protons with changes in the oxygen atom configuration. Substitution of the heavy hydrogen isotope, deuterium, usually produces major changes in the piezoelectric behavior. The ionic group includes quartz, barium titanate and related perovskites, and a variety of compounds, such as chlorates, bromates, iodates, nitrates, borates, sulfides, and oxides. Piezoelectricity in this group is caused by several types of ionic motion with rotations of polar groups often providing the chief contribution. Barium titanate and related substances possess very large piezoelectric coefficients which arise from excess lattice space available to the titanium (or equivalent) ion due to packing requirements of the remaining ions.

Applications

Piezoelectric applications may be classified into categories employing the direct, inverse, and combined piezoelectric effects. The direct or mechanical to electrical energy conversion is usually operated at low power levels and is employed in the detection and measurement of stresses or strains including pressure, sound, and vibration, and acceleration and shock. These devices include microphones, phonograph pickups, accelerometers, seismic detectors, pressure transducers, strain gages, etc. A recent application involving higher power levels is a high-voltage generator for ignition systems of gasoline engines and generation of electrical power may eventually become important. Ceramic materials, such as lead titanate-zirconate, are generally favored for these applications.

The inverse or electrical to mechanical energy conversion is usually operated at higher power levels and is used to generate motion or vibration, especially at higher frequencies where magneto-mechanical methods are less efficient. Operation of these devices at high field strengths results in an appreciable quadratic (electrostrictive) effect especially for the titanate-zirconate ceramics (see **Ferroelectricity**). Typical uses include sound generation as in earphones or loudspeakers, ultrasonic generation for cleaning, machining of hard materials, welding, etc., and coagulation or homogenization of suspensions or emulsions. The high acoustic powers attainable are also used for underwater ranging devices such as sonar.

Applications involving both input and output

signals of electrical or mechanical form are also important. The crystal resonator for frequency control of oscillator circuits is widely used in the electronics industry. In operation, the piezoelectric energy density, U_p, stored during the input half-cycle is returned to the circuit during the following half cycle with a time delay determined by the vibrational mode of the crystal. This output signal is used to control the impedance of an element in the oscillator circuit. Quartz is the preferred material for these applications because of its stable elastic properties. The same effect is used in electrical filters.

Electrooptical or piezooptical phenomena are also important for several applications. These effects depend on the birefringence due to change in refractive indices (or permittivities) with electric field or strain. The former effect depends quadratically on field strength (Kerr effect) for nonpiezoelectric materials, but has linear coefficients (Pockels effect) for piezoelectric crystals. Both effects have been used for light modulators at high frequencies. KDP, ADP, and CuCl are promising materials for this purpose.

Piezooptical effects (photoelasticity) in transparent models or coatings form an important tool in experimental stress analysis.

The piezoelectric effect in semiconductors such as CdS has recently been used to produce amplification of ultrasonic waves.

References

1. CADY, W. G., "Piezoelectricity," New York, McGraw-Hill Book Co., 1946.
2. MASON, W. P., "Piezoelectric Crystals and Their Application to Ultrasonics," Princeton, D. Van Nostrand Co., 1950.
3. FORSBERGH, P. W., JR., "Piezoelectricity, Electrostriction and Ferroelectricity," "Encyclopedia of Physics," Vol. XVII, Berlin, Springer-Verlag, 1956.
4. "IRE Standards on Piezoelectric Crystals," Proc. IRE, (now IEEE), **49**, 1161 (1961).

ROBERT D. WALDRON

Cross-references: *Electrostriction; Ferroelectricity.*

PITTING CORROSION

Pitting is a localized form of corrosion in which metal is removed preferentially at point locations on the surface to develop cavities or pits. Pitting requires the presence of an electrolyte on the metal surface, and thus occurs most commonly in liquid media. The phenomenon can occur, however, in a gaseous phase providing there is a film or droplets of liquid on the metal surface. While many pits are roughly hemispherical or conical, the shape varies greatly, from wide saucer-like depressions to small, deep cylindrical holes. The shape of the cavity at the metal surface is usually irregular, but it tends to be round while the pit walls tend to be irregular.

This description of typical pit shapes serves to distinguish pitting corrosion from intergranular corrosion (another form of localized subsurface corrosion in which metal is removed preferentially along grain boundaries). Pitting may be associated with intergranular corrosion, in which case intergranular cracks will advance from the base of the pit both laterally and inwardly.

Pitting frequently occurs in crevices, and in some cases crevice corrosion becomes a special case of pitting corrosion.

Cavitation erosion will produce a surface meeting the above description, but proceeds by a different mechanism to that to be described and should be considered separately.

Pitting is most common on metals that are normally covered with a compact adherent surface film, or which develop such a film during fabrication or by reaction with the environment upon immersion. Pits develop at defects or flaws in the surface film and at sites of mechanical damage under conditions where the film is unable to repair itself. Thus, pitting occurs under conditions when the metal is almost, but not completely, resistant to corrosion, although in the case of iron and low-alloy steels general corrosion may take place simultaneously. Pitting may also be caused by differences in electrolyte composition, concentration or condition as will be described later.

The occurrence of pitting is not necessarily damaging or detrimental since the amount of metal removed is small, and the rate of penetration usually diminishes with time. Thus, if metal thickness is adequate, perforation may not occur for a very long time. On the other hand, under special conditions, the rate of pitting may be very rapid (e.g., 5000 mpy). In some cases, for example, in the web of a load bearing structural section, perforation may not be serious. However, the most common undesirable result of pitting corrosion is perforation, and thus the most important feature of pitting is the rate of

penetration and not the incidence or number of pits.

Pits occur almost randomly with respect to surface structure, although with a preference for grain and twin boundaries. Further, pits are not mutually independent, but interact with each other over a distance depending on the conductivity of the electrolyte.

Pitting has been shown to proceed by an electrochemical mechanism. Like all forms of electrochemical corrosion, pitting is caused by electrochemical differences at two adjacent locations at the metal-liquid interface (the differences may be either in the metal itself, or in the environment). An individual pit is thus a local cell with its own anode and cathode. Current flows through the liquid medium from the local anode (the site of metal removal) to the adjacent local cathode.

Pitting may occur on a heterogeneous metal surface in a homogeneous environment, e.g., a metal surface with a separated second phase constituent of differing solution potential in a simple solution that is uniform throughout, or on a homogeneous metal surface in a heterogeneous environment, e.g., on a completely uniform metal surface partially covered by a foreign deposit or exposed to a liquid that varies from one point to another as to composition, concentration, pH, temperature, etc. Mears and Brown[1] have suggested 18 possible causes for local cell formation that can lead to the initiation of pitting; of these they considered that the most common causes of pitting were differential thermal treatment of the metal, local scratches or abrasions, differential composition or concentration of the environment, and differential aeration.

Pitting may also be caused by current entering a solution from the metal surface due to an external cause, such as an impressed emf or galvanic corrosion produced by contact with a dissimilar metal.

Since pitting is electrochemical, it can be prevented or arrested by the application of cathodic protection (current is caused to flow through the environment to the metal surface). The protective current prevents the functioning of the local cells and thus the pitting action. Pitting can also be prevented by the use of inhibitors, such as chromates, silicates, and phosphates, which alter the electrode reactions on the metal surface.

The most recent comprehensive review of pitting corrosion is that of Greene and Fontana.[2] The views of Evans[3] are also worth attention.

Electrochemistry of Pitting

(1) Reactions at the Anode. The reaction at the local anode involves the solution of the metal as ions and release of electrons into the metal:

$$M \rightarrow M^+ + e$$

If the metal ions form an insoluble hydroxide or a soluble but only partially dissociated hydroxide, there is depletion of hydroxyl ion in the vicinity of the anode, and the area tends to become acidic:

$$M^+ + H^+ + OH^- \rightarrow MOH + H^+$$

Anions such as chloride tend to migrate toward the anode and increase the acidity. The pH in active pits in neutral media may thus reach a value of 3 to 4. The development of acidity within a pit may lead to further metal dissolution and hydrogen evolution:

$$2M + 2H^+ \rightarrow H_2 + 2M^+$$

Hydrogen evolution from within pits has been reported by many investigators.

(2) Reactions at the Cathode. At the cathode the common reactions are the reduction of oxygen, metal ion, or hydrogen (leading to hydrogen evolution):

$$\tfrac{1}{2}O_2 + 1H_2O + 2e \rightarrow 2OH^-$$

$$M^+ + 1e \rightarrow M$$

$$2H^+ + 2e \rightarrow H_2$$

The cathode site tends to become alkaline. As this is initially in the bulk of the solution, diffusion occurs, and the cathode alkali concentration does not approach the acid concentration in the pit cavity. Further reason for this is that the area of the cathode is larger and thus the cathode current density is lower. The magnitude of the pit current is usually determined by the reactions at the cathode and is a function of cathode area. This in turn is often a function of the conductivity of the electrolyte. Because the anode area is small, the anode current density can be quite high, which accounts for the high rates of penetration that are sometimes observed. The rate of supply of oxygen to the cathode may become a controlling factor in pitting corrosion; indeed, with some metals pitting does not occur in the absence of oxygen.

The electrochemical nature of pitting has been demonstrated quantitatively for aluminum, iron, magnesium, and stainless steel, and qualitatively for other metals.

Stages of Pitting

(1) General. In the life cycle of a pit there are four possible stages: initiation, propagation, termination, reinitiation. Some pits initiate and terminate in a short time, after reaching only shallow depth; other pits propagate over longer periods but eventually terminate, while a few continue to propagate. It is believed that a pit may become initiated by one mechanism yet propagate for another quite different cause.

(2) The Initiation Stage. (a) *Metal Causes.* The causes of initiation of pitting have already been mentioned. Theoretically, a metal local cell (as distinct from an environment local cell) can be caused by an abnormal anodic site surrounded by a normal surface which, therefore, acts as an inadvertent cathode or by an abnormal cathodic site surrounded by normal surface which, therefore, acts as inadvertent anode. The first case is impossible to prove since the anode is consumed by corrosion and is, therefore, not available for examination at any later stage. It should be possible later to identify local cathodes in the vicinity of a pit, but this has not yet been reported. Various attempts to examine a metal surface in advance to predict the sites that will pit have not been successful. This merely means that the size and nature of the sites responsible elude present means of examination. It is believed that, at the time of initiation, the local cell currents are often feeble, in which case the prevention of initiation is quite simple. In one instance involving aluminum[4] even the slow movement (8 ft/min) of water over the surface prevented pitting that occurred in stationary water. Movement of the water prevented development of differential acidity at the local anodes and cathodes.

Edleanu and Evans[5] have suggested that the development of pitting of aluminum is autocatalytic; this view is shared by the present author. May[6] has suggested that this is also true for copper. Initiation is termed autocatalytic because, as will be described later, the functioning of the local cells produces changes at local anode and cathode sites which increase the difference in potential between them, and thus the activity of pits. In the view of the present author, only a few of the many local cells which begin to function actually develop sufficient current to initiate pits. Also, newly formed pits are unstable and may revert to inactivity because the inward migration of anion is insufficient to offset the loss of pit corrosion products by diffusion and convection.[2]

It is suggested, too, that an ordinary metal surface contains a very large number of sites that will provide local cell action upon immersion in an electrolyte. These probably vary in activity depending on their solution potential, which in turn will depend on their nature and on the electrolyte, but again the majority of these potential local cells polarize and passivate without the initiation of a visible pit. Only the stronger ones survive long enough to develop sufficient cell current to become active.

(b) *Environmental Causes.* In cases where differences in the environment cause the initiation of pitting the pit sites are completely random with respect to metal structure, and are dependent on variations in the environment. Probably the most common of these is differential aeration which may occur in a crevice or beneath a surface deposit. Oxygen, in the solution immediately in contact with the metal, becomes consumed due to corrosion, and this may lead to the production of a protective surface film. Where there is a large body of solution, the oxygen consumed is quickly replenished by diffusion. However, where there is only a small volume of solution, remote from the bulk of solution, diffusion of oxygen is slow and a difference in potential develops on the surface. Somewhat paradoxically, the site in the oxygen-depleted zone becomes the anode and corrosion (i.e., oxidation) occurs. A second function of the environment may be to supply metal ions which become reduced at the cathode and thus provide a more active cathode as mentioned earlier.

(3) The Propagation Stage. Once a pit has survived the initiation stage and develops a cavity, it propagates by local cell action now reinforced by the difference in acidity between anode and cathode. Further, the cathode surface may become activated, for example, by the deposition thereupon of copper, which lowers the hydrogen overvoltage and thus reduces polarization of the cathode. As the pit cavity grows, it begins to accumulate a cap or crust of insoluble corrosion product which restricts the oxygen supply to the cavity, and this is the cause of generation of a still stronger cell current. As the pit deepens the active cathode tends to move down into the pit, which is now self-contained and independent of the original cause of initiation.

An explanation must be provided for the localization of attack, since without a specific reason it could be expected that a new pit should proceed laterally as well as inwards. It is believed that the local cell current flowing to the adjacent surrounding cathode area provides a measure of cathodic protection which tends to prevent lateral growth of the mouth of the pit.

(4) The Termination Stage. Some pits terminate after having reached an appreciable depth, probably by stifling of the pit current, which comes about by an increase in the internal resistance of the local cell as well as by polarization of either or both anode and cathode. Other pits, possibly those with a stronger active cathode, terminate only when the pit cavity eventually becomes dry. It is suggested that the internal resistance of the local cell increases due to the buildup of corrosion products in the pit cavity.

(5) The Reinitiation Stage. If a completely dried pitted surface is returned to its original environment and rewetted, some of the pits will reinitiate while others will remain inactive. It is suggested that the reason for reinitiation is the presence of an active cathode area at the surface, or near the interior mouth of the pit, which restarts the action for the same reason that it caused the pit to initiate in the first place. Another possibility is that the film at the base of the terminated pit is imperfect or that adjacent areas have different film thickness. A third possibility is the development of differential aeration as described earlier.

Specific Metals

(1) Aluminum. The most resistant alloy series are those containing manganese or magnesium (with small amounts of chromium and/ or manganese). Alloying elements which tend to stimulate the pitting of aluminum are copper and iron. The presence of embedded foreign materials in the surface, such as particles of carbon, copper, or iron, promotes the initiation of pitting.

Pure water (distilled or demineralized) does not cause pitting of aluminum. Some natural waters tend to pit aluminum and their aggressiveness appears to increase with hardness. It is believed[7] that for pitting to occur, oxygen, copper, chloride and bicarbonate must be present. Pitting occurs only over the pH range of about 4.5 to 9.0, in which the usual corrosion product, bayerite, $Al_2O_3 \cdot 3H_2O$, is most insoluble. As the temperature increases, the number of pits tends to increase, while above about 40°C the rate of pitting decreases. Water movement tends to reduce the rate of pitting. The rate of penetration has been shown to decrease with time according to a cube root equation, $d = Kt^{1/3}$, where d is the maximum pit depth, K is a constant, and t is the time. Chromate ion is an effective inhibitor of pitting in aluminum.

(2) **Copper.** While copper is not normally considered to be very susceptible to pitting and is widely used for domestic water piping, some hard waters do pit copper. This has been shown to be due to a burned-on carbonaceous residue from the drawing lubricant. Copper may also pit in very soft acidic waters of high oxygen and carbon dioxide contents. Moderate velocities (in excess of 6–8 ft/sec) accelerate this action. On the other hand, some waters that might be expected to cause pitting of copper have been shown to contain an unidentified natural inhibitor.

(3) **Iron and Steel.** Iron and low alloy steels form less adherent and protective corrosion product films than do some other metals. Their films tend to break down in many places to allow a high incidence of pitting that leads to a general roughening of the surface, and in time to thinning of the metal section. During fabrication the surface of steel aquires a film of mill scale (oxide) that is strongly cathodic to underlying metal. If this is not removed by pickling or sand blasting, pitting will occur at breaks in the film at a much higher than normal rate. This is a common cause of pitting on ships' hulls.[8] Iron and steel may pit in a heterogeneous environment, such as soil, where differential aeration is possible, and the presence of sulfate-reducing bacteria in soil stimulates more rapid pitting through production of hydrogen sulfide. Nitrite is a common inhibitor for preventing the pitting of steel by solutions; silicates, chromates, and phosphates are also effective inhibitors.

(4) **Stainless Steels.** The pitting of stainless steels has been discussed at length by Uhlig.[9] Pitting is most likely to occur in the presence of chloride ions, combined with such depolarizers as oxygen or oxidizing salts. Movement of the solution is beneficial. The rate of pitting increases with temperature and decreases with alkalinity. The nitrates and chromates are beneficial, as are silicates and sulfates. Streicher[10] has described a valuable anodic testing technique for studying the initiation of pitting in stainless steels. There appear to be susceptible nuclei which may lead to pitting depending on the environment. The type of pit nucleus is not known, but it is influenced by composition, heat treatment, and cold work. Homogenization, followed by a rapid quench, reduces the pitting tendency, as does a passivation treatment in nitric acid.

References

1. MEARS, R. B., AND BROWN, R. H., "Causes of corrosion currents," *Ind. Eng. Chem.*, **33**, 1001–1010 (1941).
2. GREENE, N. D., AND FONTANA, M., "A critical analysis of pitting corrosion," *Corrosion*, **15**, 25–47 (1959).
3. EVANS, U. R., "The corrosion and oxidation of metals," pp. 119–132, London, Arnold, 1960.
4. WRIGHT, T. E., AND GODARD, H. P., "Laboratory studies on the pitting of aluminum in aggressive waters," *Corrosion*, **10**, 195–198 (1954).
5. EDLEANU, C., AND EVANS, U. R., "The causes of the localized character of corrosion on aluminum," *Trans. Far. Soc.*, **47**, 1121–1135 (1951).
6. MAY, R., "Some observations on the mechanism of pitting corrosion," *J. Inst. Met.*, **32**, 65–74 (1953–54).
7. PORTER, F. C., AND HADDEN, S. E., "Corrosion of aluminum in supply waters," *J. Appl. Chem.*, **3**, 385–409 (1953).
8. FFIELD, P., "Some aspects of ship bottom corrosion," *Corrosion*, **8**, 29–48, 69–88 (1942).
9. UHLIG, H. H., "Pitting in stainless steels and other passive metals," "Corrosion Handbook," p. 165–173, John Wiley & Sons, New York, 1948.
10. STREICHER, M. A., "Pitting corrosion of 18-8 stainless steel," *J. Electrochem. Soc.*, **103**, 375–390 (1956).

HUGH P. GODARD

Cross-references: *Cathodic Protection; Cavitation Erosion; Concentration Cells;* entries with *Corrosion* titles.

PLANTÉ, GASTON (1834–1889)

Gaston Planté (Raymond Louis Gaston Planté), discoverer and inventor of the lead-acid storage battery, was born in Orthez, France on April 22, 1834. His father Pierre, a cultured gentleman, moved and settled his family in

Paris to provide his sons the opportunities in education commensurate with their brilliance. Each of the three sons became distinguished in their fields. Gaston's older brother Leopold was a member of the Paris bar while his younger brother Francis was one of the most noted of French pianists. Gaston was a brilliant and outstanding student, receiving his Bachelor of Letters at the age of 16 and his Bachelor of Science at 19 from the Lycée Charlemagne, and his Master of Science from the Sorbonne at the age of 21. In 1854 he became assistant and served several years in this capacity with Edmond Becquerel at the Conservatoire des Arts & Metiers. His interests covered a broad range. He was an excellent musician, a linguist with a background in the classical languages, and a fluent ability to speak and write English, German, Spanish, and Italian, and the discoverer in 1855 of an unknown fossil bird named Gastornix Parisiensis by the Académie des Sciences and the British Museum.

His work on polarization at electrodes on conduction of current through solutions, on the lead-acid storage battery, and on the effects of electricity in natural phenomena at high voltages were described in his book, "Recherches sur l'Electricité." The prelude to his invention of the storage battery was the study of the secondary current obtained from simple cells (voltameters) in which pairs of wires were immersed in dilute sulfuric acid and subjected to the current produced by Bunsen cells. He observed the effects on pairs of wires of copper, silver, tin, aluminum, lead, iron, zinc, gold, and platinum. He noted the separate effects at the anode and cathode. In the light of modern knowledge, his observations were marked with a singular perspicuity. One need only mention his interpretation of the formation of oxide coatings on aluminum having a high resistance, the self discharge of anodized silver wire due to the interaction of the higher silver oxide with the basis silver metal, the absorption of hydrogen on and in platinum to form an alloy, and the formation of hydrogen peroxide at the cathode when electrolyzing in air.

The observation during this work that electrolysis between lead wires gave the highest secondary currents led him to the invention and development of the lead storage battery. He described and displayed the first practical model consisting of nine cells in cylindrical glass jars

at a meeting of l'Académie des Sciences on March 26, 1860. His later work was concerned with the improvement of the construction and the application of the current to the experimental study of natural phenomena in which he believed electricity and its flow played an important role.

Gaston Planté died at the age of 55 on May 29, 1889. His 100th anniversary was celebrated at a colloquium held in honor of the man and his work by the Société Française des Electriciens in 1934. The 100th anniversary of his invention of the lead-acid storage battery was celebrated at a special symposium of the Battery Division of The Electrochemical Society, Inc., in 1960. His bequest to the world was twofold: first, the example of his life as a humanitarian and second, his contribution to science and technology as a savant and scientist.

References

1. FLEISCHER, A., *J. Electrochem. Soc.*, **107**, 116C (1960).
2. JUMAU, L., *et al*, "Célébration du Centenaire de Gaston Planté," Paris, Société Française des Electriciens, 1934.
3. PLANTÉ, G., "Recherches sur L'Electricité," Paris, Aux Bureaux de la Revue La Lumière Electrique, reprinted edition, 1883.
4. VINAL, G. W., *et al*, "1860–1960 Planté Centennial Commemorative Issue and Extended Abstracts," New York, Battery Division, The Electrochemical Society, Inc., 1960.

ARTHUR FLEISCHER

Cross-references: *Anodization; Batteries, Storage; Polarization.*

PLASMA

The word "plasma" was first used in physics by Langmuir in the early 1930's to describe highly ionized gases, that is, a mixture of ions and electrons at a high energy level.

Consider the temperatures associated with the energy of various types of reactions. To begin with, chemical reactions yield maximum temperatures which do not often reach above $5000°K$. This is true even in the case of the new superfuels and processes using free radicals. The reason for this limitation is that chemical processes are molecular in nature. In nuclear reactions, on the other hand, the forces which bind the particles and entities which constitute the nucleons are many thousands and even millions of times stronger than intermolecular forces. Therefore, while enormous energies are necessary to rearrange nuclei, the energies liberated in such processes are also enormous and are accompanied by temperatures up to millions of degrees. Such temperatures exist continuously only in stars, where steady state nuclear reactions take place; they have existed on a macroscopic scale on earth for but a small fraction of a second during the explosion of nuclear devices. Their creation in the laboratory is of great concern to those physicists who are engaged in nuclear fusion experiments. However, the containment of particles or of thermal energy at these temperatures on a continuous basis is a real problem, which has been widely discussed lately, and on earth the intermittent generation of these temperatures may be a more feasible alternative. Leaving the millions of degrees and going back to our field, let us see what is there to look for, upward of the limit of chemical reactions, that is, of 5000°K.

First we find an area where all known materials, whether solid or liquid, are about to vaporize. Metals, rocks, and even the best refractories become vapor; soon beyond 10,000°K all molecular bonds are broken and atoms no longer hold to each other by the hand, so to speak. As more and more energy is added to the gas, the atoms dance frenetically around, not any more as parts of molecules but each one by itself, colliding with its neighbors, harder and harder. This is what is rightly known as thermal agitation.

As more and more energy is added and the temperature of matter, now all gaseous, goes up in the 10000°K region, another phenomenon takes place. The atoms become ionized, that is, they shed their outer electrons, which are accelerated more readily than the atoms. They generate radiation, such as light and x-rays, when they collide with atoms and with each other. If the gas can be made even warmer, say over 25,000°K, then the nuclei may be made to lose more of their electrons, and the gas becomes one comprised mostly of these small particles and of partially stripped nuclei, dashing wildly around in what is known as "random" motion, which is the real essence of heat.

However, it is not an easy matter to create a level of energy in a gas which will give us such a high value of particle energy, that is, tempera-ture which will lie in the range beyond the values obtainable with chemical reactions. One approach is to store a quantity of some type of energy and release it all at once. For example, pump a lot of air into a container at high pressure, and perhaps even warm it up to further increase its pressure and energy content; then release the gas all at once through a tube. The rushing gas will produce a sonic shock wave, like a shell traveling in a gun barrel, of temperatures as high as 20,000°K, or even higher. But such shocks travel extremely fast and the high temperature lasts only a small fraction of a second.

Another approach is to store a lot of potential energy in a missile by bringing it to great height and letting it drop. This method is certainly not very practical and it has severe limitations because the descending missile does not strike the earth with its maximum enrgy as it has been previously slowed down by the atmosphere.

Electrical energy has been used to accelerate, to very high energy values, particles and even small amounts of gas. We all know that in a metallic conductor electric charges are carried by electrons which move freely within a lattice of atoms. The higher the voltage between the ends of the wire the greater the number of electrons which will drift, which means that the current is larger. As the current increases the collisions between electrons and ions or neutral atoms become more frequent, and electrons transfer some of their kinetic energy to the atoms, with production of heat. Soon the wire is warm, and with further increase in current it glows, then becomes incandescent, the energy transferred from the electrons to the molecules increases, and when the heat generated is sufficient to break down the molecular binding forces the conductor disintegrates. So far, therefore, by this scheme it would seem that we could not produce temperatures higher than chemical temperatures. However, this is not true, because even though the conductor becomes melted or even vaporized, energy can still be electrically added to the vapor.

We can then visualize an electrical circuit energized, say, by a battery, including two wires and a gap, which has been vaporized and which contains a gas of the conductor and of electrons; this is known as an arc. If it contains no gas of the conductor but just electrons and the gas of the atmosphere where the phenomenon takes place, it is known as a spark, as in any spark plug. Arcs and sparks are known as discharges. Therefore, the electrical discharge in the gap between two electrodes comprises a mixture of electrons, neutral and ionized atoms of the gas in which the discharge takes place and, more or less, ions of the metal constituting the electrodes, depending on whether the discharge is an arc or a spark. This mixture is known as a *plasma*, which has become an important term of late, and is of great interest in many laboratories.

Plasma means a mixture of ions, electrons and at times neutral particles. Therefore plasma is present in any electrical discharge in a gas, because discharges are phenomena whereby electric charges are transported between bodies of different electrical polarity. These bodies may be two clouds in a thunderstorm, the two electrodes in an automobile spark plug, the two ends of a neon tube or of a fluorescent tube. In every case two electrodes are at a different voltage and therefore an electric potential field exists between them, capable of accelerating particles. The direction of the acceleration imparted depends on the charge of the particle.

In every case the process begins in the same manner. Electrons are accelerated from the cathode to the anode. The beginning of the process may be difficult because there may not be sufficient voltage drop at the very surface of an electrode to extract electrons from it. However, once a trickle of electrons finds its way across the gap the process easily sustains itself. The mechanism is approximately the following.

Electrons in their trip across the gas gap collide with many atoms and molecules. The collision in many cases ionizes them by translating the kinetic energy of the moving electrons into ionization energy. Every time this happens another electron is available in the gap, which increases its conductivity. The voltage drop therefore concentrates more and more near the electrodes, and at the cathode this facilitates

the extraction of electrons in much larger quantities. At this point we have electrons and ions of the gas. In effect, we may consider this flow as a flow of electron gas leaving the cathode and entering the anode, and a flow of ions being formed in the gas and moving toward the cathode and depositing themselves thereupon or acquiring electrons and again becoming neutral.

The condition described is that of an ideal spark. If the process continues, however, matters change considerably.

Soon the conductivity in the gap increases and electrons impinge with considerable energy onto the anode and the energy released in the process evidences itself as heat. When the anode becomes hot the binding energy between the atoms and molecules which make up its surface vanish, and hot ions are therefore extracted by the electric field. These travel in a direction opposite to that of the electrons.

With the appearance of hot gases of electrode material in the stream we now observe an arc. The material of the gases will deposit itself upon the cathode.

From the foregoing it is evident that the varieties of plasmas are innumerable. This becomes even more apparent if one considers that the process above described follows different trends depending on the density of the gas and the nature of the electrodes. One may have plasma extremely rich in electrode materials, as in a welding arc, or plasmas which are practically all electrons, as in a vacuum tube.

One underlying concept is common to all these plasmas, however: equilibrium of energy between electrons on one hand, and ions and neutral particles on the other. This point is of extreme importance to the user of the plasma because it establishes its nature and what is generally referred to as its "temperature." At the beginning of a discharge process the predominant part of the energy is lodged in the electrons and is transferred by them, to the ions on collision. The process of transfer depends primarily on the number of collisions. If the collisions are frequent enough, the electrons will bring the atoms to the same energy level which they themselves have and a condition of equilibrium will be reached. If, on the other hand, the collisions are few, the gas of electrons and the gas of atoms will possess different energies and will in effect be at different temperatures or in a condition of nonequilibrium.

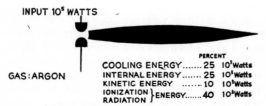

INPUT 10⁵ WATTS

GAS: ARGON

	PERCENT	
COOLING ENERGY	25	10³ Watts
INTERNAL ENERGY	25	10³ Watts
KINETIC ENERGY	10	10³ Watts
IONIZATION RADIATION } ENERGY	40	10³ Watts

FIG. 1. Energy stored in ionization

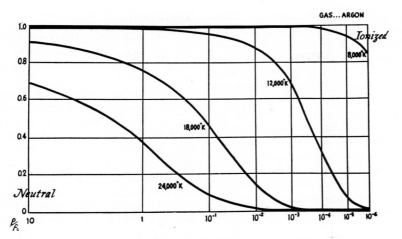

FIG. 2. Dependence of ionization on density

The first condition, of equilibrium, is reached if a discharge is carried out in a vessel containing gas at high pressure. The condition of non-equilibrium, on the other hand, exists when the pressure is low as in the case, for example, of neon signs.

Plasma is not formed only by electrical discharges. The motion of a body at hypersonic velocity through a gas will transfer enough energy to the gas so that some of the atoms will lose electrons and, therefore, become ionized, thus producing plasma. At higher atmospheric pressures, which means at low altitudes, ions and electrons will recombine quickly into neutral atoms. At higher altitudes, however, the collisions between particles being less frequent, the plasma will persist for a longer period, such as occurs in the trail of meteorites which enter the atmosphere at velocities of the order of 10 km per second. If the gas density is low enough, plasma may be created or maintained by radiation such as ultraviolet radiation from the sun, by cosmic rays and other forms of energy from outer space.

To measure the energy contained in the plasma is a tricky process because the energy is stored in different forms; for example, some of it is true thermal energy, that is, translational and rotational oscillations of the particles. This energy is recovered in the form of heat by conduction and radiation. Some of it is in directed kinetic energy, which is evidenced by the momentum of large masses of plasma moving as a whole. This energy is recovered in the form of heat if the gas is stopped. Another form in which

energy is stored is ionization; this energy is recovered in the form of radiation when electrons are recaptured by ions in reverting to a neutral atom. Some energy is dissipated within the plasma because of collisions between particles and a particularly significant type of radiation is emitted by the collision between electrons.

The heat and the light emitted by a plasma are, therefore, indications of the plasma level of energy and of the type of constituent particles. The spectral lines of the light emitted show which elements exist in the gas and the intensity of the continuous spectrum will indicate the frequency of electron-electron collisions. The appearance of certain particular spectral lines and the thickness of those lines point to the degree of ionization and, therefore, to the energy of the atoms whose light is observed.

It will be noted that the word *temperature* is conspicuously absent in this description, whereas the concept of energy is widely used. There is a reason for this, namely, that temperature denotes a concept of uniformity, while in plasma we are confronted with mixtures of particles of different energy absorbing and re-emitting energy and radiation at different rates, over different wave lengths. The concept of plasma temperature is more complex, therefore, than the concept of energy of its constituents. One way in which the mean temperature may be measured, in the case of dense plasma, is to measure the momentum change of the gas in the process of becoming enriched with plasma. This method is used widely by aerodynamicists in the development of reaction power plants such as ram jets which comprise an intake diffuser, a combustion chamber and an exhaust nozzle. The mass flow of air through the device is known and provided certain conditions of pressure at the intake diffuser and exit nozzle are respected, the thrust, or the excess velocity of the air which leaves the device over the air which enters, is directly related to the temperature of the gas in the combustion chamber. If a similar device is used in which heat is added to the gas, not by chemical combustion but by an electric discharge generating plasma, the air is accelerated in proportion to the amount of thermal energy added to it by the electrical discharge and its exit velocity will be higher than its entering velocity. This produces a thrust which will be higher, the higher the temperature at which the gas is raised by the electrical discharge. From the value of the thrust and of the mass flow one can calculate the average temperature of the gas.

The temperature in the discharge chamber is not only dependent upon the amount of energy injected into the gas, that is, by how much electrical power one can use in the discharge, but also on how small the chamber is. If one can reduce the size of the chamber and continue using the same amount of energy in it, the temperature will increase. The process goes something like this: the energy is at first practically all contained in the electrons, which transfer it by collision and otherwise to the atoms in the gas. If we reduce the size of the chamber by half and keep the number of particles the same, equilibrium conditions will be reached sooner, because of the increased number of collisions and energy transfer from the electrons to the gas.

The reduction of the size of the chamber is limited by the heat-resistance of its materials; no material exists which will withstand the temperatures generated by this method. At a certain point the gas density and pressure and the intensity of radiation will be beyond the capabilities of a solid vessel to contain it.

The energies of particles in a high temperature plasma are often measured in terms of the energy an electron acquires in being accelerated through a voltage drop of one volt. This unit, called the *electron volt*, is roughly equivalent to a temperature of $10,000°K$. Thus a gas of atoms, ions and electrons in equilibrium, where the particles have a mean energy of but one electron volt, will be at a temperature of about $10,000°K$.

Applications

If one has some plasma available, what can one do with it? An easy answer is: anything which a chemical flame cannot do because it is not hot enough. In the first place, one can fuse those materials upon which chemical flames act too slowly; in many cases, chemical flames are used in two stages, the first to warm the material, the second to change its chemical structure. For example, an oxyacetylene flame used in cutting steel first warms the steel and when the material is red-hot an excess amount of oxygen is applied to oxidize it. These two steps are not necessary when a gas hot enough to be ionized is employed, since the material melts instantly. The effect may be used to shape parts which have so far resisted thermal attack. For example, to machine a refractory metal or high melting point ceramics becomes possible. Then there is the possibility of fusing highly refractory materials such as oxides, borides and nitrides.

In this lower range, between $5000°K$ and $10,000°K$, electric arc furnaces operate, as well as many of the welding and cutting processes. However, heat at this temperature, which, incidentally, is well beyond what can be obtained from a theoretically perfect solar furnace, when free from chemical contaminants is of tremendous value to all sort of metallurgical work. It permits one to easily bond ceramics to metals, and thus may develop a whole new technology in metallurgical chemistry.

Since we can vaporize everything we know, we have the door open to thermochemistry or plasma chemistry. This is an area which is just being discovered and comprises, for instance, the creation of alloys through the vapor phase, that is, by vaporizing the metals individually and then letting them condense in appropriate order, which is what one does at much lower temperature with alcohol. A variation of this technique may lie in the direct vaporization from raw ore of one or more scarce materials into fairly pure form, and yet another in the purification of chemically active substances by controlled vaporization.

Going up in the temperature scale, beyond the point where everything is gaseous, as we continue to increase the energy added to the gas, most of it will go into ionizing the gas rather than heating it further.

Higher specific energy content of a gas and its attendant higher temperatures create an ever greater multiplicity of phenomena. We have, so far, mentioned temperatures of 10,000°K, 25,000°K, and higher; we have also mentioned that energies of 10,000°K correspond to approximately the energy of an electron which has been freely accelerated in a field of but one volt. Values are mentioned in the literature which even at the low end of the scale are a few tens or hundreds of volts; such is the case with certain potential fusion reactions between light elements where energies of this amount are generated. These correspond to electron temperatures of 100,000°K or more. But this is barely the beginning, because in the fission reactions which take place with the heavy elements at the other end of the scale, in the great accelerating machines, in cosmic rays, energies of millions and even billions of electron volts are generated. Here plasmas are of entirely different nature and characteristics from those of the lowly 1 ev gas we started from; in this region one finds nuclei coming apart in their multitudinous components, the absolute reign of nuclear physicists, complex beyond description, with ever-appearing new particles and multiple interaction between all conceivable states of energy and matter. Plasma then has a different meaning, depending on whether it is in the realm of a nuclear physics or of hydro-aerodynamics. The magnitude of the phenomena is different by a good many orders.

References

1. BROWN, S. C., "Basic Data of Plasma Physics," Cambridge, Technology Press of M.I.T., 1959.
2. SPITZER, LYMAN, "Physics of Ionizing Gases," New York, Interscience Publishers, 1956.

GABRIEL M. GIANNINI

Cross-references: *Magnetohydrodynamics; Electric Arc Properties; Vacuum Arc Properties.*

PLATING, IMMERSION-TYPE. See IMMERSION (DISPLACEMENT) PLATING.

PLATINIZED ELECTRODES

The excellent properties of platinum qualify it for a multitude of practical uses. Historically, however, price has limited its applications to those for which no other material is suited or for which platinum's superior performance outweighs all other considerations. In the elec-trochemical field platinum's position as the most favored electrode material for work on a laboratory scale has never been seriously disputed. Platinum participated in the early stages of a number of industrial processes, survived in some, and may well become reinstated in others. The natural drive toward economy has stimulated numerous efforts over a number of years in devising means to use platinum effectively and one consequence of this has been the development of platinized electrodes. It is anticipated that the new platinum-titanium combination, in particular, will considerably broaden the usefulness of both of these metals in electrochemical processes.

In 1897 Ernest LeSueur, pioneer in the electrolytic production of chlorine, employed anodes of parallel, flattened platinum wires in the first commercial diaphragm cells in a plant located at Rumford, Maine. These anodes performed well despite operation at continuous overloads of more than 50 per cent. Platinum was only $17 per ounce at that time, but in a few years it gave way to the new Acheson graphite.[1] Similarly, graphite replaced platinum anodes in the early European mercury cells. In 1901 an *Electrolytic Apparatus* was patented, a feature of which was an electrode of a "cheap metal—as for instance, lead faced with platinum or other substance substantially resistant to the action of chlorin."[2] Clad electrodes, particularly platinum-clad copper, have since taken many forms but suffer from limitations among which is the necessity of providing an appreciable thickness of platinum (0.005 in.) to ensure a pinhole-free protective covering for the underlying metal.

The possibility of using platinum in conjunction with the chemically resistant metals tungsten and tantalum was first recognized in 1913.[3] These metals develop a protective oxide film when anodized in aqueous solution. Oxidized tantalum has the "valve metal" or rectifying characteristic in that it can function as a cathode but not as an anode. It was evident that a mere coating of a noble metal, which need not be continuous, would suffice to qualify tantalum as a structural and electrically conducting anode material and at the same time provide for effective use of platinum. This combination has been exploited to some extent but not widely, due, at least in part, to the relatively high cost of tantalum. As zirconium and titanium developed into commercial metals, it became ap-

TABLE 1. PROPERTIES OF PLATINUM, TANTALUM, AND TITANIUM

	Platinum	Tantalum	Titanium
Density, g/cc	21.4	16.6	4.5
Melting point, °C	1769	2996	1660
Thermal conductivity, cgs units	0.17	0.13	0.04
Coefficient of expansion (0–100°C)	8.9×10^{-6}	6.5×10^{-6}	8.9×10^{-6}
Specific heat, cal/g/°C at 20°C	0.032	0.036	0.126
Electrical resistivity, microhm-cm at 20°C	10.6	15.5	55
Temperature coefficient of resistance, (0–100°C)	0.0039	0.0038	0.0033
Tensile strength—annealed, tons/sq in.	10	22	35
Young's modulus, psi	22×10^{6}	27×10^{6}	15.5×10^{6}

parent that they, with similar "valve metal" characteristics, could only be used as anode components when surfaced with platinum. In a patent for a battery electrode, applied for in 1949, the inventor lists platinum among the good conductors, inert to the electrolyte, which could be used to coat the outer surface of a porous titanium mass to bring about a decrease in resistance between the electrode and the electrolyte.[4] Interest in the platinum-titanium composite was stimulated a number of years later when Cotton pointed out the possibilities for application of these electrodes in the relatively new field of cathodic protection.[5]

The physical properties of platinum, tantalum and titanium are listed in Table 1.

Titanium Electrode Structures

Although only recently available as a commercial metal, titanium's technology has advanced rapidly. It is produced in the form of powder, sheet, rod, bar, tubing, and wire. Special forms, such as expanded sheet and copper-cored tubing, have received considerable developmental attention and are of interest to the electrode designer. Expanded sheet has a high surface area to weight ratio, it allows good electrolyte circulation and, when used in the horizontal position, permits direct vertical escape for gases formed at an electrode surface. Spot, seam, heliarc, and other welding techniques have been perfected so that light titanium electrode structures with good mechanical strength and electrical conductivity can now be fabricated.

In use any exposed titanium on an anode surface will be completely protected by the oxide film which, if mechanically damaged, will reform immediately with no corrosion occurring. If anode potential is allowed to reach an excessive level, 12 to 14 volts on smooth and less on roughened titanium, at points on its surface

remote from the platinum, pitting and corrosion will occur.[6] With no current flowing the presence of platinum on titanium (Pt-Ti galvanic couple) extends the conditions under which titanium will resist corrosion.

Platinum may be removed from titanium with aqua regia with no damage to the titanium. A soundly built titanium structure should be capable of many years of use; the only weight loss incurred will be that from the preparative etch which precedes each reapplication of platinum.

Types and Uses of Platinum Surfaces

Platinum-clad, rather than platinized anodes, are used in the production of per-compounds. A higher oxygen overvoltage is required for these oxidations, and this is provided by bright, massive platinum. Platinum sheet may be bonded to tantalum or titanium by hot and cold rolling processes. Considerable ingenuity has been exercised in devising platinum-tantalum electrodes for producing persulfates (and hydrogen peroxide), while platinum-clad titanium (0.0015 in. Pt) is already well established in the electrolysis of chlorate to perchlorate.

Platinized Platinum. Platinum black is electrodeposited on platinum foil from a chloroplatinic acid solution containing a small amount of lead acetate. This extremely active form of platinum has a large capacity for absorbing hydrogen and catalyzing the rapid exchange between its gaseous and ionic forms. When immersed in a normal solution of hydrogen ions and kept saturated at 25°C with hydrogen at atmospheric pressure, this is the *standard hydrogen electrode* (q.v.), the reference against which the potential differences between other electrodes and the solutions in which they are immersed are measured. Platinum black electrodes have the lowest overvoltages in electrode reactions involving the liberation of gases. Un-

TABLE 2. HYDROGEN, OXYGEN, AND CHLORINE OVERVOLTAGES ON PLATINUM AT 25°C
(From Creighton and Koehler, "Electrochemistry," Vol. I, 1943)

Current Density, amps per sq cm	Hydrogen			Oxygen			Chlorine	
	0.01	0.1	1.0	0.01	0.1	1.0	0.1	0.5
Smooth platinum	0.07	0.29	0.68	0.85	1.28	1.49	0.05	0.16
Platinum black	0.03	0.04	0.05	0.52	0.64	0.77	0.03	0.05

fortunately their fragility precludes their practical use for this purpose.

Platinum electrodeposits on titanium may be obtained from ammoniacal or acid solutions of the dinitrito-diammino-platinum salt, from sodium or potassium hexahydroxyplatinate solutions, and from the recently developed sulfatodinitrito-platinous acid solution (DNS). The writer prefers the latter bath. A preliminary etch is required to condition the titanium surface and this is best carried out in concentrated hydrochloric acid. The platinum may be annealed by heating for ten minutes at 700–800°F in air. Two and one-half grams of platinum per square foot are adequate for most purposes, but 5 or 10 grams per square foot (0.0001 in. or 0.0002 in.) may be specified for use in impressed current cathodic protection systems which are to be installed in difficultly accessible locations. Other uses as electrodes for desalting of brackish waters by electrodialysis; electroplating of platinum, rhodium, gold, nickel, chromium, and zinc; electrorefining of metals; swimming pool chlorinators; electrolytic production of chlorate and chlorine, etc.

Active Platinized Electrodes. Although the ordinary electroplated platinum deposit is suitable for most of the above mentioned applications, a more active platinum is needed on anodes for chlorine production to realize the power saving which can be obtained through the lowering of cell voltage. Platinum deposits with approximately the physical durability of the electroplate and the activity of the platinum black deposit can now be produced by various novel proprietary processes. The voltage advantage of one of these active deposits (B) over an ordinary platinum electroplate (A) is illustrated by the following results, Table 3, from a laboratory test in a diaphragm cell using concentrated brine at 90°C.

Factors Affecting Performance of Platinum Electrodes

The performance of platinum electrodes in reactions involving the liberation of gases is af-

TABLE 3

Current, amps	Current Density, amps/sq in.	Voltage Difference, (A-B)
4	1.0	0.22
8	2.0	0.31
12	3.0	0.36
16	4.0	0.45
20	5.0	0.55
22	5.5	0.66

fected by its catalytic property, surface structure, and tendency to develop surface oxide films when anodized. Platinum's catalytic activity is attributed to its d-bond character and to the arrangement of atoms in its lattice, both of which favor weak chemisorption of gases and a low energy for the transition state complexes of a reaction.[7] A high specific surface area, implying a large number of active centers—lattice dislocations, corners and edges of crystal grains, growth steps, etc.—contributes to utilization of platinum's catalytic property and lowers the true current density during electrolysis.

The presence of oxide films on platinum anodes, long assumed by investigators, was confirmed by Lingane who found by chemical analysis that both PtO and PtO_2 are present.[8] Laitinen found that, following a rapid initial oxidation, a further continuous and essentially linear increase in surface oxidation with increase in anodic potential takes place. A considerable lowering of potential is required for the reduction of the oxide film.[9] Pourbaix makes use of the following equations in constructing the diagrams, Figs. 1 and 2, which show the anode potential-pH relationship for oxide formation and which indicate conditions for the corrosion, immunity and passivation of platinum.[10]

$$Pt + 2H_2O \rightarrow Pt(OH)_2 + 2H^+ + 2e^-;$$
$$E = 0.980 - 0.0591 \text{ pH} \tag{1}$$

$$Pt(OH)_2 \rightarrow PtO_2 + 2H^+ + 2e^-;$$
$$E = 1.045 - 0.0591 \text{ pH} \tag{2}$$

$$PtO_2 + H_2O \rightarrow PtO_3 + 2H^+ + 2e^-;$$
$$E = 2.000 - 0.0591 \text{ pH} \tag{3}$$

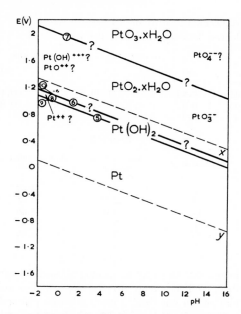

FIG. 1. Potential-pH diagram for the platinum-water system at 25°C. [From *Platinum Metals Review*, **3**, 47 (1959)]

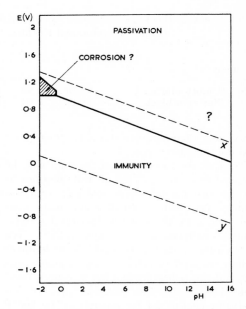

FIG. 2. Theoretical conditions for the corrosion, immunity, and passivation of platinum at 25°C. [From *Platinum Metals Review*, **3**, 47 (1959)]

$$Pt^{++} + 2H_2O \rightarrow Pt(OH)_2 + 2H^+;$$
$$\log (Pt^{++}) = -7.06 - 2pH \tag{4}$$

$$Pt \rightarrow Pt^{++} + 2e^-;$$
$$E = 1.188 + 0.0295 \log (Pt^{++}) \tag{5}$$

$$Pt^{++} + 2H_2O \rightarrow PtO_2 + 4H^+ + 2e^-;$$
$$E = 0.837 - 0.1182 \, pH - 0.0295 \log (Pt^{++}) \tag{6}$$

The oxide film is electron conducting and is said to be a monolayer in thickness. Mechanisms for oxygen formation at this surface are discussed by Latimer,[11] Laitinen,[12] and others.

The mechanism for chlorine formation during electrolysis of brine is not clear but is thought to involve the formation of hypochlorite surface compounds which react with the chloride ion to give chlorine.[13] Since chlorine discharge commences at about 1.3 volts, it is apparent that this takes place on a platinum surface which has already undergone an initial oxidation. Rise in anode potential and further oxidation to PtO_2 will take place under a condition of chloride ion depletion at the electrode surface (concentration polarization). Once an increment has been added to anode potential as a result of PtO_2 formation, it will persist at lower current density levels until the oxide film is cathodically reduced or otherwise removed. An active plati-

num anode can be regarded as one on which this further oxidation to PtO_2 has not taken place to an appreciable extent. The current density which can be maintained at the anode without loss of activity appears to be a function of its surface area.

Platinum Loss

Considering the severely corrosive conditions of its use, it is no reflection on the nobility of platinum that it suffers losses in some processes and must ultimately be replaced. Platinum consumption ranges from 0.002 to 0.006 grams per kilogram equivalent of 100 per cent H_2O_2 for commercial persulfate processes and stands at about 6 grams per ton of product for the perchlorate process.[14] In laboratory tests run in several concentrations of sodium chloride solution, Juchniewicz found that if alternating current is superimposed on d-c, overpotential decreases, and platinum loss increases as the a-c density is raised. Among results given are those below which show the influence of superimposed a-c at 50 cps in static 10 per cent sodium chloride solution at 20°C. Platinum wire 0.020 inches in diameter was used. Duration of testing was 500 hours. Weight loss is in milligrams/sq cm.[15]

TABLE 4. EFFECT OF SUPERIMPOSED A-C ON D-C
ON PLATINUM WEIGHT LOSS AT VARIOUS
CURRENT DENSITIES

Current Density, amp/sq cm	75	150	300	600
Per cent a-c	Platinum weight loss, mg/sq cm			
0	0.051	0.0643	0.149	0.169
4.5	0.0598	0.0721	0.1948	0.2284
10	0.0664	0.1184	0.2901	0.3481
14	0.0723	0.1498	0.4001	0.9964

From the practical standpoint it is important to reduce the a-c component in rectified currents to a harmless level when using platinum anodes.

Earlier testing of platinized anodes in the chlorine process led to erratic results, probably because of the variable and uncertain character of the deposits tested. More recent testing leads to the conclusion that losses of less than one gram of platinum per ton of chlorine can be expected, and there is evidence indicating that wear rates as low as a few tenths of a gram per ton are possible. Sound platinum deposits are not degraded by contact with the sodium amalgam cathode in the mercury cell.

Advantages of Platinum Surfaced Electrodes

Adoption of platinum surfaced electrodes in processes where solid platinum has previously been used results in reduction of platinum inventory and, where platinum is consumed, permits use of practically all of it without physical disintegration.

Substitution of platinized anodes for graphite in the electrolytic production of chlorine will result in a number of advantages which, collectively, are expected to more than offset the higher investment required. Savings will result from lower power, anode consumption, diaphragm replacement and maintenance costs, elimination of anode adjustment, higher current efficiency, purer products, and cleaner cells. An opportunity is presented for cell redesign for more efficient utilization of space and use of higher current densities. Similar advantages will undoubtedly appear in the application of these electrodes to other existing and new electrochemical processes.

References

1. LeSueur, E. A., *Trans. Electrochem. Soc.*, **LXIII**, 187 (1933).
2. Gibbs, W. T., U.S. Patent 665,427 (Jan. 8, 1901).
3. Stevens, R. H., U.S. Patent 1,077,920 (Nov. 4, 1913).
4. Fox, A. L., U. S. Patent 2,631,115 (March 10, 1953).
5. Cotton, J. B., *Platinum Metals Rev.*, **2,** 45 (1958).
6. Shreir, L. L., *Platinum Metals Rev.*, **4,** 15 (1960).
7. Bond, G. B., *Platinum Metals Rev.*, **1,** 87 (1957).
8. Anson, F. C., and Lingane, J. J., *J. Am. Chem. Soc.*, **79,** 4901 (1957).
9. Laitinen, H. A., *Anal. Chem.*, **33,** 1458 (1961).
10. Pourbaix, M. J. N., Van Muylder, J., and deZoubov, N., *Platinum Metals Rev.*, **3,** 47 (1959).
11. Latimer, W. L., "Oxidation Potentials," p. 41, New York, Prentice Hall, 1952.
12. Laitinen, H. A., and Enke, C. G., *J. Electrochem. Soc.*, **107,** 773 (1960).
13. Latimer, W. L., "Oxidation Potentials," p. 53, New York, Prentice Hall, 1952.
14. Mantell, C. L., "Electrochemical Engineering," p. 333 and 349, New York, McGraw Hill Book Co., 1960.
15. Juchniewicz, R., *Platinum Metals Rev.*, **6,** 100 (1962).

R. STEELE

Cross-references: *Cathodic Protection; Chlorine Production; Electrodialysis; Hydrogen Peroxide; Overvoltage; Peroxygen Chemicals; Perchlorates; Potential-pH Diagrams; Reference Electrodes.*

PLATINUM ELECTROPLATING. See PRECIOUS METAL ELECTROPLATING.

POLARIZATION

The voltage of an electrode depends on the magnitude of the current in a *nonlinear* manner. This phenomenon is called *electrolytic polarization*. The behavior of metal-electrolyte interfaces in this respect is similar to that of semiconductor-electrolyte and metal-semiconductor interfaces.

If no external current or voltage is impressed, the electrode-electrolyte interface tends to maintain its own characteristic potential. The driving force behind the establishment of the electrode potential is the tendency of the chemical species to establish *energetic equilibrium* conditions between the interface and the two bulk phases. Consider a silver electrode in a solution of silver nitrate. Statistically, a certain number of silver atoms on the silver electrode surface will continually tend to leave the lattice and enter the solution in the form of silver ions. Simultaneously, a number of silver ions in solution will tend to enter the lattice of the silver electrode. If the probability for these two reactions to occur is the same in both directions, the system is at equilibrium:

$$\text{Ag (in the lattice)} \rightleftarrows \text{Ag}^+ \text{(in solution)}$$
$$+ \ e^- \text{ (in the lattice)}$$

The reaction rates in the forward and backward direction are then identical.

The rates of the forward and backward reaction at equilibrium are called *"exchange currents,"* (q.v.) since the individual processes involve a charge-transfer mechanism. The rates of the forward and backward reaction depend on the electric potential difference across the interface. The potential difference in turn is created by the electrical double layer (q.v.). In the process of equilibration, the composition of the double layer changes until the reaction rates in the forward and backward direction become equal.

The *double layer* consists of relatively compact layers of charge on the metal side, and relatively diffuse layers of opposite charge on the solution side of the interface. The space charge, set up in this manner, shows in general the behavior of a condenser; however, the capacity of the interface condenser is constant only over limited regions of potential, within which no drastic changes in the double layer structure take place. The potential dependence of the electrochemical reaction rates stems from the electrostatic forces, acting on the charged species in the interface. The electric fields in the double layer largely determine the energetic state of the reacting species and thus the probability for reaction.

As the electrode potential is changed by application of an external current or voltage, the electrode reaction in the forward direction, and that in backward direction, become different. The relation between current and voltage for each individual reaction can be represented approximately by the expression

$$i = i_o \exp \left(Z_i e_o \alpha \eta / kT \right)$$

or

$$\eta = kT / Z_i e_o \alpha (\log i - \log i_o)$$

where i_o is the "exchange current" and η the de-

viation of the voltage from its equilibrium value, Z_i is the valency change involved in the charge transfer reaction, α the "transfer coefficient," and e_o the electronic charge. The quantity η is called "overvoltage," (q.v.) a term largely synonymous with "polarization."

However, "polarization" has a somewhat broader meaning than "overvoltage," and is not only used for deviations of the potential from the thermodynamic equilibrium value, as discussed above, but also for the deviation from any steady open circuit value, brought about by the flow of current.

Overvoltage relates to the *change* in the electrode potential caused by the flow of current, whereby experimental conditions are chosen such that only *one* electrode reaction proceeds, e.g., the evolution of hydrogen, or the evolution of oxygen, or the dissolution or deposition of a material. Polarization, in contrast, refers to changes in the electrode potential without restriction to one single reaction. Polarization, for instance, can involve a change of voltage over a range from hydrogen evolution to oxygen evolution, whereby the electrode reaction changes from one process to another.

The plot of current versus voltage is called a *polarization curve*, and is shown below for one *single electrochemical reaction* (Fig. 1). In addition to the polarization curve, indicated by the line, i, the currents for the forward and backward reactions are shown individually. At the equilibrium potential, the currents for the forward and backward reactions are equal and opposite in sign. At high anodic potential, relative to the equilibrium value, the cathodic (reduction) reaction decreases to zero, and at high cathodic potentials, the anodic (oxidation) reaction becomes zero. The disappearance of the backward process is usually thought to be complete at ±100 millivolts of overvoltage but there are exceptions to this rule for highly heterogeneous or porous electrodes. At higher overvoltage values the individual reaction is identical to the overall electrode process, and the current depends exponentially on potential.

Frequently, an apparent equilibrium potential, with no external current flowing, is established by different opposite reactions, such that the products of the anodic reaction are not identical to the reactants of the cathodic reaction. This is the case for many corrosion processes and for phenomena relating to passivity (q.v.).

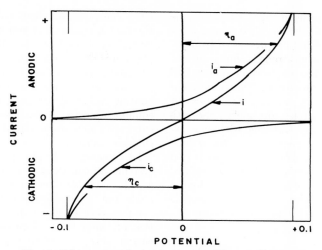

Fig. 1. Schematic polarization curve. The anodic current, i_a, and associated overvoltage, η_a, and the cathodic current, i_c, with overvoltage, η_c, are depicted individually and together with the plot for the total current, i.

For example, during the dissolution of iron in acids, the following electrochemical reactions take place:

$$\text{Fe} \rightarrow \text{Fe}^{++} + 2e^-$$

$$2e^- + 2\text{H}^+ \rightarrow \text{H}_2$$

The anodic process is the electrochemical oxidation of iron, with liberation of 2 electrons per molecule. The electrons are consumed by the cathodic process, consisting of hydrogen evolution. The potential under these circumstances is largely determined by the particular processes allowing the *largest exchange currents*. This is illustrated in the figure below, where the polarization curves for the individual electrode processes are plotted logarithmically, which renders the polarization curves more or less linear (Fig. 2). The potential established in the "active region" is neither at point A, the reversible hydrogen potential due to $2\text{H}^+ + 2e^- \rightleftarrows \text{H}_2$, nor at point B, the reversible iron potential: Fe $\rightleftarrows$ Fe^{++} + $2e^-$, but rather at C, where the *largest exchange current* become possible. This potential is called a *mixed potential* (q.v.), established by mutual *internal polarization*. Under such circumstances where *different* reactions mutually establish a mixed potential, each individual reaction is assumed to proceed at its characteristic speed, dependent only on the particular voltage and the activity of the participating species, but independent of other simultaneous electrode processes. This independence

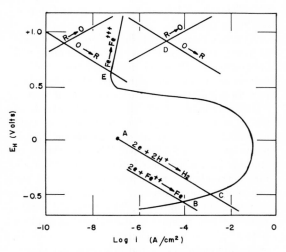

Fig. 2. Schematic polarization diagram for the electrochemical behavior of iron electrodes in acid solution.

principle was first applied by Wagner and Traud.

If, for example, an oxidizing agent with a noble redox potential is introduced into the system of an iron electrode in acid solution, the cathodic reaction changes from hydrogen evolution to O + $2e^- \rightarrow R$. The oxidizing agent is slowly reduced while iron is oxidized according to:

$$\text{Fe} \rightarrow \text{Fe}^{++} \rightarrow \text{Fe}^{+++}$$

Under these conditions one observes that the

potential of the electrode assumes a highly noble potential, falling into the so-called "passive region," where the dissolution process of iron becomes very small. The electrode is thus *polarized internally*, without the application of external current, to positive potentials. The situation is illustrated schematically in Fig. 2. Two cases, for two different redox couples, are shown; one with high exchange current, and one with low exchange current. If the redox couple has a high equilibrium exchange current on the passivated iron surface, the potential will be determined entirely by this redox process and the potential will be at point D. The dissolution of iron is then given by the current for the reaction

$$Fe \rightarrow Fe^{++} \rightarrow Fe^{+++}$$

at the potential corresponding to point D. If, on the other hand, the redox couple is weak and has a small exchange current, the potential is determined by the intersection of the curves for $2e^- + O \rightarrow R$ and $Fe \rightarrow Fe^{++} \rightarrow Fe^{+++}$ and thus is shifted to point E.

As a last example of polarization, an electrode of mercury in a solution of sodium chloride will be considered. Here, no significant quantities of mercurous ions are in solution which could maintain an equilibrium exchange current of appreciable magnitude. Chloride ions will adsorb at the mercury surface preferentially and will tend to produce a negative layer of charge on the solution side of the interface. The adsorption of chloride ions will proceed until the electrostatic forces, the short-range chemical forces, and the forces of osmotic pressure, are balanced and the system is at equilibrium. The potential established in this manner is called an "adsorption potential." No actual charge transfer occurs in either direction across the interface and no exchange currents are defined. Upon application of an external voltage, the electrode voltage changes its value until the change is identical to the one imposed externally, just as experienced with an ordinary, leakage-free condenser. The electrode potential can thus be set at any desirable value, within a certain range, without any continuous current flow of appreciable magnitude. Electrodes showing this behavior are called *ideally polarizable*. This means that polarization can be maintained with a minimum amount of current flow. If the mercury electrode is anodized, however, at a sufficiently positive potential, mercurous ions will enter the solution and will be precipitated by chloride

ions. The potential then is close to that of the Hg/Hg_2Cl_2 electrode. Upon interruption of current, the potential assumes the value of this couple, and is not changed greatly by short cathodic or anodic polarization pulses. The adsorption potential of chloride ions then has reached its limiting value, determined by thermodynamic equilibrium between the three phases liquid mercury, solid mercurous chloride, and liquid sodium chloride solution.

In contrast to ideally polarizable electrodes, systems which exhibit small polarization are called *reversible*. The more reversible an electrode, the less polarizable it is.

Substances added to an electrode composition that are intended to decrease polarization upon current flow, are called *depolarizers*. The term "depolarize" is used frequently in connection with battery technology. The electrode material in the positive electrode of the dry cells, for example, is MnO_2, which is also called the *depolarizer*. Without the MnO_2, the electrode potential would, during discharge, rapidly decrease to the point where hydrogen would evolve. With MnO_2 present, the electrode is maintained at a positive level whereby instead of

$$H^+ + e^- \rightarrow (\tfrac{1}{2})\ H_2\ (gas)$$

the reaction

$$H^+ + e^- + MnO_2 \rightarrow MnO(OH)$$

proceeds. Instead of MnO_2, oxygen can be used as the *depolarizer*, as in the oxygen, or *air depolarized* electrode.

Modern electrochemists have subdivided the polarization of an electrode into individual components as follows:

Ohmic Polarization

Many electrochemical interfaces are covered with thin films of relatively high resistance, i.e., thin oxide layers. Also, the layer of solution in the immediate vicinity of the electrode might exhibit high ohmic resistance to current flow. Since the ohmic polarization increases linearly with current, and ceases instantaneously after interruption of current, it can readily be distinguished from the other types of polarization by measuring the potential immediately after interruption of current flow.

Concentration Polarization

The flow of current causes a decrease in the concentration of the reacting species at the interface. For instance, in the deposition of silver, the silver ions are depleted by the reaction

$$e^- + Ag^+ \rightarrow Ag \text{ (metal)}$$

At the surface itself, the electrode is exposed to a smaller silver ion concentration and, thus, would have a correspondingly different equilibrium open circuit value. The associated shift in equilibrium potential is termed "concentration polarization" (q.v.). It is not necessarily connected with an actual voltage drop across the diffusion layer. With excess of supporting electrolyte no such voltage drop occurs, but concentration polarization is still present. It can be minimized by strong stirring or other means to increase convection. Particularly effective is the use of rotating disc electrodes. Concentration polarization is used in polarography as a means of determining rates of diffusion of ions to the electrode surface. In the absence of supporting electrolyte, voltage drops can appear in the diffusion layer due to different diffusion rates of various ions, a phenomena well-known as "junction potential."

Activation Polarization

The voltage change associated with the build-up of charge and potential at the interface itself is called activation polarization. It concerns the relation between current flow and the voltage drop just across the distance between Helmholtz plane and electrode surface, that is, the so-called inner electrochemical double layer. It is an immediate result of the energy barrier at the interface, associated with the electrochemical charge-transfer step. Activation polarization is thus the overvoltage for the charge-transfer reaction itself. Upon interruption of polarizing current it decays logarithmically with time. For strongly adsorbed activated species, the decay may be so slow that it interferes with concentration polarization.

Crystallization Polarization

In many electrodeposition reactions, the freshly deposited atoms are in a more active state than the one corresponding to equilibrium condition in the lattice. The atoms must migrate to these lower energy sites. The freshly deposited atoms then have a higher energy and thus constitute a different electrode material than the aged crystal surface. The disordered agglomeration of atoms exhibits a correspondingly different electrode potential.

Reaction (or Chemical) Polarization

For electrode processes where the charge transfer step is either preceded, or followed, by chemical reactions, the concentration of the reactants or product may be determined by the speed of these chemical reactions. Such reactions can be the dissociation of a weak acid or a water molecule to form H^+ ion and OH^- ion, with subsequent electrochemical deposition of the H^+ ions. The dissociation of the weak acid or water thus limits the supply of hydrogen ions. The studies of reaction polarization have led to electrochemical methods for the determination of very fast chemical reactions in solution.

The various types of polarizations can be separated experimentally to a certain degree only. It is relatively easy to separate the ohmic polarization by transient pulse techniques. After interruption of current, the various types of polarization decay in different manners. The ohmic polarization disappears immediately, within 10^{-6} seconds, which is generally the limiting resolution of the circuit. Activation polarization can be separated from concentration polarization by providing good convection, for instance with rotating electrodes. Crystallization polarization, reaction polarization, and concentration polarization are similar in nature. The immediate reactants or products of the electrode process are not in the same state or activity as the corresponding species in the bulk phases. These types of polarization can be differentiated by varying the activity of the individual reactants and products in the bulk phases.

Other Uses of the Term Polarization

The term "polarization" is used also in the theory concerning the action of electric fields on dielectrics. Polarization of dielectrics or individual molecules by electric fields, and the polarization of light, a subject of optics and electromagnetic waves, are phenomena not discussed in this article.

References

1. DELAHAY, PAUL, "New Instrumental Methods in Electrochemistry," p. 32, New York, Interscience, 1954.
2. VETTER, K. I., "Elektrochemische Kinetik," Heidelberg, Springer-Verlag Berlin, Gottingen, 1961.
3. PARSONS, R., "Equilibrium Properties of Electrified Interphases," "Modern Aspects of Electrochemistry," J. O'M. Bockris, Ed., London, Butterworths, 1954.
4. IVES, D. J. G., AND JANZ, G. J., "Reference Elec-

trodes, Theory and Practice," p. 14, New York, Academic Press, 1961.
5. WAGNER, C., AND TRAUD, W., *Z. Elektrochem.*, **44**, 391 (1938).

PAUL RUETSCHI

Cross-references: *Concentration Polarization; Electrode Double Layer; Exchange Currents; Mixed Potential; Overvoltage; Passivity; Transfer Coefficient.*

POLARIZATION, CONCENTRATION. See CONCENTRATION POLARIZATION.

POLAROGRAPHY

Polarography is an electrochemical technique based on the interpretation of the potential-current response of a micro-indicating electrode, which is commonly a dropping mercury electrode, DME. The more general term, *voltammetry*, has been applied to the responses found with all types of polarizable electrodes, including other types of response than current-potential.

Polarographic techniques and applications have been extensively developed since their introduction in 1922 by Jaroslav Heyrovsky. Polarography has become an important theoretical and practical tool in electrochemistry, analytical chemistry, and many other areas of science and technology. In 1959 Heyrovsky received the Nobel Prize in Chemistry for his discovery of polarography; this is the only Nobel Prize awarded for accomplishment in electrochemistry in many years.

Since processes involving reduction at the indicating electrode have been considerably more extensively studied and utilized than oxidative processes, the present discussion will stress reduction although the arguments and theory are equivalently applicable to oxidation.

Basic Experimental Arrangement

The essential experimental requirements for most polarographic measurements involve only the following basic elements (Fig. 1): an indicat-

Editor's Note: This and the following articles on Polarography, Inorganic and Polarography, Organic are somewhat longer than others in the *Encyclopedia of Electrochemistry*. The justification for the longer treatment is that polarography today comprises the largest field of activity in electrochemistry. The best current estimate is that between 800 and 1000 papers are published each year on polarography.

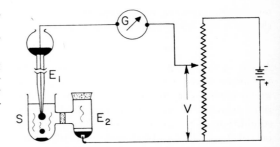

FIG. 1. Basic electrical circuit for polarography (symbols defined in text).

ing electrode, E_1, immersed in the test solution, S, which is *ca* 10^{-3} M in electroactive species and 0.1 to 1 M in *supporting electrolyte*, reference electrode, E_2, usually connected to solution, S, *via* a salt bridge, a potential source and bridge such that potentials, V, from zero to ± 2 volts may be applied across E_1 and E_2, and a suitable current indicator, e.g., a galvanometer, G. Usually, the potential applied to E_1 is made increasingly negative by small increments, while the corresponding current-flow is manually or automatically recorded. The process is discontinued when the decomposition potential of the cation in the supporting electrolyte is reached and a very large current increase occurs.

The data thus obtained are plotted, e.g., as in Fig. 2, with the potential in volts applied to the indicating electrode as abscissa (increasingly negative to the right) and the current in μa as ordinate. By convention, the current is positive when an electrochemical reduction occurs at the microelectrode. The entire plot constitutes a

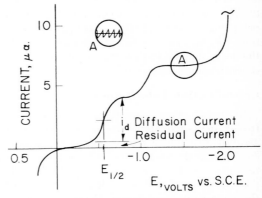

FIG. 2. An idealized polarogram showing two polarographic waves and the nomenclature of the principal features of a wave. (A illustrates the actual trace obtained by a recording polarograph.)

polarogram; the current-step centering at -0.60 v is termed a *polarographic wave*. Under controlled conditions the location of a wave ($E_{1/2}$) is characteristic of the electroactive species involved and the height of the wave is proportional to its concentration.

Electrodes. The polarizable indicator electrode, E_1, is commonly a *dropping mercury electrode* (DME) involving a 30- to 90-cm head of mercury terminated in a fine-bore capillary, which "grows" a fresh drop-electrode every 2 to 6 sec while immersed in the test solution. The reproducibility characterizing its constantly renewed surface plus the high hydrogen overvoltage of mercury are advantages outweighing the typical DME annoyance of superimposed current fluctuations due to the increasing area of the drop (A, Fig. 2). Stationary or rotating platinum microelectrodes may also be used; while usable at more positive potential, these tend to reach equilibrium more slowly and are usually inferior in terms of reproducibility of current response. Of the many other indicating electrodes described in the literature, graphite electrodes seem to show the most possibility for studying oxidation processes.

A rugged, nonpolarizable, reference electrode, e.g., the saturated calomel electrode (SCE), is commonly used for E_2; consequently, polarographic phenomena presented as in Fig. 2 should be transposed 0.25 v more positive when referred to a normal hydrogen electrode. In general, potentials in polarography are stated in reference to the SCE at 25°C.

Solution Composition. The electroactive species in solution are usually 10^{-2} to 10^{-5} M (10 to 10^{-2} mM) in concentration. An inactive salt, acid, or base present in 100-fold or greater excess is termed the *background* or *supporting electrolyte* since it functions to minimize the *IR* drop and to carry virtually all of the *migration current*. If the pH of the solution needs to be controlled as in much of the polarography involving organic species, a buffer system is used as background electrolyte. Since dissolved oxygen is reducible, test solutions are deoxygenated by presaturation with nitrogen before a run.

Automatically recording polarographs are of two general types: (1) the reflected galvanometer light beam may be photographically recorded as the potential varies, or (2) a pen recorder may be activated by the current flow or by the *IR* drop created across a standard resistor in the polarographic circuit. The choice of the latter resistor controls the "sensitivity" selection and feedback from the recorder amplifier may correct the "applied" potential.

Theory

It will be evident that the attainment of a diffusion-controlled limiting current, e.g., such as that shown in Fig. 2, for the reduction of Cd(II) to metal (amalgam at the DME), must involve an equilibrium condition rather than gross electrodeposition, where the current would soon decrease. When the potential is set at the toe of the wave, a minute amount of Cd(II) is reduced and current flow begins. The limiting current flow, i_l, occurs when the electrode potential is sufficient to reduce all of the Cd(II) reaching its surface. Since the electrical migration current is borne by the excess of supporting electrolyte, fresh Cd(II) reaches the electrode-solution interface at a rate regulated by its rate of diffusion. Once the potential determines an optimum concentration gradient near the electrode, i.e., the Cd(II) concentration approaches zero at the electrode and is that of the bulk solution concentration less than 0.1 mm distant on the solution side, mass transfer and resulting current flow are regulated by the rate of diffusion of Cd(II) across this gradient. In a given solution, no greater current will flow at more negative potential and the current-step is spoken of as a diffusion current, i_d. The concentration gradient varies with the bulk concentration of electroactive species and diffusion-controlled currents are proportional to such concentration (*cf* subsequent discussion of Ilkovic equation).

Since diffusion is a slow process, the microelectrode area is small, and the resulting current is low, little electroactive material is actually consumed during a polarographic run.

The *half-wave potential*, $E_{1/2}$, is, by definition, the potential corresponding to one-half of the diffusion current on the wave. For a reversible system, $E_{1/2}$ occurs at the inflection point of the S-shaped curve.

Successive waves resulting from mixtures of two or more electroactive species can be resolved without difficulty if the respective $E_{1/2}$ are adequately separated, e.g., a mixture of Cd(II) ($E_{1/2} = -0.6$ v) and Zn(II)($E_{1/2} = -1.0$ v) would give a curve of the type shown in Fig. 2 with a second wave at -1.0 v, whose height above the cadmium level would relate to the zinc concentration.

A given species may produce more than one wave due to successive electrode reactions. For diffusion-controlled processes, the heights of the successive waves are in the ratio of the number of electrons involved in the wave-producing processes, e.g., many organic nitro compounds are first reduced by a four-electron, i.e., $4e$, process to the hydroxylamine; the latter is then reduced by a $2e$ process to the amine.

A small nonfaradaic or capacitance current termed the *residual current* (formerly, *condenser current*), i_r, is always present and must be subtracted from the *limiting current* in reading *diffusion currents*. Impurities in the solvent and background electrolyte, reducible within the potential span covered, will also contribute to i_r.

Anodic waves corresponding to the occurrence of oxidation at the microelectrode would be plotted in the sense of negative current flows.

Ilkovic Equation. Ilkovic first derived an equation relating diffusion-controlled currents to the properties of the electroactive species and the DME, which took account of the expanding electrode of changing area. Later workers introduced a 5 to 10 per cent correction term to account for the influence of the electrode curvature, giving

$$i_d = 607nD^{1/2}\,Cm^{2/3}\,t^{1/6}\left[1 + \frac{AD^{1/2}\,t^{1/6}}{m^{1/3}}\right] \quad (1)$$

where i_d is the average diffusion current in μa and 607 embodies the *Faraday* and a collection of geometric factors and conversion factors for the units chosen. Fick's diffusion coefficient, D, sq cm/sec applies to the diffusion in the medium used of the current-producing species, whose bulk solution concentration, C, is expressed as millimolarity; n equals the number of electrons transferred per molecule reacted. The DME characteristics involve the rate of mercury flow, m, in mg/sec, and the drop-time, t, in sec. The bracketed term was omitted in the classical Ilkovic equation; the constant A has been ascribed values of from 17 to 39.

Several of the terms, but especially D, are temperature-dependent. The m and t terms, especially t, are potential-dependent for a given capillary in a given electrolyte.

Wave Equations. Equations for the polarographic wave in terms of the current, i, at the potential, E, at the DME have been more or less rigorously derived upon the basis of thermodynamic and kinetic considerations. Consider the fundamental electrode reaction

$$\text{Ox} + ne \underset{k_b}{\overset{k_f}{\rightleftharpoons}} \text{Red} \quad (2)$$

where Ox and Red represent the oxidized and reduced forms of the electroactive species concerned, n is as defined for the Ilkovic equation, and k_f and k_b represent the rates of the forward and backward heterogeneous reactions as written.

Starting with the Nernst equation and relating the effective concentrations to the diffusion coefficients and bulk concentrations of the two species, Eq. 3 is obtained for the case in which both Ox and Red are present and reacting reversibly:

$$E = E^\circ - \frac{RT}{n\mathbf{F}}\ln\frac{f_{Red}D_{Ox}^{1/2}}{f_{Ox}D_{Red}^{1/2}} - \frac{RT}{n\mathbf{F}}\ln\frac{i - (i_d)_a}{(i_d)_c - i} \quad (3)$$

where f is the activity coefficient, subscripts a and c indicate the limiting anodic and cathodic diffusion currents, respectively, and the other terms have their customary significance. The activity coefficients and D terms are essentially constant due to the large excess of supporting electrolyte; consequently, for the usual case involving reduction of a species at 25°C,

$$E = E_{1/2} - \frac{0.0591}{n}\log\frac{i}{i_d - i} \quad (4)$$

Analogous equations can be derived on the basis of rate theory, e.g.,

$$i = n\mathbf{F}A\{C_{Ox}k_f{}^\circ \exp\left[-\alpha n_a \mathbf{F}E/RT\right]$$
$$- C_{Red}k_b{}^\circ \exp\left[(1 - \alpha)n_a \mathbf{F}E/RT\right]\} \quad (5)$$

where A is the electrode area, k° the *heterogeneous rate constant* at $E = 0$ (usually *vs* the normal hydrogen electrode), and α is the *transfer coefficient*, defined on the basis that αE is the fraction of the potential favoring the cathodic reaction.

Other Types of Current Control. In addition to diffusion controlled current-producing processes, the current may be controlled by an equilibrium reaction in which the electroactive species is formed at the electrode interface from the diffusing species ("*kinetic controlled currents*") or by a so-called *catalytic process*. *Adsorption* on the electrode surface of either the reactant or product in the electrochemical reaction may result in shifting or even splitting the i-E wave into two components; splitting may also occur with certain kinetic-controlled processes. The dependence of a particular i-E wave on diffusion, rate processes or adsorption can usually be ascertained from the variation of i_1 with temperature or drop-life (i.e., effective mercury height).

General Experimental Procedure

Composition of Test Solution. The composition of the test solution is probably the critically decisive factor in the success of a polarographic investigation or method of analysis. Among the important factors involved are (1) the concentration of the electroactive species, (2) the nature and composition of the background electrolyte, (3) other additives such as maxima suppressors, (4) the solvent.

The concentration of the electroactive species is best kept in the range of 0.1 to 1 mM. When several merging waves appear on polarographing a multicomponent sample, it is of importance to remember that the potential span covered by the rising portion of the current step depends upon the concentration of the electroactive species and that the slopes of many irreversible waves are large. It is, consequently, apparent that the best possibility for separating the waves is in decreasing the concentration of the sample as far as practical.

The background electrolyte not only often controls the available potential span, but, by controlling the pH, complexing the electroactive species, altering the composition of the electrical double layer, or otherwise affecting the electroactive species or the electrode reaction, it also frequently determines the nature and characteristics of the polarographic wave observed. For much inorganic work, potassium chloride is satisfactory; a large variety of electrolytes is often used to secure preferential complexation with resulting wave resolution. In the case of organic species, pH is generally an all-important variable. Details are given in the articles on *Polarography, Inorganic* and *Polarography, Organic*.

Either rounded or sharply-peaked current *maxima* are sometimes observed, distorting the inception of the limiting current plateau. Where these complicate the proper reading of i_d or $E_{1/2}$, they may generally be removed by the addition of a low concentration of surface-active material, e.g., less than 0.01 per cent of gelatin, to the solution. Often, in the polarography of

organic compounds maxima can be minimized by keeping the concentration of organic species low.

Although water has been the most commonly used solvent for polarographic studies, a considerable number of others have been used, including alcohols, acetic acid, dioxane, dimethylformamide, and acetonitrile. Of the inorganic solvents, ammonia and sulfur dioxide have been used as liquid media at low temperatures; some work has been done at elevated temperatures in molten salts.

Procedural Requirements. Generally temperature control of the test solution to ±0.2–0.5° will be sufficient, since the average temperature coefficient of i_d is about 2 per cent. However, if the current is partially or entirely controlled by a kinetic process, temperature control to 0.1° or even better may be necessary in order to attain the desired precision. The variation of $E_{1/2}$ with temperature is generally quite small and of little practical importance.

Removal of dissolved oxygen from the test solution by purging with a stream of nitrogen or other inert gas is generally necessary because of the two reduction waves given by oxygen.

A practical limitation on the available potential range is the reduction of the background electrolyte cation at potentials of -2.2 to -2.7 v *vs* SCE. In acid solution hydrogen ion discharge may limit the working range to -1.5 v or even less negative potentials. The direct reduction of water beginning at *ca* -2.6 v at the DME sets an effective limit for all practical purposes. Positive potentials at the DME are limited by the oxidation of mercury at *ca* $+0.1$ to $+0.5$ v depending on the solution composition and for other electrodes by oxygen evolution at *ca*, $+1.0$ to 1.4 v.

Analysis of the Polarographic Curve. The diffusion or limiting current and $E_{1/2}$ of each step in the curve are usually determined geometrically by some variation of line-intersection method, which is described in the references listed at the end of this article. While the commonly used geometric methods usually correct adequately for i_r and give usable limiting currents, it is sometimes necessary to subtract the i_r-E curve (obtained on a test solution containing all but the electroactive substance under study) from the observed i-E curve in order to obtain a curve suitable for analytical or other calculations. Often, more or less empirical graphical procedures of determining currents have to be used if a succession of irreversible waves appear on the polarogram. In such situations, it is important that calibration be made on solutions yielding waves of approximately the pattern encountered with the test solution. The standard addition method of calibration (*cf.* below) is often of help here.

The large potential drop caused by the high resistance of many organic solvent solutions, when an appreciable current flows, results in a considerable distortion of the *i-E* curve, which may necessitate replotting this curve after correction for the varying *IR* drop, before reliable measurements can be made. Means of automatically correcting for the *IR* drop in such high resistance solutions have been described.

If the current steps are clearly demarcated, it is possible to obtain satisfactory data in many analytical methods by a spot-reading procedure in which *i* is read at definite potentials before and after the wave for both the sample test solution and the background solution itself in order to obtain the current increment due to the electroactive species.

Quantitative Measurement. Polarographic measurement gives a corrected i_1, which can usually be correlated with the concentration of the electroactive species in the test solution by one of the types of calibration to be described. The accuracy and precision of polarographic analysis is of the order of error of 1–3 per cent relative, which is comparable to other methods of analysis based on physical and physicochemical measurements.

In the *standard series method*, which is the fundamental method of calibrating analytical technics, the value found for the test solution is compared to those obtained for a series of samples containing varying but known amounts of the desired constituent. Generally, such a series is measured to obtain a calibration curve. This method presupposes that the essential experimental conditions are identical during calibration and analysis.

In the *additive method* one assumes that over a relatively short range of concentration there is a linear variation between the amount of the constituent being measured and the current. The sample is measured, a known amount of the desired constituent is added, the modified sample is remeasured, and the amount of constituent originally present is then determined by proportionation. Although this method requires a

standardization run for every sample, it does compensate for many environmental conditions and may compensate for a proportional variation in the relation of the current measured and the composition caused by the nature of the sample itself.

In the *internal standard* method the current due to the desired constituent is compared to that of a component present or added in known amount. The ratio of the currents for the constituent being determined and the internal standard component is compared to a prepared calibration chart of different ratios *vs* desired component concentration. This technic is sometimes called the pilot ion method and affords a way of determining relatively unstable substances for which the use of other technics would not be feasible.

The concentration of the desired constituent can be calculated from the measured current by means of the *Ilkovic equation*. Lingane pointed out that for a given set of experimental conditions, a fundamental value—the diffusion current constant, *I*—can be calculated for any substance whose behavior follows the Ilkovic equation:

$$I = i_d/Cm^{2/3}t^{1/6} \qquad (6)$$

The value of *I*, once it has been determined, permits the analyst to perform quantitative analysis without the need of calibration, standardization, or comparison, since the capillary constants, *m* and *t*, are readily measured. This technic presupposes sufficient reproducibility in experimental conditions so that the value of *D* is not significantly changed. For the most precise work, the modified form of the Ilkovic equation should be used.

In some cases such as the use of suppression of the oxygen maximum for quantitative measurement, resort may have to be made to more or less *empirical methods* of calibration.

Voltammetric Technics

A considerable number of other electrochemical technics have developed from polarography with the DME, e.g., voltammetry with solid electrodes. A few important technics are briefly described in the following paragraphs.

In *amperometric titration* a potential is applied to the indicating microelectrode, which is sufficient to oxidize or reduce the species in the solution to be titrated, the titrant to be added, or both. An inflection occurs at the equivalence-point in the plot of current flow *vs* titrant volume.

Simplified equipment can often be used. Amperometric end-point detection has become widely used in analysis.

Cathode ray oscillographic presentation of *i-E* curves, and their derivatives and integrals has been developed for both more rapid methods of analysis and the study of fundamental electrochemical phenomena. Referring to Fig. 1, a suitable alternating sweep, e.g., triangular wave of 0 to -2 v, is applied simultaneously to the electrode and the horizontal sweep of a cathode ray oscillograph. The galvanometer is replaced by a resistor, whose IR drop is presented on the vertical sweep of the oscilloscope.

Alternating current polarography in which a sinusoidal or square wave alternating potential of a few mv is superposed on the conventional d-c potential used in polarography, has come into specialized use in recent years for determining such electrochemical parameters as heterogeneous rate constants and transfer coefficients, as well as for analysis, especially at the trace level.

Chronopotentiometry, which involves measurement of the variation of the potential with time at constant current, has also become a useful tool for both analysis and electrochemical kinetics.

Stripping analysis involves two separate operations: (1) concentration of the desired constituent by electrodeposition on or into an electrode and then (2) measurement of the redissolution of the constituent. Each step may involve a complete or partial electrolysis of the amount of the desired constituent present. Stripping analysis has become an important technic in trace analysis with a sensitivity of 10^{-9} M in favorable cases.

Applications

The most extensive application of polarography has been in analysis with stress on cathodic processes. This acceptance has been due to polarography being a relatively simple experimental technique, which usually yields readily interpretable results suitable for quantitative and, often, for qualitative analysis. In addition, it offers the possibility of rapid polycomponent analysis from a single analytical record.

The polarographic technique has been widely applied for a variety of nonanalytical studies, some of which depend on using the polarograph as a specific concentration measuring device, e.g., the measurement of the rates of chemical reactions where often concentrations of both reactants and products can be followed.

In basic research, polarography has enabled investigators to gain further information on electrode processes, to elucidate their mechanism, to distinguish chemical reactions preceding and following the electron-transfer process proper, and, in some instances to obtain rate constants characterizing some of the steps in such processes. Polarography is sometimes said to have caused a renaissance in electrochemistry, e.g., polarographic studies of transport phenomena brought the interest of electrochemists back to important fields of electrochemistry, which were supposed to have been "solved" and "closed" in the nineteen twenties.

In other areas of physical chemistry, polarography permits evaluation of thermodynamic constants such as oxidation-reduction potentials and equilibrium constants of chemical reactions occurring at the electrode surface or in the bulk of the solution.

Polarography has been useful in both inorganic and organic chemistry in the elucidation of reaction mechanisms and equilibria, including the detection of reaction intermediates. Application of polarography often offers a convenient way of choosing the best conditions for synthetic reactions, separations, and isolations. Studies of the correlations between polarographic data and structure and other characteristics of chemical species are of importance not only in theoretical inorganic and organic chemistry but also form a sound basis for using polarography in the elucidation of chemical constitution.

In biochemistry, polarography is extensively used as an analytical tool and for the determination of reaction rates and mechanisms of biochemically important reactions; here, the possibilities of selectivity and of continuous measurement, sometimes even in very complicated and turbid solutions, are of importance.

Although polarography is generally less versatile than absorption spectrophotometry, this very restriction tends to build a certain amount of specificity into polarographic measurement.

Further discussion of the utilization of polarography is given in the succeeding articles on *Polarography, Inorganic,* and *Polarography, Organic.*

Analysis. Polarography has been applied to the determination of elements, functional groups, and compounds, e.g., most elements can be obtained in aqueous solution as ionic or nonionic species which will give polarographic waves suitable for analysis. The failure of a few elements and functional groups to give polarographic waves is not due to any inherent lack of reactivity, but rather to the lack of sufficient potential at the polarizable electrode to cause their oxidation or reduction (these potential limitations have been discussed).

The basis of quantitative polarographic analysis is the measurement of the i_1, which is directly related to the concentration of the electroactive species for all diffusion-controlled processes as well as for most kinetic-controlled processes. The $E_{1/2}$ as a measure of the ease of reduction is a good identifying characteristic, which also indicates the possibility of separating the waves of a mixture.

If a sample contains several components, electroactive within the potential range under consideration, whose waves are of near $E_{1/2}$, the nature of the supporting electrolyte or solvent can often be altered so as to permit resolution of the waves. If this cannot be done, it is necessary to carry out preliminary physical separation of the species involved or chemical reactions which will so change the nature of the species to be measured.

It should be emphasized that polarography as ordinarily applied is an excellent micro and even submicro technique, e.g., a typical 20 ml test solution, 0.5 mM in an electroactive species with a formula weight of 100 (a situation close to customary practice), contains only 1 mg of compound. It is possible without much difficulty to perform the analysis using 2 ml of test solution, 0.1 mM in the compound; this would require 0.02 mg.

References

The literature on specific topics in polarography is readily located in the several excellent bibliographies which are available:

1. HEYROVSKY, J. and collaborators, "Bibliography of Publications Dealing with the Polarographic Method in 19XY," published each year as a bulletin by the Czechoslovak Academy of Science.
2. SEMERANO, G. and collaborators, "Bibliografia Polarografica," published each year as a supplement to *La Ricerca Scientifica* by the Italian National Research Council.
3. "Bibliography of Polarographic Literature: 1922–1955," Chicago, E. H. Sargent and Company, 1956.

The following general references on polarography thoroughly cover theory, technique, methodology and application:

4. *Analytical Chemistry*, biennial reviews of polarography (issued in April of even-numbered years).
5. CHARLOT, G., BADOZ-LAMBLING, J., AND TREMILLION, B., "Electrochemical Reactions: The Electrochemical Methods of Analysis," New York, Elsevier, 1962.
6. DELAHAY, P., "New Instrumental Methods in Electrochemistry," New York, Interscience Publishers, 1954.
7. KOLTHOFF, I. M., AND LINGANE, J. J., "Polarography," 2nd ed., 2 Vols. New York, Interscience Publishers, 1952.
8. LONGMUIR, I. S., Ed., "Advances in Polarography," 3 Vols. London, Pergamon Press, 1960.
9. MEITES, L., "Polarographic Techniques," New York, Interscience Publishers, 1955.
10. MILNER, G. W. C., "The Principles and Applications of Polarography and Other Electroanalytical Processes," London, Longmans Green, 1957.
11. RULFS, C. L., "Polarographic Analysis," in Boltz, Ed., "Selected Topics in Modern Instrumental Analysis," Englewood Cliffs, N. J., Prentice-Hall, 1952.
12. ZUMAN, P., Ed., "Progress in Polarography," 2 Vols., New York, Interscience Publishers, 1962.

CHARLES L. RULFS AND
PHILIP J. ELVING

Cross-references: *Chronoamperometry; Chronopotentiometry;* entries with *Electrode* titles; *Electrometric Titrations; Electron Transfers at Electrodes; Fused Salt Polarography; Transfer Coefficient; Transference Numbers.*

POLAROGRAPHY IN FUSED SALTS. *See* FUSED SALT POLAROGRAPHY.

POLAROGRAPHY, INORGANIC

It will be assumed in the present discussion that the reader is familiar, as a minimum, with the features of the subject covered in the article on **Polarography.** Polarographic nomenclature and conventions regarding signs of current and potential will be employed. All potentials, not otherwise noted, will be given relative to the saturated calomel electrode, SCE.

Applicability of Inorganic Polarography

Reductions. Ionic species of most of the transition metal and heavy metal elements possess polarographically useful electrochemical reduction steps. The limited range of positive potentials polarographically available is not often a serious limitation for the observation of reductions; although it may mean that the toe of a wave (or an accurate measure of the residual current) is not definable. The polarographic limiting current for the reduction of any strong oxidant, such as permanganate, bichromate, cerate, etc., may appear at the most positive potential available. In this circumstance a transition from anodic to cathodic currents merely represents the most positive potential at which the anodic dissolution of mercury discontinues, permitting the cathodic reduction to be seen. A complication with strong oxidants may be their chemical reduction in the presence of mercury.

Alkali metal ion salts are normally used in supporting electrolytes because of their relatively negative reduction potentials, e.g., -2.3 v for Li^+. Slightly more negative potentials may be attained in aqueous or partially aqueous media by employing tetraalkylammonium halides as supporting electrolytes. Such expedients have a limited utility in inorganic polarography and do make possible the polarographic determination of barium, strontium or even calcium. Flame photometric or other methods are generally preferable, however, for the determination of the alkalies and some of the alkaline earths.

The reduction of hydrogen ion can become the limiting factor in the range of negative potential available. The use of neutral or alkaline media will sometimes be necesary for this reason. The high overpotential of hydrogen on mercury is a major advantage of the dropping mercury electrode, DME. Use of the DME permits the polarographic study even at relatively negative potentials of the noncomplexing acidic media needed to support ions of many of the heavy metals in solution. Moreover, the reduction of oxygenated species, such as MO_4^-, may occur at relatively positive potentials in acidic media, but may give ill-defined reductions at a high pH or the reduction may not occur at the most negative potential obtainable. Because of the low overpotential of hydrogen on platinum, platinum microelectrodes have a very limited range of utility in acidic media.

Oxidations. Observation of the polarographic oxidation of the lower oxidation levels of ions of many of the transition elements is possible. Such processes tend to be less frequently used for analytical purposes than are corresponding re-

duction waves. On the other hand, the anodic dissolution of mercury in the presence of certain precipitating or complexing anions, such as the halides, thiocyanate, thiosulfate, and sulfide, have been used as a measure of the anion concentrations. The mercury electrode is a reactive participant in such cases and typically, e.g.,

$$2Hg + 2Cl^- \rightarrow \underline{Hg_2Cl_2} + 2e,$$

the product has a limited solubility. While the plateau of the resulting anodic wave is diffusion-regulated by the anion, it is often distorted and difficult to define in consequence of mechanical interference by the precipitate.

Kinetic and adsorption regulated processes are more often of theoretical, than of practical, interest. Disproportionately large catalytic currents, however, have occasional value in detecting very small amounts of material. While such current-concentration relationships are nonlinear, they may be calibrated to permit estimation of concentration.

Table 1 illustrates the polarographic activity of some typical ions.

Effect of Electrolyte Composition

With an adequate, say 0.1 M, concentration of supporting electrolyte present, superimposed variations in the ionic strength of the medium have only a small effect on polarographic $E_{1/2}$ or on limiting currents. The $E_{1/2}$ and the I of most ions in 0.1 M KNO_3 would be almost the same as in 1 M KNO_3. Most reductions occur at more negative potentials in increasingly alkaline media, and amphoteric ions or hydrogen-ion dependent couples may show large shifts in $E_{1/2}$ with pH. The I_d may also vary since the species present (and diffusing to the electrode) may vary, just as in the case of complexation effects. In the case of zinc ion, e.g. (see Table 1), the simple ion or chloro complex reduces at -1.0 v, and I_d is 3.4. But the zincate anion in NaOH reduces at -1.5 v and I_d is 3.1, while the zinc ammonia complex behaves still differently. Therefore, close control of gross ionic strength is rarely critical but careful control of pH and the concentration of complexing ions may be important.

Reasonably complete removal of oxygen is requisite for most polarographic work at negative potentials. The presence of remaining oxygen is usually detectable from its two-step wave pattern, the second, peroxide-reduction step being particularly characteristic in that it extends

TABLE 1. HALF-WAVE POTENTIALS AND DIFFUSION-CURRENT CONSTANTS AT 25°C.

Ion	Supporting Electrolyte	$E_{\frac{1}{2}}$, v	I
Bi^{+++}	1 M HCl	−0.09	
	0.5 M tartrate + 0.1 M NaOH	−1.0	
Cd^{++}	0.1 M KCl	−0.60	3.51
	1 M NH$_3$ + 1 M NH$_4^+$	−0.81	3.68
Co^{++}	0.1 M KCl	−1.20	
	1 M KCNS	−1.03	
CrO_4^{--}	1 M NH$_3$ + 1 M NH$_4^+$ (VI) → (III)	−0.35	
	(III) → (0)	−1.7	
Cu^{++}	0.1 M KCl (HCl)	+0.04	3.23
	0.5 M tartrate, pH = 4.5	−0.09	2.37
	1 M NH$_3$ + 1 M NH$_4^+$ (1st wave)	−0.24	∼1.9
	(2nd wave)	−0.50	∼1.9
Fe^{+++}	0.5 M citrate, pH = 5.8 (1st wave)	−0.17	0.90
	(2nd wave)	−1.50	
Fe^{++}	1 M NH$_4$ClO$_4$	−1.46	
Mn^{++}	1 M KCl	−1.51	
Ni^{++}	1 M KCl	−1.1	
	1 M NH$_3$ + 0.2 M NH$_4^+$	−1.06	
O_2	Most buffers, pH 1 to 10 (1st wave)	−0.05	∼6.1
	(2nd wave)	−0.9	∼6.1
Pb^{++}	0.1 M KCl	−0.40	3.80
	1 M HNO$_3$	−0.40	3.67
	1 M NaOH	−0.75	3.39
Sb^{+++}	1 M HCl	−0.15	
	0.5 M tartrate + 0.1 M NaOH	−1.32	
Sn^{++}	1 M HCl	−0.47	4.07
	0.5 M tartrate + 0.1 M NaOH (anodic)	−0.71	2.86
	(cathodic)	−1.16	2.86
Sn^{++++}	1 M HCl + 4 M NH$_4^+$ (1st wave)	−0.25	
	(2nd wave)	−0.52	
Zn^{++}	0.1 M KCl	−1.00	3.42
	1 M NH$_3$ + 1 M NH$_4^+$	−1.33	3.82
	1 M NaOH	−1.50	3.14

over 0.4 to 0.5 of a volt. In trace analysis at very low concentrations or in the case of oxygen-sensitive materials, the removal must be rigorous and specially purified nitrogen will be needed. Precautions must sometimes be taken (e.g., with HTcO$_4$, OsO$_4$, etc.) against the loss of volatile substances or other concentration changes during deaerating.

Where needed, less than 0.01 per cent of any effective maximum suppressor should suffice; higher concentrations often distort waves, shifting the $E_{1/2}$ and depressing the limiting current.

Experimental Operations

Usually, a 2–3 per cent agar-sat. KCl bridge to a SCE contacts the test solution via a fritted glass disc. The reference electrode assembly may be an integral part of the polarographic cell (see, Fig. 1 of the article, **Polarography**).

The DME reservoir should be adjusted to an appropriate height, usually about 35 to 55 cm, which must be reproduced within about ±1 mm

from one run to another in a given study. With a suitable capillary the drop-time on short-circuit and in an electrolyte (*not* in air) should be within the range of 2 to 5 seconds.

Calibration and test or sample solutions should be carefully prepared using weighing and volumetric operations accurate within about ±0.5 per cent. The use of clean apparatus, distilled water, and reagent-grade chemicals is obviously requisite. The solution is deoxygenated in the polarographic cell by passing a moderate stream of nitrogen bubbles for about ten minutes. The cell should be immersed in the thermostat bath during this operation. In some cases it is important to exclude any mercury from the cell until *after* the removal of oxygen.

The polarogram must be recorded without nitrogen bubbling or other vibrations or sources of convective transport. In manual recording, six or eight points at closely spaced potentials may be read on each wave, but widely spaced points usually suffice to define the "toe" and plateau regions. Electrical damping devices should be used judiciously and not at all in the most careful work.

Overdamped galvanometers are employed in polarographs, but their average oscillation conforms approximately with the true average current. The maximum current envelope with some pen-recording instruments conforms best with true maximal currents. For most applications, either mode of treating the current may be used if the practice is consistent between calibrations and samples. A consistent and reasonable method, which gives a proper residual current subtraction, must be adopted. The $E_{1/2}$ of a polarographic wave corresponds to the point where the current (less residual current) is equal to $I_d/2$, and can be specified only after a point-by-point subtraction of the residual current.

Study of Current-Control

Nature. The irreducible minimum of residual current (about 0.2 μa at -1.5 v SCE with a DME) that can be obtained with highly purified solutions of supporting electrolytes is nonfaradaic in character. This "capacitance current" represents the charge, that must be resupplied to each new drop, necessary to build and maintain the electrical double layer at the mercury-electrolyte interface. Actual residual currents include small faradaic components resulting from the electrolysis of the traces of metal ions from impurities in the water and supporting electrolyte and any unremoved oxygen. In critical studies the residual current behavior of the background solution is usually examined separately.

Not all polarographic limiting currents are pure diffusion-controlled, and it is often of interest to establish the nature of the current control. In particular it is *requisite* for the valid application of certain useful relations that the process be diffusion-limited. Two readily available experimental parameters usually serve to characterize the current-controlling process; these involve studying the variation of the limiting current with temperature or with the height of mercury head of the DME, h.

The temperature coefficient of a diffusion-limited current is a function, primarily, of the temperature dependence of the $D^{1/2}$ term of the Ilkovic equation. The diffusion coefficient, in turn, is directly proportional to the ionic mobility or equivalent conductance, whose tempera-

TABLE 2. NATURE OF CURRENT-CONTROLLING PROCESS

Process	Temperature Coefficient, $\frac{1}{i_1}\frac{\Delta i_1}{\Delta T} \times 100$	Proportionality to h
Diffusion	ca. $+ 1.5\%$	$h^{1/2}$
Kinetic	$+2$ to 10%	h
Adsorption	$<1.0\%$	h°

ture coefficient is generally about $+2$ to 2.7 per cent per °C. Therefore, a typical temperature coefficient for a diffusion-controlled current is about $+1.5$ per cent/°C.

From the Poiseuille equation it may be deduced that the rate of mercury flow, m, at a DME should be directly proportional to the head of mercury, h, and the drop-time should be inversely proportional to h. Since I_d is proportional to $m^{2/3}t^{1/6}$, a diffusion limited current will vary, approximately, as $h^{1/2}$.

Limiting currents which are partially regulated by kinetic factors involved in the attainment of an equlibrium in the solution surrounding the interface are, not infrequently, observed, even in inorganic polarography (their nature is more fully described under *Applications* in **Organic Polarography**). While it is difficult to generalize concerning "kinetic currents," due to the many subclasses involved,[1] one can state that in general "pure" kinetic control does not obtain. The temperature coefficients of kinetically regulated currents are abnormally high, being greater than 2 per cent and sometimes approaching as a usual upper limit $+10$ per cent/°C. Kinetic currents are *in some cases* approximately independent of h. *Catalytic* currents are characterized by being abnormally large and nonlinearly related to the catalyst (or catalyst precursor's) concentration. Traces of platinum ion, for example, may be reduced on the DME, lowering the hydrogen overpotential and permitting a "catalytic" discharge of hydrogen ion.

When either the reactant or the product of a polarographic process tends to be strongly adsorbed at the electrode, the energy involved in this process causes the wave or a portion of it to appear at an abnormal position. This energy difference also results in abnormalities in the temperature and h criteria. With strong adsorption involved, i_l will appear to be directly proportional to h. Temperature coefficients will be abnormally low or negative; it is possible with a given system that a high enough temperature may be attained for desorption to occur.

Determination of "*n*"-values. It is often necessary to determine the number of electrons, *n*, transferred per molecule of reactant in a polarographic process; this may be attempted in several ways.

(a) Reversible, diffusion-controlled waves are mathematically described on their *E vs i* plots by the Heyrovsky-Ilkovic equation,

$$E_{DME} = E_{1/2} + \frac{0.0591}{n} \log \frac{i_d - i}{i}$$

Hence, a plot of *E versus* the log-term, where *i* the current observed at the potential E_{DME} on the rising portion of an actual wave, gives a straight line of slope 0.06 if $n = 1$, 0.03 if $n = 2$, etc. Integral numbers within $\pm$ 5 per cent often result with inorganic ions and can usually be relied upon.

(b) One may estimate an *n*-value by comparison of the diffusion currents of comparable concentrations of the unknown with those of a material whose reduction or oxidation behavior is well-known *and whose diffusion coefficient* (on the basis of size and charge) *would be expected to be similar*. No great reliance may be placed on this procedure.

(c) The *n*-value for any *diffusion-controlled* wave (but not necesarily a *reversible* wave) may be calculated thru the Ilkovic equation when *C*, *m*, *t*, and *D* data are all available. Limiting values of $D°$ are calculable from conductance data for infinite dilution and, as an approximation, may be used for this purpose.

(d) Lingane's coulometric technique will often serve to establish the *n*-values of either reversible or irreversible waves, even when the limiting currents are not controlled by diffusion alone. In this technique a gross electrolysis with stirring is conducted with a relatively large volume of the desired substance (say 100 to 200 ml of 1 to 10 m*M*) in the supporting electrolyte involved. The faradaic requirement for electrolysis to depletion at a suitably controlled potential on a large mercury pool is determined with a simple gas coulometer. The calculated *n*-values are usually integral within ± 1 per cent.

Various millicoulometric methods have also been described; but, in general, where method (a) does not suffice, method (d) is the most useful and reliable approach.

Nature of Half-Wave Potentials

For any serious study involving precise ($\pm$ 1 mv) measurements of potential, external potentiometer readings must supplement the humble voltmeter settings available with the majority of instruments.

Reversibility. A diffusion-limited polarographic wave may be *reversible* or *irreversible;* reversibility is not synonymous with diffusion control, and the distinction is often important. Several practical criteria of reversibility may be noted.

(a) A reversible wave should show a calculated (see, (a) above) *n*-value based on its slope which is within at least 10 per cent of an integral value; this alone is *not* a reliable criterion.

(b) The half-wave potential of the wave should not shift perceptibly over a reasonable concentration range (say, 20-fold) of electroactive species.

(c) The $E_{1/2}$ of an irreversible *reduction* may become more *positive* (easier) with increasing temperature and the magnitude of the shift may be abnormally large.

(d) For a redox system where both the oxidized and the reduced forms are available for study, $E_{1/2}$ for the reduction of the oxidized species should closely approximate the $E_{1/2}$ observed for oxidation of the reduced species, in a given supporting electrolyte. The composite polarographic wave for a solution containing *both* species should show a smooth transition from anodic to cathodic current flow.

Reversible values of $E_{1/2}$ have a valid thermodynamic significance *for the system involved*, and relate to standard values of $E°$ in a predictable fashion. The polarographic $E_{1/2}$ for the reduction of zinc ion in KCl is -1.00 v SCE, *e.g.*, or about -0.76 v NHE, the same as $E°$ of this couple. A correction of the "applied" potential for *IR* drop in the polarographic circuit is sometimes needed. A deviation which may be small or very large will be found in the case of the DME when the reaction product has a significant energy of amalgam formation. The reduction of alkali metal ions furnish a spectacular example where E of the amalgam electrode is about one volt, hence,

$$M^+ + e^- \rightarrow M°,$$
$$E° \; ca \; -3 \text{ v, but,}$$
$$M^+ + e^- + Hg \rightarrow M - Hg,$$
$$E_{1/2} \; ca \; -2 \text{ v.}$$

In general, then, choosing appropriate signs,

$$E_{1/2} = E° \pm E_{ref} \pm IR \pm E_{amal}$$

Hydrogen Ion Dependence. A change in oxidation level is often associated with a change in oxygenation of species; where the latter is involved the couple becomes hydrogen-ion dependent. For example, a (VII) state species like MO_4^- may be reduced in a three-electron step, established by coulometry, to a (IV) state. However, the (IV) state could be any of the species MO_2, M^{+4}, MO^{+2}, etc. A systematic study of the shift in polarographic $E_{1/2}$ as function of $[H^+]$ might show that the behavior of E related to $(0.0591/3) \log [H^+]^8$, confirming the M^{+4} ion as the species involved.

Complexation Effects. Shifts in half-wave potential with concentration of ligand have been used to determine the composition of complex ions and their instability constants. For the general reaction of reduction of a metal complex ion to the metal amalgam,

$$MA_p^{+(n-pb)} + ne + Hg \rightleftharpoons M(Hg) + pA^{-b}$$

the half-wave potentials for two concentrations of ligand is given by,

$$(E_{1/2})_2 - (E_{1/2})_1 = -\frac{0.059}{n} p \log \frac{(C_A)_2}{(C_A)_1}$$

This relation permits the calculation of the number of complexing addenda, p. Actually, a number of $E_{1/2}$ vs log C points are plotted and the slope of the "best fit" straight line is used to calculate p. Where successive complexes of different p exist, separate and calculable straight line portions may or may not be found in different regions over a broad range of A concentrations. Where only a smoothed curve remains, the successive p's may still be calculated by a more sophisticated process.

The instability constant of the complex may be determined from a comparison of the half-wave potential of the simple metal ion, $(E_{1/2})_c$, in the presence of a known concentration of the complexer, A. The expression takes the form,

$$(E_{1/2})_c - (E_{1/2})_s = \frac{.059}{n} \log K - p \frac{.059}{n} \log A$$

One often improves the feasibility of codetermining two species having adjacent $E_{1/2}$ values by changing the supporting electrolyte to take advantage of some selective tendency for complexation with one species.

General Remarks. The reader must be cautioned that additional considerations, which cannot be dealt with in a short article, will sometimes become important in the application of the relations just given. For example, the modified forms of Nernst equation, such as the Heyrovsky-Ilkovic and those mentioned under complexation, properly require an additional term.[2] This term at 25°C involves $(0.0591/n) \log (D_{ox}/D_{Red})^{1/2}$ and is negligible if the diffusion coefficients of the oxidized and the reduced species are approximately equal.

In the case of successive or stepwise reactions, e.g., a reduction sequence like,

$$(VI) \xrightarrow[A]{3e^-} (III) \xrightarrow[B]{1e^-} (II) \xrightarrow[C]{2e^-} (0)$$

would normally show diffusion limited currents for polarographic waves A, B, and C having a ratio of *three* to *one* to *two*. However, the diffusion current constants, I_B and I_C, characterizing waves B and C will be limited by the rate of diffusion of the (VI) species. *Bona fide, a priori* (III) or (II) species may diffuse more rapidly than the (VI) species in a given supporting electrolyte and result in larger currents per unit concentration. The analysis by polarography of a mixture of (VI) and (III) states would then require appropriate consideration of this factor.

It may also be noted with this example that if (V) or (IV) state compounds existed, the $E_{1/2}$ for their polarographic reduction to the (III) state should be the same as $E_{1/2}$ of the A-wave *only* if both processes are reversible. Actually, rather few such multielectron reductions as process A are perfectly reversible.

Applications

An experienced polarographer can usefully employ qualitative scanning for the identification of ions, but the fruitfulness of this technique is directly proportional to the breadth of experience of the user. Versatility is added by successive examination in different supporting media, and confirmations may be sought by checking for superposition of waves on the addition of known test ions.

With reasonable care and temperature control within at least ± 0.2°C, quantitative analyses of 10^{-3} to 10^{-4} M solutions of species giving well-formed waves are often accurate to better than ± 1 per cent, using a standard series or calibration technique. Routinely, results valid to ± 2 per cent can be obtained for most species. In conventional polarography preliminary dilution or concentration will be advisable when the concentration of test ion falls outside the limits of about 10^{-2} to 5×10^{-5} M.

The four approaches to quantitative measurement, described in the general article on polarography, are:

(1) Calibration or standard series.
(2) (Hohn's) Standard addition.
(3) Internal standard (or, pilot ion).
(4) "Absolute" calculation *via* Ilkovic equation or literature I_d values.

Method (3) rarely has any special virtues for inorganic polarography. Method (4) would only be used, with available I_d values, for the most casual and approximate work. Method (2) has several possible attractions; *viz.*, (a) when a given ion is to be determined infrequently, and, (b) when the supporting electrolyte composition is drastically variable between runs. Method (1) is by far the most generally satisfactory and precise technique. For optimum accuracy, however, new calibration curves should be run whenever a given capillary must be replaced. In practice, the correction of existing calibration curves to the characteristics of a new capillary, by reliance on the $m^{2/3}\,t^{1/6}$ dependence, will rarely be accurate within ±2 per cent. Accuracy could be severely compromised if a number of such "corrections" were applied over a period of time.

It is a special advantage of polarographic analysis that, while suitable electrolyte must be added, the composition of the test solution is essentially unaltered by the analysis. The examined solution may be used for subsequent controlled potential depositions, liquid-liquid extractions, spectrophotometry, precipitations or ion-exchange treatments; often, the result of such treatment can then be reexamined polarographically.

As previously mentioned, polarographic measurements are extensively used to determine such electrochemical characteristics as the heterogeneous rate constant and the transfer coefficient for electrode reactions. The possibilities for systematic study of complexation or chelation have been described. A number of polarographic studies of reaction rates have been reported.

Anodic stripping analysis at a hanging mercury drop has been used in trace analysis for metals in concentrations as low as 10^{-9} M. The derived technique of amperometric titration provides one of the best available electrometric end point detection techniques, especially for precipitation reactions. One instance of high-precision weight buret amperometry is being used for plutonium assays as good as ±0.005 relative per cent.

References

1. DELAHAY, P., "New Instrumental Methods in Electrochemistry," New York, Interscience Publishers, 1954.
2. KOLTHOFF, I. M., AND LINGANE, J. J., "Polarography," 2nd Ed., 2 Vols., New York, Interscience Publishers, 1952.
3. LINGANE, J. J., "Electroanalytical Chemistry," 2nd Ed., New York, Interscience Publishers, 1958.
4. MEITES, L., "Polarographic Techniques," New York, Interscience Publishers, 1955.
5. MILNER, G. W. C., "The Principles and Applications of Polarography and Other Electroanalytical Processes," London, Longmans Green, 1957.
6. VON STACKELBERG, M., "Polarographische Arbeitsmethoden," Berlin, de Gruyter, 1950.

CHARLES L. RULFS

Cross-references: See *Polarography.*

POLAROGRAPHY, ORGANIC

The polarographic behavior of organic compounds has been investigated from a variety of viewpoints including the determination of the mechanism of electrochemical processes, the utilization of polarographic data for the determination of elements, functional groups, and compounds, and the correlation of the half-wave potential, $E_{1/2}$, with other characteristics and properties of organic compounds, including structure.

The subsequent discussion of organic polarography is largely devoted to the reduction of organic compounds at the dropping mercury electrode, DME, since this is the situation which has been most frequently investigated and used. However, the arguments presented are generally equally applicable to the behavior of organic compounds at other electrodes and under conditions where oxidation can be observed.

In its simplest form, the electrolytic reduction

or oxidation of an organic compound at an electrode can be represented as

$$Ox + ne \rightarrow Red \qquad (1)$$

where Ox represents the oxidized form, Red the reduced form and n the number of electrons transferred.

Eq. 1 generally involves only simple integral stoichiometric ratios of oxidized and reduced forms with perhaps the addition of hydrogen ions, hydroxyl ions, and water for electrical and material balance. The physical path of the reaction, however, is usually quite complex; the reaction is heterogeneous in nature, involving electron transfer between a solution species or adsorbed or otherwise altered form and the electrode, and occurring in the interfacial region between bulk solution and electrode (the electrical double layer).

A few basic considerations need to be emphasized since these are fundamental to any detailed discussion of organic electrochemical processes:

(a) Electrochemical reduction of an organic compound involves the net transfer of electrons from the electrode to the electroactive species with an accompanying rupture of a chemical bond, resulting in a readily observed change in the structure of a functional group. Consequently, a single organic electrode reaction must involve the transfer of at least one electron, if a free radical is produced, or of 2 electrons, if a bond is completely severed without formation of an intermediate free radical.

(b) In almost all cases, such bond fission is equivalent to the conversion of a functional group involving two or more atoms into another functional group. This is in marked contrast to inorganic polarography, where the essential electrode process usually involves the transformation of an element from one oxidation state to another and, at most, may involve no more than a change in its immediate atomic environment in terms of oxygen attached to it.

(c) An electrode reaction, that gives rise to a single polarographic wave involving the transfer of more than 2 electrons per molecule of electroactive substance, is due either to a succession of processes whose potentials are so close together that a single reaction seems to be occurring, or to a $1e$ or $2e$ process occurring at a certain potential to produce species reducible at a less energetic potential, which species are consequently immediately reduced.

(d) $E_{1/2}$ for an organic compound, which generally undergoes an irreversible electrochemical reduction, is a composite function of (1) the free energy change for the electrode process, and (2) the activation energy and rate of the slow step in the process, as well as, probably, of other factors such as an energy of adsorption or orientation. Correlations of molecular structure with $E_{1/2}$, subsequently discussed, must recognize the possibility of more than one factor determining the latter.

(e) Since the observed polarographic behavior of organic compounds is usually markedly affected by experimental conditions, such as pH, buffer capacity, rate of buffer equilibration, buffer component nature (possible interaction or complexation with the electroactive species), ionic strength, and addition of organic solvent, $E_{1/2}$ for different compounds can be compared meaningfully only if determined under nearly identical experimental conditions. This is apt to be true even for members of a homologous series.

Electroactive Functions

A large variety of organic functional groups can be measured at the DME and other electrodes. Some of the most frequently encountered reducible groups are listed in Table 1.

The polarographic inertness of certain organic functional groupings, e.g., the hydroxyl and unconjugated aliphatic carbonyl groups, is not due to any inherent lack of reactivity in these groups, but rather to the unavailability of sufficient potential to effect their reduction or oxidation. The effective limiting potential for reduction processes is ca. -2.0 to -2.2 v (vs the saturated calomel electrode, as are all potentials cited in this article) due to the discharge of the usual supporting or background electrolyte cations involved. If a tetraalkyl ammonium ion is used as the cation of the background electrolyte, the working potential range can be extended to about -2.6 v, where the direct reduction of water produces an interfering current. On the positive side, the limiting usable potential with mercury electrodes is controlled by the oxidation of mercury at 0.1 to 0.4 v. With solid nonmercury electrodes, e.g., graphite, potentials as positive as ca. 1.4 v may be reached; the limitation is due to oxygen evolution.

Attempts to investigate and to utilize the electrochemical oxidation of organic compounds (anodic polarography) have not been too success-

TABLE 1. POLAROGRAPHICALLY REDUCIBLE FUNCTIONAL GROUPINGS

$\phi\overset{\mid}{C}=O$	—CHO	CX_n	—NO$_2$
$\phi\overset{\mid}{C}=\overset{/}{C}\diagdown$	$\diagdown C=N—$	ϕX	—NO
$\phi C\equiv C—$	—C≡N	$\phi\overset{\mid}{\underset{\mid}{C}}X$	—NHOH
$\diagdown C=\overset{\mid}{C}—\overset{\mid}{C}=C\diagup$	—N=N—		—ONO
$\diagdown C=\overset{\mid}{C}—\overset{\mid}{C}=O$	—O—O—	$O=\overset{\mid}{C}—\overset{\mid}{\underset{\mid}{C}}X$	—ONO$_2$
$O=\overset{\mid}{C}—\overset{\mid}{C}=O$	—S—S—		—NO=N—
Heterocyclic double bond		Polynuclear atomic ring system	

ful in the past. However, in recent years a number of interesting studies have critically discussed the application of solid platinum, gold, and graphite electrodes to organic oxidation reactions and their analytical applicability.

Effect of Experimental Conditions

The most important factors involved in the composition of the test solution from the viewpoints of obtaining well-defined waves and of securing the separation of waves of different, even related compounds, are its pH, nature and concentration of the buffer system used, ionic strength, nature of the solvent and additives added. A factor of occasional importance is the possible change in composition of the constituents of the sample due to a variety of reactions with themselves, with each other, or with the solvent.

pH. The variation of the $E_{1/2}$ of organic compounds with pH is as useful a device for securing selective reduction, i.e., separation of $E_{1/2}$, as is the addition of complex-forming reagents to solutions of inorganic species. Thus, below pH 6 the waves of the isomeric maleic and fumaric acids cannot be resolved; at pH 8, however, the wave separation is sufficient to permit the simultaneous observation of the successive reduction of the two acids.

Buffers. Simplicity of buffer system composition is desirable because of the ease of preparation and the minimization of interaction between buffer components and the organic species. Recommended simple buffering systems include HCl-KCl for the acidic region, acetate buffers for the weakly acid region, ammonia buffers for the slightly alkaline region, and KOH-KCl for the more alkaline region.

Ionic Strength. The ionic strength of the polarographic test solution will markedly affect $E_{1/2}$ and, often, the i_d of charged organic species, e.g., protonated and anionic forms of an organic acid.

In many buffer systems, e.g., those which involve polyprotic acids, the ionic strength of the solution will change considerably over the recommended optimum pH buffering region. In attempting to use a published polarographic method of organic analysis, it is important that, wherever possible, the same buffer system as that recommended by the original investigators be used. If a different system is to be used, it should first be examined in reference to the electroactive species involved to see whether it will yield the desired results.

Solvent. The selection of a solvent for polarographic study involves consideration not only of the availability, purity and solvent powers of the solvent, but also of its polarographic inertness in reference to both oxidation and reduction, its effect on electrocapillary properties, and either its lack of reactivity or its reproducible reactivity with the substance which is to be measured. Practically, water is not a satisfactory solvent for many organic compounds and the possibility of hydrolysis complicates evaluation of data. The most widely used solvents for analytical work have been 1,4-dioxane, methanol, ethanol, and, for hydrocarbon-rich samples, a mixture of more or less equal parts of benzene and methanol. For basic studies under conditions of low proton availability where the addition of electrons can be studied with little or no complication due to protonation, the favorite solvent has been dimethylformamide.

Lithium chloride dissolves to a sufficient extent in many nonaqueous media to serve as an adequate supporting electrolyte. The addition of LiOH permits some pH control in alkaline solution and gives a system which approximates that of a fairly well buffered solution. Acetate buffers have been used more or less successfully in the slightly acid region. Solutions of the usual "strong" acids in organic solvents have been used.

Due to the paucity of systematic studies on the effects of solvent nature and the difficulty of comparing the results of different investigators, in which factors other than solvent matrix, e.g., ionic strength, are also varied, only broad generalities can be made concerning the effects of organic solvents on the polarographic behavior of organic compounds. As the concentration of organic solvent is increased, the waves generally seem to be more drawn out with $E_{1/2}$ consequently becoming more negative (correction for the usually high IR drop improves the appearance of the wave considerably); the diffusion current usually decreases, although increases have been seen in a few cases.

Additives. Additives such as maxima suppressors should be used with the utmost of care in organic polarography. Frequently, troublesome maxima can be removed or minimized by decreasing the concentration of the electroactive species to *ca.* 0.1 *mM*.

Interpretation of Electrode Processes

The elucidation of the reaction mechanism of an organic polarographic process is difficult; the nature of the process prohibits the usual type of rate studies as in the case of homogeneous solution reactions. The interpretation of organic electrode processes in terms of the heterogeneous rate constant and the transfer coefficient for the electron-transfer step is still uncertain. The specific mechanism deductions in terms of substitution or free radical processes and the tests made of them are generally based on the correlation of the ease of reduction with structural

factors and products rather than on kinetic considerations.

The deduction of a polarographic reaction mechanism for an organic compound is optimumly based on the following data: (a) coulometric determination of n, the number of electrons transferred per molecule reacted; (b) evaluation of the role of hydrogen ion, e.g., effects of pH on $E_{1/2}$ and current; (c) ascertainment of the nature of the current-controlling process; (d) isolation of products by large-scale electrolysis; and (e) consideration of the chemical properties under the experimental conditions involved of the reactant and product compounds.

Cyclic voltammetry with oscillographic observation is finding increasing use as an aid to electrode reaction mechanism elucidation. Where formation of free radicals is expected, observation of the electrolyzed solution in an electron spin resonance apparatus can be helpful.

The subsequent discussion will consider as the function of the electrode process the breaking of a bond between a carbon atom and some other atom Y at the electroactive site, $R_3'C—YR_m''$, where R' and R'' represent any substituent including C and Y as in the particular cases of multiple bonds between C and Y, and of several Y connected to the same C center, and m is any number including zero. For convenience, the $R_3'C—$ entity will be represented as R and the $—YR_m''$ entity as X; the electroactive species is then R—X or R:X with the bond being adequately described by a localized electron pair. The reactive center can involve an atom other than carbon, e.g., N, O, or S.

Ionic Mechanism. In attempting to describe an electrode reaction as an ionic *substitution reaction* type, the usual factors are considered to be operative: the electrophilic nature of the carbon atom at the electroactive site and the electron density around this atom as it affects the strength of the R—X bond which is severed by the electron transfer. The S_E type of electrophilic attack need generally not be considered since the essential reagents involved in the bond fission are electrons. The S_N type of electrophilic attack is possible since the cathode is an ideal electron-donor reagent and can be described as follows:

$$S_N1 \text{ Process: } R—X \xrightarrow{\text{electrode}} R^+ + X^- \quad (2)$$

$$R^+ + 2e \rightarrow R^- \quad (3)$$

$$R^- + (H^+) \rightarrow R—H \quad (4)$$

[(H^+) represents a proton source such as water or hydrogen ion.]

S_N2 Process: R—X + $2e$ →

$$[\text{electrode complex}] \quad (5)$$

$$[\text{electrode complex}] = R^- + X^- \quad (6)$$

$$R^- + (H^+) \rightarrow R\text{—}H \quad (7)$$

Similar equations apply to the case where multiple bonds exist originally between R and X and one or more bonds between them persist in the reaction product. Hydrogen and hydroxide ions and water are not shown in the equations in this article except where necessary to indicate the final establishment of an electrically balanced species; the roles of such species as participants in potential-determining reactions are important and have been discussed.

Since the electron-transfer step in the S_N1 description ought to be potential-determining, it is necessary to assume that the energy-controlling dissociation (Eq. 2) is due to the electrical field and that consequentially the electrons enter simultaneously or in exceedingly rapid succession; this, however, is equivalent to the transition state postulated for the controlling step in the S_N2 mechanism (Eq. 5). Operationally, it is therefore probably more logical to speak of the *ionic*, rather than of the S_N1 or S_N2, mechanism.

Free Radical Mechanism. The isolation of dimeric products from some electrode processes is the strongest evidence for the formation of free radicals during the reaction. The appearance of a polarographic wave of an n of 1 is frequently taken as evidence for a free radical process. The possible steps in a *free radical type reaction* follow,

where the free radical produced in the controlling step may dimerize or be reduced:

$$R\text{—}X + e \rightarrow R\cdot + X^- \quad (8)$$

$$R\cdot + R\cdot \rightarrow R\text{—}R \quad (9)$$

$$R\cdot + e \rightarrow R^- \quad (10)$$

$$R^- + (H^+) \rightarrow R\text{—}H \quad (11)$$

Generalized Mechanism. A general sequence of reaction steps can be postulated, which accomodate the possibilities of both ionic and free radical processes and which account for the fact that some electrode processes seem to change mechanism with experimental conditions or between members of a homologous series:

$$R{:}X + e \rightarrow [\text{electrode complex}] \quad (12)$$

$$[\text{electrode complex}] \rightarrow [R\cdot] + X^- \quad (13)$$

$$[R\cdot] \rightarrow R\cdot \quad (14)$$

$$R\cdot + R\cdot \rightarrow R{:}R \quad (15)$$

$$R\cdot + e \rightarrow (R{:})^- \quad (16)$$

$$[R\cdot] + e \rightarrow (R{:})^- \quad (17)$$

$$(R{:})^- + (H^+) \rightarrow R{:}H \quad (18)$$

$$(R{:})^- \rightarrow \text{electronic rearrangement products} \quad (19)$$

Eqs. 12 and 13 represent the formation of an electrode intermediate species, which may be converted to a more or less stable trigonal free radical (Eq. 14) or reduced to a carbanion (Eq. 17). The free radical may dimerize (Eq. 15) or be reduced to a carbanion (Eq. 16). The carbanion may neutralize itself by acquisition of a proton from a solvent or interfacial species (Eq. 18) or by intramolecular electronic rearrangement (Eq. 19).

If R and X are connected by multiple bonds, the combined initial reactions (Eqs. 12 and 13) may be depicted as

$$R = X + e \rightarrow [\dot{R}\text{—}X]^- \quad (20)$$

Operationally, this mechanism is summarized in Fig. 1. The initial, generally potential-determining, step is addition of an electron to form a product, which either immediately acquires a second electron to form a carbanion or is converted to a free radical, which then adds a second electron or dimerizes. The carbanion, formed by either path, neutralizes its charge by acquisition of a Lewis acid, typically hydrogen ion, or electronic rearrangement. The latter is usually

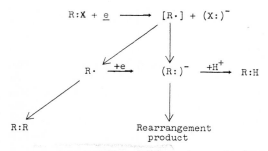

FIG. 1. Generalized chemical reaction mechanism. The initial reaction product may be (R-X-Z), if R and X are connected by multiple bonds. H^+, H_2O, and other possible participants are omitted as discussed in the text.

followed by elimination of an atom or group from an atom adjacent to the original reactive site with consequent formation of a double bond between this atom and that of the reactive site.

This general mechanism explains, for example, the reduction of vicinal dihalides, in which a *trans* elimination is involved; one carbon-halogen bond is broken by a $2e$ process to form a carbanion, which undergoes an internal electron density shift, resulting in the expulsion of the second halogen atom.

Attempts to define the physical path for the electrode reaction usually lead to a more detailed geometric description of the reaction and to the introduction of kinetic and energetic factors. The basic problems in defining the complete electrochemical mechanism of an organic electrode reaction involve answers to the questions of (a) where is the molecule when electron transfer occurs, (b) what is its state of being, and (c) how does the electron transfer occur.

The geometric treatment, which is essentially descriptive but which does help to define the kinetic and energetic factors which must be considered has been discussed by Elving and Pullman (reference at end of article), who also consider other approaches to the description of organic electrode reaction mechanisms.

Correlation of Half-Wave Potential Data

Considerable attention has been given in the polarographic literature to the search for relationships between $E_{1/2}$ and the structural and other characteristics, e.g., absorption maxima, of electroreducible and electrooxidizable organic substances.

The basis for such correlations can best be seen by briefly analyzing the physical basis for $E_{1/2}$. $E_{1/2}$ of a reversible electrode reaction is simply related to the standard electrode potential, $E°$, and to the free energy change of the reaction. However, most organic electrode reactions are irreversible.

The significance of $E_{1/2}$ for irreversible processes was first developed from absolute rate theory. For an irreversible electrode reaction involving one rate-determining step, e.g., Eq. 1, the following equation obtains at the dropping mercury electrode,

$$E_{1/2} = \frac{RT}{\alpha n_a \mathbf{F}} \ln \frac{k_{f,h}^° t^{1/2}}{\lambda_{1/2} D_0^{1/2}} \qquad (21)$$

where α is the transfer coefficient of the forward electrode process, n_a the number of electrons involved in the activation step, $k_{f,h}^°$ the specific rate constant for the forward electrode process, t the drop-time, $\lambda_{1/2}$ a constant (0.76), and D_0 the diffusion coefficient of the Ox species.

In correlating $E_{1/2}$ with structure for a series of compounds having the same type of reducible center and measured under similar experimental conditions, where temperature, drop-time and diffusion coefficients are consequently relatively constant, the variation in $E_{1/2}$ from one compound to another depends primarily upon variations in $k_{f,h}^°$ and αn_a. Since αn_a is generally constant for compounds of very similar structure, $E_{1/2}$ would be expected to vary with structure as $k_{f,h}^°$ varied with structure.

A possible solution to the problem is based on the fact that changes in reactivity are frequently related to the electron distribution in the molecules concerned. Predictions of reactivities from electron densities frequently parallel predictions based on considerations of the structure or calculations of the energy of the transition state. Calculations of electron density changes based on molecular orbital theory have been used in correlating reactivity with structure as well as correlating $E_{1/2}$ data.

Hammett Relation. At the present time, the most successful method for correlating $E_{1/2}$ of organic compounds is the use of the Hammett relation and its modifications in the form

$$E_{1/2} - (E_{1/2})_0 = \sigma\rho \qquad (22)$$

where σ a polar substituent constant based on the structure of the reacting molecule, and ρ a reaction constant which measures the susceptibility of a given reaction series to polar substituents; the zero subscript refers to some member of a series arbitrarily chosen as standard; $E_{1/2}$ sans script refers to any other member of the series.

The Taft-Hammett equation appears to be generally useful in discussing the ease of electrochemical reduction (and presumably of oxidation) of certain series of structurally related compounds. It is likely that those series or those members of a series which follow the equation are subject to polar effects only, as far as the structural effect on $E_{1/2}$ is concerned, or that the energetic magnitude of polar effects overshadows the energetic contributions of other effects such as adsorption. Thus, the Taft-Hammett relation may have possibilities for serving as a type of screen for pure polar effects due to structure.

Applications

Since the introduction of polarography and the realization of its possibilities as an analytical technique, it has found considerable favor for organic analysis. Often, polarography is the simplest method for measuring certain organic functional groups. The accuracy and precision obtainable is comparable to those obtained with other methods of functional group estimation, i.e., errors are of the order of 1 to 3 per cent relative.

Measurement and observation of the polarographic behavior of organic compounds often permits the evaluation of certain constants and quantities, which are applicable to the study of the physical phenomena of organic reactions, e.g., reaction rates, structure determination and tautomeric equilibria, and to possible methods of selective synthesis, using controlled potential techniques.

Analysis. Fundamentally, polarographic measurements made on organic compounds are almost entirely due to the functionality of certain bonds in the organic molecule. Even though the measurements may seem to involve the reactivity of an individual group, such as the carbonyl group, the effective $E_{1/2}$ is due to the nature of the molecular environment adjacent to the group, e.g., the difference in ease of reduction of a carbonyl group on an aliphatic skeleton as compared to one attached to an aromatic ring. Under favorable conditions, mixtures of such closely related compounds as *cis-trans* isomers, conjugate acid-anion forms, and members of homologous series can be analyzed.

In recent years, moderately complicated organic molecules such as steroids have been examined polarographically for both qualitative (structure determination) and quantitative (assay) purposes.

There are four general procedures available for the determination of compounds which are normally polarographically inert: (1) conversion into an electroactive isomer, (2) addition or formation of an active group, (3) formation of an electroactive complex, and (4) measurement of an electroactive reagent consumed.[5]

Reaction Rates. Experimental reaction measurement is frequently an analytical problem and polarography has frequently been used to measure chemical reaction rates. For example, the rate of condensation of urea with formaldehyde could be readily followed by observing the decrease in the limiting current of the formaldehyde wave with time.

Equilibrium Systems. In many cases the concentrations of the various components of an equilibrium system can be measured polarographically. Often, for such systems as ketol-enol, acid-anion, base-cation, lactam-lactim, and carbonyl-*gem*-glycol, $E_{1/2}$ of the two forms differ considerably or one form may be nonelectroactive within the available potential range.

If the interconversion rate of one form to the other is very rapid, only the wave of the more readily reducible form will be observed in the usual cathodic process. If this rate is very slow compared to the rates of reduction, two waves may be obtained, one for each equilibrium form. The wave at less negative potential will represent the equilibrium concentration of the more easily reduced form plus perhaps a more or less appreciable contribution from the other form, which would have been converted in the interfacial region to the more easily reduced form during the mercury drop life time as the more easily reduced is removed via reduction.

References

Specific information on the methodology, theory, technic, and applicability of various types of polarographic and voltammetric measurements to organic compounds can be readily located in the bibliographies listed at the end of the general article on **Polarography.** The following references furnish a general background for organic polarography:

1. ALLEN, M. J., "Organic Electrode Processes," New York, Reinhold Publishing Corp., 1958.
2. *Analytical Chemistry*, biennial reviews of organic polarography, issued in April of even-numbered years.
3. BREZINA, M. AND ZUMAN, P., "Polarography in Medicine, Biochemistry and Pharmacy," New York, Interscience Publishers, 1958.
4. CLARK, W. M., "Oxidation-Reduction Potentials of Organic Compounds," Baltimore, Williams and Wilkins Co., 1960.
5. ELVING, P. J., "Polarography in Organic Analysis," in Zuman, Ed., "Progress in Polarography," Vol. II, pp. 625–48, New York, John Wiley and Sons, 1962.
6. ELVING, P. J., AND PULLMAN, B., "Mechanisms of Organic Electrode Reactions," in Prigogine, Ed., "Advances in Chemical Physics," Vol. III, pp. 1–31, New York, Interscience Publishers, 1961.
7. GARDNER, H. J., AND LYONS, L. E., "The

Polarographic Reduction of Organic Compounds," *Revs. Pure Appl. Chem.*, **3**, 134 (1953).

8. MULLER, O. H., "Polarography," in Weissberger, Ed., "Physical Methods of Organic Chemistry," Part IV, 3rd. ed., pp. 3155–279, New York, Interscience Publishers, 1960.

9. SCHWABE, K., "Polarographie und Chemische Konstitution Organischer Verbindungen," Berlin, Akademie Verlag, 1957.

10. ZUMAN, P., "The Influence of Structure on the Polarographic Behavior of Organic Compounds," *Chem. Listy*, **48**, 94 (1954).

PHILIP J. ELVING

Cross-references: see *Polarography.*

POLYMERIZATION (ELECTROLYTIC) OF VINYL MONOMERS

Since the polymerization of compounds, such as vinyl acetate, methyl methacrylate, styrene, or butadiene, can be initiated by anion, cation, or radical entities, it is not surprising that attempts would be made to use electrodes to create such initiators and cause polymerization. One of the first indications of success was that of E. A. Rembold[1] who, on electrolysis of an aqueous solution of methyl methacrylate, obtained polymer at both anode and cathode, but mainly at the latter.

In the reduction at a cathode of carbonyl compounds dimerization is frequently observed. The reaction is favored by conditions of high overvoltage and is considered[2] to proceed through radical intermediates adsorbed on the cathode surface. If such radicals are to be used to initiate polymerization, then they must either get free from the metal surface or the monomer must itself be adsorbed so that it may approach the radical initiator. Using such arguments, Dineen, Schwan, and Wilson[3] electrolyzed aqueous acidic solutions containing acrylic acid, methyl acrylate, and methyl methacrylate at various cathodes and obtained polymer. The reaction was shown truly to be initiated at the cathode and was favored by high overvoltage conditions. A radical mechanism was proposed involving the simultaneous addition of an electron and a proton to the monomer molecule.

Cook[4] extended this work and studied the kinetics of the polymerization of methacrylic acid at a mercury cathode in acidic media but concluded that the reaction was initiated by radicals formed by the cathodic activation of peroxide impurities. When these were added deliberately in excess, consistent rates were obtained and were shown to be (1) independent of the nature and concentration of peroxide, (2) proportional to the current density over the range 2.5 to 75 ma/sq cm, and (3) largely independent of monomer concentration. The conclusion was drawn that both initiation and termination of the polymer chains occurred in close proximity to the cathode surface and that the cathode played a vital role in activating the peroxide in a manner analogous to the so-called "reduction-activation" well known in conventional peroxide-initiated polymerization of vinyl monomers.[5]

Cook also observed an induction period which was considered due to the presence of oxygen which frequently inhibits polymerization. This has recently been confirmed by Fedorova *et al*[6] who have shown that polymerization of methyl methacrylate in aqueous alcoholic medium at a mercury cathode can be initiated by the products of cathodic reduction of oxygen. Polymerization did not occur in the absence of oxygen and was inhibited by excess of the gas such as might be present as the result of vigorous stirring. The radical, HO_2, was believed to be the active initiator. Cook was unable to polymerize styrene or acrylonitrile which he explained by assuming that they were not sufficiently attracted to the cathode and acrylamide was reduced to dihydro-compound. On the other hand Kolthoff and Ferstandig[7] using added peroxides did observe slight polymerization of acrylonitrile after an induction period. An induction period was also noted by Parravano[8] with methyl methacrylate and a cathode of palladium, platinum, or nickel previously saturated with hydrogen. This author thought that the reaction was initiated by hydrogen atoms.

It now seems clear that cathodic initiation in aqueous medium is due to cathodic activation of peroxides or oxygen, that the reaction is inhibited by oxygen *per se*, and that polymerization is best observed using those monomers that themselves are attracted to the cathode surface. These are compounds with a tendency to undergo reduction by cathodes or dissolving metals.[9]

At the cathode in nonaqueous media the situation appears more simple and does not involve extraneous peroxidic substances. Using acrylonitrile both as polymerizable monomer and solvent and tetraethylammonium perchlorate (0.1M) as electrolyte, various cathodes give polymer.[10] Although the reaction was at first considered to involve ethyl radicals (see also Ref. 11) it is now more probable that a direct electron transfer to monomer to give an anion-radical is involved. The experimental evidence comes from copolymerization data.[12] Funt and Williams have reported[13] analogous polymerization of methyl methacrylate, acrylonitrile, styrene, and vinyl acetate in dimethylformamide solution at various cathodes using sodium nitrate as electrolyte. The chain growth is believed to be anionic rather than radical; since initiation is by an anion-radical, it could be either or both, and rate of polymerization is proportional to $[M]i^{1/2}$, where $[M]$ is the concentration of the monomer and i is the current.

At the anode, polymerization has been observed using as electrolyte salts of carboxylic acids. The discharge of such ions giving hydrocarbon forms the basis of the well-known Kolbe reaction (q.v.) and it is now believed with good experimental evidence that the reaction proceeds through the intermediate formation of acyloxy (RCO_2) and then alkyl (R) radicals.[14] It is only necessary that such radicals get free of the anode, or that the monomer is sufficiently attracted to the anode as to come into close proximity to the adsorbed radicals, for polymerization to start. Electrolysis of a solution of acetate in the presence of butadiene has been shown to give products of reaction of the diene with acetoxyl and methyl radicals including products containing two butadiene residues.[15] Using an electrolyte of potassium ethyl malonate containing butadiene and a platinum anode, a process has been devised to give dibasic acids containing twelve carbon atoms.[16] Using alkali metal acetate as electrolyte, the polymerization of vinyl acetate, vinyl chloride, and methyl methacrylate in aqueous solution[17] and acrylonitrile in acetic anhydride solution[12] has been observed. Oxygen has no effect and the chains are radical-terminated. When acetate containing radioactive carbon in the methyl group was employed, activity turned up in the polymer, confirming that the reaction involved methyl or acetoxyl radicals becoming attached to the chain.[17]

Under suitable circumstances there is no in-herent reason why cations should not be produced at the anode. At this time there is no evidence that such entities are involved in the polymerization of a monomer at an anode.

References

1. REMBOLD, E. A., Ph.D. thesis, Ohio State University, 1947.
2. WILSON, C. L., *Record of Chem. Progress*, **10**, 25 (1949).
3. DINEEN, E., SCHWAN, T. C., AND WILSON, C. L., *Trans. Electrochem. Soc.*, **96**, 226 (1949).
4. COOK, C. D., Ph.D. thesis, Ohio State University, 1951. Abstracts of the ACS Meeting, Atlantic City, September, 1949.
5. MORGAN, L. B., *Trans. Faraday Soc.*, **42**, 169 (1946); BACON, R. G. K., *ibid.*, page 141.
6. FEDOROVA, A. I., SHELEPIN, I. V., AND MOISEEVA, N. B., *Dokl. Akad. Nauk SSSR.*, **138**, 165 (1961); *Chem. Abstracts*, **57**, 577 (1962).
7. KOLTHOFF, I. M., AND FERSTANDIG, L. L., *J. Polymer Sci.*, **6**, 563 (1951).
8. PARRAVANO, G., *J. Am. Chem. Soc.*, **73**, 628 (1951).
9. FRIEDLANDER, H. Z., SWANN, S., JR., AND MARVEL, C. S., *J. Electrochem. Soc.*, **100**, 408 (1953).
10. BREITENBACH, J. W., AND GABLER, H., *Monatsch. Chem.*, **91**, 202 (1960).
11. PLUMP, R. E., AND HAMMETT, L. P., *Trans. Electrochem. Soc.*, **73**, 523 (1938).
12. BREITENBACH, J. W., AND SRNA, CH., *Pure Appl. Chem.*, **4**, 245 (1962).
13. FUNT, B. L., AND WILLIAMS, F. D., *Eleventh Canadian High Polymer Forum*, Windsor, Ontario, September 7, 1962.
14. WILSON, C. L., AND LIPPINCOTT, W. T., *J. Amer. Chem. Soc.*, **78**, 4290 (1956).
15. LINDSEY, R. V., AND PETERSON, M. L., *J. Amer. Chem. Soc.*, **81**, 2073 (1959); SMITH, W. B., AND GILDE, H. G., *ibid.*, page 5325.
16. LINDSEY, R. V., AND PETERSON, M. L., (to DuPont) U. S. Pat. 2,680,713.
17. SMITH, W. B., AND GILDE, H. G., *J. Amer. Chem. Soc.*, **82**, 659 (1960).

CHRISTOPHER L. WILSON

Cross-references: *Adiponitrile Electrosynthesis; Electro-Organic Chemistry; Kolbe and Related Brown-Walker and Hofer-Moest Reactions.*

POROUS CARBON

All manufactured carbon shapes are porous unless the pores have been filled after the shapes have been sintered. These pores are mainly generated by gasification of part of the carbonaceous binder during sintering.[1] This article will discuss carbons whose pore structures have been tailored to specific applications.

Pores in carbon range in diameter from over 100 microns (10^{-1} mm) down to a few Angstroms (10^{-7} mm). Carbon permeability or ability to pass fluid is largely a function of the size and number of pores larger than 3.5×10^{-5} mm diameter, often called "macropores." The surface areas and chemical properties of porous carbons are largely a function of the smaller or "micropore" structure. Through selection of binder and filler raw materials and of processing conditions, both macropore and micropore structure can be controlled within wide limits. Table 1[2] illustrates some of the range in properties that is commercially available.

Not all pores are the same size; hence, the distribution of void volume among pores of different diameter is of concern to most users.

Macropores. The Aminco-Winslow Mercury Porosimeter is commonly used to find the void volume in pores down to 0.035 micron (350 Å) diameter.[3] Since mercury does not wet carbon, pressure is required to force it into the carbon pores. Knowing mercury's surface tension, its contact angle with carbon, the relationship between pressure required and the volume of mercury forced into the pores of a carbon sample, one can calculate pore volume per gram of carbon as a function of pore diameter. (These calculations generally assume all pores have a circular cross section.)

It is usual to present the above calculation as a plot of cumulative pore volume vs pore diameter. Fig. 1 is such a plot for the carbons shown in Table 1. The pore diameter corresponding to the midpoint of the macropore void volume is called the "Median Pore Diameter."

Micropores. In addition to the void volume in macropores, there is often considerable void volume in pores smaller than 0.035 micron (350 Å). These pores are important because they contribute most of the surface area and, hence, control the chemical characteristics of the porous carbon. The accepted method of measuring pore diameters and void volumes in this range uses a modification of the BET procedure.[4] Recently, a simplified approximate method for determining micropore void volume has been described.[2] This method measures the difference between the volume of distilled water forced into the structure at 100 psi and of

Table 1. Physical Properties of Carbons

	Porous carbon									
	A	B	C	D	E	F	G	H	I	J
Median pore dia., microns (macropores)	0.8	1.7	2.0	2.9	3.0	4.1	4.5	5.4	6.9	11
Macropore volume, cc/g	0.05	0.29	0.43	0.26	0.49	0.20	0.11	0.13	0.20	0.61
Micropore volume, cc/g	0.01	0.33	0.14	0.01	0.07	0.01	0.00	0.01	0.03	0.31
Total pore volume, cc/g	0.06	0.062	0.57	0.27	0.56	0.21	0.11	0.14	0.23	0.93
Porosity, vol %	20	56	51	36	50	30	18	21	31	64
Surface area, sq m/g	0.3	300	9	3	7	0.5	0.2	0.4	2	560
Flow resistance, mm Hg/cm*	370	14	6	6	9	4	20	7	0.5	0.1
Average density, g/cc	1.70	0.90	0.90	1.32	0.90	1.45	1.62	1.49	1.35	0.70
Scleroscope hardness	90	50	15	40	25	35	65	90	60	20
Transverse strength, psi	10,000	1,000	500	2,000	1,000	3,500	6,500	8,000	4,000	300
Volumetric resistance, ohm-cm	0.005	0.03	0.005	0.006	0.004	0.003	0.003	0.005	0.008	0.10
Sulfur, %	1.8	0.001	0.05		0.01	0.21	0.01	0.21	0.12	0.24
Ash, %	4.7	10	0.1	0.2	0.1	0.5	0.1	0.2	0.2	6
Spectrographic analysis on ash, selected elements, %										
SiO_2	50+	50+	2	3.0	2	5.0	50+	50+	7.0	50+
Al_2O_3	0	10	0.5	5.0	0.5	0.5	10	1	3.0	2
Fe_2O_3	3	10	5	50+	5	50+	20	10	50+	10
CaO	3	1	1	20	1	0.5	1	0.05	0.1	1
MgO	2	0.8	0.1	0.25	0.1	0.25	1	0.3	2.0	0.5
TiO_2	1	0.2	50+	0.5	50+	0.15	0.5	0.2	0.05	0.08
Na_2O	0.2	8	0.1	—	0.1	0.1	3	1	0.5	2
K_2O	—	—	0.1	—	0.1	0.1	—	0.3	—	5

* Measured parallel to direction of molding.

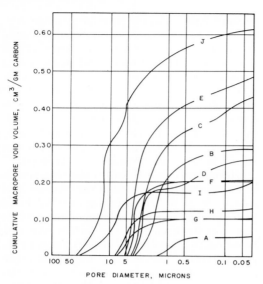

FIG. 1. Cumulative void volume in pores above 0.035 micron in diameter.

mercury forced in at 5000 psi. This difference is taken as the void volume in pores smaller than 350 Å.

Table 1 shows that for this group of porous carbons there is a rough relationship between micropore void volume as above determined and the low-temperature N_2 surface area determined by standard BET procedures.[5]

Permeability (Flow Resistance)

Permeability is that property of a porous carbon which characterizes the ease with which a fluid can be forced through the material by an applied pressure gradient. Three, possibly four, mechanisms contribute to the rate at which a fluid flows through porous carbon. Poiseuille flow, generally the major contributor, is largely governed by the macropore structure. Knudsen flow (known as slip flow or molecular streaming) can be an important contributor where the pores are very small. Diffusion (Fick flow) and adsorption-desorption transfer are usually even less important contributors to mass transfer through porous carbon.

One of the more common flow equations considers only Poiseuille flow of incompressible fluids, and uses as a unit the "darcy." A material is said to have a permeability of 1 darcy when a pressure gradient of 1 atmosphere per cm produces a flow of 1 cubic cm per sec with a fluid having a viscosity of 1 centipoise. Very few porous carbons have permeabilities as high as a darcy, and this has lead to the use of millidarcies and even microdarcies.

Another approach uses the reciprocal concept, flow resistance. The units of flow resistance are that pressure gradient, mm Hg/cm, required to force N_2 gas at room temperature through the porous carbon at the rate of 1 cc/sq cm/min. The relationship between these two units is:

$$\text{Darcies} = 0.22/\text{Flow Resistance}$$

Both these tempt the user to assume that mass flow of gas will be directly proportional to pressure gradient which is not so if the pores are small or the pressure gradient is high. When the pores are small, Knudson flow becomes predominant, and the mass rate of flow is governed by pore diameter, molecular weight of the fluid, and absolute temperature. When the pressure gradient is high, changes in specific volume must be allowed for.

Average Density, Transverse Strength, Scleroscope Hardness, Volumetric Resistance

In most applications gross physical properties are important to the user. These, too, are shown in Table 1.

Average density is calculated from the dimension of the carbon and its weight. Transverse (or flexural) strength is an indicator of the length to thickness ratio that can be used in electrode structures without excessive breakage. Hardness is an indication of machinability with carbide tools generally required to handle material in the 70 to 90 range, metal working tools for the 30 to 70 range, and wood working tools usually suitable below 30. Volumetric electrical resistance, like the other three properties, was measured using the standard NEMA/AIEE[6] method.

Sulfur, Ash, Water

Sulfur is a common impurity in raw materials needed to produce carbon. It is generally chemisorbed on the carbon, and it is difficult to remove.

Ash, like sulfur, generally enters carbons via raw materials, and it can be readily reduced below 0.2 per cent by high-temperature heat treatments (2600 to 3000°C). Further reduction in ash content generally requires careful selection of raw materials and/or chemical treatment.

Water vapor is strongly adsorbed, especially by high surface area porous carbons where contents in excess of 1 per cent by weight have been reported.

Spectrographic Analysis on Ash

Values reported were obtained using conventional emission spectrographic methods. All elements present in concentrations above 1 per cent in the ash are reported.

Applications

Porous carbon has a number of unique properties:

1. Chemically inert to most acids, bases, and solvents.

2. Thermal and electrical conductivity can be varied through a wide range. Some porous carbons have an electrical conductivity as good as brass.

3. Physical strength increases with increasing temperature up to 3000°C.

4. Excellent resistance to thermal shock.

5. Inherent lubricity, will not gall or freeze.

6. Available in a wide range of porosities, pore sizes, surface areas, and purities.

7. Low density and relatively low cost per unit volume.

Applications where porous carbon is used include fuel cell gas diffusion electrodes, catalyst supports, filter systems, adsorption beds, and ultra high-temperature insulating blocks. Carbon, of course, has a number of electrical applications—electrodes, brushes, etc.—and mechanical applications where the degree of porosity is not a major factor. Among the mechanical applications are seal faces, bearings, rocket nozzles, molds, crucibles, dies, and fixtures for high-temperature ovens.

References

1. "Proceedings of the Fourth Conference on Carbon," pp. 609–761, New York, Pergamon Press, 1960.
2. PAXTON, R. R., DEMENDI, J. F., YOUNG, G. J., AND ROZELLE, R. B., "Porous Carbon Gas Diffusion Electrodes," J. Electrochem. Soc., in press.
3. WINSLOW, N. M., AND SHAPIRO, J. J., ASTM Bulletin No. 236, February, 1959.
4. BARRET, E. P., JOYNER, L. G., AND HALENDA, P. P., J. Am. Chem. Soc., 73, 373–380 (1951).
5. BRUNAUER, S., EMMETT, P. H., AND TELLER, E., J. Am. Chem. Soc., 60, 309–319 (1938).
6. Joint Subcommittee On Carbon Brushes, "Test Code for Carbon Brushes," AIEE No. 504, New York, Amer. Inst. of Electrical Engineers, 1958.

J. F. DEMENDI AND
R. R. PAXTON

POROUS CARBON, MANUFACTURE

Almost any nonvolatile organic compound can be pyrolized to produce carbon. To produce carbons with a usable shape and controlled pore structure, however, takes special skills and experience.

The commercially produced carbons are usually made of a filler material and a carbonaceous binder.[1] The most commonly used filler materials are coke, lampblack, anthracite coal, natural graphite, and different chars. The binder can be any organic material which carbonizes easily and has high carbon residue; coal tar pitch, molasses, sugar, and synthetic resins are all common binders.[2]

The selection of the raw materials to produce a carbon with desired properties is a formidable task. Despite the fact that most of the fillers consist of carbon, there is a great variation in their response to binder addition and subsequent heating steps. Furthermore, many fillers are by-products or mined natural substances; therefore, it is not unusual to find marked difference among raw materials designated under the same name. For example, the nature of the crude oil, the coking process, the calcining operation, grinding, etc., all influence the characteristics of calcined petroleum coke. Similar factors are at work in the case of lampblack, synthetic (Acheson) graphite, and natural graphite.

The usual method of producing carbon can be described as follows. The selected filler material is mixed with a carbonaceous binder. The proportion of the components depends on the nature of the filler material and the method of manufacture. An excess amount of binder causes distortion of the shapes, blistering, and low strength, while a deficiency in binder content yields a structurally poor product due to weak bonds among the particles. The mixing is carried out either at room or at elevated temperatures depending on the type of binder used. Paddle mixers, sigma-bladed mixers, and muller mixers are the most common types. The mixers usually are equipped with heaters for the purpose of hot mixing. Since the mix is a poor thermal conductor, both the mix chamber and the blades should be heated. Mixing temperatures as high as 170°C are not unusual.

In some cases a blender is used for preliminary dispersion of the dry ingredients prior to mixing. Several types of blenders are used for mixing dry carbon powders. Tumbling mixers, such as double-cone blender, tumbling barrels, and muller mixers, are commonly used.

After mixing, the powder is formed to shape by either a molding or extrusion process.

The most widely used technique is molding. The mixture of the filler and binder is cooled and milled, then pressed in a die having the desired shape, at pressures of 2 to 20 tons/sq inch. In some cases the molding is carried out at elevated temperatures.

A more economical forming technique is extrusion. This method is a semicontinuous process. The binder-filler mix is forced under pressure from a horizontal cylinder through a die mounted at one end of the cylinder. Extrusion is usually carried out at elevated temperatures to increase plasticity of the filler-binder mixture. To reduce the die friction addition of a small amount of lubricating oil to the mixture is a common practice. The oil selected is usually insoluble in the binder and evaporates during baking.

In both forming processes, the finished product is anisotropic, that is to say properties such as strength and electrical resistance vary depending on the direction in which they are measured. When molding is used as a forming method, the particles tend to orient with their longest dimension perpendicular to the direction of applied pressure; in the extrusion process the particles align themselves with their longest dimension parallel to the direction of extrusion. The anisotropy of the extruded materials is usually higher.

The formed "green" articles are then slowly heated to 800 to 1200°C in a nonoxidizing atmosphere to carbonize the binder. During baking, pores are developed by the escape of volatile decomposition products of the binder and infusible carbon bonds are formed among the particles. In addition considerable—up to 40 per cent—shrinkage occurs due mainly to shrinkage of the binder coke. In some cases shrinkage of the filler also contributes to the overall shrinkage of the article.

The heating rate is quite important and it is selected according to the green part's size and shape, type of the binder, and baking furnace used. Two to six weeks to complete a baking cycle is not unusual. The baking in commercial scale is usually carried out in gas-fired furnaces.

During baking the "green" shapes go through a plastic stage. To avoid distortion and cracking the shapes are generally supported in a bed of sand and calcined coke. In addition the shapes may be placed in metal or ceramic saggers. This hinders escape of the pyrolysis vapors and tends to impart added strength and hardness to the baked carbon.

The product from this baking operation is often called "gas baked" carbon. It tends to be hard and have a relatively high electrical resistance. For many uses a lower resistance material is desired. This is obtained by heat treating to increase crystallite size, an operation called graphitizing. The treatment—originated by Acheson—is to heat the baked carbon in an electric furnace to about 2600 to 3000°C. At this temperature the baked carbon is not only converted to graphite, but its original ash content is greatly reduced. Graphitization also greatly reduces the number of submicron pores and fissures in carbons and the BET surface area.

Controlling total pore volume, pore size distribution, and surface area through these manufacturing steps is an interesting challenge. There is a considerable patent literature on this subject. A second rich source of background are the Carbon Conference reports,[3, 4] and the new journal, "Carbon."

Porous carbon products are produced in different shapes and sizes. The most common shapes are plates, blocks, cylinders, pipes, and rods. The size of the products is mainly determined by the method of manufacturing. Carbon cylinders as large as 48 inches in diameter are molded routinely. Extruded carbon cylinders are made as large as 60 inches in diameter.

Thin and flexible porous carbon sheets as thin as 0.005 inches[5] having a range of physical and chemical characteristics are just entering the commercial market. Sheets up to 6-inches square are being produced.

References

1. MROZOWSKI, S., "The Nature of Artificial Carbons, Industrial Carbon and Graphite," papers read at the Conference held in London 24th–26th September, 1957, pp. 7–18, Society of Chemical Industry.
2. RIESZ, C. H., AND SUSMAN, S., "Synthetic Binders for Carbon and Graphite," "Proceedings of the Fourth Conference on Carbon," pp. 609–623, New York, Pergamon Press, 1960.
3. "Proceedings of the Third Conference on Carbon," New York, Pergamon Press, 1959.

4. "Proceedings of the Fifth Conference on Carbon," Vols. 1 and 2, New York, Pergamon Press, 1962.
5. Engineering Bulletin 763, Pure Carbon Company, St. Marys, Pennsylvania.

J. F. DEMENDI AND
R. R. PAXTON

POTASSIUM ELECTROWINNING

The same general methods used in electrowinning sodium may be applied to potassium; however, potassium metal is more reactive chemically than sodium, and provision must be made for this higher reactivity in electrolytic processes.

Both the Castner and Downs patents (describing cells and processes for electrolysis of fused alkali hydroxide and alkali halide, respectively) claimed applicability to potassium as well as to sodium production. However, neither process is known to be in use for commercial potassium production. There has been only one commercial producer of potassium metal in the United States during recent years—Mine Safety Appliances Company. That company uses a thermochemical process with potassium chloride and sodium as reactants and potassium metal or sodium-potassium alloys as products.

Electrolysis of anhydrous fused potassium hydroxide in Castner-type cells is possible, but provision must be made to protect the potassium metal from atmospheric oxidation and to prevent the reaction of potassium metal with water in the melt. Water forms at the anode:

$$4OH^- \rightarrow O_2 \uparrow + 2H_2O + 4e^-$$

and dissolves appreciably in the melt at operating temperatures.

Atmospheric oxidation of potassium can be prevented by covering the electrolyte with a layer of mineral oil, and the migration of metal and water through the electrolyte can be reduced by use of a magnesite diaphragm. Alternatively, potassium bromide or iodide or mixtures of these halides can be added to the fused hydroxide to decrease water solubility, since water is less soluble in the mixed melt than in the simple hydroxide melt. Another means proposed to eliminate inefficiency caused by water is to continuously separate a portion of the melt and to heat that portion to a higher temperature while passing a stream of dry air countercurrently over the melt to vaporize the dissolved water.

A laboratory-scale preparation of potassium (15.5 grams) from potassium hydroxide has been reported, using an iron vessel with iron electrodes and a magnesite diaphragm. There were explosions when the electrolysis was started due to the reaction of potassium with air in the cell, but the electrolysis soon proceeded smoothly and a current efficiency of 58 per cent was obtained.

The high temperature requirements and corrosive nature of possible melts have deterred the development of a practical Downs-type cell for potassium reduction. Potassium chloride melts at 776°C, which is slightly above the boiling point of potassium metal, 757°C. Potassium fluoride forms a eutectic with the chloride, melting at 605°C, and barium chloride forms a eutectic melting at 660°C, but neither of these melts has been used on a large scale. Volatility of the potassium metal can be overcome by withdrawing the cathode and anode products separately at reduced pressure, but practicality of this system has yet to be demonstrated.

Potassium cyanide (melting point 634°C) has been electrolyzed on a laboratory scale using a nickel cathode, graphite anode, and a current of 2.5 amperes at 6 volts, to give potassium metal at a current efficiency of 90 to 95 per cent. The cyanogen formed at the anode is absorbed in a caustic soda solution.

A method was reported recently for electrolyzing potassium chloride—carbonate (about 50 per cent) melts at 700° with a liquid lead cathode. Current efficiencies of 80 to 90 per cent were reported. Potassium was separated from the cathode lead by fractional distillation.

Potassium ions in aqueous solutions can be reduced at a mercury cathode, taking advantage of the high overvoltage of hydrogen on mercury and the relatively low reactivity of the amalgam formed. Potassium can be recovered from amalgams: (1) by distillation of the mercury; (2) by formation, separation, and subsequent thermal decomposition of potassium hydride; (3) by electrodeposition of the potassium, using an amalgam-coated steel anode, nickel cathode, and fused salt electrolyte; or (4) by electrodeposition, using the amalgam as the anode and iron or steel as the cathode and an electrolyte of liquid ammonia containing 0.6 g per ml of potassium iodide. Evaporation of the ammonia from the upper layer formed during electrolysis then leaves potassium metal.

Potassium metal also has been prepared by electrolysis of salts such as potassium thiocyanate or potassium iodide in anhydrous solvents such as pyridine and propyleneglycol.

References

1. Dobrovolny, F. J., "Electrolysis Method," Appl. 642,936, *Official Gaz.*, **637**, 1575-6 (1950); [*Chem. Abs.*, **46**, 1895c (1952)].
2. Engelhardt, V., "Handbuch der Technischen Electrochemie," Band 3, Seite 120, Akademische Verlagsgesellschaft mbH, 1934.
3. Ewan, T., "Electrolytic Production of Alkali Metals," British Patent 218,606, April 3, 1923; [*Chem. Abs.*, **19**, 444 (1925)].
4. "Gmelins Handbuch der Anorganischen Chemie," System Number 22, Kalium, Lieferung 1, Seite 69-71, Berlin, Verlag Chemie, GMBH, 1953.
5. Kirk, R. E., and Othmer, D. F., "Encyclopedia of Chemical Technology," Vol. *I*, pages 449-50, New York, The Interscience Encyclopedia, Inc., 1947.
6. Liddell, D. M., Ed., "Handbook of Nonferrous Metallurgy, Recovery of the Metals," pages 81-2, New York, McGraw-Hill Book Company, Inc., 1945.
7. MacMullen, R. B., "By-Products of Amalgam-Type Chlorine Cells," *Chem. Eng. Prog.*, **46**, 440-55 (1950).
8. Sittig, M., "Manufacture and Availability of the Alkali Metals," *Chem. Eng. Prog.*, **52**, 337-41 (1956).
9. Smith, G. McP., and Bennet, H. C., "The Electrolytic Preparation of Amalgams of the Alkali and Alkaline Earth Metals," *J. Am. Chem. Soc.*, **31**, 799-806 (1909).
10. Zaretski, S. A. and Busse-Machukas, V. B., "Production of Potassium Through the Lead-Potassium Alloy Obtained Electrolytically," *Zhur. Priklad. Khim.*, **33**, 1823-33 (1960); [*Chem. Abs.*, **54**, 24010c (1960)].

Robert E. Davis

POTENTIAL, BILLITER. *See* BILLITER POTENTIAL.

POTENTIAL, CONTACT. *See* CONTACT POTENTIAL.

POTENTIAL, ELECTRODE. *See* ELECTRODE POTENTIALS ENTRIES.

POTENTIAL, ELECTROKINETIC. *See* ELECTROKINETIC POTENTIAL.

POTENTIAL, FLADE. *See* FLADE POTENTIAL.

POTENTIAL, LIPPMANN. *See* LIPPMANN POTENTIAL.

POTENTIAL, MEASUREMENT OF ELECTRODE. *See* ELECTRODE POTENTIALS, MEASUREMENT.

POTENTIAL MEASUREMENTS IN FUSED SALTS. *See* FUSED SALT ELECTRODE REACTIONS.

POTENTIAL, MEMBRANE. *See* MEMBRANE POTENTIALS.

POTENTIAL, MIXED. *See* MIXED POTENTIAL.

POTENTIAL, OXIDATION. *See* ELECTRODE POTENTIALS ENTRIES.

POTENTIAL-pH EQUILIBRIUM DIAGRAMS

When iron corrodes in the presence of air in tap water from a town water supply (Fig. 1), a large number of reactions take place simultaneously: the iron corrodes with the evolution of hydrogen and the water becomes alkaline according to the reaction: $Fe + 2H_2O \rightarrow Fe^{++} + H_2 \uparrow + 2OH^-$; in strongly aerated regions the ferrous ions thus formed are oxidized to ferric ions by dissolved oxygen according to the reaction: $4Fe^{++} + O_2 + 2H_2O \rightarrow 4Fe^{+++} + 4OH^-$, and these ferric ions react with the hydroxyl ions according to the reaction: $4Fe^{+++} + 12OH^- \rightarrow 4Fe(OH)_3 \downarrow$ to form a brown deposite of ferric hydroxide; in less aerated regions the action of oxygen leads to the separation, not of ferric hydroxide, but of magnetite, Fe_3O_4.

In general these oxides are deposited in the form of rust at a certain distance from the place where the iron dissolves, in which case the corrosion of the metal proceeds in a permanent manner; sometimes these oxides are deposited in an adherent form at the actual place where the iron dissolves, in which case they can cover the metal with a more or less protective coating. Other changes can occur simultaneously with these reactions: the local alkalinization of the water due to the evolution of hydrogen or the reduction of oxygen causes the conversion of bicarbonate ions, according to the reaction: $HCO_3^- + OH^- \rightarrow CO_3^{--} + H_2O$, into carbonate ions, which react with the dissolved calcium to form calcium carbonate according to the reaction $CO_3^{--} + Ca^{++} \rightarrow CaCO_3$. If this calcium carbonate deposits on the metal, which frequently happens with tap water, it can form on the surface, in combination with ferric oxide or hydroxide, an adherent coating which effectively protects the metal against further corrosion.

Finally, in the course of this corrosion of iron, other reactions can lead to the formation of small quantities of hydrogen peroxide.

Under these conditions, therefore, the corrosion of iron gives rise to the formation of a large number of substances in the dissolved, solid and gaseous states. These substances react chemically and electrochemically among themselves, and one is faced with an inextricable problem if one tries to study these reactions separately. For the study of these complex phenomena it is best to employ graphical methods which permit the study simultaneously of the equilibria of all the entangled reactions, both chemical and electrochemical, that may occur.

It is for the study of such problems that the electrochemical equilibrium diagrams discussed here are intended. The scope of these diagrams is to give a thermodynamic frame to the whole of the chemical and electrochemical reactions which may take place in the presence of aqueous solutions.

Chemical Equilibria and Electrochemical Equilibria

In electrochemistry as in chemistry, a reaction can proceed only in the direction which brings the system closer to the state of thermodynamic equilibrium, for which the affinity is null.

For a *chemical reaction*

$$\Sigma \nu \mu = 0 \tag{1}$$

the equilibrium condition is

$$\Sigma \nu \mu = 0 \tag{2}$$

This condition may be expressed, at 25°C, by the following relationship:

$$\Sigma \nu \log (M) = \log K \tag{3}$$

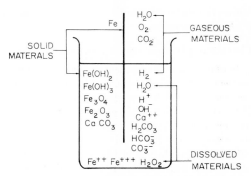

FIG. 1. Iron in the presence of tap water. [Figs. 1–6 from Ref. 2, permission Gauthier-Villars]

where

$$\log K = -\frac{\Sigma \nu \mu^\circ}{1363} \tag{4}$$

The *equilibrium constant*, K, is, according to the gaseous and/or dissolved nature of the reactants, a dissociation constant of Gulberg and Waage or of Ostwald, a solubility, a solubility product, a solubility constant of Henry, or a vapor pressure. As shown by (3) and (4) the value of these equilibrium constants may be easily calculated if one knows the standard free enthalpies of formation, μ°, of the reactants.

For an *electrochemical reaction* (or electrode reaction)

$$\Sigma \nu M + n e^- = 0 \tag{1'}$$

the equilibrium condition is

$$\Sigma \nu \mu - 23.050 \, n E_0 = 0 \tag{2'}$$

This condition may be expressed, at 25°, by the following relationship:

$$E_0 = E_0^\circ + \frac{0.0591}{n} \Sigma \nu \log (M) \tag{3'}$$

where

$$E_0^\circ = \frac{\Sigma \nu \mu^\circ}{23.050 \, n} \tag{4'}$$

The *equilibrium potential*, E_0,* is, according to the gaseous and/or dissolved nature of the reactants, usually considered as an oxidoreduction (redox) potential, or as a dissolution potential of a solid, liquid, or gaseous substance. As shown by (4'), the value of the *standard equilibrium potential*, E_0°, may be easily calculated if one

* or better, "equilibrium electrode potential," or "equilibrium tension."

knows the standard free enthalpies of formation, μ°, of the reactants.

Potential-pH Equilibrium Diagrams

If one writes all chemical and electrochemical reactions which may occur in the presence of an aqueous solution by expressing the liquid water, H_2O, the dissolved hydrogen ions, H^+, and the free electron, e^-, which eventually take part in the reaction, the Eqs. 3, 4 and 3′, 4′ express the equilibrium conditions of all reactions as a linear function of the pH and of the electrode potential, as well as of the fugacities of the gaseous species and of the activities of the dissolved species other than the H^+ ions. Each of these equilibrium conditions may thus be expressed graphically in potential-pH diagrams by a straight line, or by a series of straight lines, each of which corresponds to a given value of a given function, $\Sigma\nu \log (M)$, of the fugacities and activities of the gaseous and dissolved species.

Water. Here are three reactions relating, respectively, to the dissociation of water, and to its reduction and oxidation, and the corresponding equilibrium conditions, at 25°C:

$$H_2O \rightarrow H^+ + OH^- \quad pH = -14.00$$

(a) $H_2 \rightarrow 2H^+ + 2e^-$

$$E_0 = 0.000 - 0.591 \text{ pH} - 0.0295 \log pH_2$$

(b) $2H_2O \rightarrow O_2 + 4H^+ + 4e^-$

$$E_0 = +1.228 - 0.0591 \text{ pH} + 0.0148 \log pO_2$$

These relationships lead, for 1 atm partial pressure of hydrogen or of oxygen, to Fig. 2; according to this figure the area between lines a and b is the area of thermodynamic stability of water under 1 atm. Below line a, water may be reduced with the evolution of hydrogen and increase of pH; above line b, water may be oxidized with evolution of oxygen and decrease of pH.

Hydrogen Peroxide-Water System. Here are five reactions and equilibrium conditions relating to the dissociation, reduction and oxidation of hydrogen peroxide:

(1) $H_2O_2 \rightarrow HO_2^- + H^+$

$$\log \frac{(HO_2^-)}{(H_2O_2)} = -11.63 + \text{pH}$$

(2) $2H_2O \rightarrow H_2O_2 + 2H^+ + 2e^-$

$$E_0 = +1.776 - 0.0591 \text{ pH} + 0.0295 \log (H_2O_2)$$

(3) $2H_2O \rightarrow HO_2^- + 3H^+ + 2e^-$

$$E_0 = +2.119 - 0.0886 \text{ pH} + 0.0295 \log (HO_2^-)$$

(4) $H_2O_2 \rightarrow O_2 + 2H^+ + 2e^-$

$$E_0 = +0.682 - 0.0591 \text{ pH} + 0.0295 \log \frac{pO_2}{(H_2O_2)}$$

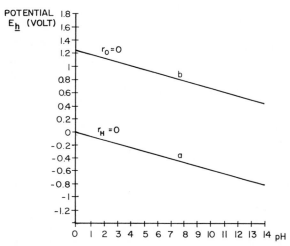

FIG. 2. Equilibrium diagram for water at 25°C. In the area above the top line (b) water may be oxidized with evolution of oxygen; in the area between the lines there is thermodynamic stability of water at 1 atm; in the area below the lower line (a) water may be reduced with evolution of hydrogen.

(5) $HO_2^- \rightarrow O_2 + H^+ + e^-$

$$E_0 = +0.338 - 0.0295 \text{ pH} + 0.0295 \log \frac{pO_2}{(HO_2^-)}$$

Fig. 3 shows that hydrogen peroxide may be reduced in water below lines 2 and 3, and may be oxidized in oxygen above lines 4 and 5. Between these two lines, hydrogen peroxide may be simultaneously reduced and oxidized and, thus, suffers double instability, leading to decomposition in water and oxygen according to the overall chemical reaction: $2H_2O_2 \rightarrow 2H_2O + O_2$.

Iron-Water System. Fig. 4, in which metastable oxide, FeO, and hydroxides, $Fe(OH)_2$ and $Fe(OH)_3$, have not been considered, shows that metallic iron and liquid water are not simultaneously stable at 25°C, under 1 atm pressure.

If one accepts, as a first approximation, that a metal is noncorrodable or corrodable in the presence of an aqueous solution initially containing none of this metal, according as the quantity of this metal which can be dissolved by the solution is lower or higher than 10^{-6} gram-atoms

per liter (0.06 mg iron per liter), the lines of Fig. 4 which correspond to this solubility (i.e., the -6 equisolubility lines) make a clear distinction between two areas where corrosion is possible and an area where corrosion is not possible. The same system is shown in Fig. 5, where the heavy lines are the equisolubility lines which define the areas of corrosion, passivation, and immunity from corrosion. In the noncorrosion area, two regions may be distinguished: one region where the solid stable form is the metal itself (area of *immunity*, or of *cathodic protection*), and one region where the solid stable form is an oxide (area of *passivation*). In this area of passivation, the metal tends to become coated with this oxide, which can, according to the circumstances, form on the metal either a nonporous film practically preventing all direct contact between the metal itself and the solution (in which case protection against corrosion is perfect), or a porous deposit which only partially prevents this contact (in which case protection is imperfect and pitting occurs). It should be thus understood that *such*

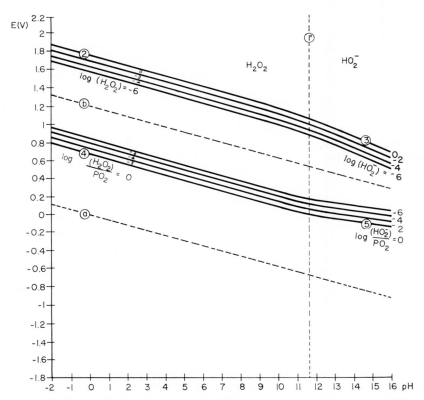

FIG. 3. Equilibrium diagram for the hydrogen peroxide-water system at 25°C.

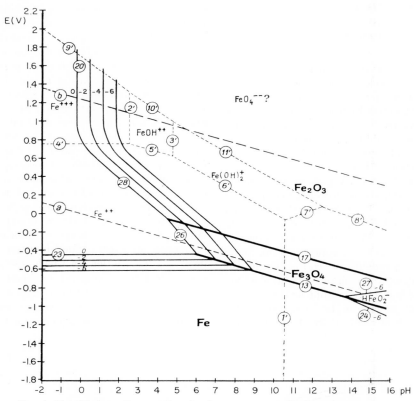

FIG. 4. Equilibrium diagram for the iron-water system at 25°C.

a passivation does not imply the absence of corrosion.

For checking the practical significance of potential-pH equilibrium diagrams, it is useful to conduct experiments, based on the measurement and on the interpretation of electrode potential values under different conditions. Particularly adequate, therefore, are experiments making use of intensiostatic and of potentiokinetic methods (with determination and interpretation of potential-current curves), of potentiostatic methods (with determination of current-time curves, and microscopic observation of the surface condition of the metal), and of various corrosimetric methods adapted to the problem to be solved.

Fig. 6 gives four "practical" potential-pH diagrams resulting from such experiments.

In Fig. 6a is given an experimental corrosion-immunity-passivation chart, resulting from intentiostatic experiments in stirred aqueous solutions,[10] with schematic indication of the speeds of corrosion; the agreement between these

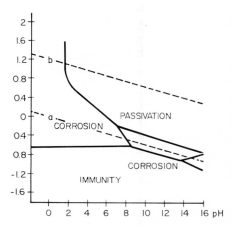

FIG. 5. Theoretical conditions of corrosion, immunity, and passivation of iron in water at 25°C.

experimental areas and the theoretical ones is satisfactory. In Fig. 6b, which is deduced from Fig. 6a, an evaluation of these corrosion velocities is given. In Fig. 6c are plotted the results of some

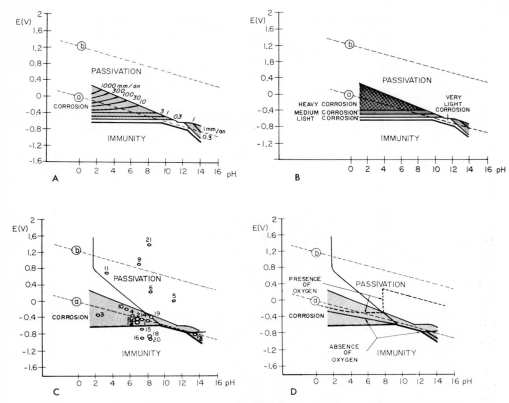

FIG. 6. Experimental conditions of corrosion immunity and passivation of iron at 25°C. (a) Corrosion rates in mm/year; (b) intensities of corrosion; (c) theoretical and experimental conditions of corrosion and of no corrosion; (d) electrode potentials of iron in the absence and in the presence of oxygen.

experiments relating to the behavior of iron in different aqueous solutions, with and without oxidizing or reducing substances (O_2, K_2CrO_4, $KMnO_2$, H_2O_2, $NaHSO_3$), with and without applied current, and with and without contact with another metal (Cu, Zn, Mg). The solid circles indicate that corrosion has been observed, and the open circles indicate no corrosion. It may be observed that corrosion always occurs in the theoretical area of corrosion, and that no corrosion ever occurs in the theoretical areas of immunity and passivation. Fig. 6d represents the influence of pH on the electrode potential of iron in the absence of oxygen, and in the presence of oxygen. It may be seen that, in the absence of oxygen, the velocity of corrosion is minimum for pH between 10 and 12. Oxygen increases the corrosion for pH lower than 8, and promotes passivation for pH higher than 8.

The Degree of Nobility of Metals. The treatment which has been applied to iron in the above section may be applied to all other metals and to metalloids.

Theoretical potential-pH corrosion charts for 43 metals and metalloids are presented in Ref. 2. In Table 1 these elements are classified in the left column by order of thermodynamic nobility.[2] According to this classification, which is based on the extent of the areas of immunity (stability of the metal) and which is somewhat similar to the classical Nernst classification, the most noble metal is gold, and the least noble of the considered metals is magnesium. If one changes this concept of nobility by adding to the areas of immunity the areas of passivation (stability of the solid oxides, hydroxides, and eventually hydrides), the classification changes as indicated in the right column of Table 1. By taking into account the conditions of passivation, the theoretical classification becomes in much better agreement with the practical classification; there is good evidence for the reason for the good

Noble Metals

A	B
1 Gold	Rhodium 1
2 Iridium	Niobium 2
3 Platinum	Tantalum 3
4 Rhodium	Gold 4
5 Ruthenium	Iridium 5
6 Palladium	Platinum 6
7 Mercury	Titanium 7
8 Silver	Palladium 8
9 Osmium	Ruthenium 9
10 Selenium	Osmium 10
11 Tellurium	Mercury 11
12 Polonium	Gallium 12
13 Copper	Zirconium 13
14 Technetium	Silver 14
15 Bismuth	Tin 15
16 Antimony	Copper 16
17 Arsenic	Hafnium 17
18 Carbon	Beryllium 18
19 Lead	Aluminum 19
20 Rhenium	Indium 20
21 Nickel	Chromium 21
22 Cobalt	Selenium 22
23 Thallium	Technetium 23
24 Cadmium	Tellurium 24
25 Iron	Bismuth 25
26 Tin	Polonium 26
27 Molybdenum	Tungsten 27
28 Tungsten	Iron 28
29 Germanium	Nickel 29
30 Indium	Cobalt 30
31 Gallium	Antimony 31
32 Zinc	Arsenic 32
33 Niobium	Carbon 33
34 Tantalum	Lead 34
35 Chromium	Rhenium 35
36 Vanadium	Cadmium 36
37 Manganese	Zinc 37
38 Zirconium	Molybdenum 38
39 Aluminum	Germanium 39
40 Hafnium	Vanadium 40
41 Titanium	Magnesium 41
42 Beryllium	Thallium 42
43 Magnesium	Manganese 43

Nonnoble metals

A

Thermodynamic Nobility

(immunity)

B

Practical Nobility

(immunity and passivation)

behavior of easily passivated metals, such as niobium, tantalum, titanium, zirconium, tin, beryllium, aluminum, and chromium.

More extensive information concerning these diagrams may be found in a thesis presented in 1945 at Delft[1] and in an "Atlas of Electrochemical Equilibria" published in 1963,[2] as well as in Technical Reports of the Centre Belge d'Etude de la Corrosion (CEBELCOR), and in publications of members of the International Committee for Electrochemical Thermodynamics and Kinetics or CITCE (q.v.).[2, 4−9] Publications of the following members of CITCE deserve a special mention: *Generalities*—P. Delahay, Ed. Deltombe, R. Piontelli, C. Vanleugenhaghe, J. Van Muylder, P. Van Rysselberghe, and N. de Zoubov; *General Chemistry*—G. Valensi; *Analytical Chemistry*—G. Charlot and L. G. Sillen; *Corrosion*—E. Mattson; *Electrodeposition*— T. P. Hoar; *Geology*—R. M. Garrels; *Metallurgy*—A. G. Guy; and *Batteries*—J. P. Brenet.

The following symbols have been used in this article:

A Affinity of a reaction (calories per molar group)
E Electrode potential (volts)
E_0 Equilibrium electrode potential (volts)
$E_0°$ Standard equilibrium potential at 25°C (volts)
e^- Negatively loaded electron
i Reaction current
log   Decimal logarithm
M   Symbol of a chemical substance
(M) Fugacity of a gaseous substance, or activity of a dissolved substance
μ Chemical potential (free enthalpy of formation at given temperature and pressure)
$\mu°$ Standard chemical potential at 25°C (free enthalpy of formation at 25°C and 1 atm)
ν Stoichiometric coefficient of a chemical substance, M
n Stoichiometric coefficient of the electron, e^-

References

1. POURBAIX, M., Thesis, Delft, 1945, "Thermodynamique des Solutions Aqueuses Diluées. Représentation Graphique du Rôle du pH et du Potential," 3rd Edition, Brussels, CEBELCOR, 1963; "Thermodynamics of Dilute Aqueous Solutions, with Applications to Electrochemistry and Corrosion," London, Edward Arnold, 1949.
2. POURBAIX, M., and coworkers "Atlas d'Equilibres Electro-chimiques," Paris, Gauthier-Villars, and Brussels, CEBELCOR, 1963.
3. "Rapports Techniques du Centre Belge d'Etude de la Corrosion (CEBELCOR)"
   (a) RT. 1, "Sur l'interprétation thermodynamiques de courbes depolarisation," 1952.
       e.12, "The utility of thermodynamic interpretation of polarization curves," 1954.
   (b) RT. 2, "Applications de diagrammes tension-pH relatifs au fer et à l'eau oxygéné. Expériences de démonstration," 1954.
   (c) RT. 66, "Electrochimie et corrosion," 1958.
       e.24, "Applications of electrochemistry to corrosion studies," 1955.
   (d) RT. 84, "Cellules d'aération différentielle," 1960.
       RT. 85e, "Conditions for the cathodic protection of metals," 1960.
   (e) RT. 89, "Les méthodes intensiostatiques et potentiostatiques. Utilisation pour le prédétermination de circonstances de corrosion et de non corrosion de métaux et d'alliages," 1960.
   (f) RT. 92, "Organisation et activité de la CEFA du CEBELCOR," 1961.
       RT. 92e, "The work of CEBELCOR's Commission des Etudes Fondamentales et Applications (CEFA)," 1961.
4. "Proceedings of the Meetings of CITCE (International Committee for Electrochemical Thermodynamics and Kinetics." 2nd Meeting, Milan, 1950; 3rd Meeting, Berne, 1951; 6th Meeting, Poitiers, 1954; 7th Meeting, Lindau, 1955; 8th Meeting, Madrid, 1956; and 9th Meeting, Paris, 1957.
5. *Electrochimica Acta*, Oxford, Pergamon Press.
6. *Journal for Corrosion Science*, Oxford, Pergamon Press.
7. GARRELS, R. M., "Mineral Equilibria at Low Temperature and Pressure," New York, Harper and Brothers.
8. SCHMITT, H. H., "Equilibrium Diagrams for Minerals at Low Temperature and Pressure," Cambridge, Geological Club of Harvard, 1962.
9. GUY, A. G., "A Firm Basis for Understanding Corrosion," *Metal Treatment and Drop Forging*, **29**, 45−54 (1962).
10. POURBAIX, M., "Corrosion, passivité et passivation du fer; le rôle du pH et du potential," 1951.

M. POURBAIX

Cross-references: *CITCE;* entries with *Corrosion* and *Electrode* titles; *Passivation; Potentiostatic Techniques in Corrosion Studies.*

POTENTIAL, SORET. See SORET POTENTIAL.

POTENTIAL, STREAMING. *See* STREAMING
    POTENTIAL.

POTENTIAL, VOLTA. *See* CONTACT POTENTIAL.

POTENTIAL, ZERO CHARGE. *See* BILLITER PO-
    TENTIAL; LIPPMANN POTENTIAL.

POTENTIAL, ZETA. *See* ELECTROKINETIC PO-
    TENTIALS; STREAMING POTENTIAL.

POTENTIALS. *See* ELECTROMOTIVE FORCE
    AND HALF-CELL POTENTIALS; ELECTRODE
    POTENTIALS; ELECTROMOTIVE SERIES.

POTENTIOMETERS

The potentiometer is an instrument for measuring an unknown electromotive force or potential difference by balancing it against a known
potential difference produced by the flow of a
known current in a resistance network. Potentiometers are used where the precision of measurement required is higher than can be obtained
by deflection instruments or where it is important
that little or no current be drawn from the source
under measurement. This latter advantage is of
particular importance in the electrochemical
field.

History

In 1841 Johann Christian Poggendorf, a German philosopher, devised two compensation
methods for measuring the voltage of polarizing
cells. His first method (see Fig. 1) is characterized

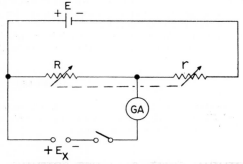

Fig. 1. Circuit for constant-current potentiometer, as devised by Poggendorf.

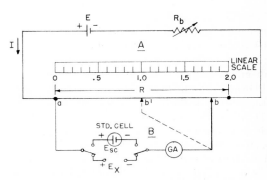

Fig. 2. Constant-current potentiometer circuit.

by a constant current flow from cell, E. The
resistors, R and r, are varied (keeping the value
$R + r$ = constant) until the current flowing
through the galvanometer is reduced to zero.
This results in the following relationship:

$$E_x = E R/(R + r)$$

By this method, the voltage, E_x, of the cell being
measured is "compensated" or balanced by the
potential difference across resistor, R. This
method forms the basis of all constant-current
potentiometers.

A simple constant-current circuit is shown in
Fig. 2. The emf, E_x, to be measured is connected
in series with a galvanometer, GA, across part of
the resistance, R, which carries the fixed current,
I, flowing in circuit, A (the battery circuit). The
section a-b, across which E_x is connected, is varied
until the galvanometer indicates that no current
is flowing in circuit B (the measuring circuit).
For this balance condition, $E_x = IR_{ab}$. In the
simplest potentiometer of this type, R is a slidewire having uniform resistance per unit length,
with a linear scale mounted beside it.

In order that E_x may be measured without
computation, the current is set to the value
needed to make the potentiometer direct reading
by the following procedure called "standardization." With a primary cell of known emf (the
standard cell) connected in the measuring circuit,
B, the slider b is set to b¹ to read the known
standard cell voltage, E_{sc}, from the scale (e.g.,
1.019 volts). Point a is set at zero on the scale
and the current in the battery circuit, A, is then
varied by means of the rheostat, R_b, until the
galvanometer indicates a null. The potentiometer
is now adjusted to read directly.

To make a measurement, E_x is substituted for
E_{sc} without changing the current, I, and the

potentiometer is balanced by varying the position of slider b. At balance, the value of E_x may be read directly from the slidewire scale (reading b). If the slidewire is uniform and the current, I, does not change between readings:

$$\frac{E_x}{E_{sc}} = \frac{\text{Reading(b)}}{\text{Reading(b}^1)} \quad \text{or} \quad E_x = E_{sc} \times \frac{\text{Reading(b)}}{\text{Reading(b}_1)}$$

but $\dfrac{E_{sc}}{\text{Reading (b}^1)} = 1$, since the reading b^1 was set equal to the numerical value of E_{sc}.

Consequently, $E_x = $ Reading (b).

It should be noted that:
1. The value of the current, I, need not be known but must be constant.
2. Only the ratio of resistances is used, their actual values in ohms are not needed for measurement.

Poggendorf's second method is characterized by a constant resistance in the E_x circuit (refer Fig. 3).

In this circuit, the resistor, R, is fixed and the meter, A, is used to measure the current from the nonpolarizing cell, which is changed by means of variable resistor, r. At balance the unknown voltage, E_x, is equal to IR. It is not necessary to know the values of E and r. This method forms the basis for all constant-resistance potentiometers. The accuracy of this method is not great due to limitations of ammeter accuracy, but has advantages over the constant-current method when measuring in the microvolt range. By using an auxiliary potentiometer instead of a deflection meter to measure the current, A, the accuracy can be considerably improved.

Because of the relative inaccuracy of the constant-resistance method, virtually all general purpose potentiometers are of the constant-current type. It should be noted that an increasing number of special-purpose potentiometers use Poggendorf's second method, a major example being the measurement of small potential differences between electrochemical cells, such as standard cells.

Many circuit variations followed publication of Poggendorf's methods—these being Dubois-Reymond, Clark, Fleming, Raps, Crompton, Fuessner, Kelvin-Varley, Diesselhorst, Waidner-Wolff, Wenner, Brooks, Stein, Leeds & Northrup, Lindeck-Rothe, Bonn, White, etc. An example of a modern, general-purpose precision potentiometer using a combination of these elements is

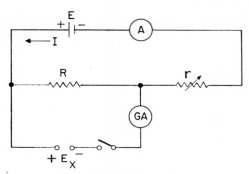

FIG. 3. Constant-resistance circuit for potentiometers.

illustrated in the schematic circuit diagram of Fig. 4.

Application

Electromotive forces are measured directly with a potentiometer in terms of the emf of a standard cell. High voltages may be measured with the aid of a volt box which in essence is a tapped, high-value resistor. This resistor is placed across the high voltage to be measured and a potentiometer is connected to a tap on this resistor which provides a voltage within the ranges of the potentiometer. The product of the potentiometer reading and the ratio of the total resistance to the resistance across the potentiometer will give the actual value of voltage being measured. This, of course, is not a true potentiometric measurement.

By measuring the voltage drop across a known resistor, the current flowing through it can be measured. Power can be calculated from potentiometric measurements of current and voltage and, if time is also measured, energy can be determined. The potentiometer is thereby one of the most fundamental and generally used instruments for electrical measurements.

Some of the more common applications are the determination of:
a) Temperature, from thermocouples.
b) Speed, by tachometer voltage.
c) Radiation, from thermopiles.
d) Pressure, from strain gages.
e) Gas analysis, by thermal conductivity cells, infrared absorption, and gas chromatography.
f) Interchecking of standard cells.
g) Calibration of deflection instruments (ammeters, voltmeters, wattmeters, pyrometers, etc.)

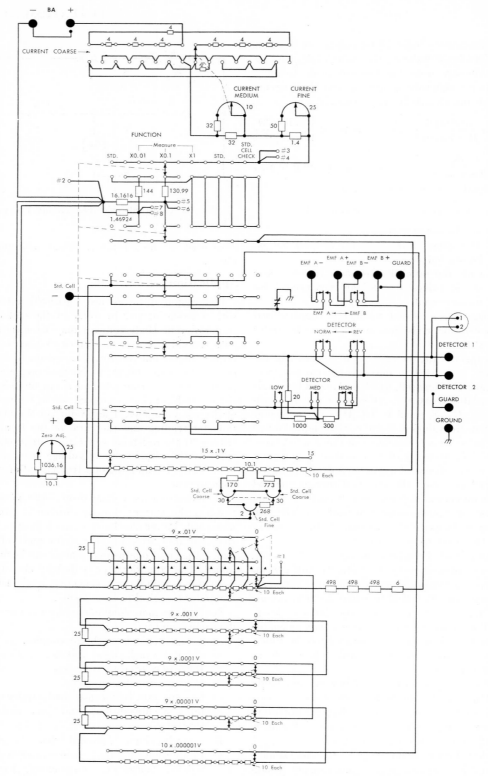

FIG. 4. Schematic circuit diagram of precision potentiometer. (*Courtesy Leeds & Northrup Co.*)

h) Battery voltage.

i) Hall effect.

j) Corrosion potential.

k) Power supply stability.

l) Differential thermal analysis.

m) pH and oxidation-reduction potential.

The potentiometer principle has such merit in accuracy and dependability and such a wide range of application that instrument makers saw the desirability of producing a potentiometer that could be used in commercial work without requiring the constant attention of an operator. Several makers now produce "self-balancing potentiometers" which operate on the true potentiometer principle with automatic balancing and draw a curve of the quantity being measured. In earlier models, the balancing process was initiated by a galvanometer pointer actuating a mechanical drive. In the most up-to-date instruments an electronic amplifier responds to an unbalance condition by driving a motor to move the potentiometer slider to balance.*

Fig. 5. A compact inexpensive self-contained potentiometer.

Commercial Instruments

An example of an inexpensive potentiometer employing Poggendorf's first method, available today, is shown in Fig. 5. This is a completely self-contained unit having a dual range of 0 to 22 millivolts and 20 to 64 millivolts and an accuracy of ±0.3 per cent of span.

An example of a highly precise potentiometer is shown in Fig. 6. It requires an external power supply, standard cell and detector. It has three ranges, the highest range going up to 1.6 volts, and the lowest range measuring in steps of 0.01 μv.

Its certified accuracy varies from ±(0.001 per cent of reading + 1 μv) on the high range to ±(0.003 per cent of reading + 0.1 μv) on the low range. (The simplified circuit of this instrument is shown in Fig. 4).

The primary characteristics of a potentiometer are range and accuracy. Other characteristics important in the choice of a potentiometer and detector are source impedance, speed of response, convenience, and cost. These data should be available from manufacturers' literature.

The selection of a potentiometer is based on the following requirements defined by the application:

Range. The range can be extended by a volt

* These instruments are described in detail in the article on *Recording Instruments*.

box for measurements over 1.5 volts. The potentiometer should, however, have a range low enough to provide the necessary resolution for small signals so that preamplification is unnecessary.

Accuracy. The rating should be compatible with the requirements of the application—extra accuracy adds complexity and cost.

External Circuit Requirements. Impedance, a-c signal components, and rate of signal change must be considered in selecting an instrument which will respond in the proper manner.

Convenience. A portable, self-contained instrument is more convenient to use under field conditions than a bench unit designed for laboratory use.

Accessories

Accessories required for use with a potentiometer include a detector (such as a galvanometer), power supply (such as a battery), standard cell, and perhaps switches for selecting more than one input. The detector is chosen according to sensitivity and also to the resistance of the combined potentiometer and emf source. In the simpler portable instruments, these are supplied in one assembly. With the more precise potentiometers, the accessories are usually not included and must be carefully selected according to application.

FIG. 6. A precision guarded potentiometer.

Precautions

Care should be taken when measuring low voltages to avoid introducing thermally generated voltages and other stray signals into the circuit. Avoiding temperature gradients, minimizing moving switch contacts, and exclusively using copper-to-copper connections (or alloys which exhibit low thermal emf's against copper) will keep thermal emf's at low levels.

Leakage currents from the high-level circuits of the potentiometer can cause serious errors in the low-level circuits.

Modern insulating materials offer some help. Prolonged exposure to humid atmospheres affects the volume resistivity of most modern dielectrics far less than hard rubber or bakelite. The surface leakage, however, can be a serious problem on even relatively short exposures to high humidity. This is particularly true unless the insulating surfaces, including binding posts, are kept free of both dust and fingerprints—a condition that is difficult to maintain in practice.

In contrast with many of the older forms of instrument construction, aluminum top panels offer distinct advantages with respect to lower weight for the same physical strength, reduction of temperature gradients by virtue of their thermal conductivity, and their possible use in electrostatic shielding. However, every switch, binding post, and other insulation supported by a metal panel becomes more vulnerable with respect to surface leakage unless the critical points of the circuit are properly guarded.

Guard circuits can be used to bypass leakage currents from the battery, standard cell, and voltage being measured, so that they will not get into the detector or other low-level circuits of the potentiometer. Guarding is especially important when making measurements involving low voltages, high-resistance circuits, or high humidity.

Guarding consists of the introduction of conducting surfaces at critical points to intercept and appropriately divert leakage currents which would otherwise cause adverse effects or measurement errors. Guarding never improves the insulation quality, but rather provides a basis for tolerating it. Guarding is effective only when the guards are judiciously connected in the circuit so that direct leakage between the guarded point and the points of higher potential is virtually eliminated while the direct leakage between the higher potential points and the guard has negligible effect.

A more complete discourse on guarding is given in ASTM Test Method D-257.

Certain forms of electrochemical cells, such as pH electrode systems, not only have a very high internal resistance, but also have equivalent internal voltage which depends markedly on how much current has been drawn from the cell in the period prior to measurement. In this case, guarding *alone* cannot help! Consideration must also be given to limiting the unbalanced current through these cells when making a measurement. The resistance of the detector circuit limits the unbalance current. If this resistance is too low, a protective resistor can be inserted in series with the detector to limit the current drawn from the cell to be measured during initial coarse balancing operations of the potentiometer. This protective resistance must be shorted out during the final balancing operation of the potentiometer if its value exceeds the maximum damping resistance recommended for the detector.

Shielding is necessary to eliminate electrostatic effects in high-impedance circuits. It can be provided by surrounding the instrument and its leads with a metallic enclosure, such as a metal case or a conducting sheath.

When inert materials must be used for electrodes, and where low signal levels are to be measured, the electrical junctions to dissimilar materials must be maintained at uniform temperature to avoid the introduction of thermal emf's.

References

1. ASTM Test Method D-257.
2. Boeing Co., Aero-Space Div., "Precision Electrical Measurement Course," Session 15, Seattle, Washington, 1962.
3. BUCKINGHAM, H., AND PRICE, E. M., "Principles of Electrical Measurements," Chapter 3, London, English Universities Press Ltd., 1955.
4. DANEMAN, H. L., "Selection Guides for Laboratory Instruments," Proceedings of the Precision Electrical Measurements Symposium, Stanford Research Institute, Page 31, Leeds & Northrup Co., MB #5–15.
5. EPPLEY, M., Trans. AIEE, 50, 1296 (1931).
6. HARRIS, F. K., "Electrical Measurements," New York, John Wiley & Sons, Inc., 1962.
7. KELLEY, J. B., AND MAROLD, H. H., "Handbook of Electrical Measurements," page 28, Pennsylvania, Instruments Publishing Co., 1960.
8. LEEDS, M. E., AND NORTHRUP, E. F., U. S. Patent 819,355 (1906).
9. LINDECK AND ROTHE, Z. Instrumentenk, 20, 293 (1900).
10. MARSHALL, R. B., "Measurements in Electrical Engineering," Ohio, J. S. Swift & Co., 1948.
11. MICHELS, W. C., "Electrical Measurements and Their Applications," Chapter 3, Princeton, New Jersey, D. Van Nostrand, 1957.
12. RAMALEY, D., "Calibration of Potentiometers," ISA Preprint 81-LA-61 (1961).
13. SCHAEFFER, W. H., Instruments & Control Systems, page 283, February, 1961.
14. SILSBEE, F. B., AND GROSS, F. J., J. Research Natl. Bur. Standards, 27 (1941).
15. SILSBEE, F. B., "Extension & Dissemination of the Electrical & Magnetic Units by the NBS," NBS Circular 531, U. S. Department of Commerce, 1952.
16. Stein, I. M., Trans. AIEE, 50, 1302 (1931).
17. STEIN, I. M., U. S. Patent 2,083,408 (1937).
18. STOUT, M. B., "Basic Electrical Measurements," Englewood Cliffs, New Jersey, Prentice-Hall, 1960.
19. WEAVER, F. D., Instruments, 23, 1236 (1950).
20. Leeds & Northrup Co., Proceedings of Symposium on Precision Electrical Measurements, George Washington University, 1963.

H. L. DANEMAN

POTENTIOMETRIC TITRATION. See ELECTROMETRIC TITRATION.

POTENTIOSTATIC TECHNIQUES IN CORROSION STUDIES

Corrosion of a pure metal is a spontaneous electrochemical reaction occurring more or less uniformly over the entire surface of the metal. On an impure metal or an alloy, this uniformity is disturbed, and pitting or preferential etching of one of the alloy constituents can take place. Basically, however, both of the above systems are similar. The over-all corrosion process involves at least one electrochemical step and consecutive chemical steps. The electrochemical step determines the corrosion current, i_{corr}, which is a measure of the corrosion rate. This rate depends in turn, on the potential prevailing at the boundary between the metal and the corrosive medium. The corrosion potential, E_{corr}, is the result of the spontaneous dissolution of portions of the specimen.

The purpose of any electrochemical corrosion study is to establish the relationship between corrosion current and potential, i.e., the polarization curve,* and to correlate this information with the theoretically predictable behavior based on electrode kinetic theory.[1]

The kinetic theory of electrode processes considers an important rate-determining step in the over-all reaction. This step may be due to mass-transport limitations at the interface (the reaction being under diffusion control), or it may be due to activation polarization. In the

---

* Generally, the electrode potential is plotted against the logarithm of the current density, i.e., the ratio of the current measured in an external circuit to the exposed area of the specimen. It will become obvious from this discussion that the "true" area of the corroding surface is changing, and also that it is not equal to the total area of the specimen, since parts of this area may still function as cathodic sites.

latter case, the rate of the over-all reaction is determined by the velocity of an essential chemical or electrochemical step. Information on reaction mechanisms and the origin of the rate-determining step can, in general, be deduced from the shape of the polarization curve and the conditions under which it is obtained.

Experimentally, the polarization curve for an anodic (or a cathodic) reaction can be obtained by one of two ways: (1) amperostatic techniques, whereby an externally imposed current is kept constant and the resulting potential (under steady-state conditions) is recorded; or (2) potentiostatic techniques, whereby the potential on the test specimen is set at some constant value and the resulting (steady-state) current is recorded.

Although it is reasonably easy to obtain polarization measurements under constant current, this approach is not always capable of completely describing the current-voltage relationship, as, for example, when "negative" resistance is encountered at the electrode-solution interface. In such cases, potentiostatic techniques are necessary. Considerable progress in this approach has been made with the development of new and more efficient instrumentation[2, 3] than that originally described by Hickling.[4] (See *Potentiostats—Principles of Design*.)

A polarization curve can be drawn automatically by the continuous-voltage-sweep method, with the use of an X-Y or strip-chart recorder, or manually through points determined by the voltage-step method. In the first case, the sweep rate is chosen to permit the recording of significant maxima and minima; in the latter case, the potential is set and kept constant for a given time interval at the end of which the steady-state current is recorded.

In the absence of any external electrical in-

fluence, the corrosion current is equal to i_a, the current crossing the anodic (actively dissolving) areas, and to i_c, the current crossing the cathodic areas on the metal surface; thus, the electrical neutrality of the system is maintained. However, the presence of an external current, i_{ext}, disturbs the equality between i_a and i_c so that

$$i_a - i_c = i_{ext}$$

In the absence of any localized effects, such as those due to polarization or surface area variations, the above condition will prevail as long as the potential on the test specimen is maintained at some constant anodic value above E_{corr}.

Experience with various metals, however, has shown that, more frequently, localized polarizations and changes in the surface area and morphology are important. Furthermore, for many metals and alloys, the current-potential plot of anodic polarization does not follow a simple Tafel-type[5] relationship, but gives an ~-shaped curve as shown in Fig. 1.[6] This behavior is the result of interaction between the anodic behavior of the anodic sites and the "anodic" behavior of the cathodic sites, since the latter are forced to attain anodic behavior by the external current.

The interaction between anodic and cathodic sites on a metal surface also determines the value of the corrosion potential of the metal or alloy on immersion in a corrosive medium. For example, if a metal exhibiting ~-shape anodic behavior (or active-passive behavior) is immersed in a corrosive medium in which the cathodic polarization of the cathodic sites is as shown by curve 1, Fig. 1, then, as expected from mixed potential theory,[7] the corrosion potential will be that indicated by the intersection of the ~-shaped (anodic) curve and the cathodic curve, i.e., point A. At this potential, the indicated current densities for the cathodic and the anodic reactions are equal.* If the polarization of the cathodic sites is as shown by curve 2 or possibly by curves 3 or 4, then, for reasons similar to those noted in the previous case, the corrosion potentials and the corresponding corrosion currents will be indicated by the points

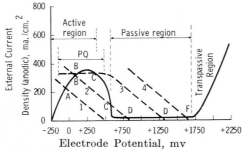

Fig. 1. Current-potential plot of anodic polarization.

* It is understood, however, that on a corroding specimen the anodic and cathodic site currents are equal but the corresponding current densities are determined by the effective areas of these sites.

of intersection B, C, D for curve 2 and curve 3 and by point F for curve 4. Thus, the specimen may be actively corroding at a corrosion potential as indicated by point B, or it may be passivated by maintaining its potential at a value indicated by point D; point C represents an unstable condition with the spontaneous tendency to revert to point D.†

Finally, it is possible to find metal-solution combinations whereby the mixed potential (the corrosion potential), (point F, curve 4) is in the passive range; i.e., the metal does not corrode actively.

When the dissolution behavior of an active-passive metal or alloy is controlled by the polarization behavior of the cathodic sites, the system is said to be under cathodic control. It is obvious that this control can be due to activation polarization characteristics or to mass-transport characteristics (i.e., when it is under diffusion control). Similar limitations, of course, apply to the anodic sites. However, since anodic and cathodic sites, in general, are not permanent sites on the metal surface, a continuous readjustment of conditions takes place.

Potentiostatic corrosion studies have been carried out successfully in each of the areas listed below:

(1) Development of corrosion-resistant alloys:[8] (a) by additions of selected alloying elements so that the resulting alloy exhibits characteristic active-passive behavior; or (b) by addition of alloying elements which, acting as cathodic sites, control the corrosion behavior of the active metal, i.e., bring about a passive state by way of cathodic control.

(2) Development of fundamental information on addition agents (corrosion inhibitors) which, through interaction with anodic or cathodic sites, will alter the respective polarization characteristics to minimize the corrosion current.[9]

(3) Development of fundamental information which will enable the use of externally applied electrical conditions to force an active alloy into the passive region and thus drastically reduce the corrosion current (anodic protection).[10, 11]

Recently, discussions on potentiostatic corrosion studies[12] and on electrochemical methods in corrosion research in general[13] have appeared in

† Curve 3 indicates polarization behavior of the cathodic sites which is characterized by a limiting current, and thus the cathodic reaction is diffusion-controlled in the region PQ.

the technical literature, to which the reader is referred for a detailed analysis of the subject.

References

1. BOCKRIS, J. O'M. "Modern Aspects of Electrochemistry," pp. 180–276, New York, Academic Press, Inc., 1954.
2. HICKLING, A., *Electrochimica Acta*, **5**, 161–168 (1961).
3. STAICOPOLUS, D. N., *Rev. Sci. Instr.*, **32**, 176–178 (1961).
4. HICKLING, A., *Trans. Faraday Soc.*, **38**, 27 (1942).
5. TAFEL, J., *Z. physik. Chem.*, **50**, 641 (1905).
6. EVANS, U. R., "The Corrosion and Oxidation of Metals," p. 230, New York, St. Martin's Press, 1960.
7. WAGNER, C., AND TRAND, W., *Z. Elektrochem.*, **44**, 391 (1938).
8. MUELLER, W. A., *Corrosion*, **18**, 73–79t (1962).
9. STERN, M., *J. Electrochem. Soc.*, **105**, 638 (1958).
10. EDELEANU, G., *Metallurgia*, **50**, 113 (1954); *Chem. and Ind.*, 301, **1961**.
11. SUDBURY, J. D., *et al*, *Corrosion*, **16**, 55–57t and 58t–62t (1960).
12. GREENE, N. D., *Corrosion*, **18**, 136t–142t (1962).
13. MAKRIDES, A. C., *Corrosion*, **18**, 338t–348t (1962).

D. N. STAICOPOLUS

Cross-references: *Anodic Protection; Corrosion Inhibition; Corrosion Inhibitors; Electrode Reactions, Kinetics; Mixed Potential; Passivity; Polarization; Potentiostats—Design Principles; Tafel Lines.*

POTENTIOSTATS—PRINCIPLES OF DESIGN

An apparatus for maintaining a constant electrode potential throughout an electrolysis—the potentiostat—was originally described by Hickling.[1] Lingane and Jones[2] further improved the design of electromechanical potentiostats to provide a closer control of the electrode potential and thus a closer control of the electrochemical reaction occurring at the electrode-solution interface.

Be it electromechanical or all-electronic, the potentiostat consists mainly of three stages: (1) the input stage, which detects differences between a "set" potential and the algebraic sum of the potentials of the test electrode and a reference electrode; (The "set" potential is usually obtained from a potential divider and battery circuit.) (2) an electronic amplifier whose output is controlled by the magnitude of the difference in potential detected by the input stage; (3) the controlled electrolysis-current stage.

In the electromechanical units, adjustment of the electrolysis current is made by a motor-driven rheostat (or variable transformer-rectifier arrangement). In the all-electronic units,[3-8] the electrolysis current is obtained from one or more current-amplifier stages, which are controlled by the output of the electronic amplifier.

Early developments in all-electronic potentiostats[3] incorporated vacuum tubes, often connected in parallel, to permit "high" output currents. Since these units were limited to a few hundred milliamperes, the size of test electrodes was also limited. Inherently, however, vacuum tubes present a high internal impedance to the electrolysis circuit, and the response of such potentiostats is greatly dependent on the load (the electrolysis cell).

With the development of low-impedance, high-current solid-state devices, i.e., transistors and silicon controlled rectifiers, potentiostats having greatly improved response characteristics and capable of delivering high currents were developed. Earliest units of this type employed an operational amplifier whose output controlled the collector current of one or more transistors.[7] Potentiostats of this type can deliver current either for anodic or for cathodic polarization, depending on the internal wiring of the unit. Although they respond rapidly to variations in test-electrode potential, they cannot correct an electrode potential in a direction opposite to that intended. To avoid "overshooting" of the desired electrode potential, one must therefore rely on a spontaneous decay of the potential back to the desired value which the potentiostat will eventually maintain.

The first transistorized, high-current potentiostat capable of delivering current for either anodic

or cathodic polarization, as required by the test electrode, has been described by Staicopolus.[8] The high-current output stage consists of two transistors (Tr_1, Tr_2)* connected in a balanced-bridge circuit (Fig. 1).

At the point of "balance," i.e., when the potential on the test electrode, Te (which is grounded), is equal to the desired potential, the current through the cell is:

$$i = i_{Tr_2} - i_{Tr_1}$$

If i_{Tr_1} is larger than i_{Tr_2} (which is set at some constant value), the cell current is negative, i.e., the test electrode is under cathodic polarization. If i_{Tr_1} is smaller than i_{Tr_2}, i is positive, and the test electrode is under anodic polarization. The balanced-bridge potentiostat[8] can instantly correct any overshooting in electrode potential by momentarily reversing the polarization current and can attain the desired values in a short time with minimum overshooting.

The basic design principles of a potentiostat can be applied to other electronic, low-impedance devices, such as the silicon controlled rectifier or the magnetic amplifier and saturable-core transformer. Use of these devices, however, has not been widely described.†[9]

References

1. HICKLING, A., *Trans. Faraday Soc.*, **38,** 27 (1942).
2. LINGANE, J. J., AND JONES, S. L., *Anal. Chem.*, **22,** 1169 (1950).
3. ROBERTS, M. H., *Brit. J. Appl. Phys.*, **5,** 351 (1954).
4. CIHAL, V., *Hutnické Listy*, **11,** 403 (1956).
5. PRAZAK, M., *Slaboprondy obzor.*, **17,** 237 (1956).
6. GERISCHER, H., AND STAUBACH, K. E., *Z. Elektrochemie*, **61,** 789 (1957).
7. BOOMAN, G. L., *Anal. Chem.*, **29,** 213 (1957).
8. STAICOPOLUS, D. N., *Rev. Scient. Instr.*, **32,** 176–78 (1961).
9. HICKLING, A., *Electrochimica Acta*, **5,** 161–168 (1961).

D. N. STAICOPOLUS

POURBAIX DIAGRAMS. See POTENTIAL-pH EQUILIBRIUM DIAGRAMS.

---

* For higher currents more than one transistor can be connected in parallel in each branch of the bridge.

† For applications of potentiostats to electrochemical technology see preceding entry by this author in this book.

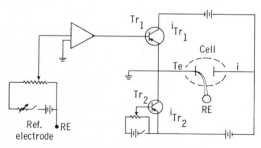

FIG. 1. Balanced-bridge circuit.

PRECIOUS METAL ELECTROPLATING

An outstanding number of new processes have been developed in the field of electrodeposition of precious metals during the past decade (1952–1962). In this field, where developments in the form of improved electrolyte compositions have been scarce, the present picture shows the issuance of numerous patents for the electrodeposition of silver, gold, rhodium, platinum, and their alloys. Silver plating is described elsewhere as a separate entry.

Gold

Jet- and space-age demands on materials have focused experimental work towards the development of superior electrolyte systems for the deposition of gold and gold alloys. As an engineering material gold has many attractive characteristics, i.e., it is the only metal that will not oxidize; it is a good electrical and thermal conductor; it is an excellent reflector of infrared; and as a coating it is relatively inexpensive. Unfortunately, the conventional, ages-old hot cyanide electrodeposit could not meet satisfactorily many of the new requirements. Deposits from such a formulation generally were dull, tended to become spongy and porous by reason of occluded cyanide polymers, and were poorly distributed.

Considered, by most observers, to be the pioneer bright gold plating process is the one developed by Rinker and first described[3] in 1953. His deposit contains a small amount of silver and has a hardness of 115 DPH, a value which enables designers to specify this coating for use in mating electrical contacts to put an end to previously encountered galling when conventional 65 DPH gold plates were utilized. This cold (room temperature) electrolyte was the forerunner of many subsequent innovations which saw the deposition of bright coatings containing up to 4 per cent antimony (of interest to semiconductor engineers who desired "doped" gold layers to produce specific transistor performance characteristics). Later Rinker and Duva,[4] in a major break-through, changed the entire concept of gold plating with their development of mild, noncorrosive, acid gold electrolyte systems. They employed mild organic acids with alkali metal gold salts at pH's ranging from about 3.0 and up. Baths were used at room temperature, or warmer, and with or without complexes of base metal additives to produce end results to satisfy any of a number of desired properties.

This basic system is used to produce high-purity, 99.999 per cent gold electroforms, 0.25 inch or more in thickness. Also, this purity level, coupled with maximum deposit density and ease of application, places this electrolyte in the forefront for usage in isotope preparation. Identical purity is attained in commercial barrel plating of transistor headers to meet the highest reliability criteria in force at this writing. Purity of deposit is maintained, even though bath contaminants are encountered during high-volume production runs, by the simple mechanism of chelation tied in with control of current density below the point at which the contaminant metal(s) complex would break down. Hardnesses of acid gold deposits range from 85 DPH upwards for the 99.999 per cent pure material and over 500 DPH for those alloyed with nickel, copper, etc. An acid gold electrodeposit of 99.9 per cent containing 0.1 per cent cobalt yields a hardness about 160 DPH whereas one with 98 per cent gold and the 2 per cent balance about equally divided between nickel, cobalt, and indium yields a hardness about 285 DPH. It should be noted that all these hardness values were determined on the cross section of a deposit, with deposit thicknesses between 0.001 inch (25 microns) and 0.0015 (37.5 microns). Also, a minimum load of 25 grams is indicated by reason of lack of uniform results that occur when loads of 1, 2, 5, and 10 grams are employed.

The former is used in a critical computer application to provide a minimum service of 100 insertions into a mating contact area. The latter has been shown to perform satisfactorily in space bearings under service conditions of 1,000 hours at 10,000 RPM. These conditions were found to be beyond attainment by regular lubricants. Oils and greases either evaporated or suffered by reason of radiation damage; and graphite, through moisture loss, became catastrophically abrasive.

The very latest contribution to this generic formulation are electrolytes which deposit gold alloys with a gold content well below the previously acknowledged floor limit. An 80–20 per cent alloy of gold-nickel which can be varied to

TABLE 1. GOLD PLATING PROCESSES

	Solution		Description of Electrodeposits				Uses
	Type	Additives	Surface Condition	Per Cent Gold Purity	Hardness DPH, 25 gram load	Other	
Conventional	Alkaline cyanide	None	Matte	99+*	60	Rough, porous, poorly distributed deposits	Not recommended. Approaching obsolescence. Most costly.
Bright Gold	Alkaline cyanide	Silver	Mirror bright	99+	To 120	Exceptional metal distribution mirror bright	"Work horse" formulation of industrial gold plating and most economical.
Gold-Silver Alloy	Alkaline cyanide	Silver	Bright	75	To 215	Mirror bright, pale color	General use. Lower gold content offers cost reductions.
Antimony Gold	Alkaline cyanide	Antimony	Bright	96–99+	To 170	Mirror bright, pale color	Good for solder joints in low temperature-high vibration service.
Gold-Copper Alloy	Neutral	Copper	Semi-bright	50–80+	To 450	Hardest alloy	Low carat alloy and hardness for sweep circuits and similar applications. Brazing of vacuum tube components.
Cobalt-Nickel-Indium-Gold Alloy	Organic acid low pH	Cobalt Nickel Indium	Bright to mirror bright	80–99.9	To 500	Alloy flexibility to yield practically any combination of properties	Printed circuits, connectors, contacts, transistors. Brazing of space metals.
24-Carat Gold	Organic acid low pH	None	Matte to semi-bright	99.99+	75	Excellent machinability. Highest purity	Electroforming and heavy build-up application. High reliability transistors.

* Maintained at this purity level only with strict quality control.

produce 82–18 per cent, etc. is in production. In color it is whiter than is nickel. It has a hardness in excess of 500 DPH and the alloy deposit has a melting point of 945°C, ideal for use in brazing of space metals, such as Waspalloy, Inco 128, Hastelloy X, and René 41. Studies to date show it will not cause undesirable intergranular cracking and that it produces strong brazed joints.

In a third and a neutral pH electrolyte system, Spreter and Mermillod[5] employ copper and other metals in conjunction with gold in an ethylenediaminetetraacetate formulation to produce gold alloys containing from 50 to 80 per cent gold.

The 75–25 per cent gold-copper alloy is copper colored, has a diamond pyramid hardness of 325 as deposited, and 450 after heat treatment. This post-plating heating step, at 300°C for 3 hours, also serves to accelerate the alloying of the as-deposited gold-copper agglomerate. Hardness of this gold-copper alloy (it is the hardest low-resistivity gold alloy when properly heat treated) suggests usage under highly abrasive conditions. Its melting point, 899°C, has led to its selection as a brazing material in the joining of vacuum tube components.

The impact of new gold and gold alloy plating formulations is readily seen in the wide number of engineering products which stipulate coatings of these metals, which are also used in decorative applications on consumer goods, such as wrist watches, jewelry, writing instruments, and optical goods. These coatings are being found on more and more products. In Europe there are well-defined regulations which assure the consumer of a floor under which the quality of gold cannot fall (with respect to karat fineness and gold thickness). These quality levels, controlled by governmental regulations, are being studied in this country for possible application here.

A summary of the above gold electrolyte processes and their applications is supplied in Table 1. Typical gold plating baths and operating conditions are listed in Table 2.

Rhodium

Over thirty years have elapsed since the introduction of rhodium plating electrolytes in the early 1930's. At that time its major use was in decorative applications where rhodium's rich blue-white color served to enhance the products of jewelry craftsmen. More recently its reported hardness of 600 has attracted the attention of printed-circuit designers for long-life rotary switching applications. The old phosphate or sulfate baths were incapable of yielding deposits of heavy thicknesses over 300 microinches which did not crack because of high tensile stresses in the coatings. Schumpelt in 1959[6] overcame the problems associated with stress cracking through use of additions of sulfamates. Deposits under the new system have been produced in barrel-production plating to 500 microinches on special bearings. Coatings to 0.015 inch (375 microns) of high purity have been deposited on copper cyclotron targets as an initial step in the production of radioisotope 103, stated to be a specific for bone cancer therapy. Deposits of this new rhodium call for a revision of the published hardness values of electrodeposited rhodium. Measurements in this country and abroad report new values at 900 or more, rather than the 600 value previously reported.

Platinum

Shortcomings in the boiling hot electrolytes commonly employed for the deposition of platinum probably contributed in a large measure to the relatively little amount of electroplating of platinum that has been observed up to the past

TABLE 2. GOLD PLATING FORMULATIONS

Typical bright gold plating formulation in a cyanide system

Gold	1 troy oz/gal (8 gpl)
Potassium cyanide	10–12 oz/gal
Brightener additives (supplied by vendor)	as needed
Cathode current density	up to 6 amp per sq ft
Temperature	55–75°F (10–24°C)
Agitation	moderate to rapid

Typical bright gold acid system

Gold	$\frac{1}{2}$ to 1 troy oz/gal
Mild organic acids-salts	to a pH 3.0–5.0
Additives (supplied by vendor)	as needed
Cathode current density	to 10 amps per sq ft
Temperature	70–110°F (20–45°C)
Agitation	moderate to rapid

Typical neutral gold plating bath

Gold	0.2–0.5 oz/gal
Ethylenediaminetetra-acetate metal complex (supplied by vendor)	to produce required alloying
Bath pH	7.0–8.0
Cathode current density	5–10 amps per sq ft
Temperature	110–120°F (45–50°C)
Agitation	moderate to rapid

couple of years. Bath performance was erratic, with fluctuating cathode efficiency a major problem. The electrolyte was sensitive to poisoning or contamination by many things, such as stop-off materials or maskants. Entrainment of organic materials into the bath often resulted in breakdown of the platinum complex and a precipitation of platinum in a dark, metallic, powdery form. The metal's high melting point offers many attractions to high-temperature product designers, who in turn prompted development of an easier-to-operate electrolyte. Thus, it was that Duva and Rinker in 1961[7] disclosed their novel use of sulfamates to promote bath stability and to extend the plateable thickness range of a commercially acceptable deposit well beyond the 25 micron maximum previously set as a practical top limit when boiling ammoniacal formulas were utilized. Today, electroforms in a thickness of 750 microns are a matter of recorded achievement.

Interestingly, the sulfamate formulation has been found to be compatible with that of the sulfamate rhodium reported above. Workers on special projects have stated they produce alloys of rhodium-platinum in an 80 to 20 percentage range that fully meet the required engineering needs of a product design.

Of major importance to electroplaters is the use of platinum coatings on titanium. Metal shapes in the form of sheets, studs, wire, and expanded mesh have and are being put through series of tortuous tests in the fields of cathodic protection and the production of electrochemicals such as chlorine. Reports from some exhaustive tests indicate that small platinum-plated titanium studs, properly positioned in a structure, will protect steel, aluminum, copper, and other metals from attack when exposed in sea water. Electrochemical producers report that a purer chlorine at a lower cost appears feasible with platinized titanium anodes. The amount of platinum required is amazingly thin, 50 microinches in the sea water applications, and about 100 microinches on anodes in the brine cells employed in manufacturing chlorine.

Additional information about precious metal electroplating can be found in References 8 and 9.

References

1. KARDOS, O., U.S. Patent 2,666,738 (1954).
2. GREENSPAN, L., U.S. Patents 2,735,808 and 2,-735,809 (1956).
3. RINKER, E. C., *Proc. Am. Electroplaters Soc.*, **40**, 19–25 (1953).
4. RINKER, E. C., AND DUVA, R., U.S. Patent 2,-905,601 (1959).
5. SPRETER AND MERMILLOD, U.S. Patent 2,724,687 (1955).
6. SCHUMPELT, K., U.S. Patents 2,895,890 and 2,895,899 (1959).
7. DUVA, R., AND RINKER, E. C., U.S. Patent 2,984,604 (1961).
8. GRAHAM, A. K., Editor, "Electroplating Engineering Handbook," New York, Reinhold Publishing Corp., 1962.
9. LOWENHEIM, F. A., Editor, "Modern Electroplating," Third Ed., New York, John Wiley and Sons Inc., 1963.

A. KORBELAK

PREECE TEST. See IMMERSION (DISPLACEMENT) PLATING.

PRIMARY BATTERIES. See BATTERIES—DRY CELLS; BATTERIES, RESERVE PRIMARY.

PROTECTION, ANODIC. See ANODIC PROTECTION.

PROTECTION, CATHODIC. See CATHODIC PROTECTION.

PROTECTION, SACRIFICIAL. See SACRIFICIAL PROTECTION.

PROTECTIVE COATINGS

Corrosion of metals may be controlled effectively by protective coatings that serve as barriers between the metal surface and the surrounding environment. Coatings owe their protective quality to their inertness or to their capacity for electrolytic reactions or to both. Where dependence is on inertness, it is necessary that the coating be continuous and free from pores or other defects that expose the underlying metal—an unnecessary requirement where protection is due to electrolytic action.

Protective coatings are of three kinds—metallic, organic, and inorganic. The type selected for the protection of a given metallic product will depend upon the nature of the product, its shape, metallic composition, and upon appearance requirements and the environment in which it is to be used. Small articles are usually metal-coated; structural steel such as used for automobile bodies and bridges is always painted; products of intermediate size may employ either metal or organic coatings. Finally, inorganic coatings are used in extreme environments, such as contact with corrosive liquids or exposure to high temperatures.

Surface Preparation for Coatings

It is essential that all foreign material be removed from metal surfaces before application of coatings. Greasy substances may be removed by dipping in solvents or preferably exposing them to solvent vapors. Trichlorethylene is widely used for this purpose. An older and common method of degreasing employs mixtures of strong alkalies, such as the hydroxide, silicates, and phosphates of sodium. Corrosion products, oxide, and scale are generally removed by abrasive blasting, acid pickling, or wire scratch-brushing.

Metallic Coatings

The nonferrous metals commonly used for the protection of iron are, in order of importance, zinc, nickel, tin, cadmium, lead, and aluminum.

Chromium is always used as a tarnish-resistant veneer on nickel coatings. Zinc, tin, and lead may be applied by dipping the product to be coated in the molten metals and by metal spraying. These metals are also electroplated, which is the only method of applying nickel-chromium coatings.

The resistance of nonferrous metals to corrosion that makes them useful as protective coatings is due to surface films of corrosion products that form as a result of chemical reactions of these metals with certain nonmetallic components of the atmosphere. Additional resistance to corrosion is conferred on such metals as zinc and aluminum by treating them with chromate or phosphate solutions. Iron and zinc are phosphated to enhance corrosion resistance and to provide surfaces more suitable for painting.

When zinc or cadmium is coupled with iron and exposed to moisture, it becomes the anodic or dissolving electrode and accordingly protects iron by electrolytic action. In this case the metal ions go into solution and hydrogen ions are plated out on iron exposed at pores or coating discontinuities, thus providing cathodic protection to iron. For coating metals cathodic to iron, such as nickel-chromium, tin, and lead, protection depends upon coating continuity and relative freedom from pores. The potential relationship and, consequently, the mechanism of protection of metals is influenced by the nature of the environment to which they are exposed. For example, as just implied, porous tin coatings are not protective in ordinary environments and yet do offer satisfactory protection inside cans used in packing foods. This is owing largely to the fact that, under these circumstances, a complex tin ion is formed that restricts the primary tin ion concentration and accordingly makes the electrolytic potential of tin anodic and therefore protective to iron exposed at pores. Were it not for the fact that foods contain substances that inhibit corrosion-cell action, much of the tin would be dissolved in protecting the bare areas of iron.

Performance of Metallic Coatings. Zinc coatings are widely used for the protection of steel sheet and wire exposed to the atmosphere. These coatings are generally produced by hot dipping, although they may be electroplated. Their service life depends on coating thickness and atmospheric conditions. In order of increasing corrosiveness atmospheric exposures may be classified as rural, marine, suburban, urban, and

industrial. Coatings are designated as extra heavy, heavy, moderately heavy, ordinary, and light. Thicknesses of these coatings in thousandths of an inch are of the order of 3.0, 2.3, 1.8, 1.0, and 0.5, respectively. Tests have indicated that the extra heavy coating should be protective for 50 years in rural atmospheres and about 15 years in highly industrialized areas, that ordinary coatings will serve about 10 years in rural and 3 years in highly industrialized locations, and, finally, that light coatings are good for about 6 years in rural and 1 to 2 years in industrial atmospheres.

Zinc coatings for indoor applications are generally electrodeposited and range in thickness from 0.15 to 1.0 thousandths of an inch. Where temperature and humidity fluctuations are such as to cause sweating or dew formation, the service life of zinc coatings may be greatly extended by chromate treatment. This is widely applied to zinc-coated products used in tropical and humid climates.

Nickel coatings have long been used for household appliances, plumbing fixtures, equipment for dairy and food industries, and automobile parts such as bumpers. Developments in recent years have included brighter plate and a very thin layer (a hundred thousandth of an inch) of chromium, which adds greatly to appearance. The protective quality of such coatings depends on the thickness of nickel, and this should exceed one thousandth of an inch, preferably twice this thickness for outdoor exposures.

The principal application of tin coatings is for the protection of steel used for cans for food and beverages. Originally applied by hot dipping, it is now largely electrodeposited. Coating thickness of tin on can stock is from a fifteen millionth to a six hundred thousandth of an inch and is porous in nature. Electrodeposited tin is sometimes given a passivating treatment by immersion in hot chromic acid solution. The inner surfaces of tinned cans for beverages and many foods are given supplementary finishes of organic coatings. For this purpose vinyl resins are largely used because these are nontoxic and do not contribute to the flavor or taste of the beverage or food.

Lead is used more widely as a lining or veneer for steel than as a typical coating, although coatings may be applied by hot dipping and by electroplating. Owing to the cathodic relation of lead to iron in ordinary environments, lead coatings are subject to pinhole rusting unless pore-free. Lead linings are employed for surfaces exposed to sulfuric acid and certain other corrosive substances.

Aluminum is used to some extent for the protection of structural steel and for this purpose is applied by metal spraying. In the form of a cladding it confers protection to certain corrodible aluminum alloys. Steel wire has been coated to a limited extent with aluminum by hot dipping, but the process is technically difficult owing to the ready oxidizability of aluminum.

Cadmium is employed for coating products for indoor use where its bright appearance and more ready solderability is desired. It resembles zinc in its anodic relationship to iron and in its protective action. Cadmium is somewhat superior to zinc for the protection of iron in marine atmospheres but less effective in rural and industrial areas.

Organic Coatings

Organic coatings have been classified generally as paints, enamels, and lacquers and comprise the most widely used means of protecting metals from corrosion. Owing to the ingenuity of the chemical industry in developing hundreds of new coating materials and blending them in many ways, the distinction between these classes has largely disappeared. Instead, organic finishing materials are now usually designated in terms of the resins that are employed. They consist essentially of a continuous film-forming liquid phase in which a pigment is dispersed.

Following the application of an organic coating material to a metal surface, the process of film formation may consist in the oxidation of an unsaturated drying oil vehicle, such as linseed oil, converting it into a gel or solid film—a reaction typical of paint drying. The combination of a resin with a drying oil provides an enamel type vehicle and, in this case, film formation may involve both oil oxidation and "curing" or cross-linking of the resin polymer by means of heat or a catalyst. Finally, film formation typical of lacquers consists in the deposition of a resin from a solution brought about by evaporation of the solvent. In some cases further polymerization of the film is induced by heat.

Coating resins may be grouped in about eight classes.[1] Among the most important are the alkyds, vinyls, styrene types, phenolics, urea-

melamines, and epoxies. Of the natural resins derived from the exudations of plants only rosin and shellac are of importance in metal finishes. Cellulosic esters, derivatives of the natural polymer cellulose, deserve mention. Nitrocellulose, at one time widely used in lacquers, is now generally blended with other resins.

The alkyds (a contraction for alcohol-acid) are polymeric esters of polyhydric alcohols and polybasic acids that are modified by partial substitution of monobasic unsaturated acids such as oleic and linoleic for the polybasic acid. The alkyds, straight and in extensive modifications, comprise more than 40 per cent of the protective coating compositions.[2] As a class they provide very satisfactory protection in a wide range of environments.

Vinyl resins and their relatives, the acrylic resins, are derived from olefinic hydrocarbons. The vinyls are widely employed in the chemical and food industries and for protection against marine environments. Acrylic resins are being increasingly used in automobile finishes.

Styrene finds use in protective coatings in the form of reaction products with drying oils, alkyd, phenolic, and other resins or as a copolymer with butadiene.

Phenolic resins, among the earliest synthetic resins, are used in very numerous modifications as air drying and baking finishes. Coatings based on these resins are remarkably resistant to moisture and many chemicals.

The urea and melamine resins obtained by polymerizing the respective amines with formaldehyde are generally blended with alkyd resins to produce rapid-curing baking resins used for finishing household equipment. Durability, retention of gloss, and alkali resistance make these finishes particularly suitable for this application.

The epoxies, one of the newest families of resins, account for only about five per cent of the sales of protective coating resins. Their outstanding properties of adhesion, flexibility, toughness, and chemical resistance are likely to bring about a marked increase in use. A variety of amines serve as curing agents. There are two broad closses of epoxies—liquids and solids. The latter are dissolved in solvents for application. Epoxy resin coatings find increasing application as air drying and baking finishes for industrial products and for household equipment.

Application and Performance of Organic

Coatings. The protection afforded by organic coatings depends upon their adherence, thickness, continuity, and composition. Adherence is improved by chemical conversion treatments applied to the carefully cleaned metal surface. Phosphate solutions, as mentioned previously, are generally employed for this purpose. This treatment may be followed in finish systems for corrosive exposures by the application of a prime coating pigmented with zinc chromate. This and other corrosion-inhibitive pigments, such as red lead, react with the metal, rendering it passive, and may even provide a measure of protection to areas of the metal exposed by scratches.

Pigmentation of the cover coats, aside from contributing to desirable appearance, serves to improve physical properties, reduce moisture permeability, and retard film deterioration caused by light and other weathering agents. Iron oxide, long used for exterior structures, is not corrosion-inhibitive but does produce hard, impervious films of high durability. The pleasing appearance of aluminum pigmented coatings has made them popular for highway bridges. The lamellar shape of aluminum pigments greatly reduces moisture permeability of these coatings.

The protective quality of organic coatings has been judged generally by their performance in exposure tests conducted in rural, marine and industrial atmospheres. A more satisfactory and rapid method for evaluation of protective quality relies upon the use of sensitive physical tests.[3]

The method of application of organic coatings is determined by the nature of the structure or product to be protected. Following is a description of a few examples.

Steel Structures. Oxide scale is removed by power-driven wire brushes, abrasive blasting, or the application of a hot gas flame. Paint is then applied by brushing or spraying. Owing to labor costs, longer coating life is desirable and is obtained by using paints with a high resin content. A minimum of three coats providing a total thickness of four or five thousandths of an inch is desirable.

Industrial Products. Since it is necessary in this case to meet appearance requirements and at the same time provide for resistance to mechanical stresses and corrosive conditions, it is customary to use enamel type coatings containing high proportions of resins. Usually surface preparation and coating application employs a conveyer system, automative spraying, and infrared drying or baking.

Underground Pipe. These structures are exposed to soil waters of varying composition and to soil stresses. While in dry soils and arid climates little or no protection may be required, it is common practice to protect most buried pipe with heavy asphalt or coal tar pitch reinforced with fabric tapes or paper. These coatings are usually applied hot in the field. The use of cathodic protection in conjunction with organic coatings for the protection of pipe lines has become common practice.

Inorganic Coatings. Porcelain enamel has been used for many years for kitchen equipment, but its largest application has been in the chemical, pharmaceutical, and food industries for the protection of large process vessels, storage tanks, and railroad tank cars for the transportation of chemicals, biochemical products, and foods.

The raw materials used in porcelain enamels are acidic substances, such as feldspar and quartz, and fluxes consisting of borax, soda ash, fluorspar, litharge, etc. Metallic oxides are used for color. These substances upon fusion produce "frit" which in powdered form when suspended in water, employing clay as a floating agent, is known as the "slip." This slip may be applied by dipping or by spraying, after which the coated part is dried and then fused in an enameling furnace.

Enamel coatings are brittle and may be damaged by mechanical impacts and sudden and extreme temperature changes; otherwise, they give excellent protection indefinitely.

Related to porcelain is a class of vitreous coatings designed for high temperature applications. These consist of admixtures of refractory materials, such as silica, chromic acid, beryllium oxide, alumina, zirconium oxide, clay, and certain fluxes. Slips composed of suspensions of these materials are then applied by dipping or spraying, dried, and fired in the temperature range 850 to 1400°C. Coatings of this type are resistant to chipping and thermal shock and may be used to protect metals for high temperature uses as, for example, in jet engines.

The newest method of application of refractory metals and metal oxides is by a plasma spray jet or gun employing plasmas at temperatures of several thousand degrees. These coatings are likely to find many applications.

An inorganic coating of considerable interest consists essentially of zinc silicate[4] prepared by suspending zinc dust in sodium silicate solutions. An acidic solution containing phosphate may be applied subsequently to cure the zinc silicate coating. In other cases a curing treatment is unnecessary since phosphates, titanates, etc., are incorporated in the silicate solution. These finishes are showing promise for protection in corrosive marine and industrial atmospheres and in sea water.

References

1. Preuss, H. P., *Metal Finish.*, **58,** 46 (June, 1960).
2. *Chem. & Eng. News,* **40,** No. 36, Part 2, 64 (Sept. 3, 1962).
3. Burns, R. M., and Bradley, W. W., "Protective Coatings for Metals," New York, Reinhold Publishing Corp., 1955.
4. *Chem. & Eng. News,* **40,** No. 26, 57 (June 25, 1962).

R. M. Burns

PYROMETRY. See RADIATION PYROMETRY.

R

RADIATION EFFECTS ON CORROSION. See CORROSION, RADIATION EFFECTS ON.

RADIATION PYROMETRY

All material bodies radiate energy, and the amount of energy radiated increases as the temperature is raised. This radiant energy may be sensed if one holds his hand near the heating element of an electric stove or if he walks from the shade into the bright sunlight. Instruments which measure this radiant energy in terms of the temperature of the radiating body are known as radiation pyrometers, and the science of such measurement is called radiation pyrometry.

Radiation pyrometry may be used advantageously to measure the temperature of a hot object from a distance when access to the hot object is difficult, when touching the object with a temperature detector would disturb the object, or when the environment of the object would disturb the reading of the temperature detector. Typical practical cases involve measuring the temperature of moving or vibrating objects, such as billets of steel during the rolling process, or of objects in a furnace atmosphere which would poison a thermocouple, or in an induction furnace where electrical interference from the high-frequency field would make it impossible to obtain a reading from a thermocouple. One very important advantage of the method is that no part of the detecting instrument is heated to the temperature being measured. Thus, radiation pyrometers may be used to measure very high temperatures.

The Laws of Radiation

Opaque objects radiate energy, absorb energy, and reflect it. Kirchhoff first expressed the relation between these processes. Thus,

$$a + r = 1 \qquad (1)$$

where a represents the absorption coefficient, or the proportion of incident radiation which is absorbed, and r represents the reflection coefficient, or the proportion of incident radiation which is reflected. If the object is in a uniform radiation field of temperature, T, which can be achieved by placing it in a furnace of uniform wall temperature, T, then it will reach this temperature; and at any later time, to stay at equilibrium, it must radiate exactly as much energy as it absorbs. Therefore,

$$\epsilon = a \qquad (2)$$

where ϵ is called the emissivity. It expresses the radiation from the body at temperature, T, in terms of the radiation field of temperature, T.

Since from its definition the absorption coefficient, a, must have a positive value between zero and unity, including these limits, ϵ is limited to this range of values; that is, a material body at temperature, T, cannot radiate more energy than the energy of the uniform radiation field of temperature, T.

A body which has a reflection coefficient of zero must have an absorption coefficient of unity. It will absorb all radiation which is incident upon it. Such a body is called a *blackbody*. The emissivity of a blackbody is unity, and it will emit the same energy as that of the uniform radiation field. This radiation is called blackbody radiation of temperature, T.

In practice it is very difficult to obtain a perfect blackbody, because there are no physical surfaces which have absolutely zero reflection. An approximation to a blackbody may be achieved by constructing an enclosure with a small opening and operating the walls of the enclosure at a uniform temperature, T. The radiation emerging from the small opening will then have approximately the characteristics of the radiation which would be emitted by a blackbody the size of the opening.

The total energy radiating from a blackbody

RADIATION PYROMETRY

of unit area is given by the Stefan-Boltzmann law

$$E = \sigma T^4 \tag{3}$$

where T is the absolute temperature in degrees Kelvin and σ, the Stefan-Boltzmann constant, has the value 5.679×10^{-12} watt cm^{-2} deg^{-4}.

The radiation from a blackbody is distributed continuously and incoherently over a wide range of wavelengths. The distribution changes with temperature, as is apparent when an object being heated first appears as a dull red, then changes color through orange and straw to a dazzling white. By the use of a spectroscope the radiation may be separated according to wavelength and displayed as a spectrum. If this is done and if a heat detector, such as a small thermometer or thermocouple, is used to investigate the distribution of energy, it will be found that most of the radiant energy is beyond the red end of the visible spectrum, in the region called infrared.

If the spectral radiance, $N_{b\lambda}$, is defined as the energy of blackbody radiation at a particular wavelength, λ, then its value is given by the Planck radiation equation

$$N_{b\lambda} = \frac{C_1 \lambda^{-5}}{\pi(e^{C_2/\lambda T} - 1)} \tag{4}$$

where C_1 and C_2 are the first and second radiation constants, respectively.

Planck first proposed this equation in 1900 as an empirical expression of the observed distribution of energy in the spectrum. It has since become one of the important milestones in the history of atomic physics because its interpretation has required recognition that the energy exchange between radiation and matter occurs in discrete quantities. The smallest amount of energy which can enter into such an exchange is $h\nu$ or hc/λ, where ν is the frequency of the radiation, which may alternatively be expressed in terms of the wavelength, λ, and the velocity of light, c, and h is called Planck's constant and has the value 6.625×10^{-27} erg sec.

The Temperature Scale

Today, almost all practical pyrometry in the laboratory and in industry is based on the International Practical Temperature Scale of 1948.[7] Temperatures on this scale are represented by the letter t and are expressed as degrees Celsius (°C). Above the melting point of gold ($t_{Au} = 1063$°C) the temperature is defined by the use of a modification of Planck's equation:[4]

$$\frac{N_{b\lambda}(t)}{N_{b\lambda}(t_{Au})} = \frac{\exp\dfrac{C_2}{\lambda(t_{Au} + T_0)} - 1}{\exp\dfrac{C_2}{\lambda(t + T_0)} - 1} \tag{5}$$

Here the second radiation constant, C_2, is defined as 1.438 centimeter-degrees, the gold point, t_{Au}, is defined as 1063°C, and T_0 is 273.15 degrees.

The wavelength may be expressed in microns. One micron (1 μ) is a millionth of a meter. When the wavelength is expressed in microns, then C_2 must be expressed as 14,380 micron-degrees.

The temperature, t, of a radiating body is determined by measuring its spectral radiance, $N_{b\lambda}(t)$, in terms of that at the gold point. An optical pyrometer which employs only a narrow band of wavelengths is used for this purpose.

The Optical Pyrometer

The optical pyrometer in most general use is the "disappearing-filament" pyrometer. Observations are made visually through a special telescope. The objective lens forms a real image of the object under observation, or target, in the plane of a lamp filament. This filament and the superimposed image are viewed through a magnifying eyepiece. A red glass filter between the filament and the eye serves to cut off radiation of wavelength shorter than about 0.62 μ. The human eye is not sensitive to light of wavelength longer than about 0.70 μ so the band of radiation used lies between these values. The effective wavelength is about 0.65 μ.

An auxiliary box is generally supplied as part of the pyrometer. This box contains an adjustable current supply for the pyrometer lamp filament, and means for reading the current. An observation consists of adjusting the filament current until the filament has the same brightness as the superimposed image of the target, and then reading the current. The current-measuring means may be either a potentiometer or an indicating milliammeter. In a commercial optical pyrometer of the industrial type the scale is calibrated directly in degrees. The measuring circuit of such a pyrometer has been adjusted at the factory so that the scale reading matches the temperature of the target. Replacement lamps then may be supplied with auxiliary re-

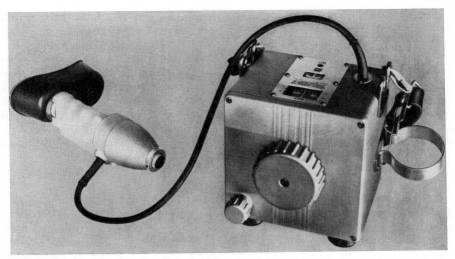

FIG. 1. Optical pyrometer, telescope, and viewer at left, auxiliary box at right. [*Courtesy, Leeds and Northrup Co.*]

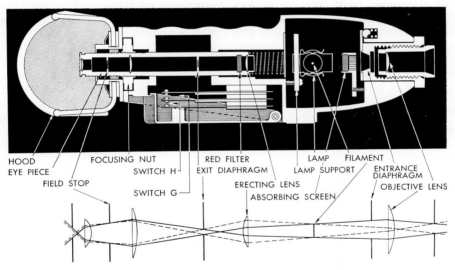

HOOD	FOCUSING NUT		RED FILTER	LAMP	FILAMENT	
EYE PIECE		SWITCH H	EXIT DIAPHRAGM	LAMP SUPPORT		ENTRANCE DIAPHRAGM
FIELD STOP				ERECTING LENS		OBJECTIVE LENS
	SWITCH G			ABSORBING SCREEN		

FIG. 2. Cross section and ray diagram of the telescope of an optical pyrometer. [*Courtesy Leeds and Northrup Co.*]

sistors and instructions for installing a new lamp so that correspondence between scale reading and target temperature is preserved.

Fig. 1 is a photograph of an optical pyrometer, showing the telescope and the auxiliary box containing the current supply and means for adjusting the current and reading the temperature. Fig. 2 shows a cross-section of the telescope of this optical pyrometer, and also a ray diagram of the optical system.

To maintain the required stability of calibra-

tion, the filament temperature of the pyrometer lamp is limited to a maximum of about 1250°C. An absorbing glass inside the pyrometer may be interposed as a filter, between the pyrometer lamp and the objective lens. This filter reduces the brightness of the target-image so that the filament brightness may be matched to it without overheating the filament. The apparent temperature, S, obtained by using this filter, may be related to the true temperature, T, by using Wien's radiation equation which is sufficiently accurate for industrial temperature measurements, and which is obtained from Planck's equation by dropping the constant term (-1) in the denominator of the exponential. The apparent spectral brightness is then

$$N'_{b\lambda} = \tau(C_1\lambda^{-5}/\pi)e^{-C_2/\lambda T} = (C_1\lambda^{-5}/\pi)e^{-C_2/\lambda S} \quad (6)$$

where τ is the transmission of the filter. From this equation the following relation may be obtained

$$\frac{1}{S} - \frac{1}{T} = -\frac{\lambda}{C_2}\ln\tau = A \quad (7)$$

The absorbing glass which is generally used as a filter has a spectral transmission such that A is a constant over the band of wavelengths employed by the pyrometer. By using this constant A value, true temperature, T, may be computed from apparent temperature, S, and a high-range calibration may be provided on the scale of the measuring instrument. With a series of such screens, the range of the optical pyrometer may be extended to extremely high temperatures with confidence that it will agree with the International Practical Temperature Scale, provided corrections are made for the divergence of Wien's radiation equation from Planck's law.

Primary Calibration

Primary calibrations are made on a precision optical pyrometer at the National Bureau of Standards (NBS) in Washington, D. C.

The first step in a primary calibration is made by sighting the pyrometer on a gold-point blackbody. This is a small, thin-walled graphite crucible immersed in molten gold. The observer adjusts the current in the pyrometer lamp until the brightness of the filament just matches the brightness of the inside of the crucible. He then records the filament current. Successive readings are taken as the gold is allowed to cool through its freezing point. A plot of the current readings as a function of time will show a plateau at the freezing point. Determination of this current constitutes a primary calibration at the gold point.

To realize a calibration point at a temperature higher than the gold point, a vacuum-lamp with a tungsten strip filament is usually used. A rotating sectored-disc placed between the strip lamp and the pyrometer acts as a neutral screen of known transmission. The pyrometer filament current is set to the value found for the gold point. The current in the strip-lamp is then adjusted until a brightness match is observed in the pyrometer. This strip-lamp current is then maintained while the sectored-disc is removed and the pyrometer lamp current is adjusted to obtain a new brightness match. The pyrometer current for this new match gives the calibration point for the brightness temperature of the strip-lamp when observed directly. The actual temperature is computed from Eq. 4 using the reciprocal of the transmission factor of the disc as the ratio of spectral radiances, and using the effective wavelength of the pyrometer for λ.

By using discs of various transmission factors, a number of primary calibration points are obtained. A calibration curve or table may then be made, giving the temperature of a blackbody source which is matched by the pyrometer filament, as a function of the filament current. Temperatures below the gold point may be included in the primary calibration. These points may be obtained by using a radiating target with a temperature near the gold point, and observing it with and without rotating discs. It is very convenient to have this downward extension of the calibration, although the optical pyrometer is not recognized as the official interpolating instrument below the gold point. The theory and procedure used in making a primary calibration have been discussed in detail by Kostkowski and Lee.[4]

Secondary Calibrations

NBS will calibrate other pyrometers from the primary pyrometer. A stabilized tungsten strip lamp is observed successively using the primary pyrometer and the secondary pyrometer under calibration, and the temperature scale is thus transferred, one point at a time, from the primary pyrometer to the secondary pyrometer. The uncertainty in the calibration of a secondary pyrometer is estimated by NBS to be not more than 4°C at 800°C, 3°C at 1100°C, 5°C at 1800°C, 8°C at 2800°C, and 40°C at 4000°C.

In laboratories engaged in precise temperature measurements, and industrial standardizing laboratories, it is customary to keep at least one secondary pyrometer with an NBS certificate of calibration. Other working pyrometers are calibrated from this pyrometer. Thus, the secondary pyrometer is used as a standard. It is not exposed to the dust and dirt and extreme temperature conditions of the factory, and its calibration may be expected to remain stable for years.

Additional assurance of the stability of calibration of the secondary standard pyrometer can be obtained by providing an additional calibrated secondary pyrometer. The two secondary pyrometers can be compared from time to time, and one of them can be returned at intervals to NBS for recalibration without interrupting the work of the laboratory.

By keeping optical pyrometers clean, and frequently checking the operation of switches and current-measuring devices, temperature readings can be reproduced with them, well within the limits of the maximum uncertainties as stated by NBS.

Emissivity

The uncertainties considered above apply to temperature measurements of blackbodies. Additional uncertainties arise in the measurement of surface temperatures. As discussed above, real surfaces emit less energy than blackbodies, and the ratio of the actual radiation to the radiation from a blackbody at the same temperature is known as the emissivity (ϵ). The emissivity may vary from less than one per cent for a highly-polished metal surface, to very nearly unity for an oxidized metal surface or a rough refractory surface. A pyrometer reading on a surface yields the "brightness-temperature" of that surface, which may be far below the true temperature if the emissivity is low.

Tables are available which give the correction to be applied to brightness-temperature to convert it to true temperature, if the emissivity of the surface is known.[6] Other tables give observed emissivities for various surfaces.[2]

At industrial temperatures, up to 1800°C, the radiation at 0.65 μ varies as a high power of the temperature. This power may be as high as 10 or 20. For this reason the error in absolute temperature is much less than error in the intensity of the radiation. For example, at the gold point an emissivity of 90 per cent causes a 10 per cent reduction in the intensity of the radiation, but at 0.65 μ the intensity is proportional to about the 16.6th power of the temperature, so the error in temperature as read by an optical pyrometer will be only 0.6 per cent or about 8°C.

There is no universal method for compensating or correcting pyrometers to eliminate the emissivity error. A number of methods have had some degree of success and have been quite useful in special applications.

The emissivity of molten cast iron is about 0.4, and special scales called "foundry scales" have been used on optical pyrometers. These scales have been constructed to include a correction for an emissivity of 0.4, and they can be used to read the true temperature of molten cast iron.

Transparent objects generally have a very low emissivity, but they may have a high emissivity within limited wavelength intervals. For example, glass radiates as a blackbody between about 4 μ and 8 μ in the infrared. A pyrometer sensitive to only this wavelength interval is very useful for measuring the surface temperature of hot glass.

It may be possible to provide a small blackbody cavity in an object for the purpose of measuring its temperature. A drilled hole of depth at least five times its diameter is adequate in most cases. A pyrometer reading made by sighting on the bottom of this hole will give the temperature within this drilled cavity. Although this may not be the same as the true surface temperature, it may be just as useful.

Other Pyrometers

It is often advantageous to record or control a temperature, in the absence of an operator. The most common form of pyrometer used for this purpose has a thermal receiver. An optical system, sometimes simply a single lens or mirror, is used to focus the radiation onto the receiver, which may be a small disc. This receiver is heated by the radiation, and the degree of heating is interpreted in terms of the temperature of the hot body supplying the radiation.[1, 3]

Fig. 3 shows schematically the arrangement of the optical system in one form of commercial radiation pyrometer. Radiation from a source enters the quartz window A, is reflected by the spherical mirror B, and is brought to a focus on the diaphragm J in the center of which there is an aperture C. Radiation passing through C is reflected by the spherical mirror D to the receiver E where an image of C is formed. The surface of J is whitened slightly with magnesium oxide, to make the image of the source visible when viewed through a lens H placed behind B. Since B produces no chromatic aberration and very little spherical aberration, the image of the source is very sharp and a very definite portion

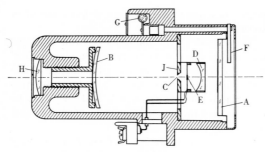

FIG. 3. Schematic diagram of a radiation pyrometer; for explanation see text. [*Courtesy Leeds and Northrup Co.*]

of the image can be made to cover C. The corresponding portion of the source, therefore, supplies the radiation which is focused on E, and the temperature of this portion of the source is measured. A light-trimmer F in front of the window may be rotated by turning the screw G, so that the output signal of the pyrometer may be adjusted. In this way, several radiation pyrometers may be matched in output so that they can be used with one multiple-point recorder.

A pyrometer of this type may be sensitive to radiation of a broad band of wavelengths, including all of the visible radiation and also infrared radiation, of longer wavelength. Such a pyrometer, called a total-radiation pyrometer, has a response approximately proportional to the fourth power of the temperature. Thus, it is more sensitive to emissivity errors than is the optical pyrometer, and therefore in practice it is often calibrated in place by means of an optical pyrometer.

On the other hand, the sensitivity of the pyrometer may be restricted to a selected wavelength band, by the use of optical filters. The glass-surface pyrometer mentioned in the previous section, is an example of such a pyrometer.

Many new pyrometers of recent development employ photoelectric detectors. When the output of a photocell is used as a measure of the temperature, then it is necessary to calibrate this cell frequently. The most promising instrument of this type has the form of an automatic optical pyrometer, in which the brightness of a standard lamp is continuously or very frequently compared with the brightness of the unknown target. The standard lamp is preferably a part of the pyrometer and in this case the brightness-comparison may be made automatically, and the sensitivity of the photocell is thus eliminated

from the measurement. Pyrometers of this type may be expected to make temperature measurements of greater accuracy than those made at present with the visual optical pyrometer,[5] and calibrations with smaller uncertainties should be available in the near future.

References

1. DIKE, P. H., "Temperature Measurements with Rayotubes," Leeds & Northrup Company, 4901 Stenton Avenue, Philadelphia 44, Pa., Technical Publication EN-33B(1), 1953.
2. GUBOREFF, G. G., JANSSEN, J. E., AND TORBORG, R. H., "Thermal Radiation Properties Survey," Minneapolis-Honeywell Regulator Company, Honeywell Research Center, Minneapolis, Minnesota, 1960.
3. HARRISON, T. R., "Radiation Pyrometry and Its Underlying Principles of Radiant Heat Transfer," New York, John Wiley and Sons, Inc., 1960.
4. KOSTKOWSKI, H. J., AND LEE, R. D., "Temperature, Its Measurement and Control in Science and Industry," Vol. 3, Part 1, p. 449, "Theory and Methods of Optical Pyrometry," New York, Reinhold Publishing Corp., 1962.
5. LEE, R. D., "Temperature, Its Measurement and Control in Science and Industry," Vol. 3, Part 1, p. 507, "The NBS Photoelectric Pyrometer of 1961," New York, Reinhold Publishing Corp., 1962.
6. POLAND, D. E., GREEN, J. W., AND MARGRAVE, J. L., "Corrected Optical Pyrometer Readings," NBS Monograph 30, Washington, D. C., Superintendent of Documents, 1961.
7. STIMSON, H. F., "International Practical Temperature Scale of 1948. Text Revision of 1960," NBS Monograph 37, Washington, D. C., Superintendent of Documents, 1961.

WILLIAM T. GRAY

RARE EARTH METAL ELECTROWINNING

The only rare earth metal product currently produced in tonnage quantities by fused salt electrolysis is mischmetal, which is a mixture of the rare earth metals consisting typically of 53 per cent cerium, 26 per cent lanthanum, 16 per cent neodymium, 5 per cent praseodymium with only slight traces of other than rare earth elements. Minor quantities of cerium, lanthanum, didymium (Nd + Pr) and cerium-free mischmetal (probably totalling no more than several thousand pounds altogether in the United States at present) are also produced electrolytically by methods resembling those used for mischmetal.

Accordingly, major emphasis in this review will be given to mischmetal, its production, properties and uses.

Feed Materials

Most production is based on compounds derived from monazite sand, a rare earth phosphate, found in India, Brazil, South Africa, Australia, and the United States. In recent years, growing use has been made of bastnasite, a rare earth fluocarbonate found in California and in the Congo, as a source of feed materials for production of mischmetal. These feed materials consist of the chlorides, fluorides, and oxides of the rare earth elements, mixed as naturally occurring in the ores used. For convenience, the symbol "Ln" will be used hereafter to designate these mixtures of rare earth elements, nowadays commonly called the "lanthanides."

Rare Earth Chloride. This compound may be produced from the ores either as a hydrate, containing approximately 30 per cent water, or directly in its anhydrous form, by chlorination. In the former case, the hydrate may be converted to the anhydrous compound by heating either alone, or together with such salts as NH_4Cl, $NaCl$, and $CaCl_2$, to yield a product with minimum oxychloride and water content. The oxychloride content can be lessened by reduced exposure to air, through use of a vacuum drier, or by the addition of common metal chlorides which reduce hydrolytic action. The latter technique can be used where such additions do not interfere with subsequent electrolysis. A recently patented procedure for production of anhydrous chloride directly from ores[1] is based on the following reaction:

$$Ln_2O_3 + 3Cl_2 + 3C \rightarrow 2LnCl_3 + 3CO.$$

This process, which has already achieved commercial significance, is likely to become increasingly important in the future.

Fluoride and Oxide. These materials are of minor commercial significance at present insofar as mischmetal is concerned, but are important in the production of the pure rare earth metals.

The anhydrous oxides are produced by dehydration of hydroxides or decomposition of carbonates. The fluorides are generally produced from the oxides by reaction with ammonium bifluoride at 200 to 600°C or by gaseous fluorination with either HF or ClF_3.

Reduction Processes

Virtually all commercial electrowinning is done by reduction of anhydrous chlorides in either ceramic or graphite cells as described below.

Ceramic Cells. A typical cell design of this type is described below (see Fig. 1).

These cells operate at 14 volts d-c and 2300 amperes with a bath temperature of 800 to 900°C, yielding 40 to 50 kgs of mischmetal daily. The ceramic material is usually fireclay or sillimanite, the anodes are carbon, and the cathodes are water-cooled iron blocks. The electrolyte consists of a mixture of $LnCl_3$ and $NaCl$. The metal collects at the bottom of the cell, where it is maintained in the molten state by the flow of direct current through it to the cathodes. At regular intervals, the metal, covered with a layer of molten electrolyte, is ladled out and poured into molds, where it solidifies under a layer of molten electrolyte. After cooling, the metal may be separated from the solidified electrolyte by breaking off the salt layer and washing.

These cells are usually connected in series, which facilitates semicontinuous operations, since molten electrolyte can be transferred from one cell to another for rapid start-up.

Graphite Cells. Contamination of the product due to iron and silica pickup may be reduced by constructing cells of graphite, which serves also as the cathode. The anodes are usually either carbon or graphite. The electrolyte consists of mixtures of $LnCl_3$ with $NaCl$, KCl, $CaCl_2$, or other salts, as preferred by various producers. The cells may be totally enclosed to exclude air, which results in reduced gas content in the mischmetal produced.

Bath temperatures are approximately 800 to 900°C. The metal collects at the bottom of the cell, where it may be maintained in the molten state by resistance heating, or allowed to solidify by use of a cooled cathode. In the latter case, it is necessary to remelt the metal by internal

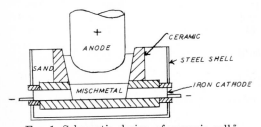

FIG. 1. Schematic design of ceramic cell.[7]

TABLE 1. COMPOSITION OF PRODUCTS MADE BY
ELECTROLYSIS OF RARE EARTH COMPOUNDS[6]

Product	Cerium	Lanth-anum	Ce-free Misch-metal	Misch-metal
Rare Earth Metal Content	99.9%	99.9%	99.8%	99.9%
Analysis of Rare Earth Metal Content				
Ce	99.9	0.09	0.26	53.0
Nd	0.07	0.04	42.0	16.0
Pr	—	.10	14.0	5.0
Gd	—	—	3.0	2.0
La + ORE*	0.03	99.7+	40.74	24.0
Al	0.005	0.007	0.053	0.010
Ca	0.010	0.010	0.010	0.010
Fe	0.014	0.043	0.120	0.050
Mg	0.010	0.010	0.060	0.025
Si	0.005	0.029	0.010	0.010

* ORE = (Other Rare Earth Metals and Yttrium).

resistance heating, sometimes supplemented by external sources of heat, before it can be removed from the cell. This type of cell may be stationary like the one described above, or tiltable, which simplifies pouring of the product into molds.

These cells are run either singly from rectifiers or in series by use of motor-generator sets. Operation is batchwise or continuous, depending on the preference of various producers.

Sometimes, iron pots are used instead of graphite crucibles in this type of commercial cell, when rare earth metals contaminated with iron are acceptable.

Experimental Cells. The Bureau of Mines at Reno has developed graphite cells with con-trolled atmosphere, pressure and temperature, which have produced cerium, lanthanum, and yttrium more than 99.9 per cent pure.[5] These cells use an electrolyte composed of LnF_3 + BaF_2 + LiF, similar to that previously used by Gray.[2] The compound reduced to metal is Ln_2O_3. The anodes are either carbon or graphite, the cathodes are molybdenum, and the bath temperatures are 800 to 900°C. Air is replaced in these cells by inert gases, such as helium or argon. To date, the economic advantages of these cells over those using chlorides have not been demonstrated.

If carefully purified feed materials are used, and air is excluded, metals of high purity can be produced by fused salt electrolysis. In Table 1 are examples of such products.

Review of the literature suggests that fused salt electrolytic methods can also be used to reduce selectively some of the rare earths to metal from their mixtures, thus making concentration of desired elements possible. Little practical use has been made to date of this principle, since it has been more convenient to produce the desired metals from relatively pure feed materials.

Properties of Electrowon Rare Earth Metals

Outlined in Table 2 are some useful data on those metals which have been produced to date by commercial electrolytic processes.

Uses

Mischmetal, which sells for less than $3.00 per pound, is the lowest cost rare earth metal product. Its oldest, and still one of the most

TABLE 2. PROPERTIES OF PRODUCTS MADE BY ELECTROLYSIS OF RARE EARTH COMPOUNDS[6]

	Cerium	Lanthanum	Neodymium	Praseodymium	Mischmetal
Specific gravity	6.81 (HCP) 6.78 (FCC)	6.162 (HCP) 6.19	7.007	6.776 (HCP) 6.805 (FCC)	6.68
Melting point, °C	804 ± 5	920 ± 5	1024 ± 5	935 ± 5	884 ± 5
Boiling point, °C	3600	4515	3300	3450	3750
Heat of fusion, kcal/mole	2.2	2.4	2.6	2.4	2.3
Heat of vaporization, kcal/mole	79	81	69	79	78
Electrical resistivity, microhm-cm	75.3	56.8	70	75	70
Thermal coef. exp. per °C × 10^{-6}	8.0	5.0	6.5	4.5	6.7
Thermal conductivity cgs units @ 28°C	0.026	0.033	0.031	0.028	0.029
Specific heat, cal/mole/°C @ 0°C	6.89	6.65	7.20	6.45	6.86

important uses, is in the manufacture of sparking-metal alloys for cigarette lighter flints and welding-gas ignitors. These contain 70 to 80 per cent mischmetal.

In recent years, important metallurgical applications for mischmetal have been developed. In ductile iron (sometimes called nodular iron) mischmetal reduces the effect of the subversive elements, helps desulfurization, and increases magnesium recovery and ladle fluidity. It may be added either separately or contained in silicon-magnesium-mischmetal or other alloys. Mischmetal increases the oxidation resistance of nickel-chromium alloys and improves the ductility and impact properties of cast steel and the hot workability of stainless steels. In magnesium alloys, mischmetal improves pressure tightness and high-temperature creep resistance. In secondary aluminum alloys, it enhances fluidity, inhibits surface oxidation, and refines grain structure. Mischmetal inhibits inverse segregation in lead bronzes and deoxidizes copper alloys. In the precision casting industry, small additions of mischmetal are made to improve the castability of superalloys, stainless, and tool steels.

While mischmetal is actually the predominant rare earth metal used in industry today, there is growing interest in cerium, lanthanum, didymium (Nd + Pr), yttrium, and cerium-free mischmetal. Some of the applications for these metals currently under investigation include additives for the improvement of alloys of copper, cobalt, beryllium, tantalum, aluminum, magnesium, and other nonferrous metals. In addition, the individual rare earth metals have received renewed consideration as desirable additives for ductile iron, heat-resistant stainless steels, and refractory metals. Other applications being studied include new cathode emitters and new getters for electronic tubes and other devices, and new materials, including intermetallics for solid state devices, such as transistors and thermoelectric elements.

References

1. BRUGGER, W., (to Th. Goldschmidt A.G.) U.S. Patent 2,755,325, (July 17, 1956).
2. GRAY, P. M. J., *Trans. Inst. Min. Met. (London)*, **61**, 141 (1951–52).
3. GSCHNEIDNER, K. A. JR., "Rare Earth Alloys," New York, D. Van Nostrand, 1961.
4. HAMPEL, C. A., "Rare Metals Handbook," New York, Reinhold Publishing Corp., 1961.
5. MORRICE, E., *et al*, Rept. of Investigation, U. S. Bureau of Mines **5549** (1960); Rept. of Investigation, U. S. Bureau of Mines **5868** (1961); Rept. of Investigation, U. S. Bureau of Mines **6075** (1962).
6. Ronson Metals Corporation, Brochure—"Rare Earth Metals & Alloys," Newark, New Jersey, 1962.
7. SINGER, R., *et al*, *BIOS Final Report No. 400* (1945).
8. SPEDDING, F. H., AND DAANE, A. H., "The Rare Earths," New York, John Wiley & Sons, Inc., 1961.

I. S. HIRSCHHORN

RECORDING INSTRUMENTS

Analytical instruments are utilized to obtain quantitative data about one or more constituents in a sample or substance. Some typical examples are: gas analysis, liquid analysis, pH, redox, and electrolytic conductivity. Recorders are also applied, for example, to temperature, pressure, flow, liquid level, force and motion measurements.

Strip chart and round chart recorders are utilized when trend data and a permanent record of concentration change with time are desired in analog form. Continuous records with one or more pens are provided, or intermittent records with multiple-point printing-type recorders are available.

In considering analytical methods in this article, the discussion is confined to electrical measurements where the concentration change of the component to be measured is made to cause a change in an electrical quantity, for example, voltage, current, resistance, capacitance, etc.

Primary elements or sensors, and analyzers or transducers are employed to create an electrical quantity which varies reliably with the change in the constituent of interest in the sample stream. The primary element or transducer most often produces a d-c voltage or d-c current, generally at the millivolt level.

Since, in a large number of cases, it is necessary to record these voltages or currents, recorders for this purpose are one of the most important classes of instruments used in the electrochemical field. In the sense of this article, a recorder is an instrument that makes a record on a chart of the quantity it is measuring.* The record may be continuous or intermittent. The recorder may record a single variable or several variables. The chart may be round or strip.

* This article will not cover direct writing recorders of the oscillograph type.

FIG. 1. A direct writing recorder.

There are two general classes of recorders, direct writing, and null balance. The direct writing instrument is the oldest type of recorder, and in its simplest form consists of some type of marking means associated with the indicating needle of the instrument that is activated by a pneumatic or electrical measuring element. If the record is to be continuous, pen and ink are usually used. This type of marking requires that the deflecting system be very carefully designed to avoid pen friction, or be designed to have sufficient torque in its system to overcome the pen friction.

If the record can be intermittent, then a depresser bar can be used to press the indicating needle of the deflecting system against a typewriter ribbon which is just above the recorder chart. A dot is produced on the chart each time this action occurs. During the time between markings the needle is free to move, and thus pen friction is eliminated. A stylus activating heat-sensitive paper, spark-sensitive paper, or pressure-sensitive paper can be used in place of the typewriter ribbon device. Electronic amplifiers can be used between the measuring

element and the deflecting system to obtain more driving power for the system.

Some of the earliest instruments in this field were made by Bristol, General Electric, Westinghouse, and Esterline Angus Companies. Fig. 1 shows the Esterline Angus recorder, which is a typical instrument of the direct acting type. For d-c current measurements, the d'Arsonval electromagnetic system was used. For voltmeters and wattmeters the Kelvin balance or electrodymometer principle was used.

The advantages of the direct writing system are that it is inexpensive and has good frequency response (down to about one cycle per second).

The disadvantages of the direct writing instruments are that they are shock- and vibration-sensitive, the readings are affected by resistance of the leads, unless a preamplifier is used their sensitivity is limited (to about 1 milliampere full scale for continuous recording and 10 microampere full scale if a depresser bar is used to obtain intermittent recording), and controls cannot conveniently be added to a recording unit of this type.

Because of these limitations, in about 1898 the Cambridge Instrument Company of England started to manufacture a recorder designed by Professor Callendar. This recorder, which was one of the earliest to appear on the market, was a continuous-balance recorder. The unbalance in a bridge or potentiometer circuit was detected by a galvanometer which actuated a motion through relays to rebalance the circuit. This null-type recorder, due to its very delicate detector system, was not satisfactory for general industrial use.

About 1910 several recorders for potentiometric and bridge-type measurements were marketed in this country, but the first really practical high-sensitivity recorder, which was rugged enough for general industrial use, appeared on the market in 1913. It was invented by M. E. Leeds, of the Leeds & Northrup Company, and was a step-by-step mechanical recorder of comparatively simple construction with a galvanometer as a detector. It required about 22 seconds for full scale rebalance.

It was not until about 1931 that the first electronic recorders for null-type measurements (potentiometric or bridge type) became available for general industrial use. One of the earliest of these was the Leeds & Northrup

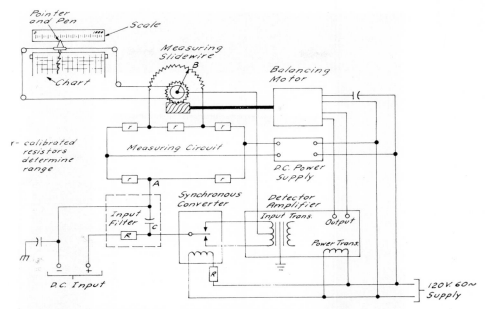

FIG. 2. Schematic drawing of a d-c potentiometer servo-balanced recorder.

"Speedomax." In this unit the galvanometer was replaced by an electronic detector.

This instrument was closely followed by other electronic recorders from the Brown Instrument Company, (now Minneapolis-Honeywell), Bailey Meter Company, C. J. Tagliabue Manufacturing Company (now Daystrom-Weston), the Foxboro Company, and later by the Bristol Company.

The advantages of the electronic null-balance recorder are: they have high sensitivity (which permits greater precision of measurement); no current is drawn from the unknown being measured; they can have wide ranges of input impedance, and they are less subject to shock and vibration than the direct writing instrument. They are, however, more expensive and not as fast as the direct writing recorders. Their maximum full scale travel speed is about ¼ second.

D-C Potential Recorders

The d-c potentiometer servo-balanced recorder is utilized for precise measurement of the output from primary elements or transducers employed in electrochemical applications. Fig. 2 is a schematic representation of such a recorder. It shows the input circuit, the detector amplifier, the measuring circuit, and the indication and analog chart record. Fig. 3 is a picture of three typical models of single-pen, strip-chart

recorders of different physical size and construction.

It will be seen from Fig. 2 that the essential internal parts of these electronic, servo-balanced, potentiometer recorders are:

1. Measuring circuit—measuring slidewire and calibrated resistors.
2. Detector amplifier.
3. Balancing motor and linkage to measuring slidewire.
4. Indicating scale and analog recording system.

The measuring circuit provides an adjustable calibrated voltage between points A and B, Fig. 2. The exact value depends on the position of the slidewire contact, B, on the measuring slidewire, S. This AB voltage is opposed by the voltage of the emf source.

When these two voltages are exactly equal, no current will flow between the measuring circuit and the emf source; thus, no current flows through the synchronous converter and input transformer. This is the "null" or balanced condition; the detector amplifier output is zero and the balancing motor remains stationary. This type of measurement is called a null-voltage measurement.

If the two millivolt values are not equal, an "error" or unbalance d-c current will flow. The synchronous converter causes this d-c current

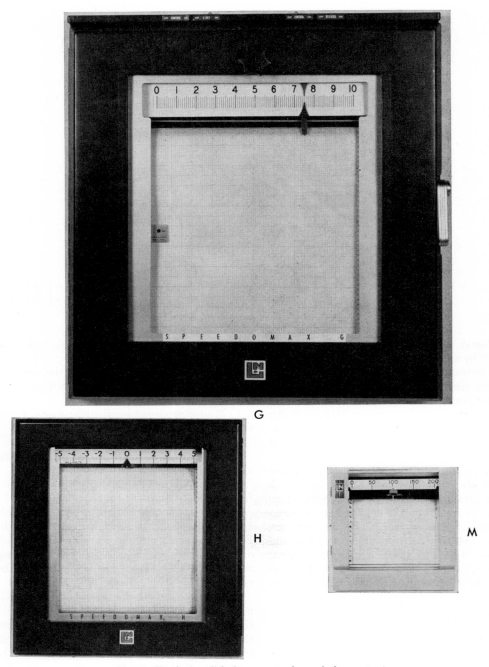

Fig. 3. Typical null-balance recorders of the servo type.

to appear as an a-c current in the primary of the input transformer. This a-c current is amplified by the detector amplifier and its output supplies power to the control winding of the two-phase balancing motor. The system is sensitive to the direction of the d-c "error" current so that the balancing motor runs in the proper direction moving slidewire contact B to reduce the "error" current to substantially zero. This causes the balancing motor to stop rotating. The mechanical linkage moves the indicating pointer and recording pen, thus indicating and recording the millivolt value of the emf source.

The d-c emf source may also include an a-c voltage due to pickup in the external circuits or a-c from d-c supplies used in the analyzers or transducers. This a-c voltage will cause an a-c current to flow through the input transformer and be amplified together with the "error" current created by the main d-c unbalance voltage. This a-c, if significantly large compared to the d-c value, will thus load the amplifier and decrease the sensitivity of the detector amplifier and increase the recorder dead band. Accordingly, care should be taken in the external primary element or transducer circuit to eliminate or minimize the a-c component. A resistance-capacitance type input filter is provided to reduce significantly the effects of any a-c component in the emf source.

Damping is provided to prevent overshooting of the unbalanced position and consequent hunting (oscillation) of the system. Damping is effected by the same resistance-capacitance as comprises the input filter. When the slidewire contact moves, a changing or damping current is caused to flow through the input filter capacitor and the input of the amplifier. This damping current opposes the error current and near the balance position exceeds the error current sufficiently to prevent overshooting of the balanced position. In some cases a d-c tachometer is used to provide the damping current.

The recorded emf value is independent of the external circuit resistance since no current flows at balance, or null position. The detector must be sufficiently sensitive to detect the small error currents with the external circuits employed and to balance the recorder at the proper emf with negligible dead band. These external circuits vary from practically zero resistance in the case of high-current shunts, to as much as 3000 megohms in the case of glass-electrode pH assemblies. No one detector can suffice for all external resistances and recorder emf ranges.

Recorder manufacturers provide a number of detectors, at different prices, for different external circuit resistances and different recorder range spans. A typical breakdown for d-c potentiometer recorders involving different detector amplifiers is as follows:

Range spans 100 to 1000 microvolts—resistance less than 2500 ohms

Range spans 1 to 5 millivolts—resistance less than 2500 ohms

Range spans 5 to 1000 millivolts—resistance less than 2500 ohms

Range spans 1 to 1000 millivolts—resistance less than 20,000 ohms

Range spans 25 to 1000 millivolts—resistance less than 1 megohm

Range spans 200 to 1000 millivolts—resistance less than 3000 megohms

Range spans 0 to 4 or 1 to 5 volts across 1000 ohms (0 to 4 or 1 to 5 milliamperes)

These types of recorders are employed with primary elements, transducers, or analyzers for typical measurements such as listed below:

pH values or redox potentials

Electrolytic conductivity

Density

Refractive index

Flow measurements

Thermal conductivity gas analysis, e.g., 0–5 per cent H_2 in O_2

Infrared gas analyzers, e.g., 0–0.5 per cent CO_2

Oxygen by thermomagnetic or paramagnetic principles

Vapor phase chromatography

Combustible gas recording

Temperature with thermocouples

Temperature with radiation pyrometers

Solar radiation with pyroheliometer or radiometer

A-c power, voltage, current with thermal converter

Pressure with vacuum gauges

Pressure and weight with load cells

Force or motion with strain gauges

D-C Current Recorders

A direct measurement of current in a circuit is most often accomplished by measuring the voltage established across a known resistor through which the current is flowing. This voltage can be recorded with the d-c potentiometer potential recorder described above.

Recorders of this type are utilized for such electrochemical measurements as:

Amperometric analysis of solutions

Dropping mercury electrode analysis of solutions

Coulometric analysis

Optical chemical analysis—photocells

Dissolved oxygen

Gas analysis—hydrogen flame, electron capture

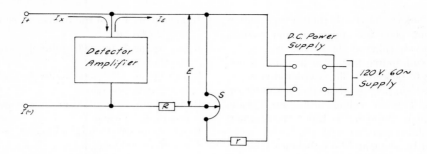

Range Resistor R equals ratio of slidewire voltage E and full scale value of unknown current $\left(R = \dfrac{E}{I_x \, Max.}\right)$.

At balance known current, I_E, and unknown current, I_x, are equal.

Fig. 4. Schematic circuit for a d-c null-current recorder.

Speed using tachometers

Pressure, temperature, flow, level with current-type transducers

A different type of measurement is often employed when barrier layer photocells are used for the primary element. This type of recorder (Fig. 4) makes a null-current type of measurement which presents zero resistance across the external photocell circuit. The current produced by a barrier-layer photocell varies with the intensity of light falling on the cell. The relationship between light and current becomes more nonlinear the higher the resistance of the current circuit. In a null-current balance circuit, the relationship is practically linear, and the temperature coefficient becomes negligible.

In the null-current circuit, the drop of potential between the input terminals of the measuring instrument is reduced to zero by applying to the terminals a known current, I_E, which is equal to the current to be measured, or unknown current, I_x. The known current, I_E, is produced by voltage, E, obtained from slidewire, S, through standard resistor, R. The detector amplifier recognizes inequality of potential of the source terminals and causes recorder balancing action until $I_E = I_s = E/R$. Ranges as low as 0 to 10^{-7} amperes may be furnished.

Such a null-current balance, "zero resistance" recorder is adaptable to a densitometer for spectrographic readout, or to liquid chemical analysis where transmission of light is a function of the concentration of the component of interest.

A-C Resistance Recorders

The electrical resistance of a solution varies with the total number of ions in the solution.

Concentration of a dissolved substance in a solution may be obtained by measuring the electrical conductivity or resistance of the solution. The conductivity cells, or electrodes, immersed in the solution are included in the circuit of a Wheatstone bridge to measure resistance.

In such a circuit, current passes between the electrodes. If d-c were used, polarization would occur at the electrodes and would create opposing voltages, or apparent resistances, at the electrodes, thus causing large errors in the resistance measurement. Therefore, a-c Wheatstone-bridge measuring circuits are employed, generally, at commercial power frequencies, to minimize polarization effects and to allow correct resistance measurements.

The resistance of a solution varies with temperature also. The a-c bridge circuit, therefore, includes a temperature compensating element. These are manually variable resistors, or temperature-sensitive resistors physically located in the solution being measured.

A typical recorder measuring circuit is shown in Fig. 5. It will be noted that the detector is sensitive to an a-c error signal and that the balancing motor moves the resistance balancing element of the bridge and also positions the recording pen.

The required damping and rejection of out of phase voltages is accomplished, as shown in Fig. 5, by the twin reed converter, resistance, capacitor circuit at the detector amplifier input.

Recorders of this type are used for such measurements as:

Purity of distilled water

Dissolved ionizable solids in water

Sulfuric acid (96.5 to 99.5 per cent)

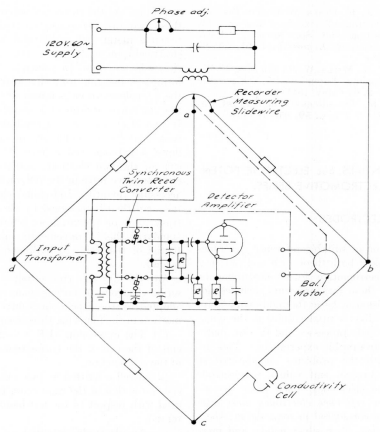

FIG. 5. Input circuit for an a-c conductivity bridge recorder.

Sulfuric acid (0 to 10 per cent)

Conductimetric titrations

Temperature (resistance thermometers, thermistors, etc.)

A-c resistance recorders are also employed utilizing photosensitive resistors in the bridge circuit. These photosensitive resistors may be located in a chemical analyzer where a sample is chemically treated so that light transmission through the sample is a function of the concentration of a component of the solution.

These recorders and analyzers are utilized for such typical measurements as silica in boiler water in the parts per billion range and chlorine in water in the parts per million range.

Other Recorder Circuits

There are many special-purpose recorder circuits employed for electrochemical analytical measurements; however, the list is extensive and their usage is small. These will not be discussed

here. Then, there are familiar circuits, such as the a-c potentiometer and d-c resistance recorders, which are also not discussed here since they are not utilized to any great extent with electrochemical analytical recorders.

References

1. "New Instruments (Speedomax)," *Instruments Magazine*, **6**, 211 (November, 1933).
2. "Electronic Recording Instruments," *Elect. Eng.*, **66** (January, 1947).
3. WILLIAMS, A. J., JR., "Combined Thyratron and Tachometer Speed Control of Small Motors," *AIEE Trans. (Electrical Engineering)*, **57**, 565–568 (October, 1938).
4. WILLIAMS, A. J., JR., "AC Null-Type Recorder with Balancing Amplifier which provides Damping and Suppresses the Quadrature Component," *AIEE Paper* **53-244,** June, 1953.
5. WILLIAMS, A. J., JR., "Electronic Recorder with Range and Precision Adequate for the Platinum Resistance Thermometer," *AIEE Trans.*, **71,** I, 289–95 (September, 1952).

6. WILLIAMS, A. J., JR., CLARK, W. R., AND TARPLEY, R. E., "Electronically balanced Recorder for Flight Testing and Spectroscopy," *AIEE Trans. (Electrical Engineering)*, **65**, 205–08 (April, 1946).
7. HARRISON, T. R., WILLS, W. P., AND SIDE, F. W., "Self Balancing Potentiometer," *Electronic Industries*, **2**, 68 (May, 1943).
8. CLARK, W. R., "Speedomax Power Level Recorder," *AIEE Trans.*, **59**, 957–64 (1940).

C. E. GREEN

REDOX POTENTIALS. See ELECTRODE POTENTIALS; ELECTROMOTIVE SERIES.

REFERENCE ELECTRODES

The definition of suitable reference electrodes forms the basis of both theoretical and practical aspects of electromotive force measurements. The scope of these measurements includes not only the provision of basic thermodynamic data but also such diverse applications as the elucidation of electrode processes and *in situ* analyses (as in polarographic experiments). This article deals with the problems encountered in assigning unequivocal emf values to electrode systems. Three electrodes which meet the requirements for *reference electrodes* most adequately will be considered in some detail: these are the hydrogen, silver-silver halide, and mercury-mercurous chloride (calomel) electrodes. An assessment, in tabular form, of additional electrode systems is also presented.

The only electrode to which the term "reference electrode" may be rigorously applied is, by definition, the standard hydrogen electrode. Of the secondary reference electrodes a distinction is often made between those for which the standard potential can be expressed in terms of strictly thermodynamic quantities (as with most electrodes involving metal-electrolyte junctions), and those less readily accounted for through purely thermodynamic considerations. The glass electrode is an extreme example of the latter type; generally speaking, all electrodes in which liquid-liquid, semiconductor-electrolyte, or membrane surface-electrolyte junctions occur fall also into this category.

Electromotive Force and Electrode Potentials

An electrode consists essentially of two conductors, one electronic and the other electrolytic, in contact. At the surface of separation between these two (as, for example, the interphase between a metal and a solution) a difference of electrical potential exists: this is termed the electrode potential. In principle, the work performed in bringing unit charge from infinity to the interphase provides a measure of this potential; no such experiment is possible in practice. If two electrodes are so combined that, when connected by a conductor, an electric current flows, a galvanic cell is formed. The algebraic sum of the two electrode potentials yields the electromotive force of the cell, an experimentally accessible quantity. Individual electrode potentials can then be assigned by choosing an arbitrary zero of potential as reference electrode standard: this is conveniently taken as the potential of the standard hydrogen electrode (see below).

An arbitrary sign convention is needed to describe electrode potentials unambiguously; that adopted by the Stockholm Convention[9] is summarized in the following three recommendations:

(1) The expression $n\mathbf{F}E = -\Delta G$ relates the emf of the cell to the Gibbs free energy change of the cell reaction.

(2) A cell is written in such a manner that the cell emf is that of the right-hand potential measured with respect to the left-hand electrode potential.

(3) An electrode potential is identical with the emf of a cell in which that electrode is on the right, with a standard hydrogen electrode on the left. Electrode potentials defined by (3) are identical in sign with those of the "European convention," and opposite in sign to "American convention" potentials. Recommendation (1) implies that a reaction for which ΔG is negative occurs spontaneously in a cell, and produces a positive emf; for such a cell (2) and (3) require that the positive electrode be placed on the right-hand side.

Reversibility

The concept of reversibility is an essential feature in the theory and practice of reference electrodes. During the operation of a cell, a reaction occurs at each electrode; it is the energy of these reactions which provides the electrical energy of the cell. [If there is an overall chemical reaction, the cell is referred to as a *chemical cell*; if, on the other hand, the change in energy is due to the transfer of solute from one concentration to another, the cell is called a *concentration cell.*] A *reversible cell* must satisfy the following conditions:

(i) If the cell is connected to an external source of emf so adjusted as to balance the emf of the cell exactly, (i.e., so that no current flows), no chemical or other change should occur in the cell.

(ii) If the external emf is decreased by an infinitesimally small amount, current will flow from the cell, and a chemical or other change, proportional to the quantity of electricity passing, should take place. If the external emf is increased similarly, current should pass in the opposite direction, and the process occurring in the cell should be exactly reversed.

Both electrodes constituting a reversible cell must be *reversible electrodes*. Three chief kinds are known:

(1) A metal or nonmetal in contact with a solution of its own ions (e.g., hydrogen in an acidic solution).

(2) A metal and a sparingly soluble salt of this metal in contact with a solution of a soluble salt of the same anion, e.g., the Ag | AgCl(s) | HCl electrode, for which the electrode reaction may be written.

$$Ag(s) + Cl^- \rightleftharpoons AgCl(s) + e$$

(3) An inert metal immersed in a solution containing both oxidized and reduced states of an oxidation-reduction system (e.g., gold immersed in a solution containing Fe^{3+} and Fe^{2+} ions). It should be noted that the oxidized and reduced states need not necessarily be ionic.

Electrodes of all three kinds are used as reference electrodes. The main qualifications which any electrode should meet in order to qualify as a suitable reference standard are: reversibility, reproducibility, and stability. The last two criteria are practical considerations, but reversibility has a theoretical aspect and is capable of quantitative assessment.

Standard Hydrogen Electrode

The choice of the hydrogen electrode as the primary standard for potential measurement is fortunate for a number of reasons. The construction of this electrode is comparatively easy. It is also by far the most reproducible; the reason for this is connected closely with the fact that the process of hydrogen ion discharge at a platinum surface permits a large exchange current density—the most important experimental qualification for a "thermodynamically well-behaved"

electrode. The most feasible way in which an electrode can be shown to meet this qualification is by testing its reversibility in micropolarization experiments.

The standard hydrogen electrode consists basically of a platinum surface in contact with a solution of hydrogen ions (of unit activity) and dissolved molecular hydrogen; the activity of the latter is specified by requiring it to be in equilibrium with hydrogen at 1 atm pressure in the gas phase. It should be noted that the standard hydrogen electrode potential is conventionally taken as zero at *all* temperatures: this assumption, though obviously not in accord with physical reality, is unavoidable if a uniform potential scale for other electrodes is to be realized.

The hydrogen electrode resembles other oxidation-reduction electrodes in that the electrons in the metal, the hydrogen ions in solution, and the dissolved hydrogen all participate in an equilibrium, but with this difference: the exchange equilibrium is catalyzed by the absorption of hydrogen ions on the metal. In other words, the equilibrium

$$H_2 \text{ (aqueous solution)} \rightleftharpoons$$
$$2H \text{ (absorbed on metal)} \rightleftharpoons$$
$$2H^+ \text{ (aqueous solution)} + 2e$$

does *not* depend solely on electron transfer.

The properties of the metal substrate are accordingly of prime importance, particularly (since the equilibrium is established at a metal-solution interface) its surface properties. It must not, of course, dissolve or otherwise react with the solution, nor must it absorb hydrogen atoms too readily; it can, in fact, be shown that the power of the substrate to absorb hydrogen atoms should fall within certain limits. Platinum metal is most suitable in this respect, particularly when electrodeposited with finely-divided platinum. Suitably applied, this coating enhances the catalytic activity of the metal, and at the same time increases the number of catalysis-active centers.

Electrolytically generated hydrogen is suitable for hydrogen electrodes, but a purification train designed to remove oxygen, carbon dioxide, and dust is advisable. Inert impurities, such as nitrogen, are objectionable only when present in amounts likely to reduce the partial pressure of hydrogen significantly. In this connection, for exacting work, corrections should be applied to account for the vapor pressure of the solution, solution supersaturation, and the nonideality of hydrogen gas.

Details on the design and construction of experimentally-proven half-cells may be found in most standard texts.[1, 2, 3] For an evaluation of hydrogen electrodes designed for specialized applications and for using substrates other than platinum (palladium, nickel, and graphite, for example), the reader is referred to a recent monograph.[1]

When kept in hydrogen-saturated media, the lifetime of a good hydrogen electrode should be quite long. The decay of an electrode which has not been exposed excessively to "poisons" (such as oxidizing agents, reducible substances, and readily absorbed surface poisons) can often be ascribed to "hydrogen poisoning." The most likely explanation of this phenomenon lies in the irreversible nature of the changes occurring in working hydrogen electrodes; with increasing age these changes ultimately terminate the useful life of these electrodes.

Silver-Silver Chloride Electrodes

Of the secondary reference electrodes the silver-silver halide system is the most popular, and for the very reasons restricting the usefulness of the primary hydrogen standard; compactness, indifference to orientation, and lack of liquid-junction requirements.

The silver-silver chloride system is an electrode of the second kind, and is customarily represented by

$$\text{Ag} \mid \text{AgCl} \mid \text{Cl}^-$$

It consists of solid silver chloride in contact with metallic silver and with a solution of a soluble chloride. Formally, it is equivalent to a silver-silver ion electrode at which the silver ion activity is controlled by the silver ion-chloride ion activity solubility product, $\alpha_{\text{Ag}^+} \times \alpha_{\text{Cl}^-}$.

The electrode can be prepared in a variety of ways, but this circumstance is responsible for continuing uncertainty in deciding its standard electrode potential. This potential is defined in terms of reproducible standard states, and in the case of the two solid components of the electrode, this implies the most stable energy state. To date, no preparative method has been devised which would eliminate the possibility of complications such as nonstoichiometry, mechanical stress, and atypical surface films. To state the situation as plainly as possible: although a set of electrodes prepared simultaneously by any one method shows a variation of 0.02 mv at worst, freshly prepared and aged

electrodes may differ by 0.1 mv, and the discrepancy between electrodes prepared by different methods is often larger. These facts serve to stress the necessity for experimental consistency when employing these electrodes, especially in high-precision measurements.

The standard electrode potential is defined as the emf of the cell

$$\text{H}_2 \text{ (ideal, 1 atm)} \mid \text{HX (ideal, } m = 1) \mid \text{AgX} \mid \text{Ag,}$$

all the components being in their standard states. The standard potential, $E°$, has been derived from experimental emf values for the cell

$$\text{H}_2 \mid \text{HX } (m_1), \text{MX}(m_2) \mid \text{AgX} \mid \text{Ag}$$

by suitable extrapolation techniques. Experiments of this kind have been made in aqueous, nonaqueous, and mixed solvents, for all of which the electrode is well-suited. $E°$ values for nonaqueous and mixed systems depend markedly on the concentration-scale used; those quoted in Table 1 are $E_m°$, based on the molal scale.

A concise survey of the various modes of preparation of silver-silver halide electrodes follows, with emphasis on those experimental aspects for which detailed guidance should be sought through reference to original publications or standard texts. Although the other halides often require modified experimental conditions, the same general principles hold.

(1) Electrolytic preparation: Electrolytically cleaned platinum (in the form of wire, gauze, or as a massive disc) is electroplated with silver, usually from a potassium silver cyanide solution. Part of the silver is then anodically converted to silver chloride using dilute hydrochloric acid as electrolyte. Adequate washing between stages in this process is important. Another stringent requirement, and this applies equally to electrodes prepared by other methods, is the removal of even trace amounts of other halides. Although until recently the most generally-used method, electrolytic preparation offers least certainty of success.

(2) Thermal preparation: An aqueous paste of silver oxide and silver chlorate—a 9:1 salt ratio is most commonly used—is applied to a platinum wire spiral; the system is then heated to the decomposition temperature (ca 650°C) for approximately one hour. Both silver oxide and chlorate should be pure; in particular, the silver oxide must be freed of water-soluble impurities by thorough and repeated washing. The comparative unreliability of thermal electrodes prob-

TABLE 1. STANDARD ELECTRODE POTENTIALS,[a] $E°_m$

Electrode	Temperature (°C)	Electrode Potential (abs. volt)	
H₂ (ideal, 1 atm)	HCl (ideal, $m = 1$)	zero at all temperatures by definition		
Ag	AgCl	HCl	0	0.2365	
	25	0.2224	
	50	0.2045	
Ag	AgBr	HBr	0	0.08168	
	25	0.07132	
	50	0.05668	
Ag	AgI	HI	25	−0.15230	

		E'	E''
		(see text)	
Hg	Hg₂Cl₂	KCl (satd)	buffer solution	25	0.2412	0.2445
Hg	Hg₂Cl₂	KCl (1N)	25	0.2801	—
Hg	Hg₂Cl₂	KCl (1N)	salt bridge	25	—	0.283
Hg	Hg₂Cl₂	KCl (0.1N)	25	0.3337	—
Hg	Hg₂Cl₂	KCl (0.1N)	salt bridge	buffer solution	25	—	0.3356
Hg	Hg₂Cl₂	HCl [metastable]	25	0.26796	
Hg	Hg₂Cl₂	HCl [stable]	5	0.27290	
	25	0.26823	
	45	0.26104	
Pt	QH₂ , Q	HCl [b]	0	0.71798	
	25	0.69976	
	40	0.68865	

[a] All data in this table refer to aqueous solutions.
[b] Q = p-benzoquinine (C₆H₄O₂).

ably stems from thermally-induced stresses and the irreproducibility of the electrode surface.

(3) Thermal-electrolytic preparation: Silver oxide, carefully purified as above, is applied in the form of an aqueous paste to a clean platinum wire spiral. The electrode is slowly heated to 450°C, and as slowly cooled; often this process is repeated with a second paste application. The silver deposited is then chloridized electrolytically (0.05N KCl or 1N HCl) until 10–20 per cent of the silver has been converted; this ratio appears to yield most stable and reproducible electrodes. Thermal-electrolytic preparation is the most uniformly successful method and is at present in general use.

Other modes of preparation include the procedures yielding "precipitated" electrodes (in which finely divided crystalline silver and silver chloride are mixed with the solution under investigation) and "silver mirror" electrodes (in which silver is deposited on platinum foil by the Rochelle salt mirror process, then chloridized as above).

As with any reference electrodes, the preparation and intercomparison of a set of several electrodes is recommended. Freshly prepared electrodes should be allowed at least 24 hours to attain an equilibrium value, and may then be compared with an aged silver-silver chloride electrode taken as a reference standard (ground energy state). The selection of the latter remains a subject of experimental art. "Long-term" aging periods, indicative of unsatisfactory electrodes from the practical viewpoint, are not uncommon; the factors contributing to the "aging" effect of silver-silver halide electrodes are still only partly understood. With chloride electrodes, the best-behaved thermal-electrolytic electrodes are light grey or white; the most satisfactory electrolytically-prepared electrodes, however, are pink or plum-colored. With either type, exposure to intense illumination is best avoided.

Mercury-Mercurous Salt Electrodes

The most commonly used mercury-mercurous salt electrodes may be represented

$$Hg \mid Hg_2Cl_2 \mid Cl^- \quad \text{(calomel electrode)}$$

and

$$Hg \mid Hg_2SO_4 \mid SO_4^=$$

Attention will be restricted here to the calomel electrode. This, like the silver-silver halide system, is an electrode of the second kind, but has, at least in theory, one obvious point of superiority: the metallic component is liquid, and irrespective of its previous history remains in a standard state. This advantage is counterbalanced by the tendency of mercurous salts to disproportionate, and further, by the entry into coordinated complex species of the mercuric ions thus formed.

Calomel electrodes with potassium chloride are used with a salt bridge, and are *calomel electrodes of fixed potential; variable potential calomel electrodes,* suitable for use in thermodynamic cells, are obtained with hydrochloric acid. A recent evaluation of variable potential calomel electrodes has elucidated a number of the factors contributing to irreversibility, and indicated ways in which such factors may be minimized. If the electrode vessel is rendered hydrophobic through the application of a layer of silicone, a markedly improved electrode is obtained. This is attributed to the elimination of the "wedge effect," an atypical annulus of aqueous solution formed between the mercury and the cell wall through capillary action. Attention to other aspects, such as the preparation of the calomel (electrolytically prepared calomel is most satisfactory, being very finely divided), and the addition of calomel to mercury (the two should be allowed to interact in the dry state—which they do with great affinity, especially when only a small amount of calomel is used—before any solution is added) contributes to electrodes of improved stability.

The mercury for these electrodes should be purified by both filtration and distillation, preferably immediately before use. The calomel and hydrochloric acid (or potassium chloride) should be free of other halides, and care should be taken to exclude oxygen from the solutions; exposure to oxygen for a short period usually proves reversible, but a long-range effect, in which the solute is slowly depleted, also occurs.

The *"variable potential"* calomel electrode (i.e., with hydrochloric acid) attains a steady emf within two hours. Some time thereafter, however, a gradual drift in electrode potential

becomes apparent; formerly this was interpreted as a departure from equilibrium conditions, but it is now generally considered that the potential change corresponds to the progress of the electrode from an initial metastable state to a final, stable equilibrium. The gradual establishment of soluble disproportionation products of calomel in the half-cell solution is believed responsible for this phenomenon. Two distinct types of electrodes can thus be recognized: the *"metastable calomel electrode"* (in which the solution contains no mercuric species) and the *"stable calomel electrode"* in which an equilibrium concentration of mercuric entities has been established in solution. Although the quantity $(E - E°)$ is often of primary importance, the evaluation of $E°$ for the calomel electrode was long frustrated by failure to distinguish between the stable and metastable types of electrode. The most reliable 25° values (on the molal scale) are:

$$E°_m = 0.26796 \text{ abs. volt}$$
(metastable calomel electrode)

and

$$E°_m = 0.26823 \text{ abs. volt}$$
(stable calomel electrode)

Calomel electrodes of fixed potential (i.e., with potassium chloride) present fewer difficulties, both in preparation and equilibration. Three forms, containing respectively saturated, $1N$, and $0.1N$ KCl, are principally used. The main limitation of these electrodes lies in the fact that a salt-bridge or liquid junction must be used to complete an electrochemical cell. For this reason potentials are seldom required to be reproducible to better than 0.1 mv, and two values of the reference electrode potential, E' and E'', are conventionally quoted. E' is taken as the standard electrode potential $(E°)$ corrected for the particular concentration of KCl used to attain the half-cell of fixed potential, while E'' includes also the liquid junction or salt-bridge increment in the value for the half-cell potential. Typical values for the saturated calomel electrode at 25° are:

$E' = 0.2412$ abs. volt, and $E'' = 0.2445$ abs. volt.

Additional values for the $0.1N$ and $1N$ calomel electrodes are given in Table 1.

Other Electrodes

The *quinhydrone electrode* is an electrode of the third kind, the reversible oxidation-reduction

TABLE 2. APPLICATIONS OF REFERENCE ELECTRODES

Electrode	Suitability				
	Aqueous solutions	Organic solvents	Fused salts	Biological systems	Special applications
standard hydrogen	****	**	*	*	Electrode standardization
silver-silver halide	****	***	***	***	Secondary reference standard; thermo-dynamic studies
calomel	****	**	*	*	Thermodynamic studies
glass	****	**	*	***	pH measurement; potentiometric titration
quinhydrone	****	*	*	**	Potentiometric studies
metal-metal oxide and sulfide	***	*	***	**	Alkaline systems; high-temperature studies
metal-metal halide	**	**	***	**	Thermodynamics of molten inorganic halides
metal-metal sulfate	***	**	**	**	Thermodynamic studies
membrane	***	**	*	**	Membrane performance studies; colloidal solutions
halogen	*	*	**	*	Molten inorganic halides
oxygen	**	*	*	**	Oxygen tension measurement
thiol	*	*	*	**	Biological oxidation—reduction experiments

Key: **** generally applicable
     *** applicable to selected systems
      ** occasionally suitable
       * insufficiently explored and/or inapplicable

system being composed of p-benzoquinone (quinone) and its hydroquinone (quinol). At present it is used infrequently, having been supplanted almost entirely by the glass electrode. It is, nevertheless, well-suited to potentiometric titration techniques (both simple and differential), and under restricted conditions responds theoretically to pH. Its limitations arise chiefly from unwanted chemical reactivity (as with concentrated hydrochloric acid solutions) and salt errors (caused by the preferential salting-out of one of the electrode components in an electrolyte solution).

The *glass electrode* occupies a prominent position in the history of pH measurement. It is, however, an "indicator" electrode rather than a standard reference electrode in the terms of this article.

Metal-metal oxide and metal-metal sulfide electrodes find application in highly alkaline systems, especially at extreme temperatures. The metals most commonly employed are silver, mercury, and antimony.

References

1. IVES, D. J. G., AND JANZ, G. J., Eds., "Reference Electrodes," New York, Academic Press, 1961.
2. HARNED, H. S., AND OWEN, B. B., "The Physical Chemistry of Electrolytic Solutions," New York, Reinhold Publishing Corp., 1958.
3. MACINNES, D. A., "The Principles of Electrochemistry," New York, Reinhold Publishing Corp., 1939.
4. BATES, R. G., "Electrometric pH Determinations," New York, John Wiley & Sons, Inc., 1954.
5. DOLE, M., "The Glass Electrode," New York, John Wiley & Sons, Inc., 1941.
6. KRATZ, L., "Die Glaselektrode und Ihre Anwendungen," Frankfurt am Main, Steinkopff, 1950.
7. ROBINSON, R. A., AND STOKES, R. H., "Electrolyte Solutions," New York, Academic Press, 1959.
8. BOCKRIS, J. O'M., MACKENZIE, J. D., AND WHITE, J. L., Eds., "Physicochemical Measurements at High Temperatures," New York, Academic Press, 1959.
9. CHRISTIANSEN, J. A., AND POURBAIX, M., *Compt. rend. conf. intern. chim. pure et appl.*, 17th Conf. Stockholm, p. 83 (1953).

GEORGE J. JANZ
AND F. J. KELLY

Cross-references: entries with *Electrode Potential* titles; *Electromotive Force and Half-Cell Potentials; EMF Measurements in Aqueous Solutions at High Temperatures; Fused Salt Electrode Reactions; Glass Electrode; Membrane Potentials; Microelectrodes; Nomenclature, Remarks on; pH Meter; Platinized Electrodes; Polarography.*

REFERENCE ELECTRODES FOR FUSED SALTS. See FUSED SALT ELECTRODE REACTIONS.

RESERVE PRIMARY BATTERIES. See BATTERIES, RESERVE PRIMARY.

RESISTANCE HEATING

Resistance heating is basically of two forms: direct and indirect. In the first case, the work is heated directly by applying voltage to it; in the latter case the work is heated indirectly through transfer of heat from a resistor. A determining test for direct resistance heating is "Does line current flow through the work,—that is, through the final material to be heated."

Direct Resistance Heating

This is an important heating method in the metals and chemical industries for such processes as the production of graphite, boron carbide, and silicon carbide, the electric melting of glass (q.v.), for reflowing tinplate, annealing wire, and for various welding and spot welding processes. It has several heating advantages: 1) high efficiency of operation due to direct application of power to the work; 2) instant control of heat input, with no thermal lag time on or off; 3) the ability to obtain accurate and repetitive heat control; 4) its applicability to continuous processes, provided that proper means are employed to conduct the current into the moving material; 5) its applicability to extremely high-temperature operation; 6) since line frequency can often be used, low-cost power is involved.

Almost invariably the resistance of the work is very small. The degree of heating obtained depends on the work resistance and the current, so the low resistance necessitates that the current be high to provide the required power input level. Thus, high-current, low-voltage sources are mainly involved. Perhaps the greatest disadvantage of this heating method is the difficulty of carrying to the work the large current involved and of getting this current into the work, whether it be with contacts, electrodes, rolls, clamps, or conductive baths.

These large a-c currents cause skin-effect, a tendency for the current to crowd close to the surface of the work. This effect is a function of the applied frequency. At line frequency it is not too pronounced, with rarely more than 5 per cent additional current density at the surface as compared to the center. Since the surface is losing energy through radiation, skin-effect can help in maintaining the temperature through the work more uniformly.

This heating method can be carried out with direct current, line-frequency (60 cps), or high-frequency power. From a least cost standpoint, power at line frequency is best for the vast majority of applications. However, there are areas where the use of direct current or high-frequency power is indicated.

In graphitizing and silicon carbide furnaces where single-phase load currents range from 30,000 to 80,000 amperes, the design problems caused by the use of line-frequency power have been solved satisfactorily by careful design of the heavy-current buswork to minimize its reactance, and by use of capacitors to provide almost complete correction of the remaining circuit reactance. The use of direct current power eliminates the furnace circuit reactance design problems and presents to the power company a steady 3-phase load which it greatly prefers to a single-phase load. In some cases the savings in buswork cost and the advantage of a 3-phase load more than offset the first cost and the slightly higher operating cost of the rectifiers required for the d-c supply.

High-frequency power has been used to overcome an apparently insurmountable contact problem that existed at 60 cycle operation in the continuous annealing of bronze wire. Sheaves or slide contacts spark severely at 60 cycle operation and cause wire damage. With 450,000 cycle power, the sparking problem is eliminated. On the other hand, the contact problems for annealing copper wire are less severe and 60 cycle operation is entirely satisfactory.

Thus, there are certain areas where each type of power does the heating task best. In general, line-frequency power is preferable, but its limitations leave a definite area of application for the other types of power source.

Temperatures obtained by this heating method can range up to several thousand degrees. As the desired temperature increases, the emission losses increase as the fourth power of the temperature. At temperature above 1000°F the radiation loss becomes extremely important and must be taken into consideration to assure proper sizing of the power supply and equipment. A standard emissivity curve or fourth-power radiation equation can be used in finding radiation loss.

During the heating process, the current and voltage required vary over a wide range. At startup the work resistivity is low, and the required voltage is also low. Toward the end of the heat time, the voltage requirement may have increased by 2- or 3-fold not only because of the increased resistivity of the work but also because of the increased power requirement to compensate for the radiated power loss. Applying too much voltage at startup results in excessive currents; applying too little voltage toward the end of the process results in excessive heating time. If the process is continuous, the power requirement is relatively constant and the control problem is merely one of employing a low-range controller to adjust the circuit as necessary to hold temperature or some other controlling function at a constant level. However, during startup or if a batch-type process is involved, some broad control means must be provided to supply the necessary control range of voltage and power.

This type of electric heating is severely limited in applicability. It is, nevertheless, a most important method that is solidly entrenched in those specific areas of usage previously mentioned.

Indirect Resistance Heating

For this heating method, voltage is applied to a resistor and the heat of the resistor is then transferred to the work material by radiation, conduction, or convection. Sometimes the resistor is sheathed, with the sheath conduction heated from the resistor and transmitting its heat onto the work by one or more of these methods.

This is by far the most prevalent and widespread type of electric heat, both in the home and in industry. Some of the advantages of indirect resistance heating are: the heating of intricate parts can be effected; it is applicable for low-, medium-, or high-temperature operation, and for either a low- or high-heat transfer rate; it is applicable to continuous processes and in areas where other heating methods would be difficult to employ; heating can be carried out in air, liquid, under controlled atmosphere conditions, or in vacuum.

The resistor material falls in one of three main classifications: metallic, nonmetallic, and salt bath type. The most widely utilized non-metallic resistor element is silicon carbide (q.v.). The rod-shaped elements of widely varying size find extensive usage in industrial furnaces for temperatures up to 3000°F. Their resistance gradually increases with use, so some means of adjusting the applied voltage is necessary to maintain a constant or nearly constant power input level with time.

The salt bath furnace is used for a great variety of applications in the metals industry. Among these are tempering, hardening, annealing, and brazing. In these furnaces, one or more pairs of electrodes are immersed in salt, and for each pair the current passes through the salt from one electrode to the other. The electrodes act only as current conductors. The molten salt is the main resistive material and heat source. Proper placement of the electrodes provides an electromagnetic stirring effect which assures uniformly distributed heat throughout the bath. The work material is immersed in the salt and heated by conduction; it is so located in the bath that current does not pass through it.

Metallic resistors can be sheathed or unsheathed. Both types are widely employed. Unsheathed or bare resistors have their most important usage in industrial furnaces for the heat treatment of metals and for melting of low-temperature metals. At temperatures up to 1500°F, convection heating plays a major role. Above this temperature, radiation heating becomes the more important heat method. The resistor may be round, ribbon, or cast type. Ribbon resistors find favor because their radiating surface is greater per unit volume and, therefore, per unit heat loss, than other resistor shapes. Cast resistors have high mechanical strength, which is their main advantage over the round or ribbon type. However, their large cross-sectional area means a low radiating surface per unit volume and also means a low value of resistance per unit length. For this reason a special low-voltage source is often required for cast resistor installations. Materials most often used for metallic resistors are steel, nichrome, and tungsten.

In pipeline heating, the pipe is the resistor. It transfers heat to the material (chocolate, molasses, water, etc.) in the pipe to prevent freezing or to assure proper flow characteristics. Most often, the heating of pipe is carried out by indirect heating of the pipe through sheathed resistors (tracers).

The sheathed resistor, with the sheath electrically insulated from the metallic resistor it encloses, finds a wide field of service in electric devices and appliances. The sheathing may be nonmetallic, such as ceramic or neoprene; or metallic, such as lead, copper, or steel; and may be tubular, flat, or finned in configuration. In each case, the heat is conducted from the resistor to the sheath and the sheath is then the source of heat for the work material. Their usage covers a large number of specialized heating tasks for heating of liquids, air, work surfaces, areas, etc., and for various uses as irons, heaters, dryers, and defrosters in many industries. Temperatures attainable range up to 2800°F.

Resistors in a glass bulb or quartz tube are also used for radiant heating. They have the protected feature of the sheath type plus the fast on-off response time of the bare type, and are used for comfort heating, drying paint, cooking foods, soft soldering, and heating of liquids to increase their fluidity. Temperatures to more than 3000°F are attainable.

References

1. TRINKS, W., "Industrial Furnace," Vol. II, New York, John Wiley and Sons, 1955.
2. PASCHKIS, V., AND PERSSON, J., "Industrial Electric Furnaces and Appliances," New York, Interscience Publishers, 1960.

E. J. BORREBACH

Cross-references: *Boron Carbide; Glass, Electric Melting of; Furnaces for Hot-Pressing; Graphite, Electrothermal Production; Silicon Carbide.*

RESISTANCE THERMOMETERS

Definition

A resistance thermometer is defined[1] as a temperature-measuring instrument comprising a resistance-measuring device, a sensing means called a resistance thermometer bulb, and electrical conductors for operatively connecting the two. In many instances the sensor alone is referred to as a resistance thermometer, but present-day tendencies toward standardization of terminology discourage this practice.

History

The resistance thermometer system was first used by Sir William Siemens about 1871, but it fell into disrepute because of instability of the sensor. The art remained inactive until Callendar and Griffiths showed that a platinum wire is remarkably stable through repeated heating and cooling cycles if it is protected against contaminating gases, is mounted on an inert support, and is not heated above the temperature at which it starts to volatilize (approx. 1200°C). Holborn and Wien also contributed to the restoration of confidence in platinum-resistance thermometry. In 1899 Callendar and Griffiths standardized the platinum element against temperatures measured with the gas thermometer and developed the Callendar formula which enabled them, by measuring three fixed points, to compute the temperature corresponding to any other resistance up to 500°C, with an error less than 0.1°C with respect to the gas thermometer. Their results were verified by many others. Measuring systems for accurately determining the resistance of sensors made their appearance.

In 1927 resistance thermometry had advanced to the point where the platinum sensor was accepted by the Seventh General Conference of Weights and Measures as defining the International Temperature scale between 0°C and +630°C by means of the Callendar formula. For temperatures from −182 to 0°C, the Conference accepted a variation of the Callendar formula proposed by Van Dusen. The acceptance was reconfirmed in the adoption of the 1948 International Practical Temperature Scale.

Since about 1900, the advantages of stability, remote indication, and sensitivity over other types of temperature-measuring devices have become slowly realized in the industrial area. Work has continued toward refining the sensors along the line of greater stability, faster response to temperature changes, and smaller size. Recording systems for precisely measuring the resistance have been developed to read directly in temperature.

Resistance Thermometer Sensors

Resistance thermometry may be divided into two general classes, precision and industrial. Precision thermometer sensors are all made of very pure platinum, are mounted in such a manner that they are free from restriction of motion resulting from expansion or contraction from temperature changes, and are sealed in a contaminant-free case. They are not adjusted closely to a predetermined resistance value and

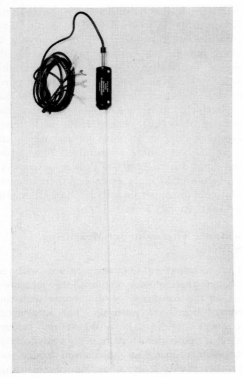

FIG. 1. Precision-type platinum sensor for general service.

$$t = \frac{(R_t - R_0)}{C\, R_0} + \delta \left(\frac{t}{100} - 1\right)\left(\frac{t}{100}\right)$$

$$+ \beta \left(\frac{t}{100} - 1\right)\left(\frac{t}{100}\right)^3$$

where t = temperature in °C

R_t = sensor resistance at temp. t

R_0 = sensor resistance at 0°C

C = fundamental coefficient of sensor,

$$\text{or} = \frac{R_{100} - R_0}{100\, R_0}$$

δ = Callendar constant

β = Van Dusen constant

Refer to Ref. 4 for a method used in determining constants.

In designing industrial sensors, qualities such as sensitivity to rapid temperature changes (or speed of response), ability to withstand environmental pressure, corrosion resistance to medium being measured, and vibration resistance must be considered. High speed of response is desirable and is a function of the thermal conductivity between the thermal-sensitive element, the specific heat of the sensor assembly, and the film coefficient of the medium being measured. These are therefore used almost entirely with measuring systems calibrated directly in electrical resistance. One type is described in Ref. 2. The temperature-sensitive element consists of a 25.5 ohm coil of pure platinum, wound on a notched mica cross. The unit is sealed in a glass tube filled with dry air. Fig. 1 shows one of these sensors. A variation of this type of sensor is shown in Fig. 2. This design, proposed by Hoge,[3] contains the same winding, but it is inserted in a small capsule-like platinum tube filled with helium and sealed. This sensor is used for cryogenic work, its small size allowing it to be mounted in the calorimeter.

Temperature values are obtained by accurately determined calibration curves of resistance *vs* temperature, based on the Callendar and Van Dusen formulas.

The Callendar formula for positive temperature is:

$$t = \frac{(R_t - R_0)}{CR_0} + \delta \left(\frac{t}{100} - 1\right)\left(\frac{t}{100}\right)$$

The Callendar-Van Dusen formula for negative temperatures is:

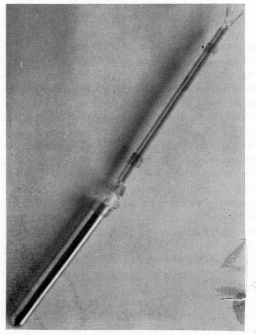

FIG. 2. Precision-type platinum sensor for cryogenic work.

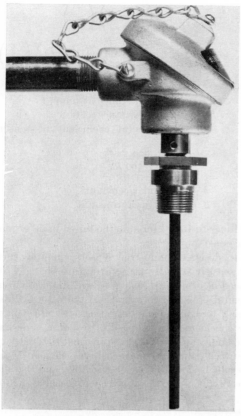

Fig. 3. Industrial-type platinum sensor.

parameters are somewhat incompatible with each other, e.g., a high-pressure environment will require increasing the mass of the case which, in turn, reduces the speed of response. On the other hand, the electrical element must be electrically insulated from the assembly, which also adds thermal resistance, reducing the response speed. Designs therefore contain compromises which are a function of the end use of the sensor. Details of specific types of construction are given in Ref. 5. The winding material is generally either platinum, copper, or nickel, although other pure metals, such as tungsten, are sometimes used. Platinum is available with closely reproducible characteristics. An industrial platinum sensor is shown in Fig. 3. Its temperature *vs* resistance relationship is not a straight line, the shape being such that the sensitivity decreases with increasing temperature as is indicated by the Callendar formula. The usual range for industrial platinum thermometers is from about −325 to +1100°F. Copper is avail-

able in reproducible condition and is usable from −325 up to 300°F, where it tends to start oxidizing and become unstable. The copper curve is a straight line in the positive range making it desirable for temperature difference measurements. Nickel is also available in a fairly pure state but its characteristics are not quite as reproducible as platinum or copper. It has an increasing resistance characteristic with temperature, making it valuable for use where an exponential curve shape is desirable.[6] The usable nickel range is from 32 to 600°F. It is inexpensive but does not make quite as stable a thermometer as platinum or copper since its resistance changes much more rapidly from straining.

Resistance Thermometer Measuring Systems

The measurement of temperature with a resistance thermometer involves the measurement of the resistance of the sensor with an adequate degree of precision. The measuring instrument used may be a Wheatstone bridge (q.v.), a potentiometer (q.v.), a deflection instrument utilizing an unbalanced bridge, or any other suitable form of resistance-measuring equipment.

To take advantage of all the capability of the platinum sensor for the precise measurement of temperature it is necessary that it be equipped with a Wheatstone bridge which is designed for the measurement of resistances within the range from 0 to about 100 ohms with the best attainable precision. The precision required may be evaluated in round numbers as follows. The temperature coefficient of the resistivity of platinum may be taken as 0.004 ohm/°C, and the resistance of the thermometer at 0°C as 25 ohms. Then its increase in resistance per °C is approximately 0.1 ohm. To detect a change in temperature of 0.001 degree it is necessary to detect a change in resistance of 0.0001 ohm in 25 ohms or of 4 parts in a million. To actually measure such a change to ±10 per cent it is necessary to have sensitivity and readability to 4 parts in ten million.

The achievement of such precision of measurement has been a matter of much study and has been arrived at in various ways, such as the potentiometer method, the Kelvin bridge and the Wheatstone bridge. The potentiometer has been preferred in Europe, the Kelvin bridge in England and the Wheatstone bridge in this country, in the form designed by Mueller at the National Bureau of Standards. The circuit of the Mueller bridge[7] is diagrammed in Fig. 4. It is essentially that of a conventional Wheatstone bridge.

Decades A, B, D, E, F, and G comprise the measuring resistors; Q and Q_1 are ratio arms; L, the thermometer coil, is the resistance to be measured.

The measurement of temperature by means of resistance thermometry requires that only the resistance of the sensitive winding be measured. The leads to the winding are usually of a material that has a temperature coefficient comparable with that of the winding. It is necessary to measure the resistance of the winding in such a way that changes in lead resistance shall not affect the results.

In industrial resistance thermometry this result is secured by providing the sensor with three copper leads, one to one end of the winding and two to the other. These may be designated A, B, and C, where B and C are the pair going to one end of the winding. (See Fig. 5).

In Fig. 5, R_1 and R_2 are equal resistors (ratio coils), S is a calibrated adjustable resistor which is used in balancing the bridge, and T is the sensor winding. Since $R_1 = R_2$, when the bridge is balanced, $S + B = T + A$. If lead a has been adjusted to be equal to lead B, and if the two wires are exposed to exactly the same temperature conditions, $s = x$ at balance; since C is a battery lead its fluctuations in resistance with changes in temperature do not affect the measurement. Errors can result from this system from variable contact resistance.

These errors are avoided by permitting only soldered connections in the bridge arms and by putting all moving contacts in series with battery or galvanometer leads, where they have no effect upon the balance conditions and produce only negligible changes in bridge current or galvanometer sensitivity.

Fig. 6 is a schematic diagram of such a bridge circuit for indicators and recorders. In this figure R_1 and R_2 are the ratio arms of the bridge; S and S_1 are uniform slidewires of equal length mounted side by side on a circular disk. S having twice as great a resistance per unit length as S_1; R is the measuring arm of the bridge and T is the sensor winding; and A, B, and C are leads to the winding. Bridge balance is attained by adjusting the position of the slidewire contacts

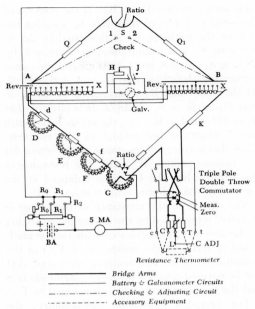

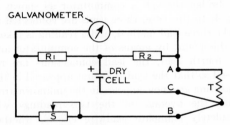

FIG. 4. Schematic of G-2 Mueller bridge circuit.

———————— Bridge Arms
———————— Battery & Galvanometer Circuits
—·—·—·—·— Checking & Adjusting Circuit
----------- Accessory Equipment

FIG. 5. Three-lead thermometer bridge.

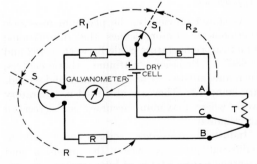

FIG. 6. Modification of three-lead thermometer bridge to eliminate effect of contact resistance.

with respect to the slidewires, either by rotating the disk past fixed contacts or by rotating an arm carrying both contacts along the slidewires. A and B are fixed resistors of values such that $A + S = B + S_1$ so that with the contacts in their zero positions $R_1 = R_2$. If the position of the contacts is moved from zero by rotating the disk or the contacts, R_1 is decreased by ΔS in slidewire S, and simultaneously increased by $PS/2$ in S_1 (since S_1 has half as great a resistance per unit length as S), so that $R_1 = A + S - PS/2$. At the same time R_2 is decreased by $\Delta S/2$ so that $R_2 = B + S_1 - \Delta S/2$. It is obvious that R_1 is still equal to R_2, i.e., the bridge ratio is still unity, whatever the setting of the contacts. Since this is true; the resistance of the sensor for any balance point is $R + \Delta S$. The resistance of the sensor when the bridge is balanced at the low end of the slidewire scale is equal to R.

The change in the resistance of the sensor is therefore represented by the change in the setting of the slidewire. The slidewire scale can be graduated in terms of the resistance of T or of the temperature of x. The temperature range that can be covered depends upon the magnitude of S and the temperature at which R is equal to T.

For precision resistance thermometry, the sensor has four leads, which are connected to the bridge through a commutator as shown in Fig. 4. In this case, three leads are connected as in the three-lead method, and a reading is taken. At this point, by means of the commutator and the fourth lead, the lead connections are reversed so that the lead that first appeared in the measuring arm now appears in the unknown arm. Thus, the average of the two readings will completely eliminate leadwire effects, whether or not the leads are precisely matched.

Applications

As stated previously, the platinum resistance thermometer sensor defines the International Practical Temperature Scale between -182 and $+630°C$. Precision platinum thermometers, therefore, are used as basic standards and secondary standards. They are also used in laboratory work where maximum accuracy and precision are required.

Industrial resistance sensors are used in industrial processes where the precision and accuracy of other types of temperature measurement are inadequate or where a simpler type of electrical measuring instrument as compared to a potentiometer, e.g., is desired.

Some general uses include

Industrial refrigeration measurement and control

Constant-temperature baths

Low-temperature furnace measurement and control

Drying ovens

Injection molding machines for plastics.

References

1. SAMA Standard RC5A Resistance Thermometers.
2. MEYERS, C. H., "Coiled Filament Resistance Thermometers," *J. Research Natl. Bur. Standards*, **9**, 807 (1932).
3. HOGE, H. J., "Electrical Conduction in the Glass Insulation of Resistance Thermometers," *J. Research Natl. Bur. Standards*, **28**, 489 (1942).
4. ROBERTSON, D., AND WALCH, K. A., "Calibration Techniques for Precision Platinum Resistance Thermometers," in "Temperature, Its Measurement and Control in Science and Industry," III, Part 1, p. 291, New York, Reinhold Publishing Corp., 1962.
5. HICKES, W. F., "Industrial Temperature Measurement with Resistance Thermometers," in "Temperature Measurement," Cleveland, American Society for Metals, 1956.
6. GRANT, D. A., AND HICKES, W. F., "Industrial Temperature Measurement with Nickel Resistance Thermometers," in "Temperature, Its Measurement and Control in Science and Industry," III, Part 2, p. 305, New York, Reinhold Publishing Corp., 1962.
7. MUELLER, E. F., "Wheatstone Bridges and Some Accessory Apparatus for Resistance Thermometry," *Bull. Natl. Bur. Standards*, **13**, 547 (1916).

D. ROBERTSON

Cross-references: *Potentiometers; Radiation Pyrometry; Thermoelectric Thermometry; Wheatstone Bridge.*

RESTORATION OF ANCIENT METALS. See ELECTROLYTIC RESTORATION OF ANCIENT METALS.

RHODIUM ELECTROPLATING. See PRECIOUS METAL ELECTROPLATING.

RIDGWAY, RAYMOND RONALD (1897–1947)

Raymond Ronald Ridgway, noted for the discovery of boron carbide and his many contributions to the science and technology of high temperature products and processing, was born in Morris, Illinois, on August 27, 1897, the son of Fred W. and Caroline K. Ridgway. He was educated at Lake Forest College and graduated with a B.S. in electrochemical engineering from Massachusetts Institute of Technology in 1920.

He married Margaret Lyman Longfellow of West Newton, Massachusetts, in 1921. They had four children, Stuart, Charlotte, Margaret, and Herbert.

After graduation, he was employed for one year by the Aluminum Company of America, mostly at Massena, New York, then for a year he worked with his father's firm, the Ridgway Electric Company in Freeport, Illinois. In 1922 he joined the staff of the Norton Company in Niagara Falls, New York. There he was active in the research department, eventually becoming associate director of research. The plant and laboratory of Norton Company meanwhile were transferred to Chippawa, Ontario but Ridgway continued to live in Niagara Falls, New York, commuting daily across the river, about six miles.

He was active in the local and national chemical organizations. After serving as secretary-treasurer and chairman of the Niagara Falls section, he was elected president of the Electrochemical Society in 1941. In the Western New York section of the American Chemical Society he was active on program and convention committees. In 1943, he became the thirteenth recipient of the Jacob F. Schoellkopf medal, awarded by the American Chemical Society for his work on boron carbide.

His outstanding accomplishments during his twenty-five years at Norton Company were the isolation and commercial production of boron carbide (known by the Norton trade-mark "Norbide") as well as methods and equipment for the fabrication of this material by "hot-pressing." He was also responsible for the invention and production of a crystalline alumina abrasive trade-marked "32 Alundum."

Twenty-six United States patents and a number of foreign patents were granted to Ridgway and his coworkers, covering a diverse range of endeavours from thermocouples to lightning arrestors. He and his associates published ten papers, nine of which were contributions to the *Transactions of the Electrochemical Society*. His work also included design of electric furnaces, processes for fusing nonconducting materials, such as boric oxide glass, and finding applications for boron carbide. Production of refractory and insulating materials, development of electrical grades of magnesia as used for insulat-

ing electric-stove heating elements, and the fabrication of resistor bars were all within the scope of his work. His studies of the temperature distribution in a silicon carbide resistance furnace are still the classical reference.

His abundance of energy, both physical and mental, overflowed his work into social and club activities and sports. He became involved in swimming, sailing, figure-skating, amateur dramatics, dancing, marionettes, and music, as well as spending much time with his growing family.

During World War II at the request of the Manhattan District, Corps of Engineers he involved the talents of the laboratory in the first commercial production of elemental boron of better than 98 per cent purity. For this contribution the laboratory was recognized by one of the awards for Chemical Engineering Achievement as a contributor to the Atomic Bomb Project.

Following the war, he was active in the designing and building of a new Research Laboratory at Chippawa. He was never to occupy this new building. On June 12, 1947 after a family sailing party, he went back alone to collect some tools left aboard the sailboat. While returning to shore he drowned in the Niagara River. A memorial plaque is located in the entrance of the Chippawa Laboratory.

References

1. Brallier, Paul S., "Raymond R. Ridgway—Obituary," *Trans. Electrochem. Soc.*, **92**, 11–13 (1947).
2. Ridgway, R. R., "Temperature Measurements in Commercial Silicon Carbide Furnaces," *Trans. Electrochem. Soc.*, **61**, 217–232 (1932).
3. "Who's Who in Engineering," 1941.

Gordon R. Finlay

RUBIDIUM AND CESIUM ELECTROWINNING

Rubidium and cesium are the most reactive of the alkali metals. Either metal will burst into flame if exposed to air, so the metals must always be prepared and handled under protective coatings such as mineral oil or in an inert atmosphere or a vacuum.

Rubidium was first reduced to the metallic state by Bunsen in 1861, the same year that Bunsen and Kirchoff discovered the element spectroscopically. In contrast, cesium salts were not successfully reduced to metal until 1881, even though the element was discovered in 1860, before the discovery of rubidium. Bunsen reduced molten rubidium chloride, using a graphite anode and an iron cathode, to obtain the metal; but attempts to reduce cesium chloride similarly were unsuccessful. Setterberg obtained cesium metal by electrolysis of a cesium cyanide-barium cyanide melt containing the two salts in a four-to-one mole ratio. The barium cyanide was used to lower the temperature of the electrolyte, and barium was not reduced.

Rubidium has been prepared by electrolysis of molten rubidium hydroxide in a nickel cell with iron electrodes and a magnesite diaphragm (cf. *Potassium Electrowinning*). A current efficiency of 30 per cent was obtained using 100 grams of rubidium hydroxide, a current density of 0.5 amp/sq cm, and a current of 5 amp for 45 minutes.

Both cesium and rubidium can be reduced from aqueous solutions at a mercury cathode. Presumably the metals can be recovered from the amalgam by any of the methods described for potassium. Rubidium metal also has been obtained through electrolysis of a nitrobenzene solution of a rubidium bromide-aluminum bromide melt.

Molten cesium chloride has been electrolyzed at 670 to 700°C using a lead cathode to form a cesium-lead alloy. A current efficiency of 59 per cent was obtained at 670°C with a cathode current density of 2 amp/sq cm. The cesium metal can be readily recovered from the lead alloy by distillation.

Both cesium and rubidium metal are more commonly prepared by thermochemical reduction methods. The high volatility of these alkali metals facilitates the vaporization that almost always occurs in thermochemical processes but which usually hinders electrochemical reductions.

References

1. "Gmelins Handbuch der Anorganischen Chemie," System Nummer 25, Cesium, Seite 16, Berlin, Verlag Chemie, GMBH, 1955.
2. *Ibid*, System Nummer 24, Rubidium, Seite 25–6, 1955.
3. HEVESY, G. VON, "Electrolytic Preparation of Rubidium," *Z. Anorg. Chem.*, **67**, 242 (1910).
4. KIRK, R. E., AND OTHMER, D. F., "Encyclopedia of Chemical Technology," Vol. I, pp. 451–3, New York, The Interscience Encyclopedia, Inc., 1947.
5. SETTERBERG, C., "Uber Die Darstellung von Rubidium und Cesium Verbindungen und uber die Gewinnung der Metalle Selbst," *Lieb. Ann.*, **211**, 112 (1882).
6. SMITH, G. McP., AND BENNETT, H. C., "The Electrolytic Preparation of the Amalgams of the Alkali and Alkali-Earth Metals," *J. Am. Chem. Soc.*, **31**, 799 (1909).
7. MOOLENAAR, R. J., "Cesium Metal—Its Production and Purification," *J. Metals*, **16**, 21 (1964).

ROBERT E. DAVIS

S

SACRIFICIAL PROTECTION

Sacrificial protection is a widely used method of combatting corrosion. It is a form of cathodic protection, and the same theory applies. The basic principle is that of using up the capacity of the cathodes in the system through the introduction of a sacrificial metal which has more active anodes than those existing on the structure to be protected. Corrosion is therefore shifted to the sacrificial metal from the metal to be protected. In the absence of complications the sacrifiical metal will be consumed at a rate greater than the equivalent rate of corrosion of the unprotected structure.

To be sacrificial, a metal must have a more negative (active) potential in the corrosive medium in question than the metal to be protected. The standard reversible single electrode potentials of two metals do not necessarily indicate which will be sacrificial to the other. In some environments tin is usefully sacrificial to steel; zinc is sacrificial to aluminum; cadmium is sacrificial to steel. It can be hazardous to employ sacrificial protection without specific knowledge of the electrochemical behavior of the metallic couple in the environment in which it is to be used.

It is essential that there be a complete electrical circuit between the two metals. The sacrificial metal must be joined to the protected structure both by direct electrical contact and by a continuous electrolytic path through the corrodent. The inside of a pipe, for example, will not be affected by protection applied to the outside since there is no continuous electrolytic path here.

A feature of cathodic protection is that, in making a structure cathodic, alkali is locally produced. The effect of this is variable: for steel, it can cause passivation and assist protection; for aluminum, alkali produced by over-protection can dissolve the protective film and actually greatly accelerate attack. In structures protected with paint or other organic coatings, alkali produced by cathodic protection, in conjunction with electroosmosis, can cause detachment and blistering of the organic coating.

Sacrificial anode systems afford greater simplicity but less flexibility than do impressed voltage systems.

Anodes

The number of metals used for sacrificial protection is rather limited. The anode must be chosen so as to supply sufficient protection to do its job throughout its life, but its local corrosion rate should be low so that it will be long-lasting. Ideally, all corrosion of the sacrificial anode should be by virtue of the current flowing between it and the protected structure, and this current should be just enough to give full protection and no more. A magnesium or zinc anode may provide good protection in an acid environment, but it would corrode so rapidly that it would very soon be completely consumed. With a very active (negative) anode metal, the galvanic current may be higher than needed. An unnecessarily high galvanic current requires more frequent replacement of the anodes.

Magnesium anodes have enjoyed wide use in cathodic protection systems. This has resulted from proved reliability in many applications, in which they have been found to deliver the required protective current until there is virtually complete consumption of the anode metal. For many applications magnesium has a favorable voltage relationship to the material to be protected. On the negative side, efficiency is rather low with magnesium anodes. They are consumed at a rate substantially greater than anticipated from Faraday's law for oxidation to the divalent state. Along with this, hydrogen is evolved, which could be a possible explosion hazard in some cases.

The current efficiency is higher with zinc anodes than with magnesium anodes. In cases where it is applicable, zinc may be more economical. However, it provides a much lower potential than magnesium and is not generally satisfactory for corrosive media which have a high electrolytic resistance. In the past, zinc anodes have been unreliable because of adherent corrosion products which increased circuit resistance and thereby sharply decreased current output. This situation has improved considerably in the last few years. Zinc anodes providing lasting protection to steel in sea water are now made from special, low-iron, high-grade zinc with small additions of aluminum and cadmium.

Although aluminum is very active in a thermodynamic sense, it is a poor sacrificial anode material, except in salt-containing media, because of the characteristics of the protective film. Aluminum alloys are used as sacrificial anodes in a few cases.

Coatings

Sacrificial protection is also involved in plated metals. The major protective effect of a coating is that of covering the vulnerable metal surface with another material, so as to greatly limit the exposed area of vulnerable metal. However, in addition, the coating metal must have a more active potential than the protected metal in the specific environment to accomplish sacrificial protection at pores, scratches, and other areas where the basis metal may be exposed. To give lasting protection, the coating must itself corrode considerably more slowly than the unprotected basis metal would.

Zinc is probably the most familiar of the sacrificial coatings. Galvanizing, as zinc plating is commonly called, represents the largest use of zinc. It is accomplished either by dipping the material to be coated in molten zinc (hot-dipping) or by electroplating. Familiar iron or steel items commonly protected by galvanizing include sheet, pipe and fittings, electrical conduit, and wire. The life of a coating increases roughly proportionally to its thickness. Conventional coatings are put on by hot-dip galvanizing, which gives the familiar spangled appearance. Electrogalvanizing gives greater control of coating thickness and uniformity, as well as a coating which has better adherence and ductility. In most common corrosion environments,

the corrosion rate of zinc is considerably lower than that of iron. However, zinc possesses useful resistance to aqueous media only in the pH range of 6 to 12.

Tinplate represents another major application of a sacrificial coating. Although tin does not sacrificially protect steel from atmospheric corrosion, conditions inside the common food can are such that tin is sacrificial. It is, perhaps, fortunate that any metal exists which has such a uniquely ideal combination of properties as tin for this purpose. The old hot-dip tinning process has been continually giving way to electrotinning processes, which uniformly coat the steel sheet with from 15 to 80 μin. of tin.

Cadmium provides much the same protection for a steel surface as zinc, along with a more attractive appearance. Cadmium plating is also applied to copper and copper alloys as well as to other metals and alloys. Because of its high price, cadmium is used over zinc only in instances where it possesses some advantage from the appearance standpoint or from other factors. Such advantages include greater resistance to alkali and sea water, solderability, and galvanic compatibility with light metal alloys. The high toxicity of cadmium salts prevents the use of cadmium plate for food and beverage containers.

The most important use of aluminum as a sacrificial coating material is for the protection of the stronger and more corrodable aluminum alloys. The method of application is by cladding, rather than by plating, and the material is familiarly known as Alclad. The cladding metal is anodic to the aluminum alloy basis metal, providing sacrificial protection where the core metal might be exposed. Considerable attention has been and is being given to the use of aluminum-coated steel sheets. Aluminum offers little, if any, sacrificial protection to ferrous metals in many environments; but, when used as a coating, the little it does afford may be just enough. This material also possesses some advantages apart from consideration of sacrificial protection.

Localized Corrosion

In most cases localized corrosion of metals appears to be more of a problem than general attack. The electrochemical principle involved in sacrificial protection is one of the factors responsible for the widespread prevalence of localized attack. In localized attack, definite anodic areas of the structure are established, resulting in localized metal destruction, with corresponding definite cathodic areas involving reduction processes also established. An established anodic area affords sacrificial protection to the cathodic areas, thereby preventing attack on the cathodes and helping to keep the attack localized.

ERNEST L. KOEHLER

Cross-references: *Cathodic Protection; Electrogalvanizing.*

SCINTILLATION COUNTERS

The scintillation counter represents an improvement, by modern electronic techniques, of one of the first counting methods used in nuclear physics. Sir William Crookes and also Elster and Geitel in 1903 observed that a screen coated with small crystals of phosphorescent zinc sulfide displayed a brilliant luminosity when bombarded by alpha particles. When the surface of the screen was viewed with a magnifying glass, the light from the screen was found to consist of individual flashes of light, or scintillations. Early experiments proved that each scintillation was caused by a single alpha particle striking the screen. The zinc sulfide screens were found to be insensitive to high-speed electrons and gamma-rays but were sensitive to protons.

A visual observation technique consisting of a ZnS screen viewed through a low-power microscope was used in the first oscillation counters. In a typical visual counter, with a microscope of numerical aperture 0.45 and magnification 50, the faintest scintillations which could be detected were those produced by low-energy alpha particles and corresponded to 300 quanta entering the eye.

In the modern scintillation counter the microscope and human eye combination has been replaced by an efficient photomultiplier tube. The scintillations from the fluorescent screen are converted into electrical pulses at the output of the multiplier tube. A major advance in this new technique resulted from the work of Kallmann, who found that single beta and gamma rays could be detected with counters using large transparent blocks of naphthalene. The original naphthalene phosphor has been superseded by more efficient organic and also inorganic phosphors.

The following list of applications shows some of the possible uses of the photomultiplier scintillation counter.

(a) The detection and energy measurement of ionizing particles with a detection efficiency of 100 per cent under suitable conditions. The flux of particles can range from a few per second to millions per second.

(b) The detection and spectroscopy of x-radiation and gamma-radiation. In general, the detection efficiency is much higher than that of a gas counter or ionization chamber owing to the increased absorption in the phosphor compared with that in the gas and surrounding walls.

(c) The detection and the energy measurement of fast neutrons by recording the scintillations from the fast recoil protons produced in an organic phosphor.

(d) The detection of thermal neutrons by the scintillations resulting from slow neutron induced nuclear reactions within the phosphor.

Photomultiplier Tubes. The photomultiplier tube used in the scintillation counter consists of a photosensitive surface and an electron multiplier which amplifies or multiplies the initial number of photoelectrons. The most widely used photocathodes are thin surfaces of antimony cesium usually deposited on glass. The spectral response of a typical photocathode enclosed in a glass envelope is shown in Fig. 1.

Since the emission spectra of most phosphors are peaked in the blue, a more precise correlation with scintillation requirements is obtained by using a suitable filter with the tungsten light source.

A thermionic emission at room temperature of 10^{-15} to 10^{-14} amp/cm^2 is observed for antimony-cesium photocathodes. A decrease in the thermionic current by a factor of about 2 per 10°C change in temperature can be produced by refrigeration of the photocathode.

In practically all scintillation counters the photoelectric current is amplified or multiplied in an electron multiplier located in the same vacuum tube which contains the photoelectric surface. By means of the electron multiplier, the initial photoelectric current may be multiplied by a factor of 10^7 without the addition of appreciable noise from the multiplier.

Photomultiplier tubes are very sensitive to magnetic fields. This effect is due to the deflection of the beam of photoelectrons in the region between the photocathode and the first

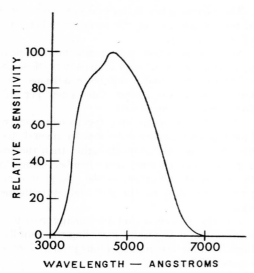

Fɪɢ. 1. Spectral sensitivity curve of an antimony-cesium photocathode.

dynode and in the region within the multiplying structure. For example, Engstrom has shown that, in the case of a 5819 tube, a field of 0.8 oersted parallel to the dynode cage axis reduces the tube gain by a factor of about three. Increasing the voltage between the cathode and first dynode reduces the effect, and high-permeability shields help to screen the tube from magnetic fields.

Inorganic Scintillation Phosphors. *Zinc sulfide*, activated with copper or silver, has the highest light conversion efficiency of any known phosphor. A value of about 25 per cent for the ratio of the energy of the emitted quanta to the energy lost in the phosphor by the incident particle is typical for the conversion efficiencies of these phosphors. The silver activated sulfide has a maximum emission near 4500Å and is well matched to the spectral response of many commercial photomultipliers. The copper activated sulfide has a maximum emission near 5200Å. The light from these sulfide phosphors has a decay time of the order of 10^{-5} sec and phosphorescence of much longer time duration has been noted. These phosphors in the form of powders show very low transparency to the emitted light and consequently are opaque in thicknesses greater than 25–50 mgm/cm². A thin layer of zinc sulfide is relatively insensitive to high energy electrons due to the low specific ionization of these particles. For this reason strongly ionizing particles,

such as low energy electrons or alpha particles, can be detected against a background of high-energy electrons or gamma radiation.

Sodium iodide, activated with thallium, is probably the most widely used inorganic phosphor. Since the crystals are highly transparent to their emitted radiation, large crystals may be used in scintillation counters. The relatively large absorption coefficient of the iodine component (85 per cent by mass) combined with large crystal size makes sodium iodide particularly suitable for the detection and spectrometry of gamma rays and x-rays. Sodium iodide may also be used as a detector of electrons and heavy particles such as protons and alpha particles.

The emission spectrum, with a peak at 4100Å, is well matched to the spectral response of most photomultiplier tubes. The decay time of the emitted light is 2.5×10^{-7} sec at room temperature, which is adequate for most counting experiments. The energy conversion efficiency is about 8.4 per cent.

Lithium iodide, activated by either thallium or tin, has been used as a scintillation crystal. The crystals have a blue-green emission spectrum and a fluorescent decay time of about 1×10^{-6} sec. A disadvantage of this phosphor is its low light conversion efficiency which is about $\frac{1}{10}$ that of sodium iodide. The most important application of lithium iodide is for the detection of thermal neutrons. Natural lithium contains 7.4 per cent of Li⁶, which has a large cross section for the absorption of thermal neutrons in the reaction Li⁶(n, α)H³. The product nuclei have a total energy of 4.8 Mev which results in scintillation pulses of constant size which may be detected against a gamma-ray background.

Organic Crystalline Phosphors. Organic phosphors have the following useful properties:

(a) The decay time of the emitted light is of the order of 10^{-8} sec.

(b) A high transparency to their fluorescence radiation.

(c) The maximum intensity of the light emitted from most organic phosphors is near the peak of the spectral sensitivity curve of many photomultipliers.

(d) The efficiency of energy-to-light conversion is high, although somewhat lower than that of ZnS (Ag) or NaI (Tl).

(e) The magnitude of the scintillation pulses produced by electrons is proportional to the energy when the energy is greater than 125 kev.

Anthracene has the highest energy-to-light conversion efficiency of the organic phosphors so far studied. For excitation by fast electrons the conversion efficiency at room temperature is about 4 per cent. The fluorescent spectrum excited by ionizing radiation has a main peak near 4450Å. The decay time of the fluorescence excited by electrons is about 2.7×10^{-8} sec at room temperature.

Stilbene combines a relatively high energy-light conversion efficiency with a very short scintillation decay time of about 7×10^{-9} sec. This phosphor has been widely used in high-speed coincidence experiments where a short resolving time is essential.

Organic Plastic and Liquid Phosphors. Liquid scintillators are useful whenever a large volume and relatively cheap scintillator is required. This type of scintillator is fast and highly transparent to its emitted radiation. At present the most efficient scintillator is a solution of *p*-terphenyl in xylene or in toluene. The scintillation efficiency of this type of scintillator at the optimum concentration of about 4 to 5 gm/liter is about 45 per cent that of solid anthracene. The decay time of the light from terphenyl solutions is 2 to 4×10^{-9} sec. The light emitted from terphenyl solutions for excitation by either ionizing radiation or by ultraviolet light has emission bands in the region 3450 to 3880Å. Since the emission spectrum is not well matched to the spectral response of most photomultiplier tubes, a wavelength shifter such as alpha naphthyl phenyloxazole is frequently added.

Plastic scintillators have been synthesized by incorporating an organic phosphor into a suitable transparent plastic. As in the case of liquid scintillators, the plastics have relatively high energy-to-light conversion efficiencies and have short decay times. Buck and Swank have described the properties of plastic scintillators formed by the polymerization of styrene and vinylstyrene solutions of organic phosphors. The most efficient scintillator was a polyvinyltoluene plastic with 4 per cent terphenyl and 0.02-percent tetraphenylbutadiene. This scintillator gave scintillation pulses 47 per cent as large as those from anthracene under similar conditions. The decay time of the light was less than 8×10^{-9} sec. Plastic scintillators of this type now are available commercially in a wide range of shapes and sizes.

Gas Scintillators. The gas scintillation counter represents the latest development in this field. This type of counter consists of a volume of gas contained in a cuplike container placed over the photocathode of a multiplier tube. The light emitted by gas molecules excited and ionized by the passage of an ionizing particle is detected by the photomultiplier. A scintillation pulse resulting from the de-excitation of the gas molecules is expected to have a time duration of about 10^{-9} sec. The amplitude of the light pulses is proportional to the energy expended by the charged particles and is independent of the charge or mass of the exciting particles.

The gases xenon, krypton, agon, and helium have been used successfully in scintillation counters. Since the light emitted from these gases extends far into the ultraviolet region, a wavelength shifter must be used to convert the shorter wavelengths to a frequency region that matches the spectral response of the photomultiplier. A thin layer of quaterphenyl on the inner surface of the gas cell has been used successfully as a wavelength shifter. The time duration of the scintillation pulses from these gases is about 10^{-8} sec.

The gas scintillation counter appears to offer definite advantages over both organic and inorganic crystals as a detector of heavy charged particles such as alpha particles and protons. The main advantage of the gas scintillator over the organic crystal is the fact that the response is linear with the energy of the heavy particle in the case of the gas but not in the organic crystal. When compared with either ZnS (Ag) or NaI (Tl) the response of a gas scintillator is much more rapid. The low sensitivity of a gas counter to gamma-rays will permit the detection of heavy particles in a large background radiation.

References

1. YUAN, C. L., AND CHIEN-SHIUNG WU, Editors, "Methods of Experimental Physics," Vol. 5, Part A, Section 1.4, "Nuclear Physics," New York, Academic Press, 1961.
2. CURRAN, S. C., "Luminescence and the Scintillation Counter," New York, Academic Press, 1953.
3. BIRKS, J., "Scintillation Counters," New York, McGraw-Hill Book Co., 1953.

JAMES S. ALLEN

Cross-references: *Electroluminescence; Fluorescence; Laser; Luminescence; Phosphorescence; Phosphors.*

SEA WATER CORROSION. See GALVANIC CORROSION; MARINE CORROSION.

SECONDARY BATTERIES. See BATTERIES, STORAGE.

SEEBECK, THOMAS JOHANN (1770–1831)

Thomas Johann Seebeck was born in Reval, Estonia on April 9, 1770. He studied medicine in Berlin and Gottingen but became intensely interested in science through discussions with his teachers and associates. Having sufficient money to follow his avocation, science, rather than his vocation, medicine, Seebeck began experiments with light and electricity. He never held a public office or academic position. From 1802 to 1810 he lived in Jena where he met and associated with such prominent men as Goethe, Hegel, Ritter, and Shelling. Seebeck's interest in science matured during this period. In 1818 he moved to Berlin where he had been elected to the Berlin Academy of Sciences.

Seebeck became interested in Oersted's observations of the deflections magnetized needles undergo when placed in the vicinity of a conductor carrying an electric current. In 1821 while working with electric circuits using dissimilar metal wires, Seebeck observed that an electric current was generated when the junction between a copper wire and a bismuth wire was heated. This discovery, the Seebeck Effect, emphasized that electricity could be produced without chemical intervention. It is the basis for temperature measurement and control by the use of thermocouples. It also provided a constant current source for many delicate experiments. Georg S. Ohm, hearing of Seebeck's discovery, arranged two copper-bismuth junctions in series. He placed one junction in boiling water and the other junction in melting ice. With this arrangement he was able to obtain currents constant enough to determine the relationship between voltage, current, and resistance now known as Ohm's law.

Seebeck was a proficient experimenter; he not only discovered the phenomena of thermoelectricity but produced a large amount of experimental data on the thermoelectric properties of materials. His lists included metals, alloys, minerals, and other chemical compounds. He arranged the materials tested into a thermoelectric series; the relative positions of materials in the list are in remarkable agreement with our present knowledge. Seebeck had found a source of electric energy that was as efficient as other sources known at that time. Seebeck misinterpreted the cause of thermoelectricity, preferring the name thermomagnetic currents. He was so convinced of the magnetic effects resulting from the temperature difference between metal contacts that he proposed that the earth's magnetic field was a result of the temperature differences between the hot equator and the cold poles. Despite these beliefs, Seebeck's discovery of and contributions to thermoelectricity are a remarkable achievement.

ALBERT J. CORNISH

Cross-references: *Ohm, Seebeck Effect, Thermoelectricity, Thermocouples.*

SEEBECK EFFECT

The observation in 1821 by Thomas Johann Seebeck that a heated junction of dissimilar metals develops an electromotive force (voltage) is called the *Seebeck Effect*. These junctions generate electricity by the direct partial conversion of heat energy to electric energy. The greatest use of the Seebeck effect has been the measurement of temperatures. However, as an understanding of the phenomena increases and materials and techniques improve, the Seebeck effect may develop into one of the major sources of electricity.

For small temperature differences the electromotive force produced is proportional to the temperature difference. The constant of proportionality, generally designated as α or S, has been called the thermoelectric power. Actually α has the dimensions of volts per degree. These dimensions are not dimensions of power. A more satisfactory name, the *Seebeck Coefficient*, has been proposed and is replacing the older term. Although the Seebeck coefficient can be determined for a single material, in the past it has been generally treated and measured as a property of junctions. Many reported values of the Seebeck coefficient designate the composition of both members of the junction. Others use a thermoelectric inert material, such as lead or platinum, as a standard. In the latter experiment a junction is made with one wire of the standard material and the other of the material to be measured.

The source of the Seebeck effect is the tendency for charge carriers, electrons, or holes, to diffuse away from the heated portion of an electric conductor. If in a closed electric circuit, a junction between different materials is heated above ambient, electrons flow from the material with the least number of electrons to the material with the most. If the junction is cooled below ambient, the electric flow will reverse itself. To maximize this effect a material that normally conducts by holes (p-type) is joined to a material that normally conducts by electrons (n-type). Several p-type materials used are Te, Sb, BiSbTe$_3$, ZnSb and GeTe. Some of n-type materials are Ge, Bi, Bi$_2$Te$_2$Se, InAs and PbTe.

When the Seebeck effect is used to measure temperatures, the junction is called a thermocouple. Two junctions give more reliable temperature measurements if they are arranged in series but oppose each other, that is, the order of the second pair is reversed. One junction is maintained at some standard temperature, such as melting ice, and the other junction placed at the temperature to be measured. When many thermocouples are connected in series alternately, the assembly, called a thermopile, is capable of detecting very small temperature differences. The Seebeck effect therefore has provided science and industry with a convenient method of temperature measurement. In the future it should provide mankind with another means of converting heat energy to electric energy.

ALBERT J. CORNISH

Cross-references: *T. J. Seebeck, Thermoelectricity, Thermoelectric Power, Thermoelectric Power Generation, Thermocouples.*

SEMICONDUCTORS

The term semiconductor generally denotes materials with an electrical conductivity between that of metals and that of insulators (i.e., between about 10^5 ohm^{-1} cm^{-1} and about 10^{-5} ohm^{-1} cm^{-1}) which increases exponentially with increasing temperature. For example, the room temperature conductivity (σ) of germanium (the best-known semiconductor) is $\sigma = 2 \times 10^{-3}$ ohm^{-1} cm^{-1}; for comparison, the conductivity of silver is 6×10^5 ohm^{-1} cm^{-1} and that of alumina, Al$_2$O$_3$, 8×10^{-12} ohm^{-1} cm^{-1}.

In most semiconductors of general interest the temperature dependence of the conductivity originates primarily in the exponential increase of the electrical carrier concentration with increasing temperature. Other forms of energy may bring about changes in the carrier concentration; such a change brought about by light leads to *photoconductivity* (q.v.).

Semiconductivity (a negative temperature coefficient of resistance) was first observed by Faraday (1833) in silver sulfide, Ag$_2$S. Photoconductivity and electrical rectification were also discovered in the 19th century. Soon thereafter the element selenium was used in photoconductivity applications (photocells). Later on the mineral galena, PbS, was used as a point contact rectifier for high-frequency currents and found applications in the early radio receivers. However, the most important landmark in the science and technology of semiconductors (solid state electronics) was the discovery of the transistor (a solid state amplifier) by Bardeen, Brattain and Shockley at the Bell Telephone Laboratories in 1949.

Electron Configuration

The electrical (as well as other) properties of materials are related to the valence electrons, i.e., the electrons of the unfilled outermost shell of the atoms. In the case of metals, these valence electrons do not participate in the formation of localized chemical bonds; that is, they are free to conduct at all temperatures. In the case of semiconductors the valence electrons form localized chemical bonds (covalent or partially ionic bonds). Actually for semiconductivity it is necessary that there be just enough electrons available to fill the chemical bonds (two electrons per bond). This is the basis of the well-known octet rule. In the germanium crystal, for example, each germanium atom (four valence electrons) forms four bonds with four other germanium atoms; each atom contributes one electron per bond; thus, each atom is surrounded by eight electrons. Thus, (at the temperature of absolute zero) all the valence electrons in semiconductors are bonded and no conduction is possible. Depending on the strength of the bonds, the electrons can be dislodged and become available for conduction. The number of dislodged electrons depends on the temperature and the energy gap of the semiconductor; this energy gap is related to the bond strength and represents the energy necessary to excite an electron from its bonded state (valence band) to its conducting state (conduction band).

According to the quantum theory of solids, electrons in crystals must be arranged in energy bands. Within an energy band, the occupancy of the individual energy levels by electrons follows the laws of quantum mechanics. Taking into consideration the wave character of the electrons and the periodic potential associated with the periodicity of the crystalline lattice, it can be shown that the above energy bands may be separated by energy regions for which no electron energy states are allowed. These forbidden energy regions are called energy gaps. Within an energy band no electron conduction is possible if the band is completely occupied (filled) with electrons. Electron conduction is possible only in a partially filled energy band. In semiconductors, there are just enough electrons to completely fill the energy bands (valence band) at 0°K; the empty energy band (conduction band) is separated by an energy gap. When this gap is overcome, electrons can be excited into the conduction band and be free to conduct. In a general way, many insulators can be considered as semiconductors with too large an energy gap to achieve conduction at ordinary temperatures. Metals, on the other hand, have partially filled energy bands and, thus, electrons are free to conduct at all temperatures.

Electrical Conductivity

In the case of a single type of carrier (see below) the electrical conductivity, σ, is related to the concentration of the carrier, n, and its mobility, μ (given in sq cm/volt-sec), as follows:

$$\sigma = nq\mu \qquad (1)$$

where q is the charge of the carrier (electronic charge). In Eq. 1, q is a constant and μ is only a weak function of temperature; n, however, depends exponentially on the energy gap, E_g and the absolute temperature, T. Thus, Eq. 1 can be written:

$$\sigma = A e^{-E_g/2kT} \qquad (2)$$

where k is Boltzmann's constant; in view of the exponential term, A can be taken approximately as a constant. Thus, Eq. 2 allows an approximate determination of the energy gap, i.e., by measuring the conductivity as a function of absolute temperature.

With the excitation of an electron to the con-

ducting state, an *electron deficiency* or a *hole* is created in the network of bonds (valence band). This hole is positively charged and it constitutes another type of electrical carrier. The conduction by holes may be crudely visualized as follows: an electron from a regular bond moves into the hole; and, thus, the hole appears in the bond from where the electron came and so on.

Since a hole is created with every electron entering the conduction band, the concentration of free electrons and that of holes is the same. Thus, the complete expression of conductivity for a semiconductor is

$$\sigma = nq\mu_e + pq\mu_h = nq(\mu_e + \mu_h) \qquad (3)$$

where n is the concentration of electrons, μ: their mobility, p the concentration of holes and μ_h their mobility.

Concentration of Electrical Carriers

Assuming that the generation of an electron and a hole is a process analogous to chemical dissociation and that the electrons and holes are free to move (quasi free particle approximation), then chemical kinetics can be readily introduced in considering the electrical carriers in semiconductors. Thus, if the thermal generation of electron-hole pairs is represented as:

$$(pn) \text{ or null} \rightleftarrows n + p \qquad (4)$$

then according to chemical kinetics:

$$n = p = \frac{2(2\pi kT)^{3/2}}{h^3} (m_e{}^* m_h{}^*)^{3/4} e^{-E_g/2kT} \qquad (5)$$

where $m_e{}^*$ and $m_h{}^*$ is the effective mass of the electron and hole, respectively. The effective masses of carriers generally are not equal to the mass of the free electron. This difference originates in the fact that carriers in a crystal move in the periodic field of the crystal in addition to the externally applied electric field. The concept of the effective mass formally accounts for the crystal field in the equation of motion.

Eq. 5 is a more accurate expression of the temperature dependence of electrical carriers than Eq. 2. Thus, the concentration of electrical carriers can be determined at any temperature if the energy gap is known. The effective masses can be approximated in many instances to be equal to the free electron mass. In the case of germanium, for example, E_g is 0.75 electron-volts (ev) and $n = p \cong 2.5 \times 10^{13}$ per cc.

The mobility of carriers—the other parameter

in the conductivity expression, Eq. 1—expressed as velocity per unit electric field is given by physical theory as:

$$\mu = q\tau/m^* \qquad (6)$$

where τ is the relaxation time of the charge carrier in the crystal (time between collisions). The parameter, τ, and, therefore, μ, varies with temperature but not as strongly as the carrier concentration. Also, τ is decreased by crystal defects or impurities.

Intrinsic and Extrinsic Semiconductors

The discussion thus far has been limited to semiconductors in which there are exactly two electrons available for each bond in the crystal. In such cases, as pointed out above, the concentration of electrons and holes is equal since to each electron excited to the conducting state there corresponds one hole. This type of semiconductors are called *intrinsic semiconductors*.

However, the exact balance of two electrons per bond can be upset in the presence of chemical impurities or crystal defects. Impurities or defects can introduce either an excess or a deficiency of electrons. The semiconductors then are called *extrinsic semiconductors*. An excess of electrons present in the crystal cannot be accommodated in the bonds (valence band) and must enter the conduction band. In this case, there are more electrons than holes, the conductivity is primarily due to electrons (majority carriers) and the semiconductor is called an *n-type semiconductor* (n stands for negative). Deficiency of electrons implies excess of holes in the valence band and therefore a concentration of holes greater than that of conducting electrons. This type of semiconductors with holes as majority carriers is called *p-type* (where p stands for positive).

As an illustration consider the substitution of arsenic atoms for germanium atoms in a germanium crystal. An arsenic atom has five valence electrons, one more than a germanium atom. This extra electron must enter the conduction band without, of course, the generation of a hole. The arsenic atom is called a donor (D) and it releases the extra electron according to:

$$D \rightleftarrows D^+ + n \qquad (7)$$

The positive charge associated with the donor atom (D^+) is localized and not free to move. On the other hand, if gallium atoms (three valence electrons) are substituted for germanium atoms, an electron deficiency is brought about in the crystal, leading directly to the formation of holes in the valence band. The electron deficient impurity atoms are called acceptors (A) and are ionized according to the equation:

$$A \rightleftarrows A^- + p \qquad (8)$$

Here again the negative ion (A^-) is localized and not free to conduct.

The excess carrier concentration in extrinsic semiconductors is, of course, determined by the concentration of impurities. At the same time, however, the concentration of carriers due to intrinsic excitation increases exponentially with temperature as in Eq. 5. Thus, at sufficiently high temperatures the intrinsic carrier concentration exceeds the concentration of carriers due to impurities and the semiconductor is rendered intrinsic.

Purity Requirements

The strong dependence of the electrical properties of semiconductors on impurities or crystal imperfections in general has necessitated the development of techniques for obtaining semiconductors with an extremely high degree of chemical purity and crystalline perfection. Silicon and germanium have been prepared in a higher degree of purity and perfection than any other solid. *Zone refining* (q.v.) has been the most successful method of purification. It is based on the fact that the composition of a freezing crystal can differ from the composition of its liquid. Thus, a short molten zone passed along a solid bar, say of germanium, draws impurities out of the body of the material. By this method, germanium has been prepared with impurities at the amazingly low level of one part in 10^9 or even less. The need for high levels of purity will be illustrated with a numerical example. Intrinsic germanium at room temperature has a carrier concentration of about 2.5×10^{13} per cc. The presence of arsenic in germanium at a level of one part in 10^8 contributes about 4.5×10^{14} electrons per cc (the number of germanium atoms per cc is 4.5×10^{22}). In view of Eq. 1, this arsenic impurity increases the conductivity of germanium by a factor of about 20.

Characterization of Semiconductors

The most important and useful parameters for characterizing a semiconductor are the carrier concentration and their mobility. The concentration of the majority carriers can be conveniently calculated from the *Hall effect* (q.v.) or Hall voltage which results when a magnetic field is applied perpendicular to the direction of current flow. In the conventionally used arrangement an electric current is passed through a uniform rectangular sample of the semiconductor (say, in the x direction) and a magnetic field is applied perpendicular to the current flow (z direction). As a result of the magnetic field, the charge carriers are deflected in the y direction (perpendicular to the other two) developing a voltage, the Hall voltage, E_H. This voltage is related to the current density, j, and the magnetic field, B as follows:

$$E_H = R_H j B \tag{9}$$

where R_H is a coefficient called the *Hall coefficient*. It can be shown that the Hall coefficient can be written as

$$R_H = \pm \frac{r}{nq} \text{ in cc/coulomb} \tag{10}$$

where n is the concentration of the carriers, q the electronic charge, and r is constant between 1 and 2, usually taken equal to 1. Thus, from R_H one obtains the concentration of the majority carrier. Since the direction of the carrier deflection depends on the sign of the carriers (positive or negative), the sign of R_H determines the type of carrier. From the carrier concentration, n, one can now determine the corresponding mobility by measuring the conductivity and using Eq. 1. The carrier concentration of commonly encountered n- or p-type germanium or silicon is 10^{14} to 10^{16} carriers per cc. The electron mobility of pure germanium and silicon at 300°K is 3,900 and 1,300 sq cm/volt-sec, respectively; the corresponding hole mobilities are 1,800 and 500 sq cm/volt-sec.

It should be emphasized that the measured values of the carrier concentration and mobility must always be examined carefully. Thus, donors and acceptors in about equal amounts will result in a very small apparent majority carrier concentration, since the two types of impurities compensate each other. Such *compensated semiconductors* may be mistaken as materials of high purity. In this type of materials or in materials which are of poor crystalline perfection, the mobility value is usually low. In many instances, proper characterization of semiconductor material requires the determination of the Hall coefficient over a broad temperature range. Analysis of such data yields important information on the nature of impurities. Depending on the material and the problem to be solved, there are, of course, other parameters which must be determined; infrared absorption and thermal conductivity are important among these parameters.

Semiconductor Surfaces

In the development of semiconductor science and technology semiconductor surfaces have played an important role. Basic measurements of the properties of the materials must in many instances be performed through the surfaces; furthermore, the function of many types of devices is intimately associated with the surface characteristics. Yet surfaces are far more difficult to understand theoretically or to deal with experimentally. They essentially constitute a giant lattice defect.

An important property of a semiconductor surface is that it introduces energy levels lying in the forbidden energy gap between the valence band and the conduction band. This type of surface state can be introduced also by the adsorption of foreign atoms or the chemical interaction of the surface atom with the environment. The tendencies of the surfaces to become contaminated and to undergo slow changes such as brought about by slow surface film formation constitute difficult problems in the semiconductor science and technology. Completely clean and well-characterized surfaces can only be achieved by very tedious techniques involving vacuum of the order of 10^{-10} mm Hg. Such "clean" surfaces, however, can be submitted to a rather limited number of measurements and are of no technological importance. "Real" surfaces remain a serious problem in solid state electronics.

Applications

Prior to the discovery of the transistor, and in fact for some years afterwards, by far the largest use of semiconductors was in rectifiers of many types and sizes. Materials such as cuprous oxide (Cu_2O), selenium, germanium, and silicon were widely employed in point contact structures. Photocells (using selenium) and other similar devices also were in use.

With the discovery of the transistor action and the development of the p-n junction (sharp transition from a p-type to n-type region within the same single crystal) the greatest use of semiconductors (most particularly silicon and germanium) is to be found in the transitor and diode industry. In the broad spectrum of electronics and communication technology, the variety of transistors and diodes employed is very large indeed and is still growing. Among the other applications of semiconductors, one may mention photocells (Cu_2O, Se, etc.), infrared detectors (PbS, PbSe, InSb, etc.), thermoelectric devices (Bi_2Te_3, etc.), and solar batteries or energy converters (q.v.). With the continuing discovery and development of new semiconductor materials (primarily semiconductor compounds), it appears that the scope of semiconductor technology will continue to broaden for some time to come.

References

1. HANNAY, N. B., Editor, "Semiconductors," New York, Reinhold Publishing Corp., 1959.
2. JOFFE, A. F., "Physics of Semiconductors," New York, Academic Press, Inc., 1960.
3. KITTEL, C., "Elementary Solid State Physics," New York, John Wiley and Sons, Inc., 1962.
4. SHOCKLEY, W., "Electrons and Holes in Semiconductors," New York, D. Van Nostrand Company, Inc., 1950.
5. SMITH, R. A., "Semiconductors," Cambridge, England, University Press, 1959.
6. SPENKE, E., "Electronic Semiconductors," New York, McGraw-Hill Book Company, Inc., 1958.

HARRY C. GATOS

Cross-references: *Hall Effect; Photoconductivity; Photovoltaic Effect in Semiconductor Junctions; Single Crystals; Solar Energy Converter; Thermoelectric Power; Zone Refining.*

SEMICONDUCTORS, ORGANIC

Perhaps surprising to some, it is a well-established fact that many organic substances can act as semiconductors, even semimetallic conductors of electricity. And by this is meant electronic conduction. Purposely excluded here is conduction by ions (as in electrolysis). Also excluded in this discussion of semiconductors are those materials which are mechanical mixtures of insulators and metallic materials, such as obtained by using conductive fillers in plastics.

To be classed as a semiconductor a substance should exhibit:[1]

(a) A specific conductivity approximately in the range 10^3 to 10^{-10} or 10^{-12} mho/cm.

(b) A negative temperature coefficient of resistance. (Some degenerate semiconductors exhibit near zero thermal activation energies, a few, such as certain pyropolymers, show semimetallic behavior and have small positive temperature coefficients).

(c) Conductivity sensitive to chemical structure, impurity, and morphology.

(d) Usually, a high thermoelectric power.

(e) Rectification or at least nonohmic behavior at junctions on occasion.

(f) Photosensitivity as a general property, exhibited as photoconduction and perhaps photovoltage if in contact with a suitable electrode.

Most of the familiar organic substances, such as benzene, napthalene, anthracene, and polystyrene, are insulators and lie outside this purview. A brief list of a few of the many organic semiconductors together with some of their known electronic properties is given in Table 1. With few exceptions they are observed to follow the relation[2]

$$\sigma = \sigma_0 \exp [-\Delta E / 2kT]$$
$$= \sigma_0 \exp [-E_a / kT]$$
$$\Delta E = 2E_a$$

where σ = specific conductivity, mho/cm; σ_0 = a constant expressing a combined product of the size of the electronic charge, the concentration of potentially available carriers, and their mobility; ΔE = energy interval, loosely related to the forbidden energy gap, E_g, in the simple band theory of semiconductors; and E_a = thermal activation energy. ΔE and E_a are conventionally expressed in units of electron volts; k = Boltzman's constant = 0.86165×10^{-4} ev/degree Kelvin, per particle = 1.380×10^{-23} joules/degree Kelvin, per particle; and T = absolute temperature, degrees Kelvin.

Units: one ev = 23.053 kcal/mole
$kT_{300°K}$ = 0.0257 ev
$\cong 1/40\ ev$

The field of organic semiconductors is presently in a most active state of flux. Literally hundreds of new examples of organic substances displaying semiconduction and related enhanced electronic behavior appear each year. This discussion will content itself with broadly classifying the organic semiconductors and their characteristics.

On a molecular scale organic semiconductors are molecular assemblies of either (a) small

TABLE 1. RESISTIVITIES OF TYPES OF SEMICONDUCTORS

Material Type	Material	Resistivity, ohm-cm
Metals (polycrystalline, crystals of three-dimensional symmetry)	silver	1.5×10^{-6}
	copper	1.7×10^{-6}
	iron	10×10^{-6}
	nickel	7.2×10^{-6}
Metals (polycrystalline, crystals of layered type)	arsenic	40×10^{-6}
	bismuth	119×10^{-6}
Organic (super layer lattice compounds)	potassium graphite (powder)	30×10^{-6}
	graphite bromide (powder)	100×10^{-6}
	graphite (powder)	1200×10^{-6}
Organic (limited-layer lattice compounds)	polymer carbons	800 to 8080×10^{-6}
	pyro-polymer (metal-doped)	10^{12} to 2000×10^{-6}
	pyro-polymer (undoped)	10^{12} to 8000×10^{-6}
Organic (molecular complexes, of limited-layer lattice type)	aromatic hydrocarbon-iodine	7.3 to 3000
	aromatic hydrocarbon-alkali metal	10^8 to 10^{11}
	quinone-amine complexes	10^4 to 10^{11}
Organic (polymers)	phenolphthalein-type	10^2 to 10^{11}
	poly copper phthalocyanine	10^4 to 10^7
	aromatic polythioethers	10^4
	chlorinated aromatic polythio-ethers	0.1 to 10^{10}
	ferrocene ketone polymer	10^{10} to 10^{11}
	polyphenyl	10^{10} to 10^{11}
	polyacrylonitrile	10^{11} to 10^{13}
	most polymeric hydrocarbons	10^{13} to 10^{21}
	most commercial polymers	10^{13} to 10^{21}
Organic (monomers) (free radicals)	violanthrone-B	10^6
	diphenyl picryl hydrazyl	10^8 to 10^9
	Banfield and Kenyon's radical (phoxyl)	10^{15}
	Coppinger's radical (galvanoxyl)	10^{13}

monomeric molecules, e.g., copper phthalocyanine, violanthrene, quaterrylene ($C_{40}H_{20}$), or (b) polymeric molecules. The polymeric assemblies can be further classified as those having monomeric portions bonded by:

(1) coordinated covalencies (i.e., the infinite order donor-acceptor complexes), such as perylene-2I_2, or imidazole,

$$\cdots N \overset{\displaystyle CH}{\underset{\displaystyle CH=CH}{<}} N-H \cdots$$

which is hydrogen-bonded, showing a conductivity of 10^{-10} mho/cm at room temperature, p-phenylene diamine-chloranil complex, and certain ferrocene polymers.

(2) covalent bonds, such as the polyphenylenes, polybenzimidazoles, and the polyacene quinone radical (PAQR) polymers. The latter can be made particularly conductive and contain high (10^{18-20} cm^{-3}) concentrations of unpaired electrons.

(3) ionic bonds, such as cationic or anionic dye salts. Very often the former appear to be n-type semiconductors, the latter being p-type.

Some semiconducting organic polymers are charge transfer (donor-acceptor) complexes in which transfer of charge between donor-acceptor pairs is nearly complete, creating ionic type bonding. Examples are the alkali metal-anthracene complex, the triethylammonium: (tetracyano-quinodimethane)$_2$ ion radical salt, and potassium graphite. All are infinite order complexes.

Again, the organic semiconductors can be classified on a morphological basis. Some can be obtained easily as single crystals, others only as polycrystaline, quasi-crystalline, or perhaps only as amorphous solids or liquids exhibiting semiconduction.

Among the many measurements of the physical properties of these interesting materials are: the specific conductivity and its temperature and pressure coefficients;[3] the thermoelectric power (Seebeck coefficient) and Hall effects and their temperature coefficients; the ohmic character; photovoltage; photoconduction; unpaired spin concentration as by electron spin resonance; infrared absorption; x-ray diffraction; and the pressure sensitivity of the Seebeck coefficient. The study of the dependence of the enhanced electronic behavior as a function of the molecular structure has been particularly active.[4, 5, 6, 7]

The conductivity of many of the molecular solids (i.e., those containing an appreciable fraction of their atoms separated by distances of the van der Waals type, 3.3 to 4 Å) is now known to be remarkably sensitive to applied pressure.[3] This piezoconductivity has led to use of these organic semiconductors in pressure transducers. The enhanced electronic properties of organic semiconductors is most pronounced in those molecules having conjugated structures.[4] It appears, however, that mere conjugation is not sufficient. There must be conjugation of a superlative degree,[6, 7] termed ekaconjugation, such that extensive pi orbital interaction occurs along the molecule. Ekaconjugation is of a degree equal to the number of contiguous pi orbitals, and of an order proportional to the orbital-orbital interaction of successive orbitals. The latter is highly sensitive to the planarity of the successive atoms and is readily interrupted by twists out of planarity along the molecule. Unlike germanium and silicon whose conductivity is particularly sensitive to foreign atoms of different valence (e.g., Al, In, P, As) but not very sensitive to those of like valence (e.g., Si in Ge or vice versa), the organic semiconductors so far examined show little such sensitivity. Instead they are sensitive to the presence of molecules of highly ekaconjugated character. Application of pressure increases intermolecular orbital overlap and therefore increases conduction.

Based upon what is now known of the organic semiconductors, their usefulness to man lies more in the future than in the past. In the past, pyropolymers obtained by pyrolysis of organic materials have been widely used to make resistors. Recently piezoconductive polymers have been used in highly sensitive transducers. Photovoltaic cells and rectifiers have been made from organic monomers on an experimental basis. There presently seems little likelihood that organic semiconductors would serve as transistors or thermoelectricity devices of high efficiency. This does not preclude their future use in other ways, and possibly on a large scale. Some success has been had in combining the semiconductive properties with the absorptive ion exchange properties of the semiconductive polymers to create electrically reversible units for the conversion of saline water to fresh water.

The biological implications of organic semiconductivity are far reaching. Use of these concepts has already permitted deep insight into the primary process of photoconduction and has provoked suggestive and partly fruitful ideas in the understanding of photosensitive carcinogenesis and of cancer mechanisms.

The study of organic semiconductors is truly interdisciplinary, interweaving physics, physical chemistry, electrochemistry, organic chemistry and biochemistry.

References

1. POHL, H. A., "Semiconduction in Polymers," Chapter II, "Modern Aspects of the Vitreous State," Ed., J. D. Mackenzie, London, Butterworths, 1962.
2. POHL, H. A., "Physico-Chemical Aspects of Organic Semiconductors," chapter in "Progress in Chemistry of the Solid State," Ed., H. Reiss, Pergamon (in press).
3. POHL, H. A., REMBAUM, A., AND HENRY, A. W., "Effects of high pressure on some organic semiconducting polymers," *J. Amer. Chem. Soc.*, **84**, 2699 (1962).
4. INOKUCHI, H., AND AKAMATSU, H., "Electrical conductivity of organic semiconductors," *Solid State Physics*, **12** (1962).
5. BROPHY, J. J., AND BUTTRY, J. W., Editors, "Organic Semiconductors," New York, Macmillan, 1962.
6. POHL, H. A., AND ENGELHARDT, E. H., "Synthesis and characterization of some highly conjugated semiconducting polymers," *J. Phys. Chem.*, **66**, 2085 (1962).
7. POHL, H. A., AND OPP, D. A., "The nature of semiconduction in some acene quinone radical polymers," *J. Phys. Chem.*, **66**, 2121 (1962).

HERBERT A. POHL

SIGN CONVENTIONS. See ELECTRODE POTENTIALS, SIGNS OF; NOMENCLATURE, REMARKS ON; TENSION, CELL AND ELECTRODE.

SILICON CARBIDE

Silicon carbide, SiC, formula weight 40.07, is a colorless[1] crystalline material. Its hardness, refractoriness, electrical, and optical properties, as well as its chemical stability, even at elevated temperatures, make it unique for many uses. The commercial product, used mainly as an abrasive and as a refractory, contains minor amounts of impurities which cause the color to vary from pale green to black. It is produced commercially by an electrochemical process discovered by Edward G. Acheson[2] in 1891 while conducting experiments in a miniature electric arc furnace. Despite the fact that it can be formed with relative ease and its principal components are abundant in the earth's crust, its only known natural occurrence has been in a meteorite from the Canon Diable in Arizona.

Silicon carbide may be formed under various time-temperature conditions from mixtures of carbon and silica or silicon as described by Ruff[3] and Baumann.[4] It can be formed as low as 525°C from Si and C under special conditions from a carbon-rich alloy of silicon, aluminum, and zinc. Silicon carbide crystals have also been produced by gaseous cracking in at least five vapor systems. One such system consists of silicon tetrachloride and toluene in the presence of hydrogen.[5] The primary form, called beta silicon carbide, has a cubic crystal form and is stable to about 2100°C. Above that temperature, it begins to transform monotropically to either the hexagonal or the rhombohedral crystalline form and does so completely at about 2400°C. Silicon carbide does not fuse at ordinary pressures but decomposes into silicon and graphite, with dissociation beginning about 2250°C.

Ramsdell[6] suggests a system of classification of silicon carbide by crystalline form. He calls the cubic-type simply beta silicon carbide as there seems to be no modification possible for this form. The designation of alpha-type silicon carbide consists of indicating the number of layers in a unit cell followed by the letter "H" or "R," depending on whether the unit cell is hexagonal or rhombohedral. To date, at least eleven of the former and seventeen of the latter type have been found.[7] The 6H polytype is the form most commonly found in the commercial furnaces.

Commercial silicon carbide is produced at strategic locations throughout the world where electric power is available at reasonable rates.

Although Canada is the principal producer, large amounts are also made in the United States. Other plants are located in Norway, U.S.S.R., France, Italy, Spain, Switzerland, Czechoslovakia, West Germany, East Germany, Brazil, Argentina, and Japan. In all cases, long, horizontal resistance furnaces are used to react high-grade silica with slightly over the stoichiometric amount of carbon in the form of coke or anthracite coal. Sawdust is added to promote mix porosity, and thus facilitate the escape of gases generated during the electrochemical reaction. According to Ruff,[3] the reaction proceeds in two steps:

$$SiO_2 + 2C \rightarrow Si + 2CO$$

$$Si + C \rightarrow SiC$$

More recent work[3] indicates that the reaction involves silicon monoxide as represented by the following sequence:

$$SiO_2 + C \rightarrow SiO + CO$$

$$SiO + C \rightarrow Si + CO$$

$$Si + C \rightarrow SiC$$

The batch type furnaces range up to 60 feet long by 10 feet wide and hold up to 200,000 pounds of mix. The furnace walls consist of removable sections of cast iron frames lined with low-grade firebrick.

The mix is delivered to the furnace by hoppers and an overhead traveling crane or by conveyors. When the furnace is one-half full, the loading is interrupted temporarily so that a loose graphite core can be placed between the electrodes located at each end of the furnace. The core is of uniform cross-section and may range up to ten inches thick and 60 inches wide, depending upon the size of the furnace. Placing the balance of the mix above the core completes the loading operation. Power is applied at rates up to 5,000 kw and at voltages ranging from 400 to 200 as the resistance of the charge changes during the heating period of about one and one-half days. The heated charge requires several days cooling to permit handling. By proper scheduling, one transformer can service four to six furnace units. Upon removing the side walls, the loose covering known as "old mix" falls away exposing the ingot. The old mix is similar in composition to the original mix and is re-used. The ingot is oval in cross-section and is encased by a crust one to two inches thick. This relatively thin crust zone forms because the sharp temperature gradient at that position favors condensation of the oxide impurities. This fortunate concentration facilitates the effective disposal of the unwanted impurities.

In making the pure or pale green type silicon carbide, the addition of sodium chloride to the mix helps to form volatile compounds of the impurities. The ingot proper containing the commercial crystals of silicon carbide is broken into large sections and removed from the furnace. The graphite core is recovered for reuse as core material and any losses due to handling are offset by adding one to two inches of coke to the top of the new core. The crystalline ingot is finally crushed and screened to desired sizes. Depending upon the end use, the grain may be further treated by cleaning with acid or alkali, then washed with water and dried.

While the theoretical power required is calculated[9] to be 2.61 kwh per pound of silicon carbide, the average power requirement for a typical run will exceed that amount due to thermal and electrical losses in the system. Several attempts have been made to produce SiC continuously but none has been found commercially successful. The production of silicon carbide for the United States and Canada in the sixty years since its discovery has been increasing as follows:

Year	Short Tons	
1891	50 pounds	(10)
1901	1,919	(10)
1911	5,188	(11)
1921	2,707	(12)
1931	8,193	(12)
1941	44,962	(12)
1951	100,498	(12)
1961	125,726	(12)

Silicon carbide is widely used for abrasive purposes by reason of its extreme hardness and its availability at reasonable costs. Its hardness is somewhere between that of corundum and diamond or between 9 and 10 on the Moh's hardness scale. By the Knoop[13] indentation method, its rank among other principal abrasive materials is as follows:

Diamond	8,000–8,500
Boron Carbide	2,230
Silicon Carbide	2,000
Fused Alumina	1,635

In addition to being hard, silicon carbide is relatively brittle. This characteristic makes it preferable to other tougher but less hard abrasives, such as fused alumina, for certain grinding applications. It is especially suitable, therefore, for grinding cast iron, chilled iron, hard alloys, marble, and ceramics, as well as the metals copper, brass, and aluminum. It is superior to other abrasives as regards the sharp cutting action in working rubber, leather, plastics, and wood. The silicon carbide grain can be used loose for lapping or for the wire sawing of quarry products. Paper or cloth coated with silicon carbide grain is available as belts, discs, and sheets for abrasive use. The grain can be formed into shapes, such as wheels, sticks, or tumbling nuggets. The bonding agents may consist of rubber, plastics, resin, or other organic materials. The inorganic or vitrified bonds contain clay, glass, feldspar, or mixtures thereof.

Its abrasive-resistant qualities make the grain useful when incorporated in brake-lining materials. It can be used to impart nonslip properties to floors or stair treads. Other such uses include incorporation in deck paint and in asphalt paving, particularly at busy intersections.

Another large use for silicon carbide is that of refractories. The properties that make it especially advantageous include high thermal conductivity, high thermal emissivity, low thermal expansion, excellent hot strength, good resistance to thermal shock, and resistance to oxidation at elevated temperatures.

The ceramic industry uses large quantities of bonded silicon carbide products in the form of setter tile, saggers, posts, pyrometer tubes, muffles, and furnace hearths.

The chemical inertness of silicon carbide to molten ash makes it especially suitable as the principal ingredient for boiler wall brick as well as for brick to line water gas generators. The high thermal conductivity and emissivity of silicon carbide, along with its excellent thermal shock resistance offer unique advantages as checker brick for use in steel-making operations. Similarly, bonded silicon carbide shapes are used in gas and petroleum industry cracking units. Special shapes are widely used in the zinc smelting and refining industry. Steel mills use skid rails made of bonded silicon carbide in working hot sheet or billets because of the resistance to abrasion at the temperatures involved. Silicon carbide-based cements are used for laying brick and other shapes as well as for rammed linings or patches in various types of furnaces.

Considerable tonnage of silicon carbide finds application in ferrous metallurgy. In cupola practice, the silicon carbide is added as a briquette and to ladles of molten steel as granules. The addition of silicon carbide results in an improvement of the microstructure and mechanical properties of the cast iron. When added to molten steel, the silicon carbide decomposes releasing Si and C. This deoxidizing reaction is strongly exothermic and increases the temperature and fluidity of the metal.

A unique combination of properties makes silicon carbide suitable for the manufacture of electric-heating elements. Furnaces using such elements can be operated as high as 1600°C, even in an oxidizing atmosphere. Elements are made by extruding rods from a mixture of silicon carbide grain and a temporary binder, drying, and then recrystallizing electrically at temperatures close to the dissociation temperature. A review of the properties of such heating elements has been made recently by Macer.[14]

The semiconductive properties of silicon carbide make it useful for devices such as Thermistors for measuring or controlling temperatures, and similar devices called Varistors for controlling voltages. A discussion of such uses is given by Shive.[15] High-tension power lines are protected by lightning arresters made of silicon carbide. It is also fabricated into shapes for use as resistors and as dummy loads.

Several new forms of silicon carbide have been developed recently. A dense type has been prepared by siliconizing shapes made of silicon carbide and carbon granules with a temporary bond.[16] The resultant product appears as a solid body of silicon carbide with the porosity approaching zero, although it contains some small inclusions of the original silicon carbide and carbon. This dense material is most suitable for wear-resistant parts, such as blasting nozzles, mold liners, dies, and wear plates. A silicon nitride- or oxynitride-bonded silicon carbide has remarkable corrosion resistance and has been found acceptable for use in aluminum reduction cells and acid-handling equipment. Ultrafine silicon carbide made in a special arc furnace possesses outstanding properties as a pigment for wear-resistant finishes and as a cryogenic insulator.[17]

References

1. SLEY, R., AND RILEY, H. L., *Nature (London)*, **160**, 468 (1947).
2. ACHESON, E. G. (to Carborundum Company), U. S. Pat. 492,767 (February 28, 1893).
3. RUFF, O., "Formation and Dissociation of Silicon Carbide," *Trans. Electrochem. Soc.*, **68**, 87–109 (1935).
4. BAUMANN, JR., H. N., "The Relationship of Alpha and Beta Silicon Carbide," *J. Electrochem. Soc.*, **99**, 109–114 (1952).
5. KENDALL, J. T., "Growing of Silicon Carbide Crystals by Gaseous Cracking," "Proc. Conference on Silicon Carbide," pp. 67–72, New York, Pergamon Press, 1960.
6. RAMSDELL, L. S., "Studies on Silicon Carbide," *Am. Minerals*, **32**, 64–82 (1947).
7. ADAMSKY, R. F., AND MERZ, K. M., *Z. Krist.*, **111**, 350–361 (1959).
8. HUMPHREY, G. L., TODD, S. S., COUGHLIN, J. P., AND KING, E. G., "Some Thermodynamic Properties of Silicon Carbide," *U. S. Bureau of Mines Reports of Investigations 4888* (July, 1952).
9. FINLAY, G. R., "Calculated Energy Requirements of Electric Furnace Products," *Chem. in Canada*, **14**, No. 2, 25–27 (February, 1952).
10. "The Mineral Industry," New York, Hill Publishing Co., Vol. XVI, pp. 149–156, 1907.
11. "The Mineral Industry," New York, McGraw-Hill Book Co., Vol. XX, p. 668, 1911.
12. "Minerals Yearbook," Washington, D. C., U. S. Bureau of Mines, for years 1921, 1931, 1941, 1951 and 1960.
13. KNOOP, F., PETERS, C. G., AND EMERSON, W. B., "A Sensitive Pyramidal Diamond Tool for Indentation Measurements," *J. Research National Bureau Standards*, **23**, 39–61 (1939).
14. MACER, E., *Ind. Heating*, **26**, 896–904, 920, 1335–1342 (1959).
15. SHIVE, J., "Properties, Physics, and Design of Semi-Conductor Devices," Princeton, New Jersey, D. Van Nostrand Co., 1959.
16. TAYLOR, K. M., "Improved Silicon Carbide for High Temperature Parts," *Materials and Methods*, **44**, No. 4, 92–95 (1956).
17. KUHN, W. E., "Formation of Silicon Carbide in the Electric Arc," Paper presented at the Los Angeles meeting of the Electrochemical Society, May, 1962.
18. BUTLER, G. M., "The Past and Future of Silicon Carbide," *J. Electrochem. Soc.*, **104**, 640–644 (1957).

JOHN C. McMULLEN

SILVER ELECTROREFINING

The treatment of copper and lead ores and, to a lesser extent, silver and gold ores provides a silver bullion containing gold, other precious metals, and various impurities, which is known as doré. This requires refining to separate and recover gold, platinum, palladium, and occa-

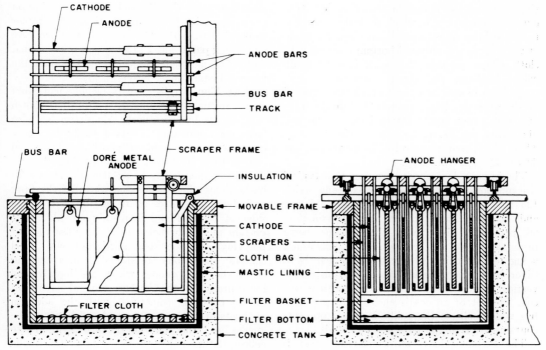

FIG. 1. Moebius cell for silver refining.

sionally the rare elements rhodium, ruthenium, iridium, and osmium. Refining is also necessary to produce silver of sufficient purity for mechanically fabricating into sheet and wire and for chemical processing into photographic emulsions.

A once widely used method of refining "parted" the silver from the other constituents by boiling the doré with concentrated sulfuric acid. This treatment dissolved the silver and some impurities while leaving the precious metals and other impurities as a sludge. After diluting with water, the acid solution was decanted and the silver precipitated on copper slabs by replacement according to the electromotive series. The cement silver was then collected, washed, and melted into bars. The sludge was treated for the recovery of its valuable constituents.

First developed in 1884, the electrolytic refining of silver is now almost universally superseding the acid parting. Similar to other such processes, the impure doré is cast into suitably shaped anodes which are electrolyzed in a solution of silver and copper nitrates containing a very small amount of free nitric acid. Crystals of commercially pure silver are loosely deposited on cathodes of silver, stainless steel, or graphite, from which the metal may be readily removed, washed free of solution, melted, and cast into

shapes for the market. Most of the impurities are electropositive to silver and remain in the electrolyte while the electronegative precious metals are collected as a slime in bags which surround the anodes or on diaphragms which separate them from the cathodes. Characteristics of the several electrolytic processes are described in the following sections. There are two such methods in active service; these differ principally in the layout and details of the cell construction, and each has certain advantages and disadvantages which will be mentioned.

The Moebius Cell

A small majority of the silver refining cells now in use are of the vertical Moebius type; this is the older of the two major processes. Fig. 1 shows the general features of the design of a typical cell, but, in practice, numerous variations in construction details are found.

Most cells are made of acid-proof stoneware, asphalt-lined concrete, or mastic-coated wood. Occasional installations using Type 316 stainless steel or even plastic have been reported. On an experimental scale, one group of stainless steel tanks has been lined with polyester resin reinforced with fibreglass in an effort to reduce pitting resulting from anodic corrosion by stray currents. Filter trays, which fit inside the cells to collect the silver crystals, are usually made of wood with a perforated bottom covered with cloth which permits the electrolyte to drain while retaining the silver; sometimes these trays have hinged bottoms to facilitate removal of the crystals. Rigid polyvinyl chloride trays are also being tried. Dimensions of the cell illustrated are 24 in. long by 26 in. wide by 22 in. deep, and the steel cells mentioned are 32 by 32 by 26 in. deep.

The impure doré anodes are cast to a typical size of about 10½ by 4¾ by ⅝ in. and weigh 125 troy ounces; some may be slightly larger and heavier. Their content is approximately 96 per cent silver with the balance being principally gold and copper. Each anode has a lug for attaching to a conducting bar by a silver hook and several anodes are suspended vertically, side by side, across the width of the cell. The set of anodes is enclosed in a canvas bag which collects the gold slime and prevents contamination of the pure silver crystals.

The cathode sheet, on which the silver is deposited, is made either of rolled silver, about ¹⁄₃₂ in. thick and with an area similar to that of the set of anodes, or of stainless steel. Each sheet is attached to a bar carrying the current and hung vertically across the cell.

In most cells, four cathode sheets are interspersed with three sets of anodes enclosed in cloth. The electrical circuit is in multiple (or parallel), similar to that in a copper refinery. The electrodes are submerged in electrolyte at 3 in. spacing. Wooden scrapers, which are mechanically oscillated before the cathode faces, continually break off the silver crystals as soon as they are deposited and thereby obviate the possibility of short circuits caused by crystal growth; the metal drops into the trays on the cell bottom. The scrapers also provide gentle agitation of the electrolyte which is beneficial. These trays and all other arrangements inside the cell, such as electrodes and scraper mechanisms, are carried on a removable frame so that the entire assembly can be periodically lifted from the cell and the silver collected. From six to eight cells are connected in series to form a single electrical circuit.

The Thum Cell

Somewhat in a minority, but nevertheless widely used, are the horizontal Thum cells,

also known as the Balbach type. In addition to being easier to construct, they are simpler to operate than the Moebius cell as they have no moving parts. Fig. 2 illustrates a conventional design but, again, details vary greatly among the various installations.

Most Thum cells are made of acid-proof stoneware or mastic-lined concrete; that shown is 52 by 24 by 9 in. deep. Aluminum has also been tried but was corroded badly by stray currents. A more modern, plastic-lined, wooden cell, is used by Cerro de Pasco; Fig. 3 gives detailed dimensions. A wooden or stoneware basket, extending across the width of the tank and about two-thirds of its length, rests on the sides of the cell and is readily movable. The bottom of this basket consists of glass rods or polyvinyl chloride rods reinforced with steel centers; these rods are spaced 3 in. apart and carry the doré anodes which are loosely laid horizontally in the basket. Several layers of muslin or duck, sometimes with the addition of sheets of filter paper, are placed between the anodes and the rods supporting them. These collect the gold slime that forms on the anode during electrolysis and prevent it from falling on and thereby contaminating the silver crystals deposited at the cathode on the cell bottom. The proper maintenance of these cloth diaphragms and filters is of great importance in keeping the gold content of the fine silver at a minimum.

A number of impure doré anodes, usually 8 by 12 by ½ in., cover the area of the bottom of the basket, resting on the filter cloth which in turn lies on the glass or plastic rods. Sometimes several layers of anodes are laid upon each other as neat fits are not essential. The anodes are similar in composition to those used in the Moebius cells. Electrical contact is made by a "door knob" of cast silver, or less frequently, by a 50 per cent silver-50 per cent gold alloy which has high corrosion resistance. This piece is relatively heavy and stable and simply stands, at the end of a flexible cable, on the top layer of anodes. The basket assembly containing the anodes may be moved from one end of the cell to the other or completely lifted out when the silver crystals are removed.

The cathode of the Thum cell is generally carbon or graphite slabs which lie on the floor of the cell to provide a conducting surface on which the silver deposits; stainless steel may also be used. The area directly beneath the

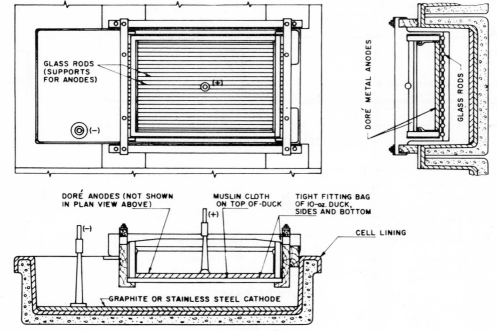

FIG. 2. Thum cell for silver refining.

anode basket receives most of the deposition, and it is necessary to remove the silver crystals at frequent intervals. Long handled rakes of wood, hard rubber, or aluminum are convenient for this purpose. The same means of electrical contact as for the anodes is made in the cathode compartment.

With high gold content in the anodes, mechanical cleaning of the lower face to remove the accumulated slimes may be needed once or even twice each day; unless this is done, the electrical resistance of the cell builds up to an undesirable point. The distance between the anode and cathode faces is about 4 in. From 20 to 30 cells are connected in series depending on the size of the plant and the capacity of the d-c electrical supply.

Identical electrolyte may be used for both the Moebius and Thum cells, but in the latter system no agitation takes place. Due to the impurities, more silver is deposited at the cathode than is dissolved at the anode; hence, the electrolyte is depleted. The deficiency is made up by the addition of fresh silver nitrate. As the electrolyte becomes foul, a portion of it is periodically drawn off, the silver cemented out on metallic copper, the copper cemented out on metallic iron, and the remaining solution discarded.

Other Cells

Another cell, used for some years by a major refiner, was a vertical type similar in many respects to the cells used for electrolytic refining of copper or lead. The doré anodes were much larger than those described above and weighed about 175 pounds; they were suspended in bags to collect the gold as usual. The cathodes were aluminum sheets, and the electrodes were arranged in multiple inside each cell with a number of cells in series. Aside from the far less labor required to cast and handle the large anodes, the novelty of the process consisted in adding tartaric acid to the otherwise conventional electrolyte; some 25 pounds of this reagent were consumed per ton of silver produced. Due to this addition, the silver crystals formed a fine-grained, adherent deposit on the cathode; moreover, as the deposit was quite brittle it could be broken and stripped with relative ease. While the installation had merit, certain factors, learned from experience, eventually made the process uneconomic.

One unique cell employed a moving belt of sheet silver as a cathode which, on its travel, carried the crystals outside the cell, thus making collection easier. Another used the surface of a rotating cylinder as a cathode from which the

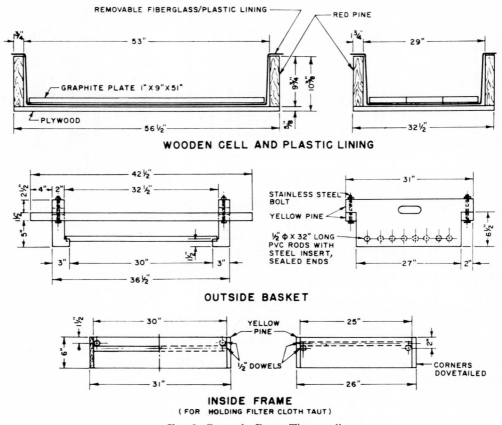

FIG. 3. Cerro de Pasco Thum cell.

silver could be scraped. All such devices endeavored to eliminate the tedious hand labor of the Moebius and Thum cells but all, other than these, have become obsolete.

Comparison of Moebius and Thum Cells

The distinct characteristics of the two principal silver refining cells permit a direct comparison between them. Local operating conditions govern their choice for any particular installation. Advantages of the Moebius cell over the Thum cell are:

1. It requires less floor area per unit of production and volume of electrolyte. This is because of the vertical, instead of horizontal, suspension of the electrodes and because both faces of the anodes are corroded simultaneously.

2. It requires less power per unit of production because of the closer spacing between electrodes, the absence of the anode basket, and consequently lowered voltage across the cell.

3. It consumes less nitric acid per unit of output.

4. It has a lower labor cost due to the mechanical scraping of the crystals from the cathode and their less frequent removal from the cell.

5. Due to more rapid rate of deposition, less precious metal is tied-up in the process.

Advantages of the Thum cell over the Moebius cell are:

1. The anodes are completely consumed, and no anode scrap is returned for remelting. This is important for metallurgical accounting accuracy as well as for the time, labor, and fuel economies.

2. Anodes may be any size or shape within the capacity of the basket.

3. Lower grade anodes can be refined, and less care is required to insure that the cathodes are not contaminated with impurities or that gold is not lost.

TABLE 1. OPERATING DATA OF SILVER ELECTROREFINING PLANTS

Item	Plant A	Plant B	Plant C	Plant D
Cells:				
Type	Moebius	Moebius	Thum	Thum
Size-inches	24 x 26 x 22	32 x 32 x 26	56 x 32 x 10	52 x 24 x 9
Material	Ceramic; rubber-covered steel	Rubber-lined steel	Plastic-lined wood	Mastic-lined concrete
Number available	180	15	100	300
Anodes:				
Weight-troy ounces	125	150	510	250
Number per cell	20	15	5	5
% Scrap returned	18	25	None	None
Silver-%	98.0	92.5	98.3	96.5
Gold-%	1.5	6.5	0.24	1.5
Copper-%	—	0.6	1.18	0.9
Cathodes:				
Number per cell	5	6	1	1
Material	Steel; silver	Silver	Graphite	Graphite
Hours between silver removal	20	12	4	4
Anode slimes—% of anode	3	—	—	5
Electrolyte composition:				
Silver-gpl	33	130	56	35
Copper-gpl	30	15	89*	80
Free nitric acid-gpl	None	1.2	1.6	1.5
Total NO$_3$-gpl	—	—	210	—
Nitric acid used-lb/1000 troy ounces silver			3.9	
Current:				
Cathode density-amps/sq ft	33	30	20	25
Amperes/cell	450	500	200	200
Volts/cell	2.5	2.8	3.0	4.0
Current efficiency-%	93.0	93.5	97.3	94.5
Troy ounces silver/kwh	42.8	43.5	39.1	24.0

Plant Identification and Recent Annual Production in Millions of Troy Ounces

A—American Smelting & Refining Co., Perth Amboy, N. J. 54
B—Canadian Copper Refiners, Montreal, Canada 8
C—Cerro de Pasco Corp., La Oroya, Peru 20
D—U. S. Metals Refining Co., Carteret, N. J. 18

* Despite some references to the contrary it has been established that the copper in the electrolyte is in the bivalent form.

4. Structural features and electrical circuit are less complex; thus, installation cost is lower.

5. Operation and maintenance are simpler as there are no moving parts.

6. Silver crystals may be removed without interrupting continuous operation.

Operating Data

The electrochemical equivalent of silver is 0.00111793 grams per coulomb or 4.02454 grams per ampere hour. Therefore, a typical refining cell operating at 200 amperes will deposit 590 troy ounces of silver per 24 hours at 95 per cent current efficiency.

Operating data from a number of actual refineries are tabulated in Table 1.

Treatment of Silver Crystals and Gold Slime

While strictly not within the scope of this article, brief mention of the disposal of the refined silver crystals and the gold slimes that result from the electrorefining of silver is warranted.

Silver crystals from the cells are washed free of entrained electrolyte and then melted; in modern practice, high frequency induction furnaces are generally used for this purpose. Older installations may still melt the metal using graphite crucibles or retorts within an oil or gas-fired tilting furnace. At one plant the crystals are melted in an oil-fired reverberatory, and sodium nitrate is added to the molten charge, to remove last traces of certain impurities such as bismuth. Rough bars are cast which are later remelted by electrical means, the oxygen adjusted with charcoal, and the standard shapes, weighing 1000 troy ounces, poured. Fine bars for the market assay 99.90 per cent silver minimum and many brands reach 99.98 per cent. Copper is usually the largest impurity.

The gold slimes remaining within the anode compartments of the cells may retain as much as 25 per cent silver. The silver is removed by boiling the slimes with concentrated sulfuric acid, diluting, and filtering off the gold residue. This material, which is about 95 per cent gold and still contains the platinum group metals and impurities, is melted for further refining.

References

The following volumes, articles, and personal records contain information on this subject:
1. BARKER, I. L., AND CERRO DE PASCO CORPORATION, personal files and records.
2. BRIDGSTOCK, G., ELKIN, E. M., AND FORBES, S. S., "Operation at Canadian Copper Refiners Limited," *Can. Mining Met. Bull.*, **53**, 773–787 (Oct. 1960).
3. KOEHLER, W. A., "Principles and Applications of Electrochemistry," Vol. 2, New York, John Wiley & Sons, Inc., 1944.
4. MANTELL, C. L., "Industrial Electrochemistry." 2nd Ed., New York, McGraw-Hill Book Co., Inc., 1940.
5. MOSHER, M. A., "Secondary Metals from Electrolytic Copper Refining," *Trans. AIME*, **106**, 427–440 (1933).
6. RICHARDS, A. E., "The Refining of Gold and Silver," chapter in "The Refining of Nonferrous Metals," London, Institution of Mining and Metallurgy, 1950.
7. SCHLOEN, J. H., AND ELKIN, E. M., "Treatment of Electrolytic Copper Refinery Slimes," chapter in "Copper," edited by A. Butts, ACS Monograph No. 122, New York, Reinhold Publishing Corp., 1954.
8. WAGOR, E. J., "Refining of Gold and Silver Bullion," chapter in "Handbook of Nonferrous Metallurgy," edited by D. M. Liddell, New York, McGraw-Hill Book Co., Inc., 1945.

I. L. BARKER

SILVER PLATING

Silver plating, first used commercially about 1840, is one of the oldest forms of electrodeposition. It is used to form a silver coating on base metals, such as copper alloys, steel, and other ferrous alloys. These deposits have both decorative and protective value on tableware and other articles in the home, as well as on musical instruments, jewelry, surgical instruments, chemical equipment, and electronic circuit components.

Electrodeposition of silver also is a basis of defining the coulomb: the quantity of electricity which must pass through a circuit to deposit 0.0011180 grams of silver from a solution of silver nitrate.

By far the chief silver electroplating bath now in use commercially is the one based on potassium silver cyanide, in which the ratio of silver to cyanide is at least one silver atom to two cyanide molecules. This is much like the bath originally introduced by Elsner in 1842 and has demonstrated superiority over other types of silver plating baths. As described below, the plating baths now used contain other components as well as $KAg(CN)_2$.

The electrodeposition of silver generally is performed through the use of a two-bath system: an initial silver or nickel strike or preplate, followed by the silver plating bath. The strike solution, though it may be eliminated from a cycle, and not without some penalties, is included in the cycle to prevent immersion deposits of silver. These, if they occur, will result in a poorly bonded plate that may peel away or blister under thermal or mechanical shock. The cost of the silver in a reasonably heavy deposit practically dictates the use of this low-cost striking operation to insure good deposits.

Silver anodes in a silver plating bath may be in the form of miscellaneous shapes—elliptical, round, flat sheet, shot, and balls. Though it is a matter of general preference to use pure silver anodes, some applications make it more practical that insoluble anodes, such as stainless steel, be used. Under special circumstances, a combination of stainless or other insoluble anode material is used with silver anodes. When only insoluble anodes are used, the silver content of the bath is maintained by addition of silver cyanide complex (potassium silver cyanide).

Tank construction may vary, ranging from unlined to lined to solid plastic. In one large application, that of a tank car, the tank car itself served as the solution container as well as the cathode, enabling the interior to be finished with a heavy silver coating at a minimum of material expense. Plastic tanks, or those lined with rubber or plastic are preferred by many electroplaters since problems with stray currents are thus eliminated.

Formulations

Basic formulas vary according to individual application. Higher plating rates are permitted with baths that are high in metal content. However, where investment in the amount of silver is of importance, the silver content may be held at a low value, i.e., 3 troy ounces per gallon rather than 10 troy ounces per gallon. Potassium formulated solutions, since they permit higher deposition rates, are the general rule and potassium baths far outnumber those compounded with sodium salts in commercial installations.

Preplate Baths

Strike Bath	(for copper and copper alloys)
Potassium silver cyanide	1.0–1.3 oz/gal
Potassium cyanide	8.0–10.0 oz/gal
Temperature	70–85°F (20–30°C)
Current density	15–25 amperes per square foot

Prestrike or conditioner	(for steel parts)
Nickel sulfate	27–32 oz/gal
Nickel chloride	6–10 oz/gal
Boric acid	4–6 oz/gal
pH	2.0–3.0 electrometric
Current density	20–40 amperes per square foot
Temperature	105–115°F (40–46°C)
Time	5 minutes

(Or)

Potassium silver cyanide	0.4 oz/gal
Potassium copper cyanide	4.0 oz/gal
Potassium cyanide	9.0 oz/gal
Temperature	70–85°F (20–30°C)
Current density	15–25 amperes per square foot

Wood chloride nickel strike
(for passive metals such as stainless steels)

Nickel chloride	32.0 oz/gal
Hydrochloric acid (conc.)	1.0 pint/gal
Temperature	70–85°F (20–30°C)

Plating Solutions. An all-around general purpose formula will operate with a metal content of 3.0 troy ounces per gallon of bath. Free cyanide will also be at the 3.0 ounce level. Carbonates are added for anode corrosion.

Proprietary brighteners, added to closely controlled limits, enable electroplaters to deposit coatings that have mirror reflecting qualities, and about double the hardness of unbrightened coatings, or both. Probably the first of the truly full-bright silver formulations was developed by Kardos.[3] In this formulation a double brightener, composed of turkey red oil (sulfonated) and the reaction produce of a ketone with carbon disulfide, is utilized.

Another recent development by Greenspan[4] utilizes bismuth or antimony as a complex polyglyceride and by reason of codeposition of the antimony or bismuth produces hardnesses double that of other systems. Silver content is high, 99.25 per cent, but hardness values of 130 DPH, approaching 90-10 per cent coin silver, have been reported.

Since the proprietary baths are controlled with a fixed amount of brightener additives, the following formulas are subject to minor modifications as stipulated by the vendors of the patented compositions.

General purpose electrolyte	
Potassium silver cyanide	10 oz/gal
Potassium cyanide	10 oz/gal
Potassium carbonate	2 oz/gal
Temperature	70–85°F (20–30°C)
Current density	5–10 amperes per square foot

High-speed electrolyte	
Potassium silver cyanide	20–30 oz/gal
Potassium cyanide	15–20 oz/gal
Potassium carbonate	2 oz/gal
Temperature	70–85°F (20–30°C)
Current density	15–50 amperes per square foot

In the high-speed formulation, the higher metal content permits higher plating speeds. Extra plating speed is effected through the use of agitation. Formulas lend themselves to both rack plating and bulk or barrel plating.

References

1. GRAHAM, A. K., Editor, "Electroplating Engineering Handbook," New York, Reinhold Publishing Corp., 1962.
2. LOWENHEIM, F. A., Editor, "Modern Electroplating," Second Ed., New York, John Wiley and Sons, Inc., 1963.
3. KARDOS, O., U. S. Patent 2,666,738 (1954).
4. GREENSPAN, L., U. S. Patents 2,735,808 and 2,735,809 (1956).

A. KORBELAK

SILVER-SILVER CHLORIDE ELECTRODE. See REFERENCE ELECTRODES.

SINGLE CRYSTALS OF METALS

Solids may exist in either an amorphous or a crystalline form. The atoms or molecules in amorphous materials are arranged in space with an order extending over an extremely short range, whereas the atoms or molecules in crystalline materials are arranged with an order extending over many atomic or molecular diameters. When this long-range order extends to the boundaries of the solid, the solid is referred to as a single crystal. Single crystals of metals are rarely found in nature because so few metals exist in nature in massive form in the elemental state. A notable exception is copper which has been found in the form of large crystals in some deposits.

A single crystal with perfect long-range order is an ideal which has rarely, if ever, been observed. Two major types of imperfections are common in metals, structural imperfections and chemical imperfections. Structural imperfections consist of two types, those in which an in-

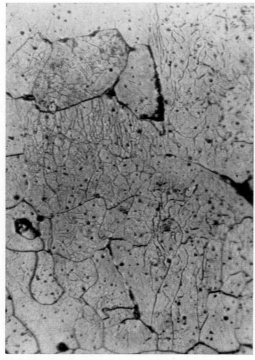

FIG. 1. A mosaic structure developed within the grains of a recrystallized single crystal of iron heated through the body-centered cubic-face-centered cubic phase transformation at approximately 900°C. Sample etched in nital. ×150.

homogeneity in order is accommodated over a large volume relative to that occupied by a single atom and those in which the inhomogeneity is accomodated over a small volume of the approximate size of an atom. The first type is known by the general term "dislocation" and the second type by the term "point defect." Under certain conditions of thermal history, many of the dislocations in a metal accumulate in lines and enclose small volumes of the metal. These volumes have a slightly different orientation than neighboring volumes and the boundaries between such volumes are detectable by etching techniques. These boundaries are referred to as "subgrain boundaries" and the structure as a whole is referred to as a "mosaic structure." Fig. 1 shows a mosaic structure within the grains of a recrystallized single crystal of iron. Point defects occur when an atom of the metal is not present in its equilibrium lattice position or when an impurity atom occupies a substitutional or interstitial position.

Defects play an important role in controlling the electrochemical properties of metals. The places where dislocations intersect the surface of a metal are often more active and thus more susceptible to chemical attack. This is particularly true in the case of pure metals. Fig. 2 shows pits developed at the sites of emerging dislocations during the etching of a copper single crystal. Dislocations often act as convenient regions for the precipitation of impurities in a metal. For example, tellurium which has a small solubility in copper at high temperature tends to precipitate at dislocations when the metal is cooled. These impurity centers are readily attacked by chemical reagents and pits develop at these sites.

Single crystals of metals are prepared by a variety of techniques and from many different environments. The most widely applied method involves controlled solidification of the molten metal. The liquid metal is confined in a crucible with a pointed tip, as in the Bridgman method, and is subjected to a slowly moving temperature gradient so that crystallization occurs first at the tip and proceeds at a controlled rate from this point. Another very useful method, the Czochralski method, involves inserting a small seed crystal into molten metal and withdrawing this seed slowly with rotation. These two procedures require good temperature control, inert atmospheres, and considerable art on the part of the experimenter and are limited to use with metals which exhibit no crystallographic phase change between the melting point and the lowest temperature to which the crystal is subjected.

Thin single crystals of metals are prepared by the deposition of metal vapor on a single crystal of a suitable substrate material. Single crystals are also prepared by electrodeposition on a seed crystal in some cases, as for example the electrodeposition of nickel as a single crystal on the (100) face of a copper crystal. Single crystals are formed by chemical reaction, such as the reduction of volatile metal halides by hydrogen and the reduction of nickel ions in fused salts by aluminum, magnesium, or other reactive metals.

Very large crystals of titanium, zirconium, hafnium, tungsten, boron, and other metals are prepared by the decomposition of a volatile halide on a hot wire of the same or different metal. Chlorides, bromides, and iodides are used. A disproportionation reaction takes place in some systems, and proper control of the pressure, temperature of the source metal, and temperature of the wire permits a continuous transport of metal (by conversion to a halide) from the source to the hot wire where metal atoms are deposited.

Many metals undergo major changes in crystal structure when cooled from high temperature to room temperature. Iron is an outstanding example of this behavior. Single crystals generally recrystallize at this phase transformation point upon either heating or cooling, with the resultant conversion of the single crystal to a solid containing many small crystals. Special techniques must be used to prepare single crystals of such metals. Iron has been successfully prepared by a strain-anneal method in which energy is imparted to a polycrystalline rod, bar, or strip by compression, tension, or torsion. Controlled heat treatment of the solid below the phase transformation results in the formation of large crystals.

Metallic single crystals have found their greatest application in basic research aimed at understanding better the principles governing the behavior of solids. However, some industrial applications have been made of metallic crystals. Single crystals of the very refractory metals such as tungsten are capable of certain metal-forming operations which cannot be carried out on similar brittle polycrystalline materials. Preparation of the single crystal is thus an important

FIG. 2. Etch pits formed at dislocation sites on the (111) surface of a copper single crystal. Dark pits are deeper than light pits and correspond to different type of dislocation. ×200. [*Photograph courtesy of Dr. Fred. W. Young, Oak Ridge National Laboratory*]

step in the metal fabrication process. Single crystals of metals prepared in needle-like form have unique high-strength properties. Their incorporation in composites yields materials with useful properties. Single crystals of an alloy of cobalt and iron have found application in neutron diffraction and single crystals of aluminum have been used in bent-crystal monochromators for x-ray diffraction.

Single crystals exhibit anisotropic behavior, that is, many of their properties are strongly dependent on the direction in which the property is measured. The magnetic properties of ferromagnetic materials, for example, are dependent on orientation of the crystal. Electrical transformer manufacturers take advantage of this phenomenon by orienting the crystals in the laminated sections of the core by rolling and heat treatment in such a way that the product has the most desirable magnetic properties and the minimum size and weight. The manner and type of deformation of metals are also dependent

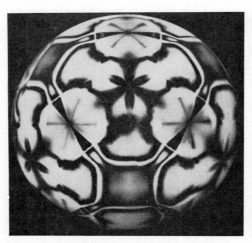

FIG. 3. Interference color pattern formed on a single crystal sphere of copper by oxidation in air at 200°C. Crystal was cleaned by thermal etching in a high vacuum prior to oxidation. [*Photograph courtesy of Dr. Kenneth Lawless, University of Virginia*]

FIG. 4. Pattern formed on a single crystal of copper during electrodeposition of nickel. The dark, highly reflecting areas are single crystal and the matte areas are polycrystalline.

on orientation. In metal-forming operations it is often necessary to adopt procedures designed to avoid a preferred orientation of the small crystals making up the materials to prevent undesirable changes in shape. In nonmetallic crystals, anistropy of electrical and optical properties are important characteristics which have been utilized in the fabrication of devices.

Single crystals in the form of spheres have proved to be extremely useful in studies of the electrochemical properties of metals. A single crystal in the form of a sphere exposes all crystal faces at the surface, and the orientational dependence of certain processes can be determined in a single experiment. Large spherical single crystals are prepared by machining a large crystal, or they are grown originally in this shape. Strain-free and brilliantly smooth surfaces are obtained on such experimental samples by chemical or electrolytic polishing. The available evidence indicates that surfaces prepared in this way approach smoothness on an atomic scale over small areas.

Studies using spherical single crystals have shown that processes such as corrosion by liquids and gases, wetting, catalysis, friction, and wear, and electrodeposition all occur at different rates or in a different manner on the various faces of a single crystal. Two examples are given. Fig. 3 shows the beautiful interference pattern observed on an electrolytically polished single crystal of copper cleaned by thermal etching in a vacuum and exposed to air at 200°C. The pattern is a result of different rates of oxidation on different crystal faces. The symmetry of this cubic metal is such that the pattern repeats itself six times on the surface of the sphere. Fig. 4 shows the symmetrical pattern observed when nickel is electrodeposited on a polished crystal of copper. The dark, highly reflecting areas represent the (100) face and other faces making a small angle with the (100) plane; the matte areas represent the (111) face and other faces making a small angle with the (111) plane. The deposit in the (100) areas is single crystal whereas the deposit in the (111) areas is polycrystalline.

Studies of the surface properties of hemispherical single crystals are also carried out in an emission microscope. Very fine wires of metals are etched in such a manner to give a hemispherical end with a radius of curvature of the order of several hundreds of atomic diameters. Wires of this type are sealed in a glass vessel whose interior is both electrically conducting and coated with a fluorescent compound. A voltage is applied between the wire and the glass vessel under conditions of high vacuum and very high field strengths are developed at the tip. Electrons are emitted with different ease from the various crystal faces and symmetrical patterns are observed on the fluorescent screen. Changes in the pattern with time are correlated with processes taking place on the crystal surface. The emission microscope has found application in studies of work function, surface diffusion of impurity atoms, kinetics of reactions, and evaporation. Field ion emission microscopes, using small amounts of helium in the glass vessel, have sufficient resolution that individual atoms may be observed. These microscopes have special utility in studies of adsorption, order-disorder phenomena, and imperfections.

References

1. AZÁROFF, L. V., "Introduction to Solids," New York, McGraw-Hill Book Co., 1960.
2. BARRETT, C. S., "Structure of Metals," 2nd Edition, New York, McGraw-Hill Book Co., 1952.
3. HURLE, D. T. J., *Progress in Materials Science*, **10**, 81 (1962).
4. ELBAUM, C., *Progress in Metal Physics*, **8**, 203 (1959).
5. LEIDHEISER, H., JR., AND GWATHMEY, A. T., *J. Electrochem. Soc.* **98**, 225 (1951).
6. LEFEVER, R. A., *J. Electrochem. Soc.*, **108**, 107 (1961).
7. MÜLLER, E. W., *J. Appl. Physics*, **28**, 1 (1957); "Advances in Electronics and Electron Physics," Vol. 13, p. 83, edited by Marton, L. New York, Academic Press, Inc., 1960.
8. YOUNG, F. W., JR., *J. Appl. Physics*, **33**, 3553 (1962).
9. GWATHMEY, A. T., AND LAWLESS, K. R., "Surface Chemistry of Metals and Semiconductors, Symposium, Columbus, Ohio," edited by Gatos, H. C., Faust, J. W., Jr., and Lafleur, W. J., p. 483, New York, John Wiley and Sons, 1960.

HENRY LEIDHEISER, JR.

Cross-references: *Metal Electrodeposition, Elementary Processes; Zone Refining.*

SINGLE CRYSTALS OF SEMICONDUCTORS

A semiconductor is, as its name implies, a material with a conductivity intermediate between that of a conductor and an insulator. The electrical conductivity of semiconductors ranges from approximately 10^3 to 10^{-9} reciprocal ohm-cm. Good conductors have a conductivity in excess of 10^7 reciprocal ohm-cm and good insulators a conductivity as low as 10^{-17} reciprocal ohm-cm. Semiconductors exhibit many useful properties which have been taken advantage of in the preparation of a variety of devices. The dependency of the resistance on temperature has been used in the manufacture of thermistors. Voltage-dependent properties have been used in the manufacture of varistors. Diode rectifiers are manufactured from semiconductors with overall nonlinear current-voltage characteristics. Semiconductor devices called transistors have the ability to perform many of the functions of vacuum tubes, particularly amplification, and are rapidly replacing these devices in electronic circuits. Certain semiconductors have the ability to convert one form of energy into another form. Photoelectric devices, in which light is converted to electricity, laser devices, in which electricity is converted to electromagnetic radiation, piezoelectric devices, in which mechanical force and electricity are converted one into the other, are examples of many types of devices which have resulted from the properties of semiconductors.

Semiconductors are of two major types, intrinsic semiconductors and impurity semiconductors. Intrinsic material contains a concentration of charge carriers which is characteristic of the material itself and is not dependent on structural and chemical imperfections for its behavior. An impurity semiconductor, of which germanium and silicon are the outstanding examples, depends on the type and concentration of impurities for its semiconducting behavior. The electrical properties of germanium and silicon are controlled by adulterating or "doping" very pure material with small amounts of elements from neighboring columns of the periodic table. Atoms having a valence of +3, such as boron, aluminum, indium, and gallium, are unable to satisfy the 4 covalent bonds of neighboring atoms in the matrix and a so-called "hole" is developed in place of a covalent bond and a positive or p-type semiconductor is formed. Atoms having a valence of +5, such as phosphorus, arsenic, and antimony, have available one more electron per atom than is required to satisfy the 4 covalent bonds of the neighboring matrix atoms, an extra electron is available, and a negative or n-type semiconductor is formed.

The electrical properties of impurity semiconductors are a function not only of the impurities but also of the structural perfection. Grain boundaries in particular act as barriers to the flow of charges and their presence causes a semiconductor to have inferior electrical properties. Great emphasis has thus been placed on the preparation of semiconductor single crystals with a high degree of structural perfection. Techniques for the preparation of semiconductor single crystals also depend critically on the avoidance of undesirable impurities during growth. The most common method for the preparation of single crystals of silicon, germanium, and 1:1 mixtures of elements from groups III and V in the periodic table is the Czochralski method (See **Single Crystals of Metals**). A crucible material which does not seriously contaminate the melt, and an inert atmosphere are essential for the preparation of high-quality crystals. Contamination by the crucible has been successfully avoided by the use of the zone melt or floating zone methods. In these two methods a rod is clamped in a vertical position or is supported in a horizontal position and a short length of the material is melted by concentrating heat in a narrow band. This molten zone is passed along the length of the rod either by moving the heat source or by moving the rod. These methods are also used to purify the material by passing a molten zone through the material many times. The different solubilities of an impurity in the solid and in the liquid phases of the semiconductor cause the impurity to concentrate at one or the other end of the rod. Local heating to form the narrow band is developed by induction coils, by resistance heating, or by electron beams impinging on the rod. (See **Zone Refining.**)

Crystals of very refractory semiconductor oxides are prepared by a process named after A. V. L. Verneuil who applied it as early as 1902 to the manufacture of synthetic rubies and sapphires. Finely divided powder is passed through an oxy-hydrogen flame or plasma arc where it melts and immediately makes contact with a single crystal seed. Only the upper portion of the boule produced in the process is maintained in the molten state. The molten area is restricted in size by slowly withdrawing the boule from the hot zone. The method requires much artistry on the part of the engineer or scientist in charge. Particular difficulties are experienced in maintaining flame stability, in feeding the powder to the flame at the proper rate, in maintaining desired stoichiometry in the product crystal, and in avoiding excessive internal stresses in the product.

One of the more promising new techniques for the preparation of useful crystals involves deposition from the vapor phase on a seed crystal of the same or different chemical composition. Vapor deposition, or epitaxial growth as it is often called, lends itself well to the preparation of single crystals in the form of thin films. This material has important potential applications in the manufacture of smaller and lighter computers and other devices. The more important vapor growth processes for the preparation of single crystals include the following: *silicon*—hydrogen reduction of $SiHCl_3$, $SiCl_4$, and SiI_4; decomposition of SiI_4; disproportionation of SiI_2; *germanium*—hydrogen reduction of $GeCl_4$; disproportionation of GeI_2; sublimation and deposition on (111) face of CaF_2; *silicon carbide*—sublimation; gaseous cracking of $SiCl_4$-toluene mixtures; *gallium arsenide*—evaporation and disproportionation in an I_2 or HCl carrier gas; *gallium phosphide*—reduction in a vacuum of a mixture of P-Ga-Ga_2O_3; evaporation and disproportionation in an I_2 carrier gas; *indium antimonide*—decomposition of an $In(CH_3)_3$-SbH_3 mixture. A variation of the epitaxial technique is used in the preparation of single crystals of cuprous oxide. Copper single crystal discs are oxidized in air at low pressure and high temperature to form cuprous oxide single crystals.

The relationship between structural perfection of semiconducting crystals and their properties has served to focus attention on means for characterizing structural defects and determining their number. The greatest effort has been devoted to etching techniques because this method makes visible, under proper conditions, the individual dislocations. A good etchant for developing dislocations as readily visible pits in silicon has the composition, 1 part HF, 3 parts HNO_3, and 8 parts CH_3COOH. Silicon crystals are moderately transparent to infrared radiation, and this property has been used to determine the number of dislocations in samples purposely contaminated with copper. Metallic copper is diffused into the crystal at 900°C. The copper precipitates in the vicinity of the dislocation and is readily detected because of its opacity to infrared radiation. X-ray techniques and specifically the diffraction micrographic technique of Lang also reveal dislocations. Single crystals in the form of thin films may be studied by transmission in the electron microscope. Individual dislocations and other imperfections such as stacking faults are readily visible because of diffraction effects as the electron beam passes through the specimen.

Organic semiconducting crystals, such as the highly conjugated polycyclic compounds and the phthalocyanines, are now being studied extensively. Many of these materials are prepared as small crystals by precipitation from solution in a foreign liquid; others are prepared from melts of the pure material. Many of the interesting electrical properties of organic semiconductors (q.v.) are dependent on chemical reactions between molecules in the surface of the crystal and the gaseous environment. Reaction of the surface with oxygen has been offered as the explanation for the different electrical conductivity of anthracene in the light and in the dark. One of the strong lures for research in this area is the hope for the development of devices which will be able to detect very low concentrations of contaminants in the atmosphere by a unique effect on the electrical properties of the crystal.

References

1. GRAY, T. J., RASE, D. E., WEST, R. R., DETWILER, D. P., LAWRENCE, W. G., AND JENNINGS, T. J., "The Defect Solid State," New York, Interscience Publishers, Inc., 1957.
2. NEWKIRK, J. B., AND WERNICK, J. H., Editors, "Direct Observation of Imperfections in Crystals," New York, Interscience Publishers, Inc., 1962.
3. SCHROEDER, J. B., Editor, "Metallurgy of Semiconductor Materials," Vol. 15, New York, Interscience Publishers, Inc., 1962.
4. GRUBEL, R. O., Editor, "Metallurgy of Elemental and Compound Semiconductors," Vol. 12, New York, Interscience Publishers, Inc., 1961.
5. GIBSON, A. F., Editor, "Progress in Semiconductors," Vol. 5, New York, John Wiley and Sons, 1960.

HENRY LEIDHEISER, JR.

Cross-references: *Laser; Photoconductivity; Piezoelectricity; Semiconductors; Solar Energy Converter; Zone Refining.*

SÖDERBERG ANODES IN ALUMINUM CELLS

History

The Söderberg electrode, invented by C. W. Söderberg, is a jointless carbon electrode formed and baked continuously as it is fed into the furnace in which the electrode is used. It was developed during World War I by Elektrokemisk A/S of Norway for use in electrothermic furnaces, as described in the subsequent entry, *"Söderberg Electrode in Electric Furnaces,"* where information on the formation of the electrode is given.

In the early twenties, Elektrokemisk A/S started to adapt the Söderberg electrode to aluminum cells or reduction pots.[1] The temperature of the molten cryolite-alumina electrolyte, about 950°C, was found to be high enough to complete a satisfactory baking of the electrode. In aluminum electrolysis introduction of impurities to the metal must be avoided. Therefore, the sheet iron casing with contact ribs, used for the electrode in electrothermic furnaces,

has been replaced by a plain aluminum casing. To obtain a sufficiently low anode voltage drop, the electrode holder with contact clamps is replaced by individual contact spikes also called studs or pins.[2] The contact spikes are inserted in the green paste near the top of the electrode, and allowed to bake into the carbon as the anode is consumed and lowered. Before reaching the lower end of the anode, where the studs might be attacked by the molten cryolite, they are pulled and reinserted in the green paste at a higher level.

Two main types of the Söderberg anode have been developed: In the "horizontal spike" (HS) anode the contact spikes are inserted in the anode from the side through the sheet aluminum casing. The first pots using this type were circular. This proved satisfactory in pot sizes of 12 to 20 ka. In larger circular pots the central part tended to be overheated and anode gas escape became unsatisfactory.

These difficulties were overcome when the French company, Pechiney, about 1930 introduced the rectangular anode, where the long sides are three to five times the short sides.[3] A cross section of a HS anode is shown in Fig. 1. The sheet aluminum casing is reinforced by interconnected steel channel frames with holes for the contact studs by which the anode is suspended. When pulling the studs, the lower frames are removed and set in the higher position together with the studs. Later on, Elektrokemisk introduced a permanent sheet steel casing with slots for the movement of the contact studs. Still, a sheet aluminum casing inside the permanent casing was necessary.

In the "vertical spike" (VS) anode the contact spikes are inserted in the anode from above. Shortly before World War II this principle was applied in Italy by Montecatini. During the war Pechiney simplified the system and arrived at an economical design that now to a large extent has replaced the horizontal stud design. A plain sheet steel casing is used. This design does not require a consumable Al-casing (inside the permanent casing). A cross section of this design is shown in Fig. 2, and Fig. 3 is a photo of a recent 80 ka installation. This modern design will be described in some detail.

Modern Vertical Spike Anodes

The anode, see Fig. 2, is suspended from above, the vertical spikes carrying the whole weight of the anode.[4] The spikes are connected

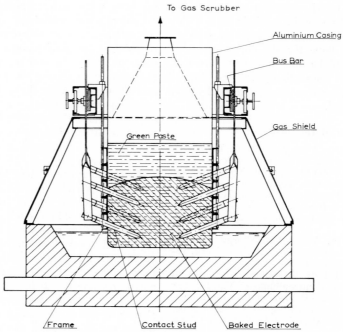

FIG. 1. Horizontal stud Söderberg anode.

to the anode bus bars by contact clamps. The anode is consumed at a rate of approximately ⅝ inch per 24 hours. The anode bus bars and the anode are lowered simultaneously by motor-driven jacks, the anode sliding through the stationary permanent casing. At regular intervals green anode paste is filled on the top of the anode to compensate for the carbon consumed by the process. When the anode bus bars have reached their lowest position, the anode is suspended by auxiliary means and the bus bars raised to their highest position under full current load.

According to pot size, the spikes are arranged in two or four rows along the bus bars. They are set at different levels. At regular intervals the spikes at the lowest level are extracted by a twisting and pulling operation. Paste is introduced into the holes, and the spikes reinserted at a suitable higher level. To facilitate the operation the lower part of the spikes is made conical. The paste introduced into the holes is rapidly baked, whereby good electric contact and mechanical bond to the baked anode is reestablished.

As is shown in Fig. 2, the baking zone of the anode drops down to the lower rim of the permanent casing. This is essential to obtain a

satisfactory sliding of the anode through the casing. The temperature of the casing, therefore, must be low enough to prevent coking of the green paste to the casing. However, below the lower rim of the casing the temperature of the anode must be high enough to assure that a solid carbon is formed.[5] Proper cooling of the casing may be obtained by cooling ribs. The anode voltage drop is 0.5–0.6 v, and the anode current density is 0.7–0.8 amp/sq cm.

Söderberg Anode Paste

The green anode paste is produced by mixing calcined low-ash coke, usually petroleum or pitch coke, with high-temperature coal tar pitch.[6] The coarser fractions of the coke are sized by screening, the fine fraction is produced in a ball mill. Maximum particle size of the coke is about half an inch, and 20 to 35 per cent of the coke is finer than 200 mesh, mainly dependant on the anode system used. The pitch content of the paste is 24 to 34 per cent, the VS anodes usually requiring a more fluid paste than the HS anodes. The softening point of the pitch is usually 80 to 100°C R & B. Paste consumption normally is 500 to 560 kg per metric ton of metal produced.

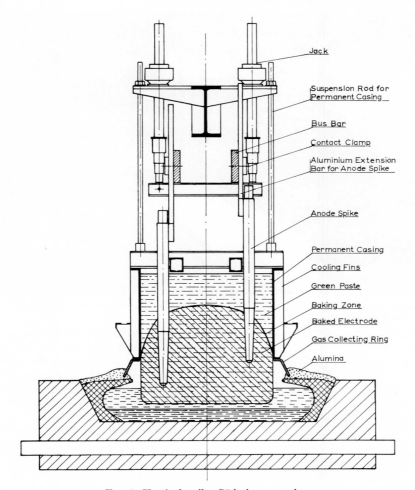

Fig. 2. Vertical spike Söderberg anode.

Anode Gas Collection

The problem of fluorine emission from aluminum pots is serious. Great efforts have been made to collect and scrub the pot gases to prevent air pollution. A further object is to recover the valuable fluorine compounds. In the early thirties Pechiney realized the advantages offered by the Söderberg anode for collection of the pot gases. They designed the first closed aluminum pots.[7]

Pot gases are evolved at a rate of approximately 0.25 Nm³/kah per pot. With open pots the pot gases are mixed with the pot room atmosphere, and for pollution control the volume of air to be treated is about 300 to 500 Nm³/kah for each pot. The HS Söderberg pots are enclosed by movable sections, see Fig. 1, and the

volume of gases to be treated is thereby reduced to 50 to 100 Nm³/kah. Still this is a large volume compared with actual pot gas evolution. The movable sections do not form a perfect sealing and a large excess of air has to be sucked off together with the pot gases to avoid leakage into the pot room atmosphere.

The VS anode system makes it possible to collect the pot gases in a very concentrated form. According to a proposal from Luzzatto in Italy shortly before World War II and to Pechiney in France,[8] a gas collecting iron ring is attached to the lower rim of the permanent casing, see Fig. 2. The gas collecting ring is sealed against the crust of frozen cryolite by the alumina charged to the pot.

The pot gases, consisting of about 40 to 60

FIG. 3. Recent 80 ka installation of aluminum cells with vertical spike Söderberg anodes.

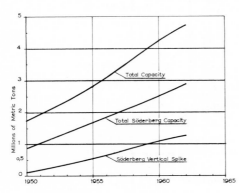

FIG. 4. Aluminum reduction capacity of the western world.

per cent CO_2 and 60 to 40 per cent CO, are contaminated by tar vapors from the baking of the anode. The tar vapors may cause some fouling in the gas pipe to the scrubber. To prevent this, each pot is equipped with a gas burner where CO and most of the tar is burned with a controlled amount of air. After combustion the gas volume is only 3 to 5 Nm^3/kah. The burnt gases contain:

SO₂ 0.5–1

HF 0.5–1

Dust 0.5–1, containing about 20% F, and tar vapors 0.1–0.5, all figures given in g/Nm^3.

By scrubbing with water, the valuable HF can be selectively absorbed[9] and thus processed to a cryolite of high purity. When breaking the

crust for feeding alumina to the pot, the sealing of the gas collecting ring by alumina is temporarily disturbed and some pot gases escape to the pot room. Large plants located in an agricultural area may, therefore, have to purify even the pot room atmosphere.

Economy and Pot Size

The Söderberg monolithic anode opened possibilities for the construction of larger and more economical units. Pot sizes have indeed been steadily increased from about 30 ka before World War II up to 100 ka and even higher at present, and the operation of larger pots is more easily mechanized. Manhours per ton of metal produced have been drastically reduced. Cathode life and electromagnetic disturbances[10] seem to limit the pot size. For these reasons the most economic size seems at present to be 80 to 100 ka.[11]

Western World Production Capacity

Fig. 4 shows the recent development of total production capacity in the western world and the capacity developed with the Söderberg system.

References

1. SEM, M., SEJERSTED, J., AND BÖCKMAN, O., "Twenty-five Years' Development of the Söderberg System in Aluminum Furnaces," *J. Electrochem. Soc.*, **94**, 220–31 (1948).

2. WESTLEY, J., U. S. Patent 1,757,695 (May 6, 1930).
3. TORCHET, P., U. S. Patent 2,073,356 (March 9, 1937).
4. U. S. Patent 2,475,452.
5. U. S. Patent 2,526,876.
6. BOWITZ, OLAV, AND SANDBERG, OVE, "Söderberg Anode Carbon in Cells for Electrolytic Production of Aluminum," *Trans. Metall. Soc. AIME*, **224**, 53–60 (1962).
7. TORCHET, P. J. M., U. S. Patent 2,031,554 (Feb. 18, 1936).
8. U. S. Patent 2,526,875.
9. ERGA, OLAV, TERJESEN, S. G., AND UTVIK, A. O., paper presented at International Symposium on the Extractive Metallurgy of Aluminum, New York, February 1962.
10. BÖCKMAN, O. CHR., AND WLEÜGEL, J., "Electromagnetic Forces in Large Aluminum Furnaces," *J. Electrochem. Soc.*, **105**, 417–420 (1958).
11. MÜLLER, AND OEHLER, "Latest Developments in Aluminum Reduction," Paper presented at Symposium on Light Metals Industry, p. 97–104, India, February 1961.

O. C. BÖCKMAN AND
M. Ö. SEM

Cross-references: *Aluminum Electrowinning; Söderberg Electrodes in Electric Furnaces.*

SÖDERBERG ELECTRODES IN ELECTRIC FURNACES

History

The Söderberg selfbaking electrode was developed during World War I by the Norwegian company Elektrokemisk A/S, based on an idea of C. W. Söderberg.[1, 3] A first public demonstration of the electrode was made in August 1919 to an international commission, headed by J. W. Richards, Professor of Lehigh University, Bethlehem, Pa., U.S.A.[2] In the next ten to twenty years the electrode was applied on a very large scale in furnaces for production of calcium carbide and various ferroalloys.

Taking advantage of this continuous and jointless electrode, allowing sizes hitherto unknown, a rapid development of the electric smelting furnaces took place.[4] As time went on they were increasingly closed and provided with gas collection. The first striking example was the development in Norway of the Tysland-Hole (ELKEM) furnace for production of pig iron. This furnace was the first commercial electric pig iron furnace using coke as a reducing agent. It has since been adopted in a num-

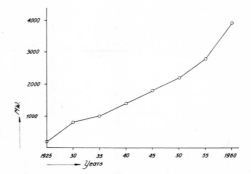

FIG. 1. Approximate capacity of furnaces with Söderberg electrodes (East block nations excluded).

ber of countries. Total capacity of these furnaces now is about 2 million tons of pig iron per year. In Europe the Söderberg electrode has also been used to a certain extent in electric steel furnaces (q.v.).

The world capacity of electric furnaces equipped with Söderberg electrodes has developed as shown in Fig. 1.

The use of the Söderberg electrode in aluminum cells is described in the previous entry.

Principle

Carbon electrodes are produced by giving the green electrode paste a desired shape, followed by a baking process to convert the green paste to a solid carbon. Prebaked electrodes are produced by extruding the paste and baking the electrodes in a separate baking furnace. By the use of prebaked electrodes, new sections are connected by screw nipples.

In the Söderberg electrode the shaping of the electrode is accomplished by feeding green paste into a sheet steel casing attached to the top of the electrode. The green paste is baked in the furnace where it is used, partly by the heat developed by the electrode current and partly by the heat conducted from the hot zone of the furnace. The electrode is extended by welding on new sections of the casing and by adding green paste on top of the electrode.

The principal parts of a Söderberg electrode are shown in Fig. 2. In the upper part the casing serves as a container for the green electrode paste. The paste is added hot or as cold blocks or briquets which melt in the electrodes. The paste must have a suitable plasticity when hot. The molten paste flows to fill the whole cross section of the casing. The electrode holder serves for

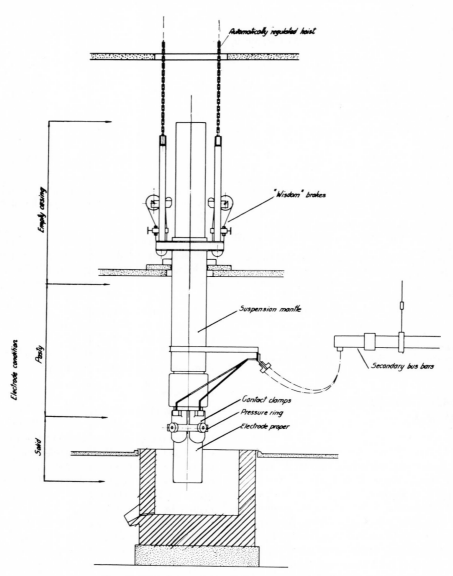

FIG. 2. Söderberg electrode in an open furnace.

introduction of the electric current and for suspension of the electrode. Above the holder a dust shield ordinarily protects the casing against the hot gases from the open furnace. The space between the shield and the electrode may also be used for controlling the temperature necessary for proper melting of the paste, by blowing preheated or cooling air, as required, from above through the annular space.

The temperature of the electrode increases downwards, and at a level corresponding to the lower part of the electrode holder carbonization of the electrode is ordinarily completed.

In the upper part of the holder the electrode is still plastic and the shape of the electrode adapts itself to the actual position of the contact clamps of the holder. Thus, a good electrical contact between the contact clamps and the casing is obtained. The electric current flows through the casing and is gradually taken over by the carbon electrode. To obtain a sufficient electric contact and mechanical bond between the casing and the carbon, the casing is provided with a number of internal ribs. At a certain distance below the electrode holder the casing melts or is oxidized by the atmosphere, and the carbon takes the whole electrode current.

As the electrode is consumed at the tip, it is lowered by slipping through the holder. The electrode consumption in the furnace depends on the smelting process carried out; normally it is within the range 8 to 24 inches per 24 hours. It is preferable to lower the electrodes only a small distance at a time, usually 1 to 3 inches, to obtain uniform conditions for the baking of the electrode. For extension of the casing by welding on new sections and for other electrode work the furnace building usually is provided with an overhead electrode cabin surrounding the top of the electrode.

The Söderberg electrode in smelting furnaces may thus be operated continuously with no joints for the whole life of the furnace.

No fundamental change has been made since the electrode was first developed, but the equipment, such as the electrode holder and the slipping device, has been improved considerably. The electrode has also influenced the design of smelting furnaces. These aspects of the Söderberg electrode will be considered in some detail.

In electric steel furnaces it was found too difficult to lengthen the electrode on top of the furnace. This operation is, therefore, carried out outside the steel furnace, and the electrode operates in a semicontinuous way.

Electrode Holders

Originally the holder consisted of a number of water-cooled contact clamps surrounded by a pressure ring. The clamps were pressed against the electrodes by large screws through the pressure ring with manual operation from the furnace floor. As the electrodes grew larger, remote operation became desirable. For closed furnaces the need is for a compact, slender electrode holder, making possible the submerging of the holder in the roof with a close fit. To meet these requirements various types of modern electrode holders have been developed. Fig. 3 shows a cross section of such a modern electrode holder using hydraulic pressure. Between the water-cooled contact clamp and the likewise water-cooled pressure ring, a rubber bag filled with water is inserted, pressing the clamps to the

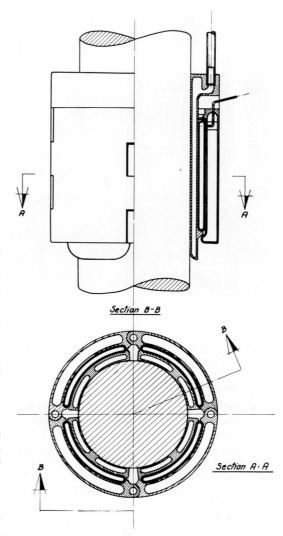

Section B-B

Section A-A

FIG. 3. Electrode holder for a closed furnace.

electrode by 2–4 kg/sq cm water pressure. Instead of a rubber bag, a rubber membrane is also being used. Even a purely mechanical holder hydraulically operated is being used.

Fig. 4 shows the electrode holder in high position in the roof of a large carbide furnace. The holder is seen to be compact and with a smooth outer surface. This allows a close fit in the roof and an efficient collection of the furnace gas. By submerging the electrode holder in the roof the free length of the electrode is reduced, thereby reducing the power loss and increasing the strength of the electrode. To avoid eddy

FIG. 4. Electrode holder in high position in the roof of a large carbide furnace.

current losses, modern electrode holders are made of nonmagnetic materials.

Slipping Device

An early device for controlled slipping is the "Wisdom Ribbon" which is still widely used. It is shown in Fig. 2. It consists of two steel ribbons, one on each side of the electrode, at one end wound on a drum and at the other fixed to the casing by welding. In between a friction brake on each ribbon is inserted. When lowering the electrode, the pressure on the contact clamps of the electrode holder is somewhat reduced, and the electrode slides through the holder by its own weight. The brakes on the "Wisdom Ribbons" are used for controlling the slipping.

A modern device for controlling the electrode slipping is shown in Fig. 5. In the upper part of the electrode, a pressure ring with rubber membranes, most similar to the modern electrode holder mentioned above, is pressed against the electrode casing. By hydraulic jacks fastened to the pressure ring the electrode is forced downwards through the holder ordinarily without releasing the pressure on the contact clamps and with full current load on the electrode. This device allows a close control of the slipping. Sometimes it is made so strong that it can raise the electrode through the holder in case of repairs or in case of electrode breakage.

For steel furnaces a special clamping device on top of the electrode holder has been developed, see Fig. 6. When releasing the pressure

FIG. 5. Electrode slipping device.

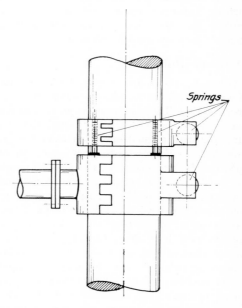

FIG. 6. Electrode holder for electric steel melting furnaces.

on the contact clamps of the electrode holder, the electrode slides through the holder until the clamping device rests on the holder. Pressure is again applied on the electrode holder, the clamping device is released and returned to the original position by springs. This operation in steel furnaces ordinarily takes place when power is off.

Influence on Furnace Design

The simple construction and easy operation of the Söderberg electrode has made possible a large increase in electrode size and, hence, in furnace size. Electrodes 59 inches in diameter have been in operation in three-phase furnaces for several years with electrode currents about 100 ka and even more. In monophase furnaces (Miguet type) a 3½ m diameter electrode is in operation, carrying more than 200 ka.

Furnaces are under construction with electrodes 75 inches diameter and with a design electrode current of 140 ka. Power load on the furnaces has been steadily increasing. Before World War II the largest furnaces rated about 10 mw, but today several furnaces operate with 40 mw and even more. Still larger furnaces are contemplated.

Some big carbide producers still retain the rectangular carbide furnaces. The old packet electrodes of the same have been replaced by oblong Söderberg electrodes. To avoid deformation of the upper soft part of the electrode the long sides of the oblong electrode casing are connected by extensions of the ribs through the electrode casing (Fig. 7).

Where it is found possible, most big furnaces have now been enclosed to collect the furnace gas and for cleaning the gas to avoid air pollution. The modern submerged electrode holders developed for Söderberg electrodes have made this gas collection most efficient. In calcium carbide furnaces a gas containing 90 per cent CO can be collected. After purification the gas is used in various ways for heating purposes, such as in lime kilns, as well as for synthesis of methanol and other hydrocarbons, etc.

Söderberg Electrode Paste

The same raw materials are used for Söderberg as for prebaked electrodes, mainly anthracite calcined to partial graphitization and high-temperature coal tar pitch. The paste used for

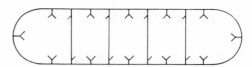

FIG. 7. Electrode casing for oblong electrodes.

Söderberg electrodes, however, must be more fluid to insure proper flow of the paste to fill the casing. More binder is, therefore, used, Söderberg paste normally containing 20 to 26 per cent of binder. The baked electrode will show approximately the same physical properties as those of large prebaked electrodes.

The electrode consumption of a few smelting furnaces is normally too small to warrant installation of a paste plant. The paste is, therefore, usually produced in centrally located paste plants which ship the paste in blocks of 40 to 60 lb. Recently, the paste is also cast into cylinders of 500 to 2000 lb, the size of the cylinders adjusted to the electrode size. Briqueted paste is also shipped. In countries of moderate temperature the paste is normally shipped without any special packing.

References

1. SÖDERBERG, C. W. (to Elektrokemisk A/S Oslo), U. S. Patent 1,441,037 (Jan. 2, 1923); U. S. Patent 1,440,724 (Jan. 2, 1923); and U. S. Patent 1,670,052 (May 15, 1928).
2. RICHARDS, J. W., "The Söderberg Selfbaking, Continuous Electrode," Trans. Am. Electrochem. Soc., **37**, 169 (1920).
3. SÖDERBERG, C. W., AND SEM, M. Ö., "Söderberg Electrodes," Chem. Met. Eng., **26**, 1128 (1922).
4. SEM, M. Ö., "Les Electrodes Söderberg et leur Influence sur la Construction des Fours Electriques de Fusion," J. du Four Electrique, **61**, No. 2 et 3, 39–44, 72–77 (1952).

O. C. BÖCKMAN AND
M. Ö. SEM

Cross-references: *Aluminum Electrowinning; Calcium Carbide; Electric Smelting Furnaces; Lead, Electrothermic Smelting; Phosphorus, Electrothermal Production; Söderberg Electrodes in Aluminum Cells; Steel Making in Electric Arc Furnaces.*

SODIUM CHLORATE. See CHLORATES, ELECTROLYTIC PRODUCTION.

SODIUM, ELECTROLYTIC PRODUCTION

The first electrolytic sodium produced commercially was made from sodium hydroxide. Later, in the 1920's sodium chloride was introduced as the raw material. These two processes were demonstrated in the laboratory many years before electrical machinery was developed to supply the great amperage needed for commercial operation.

Humphry Davy[2] discovered sodium and potassium in 1807. He electrolyzed moist lumps of the metal hydroxide, which rested on a platinum-sheet anode and were contacted above by a platinum-wire cathode. The lumps of hydroxide were $\frac{1}{8}$ to $\frac{1}{4}$ in. thick.

The much more difficult electrolysis of sodium chloride was demonstrated about 50 years later in Bunsen's laboratory, and was described by his student, A. Matthiessen.[4] They electrolyzed a mixture of sodium and calcium chlorides, in a porcelain crucible, using an iron-wire cathode and a carbon anode. None of these experimenters isolated more than a few grams of the metal.

Castner Cell

H. Y. Castner (q.v.) developed the first commercial cell, using sodium hydroxide as the main raw material, the carbonate as a melting-point depressant, and chloride to improve conductivity. Castner's patent[1] claimed operation at not more than 20°C above the melting point of the bath. This was, indeed, essential for efficient performance. The first plant was started at Oldbury, England, in 1891.

The major reactions in the Castner cell are:

$$4NaOH + 4e \rightarrow 4Na + 2H_2O + O_2 \quad (1)$$

$$\underline{2H_2O + 2Na \rightarrow H_2 + 2NaOH} \quad (2)$$

$$2NaOH + 4e \rightarrow 2Na + H_2 + O_2 \quad (3)$$

Water formed in reaction (1) dissolves in the bath and diffuses toward the cathode until decomposed according to reaction (2).

Minor reactions involve impurities, many of which are reduced to insoluble products that accumulate at the bottom of the cell.

The container for those cells was a cast-iron pot, 15 in. diameter at the top, by 20 in. deep. Below this pot, a pipe extended downward for 20 in. to serve as a seal around the conductor to the cathode. Rows of pots were housed in brick benches set above access tunnels for the bus bars. An empty pot, with cathode conductor held in place by wooden wedges, was placed in a bench. Then some starting bath was poured into the seal and allowed to freeze. Next, a copper cathode, $4\frac{1}{2}$ in. diameter and $8\frac{1}{2}$ in. high, was screwed onto the conductor. This located the cathode centrally in the lower half of the pot. Then a cast nickel anode, 6 in. inside diameter by $8\frac{7}{8}$ in. high, was placed around the cathode. The anode was suspended from the top of the pot, but insulated therefrom by an asbestos gasket. Finally, the diaphragm, attached to a short, open-ended iron tube was inserted from the top. The diaphragm was a plain cylinder of 28-mesh iron gauze, positioned half way between the electrodes. The tube above the diaphragm formed a well to collect the sodium.

The cell was then filled with molten starting bath, and the power was promptly switched on. Starting bath was sodium hydroxide diluted with 4 to 10 per cent sodium carbonate plus 10 to 16 per cent sodium chloride.

Routine operation required that sodium be bailed out of cells every hour, that pure sodium hydroxide be fed as needed to maintain bath level, and that the electrical load on each bench be adjusted occasionally to keep cell temperatures as low as practical.

When a cell failed to produce efficiently, some damp salt was added or a clean diaphragm was installed. When these expedients failed, the cell was cut out, dumped, and cleaned. See Table 1 for performance data on these and subsequent sodium cells.

Auxiliary facilities were an electrical substation to supply d-c power; an overhead crane to handle cell parts; a wash tank for dirty equipment; a system to recover impure sodium hydroxide; two large melting kettles, one for pure caustic, and one for starting bath; a small kettle to recover scrap sodium; perforated ladles to bail sodium from the cells (molten bath drained through the holes, but high surface tension kept the sodium back); two-handled, small-mouth jugs to carry either bath to the cells or sodium from them; and molds and drums to pack and ship the sodium.

At the Niagara Electrochemical Company plant (which is now the Niagara Falls plant of E. I. du Pont de Nemours & Co.), a Castner sodium plant was started in 1896. Niagara Electrochemical introduced a larger but similar cell in 1912 (see Table 1). An improved bailing apparatus was developed and the bath was fed from an insulated bucket carried by the overhead crane.

Downs Cell

All Castner cells at Niagara Falls were superseded by Downs cells[3] in May, 1925. (See entry on **J. C. Downs.**) This cell uses sodium chloride as the raw material. Elsewhere, Castner cells continued in use for many years. An English plant that ceased operation in 1952 is described by Wallace.[6]

The major reactions in the Downs cell are:

$$2NaCl + 2e \rightarrow 2Na + Cl_2 \qquad (4)$$

$$2Na + CaCl_2 \rightleftharpoons Ca + 2NaCl \qquad (5)$$

The minor reactions are mainly reductions of impurities to insoluble materials that collect at the bottom of the cell.

A recent type of Downs cell is described below, while Table 1 gives data for both that cell and the original Downs cell.

Downs cells are housed in two-story buildings, where the 9 ft high containers for the cells project 4 ft above the second floor. A new cell is assembled by first setting a base with anodes upon the supporting steel. This base is a welded, steel box with sockets for four anodes, and compartments for cooling water. Each graphite anode is in the form of a cylinder, 6 ft overall height, containing a cylindrical well that extends 3 ft down from the top and comprises about half the diameter of the anode. Four radial slots from each well permit the bath to circulate through the anode. Bus bars are connected to the underside of the base, while the top is insulated from the bath by a layer of ceramic cement.

The sheet-iron wall of the cell is made in sections. The lower half, which supports the cathode assembly, is set on the base in such a manner that there is no electrical contact from metal to metal. This shell is then lined with firebrick to a thickness of $4\frac{1}{2}$ in.

Next, the cathode assembly is lowered into place. This has four steel tubes side by side in a square array. Iron conductor arms on opposite sides project through the cell walls and are attached to bus bars just outside the cell. Each cathode tube is 40 in. high and has an annular clearance of not more than 2 in. between it and the anode. These small spaces are the sites where all the electrolysis takes place.

TABLE 1. AVERAGE PERFORMANCE OF
SODIUM CELLS

	Type of cell			
	Castner		Downs	
Approximate year	1910	1920	1925	1955
Load per cell, amperes	1200	7500	8600	38000
Sodium, lb per cell day	24	135	165	1420
Chlorine, lb per cell day	*	*	250	2180
Current efficiency, per cent	44†	40†	42	83
Volts across cell	4.7	4.3	7.4	6.9
A-C power, kwh per lb Na	7.3	6.8	9.9	4.8
Diaphragm life, months	‡	‡	?	1
Cell life, months	4**	4**	6	18
Operating temperature, °C	320	320	640	590

* The Castner cell made no chlorine: its coproducts were oxygen and hydrogen gases. These were not recovered as a rule.
† Current efficiency of a Castner cell never could exceed 50 per cent because enough water was formed at the anode by the electrolysis to react with half the sodium concurrently formed.
‡ Diaphragms in the Castner cell corroded very slowly, but they often became so heavily encrusted with impurities that they had to be removed, washed and dried before they could be reused.
** Cell life was dependent on purity of the NaOH used, especially on the silicate content. If mercury cell NaOH were used, a life of 4 months was average.

The upper sheet iron wall is added and lined with brick; starter blocks of graphite are wedged in at the top of the electrodes; the cell is filled with chunks of recovered bath having a nominal composition of 40 per cent NaCl-60 per cent $CaCl_2$ and a melting point of about 560°C. Power is switched on and when molten bath covers the electrodes the graphite blocks are manually removed.

Meanwhile, the diaphragms, sodium collector, and supporting steel have been assembled inside a guide cage, upon a jig that aligns the diaphragms so that they will slip between the electrodes. The diaphragms are cylinders of iron gauze, having 26 meshes per lineal inch. The top of each diaphragm is firmly held by the sodium collector and additional stiffening is provided by three horizontal hoops, stapled outside the gauze. The sodium collector consists of inverted, interconnected troughs surrounding each gauze at the top. The roof of the troughs slopes upward toward one corner where a vertical "riser" pipe extends to a point above the cell cover.

When all the bath is molten, the electrical load is cut off and an overhead crane moves the cage and assembled parts to a marked position on top of the cell. The collector-gauze assembly is lowered until its supports rest on the rim of the cell. The cage is removed, a sheet-nickel gas dome placed over the central opening in the sodium collector, and the cell cover installed. A "cross-over" pipe from the dome delivers chlorine averaging 98 per cent purity and at a slight negative pressure to a gas main alongside the cell. The sodium collection system is completed by a pipe provided with cooling fins and a side outlet from which sodium flows, via a small, intermediate receiver, to a portable receiver that holds one day's output. The pipe with the cooling fins is bolted to the pipe that rises from the collecting troughs.

Calcium is formed at the cathode, as well as sodium. It is soluble in liquid sodium, the solubility varying directly with the temperature. Thus, sodium in contact with the hot cell-bath contains about 5 per cent calcium metal. Much of this crystallizes as the sodium cools in the "riser" pipe, so that the discharge into the receivers contains only 1 per cent calcium. Most of the crystals descend to the interface between sodium and bath, where they react to form more impure sodium. Other calcium crystals cling to the wall of the riser, from which they are dislodged, every half hour, by a hand-operated scraper.

Pure, dry salt is fed continuously, from an overhead conveyor, to maintain bath level. There is a solid crust on top the bath, except for a small hole kept open by an air jet immersed in the bath. Periodically, dry calcium chloride is fed by hand to replace calcium removed with the sodium.

The portable sodium containers are removed daily with a lift truck; they are weighed, emptied, reweighed, and returned to the cells. The raw sodium is filtered at a temperature slightly above its melting point to remove calcium metal and sodium oxide, leaving a saleable product containing less than 0.04 per cent Ca. The calcium-containing filter sludge is reacted with molten NaCl: $Ca + 2NaCl \rightarrow 2Na + CaCl_2$, thereby recovering additional sodium.

Diaphragms have an average life of one month, failing because of wire failure or gauze plugging. A decrease in daily sodium output indicates when a diaphragm replacement is needed. In addition to this, the cells deteriorate slowly because of corrosion of the anodes. Anode consumption increases the clearance between electrodes, thereby raising cell voltage and decreasing production. When a cell becomes too inefficient, it is replaced.

Economic Comparison

One way to compare the economics of the Castner and Downs processes is to assume that both start with NaCl, so that the Castner would be a two-stage process, first making caustic and chlorine from the salt. Then, comparative power requirements would be:

	KWH/lb Na
Castner Process	
1.8 lb NaOH @ 1.35 KWH per lb	2.4
1.0 lb Na ex NaOH	6.8
Total for Castner	9.2
Downs Process	
1.0 lb Na	4.8

Since power is the greatest single item in the operating cost for these processes, and since a two-stage process is inherently more expensive than a one-stage one, the operating cost for the Castner sodium is greater than for Downs. The same reasons also make the investments greater for Castner than for Downs. Hence, the economics are definitely in favor of the Downs process.

Production Data

United States sodium production, all made from sodium chloride, has reached a plateau in recent years. Recorded recent annual productions have been:

Year	1958	1959	1960	1961	1962
MMlb.	221	224	226*	218	238

* Extrapolated from the data for first 9 months only.

Roughly 70 per cent of this sodium is now used to make tetraethyl lead. The remainder is mainly used to make sodium peroxide, titanium, and other difficultly reducible metals, for descaling metals, for synthesis of organic compounds, and as a heat-transfer medium.

References

1. CASTNER, H. Y., U. S. Patent 542,030 (May 12, 1891).
2. DAVY, H., *Phil. Trans. Roy. Soc., London,* **98,** 1 (1808).
3. DOWNS, J. C., U. S. Patent 1,501,756 (July 15, 1924).

4. Matthiessen, A., *Ann. Chem. Pharm.*, **93**, 277 (1855).
5. Sittig, M., "Sodium, Its Manufacture, Properties and Uses," New York, Reinhold Publishing Corp., 1956.
6. Wallace, T., *J. Soc Chem. Ind.*, **72**, 876 (1953).

Leo D. Williams

SODIUM SULFATE SOLUTION ELECTROLYSIS

History

The electrolysis of sodium sulfate solution to convert it into caustic soda and sulfuric acid has not yet been carried out commercially, while the electrolysis of sodium chloride is now a great electrochemical industry. Difficulty in separating the anolyte and catholyte from each other, lack of good materials for anodes and diaphragms, high energy consumption, and other unsolved problems have retarded the development of the electrolysis of sodium sulfate solution.

The fundamental researches, however, have been continued from the early part of this century. The first achievement was Grube's cell.[1] He studied two sorts of the cell: the diaphragm and the amalgam. The diaphragm cell was made from porcelain and bakelite, the anode was platinum-iridium alloy screen, and the diaphragm was a special porous porcelain. He studied both vertical and horizontal types of the diaphragm cell. However, the terminal voltage of his cell was very high. The horizontal cell resembles a Billiter-Siemens chlorine cell, that is, the woven steel cathode supports the diaphragm, which is composed of asbestos cloth and finely-ground barium sulfate paste. The anode chamber is cylindrical porous porcelain, set horizontally above the asbestos diaphragm, the oxygen gas accumulates at the upper part (of its horizontal cathode chamber). Grube obtained $3N$ H_2SO_4 and $3N$ NaOH under the conditions of 6 amp/sq dm current density, 5 volts terminal voltage, and a current efficiency of about 80 per cent. The concentration of the Na_2SO_4 brine was $4N$. Some Na_2SO_4 contaminated the NaOH product.

Grube's amalgam cell is essentially similar to his own horizontal diaphragm cell except for the cathode and asbestos diaphragm. The cathode is flowing sodium amalgam. Of course, good quality NaOH product is obtained, but the energy consumption is quite large, more than 4,000 kwh per ton of NaOH. Researches on the electrolysis of sodium sulfate solution have also been conducted in Russia, U.S.A., Japan, and other countries.[2]

During World War II, the German I.G. Farbenindustrie operated two kinds of amalgam cell: the horizontal and the vertical.[3] The horizontal cell of I.G. is essentially similar to Grube's cell, but distance between electrodes is narrow. Because of good corrosion resistivity, a Pb-Ag (10 per cent) alloy anode was employed. I.G. cell was 9 ka in capacity, and 240 to 260 gpl H_2SO_4 anolyte containing about 200 gpl Na_2SO_4 was obtained under the conditions of 10 amp/sq dm current density and 5.5 to 6 volts terminal voltage. The energy consumption was 3,900 to 4,250 kwh per ton of NaOH.

Most success was achieved by the vertical type cell with a falling amalgam film formed on steel plate cathodes. The 1,000 ampere cell operated by I.G., was about 2 meters high and 20 cm in diameter. The energy consumption was 3,100 to 3,400 kwh per ton of NaOH under the conditions of 10 amperes per sq dm current density, 4.4 volts terminal voltage, and 95–97 per cent in current efficiency.

De Nora in Italy has also operated the falling film type cell, which resembles a filter press.[4] A woven steel cathode was used.

Cell Reactions in Diaphragm Process and in Amalgam Process

The anodic reactions in the diaphragm and amalgam processes are the same. Oxygen gas evolves from the anode surface; the solution is very acidic, so that the reaction:

$$H_2O \rightarrow 2H^+ + \tfrac{1}{2}O_2 + 2e \qquad (1)$$

may take place.

The cathodic reactions in both processes are, however, quite different. Although hydrogen gas comes from the cathode surface of the diaphragm cell, the deposition of sodium into the amalgam cathode takes place in the amalgam process. Therefore, the respective reactions of the processes are as follows:

Diaphragm process:
$$H_2O + e \rightarrow \tfrac{1}{2}H_2 + OH^- \qquad (2)$$

Amalgam process:
$$Na^+ + e\ (+ Hg) \rightarrow Na\text{-}Hg \qquad (3)$$

Two sets of diaphragms, one of which is put around the anode and the other around the cathode, must be used in the diaphragm process. The sodium sulfate solution is sent into the space between these two sets, and passes through the diaphragms toward anode and cathode to prevent, respectively, the migration of H^+ and OH^-. In the amalgam process, only one diaphragm is used between the anode and cathode to prevent the migration of H^+ formed at the anode by the electrolyte flow from cathode to anode. Finally, the overall reactions of both diaphragm and amalgam processes for electrolysis of sodium sulfate solution are:

Diaphragm process:
$$3H_2O + Na_2SO_4 \rightarrow H_2 + \frac{1}{2}O_2 + 2NaOH + H_2SO_4 \quad (4)$$

Amalgam process:
$$Na_2SO_4 + H_2O \rightarrow 2Na(Hg) + H_2SO_4 + \frac{1}{2}O_2 \quad (5)$$

The theoretical decomposition voltages for the electrolysis of sodium sulfate solution can be calculated: 2.03 volts for the diaphragm process, and 3.14 volts for the amalgam process at 25°C or 298°K, based on the unit activities of water, oxygen, and hydrogen.

The anode for electrolysis of sulfate solution consists of lead alloy in general because of its corrosion resistance. But the oxygen overpotential of lead alloy is usually high; moreover, some of ohmic voltage drop is due to the thin oxide film which forms on the anode surface during electrolysis.

The voltage drop in the diaphragm is also considerable because of its low permeability.

However, the hydrogen overpotential of the steel cathode of the diaphragm cell is low, and the overpotential of the amalgam cathode where sodium deposits is also negligible.

There is some ohmic voltage drop in the solution. Thus, the voltage balance consists of the decomposition voltage, the ohmic drops of diaphragm and the brine, and the anodic overpotential containing the voltage drop of the thin oxide film. However, details of each value have not yet been studied. The terminal voltages of the I.G. cells are about 5 to 6 volts for the diaphragm cell and 5.5 to 6.0 volts for the amalgam cell at 10 amperes per sq dm current density, as mentioned above. The terminal voltage of the sulfate cell is considerably higher than that of the chlorine cell. It is one of the weak points of the electrolysis of sodium sulfate solution.

There are many other difficult problems for this electrolysis. Development of good corrosion-resistant materials for the anode and the diaphragm is the key-point. Construction of the cell is also a big problem.

These significant items have been studied by Japanese researchers at Kyoto University.[5]

Summary of the Studies at Kyoto University

Fundamental Research. These studies have emphasized the economic point of view: (1) studies on corrosion-resistant materials for the anode and the diaphragm, (2) consideration of the most desirable process for the electrolysis of sodium sulfate solution, and (3) how to operate the cell at high current density and low terminal voltage conditions.

I.G. employed a high-silver (10 per cent) lead alloy in its electrolyzer during World War II. While very expensive, it is an excellent material as regards anodic corrosion.

A new economical and good corrosion-resistant alloy anode has been investigated by Okada's laboratory at Kyoto University.[6] It is the eutectic Ag(2 per cent)-Pb alloy containing a third metal. After the consumption of a great many alloys was measured in a small cell for a long time, three alloys, consisting of 1 per cent, 10 per cent, and 15 per cent Te with 2 per cent Ag, were selected.

For the diaphragm, unglazed pottery plate, pieces of blue asbestos and white asbestos cloth, some synthetic fabrics, porous synthetic-resin plates, and porous rubber sheets were examined in a small cell. Of these, the blue asbestos cloth and the fine-pore rubber sheet, which is used for lead batteries, were selected.

The synthetic fabrics were also of great use in practice. However, the fabric should be isolated from the anode surface during electrolysis because of anodic oxidation. This property is to be compared with that of the asbestos and rubber diaphragms which are much more resistant to oxidation than synthetic fabrics. To prevent oxidation, a thin, glass-fiber fabric was usually placed between the diaphragm and anode surfaces as protection from electrochemical attack. Moreover, the layer diaphragm is favorable to the production of concentrated sulfuric acid. For this purpose two or three sheets were sometimes installed in practice.

Both the process and the type of electrolyzer have been considered in detail, with the results that the vertical rotating cathode mercury cell was selected for technical reasons. The research on the electrolysis of sodium sulfate solution was carried out with several purposes in mind, one of the most important of which is, of course, to convert the by-product Na_2SO_4 of the rayon industry to obtain high-purity caustic soda.

The vertical rotating cathode cell has been developed as the electrolyzer of sodium chloride solution by Okada.[7] The cell employed for the electrolysis of sodium sulfate solution is a modification of Okada's cell.

The first pilot cell was of a 200 ampere scale. The inside of the cell was covered with polyvinyl chloride sheet of 0.6 mm thickness. Three sheet disc cathodes and six lead alloy anodes were placed in parallel position; that is, each cathodic disc was placed between two anode plates. Total area of the cathode surface was about 13.2 sq dm, which corresponds to 15 amp/sq dm current density at 200 amperes total current. As a result of this experiment, it was concluded that the alloy consisting of Ag(2 per cent)-Te(1 per cent)-Pb, is the most economical material for the anode; its consumption is about 0.2 to 0.5 mg/amp-hr. Concentrated sulfuric acid, 200 to 250 gpl H_2SO_4, is obtained under the conditions of less than 5 volts of terminal voltage and 95 to 98 per cent of current efficiency.

Operation at High Current Densities. From the economic point of view, more than 30 amperes per sq dm current density will be neces-

sary to compete with the chlor-caustic industry.

The three factors which contribute most of the potential drop of the cell will be considered: the high anodic overpotential, the voltage drop in the diaphragm, and the ohmic drop in the bulk of the solution, especially at the vicinity of the anode because of the suspension of the oxygen gas generated. The overpotential of the anode could be decreased if the gas generated were carried away from the surface of the anode as soon as possible, since the majority of the surface of the anode is covered by oxygen gas. The bubbles also contribute to the ohmic voltage drop in the neighborhood of the anode, as indicated above.

The following items were investigated in relation to these problems by using the 1,500 ampere cell shown in Fig. 1.

The Anode. For the convenience of the escape of the oxygen gas, a drilled anode was employed. The percentage of area of the holes to the total area of the electrode surface and the diameter of the holes were important factors. A hole-area of 7 to 14 per cent of the total area of the electrode seems desirable from both the economic and technical points of view and also in consideration of the strength of the anode. The consumption of the anode material at a current density as high as 32 amperes per sq dm was less than 3.0 mg/amp-hr.

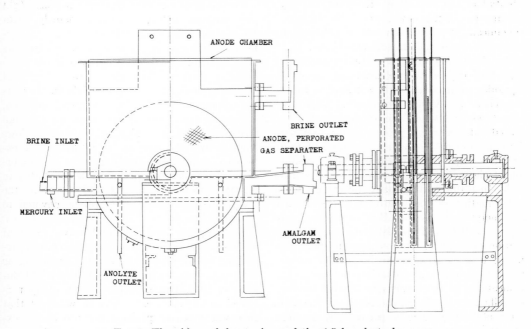

FIG. 1. The side and front views of the 1.5 ka electrolyzer.

The Diaphragm. Although a three-layer diaphragm of fine pore rubber sheet was recommended for producing concentrated sulfuric acid at low current densities; a thinner diaphragm can be employed at high current densities, so as to maintain the constant voltage drop in the diaphragm, and then, because of the increased flow of electrolyte through the diaphragm to prevent the increased migration of acid per unit area.

The cell was operated continuously during several months under a current density as high as 32 amp/sq dm, and as a result, 230 to 250 gpl H_2SO_4 containing 200 gpl Na_2SO_4 was obtained as the anolyte. The terminal voltage was less than 5 volts, and the current efficiency was 90 to 95 per cent. The energy consumption is about 3,500 kwh per ton of NaOH. The concentration of caustic soda solution which flooded from the amalgam decomposer was high, 20 to 70 per cent NaOH, and no contamination was determined.

The Unique Electrochemical Process to Make Persulfate as By-product of Caustic and Sulfuric Acid. The electrolysis of sodium sulfate solution for production of sodium hydroxide and sulfuric acid has had a weak point that the electric energy consumption is larger than that of the electrolysis of sodium chloride solution. It is caused by the high oxygen overpotential of the lead alloy. However, the high consumption of the power would be warranted economically if persulfate could be produced by the electrolysis of sodium sulfate solution.

The electrolysis using a platinum anode, for which both oxygen overpotential and the ability for oxidation are quite high, was studied by the researchers at Kyoto University.[5] They considered the kinetics of the anodic process, and worked out a mercury process electrolyzer with platinum anodes to convert sodium sulfate to persulfate and sodium amalgam. The consumption of the anode and its chamber, the control of the operating temperature, and the effects of contamination in the electrolyte were studied. The anolyte used is $15N$ H_2SO_4 saturated with Na_2SO_4 at $10°C$, and the catholyte is a saturated solution of Na_2SO_4. Sintered alumina plate was employed as the diaphragm because of its corrosion resistance to persulfate solution. The permeability of the diaphragm affected the current efficiency of the anodic reaction. The yield of persulfate was 50 to 95 per cent. While some experimental research has already been carried

out in a 20 ampere cell, a large 500 ampere cell is now operated to obtain several conditions proposed from an industrial point of view. The distillation and the rectification of the anolyte to produce hydrogen peroxide are also being studied. Results will be reported in the not too distant future.

References

1. GRUBE, H. G., *Z. Elektrochem.*, **44**, 640 (1938).
2. ZELINSKY, N. D., *et al.*, *Chem. Zentralblatt*, **103**, II, 2219 (1932). STENDER, W. W., *et al.*, *Trans. Electrochem. Soc.*, **68**, 493 (1935). OKUNO, T., SAKAI, W., AND ISHIMURA, M., *Kogyo Kagaku Zassi (Journal of the Society of Chemical Industry, Japan)*, **42**, 86, 919 (1939).
3. P. B. Fiat Final Report No. 831 (1946).
4. DE NORA, V., *Chem. Eng.*, **62**, 103 (1955).
5. OKADA, S., *et al.*, *Memoirs of the Faculty of Engineering, Kyoto Univ.*, **26**, Part 1, 112 (1962).
6. Japanese Patents 204,853; 210,923.
7. OKADA, S., AND YOSHIZAWA, S., *J. Electrochem. Soc. Japan*, **20**, 471 (1952).
8. YOSHIZAWA, S., HINE, F., AND YAMASHITA, M., *ibid.*, **30**, E-60 (1962).

SHINZO OKADA AND
SHIRO YOSHIZAWA

SOIL CORROSION

Corrosion of metallic structures in soils might be considered in three categories, namely, natural, galvanic, and stray-current corrosion. Natural corrosion can be defined as the normal deteriorating effect of the soil environment on a metallic surface. Galvanic corrosion is that caused by the metallic contact of dissimilar metals exposed to the soil. Stray-current corrosion, sometimes called electrolysis, occurs on a foreign structure (such as a pipeline) as current flows from it into the soil on its return to an external power source. Today, most of the underground corrosion can probably be attributed to natural effects of the soil and therefore the greater part of this section will be devoted to natural corrosion.

Probably the most comprehensive study of underground corrosion ever undertaken was carried out by the National Bureau of Standards as the result of an authorization by an act of Congress in 1910. The early part of the study pertained to stray-current corrosion which at that time was a severe problem because of the extensive use of direct-current railway systems. As a result of that investigation, it soon became evident that some soils also cause serious corrosion, even in the absence of stray-currents. At this early date, it also was concluded that the corrosion of iron exposed to soils caused by alternating current of commercial frequencies was negligible.[1] Today, this is still believed to be so. However, the effects of alternating current continue to be regarded with suspicion, especially as regards the possibility of rectification by metallic oxides. The reader is referred to an article by Kulman[2] on the subject of corrosion by alternating current in which many references are listed and also to other communications[3] on the same subject.

Natural Corrosion

Natural corrosion is thought of in connection with iron and steel structures because they comprise the greater part of the metals used underground. Nature has the tendency to change metals back to the state from which they came. The metal ore represents the more stable state, and the process of corrosion brings this about, destroying the man-made structure during the transition period. Natural corrosion in soils is now regarded chiefly as an electrochemical process. The soil is the electrolyte and the areas of metal exposed to the soil react as the electrodes (anode and cathode) of a battery. The metal forms a highly conductive path through which the corrosion current flows. Corrosion occurs where the current enters the electrolyte. This current is opposite in direction to the movement of electrons in the metallic path. The metal goes into solution as positive metal ions at the anode. Thus, the corrosion process continues as long as there is a difference of electrical potential generated by anodic and cathodic areas. This difference in potential or, strictly speaking, driving potential is influenced by a factor termed polarization which reduces the driving potential and consequently the corrosion current. On metals, such as iron, copper, and lead, exposed to soils there are innumerable corrosion cells operating collectively. The potency of such cells is also affected to a large extent by the ohmic resistance of the electrolytic path. Soil resistivities vary greatly, from less than 100 ohm-cm to over 100,000 ohm-cm. Generally speaking, all soils having resistivities less than 1000 ohm-cm are considered as being potentially corrosive, while soils over 10,000 ohm-cm are usually not inher-

ently corrosive. However, there are isolated exceptions due to the inclusion of soil patches of high conductivity. Low-resistivity soils are usually associated with sea-level or swampy areas. In general, very corrosive soils contain large amounts of soluble salts, accounting for low resistivities, while soils not so corrosive lack these salts which produce ionization. The least corrosive soils are usually well-aerated and low in moisture content because of good drainage. The soil conductivity is also related to the physical structure of the soil which ranges from clays (small soil particles) to sands (large soil particles). Clays usually have the lower resistivities because of their fine texture, compactness, and ability to hold moisture and soluble salts.

The small voltages (usually less than 0.5 volt) of natural soil corrosion cells are believed to be caused primarily by differences in oxygen concentration on the metal surface. The areas deficient in oxygen become anodes and better-aerated areas are the cathodes. The process is called differential aeration. The classical example is that of a pipeline where the underlying soil is moist and compacted by the weight of the pipe while the soil on top is comparatively well-aerated. Under these conditions, corrosion would take place on the bottom of the pipeline. Actually, this is not always what takes place, for corrosion also occurs on the top surface of pipelines. In the classical situation, a potential measurement made between the pipe and a reference electrode placed adjacent to the pipe at the bottom would show a reading electronegative to the potential when the electrode is located adjacent to the pipe at the top. On long pipelines, engineers sometimes measure potentials along the length of the pipeline with the reference cell (copper-copper sulfate) placed on the ground surface over the line. Assuming the absence of stray-currents, this procedure, known as a potential profile, will reveal "hot-spots" (areas of maximum electronegative potential), which are areas usually most severely affected by corrosion.

As the corrosion of metals underground is partly chemical in nature, the rate of corrosion is influenced by the length of exposure time. Corrosion rates during the early periods of exposure are usually comparatively high even in well-aerated soils. After a year or more the rates of corrosion in well-aerated soils decrease considerably, sometimes almost to the point of cessation. On the other hand, corrosion rates in poorly drained soils of low resistivity are nearly constant for the duration of exposure after the initial period of exposure. Thus, these factors will have an influence on the kind of protection required.

Comparison of some of the metals commonly used underground is of interest. For practical purposes, all of the ferrous materials, such as steel, cast iron and wrought iron, corrode at approximately the same rate in the same soil environment. The graphitization which takes place as cast iron corrodes can be advantageous for certain uses. In almost all soils, plain iron and steel corrode at a considerably faster rate than does copper or lead. In a soil of high acidity and high in sulfates, only lead will withstand the corrosive action for a long time, because of the deposition of insoluble salts on the metallic surface. Romanoff[4] goes into great detail about the behavior of metals and alloys exposed to all kinds of underground environments. During 30 years of field exposure programs, the National Bureau of Standards has obtained data on approximately 37,000 specimens representing over 330 varieties of materials for exposures up to 17 years in 128 test sites that included 95 soil types.

Romanoff[5] has recently made a study of the effect of soils on the corrosion of steel pilings. All previous field studies conducted by the National Bureau of Standards were confined to the exposure of metals in back-filled trenches, and, except for the size of specimens, conditions simulated the exposure of pipelines. When a pile is driven, the soil is left, relatively speaking, undisturbed in comparison with the soil in back-filled trenches. It was found that environments which cause severe corrosion under disturbed soil conditions were only mildly corrosive to steel pilings. It was concluded that the difference was probably due to oxygen deficiency at levels a few feet below the ground line or the water table zone. Under such conditions, one might wonder about the effect of anaerobic bacteria, specifically sulfate-reducing bacteria. In three locations where piles were pulled the soil conditions were favorable for such bacteria to thrive, yet the pilings were reported as being little affected by corrosion.

The action of sulfate-reducing bacteria and their effect on corrosion has recently received renewed emphasis in corrosion literature.[6, 7] The work of Starkey and Wight[8] has been the basis for a probe for measuring the oxidation-reduction potential (redox potential) of a soil and the pH, which together are used to formulate an index of corrosiveness. Anaerobic corrosion is classified in four degrees by a range of specified potentials. A more practical redox probe has been developed by Deuber and Deuber[9] and further refined by Costanzo and McVey.[10]

The corrosion rates of steel and aluminum underground have been measured by a polarization technique.[11] One specimen of each metal was exposed for 16 months during which current-potential curves were obtained at periodic intervals. Instantaneous corrosion currents were calculated during the intervals from significant changes in slope in the cathodic and anodic current-potential curves. By substituting the average value of corrosion current for one interval in the Faraday equation, the weight loss for the interval was calculated. The cumulative weight loss for all intervals compared favorably with actual weight losses.

The foregoing described polarization measurements revealed that both the steel and aluminum corroded at a faster rate during early months of exposure than later. For the particular environment, the corrosion rate of the aluminum diminished more rapidly and to a greater degree than did that of the steel. The corrosion rate of the steel was more affected by temperature and rainfall than was that of the aluminum and was a minimum during the coldest time of the year. The technique of measurement might be put to practical use for measuring corrosion rates or soil corrosivity.

Galvanic Corrosion

Galvanic corrosion currents are produced by the intrinsic difference in electrical potential of two or more dissimilar metals when exposed to a soil and in metallic contact with each other. A combination of steel and copper serves as a good example. The severity of corrosion on the anodic member (steel) depends on the area of each metal in contact with the soil. If the area of the anodic metal is relatively small compared to the cathodic metal, the corrosion on the former will be severe. Should the area of the anodic metal be relatively large, the corrosion on it because of galvanic action might be insignificant compared with the natural corrosion. As a general rule, metallic contact of dissimilar metals ought to be avoided or prevented by the use of insulating devices. The cathodic metal (copper) in direct contact with the steel will receive galvanic protection even though it would not be seriously affected by natural corrosion.

Stray-Current Corrosion and Cathodic Protection

Years ago, when direct-current railways were in common use, currents often leaked from the rails to pipelines on their return to the power source. Serious corrosion occurred on the pipeline where the current re-entered the soil. However, it was observed that the elimination of that problem and the additional benefit of cathodic protection was possible by simply connecting a bonding wire from the pipeline to the rail. Today, with the increasing use of cathodic protection, stray-current corrosion can continue to be a problem unless the cathodic protection systems are properly engineered to keep protective currents away from neighboring lines. Utility companies in some cities form correlating committees to coordinate their cathodic protection activities.

References

1. McCollum, Burton, and Ahlborn, G. H., "Influence of Frequency of Alternating or Infrequently Reversed Current on Electrolytic Corrosion," *Bureau of Standards Tech. Paper No.* **72** (1916).
2. Kulman, F. E., "Effects of Alternating Currents in Causing Corrosion," *Corrosion*, **17**, 34 (March 1961).
3. *Ibid*, page 60.
4. Romanoff, Melvin, "Underground Corrosion," *National Bureau of Standards Circular* **579** (1957).
5. Romanoff, Melvin, "Corrosion of Steel Pilings in Soils," *J. Research NBS*, **66C**, 223 (July–September 1962) or NBS Monograph **58.**
6. von Wolzogen Kühr, C. A. H., "Unity of Anaerobic and Aerobic Iron Corrosion Process in the Soil," *Corrosion*, **17**, 293t (June 1961).
7. Harris J. O., "Soil Microorganisms in Relation to Cathodically Protected Pipe," *Corrosion*, **16**, 441t (September 1960).
8. Starkey, R. L., and Wight, K. M., "Anaerobic Corrosion of Iron in Soil," American Gas Association Report, New York, 1945.
9. Deuber, C. G., and Deuber, G. B., "Development of the Redox Probe," final report of the American Gas Association Research Project PM-20, New York, 1956.
10. Costanzo, F. E., and McVey, R. E., "Development of the Redox Probe Field Technique," *Corrosion*, **14**, 268t (June 1958).
11. Schwerdtfeger, W. J., "A Study by Polarization Techniques of the Corrosion Rates of Aluminum and Steel Underground for 16 Months," *J. Research NBS*, **65C**, 271 (Oct.–Dec. 1961).

William J. Schwerdtfeger

Cross-references: *Microbiological Corrosion, Cathodic Protection, Concentration Cells, Corrosion, Polarization, Corrosion of Metals Due to Alternating Currents.*

SOLAR BATTERIES. See SOLAR ENERGY CONVERTERS.

SOLAR ENERGY CONVERTER

The conversion of solar energy into electrical energy by means of a photovoltaic cell was discovered by Becquerel[1] in 1839. In a wet cell he noticed an electromotive force was generated when light fell on one of the electrodes. Around 1876 Adams and Day[2] were the first to discover a dry photovoltaic cell using selenium. However, it was not until about 1930 that the first practical use was made of this system in the form of selenium cells for light meters, the operation of relays, and other mechanisms.

Extensive research into more efficient elements resulted in higher energy capabilities of the photovoltaic system. Thus, the present solar energy converters were developed by Chapin, Fuller and Pearson of Bell Telephone Laboratories[3,4] in 1954. This was a silicon system having a p-n junction similar to that found in transistors and semiconductors.

One type of solar energy converter consists of n-type silicon on which boron is diffused into the surface layer to a predetermined depth giving a p-type layer. Electrical contacts made to each type gives a cell (Fig. 1). Other combinations of materials beside silicon may be used, such as indium-phosphorus, gallium-arsenic, cadmium, tellurium, etc.

To make the p-n junction work, there must be a difference in energy level between the valence band and the conducting band, which is known as the Fermi level in semiconductors. Fig. 2 shows this schematically. This difference should be 1 to 2 electron volts to make the best photovoltaic cells; if it is higher, the materials become insulators. When the light strikes the valence

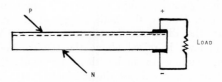

Fig. 1. Solar cell.

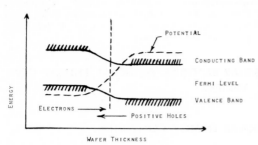

FIG. 2. Mechanism of energy conversion.

band it raises the electrons to the conducting band, leaving positive holes in the valence band. The electrons move to the right and holes to the left, producing an electric current. Junctions of this type are capable of operation by any type of radiation with sufficient energy to create electrons and positive holes, i.e., the quantum energy equals or exceeds the energy of the Fermi level. The present summary deals only with solar radiation.

The efficiency of solar energy converters is affected by temperature, amount of incident radiation, spectral distribution, and the angle of incidence. The cells are usually rated at 30°C. Higher temperatures reduce the efficiency, and lower temperatures, down to 10°C, increase the efficiency; below this, the change is small.

If the incident radiation is above 40 mw/sq cm, there is little change in energy. If it is below this level, the energy drops off rapidly. The spectral distribution may range from wavelengths of 0.4 to 1.1 microns with 0.8 microns giving the highest efficiency. The power converted is a cosine function of the angle of incidence. Thus, in the operation of the cell, all of these factors must be considered to get the maximum efficiency. It has been found in satellite applications that other radiation has a harmful effect on the operation of cells. Radiation damage[5] occurs principally from the Van Allen belt and more recently from high-altitude nuclear detonations. The latter injects large numbers of high-energy electrons into the magnetic field around the earth and forms a second belt. Since the latter is of much higher intensity, its effect is more pronounced. Due to the high energy of the electrons, the difference in electron volts in the Fermi level is raised above the semiconductor level, tending to make them nonconducting. This tendency reduces the efficiency very rapidly.

Various means are being used to reduce these effects, such as forming the p-junction on a glass surface and placing it over the n-type silicon. Here the glass acts as a shield to reduce the effect of radiation. Recently new materials have been investigated, and the old p-n junction has been reversed to an n-p junction giving a cell which is much more resistant to radiation damage.

The maximum power transfer at 30°C with an incident energy of 100 mw/sq cm on a surface area of 1.75 sq cm with an 8 per cent efficiency would give 0.4 volts at 35 ma. If the efficiency is 4 per cent, the current at 0.4 volts would be 17.5 ma. The silicon-boron n-p junction cell is the most efficient. In recent studies, efficiencies of up to 11 per cent have been achieved.

The actual maximum utilization of the solar energy converter depends on the type of collector and mounting used. The intercell connection must be made to give the least resistance. This is usually accomplished by using a grid network.

To get maximum efficiency, the solar arrays are so arranged that maximum amount of light is received on the cell surface and likewise the dissipation of heat must be at a maximum.

Various solar arrays have been used in most of the satellites. The first Vanguard has been transmitting for many years from the power supplied by the solar cells on its surface. At present, the solar arrays are used in conjunction with storage batteries to furnish the power of all recent satellites.

It must be pointed out that the solar energy converter is not a true battery since the energy is directly converted and can not be stored. For this reason the "solar battery" so-called is really a misnomer and truly should be called a solar energy converter.

References

1. BECQUEREL, E., "On Electric Effects under the Influence of Solar Radiation," *Compt. Rend.*, **9,** 561 (1839).
2. ADAMS, W. G., AND DAY, R. E., "The Action of Light on Selenium," *Proc. Roy. Soc.*, **A25,** 113 (1877).
3. CHAPIN, D. M., FULLER, C. S., AND PEARSON, G. L., "A New Silicon p-n Junction Photocell for Converting Solar Radiation into Electric Power," *J. Appl. Phys.*, **25,** 676 (1954).
4. CHAPIN, D. M., FULLER, C. S., AND PEARSON, G. L., "The Bell Solar Battery," *Bell Labs. Rec.* (July 1955).

5. SANDERS, NEWELL D., *et al*, "Power for Space-craft," *NASA, SP-21*, p. 4 (Dec. 1962).

PAUL L. HOWARD

Cross-references: *Photoconductivity; Semiconductors; Space Power.*

SOLID ELECTROLYTE BATTERIES. See BATTERIES, SOLID ELECTROLYTE.

SOLION

The term "Solion" is a derived name for a group of electrochemical control and measurement devices which use a solution of ions as a working medium. These devices have some functional similarity to vacuum tubes and transistors, in that the internal flow of charged particles is controlled through various factors of design to yield a desired behavior in an external electrical circuit. In the vacuum tube, the internal particles are electrons, the working medium is a vacuum, and the control is obtained through imposition of selective fields. In the transistor, the internal particles are both electrons and "holes," the working medium a crystal lattice, and the control is again obtained through electric fields. In the solion, the internal particles are ions, the working medium an electrolyte solution, but control in this case can be exercised through both electric fields and mass transport (diffusion and bulk fluid motion).

Because the velocities of ion movement in solution are low in comparison to the electron velocities in vacuum tubes and transistors, solions are inherently lower frequency devices (<1000 cps). Although this limitation to low frequencies places the solions at a disadvantage insofar as incorporation into present electronic circuitry is concerned, they possess distinct advantages in applications which require measurement or control of phenomena at low frequencies.

Components

Almost all solions employ an electrochemical system of iodine and potassium iodide dissolved in water or an alcohol. In these solutions, the iodine exists predominantly as the tri-iodide ion, I_3^-, formed by the equilibrium,

$$I_2 + I^- \rightleftharpoons I_3^-. \qquad (1)$$

The electrodes are usually fabricated of platinum, although other materials (carbon, tantalum carbide) are used for certain specialized applications. As in vacuum tubes, the size, dimension, and form of the electrodes and the spatial arrangement of several electrodes throughout the system are used to obtain performance variations from different units.

Solions can be divided into two major categories: (1) those in which the solution is either allowed or forced to move in response to external electrical or pressure signals, and (2) those in which the solution remains stationary. The housings of units in the first group are of an inert plastic, preferably polymonochlorotrifluoroethylene (Kel-F), with flexible plastic diaphragms forming two of the walls so that external pressure signals can be transmitted to the solution. These units are generally pressure detectors or transducers. The second group units (diodes and integrators) are usually housed in glass, although plastics can be used.

Some idea of the physical size and shape of solions can be gathered by reference to Fig. 1, and of electrode layout by reference to Figs. 2, 3, and 6.

Electrochemical Phenomena Involved in Solion Operation

Passage of current through the iodine-iodide electrolyte solutions used in most solions is accompanied by the following electrode reactions:

At the cathode,

$$I_3^- + 2e \rightarrow 3I^-, \qquad (2)$$

and at the anode,

$$3I^- - 2e \rightarrow I_3^-. \qquad (3)$$

There is thus no net change in any component in the solution, so that in the absence of undesired side reactions, current can flow through the solution indefinitely with no change in the total system, although there will be local changes in the concentration of iodine and iodide. In general, solion operation revolves around the interrelationships between current flow and applied voltage, and between current flow and local concentration changes, and how these are affected by electrode design, solution concentration, mass transfer of the solution, and many other such factors. Only the most important of these will be discussed.

Polarization Characteristics. Considering only two platinum electrodes in an iodine-iodide solution, the functional relationship between

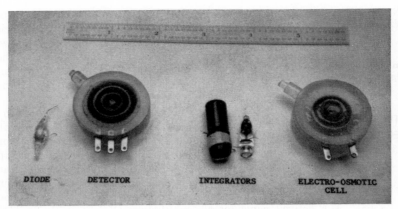

FIG. 1. Typical solion units.

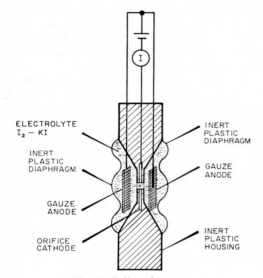

ELECTROLYTE
$I_2 - KI$

INERT
PLASTIC
DIAPHRAGM

GAUZE
ANODE

ORIFICE
CATHODE

INERT
PLASTIC
DIAPHRAGM

GAUZE
ANODE

INERT
PLASTIC
HOUSING

FIG. 2. Solion detector.

current and applied voltage will depend on the electrolytic resistance through the solution and the flux density (ions/sq cm/sec) of tri-iodide ions to the cathode. In the usual solion operation, the electrolytic resistance is made negligible by using a large excess of potassium iodide.

A typical plot of the current-voltage relationship is shown in Fig. 4 for solutions of three different concentrations of iodine. The current increases rapidly with voltage, following Ohm's law for the electrolytic resistance of the solution, until the supply of iodine to the cathode becomes limited, at which point the current levels out and becomes voltage independent or "concentration polarized." The second increase in current at about 1.0 v is due to reduction of hydrogen ions from the solvent; this undesired

side reaction is avoided by limiting the bias to < 0.9 v.

The plateau regions of Fig. 4 are called "limiting diffusion currents;" for quiet, isothermal conditions, their values are given by

$$I = n\mathbf{F}AD(dc/dx) \qquad (4)$$

where n is the number of electrons involved in the electrochemical reaction (for the iodine reaction, two), $\mathbf{F}$ the value of the Faraday, A the cathode area, D the diffusion coefficient of the tri-iodide species, and dc/dx the concentration gradient of tri-iodide at the cathode. The value of dc/dx in Eq. (4) is a function of:

(1) The bulk concentration of iodine (cf curves of Fig. 4). This makes it possible to read electrically the concentration of iodine at any point in the solion.

(2) The degree of stirring or bulk fluid movement in the vicinity of the cathode. Thus, the curves of Fig. 4 could be obtained from the solion of Fig. 2 by using three different flow rates through the orifice cathode, even though the bulk concentration of iodine is constant.

(3) The spacing between the anode and cathode, provided they are close enough together that the concentration gradient extends all the way from one electrode to the other. Thus, the curves of Fig. 4 could be obtained from the solion shown in Fig. 3 by using three different spacings between electrodes R and C.

Faraday Equivalence. The exact equivalence between the total quantity of electricity passed through an electrochemical system and the changes in chemical content which occur at the electrodes (Faraday's law) is used as the basic phenomenon in several types of solion integrators.

In operation, a current (usually in the order of microamperes) is passed through the solution, and the change in concentration around one of the electrodes is determined. Since the number of coulombs passed is given by

$$\int idt \, ,$$

then by Faraday's law,

$$\int idt = \frac{\text{(g iodine transferred) (value of the Faraday)}}{\text{(equivalent weight of iodine)}} \quad (5)$$

and the value of the integral is obtained by any method which determines the amount of iodine transferred. This is usually done by confining the iodine to a fixed volume and reading concentration.

Concentration Voltage. Two platinum electrodes immersed in different concentrations of iodine at room temperature will exhibit a potential difference of

$$E_{conc} = 0.030 \log \frac{C_1}{C_2} , \quad (6)$$

provided only that there is a continuous electrolytic path between the two electrodes. The potential developed can be used for either reading a concentration or as a supply voltage to drive another element (such as another solion, a relay, or a transistor).

Electroosmotic Pumping. The electroosmotic cell serves as a complementary unit to a variety of other solions, in that it is used exclusively as a micropump to feed fluid flows into other coupled units. The electrochemical phenomena involved in these units are quite different from those of the iodine-iodide system used in most solion devices. Electroosmosis (q.v.) is the movement of a liquid through a porous medium, such as fritted glass, under the influence of a potential gradient.

Fig. 5 is a schematic of the electroosmotic cell. In these cells, unlike the units using the iodine-iodide system, it is desired that the liquid exhibit a very low conductivity, so that electrode polarization will be minimized, and most of the applied voltage will appear as IR drop. The best electrodes have been found to be finely-divided silver compressed into a disc shape. It should be noted that as current flows through the cell, there is a transfer of silver from anode to cathode, so that current flowing constantly in one

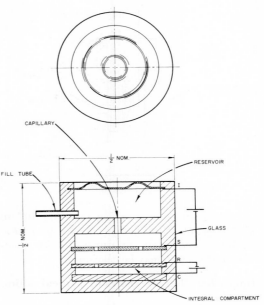

FIG. 3. Solion electrical readout integrator.

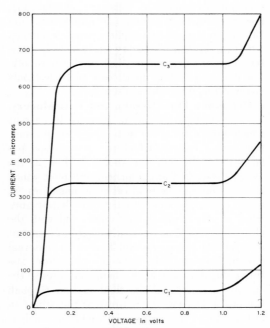

FIG. 4. Limiting diffusion currents as a function of iodine concentration.

direction would eventually consume the anode, and the cell would cease to function. Currents are only a few microamperes on the average, however, so a few grams of silver will suffice for several years of operation.

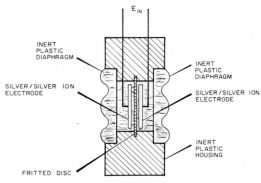

FIG. 5. Electroosmotic cell.

Typical values of pumping rates are 10^{-3} to 10^{-5} cc/sec, or, if the flow is impeded by pumping into a diaphragm, pressures of a few thousand dynes/sq cm may be developed.

Operating Characteristics of Typical Solion Units

Solions may be classified according to the function performed, as follows: (1) detectors, flow meters, transducers, (2) integrators, and (3) differentiators, multipliers, and amplifiers. Units in the third category are generally combinations of single solions, i.e., an electroosmotic cell plus a detector, integrators plus electronic components, integrators in series, etc.

Detectors, Flow Meters, and Transducers. These units operate on the increase in current which results from the disturbance of the solution near a cathode which is concentration polarized. In the detector shown in Fig. 2, the cathode is in the form of an orifice through which the solution may be pumped by means of an external pressure across the detector diaphragms. With no flow through the orifice, and with the electrodes biased at 0.9 v, a background current of a few microamperes will flow in the external circuit. Forcing fluid through the orifice disturbs the diffusion layer there and causes the current to increase. The fluid motion through the orifice can be either direct or pulsating; in either case, a d-c current is produced which is a function of the amplitude of the flow. By suitable design of the detecting cathode, the functional nature of the response to flow may be varied. The simple orifice, when properly designed, gives an output which is logarithmic; a porous cathode gives a linear output; and a small box containing offset pinhole orifices gives a square root response.

Integrators. At the present time, the integrators are clearly the most important solion units, and the only ones to have reached commercial production. The solion integrator is essentially an iodine coulometer of unique design; the design factors which make the solion integrator a practical device are the method of readout and the method of retaining the integral.

Readout of the integral is accomplished by any method which determines concentration. The three methods used most extensively are (1) the diffusion-limited current at a cathodic element in the integral compartment; (2) the concentration cell voltage between an electrode in the integral compartment and another electrode in a constant reference concentration; and (3) the color density of the solution in the integral compartment. The diffusion-limited current readout is preferred in most cases, since enough power is available through the readout current to operate subsequent electrical circuits for control purposes. However, the other two readout methods are uniquely suited to certain integrating applications.

All solion integrators contain an integral compartment and an iodine reservoir, connected by a solution bridge. During integration, iodine is transferred by electrolysis from the reservoir into the integral compartment, after first removing all the iodine from this compartment. For high accuracy, it is essential to retain all of the transferred iodine in the integral compartment and at the same time prevent any iodine reaching this compartment by any process other than the desired electrochemical transfer. However, since there must be a solution bridge between the two compartments, iodine will diffuse from one to the other at a rate dependent on the concentration gradient and the geometry of the diffusion path. The two methods used to "retain the integral" (i.e., to minimize diffusion transfer) are electrical shielding with a negatively biased electrode, and the use of a two-phase solvent system with a high distribution coefficient for iodine between the two solvents.

Electrical shielding can be illustrated by referring to Fig. 3 and describing briefly the operation of this integrator. Before operation, the "readout" electrode, R, is shorted to the "shield" electrode, S; the negative bias on these two electrodes will quickly transfer all the iodine from the volume below the shield into the reservoir. The readout electrode is then returned to its original connection, but since there is now no iodine in the lower region, no current flows between the readout and the "common" electrode, C. Some iodine will diffuse through the capillary, but it will be "picked up" (reduced) by the shield electrode and transferred electrochemically back into the reservoir. The current to be integrated is passed through the integrator between the "input" electrode, I, and the "common" electrode, C, so that iodine is transferred from the reservoir into the integral compartment. The iodine thus transferred is formed on the surface of electrode C, and diffuses across to electrode R, where it is picked up and redeposited at C. The transferred iodine is thus retained inside the integral compartment.

Where the integral must be retained over very long periods (months), the two-phase solvent system is used. Referring again to Fig. 3, imagine the separator containing the capillary to be replaced by a fritted-glass disc. If the fritted structure contains a water phase saturated with an iodine salt, and the volumes on either side contain butyl alcohol in which the iodine-iodide system is dissolved, the concentration of iodine in the aqueous phase at equilibrium will be very small due to the high distribution coefficient for iodine between butyl alcohol and water. The concentration *gradient* of iodine across the water phase is therefore very small, and diffusion transfer is essentially negligible.

Differentiators, Multipliers, and Amplifiers. These are "compound" units, in which two or more solions are hydraulically or electrically coupled to perform a desired mathematical function, or in which transistor circuits are combined with solion circuits. Most of these involve coupling the electroosmotic cell to solion detectors of various designs. Because of the very low frequency response of the electroosmotic cell, all of these devices operate from very low frequencies down to very near d-c.

In the amplifier the solion detector operates linearly, and since the pressure developed by the electroosmotic cell is linear with applied voltage, the output of the detector follows the input to the micropump, but with large current gains. Typical inputs to the micropump are a few microamperes at less than a volt (i.e., microwatts), while outputs from the coupled detector are milliamperes at about a volt (i.e., milliwatts).

The solion differentiator consists of the same two units as does the amplifier, but with a hydraulic capacitance, such as a stiff diaphragm or bellows, inserted in the fluid flow circuit. An understanding of how the solion differentiator works is best gained by drawing an analogy to the corresponding electrical network. In general, the important parameters of hydraulic circuits have exact analogies in electrical circuits, and the most common of these are

Electrical	*Hydraulic*
Voltage	Pressure
Current	Fluid flow rate
Resistance	Hydraulic resistance (fritted disc)
Capacity	Hydraulic compliance (diaphragm or bellows)
Inductance	Hydraulic inertance (capillary tube)

One of the simplest electrical networks is a resistor, R, and a capacitor, C, in series (RC differentiator). A voltage, E_t, applied to the terminals of this network results in a current which follows the equation

$$I_t = C \frac{dE}{dt}\left(1 - \exp - \frac{t}{RC}\right). \qquad (7)$$

The analogous equation for the RC series hydraulic circuit is

$$\frac{dv}{dt} = C \frac{dP}{dt}\left(1 - \exp - \frac{t}{RC}\right). \qquad (8)$$

The flow rate, dv/dt, can be converted into a current, I_{out}, by a solion detector, while dP/dt can be generated by a voltage dE/dt fed into an electroosmotic cell. Under these conditions, Eq. (8) becomes

$$I_{out} = 10^{-3}\, \mathbf{F}NkC \frac{dE}{dt}\left(1 - \exp - \frac{t}{RC}\right), \qquad (9)$$

where $\mathbf{F}$ is the value of the Faraday, N the normality of the iodine, and k is the pressure output of the electroosmotic cell (in dynes/sq cm) at 1.0 v applied.

Comparison of Eq. (9) with Eq. (7) shows that the solion differentiator works essentially like the simple RC electrical differentiator, but with some rather important practical differences. First, the value of the RC product, which determines the frequency range over which differentiation occurs, can be made quite large in the hydraulic case, and good derivatives are obtainable down to frequencies as low as cycles per kilosecond. The solion, however, cannot compete at frequencies above about 10 cycles/sec. Second, amplification is inherent in the solion differentiator, the power being obtained from the battery

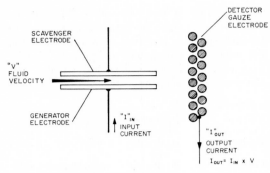

FIG. 6. Schematic of electrode arrangement for the solion multiplier.

in the linear detector circuit. The third difference of some importance is the absence of electrical coupling between the output and input of the solion, which greatly simplifies the design of circuits containing these units.

The solion multiplier is somewhat more complex than the differentiator and amplifier, but illustrates nicely the wide variety of functions which can be obtained by combining the various electrochemical phenomena in different ways. The detector for the multiplier is essentially a linear detector in which the fluid flowing to the detecting cathode contains no iodine unless it is formed in place by a second external current. This is accomplished by the electrode arrangement shown schematically in Fig. 6. Here the "generator" electrode and the "scavenger" electrode form the opposite faces of a very narrow corridor through which the electrolyte flows before it reaches the detector electrode. These electrodes are insulated so that their inner faces only are exposed to the solution. If the electrolyte initially contains no iodine, and if there is no input current to the generator electrode, no iodine reaches the detector gauze regardless of the magnitude of flow. Conversely, if there is no flow, any iodine formed at the generator electrode by making it an anode will simply diffuse across to the scavenger where it is reduced to iodide, and again no iodine reaches the detector gauze. If, however, both flow and generating current are present, the amount of iodine reaching the detector gauze, and hence the output current, is proportional to the product of flow and generating current. By remembering that with other solion units flows may be produced from electrical currents or electrical currents from flows, it may be seen that a product of any combination may be taken. Further, by in-

corporating suitable values of hydraulic capacitance in the circuits, products of derivatives in various forms may be obtained in the same unit.

Conclusion

Solion units other than those described here have been developed; still others are in the experimental stage. The technology of solions is young, having been developed over a period of about the last 15 years. Many problems in design and fabrication remain to be solved; however, the basic theory is new well understood, and it is felt that solions will occupy an important position in the future of such things as control circuits and automation for chemical plants, where low-frequency hydraulic measurements are common; in instrumentation, where long-period differentiation, integration, etc., are often desired; and as components in almost any situation where low-frequency hydraulic or electrical signals are available.

References

1. EULER, J., "The Solion, an Electrochemical Control Element," *Electrotech. Z.*, Part B, **12**, (22), 537–540 (1960).
2. HURD, R. M., AND JORDAN, W. H., JR., "The Principles of the Solion," *Platinum Metals Review*, **4**, No. 2, 42 (April, 1960).
3. HURD, R. M., AND LANE, R. N., "Principles of Very Low Power Electrochemical Control Devices," *J. Electrochem. Soc.*, **104**, 727 (1957).
4. KEMP, G. T., AND HURD, R. M., "Solion Integration," *Research*, **14**, No. 10, 382 (October, 1961).
5. MARTIN, JAMES W., AND COX, JAMES R., "Solion Tetrode Integrates Chromatograph Signals," *Electronics*, **35**, 46–47 (March 23, 1962).
6. REED, H. B., AND McQUITTY, J. B., "The Solion," *Yale Scientific Magazine*, **32**, No. 5 (February, 1958).
7. WITTENBORN, A. F., "Analysis of a Logarithmic Solion Acoustic Pressure Detector," *J. Acoust. Soc. Am.*, **31**, No. 4, 475 (April, 1959).

RAY M. HURD

SORET POTENTIAL

If a temperature gradient exists in a solution, there is a tendency for a concentration gradient (Soret effect) to be established, i.e., one component becomes concentrated in either the hot or the cold portion of the solution. The change in concentration is distinct from changes associated with convection processes. If suitable precautions are taken, a cell can be set up in which a dynamic equilibrium is established after a sufficient time and a reproducible concentration difference, δc, observed for a temperature difference, δT. The quantity $(1/c)(dc/dT)$ is called the Soret coefficient, σ. In the case of an electrolyte solution a simultaneous potential gradient (the Soret potential) is established, which reaches a constant limiting value when a condition of dynamic equilibrium has been established in the cell. The value of $d\Phi/dT$, where Φ is the potential observed, depends on the activity of the ion to which the electrodes used are reversible and on the nature and relative concentrations of all the ions present in the solution.

Reference

Tyrrell, H. J. V., "Thermal-Diffusion Phenomena in Electrolytes and the Constants Involved," in "Electrochemical Constants," *NBS Circular 524*, p. 119, U. S. Dept. of Commerce, 1953.

M. H. Lietzke and
R. W. Stoughton

SPACE POWER

Space power requirements involve both nonpropulsive and propulsive electrical power. The power levels for the nonpropulsive applications range from less than 100 watts in the early satellite systems to a predicted level of several hundred kilowatts for the mission patterns of the 1970's. Electrical propulsive requirements are estimated to start at the 100-kw level and eventually will require megawatt levels. The accompanying table indicates some of the power requirements for various satellites and missions.

There are several parameters that are used for selecting and evaluating space power systems. These will be discussed by paragraphs below.

Mass and Power Level

In general the main parameters for selection of a system have been based on system mass for a given power level. Chemical systems become prohibitively heavy for missions that require more than a few weeks. Primary batteries are useful for missions of a day or so. The most efficient devices for converting chemical to electrical energy are fuel cells (q.v.) and these devices (of which there are many types) can be considered for missions of several weeks. Solar and nuclear energy receive consideration for missions of more than one month. Power requirements of several kilowatts can be satisfied by solar cells (see *Solar Energy Converter*), and solar collectors wtih thermionic convertors and nuclear reactor thermo-electric devices are given consideration. The solar devices have a specific mass of 200 lb/kw. These devices usually require thermal energy storage or supplementary battery power due to periods of darkness or peak power demand. The specific mass then varies from 200 to 1000 lb/kw. Radioisotope power cells with thermionic convertors have specific mass of 1000 lb/kw.

A power level of a few kilowatts can be satisfied by solar and nuclear turbogenerators and nuclear reactor systems are preferred for the 100-kw range. This latter level can also be satisfied by utilizing turbogenerators and thermionic devices.

Relationship to the Complete Vehicle System

The power conversion device must be compatible with the other components of the vehicle system. The volume and shape must be selected in terms of the other subsystems. The effects of radiation, heat, and altitude control must all be considered. In addition electrical compatibility must be considered in terms of the output characteristic of the power convertor and the electrical load imposed by the vehicle mission. The design of the radiator must also be considered in terms of area requirements and geometry. In the solar energy convertors, the collector design and orientation are critical. Shelding and special geometries are required for nuclear reactors to eliminate the radiation hazards.

Table 1. Typical Space Power Requirements

Mission	Power	Performance
Communication satellite	150 w	
Meteorological satellite	300–450 w	Several months
Apollo	2 kw	Two weeks
Manned-orbiting space system	10 kw	One year
Manned-lunar station	100 kw	
Unmanned-Jupiter probe	1 mw	
Electrical propulsion to Mars and return	10–30 mw	1½–2 years

Space Environment

The complexities of the space environment in terms of meteoroid damage, space radiation (e.g., van Allan belt), etc., must be taken into account in selecting and designing energy conversion devices. The vacuum of outer space and solar radiation influences dramatically the selection of materials of construction as well as the design of the power unit. The zero-g environment cannot be overlooked.

Reliability and Lifetime

In terms of space exploration, the power device must be reliable and preferably fail-proof. In this connection redundancy must be considered to insure a proper functioning of the space vehicle. The lifetime of the unit must be compatible with the mission.

Cost and Availability

The selection of a specific power convertor is predicated on the fact that the technical areas associated with the device are understood and workable. It is only good sense to use state-of-the-art devices. It is also necessary in this regard to make sure that devices contemplated for use in the 1970's are now undergoing a concerted research and development effort.

The last parameter to be used in selecting devices is cost. Certainly the cheaper unit should be selected providing all other parameters are the same. As a result of current developments, the cost parameter is considered to be a minor consideration.

References

SNYDER, NATHAN W., Editor, "Progress in Astronautics and Rocketry," Vol. 3, "Energy Conversion for Space Power," and Vol. 4, "Space Power Systems," New York, Academic Press, 1961.

Aeronautics and Aerospace Engineering, whole issue devoted to "Space Electric Power," **1**, No. 4 (May 1963).

CHARLES K. HERSH

Cross-references: *Fuel Cells; Solar Energy Converter.*

STABILITY CONSTANTS OF METAL COMPLEXES

The work of Bjerrum (1941)[1] first clearly stressed the importance of considering the formation of metal complexes as taking place by successive equilibria. For a ligand, L, attaching to a metal, M, successive complexes are assumed to form in solution, ML, ML_2, ML_3 $\cdots$, with formation or stability constants, K_1, K_2, K_3 $\cdots$, respectively. This concept has gradually superseded that of a unique complex being present in a given solution; under differing conditions one or another complex may predominate.

Ligands may be neutral molecules or negative ions, and the charge borne by a particular complex ion is the algebraic sum of that of the simple ion plus those of the attached ligands. The maximum number of ligand molecules that can be bonded to the metal atom depends on the coordination number of the latter (commonly 6 or 4, less commonly 2 or 8) and the number of covalent bonds which a particular ligand can form. Ligands, such as ammonia or the cyanide ion, are univalent, and one molecule (or ion) occupies one coordination site. Ligands with more than one atom capable of forming bonds to the metal, e.g., ethylenediamine or citric acid, form so-called chelate complexes with ring structures incorporating the metal atom. In such cases the maximum number of ligand molecules is the coordination number divided by the number of bonds formed per ligand molecule.

The majority of experimental studies of complex ion equilibria have been carried out in media of constant ionic strength. The equilibrium constants derived from these are therefore mainly "conditional" constants; in the principal collection of published stability constants the ionic medium to which these apply is specified in each case.[2]

Bjerrum introduced the concept of the degree of complex formation, $\bar{n}$, the average number of ligand molecules bound per metal atom. He showed

$$\bar{n} = \frac{\Sigma\, n\beta_n\, [\text{L}]^n}{1 + \Sigma\, \beta_n\, [\text{L}]^n}$$

(Here $\beta_n = K_1 K_2 \cdots K_n$, the cumulative product of formation constants for the nth complex).

The extent of complex formation at any particular concentration of ligand is given by a plot of $\bar{n}$ vs pL, so-called formation curve. Among a series of metal complexes the distribution of the metal may be represented by a conservation equation such as

$$[\text{M}]_T = [\text{M}] + [\text{ML}] + [\text{ML}_2] + \cdots [\text{ML}_n]$$

This representation shows only mononuclear

complexes; the conservation equation might have to be modified to show polynuclear complexes (e.g., M_2L_2), protonated complexes (e.g., MHL), etc. For the above conservation equation it can be shown that the relative proportions of the several constituents in the order as written are

$$1 : \beta_1[L] : \beta_2[L]^2 : \cdots : \beta_n[L]^n$$

It is instructive to note the formal similarity between this and the set of ratios for the constituents in solutions of acids discussed under Case 2, in **Ionic Equilibria** (q.v.). The fraction of metal in each complex species may thus be shown graphically as a function of pL; this is illustrated in Fig. 1 (a) ferric ion + sulfosalicylic acid, (b) ferric ion + 8-quinolinol-5-sulfonic acid.

Information about the formation of metal complexes is frequently derived indirectly from pH measurements. The majority of ligands that form metal complexes are strong bases, and readily accept protons to assume the form of the conjugate acid. In such cases the formation of a metal complex is a proton-transfer process, thus:

$$M + nHL \rightleftarrows ML_n + nH$$

(The charges are omitted for simplicity. The ligand may, of course, be dibasic or polybasic in which case twice or some multiple the number of protons is released.) It is seen from this equation that the number of ligand molecules bound to the metal can be simply determined from the number of protons set free. The amount of hydrogen ion liberated in this way can be measured by titration. An acidified solution of ligand containing the metallic ion is titrated with an alkaline solution of known concentration, and the volume of the latter required to bring the pH to some particular value is compared with the volume required for an equivalent acidified solution of ligand containing no metal. The following equation applies in each case:

$$[H]_T - \bar{n}_H[L]_T - [H] = [B]_T - [OH]$$

Here $[H]_T$ is the total number of equivalents per litre of mineral acid and/or protonated ligand taken initially, and $\bar{n}_H$ is the degree of protonation of the ligand. For the same pH in the two solutions all terms except $[B]_T$ are identical; the difference in $[B]_T$ is equivalent to the number of protons set free by metal-complex formation.

For calculation of the stability constants for a series of metal complexes a range of corre-

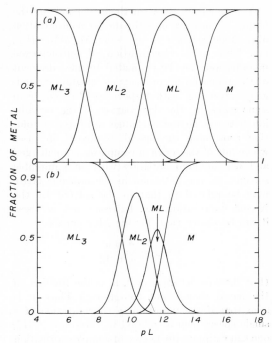

FIG. 1. Representation of the distribution of metal in solution as free and complex ions, as a function of pL = −log[L]: (a) iron (III) + 5-sulfosalicylic acid, (b) ferric iron + 8-quinolinol-5-sulfonic acid.

sponding values of $\bar{n}$, the degree of complex formation (see **Ionic Equilibria**), and pL is required. At selected pHs in the preceding titrations one may immediately determine $\bar{n}$; it is given by the number of moles of ligand per liter bound to metal (related to the difference in $[B]_T$) divided by the total molarity of metal in solution. At the same pHs one calculates pL = −log [L] from the relationship

$$[L] = \frac{[L]_T - \bar{n}[M]_T}{1 + a_H/K''_{a1} + a_H^2/K''_{a1}K''_{a2} + \cdots}$$

in which K''_{a1}, etc., is the acidity constant(s) of the protonated form of the ligand (Brönsted constants). A variety of numerical procedures have been described for the extraction of stability constants given a formation curve based on corresponding values of $\bar{n}$ and pL.[3]

A variety of other methods for obtaining stability constants of metallic complexes have been developed, and a recent monograph[3] is devoted to this subject; in addition, the introduction to the published tables[2] summarizes many of these methods.

A number of these methods depend on the ability to measure or estimate the concentration of a single member of the series M, ML, ML$_2$, etc. Thus, the concentration of uncomplexed metallic ion may be estimated by measurement of the potential of an electrode (metal or amalgam) reversible with respect to the ion, or in some cases by the distribution of the metallic ion between an ion exchange resin and a solution containing the ligand. Similarly, in cases where one of the series of complexes is uncharged and will undergo partition with an immiscible solvent, its concentration in the aqueous phase may be related to that in the solvent by the Nernst distribution law. In cases such as these it can be shown that, for the jth complex

$$\bar{n} = j - \frac{\partial \ln \alpha_j}{\partial \ln [\mathrm{L}]}$$

(For the case where $j = 0$, α_j is the fraction of the metal that is not complexed.) Thus, it is seen that if the variation in concentration of a single species can be related to variations in [L], one can estimate the degree of complex formation and, given sufficient measurements, the stability constants of the complexes.

It has been shown that the half-wave potential of a given metallic ion is shifted by incorporation of the metal in a complex ion, and a number of investigators have determined stability constants by polarographic methods.[4] A more recent electrochemical method has been the use of an electrode of the "second kind" in which a mercurous complex in contact with mercury serves as a device to estimate the free ligand concentration.[5]

A great many optical methods have been used to determine stability constants of complexes. These usually depend on shifts in absorption spectra resulting from the formation of one or more complexes.[6, 7] These are usually most successful when applied to systems of complexes such as that illustrated in Fig. 1 (a), in which each of a series of complexes can be produced in solution without serious interference from the others by control of the pH (and hence of the pL) in the medium.

References

1. Bjerrum, J., "Metal Ammine Formation in Aqueous Solution," Copenhagen, P. Haase & Son, 1941.
2. The Chemical Society, London (1958). "Stability Constants," Part I, "Organic Ligands," Part II, "Inorganic Ligands."
3. Rossotti, F. J. C., and Rossotti, H., "The Determination of Stability Constants," Chapter 5, New York, McGraw Hill Book Co., Inc., 1961.
4. Lingane, J. J., Chemical Reviews, 29, 1 (1941); Ringbom, A., and Erikson, L., Acta Chem. Scand., 7, 1105 (1953).
5. Schmid, R. W., and Reilley, C. N., J. Am. Chem. Soc., 78, 5513 (1956); Anderigg, G., Helv. Chim. Acta, 42, 344 (1959).
6. Vosburgh, W. C., and Cooper, G. R., J. Am. Chem. Soc., 63, 437 (1941); Job, P., Ann. chim., 9 (10), 113 (1928).
7. Vareille, L., Bull. soc. chim. France, 870 (1955).

W. A. E. McBryde

Cross-references: *Acidimetry and Alkalimetry; Complex Ions in Electroplating; Dissociation; Ionic Equilibria; pH; pH Titration Curves; Polarography.*

STANDARD ELECTRODE POTENTIALS, See ELECTRODE POTENTIALS entries; REFERENCE ELECTRODES.

STEEL MAKING IN ELECTRIC ARC FURNACES

The electric furnace offers many advantages in steel making. It provides a ready source of heat at very high temperatures which is quickly available and easily regulated. In contrast to fuel-fired furnaces, the furnace atmosphere can be maintained free of contaminating gases and can be controlled to provide the desired conditions for melting and refining of the steel. In addition to being clean, electric furnaces operate at greater thermal efficiency than fuel-fired types, and can be maintained constantly at any desired temperature. For these and other reasons the use of the electric arc furnace for steel making has grown steadily.

The first electric furnace put into successful commercial operation for melting steel was installed in France in 1899 by Héroult (q.v.). The first electric furnace used in the United States was installed by Halcomb Steel in Syracuse, New York, in 1906. This four ton furnace was single-phase and rectangular. Two years later Firth-Sterling started up a similar unit at McKeesport, Pennsylvania, and in 1909 Illinois Steel installed a fifteen ton, three-phase, circular furnace at South Chicago. These furnaces produced ingot steels. The first electric furnace for melting foundry steels was installed at Easton, Pennsylvania, in 1911.

Considerable expansion in electric melting took place throughout World War I. During that time and afterward crucible melting furnaces and foundry converters were widely replaced due to their higher metal costs. The electric furnace then invaded the billet-size ingot field where small open-hearth furnaces were more expensive to use. Top charging of electric furnaces increased the advantages of this type of equipment, particularly when coupled with higher powering.

By the end of 1962 nearly nine per cent of all steel made into ingots and castings in the United States was melted electrically, the direct-arc, three-phase, top-charge furnace being used to tap essentially all of this tonnage. In addition to their operations on steel, direct-arc furnaces also are used to melt copper and nickel.

At present ingot furnaces most generally are installed in sizes making from 10 to somewhat over 100 ton heats. The 20 ft diameter top-charge furnace, for example, when backed with 25,000 kva, usually makes 110 ton heats in less than four hours tap to tap. In the case of foundry furnaces, the heats ordinarily are from one to 20 tons. Table 1 lists heat sizes and the powering of the more popular sizes of three-phase, direct-arc furnaces. To date the 25 ft I.D. 40,000 kva unit is the largest size in operation. When melting plain carbon steels many shops exceed the nominal charges listed, whereas on high-grade alloy steels the converse is more usual. When tapping structural-grade and foundry steels a productive rate of one ton per hour per 1,000 kva of furnace powering is a general rule. However, oxygen injection and supplemental heating with gas burners is increasing the melting rate in numerous instances as described later.

The electric furnace using scrap charges is very much favored by the fact that the heat to effect the melting is released by the arcs right in the charge itself so high thermal efficiency is insured. On the order of 320 kwh is needed at 100 per cent thermal efficiency to fluidize one ton of miscellaneous cold steel scrap charge with adherents, and it is customary—without aid with oxygen—to melt down one ton of charge with the expenditure of 400 kwh or less.

General Operating Procedure

In general, foundries in the United States operate with acid-lined electric furnaces, but essentially all electric steel ingots are cast of metal from furnaces having magnesite hearths

TABLE 1. PRINCIPAL SIZES OF DIRECT-ARC STEEL MELTING FURNACES

Furnace Diameter, ft	Nominal Charge, tons	Usual Powering, kva
6	3	1,500
8	6	2,500
10	12	5,000
12	22	7,500
14	40	10,000
16	60	15,000
18	75	18,000
20	100	25,000

and lower sidewalls. Linings of magnesite are termed basic linings, whereas silica linings are termed acid linings. Foundry melting units delivering maganese steel or heat-resistant alloy steels also are operated with basic linings since these best withstand the high-lime slags of this type of operation.

The operating procedure with modern electric furnaces consists of first charging on the furnace hearth a weighed amount of suitable scrap. Since modern electric furnaces universally are of the swing-roof type, clam shell buckets are used in charging. The amounts of various grades of scrap which will be most economical to use for any particular operation will be determined by the specifications of the steels to be produced.

The charge is melted with arcs which exceed 6000°F, and once the charge has been fluidized, it must be brought to the condition required by the type of product to be made. Usually, burned lime with some fluorspar or sand to act as a flux is first added to the bath to form a slag with the oxides resulting from the melting of the scrap. This is an oxidizing slag.

Copper, molybdenum, and nickel strongly resist oxidation with the result that they are retained by the molten bath of metal on meltdown. Zinc volatilizes during melting. Aluminum, silicon, and titanium oxidize readily. Hence, they pass into the slag. Chromium, phosphorus, and manganese dioxide oxidize to a lesser extent and become slag components.

Either a single-slag or a two-slag process can be used as required by the demands of the product and the charge. Foundry steels are made by the single-slag, acid-lining practice since silica refractories cost less than basic refractories and stand up well to the approximately 3000°F molten bath temperature needed for pouring relatively intricate shapes. The acid slag is composed largely of molten silica together with iron and manganese oxides. This operation is one which carbon and oxidized metal and metalloids are eliminated by oxidation. Phosphorus and sulfur are not removed from the metal in acid-lining working.

Basic steels normally are made by either single-slag or two-slag practice. However, there are several modifications of these basic-lining processes, because the steels tapped may be used to make various products, i.e., reinforcing bars or stainless or tool steels. Single-slag, basic oxidizing-slag practice is used largely for tonnage operations on plain carbon steels and has the advantage that it permits the ready removal of phosphorus. This element is contained chiefly in the slag on the bath following meltdown, the slag being composed mainly of lime with the oxides of manganese, silicon, and iron. Burned lime or limestone is charged into the furnace to supply the lime needed by the slag.

In two-slag practice the initial, black slag is removed from the bath by back tilting the furnace and skimming off the slag. This permits a new slag which is highly reducing in nature to be formed to cover the bath. The second slag generally contains 70 per cent lime and is made highly reducing in its action on the molten metal by spreading carbon or a metallic reducer, such as crushed ferrosilicon, on the slag surface. This two-slag procedure is followed when thorough deoxidation is essential, when maximum sulfur elimination must be effected, and when maximum recovery of oxidizable alloying elements added through the slag must be realized.

One useful modification of this operation eliminates the initial oxidizing slag stage, and the operators proceed after meltdown to form a highly reducing slag on the bath. This practice serves well where the charges contain readily oxidizable elements, since these are then retained in the molten metal.

As indicated above, the electric arc furnace is very flexible in its operations because oxidizing, reducing, or neutral slags can be employed, and the furnace atmosphere can be either oxidizing or reducing. Improvement in refractories has aided in all phases of melting and refining. Of much interest, increasing amounts of quality, basic, electric furnace steels are being treated under vacuum in the molten state separately from the furnace, or are being remelted under vacuum as cast to further improve their properties.

Construction of the Furnace

Fig. 1 shows in cross section a furnace of medium size such as now is being used in quite a number of shops for the production of steel for casting into billet size ingots. Newer furnaces of this size are under construction for installation with continuous casting machines.

The furnace itself is heavy and of the spheroidal bottom construction. The furnace rests on steel tilting rockers of the offset type. Hydraulic tilting cylinders provide forward tilt for tapping and backward tilt for slagging. These cylinders in conjunction with the tilting rockers provide sturdy four-point support to the furnace itself.

The furnace is equipped with a hydraulic ram for raising and swinging the roof and superstructure clear of the interior of the furnace to permit charging with a clam shell charging bucket. The furnace roof can be swung either over the tapping spout or back over the working door. There is four-point suspension of the roof and roof ring. The roof rings are of greater diameter than the furnace shell.

The furnace is fitted with air-release power operated clamps. The furnace shown is 12 ft in diameter. This size in ingot shops normally is backed with 7,500 kva electric substation and control equipment. Fourteen inch diameter graphite electrodes carry the power from the clamps to the metallic charge. In an operation of this kind the current in each arc approximates 20,000 amperes.

Figs. 2, 3 and 4 show large electric steel furnaces. Smaller furnaces, such as are most popular in steel foundries, are very similar in construction except in the matter of tilting; they generally have the tilting rockers welded to the furnace sideplates. There are other types of tilt termed nose and roller tilt, but these have their greatest use in iron foundries in which molten cupola iron is increased in temperature, mixed, and adjusted in composition by the addition of steel scrap or ferrosilicon. Foundry furnaces used in cold melting, like steel works furnaces, have been increased in their powering until units of six tons charge size frequently use 3,000 kva substations and furnaces of ten tons charge size use 4,000 kva and more in substation capacity.

Both foundry and steel works furnaces presently are built considerably deeper than formerly was standard. This has the advantage of permitting light scrap to be used with less back-charging. In addition, the electrode arms and

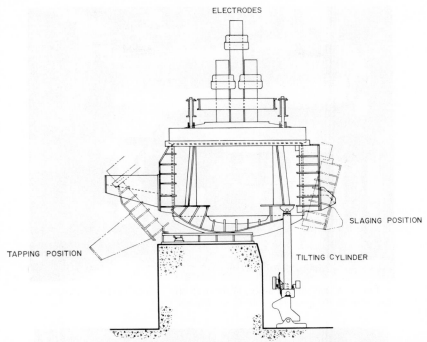

FIG. 1. Side elevation of electric arc furnace for steel making, showing chief components and tilting positions. [*Courtesy Lectromelt Furnace Div., McGraw-Edison Co.*]

FIG. 2. A 24-ft diameter, 36,000-kva top-charge furnace making 200 ton heats. [*Courtesy Lectromelt Furnace Div., McGraw-Edison Co.*]

columns are supplied in much stronger construction, for the speed of electrode movement today is on the order of three times faster than was available in the case of earlier installations.

Electric Substation and Control Equipment

Electric furnaces are supplied with substation equipment to accommodate the voltage of the

FIG. 3. A 200-ton capacity, 37,000-kva top-charge furnace. [*Courtesy Lectromelt Furnace Div., McGraw-Edison Co.*]

FIG. 4. Tapping a 115-ton heat from a 20-ft diameter, 25,000-kva top-charge furnace. [*Courtesy Lectromelt Furnace Div., McGraw-Edison Co.*]

power company at any particular plant site. The most common voltages are 6,600, 13,800, and 33,000. Equipment has been installed on 44,000 volts. When the power supply is higher than 33,000 volts, it is usual to operate the furnace from 13,800 volts with power at this voltage being supplied by a step-down sub-station. Some smaller furnaces are in use on 2,200 and 4,160 volts.

The substation equipment of the electric furnace is housed in a transformer room. This room preferably is located very close to the furnace itself. All effort is directed to keeping the secondary conductors between the main transformer and the electrode arms minimum in length.

The primary circuit breaker for a 7,500 kva installation on 13,800 volts normally is of the air-break type and of 250 mva interrupting capacity. This breaker is interlocked with the disconnects. Breakers often include the high-tension current transformers and high-tension potential transformers.

The main transformer normally provides a range of secondary voltages of from over 250 volts down to about 100 volts. The transformer is of low inherent impedance but sufficient adjustable reactance is provided to stabilize the load. In general, melting is carried out at about 85 per cent power factor which, of course, makes over 6,000 kw available for the fluidizing stage in the case of a 7,500 kva installation. When so operating, secondary watts are at maximum and increasing the secondary current reduces the power delivery.

Furnaces of 12 ft inside diameter are usually operated on about 25 ton heats. The automatic regulators provide an electrode speed of up to 160 inches per minute. The newest system of regulator for automatically providing smooth, uninterrupted control for the raising and lowering of the electrodes is a low-inertia static regulating and electrode movement system in which a transistor balancing-signal assembly feeds current and voltage signals to an eddy-current type of clutch.

Operating Data

With the increasing use of oxygen and gas to boost furnace production there is apt to be confusion as to the work any particular unit can do unless all the details are known. Another aspect is that many shops overload their transformers substantially beyond rated kva. As an instance of fast working with supplemental gas and oxygen, a user of an 8 ft diameter 2,500 kva top-charge foundry furnace produces 131 lb of acid foundry steel per minute with the usage of under 400 kwh per ton tapped. This foundry uses a gas-oxygen burner during the melt-down stage and inserts the oxygen lance before tapping. The advantages of burner use are listed as follows:

(1) Production increased from 113 lb per minute to 131 lb per minute.
(2) Refractory costs decreased 15 per cent.
(3) Power per ton decrease by 57 kwh.
(4) Electrode consumption per ton, 9 lb of 8 in. graphite.

Concerning basic practice on stainless and superalloys, the following gives the results in a plant making two ton heats in a 1,600 kva furnace on single-turn operation:

(1) Tapping temperature, above 3100°F.
(2) Power, 465 kwh per ton.
(3) Electrodes per ton, 9 lb of graphite.
(4) Heats per roof, 220.
(5) Heats per sidewall, 230.
(6) Oxygen per ton, 850 cubic feet.
(7) Heats in eight hours, 5.
(8) Pounds per minute, 41.5.
(9) Power off between heats for 10 minutes.
(10) Time of oxygen blow, 12 minutes.
(11) Finish carbon, 0.06 per cent.
(12) Carbon drop per minute, 0.018 per cent.

In the case of an operation where a 12,500 kva, 15 ft I.D. furnace is used on plain carbon steels for light structurals, reinforcing bars, and similar products, the following is a typical operation:

(1)	Size of heat	52 tons
(2)	Time tap to tap	3¾ hours
(3)	Power per ton of ingots with little oxygen use	485/490 kwh
(4)	Back charges per heat	2
(5)	Heats per roof (clay brick)	80–90
(6)	Heats per sidewall (metal-case)	165–170 —
(7)	Electrodes (18 in. graphite) (11 lb with 15/20 per cent bundles in charge)	9 to 12 pounds per ton of ingots
(8)	Normal operation	120 hours per week

The foregoing particulars have been directed principally to the production of steel for ingots and for castings. The power required in cold melting irons is moderately less than that used in melting steels, and copper melting takes about half as much power as steel melting.

Many other products are made in electric furnaces which are built with constructions employing submerged arcs. This work involves delivering the power at lower voltages and at much higher amperage than in the case of direct arc installations. Among the materials produced in submerged arc furnaces are: ferroalloys, calcium carbide, sublimated phosphorus, fused refractories, and silicon metal. While conditions in the United States have not favored making electric pig iron in most localities, considerable attention is being given to melting reduced and partially reduced charges since this combination of operations greatly lowers the amount of electric power needed. Consequently, the furnace output is correspondingly increased.

References

1. "Electric Furnace Proceedings," covering the annual conferences 1943–1962 sponsored by the Electric Furnace Committee of the Iron and Steel Division of The Metallurgical Society of the American Institute of Mining, Metallurgical, and Petroleum Engineers.
2. "Electric Furnace Steelmaking," sponsored by the Physical Chemistry of Steelmaking Committee, Iron and Steel Division, The Metallurgical Society of AIME, two volumes, New York, Interscience Publishers, a division of John Wiley and Sons, Inc., 1962.
3. ROBIETTE, A. G. E., "Electric Melting and Smelting Practice," London, Charles Griffin and Company Limited, 1955.
4. PASCHKIS, V., "Industrial Electric Furnaces," two volumes, New York, Interscience Publishers Inc., 1945, 1948.
5. "Continuous Casting," containing technical papers on continuous casting developments and the working of cast structures as presented at the 1961 Fall Meeting of the AIME in Detroit, New York, Interscience Publishers, a division of John Wiley and Sons, Inc., 1962.

Cross-references: *Electric Smelting Furnaces* (three articles).

W. E. LEWIS

STORAGE BATTERIES. See BATTERIES, STORAGE.

STORAGE BATTERIES, SEALED. See BATTERIES, SEALED STORAGE.

STREAMING CURRENT

Streaming current is an electrical current which is developed when a liquid is forced through a capillary or a network of capillaries (fritted material). The magnitude of this current (micro-microamperes) is measured by placing electrodes at the ends of the capillary or frit and shunting the current through a low impedance external circuit. The more common measurement is that of "Streaming Potential," for which a high impedance circuit is used. A detailed description of the measurement and the origin of this phenomenon is given under "Streaming Potential" below.

RAY M. HURD

STREAMING POTENTIAL

Streaming potential is one of a series of four electrokinetic effects, the others being electro-osmosis, electrophoresis, and sedimentation potential. All of these effects are due to the disturbance, by external forces, of the static equilibrium conditions in the electrical double layer which exists at a solid/liquid (and occasionally at a liquid/liquid) interface. In the case of the streaming potential, the external disturbing force is a hydrostatic pressure drop across the ends of a capillary containing a liquid; as the liquid flows, an electric potential is set up between the ends of the capillary. This phenomenon was discovered in 1859 by Quincke, who reported a linear relationship between the applied pressure and the potential developed for a variety of solutions in glass capillaries. The original theory for all electrokinetic effects was developed by Helmholtz; refinements in his theory have been made (see, e.g., Smoluchowski and Bikerman) parallel with refinements in the concept of the electrical double layer.

A simple apparatus for making streaming potential measurements on a glass capillary is shown in Fig. 1. If a pressure drop, P, is imposed across the ends of the capillary tube (radius, r, and length, ℓ), the velocity, v, of liquid movement in the tube at any distance, x, from the center may be calculated from Poiseuille's law:

$$v_x = \frac{P}{4\eta\ell} (r^2 - x^2) \qquad (1)$$

where η is the viscosity of the liquid. This equation assumes laminar flow, and the resultant velocity profile is parabolic.

The distribution of ions near the capillary wall can be represented schematically as in Fig. 2; they exist as a layer of ions of one sign (in this case, negative) close up against the wall and a second layer of equal and opposite charge in a "diffuse" distribution. The potential drop associated with this type of ionic distribution is represented schematically in Fig. 3. At some distance very near the wall (represented by the dashed line in both figures), there exists a "surface

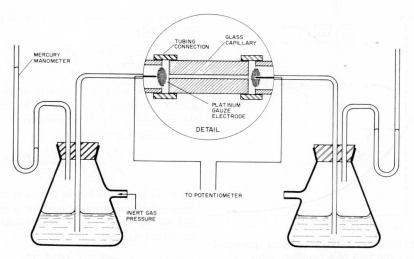

Fig. 1. Simple apparatus for streaming potential measurements.

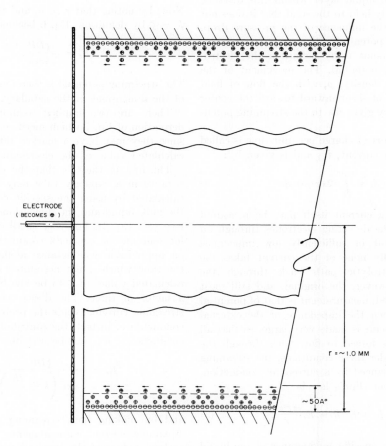

Fig. 2. Schematic of ion distribution near a capillary wall. (Arrows
represent movement of ions outside surface of shear with fluid flow.)

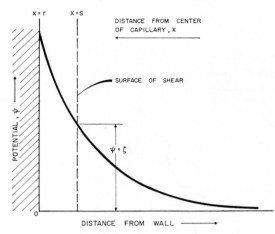

x = r   x = s

DISTANCE FROM CENTER
OF CAPILLARY, X ←

SURFACE OF SHEAR

POTENTIAL, ψ →

$\psi = \zeta$

O

DISTANCE FROM WALL →

FIG. 3. Schematic representation of potential variation near the wall of a capillary tube.

of shear," the liquid layer within this distance being so tightly held to the solid that it does not move under the influence of the pressure drop. The value of potential with respect to the solution at this point is by definition the electrokinetic, or ζ, potential. The movement of the excess charge density, ρ, with the flow of fluid from the line of shear inward toward the center of the capillary gives rise to the streaming potential.

The transport of charge per unit time is called the streaming current, i_s, and is given by:

$$i_s = \int_0^s 2\pi x \cdot \rho \cdot v_x dx \qquad (2)$$

The streaming current itself may be measured directly by the detecting electrodes through an external circuit of sufficiently low impedance that essentially none of the current takes the internal electrolytic path back through the capillary. However, the original, and still most frequently used, measurement is that of potential developed when the impedance of the external measuring circuit is made very large, so that all the current is forced to flow back through the capillary. Under these conditions, the streaming current is balanced by a current of conduction, i_k, which from Ohm's law is

$$i_k = E_s/R = E_s \cdot \frac{\pi r^2 k}{\ell}, \qquad (3)$$

where k is the specific conductance of the liquid in the capillary and E_s the streaming potential.

Since at the steady state, $i_s = i_k$, then from (2) and (3):

$$E_s \frac{\pi r^2 k}{\ell} = \int_0^s 2\pi x \cdot \rho \cdot v_x dx \qquad (4)$$

Poisson's relation between charge density, ρ, and potential, ψ, is required for evaluation of the integral of Eq. 4; for cylindrical coordinates, this equation has the form:

$$\frac{1}{x}\frac{d}{dx}\left(\frac{xd\psi}{dx}\right) = -\frac{4\pi\rho}{D}, \qquad (5)$$

where D is the dielectric constant of the fluid. After substitution into Eq. 4 for ρ (from Eq. 5) and for v_x (from Eq. 1), the equation can be integrated to yield:

$$E_s \frac{\pi r^2 k}{\ell} = -\frac{DPa^2}{4\eta\ell}\int_0^s dx \qquad (6)$$

Now, by noting that $r \simeq a$, and that at $x = s$, $\psi = \zeta$ by definition, Eq. 6 becomes:

$$E_s = -\frac{\zeta DP}{4\pi\eta k}. \qquad (7)$$

The streaming potential is therefore independent of the dimensions of the capillary.

There are two implicit assumptions in the derivation of Eq. 7 which merit some discussion, since they may have a marked influence on the calculated value of the electrokinetic potential.

The first of these is that the electrolytic resistance in a capillary tube may be accurately calculated by using the specific conductance of the bulk liquid and the dimensions of the capillary (cf., Eq. 3). For very small capillaries and for solutions of low bulk conductivity, there is an appreciable conductance along the wall of the tube which if not accounted for will cause calculated values of ζ to be low by as much as a factor of three. The direct measurement of streaming current avoids the problem of surface conductance. In fact, the contribution of surface conductance, K_s, can be introduced into Eq. 7:

$$E_s = -\frac{\zeta DP}{4\pi\eta\left(k + \dfrac{2K_s}{r}\right)}, \qquad (8)$$

and by making both streaming potential and streaming current measurements on the same system, values of the interesting quantity, K_s, can be obtained. For metal capillaries, still another conducting path is possible for the return current via electrode reactions and electronic conduction through the metal itself. In this case, streaming potential measurements are meaningless, and the streaming current method must be used to obtain values of ζ.

The second assumption which causes difficulty is that the values of dielectric constant and viscosity of the liquid in the double layer region are equal to those of the bulk liquid. This is almost certain not to be the case, so only the composite quantity, $D\zeta/\eta$, can be obtained with confidence. The values of D and η at the probable field strengths existing in the mobile part of the double layer may be estimated, and corrections to the value of ζ made on this basis, but this has been attempted only rarely. Typical numbers quoted for such estimates are 10^5 to 10^6 volts/cm for the field in aqueous solutions, which reduces D by some 50 per cent and increases the viscosity by some 5 per cent. Most of the quoted values of ζ in the literature are based on calculations using the usual bulk values for D and η.

Values of the electrokinetic potential on a variety of materials with a variety of solutions fall typically in the range -200 to $+100$ millivolts, so that streaming potentials fall in the range of some 10 millivolts per cm of Hg pressure drop. Streaming currents are in the order of 10^{-9} to 10^{-11} amperes, again depending on the system and the pressure drop.

Very little practical use of the streaming potential phenomenon has been found, although patents have been issued on an electrokinetic transducer, which gives an electrical output proportional to an alternating hydraulic flow of fluid through a porous plug.

References

1. BOOTH, F., "Theory of Electrokinetic Effects," *Nature*, **161**, 83 (1948).
2. BUTLER, J. A. V., Ed., "Electrical Phenomena at Interfaces," London, Methuen and Co., 1951.
3. DAVIES, J. T., AND RIDEAL, E. K., "Interfacial Phenomena," New York, Academic Press, 1961.
4. KRUYT, H. R., Ed., "Colloid Science," Vol. I, Chapters IV and V, New York, Elsevier Publishing Co., 1952.

RAY M. HURD

Cross-references: *Electrokinetic Potentials; Electroosmosis; Electrophoresis.*

STRESS   CORROSION

The corrosion rate of a metal is dependent upon the environment, temperature, agitation, and the metallurgical microstructure. Inhomogeneities in the microstructure contribute to localized corrosion. As we learn more about the defect structure of the metal lattice, we are beginning to understand the effects of plastic deformation on corrosion. It has been known for many years that stresses accelerate corrosive attack, although there still is disagreement in the literature as to the nature and amount of stress required, its effect on the emf of the corrosion reaction, and its effect on the anode and cathode kinetics. There is general agreement, however, that if the tensile stresses are sufficiently large to cause yielding of the metal, the anodic processes are accelerated and the corrosion rate increases locally. Stress-accelerated corrosion is simply referred to as "stress corrosion" and is the resultant of the interaction between stress, structure, the surface, and the environment. A very common manifestation of the interplay of these variables is a localized cracking phenomenon known as "stress corrosion cracking."

At first glance it would appear that there are no great differences between stress corrosion cracking and corrosion fatigue. Yet, these two corrosion-induced metal fracture phenomena are distinctly separated by workers in the field of corrosion. The primary distinction is made on the basis of the nature of the stresses. A second significant difference lies in the importance of a particular environment. Stress corrosion cracking requires static tensile stress although the stress may be applied or residual after fabrication, but relatively few media are capable of causing stress corrosion cracking. On the other hand, any environment capable of some localized attack is probably sufficient to accelerate a fatigue failure.

Practically all classes of alloys are susceptible to stress corrosion cracking. Stainless steels crack in chlorides, and strong caustic; copper alloys crack in ammonia and amines; gold alloys crack in ferric chloride; aluminum alloys crack in chlorides, etc. It is a very difficult thing to prove experimentally, but it is a currently accepted idea that very pure metals are immune to stress corrosion cracking.

The fracture path through the metal is another perplexing aspect of stress corrosion cracking. Homogeneous alloys can crack intergranularly or transgranularly, rarely both simultaneously. Lattice structure is not a clue to a correct prediction of crack path, although certain crystallographic planes may be preferentially attacked. Face-centered cubic silver-gold and copper-gold alloys crack intergranularly; face-centered cubic austenitic stainless steels and ordered body-centered cubic β-brass crack transgranularly. Precipitated alloys will generally crack intergranularly. Redissolving the precipitate by altering the heat treatment will prevent cracking (common in aluminum alloys) or may cause transgranular cracking (common in stainless steels).

The literature abounds with articles on stress corrosion. No other field of corrosion today is being written about and discussed as much as this. Besides being a rather dramatic phenomenon, stress corrosion cracking is easy to study in the laboratory. Stressed specimens of any size, shape, or geometry can be fabricated and tested at a predetermined stress level while either totally immersed, partially immersed, or alternately wetted and dried in a particular environment. Cracks appear rapidly (stainless steels crack in less than 1 hour in boiling 42 per cent by weight $MgCl_2$). The failure of a specimen can be used to stop a clock, ring a bell, etc.

There is much disagreement over the probable mechanism of stress corrosion cracking. In fact it is doubtful that only one mechanism (even excluding hydrogen cracking from consideration) applies, since it is fairly easy to cite at least one case where no one theory fails to satisfy all the reported facts and observations. Major differences between theories concern the mode of crack nucleation and propagation. Cracks are believed to nucleate and propagate by purely electrochemical means, by a combination of electrochemical and mechanical processes, or by purely mechanical processes. The reason for the difficulty in agreement on the means of crack development (as contrasted to fatigue where there is much less controversy) arises from the well-documented observation that stresses much lower than 20 per cent of yield strength can cause stress corrosion cracking. One is therefore forced to devise a theory which would explain how the stress is intensified, how the fracture strength of the material is lowered, or how the electrochemical dissolution process is locally accelerated. Current theories

attempt to supply the answers to one or more of these three important questions.

Some investigators believe that the crack will originate by rupture of a passivating film after the film reaches definite proportions while under stress. Others, cognizant of a lack of films in certain systems, suggest selective dissolution of an alloying element, much like the familiar dezincification of α-brass, is the cause of pit-like attack. The stress intensification at the base of a pit or root of a crack is supposedly sufficient to cause yielding and brittle fracture. Another theory suggests that additional stress intensification arises from a wedging action caused by growing corrosion products along the walls of the crack behind the advancing edge.

Since a relationship is known between surface energy and fracture strength, one current theory assumes crack nucleation and brittle fracture are both resultants of surface energy lowering. It is stated that ionic adsorption of a particular species from solution would reduce the surface energy, and hence the fracture strength, sufficiently that microcracks would appear at the surface. The newly exposed surface would be an active area for rapid adsorption and would thereby "catalyze" crack propagation. The stress intensification at the root of the crack would also assist in causing a rapid fracture.

By far the largest amount of experimental work has dealt with the electrochemistry of the cracking phenomenon. There are many curves in the literature showing the relationship between emf and time for specimens under tensile load in a corroding media. Using these curves and ordinary polarization data one can predict the nature and quantity of applied current necessary to either prevent or accelerate failure. Polarizing to a desired emf by means of a potentiostat has eliminated the incubation period and caused immediate failure by stress corrosion cracking. Likewise, by using the same technique but an opposing current, protection has been afforded the specimen which lasted indefinitely. These remarkable accomplishments have been used as strong evidence to support the contention that stress corrosion cracking is, at least partially, electrochemical. It is very difficult, however, to understand very rapid anodic dissolution only along a narrow path. One theory prefers to explain this as an "electromechanical" effect and describes the dissolution process as activated dissolution of unfilmed, yielding metal. In other words, this theory assumes that the maximum effect of stress-accelerated corrosion comes into play along a narrow path in specific alloy systems in very specific environments. The calculated anodic current density equivalent to the observed crack penetration rate in austenitic stainless steels in chlorides is 1.5 amp/sq cm. This is not too unreasonable to attain experimentally. On the other hand, a similar calculation for mild steel cracking in nitrates results in an anticipated anodic current density of 400 amp/sq cm.

As was stated earlier, recent research into the metal physics of deformation seems to be leading to a more unified theory of the stress corrosion cracking phenomenon. This theory utilizes the defect structure of a metal to explain chemical reactivity at certain structural sites and also to show how the defects can intensify stress during deformation. A very important consequence of this work has been an apparent dependence of susceptibility to stress corrosion cracking on stacking-fault energy. This fact alone has been used to explain why pure metals may not be susceptible to stress corrosion cracking (higher stacking-fault energy) and why certain alloying elements or impurities increase susceptibility to cracking. Another result gained by considering the behavior of stacking faults during deformation is an insight into the reason why cracks may be intergranular or transgranular but rarely both.

Very recent work using the technique of thin film electron transmission microscopy has brought attention to the superior resistance to transgranular stress corrosion cracking of alloys whose deformed films exhibit a cellular arrangement of dislocation tangles. Susceptible alloys are more likely to have a planar dislocation network after strain is applied to the thin foil. While it is true that the distribution of dislocations is dependent on the stacking fault energy, it is also, unfortunately, true that the stacking fault energy parameter, γ, is very difficult to measure experimentally. Confounding the picture still further is the fact that certain interstitial elements which do not apparently alter γ have a very decided effect on the dislocation arrangement. In any event, current thinking on the cause of initiation in austenitic stainless steels are dislocations arriving at the surface on active slip planes during plastic deformation. The dislocation process is electrochemical.

Some persons consider a type of fracture caused by cathodic discharge of hydrogen as a special case of stress corrosion. This phenomenon is usually called "hydrogen embrittlement" or "hydrogen cracking" and is best understood if one does not attempt to include it as part of stress corrosion cracking. The fracture apparently occurs only after hydrogen has entered the alloy, and only metals with relatively low solubility for hydrogen are susceptible. Cracking is accelerated by cathodic currents (increasing the hydrogen discharge rate) and by the presence of poisons or films interfering with the evolution of molecular hydrogen at the surface. Effective poisons for the recombination of atomic hydrogen to molecular hydrogen and, therefore, capable of forcing hydrogen into the metal, are: arsenic, sulfur, selenium, and phosphorus. Martensitic structures are exceedingly susceptible to this form of stress cracking due to low tolerable solubility for hydrogen.

In summary, an attempt has been made to describe the current status of stress corrosion. Preventative measures consist of: cathodic protection, stress relieving, shot-peening, purification and adjustment of composition of alloys and environments, etc. The literature includes many thought-provoking articles on the subject, and the reader is directed to the bibliography at the end of this article to read and decide for himself whether one theory has more merit than another. The practicing design engineer who fears the possibility of stress corrosion cracking often has little recourse other than to select the least susceptible alloy in its best metallurgical condition.

References

1. ROBERTSON, W. D., AND TETELMAN, A. S., "A Unified Structural Mechanism for Intergranular and Transgranular Corrosion Cracking," p. 217–252, "Strengthening Mechanisms in Solids," Cleveland, American Society for Metals, 1960.
2. BARNARTT, S., "General Concepts of Stress-Corcosion Cracking," *Corrosion*, **18**, No. 9, 322t–331t, (September, 1962).
3. "Physical Metallurgy of Stress Corrosion Fracture," New York, Interscience Publishers, 1959.
4. "Stress Corrosion Cracking and Embrittlement," New York, John Wiley and Sons, Inc., 1956.
5. EVANS, U. R., "The Corrosion and Oxidation of Metals: Scientific Principles and Practical Applications," pp. 665–700, New York, St. Martin's Press Inc., 1960.
6. HINES, J. G., AND HOAR, T. P., *J. Applied Chem.*, **8**, 764 (1958).
7. UHLIG, H. H., WHITE, R. A., AND LINCOLN, J., *Acta Metallurgica*, **5**, 473, (1957).

8. UHLIG, H. H., AND WHITE, R. A., *Trans. ASM*, **52**, 830 (1960).
9. LANG, F. S., "Effects of Trace Elements on Stress Corrosion Cracking....," *Corrosion*, **18**, No. 10, 378t–382t (October, 1962).
10. Swann, P. R., "Dislocation Substructure vs Transgranular Stress Corrosion Susceptibility of Single Phase Alloys," *ibid.*, **19**, No. 3, 102t–112t (March, 1963).
11. Hoar, T. P., "Stress Corrosion Cracking," *ibid.*, **19**, No. 10, 331t–338t (October, 1963).
12. Douglass, D. L., Thomas, G., and Roser, W. R., "Ordering, Stacking Faults and Stress Corrosion Cracking in Austenitic Alloys," *ibid.*, **20**, No. 1, 15t–28t (January, 1964).

LAWRENCE R. SCHARFSTEIN

Cross-references: *Corrosion Fatigue; Hydrogen Embrittlement; Pitting Corrosion.*

STRESS CORROSION CRACKING. See STRESS CORROSION.

SULFUR HEXAFLUORIDE

Sulfur hexafluoride, SF_6, is a colorless, odorless, nontoxic gas. The French chemist Moisson first prepared it in 1900. SF_6 is very inert. It has high dielectric strength and great ability to quench electric arcs. Thus, it is used as a dielectric in transformers, circuit breakers, capacitors, and microwave equipment.

Sulfur hexafluoride is commercially produced by burning lump sulfur in fluorine. Several purification steps are used to insure adequate removal of the lower fluorides of sulfur and other unwanted impurities. Commercial SF_6 contains very small amounts of CF_4, moisture, and N_2. These have little effect on the dielectric strength of the gas. It is shipped in steel cylinders as a liquefied gas.

The chemical and physical properties that make SF_6 a good dielectric are listed in the following table.

TABLE 1. SELECTED PROPERTIES OF SF_6

Sublimation point (1 atm)	−63.8°C
Melting point (32.5 psia)	−50.8°C
Critical temperature	45.547°C
Critical pressure	545.47 psia
Vapor density at 1 atm. and 21°C	6.14 g/liter
Gaseous viscosity at 1 atm and 30°C	0.0152 centipoises
Thermal conductivity at 1 atm and 30°C	3.36×15^5 cal/sec/cm/°C
Heat capacity (Cp) at 15 psia and 25°C	23.22 cal/mole/°C

The low sublimation temperature of SF_6 allows its use as gas-phase insulation over a wide temperature range. Even if equipment is filled with the gas at about 1 atmosphere, the temperature must be quite low to condense SF_6. When placed in a chamber at 45 psia and 21°C it will not condense until the temperature drops below −50°C.

The thermal conductivity of SF_6 is much lower than that of gases such as helium or hydrogen. It has been shown, however, that when heat transfer by natural convection is considered, the overall heat transfer coefficient of SF_6 is actually higher than that of helium or hydrogen. The low gaseous viscosity of SF_6 and its high specific heat are two factors that help explain this high coefficient.

Because SF_6 is inert, it is unaffected by quartz at temperatures as high as 500°C. In contact with most materials, it is stable well above the temperature at which oil oxidizes and decomposes, but in contact with some metals, such as silicon and carbon steels, at temperatures above 150°C, SF_6 slowly decomposes. Copper, aluminum, stainless steel, and silver have little effect on SF_6 at temperatures of 250°C or below.

Sulfur hexafluoride is physiologically inert. Prolonged exposure to 80 per cent SF_6 and 20 per cent oxygen causes no ill effects in albino rats. Thermal and electrical breakdown products of SF_6, however, include lower fluorides and oxyfluorides of sulfur, some of which are toxic. These arced gases can be easily removed by passing them through or over a mixture of activated alumina and soda lime.

The high dielectric strength of SF_6 is attributed to its molecular complexity and ability to form stable negative ions. The electrical breakdown of a gas is thought to begin when an electron is excited and released at the cathode. As it accelerates across the electrode gap to the anode, it collides with gas molecules, forming ions and releasing more electrons. These secondary electrons collide with other molecules, and the process continues. Thus, an avalanche of electrons makes its way to the anode, causing breakdown. This process is called Townsend discharge. A dielectric impedes this process. The large molecular cross-section and the electrophilic nature of SF_6 make it a good target for free electrons. The complexity of the SF_6 molecule permits it to absorb electrons of 2 ev or less by resonance capture. This electron capture causes formation of negative ions. These have low mobility and do not contribute to further ionization. Thus, many electrons are captured before they gain enough energy to release secondary electrons from the molecule.

The dielectric strength of SF_6 and other electronegative gases depends on several factors, among which are gas pressure and electrode spacing and configuration. In a uniform field, such as two parallel plates or two spheres of large diameter, SF_6 follows Paschen's law. The breakdown voltage is a linear function of the product of gas pressure and gap distance. This relationship is only true at small electrode gap distances or at relatively low pressures. Deviations occur at larger gaps and at higher pressures. In nonuniform fields, as found in an electrode system consisting of a sharp pointed electrode and a flat plate, the dielectric strength of SF_6 does not follow Paschen's law. In plotting the breakdown strength of SF_6 versus gas pressure for a nonuniform electrode system, the breakdown strength in volts does not increase proportionately with increased pressure. The curve goes to a maximum value and then actually decreases with increased pressure. The pressure at which this maximum occurs is dependent upon the distance between electrodes. As this gap distance becomes larger, the maximum occurs at lower and lower pressures. Usually this maximum is in the pressure region of 1–5 atmospheres. This phenomenon is attributed to space charge effects around the sharp electrode and is only observed with electronegative gases and air. At the pressure at which this maximum occurs, corona always precedes sparkover.

Sulfur hexafluoride is used as a gaseous dielectric in power transformers with ratings up to 69 kv and 10,000 kva. Its use in transformers brings several advantages. Electrical failure causes no explosion or fire hazard as it does in transformers filled with a liquid dielectric. The reason is that pressure buildup is much smaller. After a failure, SF_6 is selfhealing, preventing insulation from weakening to cause further sparkover. A pound of SF_6 at atmospheric pressure and room temperature occupies the same volume as 15 gallons of oil, giving a sizable weight advantage. The noise level of gas-filled transformers is much lower than liquid-filled units.

Sulfur hexaflouride has been used as the interrupting medium in power circuit breakers, being about 100 times better than air. At 60 psig, the gas can arrest currents up to 74,000 amperes at 13.2 kv. Some circuit breakers using SF_6 can interrupt 15,000 Mva at 230 kv.

Besides being used in power frequency equipment, SF_6 is used in high-frequency applications, such as in HF filterplexers, coaxial cables, and microwave cavities. It is also used in the power supplies of Van de Graaff generators.

References

1. Howard, P. R., "Insulation Properties of Compressed Electronegative Gases," *Proc. Inst. Elect. Eng. (London)*, **104**, Part A, 123–138 (1957).
2. Camilli, G., Gordon, G. J., and Plump, R. E., *A. I. E. E. Trans.*, III, **71**, 348–356 (1952).
3. Works, C. N., and Dakin, T. W., "Dielectric Breakdown of SF_6 in Nonuniform Fields," *A. I. E. E. Trans.*, I, **72**, 682–4 (1953).

JAMES A. BROWN

Cross references: *Dielectrics, Gaseous; Paschen's Law.*

SUTHERLAND, WILLIAM (1859–1911)

William Sutherland was born in Dumbarton, Scotland, on August 4, 1859. To improve the father's health the family moved to Australia in 1864 and settled in Melbourne in 1870. William's health also prospered in Australia, and he changed from a sickly child to a normally robust boy. He developed the habit of study early, and his exceptional brightness was recognized and encouraged by his teachers. In Wesley College, a secondary school, he received individual attention and rigorous training in mathematics and science as well as in the humanities and history.

In February, 1876, he entered Melbourne University, studying both arts and engineering. He was graduated in 1879 with first class honors and a scholarship in natural science and third class honors in engineering. He gained a master's degree from Melbourne in 1883 by examination.

Family life has rarely exerted a stronger influence on a man's life than it did on Sutherland's. The seven brothers and sisters were extremely talented, well-read, and open to the exciting ideas of the day, several attaining prominence in education, art, music, and literature. The household rang with classical music and with stimulating discussions, especially of Darwin's theories. The attractions of this lively group apparently made other associations seem mundane, for several of the members, including William, were unable to remain long away from it.

William was awarded a Gilchrist scholarship for three years of study at University College, London, embarking with high hopes in July, 1879. Although disappointed in his studies at first, he thrived under Professor Carey Foster, doing research and forming habits of reading widely. In 1881 he received his degree with first class honors in experimental physics. Employment in England was offered to him, but the pull of home was too strong, and after a brief trip through Europe he returned to Melbourne.

The Superintendency of the School of Mines at Ballarat was open to him in 1882, but he declined it, preferring to stay close to his family and to the excellent public library at Melbourne. Salary never interested him; as long as he could cover his simple needs, he preferred to spend his time in independent study. Tutoring and examining for his friends at Melbourne University and writing for the *Age* newspaper—beautifully written articles popularizing science or discussing current issues—appear to have covered those needs. The library and his correspondence furnished the data for his research, although he did regret the lack of a laboratory in which to conduct his own experiments.

In 1888 he held an interim appointment as lecturer in physics at Melbourne, failing to receive the permanent post because of a mixup. In 1897 he again served as lecturer, but the strain of large classes and administrative duties proved distasteful.

Most of Sutherland's research lies in the general field of attractions between bodies, from atoms to planets, from gases to solids. His first serious paper presented the relationship between distances and forces of attraction in gases. Subsequent papers extended these relationships to liquids, solids, solutions, etc., and used them to explain other phenomena, such as the variation of viscosity with temperature in gases and some observed deviations from Boyle's law.

In 1902 he published his first paper on ionization, in which he set forth the electric doublet hypothesis, that the forces exerted by atoms are those of one or more pairs of oppositely charged units whose moment is characteristic of the atom. Further researches developed the idea that many of the properties of matter are electric in origin, e.g., viscosity, rigidity, valency. He ascribed the vibration frequencies of solids to the motions of the electric charges and found that the frequencies followed the periodic law in predictable fashion.

In 1911 he proposed the theory that strong electrolytes are completely ionized in solution. This contradicted Arrhenius's idea that in a concentrated solution only a certain fraction of the molecules are dissociated. Sutherland theorized that the electrical attractions between the ions introduced viscous resistance which reduced the mobility of the ions. Much debate ensued, culminating in agreement on the total ionization of strong electrolytes and in the quantitative explanation of the electric forces between ions and ions and molecules by Debye and Hückel in 1923.

Other studies dealt with side interests. Between 1900 and 1910 he published papers on the constitution of water, deducing degrees of polymerization that vary with phase and temperature. Two papers dealt with the relationship between rigidity and the spectrum of an element. Molecular refraction, the heat of formation of compounds, and nerve impulses each elicited a share of his attention.

In death he was as quiet as in life, for he died in his sleep on October 5, 1911.

References

1. OSBORNE, WILLIAM ALEXANDER, "William Sutherland—a Biography," Melbourne, Lothian Book Publishing Co., 1920.
2. SERLE, P., "Dictionary of Australian Biography," Vol. 2, p. 394–395, Sydney, Angus and Robertson, 1949.

ELIZABETH S. BENFORD

T

TAFEL LINES

A Tafel line can best be defined by the equation,

$$E = a + b \log |i| \qquad (1)$$

where E is the electrode potential with respect to an arbitrary fixed potential, i is the partial current density corresponding to either the anodic or cathodic reactions occurring at the electrode/solution interface, and a and b are constants. Eq. 1 is known as the Tafel equation, in honor of its discoverer.[3] A graph of E vs $\log |i|$ is called a Tafel diagram. The electrode potential is generally given relative to the standard hydrogen electrode, the saturated calomel electrode, or the potential of the electrode when the net current density at the electrode/solution interface is zero, i.e., the open-circuit potential. In the latter case, the symbol for the electrode potential is changed from E to η and is referred to as either an overvoltage or a polarization, depending upon whether the open-circuit potential is the reversible potential of the electrode or a mixed potential. Thus, several types of Tafel diagrams, differing only in the choice of the fixed potential, are encountered in the modern literature of electrochemistry. The following discussion is designed to illustrate the significance of the Tafel equation as applied to the kinetics of a typical electrode reaction.

Consider the following elemental charge-transfer reaction occurring at an electrode/solution interface,

$$X^{z+} + \lambda e^- \rightleftharpoons X^{(z-\lambda)+}. \qquad (2)$$

The rate equation for reaction 2 may be written in the form,

$$\frac{-d(X^{z+})}{dt} = \bar{k}_c A^*_{X^{z+}} - \bar{k}_a A^*_{X^{(z-\lambda)+}} \qquad (3)$$

where $[-d(X^{z+})/dt]$ is the net rate of reduction of X^{z+} in moles/sec per unit area of electrode surface. The significance of the remaining terms in Eq. 3 will be shown in the following discussion. In the absence of specific adsorption of ions, the solution side of the electrode surface may be viewed as a simple double layer, consisting of the usual inner and diffuse regions separated by the outer Helmholtz plane, i.e., a plane parallel to the electrode surface and passing through the centers of solvated ions at their distance of closest approach to the electrode surface. The charge-transfer reaction occurs across the inner region of the double layer. Consequently, the activities of X^{z+} and $X^{(z-\lambda)+}$ appearing in the rate equation as $A^*_{X^{z+}}$ and $A^*_{X^{(z-\lambda)+}}$, are the activities at the outer Helmholtz plane. If the mass transport processes are rapid relative to the charge-transfer processes, the activities at the outer Helmholtz plane are related to the activities in the bulk of the solution, $A_{X^{z+}}$ and $A_{X^{(z-\lambda)+}}$, by the Boltzmann distribution law,

$$A^*_{X^{z+}} = A_{X^{z+}} \exp \frac{-z\mathbf{F}\zeta}{RT} \qquad (4)$$

$$A^*_{X^{(z-\lambda)+}} = A_{X^{(z-\lambda)+}} \exp \frac{-(z-\lambda)\mathbf{F}\zeta}{RT} \qquad (4a)$$

where $RT/\mathbf{F}$ has its customary meaning, and ζ is the Galvani potential difference across the diffuse region of the double layer (cp., the familiar zeta-potential). For simplicity, it has been assumed that the cathodic and anodic reactions, i.e., the forward and reverse reactions of Eq. 2, are first order in the activities of X^{z+} and $X^{(z-\lambda)+}$, respectively. The electrochemical rate constants for the cathodic and anodic reactions, $\bar{k}_c$ and $\bar{k}_a$, are functions of the Galvani potential difference across just the inner region of the double-layer. In accordance with absolute rate theory, the electrochemical rate constants are given by Eqs. 5 and 5a

$$\bar{k}_c = k_c \exp \frac{-(1-\alpha)\lambda \mathbf{F}}{RT}(E-\zeta) \qquad (5)$$

$$\bar{k}_a = k_a \exp \frac{\alpha\lambda \mathbf{F}}{RT}(E-\zeta) \qquad (5a)$$

where α is the transfer coefficient $(0 < \alpha < 1$ and frequently $\alpha = \frac{1}{2})$, and E is the electrode potential referred to a fixed potential such as the standard hydrogen electrode.[1, 2, 4]

The net current density, i_n, corresponding to the net reduction of X^{z+} is given by Eq. 6,

$$i_n = -\mathbf{F}\lambda \left[\frac{-d(X^{z+})}{dt}\right] \qquad (6)$$

By convention, a negative net current density corresponds to a net cathodic process. Eq. 7 is obtained by substituting $[-d(X^{z+})/dt]$ from Eq. 3 into Eq. 6,

$$i_n = -\mathbf{F}\lambda \bar{k}_c A^*_{X^{z+}} + \mathbf{F}\lambda \bar{k}_a A^*_{X^{(z-\lambda)+}} \qquad (7)$$

The partial current densities of the cathodic and anodic reactions, i_c and i_a, respectively, are given by Eqs. 8 and 8a,

$$i_c = -\mathbf{F}\lambda \bar{k}_c A^*_{X^{z+}} \qquad (8)$$

$$i_a = \mathbf{F}\lambda \bar{k}_a A^*_{X^{(z-\lambda)+}} \qquad (8a)$$

where it should be observed that a partial cathodic current density is always negative, and a partial anodic current density is always positive. The net current density may then be expressed as the sum of the partial current densities in the following abbreviated form:

$$i_n = i_c + i_a \qquad (9)$$

When the activities from Eqs. 4 and 4a and the rate constants from Eqs. 5 and 5a are inserted, Eqs. 8, 8a, and 9 may be rewritten to give,

$$i_c = -\mathbf{F}\lambda k_c A_{X^{z+}} \cdot f(\zeta) \cdot \exp \frac{-(1-\alpha)\lambda \mathbf{F}E}{RT} \qquad (10)$$

$$i_a = \mathbf{F}\lambda k_a A_{X^{(z-\lambda)+}} \cdot f(\zeta) \cdot \exp \frac{\alpha\lambda \mathbf{F}E}{RT} \qquad (11)$$

$$i_n = \left[\mathbf{F}\lambda k_a A_{X^{(z-\lambda)+}} \exp \frac{\alpha\lambda \mathbf{F}E}{RT} \right.$$
$$\left. - \mathbf{F}\lambda k_c A_{X^{z+}} \exp \frac{-(1-\alpha)\lambda \mathbf{F}E}{RT}\right] \cdot f(\zeta) \qquad (12)$$

where

$$f(\zeta) = \exp \frac{[(1-\alpha)\lambda - z]\mathbf{F}\zeta}{RT} \qquad (13)$$

At the reversible potential of the electrode, the net current density is zero. Consequently, from Eq. 9,

$$|i_c| = i_a = i_0 \qquad (14)$$

where i_0 is the exchange current density. Expressions for i_0 may be obtained by replacing E and ζ in Eqs. 10 and 11 by their respective values at the reversible potential, E_r and ζ_r, i.e.,

$$i_0 = \left| \mathbf{F}\lambda k_c A_{X^{z+}} \cdot f(\zeta_r) \cdot \exp \frac{-(1-\alpha)\lambda \mathbf{F}E_r}{RT}\right|$$
$$= \mathbf{F}\lambda k_a A_{X^{(z-\lambda)+}} \cdot f(\zeta_r) \cdot \exp \frac{\alpha\lambda \mathbf{F}E_r}{RT} \qquad (15)$$

Furthermore, by equating $|i_c|$ and i_a, i.e., Eqs. 10 and 11, one obtains the Nernst equation,

$$E_r = E_r{}^\circ - \frac{2.303RT}{\lambda \mathbf{F}} \log \frac{A_{X^{(z-\lambda)+}}}{A_{X^{z+}}} \qquad (16)$$

where $E_r{}^\circ$ is the standard half-cell potential for reaction 2 if E is referred to the standard hydrogen electrode.

Finally, if the expressions derived for i_c, i_a, and i_n, Eqs. 10, 11, and 12, are divided by i_0, Eq. 15, the following alternate expressions are obtained,

$$i_c = -i_0 \cdot \frac{f(\zeta)}{f(\zeta_r)} \cdot \exp \frac{-(1-\alpha)\lambda \mathbf{F}\eta}{RT} \qquad (17)$$

$$i_a = i_0 \cdot \frac{f(\zeta)}{f(\zeta_r)} \cdot \exp \frac{\alpha\lambda \mathbf{F}\eta}{RT} \qquad (18)$$

$$i_n = i_0 \cdot \frac{f(\zeta)}{f(\zeta_r)} \cdot \left[\exp \frac{\alpha\lambda \mathbf{F}\eta}{RT}\right.$$
$$\left. - \exp \frac{-(1-\alpha)\lambda \mathbf{F}\eta}{RT}\right] \qquad (19)$$

where η is the electrode overvoltage defined by Eq. 20.

$$\eta = E - E_r \qquad (20)$$

It should be apparent that a negative overvoltage corresponds to a net cathodic process, a positive overvoltage to a net anodic process.

For constant activities of X^{z+} and $X^{(z-\lambda)+}$, the equations for i_c and i_a in terms of E or η can be reduced to the form of the Tafel equation only if ζ is either proportional to E or may be regarded as a constant over the range of E of interest. While the former situation is occasionally encountered, the general practice is to achieve the latter by employing an excess of electrochemically inert electrolyte to suppress the magnitude of the ζ potential.[4] Then, for the cathodic process, Eqs. 10 and 17 can be reduced to the Tafel equations,

$$E = \frac{2.303RT}{(1-\alpha)\lambda\mathbf{F}} \log \mathbf{F}\lambda k_c A_{X^{z+}} \cdot f(\zeta)$$

$$- \frac{2.303RT}{(1-\alpha)\mathbf{F}\lambda} \log |i_c| \qquad (21)$$

$$\eta = \frac{2.303RT}{(1-\alpha)\mathbf{F}\lambda} \log i_0 - \frac{2.303RT}{(1-\alpha)\mathbf{F}\lambda} \log |i_c|. \quad (22)$$

Similarly, Tafel equations for the anodic process are obtained from Eqs. 11 and 18.

$$E = \frac{-2.303RT}{\alpha\lambda\mathbf{F}} \log \mathbf{F}\lambda k_a A_{X^{(z-\lambda)+}} \cdot f(\zeta)$$

$$+ \frac{2.303RT}{\alpha\lambda\mathbf{F}} \log i_a \qquad (23)$$

$$\eta = \frac{-2.303RT}{\alpha\lambda\mathbf{F}} \log i_0 + \frac{2.303RT}{\alpha\lambda\mathbf{F}} \log i_a \qquad (24)$$

The Tafel diagram for reaction 2 may be obtained by plotting E vs log $|i|$ in accordance with Eqs. 21 and 23, or by plotting η vs log $|i|$ in accordance with Eqs. 22 and 24, the results necessarily being the same in either case. In the accompanying Fig. 1, E has been plotted against log $|i|$. The intersection of the Tafel lines for the cathodic and anodic processes gives i_0 and E_r, in agreement with Eqs. 14 and 16. The slopes of the cathodic and anodic Tafel lines, $[-2.303RT/(1-\alpha)\lambda\mathbf{F}]$ and $2.303RT/\alpha\lambda\mathbf{F}$, respectively (see Eqs. 21 and 23), are of diagnostic value in that they are functions of α and λ, quantities which characterize the particular electrode reaction. In the figure, α and λ have been arbitrarily set equal to $\frac{1}{2}$ and 1, respectively. The dashed curve gives $|i_n|$, the net current density. As the electrode potential is shifted in the negative direction, i_n approaches i_c (see Eq. 12). Similarly, when E is shifted in a positive direction, i_n approaches i_a. The dashed straight line, $|i_c'|$, represents the cathodic Tafel line resulting from a tenfold increase in $A_{X^{z+}}$, all other factors remaining constant. The new values of i_0' and E_r', resulting from the increase in $A_{X^{z+}}$, may be determined directly from the graph, i.e., from the intersection of the anodic and the new cathodic Tafel lines.

As the preceding example illustrates, the electrochemical behavior of an electrode under speci-

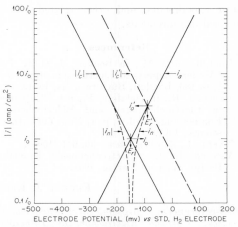

FIG. 1. Tafel diagram for typical electrode reaction.

fied environmental conditions can frequently be represented by a simple diagram. The procedures outlined above can be extended to those cases where the electrode behavior is complicated by such factors as simultaneous consecutive and/or parallel reactions, slow mass transport, and specific adsorption. From the practical viewpoint, the value of Tafel lines and Tafel diagrams is to be found in their application to the problem of unraveling the mechanisms of such complex electrode reactions. Numerous examples of the successful utilization of Tafel diagrams for this purpose can be found in the field of metallic corrosion and corrosion inhibition.

Typically, the investigation of an electrochemical reaction begins with the accumulation of experimental $E/\log|i|$ data under varying conditions of solution composition. Other factors such as temperature and solution stirring rate may also be varied. If the $E/\log|i|$ data obey the Tafel equation, then the anodic and cathodic Tafel slopes, and the displacement of the Tafel lines accompanying changes in solution composition can, as shown previously, serve to elucidate the mechanism of the electrochemical reaction. Over certain potential regions, the data may exhibit deviations from the Tafel equation. Systematic deviations from Tafel behavior are also important because they can often be interpreted qualitatively or, under favorable circumstances, quantitatively in terms of specific adsorption or other complicating factors. In more difficult cases, it is advantageous or even necessary to supplement the current-potential data with electrode capacity measurements, radioactive tracer experiments, and other related electrochemical measurements.

References

1. BOCKRIS, J. O'M., in Bockris, J. O'M., Ed., "Modern Aspects of Electrochemistry," Vol. 1, p. 180, London, Butterworths, 1954.
2. PARSONS, R., in Delahay, P., Ed., "Advances in Electrochemistry and Electrochemical Engineering," Vol. 1, p. 1, New York, Interscience, 1961.
3. TAFEL, J., *Z. phys. Chem.*, **50**, 641 (1905).
4. VETTER, K. J., "Electrochemische Kinetik," Berlin, Springer-Verlag, 1961.

EUGENE J. KELLY

Cross-references: *Corrosion, Electrochemical Kinetics; Corrosion-Electrochemical Principles; Electrode Double Layer; Electrode Reactions, Kinetics; Electrode Potentials; Exchange Currents; Overvoltage; Polarization; Streaming Potential.*

TANTALUM ELECTROWINNING

Tantalum, in common with aluminum and magnesium, is one of the very few structural metals produced commercially by electrodeposition from fused salts. The success of the aluminum process was, in fact, an important consideration in C. W. Balke's decision to investigate electrolysis as a means of obtaining tantalum. This study culminated in the development of a practical production method which, over the years, has provided tantalum in sufficient quantity and of adequate purity for the evaluation and utilization of the metal in a variety of industrial applications.

Efforts to prepare tantalum metal have a historical record dating back to the early part of the nineteenth century. Although early investigators made several attempts to obtain the element by active metal (and carbon) reduction of the oxide, high-purity metal was not prepared. It is generally recognized that von Bolton, of the Siemens and Halske Company in Germany, produced the first ductile tantalum in 1903, through reduction of potassium fluotantalate by sodium. His success resulted from appropriate modifications and improvements of a method which had been tried previously by Berzelius (1825) and Rose (1856). Balke was the first worker to provide high-purity tantalum by electrodeposition, and this accomplishment, achieved during the period 1916 to 1922, was the primary stimulus

for the commercial development of the metal, particularly in the United States.

The electrodeposition of tantalum from aqueous solutions has not been achieved. From a practical standpoint, this places tantalum in the category of active metals, even though its exact position in the electromotive series has not been determined experimentally in a water solution. The latter remains to be accomplished because of the ease with which an insulating oxide film forms on the surface of the metal. The single electrode potential for the reaction: $2Ta + 5H_2O \rightarrow Ta_2O_5 + 10H^+ + 10\ e^-$, is $E° = 0.81$ volts, as calculated from thermodynamic data. Tantalum, on the basis of this value, is considerably more noble (less reactive) than aluminum and slightly less noble than zinc. Hydrogen is discharged in preference to the metal during the electrolysis of aqueous tantalum solutions; and it appears unlikely that the situation can be changed.

Codeposition of tantalum with more noble metals, e.g., nickel, cobalt, tungsten, has been reported, but it was not established definitely that the tantalum contained in the deposits was present in the elemental condition, rather than in the form of an occluded compound. Similarly, it has not been demonstrated that tantalum metal can be deposited from nonaqueous solutions by electrolysis.

In the tantalum electrowinning method developed by Balke and used by Fansteel Metallurgical Corporation for the commercial production of the metal, potassium fluotantalate, K_2TaF_7, is the source of the element. Electrolysis is performed in open cast-iron pots with the temperature of the electrolyte being maintained at approximately 900°C by self-resistance heating. The pot serves as the cathode and a graphite rod, centered in the melt, is the anode. Polarization, and hence the "anode effect" which is intolerable during electrolysis, is prevented by the addition of Ta_2O_5. Replenishment of the electrolyte is made at intervals during electrolysis. As reduction proceeds, the liberated metal causes solidification of the bath, which eventually leads to the termination of the flow of current. During the normal 14-hour electrolysis period about 50 per cent of the contained tantalum is deposited, with each pot providing approximately 15 pounds of metal. After pulverizing, the metal product, a relatively coarse crystalline powder, is separated from the unreduced salts by water washing on a concentrating table. Final purification is achieved through leaching with strong acids, e.g., aqua regia. Typically, the finished powder contains 99.9 per cent tantalum with the major impurities being columbium, carbon, iron, and silicon.

The tantalum reduction investigations of Driggs and Lilliendahl were reported in 1931. Electrodeposition of the metal from fused potassium fluotantalate containing alkali metal halides, e.g., KCl, KF, was studied. They, like Balke, found that tantalum pentoxide was effective in eliminating the anode effect. Several container and electrode materials were tried, including graphite or nickel crucibles as cathodes and a carbon rod anode, and molybdenum or nickel rod cathodes and a graphite crucible as anode. Using the latter combinations, essentially continuous operation was possible because the reduced metal adhered well to the cathode, thus permitting removal of the deposit from the molten electrolyte and cathode replacement. In a series of experiments employing this arrangement and an operating temperature of 750°C, a current efficiency of 83 per cent was obtained at 90 amp/sq dm current density. The tantalum

powder produced was low in metallic impurities and, after removal of adsorbed gases, was ductile.

The increasing importance of tantalum in industrial applications has stimulated research activity in the development of improved reduction methods. This activity is widespread as evidenced by the fact that during recent years information on the electrowinning of tantalum has appeared in the technical literature of many countries, including Australia, England, France, Germany, Russia, and the United States.

A modification of the methods described previously is being used by Union Carbide Metals Company for tantalum metal production. The electrolyte, a fused mixture of potassium fluotantalate and alkali metal chloride, is electrolyzed in a cell consisting of a graphite container which is also the anode and a removable metal rod as cathode. See Fig. 1. During operation the cell is evacuated or provided with an inert atmosphere, and the temperature is maintained in the 800 to 950°C range. The impurity content of the metal product is reported as 0.05 per cent.

Recent investigations by Myers and others

Fig. 1. At its cathode, this electrolytic cell wins pure dendritic tantalum metal from fused potassium fluotantalate. This is one of the electrolytic cells for producing tantalum at the Niagara Falls, New York, plant of Union Carbide Metals Company.

have provided additional information regarding several aspects of tantalum deposition. As mentioned previously, the anode effect is a frequent and troublesome occurrence during the electrolysis of molten tantalum compounds. Advent of this phenomenon is immediately obvious because the electrolyzing current drops drastically, as much as 80 per cent, and the voltage increases by a factor of five or so. Arcing occurs across the anode-electrolyte interface, and the surface of the anode becomes luminous. Possibly the anode effect results when fluorine, rather than oxygen, is discharged at the anode. There is support for this possibility because the effect is eliminated when the electrolyte contains oxygen, in the form of Ta_2O_5 or otherwise. Also, the gases evolved during normal electrolysis (graphite anode) are oxides of carbon and contain no fluorine.

Oxygen apparently has another essential role during electrolysis. Deposition of tantalum from oxygen-free fluotantalate baths has not been accomplished. This has led to the conclusion that a soluble tantalum-oxygen substance must be present for electrodeposition of the metal. In addition to functioning as a solvent electrolyte, the potassium fluotantalate can provide, through appropriate reactions with oxygen or water vapor, the oxygen compounds required for the electrolytic preparation of tantalum.

Potassium chloride, potassium fluoride, and mixtures of the two salts are poor solvents for Ta_2O_5, unless K_2TaF_7 is present. In suitable combinations these materials provide baths which can be electrolyzed at a relatively low temperature, thus reducing the volatilization of tantalum compounds. One such bath consisting of 90 per cent KCl-KF eutectic mixture (melting point 610°C) and 10 per cent K_2TaF_7 dissolves 5 per cent Ta_2O_5 at 650°C. The eutectic mixture contains 39 per cent KF. Frequent additions of tantalum salts are required because of the low concentration of tantalum in the bath. The tantalum decomposition potential is approximately 1 volt. Both lower current density and higher bath temperature increase the particle size of the metal powder product.

While fused-bath electrolysis is an industrially important process, both historically and presently, for the preparation of tantalum, it is not the only commercial method, as in the instance of aluminum, for obtaining the metal. Nonelectrolytic processes, e.g., active metal, carbon and hydrogen reduction, can be expected to grow in importance.

References

1. HAMPEL, C. A., Editor, "Rare Metals Handbook," 2nd Edition, Chapter 25, New York, Reinhold Publishing Corp., 1961.
2. LATIMER, W. M., "The Oxidation States of the Elements and Their Potentials in Aqueous Solutions," p. 265, New York, Prentice-Hall, Inc., 1952.
3. MELLOR, J. W., "A Comprehensive Treatise on Inorganic and Theoretical Chemistry," Vol. IX, p. 883, London, Longmans Green and Co., 1933.
4. MILLER, G. L., "Tantalum and Niobium," Chapter 5, New York, Academic Press Inc., 1959.
5. BALKE, C. W., *Ind. Eng. Chem.*, **27**, 1166 (1935).
6. BALKE, C. W., *Chem. and Ind.*, **6**, 83 (1948).
7. CHILTON, C. H., *Chem. Eng.*, **65**, 104 (Nov. 3, 1958).
8. MYERS, R. H., *Proc. Aust. Inst. Min. Engrs.*, **144**, 297 (1946).
9. TAYLOR, D. F., *Chem. Eng. Prog.*, **54**, 47 (1958).
10. VON BOLTON, W., *Z. Elektrochem.*, **11**, 45 (1905).

RALPH WEHRMANN

TENSION, CELL AND ELECTRODE

The term cell tension (electrode tension) is an English equivalent of the German *Zellspannung* (*Elektrodenspannung*) and the French *tension de cellule* (*tension d'électrode*) and is roughly synonymous with the English "electromotive force" and "potential." Technically, the *cell tension*, U(cell), has been defined by

$$U(\text{cell}) = V(\text{left}) - V(\text{right}) \qquad (1)$$

where the V's denote the electrical potentials of the two terminals (of the same kind of metal) of the d-c potential-measuring instrument with which the cell is in balance. Since the *cell emf* has been defined by

$$E(\text{Cell}) = V(\text{right}) - V(\text{left}), \qquad (2)$$

it follows that

$$U(\text{Cell} = -E(\text{Cell}). \qquad (3)$$

The *electrode tension* is defined as the tension of the cell: electrode//SHE, where SHE denotes the standard hydrogen electrode and the double bar // indicates that the liquid junction potential has been eliminated or minimized. From this, it follows that the *electrode tension* corresponds exactly to the *electrode potential, V* (*Gibbs—Stockholm electrode potential*).

References

1. VAN RYSSELBERGHE, P., "Electrochemical Nomenclature and Definitions," "Report of Commission No. 2 of CITCE, *Proc. 6th Meeting CITCE*," pp. 20–49, Poitiers, 1954.
2. CHRISTIANSEN, J. A., AND POURBAIX, M., *Compt. rend. 17th Conf. I.U.P.A.C.*, pp. 82–84, Stockholm, 1953; Christiansen, J. A., *J. Am. Chem. Soc.*, **82**, 5517 (1960).
3. LICHT, T. S., AND DEBETHUNE, A. J., *J. Chem. Educ.*, **34**, 433 (1957).

ANDRE J. DE BETHUNE

Cross-references: *Electrode Potentials; Electromotive Force; Electromotive Series; Nomenclature, Remarks on.*

TESLA, NIKOLA (1856–1943)

Nikola Tesla, one of the world's greatest electrical inventors, was born July 10, 1856, at Smiljan, Lika, in Yugoslavia. His father was a Greek-Catholic clergyman and his mother a Serbian. He received his early education in Smiljan, Gospic, and Karlstadt and even then demonstrated unusual ability in mathematics and science. In 1878 he entered the Polytechnic Institute at Graz to study mathematics and physics and showed unusual dedication to his studies by observing a day of study extending from three in the morning until eleven at night. In 1880 he transferred to the University of Prague.

During the following year, Tesla became interested in Bell's invention of the telephone. Thereupon he went to Budapest, where he began his practical career as chief electrician for the newly formed telephone company. At this time he invented a telephone repeater, which he patented in Budapest, and also conceived the idea of a rotating magnetic field.

Upon finishing his work in Budapest, Tesla joined the Continental Edison Company in Paris where his inability to interest anyone in his theory of alternating current brought about his emigration to the United States and eventual citizenship.

For a while he worked for Thomas A. Edison in New York designing direct-current dynamos.

Tesla considered Edison "by far the most successful and probably the last exponent of the purely empirical method of investigation." Edison, however, favored direct current and Tesla the new theory of alternating current, so their association eventually terminated.

As a result, Tesla established his own laboratory and constructed working models of motors which previous to this time he had merely visualized. He forwarded his first patent applications, concerning the induction motor, to the U.S. Patent Office in October of 1887. This invention made it possible to convert electrical energy into mechanical energy more efficiently and economically than by direct current. In May of the following year, patents on this process were granted.

Shortly thereafter Tesla made his invention public through a paper presented to the American Institute of Electrical Engineers and entitled, "A New System of Alternating Current Motors and Transformers." At this time, those supporting the theory of alternating current were looking for such an induction motor. George Westinghouse, one of these advocates, lost no time acquiring rights to the patents and hiring Tesla. While in Pittsburgh, Tesla successfully applied the principle of the rotary magnetic field which is used today for transmitting power from Niagara Falls.

Legal troubles over patents in this field forced Tesla to return to New York and his own laboratory. Once there he carried out experimental research on the generation of high-frequency currents, transmission of energy over single wires without return, methods of conversion, oscillatory charges, and mechanical vibration.

His dream of sending electric power without wires was realized in 1900 in Colorado. There he was able to prove that the earth was a conductor and in this respect formulated the fundamental laws of radio broadcasting which were applied some twenty years later.

Tesla considered hardship and pain as being essential to creative work. Money, degrees, and decorations held little attraction for this man who lived apart from other scientists. He placed more value on his American citizenship papers, kept in a safe, than his honorary degrees, which were kept in a dresser drawer. When Kaiser Wilhelm II invited him to perform some experiments and receive an honor in Germany, Tesla refused, stating that his inventive work in the United States kept him too busy.

Financial difficulties forced him into retirement and his final years were spent alone in theoretical research. His death occurred at the Hotel New Yorker on January 7, 1943.

In recognition of his contributions and achievements in electricity, the International Electrochemical Commission in 1956 named the unit of magnetic flux density in the meter-kilogram-second or Giorgi system a "Tesla." Although he left many of his ideas unpublished, he greatly influenced men of future generations. In 1892, before the Institution of Electrical Engineers of London, he stated his aim was, "to advance ideas which I am hopeful will serve as starting points for new departures." Certainly his success in this endeavor is beyond a doubt.

MARY L. CHEKEWICZ

THERMOCOUPLES. See THERMOELECTRIC THERMOMETRY.

THERMODYNAMICS OF IRREVERSIBLE ELECTROCHEMICAL PROCESSES. See IRREVERSIBLE ELECTROCHEMICAL PROCESSES, THERMODYNAMICS OF.

THERMOELECTRIC FIGURE OF MERIT. See FIGURE OF MERIT.

THERMOELECTRIC POWER (SEEBECK COEFFICIENT)

Consider a homogeneous isotropic substance situated in a field-free medium; i.e., no microscopic electric or magnetic fields and no temperature gradients exist in the material. For the time being this treatment will be concerned only with that case in which electrons are the sole source of charge carriers. Conduction by holes, as is common in semiconductors, will be introduced later. Under such conditions, the electrons in the system will have various energies, the fractional density having a given energy being determined by an appropriate statistical distribution function. For the time being, it will be considered that the Fermi-Dirac statistics apply, i.e., the probability, f, that an electronic state having energy, E, is occupied is given by

$$f = \frac{1}{e^{(E-\zeta)/kT} + 1} \qquad (1)$$

where ζ is referred to as the Fermi energy, or Fermi level; k is Boltzmann's constant ($= 1.38 \times 10^{-16}$ erg/°K); and T is the absolute temperature. From examination of the form of f, it can be seen that at absolute zero the distribution is given by a step function: $f = 1$ for $E < \zeta$ and $f = 0$ for $E > \zeta$. For $T > 0°$K, a few electrons near $E = \zeta$ can acquire sufficient thermal energy to exceed ζ and the distribution function changes accordingly, as is shown in Fig. 1.

Up to this point, it has been implicitly assumed that an electron in a solid can have all possible values of energy. This is, in fact, not true in general. To be sure, there are only certain allowable values of the energy which a charge carrier can assume and these are, in the simplest case, grouped into "allowed bands" separated by "forbidden gaps." As the temperature is increased above absolute zero, the electrons tend to be raised within a band. If sufficient thermal energy is imparted to the electrons, they may be excited across a forbidden gap into the next allowable band.

In a metal, the Fermi level is situated in the highest partially filled band, whereas in a pure semiconductor, ζ lies in the band gap between the highest "valence band," which is completely full, and the lowest "conduction band," which is completely empty.

Let it now be supposed that a temperature difference is imposed and maintained along the homogeneous material discussed in the opening paragraph. The electrons in this specimen will redistribute themselves according to the new conditions, i.e., the distribution function at the warmer end will differ from the distribution

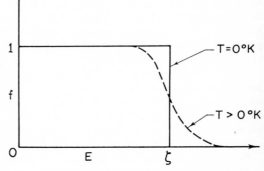

FIG. 1. Fermi-Dirac distribution function for $t = 0°K$.

function at the cooler end. In an effort to effect a minimum-energy configuration, the more energetic electrons will attempt to congregate at the cooler side of the specimen and an imbalance of charge will result. An equilibrium situation is soon established where the accumulation of charge on one end and an impoverishment on the other end give rise to a steady electric field (provided that the ends of the sample are not short-circuited). The size of the electromotive force per unit temperature difference is termed the *thermoelectric power* (TEP) or Seebeck coefficient, expressed in units of volts/degree, and shall be denoted by the symbol, α.*

Theoretical Expression for α

From the qualitative description given above for the mechanism giving rise to the thermoelectric power, it can be seen that there are two competing phenomena contributing to a steady-state voltage difference. First, there is the potential energy term associated with the fact that on the average, the electrons at one end of the crystal have a higher energy than those at the opposite end. Second, there is a kinetic energy associated with the thermal motion of charge carriers. In the free-electron approximation, a rigorous derivation of the theoretical value of α, using the Boltzmann transport equation, shows that the general form for α can be expressed as

$$\alpha = \frac{k}{e}\left[\frac{p + 5/2}{p + 3/2}\frac{F_{p+3/2}(\zeta^*)}{F_{p+1/2}(\zeta^*)} - \zeta^*\right] \qquad (2)$$

where

$\zeta^* = \zeta/kT =$ "reduced Fermi level" and ζ is measured positive upward from the bottom of the conduction band.

$e =$ electronic charge

$k/e = 86.3$ microvolts/°K.

The first term in brackets represents the contribution from the kinetic energy. The F's are Fermi-Dirac integrals which may be written as

$$F_n(\zeta^*) = \int_0^\infty \frac{x^n\, dx}{e^{x-\zeta^*} + 1}$$

These integrals have been tabulated for a wide

* In much of the modern literature, it will be noted that the TEP is expressed as α, Q, or S, especially in work on semiconductors and thermoelectric devices. It is quite common, however, to find the TEP expressed as θ or S, where this latter symbolism has been closely adhered to by those concerned with the properties of metals. It is merely the author's preference, here, to use α.

range of values of both n and ζ^*. In Eq. (2), the significance of the index, p, is as follows. It is assumed that the motion of an electron through a crystal lattice is impeded by various scattering mechanisms. Any factor which disrupts the perfect periodicity of a lattice will scatter carriers from otherwise straight paths. Among these scattering mechanisms are: (1) thermal oscillations of atoms; (2) ionized or neutral impurities; (3) dislocations and other "mechanical faults"; (4) vacant sites or interstitial atoms.

In the simplest case, it is assumed that an electron will drift in a preferred direction under the action of an impressed electric field and that it will travel for an average period of time, 2τ, between two scattering events. The collision (or "relaxation") time, τ, is usually a function of the energy and may be given approximately as $\tau \sim E^p$, where the particular value of p depends upon which scattering mechanism is predominant.* The two most common cases are scattering by lattice vibrations ($p = \frac{1}{2}$) and by ionized impurities ($p = \frac{3}{2}$), hence

$$\alpha = \frac{k}{e}\left[\frac{2F_1(\zeta^*)}{F_0(\zeta^*)} - \zeta^*\right] \text{ lattice scattering} \qquad (3a)$$

$$\alpha = \frac{k}{e}\left[\frac{4F_3(\zeta^*)}{3F_2(\zeta^*)} - \zeta^*\right] \begin{array}{l}\text{ionized impurity}\\\text{scattering}\end{array} \qquad (3b)$$

Effects of Degeneracy

One of the primary differences between metals and semiconductors is the position of the Fermi energy relative to the energy of the mobile charge carriers. As can be inferred from the earlier discussion, the Fermi level in metals is positive [in accordance with the convention mentioned following Eq. (2)] and lies within a band which is only partially filled. Hence, the average carrier energy is not significantly different from ζ. On the other hand, the Fermi level in pure semiconductors usually lies within the forbidden gap and is, therefore, negative (being measured *downward* from the bottom of the conduction band). In this latter case, the charge carrier energies are usually significantly larger than ζ. With $\zeta < 0$, $e^{(E-\zeta)/kT} \ll 1$, so that the Fermi distribution function, Eq. (1), becomes $f \sim e^{-(E-\zeta)/kT}$, which is merely the classical Maxwell-Boltzmann distribution. In the lan-

* In many instances, more than one mechanism is important and the expression for τ is more complex. In that case, the resulting value of α is similarly more complicated.

guage of statistical mechanics, this is referred to as a nondegenerate distribution, whereas the electron distribution in metals is said to be degenerate.

Although extensive tables are required for the determination of α in terms of the reduced Fermi level, closed expressions may be obtained for α for the limits of very degenerate ($\zeta^* > 20$) or nondegenerate ($\zeta^* < -4$) electron distributions. Using the limiting values

$$F_k(\zeta^*) \approx \frac{(\zeta^*)^{k+1}}{k+1} + \frac{k\pi^2}{6}(\zeta^*)^{k-1} \quad \zeta^* > 20$$

$$F_k(\zeta^*) \approx k!\,e^{\zeta^*}, \qquad\qquad \zeta^* < -4$$

it is found that

$$\alpha \approx \frac{\pi^2}{3}\frac{k}{e}\frac{(p + \frac{3}{2})}{\zeta^*} \qquad \zeta^* > 20 \text{ (metals)}$$

$$\alpha \approx \frac{k}{e}(p + \frac{5}{2} - \zeta^*) \quad \zeta^* < -4 \text{ (semiconductors)}.$$

As a result of the extreme degeneracies encountered in metals, as opposed to the case of relatively pure semiconductors, the TEP of metals is much the smaller of the two classes of materials. While typical TEP's of metals will be on the order of a few tens of microvolts/degree near room temperature, semiconductors may exhibit TEP's of several hundreds of microvolts/degree or a few millivolts/degree. As will be briefly discussed later, the larger TEP's of certain semiconducting materials coupled with smaller thermal conductivities, make them qualified candidates for efficient thermoelectric devices.

Conduction by Holes

Thus far, the conduction by electrons in metals and semiconductors has been discussed. The concept of hole conduction is most easily described in terms of the example of a slightly impure semiconductor at low temperatures. Certain impurities (such as Group III impurities in Ge and Si or Group II impurities in III-V compounds) introduce localized impurity levels usually situated (in energy) as positions in the forbidden gap and close to the highest filled band, termed the valence band. At low temperatures, there is insufficient energy to excite electrons from the valence band to the conduction band. However, the localized states arising from the impurities provide a site for a few electrons

and these are then filled by excitation from the valence band.

The ensuing absence of an electron thus results in a vacant location which may be filled by another electron from the valence band. Thus, the deficit-electron, or "hole," is free to roam through the crystal and can be regarded as a charge carrier similar to the single electron in the conduction band (but with opposite sign).

The pictorial account given before regarding the TEP for electrons can be straightforwardly applied to holes, with two exceptions arising in the final expressions. First, the sign of the hole is opposite to that of the electron. Second, the expression for α as given in Eq. (2) is still applicable with the exception that the Fermi level for holes, ζ_h, is measured positive *downward* from the top of the valence band. It can be shown that ζ_h and ζ_e, the Fermi level for electrons as defined following Eq. (2), are related by $\zeta_e + \zeta_h = E_G$, where E_G is the value of the energy gap.

Mixed Conductors

Thus far, consideration has been only to those cases in which either holes or electrons alone contribute to the total current. At sufficiently high temperatures (where electrons in the valence band obtain enough energy to be excited to the conduction band), both types of charge carriers may be present in a density large enough to be significant. It can be shown that the resulting value of the TEP is given by

$$\alpha = \frac{\sigma_e\alpha_e + \sigma_h\alpha_h}{\sigma_e + \sigma_h}$$

where

σ_e = electron contribution to conductivity = $n_e e \mu_e$

σ_h = hole contribution to conductivity = $n_h e \mu_h$ and n_e, n_h, μ_e, μ_h = densities and mobilities of electrons and holes. It must be recalled, of course, that α_e and α_h have different algebraic signs.

More generally, there are several materials in which more than one type of conduction or valence band may be important. Specifically, the semiconductors GaAs and GaSb are known to have two conduction bands, each of which may be important under ordinary conditions. Furthermore, p-type germanium exhibits two types of holes, each of which is important at almost all temperatures. Under such conditions, the expression for TEP may be generalized as

$$\alpha = \frac{\sum_i \sigma_i \alpha_i}{\sum_i \sigma_i}$$

where the summation extends over all important bands and care is taken that the appropriate algebraic signs are used for the respective α_i's.

Measurement of TEP

In the measurement of the TEP, the methods and analysis required are relatively straightforward, but a certain degree of caution must be used in the interpretation of experimental data. The usual circuit required for the simplest case is shown in Fig. 2. Bimetallic thermocouples (composed of materials M_1 and M_2) measure the steady-state temperatures at the hot and cold ends of the specimen, T_h and T_c, respectively, when the pairs of contacts $(1,2)$ and $(3,4)$ are connected to a potentiometer at ambient temperature, T_a. The thermocouple reference temperature, T_R, is usually chosen to be at 0°C to facilitate the use of standard reference tables. A measure of the total thermoelectric voltage induced along the specimen may be found from determining the voltage difference between the two M_1 leads (Contacts 1,4) or the two M_2 leads (2,3). In either case, corrections must be made to account for the thermoelectric voltage generated in each set of leads, which can be shown to be $(T_h - T_c)\alpha_{M_1}$ or $(T_h - T_c)\alpha_{M_2}$. Either of these voltages may be positive or negative depending on the absolute TEP of the metals so employed. Inasmuch as more efficient thermocouples result when α_{M_1} and α_{M_2} have different algebraic signs, it shall be necessary to, say, add $(T_h - T_c)\alpha_{M_1}$ to the voltage measured across (1,4) and subtract $(T_h - T_c)\alpha_{M_2}$ from the voltage measured across (2,3), or *vice versa*. The resultant corrected voltages should be equal within experimental error and need only to be divided by the temperature difference to determine the TEP for the sample.

A final word should be said about the measurement problem. In order that the temperature measured by the thermocouples be very nearly the same as the temperature at the ends of the specimen, it is required that the thermocouple leads be small enough to offer reasonable values of thermal resistance. Otherwise, the heat transport along the thermocouple wires may be large enough to result in erroneous data.

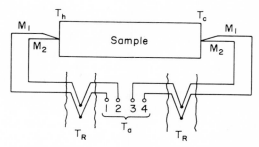

Fig. 2. Schematic circuit for measurement of thermoelectric power.

Peltier Effect

In review of the above sections, it is seen that the presence of a thermal gradient along a conducting material will result in an electric field either parallel or antiparallel to the gradient. As will be mentioned below, this process serves as the source of power for thermoelectric generation, i.e., one may attach a resistive load to the ends of the specimen and an electric current will be established in the system.

The reverse effect can also be established, as can be shown not only by the same type of purely physical arguments forwarded in the first section, but also by a mathematical inversion of the phenomenological equations relating electrical and thermal potential gradients and currents. In brief, the Peltier effect (which is described in more detail in another entry in this Encyclopedia) is related to the absorption or emission of heat at the junction of two conductors when current passes through this junction in a prescribed direction, this heat being in addition to any Joule heating due to the electrical resistance in the conductors. It can be shown that the phenomenon is reversible, i.e., if the temperature at the junction is raised for one direction of current flow, it will be lowered for the other direction of current flow. Furthermore, the Peltier coefficient, Π, being the ratio of the amount of heat generated to the current through the junction is given by $\Pi = \alpha T$. The Peltier and Seebeck coefficients are here connected by the well-known 2nd Kelvin Relation.

Applications

Although specific applications of both the thermoelectric power (Seebeck effect) and Peltier effect will be covered in more detail in other articles in the Encyclopedia, two of the more common uses which have been the subject of considerable investigation are mentioned here. The most common use of the thermoelectric effect has already been cited: the development of thermocouples for the precise measurement of temperature. Many combinations of pairs of metals and alloys have been standardized to provide an accurate means of measuring temperatures over a wide range. Comprehensive tables of thermocouple voltages (referred to a standard junction temperature of 0°C) for a number of different thermocouples have been published by the National Bureau of Standards (Circular 561).

Metallic thermocouples have found limited use as power-generating devices inasmuch as the TEP's are relatively small. However, several thermocouples connected in series ("thermopile") are capable of providing small currents for certain applications. On the other hand, much effort has been expended on certain semiconductors which have sufficiently large TEP's so that more efficient direct conversion of heat to electricity is feasible. In applications, heat to one junction is usually supplied as a by-product from other essential operations, such as nuclear energy from a reactor, solar energy, or a furnace. The temperature of the "cold" junction may be at ambient. Under such conditions, a sufficient amount of power may be obtained for relatively heavy operations.

The Peltier effect has been used for cooling where the temperature of the "hot" junction is maintained at ambient. By passing a current through an appropriate material, the temperature at the cold junction can be lowered as much as 70 to 80°C. Many applications for this effect have been suggested, not the least of which are food storage, heating and cooling of buildings, controlled temperature baths for references, cooling of other electronic equipment, etc.

In the use of either the Seebeck or Peltier effect, the efficiency and operation of a device depends upon not only the thermoelectric power but also on the thermal and electrical conductivities (κ and σ, respectively). It can be shown that the performance of a thermoelectric device is related to the dimensionless parameter, $ZT = \alpha^2 \sigma T / \kappa$, often referred to as the "figure of merit" (q.v.). Much of the research effort on thermoelectricity has been devoted to modification or discovery of materials in which the figure of merit is as high as possible. At the present stage of development, a value of $ZT \approx 1$ is readily

available in a number of semiconductor or semi-metal materials systems, and some higher values have been reported.

References

1. BEER, A. C., in "Progress in Astronautics and Rocketry," Vol. 3, p. 3, New York, Academic Press, Inc., 1961.
2. BEER, A. C., CHASE, M. N., AND CHOQUARD, P. F., *Helv. Phys. Acta*, **28**, 529 (1955).
3. CADOFF, I. B., AND MILLER, E., "Thermoelectric Materials and Devices," New York, Reinhold Publishing Corp., 1960.
4. EGLI, P. H., "Thermoelectricity," New York, John Wiley & Sons, Inc., 1960.
5. HEIKES, R. R., AND URE, R. W., JR., "Thermoelectricity: Science and Engineering," New York, Interscience Publishers, 1961.
6. IOFFE, A. F., "Semiconductor Thermoelements and Thermoelectric Cooling," London, Infosearch Ltd., 1957.
7. WILSON, A. H., "The Theory of Metals," Cambridge, University Press, 1958.

JULES J. DUGA

Cross-reference: *Figure of Merit, Peltier Effect, Seebeck Effect, Thermoelectric Power Generation, Thermoelectricity, Thermoelectric Thermometry, Semiconductors.*

THERMOELECTRIC POWER GENERATION

When the two junctions of dissimilar conductors are held at different temperatures, a potential difference or Seebeck emf will be established between the two junctions. This thermoelectric effect, the Seebeck effect (q.v.), initially discovered by T. J. Seebeck (q.v.) in 1822, forms the basis for the practical generation of electrical power by thermocouples. To illustrate the concepts involved, consider a junction composed of a p-type (positive Seebeck coefficient) element and an n-type element (negative Seebeck coefficient). The arrangement is shown in Fig. 1. One junction is held at temperature, T_h, and the other at temperature, T_c. The open-circuit potential difference, E_0, is given by $(\alpha_2 - \alpha_1)(T_h - T_c)$, where α_2, a positive quantity, is the Seebeck coefficient or thermoelectric power of the p-type material, and α_1, a negative quantity, is the thermoelectric power of the n-type material. Thus, in this case, E_0 may be written as $(\alpha_2 + |\alpha_1|)\Delta T$ where $\Delta T = T_h - T_c$. If the temperature is expressed in Centigrade degrees, the thermoelectric power is usually expressed in volts/°C.

A related thermoelectric effect, the Peltier effect (q.v.), discovered in 1834 by Jean C. A. Peltier (q.v.), pertains to the reversible heating or cooling that occurs at a junction between two dissimilar conductors when charge is flowing in the circuit. The rate of heat absorption, $\dot{Q}$, is given by $\dot{Q} = \pi_{21}\dot{q}$ where π_{21} is the Peltier coefficient of the junction and $\dot{q}$ is the rate of charge flow across the junction. If π_{21} is measured in volts and $\dot{q}$ in coulombs/second, then $\dot{Q}$ is measured in watts. From thermodynamic relations, it has been shown that the Peltier coefficient is related to the Seebeck coefficient as $\pi_{21} = (\alpha_2 - \alpha_1)T$, where T is the absolute temperature in degrees Kelvin. This is commonly known as Kelvin's second relation.

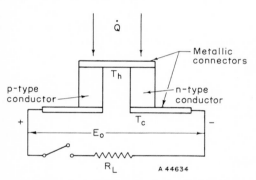

FIG. 1. Basic thermoelectric generator circuit.

Working Expressions

To arrive at the expressions which predict the efficiency of thermoelectric power generation, consider the idealized case of a homogeneous conductor of uniform cross-sectional area, A, length, L, and material properties independent of temperature, as depicted in Fig. 2a. It is assumed that the element is surrounded by perfect insulation. The end, $x = 0$, is held at temperature, T_h, and the end, $x = L$, is held at temperature, $T_c < T_h$. Under steady-state conditions, with a current, I (expressed in amperes), existing in the specimen, the rate of heat input to a segment of length Δx is balanced by the heat flow out of Δx. Referring to Fig. 2b, this can be expressed:

$$-\kappa A \left.\frac{dT}{dx}\right|_{x=x_1} + I^2 \frac{\rho \Delta x}{A} = -\kappa A \left.\frac{dT}{dx}\right|_{x=x_2} \quad (1)$$

(heat input)   =   (heat loss)

where κ is the thermal conductivity of the material composing the specimen and ρ is the electrical resistivity. The first term on the left side of Eq. (1) is the total power input to the segment by thermal conduction, the second term is the internal Joule heating in the segment, and the term on the right side is the total power lost from the segment by thermal conduction. With κ in watts/cm-°C and ρ in ohm-cm, the three terms in Eq. (1) are expressed in watts.

Now a Taylor's series expansion of a general

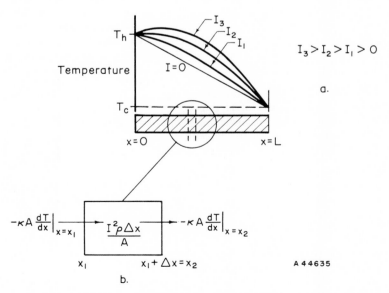

Fig. 2. Temperature distribution in a homogeneous element with internal Joule heating.

function evaluated at a point x_2 in terms of the value of the function at point x_1, where $x_2 - x_1 = \Delta x$, states that to first order terms in Δx,

$$f(x_2) = f(x_1) + \frac{df}{dx}\,\Delta x.$$

One thus obtains

$$\left.\frac{dT}{dx}\right|_{x=x_2} = \left.\frac{dT}{dx}\right|_{x=x_1} + \frac{d^2T}{dx^2}\,\Delta x$$

The above relation permits Eq. (1) to be put into the form

$$-\kappa A\,\frac{d^2T}{dx^2}\,\Delta x = I^2\,\frac{\rho\Delta x}{A}$$

which may simply be written as

$$\frac{d^2T}{dx^2} = -\frac{I^2\rho}{\kappa A^2} \tag{2}$$

Eq. (2) is the basic differential equation satisfied by the temperature, $T(x)$, in the element. With the assumption that ρ and κ are independent of temperature, it can be shown that the solution of Eq. (2), subject to the appropriate boundary conditions, is given by

$$T(x) = T_h - \frac{(T_h - T_c)x}{L} + \frac{I^2\rho}{2\kappa A^2}\,(Lx - x^2) \tag{3}$$

From this it follows that the rate of heat flow by thermal conduction into the element at $x = 0$ is

$$-\kappa A\,\left.\frac{dT}{dx}\right|_{x=0}
\begin{aligned}
&= \frac{\kappa A}{L}\,\Delta T - \frac{I^2\rho L}{2A} \\
&= \kappa\lambda\Delta T - \frac{I^2}{2}\,\frac{\rho}{\lambda},
\end{aligned} \tag{4}$$

where $\Delta T = T_h - T_c$ and $\lambda = A/L$. Eq. (4), which holds for any homogeneous conducting medium having parameters independent of temperature, indicates that one-half of the Joule heat flows *to* the hot junction. In a similar way, from the expression for

$$-\kappa A\,\left.\frac{dT}{dx}\right|_{x=L}$$

it can be shown that the remaining half of the Joule heat flows to the cold junction.

In the more general case, the amount of thermal power which must be supplied to maintain the temperature difference, ΔT, is given by Eq. (4) plus additional terms. If the elements are used as a generator to deliver current, I, one principal additional term entails the heat extracted from the hot junction by the Peltier effect. Thus, the required thermal power input to the idealized thermoelectric element is

$$\dot{Q} = IT_h\alpha + \kappa\lambda\Delta T - \frac{I^2}{2}\,\frac{\rho}{\lambda}\ \text{watts} \tag{5}$$

where the first term on the right side of Eq. (5) is the Peltier term. (In thermoelectric refrigeration, where current, I, is supplied by an external source, the net rate of heat *absorption* at the *cold* junction is

$$\dot{Q}_a = IT_c\alpha - \kappa\lambda\Delta T - \frac{I^2}{2}\,\rho/\lambda.)$$

Making use of Eq. (5), the net power input at the hot junction of a thermocouple of n- and p-type elements (whose properties are designated by subscripts 1 and 2, respectively) is

$$\dot{Q}_h = IT_h(\alpha_2 - \alpha_1) - \frac{I^2}{2}\left(\frac{\rho_1}{\lambda_1} + \frac{\rho_2}{\lambda_2}\right)$$
$$+ (\kappa_1\lambda_1 + \kappa_2\lambda_2)\Delta T \tag{6}$$

$$= IT_h\epsilon - \frac{I^2R}{2} + K\Delta T\ \text{watts},$$

where

$\epsilon = \alpha_2 - \alpha_1$, volts/deg
$R = (\rho_1/\lambda_1) + (\rho_2/\lambda_2)$, the electrical resistance of the thermocouple, ohms
$K = \kappa_1\lambda_1 + \kappa_2\lambda_2$, the thermal conductance of the thermocouple, watts/° C.

The efficiency is simply the ratio of power delivered, P, to the thermal-power input.

$$\eta = \frac{P}{\dot{Q}_h}. \tag{7}$$

The power delivered is

$$P = I^2R_L = \left(\frac{\epsilon\,\Delta T}{R + R_L}\right)^2 R_L \tag{8}$$

where R_L is the load resistance. Setting $m = R_L/R$, the delivered power is expressed more conveniently as

$$P = \left(\frac{\epsilon\,\Delta T}{1 + m}\right)^2 \frac{m}{R} \tag{9}$$

Inserting Eqs. (6) and (9) into (7), yields, after some rearrangements,

$$\eta = \frac{\Delta T}{T_h} \frac{\dfrac{m}{m+1}}{1 + \dfrac{KR}{\epsilon^2} \dfrac{m+1}{T_h} - \dfrac{1}{2} \dfrac{\Delta T}{T_h} \dfrac{1}{m+1}} \qquad (10)$$

From Eq. (10) it is seen that the efficiency of generation depends entirely on the temperature, the factor m, and a material factor or figure of merit, ϵ^2/KR. The latter quantity (q.v.) is usually designated as Z. When one speaks of a single material, the figure of merit is simply $Z = \alpha_2/\kappa\rho$. The term, $\Delta T/T_h$, is recognized as the efficiency of a Carnot cycle. Also note that the product, KR should be minimized to obtain a maximum thermocouple figure of merit and efficiency. Then,

$$KR = (\kappa_1\lambda_1 + \kappa_2\lambda_2)\left(\frac{\rho_1}{\lambda_1} + \frac{\rho_2}{\lambda_2}\right)$$

$$= \kappa_1\rho_1 + \kappa_2\rho_2 + \kappa_1\rho_2 s + \kappa_2\rho_1 \frac{1}{s} \qquad (11)$$

where
$s = \lambda_1/\lambda_2$. Minimizing KR with respect to s yields

$$\left(\frac{\lambda_1}{\lambda_2}\right)_{opt} = \sqrt{\frac{\rho_1\kappa_2}{\rho_2\kappa_1}} = \left(\frac{A_1/L_1}{A_2/L_2}\right)_{opt} \qquad (12)$$

as the optimum ratio. Inserting Eq. (12) into Eq. (11) yields

$$(KR)_{opt} = (\sqrt{\rho_1\kappa_1} + \sqrt{\rho_2\kappa_2})^2 \qquad (13)$$

It then follows that the optimum thermocouple figure of merit is given by

$$Z_{opt} = \left(\frac{\epsilon}{\sqrt{\rho_1\kappa_1} + \sqrt{\rho_2\kappa_2}}\right)^2 \text{ per °C} \qquad (14)$$

Returning to Eq. (10), the efficiency at the matched load ($m = 1$) or maximum power condition becomes

$$\eta_\rho = \frac{2\Delta T}{8/Z + 3T_h + T_c} \qquad (15)$$

To obtain the maximum efficiency, Eq. (10) must be maximized with respect to m. The result is

$$m_{opt} = M = \sqrt{1 + Z\overline{T}} \qquad (16)$$

where

$$\overline{T} = \frac{T_h + T_c}{2},$$

the mean temperature, °K. Substituting Eq.

(16) into Eq. (10) yields*

$$\eta_{max} = \frac{\Delta T}{T_h} \frac{M-1}{M + \dfrac{T_c}{T_h}} \qquad (17)$$

Actually, η_{max} differs little from η_ρ. In fact

$$\lim_{Z\to\infty}\left(\frac{\eta_{max}}{\eta_\rho}\right) = 1.5 \times T_c/2T_h \text{ and } \lim_{Z\to\infty}\left(\frac{\eta_{max}}{\eta_\rho}\right) = 1$$

With the relatively small values of Z presently available, the above ratio, η_{max}/η_ρ is essentially unity, and the design is usually centered around maximum-power operation.

The above discussion is a simplified approach to the development of working relations for predicting thermoelectric-generator performance. The thermoelectric parameters, α, κ, and ρ, have been assumed to be independent of temperature. In actuality the parameters may be highly dependent on temperature. If the thermoelectric power, α, varies with temperature, there is a Thomson heat, $\dot{Q}_T$, generated in the element at the rate

$$\dot{Q}_T = I \int_{T_c}^{T_h} T \frac{d\alpha}{dT} dT \qquad (18)$$

$\dot{Q}_T$ is zero if α is independent of temperature or if α has the same value at temperatures, T_c and T_h. Ioffe[1] has indicated that the Thomson heat tends to be accounted for in efficiency calculations if α is replaced by its mean value between the two temperature extremes, i.e.,

$$\bar{\alpha} = \frac{\alpha_c + \alpha_h}{2} \qquad (19)$$

Also, in this average-parameter approach, the product, $\kappa\rho$, is replaced by its average, $\overline{\kappa\rho}$, given by

$$\overline{\kappa\rho} = \int_{T_c}^{T_h} \frac{\kappa(T)\, \rho(T)\, dT}{T_h - T_c} \qquad (20)$$

Thus, the expression for the average thermocouple figure of merit becomes

* In the case of thermoelectric cooling, one is interested in the coefficient of performance, that is, the net heat absorbed divided by the total power input. The maximum COP, analogous to Eq. (15), is given by

$$(COP)_{max} = \frac{T_c}{\Delta T} \frac{M - \dfrac{T_h}{T_c}}{M+1}.$$

$$\bar{Z} = \left\{ \frac{\frac{1}{2}[(\alpha_2 - \alpha_1)_h + (\alpha_2 - \alpha_1)_c]}{\sqrt{\overline{\rho_1 \kappa_1}} + \sqrt{\overline{\rho_2 \kappa_2}}} \right\}^2 \quad (21)$$

Sherman, Heikes, and Ure[2] have developed an exact procedure for computing the performance of thermoelectric generators when the material parameters have an arbitrary temperature dependence. Using the characteristics of typical thermoelectric materials, they found that the average-parameter approach agrees with the exact formulation to within about 5 per cent in the case of power generation. This agreement is sufficient in most practical cases.

Materials

There are a considerable number of materials being explored for thermoelectric applications. Just as the semiconductor, bismuth telluride, and its alloys have been the most prominant for thermoelectric cooling, lead telluride has been the most frequent choice for thermoelectric generator material in recent years. In spite of the tremendous research effort, experimentally attained efficiencies are not greatly different than those noted by Telkes[3] in 1947. For example, Telkes investigated the intermetallic compound, zinc antimonide, and found an efficiency of 5.6 per cent when used in combination with constantan. Many other materials, such as silicon alloys, sulfides, and oxides, received attention at that time. At this writing, the most recent advances for high-temperature generation have been made with the germanium-silicon alloy.

Some useful p-type materials include PbTe, ZnSb, GeTe, $AgSbTe_2$-GeTe alloys, $Ge_{0.9}Bi_{0.1}Te$, and $MnSi_2$; n-type materials, such as PbTe, InAs, and the semiconductor alloy, $InAs_xP_{1-x}$, have been studied. White, et al.,[4] have compiled the product, ZT, versus T for many materials and have also listed their suppliers. As materials are sought with a high value of ZT over a wide range of temperature, semiconductors with high melting points and large forbidden-energy gap are required.

Some refractory oxides which exhibit semiconductor properties at elevated temperature are NiO, CoO, and Cr_2O_3. Many sulfides, such as CrS, BaS, and NiS, are also being explored. Gambino[5] has given the thermoelectric properties of these materials as well as for some carbides, borides, nitrides, and silicides. In addition to these and other solids, research efforts are also being directed toward the properties of liquid materials.[6]

In addition, there has been increased attention given to the use of segmented thermocouples, that is, those in which the n- or p-type elements are composed of more than one material. For example, n-type elements with a high-temperature segment of PbTe joined to a low-temperature segment of a Bi_2Te_3 alloy is one arrangement which has been investigated. The interesting approach of using a continuously graded element, such as one composed of InAs-GaAs alloy, has also been discussed.[7] In this alloy system, the composition of the element changes continuously along its length, with a high GaAs content at the "hot" end and a high InAs content at the "cold" end.

Design

Thermoelectric generators are being developed for a variety of uses. Among these are ground-based portable units for powering communications systems, satellite power supplies, and special shipboard generators. The source of heat may be liquid or solid combustible fuels, concentrated solar energy, or radioactive isotopes. Propane and gasoline burners have been perfected; isotopes, such as polonium-210, strontium-90, uranium-235–zirconium hydride, cerium-144, and plutonium-238, have been used to date. There have been several discussions of thermoelectric generator design and construction for various applications.[8-12]

The major experimental problem encountered in the construction of thermoelectric generators has been the deterioration of performance with operating time. There are a variety of factors which can cause this degradation: unstable electrical contacts to the thermoelectric material, sublimation or vaporization of the thermoelectric components, diffusion of contacting elements or impurities into the material, oxidation or exposure to corrosive fumes, and mechanical stress (particularly shear stress) are examples.

Electrical contacts can be fabricated with extremely low resistance at room temperature. One useful technique employs nickel plating the ends of the thermoelectric elements and then "tinning" with a lead-tin solder.[13] However, the useful range of hot-junction temperature is usually above the melting point of conventional solders so that iron pressure contacts are frequently used.[10] This requires compression loading of the element by a spring to maintain the pressure contact. A major drawback to this technique relates to the fact that the contact resistance may sometimes contribute to at least 10 per cent of the total thermocouple resistance in a generator.

Thermoelectric elements are sometimes encapsulated to suppress decomposition and attack by impurities. Forsterite ceramics with iron-titanium seals have been successfully used.[14] The disadvantage to encapsulation is the added weight and the bypassing of some heat flux through the encapsulant.

Frequently, a large number of thermocouples must be placed in series (electrically) if certain voltage and current relations are to be met. The reliability problem can be serious, since an open circuit in any single element affects the operation of the entire generator. Redundancy, that is, the use of parallel systems, offers improvement in reliability at the expense of an additional number of thermocouples.[15]

Thermoelectric generators will undoubtedly find increased future use in specialized applications. The number of applications will be in direct proportion to the overall state of technology in thermoelectric materials.

References

1. IOFFE, A. F., "Semiconductor Thermoelements and Thermoelectric Cooling," London, Infosearch Ltd., 1957.
2. SHERMAN, B., HEIKES, R. R., AND URE, R. W., JR., *J. Appl. Phys.*, **31,** 1 (1960).
3. TELKES, M., *J. Appl. Phys.*, **18,** 1116 (1947).
4. WHITE, D. C., WEDLOCK, B. D., AND BLAIR, J., "Proceedings of 15th Annual Power Sources Conference," p. 125, 1961.
5. GAMBINO, J. R., "Thermoelectric Properties of Refractory Materials," "Thermoelectric Materials and Devices," Edited by I. B. Cadoff and E. Miller, pp. 163–172, New York, Reinhold Publishing Corp., 1960.
6. MARCUS, R. J., AND KELLEY, C. M., "Liquids as Thermoelectric Materials," "Thermoelectric Materials and Devices," Edited by I. B. Cadoff and E. Miller, pp. 184–193, New York, Reinhold Publishing Corp., 1960.
7. EGLI, P. H., "Thermoelectricity," pp. 152–154, New York, John Wiley and Sons, Inc., 1960.
8. FISHER, M. D., KASTOVICH, J. C., MORELAND, W. C., AND CORRY, T. M., *Adv. Energy Conversion*, **2,** 275 (1962).
9. MERRILL, P. S., FOREJT, D. A., PITYK, P. E., SPIRA, G., AND KUESER, P. E., *Adv. Energy Conversion*, **2,** 281 (1962).
10. WILSON, R. J., *Adv. Energy Conversion*, **2,** 287 (1962).
11. SCHLICTIG, R. C., *Adv. Energy Conversion*, **2,** 299 (1962).
12. CORRY, T. M., AND SPIRA, G., *IRE Trans.*, **MIL-6,** 34 (1962).
13. MENGALI, O. J., AND SEILER, M. R., *Adv. Energy Conversion*, **2,** 59 (1962).
14. FISCHER-COLBRIE, E., AND WILLIS, W. L., *Adv. Energy Conversion*, **2,** 115 (1962).
15. SEILER, M. R., AND SHILLIDAY, T. S., *Proc. IRE*, **49,** 1952 (1961).

M. R. SEILER

Cross-references: *Figure of Merit, Joule Effect, Peltier Effect, Seebeck Effect, Thermoelectric Power, Thermoelectricity, Thomson Effect.*

THERMOELECTRIC THERMOMETRY

Thermocouples

The temperature-sensing device used in thermoelectric thermometry is called a thermocouple. It consists of two dissimilar electrical conductors (usually wires) joined to form a measuring junction with the free ends constituting the reference junction of the device. An electromotive force (emf) is developed between the free ends whenever there is a temperature difference between the reference junction and the measuring junction. This emf is a function of the temperature difference and is used as a means of determining the temperature of the measuring junction if the reference junction is at a constant known temperature.

Thermoelectric Thermometers

A thermocouple with its emf measuring device (attached at its free ends) becomes a thermoelectric thermometer or pyrometer.[1, 2] Such a device, with the proper choice of thermoelectric materials, can be used for measuring temperatures from close to absolute zero to temperatures above 2700°C (about 5000°F). The resultant emf, developed by thermocouples generally used for measuring temperatures, ranges from about 1 millivolt to about 7 millivolts when the temperature difference between the junctions is 100°C. The emf is readily measured by measuring the current produced in a circuit of fixed and known resistance using a millivoltmeter, or by balancing it against an equal and opposite emf by means of a potentiometer.

The millivoltmeter consists of a galvanometer with a rigid pointer which moves over a scale graduated in millivolts or in °F or °C. The galvanometer indicates by its deflection the magnitude of the current passing through it; if the circuit in which it is placed includes a thermocouple, it measures the current, I, generated by the thermocouple in the circuit. If the circuit has a resistance, R, and the emf is E, by Ohm's law, $E = RI$, and if R is kept constant, E is proportional to I and the scale can be calibrated in terms of millivolts rather than in milliamperes or microamperes. This calibration holds good only as long as R remains constant. Any change in R introduces an error in the indicated value of E.

The potentiometer (q.v.) is an instrument for measuring an unknown emf or potential difference by balancing it against a known potential difference produced by the flow of a known current in a resistance network. Potentiometers are used where the precision required is higher than can be obtained by deflection instruments (millivoltmeters) or where it is important that little or no current be drawn from the source under measurement. Accessories required for use with a potentiometer include a detector (such as a galvanometer), power supply (such as a battery), standard cell, and perhaps switches for selecting more than one emf input. The detector is chosen according to sensitivity and also to the resistance of the combined potentiometer and emf source. When measuring millivoltages, great care should be exercised to exclude thermal voltages and other stray signals from the circuit. Proper guarding, exclusive use of copper-to-copper connections, minimization of moving switch contacts in the measuring circuit, and avoidance of temperature gradients will reduce interference with the measured signal.

Commercial Thermocouples

The thermoelement combinations most commonly used as thermocouples are Types S, R, J, T, K, and E, following the recommended practice of thermocouple designations as established by the Instrument Society of America.

The Type S (Pt-Pt$_{90}$Rh$_{10}$) thermocouple is often called the Le Chatelier thermocouple. It is, from the scientific standpoint, the most important of the thermocouples now in use. It is used for defining the International Temperature Scale[3] from 630.5 (the freezing point of antimony) to 1063°C (the gold point), for intermittent temperature measurements as high as 1600°C, for precise continuous temperature measurements between 0 and 1500°C, and for temperature measurements where its chemical inertness and its stability at high temperatures in oxidizing atmospheres make its choice imperative in preference to base-metal couples (Types J, T, K, and E). It is not used for subzero temperatures since its thermoelectric power becomes too low for accurate measurements and becomes zero at about −138°C. Its thermoelectric power is only about 6 μv/°C between 0 and 100°C, but its advantages outweigh its relatively low sensitivity, which is not a serious drawback with modern instrumentation.

The Type R (Pt-Pt$_{87}$Rh$_{13}$) thermocouple has seen limited industrial use although it exhibits all of the characteristics (except temperature-emf) of the Type S thermocouple. It was introduced when it was found that readings on instrument scales calibrated to correspond to somewhat impure Pt-Pt$_{90}$Rh$_{10}$ thermocouples were in error when purer materials became available. The purer thermocouples exhibited a lower emf. The substitution of Pt$_{87}$Rh$_{13}$ for Pt$_{90}$Rh$_{10}$ compensated for this error and allowed the existing instruments to read correctly.

The Type J or iron-constantan thermocouple is the most widely used of all thermocouples in industrial pyrometry. It is usable from −200°C up to about 760°C in oxidizing atmospheres and up to about 980°C in reducing atmospheres. The composition of the iron is carefully controlled, and the constantan is an alloy of approximately 57 per cent copper and 43 per cent nickel with manganese and iron as addition elements. The thermoelectric power of the iron-constantan thermocouple increases rather uniformly from about 26 μv/°C at −190°C to 63 μv/°C at 800°C.

The Type T or copper-constantan thermocouple is usable in the range from about −250 to +300°C and for short intervals as high as 400°C, being restricted by the oxidation of copper at higher temperatures. It develops a thermoelectric power which also increases rather uniformly from about 15 μv/°C at −200°C to 60 μv/°C at 350°C. The constantan (Adam's) differs slightly from that used with iron.

The Type K thermocouple (formerly the Chromel*-Alumel* thermocouple only) now des-

* Registered trade mark of the Hoskins Manufacturing Co.

ignates any thermocouple which exhibits, within specified limits, the thermal emf relationships as given in the Chromel-Alumel Tables in NBS Circular No. 561 over the range of temperatures from −190 to 1371°C. The thermoelectric power of this couple is fairly constant; about 40 $\mu v/°C$ over the range from 250 to 1000°C, and even up to 1300°C it does not drop below 35 $\mu v/°C$. The oxidation-resistant characteristics of the Type K thermocouple are better than those of other base-metal thermocouples in general use, and permit its continuous use at temperatures up to 1200°C without rapid deterioration, and for limited times as high as 1300°C. It is not recommended for use in reducing atmospheres.

The Type E or Chromel-constantan (Adam's) thermocouple is becoming more commonly used and, therefore, has been added to the ISA recommended practice for thermocouples. It has very good emf stability over the range from 0 to 870°C, and its thermoelectric power is the highest of the commonly-used thermocouples. This characteristic makes it useful for differential temperature measurements since the greater generated emf allows for easier amplification. The thermoelectric power increases from 68 $\mu v/°C$ at 100°C to 81 $\mu v/°C$ at 500°C, and then reduces to 77 $\mu v/°C$ at 900°C.

Many combinations of metals and alloys are available which have not been put to as general use as the ones just described. With the considerable interest in the cryogenics and high-temperature fields, a number of these combinations have been favored. The most prominent of these are the CoAu-silver normal thermocouple for low-temperature measurements and the $Pt_{94}Rh_6$-$Pt_{70}Rh_{30}$, Ir-$Ir_{40}Rh_{60}$, and the W-$W_{74}Re_{26}$ thermocouples for the high-temperature range.

Accuracy

The emf-temperature relationships of the six most commonly-used thermocouples have been determined and are published in convenient tabular form by most thermocouple manufacturers and by the National Bureau of Standards in its Circular No. 561.[4] With the aid of such tables, the temperature of the measuring junction can be determined by a measurement of the emf generated when the reference junction is held at the melting point of ice or where means are provided in the measuring instrument to compensate its indication for the difference be-

tween the actual temperature of the reference junction and the ice point. The precision attainable depends on the precision of the measurement of the emf and on the accuracy with which the particular thermocouple agrees with its standard table. Commercial base-metal thermocouples are usually guaranteed to match the corresponding table to ±0.75 per cent of the measured emf at temperatures above 260°C and ±2.2°C below 260°C. With selected and calibrated thermocouples,[5] the agreement may be better than ±0.375 per cent, and correspondingly accurate temperature measurements can be made if the potentiometric method of measuring emf is employed.

Extension Leads

It is not usually convenient to locate the measuring instrument of a thermocouple close to the location where the thermocouple is being used. Therefore, in industrial applications, where it is impractical to use ice baths as reference junctions, it is customary to employ automatic reference-junction compensation. The compensator is usually located at the instrument, and the thermocouple wires should extend to the instrument. However, thermocouple wires are not generally suited for use as lead wires to extend for considerable distances. No. 8 gage (0.128 inch) base-metal thermocouple wires are too cumbersome and expensive and not properly insulated for such a purpose. Consequently, smaller gage pairs of the same materials as the thermocouple are made up for extension-wire purposes, as duplex conductors. The same sizes can also be supplied as single insulated conductors. Extension wires of Pt and $Pt_{90}Rh_{10}$ for the Type S thermocouple are very expensive. Thus, extension lead wires of copper and of an alloy of copper and nickel are used. These have approximately the same emf characteristics as the Pt-$Pt_{90}Rh_{10}$ combination in the limited temperature range to which the reference junctions will be normally exposed.

Protecting Tubes

With few exceptions, the thermocouple wires are insulated from each other and enclosed in protecting tubes. For insulation, the wires may be enameled for use up to 100°C; glass fiber insulation may be used up to 500°C and ceramic tubes or beads may be used from the lowest to the highest temperatures. The protecting tube may be of metal, ceramic, graphite, cermets, etc., depending on the temperature to be measured and the nature of the atmosphere or liquid in which it is placed. The function of the protecting tube is to keep the thermocouple in an atmosphere of dry air and to shield it from mechanical and chemical damage.

Uses

While thermocouples were first used in pyrometry (above 500°C), they are competitive with resistance thermometers and various expansion and pressure types of thermometers in the lower ranges of temperature. They are competitive with radiation methods of measuring temperature even above 1700°C. They are well-adapted to the recording and control of temperatures throughout this wide range, and they have achieved predominance in many diversified fields of industry because of their reliability and low maintenance.

Precautions

Thermocouples should be made of wires which have been carefully tested to match the appropriate emf vs temperature table, for stability under operating conditions, and should be rechecked at suitable intervals. If a permanent thermocouple installation is made, extension wires should have weatherproof, heat-resistant insulating covering and should be run in grounded metal conduits. All joints, except at the thermocouple head, should be soldered and carefully insulated. The leads should not be run through excessively hot regions; for example, over poorly thermally-insulated furnaces where the insulation may be damaged. Where more than one thermocouple is to be monitored by a single measuring instrument, the selector switch should be of the double-pole variety, so that both leads of each thermocouple are disconnected from the circuit when transferring to another thermocouple.

References

1. ROESER, W. F., "Temperature—Its Measurement and Control in Science and Industry," p. 180, New York, Reinhold Publishing Corp., 1941.
2. FINCH, D. I., "Thermoelectric Thermometry," in "Temperature—Its Measurement and Control in Science and Industry," Vol. 3, Part 2, New York, Reinhold Publishing Corp., 1962.
3. STIMSON, H. F., "International Practical Temperature Scale of 1948—Text Revision of 1960," National Bureau of Standards Monograph 37, Washington 25, D. C., September 8, 1961.
4. SHENKER, H., LAURITZEN, J. I., JR., CORRUCCINI, R. J., AND LONBERGER, S. T., "Reference Tables for Thermocouples," National Bureau of Standards Circular 561, Washington 25, D. C., April 27, 1955.
5. ROESER, W. F., AND LONBERGER, S. T., "Methods of Testing Thermocouples and Thermocouple Materials," National Bureau of Standards Circular 590, Washington 25, D. C., February 6, 1958.

DONALD I. FINCH

Cross-references: *Galvanometers; Potentiometers.*

THERMOELECTRICITY

Any phenomena involving relations between electric energy and heat can be considered as part of thermochemistry. Historically, Thomas Johann Seebeck discovered thermoelectricity when he observed electric currents generated in a junction between two different electric conductors when the junction was heated. Shortly after Seebeck's discovery, Jean Charles Athanase Peltier observed the reverse phenomena, an electric current when passed through a junction between different materials would either heat or cool the junction depending on the direction of the current. It was not until the work of William Thomson, later known as Lord Kelvin, that the present understanding of the phenomena became possible. Using the thermodynamic principles available at that time, Thomson derived the relation between the Seebeck and Peltier effects. In addition, he predicted that heat would be evolved or absorbed reversibly when an electric current passes through an electric conductor in which a temperature gradient exists. Such an evolution or absorption of heat was observed and called the Thomson effect. One irreversible phenomenon associated with thermoelectricity is the Joule effect or the resistance heating of a conductor by an electric current. These four effects are explained by our present concepts of the conduction of heat and electricity.

The Seebeck effect is used extensively for the measurements of temperatures. By proper choice of materials to make the junctions, called thermocouples, temperatures can be measured from near absolute zero Kelvin to 2500°C. In recent years increasing effort has been spent looking for materials and techniques to convert large quantities of heat directly to electric energy by use of the Seebeck effect. Efficiencies of thermoelectric power-generators now rival other forms of energy conversion. Since they operate over a temperature range, their maximum efficiency is governed by the Carnot efficiency. The Peltier effect has been used to develop cooling devices, such as thermoelectric refrigerators and air conditioners. These products are entering the market in increasing numbers. A few years ago they were a novelty.

ALBERT J. CORNISH

Cross-references: *Joule Effect, Peltier Effect, Seebeck Effect, Thermoelectric Power, Thermoelectric Power Generation, Thomson Effect.*

THERMOMETERS, RESISTANCE-TYPE. See RESISTANCE THERMOMETERS.

THOMSON EFFECT

During the decade 1850–1860 William Thomson, later known as Lord Kelvin, applied the concepts of thermodynamics to thermoelectricity. He developed an understanding of the principles involved, showed relationships between the Peltier and Seebeck coefficients (q.v.) and predicted a new phenomena which is called the *Thomson Effect*. Thomson predicted that if an electric current passes through a homogeneous conductor in which a temperature gradient exists, heat must be evolved or absorbed by the conductor if the pre-existing temperature gradient is to be maintained. This is a reversible phenomena, and a property of a single homogeneous material. It is independent of and in addition to any irreversible heating of the conductor by the Joule effect (q.v.). The reversible heat evolved or absorbed per unit temperature gradient is proportional to the magnitude of the electric current. The constant of proportionality is called the *Thomson Coefficient*. This phenomena demonstrates vividly the contributions made by charge carriers, electrons, and holes to the conductivity of heat and electricity. Charge carriers in heated portions of a conductor have their random velocities increased. If an electric current is passing through the bar, this portion of charge carriers with higher velocities would drift and disturb the pre-existing temperature gradient. It is possible to distinguish between

electrons and holes as charge carriers by the sign of the Thomson coefficient.

ALBERT J. CORNISH

Cross-references: *Thermoelectricity.*

THROWING POWER

The current distribution on the surface of a cathode rarely determines the metal distribution on it during electrodeposition, and the difference between them is called the *throwing power*. Electroplaters once thought that throwing power was truly a property of electroplating solutions, but they recognized in the 1930's that it is only a vaguely defined idea or concept, and that it is not a single property susceptible to measurement and expressible by a number.

The term is properly used only in electrodeposition and its careless extension to such processes as vapor deposition or electroless plating has no justification whatever, for no electrical current distribution is involved in these processes.

Except for a few instances of little commercial interest, uniformity of metal distribution on a cathode is a prime objective of electroplating. Most workpieces, however, are so irregularly shaped that the current distribution over them in the absence of polarization or other complicating factors is extremely irregular. In addition to the shape of the cathode, its size, spatial relationship to the other electrodes in the bath (both anodes and other cathodes), position with respect to the tank walls and floor, and relationship to other conductors and nonconductors in the tank, such as heaters and racks, must be taken into account in the determination of the *primary current distribution*, i.e., the distribution in the absence of electrolytic factors that prevail at the electrode surface, principally polarization. The primary current distribution can be calculated only for the simplest kinds of plating setups; hence, it is only for these that any kind of experimental numerical evaluation of throwing power can be undertaken. Kasper[1] has dealt with the techniques of calculation. Such systems, however, are not acceptable for determining absolute values of throwing power because the variability of polarization effects with cathode shape is excluded. The value of the many schemes that have been advanced for arriving at some kind of throwing power number lies wholly in the comparison of several solutions to obtain a relative rating of them. Secondary current distribution caused by polarization and other factors arising from bath composition and plating conditions complicate the calculation of actual current distribution under working conditions. Pinkerton[2] has discussed the practical aspects of this problem as well as the interrelation of it with primary current distribution and throwing power.

Probably the most popular device for measuring throwing power was one of the first to be described. Devised by Haring and Blum,[3] it comprises a rectangular box with a weighed cathode at either end and an anode between them, considerably closer to one cathode than the other. A 5 to 1 distance ratio is often used, but it may vary from 2 to 1 to 10 to 1. The primary current distribution can be easily calculated and the expected ratio of deposit weights can be determined. The difference between the actual ratio and the expected ratios is taken as a measure of throwing power. It is often expressed as a percentage. The results will vary with the size of the box, the length of the run, and the ratio of the interelectrode distances. Comparison of results by various workers must, therefore, be made with great caution.

Another and even more qualitative device that is quite popular is a block of metal containing several holes drilled to various depths. The amount of metal plated as a function of hole depth is a measure of throwing power. Pan[4] has investigated rather thoroughly the complexities and niceties of using this cavity scale. If one only inspects the cavities to find the deepest one that has received a deposit, he is evaluating *covering power* rather than throwing power. Thickness of the coating or its weight per unit area must be measured to evaluate throwing power. Pan's device is only one of many qualitative schemes, but the others have little to recommend them.

Although many factors contribute to the overall effect known as throwing power, the relationship between current density and efficiency is by far the most important. If the efficiency decreases rapidly with an increase in current density, the throwing power is likely to be good, as in a copper cyanide bath. A copper sulfate solution has poor throwing power because efficiency is almost constant over a wide range of current density. In the case of chrom-

ium plating, the increase in efficiency with an increase in current density leads to "negative throwing power" and very poor metal distribution.

Since the 1940's much attention has been directed toward *microthrowing power*. When the depth of a cavity, scratch, pore, or other irregularity on a cathode surface is of about the same order of magnitude as the thickness of the catholyte film (a few thousandths of an inch under normal circumstances) unusual metal-distribution effects are often observed. In general the pores and other defects are best filled by deposition from solutions that have poor throwing power in the usual sense, e.g., chromic acid plating baths. In some instances the effect is so pronounced that an initially matte surface can be made bright and shiny by depositon of a comparatively thin layer of metal. This process is known as *smoothing* or *levelling*. The improvement that can be achieved with practical deposit thicknesses varies considerably with many circumstances. In general it will be in the order of a few tens of microinches, but this will often make possible the attainment of a bright finish without expensive buffing of the workpiece.

In contrast to throwing power, microthrowing power is but little affected by the geometry of electrodes and tank. Even more striking is the effect of addition agents. They are not of much value for alteration of throwing power, but the effective utilization of microthrowing power as exemplified by levelling depends heavily upon addition agents used specifically for that purpose as opposed to those used for stress control or brightness. As might be expected, developments in this direction have resulted in proprietary solutions that are used for most industrial work.

Obviously the mechanisms involved in microthrowing power are quite different than those for throwing power. The detailed and elegant treatment by Kardos[5] accounts for the basic observations and phenomena.

References

1. KASPER, C., *Trans. Electrochem. Soc.*, **77**, 353 (1940); **77**, 365 (1940); **78**, 131 (1940); **78**, 147 (1940); **82**, 153 (1942).
2. PINKERTON, H. L., "Electroplating Engineering Handbook," edited by A. K. Graham, 2nd Ed., pp. 480–490, New York, Reinhold Publishing Corp., 1962.
3. HARING, H. E., AND BLUM, W., *Trans. Electrochem. Soc.*, **44**, 313 (1923).

4. PAN, L. C., *Metal Ind. (N. Y.)*, **28**, 271 (1930).
5. KARDOS, O., *Proc. Am. Electroplaters' Soc.*, **43**, 181 (1956).

HAROLD J. READ

TIN ELECTRODEPOSITION

Tin, one of the easiest metals to electrodeposit, has attained widespread use as an electrodeposited coating for metals because of its unique properties. Tin coatings are ductile, nontoxic, resist tarnishing and corrosion by near neutral solutions. Four basic electrolytes are used commercially and each is suitable for plating in still, barrel, semiautomatic, and continuous tinning equipment ranging in capacity from a few gallons to thousands of gallons.

This article describes the electrodeposition of tin, the electrotinning of steel strip, and the electrodeposition of tin alloy coatings.

A tin coating is electrodeposited as a pleasing, white, matte finish from the conventional electrolytes. The matte coating may be flow-brightened with heat to give a bright finish. An electrolyte, with special addition agents, has been developed which deposits tin in a bright condition. Tin coatings are applied to metals for four main purposes, viz: hygienic protection, solderability, corrosion protection, and for antifrictional purposes.

Steel sheet is given a hygienic coating by a continuous electrotinning process. The manufacture of tinplate for food containers and packaging is the largest outlet for tin. The process is flexible in that steel, 0.005 to 0.010 inch thick, may be coated with a few millionths to several ten thousandths of an inch of tin to meet service requirements. Electrodeposited tincoated steel sheet accounted for 5,000,000 long tons of steel in 1961, about one eighth (⅛) of all the U.S. flat-rolled steel production. The tin metal consumed in producing this amount of tinplate amounted to 31,185 long tons. Some tinplated copper is used for food handling equipment, parts for water coolers and refrigerators, and in equipment for high-purity water distribution systems.

The second important application for electrotinned coatings is to facilitate the joining and soldering of steel, copper, brass, nickel, and aluminum components used by the electronics industry. Pretinned condenser and capacitor cans, switch parts, transistors, connector pins and lugs, contacts, printed circuitry and component leads are typical examples. Where *good* solderability and long shelf life are required, a tin coating 0.0003 inch thick meets all the requirements.

The third important function of a tin coating deals mainly with its value as a corrosion-resistant coating. A plated coating will corrode at pore sites. If the electrodeposited tin coating is applied in a thickness of 0.0005 inch or more, it will be pore-free, and the only available method of applying thick coatings is by electrodeposition. The oil industry uses large steel couplings in oil well drilling equipment, and electrodeposited tin coatings 0.002 inch thick provide internal protection from corrosion and abrasive wear. The nitriding of steel parts is simplified if a pore-free tin coating is used as a stop-off. Bright tin plating provides a means of obtaining a thick coating which is not only corrosion resistant but is decorative.

The fourth important application utilizes the antifrictional properties of tin. Cast iron piston rings, aluminum pistons, and steel-backed automotive bearings, are tinplated to reduce friction during the running-in period. The tin coating also protects the parts while in storage.

Electrodeposition Processes[1, 3]

Tinning by electrodeposition affords a means of applying a tin coating of accurately controlled and uniform thickness over a wide range. Tin plating baths have high throwing power, and it is possible to plate articles of complex shape without the use of internal anodes. The job plater and "captive" plating shops in manufacturing plants operate tin plating units with a minimum of control and without undue trouble. The commonly used processes are summarized in Table 1.[3]

Sodium Stannate Electrolyte. This bath is widely used for general purposes. It is simple and reliable. Owing to its extremely high throwing power, it is particularly suitable for the plating of fabricated articles. The current density limit is 25 amp per sq ft and the plating speed is slow.

Potassium Stannate Electrolyte. The potassium bath is used extensively for general purposes. Potassium salts are more soluble than sodium salts. The concentration of salts can be

TABLE 1. SUMMARY OF TIN ELECTRODEPOSITING PROCESSES

Electrolyte	Gpl				Temp., °C	Bath Volts	Cathode C.D. A.S.F.	†Anode C.D. A.S.F.	Cathode Efficiency, %	Mins. to Plate 0.0001 in.
	Tin	Alkali free	Acid	Addition						
Sodium Stannate (still baths)	40	NaOH 12.5		none	80	3 to 4	15	20	82 to 87	7.3
(barrel plating)	80	22.5		none	70 to 80	3 to 4	7.5	20		
Potassium Stannate	40	KOH 15		none	65 to 88	4 to 8	30 to 100	30 to 40	85 to 90	3.6 1.2
(barrel plating)	80	22.5			65 to 88	4 to 14	1 to 150	40	85 to 90	
Stannous Sulfate	40		H_2SO_4 50	C.S.A.* 40 Glue 2 β-naphthol 1	Room	0.4 to 0.8	10	10	100	5
Stannous Fluoborate	80		Fluoboric 150	Glue 6 β-naphthol 1	Room	1 to 3	20	20	100	2.5

* C.S.A. = cresolsulfonic acid.
† Anode C.D. based on that area facing only the cathode.

increased, the conductivity is raised, and a high working current density up to 150 amp per sq ft gives a higher rate of tin deposition.

Stannous Sulfate Electrolyte. The acid electrolyte has a high current efficiency and operates at room temperature. With a moving cathode, when used, for example, in electrotinning of strip, high current densities are possible. Addition agents are needed but the bath operation is easy to control.

The sulfate bath, with the addition of a brightening agent prepared from acetaldehyde and ortho-toluidine, is the basis of the recently developed bright tinning process.[8]

Stannous Fluoborate Electrolyte. The fluoborate bath is gaining in popularity because of its simplicity in operation, high electrode efficiencies, and ability to produce fine-grained deposits at high current densities.

Halogen Electrolyte. This high-speed tin-plating solution contains stannous chloride and alkali fluorides. Its use is confined mainly to the United States in tinplate manufacturing and in a wire tinning process. Plating speeds of 1500 feet per minute and up are possible.

Precleaning and Post Treatment

It is essential to prepare the basis metal for plating by vapor degreasing, acid pickling, or alkaline cleaning. The appearance of the matte tin coating can be improved by heating the article in hot vegetable oil or by induction to change the structure to that of melted tin. Coatings that are to be flow melted should not be more than 0.0003 inch in thickness.

Electrotinning Steel Strip[1, 4]

A schematic diagram of the three general types of electrotinning lines (alkaline tin, acid tin, halogen) for tinplate is shown in Fig. 1. Each unit is equipped with a section for surface preparation, plating, and finishing. An illustration of a typical unit is shown in Fig. 2.

Coils of low-carbon steel sheet weighing about 30,000 lb are cold-rolled to 0.010 inch or thinner. The entry end of the electrotinning line is

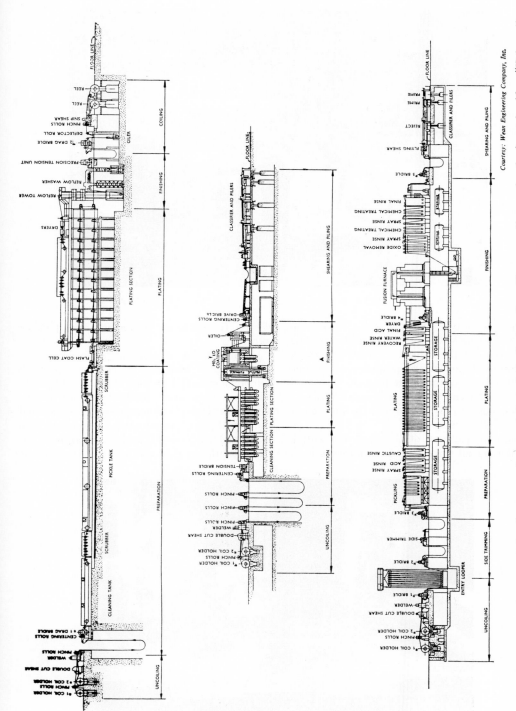

Courtesy: Wean Engineering Company, Inc.

FIG. 1. Schematic diagrams of the three general types of electrolytic tinplate lines. The upper diagram is a horizontal acid or "Halogen" line; the middle diagram is a vertical acid or Ferrostan line; and the lower one is an alkaline line. All are schematically to the same scale.

FIG. 2. Ferrostan electrotinning line. [*Courtesy U. S. Steel Corp.*]

equipped with two coilers, a shear, and seam welder. A new coil is seam welded to the trailing end of the coil preceding it. About 10 seconds are required to join the strips during which time the processing section is running at a reduced speed. A sufficient amount of strip is held in a free hanging loop in a pit to feed the line at low speed for 10 seconds.

Surface preparation of the sheet for plating is similar for all three processes and consists of electrolytic cleaning, scrubbing, and pickling steps.

In the plating section, the electrolyte and anodes for the acid lines are contained in small individual cells and the electrolyte is continually circulated from tanks in the basement. In the horizontal "Halogen" line, the anodes are located underneath the moving strip on each of two levels and each side is plated separately, see Fig. 3. In the vertical acid line (Ferrostan), the

FIG. 3. Replacing tin anode in "Halogen" line. [*Courtesy Weirton Steel Co.*]

TABLE 2. ELECTROLYTIC TINNING LINES DESIGNED AND INSTALLED IN UNITED STATES

Plant and location	Year put in operation*	Horizontal acid	Ferrostan	Alkali	Others	Coiling in line	Shear in line	Remarks
Bethlehem Steel Co.—Sparrows Point, Md.	1942			3		3		Rearranged 1951 & 1952. Capacity increased approx. 1947.
	1951			1		1		
	1953				1	1		Experimental acid line (neither Ferrostan nor standard horizontal acid).
	1955		1			1		
	1956		1			1		
	1957		2			2		
	1958		1			1		
	1963	1				1		
Granite City Steel Co.—Granite City, Ill.	1942			1		1		Capacity increased 1949.
	1959			1		1		
Inland Steel Co.—East Chicago, Ind.	1942			1			1	
	1949			1		1		Rebuilt one 1942 line.
	1959			1		1	1	
Jones & Laughlin Steel Corp.—Aliquippa, Pa.	1951	1				1		
	1954	1				1		Changed one 1942 line from alkali to horizontal acid. 1942 alkali line decommissioned 1960 & replaced by horizontal acid line.
	1961	1				1		
Kaiser Steel Co.—Fontana, Calif.	1952			1		1		
	1957			1		1		
National Steel Corporation								
Midwest Steel Div.—Portage, Ind.	1960	1				1		
Weirton Steel Co.—Weirton, W. Virginia	1942	2				2		Three lines built; one used for zinc exclusively.
	1949	1				1		
	1956	1				1		
Weirton Steel Co.—Steubenville, Ohio	1963	1						In operation February, 1963
Republic Steel Corp.—Niles, Ohio	1943	1				1		Two lines built; one used for zinc exclusively.
U. S. Steel Corporation								
Columbia-Geneva Steel Div.—Pittsburg, Calif.	1947		1			1	1	Originally installed at T.C. & I.
	1952		1				1	
	1957		1			1	1	
Fairless Works—Morrisville, Pa.	1952		1			1	1	
	1959		1			1	1	
Gary Sheet & Tin Mill—Gary, Ind.	1937		1				1	Original capacity 50,000 tons/year. Decommissioned 1943.
	1942		3			1	3	One rebuilt 1951 for 1 ℔ plate. Same capacity.
	1951		1			1	1	For ¼ ℔ plate only.
	1957		1			1	1	
Irvin Works—Dravosburg, Pa.	1942		3			2	2	
Tennessee Coal & Iron Div.—Fairfield, Ala.	1942		2			1	2	One of three original lines later rebuilt & transferred to Columbia.
	1955		1			1	1	
Wheeling Steel Corp.—Yorksville, Ohio	1943			1		1	1	
	1951			1		1	1	
Youngstown Sheet & Tube Co.—Indiana Harbor, Ind.	1942			2		2		Capacity increased approx. 1947.
	1956	1				1		
U. S. A. Total		**12**	**22**	**15**	**1**	**42**	**20**	

* As published in "Electrolytic Tin Plate," copyright 1959, The Wean Engineering Company, Inc., and corrected to 1963.

anodes are relatively small and are placed on both sides of the sheet. Anodes for the alkaline lines are extremely large, weighing over 2000 lb, and are changed once a month. The electrolyte is contained in a large tank, over which the conductor rolls are mounted. The solution is not recirculated from the storage tanks.

The coating thickness on each side of the sheet can be controlled by anode arrangement. Regular tinplate is available with a tin coating of equal thickness on both sides and may vary in thickness from 15 to 75 millionths of an inch. Differential tinplate is available in a variety of coating thicknesses applied to either side of the sheet. The more heavily coated side is used for the inside surface of containers, while the thinly coated side is used on the outside where corrosion resistance is not so important.

The finishing section includes flow melting, chemical treatment, and final oiling operations. Tinplate is shipped in coils or may be cut up into sheets 20 x 14 inches.

Electrotinning installations in the United States and foreign countries are given in Tables 2 and 3.

Electrodeposited Tin Alloy Coatings

Tin alloy plating processes have been improved in the last ten years, and simple plating procedures are available.[2] Most plating shops are equipped to deposit tin-copper, tin-lead, tin-zinc, tin-cadmium, and tin-nickel coatings.

TABLE 3. ELECTROLYTIC TINNING LINES DESIGNED IN UNITED STATES AND INSTALLED ABROAD

| Plant and location | Year put in operation | Type and number of lines | | | | Coiling in line | Shear in line | Remarks |
		Horizontal acid	Ferrostan	Alkali	Others			
Altos Hornos—Mexico	1956		1				1	
Altos Hornos—Spain	1962		1				1	
Australian Iron & Steel—Australia	1962	1				1		
Breedband—Holland	1957		1				1	
	1962		1				1	
J. J. Carnaud—France	1960		1				1	
Cornigliano—Italy	1957		1				1	
Dominion Foundries & Steel Co.	1949		1				1	
Hamilton, Ont.	1956		1			1	1	
Elizalde—Manila, Philippines	1963	1					1	
Ferblatil—Belgium	1951		1				1	
Fuji Iron & Steel—Japan	1957		1				1	
Huta-Im-Lenina—Poland	1963		1				1	
Kloeckner—Germany	1963		1			1		
Brazilian National Steel—Brazil	1955		1				1	
Nippon Kokan–Japan	1963		1			1	1	
Phenix Works—Belgium	1961		1				1	
Richard Thomas & Baldwins—Great	1947		1				1	
Britain	1961		1			1		
Sollac—France	1953		1				1	
	1958		1				1	
	1962		1			1	1	One coiler, experimental
Somisa—Argentina	1963		1				1	
Steel Co. of Canada—Hamilton,	1948		1				1	
Ontario	1957		1			1	1	
Steel Co. of Wales. Trostre Works—	1952		2				2	
Great Britain	1961		1			1	1	
Steel Co. of Wales. Velindre Works —Great Britain	1956		3			1	3	
Toyo Kohan Co., Ltd.—Japan	1955		1				1	
	1959		1				1	
Yawata Iron & Steel—Japan	1955		1				1	
	1958		1			1	1	
	1963		1				1	
World Total		14	56	15	1	52	53	

In general, tin-alloy coatings are denser and harder, more protective to the basis metal, brighter or more easily buffed than the single metals. Red bronze (5–20 per cent tin) is an excellent undercoat for nickel-chromium plating. Tin-lead plating[7] is used on electronic components, printed circuit boards, and bearings. Tin-zinc (80 per cent tin) is a sacrificial coating to steel, and has outstanding solderability.[5] The bright tin-nickel coating (66 per cent tin) has exceptional corrosion resistance and is well suited as a decorative finish for surgical instruments, drawing instruments, computor parts, electronic connectors, watch parts, tableware, etc.[6]

References

1. HEDGES, E. S., "Tin and Its Alloys," Chapter 5, London, Edward Arnold Ltd., 1960.
2. PRICE, J. W., Tin Research Institute, Columbus, Ohio, Publication No. 259, 1956.
3. Tin Research Institute, Columbus, Ohio, Publication No. 92, 1961.
4. Tin Research Institute, Columbus, Ohio, Publication No. 181, 1958.
5. Tin Research Institute, Columbus, Ohio, Publication No. 202, 1961.
6. Tin Research Institute, Columbus, Ohio, Publication No. 235, 1960.
7. Tin Research Institute, Columbus, Ohio, Publication No. 325, 1961.
8. Tin Research Institute, Columbus, Ohio, Publication No. 330, 1962.

Editor's Note: The publications given in Refs. 2–8 are available free of charge from the Tin Research Institute, Inc., 483 West Sixth Ave., Columbus 1, Ohio.

R. M. MacINTOSH

TITANIUM DIBORIDE AND ZIRCONIUM DIBORIDE ELECTRODES

A great deal of effort has been expended in the last decade developing borides for application as electrode materials. Perhaps the greatest contribution has been made by Ransley[1,2] and his associates who have pioneered the use of titanium diboride as a cathode material in aluminum reduction cells. Ransley[3] reported on the use of these materials in various ways at the First International Symposium on Aluminum held in New York City in 1962. The advantages mentioned in using such a cathode system were: 1) voltage drop could be considerably reduced, 2) new types of cells become feasible, 3) the cell lining could be made electrically neutral, and 4) magnetic fields could be reduced or eliminated.

An aluminum reduction cell normally consists of a carbon receptacle containing iron cathode collector bars buried in the bottom about 10 inches below the inner surface. Cryolyte and alumina are charged into the cell, and a carbon anode lowered until proper spacing is achieved. High current ranging from 40,000 to 120,000 amperes, at low potentials, 4 to 5 volts, is applied. It fuses the charge and produces the temperature and potential necessary to electrolyze the alumina, producing aluminum at the cathode and oxygen (burning to CO and CO_2) at the anode.

The use of borides eliminates several high resistance barriers in the cathode system. In the present cell, current must flow from iron to carbon, through a sludge which collects in the bottom of the cell, and finally to the aluminum. These barriers represent a resistance which accounts for a voltage drop of from 0.4 to 0.8 volts. Boride cathodes which protrude directly into the aluminum from the main bus eliminate this high loss of power. Interfacial resistance between borides and aluminum have been found to be insignificant as measured in a small 200 ampere cell.

An additional side benefit would be the possibilities of eliminating the present rammed or built-up carbon linings. The electrolyte components presently used quite easily penetrate these linings, causing swelling, heaving, and buckling, thereby requiring that the steel outer shell be reinforced and solidly constructed.

At the same meeting, this author (4) reported on the application of borides as cathodic elements in experimental aluminum cells in the United States. Tests have confirmed the savings in power and the general increase in smoothness of cell operation reported by Ransley. In these cells, the boride material can be placed directly in contact with the molten aluminum, cryolite, and dissolved alumina because of its excellent resistance to erosion, corrosion, and dissolution.

In the case of the electrolytic production of uranium metal from uranium oxides,[5] a boride could be used but would have to be buried in the cell bottom to avoid poisoning the uranium. Here again, the excellent refractoriness and electrical conductivity of the boride could be used to full advantage.

Additional uses have been suggested: 1) in the spot welding of galvanized steel, electrode life could be extended by using a boride tip, 2) in the fusion of borides, boride electrodes would improve the purity of an otherwise carbon-contaminated pig, and 3) for certain electrolytic processes for hard-to-refine metals (titanium for instance), the metal boride could act as a cathode material.

This family of materials cannot, however, be used in the anodic state since rapid and damaging dissolution occurs.

Fabrication and Properties

The physical properties of borides, and in this entry only titanium and zirconium diborides will be discussed, are in many ways similar; but very little correlation exists between properties reported by investigators because of the manner of preparation, purity, and degree of densification of the specimen. Electrical resistivity, for instance,[6] for titanium diboride is reported to be between 10 and 50 microhm-cm. Other reported properties are similarly conflicting. Again the reasons for this are material of questionable purity, the gross effects of some impurities on these properties, and crystal size.

The lowest electrical resistivities for zirconium and titanium diboride measured and reported have been by the author; 7.0 microhm-cm for ZrB_2 hot-pressed to 95 per cent density (5.72 g/cc) and 10.5 microhm-cm for TiB_2 hot-pressed to 93 per cent density (4.20 g/cc). Stoichiometry plays a very important part in determining optimum electrical resistivity. In a test conducted at the Norton Company, the ratio of Ti to B was varied from 1.9:1 to 2.1:1. At a ratio of 1.98:1, optimum resistivity was reached; deviating to either side resulted in rapid increases in resistivity.

Material Preparation. Borides are commercially prepared by the carbothermic reaction[7] of titania, boric acid, and carbon, or boron carbide, titania, and carbon. These materials are blended together and brought to a temperature

in the 2000 to 2400°C range where the following reactions occur:

$$TiO_2 + B_2O_3 + 5C \rightarrow TiB_2 + 5CO \quad (1)$$

$$2TiO_2 + B_4C + 3C \rightarrow 2TiB_2 + 4CO \quad (2)$$

The resulting material can be easily crushed and processed into a moldable powder. Normally, reduction to an average particle size of less than 10 microns is necessary to achieve the surface activity necessary for successful sintering or hot-pressing. Jet milling provides this with a minimum of cost and more important, a minimum of contamination and material loss. In jet milling, particles carried in a fast moving air stream are worked against themselves, thereby causing a rapid and contamination-free reduction in particle size. Various devices may be used for measuring average particle size: micromerograph, Coulter counter, and Fisher sub-sieve sizer, to mention a few. A material with a range of between 5 to 8 microns as measured on a micromerograph provides a readily moldable powder.

Material Purity. Extremely pure material is difficult to fabricate because of its very high melting point on the one hand and its tendency to be mineralized by the carbon or graphite containers on the other. This usually results in excessive crystal growth without appreciable densification. The first two materials in Table 1 because of the impurities present, can be densified without rapid crystal growth occurring, while the third, the higher purity one, resists densification using conventional hot-pressing techniques.

Fabrication. Blum[8] describes a method of fabrication of RHM (refractory hard metal) materials using powder metallurgy techniques involving cold-pressing and sintering. In this technique, extremely fine particles of material are combined with organics (such as Carbowax and methylene chloride) cold-pressed at very high pressures, 2 to 50 tsi, and sintered at temperatures in excess of 2000°C. It is extremely difficult to produce dense borides using sintering techniques. However, the addition of densifying agents allows the production of shapes approaching theoretical density, usually in the 95 to 98 per cent range. Usually when this technique is used, a protective atmosphere such as hydrogen aids in sintering by keeping particles oxide-free and extremely active.

Brewer and Sawyer[9] describe an experiment

TABLE 1. COMPOSITION OF BORIDES

	TiB_2	ZrB_2	TiB_2*
Ti	68.44	0.20	68.7
Zr	—	78.18	—
B	29.93	19.66	30.4
C	0.65	0.72	0.2
N	0.45	0.35	low
Fe	0.25	0.45	low

* Extreme difficulty in molding.

wherein titanium diboride was sintered under a ½ atmosphere of argon for 15 minutes at 1600°C with no shrinkage, while under an atmosphere of nitrogen, a sample containing titanium nitride shrank and sintered well after 15 minutes at 1515°C.

This author prefers the technique of hot-pressing since this technique permits the making of simple geometric shapes in a positive manner, that is, the final configuration is accurately dimensioned, density is controlled, and particle size range can be kept to any desired tolerance.

Powders can be loaded in graphite molds or combined with organics, such as Carbowax and methylene chloride, and pressed into compacts called preforms. The preforms in turn can be loaded in any number into molds.

Two basic types of heating units are used in hot-pressing: 1) the resistance unit which utilizes a graphite tube electrically heated by passing high-amperage current directly through it, and 2) the induction unit whereby a graphite susceptor is heated in a 100 to 40,000 cps electric field. (See **Furnaces for Hot-Pressing.**) The loaded mold is simultaneously subjected to pressure and heat until the desired level of densifi-

cation is attained. Temperature-pressure relationship controls the degree of crystal growth, i.e., high pressure-low temperature results in a small crystal size, high-strength body, while low pressure-high temperature results in a large crystal size, low-strength body. Holliday, Mogstad, and Henry[10] took this high pressure-low temperature to extremes and produced bodies having cross bending strengths in the 100,000 psi region. Their process involved using partially reacted components which during hot pressing further reacted, resulting in extremely active, fine material, which readily densified under the effects of fairly high pressures and low heat.

Properties. Tables 2 and 3 describe in condensed form the relationships that exist between the molding conditions and physical properties. This represents some work by Alliegro and Schultz[11] where the hot-pressing conditions were deliberately shifted so that the physical properties measured were then a function of these changes. The properties are not considered to be optimum but represent characteristics of commercially available materials.

Fig. 1 indicates the crystal size increase for zirconium diboride ranging from 8 to 18 to 25

TABLE 2. ZIRCONIUM DIBORIDE PROPERTIES

	1	2	3	4	1A	2A	3A
Temp., °C	1990	2075	2150	2075	1930	2040	2150
Press., psi	1990	1600	1100	1990	1680	920	610
Time above 1950°C (min.)	30	22	18	55	60	60	60
Density, g/cc	5.59	5.66	5.67	6.04	5.96	5.95	5.84
Elect. resistivity, microhm-cm	15.4	16.8	18.6	17.0	15.7	17.7	19.2
MOR, psi, 20°C	47,100	58,200	43,000	53,300	47,300	42,600	33,900
MOR, psi, 1000°C	59,100	55,900	51,700	37,800	44,400	50,000	27,100
Comp., psi, 20°C	233,000	247,000	222,500	218,000	227,400	218,800	217,000
Crystal size, micron	7	9	10	16	8	18	25
Mod. of elast., 10^6 psi	61.7	66.0	65.0	73.4	71.1	69.7	68.2

TABLE 3. TITANIUM DIBORIDE PROPERTIES

	1	2	3	4	5*
Temp., °C	1850	2000	2000	2100	2350
Press., psi	2930	2070	1460	2070	3000
Time above 1950°C (min)	22	60	22	24	50
Density, g/cc	4.56	4.56	4.56	4.56	4.23
Elect. resistivity, microhm-cm	13.3	14.3	14.5	14.3	21.0
MOR, psi, 20°C	73,200	59,000	48,700	45,700	26,400
MOR, psi, 1000°C	53,100	57,500	54,500	52,600	27,300
Comp., psi, 20°C	337,900	344,500	314,000	337,500	158,000
Crystal size, microns	12	18	20	25	50
Mod. of elast., 10^6 psi	83.9	84.2	84.5	83.3	72.1

* High purity material.

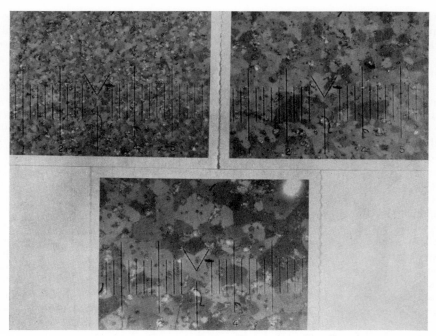

FIG. 1. Crystal structure—ZrB₂ (top left, 8 micron; top right, 18 micron; bottom, 25 micron).

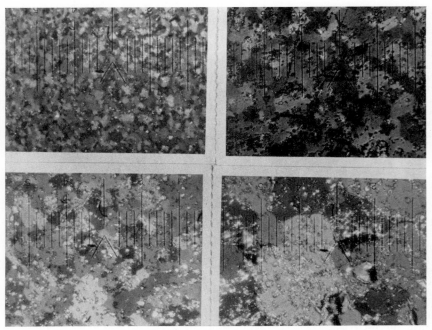

FIG. 2. Crystal structure—TiB₂ (top left, 12 micron; top right, 18 micron; bottom left, 25 micron; bottom right, 50 micron).

microns. Fig. 2 is a composite of titanium diboride photomicrographs illustrating the increase over the range of 12, 18, 25, and 50 microns. The characteristic hexagonal crystal structure can be clearly seen for the titanium diboride while the zirconium diboride tends to be less defined.

Shapes. A great variety of shapes have been fabricated, but perhaps the most useful at the present time is a cylindrical rod. Shapes[12] as large as 6 in. diameter × 20 in. long weighing over 100 pounds have been described. Cathodes from an experimental aluminum cell are shown in Fig. 3. These bars, 6 in. diameter × 8 in. long welded to 15 in. long iron shanks were exposed to cell conditions for 133 days. During that time, the bar having the thermal shock-resistant properties built into it remained relatively unscathed

while the other more conventional one was severely cracked, illustrating the importance of crystal size control. Fig. 4 shows another typical cathode bar measuring approximately 3 in. diameter by 16 in. long. These bars used in either side or bottom entry permit the operation of electrolytic cells with a minimum of voltage drop due to interfacial contact resistance.

Summary

Titanium and zirconium diboride, because of their unique properties of excellent electrical conductivity, high resistance to corrosion and erosion, excellent oxidation resistance to 1200°C in air, resistance to hydrochloric and hydrofluoric acids, and extreme refractoriness, offer the electrochemist a tool to be put to use. Presently, extensive exploration with the basic Hall-Héroult cell indicates definite advantages in using a boride cathode system. Because of the nature of these materials, other electrolytic processes could very well use this family of materials to advantage.

FIG. 3. Cathodes from aluminum test cell.

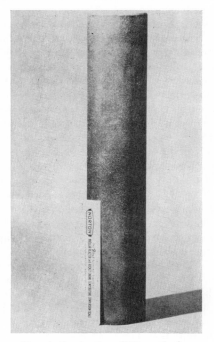

FIG. 4. Production TiB₂ cathode.

References

1. RANSLEY, C. E., (to British Aluminum Company). British Patent 784,696 (Oct. 16, 1957), "Improvements in or Relating to Eelectrolytic Cells for the Production of Aluminum."
2. RANSLEY, C. E., (to British Aluminum Company). British Patent 826,635 (Jan. 13, 1960), "Improvements in or Relating to Electrolytic Cells for the Production of Aluminum."
3. RANSLEY, C. E., "The Application of the Refractory Carbides and Borides to Aluminum Reduction Cells," presented at First International Symposium on Aluminum, Feb. 1962, New York (to be published).
4. ALLIEGRO, R. A., "Borides and Boride-Steel Cathode Leads," presented at First International Symposium on Aluminum, Feb. 1962, New York (to be published).
5. PIPER, R. D., AND LEIFIELD, R. F., *Ind. Eng. Chem.*, **1**, No. 3, 208–212 (July 1962).
6. CAMPBELL, I. E., "High-Temperature Technology," New York, John Wiley & Sons, Inc., 1956.
7. SCHWARZKOPF, P., AND KIEFFER, R., "Refractory Hard Metals," New York, The Macmillan Co., 1953.
8. BLUM, A., "Furnaces, Supports, and Atmospheres for the Sintering of Some Borides, Nitrides, and Silicides," presented at the Electrochemical Society Meeting, Oct. 3, 1961, Detroit, Michigan.
9. BREWER, L., AND SAWYER, D. L., Univ. of Calif. Radiation Lab., Ref. 610, 1950.
10. HOLLIDAY, R. D., MOGSTAD, R., AND HENRY, J. L., "Gas Evolution During Consolidation of

Carbothermic TiB₂ Powders to High Density," *Electrochem. Tech.*, **1**, 183 (1963).

11. ALLIEGRO, R. A., AND SCHULTZ, A. R., "The Effect of Hot-Pressing Variations on the Properties of Zirconium and Titanium Diboride," presented at the Hot Pressing Symposium, Sept. 1962, Boston Electrochemical Society Meeting.

RICHARD A. ALLIEGRO

Cross-references: *Aluminum Electrowinning; Furnaces for Hot-Pressing.*

TITANIUM, ELECTROLYTIC PREPARATION

Attempts to electrodeposit titanium date back to the beginning of this century. However, it was during the period 1945–55 that the most intensive process development occurred. As a result of this effort, several processes have been developed to a near-commercial point. Recent work has adequately established the fact that aqueous electrolytes cannot be used for titanium electroprocessing. The presence of available oxygen results in the formation of titanium-oxygen materials rather than free metal. Thus, current consideration of electrolytic processes for titanium is restricted to nonaqueous systems—principally molten salt systems.

As in the processing of other metals, two general types of approach have been developed: (a) electrowinning or primary metal production by electrodecomposition of titanium-bearing materials, and (b) electrorefining or metal purification by anodic dissolution of metal from a high-titanium content material followed by cathodic deposition of pure metal.

Electrowinning

Approach. The general approach to titanium electrowinning is comparable to other similar processes. The only differences are in the nature of solvents employed and in the operating temperature. A titanium-bearing source material is dissolved in the solvent and subjected to direct current. The metal is cathodically deposited; simultaneously an anodic product, usually a gas, is liberated. All present potential titanium electrodeposition procedures utilize molten salt solvents made from various alkali and alkaline earth halides, most commonly chlorides. Source materials are largely confined to titanium fluorides, chlorides, and oxides.

Previous reports of titanium deposition from

aqueous or organic-based systems have not been substantiated. Such aqueous systems include: sulfanilic acid—$Ti(OH)_4$, TiO_2—H_2SO_4—Na_2SO_4, $Ti_2(SO_4)_3$, alkaline $Ti(OH)_4$, Ti tartrate, and Ti salicylates. Electrolysis of all such materials yields Ti oxides, hydroxides, or complex oxygen-containing products.

Similarly, organic electrolytes yield comparable nonmetallic deposits. Efforts have been made to prepare the metal from halides, oxides, and titanium metalorganics with solvents, such as hydrocarbons, halogenated hydrocarbons, alcohols, ethers, nitrites, ketones, amides, amines, and acids.

Electrolytic Cells. Cells employed for molten salt electrolytic titanium processes differ widely in detail, but have many basic characteristics in common. Many aspects of cell design are dictated by the operating temperature range of 600–1,000°C or by the requirement for inert atmosphere operation. Argon or helium is employed as an atmosphere, since any other common gas reacts with both the product metal and many of the source electrolytes. Use of an inert atmosphere permits carbon or graphite resistance heating. Both external and immersion heating elements have been used.

Crucible materials are of graphite or steel. Steel cannot be used with fluorides, but can be used with chloride melts. The melt container also frequently serves as the anode. Cells have also been built with a temperature gradient across the container wall such that a layer of solidified melt actually acts as the container. Obviously, such cells must employ immersion heating. Cathode materials may consist of any metal with a sufficiently high solid-state range, provided it does not react excessively with the deposited titanium. Steels are most commonly used.

Electrolytic cells for titanium primary production generally share the following design characteristics: graphite resistance heating; graphite anode; steel cathode; air-lock for deposit and for melt removal; argon or helium atmosphere, vacuum-pumping provision, and materials of construction inert to melts and vapors.

Some designs have additional features, such as: salt-feed provision either in liquid or solid state, salt-drain provision, and diaphragm barrier between anode and cathode. Cells of this general type have been operated on a pilot-plant basis on scales of up to 20,000 amp.

Electrolytes. The most commonly used solvent material is molten NaCl. Other chlorides,

TABLE 1. PROPERTIES OF ELECTROLYTE CONSTITUENTS

Compound	Melting Point (°C)	Boiling Point (°C)	Form	Density Liquid at 850°C (g/cc)	Specific Electrical Conductance at 850°C (ohm-cm^{-1})
			Solvents		
LiCl	613	1353	colorless crystal	1.394	7.66
NaCl	801	1413	colorless crystal	1.505	3.77
KCl	776	1500	colorless crystal	1.480	2.36
$MgCl_2$	708	1412	hygroscopic crystal	1.646	1.33
$CaCl_2$	772	>1600	hygroscopic crystal	2.03	2.34
$SrCl_2$	873		hygroscopic crystal	2.71	1.18
NaF	980	1200	colorless crystal	2.05	5.5^{mp}
KF	880	1500	deliquesent crystal	1.91	3.2^{mp}
			Source Electrolytes		
TiF_3	s950		violet crystal	—	
TiF_4	sublimes	284	colorless solid	2.798$^{20°}$	
K_2TiF_6	780	—	colorless crystal	—	~3.7
$TiCl_2$	677	d850	black crystal	—	
$TiCl_3$	d440	927	violet crystal	—	
$TiCl_4$	−30	136.4	colorless liquid	1.726$^{20°}$	—
TiO	1750	—	bronze crystal	4.92$^{20°}$	
TiO_2	1640	—	colorless crystal	4.26$^{20°}$	10^{-4}

including those of Li, K, Mg, and Ca, and mixtures of these, have also been utilized. Limited use as melt constituents has also been made of fluorides of Li, Na, and K. Titanium source materials of major interest are $TiCl_2$, $TiCl_3$, $TiCl_4$, TiF_4, K_2TiF_6, TiO_2, and TiO. Complex chlorides have also been considered. The Ti bromides and iodides could also be used in electrolytic processing, but have not been seriously considered because of economic factors. Pertinent properties of major electrolytic constituents are shown in Table 1.

A satisfactory source electrolyte must possess a finite solubility in the solvent. Oxides are generally only slightly soluble in alkaline earth chlorides and are almost insoluble in alkali chlorides. The oxides are more soluble in fluorides. All reduced Ti halides are compatible with the alkali or alkaline earth chloride solvents. The materials, TiF_4 and $TiCl_4$, are not directly compatible because of their restricted liquidus range. Thus, these materials must be introduced as vapors and immediately reduced, or they must be utilized in complex form, e.g., K_2TiF_6.

Regardless of the salt system employed, product metal purity is in large measure a function of melt purity and effectiveness of the inert atmosphere. Impurities, such as moisture, free oxygen, or nitrogen, will react directly with deposited metal. Other impurities, such as Fe, Cr, V, Zr, and Mn, deposit below or at about the

TABLE 2. DECOMPOSITION VOLTAGES

Material	Decomposition Voltage (1,000°K)		
	Oxide	Fluoride	Chloride
K$^+$	2.35	4.76	3.53
Sr^{2+}	2.51	5.41	3.51
Li$^+$	4.85	5.28	3.41
Na$^+$	2.84	4.86	3.31
Ca^{2+}	2.84	5.41	3.38
Mg^{2+}	2.57	4.78	2.49
Zr^{2+}	—	4.25	2.47
Zr^{3+}	—	4.32	2.33
Mn^{2+}	1.62	3.42	1.77
Zr^{4+}	—	4.10	1.92
Ti^{2+}	2.6*	3.46	1.82
Ti^{3+}	—	3.85	1.72
Ti^{4+}	2.05*	3.51	1.55
V^{2+}	1.69	3.48	1.74
Cr^{2+}	—	3.34	1.40
Fe^{2+}	1.02	2.98	1.16
K_2TiF_6	—	1.85*	—
H$^+$	0.8	—	—

* Measured values.

same voltage as titanium. This is apparent from the decomposition voltage data in Table 2. Thus, only CP grades of materials are employed in melts. Various recrystallization, distillation, and sublimation procedures are employed to insure high-purity reagents. In addition, most melts are subjected to a pre-electrolysis step at 1–1.5 volts to insure removal of traces of moisture and other low decomposition-voltage materials.

Oxide Processes. Since titanium oxide is a readily available material, it is frequently employed as a source electrolyte for primary titanium process study. However, there is no confirmed evidence of pure metal being prepared in this manner. Preparation of Ti from TiO_2 has been reported with melts such as $CaCl_2$, alkali metal phosphates, alkali metal borates, and alkali metal fluorides. A process analogous to the cryolite process for aluminium is also of interest. This process involves a system based on TiO_2 dissolved in K_2TiF_6.

The major difficulty with oxide processes is twofold: (a) it is difficult to effect a complete electrolytic separation of titanium and oxygen because of the high affinities for each other of these two elements, both in ionic and elemental form; (b) metal recovery from the deposit is difficult because of insoluble oxide inclusion from the melt. One approach toward overcoming the second problem involves use of liquid metal cathodes. Titanium of 99.5 per cent purity has been reported deposited in such a cathode from a TiO_2-$CaCl_2$ electrolyte. A second approach would be deposition of metal in massive form. However, this has not yet been achieved.

Reduced titanium oxides have also been subjected to molten salt electrolysis. The sesquioxide, Ti_2O_3, yields a high oxygen product, but the monoxide, TiO, can be electrolyzed in an alkaline earth halide, such as $CaCl_2$ to yield metal of up to 98.8 per cent purity. The monoxide itself may be electrolytically prepared from TiO_2 by electrolysis in $CaCl_2$. The present status of oxide processes indicates that their primary utility would be as methods for obtaining high-titanium content materials. These materials could be employed as feeds in subsequent refining operations.

Halide Processes. Electrolysis of titanium halides is the only primary metal-electrolytic approach to pure titanium which may be potentially competitive with existing thermal reduction processes. All currently reported processes have utilized either K_2TiF_6, TiF_4, or $TiCl_4$ as the source material in a chloride solvent. The $TiCl_4$ is, of course, immediately reduced to $TiCl_3$-$TiCl_2$ to form a stable electrolyte. The chloride has also been used in complex forms, such as $KTiCl_5$, as well as directly as $TiCl_3$ or $TiCl_2$. Voltametric studies indicate that titanium is reduced in stepwise fashion, i.e., $Ti^{4+} \rightarrow Ti^{3+} \rightarrow Ti^{2+} \rightarrow Ti$.

Another possible reaction mechanism involves a two-step process whereby an alkali or alkaline earth metal is electrolytically produced. This metal product could then react with the titanium source material to yield metallic titanium. The anode reaction is simple; it consists of the liberation of a halogen gas. In all cases of interest, chlorine is produced. Where fluorides are source materials, chlorine is still preferentially liberated, provided, of course, that a chloride solvent is used.

Electrolysis conditions vary over a considerable range and depend on characteristics of the particular salt system used. However, in general, pertinent variables fall in the following ranges:

Temperature	600–900°C
Cathode current density (initial)	100–500 amp/sq dm
Concentration of Ti in melt	3–6 wt %
Voltage	>2

All of these factors are interdependent, each affecting one or more of the others. Secondary effects manifest themselves in the form of current efficiency, particle size of product, salt content of deposit, etc.

Temperature primarily affects the type of deposit obtained. Normally, titanium is deposited as an HCP structure, but above 882°C, a BCC structure is formed. Temperatures greater than 800°C in general also tend to reduce particle size and current efficiency. The latter effect is largely the result of physical loss of source electrolyte from the melt. Cathode current density has only nominal process effects within the stated limits. There is a tendency toward higher efficiency with an increase in current density. Average efficiencies are 50 to 60 per cent based on a four-electron change. Concentration of source electrolyte in the melt has profound processing effects, because it appears that such concentrations affect the equilibrium of back reactions that may interfere with process efficiency. Applied voltage is of importance only insofar as it exceeds the decomposition potential of the source electrolyte.

Specific systems which show promise as commercial methods include: K_2TiF_6-LiCl-KCl, NaCl-KCl, or NaCl; $TiCl_3$-LiCl-KCl; $TiCl_4$-NaCl-KCl-$CaCl_2$; $TiCl_4$-NaCl-$SrCl_2$; $NaTiCl_4$-NaCl-KCl. Most of these have been used with larger than laboratory-scale cells.

Fluoride-source electrolytes possess the disadvantage of producing by-product fluorides in the melt, i.e., NaF, KF, CaF_2, etc. These raise the melting point of the electrolyte, increase the tendency toward anodic polarization, and ultimately reduce metal recovery efficiency because of their water insolubility. On the other hand, K_2TiF_6 is much easier to handle than salts, such as $TiCl_4$ or $TiCl_3$, which are extremely reactive with moisture.

Electrorefining

Of presently envisioned processes, the electrorefining of titanium has perhaps the greatest commercial potential. These processes utilize relatively crude forms of metal, such as scrap, off-grade sponge, or even carbides, alloys, and possibly TiO, TiN, or TiS, and result in production of very high-purity metal, even, in some cases, exceeding that of metal prepared by iodide methods.

Melts employed are very similar to those used for electrowinning. With electrorefining, however, the melt meets only two basic requirements: (a) it must be electrically conductive, and (b) it must contain a carrier salt of titanium to permit transport from anode to cathode.

Electrolytic Cells. Cells similar to those used in electrowinning are employed for electrorefining. Where other than massive feed materials are employed, an anode basket arrangement is used to contain the source material. This may be of graphite or of steel (since the solution potential of steel is greater than that of Ti).

Electrolytes. Any of the halide materials used in electrowinning processes also behave satisfactorily as carrier electrolytes. These may be present in amounts of 30 to 70 wt per cent. Operating conditions, except those for current and voltage, are also very similar to those for electrowinning. Electrorefining procedures are conducted at very low voltages—well below the decomposition voltages of any materials used. Thus the current density values are also of a lower order of magnitude. This condition generally results in the deposition of large, dendritic, cathodic crystal growths.

Voltametric data and cathodic efficiencies indicate that Ti anodically dissolves primarily as a Ti^{2+} species. Processes operate at 80 to 90 per cent cathode current efficiency with a two-electron change. These procedures are extremely effective in removal of the following impurities from titanium: oxygen, nitrogen, iron, and chromium. Manganese and vanadium separa-

tions are the most difficult, their potentials being very close to that of Ti^{2+}.

The most effective processes use an electrolyte with a high titanium content (up to 35 wt per cent). It is also important to maintain the carrier salt in a maximum state of reduction, that is, in a Ti^{2+} state. The specific carrier species is also of concern, but little definitive information is available in this area.

Metal Recovery

Because of the inclusion of electrolyte salts in the deposit—regardless of the particular processing method employed—all fusion electrolysis procedures require a metal recovery step. Since washing procedures are the simplest approach to metal recovery, water solubility is a desirable property of all salts employed. Deposits vary in character from very fine granules for very high-current density processes to large dendrites or flakes up to several inches in length. The amount of salts contained in a deposit is less in the larger particle sizes, probably because of improved salt drainage. Salt contents may vary from at least 15 to 60 wt per cent.

Specific aqueous recovery procedures vary with the material used, but in general, these procedures consist of a base cathode removal step, a crushing operation, water elution and circulation, filtering or centrifuging, and low-temperature drying. In some cases, deposits are removed hot from the base cathode within the cell.

Recovery is considerably complicated in cases where insoluble materials, such as oxides or certain fluorides, are present in the deposit. Fluorides may be removed by vacuum distillation. Some success in oxide removal has been achieved by use of flotation procedures. Use of liquid cathodes in oxide processes may at least partially overcome the difficulties of oxide removal. The presence of residual hydrolyzable titanium species requires special attention. These materials may produce insoluble hydroxides which may result in oxide contamination of the product metal. Acid washes are generally employed to suppress the hydrolysis process. Such washes do not affect titanium to any significant degree.

Electrolytic Titanium Products

The purity and the type of product obtained from electrolytic processing varies widely. In general, material produced from oxides is suit-

TABLE 3. ELECTROLYTIC TITANIUM—TYPICAL PROPERTIES

Primary Metal

Source Electrolyte	Ti Content, wt %	Hardness, BHN	Product Type	Product Impurities (ppm)				Total Ti, wt %
				O_2	N_2		Fe	
TiO	75	250–400	Powder	2,000	<500	15,000	,000–2,000	98.5
$TiCl_3$	31	180	Granules	1,000–1,500	<200	200–400	500–1,000	>99
K_2TiF_6	20	150	Flake	500–1,000	20–40	300–500	50–500	>99.8
Kroll	—	150	Sponge	1,000		300	200	1,000	>99.8

Electrorefined Metal

Source Anode	Ti Content, wt %	Anode Impurities (ppm)				Product Type	Hardness, BHN	Product Impurities (ppm)			
		O_2	N_2	C	Fe			O_2	N_2	C	Fe
Ti Scrap	96–99	5,200	200	1,150	2,500	Dendritic	50–80	300	50	100	200
TiC	79	—	—	200,000	300	Dendrites	157	1,200–5,000	—	200–4,000	1,000–5,000
Deposit from TiC	99.4	—	—	1,500	1,000	Dendrites	120	1,200	—	200	300
Iodide	—	—	—	—	—	Crystal bar	50–80	100	30	200	200

able only as feed material for further refining. Products from electrodecomposition of chlorides and fluorides are comparable in quality to the presently produced Kroll process sponge. Electrorefined titanium is a maximum-purity product analogous to or superior to iodide process material. Some average typical properties are shown in Table 3. For comparison, values are also shown for Kroll and iodide process material.

Future commercial utilization of electrolytic titanium depends primarily on the extent to which demand for the metal increases. Further development of primary metal electrolytic processes and advanced cell development could result in advantages both in cost and quality over existing processes. However, further development is unlikely without substantial increase in use of the metal.

Development of electrorefining processes is likely to take place more rapidly. The stockpile of scrap titanium at present is considerable; the molten salt electrorefining process seems the logical answer to this problem. On a large-scale continuous production basis, a high-purity product could be prepared at competitive cost.

Additional impetus will be given toward the use of electrolytic processing techniques as powder metallurgy technology develops. If electrolytic products could be used directly for fabrication of mill products, substantial cost savings would result. Present technology requires use

of a consolidation and arc melting step prior to manufacture of mill products.

Currently, electrolytic titanium is available only in laboratory quantities. Organizations having experience in electrolytic titanium processing include: U. S. Bureau of Mines, Horizons Incorporated, Mallory-Sharon, Union Carbide Metals, Chicago Development Corp., Titanium Metal Corp., Kennecott Copper Corp., New Jersey Zinc Co., National Lead Co., The Norton Co., National Research Corp., E. I. duPont deNemours, Shawinigan Water and Power Co., Imperial Chemical Co. Ltd., and Battelle Memorial Institute.

References

1. BIRMINGHAM, J., *Met. Soc.*, **35**, #3, 248–302 (1955).
2. DELIMARSKII, IU. K., AND MARKOV, B. F., "Electrochemistry of Fused Salts," (English translation), Washington, Sigma Press, 1961.
3. DROSSBACH, P., *Z. Elektrochem.*, **58**, #9, 686–697 (1954).
4. HAMPEL, C. A., Ed., "Rare Metals Handbook," 2nd Ed., Chap. 29, New York, Reinhold Publishing Corp., 1961.
5. KROLL, W. J., *Met. Ind.*, 243–46, Sept. 26, 1952; 269–71, Oct. 3, 1952; 284–86, Oct. 10, 1952; 307–11, Oct. 17, 1952; 325–26, Oct. 24, 1952; 341–43, Oct. 31, 1952; 365–66, Nov. 7, 1952; 81–82, July 31, 1953; 101–04, Aug. 7, 1953; 124–26, Aug. 14, 1953; and 141–43, Aug. 21, 1953.
6. McQUILLAN, A. D., AND McQUILLAN, M. K., "Titanium," London, Butterworths Scientific Publications, 1956.

7. Sibert, M. E., and Steinberg, M. A., *J. Metals*, **8**, 1162–68, (Sept., 1956).

Merle E. Sibert

Cross-references: *Fused Salt Electrode Reactions; Fused Salt Electromotive Force Series; Hafnium, Electrolytic Preparation; Zirconium, Electrolytic Processing.*

TONE, FRANK JEROME (1868–1944)

A pioneer in the development of the electro-thermic industry, Frank Jerome Tone was born in Bergen, N.Y., on October 16, 1868. He graduated as a mechanical engineer from Cornell University in 1891 and spent four years as engineer with the Thomson-Houston Electric Company, Lynn, Massachusetts, and with the Pittsburgh Traction Company before being engaged by Edward G. Acheson in 1895 as plant engineer at the new Niagara Falls plant producing the "Carborundum" (silicon carbide) discovered by Acheson. This association with the abrasives industry and the Carborundum Company at Niagara Falls was to last throughout his life, and he made notable contributions to the growth of both the industry and his company.

His achievements include the study of the production, properties and applications of the abrasives, silicon carbide and fused aluminum oxide, products which revolutionized the abrasives industry. Tone's work led to the development of grinding wheels and coated abrasive products (sanding and finishing papers and cloth), and of improved production and processing operations. He also contributed to the development and application of super-refractories and to the production of silicon metal in large quantities at reasonable prices. His creative and inventive ability resulted in his being granted well over 150 patents.

In 1919 Tone was made president of the Carborundum Company and in 1942 he became chairman of the board of directors.

Active in the Electrochemical Society from its beginning, he was president of it in 1918–1919 and was awarded its Acheson Medal in 1935. He belonged to many other scientific societies and received the first Schoelkopf Medal in 1931 and the Perkin Medal in 1938. Among the many honors given him during his long and distinguished career, beginning with the Paris Exposition Medal in 1900, was the degree of Doctor of Science from the University of Pittsburgh in 1935.

Tone died at his home in Niagara Falls on July 26, 1944, survived by his widow, Gertrude Franchot Tone, and two sons, Frank J. Tone, Jr., of Niagara Falls, and Franchot Tone of Hollywood.

Reference

Bowman, F. D., *Trans. Electrochem. Soc.*, **86**, 44 (1944).

Clifford A. Hampel

TRANSDUCERS, BIOLOGICAL. See BIOLOGICAL TRANSDUCERS.

TRANSFER COEFFICIENT

The rate of any electrochemical reaction, such as, e.g., the deposition of hydrogen ions to form hydrogen gas, may be represented by an Arrhenius-type rate equation of the form

$$v_i = C_i k_i \exp\left[-E/RT\right] \qquad (1)$$

where v_i is the velocity of the reaction, C_i the concentration of the reacting species, k_i, the rate constant, E the activation energy, R the gas constant, and T the absolute temperature. The velocity is here expressed in moles reacted per sq cm of electrode surface and per second. However, it is more natural to express electrochemical reaction rates in terms of a current density

$$i = Z_i \mathbf{F} C_i k_i \exp\left[-E/RT\right] \qquad (2)$$

where $\mathbf{F}$ is the Faraday and where Z_i is the number of electrons produced or consumed per unit reaction

The activation energy, E, must depend more or less linearly on the electrode potential, ψ, since a wealth of experimental data accumulated during the last sixty years clearly indicates that the current is an exponential function of the electrode potential, hence:

$$E = A + B(\psi - \psi_0) \qquad (3)$$

and

$$i = Z_i \mathbf{F} C_i k_i{}^\circ \exp\left[-B(\psi - \psi_0)/RT\right] \qquad (4)$$

where A and B are constants and

$$k_i{}^\circ = k_i \exp\left[A/RT\right] \qquad (5)$$

The absolute values of electrode potentials are

not accessible to measurement or indirect determination. However, changes in ψ are readily observable by polarization experiments, using half-cell potential measurements. Therefore, the meaning attached to $(\psi - \psi_0)$ in the present discussion is the difference in potential from an arbitrarily selected origin ψ_0. Equations of the type represented by (4) have been applied to describe kinetics for many different electrode reactions: metal deposition and dissolution, hydrogen evolution and oxidation, oxygen evolution and reduction, and to redox processes in solution. It was first discovered for the hydrogen evolution reaction, and later confirmed for many other electrode processes that the constant, B, may be expressed by

$$B = (1 - \alpha)Z_i\mathbf{F} \qquad (6)$$

where α has a surprisingly constant value of about 0.5 for a wide variety of different reactions under completely different conditions and extremely broad ranges of current densities. For instance, the constant, α, holds the value of 0.50 for the hydrogen evolution reaction on mercury between current densities of 10^{-8} amp/sq cm and 10^1 amp/sq cm.

Introducing (6) into (4) one obtains for the rate equation of a first-order electrode reaction

$$i = Z_i\mathbf{F}C_ik_i{}^\circ \exp\left[(1 - \alpha)\,Z_i\mathbf{F}(\psi - \psi_0)/RT\right] \qquad (7)$$

Eq. (7) is probably the most important and most frequently used equation in the field of theoretical electrochemistry as it relates to electrode processes. In this important equation "α" must *a*

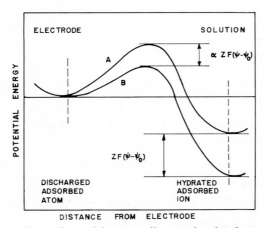

FIG. 1. Potential energy diagram for the theoretical interpretation of the transfer coefficient according to the "symmetrical energy barrier theory."

priori be considered strictly as a parameter introduced to fit experimental data. Indeed, with $\alpha = \frac{1}{2}$ a large number of electrode processes may be represented by (7) with fair accuracy. It is thus only natural that the factor, α, has been the subject of special interest and extensive theoretical discussion, as well as broad speculative consideration.

The factor, α, has been named *transfer coefficient*, in German "Durchtrittsfaktor." In a strict sense, it is, as pointed out, a numerical parameter to fit Eq. (7) to the experimental findings. Eqs. (3) and (6) state that the voltage changes the activation energy by the amount

$$(\Delta E) = (1 - \alpha)\,Z_i\mathbf{F}(\psi - \psi_0) \qquad (8)$$

The electrical energy required to transport a charge, $Z_i\mathbf{F}$, across a potential difference, $\Delta\psi$, would be $Z_i\mathbf{F}(\psi - \psi_0)$. The Eq. (8) indicates that only a fraction, α, of this energy is relevant to the activation energy of the process as influenced by the potential, ψ. To interpret this phenomenon, one has used in the past the picture of a potential energy barrier, located half-way between initial and final stage of the reaction. The potential energy barrier in this model is usually plotted as a function of the distance from the electrode. If this model is applied to the discharge of an ion from solution, the peak of the activation energy barrier would be located about in the middle between the hydrated ion in solution and the discharged atom on the electrode surface. Fig. 1 illustrates this concept. As the potential, $\Delta\psi$, is applied, curve A changes to B. The potential energy of one mole of ion in solution is assumed to increase by $Z_i\mathbf{F}(\psi - \psi_0)$ through the application of $\Delta\psi$. At the peak of the activation energy barrier, however, the potential energy changes only by $\alpha Z_i\mathbf{F}(\psi - \psi_0)$ since the effect due to ψ must disappear to zero towards the metal side of the interface. For the deposition reaction the activation energy thus changes by $(1 - \alpha)Z_i\mathbf{F}(\psi - \psi_0)$. This model then appears to explain the unusual factor of $(1 - \alpha)$ in the exponential term of the rate equation, in justification of Eq. (7).

However, this widely accepted argument to explain the appearance of $(1 - \alpha)$ in (7) may be shown to be theoretically on weak ground. Firstly, it is inconceivable that the energy barrier should remain exactly symmetrical and the activated complex located physically exactly at half-distance between the hydrated ion in solution and the discharged atom for a variety of electrode surfaces, having widely different lattice spacings, and for a variety of ions with different ionic diameters, charge, and hydration energies. Secondly, it can be shown that the electrostatic part of the free enthalpy, or Gibbs free energy, of an individual charged ion in a field generated by a large number of other identical point charges, cannot be determined separately, but only in conjunction with an opposite counter charge. Each charged particle must be considered jointly with its complementary countercharge, and the electrostatic potential energy determined for an ion-pair, rather than for an individual ion. In an electrical double layer (q.v.) the positive ions on the solution side, e.g., must be considered jointly with the opposite negative charges on the electrode. The electrostatic energy of each charge pair may be obtained by a charging process, as used in determining the electrostatic energy of electric condensers. Applying this principle one can derive that the electrostatic potential energy of the reacting ions and electrons in the interface depends on the potential across the double layer in the following manner

$$\Delta E = (\tfrac{1}{2}) \, Z_i \mathbf{F} (\psi - \psi_0)$$

Thus, the value $(1 - \alpha) = \tfrac{1}{2}$ is derived naturally. This result may be refined by taking into account the fine structure of the double layer, including the effect of foreign, nonreacting species to give

$$\Delta E = (\tfrac{1}{2}) \, (1 - \gamma) \, Z_i \mathbf{F} (\psi - \psi_0)$$

where γ is usually a small positive or negative fraction; hence $\alpha = (1 - \gamma)/2$. All species in reach of the field of the double layer are subject to this potential energy term. The electrostatic forces between charged particles are of much longer range than chemical short-range forces. Thus, energetics of the reaction pathway may be schematically depicted as in Fig. 2. The energetic state prior to the short-range chemical activation hump is changed due to the presence of the electrostatic forces. Only the statistically small fraction of ions in the double layer which have acquired enough energy to overcome the energy hump will react. The activation energy shown at $\Delta\psi = 0$ in Fig. 2 is not meant to imply that this is a truly chemical activation energy at an absolute electrode potential of zero. Rather, as seen from (3) it represents the term, $A + B\psi_0$, and thus does include an electric term. With this

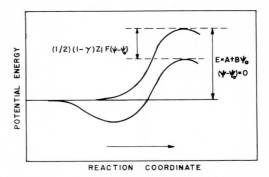

FIG. 2. Potential energy diagram for the interpretation of the transfer coefficient according to the electrostatic interaction energy model.

model, the limitation that the activation energy peak must be located symmetrically between hydrated ions in solution and discharged atoms on the surface is removed. The transfer coefficient is then explained as a natural effect of the mutual electrostatic interaction of point charges.

The values of $\alpha = \tfrac{1}{2}$ can be expected to appear for widely different reactions, since the model is no longer sensitive to the position of the activated complex along the reaction coordinate, because the energetic state all along the short-range activation process is influenced similarly by the long-range field of the double layer.

References

1. GLASSTONE, S., LEIDER, K. J., AND EYRING, H., "The Theory of Rate Processes," p. 575, New York-London, McGraw-Hill Book Company, Inc., 1941.
2. VOLMER, M., AND ERDEY-GRUZ, T., *Z. physik. Chem.*, **A159**, 165 (1931).
3. BUTLER, J. A. V., *Trans. Faraday Soc.*, **19**, 729, 734 (1924).
4. VETTER, K. J., *Z. Elektrochem.*, **59**, 596 (1955).
5. RUETSCHI, P., *J. Electrochem. Soc.*, **110**, 835 (1963).

PAUL RUETSCHI

Cross-reference: *Electrode Double Layer.*

TRANSFERENCE NUMBERS IN SOLVENTS

In contrast to the electron flow found in metallic conductors, electrical current passes through an electrolyte solution by means of a flow of ions. Cations (positive ions) move to the cathode (reducing electrode) while anions (negative ions) move to the anode (oxidizing electrode).

The fraction of the total electrical current carried by any ionic species is called the transference number or transport number of that ionic species. It can be shown that the current per sq cm carried by any ionic species under a potential gradient of one volt per cm is given by

$$I_i = .001 \mathbf{F} c_i u_i \tag{1}$$

and consequently, the total current under the same conditions is given by

$$I = .001 \mathbf{F} \sum_i c_i u_i \tag{2}$$

Here $\mathbf{F}$ is the Faraday (96,500 coulombs gm-equiv.$^{-1}$) and u_i is the mobility (velocity per unit potential gradient) of ionic species, i. The equivalent ion concentration, c_i, is equal to the molar concentration times the valence of the ion without the sign. From Eqs. 1 and 2 the transference number of the species, i, can be expressed as

$$t_i = \frac{c_i u_i}{\sum_i c_i u_i} = \frac{c_i \lambda_i}{\sum c_i \lambda_i} \tag{3}$$

since the equivalent ionic conductance, λ_i (cm^{2}gm-equiv^{-1} ohm^{-1}), is given by

$$\lambda_i = \mathbf{F} u_i \tag{4}$$

Eq. 3 illustrates the fact that the transference numbers of all ionic species present must add up to unity. It follows from Eq. 3 that the transference numbers, for any electrolyte which dissociates into only two kinds of ions, can be expressed as

$$t^+ = \lambda^+/\Lambda \qquad t^- = \lambda^-/\Lambda \tag{5}$$

where λ and Λ are, respectively, the ion and electrolyte equivalent conductances based on the electrolyte equivalent concentration, c. It can be seen that incomplete dissociation does not invalidate these relationships since $c_i = \alpha c$ and $\lambda_i = \lambda/\alpha$ and the degree of dissociation α cancels. The transference number under these conditions refers to an ionic concentration, αc, instead of c. The fact that transference numbers, in contrast to conductances, are not affected by ion association, provided no new charged species are formed in the association process, is an important property of transference numbers.

If the electrolyte can form more than two conducting species the above definition and equations are not applicable to the measured transference numbers. Such is the case for many unsymmetrical electrolytes, like $CdCl_2$ which can give a variety of charged complexes, such as $CdCl^+$ and $CdCl_3^-$, in solution. The problem is that the various methods of measurement give the transference number of the ion constituent Cd rather than that of an ionic species, such as Cd^{++}, in much the same way that a chemical analysis gives the total amount of the ion constituent Cd in the solution and not the concentration of cadmium as free Cd^{++} ion. Due to complex formation, negative transference numbers have been obtained for concentrated solutions of CdI_2.

To include all possibilities, the transference numbers of a cation constituent can be defined in a more general way as the number of gram-equivalents of that ion constituent that crosses an imaginary plane in the solution in the direction of the cathode per faraday of current passing across the plane. The choice of ion constituents is restricted to those species which cannot dissociate further under the conditions of the experiment. This somewhat neglected aspect of transference measurements has been discussed most thoroughly by Spiro.

Concentration, Temperature, and Pressure Dependence

Transference numbers are insensitive to moderate changes in temperature and pressure. Although ion mobilities are quite sensitive to temperature changes, transference numbers are a measure of relative mobilities and the temperature coefficient of mobility, to a first approximation, is about the same for most ions. The magnitude of the temperature coefficient for cation transference numbers depends to a considerable extent on the electrolyte investigated. Some typical values are +0.2 per cent per degree for LiCl, −0.04 per cent for KCl, and +0.12 per cent for HCl. No simple explanation for these differences can be given.

Cation transference numbers of NaCl and KCl in water have been found to decrease 2 to 3 per cent for a pressure increase of 1000 atmospheres. Under the same conditions t^+ for HCl increases about 0.5 per cent. The different behavior for the acid has been attributed to the proton jump mechanism in operation in acid solutions.

The change of transference numbers with concentration depends to a considerable extent on the valence of the ions involved. Empirically it has been found that all symmetrical electrolytes, such as KCl and $ZnSO_4$, have transference numbers which approach 0.5 as the concentration approaches infinite dilution. Also, the concentration dependence is proportional to the difference between the transference number and 0.5. These observations are explained by theory as shown in Eq. 9 below. For unsymmetrical electrolytes, such as $CaCl_2$, the situation is complicated by valence factors and a detailed text should be consulted.

The concentration dependence of transference numbers in dilute solution can be explained by existing theories based on the Debye-Hückel ion atmosphere model. This theory attributes the concentration dependence of mobilities to two effects, both of which decrease the mobility with increasing concentration. The electrophoretic effect takes into account the decrease in velocity of an ion due to the counterflow of solvent in the ion atmosphere. The relaxation effect results from the asymmetry produced in the ion atmosphere due to the movement of the central ion. The asymmetric atmosphere exerts a force on the ion opposing its motion under the applied field. As applied to equivalent conductances this theory gives

$$\lambda = (\lambda_0 - \lambda_e)(1 + \Delta x/x) \qquad (6)$$

where λ_e is the electrophoretic contribution to the ion conductance, $\Delta x/x$ is the fractional change in the applied field, x, due to the relaxation effect, and the subscript zero indicates infinite dilution. For symmetrical electrolytes λ_e and $\Delta x/x$ are the same for both ions. Setting $2\lambda_e = \Lambda_e$, the electrolyte equivalent conductance can be expressed as

$$\Lambda = (\Lambda_0 - \Lambda_e)(1 + \Delta x/x) \qquad (7)$$

and from Eq. 5 the cation transference number becomes

$$t^+ = (\lambda_0^+ - \lambda_e)/(\Lambda_0 - \Lambda_e) \qquad (8)$$

since the relaxation effect cancels in the ratio. Introduction of $t_0^+ \Lambda_0 = \lambda_0^+$ into Eq. 8 and rearrangement gives a general expression for the concentration dependence of transference numbers

$$t^+ = \lambda_0^+ + \frac{(t^+ - 0.5)}{\Lambda_0} \Lambda_e \qquad (9)$$

Using the hard-sphere, solvent-continuum model, Fuoss and Onsager have evaluated the electro-

phoretic effect in terms of the dielectric constant, D, the viscosity of the solvent, η, and the distance of closest approach of the ions, a. Their result for uni-univalent electrolytes is

$$\Lambda_e = \frac{\beta}{1 + \kappa a} c^{1/2} \qquad (10)$$

where

$\beta = 82.50/\eta(DT)^{1/2}$ and

$$\kappa = 50.29 \times 10^8 c^{1/2}/(DT)^{1/2}$$

Eq. 10 reduces to the limiting Onsager equation for point charges when a is reduced to zero. Eqs. 9 and 10 successfully reproduce the concentration dependence of transference numbers for aqueous, methanol, and nitromethane solutions using the same a that is required to fit conductance data. For ethanol solutions Eq. 10 appears to give too low a value for the electrophoretic effect.

This theory is applicable to dilute solutions only. The maximum concentration is about $0.03N$ for aqueous solutions and about $0.01N$ for methanol solutions. The upper limit decreases with decreasing dielectric constant and increasing ion size. No suitable theory is available for higher concentrations.

Uses

Transference data can be used in conjunction with conductance data to obtain individual ion conductances from Eq. 5 and mobilities from Eq. 4. This is one of the few measurements which permit the ion rather than electrolyte properties to be studied. It is the properties of the ions that are important for the development of a suitable hydrodynamic theory to explain the magnitude of ionic mobilities in various solvents.

Transference data can be extrapolated to infinite dilution by means of Eqs. 9 and 10 and when combined with Λ_0 give limiting ionic conductances and mobilities. Such mobilities are independent of the particular electrolyte used in the determination (Kohlrausch's law of independent ion mobilities). Consequently, transference data for only one electrolyte in any one solvent are needed to obtain the mobilities of all ions in that solvent from conductance measurements alone. Of course, transference data for more than one salt provides an essential check of the measurements and extrapolation procedures.

Transference numbers can be helpful in obtaining Λ_0 for electrolytes which are highly associated. The conductance data for $CdCl_2$ in aqueous solution are extremely difficult to extrapolate due to complex formation and hydrolysis. The extrapolation of transference data on the other hand is much simpler and the limiting value when combined with the known limiting conductance of the chloride ion gives Λ_0.

Transference measurements have been used for some time to detect complex formation. At high concentrations negative cation transference numbers can be obtained for electrolytes such as the cadmium and zinc halides. Complex formation can be detected even in dilute solution by the concentration dependence of transference numbers since it is often in the opposite direction to that predicted by Eq. 9.

The electrophoretic contribution to conductance can be determined from the concentration dependence of transference numbers for symmetrical electrolytes. Eq. 9 can be rearranged to give

$$\Lambda_e = \Lambda_0 \left[\frac{t_0{}^+ - t^+}{0.5 - t^+} \right] \qquad (11)$$

The relaxation contribution to conductance can be calculated from transference and conductance data since the combination of Eqs. 7 and 11 gives

$$1 + \frac{\Delta x}{x} = \frac{\Lambda}{\Lambda_0} \left(\frac{1 - 2t^+}{1 - 2t_0{}^+} \right) \qquad (12)$$

This method of determining the two effects separately is of considerable importance to theory. For example, the good fit of conductance data obtained with the limiting Onsager theory has been shown to be due to a cancellation of errors in the two effects.

If transference data are available, precise activity coefficients at low concentrations can be obtained from emf measurements of concentration cells, a method which requires electrodes reversible to only one ion of the electrolyte.

References

1. ROBINSON, R. A., AND STOKES, R. M., "Electrolyte Solutions," 2nd Edition, London, Butterworths, 1959.
2. KAY, R. L., AND DYE, J. L., *Proc. Natl. Acad. Sci.*, **49,** 5 (1963).
3. MACINNES, D. A., AND LONGSWORTH, L. G., *Chem. Revs.*, **11,** 171 (1932).

ROBERT L. KAY

Cross-references: *Activity and Activity Coefficient, Conductance, Conductivity, Fused Salt Transport Numbers.*

TRANSFERENCE NUMBERS: MEASUREMENT AND DATA

Measurement

The most direct method of measuring transference numbers is by the Hittorf or analytical method which can best be illustrated by an example. Two electrode compartments, each of which contains a silver electrode, are filled with $AgNO_3$ solution and connected by a tube fitted with two stopcocks so that the contents of the tube can be isolated from the electrode compartments. Due to the electrode reactions, one equivalent of Ag^+ will appear in the anode compartment and one equivalent of Ag^+ will disappear from the cathode compartment when one faraday of current has passed. At the same time, t^+ equivalents of Ag^+ will move into the cathode compartment and t^- equivalents of NO_3^- will move out due to ion migration. On the other hand, t^+ equivalents of Ag^+ will move out of the anode compartment and t^- equivalents of NO_3^- will move in due to ion migration. The net result will be a gain of t^- equivalents of $AgNO_3$ in the anode compartment, a loss of t^- equivalents of $AgNO_3$ in the cathode compartment, and no change in the connecting tube if bulk mixing has been avoided. The transference number can be calculated by measuring the change in the amount of $AgNO_3$ in either electrode compartment due to the passage of one faraday of current. Actually, the change in concentration and the weight or volume of the electrode compartments are the quantities generally measured. The measurement is valid only if the solution in the connecting tube is shown not to change concentration during the experiment, since the amount of each ion species entering this tube by migration is just balanced by an equal amount leaving by migration. A solvent correction must be made for the amount of current carried by solvent impurities.

The Hittorf method is capable of a precision of about 0.1 per cent at concentrations above $0.01N$. Better precision is not possible because the results depend on the measurement of small differences between relatively large concentrations. There is no upper limit of concentration and, in spite of the rather laborious measurements required, the Hittorf method is to be preferred at high concentration, since it is an absolute measurement requiring no significant corrections.

Most of the accurate data available at present for dilute solutions have been obtained by the moving boundary method. This method is based on the fact that a boundary, formed between solutions of two electrolytes with a common ion, remains sharp during the passage of current provided the slower ion is permitted to follow the faster ion. The solution containing the faster ion is known as the leading solution; whereas, the solution containing the slower ion is known as the following or indicator solution. To maintain density stabilization the boundary must move in a vertical direction, up if the following solution has the higher density, down if the leading solution is more dense.

Two types of cells, known as the autogenic and the sheared cell, have been employed in this method. The autogenic cell consists of a tube sealed at one end by a metal anode which is generally cadmium. The other end of the tube is connected to an electrode chamber containing an appropriate cathode. The tube through which the boundary passes is generally about 3 mm ID and of such a length that it contains about 1 ml between finely etched lines situated near the top and bottom of the tube. If the cell is filled with KCl solution and a constant current passed so that the cadmium plug is the positive electrode, a sharply boundary between KCl and $CdCl_2$ moves up the tube at a constant velocity. The mechanism in operation, which overcomes the spreading effect at the boundary due to diffusion and convection, is well understood. For a stable boundary the leading and following ions must move with the same velocity or a space charge will result. Although the mobility of Cd ion constituent is less than that of K^+, the concentration of the $CdCl_2$ solution is automatically adjusted so that the velocity of the Cd ion constituent equals that of the K^+ ion. This results in a higher potential gradient in the following solution than in the leading solution. If a Cd^{++} ion diffuses across the boundary, it enters a region of lower potential gradient and slows down until the boundary reaches it. A K^+ ion diffusing across the boundary is speeded up by the higher potential gradient in the following solution. This automatically adjusted concentration of following solution is known as the Kohlrausch concentration.

In a sheared cell the metal anode is replaced by a stopcock which leads to a second electrode chamber. One side of the cell is filled with leading solution and the other with following solution, and the boundary is formed by turning the stopcock. This type of cell is not as convenient to use as the autogenic cell since it is necessary to show that the boundary velocity is independent of the initial concentration of following solution as well as the current. At the point at which the boundary is sheared a concentration boundary forms between the Kohlrausch concentration and initial concentration of following solution. Fortunately this boundary moves very slowly, its velocity being a function of the concentration dependence of the transference number for the following ion.

If the boundary sweeps out a volume V' liters per faraday passed, then $C_L V'$ equivalents of leading ion and $C_F V'$ equivalents of following ion must pass imaginary planes in the leading solution and following solutions, respectively. Here C_F is the Kohlrausch concentration of following solution. For lesser amounts of current the transference number of the leading solution therefore is given by

$$t_L = \frac{C_L V \mathbf{F}}{IS} \qquad (1)$$

and that of the following ion by

$$t_F = \frac{C_F V \mathbf{F}}{IS} \qquad (2)$$

where I is the current in amperes and S the time in seconds and V is the volume of leading solution swept out by the boundary upon passage of IS coulombs. Combining Eqs. 1 and 2 gives the Kohlrausch regulating function in the form

$$\frac{t_L}{t_F} = \frac{C_L}{C_F} \qquad (3)$$

The volumes between the etched lines on the capillary tube are determined either directly by mercury weighing or indirectly by calibration with electrolytes whose transference numbers are known. Transference numbers determined from Eq. 1 must be corrected for solvent conductance and for the volume change that occurs at the electrode on the closed side of the cell. All moving boundary experiments must be carried out with one side of the cell closed to insure that all boundary displacement is the result of ion migration. Boundary displacement must be measured relative to the solvent to agree with the Hittorf measurement and volume changes at the closed electrode can cause movement in the solvent and therefore in the boundary.

Boundary movement can be detected by optical and by electrical methods. The optical methods require a substantial refractive index gradient across the boundary, thereby restricting the choice of following solution and limiting the lower concentration limit to approximately $0.005N$ in most cases. Recently developed electrical methods, which detect the change in potential or resistance as the boundary passes probe electrodes sealed into the tube, have reduced the lower concentration limit to $0.001N$ and even $0.0001N$ in some cases. The precision of the moving boundary method is about 0.03 per cent under favorable circumstances. The magnitude of the solvent correction often limits the lower concentration possible, while the volume correction limits the upper concentration to $0.2N$ for precise measurements.

In the indirect moving boundary method t_L and C_F are measured, permitting t_F to be calculated from Eq. 3. t_L is determined from the volume swept out by the boundary and C_F is obtained by conductance measurements on the following solution *in situ* or on samples removed from the cell. This method is of considerable importance because transference numbers for ions which can act as suitable indicators are difficult to obtain by the direct procedure. Also, if t_L is known, no measurements of time, current, or volume are necessary.

A method known as the analytical boundary method utilizes a porous glass disc to separate the leading and following solutions. The transference number, t_F, is calculated from the amount of following ion which crosses the disc for a given number of coulombs. The analysis is simplified considerably if the following ion is radioactive. Both the solvent and volume correction must be applied to this method and at concentrations below $0.01N$ surface effects in the glass disc produce erroneous results.

Two emf methods have been used to measure transference numbers. The first method consists of placing a galvanic cell, consisting of a homogeneous solution of say KI and I_2 and two platinum electrodes, in a centrifugal field and measuring the emf generated. Provided sedimentation does not change the solution concentration at the electrodes, a transference number can be calculated from the emf. The method suffers from the need for rather elaborate equipment but would be an excellent method for the study of concentrated solutions. The second emf method involves the measurement of the emf of concentration cells. If activity data are available, transference number can be obtained. In the absence of activity data, the emf of cells without liquid junctions must be measured and the transference number is obtained from the change of such emf's with the emf of the corresponding concentration cell. The interpretation of the emf data can be difficult and, in any case, the method is generally not applicable to nonaqueous solvents due to the lack of reversible electrodes.

Data

There is a general lack of precise transference data, particularly for dilute solutions. Very few measurements have been made at concentrations below $0.01N$ even in aqueous solution. Due to the new electrical methods of detecting moving boundaries, precise transference data are now available at concentrations as low as $0.001N$ for ethanol and nitromethane solutions. The only other precise data available for nonaqueous solvents are those for the alkali halides in methanol-water mixtures and for HCl in dioxane-water mixtures. Some of the available limiting transference numbers for aqueous and nonaqueous solvents and mixtures at 25°C are given below.

Electrolyte	Solvent	t_0^+
HCl	H_2O	0.8209
LiCl	H_2O	.3364
NaCl	H_2O	.3964
KCl	H_2O	.4905
KBr	H_2O	.4849
KI	H_2O	.4887
$CaCl_2$	H_2O	.4380
$LaCl_3$	H_2O	.477
Na_2SO_4	H_2O	.386
$ZnSO_4$	H_2O	.398
NaCl }	50 mole % (-)	.4437
KCl }	methanol-water	.5068
NaCl	methanol	.4633
KCl	methanol	.5001
LiCl	ethanol	.5607
NaCl	ethanol	.5187
HCl	82% dioxane-water	.670

References

1. Spiro, M., "Techniques of Organic Chemistry," Vol. 1, Part IV, 3rd Edition, Weisbserger, Editor, New York, Interscience Publishers, 1960.
2. MacInnes, D. A., and Longsworth, L. G., *Chem. Revs.*, **11**, 171 (1932).
3. Harned, H. S., and Owen, B. B., "The Physical Chemistry of Electrolytic Solutions," 3rd ed., New York, Reinhold Publishing Corp., 1958.

Robert L. Kay

TRANSPORT NUMBERS IN FUSED SALTS. See FUSED SALT TRANSPORT NUMBERS.

U

UDY, MARVIN J. (1892–1959)

Marvin J. Udy, known for his work in electrometallurgy and electrodeposition, was born in Farmington, Utah on February 19, 1892, the son of Mathias C. and Emily Rebecca (Hess). He received the B.S. in chemical engineering in 1915 and the M.S. in metallurgy in 1916 from the University of Utah.

From 1916 to 1918 Udy was assistant research chemist at the United States Mining, Smelting, and Refining Company at Midvale, Utah. With J. F. Cullen he patented a process for treating bismuth-carrying lead ores. In 1918, as a chemist for the Hooker Electrochemical Company at Niagara Falls, New York, he worked on the use of chlorine in the metallurgy of nonferrous ores. With O. C. Ralston he patented a process for the separation of nickel and cobalt, using chlorine and calcium carbonate.

From November, 1918, to November, 1919, Udy was chief chemist at the Haynes Stellite Company in Kokomo, Indiana. His work on the treatment of cobalt ores from Idaho resulted in a patent for recovery of cobalt by electrodeposition which is essentially the same process now being used in the Congo. While at Haynes Stellite Company, Udy patented a process for cadmium plating which became the basis of the Udylite Company, now of Detroit, Michigan. He was manager of the Haynes cobalt mine at Leesburg, Idaho from November, 1919 to November, 1920.

From November, 1920 to July 1931, he was a research and development engineer for Union Carbide and Carbon Research Laboratories and the Electrometallurgical Company of Niagara Falls, New York. He developed methods for treating cobalt ores and African vanadate ores and also made a complete investigation of the electrodeposition of chromium. He spent seven years in the commercialization of the chromium plating process he developed in this study.

From 1931 to 1934, Udy was research and development engineer for the Swann Chemical Company (now Monsanto) at Anniston, Alabama. He worked on chlorinated diphenyls and on improving electric furnace production of phosphorus, calcium carbide, and alumina for abrasives. He was among the first to use sintered burden in producing phosphorus.

From 1934 to 1937, Udy was a research and development engineer for Oldbury Electrochemical Company in Niagara Falls, New York, where he studied phosphorus production and supervised the operation of the first three-phase electric furnace used for this operation.

In 1937 a process for treating low-grade chromium ores developed by Udy led to the formation by Leo H. Timmins and associates of a company, the Chromium Mining and Smelting Corporation, to manufacture exothermic ferroalloys. Udy stayed with this company as vice president of research until 1941.

From 1941 through 1955 Udy served as a consultant for many companies including New Jersey Zinc, Quebec Iron and Titanium, Vanadium Corporation of America, Fabrica Nacional De Carburo Y Metallurgie (Chile), Bradley Mining, Carborundum, Midwest Carbide, Pittsburgh Lectromelt Furnace, Eldorado Mining and Refining, Pacific Carbide and Alloys, Ebasco Engineering Services, Tennessee Products, American Chrome, Mallinckrodt Chemical, Keokuk Electrometals, Battelle Memorial Institute, U.S. Bureau of Mines, and Bonneville Power Authority.

In 1952 Udy formed a partnership with R. O. Denman for continued development of electric furnace smelting of iron, chromium, manganese, and other ores. The processes involved prereduction treatment to reduce power requirements, and with off-grade ores, selective reduction, and multiple stages so that standard grades of products could be produced.

In September 1955, Udy and Denman sold to

Strategic Materials Corporation all rights to the processes. The sale involved Udy's services as research director for Strategic Materials Corporation and as vice president of the two subsidiary research and development companies set up to further develop and exploit Udy's processes and ideas. These companies, Strategic-Udy Processes, Inc., and Strategic-Udy Metallurgy, Ltd., are located in Niagara Falls, New York, and Niagara Falls, Ontario, respectively. Udy was active with these companies until his death April 11, 1959.

He was the author of numerous technical papers, editor of Vol. I and II of the book, "Chromium," and holder of over 100 patents. He was an active member in many technical and professional societies and was national president of The Electrochemical Society in 1954–55.

His honors include Tau Beta Pi in 1935 and the Schoellkopf Medal of the American Chemical Society in 1948. In 1956 he was granted a Doctor of Science degree from Alfred University.

Udy was not only a brilliant scientist, but was active in sports. His specialties were basketball and baseball. As a baseball pitcher, he refused the opportunity to become a professional in the farm system of one of the major league teams. Udy was also active in church affairs. At the time of his death, he had served several years as president of the Niagara Falls Branch of the Church of Jesus Christ of Latter-day Saints.

Udy was married in 1915 to Tessa McMurray. They were the parents of three sons: Murray C., Lynn S., who died in maturity, and Kay N. who died as an infant.

MURRAY C. UDY

ULTRAVIOLET LAMPS

Conversion of electrical energy into radiation and observations of the accompanying chemical reactions due to ultraviolet radiation have been of interest to the electrochemist for more than 60 years.[6] Within the past 30 years, about 75 new types of ultraviolet lamps have been developed and placed on the market.[4] These lamps vary in size, wattage, and emitted spectrum. The lamps have been designed for specific applications, for example, photochemical reactions, suntanning and vitamin D production, generation of light, and for bactericidal effect or ozone production.

Most of the commercially available ultraviolet lamps contain mercury vapor. The passage of current through the vapor results in exciting the mercury atoms to various energy states. In making transitions from one state to another, the atoms emit radiation of definite wavelengths. The emission of radiation in different regions depends on the pressure of the mercury vapor, the amount and type of other gases, and the electrical conditions in the discharge.

At very low mercury vapor pressures, e.g., 10 microns, most of the emitted radiation is the result of a transition from the excited state at 4.88 ev to the ground state. This is known as resonance radiation. In a low-pressure mercury discharge over 85 per cent of the radiation emitted is at 2537 Å; see Table 1. The amount of 1849 Å radiation is dependent on the transmission of the envelope. Most bactericidal lamps are made of glasses that transmit less than 0.1 to 2.0 per cent of the energy generated at 1849 Å wavelength. The so-called "cold quartz" lamps emit 50 to 90 per cent of the 1849 Å radiation depending on the quality of the quartz.

Two types of low-pressure mercury lamps are manufactured, the hot-cathode and the cold-cathode type. In the former, a localized hot spot is produced by ion bombardment to supply the electrons necessary for the discharge. The lamps operate at low voltage, at high current, and with a low cathode drop. The electron emission from the cold cathode is supplied by an ion

TABLE 1. RELATIVE INTENSITIES OF WAVE LENGTHS EMITTED BY LOW-PRESSURE MERCURY DISCHARGE LAMP

New Length, Å	Relative Energy
1849	5.0 (approximate)
1942	nil
2054	nil
2260	nil
2537	100.0
2652	0.14
2753	0.05
2893	0.07
2967	0.37
3022	0.17
3126–3132	1.43
3650–3663	1.30
3906–4077	1.60
4339–4358	3.40
5461	2.25
5770–5791	0.60

TABLE 2. RELATIVE SPECTRAL ENERGY DISTRIBUTION OF A QUARTZ HIGH-PRESSURE MERCURY VAPOR DISCHARGE LAMP

TABLE 2. RELATIVE SPECTRAL ENERGY DISTRIBUTION OF A QUARTZ HIGH-PRESSURE MERCURY VAPOR DISCHARGE LAMP

Wave Length, Å	Relative Energy
6234	4.9
5700	88.5
5400	63.0
4960–4358	57.2
4045–3906	48.5
3660	100.0
3351	11.1
3130	68.7
3025	34.3
2967	14.2
2925–2893–2803	12.8
2752–2700	8.0
2652	24.0
2571	9.7
2537	25.6
2482–2400–2360–2300	24.0
1942–1849	6.2

bombardment of a large metal surface. These lamps require high voltage and operate at low current and have a high cathode drop.

There are many types of high-pressure mercury lamps. Some operate at a fraction of an atmosphere of mercury vapor pressure while others may operate at over a hundred atmospheres pressure. At low pressure the characteristic mercury lines predominate. At higher pressures the lines broaden and a continuous background radiation appears. In typical quartz lamps the amount of energy below 3800 Å is approximately 30 to 50 per cent greater than the visible energy radiated, depending on the mercury pressure; see Table 2.

Two fluorescent-type ultraviolet lamps are used in medicine and industry. The fluorescent sunlamp is a low-pressure mercury vapor lamp with a special ultraviolet transmitting glass envelope. The glass is coated internally with a calcium zinc phosphate:Tl phosphor which has its peak emission at 3220 Å. (See entry on **Phosphors.**) A low-pressure mercury discharge in regular lime glass coated with a barium silicate:Pb phosphor produces the "blacklight" fluorescent lamp. The peak emission of this phosphor is at 3500 Å.

Applications

The low-pressure mercury discharge lamps are used extensively to destroy air-borne and surface bacteria, viruses, yeasts, and molds. Since about 90 per cent of the ultraviolet energy from these lamps is radiated in the 2537 Å line, which is near the peak of the maximum bactericidal activity, at 2650 Å, these lamps are ideal generators for this purpose. The amount of 2537 Å energy necessary to destroy various bacteria, yeasts, and mold is shown in Table 3.

Hart and Nicks[3] have shown that postoperative infections could be reduced by 85 per cent by the use of direct radiation in the operating room. The intensity of radiation at the operating site is of the order of 20 to 24 microwatts/sq cm. Indirect bactericidal radiation is used in school rooms and nurseries. The ultraviolet lamps are mounted on the walls in parabolic reflectors to produce a high intensity of radiation in the upper portion of the room. Various tests have shown that such installations can reduce the incidence of respiratory diseases by 15 to 50 per cent depending on the intensity of radiation. Both direct and indirect bactericidal radiation is used in hospitals to control *Staphylococcus aureus* and *Mycobacterium tuberculosis* organisms in the air. In air conditioning ducts high-intensity lamps can destroy from 90 to 99 per cent of the air-borne organisms. The amount of 2537 Å energy necessary for such an application would be determined by the velocity of air, size of duct, and reflectivity of the duct walls.

Bactericidal lamps are used extensively in industry. In the preparation of biotics and serums bactericidal lamps are used to destroy air-borne organisms to prevent contamination of the products. In the preservation and tenderization of meat ultraviolet lamps are used to destroy mold and bacteria growth on the surface of the meat. In these latter applications the ultraviolet lamps are made from a special glass to permit a controlled amount of 1849 Å radiation to be emitted. This radiation dissociates oxygen in air resulting in the formation of pure ozone. Ozone will also oxidize organic vapors and is sometimes used to oxidize odors in air ducts.[1]

Most liquids, except water, are opaque to 2537 Å radiation. In the preparation of many vaccines and in the irradiation of blood plasma, the solutions are exposed in very thin layers to inactivate viruses or bacteria. Under proper conditions large volumes of water can be sterilized or made potable by the use of bactericidal lamps. The coefficient of absorption of water ranges from 0.08 to 0.25/cm depending on the amount of organic matter or iron salts in the

TABLE 3. INCIDENT ENERGIES AT 2537Å RADIATION NECESSARY TO INHIBIT COLONY FORMATION IN 90 PER CENT OF THE ORGANISMS AND FOR COMPLETE DESTRUCTION

Organism	Energy (Microwatt-sec/sq cm)	
	90%	100%
Bacillus anthracis	4520	8700
S. enteritidis	4000	7600
B. Metatherium sp. (veg.)	1300	2500
B. Megatherium sp. (spores)	2730	5200
B. paratyphosus	3200	6100
B. subtilis	5800	11000
B. subtilis spores	11600	22000
Corynebacterium diphtheriae	3370	6500
Eberthella typosa	2140	4100
Escherichia coli	3000	6600
Micrococcus candidus	6050	12300
Micrococcus sphaeroides	10000	15400
Neisseria catarrhalis	4400	8500
Phytomonas tumefaciens	4400	8500
Proteus vulgaris	3000	6600
Pseudomonas aeruginosa	5500	10500
Pseudomonas fluorescens	3500	6600
S. typhimurium	8000	15200
Sarcina lutea	19700	26400
Seratia marcescens	2420	6160
Dysentery bacilli	2200	4200
Shigella paradysenteriae	1680	3400
Spirillum rubrum	4400	6160
Staphylococcus albus	1840	5720
Staphylococcus aureus	2600	6600
Streptococcus hemolyticus	2160	5500
Streptococcus lactis	6150	8800
Streptococcus viridans	2000	3800
Yeast		
Saccharomyces ellipsoideus	6000	13200
Saccharomyces sp.	8000	17600
Saccharomyces cerevisiae	6000	13200
Brewers' yeast	3300	6600
Bakers' yeast	3900	8800
Common yeast cake	6000	13200
Mold Spores	*Color*		
Penicillium roqueforti	Green	13000	26400
Penicillium expansum	Olive	13000	22000
Penicillium digitatum	Olive	44000	88000
Aspergillus glaucus	Bluish green	44000	88000
Aspergillus flavus	Yellowish green	60000	99000
Aspergillus niger	Black	132000	330000

TABLE 3.—*Continued.*

Organism		Energy (Microwats-sec/sq cm)	
		90%	100%
Rhisopus nigricans	Black	111000	220000
Mucor racemosus A	White gray	17000	35200
Mucor racemosus B	White gray	17000	35200
Oospora laetis	White	5000	11000

water. Generally, the ultraviolet lamps are enclosed in quartz tubes to protect them from the cold water. The quartz tubes are placed into a larger pipe which is the irradiation chamber. Approximately 100 gallons per hour of potable water can be produced by one watt of 2537 Å radiation.

A number of investigators have reported that quartz ultraviolet lamps will ionize air. Even the shortest radiation, 1849 Å, from such lamps does not have sufficient energy to ionize oxygen or nitrogen. However, copious amounts of electrons are released by the radiation from bactericidal lamps from metals or dirt particles near the lamp. (See entry on **Air Ion Generation.**) These electrons attach themselves to oxygen, water vapor or dirt particles, resulting in negatively ionized air. There may be as few as a hundred or as many as a million ions/cc near a bactericidal lamp depending on the photoemissive metal near the lamp and the amount of ultraviolet radiation emitted.

For the past 60 years there have been many investigators that have reported on the physiological action of air ions. Kornblueh[5] has summarized the world literature. The conclusions are that negative air ions relieve certain forms of asthma, hayfever, bronchitis, emphysema and other types of respiratory ailments. Negative air ions have been shown to relieve pain and hasten the healing of burn wounds. Positive air ions have been shown to produce such minor discomforts as headache, dry throat, and closing of nasal passages. Introduction of simple methods of generation of air ions and accurate methods of measurement of ions have greatly expanded interest in this field.

The medium- and high-pressure mercury lamps are for the most part used for lighting purposes. However, since these lamps are rich in radiation from 1849 to 4000 Å, they are applicable for many photochemical reactions. Ellis and Wells[2] and Noyes and Leighton[7] have summarized various photohalogenization, photoxidation, photopolymerization, and photodecomposition reactions.

The spectral region between 3200 and 4000 Å, generally called "blacklight," has been used for identification of skin diseases, minerals, adulterants, viruses, and end-points in chemical reactions.[8] The spectral region between 2800 and 3200 Å is used in the production of vitamin D, and it will cause a "sunburn" and tanning of the skin. The so-called therapeutic lamps emit radiation from 1849 Å to the infrared region. An understanding of the radiation emitted by various mercury lamps and the effect of this radiation on matter will enable the electrochemist to select the lamp best suited for use in industry, the laboratory or in medicine.

References

1. A.C.S. Advances in Chemistry Series No. 21, "Ozone Chemistry and Technology," p. 57, Washington 6, D.C., American Chemical Society, 1959.
2. ELLIS, C., AND WELLS, A. A., "Chemical Action of Ultraviolet Rays," Chap. 12 to 33, New York, Reinhold Publishing Corp., 1941.
3. HART, D., AND NICKS, J., *Arch. Surgery*, **82**, 449 (1961).
4. "IES Lighting Handbook," Third Edition, p. 8-108 to 8-110, New York, Illuminating Enigneering Society, 1959.
5. KORNBLUEH, I. H., *Arch. Med. Hydrology*, **21**, 1 (1961).
6. NAGY, R., *J. Electrochem. Soc.*, **99**, 81C (1952).
7. NOYES, W. A., JR., AND LEIGHTON, P. A., "The Photochemistry of Gases," Chap. 5 to 7, New York, Reinhold Publishing Corp., 1941.
8. RADELY, J. A., AND GRANT, J., "Fluorescence Analysis in Ultraviolet Light," London, Chapman and Hall, Ltd., 1954.

RUDOLPH NAGY

Cross-references: *Air Ion Generation; Ozone; Phosphors.*

V

VACUUM ARC MELTING. *See* FURNACES, IN-ERT ATMOSPHERE AND VACUUM ARC; VACUUM ARC PROPERTIES.

VACUUM ARC PROPERTIES

This article will describe the metallurgical vacuum arc and its relation to other electrical discharge phenomena.

The term "vacuum arc" may seem self-contradictory, since an electric arc is obviously a material phenomenon while "vacuum" means the absence of matter. The inability of arcs to exist in vacuum is exemplified by the operation of the vacuum circuit breaker, which takes advantage of the high dielectric strength of vacua of the order of 10^{-5} Torr ($= 10^{-5}$ mm Hg). (See **Dielectric Properties of Vacuum.**) There is also the familiar electron beam used in electronic and x-ray tubes and in metallurgical vacuum furnaces. (See **Electron Beam Melting.**) Here, potentials of tens of kilovolts are maintained without difficulty if the pressure remains below about 10^{-4} Torr.

It is also true, however, that one can readily initiate and maintain a stable arc between gas-free metal electrodes in an evacuated space. This is the phenomenon of the vacuum arc. A requirement is that the arc power be sufficient to vaporize some of the electrode material, which is necessary to sustain the arc. Since the vapor is condensible and would not be sensed by vacuum gauges, the arc *appears* to exist in vacuum.

Vacuum arc formation could occur in vacuum circuit breakers if the arc power were high enough for electrode vaporization at the instant of contact separation. The arc can also form in high-current electron-beam devices if the pressure exceeds about 10^{-4} Torr. Such *breakdown* is an integral part of electrical discharge phenomenology, a brief summary of which follows.

Electron Beams, Breakdown, Glow Discharges and Arcs*

An apparatus for studying electrical breakdown and related phenomena is sketched in Fig. 1. An enclosure for vacuum or gas at any pressure contains an anode ($+$), a cathode ($-$), and a cathode heater. (Unless otherwise specified, the spacing between anode and cathode is of the order of 1 cm.) A d-c source with the open-circuit potential, E, is connected to the electrodes through a resistance, R. With the space evacuated and the cathode cold, no current will flow unless E is high enough (around 10^6 volts) for field emission. Usually E is not this high, and the vacuum is an insulator with the cold cathode.

If the cathode is heated in vacuum, an electron beam is initiated due to thermionic emission of electrons from the cathode and their acceleration to the anode by the potential, V. The current, I, is a sensitive function of the cathode temperature. The potential drop, V, between anode and cathode is related to the other circuit parameters by

$$V = E - IR \qquad (1)$$

If gas at low pressure is permitted to enter the enclosure while the electron beam is operative, breakdown to form either a glow discharge or an arc will occur if V is sufficiently high. V then drops to the voltage characteristic of the discharge formed, while I increases to satisfy Eq. 1. The conditions and consequences of electrical breakdown are diagrammed in Figs. 2 and 3, which represent two projections of a three-dimensional plot of V against I and pres-

* For an exhaustive, quantitative treatment of breakdown, glow discharges, and arcs in various gases, see Vol. 22 of "Encyclopedia of Physics" ("Handbuch der Physik"), S. Flügge, Editor, Berlin, Springer-Verlag, 1956. A more recent review of electrical breakdown is in Ref. (2).

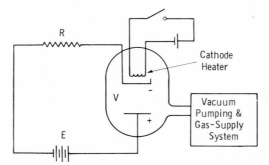

FIG. 1. Schematic diagram of apparatus for studying electron beams, breakdown, glow discharges, and arcs in gases at various pressures.

sure, the latter two quantities on logarithmic scales. Curves A, B, and C in Fig. 2 are plots of V against I (at constant E and R) satisfying Eq. 1. These curves are determined by only the E and R values of the various power supplies.

The remaining curve in Fig. 2 is not related to any power supply but represents the characteristic voltages of the different electrical discharges obtainable in a particular gas at a particular pressure and with a particular electrode configuration.[1] (The curve shown is for neon at 1 Torr and with 50 cm electrode separation. A similar curve for air is obtained at 1 Torr and about 3 cm electrode separation.) The terms "Glow Discharge" and "Arc" in Fig. 2 indicate the mutually exclusive ranges of both current and voltage at which these two discharge forms occur. The glow discharge is characterized by a potential drop of several hundred volts and currents below 1 ampere, while the arc is characterized by much higher currents and lower voltages.

With a given power supply, the type of discharge that will be obtained, as well as its current and voltage, are indicated by an "operating point" defined by the intersection of the power supply characteristic curve and the discharge curve. For Curve A in Fig. 2, a glow discharge of 320 volts and 9 milliamperes is obtained with a power supply having $E = 1000$ volts and $R = 75,000$ ohms.

Curve C is for a power supply having $E = 1000$ volts and $R = 10$ ohms. Such a supply might be used for powering an electron beam at 800 volts and 20 amperes. On breakdown accompanying a gas pressure increase, an arc rather than a glow discharge would form due to the high current available.

The maximum discharge power obtainable

from a power supply of the type diagrammed in Fig. 1 occurs where V is one-half of E. Vacuum metallurgical arcs usually have voltages between 20 and 40, and a suitable open-circuit voltage is 75. Curve B (Fig. 2) represents such a power supply having $R = 0.038$ ohm. Since E is below the glow-discharge voltage, the arc is the only discharge that can form. Of the two intersections with the discharge curve, only that at the higher current is a stable operating point; this is at 25 volts, 1300 amperes.

Both the glow discharge and the arc (as distinct from the electron beam) are said to be self-sustaining because they can persist without auxiliary heating of the cathode. If the cathode heater is "off" and evacuation of the enclosure

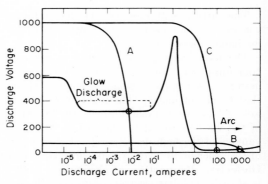

FIG. 2. Types and characteristics of discharges obtained with different power supplies. (Operating points are indicated by intersections ($\oplus$) of the respective curves.)

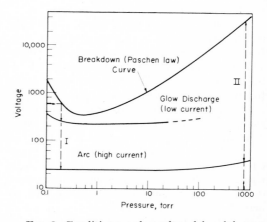

FIG. 3. Conditions and results of breakdown. (Schematic for 1 cm electrode spacing in air.)
I. Breakdown on increasing pressure from vacuum.
II. Arc breakdown at atmospheric pressure.

is commenced while a glow discharge is operative, the discharge will eventually be extinguished and V will become equal to E as the current drops to zero. If the cathode is heated during pressure reduction, however, an electron beam will eventually replace the glow discharge.

The thermal power of the arc is much greater than that of the glow discharge due to its much higher current. If the arc power is sufficient for electrode vaporization, the container may be vacuum-pumped for an indefinite period without arc extinction, since the arc would be sustained by vapor from the electrodes.

With unheated electrodes in an evacuated space and zero current (or $V = E$), a gradual increase in gas pressure will result in breakdown at a pressure-voltage combination given by Paschen's law (q.v.). This is diagrammed in Fig. 3, where Path I is for an initial potential drop, V (or E), of 600 volts. As the pressure increases until Path I touches the Paschen law curve (at about 0.2 Torr), breakdown to form either a glow discharge at about 300 volts or an arc at 25 volts, depending on the value of R, will occur. The same discharge voltage levels are seen in Fig. 2. The 600-volt plateau at the far left represents the Paschen-law breakdown potential at initial currents below 10^{-5} ampere. Raising the potential drop between the unheated electrodes to this plateau results in breakdown. V then decreases to the value characteristic of the discharge formed, while the current increases to satisfy Eq. 1. With unheated electrodes, then, V can never exceed the low-current plateau voltage of the discharge curve at the pressure where this curve applies. With varying pressure, the maximum possible value of V is given by the Paschen-law curve. (Figure 3 shows this curve for air.)

If the cathode is heated, the highest attainable value of V at a given gas pressure is lower than that for the unheated cathode, being given by, for example, the voltage values on the discharge curve at the right of the low-current plateau in Fig. 2. For a heated cathode that may be emitting an electron beam at a current between 10^{-4} and 10^{-1} ampere, the maximum attainable value of V (at the pressure of Fig. 2) is given by the "Glow Discharge" voltage. With any given gas pressure and electrode configuration, the permissible conditions for either zero current or maintenance of an electron beam are confined to the region *below* the applicable discharge curve. With varying pressure the allowed operating points are below the Paschen-law curve, and are either upon or below the respective discharge contour curves (representing different current ranges) as illustrated in Fig. 3.

Path II in Fig. 3 represents high-voltage arc breakdown at atmospheric pressure. Such breakdown is commonly used for arc initiation without the necessity of physical contact between the electrodes.

As the pressure decreases below 1 atm, the Paschen-law or breakdown voltage passes through a minimum. For air (Fig. 3) the minimum breakdown potential is 330 volts; this is obtained at 0.5 Torr with an electrode spacing of 1 cm.

The abscissa of the Paschen-law curve is actually the pressure multiplied by the electrode spacing. The minimum breakdown potential of 330 volts in air would also occur, for example, at a pressure of 0.005 Torr and an electrode spacing of 100 cm. At the left of the Paschen-curve minimum, the breakdown potential decreases as either the pressure *or* the electrode spacing increases. The effective electrode spacing is then not only the narrowest gap between the oppositely polarized members, but it may be any possible distance between exposed areas on the respective conductors. As the pressure is decreased, there is a tendency for the breakdown potential to remain constant at the minimum value while the regions on the respective conductors where breakdown and discharge formation occur move away from each other.[2] Attempts to use high-voltage breakdown for arc initiation in vacuum would be expected, therefore, to result in the arc terminals' being formed at locations well removed from the intended arc gap. Fortunately, the use of breakdown for vacuum arc initiation is unnecessary, since the vacuum arc may be readily initiated by momentary electrode contact.

Vacuum Arcs of Metals with Melting Points between 1000 and 2000°C

Since the vacuum arc is primarily a metal vapor phenomenon, its characteristics depend mainly on the properties of the electrode materials. A prominent variation in arc properties occurs with increasing melting point of the cathodic electrode, probably due to the increasing ease of thermionic emission. Thus, vacuum arcs with tungsten, tantalum, and molybdenum electrodes are different from those with zirconium, titanium, and steels. The remarks in this section are based mainly on observations of iron-electrode arcs; quite similar arc behavior has been noted with other metals having melting points between 1000 and 2000°C.

The appearance of the vacuum arc is strikingly different from that of an atmospheric-pressure arc.[3] The highly luminous core of the latter is not seen in the vacuum arc; this is true also of the small, intensely heated anode spot and its luminous vapor plume or *anode flame*. The vacuum arc plasma is diffuse and relatively dark. The anode terminal is spread over an area as large as several square inches, which is heated uniformly. The most luminous parts of the vacuum arc are the "cathode spots," the number of which is proportional to the arc current at about 50 to 100 amperes per spot. These small, bright spots move slowly over molten metal, while on unheated metal they tend to move rapidly away from the main arc plasma.[4] The tracks left by the cathode spots on the electrode surface are often brighter than the parent metal surface, indicating that the cathode spots have a scavenging or cleansing effect with respect to cathode surface impurities.

The role of permanent gases in the operation of the vacuum arc is of considerable interest. In the vacuum circuit breaker, where arcing is intolerable, the maximum allowed gas content of the contact members is 0.1 ppm, and the maximum tolerable pressure is 5×10^{-5} Torr.[5] These limits suggest that a small amount of permanent gas is at least helpful in aiding arc initiation. Since the vapor pressures of molten metals are usually above 10^{-3} Torr, it seems clear that no permanent gas need be present after the arc is established.

The predominant use of the vacuum arc is in the consumable-electrode melting of numerous metals and alloys. (See **Furnaces, Inert Atmosphere and Vacuum Arc.**) A primary function of this process is the elimination of gaseous impurities. The arc is maintained between the lower end of a consumable electrode and a melt supported on a continuously freezing ingot. The usually preferred arrangement is to use a d-c arc with the consumable electrode negative. The arc melting and refreezing of the metal to form the ingot are performed in a crucible that is conventionally of water-cooled copper with its upper end continuously vacuum pumped. Thus, the metallurgical vacuum arc is sustained in most cases by a mixture of metal vapor and permanent gases.

The degree of metal degassing achievable during vacuum arc melting is related inversely to the total pressure of permanent gases over the melt surface. Novel probe techniques for measuring this pressure have been described for arcs with titanium,[6] molybdenum,[7] and steels.[8, 9] With the latter two materials the measured pressures are surprisingly high, being up to 20 Torr, while the pressures at the *top* of the crucible are only $\frac{1}{1000}$ as high. Since such pressure differences are not consistent with gas flow theory, their explanation must be sought elsewhere. T. E. Browne has kindly suggested[10] that the high pressure in the arc region may be due to *magnetic bottling* of the plasma gases due to the magnetic field of the arc current, which converges between anode and cathode. This theory is consistent with the additional observation that the gas pressure over the melt decreases by an order of magnitude or more as the arc length is increased[9] (because the current convergence decreases as the arc length increases). A prediction based on this view is that the maximum possible degree of metal degassing during vacuum arc melting should be obtained by minimizing or even eliminating, if possible, the arc current convergence.

Under certain conditions the consumable-electrode arc exhibits *positional instability*, where the arc terminals leave their intended positions and migrate upward within the annulus between the electrode and the crucible wall. This phenomenon has been studied in a "vacuum arc study chamber"[11] having open geometry. With a sandblasted, 2-inch-diameter iron cathode and 1600 amperes arc current, the degree of positional instability was at a maximum at a gas pressure of about 0.5 Torr.[3] The greatest assurance of freedom from positional instability is gained by using the lowest possible pressures or highest vacuum-pumping speeds, the smallest practicable arc length and the highest feasible arc current. At pressures below 0.02 Torr, the arc was positionally stable until the current was reduced (in steps) to about 600 amperes, below which the arc was positionally unstable continuously.[4]

Arc positional instability has been seen with many electrode materials. It is not an inherent property of the vacuum arc itself as much as it is attributable to gas-forming impurities on the cathode surface, being intimately related to the mobility and impurity-scavenging action of the cathode spots. An iron cathodic electrode having a freshly machined surface would not support a positionally unstable arc in vacuum; instead, all attempts to reduce the arc current to 600 amperes resulted in arc extinction.[4] With an unclean-surfaced (e.g., sandblasted) cathode, the onset of positional instability was often accompanied by a gas pressure burst—another indication that the arc cathode terminal vigorously scavenges and decomposes surface impurities. Allowing a positionally unstable arc to burn for 74 seconds resulted in migration of the cathode spots to a height of 2 feet on the electrode, the entire surface of which was thoroughly cleaned.[4]

Arcs with Refractory Metal Cathodes

With increasing cathode melting point the arc heat distribution tends to shift away from the cathode and toward the anode. This effect has been observed both at atmospheric[3] and lower pressures. Extreme arc heat unbalance occurs with tungsten, such that the cathode will often remain unmelted at arc power levels sufficient to overheat and to damage severely the crucible and its molten contents.[12] Under certain conditions, however, a tungsten cathode may be readily arc melted. For example, Noesen[12] found that a tungsten cathode which would not melt at all in a 2.25-inch-diameter crucible was rapidly melted at the same arc power level in a 3.75-inch-diameter crucible. This observation and those of Butler and Morgan[13] suggest that there may be a critical pressure above which the tungsten cathode cannot be arc melted.

The paper by Butler and Morgan[13] is a comprehensive, quantitative description of d-c vacuum arcs with consumable cathodic electrodes of tungsten, tantalum, and columbium. "Open-arc" rather than deep-crucible geometry was employed with high-vacuum pumping at pressures down to 10^{-6} Torr. Both tungsten and tantalum exhibit broad operating arc current ranges between the 3500 to 4500 amperes required for arc ignition and the 1200 to 2000 amperes needed for maintenance of a stable arc. Rapid cathode melting occurs at the highest currents of these ranges. With decreasing current, the melting rate goes to zero at a current that is still well above that required for arc stability. This fact affords precise control of the rate of molten metal addition to the bath. By melting slowly and allowing sufficient time for thorough degassing of the melt and maintenance of a high vacuum, Butler and Morgan have achieved refinement of both tungsten and tantalum comparable to that obtained in electron beam melting (q.v.).

With columbium, whose melting point (2468°C) is below those of tungsten (3410°C) and tantalum (2996°C), the cathode melting rate is still appreciable (rather than zero) at the minimum current required for arc stability. Consequently, the degree of purification achieved is less than that with tungsten and tantalum.

Summary

Cathodic electrodes of the very highest-melting-point metals can be arc melted at any desired rate in a suitably designed furnace equipped with high-vacuum pumping. Metal refinement comparable to the best achieved in other vacuum melting processes is then possible. With lower-melting-point metals, the minimum arc current required for arc stability may give rise to an appreciable melting rate, and thorough degassing may not be possible.

In vacuum arc furnaces having deep crucibles, the maximum possible degree of metal refinement is often limited by a surprisingly high gas pressure over the molten metal. Through suitable changes of the furnace design, this pressure may be reduced appreciably. Substantially improved metal refinement is then possible, not only because of the improved furnace geometry but also because of the feasibility of using lower arc currents and melting rates without difficulties due to arc positional instability.

The formation of positionally unstable arcs on current reduction in vacuum may be avoided with iron and steel, at least, by thoroughly cleaning the cathodic electrode surface prior to arcing. A minimum arc current between 500 and 1000 amperes is still necessary, however, to prevent arc extinction. The vapor pressure of the molten metal is then sufficient to sustain the arc in the complete absence of any permanent gas.

References

1. JOHNSON, E. W., "Arc Phenomena, Basic and Applied" in "Vacuum Metallurgy," R. F. Bunshah, Editor, Chapter 6, pp. 101–120, New York, Reinhold Publishing Corp., 1958.
2. DAKIN, T. W., AND BERG, D., "Theory of Gas Breakdown" in "Progress in Dielectrics—4," pp. 153–198, London, Heywood and Company, Ltd., 1962.
3. JOHNSON, E. W., HAHN, G. T., AND ITOH, R., "Characteristics of Consumable Electrode D. C. Arcs in Argon, Helium and Vacuum" in "Arcs in Inert Atmospheres and Vacuum,"

W. E. Kuhn, Editor, pp. 19–40, New York, John Wiley and Sons, 1956; see also Ref. (1), p. 114.

4. JOHNSON, E. W., AND ITOH, R., "Positional Instability Behavior of Low-Pressure D. C. Arcs," to be published in *Electrochemical Technology* (1964).

5. COBINE, J. D., Lecture on "Vacuum Switches" at Carnegie Institute of Technology, Oct. 25, 1962.

6. GRUBER, H., "Survey of European Arc Melting" in "Vacuum Metallurgy," R. F. Bunshah, Editor, Chapter 8, pp. 145–147, New York, Reinhold Publishing Corp., 1958.

7. Noesen, S. J., "The Removal of Gaseous Impurities by Vacuum Arc Melting" in "Transactions of the Fourth National Symposium of the Committee on Vacuum Techniques," (Boston Symposium, 1957).

8. SUITER, J. W., "Pressure Distribution within a Vacuum Arc Furnace," *J. Electrochem. Soc.*, **105**, 44–46 (1958).

9. JOHNSON, E. W., ITOH, R., READAL, R. L., AND HILL, M. L., "Determination of Composition and Pressure of Gases over the Melt in a Vacuum Arc Furnace" in "1961 Transactions of the Eighth Vacuum Symposium and Second International Congress on Vacuum Science and Technology," L. E. Preuss, Editor, pp. 751–755, Oxford, Pergamon Press, 1962.

10. BROWNE, T. E., JR., Private Communication.

11. JOHNSON, E. W., AND ITOH, R., "A Vacuum Arc Study Chamber" in 1956 "Vacuum Symposium Transactions," pp. 170–174, London, Pergamon Press, 1957.

12. NOESEN, S. J., "Consumable Electrode Melting of Reactive Metals," *J. Metals*, **12**, 846 (1960); original publication: *Electric Furnace Conference Proceedings*, AIME, **17**, 37 (1960).

13. BUTLER, T. E., AND MORGAN, R. P., "Arc Melting in High-Vacuum Environments," *J. Metals*, **14**, 200–203 (1962).

E. W. JOHNSON

Cross-references: *Dielectric Properties of Vacuum; Dielectrics, Gaseous; Electric Arc Properties; Electron Beam Melting; Furnaces, Inert Atmosphere and Vacuum Arc; Gases, Electrical Conductance and Ionization; Paschen's Law.*

VISCOELECTRIC EFFECT. See ELECTROVISCOUS EFFECT.

VOLT, ABSOLUTE. See ELECTRICAL UNITS AND STANDARDS.

VOLTA, ALESSANDRO (1745–1827)

From ancient times to the close of the eighteenth century, knowledge of electricity accumulated slowly. Experiments were limited to static phenomena, often spectacular but of little practical value prior to the new era that opened in 1800 with Volta's discovery of a new and adequate source of continuous electric current. Alessandro Volta was then Professor of Natural Philosophy at the University of Pavia, Italy. He had already achieved fame for his electrical experiments in induced electricity (the electrophorus) and his invention of a sensitive electroscope. For the latter he had been awarded the Copley Medal of the Royal Society of London in 1794.

A fellow countryman, Luigi Galvani, at the University of Bologna had published in 1791 the account of his famous experiment with the twitching frogs' legs and with it his theory of animal electricity. This influenced Volta's line of thought and experiment, but Volta ultimately reached a far different and more correct conclusion. Volta reasoned that the source of the electricity was in the contact of different metals.

Volta's experiments that finally led to his announcement of the pile and crown of cups probably began seven or eight years earlier, following closely on publication of Galvani's theories. Volta probably constructed a pile as early as 1796. His discovery of the production of electricity by the pile and crown of cups ranks with the great discoveries of all time. It was announced in his letter dated March 20, 1800, addressed to the President of the Royal Society. Batteries as we know them today became possible, and for the first time experimenters were provided with a means of generating electricity in considerable and manageable quantity.

The immediate effect of Volta's letter in England was felt within six weeks of the time it was dispatched from Italy. Even before it had been formally read before the Royal Society, (June 26, 1800), Nicholson and Carlisle had constructed a pile and with it effected the decomposition of water. Soon after, Sir Humphry Davy decomposed electrolytically the fixed alkalies, as they were then called, and saw the first metallic potassium. With a battery of many cells he demonstrated the "full splendors of the electric arch" (arc) between carbon electrodes.

The pile and crown of cups are described in great detail in Volta's letter. Discs of copper, or better silver, against tin, or better zinc, as he said in his quaint way, and an equal number of discs of pasteboard or hide well soaked in water were arranged in a certain manner. He laid great stress on this "certain manner." There were many ways in which these pieces could have been piled up to produce no worthwhile result, but the certain manner is clearly of first importance. He assembled piles of 20, 40, 60 or as many pairs of metals in vertical columns as could sustain themselves without falling. Another great contribution was the series connection of individual cells.

The crown of cups was fundamentally the same in principle, but better adapted to some of his experiments. Goblets or other glass vessels may have been placed on a table in a more or less circular arrangement, but one illustration shows the cups arranged in six rows of nine cells each. The metals, either copper or silver against tin or zinc, were connected in pairs which linked adjacent vessels throughout the entire line. The solution which filled the vessels was dilute lye when he used tin, or a solution of common salt when zinc was employed. With this arrangement of cups he could immerse his fingers or his whole hand in any of the vessels and thus test the strength of the "electric fluid," as he called it.

Volta found that the current of "electric fluid" excited not only the muscles of the body more or less violently, but also the organs of taste, of sight, of hearing, and of touch. One wonders that he did not do himself bodily harm in some of these experiments. Only the sense of smell was unaffected by the current. He thought of the "electric fluid" as flowing perpetually when the circle, as he called it, was closed.

The pile and crown of cups had their limitations. The pile dried out in a few days and the crown of cups was too voluminous to be convenient. Other early experimenters were quick to make improvements. Duplex electrodes appeared in 1800; plunge batteries came a few years later; batteries grew in size and power but the principles remained essentially the same.

Volta gave to the world the first practical battery and with it a demonstration of convincing experiments. His name is honored for all time by the universally used designation for the unit of electromotive force, the "volt."

Except for his wide travels, Volta spent his life in Italy. He was born February 18, 1745, at Como and died there March 5, 1827. From 1774 to 1779 he was professor of physics at the Como Gymnasium, and then became professor of natural philosophy at the University of Pavia, where he remained until his retirement from that post in 1804. He was one of the most renowned European scientists and was given high honors during his life. The great regard in which he is held in Italy is attested by the two impressive monuments to him at Como.

George W. Vinal

Cross-references: *Batteries; Galvani, Luigi.*

VOLTA POTENTIAL. See CONTACT POTENTIAL.

VOLTAMMETRIC TITRATION. See ELECTROMETRIC TITRATION.

VOLTMETERS, MICRO-. See MICROVOLTMETERS AND MICRO-MICROAMMETERS.

W

WATER DEMINERALIZATION. See DEMINERAL-
IZATION OF WATER, DIRECT ELECTRO-
CHEMICAL; DEMINERALIZATION BY ELEC-
TRODIALYSIS.

WATER ELECTROLYSIS

History

The first recorded decomposition of water into its elementary components, hydrogen and oxygen, under the action of an electric current, was carried out by A. Paets van Troostwijk and J. R. Deimann in 1789, using an electrostatic machine. However, due to the limitations of this sort of electric generator, these workers were unable to detect the development of hydrogen and oxygen at the two poles, so as to interpret the nature of the chemical reaction they had observed.

In 1800, W. Nicholson and A. Carlisle were able to achieve the decomposition of water by means of Volta's pile, as soon as they heard of this invention. However, to H. Davy goes the merit of having proved that hydrogen and oxygen thus produced are in the same proportions as required for their synthesis to generate water.[3]

Electrochemical Reactions

When an aqueous solution of an inorganic acid, such as sulfuric acid, or an alkali metal hydroxide, such as caustic soda or caustic potash, is submitted to the passage of a direct current through a pair of nonreactive electrodes, so as to prevent any adverse side-reactions, hydrogen and oxygen develop at the cathode and the anode, respectively, in gaseous form and in quantities conforming to Faraday's law. Accordingly, the quantity of electricity of 26.8 amp-hr (or 1 faraday) liberates one gram equivalent of each element, that is, 11.2 liters of hydrogen and 5.6 liters of oxygen, measured at 0°C and 760 mm mercury.

In an acid solution, where H^+ ions are strongly predominant over OH^- ions, the half-reactions that can be considered as the most likely at each electrode are the following:[6]

cathodic half-reaction:
$$2H^+ + 2e^- \rightarrow 2H$$
$$2H \rightarrow H_2$$
anodic half-reaction:
$$2H_2O \rightarrow 2OH + 2H^+ + 2e^-$$
$$2OH \rightarrow H_2O + O$$

overall reaction: $\quad \overline{H_2O \rightarrow H_2 + \tfrac{1}{2}O_2}$

In alkaline solutions, where OH^- ions strongly predominate, the following half-reaction mechanisms can explain the two electrode processes:

cathodic half-reaction:
$$2H_2O + 2e^- \rightarrow 2H + 2OH^-$$
$$2H \rightarrow H_2$$
anodic half-reaction:
$$2OH^- \rightarrow 2OH + 2e^-$$
$$2OH \rightarrow H_2O + O$$

overall reaction: $\quad \overline{H_2O \rightarrow H_2 + \tfrac{1}{2}O_2}$

It can thus be seen that, irrespective of the acid or basic nature of the electrolyte, the ions into which it is dissociated will perform, under the conditions formerly assumed, the main function of carrying the electrolytic current, in that their presence in the aqueous medium improves its conductivity, without affecting the overall electrolysis process.

Thermodynamic Aspects

As a consequence of the foregoing, the cell voltage, under thermodynamic equilibrium conditions at 25°C and atmospheric pressure, is in both the aforesaid cases equal to 1.229 v. Indeed, thermodynamics show that this value can be correlated with the standard free enthalpy (or the maximum amount of chemical energy that can be converted into useful, e.g., electrical, work) that is characteristic of the synthesis of hydrogen and oxygen gas into liquid water. Since the standard free enthalpy for this reaction is −56,690 cal/mole, the relationship between this value and cell voltage, E, is established by the following formula:[2]

$$E = \frac{56,690}{2 \times 23,060} = 1.229 \text{ v}$$

in which the first factor in the denominator represents the reaction charge, or the two electrons involved in the electrochemical reaction, while the other factor is the product of 0.239 (calories per joule) by 96,484 (coulombs per faraday). Under practical conditions, however, the actual cell voltage is considerably higher than that at thermodynamic equilibrium, on account of the following factors:

(a) The high irreversibility that characterizes the hydrogen as well as the hydrogen discharge on technically applicable electrode materials and at practical current density values: this irreversibility is expressed in terms of *hydrogen* and *oxygen overvoltage.*

(b) The voltage drop through the electrolyte, due to its ohmic resistance.

(c) The concentration polarization in the electrolyte zone surrounding each electrode. The inevitable formation of a concentration gradient, for instance in an alkaline solution, is pointed out in the above equations by the fact that, for each water molecule which is decomposed in the overall reaction, two molecules are consumed in the cathodic reaction, while one molecule is formed in the anodic process. However, a very effective counteraction to the tendency for the concentration gradient to build up to a large extent is exerted by the intense agitation that the rising gas bubbles bring about in the solution.

Consequently, of the above noted factors of irreversibility, hydrogen and oxygen overvoltage are by far the most important: indeed, under practical operating conditions, they account together for about 90 per cent of the electrical energy that is dissipated into an irreversible production of heat, over and above the quantity of electric work that is usefully converted into chemical energy.

Within the usual range of operating temperatures (60 to 80°C) the equilibrium voltage may be assumed, with reasonable accuracy for all practical purposes, to be 1.25 v. Therefore, this represents the ideal lower limit that can never be attained. It is, however, to be noted that, albeit any voltage in excess of this value represents an unwanted waste of energy, the actual heat output of the system is appreciably lower

than would be calculated on the basis of such excess. Indeed, if the decomposition of liquid water into gaseous hydrogen and oxygen could be achieved under equilibrium conditions, it would be an endothermic reaction, so that, due to a reversible entropy increase of the system, heat would be absorbed by the system from the surroundings, in the amount of about 11,600 cal per mole of water. This quantity is equivalent to a voltage excess of 0.25 v, so that, by adding it to the equilibrium value, it results that the actual reaction, in spite of irreversibility, would still be endothermic for any measured cell voltage up to 1.5 v and would give up heat to surroundings only for any measured voltage exceeding 1.5 v. This consideration is quite important for the purpose of calculating the thermal balance of the reaction, as required for designing and providing the cooling facilities that are usually needed to keep the most suitable operating temperature. Beside the heat that is spontaneously given up by the equipment through radiation and convection, such thermal balance must take, of course, into account the even greater amount that leaves with the water vapor saturating both warm gas streams.[5]

Technology

Iron, beside being the most practical construction material for the general cell structure, ranges among the metals characterized by a relatively low hydrogen overvoltage; accordingly, it is particularly suitable to work as a cathode.

As regards anode material, nickel, beside being distinguished by a relatively low oxygen overvoltage, has the further advantage of becoming easily passivated, so as to withstand chemical attack by nascent oxygen. Consequently, nickel-plated steel is universally used for this application.

Since overvoltage depends, among others, upon *real* current density, that is, the current intensity referred to *real* unit area of electrode, particular techniques have been developed to provide the maximum possible roughness or "sponginess" on the iron surface of the cathode and on the nickel deposit on the anode. The thickness of the nickel deposit is usually about 0.05 mm.[1, 7]

The behavior of iron and nickel in contact with alkaline solutions, at temperatures and concentrations as normally used in water electrolysis, is quite satisfactory; however, these metals do not withstand the aggressiveness of acid media, which offer no appreciable advantage, regarding cell voltage and other operating conditions, over alkaline hydroxides, such as caustic soda and caustic potash. Consequently, these two electrolytes only are used for industrial production of hydrogen and oxygen.

For temperatures in the neighborhood of 75°C, the highest conductivities of sodium hydroxide and potassium hydroxide are obtained at concentrations close to 25 per cent NaOH (1.2 ohm^{-1} cm^{-1}) and 30 per cent KOH (1.4 ohm^{-1} cm^{-1}), respectively. In practice, a concentration of 25 per cent for either NaOH or KOH is used.

Since voltage drop through the electrolyte accounts only for about 10 per cent of the total cell voltage, the slightly higher conductivity of KOH over NaOH does not involve any remarkable reduction in energy consumption, although in practice the apparent resistance of the electrolyte is increased by 25 to 30 per cent over the actual value, owing to the presence of gas bubbles. However, at the aforesaid concentration and temperature, the aqueous vapor pressure is appreciably lower over caustic potash, so that evaporation losses are also less. Therefore, potassium hydroxide is to be preferred for those cell constructions that are designed for high current densities and correspondingly higher temperatures.

As overvoltage decreases with temperature increase, there would be an advantage in operating at a temperature as high as possible. On the

other hand, beyond the temperature of 80°C, the volume of water vapor developing with the gases amounts to about 30 per cent of the total and the vapor bubbles rising in the solution contribute to increasing further the resistance to the passage of current. Moreover, the energy absorbed in the work of evaporation becomes so appreciable that the decrease in overvoltage obtainable by raising the temperature is counterbalanced by the aforesaid intervening sources of energy dissipation. Consequently, any voltage reduction beyond 80°C becomes negligible.[1]

Cell Types

The first industrial cells were of the so-called *tank type* with *unipolar electrode* arrangement, as schematically illustrated in Fig. 1. The first denomination refers to the typical shape of the container or cell proper. Each electrode plate, irrespective of the number of electrodes in the cell, performs only one function, in that it behaves on both sides only as an anode or as a cathode: hence its unipolar characteristic. The anodes are all connected together in parallel and so are the cathodes.

Another class of apparatus, which was developed at the turn of the century, is characterized by a bipolar, *filter-press* type of assembly, as schematically shown in Fig. 2. An industrial cell of this type is shown in Fig. 3. In this system the electrodes transfer the current from one to the next in series. Accordingly, whereas the unipolar arrangement requires as many connections with the outer circuit as are the electrodes in parallel, a filter-press electrolyzer is directly tied-in with the positive and the negative bus bar by means of its two terminal electrode plates. The electric field thus applied through the system obliges cations to migrate within each compartment between two plates in the direction of the negative terminal and the anions toward the positive terminal. The two metallic sides of each electrode plate can be assumed to be equipotential, since the ohmic drop through the small plate thickness is negligible. However, a half-cell voltage builds up at each side; the metal face over which hydrogen is discharged becomes cathodic, while the other face becomes anodic and oxygen discharge takes place on it. In this sense each electrode performs a bipolar function: hence the denomination proper to this cell.

In all modern electrolyzers, whether of uni-

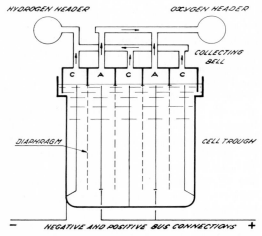

Fig. 1. Unipolar electrolyzer typical arrangement (schematic).

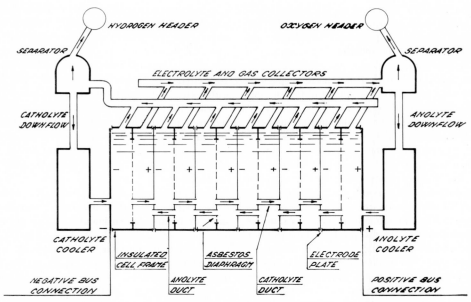

FIG. 2. Bipolar electrolyzer typical arrangement (schematic).

FIG. 3. De Nora water electrolyzer; rated capacity: 450 cubic meter STP hydrogen per hour at 10,000 amp (*Courtesy of Oronzio de Nora, Impianti Elettrochimici*)

polar or bipolar type, each anodic surface is separated from the cathodic surface of the next plate in the series by means of a porous diaphragm (usually of asbestos cloth) which prevents hydrogen and oxygen from mixing together.

Specially because of limitations in heat removal and electrolyte circulation, the current density allowable in unipolar cells seldom exceeds 700 amp/sq m, while in bipolar electrolyzers it can be even higher than 1500 amp/sq m. Such improvement is rendered possible mainly by the possibility to make complete use of the difference in density between the liquid-and-gas system inside the cell block and the degasified electrolyte stream, in order to carry out an active gravity circulation through external coolers. Moreover, the bipolar plates can be provided on each face with a perforated electrode which becomes the main seat of the gas discharge: this system allows the bubbles to escape through the perforations backward into the compartment between the fore-electrode and the back-plate, away from the main path of the current; it is thus possible to obtain a considerable decrease in voltage.

On account of the aforesaid limitations, unipolar assemblies require, per unit of production capacity, much more floor space than the filter-press construction. Therefore, in all the modern plants with high capacity rates, such as required for production of ammonia and fertilizers, the latter cell-type is to be preferred.

Typical, even though not exclusive, examples of unipolar design are the models known under the names of Electrolabs, Fauser, Knowles, Holmboe, and Trail. The best-known types of filter-press construction are those known under the names of Bamag, Demag, de Nora, Oerlikon, Pechkranz, and Zdansky-Lonza.[4] This last model is characterized by operating at a pressure of 450 psi and a temperature around 95°C. The higher temperature is allowed by the higher pressure, since the water vapor content in the gases is correspondingly reduced. The combined effect of temperature and pressure is to reduce overvoltage and gas bubble size, thus resulting in a considerable voltage decrease.

The energy requirement at rated capacity ranges for most models between 4.8 and 5 kwh/cu m STP of hydrogen, which corresponds to a cell voltage close to 2 v and a current efficiency usually higher than 0.98.

Since the electrolyte losses in well-designed equipment are almost negligible, the only consumption material consists of distilled or demineralized water, at the rate of about 0.9 liter/cu m STP of hydrogen (taking into account also evaporation losses).

Uses

Electrolytic hydrogen and oxygen are usually very pure (99.8 per cent or better). The small quantity of alkaline mist entrained with the gases is normally removed by passage through scrubbing towers, countercurrent to wash-water; however, for some particular applications, like the production of nitric acid by catalytic combusion of ammonia with oxygen, more efficient methods, such as electrostatic precipitation, are needed.

For hydrogen production in tonnage quanti-

ties, such as required in the nitrogen fertilizer industry, there is now a tendency to prefer non-electrolytic processes, unless very cheap and plentiful hydroelectric power is available. In this case, water electrolysis can be conveniently associated also with the recovery of *heavy water* (q.v.), as a valuable byproduct.

For relatively small production rates, such as required for the hydrogenation of oils and fats and in the pharmaceutical industry, the electrolytic process still remains outstanding, in view of the high purity of its products, as well as of its simplicity and flexibility.

An interesting possibility for water electrolysis to perform another important function resides in future developments of *hydrogen-oxygen fuel cells*. Indeed, it has already been visualized that the latter might provide a convenient means to store power, by reconverting into electrical work the recombination of hydrogen with oxygen, if their source of supply is electrolysis to be carried out at periods when a surplus of hydroelectric power is available.[7]

References

1. BILLITER, J., "Die technische Elektrolyse der Nichtmetalle," Chapt. 1, Wien, Springer-Verlag, 1954.
2. LATIMER, W. M., "Oxidation Potentials," p. 39, Englewood Cliffs, Prentice-Hall, Inc., 1961.
3. LEICESTER, H. M., "The Historical Background of Chemistry," Chapt. 17, New York, John Wiley & Sons, Inc., 1956.
4. MANTELL, C. L., "Electrochemical Engineering," p. 315, New York, McGraw-Hill Book Co., Inc., 1960.
5. PICHLER, A. v., *Chem. Ing. Tech.*, **33**, 95 (1961).
6. POTTER, E. C., "Electrochemistry," Chapt. 6, London, Cleaver-Hume Press Ltd., 1956.
7. VIELSTICH, W., *Chem. Ing. Tech.*, **33**, 75 (1961).

PATRIZIO GALLONE

Cross-reference: *Heavy Water; Overvoltage, Hydrogen; Overvoltage, Oxygen.*

WATTS, OLIVER PATTERSON (1865–1953)

A twentieth century scientist noted for his contributions to the field of electrochemistry, particularly in electroplating, Watts was born July 16, 1865 in Thomaston, Maine to Joseph and Maria Patterson Watts. After graduation from Bowdoin College in Brunswick, Maine in 1889 and a year of graduate work at Clarke University, in Worcester, Massachusetts, Watts began teaching as Thomaston grammar school principal for two years. Then he taught physics at Franklin Academy for six years and at a Waltham, Massachusetts high school for five years.

These years were a prelude to his thirty-two years as an instructor and professor of applied electrochemistry at the University of Wisconsin. An interest in this field brought him to the university in 1902, where he studied under Charles Burgess and Louis Kahlenberg. Burgess had established the Department of Applied Electrochemistry (later merged with the Department of Chemical Engineering) in 1898. Watts received the first doctorate degree offered by either department in 1905. His thesis was "An Investigation of the Borides and Silicides."

In 1905, the Trustees of the Carnegie Institution of Washington established a five year grant, at $2500 per year, to investigate the properties of electrolytic iron and its alloys. The grant was awarded to Watts.

Thus, he began an exploration of the complex problems of corrosion and electrochemistry. Thirty-one of his papers appeared in the *Transactions of the American Electrochemical Society* attesting to his fifty years of scientific investigation. The subjects of his works include: 1) general theories and applications of electrochemistry; 2) corrosion rates; 3) iron rusting; 4) effects of dissolved oxygen and water on corrosion; 5) grading of corrosion-resistant alloys; 6) behavior of voltaic couples; 7) electroplating, especially the problems of embrittlement and dezincification, the structure of electrodeposits, the effect of addition agents and the hot nickel-plating bath; 8) electrometallurgy, especially the production of borides, calcium carbide, carborundum, silicides, and nitrides of metals plus hundreds of alloys.

His hot nickel-plating bath, known as the "Watts Bath," is the ancestor of most modern nickel-plating solutions. It is a high-speed method of nickel-plating on iron and steel. This process made millions of dollars for the plating industry. Watts neither asked nor received any financial compensation for his bath. Rewards of this nature did not concern him.

In 1913, the Chicago Branch of the National Electro-Platers Association elected both Watts and Burgess honorary members of the branch, showing that the value of their research was well recognized. When this association became the American Electro-Platers Society, they were given national honorary membership. Bowdoin

College honored Watts by awarding him the honorary degree of Doctor of Science in 1924. He also was elected to serve as vice-president of the Electrochemical Society in 1926 and 1927. These displays of appreciation were reward enough for him, as was freely giving advice to all who sought it.

This scholarly man had a deep devotion for research and a strong belief in the inquiring approach to science. Experimentation, not reliance on results derived from extrapolation of mathematical formulas, was stressed even in his classes. His students had to reason scientifically, stating full explanations of the results of their experiments without using statements memorized from textbooks.

Research and teaching were not Watts' only interests. He regularly enjoyed several hobbies, including iceskating, photography, astronomy, and sailing in the summer along the coast of Maine in his sloop, the Kestrel. Retirement from teaching in 1937, at the age of seventy-two, did not stop him from continuing experimentation or an active life. During this period, he toured the United States by car, always camping out. He also toured Canada driving on some of the roughest roads in the Northwest Territory. The winters were spent in Florida. Still he continued iceskating, for at the age of 80, he bought a pair of shoe skates to replace the detachable type he had used for sixty years.

He had two devoted wives who were fine helpmates. Jary J. Orton, the daughter of a president of Ohio State University, was his first wife. She passed away shortly after his retirement. His second wife was Estella Nuzum Jones, whom he married in 1948.

Five years later on the evening of February 5, 1953, Dr. Watts passed away in Madison, Wisconsin. His character and importance are best summed up in a short biography by O. A. Hougen of the Department of Chemical Engineering at the University of Wisconsin. He described Dr. Watts as being "of that school of rugged individualists in applied science who has persisted in his own unaided investigational efforts. He is responsible for the emphasis on applied electrochemistry in the Department of Chemical Engineering at Wisconsin and has been a source of inspiration to hundreds of students in his classes." [*J. Electrochem. Soc.*, **99**, 277C–278C (1952).].

FLORENCE H. LARKOWSKI

WESTON, EDWARD (1850–1936)

A pioneer American electrical engineer, Edward Weston, was born May 9, 1850 at Brynn Castle near Owestry, Shropshire, England. He early evidenced interest in scientific research and at the age of 16 delivered lectures on the marvels of electricity. Weston was given the best education possible, but after a period of three years as apprentice to a physician, he abandoned this career and in 1870 came to the United States. Weston's first job was as a chemist with a company making photographic materials, but he soon joined the American Nickel Plating Co. Here he made improvements in the methods and baths for the then new nickel plating business and laid the foundation for many of the electroplating practices in use over 60 years later.

Recognizing the limitations of batteries, then the source of electricity for electroplating, Weston developed an electric generator in 1873 and formed the Weston Dynamo Electric Machine Co. in Newark, the first company in this country devoted exclusively to the manufacture of these machines. From the manufacture of plating dynamos, the company branched into the production of improved lighting generators which became known as the most efficient on the market. In 1878 this company was sold to U. S. Electric Lighting Co., which opened a new plant in Newark that was later consolidated in 1888 with Westinghouse. Weston remained as an electrical engineer at the new plant until 1888.

One of the pioneers in the field of electric lighting, Weston worked from 1875 to 1886 in the development of arc and incandescent illumination, and at the Centennial Exposition in 1876 he exhibited his carbon incandescent lamps. Among other things, he discovered the means of equalizing the diameter of carbon filaments by flashing them in a hydrocarbon vapor. At the Franklin Exposition in 1883, Weston exhibited 300-candlepower, gas-filled ($CHCl_3$) carbon lamps. He also made many other developments in arc and incandescent lamps and in complete lighting systems.

Aware that electrical instruments had lagged behind other advances in the electrical field, Weston in 1885 set out to develop suitable ones. In 1888 he produced the first accurate direct-reading electrical indicating instrument. This included the first really permanent magnet with shaped pole pieces and a core, and spiral springs to conduct the current to and from the moving coil. To manufacture the instruments he invented, Weston in 1888 formed the Weston Electrical Instrument Co., Waverly, N. J., and served as its president. The Weston ammeters and voltmeters revolutionized the everyday measurements of amperes and volts.

His multitude of inventions includes the famous Weston standard cadmium cell in 1892, the basis for the international volt; and manganin (11 to 12 per cent Mn, 3 to 4 per cent Ni, and balance Cu), a better high-resistance alloy. Several hundred patents were granted to him, 299 in the period to 1915.

In addition to working to provide the growing electrical industry with fundamental equipment, he was also interested in advancing the science of electricity. He was a charter member (1884) of the American Institute of Electrical Engineers and served as its president in 1888. He was a charter member (1902) and honorary member (1926) of the Electrochemical Society, a fellow of the American Association for the Advancement of Science, and a member of the American Physical Society, the American Chemical Society, and the National Electric Light Association. His other interests are exemplified by membership in the Society for the Encouragement of Art, the Metropolitan Museum of Art, and the American Museum of Natural History. In 1929 he endowed the Weston Fellowship of the Electrochemical Society.

His many contributions to science and industry were recognized internationally by a variety of awards, degrees and honors. Weston died at the age of 86 on August 20, 1936.

Reference

WOODBURY, DAVID O., "A Measure of Greatness," New York, McGraw-Hill Book Co., 1949.

CLIFFORD A. HAMPEL

WHEATSTONE BRIDGE

This null balance comparison method for precise measurement of resistance is based on a network invented by S. H. Christie in 1833. Sir Charles Wheatstone, in 1843, called attention to Christie's network, and its application to precise resistance measurement. The method became known as the Wheatstone Bridge. The basic network is in Fig. 1.

X is the resistance to be measured. A and B are fixed resistors of known ratio value. R is an adjustable standard resistance. G is a galvanometer to detect current flow in the "bridge" between corners b and d. E is a battery supplying current to the circuit when the key is closed. Resistance of the battery arm is C. Currents in the arms of the network are designated by α, β, ρ, χ, γ, and ϵ.

Ohm's Law and Kirchhoff's Laws give the following equations for the relationships of current, voltage and resistance in the six bridge arms:

$$E - \epsilon C = \rho R + \chi X \qquad -\rho + \gamma + \chi = 0$$

$$\beta B = \rho R + \gamma G \qquad \alpha + \chi - \epsilon = 0$$

$$\alpha A = \chi X - \gamma G \qquad \beta + \gamma - \alpha = 0$$

$$E - \epsilon C = \beta B + \alpha A \qquad \epsilon - \rho - \beta = 0$$

Balance is achieved when $\beta B = \rho R$, and $\gamma = 0$. Then, by substitution and division:

$$\rho = \chi, \quad \beta = \alpha, \quad \beta B = \rho R, \quad \alpha A = \chi X$$

and

$$X = \frac{A}{B} R.$$

The balancing process is analogous to the comparison of masses in a chemical balance. Ratio A/B is the lever arm ratio in the "scales." Standard resistance, R, is adjusted until no current flows in the galvanometer, thus null balance is achieved. Alternately, a fixed standard resistance is used, and the ratio arms, A/B, are a slidewire resistor. The sliding contact position is adjusted to achieve null balance, and the ratio is calculated from the slidewire contact position.

The network permits comparison of resistors over a wide range of values. Precision and accuracy in a particular bridge network are controlled by the care used in construction and adjustment of the resistors, R, A, and B; the choice of operating voltage; and the choice of galvanometer sensitivity.

Sensitivity of a bridge circuit is determined by the current available to deflect the galvanometer when the bridge is unbalanced by a small amount. A convenient simplification of the equation for voltage across the detector, γG, is

$$\gamma G = \frac{RXKE}{(R + X)^2}$$

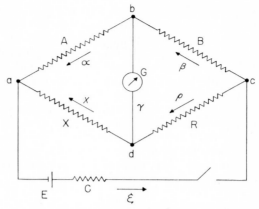

FIG. 1. Basic Wheatstone bridge network.

where K is the error in the bridge balance in parts. Then detector current is

$$\gamma = \frac{\gamma G}{\dfrac{(A + X)(B + R)}{A + B + R + X} + G}.$$

When A/B is greater than 10, the (B + R) controls the denominator; when A/B is less than 0.1, then (A + X) controls the denominator for all practical purposes.

Galvanometer sensitivity and resistance, and needed operating voltage may be selected from these relationships according to the sensitivity desired. Constant, K, will be 0.01 for 1 per cent sensitivity, 10^{-6} for 1 part/million sensitivity.

In selecting the voltage for a particular measurement, current through the resistors, A, B, R and X must be considered, since the I^2R heating effect will increase resistor temperatures. Temperature rise must be kept low, since even the manganin resistors used at A, B and R have a temperature coefficient of a few parts per million per °C. The X resistor in many cases will be of a material, such as copper or carbon, which has a substantial temperature coefficient of resistance. Extreme overload of resistors will cause burnout or permanent damage to their adjustment.

Heating effects in the individual resistors will be approximately

$$\left[\frac{E}{A + B}\right]^2 A, \quad \left[\frac{E}{A + B}\right]^2 B, \quad \left[\frac{E}{X + R}\right]^2 X,$$

$$\text{and} \quad \left[\frac{E}{X + R}\right]^2 R, \text{ in watts.}$$

As a general rule, if the largest of these heating effects is less than 0.1 watt, at a bridge voltage which will give the desired sensitivity with the galvanometer available, heating effects will need no further consideration and can be neglected.

There may be an advantage to interchanging the battery and galvanometer connections—placing the battery across the bd corners and the galvanometer across the ac corners. The balance equations do not change, but the distribution of currents and voltages may produce a higher sensitivity, a lower heating effect in the resistors, or a more favorable damping condition for the galvanometer. The sensitivity equation will change to

$$\gamma G = \frac{RBKE}{(R + B)^2}$$

and the heating effects will be

$$\left(\frac{E}{A + X}\right)^2 A, \ \left(\frac{E}{A + X}\right)^2 X, \ \left(\frac{E}{B + R}\right)^2 B,$$

$$\text{and} \ \left(\frac{E}{B + R}\right)^2 R.$$

Measurement of High Resistance

General-purpose Wheatstone bridges usually provide range of ratio A/B and standard resistance, R, to measure up to about 10 megohms. For precise measurement at higher values, leakage currents are a limiting factor on accuracy. Guarding to intercept leakage currents, and extremely good insulation of the bridge elements and terminals are needed, and provided, on bridges intended for measurement up to a few thousand megohms. Requirements for high-resistance measurements are discussed by Wyeth *et al.* in Ref. (4). Bridge power voltage must be increased, and detector sensitivity increased, for very high resistance measurements. The "X" resistors must be well designed for stability if bridge measurement is to be justified, and they must be carefully handled to prevent surface leakage from degrading the resistor itself.

Commerical Forms of Wheatstone Bridges

The bridges illustrated are commercial forms of self-contained units. The portable bridge in-

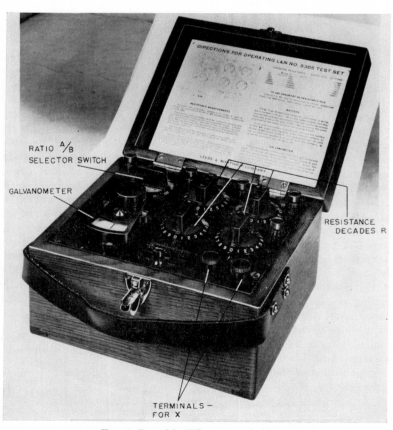

FIG. 2. Portable Wheatstone bridge.

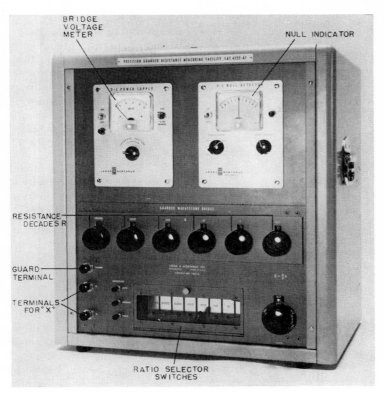

FIG. 3. Precise, guarded resistance measuring facility.

cludes the battery, galvanometer, and a resistor network having seven A/B ratio values from 0.001 to 1000, and a four-decade standard R. It is designed to measure to about 0.1 per cent accuracy over the range from 1 ohm to a few megohms. The console facility (Fig. 3) includes a regulated power supply, an electronic null detector, eleven ratio values from 0.00001 to 100,000 and a six-decade standard. It is designed to measure to about 0.01 per cent accuracy over the range from 1 ohm to a few megohms, and to measure reliably, at somewhat lower accuracy, up to 1000 megohms. Other commercial forms of bridges are available with accuracy ranging from about 1 per cent for low-cost simplified bridges to the bridges accurate to a few parts per million used at National Bureau of Standards and other standardizing laboratories for comparisons to the national standard ohms.

Measurement of Low Resistance

In the basic Wheatstone bridge network, the resistance in the X arm necessarily includes everything in the circuit between the a and d corners. This is resistor, X, plus its leads, plus the resistance of the bridge terminals and the internal wiring from the terminals to the a and d corners.

These lead and contact resistances can be measured, with X short circuited, and the measured value can be subtracted from the measured value of X which includes these lead and contact resistances. This procedure is usually satisfactory when X is greater than about 1 ohm, and it is not usually necessary when X is greater than about 100 ohms.

When X is less than about 1 ohm, the lead and contact corrections will be a serious limitation in accuracy. Reference to the sensitivity equations, when X is small, will demonstrate that it will also be difficult to obtain sufficient sensitivity with safe current through the bridge.

The Kelvin bridge network is an extension of the Wheatstone bridge network to provide measurement of low value resistors. This network measures X as a four-terminal resistor—two terminals carry current to the resistor, and two potential terminals define the resistance of interest. The Kelvin bridge network and its transformation to a Wheatstone network are:

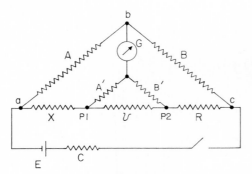

FIG. 4a. Kelvin bridge.

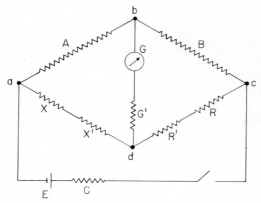

FIG. 4b. Kelvin bridge transformed to Wheatstone bridge.

Delta-wye transform of A¹ and B¹ gives the values

$$G' = \frac{A'B'}{A' + B' + v}, \ X' = \frac{A'}{A' + B' + v},$$

$$R' = \frac{B'}{A' + B' + v}$$

The complete balance equation is:

$$X + X' = \frac{A}{B}(R + R')$$

which, by substitution, simplifies to

$$X = \frac{A}{B}R + \frac{v(AB - BA')}{A + B + v}$$

By design, A = A', B = B', which reduces the second member to zero.

In Figs. 4a and 4b, the points designated a and p1 are the potential terminals of resistor X, and points p2 and c are the potential points of the standard resistor. Lead and contact resistances associated with the a and c corners are outside the measuring network, those associated with p1 and p2 are part of the yoke arm, v, and transform to part of X' and R'. R is a low resistance designed to carry the substantial current required to obtain good sensitivity. Galvanometer current for the transformed Kelvin bridge is determined from the equation for galvanometer current in the Wheatstone bridge. Heating effects need to be considered in the X and R resistors only.

Temperature Measurement with Resistance Thermometers

The network is arranged for A/B ratio of 1/1. The rheostat arm is made adjustable either continuously or in very small decade steps. Leads are arranged to the three- or four-lead thermometer, so that resistance of one lead adds to X, and resistance of the other lead adds to R in equal amounts. This provides compensation for lead resistance. Commercial resistance thermometer bridges, Fig. 6, calibrated to be direct reading in temperature, provide about 0.2°C accuracy at low cost for the convenience of reading thermometers located at a considerable distance from the measuring bridge. The Mueller resistance thermometer bridge, Fig. 7, is designed for very high-accuracy measurement of the strain-free platinum resistance thermometers used to maintain the International Temperature Scale through the range −183°C to 630°C and the platinum resistance thermometers used in cryogenic and calorimetric work.

Temperature Measurement with Thermistors

Thermistors used in temperature measurement are commonly measured with general purpose Wheatstone bridges. Resistance readings are converted to temperature from calibration data. Thermistor bridges calibrated directly in temperature for thermistors of standardized calibration are also available.

Resistance of Semiconductors

Resistance characteristics of semiconductors, diodes, and rectifiers are readily made with general-purpose Wheatstone bridges. Forward and reverse readings are needed. These are obtained by reversing the battery voltage between measurements. Voltage applied to the tested article must be within the proper range for the

FIG. 6. Portable Wheatstone bridge for temperature measurements with resistance thermometers.

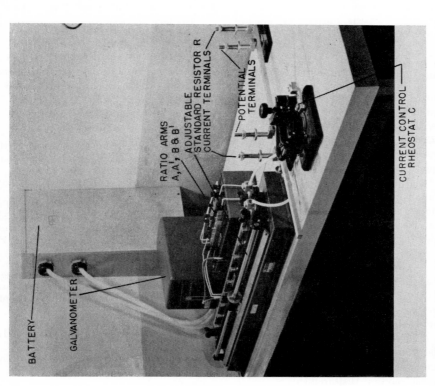

FIG. 5. Kelvin bridge for measuring resistance of a copper bar.

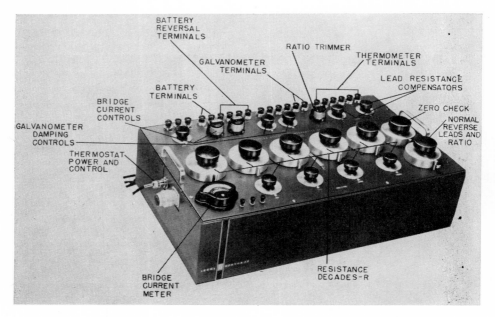

Fig. 7. G-4 Mueller bridge for precise temperature measurement with strain-free platinum resistance thermometer.

device tested; the voltage relationships provide for calculating this. Special-purpose bridges are available for rapid routine testing of semiconductors.

Conductance of Electrolytes

In electrochemistry the Wheatstone bridge is widely used for measuring the conductance of electrolytes. The bridge network is provided with low-frequency a-c power. An a-c null detector or telephone receiver replaces the galvanometer. The balance equation is unchanged. The effects of capacitance and inductance are negligible for ordinary accuracy measurement.

A conductivity cell comprising electrodes of known area and spacing supported in a glass or plastic insulating structure is immersed in or filled with the test sample and measured as X. Resistance measured is the reciprocal of the conductance. Measurement is usually corrected to a standard temperature and to specific conductance/cc, using temperature-coefficient data for the electrolyte and the calibrated constant of the cell used.

A complete discussion of electrolytic conductivity bridges will be found in the article "Conductivity (Electrolytic) Measurement."

Automatically-Balanced Wheatstone Bridges

Self-balancing bridges, widely used in the measurement of temperature with resistance thermometers (q.v.) and the measurement of electrolytic conductivity, are discussed in the articles "Recorders" and "Controllers."

References

1. STOUT, M. B., "Basic Electrical Measurements," Second Edition, Englewood Cliffs, N. J., Prentice-Hall, Inc., 1960.
2. HARRIS, F. K., "Electrical Measurements," New York, John Wiley & Sons, 1952.
3. National Bureau of Standards, "Precision Measurement & Calibration," Handbook 77—Volume I. "Electricity;" Volume II, "Heat & Mechanics," U. S. Gov't. Printing Office, Washington, D. C., 1961.
4. WYETH, F. H., HIGLEY, J. B., AND SHIRK, W. H., JR., "Precision Guarded Resistance Measuring Facility," *AIEE Transactions,* Communications & Electronics," September, 1958.

JOHN C. MELCHER

Cross-references: *Conductivity (Electrolytic) Measurement; Galvanometers; Resistance Thermometers.*

WHITNEY, WILLIS RODNEY (1868–1958)

Willis Rodney Whitney stands unique among American scientists. A creative research worker in his own right, he became even more pre-eminent as the spiritual architect and builder of the first industrial research laboratory in the United States. He developed and guided it from original vague concepts, through its forming and growing stages, to an ultimately large and world-famous institution which served as a model and inspiration for many other research laboratories to follow elsewhere.

At the time of its inception, a laboratory of this kind was unknown; basic research was carried on at academic institutions. It was E. W. Rice, an official of the General Electric Co., who in 1900 conceived the idea of a true research laboratory for the growing electrical industry. The laboratory was to be charged with creating new scientific ideas and fundamental knowledge, and thereby new materials, processes, or products as well, in the expectation that this would assure the company's leadership in an expanding industry. Rice sought and found in Whitney the right man at the right time to translate these visions into reality.

Whitney was born on August 22, 1868, in Jamestown, N.Y., where he attended the public schools through graduation. Although deeply interested in microscopy and the biological sciences, he chose to study chemistry at Massachusetts Institute of Technology. Having obtained his B.S. degree in 1890, he served as an instructor for four more years, then went abroad to earn his Ph.D. degree under W. Ostwald at the University of Leipzig (in 1896), and then for six months of post-doctoral work at the Sorbonne in Paris. From this time dates his continued interest in solution and in colloid chemistry. He returned to M.I.T. first as assistant professor, later as full professor, intent on devoting his life's work to teaching and doing research. This is the field in which he expected to find greatest personal satisfaction and proficiency. When approached about the new job, therefore, he accepted only with hesitation and with the reservation that he could divide his time between his duties at M.I.T. and the new ones of planning and organizing the new laboratory which he was to head. Gradually, however, he became so intrigued with the great and un-usual opportunities offered by the new venture that he resigned his position at M.I.T. to devote full time to the building of the envisioned research organization.

From an initial complement of three people (Whitney, Steinmetz and an assistant) who were installed to conduct research in a barn on Steinmetz's property, this organization was to grow until by the time of Whitney's retirement from administrative duties in 1932 it comprised several hundred people in two large buildings. By the time of his death on January 9, 1958, it had grown larger yet; it had been organized along several disciplines, such as chemistry, physics, ceramics, metallurgy, etc.; and it was given larger and more modern quarters in a group of prominent buildings at the Knolls near Schenectady. The quality and importance of the research work done under the guidance of Whitney's managerial principles is attested to by the fact that scientific publications from this institution are among the most frequently quoted papers in their respective fields.

Whitney had an unusually keen and observing eye and mind, and his searching inquisitiveness into the workings of nature stayed with him until the end. He inspired people with his own enthusiasm for meaningful research, and he was exceptionally successful in surrounding himself with some of the ablest scientists in their fields. The fruits of their work soon became apparent, and, thus, Whitney succeeded early in demonstrating that an industrial research laboratory could well progress from an important to an essential part of a business.

Although his ideas and suggestions were crucial for the success of unnumbered developments for which he refused to take any credit himself, a few of these are so singularly his own that his name must be attached to them. Among these are the electrochemical theory of corrosion published in 1903, the metallized carbon filament for incandescent lamps, the inductotherm machine for the production and medical application of artificial fever, the Calrod heating unit, the principle of hydrogen cooling for turbine generators, and several others.

In addition to his earned degrees, Whitney received five honorary doctor's degrees from American universities and a number of prominent medals and honors, among the most important of which are the following: Willard Gibbs Medal (1916), Perkin Medal (1921),

Franklin Medal (1931), Edison Medal (1934) and the John Fritz Medal (1943). In 1937 he was elected a Chevalier of the French Legion of Honor.

A charter member of the Electrochemical Society, he was active in policy matters during its early years, served as its president in 1911–12, and was made an honorary member in 1944. He was president of the American Chemical Society in 1909 and one of ten honorary members of the Chemists' Club in New York. In 1947 the National Association of Corrosion Engineers established the Willis Rodney Whitney Award.

References

1. "WILLIS R. WHITNEY," by L. A. Hawkins, General Electric Monogram, 1950 (September–October issue).
2. "WILLIS RODNEY WHITNEY," by John T. Broderick, Albany, N.Y., Fort Orange Press, 1945.

H. C. FROELICH

WIEN EFFECT

The Wien Effect, demonstrated experimentally by Max Wien in 1927,[1] is an increase of conductance of an electrolytic solution under the influence of an electrical field. Wien plotted the quotient, $\Delta\Lambda/\Lambda(0)$, the change in the conductance as a result of the applied field divided by the conductance at very low (near zero) field, expressed as per cent, as a function of the field. The results of many measurements may be grouped into two distinctive types in terms of the kinds of plots thus obtained, examples of which are shown in Fig. 1.

In strong or wholly ionized electrolytes the conductance rises rapidly in a range of fields up to about 50 kv/cm and then rises only a small fraction further during the application of higher fields up to those which cause dielectric breakdown (~500 kv/cm). For weak, associated, or not wholly ionized electrolytes a second effect predominates, the form of which is distinctively different. The conductance increases with field, curves gently upward at lower fields, 0 to 30 kv, and increases linearly with field after this point. The section of linear increase extrapolates to a negative value of the quotient, $\Delta\Lambda/\Lambda(0)$, at zero field.

The valence type, degree of association, and concentration are the characteristics of the elec-

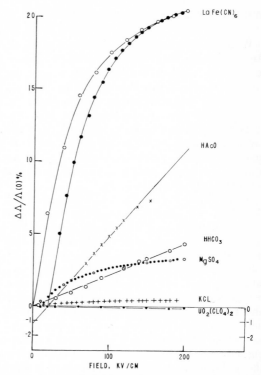

FIG. 1. High-field conductance quotient, $\Delta\Lambda/\Lambda(0)$, per cent, plotted against field, in kilovolts/centimeter, for a variety of electrolytes. Top curve, lanthanum (III) iron (III) cyanide, 1.025×10^{-4} M; open circles, experimental results; filled circles, theoretical calculation for $K(O) = 2.20 \times 10^{-4}$. Second from top, acetic acid, 7.405×10^{-4} M; crosses, experimental results; straight line, Onsager theory, Ref. 2. Third from top: carbonic acid first ionization, 0.0152 M carbon dioxide solution; $K(O)$ calculated, 1.72×10^{-4}. Fourth from top, magnesium sulfate, 1.39×10^{-4} M; small open circles, experimental results; small filled circles, theoretical calculation for $K(O) = 6.3 \times 10^{-3}$. Just above zero conductance quotient axis, crosses, calculation for potassium chloride, 3.00×10^{-4} M. Below zero axis, small filled circles, experimental results, uranyl perchlorate, 1.018×10^{-4} M. All for temperature of 25.00°C.

trolyte most important in determining the character of the observed effect. With strong electrolytes the fractional amount of the increase is principally dependent upon the valence type, being in the vicinity of 0.4 per cent for 1-1 electrolytes, 0.6 per cent for 1-2 or 2-1, 4 per cent for 2-2, 9 per cent for 2-3 or 3-2, and 20 per cent for 3-3 electrolytes at 200 kv/cm. The dependence on concentration is less marked, the relative effect becoming larger for more concentrated solutions of a given valence type. For weak electrolytes the slope of the linear increase is proportional to the weakness of the electrolyte, the weaker the electrolyte, the greater the fractional increase with increasing field. At 200 kv/cm, the value of $\Delta\Lambda/\Lambda(0)$ for carbonic acid, $K_1 = 1.72 \times 10^{-4}$, is 4.1 per cent; for acetic acid $K = 1.8 \times 10^{-5}$, it is 11.6 per cent. To understand these effects a satisfactory theory is clearly necessary.

Theory

Fortunately, theories are available for the high-field conductances of weak and strong electrolytes of any valence type. All are the work of Lars Onsager.[2, 3] They are critically presented and summarized in the book of Harned and Owen.[4]

The result of Onsager and Wilson (Ref. 4, pp. 136–138), though less general than that of Onsager and Kim,[3] is entirely adequate for the present discussion and rather easier to appreciate since it is directly reducible to the ordinary conductance equation of Onsager at zero field, and gives rise to two factors convenient to associate with the behavior of strong electrolytes. The mathematical form of the theory is:

$$\lambda_j = \lambda_j^0 - \left[\frac{e_j^2 \kappa \lambda_j^0}{2DkT}\right] g(x) - \left[\frac{\mathbf{F} e_j \kappa}{6\sqrt{2}\pi\eta_0 c \times 10^{-8}}\right] f(x) \tag{1}$$

The symbols are as usual: λ_j and λ_j^0, the conductances of ion j at finite and infinite dilution; e, the charge of the ion in units of the electronic charge; κ, the Debye-Hückel reciprocal of the average radius of the ion atmosphere surrounding ion j; D, the bulk dielectric constant of the solvent; k the Boltzmann constant; T the absolute temperature; $\mathbf{F}$, the value of the Faraday; η_0, the viscosity of the solvent; c, the molar concentration of the solute; $g(x)$, a factor accounting for the influence of the applied field in competition with the ionic field surrounding the ion, j; and $f(x)$ a factor expressing the effect of electrophoresis on the velocity of the ion in the external electric field. The quantity $g(x)$ falls rapidly from the value $g(0) = (2 - \sqrt{2})/3$, or 0.19526, at zero field, to only 0.00972, 20 times smaller, at 50 kv/cm and becomes zero at infinite field. In contrast, the quantity $f(x)$ falls

appreciably more slowly from $\sqrt{2} = 1.4142$ at zero field to 1.0710 at 50 kv/cm, a factor of 1.3-fold, and to unity at infinite field.

The initial and rapid rise of the conductance quotient with field is due to the rapid decrease of $g(x)$, reducing the size of the quantity which it multiplies and, since it is subtracted from λ_j^0, causing the conductance to increase. The function $g(x)$ expresses mathematically the influence of the surrounding ionic atmosphere (see Debye-Hückel theory) on the reference ion, j, and the interaction of the ion with the externally applied field and with the field of the ion atmosphere. Under the applied field, the ion, j, moves in one direction (toward the electrode of opposite sign) at a speed proportional to the magnitude of the field while the bulk of the ion atmosphere moves in the opposite direction. Since a finite time is required for the equilibrium stabilization of the cloud of ions of one charge surrounding an ion of opposite charge, the atmosphere will not have a chance to form if the ions move with sufficient speed. The effects of interionic attraction are the principal ones in solutions of wholly ionized electrolytes reducing the conductance from the higher value it would have at infinite dilution. The effect of the external field is thus to negate rapidly the effects of interionic attraction, so the conductance approaches the infinite dilution value.

At the same time, that portion of the conductance equation governed by $f(x)$ decreases in magnitude, further contributing to the rise in conductance; this change is small and does not vanish. Consequently, the conductance, λ_j, never reaches the value, λ_j^0, even at infinite field, because of the influence of the $f(x)$ factor. The quantity $f(x)$ expresses mathematically the retarding force on the movement of a hydrated ion due to the bulk viscosity of the solvent. Both positive and negative ions must make their way through water moving in different directions on hydrated ions. No matter how high the applied field, this hydrodynamic or electrophoretic retardation is never overcome, with the result that the λ_j at infinite field does not reach the value of λ_j^0.

The theory described is applicable only to electrolytes of symmetrical valence type. A more general statement of the problem is that of Onsager and Kim, Ref. 4, pp. 146–153.

The theory of Onsager for weak electrolytes in one form is expressed mathematically as

$$\frac{K(x)}{K(0)} = F(b) = 1 + b + \frac{b^2}{3}$$

$$+ \frac{b^3}{18} + \frac{b^4}{180} + \frac{b^5}{2700} + \cdots$$

for small values of b, where

$$b = \frac{z_1^2 z_2^2 (\lambda_1 + \lambda_2)}{z_2 \lambda_1 + z_1 \lambda_2} \frac{300 X \epsilon^3}{2Dk^2T^2} \qquad (2)$$

and if the electrolyte is 1-1,

$$b = 9.695 \frac{X}{DT^2}$$

The K's are the ionization constants at fields X and zero, z_1 and λ_1 are the valence (with sign) and the equivalent conductance of ion$_1$, etc; X is the field applied in volts/cm, and the remaining symbols have the same significance as before.

From an inspection of Eq. (2), it can be seen that the ratio of the equilibrium constants is linear in terms of the field, X, and dependent on the valences and mobilities of the ions. Inherent in the theory is the assumption that the applied field increases the rate of ionization of the weak electrolyte but has no effect on the rate of recombination of ions. Thus, application of a field increases the number of ions present and increases the conductance. The smaller $K(0)$, the larger is a proportional increase in $K(X)$ and, thus, in the number of ions and the conductance at a given field. The explanation for the experimentally observed linear increase of the conductance quotient with applied field and the influence of $K(0)$ is found in the facts just mentioned. However, as will be recalled, see Fig. 1, the plot for $\Delta\Lambda/\Lambda(0)$ vs field for a weak electrolyte extrapolates to a negative intercept. This is due to the influence of interionic attractions ordinarily neglected with weak electrolytes, or hidden in estimates of degrees of dissociation.

Methods of Measurement

Aqueous electrolytic solutions are usually highly conducting. To demonstrate conductance changes large enough to be measurable with precision, very large fields, ranging up to 300 kv/cm, must be applied. The combination of high conductivity and large fields results in the passage of very large currents through the solution, with consequent Joule heating at a rate easily reaching the megawatt range. As a consequence, nearly all investigators from Wien's time until now have chosen to work with short pulses in the microsecond range, thus reducing the power dissipated to a watt or so. With solutions of highly associated compounds of low conductivity, especially in nonaqueous solvents, the magnitude of the Wien effect is much larger and lower fields can be used, so that continuously sine-wave powered bridges, e.g., the Schering bridge, are entirely adequate. In the more usual case, a design to accomodate high-voltage pulses of short duration and consequent wide band width or high frequency is required in the bridge network. Balances for R + C components of the cell and bridge impedances are necessary. The designs of Gledhill and Patterson[5] and of Eigen[6] are typical. Of equal importance and special character are the conductance cells required in the measurement. All the usual design characteristics (see **Conductivity Measurement**) are desired, plus the ability to withstand high voltage and to maintain a definite electrode spacing so the field will be known and well defined.

Principal interest in the Wien effect has centered on using the phenomenon to study other chemical manifestations of interest, especially ion association and relaxation phenomena.

Patterson, Bailey and Freitag[7] have shown that higher valence types of strong electrolytes, e.g., $MgSO_4$, $La(III)Fe(III)(CN)_6$, deviate markedly from the predictions of the O-K theory, the measurements lying above the theory. They successfully corrected for this disagreement by assuming that an equilibrium such as

$$[Mg^{++}SO_4^{--}]^0 \rightleftharpoons Mg^{++} + SO_4^{--}; \quad K = 0.0063$$

was involved and also influenced by the field to contribute more ions, accounting for this by combining the weak and strong electrolytic theories of Onsager and coworkers in appropriate fashion and employing estimates of the value of K obtained from independent low-field conductance measurements. The results are shown also in Fig. 1. They add credence to the view that solutions of electrolytes of higher valence type, above 1-1, are significantly associated.

In another application of the method to determine a value of K not otherwise easily accessible, Patterson, Berg and Wissbrun[8] measured the HF conductance of solutions of carbon dioxide in water, and analyzed the data to obtain K, for the reaction

$$H_2CO_3 \rightarrow H^+ + HCO_3^-, \quad K = 1.72 \times 10^{-4} \text{ at } 25°.$$

Eigen, as he describes in Ref. 6, has used measurements of high-field conductance to study relaxation phenomena in a number of chemical systems. In addition to the experimental variables previously mentioned, the pulse length can also be varied. If there is a chemical reaction responsible for the presence of ions in solution, the reciprocal of the rate of which falls within the range of times conveniently available to the experimenter, then at a given field different conductance quotients will be measured as a function of pulse length. Another possibility of variation on the conductance with pulse length might be found in the times required for formation of the ionic atmosphere. Although these times are normally much shorter than the durations of the pulses ordinarily used, for large particles, such as colloid micelles, bulky ions, or polyelectrolytes, time-dependent effects may be observed to which ion atmosphere and other electrical and mechanical properties of the solute ions contribute. Eigen[6] has been strikingly successful in interpreting high-field conductance data to obtain rates of reactions and to investigate many other details of ionic behavior.

New evidence that the application of a high field to an electrolyte does not inevitably lead to an increase of conductance, as the foregoing discussion would suggest, is found in results of Patterson, Bailey, and Spinnler.[9] The high-field conductance of solutions of uranyl nitrate and perchlorate decreases in some cases when a high field is applied, the more spectacular examples of the phenomenon occurring at higher temperatures, 35 to 55°, where the hydrolysis of the solutions is extensive. A possible explanation of this unexpected phenomenon is that the high field reverses the hydrolysis reaction, and decreases the number of ions available to conduct.

References

1. WIEN, M., Ann. Physik., 4, 83, 327 (1927); ibid., 85, 795 (1928); Physik. Z., 28, 834 (1927); ibid., 29, 751 (1928).
2. ONSAGER, L., J. Chem. Phys., 2, 599 (1934).
3. ONSAGER, L., AND KIM, S. K., J. Phys. Chem., 61, 198 (1957).
4. HARNED, H. S., AND OWEN, B. B., "The Physical Chemistry of Electrolytic Solutions," 3rd ed., pp. 127–153, 183–193, 327–330, New York, Reinhold Publishing Corp., 1958.
5. PATTERSON, A., AND GLEDHILL, J. A., J. Phys. Chem., 56, 999 (1952).
6. EIGEN, M., in WEISSBERGER, A. (Ed.), "Technique of Organic Chemistry," Vol. 8, Part 2, 2nd Edition, New York, Interscience Publishers, 1963.
7. PATTERSON, A., AND FREITAG, H., J. Electrochem. Soc., 108, 529 (1961).
8. PATTERSON, A., AND WISSBRUN, K. F., J. Phys. Chem., 58, 693 (1954).
9. BAILEY, F. E., SPINNLER, J. F., AND PATTERSON, A., J. Am. Chem. Soc., 83, 1761 (1961).

ANDREW PATTERSON, JR.

Cross-references: *Activity and Activity Coefficient; Conductivity; Dissociation; Ion Association.*

WILLSON, THOMAS LEOPOLD (1861–1915)

Thomas Leopold Willson was born March 14, 1861 at Princeton, Ontario, near Hamilton, and was educated in the Hamilton public schools. At the Collegiate Institute he became interested in science, particularly electricity, and subsequently built one of Canada's first dynamos.

His interest in dynamos and electric furnaces led him to New York, where in 1885 he obtained a patent on an electric arc lamp. Several patents on dynamos and electrical machinery followed, and in 1889 he filed his first application on using an arc-type electric furnace to melt and reduce metals.

His work on the reduction of alumina by base metals interested James Turner Moorehead, of Spray, North Carolina, and the Willson Aluminum Company was formed. Large scale production, however, presented difficulties. In May, 1892, attempting to obtain metallic calcium for experiments with this process, Willson heated coal tar and lime together in his electric furnace. The resulting crystalline compound was a disappointing surprise. The usual story tells of the charge being dumped into a bucket of water and the resulting gas igniting from a heater. Another story—more logical but less romantic—says that the substance was tested for metallic calcium by being reacted with water and the evolved gas ignited. Instead of a hydrogen flame there appeared a very luminous, smokey flame indicative of a hydrocarbon!

The solid and the gas were sent to various authorities for analysis and were found to be calcium carbide and acetylene. Neither substance was new, having been discovered in 1840 and 1836, respectively, but no way of making them economically had yet been found. Willson obtained patents on his processes in 1895. The process was widely discussed in both Europe and United States, and acetylene was hailed as a boon to illumination.

A plant was started near Lynchburg, Va., but the difficulties of getting dynamos, coke, and capital caused Willson to sell his U.S. patent rights to the Electro Gas Company, which later became Union Carbide.

He moved to Merriton, Ontario, on the old Welland Canal, and set up the first hydroelectric plant in Canada, producing about one ton of calcium carbide per day in single-phase, batch-type furnaces. When the hydroelectric development at Shawinigan Falls, Quebec was opened up, the Shawinigan Carbide Company was formed with Willson as vice president, starting production in 1904.

Although Willson continued to experiment with the electric furnace, obtaining patents on reducing alumina in 1897, reducing calcium oxide in 1906, and producing metallic silicides in 1907 and 1909, most of his work during this period consisted of improvements in his process and means of storing, packaging, and use of acetylene. At least once the explosive nature of his product almost cost his life. Many patents were issued to him for signal buoys which generated and burned acetylene; other patents covered mechanical sounding buoys for fog. The International Marine Signal Company was formed with Willson as president, and his buoys were officially adopted by many governments.

Willson experienced success during his lifetime, since acetylene was so widely used for illumination and in the steel industry. However, the tremendous growth of calcium carbide as a chemical intermediate through acetylene and cyanamid gives his invention an importance he could not have imagined.

In 1911 Canada Carbide purchased Willson's manufacturing rights in Canada, and Willson's interests switched to the field of phosphatic fertilizers. He and Maximilian Mattheus Haff obtained many patents in this field over the next four years, none involving any of his old interests. One of these was issued to him eight days after his death in a New York hotel on December 20, 1915.

References

1. EIMER, AUGUST, *J. Electrochem. Soc.*, **51**, 73 (1927).
2. WARRINGTON, C. J. S., AND NICHOLLS, R. V. V., "A History of Chemistry in Canada," Chapter 7, Toronto, Sir Isaac Pitman and Sons (Canada) Ltd., 1949.
3. WILLSON, T. L., AND SUCKERT, J. J., *J. Franklin Inst.*, **139**, 321 (May, 1895).

ELIZABETH S. BENFORD

WORK FUNCTION

The work function is the energy required to remove an electron from a solid in the absence of all external potentials or fields. It may be considered as the latent heat of evaporation for electrons, although it is usually expressed as the energy required to remove a single electron rather than in molar quantities. The work function is commonly expressed in electron volts, but it is sometimes given in volts which must be multiplied by the electronic charge to obtain the energy. The work functions of the elements range from about 1.5 to 6.0 ev, and vary periodically with the atomic number. There is a good correlation[1] with various other properties, including ionization energy, standard electrode potential, and cohesive energy.

More precisely, in a metal, the work function is the energy required to take an electron from the Fermi level to a point just outside the surface. The Fermi level, in any solid, is that energy which is equal to the electrochemical potential of the electrons and, furthermore, in a metal it is the maximum energy an electron can have at zero degrees Kelvin. By defining the work function as the work done in taking the electron just outside the surface any difficulty with arbitrary potentials and stray fields is eliminated, but the concept of "just outside" must be defined. By considering electrostatic image forces it has been shown[2] that a distance of 100 to 1000 Å is sufficiently large to include all the work,

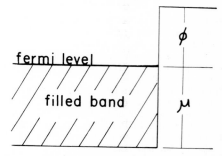

FIG. 1. Idealized energy levels in a metal.

but small enough to eliminate other effects. The work that must be done to remove an electron may be separated into two parts:[3] the internal work, which is the electrostatic work in separating the electron from the solid, and that due to the electrical double layer that exists at the surface of any solid. The original calculation by Wigner and Bardeen[4] shows that the internal work provides the largest contribution in pure, clean metals, and for the alkali metals this contribution alone gives good agreement with the experimental values. The double layer at the surface will contribute about 0.5 ev in clean metals, but may be the major factor when absorbed films are involved (e.g., a monolayer of cesium on tungsten lowers the work function from 4.5 to approximately 2.0 ev).[5] The work function will be a very sensitive function of surface condition and all measurements must be made under ultrahigh vacuum or other controlled conditions. The work function will also depend on the crystal direction, because the different crystal planes have different surface dipole moments. The work function is also a function of the temperature. This is due both to changes in the electrochemical potential and to other changes in the solid with temperature. The total effect is small for metals, amounting to something on the order of 10^{-5} to 10^{-4} ev/°K. In semiconductors, where the free electron density and the Fermi level change rapidly with temperature, one expects larger changes in the work function. The definition given here also applies to semiconductors and insulators. However, due to the band structure the electrochemical potential may fall in the forbidden gap, and there will be no electrons with that energy. This does not affect the basic concepts, but one must be careful in making measurements.

In Figs. 1 and 2 are shown the idealized energy levels in a metal and in an intrinsic semiconductor. The work function, ϕ, is as shown and μ is the electrochemical potential of the electrons.

This definition may be called the "true work function." It is an idealization that applies to clean, perfect surfaces. Measurements of the work function do not yield the true work function, but always reflect the measurement technique. Three methods of measurement are in common use; thermionic emission, photoelectric emission, and contact potential difference. The collected data are usually labeled as to the measurement technique. The first two methods

give absolute values which agree fairly well if temperature and other corrections are made. The contact potential difference method yields a relative value with respect to a standard surface (e.g., well-aged polycrystalline tungsten or gold).

The thermionic emission from a solid follows the well-known Richardson-Dushman equation:

$$J = AT^2 e^{-\phi/kT} \tag{1}$$

where J is the emission current density, A is a constant theoretically equal to 120 amp/(°K)^2, T is the absolute temperature, k is Boltzmann's constant and ϕ is the work function. If the current density is measured as a function of temperature, then the work function can be calculated. This method obviously is limited to those materials that will give measurable currents below their melting point. This may also preclude measurement of certain phases which exist only at the lower temperatures and, of course, it cannot be used to study the effect of surface conditions unless they are stable at elevated temperatures. Various values of the work function result from this technique. This has been discussed by Hensley[6] who has defined the following terms: "effective work function," which is the value obtained by solving the equation for ϕ using the theoretical value of A and "Richardson work function," which is obtained by plotting log J/T^2 vs $1/T$. The slope of that line yields ϕ_r and the intercept, A_r. Much of the older thermionic data is given in terms of the Richardson work function. However, the effective work function is preferred because it gives a value for a specific value of temperature rather than averaging over temperature. The effective work

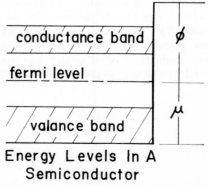

Energy Levels In A Semiconductor

Fig. 2. Idealized energy levels in an intrinsic semiconductor.

function also gives better agreement with measurements made by other techniques. Nottingham[7] has given a thorough discussion of the theory and practical measuring techniques.

The photoelectric values are obtained by measuring photoemission current against photon energy. As Einstein has shown, there is a minimum energy $h\nu = \phi$ (where h is Planck's constant, and ν is the frequency) below which no electrons are ejected. Because of the statistical nature of the problem it is not possible to accurately determine ϕ from a simple plot and the Fowler-Dubridge[8] technique is used. Photoelectric measurements may be made at all temperatures below that for which thermionic emission is detected. The anomalous behavior near the curie point is discussed by Ames and Christensen[9] who also have a good description of the techniques used to determine the photoelectric work function. Photoelectric work functions for semiconductors must be examined carefully. In a semiconductor there may not be any electrons at the Fermi level and all the photoelectrons come either from the conduction band or the valence band. Semiconductors also have surface states which affect the band structure over a much larger range than in a metal. These surface states may extend into the material a distance greater than the depth of penetration for the photons. This must be considered in interpreting such measurements.

A contact potential difference arises whenever two dissimilar conductors or semiconductors are placed in contact. This potential arises because the electrochemical potential of the two conductors must be the same when they are in contact, hence electrons will flow from one metal into the other until this condition is satisfied. This will result in a potential difference at the free surfaces equal to the difference in the work functions. This potential can be measured in various ways. A vibrating capacitor technique (Kelvin method) is often used.[10] The contact potential method may be used to study the effects of various absorbed films, and even to watch the formation of such films in various atmospheres. Anderson,[11] in a long series of papers, and more recently Riviere[12] have used this method. Because it gives only the difference in work functions, one must have an absolute determination of the work function of a reference surface. Tungsten is often used because it can be cleaned at high temperatures and because its work function is well known. Gold has also been used, especially in studies of absorbed films and semiconductors. This technique is often used for semiconductors where the thermionic emission technique is not applicable because of temperature limitations and because photoemission depends on the band structure and surface states.

References

1. MICHAELSON, H. B., *Jour. Appl. Phys.*, **21**, 536 (1950).
2. CUSACK, N., "The Electrical and Magnetic Properties of Solids," p. 35 ff, London, Longmans Green and Co., 1958.
3. SEITZ, F., "The Modern Theory of Solids," Chapt. XI, New York, McGraw-Hill Book Co., 1940.
4. WIGNER, E., AND BARDEEN, J., *Phys. Rev.*, **48**, 84 (1935).
5. BOER, J. H., "Electron Emission and Absorption Phenomena," London, Cambridge Univ., 1935.
6. HENSLEY, E. B., *Jour. Appl. Phys.*, **32, 301** (1961).
7. NOTTINGHAM, W. B., "Handbuch der Physik," Vol. 21, p. 1, Berlin, Springer, 1956.
8. DUBRIDGE, L. A., "New Theories of the Photoelectric Effect," Paris, Hermann and Cie., 1935.
9. AMES, I., AND CHRISTENSEN, R. L., *I.B.M. Jour.*, **7**, 34 (1963).
10. ZISMAN, W. A., *Rev. Sci. Inst.*, **3**, 367 (1932).
11. ANDERSON, P. A., *Phys. Rev.*, **115**, 553 (1959).
12. RIVIERE, S. C., *Proc. Phys. Soc. (London)*, **70B,** 696 (1957).

LAWRENCE C. SCHOLZ

Cross-references: *Contact Potential; Semiconductors.*

X

XEROGRAPHY

Xerography is a relatively new photographic process based on the physical phenomena of photoconductivity and electrostatic attraction, rather than on photochemical reactions as are other photographic processes. Briefly, xerography involves a thin, highly insulating photoconductive film, on an electrically conductive base plate, which is given a strong electrical surface charge and then exposed to a light or an x-ray image. Where light or x-rays strike the plate, the photoconductive film becomes conductive and the surface charge flows through the film to the base plate. In dark areas of the image, the surface charge remaining is used to attract and hold colored particles of powder which are brought close to the plate in a development step, thus producing a visible image corresponding to the original light image. The powder image thus produced can be examined on the plate, fixed to the plate to form a permanent image, or transferred to another surface—such as a sheet of ordinary paper—and fixed thereon to form the final image. The whole process is dry and rapid, certain xerographic plates can be reused many times, and images produced are of good quality. The process is particularly adaptable to the making of photocopies of graphic materials and promises to be good enough for reproducing microimages or for continuous-tone photography.

Xerography, formerly called electrophotography, was invented and patented by Chester F. Carlson. In a nomenclature adopted by the Institute of Electrical and Electronic Engineers, it is considered as a subclass under more general classes of processes called electrostatography and electrostatic electrophotography. Early developmental research on the process was carried out at Battelle Memorial Institute of Columbus, Ohio and first commercial applications of the process were made by Xerox Corporation of Rochester, New York. RCA has contributed to a number of processes in the field, for example, in the areas of disposable paper plates and magnetic-brush development, and many other companies now are offering commercial equipment using the process or are conducting research toward that end, including IBM, Stromberg-Carlson, Charles Bruning Co., American Photocopy Equipment Co., Keuffel & Esser Co., Smith-Corona-Marchant, and others.

In greater detail, xerography requires the following process elements:

(1) A xerographic plate consisting, for example, of a photoconductive insulating film on an electrically conductive base plate, perhaps 20 to 100 microns thick and having a resistivity in darkness of over 10^{14} ohm-centimeters.

(2) The surface of this plate is given an electrical charge by placing it near wires perhaps 90 microns in diameter raised to a potential of something like 7,000 volts. Ions, formed in the corona discharge resulting from these conditions, accumulate on the plate to produce a potential difference across the photoconductive film of 600 volts in a typical case.

(3) This sensitized plate is exposed to a light image, by projection or contact, or to an x-ray image. During exposure the electrical potential across the photoconductive film in each increment of area is decreased in proportion to the intensity of the light and the time of exposure for that area.

(4) The resulting electrostatic image left on the plate after exposure is developed by bringing to its surface finely divided resinous powders whose particles carry an electrostatic charge. Perhaps the simplest way to do this is by gently brushing such powders across the plate and blowing off the excess. Much more sophisticated methods are used in practical machines.

(5) With inexpensive and light colored photoconductive films on paper supports, the final image may be fixed to the plate, typically by

heating or exposure to solvent vapors. With more expensive reusable plates, the image is transferred to inexpensive paper by laying the paper on the powder image and passing the combination a second time under the corona wires which were used to sensitize the plate. After this, the image is fixed to the final paper, commonly by heating or exposure to solvent vapors.

(6) With expendable paper plates the process is complete at this point. With reusable plates, the residual image must by cleaned off of the plate, after which it is ready for another use.

The Photosensitive Surface

Xerographic plates are made by coating a conductive base plate or conductive paper with a thin layer of an insulating photoconductor. The most successful reusable plates are made by vacuum evaporating onto a metal plate a 20 to 100 micron layer of vitreous selenium. Such films exhibit resistivities in darkness greater than 10^{16} ohm-centimeters, are sensitive to light in the blue half of the visible spectrum, have a sensitivity roughly equivalent to an ASA Exposure Index of 2, and can be used to produce from tens to hundreds of thousands of images before they cease to function properly. Ordinarily such members are made in the form of rigid flat plates or cylinders, but they can be made as flexible belts for special purposes.

One-use xerographic surfaces are frequently made on a slightly conductive paper base with paint-like films of a resin binder loaded with particulate forms of zinc oxide. An interesting property of such films is that dye sensitization works with them much as it does with silver halide photographic emulsions.

More recently, considerable promise is being shown by organic photoconductors as xerographic films, particularly as mixed with resinous binders. It appears likely that only a beginning has been made in this area.

Ordinarily one might expect the light sensitivity of xerographic plates to be limited to 100 per cent quantum efficiency, that is, where every photon of light liberates one current carrier in the photoconductor. A maximum quantum efficiency of 30 per cent is achieved by selenium for blue light. However, phenomena exist that might lead to plates with more than a 100 per cent efficiency.

Sensitizing the Plate

The above brief description of this operation is sufficient. Thought has been given to frictional and other methods for producing an electrical charge on the photoconductive surface, but none of these methods has challenged the simplicity and effectiveness of the corona-discharge method in practical applications.

Xerographic Development

Xerographic developers and development are extremely simple in principle but much more complex in practice. In principle, it is necessary only to bring finely divided electrically charged powder into the electrostatic fields extending above the charged image areas of the exposed plate. Such powder might consist of almost anything from simple carbon or pigments for colored images to complex mixtures of pigments and special binders to produce images for special purposes, even up to reactive chemicals or ceramic frits for very specialized applications where images have purposes other than just to be viewed.

In commercial xerography today, developer powders—sometimes called toners—comprise resins and pigments, and are approximately equivalent in composition to dried black paint or some forms of printing ink. However, practical developers must have, in addition, the right polarity and quantity of electrical charge when used in particular development processes; they must melt at a temperature suitable for fixing the final image onto real substances such as on paper; they must be quite hydrophobic if they are to be used in summer climates; and they must not soften at common ambient temperatures or leave soiling films on plates or equipment. Ordinarily, developer powders are reduced to a size range of 10 to 15 microns, generally in fluid-energy mills.

The mechanical process of development can take may forms. The most common commercial form has been called carrier development or cascade development because it involves a second coarse granular material whose function is to "carry" the toner across the photoconductive surface, or because the process is normally performed by "cascading" across the surface this mixture of carrier and toner. The coarser carrier serves to make it easy to manipulate the toner over the plate; powders as finely ground as xerographic toners are difficult to handle in practical conveyor systems. A second and most important function of the carrier is to produce an electrical charge of the right polarity on the toner particles. This is achieved by selecting, as the carrier material, or as a coating over carrier particles, a substance which is far from the finer material in the triboelectric series and that is on the proper side of the toner in this series to give the desired polarity. When this relationship exists, the jostling of a mixture of the two powders produces the correct charge on the toner powder by contact electrification so that it will be attracted and held to image areas of the latent electrostatic image on the exposed plate.

Many other arrangements can be used to charge the toner powder and to convey it to the plate. Properly selected fur brushes can be used, or magnetic brushes formed on the poles of a magnet from a ferromagnetic carrier material. Shaded images can be produced from air suspensions of powder brought close to the exposed plate, either in an open chamber near the plate or in a confined slot between the plate and a "development electrode" quite close to the plate. Open-chamber powder-cloud development is normally used in commercial xeroradiography. A most interesting form of development involves immersing the exposed plate in a highly insulating liquid bearing finely divided pigment, such as an artists' color. Such mixtures almost inevitably produce electrical charges on the pigment particles and such charges lead to the development of the latent electrostatic image. Still other forms of development may be devised based on bringing close to the exposed plate webs of various substances bearing toner powder.

It appears very likely that many forms of development will find commercial application, with the form selected depending on requirements of the process. Powder-cloud and liquid-immersion development are elaborate but can give very good image rendition, particularly where gradations of density must be reproduced. Liquid-immersion development is now being used in at least one commercial photocopy machine. Granular-carrier and magnetic-brush development have properties suiting them for machines designed to copy documents.

Transfer and Fixing of the Image

These process steps are so simple that the earlier description suffices for this short article.

Where transfer is required, from 50 to 90 per cent of the powder image on the plate can be transferred to the final paper and, with proper fixing, this forms an image quite like that formed in good printing processes as far as permanence and wear resistance are concerned.

Applications of Xerography

Xerography promises to find many uses. Its most obvious application is that of present photocopy xerographic machines in making inexpensive reproductions of primarily line originals, to make paper offset lithographic masters, and to enlarge from microfilm. Xerographic resist images have been used for etched printed circuits, and images have been placed on cloth, wood, and ceramics. Continuous-tone images for black and white photography can be made of sufficient quality for commercial and amateur use in prints. Color reproductions involve only the use of three separate applications of this process with colored powders and with a very nice control over the reproduction characteristics of the process. As mentioned above, extremely small images can be made so that microimage systems seem attainable eventually, with the advantages of low cost and rapid delivery of the final image.

The above applications involve the production of images that are used in and of themselves. Xerography also has found and will find uses in producing special-purpose images for other processes. It probably will be used for applying resists to metal plates in the making of letterpress printing plates or in the preparation of etched electronic circuits. It very likely will find application for other purposes, such as the forming of objects of metal or in the applications of adhesives in special patterns.

One promising application is to the production of radiographs of industrial objects and to medical radiography for special purposes where radiation limits are not important.

Reference

RHEINFRANK, J. J., AND WALKUP, L. E., "Current Status of Electrostatic Reproduction Processes," Proceedings of the Technical Association of the Graphic Arts, pp. 112–143, Rochester, N.Y., 1961. This status report contains over 90 references.

LEWIS E. WALKUP

Cross-references: *Electrostatic Coating Processes; Photoconductivity.*

Z

ZERO CHARGE POTENTIAL. See BILLITER PO-
TENTIAL; LIPPMANN POTENTIAL.

ZETA POTENTIAL. See ELECTROCAPILLARY
PHENOMENA; ELECTROKINETIC POTEN-
TIALS; STREAMING POTENTIAL.

ZINC AND CADMIUM ELECTROWINNING

Zinc

Approximately 38 per cent of all slab zinc
produced in the United States and in the world
is derived by electrowinning processes in which
a solution of zinc sulfate, made by the leaching
of zinc oxide from ores and concentrates with
sulfuric acid, is electrolyzed in cells containing
aluminum cathodes and lead anodes. In recent
years the United States production of electrolytic zinc has been about 360,000 tons annually,
and the total world production has been about
1,400,000 tons annually, indicating that the electrowinning of zinc is one of the major electrochemical industries.

As shown in Table 1, there are four companies
operating five plants in the United States, and
two companies with one plant each operating in
Canada. The American companies have operated
at about three-quarters to full rated capacity in
recent years and the Canadian companies at
slightly above rated capacities. For the world as
a whole, production of electrolytic zinc has been
well over 80 per cent of total rated plant
capacity.

While the electrolytic process was proposed
and patented by Léon Létrange of France in
1881, the first successful electrolytic zinc plant
began began production at Anaconda, Montana,
in 1915. The process offers the means of producing high-purity zinc from complex sulfide ores
not readily exploited by pyrometallurgical processes and of recovering the other desirable constituents present in the ore.

The principal raw material for the process is
zinc calcine, obtained by the furnace roasting of
sulfide-type ores or concentrates which converts
the sulfides to oxides. Other sources of zinc-
bearing materials, such as zinc oxide fume from
lead smelters, can also be used. The zinc calcine
contains 50 to 65 per cent zinc, the bulk of
which is zinc oxide, with a smaller portion, up
to 4 per cent, of zinc sulfate and a few per cent
of zinc ferrite.

The process consists essentially of three steps:
the leaching of the calcine or other material containing zinc oxide with dilute sulfuric acid obtained from the electrolysis cells; the purification of the zinc sulfate solution to eliminate the
several undesired elements which profoundly
affect the electrolysis; and the electrolysis of
this purified zinc sulfate solution. The leaching
stage can be exemplified by the reaction:

$$ZnO + H_2SO_4 \rightarrow ZnSO_4 + H_2O.$$

The electrolysis operation is represented by the
reaction:

$$2ZnSO_4 + 2H_2O \rightarrow 2Zn + 2H_2SO_4 + O_2.$$

The zinc is deposited on the cathode and oxygen is liberated at the anode of the cell. The
sulfuric acid generated in the cell is recirculated
to the leaching operation with such additional
acid as is needed to replace process losses.

Although the process appears simple, it is
actually quite complex as operated on the large
scale, chiefly because of the extreme care which
must be taken to attain high extraction efficiency and to provide the very high purity required in the zinc sulfate solution fed to the
cells. The schematic flowsheet of Fig. 1 indicates
this complexity.

Leaching. The leaching of the zinc oxide raw
material is associated with the various purification operations, and the methods used can be
divided into two types, the single and the double
leach, both conducted in a combination of batch

TABLE 1. ELECTROLYTIC ZINC PLANTS IN THE UNITED STATES AND CANADA

	Capacity, annual tons	1962 Production, tons
American Smelting and Refining Company, Corpus Christi, Texas	105,000	89,832
American Zinc Company of Illinois, Monsanto, Illinois	60,000	59,918
Anaconda Company, Great Falls, Montana	162,000	129,144
Anaconda Company, Anaconda, Montana	80,500	58,400
Bunker Hill Company, Kellogg, Idaho	77,000	76,756
Consolidated Mining and Smelting Company of Canada Ltd., Trail, B.C.	195,000	199,393
Hudson Bay Mining and Smelting Company, Flin Flon, Manitoba	80,000	80,766

and continuous operation steps. The double-leach method shown in Fig. 1 will be described.

Zinc calcine is added to some of the spent electrolytic cell liquor, which usually contains 10 to 12 per cent H_2SO_4 and 3 to 4 per cent $ZnSO_4$, in a mechanically agitated tank. The major portion of the ZnO reacts to form $ZnSO_4$; and, simultaneously, other elements, such as arsenic, antimony, copper, cadmium, iron, nickel, tin, germanium, selenium, tellurium, silicon, and aluminum, also are dissolved. Ferrous sulfate, derived from the iron in the calcine (or from scrap iron if not extractable in sufficient amount from the calcine), is oxidized to ferric sulfate by the addition of MnO_2 and plays an important role in the purification of the solution. It is precipitated as ferric hydroxide as the neutralization of the leach solution with ZnO occurs and carries with it such impurities as arsenic, antimony, tellurium, germanium,

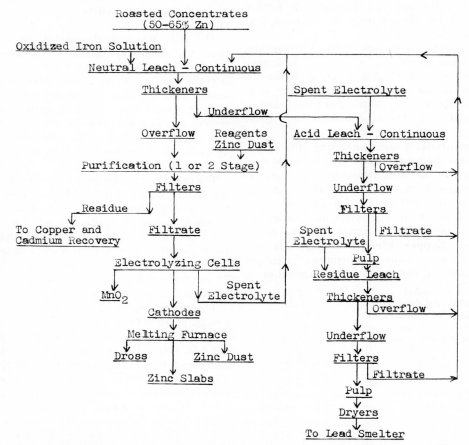

FIG. 1. Simplified flowsheet of electrolytic zinc plant using double leach process. (From Ref. 1)

alumina, and silica. The precipitation of ferric hydroxide is represented by the equation:

$$Fe_2(SO_4)_3 + 3ZnO + 3H_2O \rightarrow 2Fe(OH)_3 + 3ZnSO_4 .$$

The slurry from the neutral leach stage is thickened, the overflow being treated with zinc dust and other reagents to remove undesired impurities. The zinc dust displaces copper and cadmium by a cementation reaction, for example, $Zn + CuSO_4 \rightarrow Cu + ZnSO_4$. Other metals below zinc in the electromotive series are similarly precipitated. After filtration the filtrate enters the electrolysis cells. The underflow from the neutral leach stage thickeners is treated in the second or acid leach process with spent cell liquor to dissolve the remainder of the extractable zinc and copper content. After thickening and filtration, the solution is returned to the initial leach stage, and the solids are sent to a lead smelter for recovery of lead. The solids formed by the zinc dust treatment are further processed for the recovery of cadmium and copper.

The specific operations in the leaching and purification of the zinc sulfate cell feed vary considerably from plant to plant, as do the operations of the electrolysis part of the total process. Many of the details about the practices in individual plants can be found in Refs. 1 and 2.

Electrolysis. A high-purity zinc sulfate solution is easily electrolyzed between insoluble electrodes, with zinc being deposited at the cathode and oxygen at the anode. While the theoretical decomposition voltage is 2.25 volts, commercial cells operate at 3.0 to 3.7 volts, most commonly at the upper end of this range. As Butts points out (see **Copper Electrowinning**), the cell voltage is about twice that required for copper electrowinning, and typically is comprised of:

Reaction potential	2.25 v
Electrolyte IR drop	0.75
Resistance of contacts, etc.	0.15
Oxygen gas voltage	0.45
Hydrogen gas voltage	0.10
	3.70

The decomposition voltage of 2.25 v is higher than the decomposition voltage for water, but the high hydrogen overvoltage on a zinc electrode, 2.4 v, permits the deposition of zinc rather than hydrogen at the cathode in the $ZnSO_4$ electrolysis cell. Many factors influence the hydrogen

overvoltage in commercial cells, and those which lower it must be avoided. Among the most important are impurities in the $ZnSO_4$ solution, for example, germanium, arsenic, antimony, cobalt, nickel, and copper.

The zinc sulfate solution enters the cell at a zinc concentration of 110 to 135 gpl, although some plants operate at higher concentrations of 170 and 215 gpl. Only a portion of the zinc content is depleted in each cycle, and the solution leaves the cell at a concentration of 45 to 55 gpl of zinc. The sulfuric acid formed during electrolysis increases until the final depleted solution leaving the cell contains 100 to 110 gpl, although the plants operating with the higher $ZnSO_4$ content solutions discharge a solution containing 20 to 27 per cent H_2SO_4. Actually, the cells are arranged in cascades of 6 to 9 cells for flow purposes with the discharge from each cell passing through the rest of the cells in the cascade. Each cell is fed individually. Thus, the acid and zinc concentrations vary slightly in any one cell.

The cells are large, horizontal, rectangular tanks that usually are constructed of lead-lined wood or concrete. The sheet electrodes hang laterally from conductor bars into the tank and usually are arranged alternately anode and cathode, spaced about 3 inches anode to anode center. A plant will contain several hundred cells. They are connected in series electrically by banks whose number is based on the available d-c voltage.

The cathodes are high-purity aluminum sheets $\frac{3}{32}$ to $\frac{3}{16}$ inches thick welded or riveted at the top to aluminum header bars. Edge strips of wood, rubber, or plastic are sometimes fastened to the sheets to prevent zinc being deposited on the edges. Several months of service life can be attained for the aluminum cathodes. At intervals of 8 to 24 hours the cathodes are removed and the zinc deposits stripped.

The anodes are pure lead or lead-silver alloys containing 0.5 to 1 per cent Ag and range in thickness from $\frac{3}{16}$ to $\frac{3}{8}$ inches. Most of the plants use solid sheets, but in some cases the anode is perforated to improve electrolyte circulation. The anodes are cast around or welded to copper header bars. Their life may be as high as 2 to 4 years. Spacers or guides attached to the cell walls maintain uniform spacing between anodes and cathodes and also prevent warping of the anodes. Manganese present in the cell feed is deposited on the anodes as manganese dioxide in the form of a loose deposit, which is removed periodically together with the MnO_2 sludge on the cell bottom. This MnO_2 is used to oxidize ferrous ion to ferric in the $ZnSO_4$ purification steps, and the excess is washed, filtered, dried, and sold.

The cathode current density in zinc cells is in the range of 30 to 40 amp/sq ft in low-density plants and 60 and 100 in the higher density plants. The operating temperature is maintained at 30 to 40°C for optimum electrolysis conditions. It varies directly with the current density. Heat must be removed from the cells, either by internal cooling coils of lead, aluminum, or stainless steel, or by external cooling in tanks, coils, or evaporative-type towers through which the electrolyte is circulated. Current efficiency is usually 90 per cent or more, and the power consumption is 1.4 to 1.6 kwh/lb of zinc.

The principal metallic impurities in the zinc deposited in the cells are copper, cadmium, and lead, each of which deposits at a lower voltage than does zinc. The purification of the electrolyte is the main factor which controls the amounts of copper and cadmium in the final zinc metal. However, corrosion of the lead anodes and tank linings and of the copper bus bars and header bars by the acidic cell solutions, chiefly by acid mist, can introduce both metals into the deposited zinc. The use of a frothing agent, for instance, a mixture of cresylic acid, sodium silicate, and gum arabic, is effective in decreasing the acid mist above the solution caused by oxygen evolution from the anodes. A slurry of strontium carbonate or barium hydroxide added to the cells is effective in reducing the lead content of the zinc deposit.

The zinc is stripped from the cathodes at intervals, melted in reverberatory or induction furnaces, and cast into 56 pound slabs. The bulk of the cathode zinc meets Special High Grade specifications, but High Grade, Prime Western, and other grades are also produced in the melting furnaces.

Cadmium

About 40 per cent of the approximately 10 million pounds of cadmium produced annually in the United States is a by-product of electrolytic zinc plants. The chief source is the zinc-dust purification residue resulting from the preparation of zinc sulfate solutions. The residue, containing cadmium, copper, and zinc, is dissolved in acid zinc-cadmium sulfate cell liquor and the solution subsequently electrolyzed with lead anodes and aluminum cathodes. Other sources of cadmium, such as flue dust, can also be used.

The initial leaching of the residues is done with zinc cell solution containing 10 to 12 per cent H_2SO_4, and the resulting solution is thickened before the overflow is treated with sufficient zinc dust to remove copper as a solid. The high-copper residue is filtered off and shipped to a copper smelter. The solution (filtrate) is treated with excess zinc dust to precipitate all of the cadmium as a sponge which is filtered off, the filtrate being returned to the zinc plant. After the sponge has been allowed to oxidize in the air for several weeks to improve the solution rate, it is then leached with spent electrolyte from the cadmium cells. The latter solution contains 60 to 90 gpl H_2SO_4, about 65 gpl zinc, and about 30 gpl cadmium.

Electrolyte entering the cadmium cells contains 100 to 200 gpl cadmium, about 60 gpl zinc, and a small amount of sulfuric acid. Glue is added to reduce the tendency of cadmium to deposit in irregular forms. It is electrolyzed in cells essentially the same as those used for zinc sulfate electrolysis with closely spaced, alternately arranged, vertical lead anodes and aluminum cathodes. Cell voltage is 2.5 to 2.7 v, and the cathode current density is 4 to 10 amp/sq ft, much lower than that in zinc cells. The current efficiency is about 90 per cent and the power consumption is 0.65 to 0.82 kwh/lb Cd. The operating temperature is maintained at 20 to 35°C by the use of cooling coils usually located in the cell. Zinc is not deposited with the cadmium in the cells.

The cells are arranged in cascades and fed individually. A portion of the spent electrolyte is replaced each cycle to keep down the zinc content and may be used to leach the zinc-dust purification residue. The portion withdrawn is replaced with fresh acid or by spent zinc electrolyte of low zinc content.

At daily intervals the cathodes are stripped of the deposited cadmium sheets which are washed and dried before being melted in pots under a layer of caustic soda. The molten cadmium of very high purity is then cast into bars, balls, pencils, anodes, and other commercial forms.

References

1. WEIMER, F. S., WEVER, G. T., AND LAPEE, R. J., "Electrolytic Zinc Processes," pp. 174–224, in "Zinc, the Metal, Its Alloys and Compounds," C. H. Mathewson, Editor, New York, Reinhold Publishing Corp., 1959.
2. MANTELL, C. L., "Electrochemical Engineering," pp. 210–231, New York, McGraw-Hill Book Co., Inc., 1960.
3. AUSTIN, E., AND McFADDEN, W. F., "The Electrolytic Zinc Plant of the Hudson Bay Mining and Smelting Company Ltd.," *Trans. Can. Inst. Mining Met.*, **59**, 208 (1956).
4. CUNNINGHAM, G. H., AND JEPHSON, A. C., "Electrolytic Zinc at Corpus Christi, Texas," *Trans. Am. Inst. Mining Met. Engrs.*, **159**, 194 (1944).
5. MOORE, T. I., AND PAINTER, L. A., "Electrolytic Zinc Plant at Monsanto, Illinois," *J. Metals*, **4**, 1149 (1952).
6. SNOW, W. C., "Electrolytic Zinc Plant at Risdon, Tasmania," *Trans. Am. Inst. Mining Met. Engrs.*, **121**, 482 (1936).
7. STIMMEL, B. A., HANNAY, W. H., AND McBEAN, K. D., "Electrolytic Zinc Plant of the Consolidated Mining and Smelting Company of Canada Ltd., *ibid.*, p. 540.

Additional specific references are given in Refs. 1 and 2.

CLIFFORD A. HAMPEL

Cross-references: *Copper Electrowinning; Electrogalvanizing.*

ZINC, ELECTROTHERMIC PRODUCTION

Energy requirements for producing zinc are higher than for most common metals, such as copper, lead, iron, and tin. Favorable equilibrium for the reduction of zinc oxide by carbon is achieved only at temperatures greater than the boiling point of zinc (907° C). Commercially feasible reaction rates require even higher temperatures. These considerations place great economic importance on the method of supplying thermal energy to the zinc oxide-carbon charge.

Difficulty in heating the charge delayed for many years the development of large-scale zinc smelting furnaces. The externally-heated retort method was the only one employed. Thermal efficiency was low. To achieve a reasonable degree of zinc reduction required many hours of treatment time.

Early investigators recognized the inherent potential of an electric furnace for overcoming these problems. The Cowles Brothers[6] in Cleveland, Ohio, designed and patented a process in 1885. This did not attain commercial success. Gustave De Laval[3] developed an open arc furnace in 1898 at Trolhättan, Sweden. Over the years, considerable development took place and a commercial process resulted. Due to difficulty in condensing the zinc vapor, the furnace production was principally blue powder, a mixture of metallic zinc and zinc oxide particles. A separate electrically-heated liquating furnace coalesced this powder. Overall power consumption amounted to 6,550 kwh/ton of product metal, and operations were eventually terminated.

Others worked on various types of furnaces, including one which was resistance heated,[6] but with no commercial success. The major problem, until the St. Joseph Lead Company development, was that the condensing systems were not capable, as single units, of condensing sufficient zinc vapor into liquid metal.

Today there are five electrothermic zinc smelters in the world: one in Germany, one in Argentina, one in Japan (of which little is known), one in Missouri, and the large Josephtown Smelter of the St. Joseph Lead Company. The Argentina plant employs the Josephtown process.

The St. Joseph Lead Company Vertical Electrothermic Furnace

The St. Joseph Lead Company developed the first commercially successful electrothermic process in the Western Hemisphere. The process employs resistance heating of the reactants. In 1930, at Josephtown, Pennsylvania, a plant was built for producing zinc oxide. In 1936, a liquid zinc condenser was developed which matched in condensation capability the vapor production of the furnace. Today, individual furnace-condenser units are producing in excess of 65 tons daily of zinc metal.

There is no basic difference between oxide and metal-producing furnaces. To produce zinc oxide, the vapors venting from the furnace are oxidized with air. To produce metal, the vapors are bubbled through a large U-tube filled with molten zinc—the Weaton-Najarian condenser.

The furnaces are vertical refractory cylinders up to nine feet in internal diameter and fifty feet high. The barrel is constructed in cylindrical sections. Each section is supported on independent skew rings. The bottom section is supported by a water-cooled ring. Most of the furnace barrel is constructed of high-duty, low-porosity firebrick. Fig. 1 shows general features of a metal furnace.

Operation is continuous. A rotary distributor seals the furnace top and positions a preheated (750°C) mixture of sized coke and zinc oxide-containing sinter (56 to 59 per cent zinc) about ten inches inside the periphery of the furnace wall, an action which promotes development of optimum temperature distribution. By depositing the charge close to the furnace wall, the larger particles of coke tend to roll toward the furnace axis. This causes the axial region of the furnace to be more electrically conductive than the outer region which helps prevent over-heated walls. The rotary discharge table regulates the withdrawal rate of smelted charge from the furnace (some liquid slag is present in the spent charge, but the excess of coke present makes the charge behave as if it were dry).

The charge, containing about equal volumes of sinter and coke, is the electrical resistance.

Twelve-inch diameter graphite electrodes, positioned near the top of the furnace and near the bottom, introduce electricity. The arrangement forms eight individual single-phase circuits, each with a vertical resistance path of about thirty feet through the furnace charge.

The upper electrodes are sloped downward thirty degrees from the horizontal. They are normally inserted fifteen to seventeen inches inside the furnace. Electrodes, consumed at the rate of about 1¼ inches per day, are repositioned every five days. Nonscheduled adjustments are made if temperature excursions are experienced near the furnace walls. The lower electrodes are inserted horizontally; they do not require repositioning but are occasionally replaced. Total electrode consumption is about 2.3 pounds per ton of zinc produced.

Power input per electrode circuit ranges upwards to 950 kw. Normally each circuit draws 700 to 800 kw, corresponding to about 5500 to 6500 kw per furnace. The voltage can be regulated from 160 to 300 volts; normally it is 200

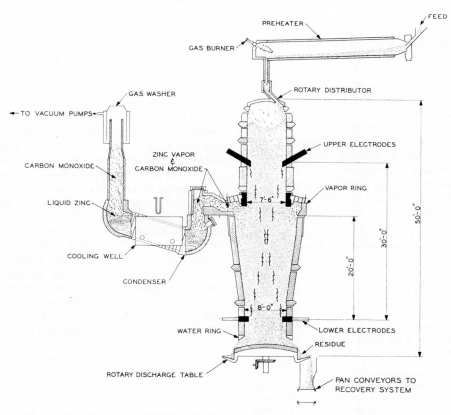

FIG. 1. Josephtown electrothermic zinc furnace. [*Courtesy St. Joseph Lead Co.*]

to 230 volts. Automatic regulators control furnace power. Within the furnace, temperature ranges from about 900°C near the wall, 1200°C in the main charge, to 1300 or 1400°C at the center.

The furnace charge approximates a 100 per cent resistive load. However, the overall power factor of the transformers, bus bars, voltage regulators, and furnace is 80 to 98 per cent, depending on furnace voltage and power level; it averages about 94 per cent. Power losses through the transformer and distribution system range from 2.5 to 5.5 per cent, averaging about 3.0 per cent. Furnace power consumption amounts to 78 per cent of the total consumed in the smelter.

About ten feet below the upper electrodes, the furnace widens out. This expanded diameter and a suspended curtain wall, built of shaped carbon blocks, cause the descending charge to form a disengaging surface through which the furnace gases are vented to the condenser. The furnace gases contain approximately equal portions of zinc vapor and carbon monoxide; the sum of the nitrogen, carbon dioxide, and hydrogen amounts to about ten per cent.

The condenser and cooling arrangement for removing latent and sensible heat has undergone extensive development.[4] Units currently in use have condensed in excess of 90 tons of metal per day. Condensation efficiency is 91 to 97 per cent, averaging about 95.5 per cent.

The condenser is shaped in the form of a U-tube with a vertical inlet, an inclined connecting tube at about nineteen degrees with the horizontal, and a vertical outlet. The condenser and associated cooling well hold about 50 tons of molten zinc. The gas exhaust leg of the condenser operates under ten to twelve inches of

mercury vacuum. Gases leaving the furnace at essentially atmospheric pressure bubble through the molten zinc. The head of zinc developed by gas pushing through the metal causes rapid circulation of molten zinc through a cooling well, which is open to atmosphere. Temperature of metal is controlled at 480 to 500°C by water-cooled pipe coils. Gases venting the condenser are water scrubbed in a high-velocity impinger. The clean gas, containing 80 per cent carbon monoxide, furnishes fuel for smelter use.

Typical performance for a metal furnace is shown in Table 1. Single-pass recovery is the order of 85 per cent. Residues discharged from the furnace are processed to reclaim a major fraction of the contained zinc and carbon. This results in high overall smelter zinc recovery, which exceeds 95 per cent. The smelter has an annual capacity of 34,000 tons of zinc oxide and 174,000 tons of slab zinc. Detailed descriptions of the process appear elsewhere.[5, 7]

Electrothermal Furnace of Duisburger Kupferhütte

Duisburger Kupferhütte in Duisburg, Germany, has recently developed an electrothermal furnace for producing zinc metal from zinc oxide clinker. The zinc oxide clinker is recovered from salt-roasted pyrite cinder. This involves leaching the roasted pyrite, treating the leach solutions with quicklime, and calcining the crude zinc hydroxide in a rotary kiln. Clinker composition is approximately 70 per cent zinc, 0.5 per cent nickel, 0.2 per cent iron, 0.1 per cent cobalt, 3 per cent lime, 3 per cent magnesia, and 1 to 2 per cent each of silica and alumina.

Following several years of development work, a 30 metric ton commercial furnace was built in 1961. The furnace is a truncated cone having an inside diameter of approximately six meters at the slag line. The upper walls are inclined slightly toward the center line. Energy is supplied through four electrodes in three-phase hookup. Charge is fed in batches through seven charging ports. The furnace is equipped with three splash condensers, but only two operate at a given time. A diagrammatic sketch is shown in Fig. 2.

Typical daily charge comprises fifty metric tons of zinc oxide clinker containing 34 tons of zinc, 8 tons of coke, 0.6 tons of coal, 3.0 tons of silica, and 2.4 tons of other additives. Furnace electric energy input amounts to 1.32 kwh per

TABLE 1. TYPICAL PERFORMANCE—ST. JOE ELECTROTHERMIC METAL FURNACE (1962)

Nominal power input	6,500 kw
Zinc in feed per day	75.8 tons
Carbon in feed per day	35.8 tons
Furnace carbon consumption per day	18.9 tons
Zinc produced per day	64.2 tons
Power consumed per pound zinc produced	1.14 kwh
Power off time for maintenance	6.5 percent
Furnace campaign life	154 days
Zinc in blue powder per day	2.6 tons
Zinc in circulated residue per day	7.7 tons
Zinc in discarded residue per day	1.3 tons

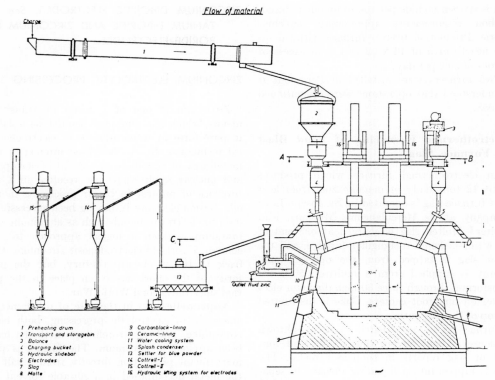

FIG. 2. Duisburger Kupferhütte electrothermal zinc furnace. [*Courtesy Duisburger Kupferhütte*]

pound of zinc vaporized. The electrode consumption is 0.15 tons per day. Thermal losses are 22.5 per cent of energy input.

Of the zinc in furnace charge, 90 per cent reports in the slab zinc product, 8 per cent in zinc dust which escapes the condenser, and only 0.4 per cent in the liquid slag which is tapped from the furnace. Slag weight averages ten metric tons per day with a composition of 1.3 per cent zinc oxide. Slag temperatures are held at 1300 to 1340°C. Life of the carbon lining is about eighteen months.

The Sterling Process of the New Jersey Zinc Company

An electrothermal furnace of commercial size was placed in operation by The New Jersey Zinc Company in 1951 for recovering zinc from oxidic zinc-bearing materials. In the Sterling Process,[1] the heat is supplied by open electric arcs between the electrodes and the slag bath. The charge, consisting of the zinc-bearing feed stock, slag-modifying additives, and coal, is first pre-

heated to 850 to 900°C and then introduced around the periphery of the furnace. The banks of charge protect the sides and end walls from the corrosive attack of molten slag and iron. The heat generated by the open arc is, for the most part, absorbed by the banks of charge so that substantial zinc reduction is effected before the slag constituents melt. By maintaining a clear slag bath surface to which arcing takes place preferentially, arcing to the charge banks is largely avoided. This minimizes dusting and volatilization of fume detrimental to good zinc condensation.

Several splash condensers of New Jersey Zinc Company design are attached to the furnace. In these condensers, the gases pass through a shower of molten zinc maintained at 500°C by water-cooled coils immersed in the liquid zinc bath.

The furnace reportedly requires about 2800 kwh per ton of combined nonferrous metals and iron reduced, when treating roasted high-grade zinc concentrates. Graphite electrode consumption is sixteen pounds per ton of metals reduced. Carbon requirements approximate stoichiometric. Production from a furnace with an inside hearth area of 16 x 32 feet is in excess of 35 tons of zinc per day.

Two furnaces were installed in Peru, but it is understood that operations were discontinued in 1958.

Electrothermic Furnacing of Lead Blast Furnace Slag

An electrothermal furnace which produces about 12 tons daily of metallic zinc from lead blast furnace slag is operated by St. Joseph Lead Company at its Herculaneum, Missouri, lead smelter.[2] Molten slag is charged at one end of the water-jacketed rectangular furnace, and the spent slag is tapped from the opposite end. Energy is supplied from a multitap 5000 kw transformer through three 30-inch diameter electrodes on nine-foot centers. Coke is distributed on top of the slag bath.

Furnace gases are treated in a Josephtown condenser. About 50 per cent of the lead content of slag reports in condenser metal. The zinc is tapped into a liquating furnace to separate excess lead and iron.

About 150 tons daily of blast furnace slag are treated. Single-pass zinc recovery is 50 to 54 per cent; recirculation of drosses results in 70 per cent overall recovery. Coke consumption is 4.6 tons per day and power consumption 4.7 kwh per pound of zinc produced.

References

1. HANDWERK, E. C., MAHLER, G. T., AND FETTEROLF, L. D., *J. Metals*, **4**, 581–586 (1952).
2. ISBELL, W. T., AND LONG, C. C., *Trans. Am. Inst. Min., Met. & Petr. Engrs.*, **159**, 176–81 (1944).
3. LANDIS, W. S., *Trans. Am. Inst. Min., Met. & Petr. Engrs.*, **121**, 573–98 (1936).
4. NAJARIAN, H. K., *Trans. Am. Inst. Min., Met. & Petr. Engrs.*, **212**, 493–497 (1958).
5. NAJARIAN, H. K., PETERSON, K. F., AND LUND, R. E., *Trans. Am. Inst. Min., Met. & Petr. Engrs.*, **191**, 116–119 (1951).
6. O'HARRA, B. M., *U. S. Bur. Mines Bull.* **208**, (1922).
7. WEATON, G. F., AND LONG, C. C., *Trans. Am. Inst. Min., Met. & Petr. Engrs.*, **159**, 141–160 (1944).

ROBERT E. LUND

ZINC PLATING. See ELECTROGALVANIZING.

ZIRCONIUM DIBORIDE ELECTRODES. See TITANIUM DIBORIDE AND ZIRCONIUM DIBORIDE ELECTRODES.

ZIRCONIUM, ELECTROLYTIC PROCESSING

Zirconium is one of a series of transition metals, which like aluminum cannot be isolated in pure form by usual aqueous or electrochemical techniques. Recent increased interest in the metallurgy of zirconium as a result of aerospace and nuclear applications has resulted in a resurgence of interest in better processing methods. Fusion electrolysis, having been successfully used to electrowin metals such as aluminum and tantalum, is then a logical approach to zirconium. Efforts to electrodeposit zirconium date back to the nineteenth century, but the majority of the effort has taken place in the period since the Second World War.

Approaches. As in the case of other metals amenable to electrolytic processing, both electrowinning and electrorefining methods have been applied to zirconium. The former is primary metal production directly from a salt of the metal decomposed in a suitable solvent by virtue of an applied direct current. The latter is employed as a purification method involving anodic dissolution of a crude metallic source and cathodic deposition of the metal in pure form; impurities are then retained at the anode or in the electrolyte.

It has been adequately demonstrated that zirconium is not amenable to processing in aqueous media due to its highly oxyphillic nature. Thus, all successful processing of the metal by electrolytic techniques has been carried out in molten salt media. Similar melts are used for both approaches. These are in turn quite similar to the melts utilized for related titanium processes. In general, the solvent consists of one or more salts of the alkali or alkaline earth metal chlorides. The source electrolyte in the case of electrowinning procedures, or the carrier electrolyte for electrorefining processes, is most commonly a zirconium chloride or fluoride, or a double fluoride of zirconium and a Group IA or 2A metal. Other halides could probably be employed with equal success, with the exception of some of the fluorides which are not water soluble and would thus present a problem in recovery of the metal values. Pertinent properties

TABLE 1. PROPERTIES OF MELT CONSTITUENTS

Salt	M.P., °C	B.P., °C	Form	Density at 850°C, g/cc	Specific Electrical Conductance at 850°C (ohm-cm^{-1})	Decomp. Voltage (1000°K)
NaCl	801	1413	cl†-crystal	1.505	3.77	3.31
KCl	776	1500	cl-crystal	1.480	2.36	3.53
NaF	980	1700	cl-crystal	5.5$^{M.P.}$	5.5$^{M.P.}$	4.86
KF	880	1500	deliq-cryst.	3.2$^{M.P.}$	3.2$^{M.P.}$	4.76
ZrCl$_4$	subl.	—	hygrosc. cryst.	2.8	—	1.5*
K$_2$ZrF$_6$	700	—	cl-crystal	3.58	—	1.25*

* measured values; † cl = colorless.

of some electrolyte constituents are given in Table 1.

Electrolytic Cells. Cells employed in zirconium electrolytic extraction processes may take a variety of configurations, but all possess several features in common necessary for successful process operation.

1. An inert atmosphere is required to prevent reoxidation of deposited metal and to prevent oxidation of the zirconium salt in the melt.

2. Refractory materials of construction must be employed in the cell since most processes operate between 700 to 1000°C. Graphite is the most commonly employed material; other ceramic and metallic materials have limited application.

3. Provision is made for venting of anode gas (chlorine in all present cases of electrowinning processes); no gas is produced in electrorefining approaches.

4. Anode area is greater than cathode area by at least a 2:1 ratio.

5. Provision for heating the melt is provided since current level for electrolysis is insufficient to maintain temperature.

6. Container must be nonporous to melt and nonreactive toward the melt. Container also frequently acts as anode in electrowinning processes.

In addition to these general considerations, many cells have provision for charging of salt either as a solid through an air lock or as a liquid under an atmosphere. Cells are also frequently fitted with facilities for withdrawal of cathode deposits through an air lock, enabling continuous operation.

Most cells are of steel external construction and many have a water-cooled wall. Graphite powder, lampblack and silica flour are frequently employed as insulation materials. All cells are of closed construction such that they may be vacuum purged.

Electrowinning Processes

All current zirconium electrowinning processes utilize a chloride or fluoride as the source electrolyte. Iodides or bromides might be used as well were it not for economic considerations. Specific procedures have been developed for ZrCl$_4$, ZrCl$_3$, ZrF$_4$, and K$_2$ZrF$_6$.

In all cases these are ionic materials, and the cationic species, Zr^{4+}, Zr^{3+}, or a Zr halide ion, migrates to the cathode and deposits as metal. The chloride ions in the first two cases behave similarly anionically, liberating chlorine gas. In the case of the fluoride, chlorine is also liberated since the process is carried out in a chloride solvent and chlorine is liberated preferentially over fluorine. The double fluoride apparently acts as though it were two separate salts and behaves in the same manner as the simple fluoride.

Indications are that zirconium is deposited as a one-step process whether from the trivalent or tetravalent state. This is equivalent to 1.13 g/amp-hr from the 3+ state and 0.85 g/amp-hr from the 4+ state. The most successful zirconium electrodeposition processes have utilized the starting material in the 4+ state.

Representative systems which have yielded zirconium of practical purity include the following:

K$_2$ZrF$_6$-NaCl-KCl	ZrCl$_4$-NaCl
K$_2$ZrF$_6$-NaF-KF	ZrCl$_4$-NaCl-KCl
K$_2$ZrF$_6$-NaCl-CaCl$_2$	ZrCl$_4$-KCl-KF
K$_2$ZrF$_6$-NaCl	ZrCl$_4$-MgCl$_2$
ZrCl$_3$-NaCl	
ZrCl$_3$-NaCl-KCl	

Systems are generally operated such that the melt contains about 8 to 10 wt per cent Zr. This results in a maximum current efficiency which averages 65 to 70 per cent. Most melts are operated in the vicinity of 700 to 800°C. Initial cathode current density values range from about

TABLE 2. ELECTROLYTIC ZIRCONIUM
PRODUCTION FROM K$_2$ZrF$_6$*

K$_2$ZrF$_6$, wt %	NaCl, wt %	Temp, °C	Cathode c. d., initial, a/sq dm	Anode c.d., a/sq dm	Current effici-ency, %	Rate, lb/hr Zr
33	67	870	330	45	67	5.5
33	67	835	330	55	62	5.0
33	67	855	370	50	64	5.3

* Pilot plant cell, 30–40 lb. Zr/cathode deposit.

50 to 500 amps/sq dm; in most cases current density has little effect on process operation. Purity of the product metal is in large measure a function of purity of the melt and its constituents, together with purity of the inert atmosphere.

It is essential that moisture and oxides be absent from all phases of processing; otherwise these decompose preferentially and impart oxygen to the metal. Most investigators have carried out a low-voltage pre-electrolysis on melt constituents prior to actual metal deposition. This insures removal of last traces of moisture and many potential contaminant oxides.

The K$_2$ZrF$_6$-NaCl system has received the most intensive investigation and has been operated on a pilot plant scale. Some typical operation data are given in Table 2. This procedure produces metal comparable in quality to that produced by the magnesium reduction process. Such a cell can be operated on a continuous basis up to the point where the melt becomes too concentrated in alkali fluoride content; this manifests itself in anodic polarization.

Less extensive investigations have been made utilizing the oxide as a source electrolyte, but there is no conclusive evidence for preparation of a product of acceptable purity by this approach. The oxide has been utilized successfully to combat anode effect or polarization, particularly in fluoride melts; however, it is likely that oxygen contamination of the product metal is a necessary consequence.

Electrorefining Processes

Electrorefining of zirconium metal has not been investigated to the extent carried out for titanium. However, work completed is sufficient to demonstrate feasibility of the approach. Such studies have utilized melts employed in electrowinning processes coupled with a soluble anode of impure zirconium. No definitive data have

been released on operational parameters of such procedures. It is apparent that current efficiencies observed have been less than for comparable titanium procedures. Indications are that the degree of purification achieved is also somewhat less in the case of zirconium.

It is probable that zirconium electrorefining would take place on a 3+ electron-change basis due to the apparent instability of the 2+ state. It would also be expected that such procedures would operate at maximum effectiveness with a high concentration of carrier salt.

Metal Recovery

Typical metallic deposits from molten salt procedures contain from 35 to 60 wt per cent metal and the balance occluded salts. Particles include granules of a crystalline nature and dendritic crystal growth. In general, lower current densities promote growth of larger crystals. In most cases occluded salts are largely alkali metal chlorides; in the cases where K$_2$ZrF$_6$ is the source electrolyte, small amounts of KF, NaF and KCl will also be present.

In all processes evaluated to date, aqueous washing procedures have been successfully employed to remove residual salts. The deposit is broken off the cathode, crushed, and washed either in a continuous process or by a series of washes and decantations. The cone washer has been successfully adapted to zirconium recovery. Generally initial washing is carried out in slightly acidic solution to prevent hydrolysis of any residual zirconium salts present. Completeness of salt removal is generally ascertained by a suitable test for absence of chloride ion. Following the salt removal, the metal powder is filtered or centrifuged and dried in a low-temperature oven.

The resultant product is then amenable to processing by usual powder metallurgical methods. Such approaches include pressing and inert atmosphere sintering or arc melting; the latter approach is generally the one taken. The arc melted stock may then be subjected to various rolling, drawing, and swaging processes according to standard refractory metal practice. Work is also in progress directed toward direct processing of metal powders into mill products. Successful development of such procedures would most certainly create an enhanced interest in molten salt extraction methods for zirconium.

TABLE 3. ELECTROLYTIC ZIRCONIUM

Source electrolyte	Ti content, wt %	Product type	Hardness, BHN	Impurities (ppm)				Total Zr, wt %
				O_2	N_2	C	Fe	
K_2ZrF_6	32	Cryst. granules	150	350–700	20–100	300–500	200–800	>99.9
$ZrCl_4$	39	powder	200					99.3
$ZrCl_3$	46	powder						99.5
Kroll Reactor Grade		sponge	150	1400*	50*	500*	1500*	>99.6

* Maximum values

Electrolytic Zirconium Products

Primary electrolytic zirconium is of equivalent or superior purity and properties to commercial material as produced by Mg reduction of $ZrCl_4$. Analytical and hardness data for electrolytic material from K_2ZrF_6 are compared with specifications for commercial material in Table 3.

Data are not available for electrorefined material. These procedures have not yet been fully investigated and existing data have not yet been released. It is expected that this approach would yield a substantially higher quality product than those prepared by electrodecomposition procedures.

At present electrolytic zirconium is not available except in laboratory quantities. Organizations known to have interests in this area include U.S. Bureau of Mines, Kennecott Copper Corporation, and Horizons Incorporated.

Further utilization of electrolytic methods for zirconium production will depend largely on increased usage of the metal together with development of advanced techniques in powder metallurgy enabling direct use of an electrolytic product without intermediate consolidation steps.

References

1. "Zirconium and Zirconium Alloys," pp. 5–120, Cleveland, Ohio, *American Society for Metals*, 1953.
2. DELIMARSKII, IU. K., AND MARKOV, B. F., "Electrochemistry of Fused Salts," (English translation), Washington, D. C., Sigma Press, 1961.
3. HAMPEL, C. A., Ed., "Rare Metals Handbook," 2nd Ed., Ch. 34, New York, Reinhold Publishing Corp., 1961.
4. LUSTMAN, B., AND KERZE, F., Eds., "The Metallurgy of Zirconium," Ch. 4–5, New York, McGraw-Hill Book Co., 1955.
5. MILLER, G. L., "Zirconium," Ch. 5–7, London, Butterworths Scientific Publications, 1957.
6. PASCAL, P., Ed., "Nouveau Traite de Chimie Minerale," Vol. 9, pp. 246–317, Paris, Masson et Cie., 1963.
7. STEINBERG, M. A., SIBERT, M. E., AND WAINER, E., *J. Electrochem. Soc.*, **101**, 63–78 (1954).

MERLE E. SIBERT

Cross-references: *Fused Salt Electrode Reactions; Fused Salt Electromotive Force Series; Hafnium, Electrolytic Preparation; Titanium, Electrolytic Preparation.*

ZONE REFINING

Zone refining may be defined as the performance of repeated crystallizations, each of which causes a segregation of impurities, during the passage of a series of molten zones, in one direction, through the charge to be purified.[14, 16]

The elucidation of the transistor in 1948 by Bardeen and Brattain[2] gave rise to what is now the $290,000,000/year transistor industry.[25] If, however, the art of zone refining had not been discovered by Pfann[13, 15] at about the same time, it is doubtful that the development of solid-state devices could have proceeded beyond a small fraction of their present importance. The need for highly purified germanium could only be satisfied by Pfann's technique which was later extended to the refining of silicon as the need for that element developed.

After more than a decade of rapidly developing technology, zone refining is still the only method capable of producing the elemental semiconductors with the desired purity. It is now also playing an important part in the preparation of compound-semiconductor materials, such as the III-V compounds, gallium arsenide and indium antimonide.

It is interesting to note that germanium, the material to which zone refining was first applied, is still the substance which responds most favorably to the method. Germanium, whose electrical characteristics show it to be essentially without impurities, is routinely made by the use of the technique. The zone refining of silicon, although of great value, is unable, however, to remove the last traces of boron except when a chemical purification is simultaneously applied.[22]

Although zone refining has been of paramount importance in the purification of semiconductor materials, attempts to apply it to other substances have been somewhat less successful. Advances have been made, however, in the refining of metals,[1] inorganic,[7] and organic[9] compounds.

Theory

In a system in which the freezing point of the solvent is lowered by the solute, careful partial freezing of the solution will result in a solid phase in which the solvent is purer than it is in the liquid phase. Such a system is illustrated in Fig. 1 where a solution whose solute concentration is C_1 is carefully cooled under equilibrium conditions. The first solid to appear has the solute concentration, C_s. The equilibrium distribution coefficient, k_{eq}, of the system is defined as

$$k_{eq} = C_s/C_1.$$

For the system of Fig. 1, k_{eq} is smaller than unity and purification of the solvent occurs. In a system where the freezing point of the solvent is raised by the solute, K_{eq} would be larger than unity and an increase in the concentration of the solute in the solvent would take place on freezing. For practical rates of freezing, especially if no stirring of the mixture can be achieved, true equilibrium cannot be attained and the effective distribution coefficient, k, will have a value between the equilibrium value, k_{eq}, and unity.

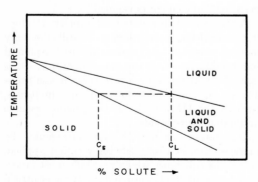

FIG. 1. Constitutional diagram of a system in which the freezing point is lowered by the solute.

If the solution illustrated by Fig. 1 is placed in a boat and carefully cooled from one end, normal freezing occurs. The resulting bar of solid then contains a solute distribution ranging from $C_s = kC_1$ at the first-to-freeze end to $C_s > C_1$ at the last-to-freeze end, the constant, k, being the effective distribution coefficient. The value of this parameter will approach theoretical only under ideal conditions which include a) complete mixing in the liquid phase (or very rapid diffusion), b) no diffusion in the solid phase, and c) a slow rate of crystallization.

If one end of a solid bar is melted and the molten zone slowly moved into the remaining solid while refreezing occurs at the zone's trailing face, the basic arrangement for zone refining is met. The first solid to crystallize will have the concentration, kC_0, where C_0 is the concentration of the solute (impurity) in the original material. As further solid is melted into the liquid zone, however, the concentration of the impurity, C_1, in the liquid rises because the quantity of liquid solvent remains essentially constant while the rate of dissolution of the impurity at the melting face is greater than the rate of precipitation of the impurity at the freezing face.

When the concentration of the impurity in the liquid zone rises to C_0/k, the material crystallizing is of the same impurity content as the material dissolving and no further purification occurs.

As the molten zone "moves off" the end of the bar, however, normal freezing takes place and the impurity concentration rises sharply toward the last-to-freeze end. At the end of the first pass, the impurity concentration in the bar is similar to that shown by the solid curve in Fig. 2.

If the process is repeated, the concentration at the first-to-freeze end is lowered, the point at which the freezing solid has the concentration, C_0, is moved farther along the bar, and the concentration in the last-to-freeze portion rises. After n passes, the impurity distribution in the bar resembles the broken curve of Fig. 2.

The distance, l, in Fig. 2 is the length of the zone. For the most efficient separation of the impurity, l should be as small as possible with respect to L, the length of the bar. Because the separation increases with the number of passes, n, it is therefore desirable to make both n and the ratio, L/l as large as possible. When properly applied, then, zone refining is, in essence, a series of fractional-crystallization steps, each of which accomplishes a small amount of purification.

Practice

In general, zone refining offers a technique which keeps handling of the material and its consequent contamination to an absolute minimum. In addition, the use of a controlled atmosphere or a vacuum in the system removes the danger of atmospheric contamination or reaction with the elements of the air.

When the material to be purified can be melted in a nonreactive boat, horizontal zone refining can be used. The familiar zone refining of germanium is a good example where boats of either quartz or graphite are employed. The boat, loaded with germanium, is placed in a quartz or "Vycor" tube around which a series of coils, forming part of the tank circuit of a radio-frequency generator, are wound. The tube may be evacuated or flushed with a protective, flowing gas, such as argon, helium, or nitrogen, to prevent oxidation of the germanium.

Each coil of the series causes a molten zone to form in the ingot by induction. The series of molten zones may be made to traverse the ingot by movement of the coils, movement of the boat in the tube, or movement of the tube and boat together in the coils. Thus, in one cycle, several zones can be passed through the bar. The length of the individual zone is generally held at approximately one-tenth of the length of the ingot.

Usually, the zones are made to move at speeds in the neighborhood of six inches an hour, at which rate the distribution coefficients of most of the impurities are fairly favorable.[4] With good starting material, germanium of very fine quality can be produced by the passage of fewer than 20 zones.

When a change in volume occurs with the liquid-to-solid transition in the material being purified, the ingot will become progressively more tapered as further zones are passed. When the solid is less dense than the liquid, as is the situation with germanium, the freezing solid pushes liquid forward, slowly raising the liquid level and causing the ingot to be larger at the last-to-freeze end. To overcome this effect, materials such as germanium are zoned "uphill" at an angle of a few degrees.

In contrast, when the solid material is more dense than the liquid, the transport of matter causes the first-to-freeze end of the ingot to become larger. Zoning "downhill" overcomes the effect.

Many other techniques have been used in place of radio-frequency heating in horizontal zone refining and numerous ingenious methods have been worked out to permit the motion of the zones with a minimum motion of the heat sources.[19] When a boat cannot be found which does not react with the molten material to be refined, the floating-zone modification of zone refining[10, 11, 22, 23] may be used. In this, a bar of the material is held vertically between two supports in a protective tube of quartz or "Vycor." A narrow molten zone in which the liquid is retained largely by its own surface tension can be formed in the rod by heating created by energy from the outside of the tube. Thus, the molten zone comes in contact only with the solid material and no contamination from a container is encountered.

Silicon is zone-refined by the floating-zone technique with radio-frequency heating in either a vacuum or an ambient of a protective gas such as helium. Although the distribution coefficients are less favorable in silicon than they are in germanium,[4] extensive purification is gained, possibly by evaporation as well as by segregation of the impurities. Because the arrangement of the bar permits only one molten zone to be formed at a time, a very large number of passes may be necessary to allow the desired purity to be reached.

In a special example of floating-zone refining, the heating is carried out by electron bombardment in a vacuum. In practice, the setup is a large thermionic diode in which the work forms the anode, and the cathode is a heated filament of tungsten or some other refractory metal. The technique was first applied to the refining of tungsten[5, 6] for which no satisfactory crucible material is known. As in the vacuum zone refining of silicon, part of the purification is achieved by evaporation of the impurities as well as by their segregation.

Because of the size limitation inherent in the floating-zone technique, attempts have been made to circumvent the interaction between the molten zone and the containing boat to allow larger charges to be purified more rapidly. In one of these, silicon was zone-refined in thin-walled quartz boats in such a way that the solid zones of silicon were heated sufficiently to be kept plastic. When the purification was finished and the boat allowed to cool, extensive breakage of both the bar and the boat took place because of the difference in thermal expansivities of silicon and quartz and because the molten silicon had wetted the container. The quartz adhering to the silicon was removed by etching.[20] In the second technique in this category, silicon was zone-refined in a water-cooled metal boat in which no reaction of the molten silicon took place with the metal of the boat. Although the

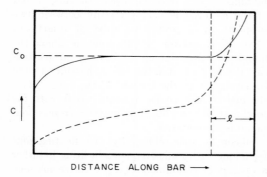

Fig. 2. Impurity distribution as a result of zone refining.

power consumption of the method (radio-frequency) was very large, the finished ingot could be easily removed in one piece and the boat reused.[18]

As may be seen from the above discussion and from Fig. 2, zone refining results merely in a redistribution of impurities if losses by volatilization are ignored. To obtain the purified material one must, therefore, cut the final ingot at some point beyond which the impurity content is higher than desired. The impurity-rich section is then discarded or reprocessed as desired.

Fig. 3 is a photograph of a production zone-refining plant for germanium in which heating is carried out by radio-frequency induction and the traverse of the bar by the heating coils is entirely automatic. A wide range of zoning speeds is possible and the machines will complete any predetermined number of passes before turning off automatically.

The principles of zone refining have also been applied to the growth of monocrystals, especially in the semiconductor industry. In addition to the very important Teal and Little modification[21] of the Czochralski technique[8] which is used to grow crystals of silicon, ger-

Fig. 3. Germanium zone-purification plant. (*Courtesy Chemical and Metallurgical Div., Sylvania Electric Products, Inc.*)

manium, and the III-V compounds, the zone-levelling modification of zone refining[3, 17] is used very extensively to grow monocrystals of germanium and other materials for which nonreactive boats are available. When nonreactive boats are not available, monocrystals may be grown by the floating-zone technique. Silicon[22] and alkali halide[24] crystals have been grown by radio-frequency induction heating, while tungsten and rhenium crystals[5] have been grown by electron beam heating.

In both methods of growing crystals, oriented seeds of the material to be grown are used. A molten zone is established at the point of contact of the seed and a bar of stock which has been purified by zone refining. As the zone is moved slowly away from the seed, monocrystalline growth results as the liquid solidifies.

If the controlled addition of an impurity is desired in the monocrystal, a very uniform impurity content can be achieved if the effective distribution coefficient of the impurity is small. In practice, a small amount of the desired impurity is added to the melt as it is first formed at the junction of the seed and the stock. Because a) the stock is of high purity, b) the volume of the liquid is constant, and c) only a very small proportion of the impurity is lost to the freezing face (if k is small), the concentration of the impurity in the liquid phase is essentially constant and the concentration of the impurity in the growing crystal, therefore, is also essentially constant.

As the zone passes off the end of the bar, normal freezing occurs as in the case of simple zone refining and a very rapid rise in the impurity content takes place. This last-to-freeze section of the bar can then be cut off and discarded to leave a very uniformly "doped" crystal.

Reference may be made to Pfann[16] or to Parr[12] for an extensive and thorough study of zone refining.

References

1. ALBERT, PH., *Chimia*, **14**, 218 (1960).
2. BARDEEN, J., AND BRATTAIN, W. H., *Phys. Rev.*, **74**, 230 (1948).
3. BENNETT, D. C., AND SAWYER, B., *Bell System Tech. J.*, **35**, 637 (1956).
4. BURTON, J. A., *Physica*, **20**, 845 (1954).
5. CALVERLY, A., DAVIS, M., AND LEVER, R., *J. Sci. Instr.*, **34**, 142 (1957).
6. CARLSON, R. G., *J. Electrochem. Soc.*, **106**, 49 (1959).
7. Centre national de la recherche scientifique (P. Süe and J. Pauly) French Patent 1,171,-560 (January 28, 1959).
8. CZOCHRALSKI, J., *Z. physik. Chem.*, **92**, 219 (1918).
9. DOEDE, C. M., *Ind. Chemist*, **38**, 462 (1962).
10. EMEIS, R., *Z. Naturforsch.*, **9a**, 67 (1954).
11. KECK, P. H., AND GOLAY, M. J. E., *Phys. Rev.*, **89**, 1297 (1953).
12. PARR, N. L., "Zone Refining," London, The Royal Institute of Chemistry (Monograph No. 3), 1957.
13. PFANN, W. G., *Trans. AIME*, **194**, 747 (1952).
14. PFANN, W. G., *Chem. Eng. News*, **34**, 1440 (1956).
15. PFANN, W. G., (to Bell Telephone Laboratories, Inc.) U.S. Patent 2,739,045 (March 20, 1956).
16. PFANN, W. G., "Zone Melting," New York, John Wiley and Sons, Inc., 1958.
17. PFANN, W. G., AND OLSEN, K. M., *Phys. Rev.*, **89**, 322 (1953).
18. PORTER, J. L., AND LAMB, D. M., Paper No. 155, Electrochem. Soc. 120th Meeting, Detroit, October, 1961.
19. Reference 16, Chapter 4.
20. TAFT, E. A., AND HORN, F. H., *J. Electrochem. Soc.*, **105**, 81 (1958).
21. TEAL, G. K., AND LITTLE, J. B., Paper No. I 15, Am. Phys. Soc. Meeting, Oak Ridge, 1950.
22. THEUERER, H. C., *Trans. AIME*, **206**, 1316 (1956).
23. THEUERER, H. C., (to Bell Telephone Laboratories, Inc.) U.S. Patent 3,060,123 (October 23, 1962).
24. WARREN, R. V., *Rev. Sci. Instr.*, **33**, 1378 (1962).
25. *Weekly Report to the Electronics Industry* (Electronic Industries Assocn.), **19**, No. 3, January 21, 1963.

A. STUART TULK

Cross-references: *Electron Beam Melting; Induction Heating; Single Crystals.*

INDEX

(Capitalized words refer to specific article titles. Boldface numbers refer to main articles or to important passages.)